HANS CHRISTIAN ANDERSEN

The Complete Fairy Tales

HANS CHRISTIAN ANDERSEN

The Complete Fairy Tales

WORDSWORTH LIBRARY COLLECTION

For my husband
ANTHONY JOHN RANSON
with love from your wife, the publisher.
Eternally grateful for your unconditional love,
not just for me but for our children,
Simon, Andrew and Nichola Trayler

3

Readers who are interested in other titles from
Wordsworth Editions are invited to visit our website at
www.wordsworth-editions.com

For our latest list and a full mail-order service, contact
Bibliophile Books, 5 Datapoint, South Crescent, London E16 4TL
TEL: +44 (0)20 7474 2474 FAX: +44 (0)20 7474 8589
ORDERS: orders@bibliophilebooks.com
WEBSITE: www.bibliophilebooks.com

This edition, part of the Wordsworth Library Collection,
published 2009 by Wordsworth Editions Limited
8B East Street, Ware, Hertfordshire SG12 9HJ

ISBN 978 1 84022 173 2

Text © Wordsworth Editions Limited 2009

Wordsworth® is a registered trademark of
Wordsworth Editions Limited,
the company founded by Michael Trayler in 1987

Cover design by Robert Mathias, Publishing Workshop

Cover illustration: *The Little Red Shoes* (watercolour)
by Honor C. Appleton (1879–1951)
Private Collection / © Chris Beetles, London, UK /
Bridgeman Art Library, London

Text typeset in Great Britain by Antony Gray
Printed and bound by Clays Ltd, St Ives plc

Contents

The Tinder-Box

THERE came a soldier marching along the high road – *one, two!*
one, two! He had his knapsack on his back and a sabre by his side,
for he had been in the wars, and now he wanted to go home.
And on the way he met with an old witch: she was very hideous, and
her under lip hung down upon her breast. She said, 'Good-evening,
soldier. What a fine sword you have, and what a big knapsack! You're
a proper soldier! Now you shall have as much money as you like to
have.'

'I thank you, you old witch!' said the soldier.

'Do you see that great tree?' quoth the witch; and she pointed to a
tree which stood beside them. 'It's quite hollow inside. You must climb
to the top, and then you'll see a hole, through which you can let
yourself down and get deep into the tree. I'll tie a rope round your
body, so that I can pull you up again when you call me.'

'What am I to do down in the tree?' asked the soldier.

'Get money,' replied the witch. 'Listen to me. When you come down to the earth under the tree, you will find yourself in a great hall: it is quite light, for many hundred lamps are burning there. Then you will see three doors; these you can open, for the keys are in the locks. If you go into the first chamber, you'll see a great chest in the middle of the floor; on this chest sits a dog, and he's got a pair of eyes as big as two teacups. But you need not care for that. I'll give you my blue-checked apron, and you can spread it out upon the floor; then go up quickly and take the dog, and set him on my apron; then open the chest, and take as many farthings as you like. They are of copper: if you prefer silver, you must go into the second chamber. But there sits a dog with a pair of eyes as big as mill-wheels. But do not you care for that. Set him upon my apron, and take some of the money. And if you want gold, you can have that too – in fact, as much as you can carry – if you go into the third chamber. But the dog that sits on the money-chest there has two eyes as big as the round tower of Copenhagen. He is a fierce dog, you may be sure; but you needn't be afraid, for all that Only set him on my apron, and he won't hurt you; and take out of the chest as much gold as you like.'

'That's not so bad,' said the soldier. 'But what am I to give you, you old witch? for you will not do it for nothing, I fancy.'

'No,' replied the witch, 'not a single farthing will I have. You shall only bring me an old tinder-box which my grandmother forgot when she was down there last.'

'Then tie the rope round my body,' cried the soldier.

'Here it is,' said the witch, 'and here's my blue-checked apron.'

Then the soldier climbed up into the tree, let himself slip down into the hole, and stood, as the witch had said, in the great hall where the many hundred lamps were burning.

Now he opened the first door. Ugh! there sat the dog with eyes as big as teacups, staring at him. 'You're a nice fellow!' exclaimed the soldier; and he set him on the witch's apron, and took as many copper farthings as his pockets would hold, and then locked the chest, set the dog on it again, and went into the second chamber. Aha! there sat the dog with eyes as big as mill-wheels.

'You should not stare so hard at me,' said the soldier; 'you might strain your eyes.' And he set the dog upon the witch's apron. When he saw the silver money in the chest, he threw away all the copper money he had, and filled his pockets and his knapsack with silver only. Then he went into the third chamber. Oh, but that was horrid! The dog there really had eyes as big as the round tower, and they turned round and round in his head like wheels.

'Good-evening!' said the soldier; and he touched his cap, for he had never seen such a dog as that before. When he had looked at him a little more closely, he thought, 'That will do,' and lifted him down to the floor, and opened the chest. Mercy! what a quantity of gold was there! He could buy with it the whole of Copenhagen, and the sugar-pigs of the cake-woman, and all the tin soldiers, whips, and rocking-horses in the whole world. Yes, that was a quantity of money! Now the soldier threw away all the silver coin with which he had filled his pockets and his knapsack, and took gold instead: yes, all his pockets, his knapsack, his boots, and his cap were filled, so that he could scarcely walk. Now indeed he had plenty of money. He put the dog on the chest, shut the door, and then called up through the tree, 'Now pull me up, you old witch.'

'Have you the tinder-box?' asked the witch.

'Plague on it!' exclaimed the soldier, 'I had clean forgotten that.' And he went and brought it.

The witch drew him up, and he stood on the high road again, with pockets, boots, knapsack, and cap full of gold.

'What are you going to do with the tinder-box?' asked the soldier.

'That's nothing to you,' retorted the witch. 'You've had your money – just give me the tinder-box.'

'Nonsense!' said the soldier. 'Tell me directly what you're going to do with it, or I'll draw my sword and cut off your head.'

'No!' cried the witch.

So the soldier cut off her head. There she lay! But he tied up all his money in her apron, took it on his back like a bundle, put the tinder-box in his pocket, and went straight off towards the town.

That was a splendid town! He put up at the very best inn, asked for the finest rooms, and ordered his favourite dishes, for now he was rich, having got so much money. The servant who had to clean his boots certainly thought them a remarkably old pair for such a rich gentleman; but he had not bought any new ones yet. The next day he procured proper boots and handsome clothes. Now our soldier had become a fine gentleman; and the people told him of all the splendid things which were in their city, and about the king, and what a pretty princess the king's daughter was.

'Where can one get to see her?' asked the soldier.

'She is not to be seen at all,' said they all together; 'she lives in a great copper castle, with a great many walls

and towers round about it; no one but the king may go in and out there, for it has been prophesied that she shall marry a common soldier, and the king can't bear that.'

'I should like to see her,' thought the soldier; but he could not get leave to do so. Now he lived merrily, went to the theatre, drove in the king's garden, and gave much money to the poor; and this was very kind of him, for he knew from old times how hard it is when one has not a shilling. Now he was rich, had fine clothes, and gained many friends, who all said he was a rare one, a true cavalier; and that pleased

the soldier well. But as he spent money every day and never earned
any, he had at last only two shillings left; and he was obliged to turn out
of the fine rooms in which he had dwelt, and had to live in a little garret
under the roof, and clean his boots for himself, and mend them with a
darning-needle. None of his friends came to see him, for there were
too many stairs to climb.

It was quite dark one evening, and he could not even buy himself a
candle, when it occurred to him that there was a candle-end in the
tinder-box which he had taken out of the hollow tree into which the
witch had helped him. He brought out the tinder-box and the candle-
end; but as soon as he struck fire and the sparks rose up from the flint,
the door flew open, and the dog who had eyes as big as a couple of
teacups, and whom he had seen in the tree, stood before him, and said,
'What are my lord's commands?'

'What is this?' said the soldier. 'That's a famous tinder-box, if I can
get everything with it that I want! Bring me some money,' said he to
the dog; and *whisk!* the dog was gone, and *whisk!* he was back again,
with a great bag full of shillings in his mouth.

Now the soldier knew what a capital tinder-box this was. If he struck
it once, the dog came who sat upon the chest of copper money; if he
struck it twice, the dog came who had the silver; and if he struck it three
times, then appeared the dog who had the gold. Now the soldier moved
back into the fine rooms, and appeared again in handsome clothes; and
all his friends knew him again, and cared very much for him indeed.

Once he thought to himself, 'It is a very strange thing that one
cannot get to see the princess. They all say she is very beautiful; but
what is the use of that, if she has always to sit in the great copper castle
with the many towers? Can I not get to see her at all? Where is my
tinder-box?' And so he struck a light, and *whisk!* came the dog with
eyes as big as teacups.

'It is midnight, certainly,' said the soldier, 'but I should very much
like to see the princess only for one little moment.'

The dog was outside the door directly, and, before the soldier
thought it, came back with the princess. She sat upon the dog's back
and slept; and everyone could see she was a real princess, for she was

so lovely. The soldier could not refrain from kissing her, for he was a thorough soldier. Then the dog ran back again with the princess. But when morning came, and the king and queen were drinking tea, the princess said she had had a strange dream the night before, about a dog and a soldier – that she had ridden upon the dog, and the soldier had kissed her.

'That would be a fine history!' said the Queen.

So one of the old court ladies had to watch the next night by the princess's bed, to see if this was really a dream, or what it might be.

The soldier had a great longing to see the lovely princess again; so the dog came in the night, took her away, and ran as fast as he could. But the old lady put on waterboots, and ran just as fast after him. When she saw that they both entered a great house, she thought, 'Now I know where it is;' and with a bit of chalk she drew a great cross on the door. Then she went home and lay down, and the dog came up with the princess; but when he saw that there was a cross drawn on the door where the soldier lived, he took a piece of chalk too, and drew crosses on all the doors in the town. And that was cleverly done, for now the lady could not find the right door, because all the doors had crosses upon them.

In the morning early came the King and the Queen, the old court lady and all the officers, to see where it was the princess had been. 'Here it is!' said the King, when he saw the first door with a cross upon it. 'No, my dear husband, it is there!' said the Queen, who descried another door which also showed a cross. 'But *there* is one, and *there* is one!' said all, for wherever they looked there were crosses on the doors. So they saw that it would avail them nothing if they searched on.

But the Queen was an exceedingly clever woman, who could do more than ride in a coach. She took her great gold scissors, cut a piece of silk into pieces, and made a neat little bag; this bag she filled with fine wheat flour, and tied it on the princess's back; and when that was done, she cut a little hole in the bag, so that the flour would be scattered along all the way which the princess should take.

In the night the dog came again, took the princess on his back, and ran with her to the soldier, who loved her very much, and would gladly have been a prince, so that he might have her for his wife. The dog did not notice at all how the flour ran out in a stream from the castle to the windows of the soldier's house, where he ran up the wall with the princess. In the morning the King and the Queen saw well enough where their daughter had been, and they took the soldier and put him in prison.

There he sat. Oh, but it was dark and disagreeable there! And they said to him, 'Tomorrow you shall be hanged.' That was not amusing to hear, and he had left his tinder-box at the inn. In the morning he could see, through the iron grating of the little window, how the people were hurrying out of the town to see him hanged. He heard the drums beat and saw the soldiers marching. All the people were running out, and among them was a shoemaker's boy with leather apron and slippers, and he galloped so fast that one of his slippers flew off, and came right against the wall where the soldier sat looking through the iron grating.

'Halloo, you shoemaker's boy! you needn't be in such a hurry,' cried the soldier to him: 'it will not begin till I come. But if you will run to where I lived, and bring me my tinder-box, you shall have four shillings; but you must put your best leg foremost.'

The shoemaker's boy wanted to get the four shillings, so he went and brought the tinder-box, and – well, we shall hear now what happened.

Outside the town a great gallows had been built, and round it stood the soldiers and many hundred thousand people. The king and queen sat on a splendid throne, opposite to the judges and the whole council. The soldier already stood upon the ladder; but as they were about to put the rope round his neck, he said that before a poor criminal suffered his punishment an innocent request was always granted to him. He wanted very much to smoke a pipe of tobacco, and it would be the last pipe he should smoke in the world. The king would not say 'No' to this; so the soldier took his tinder-box, and struck fire. One – two – three! – and there suddenly stood all the dogs – the one with eyes as big as teacups, the one with eyes as large as mill-wheels, and the one whose eyes were as big as the round tower.

'Help me now, so that I may not be hanged,' said the soldier.

And the dogs fell upon the judge and all the council, seized one by the leg and another by the nose, and tossed them all many feet into the air, so that they fell down and were all broken to pieces.

'I won't!' cried the King; but the biggest dog took him and the Queen, and threw them after the others. Then the soldiers were afraid, and the people cried, 'Little soldier, you shall be our king, and marry the beautiful princess!'

So they put the soldier into the king's coach, and all the three dogs danced in front and cried 'Hurrah!' and the boys whistled through their fingers, and the soldiers presented arms. The princess came out of the copper castle, and became queen, and she liked that well enough. The wedding lasted a week, and the three dogs sat at the table too, and opened their eyes wider than ever at all they saw.

Great Claus and Little Claus

THERE lived two men in one village, and they had the same name – each was called Claus; but one had four horses, and the other only a single horse. To distinguish them from each other, folks called him who had four horses Great Claus, and the one who had only a single horse Little Claus. Now we shall hear what happened to each of them, for this is a true story.

The whole week through, Little Claus was obliged to plough for Great Claus, and to lend him his one horse; then Great Claus helped him out with all his four, but only once a week, and that was on Sunday. Hurrah! how Little Claus smacked his whip over all five horses, for they were as good as his own on that one day. The sun shone gaily, and all the bells in the steeples were ringing; the people were all dressed in their best, and were going to church, with their hymn-books under their arms, to hear the clergyman preach, and they saw Little Claus ploughing with five horses; but he was so merry that he smacked his whip again and again, and cried, 'Gee up, all my five!'

'You must not talk so,' said Great Claus, 'for only one horse is yours.'

But when anyone passed Little Claus forgot that he was not to say this, and he cried, 'Gee up, all my horses!'

'Now, I must beg of you to stop that,' cried Great Claus, 'for if you say it again, I shall hit your horse on the head, so that it will fall down dead, and then it will be all over with him.'

'I will certainly not say it any more,' said Little Claus.

But when people came by soon afterwards, and nodded 'good-day' to him, he became very glad, and thought it looked very well, after all, that he had five horses to plough his field; and so he smacked his whip again, and cried, 'Gee up, all my horses!'

'I'll "gee up" your horses!' said Great Claus. And he took a mallet and hit the only horse of Little Claus on the head, so that it fell down, and was dead immediately.

'Oh, now I haven't any horse at all!' said Little Claus, and began to cry.

Then he flayed the horse, and let the hide dry in the wind, and put it in a sack and hung it over his shoulder, and went to the town to sell his horse's skin.

He had a very long way to go, and was obliged to pass through a great dark wood, and the weather became dreadfully bad. He went quite astray, and before he got into the right way again it was evening, and it was too far to get home again or even to the town before nightfall.

Close by the road stood a large farmhouse. The shutters were closed outside the windows, but the light could still be seen shining out over them.

'I may be able to get leave to stop here through the night,' thought Little Claus; and he went and knocked.

The farmer's wife opened the door; but when she heard what he wanted she told him to go away, declaring that her husband was not at home, and she would not receive strangers.

'Then I shall have to lie outside,' said Little Claus. And the farmer's wife shut the door in his face.

Close by stood a great haystack, and between this and the farmhouse was a little outhouse thatched with straw.

'Up there I can lie,' said Little Claus, when he looked up at the roof; 'that is a capital bed. I suppose the stork won't fly down and bite me in the legs.' For a living stork was standing on the roof, where he had his nest.

Now Little Claus climbed up to the roof of the shed, where he lay, and turned round to settle himself comfortably. The wooden shutters did not cover the windows at the top, and he could look straight into the room. There was a great table, with the cloth laid, and wine and roast meat and a glorious fish upon it. The farmer's wife and the parish-clerk were seated at table, and nobody besides. She was filling his glass, and he was digging his fork into the fish, for that was his favourite dish.

'If one could only get some too!' thought Little Claus, as he stretched out his head towards the window. Heavens! what a glorious cake he saw standing there! Yes, certainly, that *was* a feast.

Now he heard someone riding along the high road. It was the woman's husband, who was coming home. He was a good man enough, but he had the strange peculiarity that he could never bear to see a clerk. If a clerk appeared before his eyes he became quite wild. And that was the reason why the clerk had gone to the wife to wish her good-day, because he knew that her husband was not at home; and the good woman therefore put the best fare she had before him. But when they heard the man coming they were frightened, and the woman begged the clerk to creep into a great empty chest which stood in the corner; and he did so, for he knew the husband could not bear the sight of a clerk. The woman quickly hid all the excellent meat and wine in her baking-oven; for if the man had seen that, he would have been certain to ask what it meant.

'Oh, dear!' sighed Little Claus, up in his shed, when he saw all the good fare put away.

'Is there anyone up there?' asked the farmer; and he looked up at Little Claus. 'Why are you lying there? Better come with me into the room.'

And Little Claus told him how he had lost his way, and asked leave to stay there for the night.

'Yes, certainly,' said the peasant, 'but first we must have something to live on.'

The woman received them both in a very friendly way, spread the cloth on a long table, and gave them a great dish of porridge. The farmer was hungry, and ate with a good appetite; but Little Claus could not help thinking of the capital roast meat, fish, and cake, which he knew were in the oven. Under the table, at his feet, he had laid the sack with the horse's hide in it; for we know that he had come out to sell it in the town. He could not relish the porridge, so he trod upon the sack, and the dry skin inside crackled quite loudly.

'Hush,' said Little Claus to his sack; but at the same time he trod on it again, so that it crackled much louder than before.

'Why, what have you in your sack?' asked the farmer.

'Oh, that's a magician,' answered Little Claus. 'He says we are not to eat porridge, for he has conjured the oven full of roast meat, fish, and cake.'

'Wonderful!' cried the farmer; and he opened the oven in a hurry, and found all the dainty provisions which his wife had hidden there, but which, as he thought, the wizard had conjured forth. The woman dared not say anything, but put the things at once on the table; and so they both ate of the meat, the fish, and the cake. Now Little Claus again trod on his sack, and made the hide creak.

'What does he say now?' said the farmer.

'He says,' replied Claus, 'that he has conjured three bottles of wine for us, too, and that they are also standing there in the oven.'

Now the woman was obliged to bring out the wine which she had hidden, and the farmer drank it and became very merry. He would have been very glad to own such a conjuror as Little Claus had there in the sack.

'Can he conjure the demon forth?' asked the farmer. 'I should like to see him, for now I am merry.'

'Oh, yes,' said Little Claus, 'my conjuror can do anything that I ask of him. Can you not?' he added, and trod on the hide, so that it crackled. 'He says "Yes." But the demon is very ugly to look at: we had better not see him.'

'Oh, I'm not at all afraid. Pray, what will he look like?'

'Why, he'll look the very image of a parish-clerk.'

'Ha!' said the farmer, 'that *is* ugly! You must know, I can't bear the sight of a clerk. But it doesn't matter now, for I know that he's a demon, so I shall easily stand it. Now I have courage, but he must not come too near me.'

'Now I will ask my conjuror,' said Little Claus; and he trod on the sack and held his ear down.

'What does he say?'

'He says you may go and open the chest that stands in the corner, and you will see the demon crouching in it; but you must hold the lid so that he doesn't slip out.'

'Will you help me to hold him?' asked the farmer. And he went to the chest where the wife had hidden the real clerk, who sat in there and was very much afraid. The farmer opened the lid a little way and peeped in underneath it.

'Ugh!' he cried, and sprang backward. 'Yes, now I've seen him, and he looked exactly like our clerk. Oh, that was dreadful!'

Upon this they must drink. So they sat and drank until late into the night.

'You must sell me that conjuror,' said the farmer. 'Ask as much as you like for him: I'll give you a whole bushel of money directly.'

'No, that I can't do,' said Little Claus: 'only think how much use I can make of this conjuror.'

'Oh, I should so much like to have him!' cried the farmer; and he went on begging.

'Well,' said Little Claus, at last, 'as you have been so kind as to give me shelter for the night, I will let it be so. You shall have the conjuror for a bushel of money; but I must have the bushel heaped up.'

'That you shall have,' replied the farmer. 'But you must take the chest yonder away with you. I will not keep it in my house an hour. One cannot know – perhaps he may be there still.'

Little Claus gave the farmer his sack with the dry hide in it, and got in exchange a whole bushel of money, and that heaped up. The farmer also gave him a big truck, on which to carry off his money and chest.

'Farewell!' said Little Claus; and he went off with his money and the big chest, in which the clerk was still sitting.

On the other side of the wood was a great deep river. The water rushed along so rapidly that one could scarcely swim against the stream. A fine new bridge had been built over it. Little Claus stopped on the centre of the bridge, and said quite loud, so that the clerk could hear it, 'Ho, what shall I do with this stupid chest? It's as heavy as if stones were in it. I shall only get tired if I drag it any farther, so I'll throw it into the river: if it swims home to me, well and good; and if it does not, it will be no great matter.'

And he took the chest with one hand, and lifted it up a little, as if he intended to throw it into the river.

'No! let be!' cried the clerk from within the chest; 'let me out first!'

'Ugh!' exclaimed Little Claus, pretending to be frightened, 'he's in there still! I must make haste and throw him into the river, that he may be drowned.'

'Oh, no, no!' screamed the clerk. 'I'll give you a whole bushel-full of money if you'll let me go.'

'Why, that's another thing!' said Little Claus; and he opened the chest.

The clerk crept quickly out, pushed the empty chest into the water, and went to his house, where Little Claus received a whole bushel-full of money. He had already received one from the farmer, and so now he had his truck loaded with money.

'See, I've been well paid for the horse,' he said to himself when he had got home to his own room, and was emptying all the money into a heap in the middle of the floor. 'That will vex Great Claus when he hears how rich I have grown through my one horse; but I won't tell him about it outright.'

So he sent a boy to Great Claus to ask for a bushel measure.

'What can he want with it?' thought Great Claus. And he smeared some tar underneath the measure, so that some part of whatever was measured should stick to it. And thus it happened; for when he received the measure back, there were three new threepenny pieces adhering thereto.

'What's this?' cried Great Claus; and he ran off at once to Little Claus. 'Where did you get all that money from?'

'Oh, that's for my horse's skin. I sold it yesterday evening.'

'That's really being well paid,' said Great Claus. And he ran home in a hurry, took an axe, and killed all his four horses; then he flayed them, and carried off their skins to the town.

'Hides! hides! who'll buy any hides?' he cried through the streets.

All the shoemakers and tanners came running, and asked how much he wanted for them.

'A bushel of money for each!' said Great Claus.

'Are you mad?' said they. 'Do you think we have money by the bushel?'

'Hides! hides!' he cried again; and to all who asked him what the hides would cost he replied, 'A bushel of money.'

'He wants to make fools of us,' they all exclaimed. And the shoemakers took their straps, and the tanners their aprons, and they began to beat Great Claus.

'Hides! hides!' they called after him, jeeringly. 'Yes, we'll tan your hide for you till the red broth runs down. Out of the town with him!' And Great Claus made the best haste he could, for he had never yet been thrashed as he was thrashed now.

'Well,' said he when he got home, 'Little Claus shall pay for this. I'll kill him for it.'

Now, at Little Claus's the old grandmother had died. She had been very harsh and unkind to him, but yet he was very sorry, and took the dead woman and laid her in his warm bed, to see if she would not come to life again. There he intended she should remain all through the night, and he himself would sit in the corner and sleep on a chair, as he had often done before. As he sat there, in the night the door opened, and Great Claus came in with his axe. He knew where Little Claus's bed stood; and, going straight up to it, he hit the old grandmother on the head, thinking she was Little Claus.

'D'ye see,' said he, 'you shall not make a fool of me again.' And then he went home.

'That's a bad fellow, that man,' said Little Claus. 'He wanted to kill me. It was a good thing for my old grandmother that she was dead already. He would have taken her life.'

And he dressed his grandmother in her Sunday clothes, borrowed a horse of his neighbour, harnessed it to a car, and put the old lady on the back seat, so that she could not fall out when he drove. And so they trundled through the wood. When the sun rose they were in front of an inn; there Little Claus pulled up, and went in to have some refreshment.

The host had very, very much money; he was also a very good man, but exceedingly hot-tempered, as if he had pepper and tobacco in him.

'Good-morning,' said he to Little Claus. 'You've put on your Sunday clothes early today.'

'Yes,' answered Little Claus; 'I'm going to town with my old grand-mother: she's sitting there on the car without. I can't bring her into the room – will you give her a glass of mead? But you must speak very loud, for she can't hear well.'

'Yes, that I will,' said the host. And he poured out a great glass of mead, and went out with it to the dead grandmother, who had been placed upright in the carriage.

'Here's a glass of mead from your son,' quoth mine host. But the dead woman replied not a word, but sat quite still. 'Don't you hear?' cried the host, as loud as he could, 'here is a glass of mead from your son!'

Once more he called out the same thing, but as she still made not a movement, he became angry at last, and threw the glass in her face, so that the mead ran down over her nose, and she tumbled backwards into the car, for she had only been put upright, and not bound fast.

'Hallo!' cried Little Claus, running out at the door, and seizing the host by the breast; 'you've killed my grandmother now! See, there's a big hole in her forehead.'

'Oh, here's a misfortune!' cried the host, wringing his hands. 'That all comes of my hot temper. Dear Little Claus, I'll give you a bushel of money, and have your grandmother buried as if she were my own; only keep quiet, or I shall have my head cut off, and that would be so very disagreeable!'

So Little Claus again received a whole bushel of money, and the host buried the old grandmother as if she had been his own. And when Little Claus came home with all his money, he at once sent his boy to Great Claus to ask to borrow a bushel measure.

'What's that?' said Great Claus. 'Have I not killed him? I must go myself and see to this.' And so he went over himself with the bushel to Little Claus.

'Now, where did you get all that money from?' he asked; and he opened his eyes wide when he saw all that had been brought together.

'You killed my grandmother, and not me,' replied Little Claus; 'and I've been and sold her, and got a whole bushel of money for her.'

'That's really being well paid,' said Great Claus; and he hastened home, took an axe, and killed his own grandmother directly. Then he put her on a carriage, and drove off to the town with her, to where the apothecary lived, and asked him if he would buy a dead person.

'Who is it, and where did you get him from?' asked the apothecary.

'It's my grandmother,' answered Great Claus. 'I've killed her to get a bushel of money for her.'

'Heaven save us!' cried the apothecary, 'you're raving! Don't say such things, or you may lose your head.' And he told him earnestly what a bad deed this was that he had done, and what a bad man he was, and that he must be punished. And Great Claus was so frightened that he jumped out of the surgery straight into his carriage, and whipped the horses, and drove home. But the apothecary and all the people thought him mad, and so they let him drive whither he would.

'You shall pay for this!' said Great Claus, when he was out upon the high road: 'yes, you shall pay me for this, Little Claus!' And directly he got home he took the biggest sack he could find, and went over to Little Claus and said, 'Now, you've tricked me again! First I killed my horses, and then my old grandmother! That's all your fault; but you shall never trick me any more.' And he seized Little Claus round the body, and thrust him into the sack, and took him upon his back, and called out to him, 'Now I shall go off with you and drown you.'

It was a long way that he had to travel before he came to the river, and Little Claus was not too light to carry. The road led him close to a church: the organ was playing, and the people were singing so beautifully! Then Great Claus put down his sack, with Little Claus in it, close to the church door, and thought it would be a very good thing to go in and hear a psalm before he went farther; for Little Claus could not get out, and all the people were in church; and so he went in.

'Oh, dear! Oh, dear!' sighed Little Claus in the sack. And he turned and twisted, but he found it impossible to loosen the cord. Then there came by an old drover with snow-white hair, and a great staff in his hand: he was driving a whole herd of cows and oxen before him, and they stumbled against the sack in which Little Claus was confined, so that it was overthrown.

'Oh, dear!' sighed Little Claus, 'I'm so young yet, and am to go to heaven directly!'

'And I, poor fellow,' said the drover, 'am so old already, and can't get there yet!'

'Open the sack,' cried Little Claus; 'creep into it instead of me, and you will get to heaven directly.'

'With all my heart,' replied the drover; and he untied the sack, out of which Little Claus crept forth immediately.

'But will you look after the cattle?' said the old man; and he crept into the sack at once, whereupon Little Claus tied it up, and went his way with all the cows and oxen.

Soon afterwards Great Claus came out of the church. He took the sack on his shoulders again, although it seemed to him as if the sack had become lighter; for the old drover was only half as heavy as Little Claus.

'How light he is to carry now! Yes, that is because I have heard a psalm.'

So he went to the river, which was deep and broad, threw the sack with the old drover in it into the water, and called after him, thinking that it was little Claus, 'You lie there! Now you shan't trick me any more!'

Then he went home; but when he came to a place where there was a cross-road, he met Little Claus driving all his beasts.

'What's this?' cried Great Claus. 'Have I not drowned you?'

'Yes,' replied Little Claus, 'you threw me into the river less than half an hour ago.'

'But wherever did you get all those fine beasts from?' asked Great Claus.

'These beasts are sea-cattle,' replied Little Claus. 'I'll tell you the whole story, and thank you for drowning me, for now I'm at the top of the tree. I am really rich! How frightened I was when I lay huddled in the sack, and the wind whistled about my ears when you threw me down from the bridge into the cold water! I sank to the bottom immediately; but I did not knock myself, for the most splendid soft grass grows down there. Upon that I fell; and immediately the sack was opened, and the loveliest maiden, with snow-white garments and a green wreath upon her wet hair, took me by the hand, and said, "Are you come, Little Claus? Here you have some cattle to begin with. A mile farther along the road there is a whole herd more, which I will give to you." And now I saw that the river formed a great highway for the people of the sea. Down in its bed they walked and drove directly from the sea, and straight into the land, to where the river ends. There it was so beautifully full of flowers and of the freshest grass; the fishes, which swam in the water, shot past my ears, just as here the birds in the air. What pretty people there were there, and what fine cattle pasturing on mounds and in ditches!'

'But why did you come up again to us directly?' asked Great Claus. 'I should not have done that, if it is so beautiful down there.'

'Why,' replied Little Claus, 'just in that I acted with good policy. You heard me tell you that the sea-maiden said, "A mile farther along the road" – and by the road she meant the river, for she can't go anywhere else – "there is a whole herd of cattle for you." But I know what bends the stream makes – sometimes this way, sometimes that; there's a long way to go round: no, the thing can be managed in a shorter way by coming here to the land, and driving across the fields towards the river again. In this manner I save myself almost half a mile, and get all the quicker to my sea-cattle!'

'Oh, you are a fortunate man!' said Great Claus. 'Do you think I should get some sea-cattle too if I went down to the bottom of the river?'

'Yes, I think so,' replied Little Claus. 'But I cannot carry you in the sack as far as the river; you are too heavy for me! But if you will go there, and creep into the sack yourself, I will throw you in with a great deal of pleasure.'

'Thanks!' said Great Claus; 'but if I don't get any seacattle when I am down there, I shall beat you, you may be sure!'

'Oh, no; don't be so fierce!'

And so they went together to the river. When the beasts, which were thirsty, saw the stream, they ran as fast as they could to get at the water.

'See how they hurry!' cried Little Claus. 'They are longing to get back to the bottom.'

'Yes, but help me first!' said Great Claus, 'or else you shall be beaten.'

And so he crept into the great sack, which had been laid across the back of one of the oxen.

'Put a stone in, for I'm afraid I shan't sink else,' said Great Claus.

'That will be all right,' replied Little Claus; and he put a big stone into the sack, tied the rope tightly, and pushed against it. *Plump!* There lay Great Claus in the river, and sank at once to the bottom.

'I'm afraid he won't find the cattle!' said Little Claus; and then he drove homeward with what he had.

The Princess on the Pea

THERE WAS once a Prince who wanted to marry a princess; but she was to be a *real* princess. So he travelled about, all through the world, to find a real one, but everywhere there was something in the way. There were princesses enough, but whether they were *real* princesses he could not quite make out: there was always something that did not seem quite right. So he came home again, and was quite sad; for he wished so much to have a real princess.

One evening a terrible storm came on. It lightened and thundered, the rain streamed down; it was quite fearful! Then there was a knocking at the town-gate, and the old King went out to open it.

It was a Princess who stood outside the gate. But, mercy! how she looked, from the rain and the rough weather! The water ran down her hair and her clothes; it ran in at the points of her shoes, and out at the heels; and yet she declared that she was a real princess.

'Yes, we will soon find that out,' thought the old Queen. But she said nothing, only went into the bedchamber, took all the bedding off, and put a pea on the bottom of the bedstead; then she took twenty mattresses and laid them upon the pea, and then twenty eiderdown quilts upon the mattresses. On this the Princess had to lie all night. In the morning she was asked how she had slept.

'Oh, miserably!' said the Princess. 'I scarcely closed my eyes all night long. Goodness knows what was in my bed. I lay upon something hard, so that I am black and blue all over. It is quite dreadful!'

Now they saw that she was a real princess, for through the twenty mattresses and the twenty eiderdown quilts she had felt the pea. No one but a real princess could be so tender-skinned.

So the Prince took her for his wife, for now he knew that he had a true princess; and the pea was put in the museum, and it is still to be seen there, unless somebody has carried it off.

Look you, this is a true story.

Little Ida's Flowers

'MY POOR FLOWERS are quite dead!' said little Ida. 'They were so pretty yesterday evening, and now all the leaves hang withered. Why do they do that?' she asked the student, who sat on the sofa; for she liked him very much. He knew the prettiest stories, and could cut out the most amusing pictures – hearts, with little ladies in them who danced, flowers, and great castles in which one could open the doors: he was a merry student. 'Why do the flowers look so faded today?' she asked again, and showed him a whole bouquet, which was quite withered.

'Do you know what's the matter with them?' said the student. 'The flowers have been at a ball last night, and that's why they hang their heads.'

'But flowers cannot dance!' cried little Ida.

'Oh, yes,' said the student, 'when it grows dark, and we are asleep, they jump about merrily. Almost every night they have a ball.'

'Can no children go to this ball?'

'Yes,' said the student, 'quite little daisies, and lilies of the valley.'

'Where do the most beautiful flowers dance?' asked little Ida.

'Have you not often been outside the town-gate, by the great castle, where the king lives in summer, and where the beautiful garden is, with all the flowers? You have seen the swans, which swim up to you when you want to give them bread crumbs? There are capital balls there, believe me.'

'I was out there in the garden yesterday, with my mother,' said Ida; 'but all the leaves were off the trees, and there was not one flower left. Where are they? In the summer I saw so many.'

'They are within, in the castle,' replied the student. 'You must know, as soon as the king and all the court go to town, the flowers run out of the garden into the castle, and are merry. You should see that. The two most beautiful roses seat themselves on the throne, and then they are king and queen; all the red coxcombs range themselves on either side, and stand and bow; they are the chamberlains. Then all the pretty flowers come, and there is a great ball. The blue violets represent little naval cadets: they dance with hyacinths and crocuses, which they call young ladies; the tulips and the great tiger-lilies are old ladies who keep watch that the dancing is well done, and that everything goes on with propriety.'

'But,' asked little Ida, 'does nobody do anything to the flowers, for dancing in the king's castle?'

'There is nobody who really knows about it,' answered the student. 'Sometimes, certainly, the old steward of the castle comes at night, and he has to watch there. He has a great bunch of keys with him; but as soon as the flowers hear the keys rattle they are quite quiet, hide behind the long curtains, and only poke their heads out. Then the old steward says, "I smell that there are flowers here," but he cannot see them.'

'That is famous!' cried little Ida, clapping her hands. 'But should not I be able to see the flowers?'

'Yes,' said the student; 'only remember, when you go out again, to peep through the window; then you will see them. That is what I did today. There was a long yellow lily lying on the sofa and stretching herself. She imagined herself to be a court lady.'

'Can the flowers out of the Botanical Garden get there? Can they go the long distance?'

'Yes, certainly,' replied the student; 'if they like they can fly. Have you not seen the beautiful butterflies, red, yellow, and white? They almost look like flowers; and that is what they have been. They have flown off their stalks high into the air, and have beaten it with their leaves, as if these leaves were little wings, and thus they flew. And because they behaved themselves well, they got leave to fly about in the daytime too, and were not obliged to go home again and to sit still upon their stalks; and thus at last the leaves became real wings. That you have seen yourself. It may be, however, that the flowers in the Botanical Garden have never been in the king's castle, or that they don't know of the merry proceedings there at night. Therefore I will tell you something: he will be very much surprised, the botanical professor, who lives close by here. You know him, do you not? When you come into his garden, you must tell one of the flowers that there is a great ball yonder in the castle. Then that flower will tell it to all the rest, and then they will fly away: if the professor then comes out into the garden, there will not be a single flower left, and he won't be able to make out where they are gone.'

'But how can one flower tell it to another? For, you know, flowers cannot speak.'

'That they cannot, certainly,' replied the student; 'but then they make signs. Have you not noticed that when the wind blows a little, the flowers nod at one another, and move all their green leaves? They can understand that just as well as if they talked.'

'Can the professor understand these signs?' asked Ida.

'Yes, certainly. He came one morning into his garden, and saw a great stinging-nettle standing there, and making signs to a beautiful red carnation with its leaves. It was saying, "You are so pretty, and I love you so much." But the professor does not like that kind of thing, and he directly slapped the stinging-nettle upon its leaves, for those are its fingers; but he stung himself, and since that time he has not dared to touch a stinging-nettle.'

'That was funny,' cried little Ida; and she laughed.

'How can anyone put such notions into a child's head?' said the tiresome privy councillor, who had come to pay a visit, and was sitting on the sofa. He did not like the student, and always grumbled when he saw him cutting out the comical funny pictures – sometimes a man hanging on a gibbet and holding a heart in his hand, to show that he stole hearts; sometimes an old witch riding on a broom, and carrying her husband on her nose. The councillor could not bear this, and then he said, just as he did now, 'How can anyone put such notions into a child's head? Those are stupid fancies!'

But to little Ida, what the student told about her flowers seemed very entertaining; and she thought much about it. The flowers hung their heads, for they were tired because they had danced all night; they were certainly ill. Then she went with them to all her other toys, which stood on a pretty little table, and the whole drawer was full of beautiful things. In the doll's bed lay her doll Sophy, asleep; but little Ida said to her, 'You must really get up, Sophy, and manage to lie in the drawer for tonight. The poor flowers are ill, and they must lie in your bed; perhaps they will then get well again.'

And she at once took the doll out; but the doll looked cross, and did not say a single word; for she was angry because she could not keep her own bed.

Then Ida laid the flowers in the doll's bed, pulled the little coverlet quite up over them, and said they were to lie still and be good, and she would make them some tea, so that they might get well again, and be able to get up tomorrow. And she drew the curtains closely round the little bed, so that the sun should not shine in their eyes. The whole evening through she could not help thinking of what the student had told her. And when she was going to bed herself, she was obliged first to look behind the curtain which hung before the windows where her mother's beautiful flowers stood – hyacinths as well as tulips; then she whispered quite softly. 'I know you're going to the ball tonight!' But the flowers made as if they did not understand a word, and did not stir a leaf; but still little Ida knew what she knew.

When she was in bed she lay for a long time thinking how pretty it must be to see the beautiful flowers dancing out in the king's castle. 'I wonder if my flowers have really been there?' And then she fell asleep. In the night she awoke again: she had dreamed of the flowers, and of the student with whom the councillor found fault. It was quite quiet in the bedroom where Ida lay; the night-lamp burned on the table, and father and mother were asleep.

'I wonder if my flowers are still lying in Sophy's bed?' she thought to herself. 'How I should like to know it!' She raised herself a little, and looked at the door, which stood ajar; within lay the flowers and all her playthings. She listened, and then it seemed to her as if she heard someone playing on the piano in the next room, but quite softly and prettily, as she had never heard it before.

'Now all the flowers are certainly dancing in there!' thought she. 'Oh, how much I should like to see it!' But she dared not get up, for she would have disturbed her father and mother.

'If they would only come in!' thought she. But the flowers did not come, and the music continued to play beautifully; then she could not bear it any longer, for it was too pretty; she crept out of her little bed, and went quietly to the door, and looked into the room. Oh, how splendid it was, what she saw!

There was no night-lamp burning, but still it was quite light: the moon shone through the window into the middle of the floor; it was almost like day. All the hyacinths and tulips stood in two long rows on the floor; there were none at all left at the window. There stood the empty flowerpots. On the floor all the flowers were dancing very gracefully round each other, making a perfect chain, and holding each other by the long green leaves as they swung round. But at the piano sat a great yellow lily, which little Ida had certainly seen in summer, for she remembered how the student had said, 'How like that one is to Miss Lina.' Then he had been laughed at by all; but now it seemed really to little Ida as if the long yellow flower looked like the young lady; and it had just her manners in playing – sometimes bending its long yellow face to one side, sometimes to the other, and nodding in tune to the charming music! No one noticed little Ida. Then she saw a great blue crocus hop into the middle of the table, where the toys stood, and go to the doll's bed and pull the curtains aside; there lay the sick flowers, but they got up directly, and nodded to the others, to say that they wanted to dance too. The old chimney-sweep doll, whose under lip was broken off, stood up and bowed to the pretty flowers: these did not look at all ill now; they jumped down among the others, and were very merry.

Then it seemed as if something fell down from the table. Ida looked that way. It was the Shrovetide birch rod which was jumping down! it seemed almost as if it belonged to the flowers. At any rate it was very neat; and a little wax doll, with just such a broad hat on its head as the councillor wore, sat upon it. The birch rod hopped about among the flowers on its three red legs, and stamped quite loud, for it was dancing the mazurka; and the other flowers could not manage that dance, because they were too light, and unable to stamp like that.

The wax doll on the birch rod all at once became quite great and long, turned itself over the paper flowers, and said, 'How can one put such things in a child's head? Those are stupid fancies!' and then the wax doll was exactly like the councillor with the broad hat, and looked just as yellow and cross as he. But the paper flowers hit him on his thin legs, and then he shrank up again, and became quite a little wax doll. That was very amusing to see; and little Ida could not restrain her laughter. The birch rod went on dancing, and the councillor was obliged to dance too; it was no use whether he might make himself great and long, or remained the little yellow wax doll with the big black hat. Then the other flowers put in a good word for him, especially those who had lain in the doll's bed, and then the birch rod gave over. At the same moment there was a loud knocking at the drawer, inside where Ida's doll, Sophy, lay with many other toys. The chimney-sweep ran to the edge of the table, lay flat down on his stomach, and began to pull the drawer out a little. Then Sophy raised herself, and looked round quite astonished.

'There must be a ball here,' said she; 'why did nobody tell me?'

'Will you dance with me?' asked the chimney-sweep.

'You are a nice sort of fellow to dance!' she replied, and turned her back upon him.

Then she seated herself upon the drawer, and thought that one of the flowers would come and ask her; but not one of them came. Then she coughed, 'Hem! hem! hem!' but for all that not one came. The chimney-sweep now danced all alone, and that was not at all so bad.

As none of the flowers seemed to notice Sophy, she let herself fall down from the drawer straight upon the floor, so that there was a great noise. The flowers now all came running up, to ask if she had not hurt herself; and they were all very polite to her, especially the flowers that had lain in her bed. But she had not hurt herself at all; and Ida's flowers all thanked her for the nice bed, and were kind to her, took her into the middle of the floor, where the moon shone in, and danced with her; and all the other flowers formed a circle round her. Now Sophy was glad, and said they might keep her bed; she did not at all mind lying in the drawer.

But the flowers said, 'We thank you heartily, but we cannot live so long. Tomorrow we shall be quite dead. But tell little Ida she is to bury us out in the garden, where the canary lies; then we shall wake up again in summer, and be far more beautiful.'

'No, you must not die,' said Sophy; and she kissed the flowers.

At that moment the door opened, and a great number of splendid flowers came dancing in. Ida could not imagine whence they had come; these must certainly all be flowers from the king's castle yonder. First of all came two glorious roses, and they had little gold crowns on; they were a king and a queen. Then came the prettiest stocks and carnations; and they bowed in all directions. They had music with them. Great poppies and peonies blew upon pea-pods till they were quite red in the face. The blue hyacinths and the little white snow-drops rang just as if they had bells on them. That was wonderful music! Then came many other flowers, and danced all together; the blue violets and the pink primroses, daisies and the lilies of the valley. And all the flowers kissed one another. It was beautiful to look at!

At last the flowers wished one another good-night; then little Ida, too, crept to bed, where she dreamed of all she had seen.

When she rose next morning, she went quickly to the little table, to see if the flowers were still there. She drew aside the curtains of the little bed; there were they all, but they were quite faded, far more than yesterday. Sophy was lying in the drawer where Ida had laid her; she looked very sleepy.

'Do you remember what you were to say to me?' asked little Ida.

But Sophy looked quite stupid, and did not say a single word.

'You are not good at all!' said Ida. 'And yet they all danced with you.'

Then she took a little paper box, on which were painted beautiful birds, and opened it, and laid the dead flowers in it.

'That shall be your pretty coffin,' said she, 'and when my Norwegian cousins come to visit me by and by, they shall help me to bury you outside in the garden, so that you may grow again in summer, and become more beautiful than ever.'

The Norwegian cousins were two smart boys. Their names were Jonas and Adolphe; their father had given them two new crossbows, and they had brought these with them to show to Ida. She told them about the poor flowers which had died, and then they got leave to bury them. The two boys went first, with their crossbows on their shoulders, and little Ida followed with the dead flowers in the pretty box. Out in the garden a little grave was dug. Ida first kissed the flowers, and then laid them in the earth in the box, and Adolphe and Jonas shot with their crossbows over the grave, for they had neither guns nor cannons.

Thumbelina

THERE WAS once a woman who wished for a very little child; but she did not know where she should procure one. So she went to an old witch, and said, 'I do so very much wish for a little child! can you not tell me where I can get one?'

'Oh! that could easily be managed,' said the witch. 'There you have a barleycorn: that is not of the kind which grows in the countryman's field, and which the chickens get to eat. Put it into a flowerpot, and you shall see what you shall see.'

'Thank you,' said the woman; and she gave the witch a groat.

Then she went home and planted the barleycorn, and immediately there grew up a great handsome flower, which looked like a tulip; but the leaves were tightly closed, as though it were still a bud.

'It is a beautiful flower,' said the woman; and she kissed its beautiful yellow and red leaves. But just as she kissed it the flower opened with a loud crack. It was a real tulip, as one could now see; but in the middle of the flower there sat upon the green stamens a little maiden, delicate and graceful to behold. She was scarcely half a thumb's length in height, and therefore she was called Thumbelina.

A neat polished walnut-shell served Thumbelina for a cradle, blue violet-leaves were her mattresses, with a rose-leaf for a coverlet. There she slept at night; but in the daytime she played upon the table, where the woman had put a plate with a wreath of flowers around it, whose stalks stood in water; on the water swam a great tulip-leaf, and on this the little maiden could sit, and row from one side of the plate to the other, with two white horse-hairs for oars. That looked pretty indeed! She could also sing, and, indeed, so delicately and sweetly, that the like had never been heard.

One night as she lay in her pretty bed, there came a horrid old Toad hopping in at the window, in which one pane was broken. The Toad was very ugly, big, and damp: it hopped straight down upon the table, where Thumbelina lay sleeping under the red rose-leaf.

'That would be a handsome wife for my son,' said the Toad; and she took the walnut-shell in which Thumbelina lay asleep, and hopped with it through the window down into the garden.

There ran a great broad brook; but the margin was swampy and soft, and here the Toad dwelt with her son. Ugh! he was ugly, and looked just like his mother. 'Croak! croak! brek kek-kex!' that was all he could say when he saw the graceful little maiden in the walnutshell.

'Don't speak so loud, or she will awake,' said the old Toad. 'She might run away from us yet, for she is as light as a bit of swan's-down. We will put her out in the brook upon one of the broad water-lily leaves. That will be just like an island for her, she is so small and light. Then she can't get away, while we put the state-room under the mud in order, where you are to live and keep house together.'

Out in the brook there grew many water-lilies with broad green leaves, which looked as if they were floating on the water. The leaf which lay farthest out was also the greatest of all, and to that the old Toad swam out and laid the walnutshell upon it with Thumbelina. The poor little thing woke early in the morning, and when she saw where she was, she began to cry very bitterly; for there was water on every side of the great green leaf, and she could not get to land at all. The old Toad sat down in the mud, decking out her room with sedges and yellow water-lilies – it was to be made very pretty for the new daughter-in-law; then she swam out, with her ugly son, to the leaf on which Thumbelina was. They wanted to take her pretty bed, which was to be put in the bridal chamber before she went in there herself. The old Toad bowed low before her in the water, and said, 'Here is my son; he will be your husband, and you will live splendidly together in the mud.'

'Croak! croak! brek-kek-kex!' was all the son could say.

Then they took the elegant little bed, and swam away with it; but Thumbelina sat all alone upon the green leaf and wept, for she did not like to live at the nasty Toad's, and have her ugly son for a husband. The little fishes swimming in the water below had both seen the Toad, and had also heard what she said; therefore they stretched forth their heads, for they wanted to see the little girl. So soon as they saw her they considered her so pretty that they felt very sorry she should have to go down to the ugly Toad. No, that must never be! They assembled together in the water around the green stalk which held the leaf on which the little maiden stood, and with their teeth they gnawed away the stalk, and so the leaf swam down the stream; and away went Thumbelina far away, where the Toad could not get at her.

Thumbelina sailed by many places, and the little birds which sat in the bushes saw her, and said, 'What a lovely little girl!' The leaf swam away with her, farther and farther; so Thumbelina travelled out of the country.

A graceful little white butterfly continued to flutter round her, and at last alighted on the leaf. Thumbelina pleased him, and she was so delighted, for now the Toad could not reach her; and it was so beautiful where she was floating along – the sun shone upon the water, it was just like shining gold. She took her girdle and bound one end of it round the butterfly, fastening the other end of the ribbon to the leaf. The leaf now glided onward much faster, and Thumbelina too, for she stood upon the leaf.

There came a big cockchafer flying up; and he saw her, and immediately clasped his claws round her slender waist, and flew with her up into a tree. The green leaf went swimming down the brook, and the butterfly with it; for he was fastened to the leaf, and could not get away from it.

Mercy! how frightened poor little Thumbelina was when the Cockchafer flew with her up into the tree! But especially she was sorry for the fine white butterfly whom she had bound fast to the leaf, for, if he could not free himself from it, he would be forced to starve to death. The Cockchafer, however, did not trouble himself at all about this. He seated himself with her upon the biggest green leaf of the tree, gave her the sweet part of the flowers to eat, and declared that she was very pretty, though she did not in the least resemble a cockchafer. Afterwards came all the other cockchafers who lived in the tree to pay a visit: they looked at Thumbelina, and the lady cockchafers shrugged

their feelers and said, 'Why, she has not even more than two legs! that
has a wretched appearance.'

'She has not any feelers!' cried another.

'Her waist is quite slender – fie! she looks like a human creature –
how ugly she is!' said all the lady cockchafers.

And yet Thumbelina was very pretty. Even the Cockchafer who had
carried her off thought so; but when all the others declared she was
ugly, he believed it at last, and would not have her at all – she might go
whither she liked. Then they flew down with her from the tree, and set
her upon a daisy, and she wept, because she was so ugly that the
cockchafers would not have her; and yet she was the loveliest little
being one could imagine, and as tender and delicate as a rose-leaf.

The whole summer through poor Thumbelina lived quite alone in
the great wood. She wove herself a bed out of blades of grass, and hung
it up under a large burdock leaf, so that she was protected from the
rain; she plucked the honey out of the flowers for food, and drank of
the dew which stood every morning upon the leaves. Thus summer

and autumn passed away; but now came winter, the cold long winter. All the birds who had sung so sweetly to her flew away; trees and flowers shed their leaves; the great burdock leaf under which she had lived shrivelled up, and there remained nothing of it but a yellow withered stalk; and she was dreadfully cold, for her clothes were torn, and she herself was so frail and delicate – poor little Thumbelina! she was nearly frozen. It began to snow, and every snowflake that fell upon her was like a whole shovel-full thrown upon one of us, for we are tall, and she was only an inch long. Then she wrapped herself in a dry leaf, but that would not warm her – she shivered with cold.

Close to the wood into which she had now come lay a great corn-field, but the corn was gone long ago; only the naked dry stubble stood up out of the frozen ground. These were just like a great forest for her to wander through; and, oh! how she trembled with cold. Then she arrived at the door of the Field Mouse. This mouse had a little hole under the stubble. There the Field Mouse lived, warm and comfortable, and had a whole room-full of corn – a glorious kitchen and larder. Poor Thumbelina stood at the door just like a poor beggar girl, and begged for a little bit of a barleycorn, for she had not had the smallest morsel to eat for the last two days.

'You poor little creature,' said the Field Mouse – for after all she was a good old Field Mouse – 'come into my warm room and dine with me.'

As she was pleased with Thumbelina, she said, 'If you like you may stay with me through the winter, but you must keep my room clean and neat, and tell me stories, for I am very fond of them.'

And Thumbelina did as the kind old Field Mouse bade her, and had a very good time of it.

'Now we shall soon have a visitor,' said the Field Mouse. 'My neighbour is in the habit of visiting me once a week. He is even better off than I am, has great rooms, and a beautiful black velvety fur. If you could only get him for your husband you would be well provided for; but he cannot see at all. You must tell him the very prettiest stories you know.'

But Thumbelina did not care about this; she would not have the

neighbour at all, for he was a Mole. He came and paid his visits in his black velvet coat. The Field Mouse told how rich and how learned he was, and how his house was more than twenty times larger than hers; that he had learning, but that he did not like the sun and beautiful flowers, and said nasty things about them, for he had never seen them.

Thumbelina had to sing, and she sang 'Cockchafer, fly away,' and 'When the parson goes afield.' Then the Mole fell in love with her, because of her delicious voice; but he said nothing, for he was a sedate man.

A short time before, he had dug a long passage through the earth from his own house to theirs; and Thumbelina and the Field Mouse obtained leave to walk in this passage as much as they wished. But he begged them not to be afraid of the dead bird which was lying in the passage. It was an entire bird, with wings and a beak. It certainly must have died only a short time before, when the winter began, and was now buried just where the Mole had made his passage.

The Mole took a bit of decayed wood in his mouth, for that glimmers like fire in the dark; and then he went first and lighted them through the long dark passage. When they came where the dead bird lay, the Mole thrust up his broad nose against the ceiling and pushed the earth, so that a great hole was made, through which the daylight could shine down. In the middle of the floor lay a dead Swallow, his beautiful wings pressed close against his sides, and his head and feet drawn in under his feathers: the poor bird had certainly died of cold. Thumbelina was very sorry for this; she was very fond of all the little birds, who had sung and twittered so prettily for her through the summer; but the Mole gave him a push with his short legs, and said, 'Now he doesn't pipe any more. It must be miserable to be born a little bird. I'm thankful that none of my children can be that: such a bird has nothing but his "tweet-tweet", and has to starve in the winter!'

'Yes, you may well say that, like a sensible man,' observed the Field Mouse. 'Of what use is all this "tweet-tweet" to a bird when the winter comes? He must starve and freeze. But they say that's very aristocratic.'

Thumbelina said nothing; but when the two others turned their backs on the bird, she bent down, put the feathers aside which covered his head, and kissed him upon his closed eyes.

'Perhaps it was he who sang so prettily to me in the summer,' she thought. 'How much pleasure he gave me, the dear beautiful bird!'

The Mole now closed up the hole through which the daylight shone in, and accompanied the ladies home. But at night Thumbelina could not sleep at all; so she got up out of her bed, and wove a large beautiful carpet of hay, and carried it and spread it over the dead bird, and laid soft cotton, which she had found in the Field Mouse's room, at the bird's sides, so that he might lie warm in the cold ground.

'Farewell, you pretty little bird!' said she. 'Farewell! and thanks to you for your beautiful song in the summer, when all the trees were green, and the sun shone down warmly upon us.' And then she laid her head on the bird's breast, but at once was greatly startled, for it felt as if something were beating inside there. That was the bird's heart. The bird was not dead; he was only lying there torpid with cold; and now he had been warmed, and came to life again.

In autumn all the swallows fly away to warm countries; but if one happens to be belated, it becomes so cold that it falls down as if dead, and lies where it falls, and then the cold snow covers it.

Thumbelina fairly trembled, she was so startled; for the bird was large, very large, compared with her, who was only an inch in height. But she took courage, laid the cotton closer round the poor bird, and brought a leaf of mint that she had used as her own coverlet, and laid it over the bird's head.

The next night she crept out to him again – and now he was alive, but quite weak; he could only open his eyes for a moment, and look at Thumbelina, who stood before him with a bit of decayed wood in her hand, for she had no other lantern.

'I thank you, you pretty little child,' said the sick Swallow; 'I have been famously warmed. Soon I shall get my strength back again, and I shall be able to fly about in the warm sunshine.'

'Oh,' she said, 'it is so cold without. It snows and freezes. Stay in your warm bed, and I will nurse you.'

Then she brought the Swallow water in the petal of a flower; and the Swallow drank, and told her how he had torn one of his wings in a thorn bush, and thus had not been able to fly as fast as the other swallows, which had sped away, far away, to the warm countries. So at last he had fallen to the ground, but he could remember nothing more, and did not know at all how he had come where she had found him.

The whole winter the Swallow remained there, and Thumbelina nursed and tended him heartily. Neither the Field Mouse nor the Mole heard anything about it, for they did not like the poor Swallow. So soon as the spring came, and the sun warmed the earth, the Swallow bade Thumbelina farewell, and she opened the hole which the Mole had made in the ceiling. The sun shone in upon them gloriously, and the Swallow asked if Thumbelina would go with him; she could sit upon his back, and they would fly away far into the green wood. But Thumbelina knew that the old Field Mouse would be grieved if she left her.

'No, I cannot!' said Thumbelina.

'Farewell, farewell, you good, pretty girl!' said the Swallow; and he flew out into the sunshine. Thumbelina looked after him, and the tears came into her eyes, for she was so fond of the poor Swallow.

'Tweet-weet! tweet-weet!' sang the bird, and flew into the green forest. Thumbelina felt very sad. She did not get permission to go out into the warm sunshine. The corn which was sown in the field over the house of the Field Mouse grew up high into the air; it was quite a thick wood for the poor girl, who was only an inch in height.

'Now you must work at your outfit this summer,' said the Field Mouse to her; for her neighbour, the tiresome Mole with the velvet coat, had proposed to her. 'You shall have woollen and linen clothes both; you will lack nothing when you have become the Mole's wife.'

Thumbelina had to turn the spindle, and the Mole hired four spiders to spin and weave for her day and night. Every evening the Mole paid her a visit; and he was always saying that when the summer should draw to a close, the sun would not shine nearly so hot, for that now it burned the earth almost as hard as a stone. Yes, when the summer should have gone, then he would keep his wedding day with Thumbelina. But she was not glad at all, for she did not like the tiresome Mole. Every morning when the sun rose, and every evening when it went down, she crept out at the door; and when the wind blew the corn ears apart, so that she could see the blue sky, she thought how bright and beautiful it was out here, and wished so much to see her dear Swallow again. But the Swallow did not come back; he had doubtless flown far away, in the fair green forest. When autumn came on, Thumbelina had all her outfit ready.

'In four weeks you shall celebrate your wedding,' said the Field Mouse to her.

But Thumbelina wept, and declared she would not have the tiresome Mole.

'Nonsense,' said the Field Mouse; 'don't be obstinate, or I will bite you with my white teeth. He is a very fine man whom you will marry. The queen herself has not such a black velvet fur; and his kitchen and cellar are full. Be thankful for your good fortune.'

Now the wedding was to be held. The Mole had already come to fetch Thumbelina; she was to live with him, deep under the earth, and never to come out into the warm sunshine, for that he did not like. The poor little thing was very sorrowful; she was now to say farewell to the glorious sun, which, after all, she had been allowed by the Field Mouse to see from the threshold of the door.

'Farewell, thou bright sun!' she said, and stretched out her arms towards it, and walked a little way forth from the house of the Field Mouse, for now the corn had been reaped, and only the dry stubble stood in the fields. 'Farewell!' she repeated, and threw her little arms round a little red flower which still bloomed there. 'Greet the dear Swallow from me, if you see her again.'

'Tweet-weet! tweet-weet!' a voice suddenly sounded over her head. She looked up; it was the Swallow, who was just flying by. When he saw Thumbelina he was very glad; and Thumbelina told him how loth she was to have the ugly Mole for her husband, and that she was to live deep under the earth, where the sun never shone. And she could not refrain from weeping.

'The cold winter is coming now,' said the Swallow; 'I am going to fly far away into the warm countries. Will you come with me? You can sit upon my back, only tie yourself fast with your sash, then we shall fly from the ugly Mole and his dark room – away, far away, over the mountains, to the warm countries, where the sun shines more beautifully than here, where it is always summer, and there are lovely flowers. Only fly with me, you dear little Thumbelina, you who saved my life when I lay frozen in the dark earthy passage.'

'Yes, I will go with you!' said Thumbelina, and she seated herself on the bird's back, with her feet on his outspread wings, and bound her girdle fast to one of his strongest feathers; then the Swallow flew up into the air over forest and over sea, high up over the great mountains, where the snow always lies; and Thumbelina felt cold in the bleak air, but then she crept under the bird's warm feathers, and only put out her little head to admire all the beauties beneath her.

At last they came to the warm countries. There the sun shone far brighter than here; the sky seemed twice as high; in ditches and on the hedges grew the most beautiful blue and green grapes; lemons and oranges hung in the woods; the air was fragrant with myrtles and balsams, and on the roads the loveliest children ran about, playing with the gay butterflies. But the Swallow flew still farther, and it became more and more beautiful. Under the most glorious green trees by the blue lake stood a palace of dazzling white marble, from the olden time. Vines clustered around the lofty pillars; at the top were many swallows' nests, and in one of these the Swallow lived who carried Thumbelina.

'Here is my house,' said the Swallow. 'But if you will select for yourself one of the splendid flowers which grow down yonder, then I will put you into it, and you shall have everything as nice as you can wish.'

'That is capital,' cried she, and clapped her little hands.

A great marble pillar lay there, which had fallen to the ground and had been broken into three pieces; but between these pieces grew the most beautiful great white flowers. The Swallow flew down with Thumbelina, and set her upon one of the broad leaves. But how great was the little maid's surprise! There sat a little man in the midst of the flower, as white and transparent as if he had been made of glass; he wore the daintiest of gold crowns on his head, and the brightest wings on his shoulders; he himself was not bigger than Thumbelina. He was the angel of the flower. In each of the flowers dwelt such a little man or woman, but this one was king over them all.

'Heavens! how beautiful he is!' whispered Thumbelina to the Swallow.

The little prince was very much frightened at the Swallow; for it was quite a gigantic bird to him, who was so small. But when he saw Thumbelina, he became very glad; she was the prettiest maiden he had ever seen. Therefore he took off his golden crown, and put it upon her, asked her name, and if she would be his wife, and then she should be queen of all the flowers. Now this was truly a different kind of man to the son of the Toad, and the Mole with the black velvet fur. She therefore said 'Yes' to the charming prince. And out of every flower came a lady or a lord, so pretty to behold that it was a delight: each one brought Thumbelina a present; but the best gift was a pair of beautiful wings which had belonged to a great white fly; these were fastened to Thumbelina's back, and now she could fly from flower to flower. Then there was much rejoicing; and the Swallow sat above them in her nest, and sung for them as well as she could; but yet in her heart she was sad, for she was so fond of Thumbelina, and would have liked never to part from her.

'You shall not be called Thumbelina!' said the Flower Angel to her; 'that is an ugly name, and you are too fair for it – we will call you Maia.'

'Farewell, farewell!' said the Swallow, and she flew away again from the warm countries, far away back to Denmark. There she had a little nest over the window of the man who can tell fairy tales. To him she sang 'Tweet-weet! tweet-weet!' and from him we have the whole story.

The Naughty Boy

THERE was once an old poet – a very good old poet. One evening, as he sat at home, there was dreadfully bad weather outside. The rain streamed down: but the old poet sat comfortably by his stove, where the fire was burning and the roasting apples were hissing.

'There won't be a dry thread left on the poor people who are out in this weather!' said he, for he was a good old poet.

'Oh, open to me! I am cold and quite wet,' said a little child outside; and it cried, and knocked at the door, while the rain streamed down, and the wind made all the casements rattle.

'You poor little creature!' said the poet; and he went to open the door. There stood a little boy; he was quite naked, and the water ran in streams from his long fair curls. He was shivering with cold, and had he not been let in, he would certainly have perished in the bad weather.

'You poor little creature!' said the poet, and took him by the hand, 'come to me, and I will warm you. You shall have wine and an apple, for you are a pretty boy.'

And so he was. His eyes sparkled like two bright stars, and though the water ran down from his fair curls, they fell in beautiful ringlets. He looked like a little angel-child, but was white with cold and trembled all over. In his hand he carried a lovely bow, but it looked quite spoiled by the wet; all the colours in the beautiful arrows had been blurred together by the rain.

The old poet sat down by the stove, took the little boy on his knees, pressed the water out of the long curls, warmed his hands in his own, and heated sweet wine for him; then the boy recovered himself, and his cheeks grew red and he jumped to the floor and danced round the old poet.

'You are a merry boy,' said the old poet. 'What is your name?'

'My name is Cupid,' he replied; 'don't you know me? There lies my

bow – I shoot with that, you may believe me! See, now the weather is
clearing up outside, and the moon shines.'

'But your bow is spoiled,' said the old poet.

'That would be a pity,' replied the little boy; and he took the bow
and looked at it. 'Oh, it is quite dry, and has suffered no damage; the
string is quite stiff – I will try it!' Then he bent it, and laid an arrow
across, aimed, and shot the good old poet straight into the heart. 'Do
you see now that my bow was not spoiled?' said he, and laughed out
loud and ran away. What a naughty boy to shoot at the old poet in that
way, who had let him into the warm room, and been so kind to him,
and given him the best wine and the best apple!

The good poet lay upon the floor and wept; he was really shot straight into the heart. 'Fie!' he cried, 'what a naughty boy this Cupid is! I shall tell that to all good children, so that they may take care, and never play with him, for he will do them harm!'

All good children, girls and boys, to whom he told this, took good heed of this naughty Cupid; but still he tricked them, for he is very cunning. When the students come out from the lectures, he runs at their side with a book under his arm, and has a black coat on. They cannot recognise him at all. And then they take his arm and fancy he is a student too; but he thrusts the arrow into their breasts. When the girls are being prepared for confirmation, he is also after them. Yes, he is always following people! He sits in the great chandelier in the theatre and burns brightly, so that the people think he is a lamp; but afterwards they see their error. He runs about in the palace garden and on the promenades. Yes, he once shot your father and your mother straight into the heart! Only ask them, and you will hear what they say. Oh, he is a bad boy, this Cupid; you must never have anything to do with him. He is after everyone. Only think, once he shot an arrow at old grandmamma; but that was a long time ago. The wound has indeed healed long since, but she will never forget it. Fie on that wicked Cupid! But now you know him, and what a naughty boy he is.

The Travelling Companion

POOR JOHN was in great tribulation, for his father was very ill, and could not get well again. Except these two, there was no one at all in the little room: the lamp on the table was nearly extinguished, and it was quite late in the evening.

'You have been a good son, John,' said the sick father. 'Providence will help you through the world.' And he looked at him with mild earnest eyes, drew a deep breath, and died: it was just as if he slept. But John wept; for now he had no one in the world, neither father nor mother, neither sister nor brother. Poor John! He knelt down beside the bed, kissed his dead father's hand, and shed very many salt tears; but at last his eyes closed, and he went to sleep, lying with his head against the hard bed-board.

Then he dreamed a strange dream: he saw the sun and moon curtsy to him, and he beheld his father again, fresh and well, and he heard his father laugh as he had always laughed when he was very glad. A beautiful girl, with a golden crown upon her long beautiful hair, gave him her hand; and his father said, 'Do you see what a bride you have gained? She is the most beautiful in the whole world!' Then he awoke, and all the splendour was gone. His father was lying dead and cold in the bed, and there was no one at all with them. Poor John!

In the next week the dead man was buried. The son walked close behind the coffin, and could now no longer see the good father who had loved him so much. He heard how they threw the earth down upon the coffin, and stopped to see the last corner of it; but the next shovel-full of earth hid even that; then he felt just as if his heart would burst into pieces, so sorrowful was he. Around him they were singing a psalm; it sounded so beautifully, and the tears came into John's eyes; he wept, and that did him good in his sorrow. The sun shone magnificently on the green trees, just as if it would have said, 'You shall no longer be sorrowful, John! Do you see how beautifully blue the sky is? Your father is up there, and prays to the Father of all that it may be always well with you.'

'I will always be good,' said John, 'then I shall go to heaven to my father; and what joy that will be when we see each other again! How much I shall then have to tell him! and he will show me so many things, and explain to me so much of the glories of heaven, just as he taught me here on earth. Oh, how joyful that will be!'

He pictured that to himself so plainly, that he smiled, while the tears were still rolling down his cheeks. The little birds sat up in the chestnut trees, and twittered, 'Tweet-weet! tweet-weet!' They were joyful and merry, though they had been at the burying, but they knew quite well that the dead man was now in heaven; that he had wings, far larger and more beautiful than theirs; that he was now happy, because he had been a good man upon earth, and they were glad at it. John saw how they flew from the green trees out into the world, and he felt inclined to fly too. But first he cut out a great cross of wood to put on his father's grave; and when he brought it there in the evening the grave was decked with sand and flowers; strangers had done this, for they were all very fond of the good father who was now dead.

Early next morning John packed his little bundle, and put in his belt his whole inheritance, which consisted of fifty dollars and a few silver shillings; with this he intended to wander out into the world. But first he went to the churchyard, to his father's grave, repeated the Lord's Prayer, and said, 'Farewell, dear father, I will always be good, and so you may well venture to pray to the good God that things may go well with me.'

Out in the field where he was walking all the flowers stood fresh and beautiful in the warm sunshine; and they nodded in the wind, just as if they would have said, 'Welcome to the green wood! Is it not fine here?' But John turned back once more to look at the old church, in which he had been christened when he was a little child, and where he had been every Sunday with his father at the service, and had sung his psalm; then, high up in one of the openings of the tower, he saw the church-goblin standing in his little pointed red cap, shading his face

with his bent arm, to keep the sun from shining in his eyes. John
nodded a farewell to him, and the little goblin waved his red cap, laid
his hand on his heart, and kissed his hand to John a great many times,
to show that he wished the traveller well and hoped he would have a
prosperous journey.

John thought what a number of fine things he would get to see in
the great splendid world; and he went on farther – farther than he had
ever been before. He did not know the places at all through which he
came, nor the people whom he met. Now he was far away in a strange
region.

The first night he was obliged to lie under a haystack in the field to
sleep, for he had no other bed. But that was very nice, he thought; the
king could not be better off. There was the whole field, with the brook,
the haystack, and the blue sky above it; that was certainly a beautiful
sleeping-room. The green grass with the little red and white flowers
was the carpet; the elder bushes and the wild rose hedges were garlands
of flowers; and for a wash-hand basin he had the whole brook with the
clear fresh water, where the sedges bowed before him and wished him
'good-evening' and 'good-morning'. The moon was certainly a great
night-lamp, high up under the blue ceiling, and that lamp would never
set fire to the curtains with its light. John could sleep quite quietly, and
he did so, and never woke until the sun rose and all the little birds were
singing around, 'Good-morning! good-morning! Are you not up yet?'

The bells were ringing for church; it was Sunday. The people went
to hear the preacher, and John followed them, and sang a psalm and
heard God's Word. It seemed to him just as if he was in his own
church, where he had been christened and had sung psalms with his
father.

Out in the churchyard were many graves, and on some of them the
grass grew high. Then he thought of his father's grave, which would at
last look like these, as he could not weed it and adorn it. So he sat down
and plucked up the long grass, set up the wooden crosses which had
fallen down, and put back in their places the wreaths which the wind
had blown away from the graves; for he thought, 'Perhaps someone
will do the same to my father's grave, as I cannot do it.'

Outside the churchyard gate stood an old beggar, leaning upon his crutch. John gave him the silver shillings which he had, and then went away, happy and cheerful, into the wide world. Towards evening the weather became terribly bad. He made haste to get under shelter, but dark night soon came on; then at last he came to a little church, which lay quite solitary on a small hill.

The door luckily stood ajar, and he crept in; here he decided to remain till the storm had gone down.

'Here I will sit down in a corner,' said he; 'I am quite tired and require a little rest.' Then he sat down, folded his hands, and said his evening prayer; and before he was aware of it he was asleep and dreaming, while it thundered and lightened without.

When he woke it was midnight; but the bad weather had passed by, and the moon shone in upon him through the windows. In the midst of the church stood an open coffin with a dead man in it who had not yet been buried. John was not at all timid, for he had a good conscience; and he knew very well that the dead do not harm anyone. It is living people who do harm. Two such living bad men stood close by the dead man, who had been placed here in the church till he should be buried. They had an evil design against him, and would not let him rest quietly in his coffin, but were going to throw him out before the church door – the poor dead man!

'Why will you do that?' asked John; 'that is wrong and wicked. Let him rest, for mercy's sake.'

'Nonsense!' replied the bad men; 'he has cheated us. He owed us money and could not pay it, and now he's dead into the bargain, and we shall not get a penny! So we mean to revenge ourselves properly: he shall lie like a dog outside the church door!'

'I have not more than fifty dollars,' cried John, 'that is my whole inheritance; but I will gladly give it you, if you will honestly promise me to leave the poor dead man in peace. I shall manage to get on without the money; I have hearty strong limbs, and Heaven will always help me.'

'Yes,' said these ugly bad men, 'if you will pay his debt we will do nothing to him, you may depend upon that!' And then they took the money he gave them, laughed aloud at his good nature, and went their way. But he laid the corpse out again in the coffin, and folded its hands, took leave of it, and went away contentedly through the great forest.

All around, wherever the moon could shine through between the trees, he saw the graceful little elves playing merrily. They did not let him disturb them; they knew that he was a good innocent lad; and it is only the bad people who never can see the elves. Some of them were not larger than a finger, and had fastened up their long yellow hair with golden combs: they were rocking themselves, two and two, on the great dewdrops that lay on the leaves and on the high grass; sometimes the drop rolled away, and then they fell down between the long grass-stalks, and that occasioned much laughter and noise among the other little creatures. It was extremely amusing. They sang, and John recognised quite plainly the pretty songs which he had learned as a little boy. Great coloured spiders, with silver crowns on their heads, had to spin long hanging bridges and palaces from hedge to hedge; and as the tiny dewdrops fell on these they looked like gleaming glass in the moonlight. This continued until the sun rose. Then the little elves crept into the flower-buds, and the wind caught their bridges and palaces, which flew through the air in the shape of spider's webs.

John had just come out of the wood, when a strong man's voice called out behind him, 'Halloo, comrade! whither are you journeying?'

'Into the wide world!' he replied. 'I have neither father nor mother, and am but a poor lad; but Providence will help me.'

'I am going out into the wide world, too,' said the strange man: 'shall we two keep one another company?'

'Yes, certainly,' said John; and so they went on together. Soon they became very fond of each other, for they were both good souls. But John saw that the stranger was much more clever than himself. He had travelled through almost the whole world, and could tell of almost everything that existed.

The sun already stood high when they seated themselves under a great tree to eat their breakfast; and just then an old woman came up. Oh, she was very old, and walked quite bent, leaning upon a crutch;

upon her back she carried a bundle of firewood which she had collected in the forest. Her apron was tucked up, and John saw that three great stalks of fern and some willow twigs stuck out of it. When she was close to them, her foot slipped; she fell and gave a loud scream, for she had broken her leg, the poor old woman!

John directly proposed that they should carry the old woman home to her dwelling; but the stranger opened his knapsack, took out a little jar, and said that he had a salve there which would immediately make her leg whole and strong, so that she could walk home herself, as if she had never broken her leg at all. But for that he required that she should give him the three rods which she carried in her apron.

'That would be paying well!' said the old woman, and she nodded her head in a strange way. She did not like to give away the rods, but then it was not agreeable to lie there with a broken leg. So she gave him the wands; and as soon as he had only rubbed the ointment on her leg, the old mother arose, and walked much better than before – such was the power of this ointment. But then it was not to be bought at the chemist's.

'What do you want with the rods?' John asked his travelling companion.

'They are three capital fern brooms,' replied he. 'I like those very much, for I am a whimsical fellow.'

And they went on a good way.

'See how the sky is becoming overcast,' said John, pointing straight before them. 'Those are terribly thick clouds.'

'No,' replied his travelling companion, 'those are not clouds, they are mountains – the great glorious mountains, on which one gets quite up over the clouds, and into the free air. Believe me, it is delicious! Tomorrow we shall certainly be far out into the world.'

But that was not so near as it looked; they had to walk for a whole day before they came to the mountains, where the black woods grew straight up towards heaven, and there were stones almost as big as a whole town. It might certainly be hard work to get quite across them, and for that reason John and his comrade went into the inn to rest themselves well, and gather strength for the morrow's journey.

Down in the great common room in the inn many guests were assembled, for a man was there exhibiting a puppet-show. He had just put up his little theatre, and the people were sitting round to see the play. Quite in front a fat old butcher had taken his seat in the very best place; his great bulldog, who looked very much inclined to bite, sat at his side, and made big eyes, as all the rest were doing.

Now the play began; and it was a very nice play, with a king and a queen in it; they sat upon a velvet throne, and had gold crowns on their heads and long trains to their cloaks, for their means admitted of that. The prettiest of wooden dolls with glass eyes and great moustaches stood at all the doors, and opened and shut them so that fresh air might come into the room. It was a very pleasant play, and not at all mournful. But – goodness knows what the big bulldog can have been thinking of! – just as the queen stood up and was walking across the boards, as the fat butcher did not hold him, he made a spring upon the stage, and seized the queen round her slender waist so that it cracked again. It was quite terrible!

The poor man who managed the play was very much frightened and quite sorrowful about his queen, for she was the daintiest little doll he possessed, and now the ugly bulldog had bitten off her head.

But afterwards, when the people went away, the stranger said that he would put her to rights again; and then he brought out his little jar, and rubbed the doll with the ointment with which he had cured the old woman when she broke her leg. As soon as the doll had been rubbed, she was whole again; yes, she could even move all her limbs by herself; it was no longer necessary to pull her by her string. The doll was like a living person, only that she could not speak. The man who had the little puppet-show was very glad, now he had not to hold this doll any more. She could dance by herself, and none of the others could do that.

When night came on, and all the people in the inn had gone to bed, there was someone who sighed so fearfully, and went on doing it so long, that they all got up to see who this could be. The man who had shown the play went to his little theatre, for it was there that somebody was sighing. All the wooden dolls lay mixed together, the king and all his followers; and it was they who sighed so pitiably, and stared with their big glass eyes; for they wished to be rubbed a little as the queen had been, so that they might be able to move by themselves. The queen at once sank on her knees, and stretched forth her beautiful crown, as if she begged, 'Take this from me, but rub my husband and my courtiers!' Then the poor man, the proprietor of the little theatre and the dolls, could not refrain from weeping, for he was really sorry for them. He immediately promised the travelling companion that he would give him all the money he should receive the next evening for the performance if the latter would only anoint four or five of his dolls. But the comrade said he did not require anything at all but the sword the man wore by his side; and, on receiving this, he anointed six of the dolls, who immediately began to dance so gracefully that all the girls, the living human girls, fell a dancing too. The coachman and the cook danced, the waiter and the chambermaid, and all the strangers, and the fire-shovel and tongs; but these latter fell down just as they made their first leaps. Yes, it was a merry night!

Next morning John went away from them all with his travelling companion, up on to the high mountains, and through the great pine woods. They came so high up that the church steeples under them looked at last like little red berries among all the green; and they could see very far, many, many miles away, where they had never been. So much splendour in the lovely world John had never seen at one time before. And the sun shone warm in the fresh blue air, and among the mountains he could hear the huntsmen blowing their horns so gaily and sweetly that tears came into his eyes, and he could not help calling out, 'How kind has Heaven been to us all, to give us all the splendour that is in this world!'

The travelling companion also stood there with folded hands, and looked over the forest and the towns in the warm sunshine. At the same time there arose lovely sounds over their heads: they looked up, and a great white swan was soaring in the air, and singing as they had never heard a bird sing till then. But the song became weaker and weaker; he bowed his head and sank quite slowly down at their feet, where he lay dead, the beautiful bird!

'Two such splendid wings,' said the travelling companion, 'so white and large, as those which this bird has, are worth money; I will take them with me. Do you see that it was good I got a sabre?'

And so, with one blow, he cut off both the wings of the dead swan, for he wanted to keep them.

They now travelled for many, many miles over the mountains, till at last they saw a great town before them with hundreds of towers, which glittered like silver in the sun. In the midst of the town was a splendid marble palace, roofed with red gold. And there the king lived.

John and the travelling companion would not go into the town at once, but remained in the inn outside the town, that they might dress themselves; for they wished to look nice when they came out into the streets. The host told them that the king was a very good man, who never did harm to anyone; but his daughter, yes, goodness preserve us! she was a bad princess. She possessed beauty enough – no one could be so pretty and so charming as she was – but of what use was that? She was a wicked witch, through whose fault many gallant princes had lost their lives. She had given permission to all men to seek her hand. Anyone might come, be he prince or beggar; it was all the same to her. He had only to guess three things about which she questioned him. If he could do that she would marry him, and he was to be king over the whole country when her father should die; but if he could not guess the three things, she caused him to be hanged or to have his head cut off! So evil and so wicked was the beautiful princess. Her father, the old king, was very sorry about it; but he could not forbid her to be so wicked, because he had once said that he would have nothing to do with her lovers; she might do as she liked. Every time a prince came, and was to guess to gain the princess, he was unable to do it, and was hanged or lost his head. He had been warned in time, you see, and might have given over his wooing. The old king was so sorry for all this misery and woe, that he used to go down on his knees with all his soldiers for a whole day in every year, praying that the princess might become good; but she would not, by any means. The old women who drank brandy used to colour it quite black before they drank it, they were in such deep mourning – and they certainly could not do more.

'The ugly princess!' said John; 'she ought really to have the rod; that would do her good. If I were only the old king she should be punished!'

Then they heard the people outside shouting 'Hurrah!' The princess came by; and she was really so beautiful that all the people forgot how wicked she was, and that is why they cried 'Hurrah!' Twelve beautiful virgins, all in white silk gowns, and each with a golden tulip in her hand, rode on coal-black steeds at her side. The princess herself had a snow-white horse, decked with diamonds and rubies. Her riding-habit was all of cloth of gold, and the whip she held in her hand looked like a sunbeam; the golden crown on her head was just like little stars out of the sky, and her mantle was sewn together out of more than a thousand beautiful butterflies' wings. In spite of this, she herself was much more lovely than all her clothes.

When John saw her, his face became as red as a drop of blood, and he could hardly utter a word. The princess looked just like the beautiful lady with the golden crown, of whom he had dreamt on the night when his father died. He thought her so enchanting that he could not help loving her greatly. It could not be true that she was a wicked witch, who caused people to be hanged or beheaded if they could not guess the riddles she put to them.

'Everyone has permission to aspire to her hand, even the poorest beggar. I will really go to the castle, for I cannot help doing it!'

They all told him not to attempt it, for certainly he would fare as all the rest had done. His travelling companion too tried to dissuade him; but John thought it would end well. He brushed his shoes and his coat, washed his face and his hands, combed his beautiful yellow hair, and then went quite alone into the town and to the palace.

'Come in!' said the old king, when John knocked at the door.

John opened it, and the old king came towards him in a dressing-gown and embroidered slippers; he had the crown on his head, and the

sceptre in one hand and the orb in the other. 'Wait a little!' said he, and put the orb under his arm, so that he could reach out his hand to John. But as soon as he learned that his visitor was a suitor, he began to weep so violently that both the sceptre and the orb fell to the ground, and he was obliged to wipe his eyes with his dressing-gown. Poor old king!

'Give it up!' said he. 'You will fare badly, as all the others have done. Well, you shall see!'

Then he led him out into the princess's pleasure-garden. There was a terrible sight! In every tree there hung three or four kings' sons who had wooed the princess, but had not been able to guess the riddles she proposed to them. Each time that the breeze blew all the skeletons rattled, so that the little birds were frightened, and never dared to come into the garden. All the flowers were tied up to human bones, and in the flowerpots skulls stood and grinned. That was certainly a garden for a princess.

'Here you see it,' said the old king. 'It will chance to you as it has chanced to all these whom you see here; therefore you had better give it up. You will really make me unhappy, for I take these things very much to heart.'

John kissed the good old king's hand, and said it would go well, for that he was quite enchanted with the beautiful princess.

Then the princess herself came riding into the courtyard, with all her ladies; and they went out to her and wished her good-morning. She was beautiful to look at, and she gave John her hand. And he cared much more for her then than before – she could certainly not be a wicked witch, as the people asserted. Then they betook themselves to the hall, and the little pages waited upon them with preserves and gingerbread nuts. But the old king was quite sorrowful; he could not eat anything at all. Besides, gingerbread nuts were too hard for him.

It was settled that John should come to the palace again the next morning; then the judges and the whole council would be assembled, and would hear how he succeeded with his answers. If it went well, he should come twice more; but no one had yet come who had succeeded in guessing right the first time, and so they had to lose their lives.

John was not at all anxious as to how he should fare. On the contrary, he was merry, thought only of the beautiful princess, and felt quite certain that he should be helped; but *how* he did not know, and preferred not to think of it. He danced along on the road returning to the inn, where his travelling companion was waiting for him.

John could not leave off telling how polite the princess had been to him, and how beautiful she was. He declared he already longed for the next day, when he was to go into the palace and try his luck in guessing.

But the travelling companion shook his head and was quite downcast. 'I am so fond of you!' said he. 'We might have been together a long time yet, and now I am to lose you already! You poor dear John! I should like to cry, but I will not disturb your merriment on the last evening, perhaps, we shall ever spend together. We will be merry, very merry! Tomorrow, when you are gone, I can weep undisturbed.'

All the people in the town had heard directly that a new suitor for the princess had arrived; and there was great sorrow on that account. The theatre remained closed; the women who sold cakes tied bits of crape round their sugar pigs, and the king and the priests were on their knees in the churches. There was great lamentation; for John would not, they all thought, fare better than the other suitors had fared.

Towards evening the travelling companion mixed a great bowl of punch, and said to John, 'Now we will be very merry, and drink to the health of the princess.' But when John had drunk two glasses, he became so sleepy that he found it impossible to keep his eyes open, and he sank into a deep sleep. The travelling companion lifted him very gently from his chair, and laid him in the bed; and when it grew to be dark night, he took the two great wings which he had cut off the swan, and bound them to his own shoulders. Then he put in his pocket the longest of the rods he had received from the old woman who had fallen and broken her leg; and he opened the window and flew away over the town, straight towards the palace, where he seated himself in a corner under the window which looked into the bedroom of the princess.

All was quiet in the whole town. Now the clock struck a quarter to twelve, the window was opened, and the princess came out in a long white cloak, and with black wings, and flew away across the town to a great mountain. But the travelling companion made himself invisible, so that she could not see him at all, and flew behind her, and whipped the princess with his rod, so that the blood actually came wherever he struck. Oh, that was a voyage through the air! The wind caught her cloak, so that it spread out on all sides like a great sail, and the moon shone through it.

'How it hails! how it hails!' said the princess at every blow she got from the rod; and it served her right. At last she arrived at the mountain, and knocked there. There was a rolling like thunder, as the mountain opened, and the princess went in. The travelling companion followed her, for no one could see him – he was invisible. They went through a great long passage, where the walls shone in quite a peculiar way: there were more than a thousand glowing spiders running up and down the walls and gleaming like fire. Then they came into a great hall built of silver and gold; flowers as big as sunflowers, red and blue, shone on the walls; but no one could pluck these flowers, for the stems were ugly poisonous snakes, and the flowers were streams of fire pouring out of their mouths. The whole ceiling was covered with shining glowworms and sky-blue bats, flapping their thin wings. It looked quite terrific! In the middle of the floor was a throne, carried by four skeleton horses, with harness of fiery red spiders; the throne itself was of milk-white glass, and the cushions were little black mice, biting each other's tails. Above it was a canopy of pink spider's web, trimmed with the prettiest little green flies, which gleamed like jewels. On the throne sat an old magician, with a crown on his ugly head and a sceptre in his hand. He kissed the princess on the forehead, made her sit down beside him on the costly throne, and then the music began. Great black grasshoppers played on Jew's harps, and the owl beat her wings upon her body, because she hadn't a drum. That was a strange concert! Little black goblins with a Jack-o'-lantern light on their caps danced about in the hall. But no one could see the travelling companion: he had placed himself just behind the throne, and heard and saw everything. The courtiers, who now came in, were very grand and stately; but he who could see it all knew very well what it all meant. They were nothing more than broomsticks with heads of cabbages on them, which the magician had animated by his power, and to whom he had given embroidered clothes. But that did not matter, for, you see, they were only wanted for show.

After there had been a little dancing, the princess told the magician that she had a new suitor, and therefore she enquired of him what she should think of to ask the suitor when he should come tomorrow to the palace.

'Listen!' said the magician, 'I will tell you that: you must choose something very easy, for then he won't think of it. Think of one of your shoes. That he will not guess. Let him have his head cut off: but don't forget, when you come to me tomorrow night, to bring me his eyes, for I'll eat them.'

The princess curtsied very low, and said she would not forget the eyes. The magician opened the mountain, and she flew home again; but the travelling companion followed her, and beat her again so hard with the rod that she sighed quite deeply about the heavy hailstorm, and hurried as much as she could to get back into the bedroom through the open window. The travelling companion, for his part, flew back to the inn, where John was still asleep, took off his wings, and then lay down upon the bed, for he might well be tired.

It was quite early in the morning when John awoke. The travelling companion also got up, and said he had had a wonderful dream in the night, about the princess and her shoe; and he therefore begged John to ask if the princess had not thought about her shoe. For it was this he had heard from the magician in the mountain.

But he would not tell John anything about that; he merely told him to ask if she had not thought about one of her shoes.

'I may just as well ask about that as about anything else,' said John. 'Perhaps it is quite right, what you have dreamed. But I will bid you farewell; for, if I guess wrong, I shall never see you more.'

Then they embraced each other, and John went into the town and to the palace. The entire hall was filled with people: the judges sat in their armchairs and had eiderdown pillows behind their heads, for they had a great deal to think about. The old king stood up, and wiped his eyes with a white pocket-handkerchief. Now the princess came in. She was much more beautiful than yesterday, and bowed to all in a very affable manner; but to John she gave her hand, and said, 'Good-morning to you.'

Now John was to guess what she had thought of. Oh, how lovingly she looked at him! But as soon as she heard the single word 'shoe' pronounced, she became as white as chalk in the face, and trembled all over. But that availed her nothing, for John had guessed right!

Wonderful! How glad the old king was! He threw a somersault beautiful to behold. And all the people clapped their hands in honour of him and of John, who had guessed right the first time!

The travelling companion beamed with delight, when he heard how well matters had gone. But John folded his hands and thanked God, who certainly would help him also the second and third time. The next day he was to guess again.

The evening passed just like that of yesterday. While John slept the travelling companion flew behind the princess out to the mountain, and beat her even harder than the time before, for now he had taken two rods. No one saw him, and he heard everything. The princess was to think of her glove; and this again he told to John as if it had been a dream. Thus John could guess correctly, which caused great rejoicing in the palace. The whole court threw somersaults, just as they had seen the king do the first time; but the princess lay on the sofa, and would not say a single word. Now, the question was, if John could guess properly the third time. If he succeeded, he was to have the beautiful princess and inherit the whole kingdom after the old king's death. If he failed, he was to lose his life, and the magician would eat his beautiful blue eyes.

That evening John went early to bed, said his prayers, and went to sleep quite quietly. But the travelling companion bound his wings to his back and his sword by his side, and took all three rods with him, and so flew away to the palace.

It was a very dark night. The wind blew so hard that the tiles flew off from the roofs, and the trees in the garden where the skeletons hung bent like reeds before the storm. The lightning flashed out every minute, and the thunder rolled just as if it were one peal lasting the whole night. Now the window opened, and the princess flew out.

She was as pale as death; but she laughed at the bad weather, and thought it was not bad enough yet. And her white cloak fluttered in the wind like a great sail; but the travelling companion beat her with the three rods, so that the blood dripped upon the ground, and at last she could scarcely fly any farther. At length, however, she arrived at the mountain.

'It hails and blows dreadfully!' she said. 'I have never been out in such weather.'

'One may have too much of a good thing,' said the magician. Now she told him that John had also guessed correctly the second time; if he did the same on the morrow, then he had won, and she could never more come out to him in the mountain, and would never be able to perform such feats of magic as before, and so she was quite dejected. 'He shall not be able to guess,' said the magician. 'I shall think of something of which he has never thought, or he must be a greater conjuror than I. But now we will be merry.' And he took the princess by the hands, and they danced about with all the little goblins and Jack-o'-lanterns that were in the room. The red spiders jumped just as merrily up and down the walls: it looked as if fiery flowers were spurting out. The owl played the drum, the crickets piped, and the black grasshoppers played on the Jew's harp. It was a merry ball.

When they had danced long enough the princess was obliged to go home, for she might be missed in the palace. The magician said he would accompany her, then they would have each other's company on the way.

Then they flew away into the bad weather, and the travelling companion broke his three rods across their backs. Never had the magician been out in such a hailstorm. In front of the palace he said goodbye to the princess, and whispered to her at the same time, 'Think of my head.' But the travelling companion heard it; and just at the moment when the princess slipped through the window into her bedroom, and the magician was about to turn back, he seized him by his long beard, and with his sabre cut off the ugly conjuror's head just by the shoulders, so that the magician did not even see him. The body he threw out into the sea to the fishes; but the head he only dipped into the water, and then tied it in his silk handkerchief, took it with him into the inn, and then lay down to sleep.

Next morning he gave John the handkerchief, and told him not to untie it until the princess asked him to tell her thoughts.

There were so many people in the great hall of the palace, that they stood as close together as radishes bound together in a bundle. The council sat in the chairs with the soft pillows, and the old king had new clothes on; the golden crown and sceptre had been polished, and everything looked quite stately. But the princess was very pale, and had a coal-black dress on, as if she were going to a funeral.

'Of what have I thought?' she asked John. And he immediately untied the handkerchief, and was himself quite frightened when he saw the ugly magician's head. All present shuddered, for it was terrible to look upon; but the princess sat just like a statue, and could not utter a single word. At length she stood up, and gave John her hand, for he had guessed correctly. She did not look at anyone, only sighed aloud, and said, 'Now you are my lord! this evening we will hold our wedding.'

'I like that!' cried the old king. 'So I would have it.'

All present cried, 'Hurrah!' The soldiers' band played music in the streets, the bells rang, and the cake-women took off the black crape from their sugar pigs, for joy now reigned everywhere; three oxen roasted whole, and stuffed with ducks and fowls, were placed in the middle of the market, that everyone might cut himself a slice; the fountains ran with the best wine; and whoever bought a penny cake at a baker's got six buns into the bargain, and the buns had raisins in them.

In the evening the whole town was illuminated; the soldiers fired off the cannon, and the boys let off crackers; and there was eating and drinking, clinking of glasses, and dancing, in the palace. All the noble gentlemen and pretty ladies danced with each other, and one could hear, a long distance off, how they sang:

> Here are many pretty girls, who all love to dance;
> See, they whirl like spinning-wheels, retire and advance.
> Turn, my pretty maiden, do, till the sole falls from your shoe.

But still the princess was a witch, and did not like John. This had been expected by the travelling companion; and so he gave John three feathers out of the swan's wings, and a little bottle with a few drops in it, and told John that he must put a large tub of water before the princess's bed; and when the princess was about to get into bed, he should give her a little push, so that she should fall into the tub; and then he must dip her three times, after he had put in the feathers and poured in the drops; she would then lose her magic qualities, and love him very much.

John did all that the travelling companion had advised him to do. The princess screamed out loudly while he dipped her in the tub, and struggled under his hands in the form of a great coal-black swan with fiery eyes. When she came up the second time above the water, the swan was white, with the exception of a black ring round her neck. John let the water close for the third time over the bird, and in the same moment it was again changed to the beautiful princess. She was more beautiful even than before, and thanked him, with tears in her lovely eyes, that he had freed her from the magic spell.

The next morning the old king came with his whole court, and then there was great congratulation till late into the day. Last of all came the travelling companion; he had his staff in his hand and his knapsack on his back. John kissed him many times, and said he must not depart, he must remain with the friend of whose happiness he was the cause. But the travelling companion shook his head, and said mildly and kindly, 'No, now my time is up. I have only paid my debt. Do you remember the dead man whom the bad people wished to injure? You gave all you possessed in order that he might have rest in the grave. I am that man.'

And in the same moment he vanished.

The wedding festivities lasted a whole month. John and the princess loved each other truly, and the old king passed many pleasant days, and let their little children ride on his knees and play with his sceptre. And John afterwards became king over the whole country.

The Little Sea Maid

F AR OUT in the sea the water is as blue as the petals of the most
beautiful cornflower, and as clear as the purest glass. But it is
very deep, deeper than any cable will sound; many steeples must
be placed one above the other to reach from the bottom to the surface
of the water. And down there live the sea people.

Now, you must not believe there is nothing down there but the
bare sand; no, the strangest trees and plants grow there, so pliable in
their stalks and leaves that at the least motion of the water they move
just as if they had life. All fishes, great and small, glide among the
twigs, just as here the birds do in the trees. In the deepest spot of all
lies the Sea King's castle: the walls are of coral, and the tall pointed
windows of the clearest amber; mussel shells form the roof, and they
open and shut according as the water flows. It looks lovely, for in each
shell lie gleaming pearls, a single one of which would be a great
ornament in a queen's diadem.

The Sea King below there had been a widower for many years, while
his old mother kept house for him. She was a clever woman, but proud
of her rank, so she wore twelve oysters on her tail, while the other great
people were only allowed to wear six. Beyond this she was deserving
of great praise, especially because she was very fond of her grand-
daughters, the little sea princesses. These were six pretty children; but
the youngest was the most beautiful of all. Her skin was as clear and as
fine as a rose leaf, her eyes were as blue as the deepest sea, but, like all
the rest, she had no feet, for her body ended in a fishtail.

All day long they could play in the castle, down in the halls, where
living flowers grew out of the walls. The great amber windows were
opened, and then the fishes swam in to them, just as the swallows fly in
to us when we open our windows; but the fishes swam straight up to
the princesses, ate out of their hands, and let themselves be stroked.

Outside the castle was a great garden with bright red and dark blue flowers: the fruit glowed like gold, and the flowers like flames of fire; and they continually kept moving their stalks and leaves. The earth itself was the finest sand, but blue as the flame of brimstone. A peculiar blue radiance lay upon everything down there: one would have thought oneself high in the air, with the canopy of heaven above and around, rather than at the bottom of the deep sea. During a calm the sun could be seen; it appeared like a purple flower, from which all light streamed out.

Each of the little princesses had her own little place in the garden, where she might dig and plant at her good pleasure. One gave her flower-bed the form of a whale; another thought it better to make hers like a little mermaid; but the youngest made hers quite round, like the sun, and had only flowers which gleamed red as the sun itself. She was a strange child, quiet and thoughtful; and when the other sisters made a display of the beautiful things they had received out of wrecked ships, she would have nothing beyond the red flowers which resembled the sun, except a pretty marble statue. This was a figure of a charming boy, hewn out of white clear stone, which had sunk down to the bottom of the sea from a wreck. She planted a pink weeping willow beside this statue; the tree grew famously, and hung its fresh branches over the statue towards the blue sandy ground, where the shadow showed violet, and moved like the branches themselves; it seemed as if the ends of the branches and the roots were playing together and wished to kiss each other.

There was no greater pleasure for her than to hear of the world of men above them. The old grandmother had to tell all she knew of ships and towns, of men and animals. It seemed particularly beautiful to her that up on the earth the flowers shed fragrance, for they had none down at the bottom of the sea, and that the trees were green, and that the fishes which one saw there among the trees could sing so loud and clear that it was a pleasure to hear them. What the grandmother called fishes were the little birds; otherwise they could not have understood her, for they had never seen a bird.

'When you have completed your fifteenth year,' said the grandmother, 'you shall have leave to rise up out of the sea, to sit on the rocks in the moonlight, and to see the great ships sailing by. Then you will see forests and towns!'

In the next year one of the sisters was fifteen years of age, but each of the others was one year younger than the next; so that the youngest had full five years to wait before she could come up from the bottom of the sea, and find out how our world looked. But one promised to tell the others what she had seen and what she had thought the most beautiful on the first day of her visit; for their grandmother could not tell them enough – there was so much about which they wanted information.

No one was more anxious about these things than the youngest – just that one who had the longest time to wait, and who was always quiet and thoughtful. Many a night she stood by the open window, and looked up through the dark blue water at the fishes splashing with their fins and tails. Moon and stars she could see; they certainly shone quite faintly, but through the water they looked much larger than they appear in our eyes. When something like a black cloud passed among them, she knew that it was either a whale swimming over her head, or a ship with many people: they certainly did not think that a pretty little sea maid was standing down below stretching up her white hands towards the keel of their ship.

Now the eldest princess was fifteen years old, and might mount up to the surface of the sea.

When she came back, she had a hundred things to tell – but the finest thing, she said, was to lie in the moonshine on a sandbank in the quiet sea, and to look at the neighbouring coast, with the large town, where the lights twinkled like a hundred stars, and to hear the music and the noise and clamour of carriages and men, to see the many church steeples, and to hear the sound of the bells. Just because she could not get up to these, she longed for them more than for anything.

Oh, how the youngest sister listened! and afterwards when she stood at the open window and looked up through the dark blue water, she thought of the great city with all its bustle and noise; and then she thought she could hear the church bells ringing, even down to the depth where she was.

In the following year, the second sister received permission to mount upward through the water and to swim whither she pleased. She rose up just as the sun was setting; and this spectacle, she said, was the most beautiful. The whole sky looked like gold, she said, and as to the clouds, she could not properly describe their beauty. They sailed away over her head, purple and violet-coloured, but far quicker than the clouds there flew a flight of wild swans, like a long white veil, over the water towards where the sun stood. She swam towards them; but the sun sank, and the roseate hue faded on the sea and in the clouds.

In the following year the next sister went up. She was the boldest of them all, and therefore she swam up a broad stream that poured its waters into the sea. She saw glorious green hills clothed with vines; palaces and castles peeped forth from amid splendid woods; she heard how all the birds sang; and the sun shone so warm that she was often obliged to dive under the water to cool her glowing face. In a little bay she found a whole swarm of little mortals. They were quite naked, and splashed about in the water: she wanted to play with them, but they fled in affright, and a little black animal came – it was a dog, but she had never seen a dog – and it barked at her so terribly that she became frightened, and made out to the open sea. But she could never forget the glorious woods, the green hills, and the pretty children, who could swim in the water though they had not fishtails.

The fourth sister was not so bold: she remained out in the midst of the wild sea, and declared that just there it was most beautiful. One could see for many miles around, and the sky above looked like a bell of glass. She had seen ships, but only in the far distance – they looked like seagulls; and the funny dolphins had thrown somersaults, and the great whales spouted out water from their nostrils, so that it looked like hundreds of fountains all around.

Now came the turn of the fifth sister. Her birthday came in the winter, and so she saw what the others had not seen the first time. The sea looked quite green, and great icebergs were floating about; each one appeared like a pearl, she said, and yet was much taller than the church steeples built by men. They showed themselves in the strangest forms, and shone like diamonds. She had seated herself upon one of the greatest of all, and let the wind play with her long hair; and all the sailing ships tacked about in great alarm to get beyond where she sat; but towards evening the sky became covered with clouds, it thundered and lightened, and the black waves lifted the great iceblocks high up, and let them glow in the red glare. On all the ships the sails were reefed, and there was fear and anguish. But she sat quietly upon her floating iceberg, and saw the forked blue flashes dart into the sea.

Each of the sisters, as she came up for the first time to the surface of the water, was delighted with the new and beautiful sights she saw; but as they now had permission, as grown-up girls, to go whenever they liked, it became indifferent to them. They wished themselves back again, and after a month had elapsed they said it was best of all down below, for there one felt so comfortably at home.

Many an evening hour the five sisters took one another by the arm and rose up in a row over the water. They had splendid voices, more charming than any mortal could have; and when a storm was approaching, so that they might expect that ships would go down, they swam on before the ships and sang lovely songs, which told how beautiful it was at the bottom of the sea, and exhorted the sailors not to be afraid to come down. But these could not understand the words, and thought it was the storm sighing; and they did not see the splendours below, for if the ships sank they were drowned, and came as corpses to the Sea King's palace.

When the sisters thus rose up, arm in arm, in the evening time, through the water, the little sister stood all alone looking after them; and she felt as if she must weep; but the sea maid has no tears, and for this reason she suffers far more acutely.

'Oh, if I were only fifteen years old!' said she. 'I know I shall love the world up there very much, and the people who live and dwell there.'

At last she was really fifteen years old.

'Now, you see, you are grown up,' said the grandmother, the old dowager. 'Come, let me adorn you like your sisters.'

And she put a wreath of white lilies in the little maid's hair, but each petal in the flower was half a pearl; and the old lady let eight great oysters attach themselves to the princess's tail, in token of her high rank.

'But that hurts so!' said the little sea maid.

'Yes, one must suffer something for the sake of rank,' replied the old lady.

Oh, how glad she would have been to shake off all the tokens of rank and lay aside the heavy wreath! Her red flowers in the garden suited her better; but she could not help it. 'Farewell!' she said, and then she rose, light and clear as a water-bubble, up through the sea.

The sun had just set when she lifted her head above the sea, but all the clouds still shone like roses and gold, and in the pale red sky the evening star gleamed bright and beautiful. The air was mild and fresh and the sea quite calm. There lay a great ship with three masts; one single sail only was set, for not a breeze stirred, and around in the shrouds and on the yards sat the sailors. There was music and singing, and as the evening closed in, hundreds of coloured lanterns were lighted up, and looked as if the flags of every nation were waving in the air. The little sea maid swam straight to the cabin window, and each time the sea lifted her up she could look through the panes, which were clear as crystal, and see many people standing within dressed in their best. But the handsomest of all was the young prince with the great black eyes: he was certainly not much more than sixteen years old; it was his birthday, and that was the cause of all this festivity. The sailors were dancing upon deck; and when the young prince came out, more than a hundred rockets rose into the air; they shone like day, so that the little sea maid was quite startled, and dived under the water; but soon she put out her head again, and then it seemed just as if all the stars of heaven were falling down upon her. She had never seen such fireworks. Great suns whirled around, glorious fiery fishes flew up into the blue air, and everything was mirrored in the clear blue sea. The ship itself was so brightly lit up that every separate rope could be seen, and the people therefore appeared the more plainly. Oh, how handsome the young prince was! And he pressed the people's hands and smiled, while the music rang out in the glorious night.

It became late; but the little sea maid could not turn her eyes from the ship and from the beautiful prince. The coloured lanterns were extinguished, rockets ceased to fly into the air, and no more cannons were fired; but there was a murmuring and a buzzing deep down in the sea; and she sat on the water, swaying up and down, so that she could look into the cabin. But as the ship got more way, one sail after another was spread. And now the waves rose higher, great clouds came up, and in the distance there was lightning. Oh! it was going to be fearful weather, therefore the sailors furled the sails. The great ship flew in swift career over the wild sea: the waters rose up like great black mountains, which wanted to roll over the masts; but like a swan the ship dived into the valleys between these high waves, and then let itself be lifted on high again. To the little sea maid this seemed merry sport, but to the sailors it appeared very differently. The ship groaned and creaked; the thick planks were bent by the heavy blows; the sea broke into the ship; the mainmast snapped in two like a thin reed; and the ship lay over on her side, while the water rushed into the hold. Now the little sea maid saw that the people were in peril; she herself was obliged to take care to avoid the beams and fragments of the ship which were floating about on the waters. One moment it was so pitch dark that not a single object could be descried, but when it lightened it became so bright that she could distinguish everyone on board. Everyone was doing the best he could for himself. She looked particularly for the young prince, and when the ship parted she saw him sink into the sea. At first she was very glad, for now he would come down to her. But then she remembered that people could not live in the water, and that when he got down to her father's palace he would certainly be dead. No, he must not die: so she swam about among the beams and planks that strewed the surface, quite forgetting that one of them might have crushed her. Diving down deep under the water, she again rose high up among the waves, and in this way she at last came to the prince, who could scarcely swim longer in that stormy sea. His arms and legs began to fail him, his beautiful eyes closed, and he would have died had the little sea maid not come. She held his head up over the water, and then allowed the waves to carry her and him whither they listed.

When the morning came the storm had passed by. Of the ship not a fragment was to be seen. The sun came up red and shining out of the water; it was as if its beams brought back the hue of life to the cheeks of the prince, but his eyes remained closed. The sea maid kissed his high fair forehead and put back his wet hair, and he seemed to her to be like the marble statue in her little garden: she kissed him again and hoped that he might live.

Now she saw in front of her the dry land – high blue mountains, on whose summits the white snow gleamed as if swans were lying there. Down on the coast were glorious green forests, and a building – she could not tell whether it was a church or a convent – stood there. In its garden grew orange and citron trees, and high palms waved in front of the gate. The sea formed a little bay there; it was quite calm, but very deep. Straight towards the rock where the fine white sand had been cast up, she swam with the handsome prince, and laid him upon the sand, taking especial care that his head was raised in the warm sunshine.

Now all the bells rang in the great white building, and many young girls came walking through the garden. Then the little sea maid swam farther out between some high stones that stood up out of the water, laid some sea foam upon her hair and neck, so that no one could see her little face, and then she watched to see who would come to the poor prince.

In a short time a young girl went that way. She seemed to be much startled, but only for a moment; then she brought more people, and the sea maid perceived that the prince came back to life and that he smiled at all around him. But he did not cast a smile at her: he did not know that she had saved him. And she felt very sorrowful; and when he was taken away into the great building, she dived mournfully under the water and returned to her father's palace.

She had always been gentle and melancholy, but now she became much more so. Her sisters asked her what she had seen the first time she rose up to the surface, but she would tell them nothing.

Many an evening and many a morning she went up to the place where she had left the prince. She saw how the fruits of the garden

grew ripe and were gathered; she saw how the snow melted on the
high mountain; but she did not see the prince, and so she always
returned home more sorrowful still. Then her only comfort was to sit
in her little garden, and to wind her arms round the beautiful marble
statue that resembled the prince; but she did not tend her flowers; they
grew as if in a wilderness over the paths, and trailed their long leaves
and stalks up into the branches of trees, so that it became quite dark
there.

At last she could endure it no longer, and told all to one of her
sisters, and then the others heard of it too; but nobody knew of it
beyond these and a few other sea maids, who told the secret to their
intimate friends. One of these knew who the prince was; she too had

seen the festival on board the ship; and she announced whence he came and where his kingdom lay.

'Come, little sister!' said the other princesses; and, linking their arms together, they rose up in a long row out of the sea, at the place where they knew the prince's palace stood.

This palace was built of a kind of bright yellow stone, with great marble staircases, one of which led directly down into the sea. Over the roof rose splendid gilt cupolas, and between the pillars which surrounded the whole dwelling stood marble statues which looked as if they were alive. Through the clear glass in the high windows one looked into the glorious halls, where costly silk hangings and tapestries were hung up, and all the walls were decked with splendid pictures, so that it was a perfect delight to see them. In the midst of the greatest of these halls a great fountain plashed; its jets shot high up towards the glass dome in the ceiling, through which the sun shone down upon the water and upon the lovely plants growing in the great basin.

Now she knew where he lived, and many an evening and many a night she spent there on the water. She swam far closer to the land than any of the others would have dared to venture; indeed, she went quite up the narrow channel under the splendid marble balcony, which threw a broad shadow upon the water. Here she sat and watched the young prince, who thought himself quite alone in the bright moonlight.

Many an evening she saw him sailing, amid the sounds of music, in his costly boat with the waving flags; she peeped up through the green reeds, and when the wind caught her silver-white veil, and anyone saw it, they thought it was a white swan spreading out its wings.

Many a night when the fishermen were on the sea with their torches, she heard much good told of the young prince; and she rejoiced that she had saved his life when he was driven about, half dead, on the wild billows: she thought how quietly his head had reclined on her bosom, and how heartily she had kissed him; but he knew nothing of it, and could not even dream of her.

More and more she began to love mankind, and more and more she wished to be able to wander about among those whose world seemed far larger than her own. For they could fly over the sea in ships, and mount up the high hills far above the clouds, and the lands they possessed stretched out in woods and fields farther than her eyes could reach. There was much she wished to know, but her sisters could not answer all her questions; therefore she applied to the old grandmother; and the old lady knew the upper world, which she rightly called 'the countries above the sea', very well.

'If people are not drowned,' asked the little sea maid, 'can they live for ever? Do they not die as we die down here in the sea?'

'Yes,' replied the old lady. 'They too must die, and their life is even shorter than ours. We can live to be three hundred years old, but when we cease to exist here, we are turned into foam on the surface of the water, and have not even a grave down here among those we love. We have not an immortal soul; we never receive another life; we are like the green seaweed, which when once cut through can never bloom again. Men, on the contrary, have a soul which lives for ever, which lives on after the body has become dust; it mounts up through the clear air, up to all the shining stars! As we rise up out of the waters and behold all the lands of the earth, so they rise up to unknown glorious places which we can never see.'

'Why did we not receive an immortal soul?' asked the little sea maid, sorrowfully. 'I would gladly give all the hundreds of years I have to live to be a human being only for one day, and to have a hope of partaking the heavenly kingdom.'

'You must not think of that,' replied the old lady. 'We feel ourselves far more happy and far better than mankind yonder.'

'Then I am to die and to float as foam upon the sea, not hearing the music of the waves, nor seeing the pretty flowers and the red sun? Can I not do anything to win an immortal soul?'

'No!' answered the grandmother. 'Only if a man were to love you so that you should be more to him than father or mother; if he should cling to you with his every thought and with all his love, and let the priest lay his right hand in yours with a promise of faithfulness here and in all eternity, then his soul would be imparted to your body, and you would receive a share of the happiness of mankind. He would give a soul to you and yet retain his own. But that can never come to pass.

What is considered beautiful here in the sea – the fishtail – they would consider ugly on the earth: they don't understand it; there one must have two clumsy supports which they call legs, to be called beautiful.'

Then the little sea maid sighed, and looked mournfully upon her fishtail.

'Let us be glad!' said the old lady. 'Let us dance and leap in the three hundred years we have to live. That is certainly long enough; after that we can rest ourselves all the better. This evening we shall have a court ball.'

It was a splendid sight, such as is never seen on earth. The walls and the ceiling of the great dancing-saloon were of thick but transparent glass. Several hundreds of huge shells, pink and grass-green, stood on each side in rows, filled with a blue fire which lit up the whole hall and shone through the walls, so that the sea without was quite lit up; one could see all the innumerable fishes, great and small, swimming towards the glass walls; of some the scales gleamed with purple, while in others they shone like silver and gold. Through the midst of the hall flowed a broad stream, and on this the sea men and sea women danced to their own charming songs. Such beautiful voices the people of the earth have not. The little sea maid sang the most sweetly of all, and the whole court applauded her, and for a moment she felt gay in her heart, for she knew she had the loveliest voice of all in the sea or on the earth. But soon she thought again of the world above her; she could not forget the charming prince, or her sorrow at not having an immortal soul like his. Therefore she crept out of her father's palace, and while everything within was joy and gladness, she sat melancholy in her little garden. Then she heard the bugle horn sounding through the waters, and thought, 'Now he is certainly sailing above, he whom I love more than father or mother, he on whom my wishes hang, and in whose hand I should like to lay my life's happiness. I will dare everything to win him and an immortal soul. While my sisters dance yonder in my father's palace, I will go to the sea witch of whom I have always been so much afraid: perhaps she can counsel and help me.'

Now the little sea maid went out of her garden to the foaming whirlpools behind which the sorceress dwelt. She had never travelled that way before. No flowers grew there, no sea grass; only the bare grey sand stretched out towards the whirlpools, where the water rushed round like roaring mill-wheels and tore down everything it seized into the deep. Through the midst of these rushing whirlpools she was obliged to pass to get into the domain of the witch; and for a long way there was no other road except one which led over warm bubbling mud: this the witch called her peat-moss. Behind it lay her house in the midst of a singular forest, in which all the trees and bushes were polypes – half animals, half plants. They looked like hundred-headed snakes growing up out of the earth. All the branches were long slimy arms, with fingers like supple snakes, and they moved joint by joint from the root to the farthest point; all that they could seize on in the water they held fast and never again let it go. The little sea maid stopped in front of them quite frightened; her heart beat with fear, and she was nearly turning back; but then she thought of the prince and the human soul, and her courage came back again. She bound her long flying hair closely around her head, so that the polypes might not seize it. She put her hands together on her breast, and then shot forward as a fish shoots through the water, among the ugly polypes, which stretched out their supple arms and fingers after her. She saw that each of them held something it had seized with hundreds of little arms, like strong iron bands. People who had perished at sea and had sunk deep down, looked forth as white skeletons from among the polypes' arms; ships' rudders and chests they also held fast, and skeletons of land animals, and a little mermaid whom they had caught and strangled; and this seemed the most terrible of all to our little princess.

Now she came to a great marshy place in the wood, where fat water-snakes rolled about, showing their ugly cream-coloured bodies. In the midst of this marsh was a house built of white bones of shipwrecked men; there sat the sea witch feeding a toad out of her mouth, just as a person might feed a little canary bird with sugar. She called the ugly fat water-snakes her little chickens, and allowed them to crawl upwards and all about her.

'I know what you want,' said the sea witch. 'It is stupid of you, but you shall have your way, for it will bring you to grief, my pretty princess. You want to get rid of your fishtail, and to have two supports instead of it, like those the people of the earth walk with, so that the young prince may fall in love with you, and you may get him and an immortal soul.' And with this the witch laughed loudly and disagreeably, so that the toad and the water-snakes tumbled down to the ground, where they crawled about. 'You come just in time,' said the witch: 'after tomorrow at sunrise I could not help you until another year had gone by. I will prepare a draught for you, with which you must swim to land tomorrow before the sun rises, and seat yourself there and drink it; then your tail will part in two and shrink in and become what the people of the earth call beautiful legs, but it will hurt you – it will seem as if you were cut with a sharp sword. All who see you will declare you to be the prettiest human being they ever beheld. You will keep your graceful walk; no dancer will be able to move so lightly as you; but every step you take will be as if you trod upon sharp knives, and as if your blood must flow. If you will bear all this, I can help you.'

'Yes!' said the little sea maid, with a trembling voice; and she thought of the prince and the immortal soul.

'But, remember,' said the witch, 'when you have once received a human form, you can never be a sea maid again; you can never return through the water to your sisters or to your father's palace; and if you do not win the prince's love, so that he forgets father and mother for your sake, is attached to you heart and soul, and tells the priest to join your hands, you will not receive an immortal soul. On the first morning after he has married another, your heart will break and you will become foam on the water.'

'I will do it,' said the little sea maid; but she became as pale as death.

'But you must pay me, too,' said the witch; 'and it is not a trifle that I ask. You have the finest voice of all here at the bottom of the water; with that you think to enchant him; but this voice you must give to me. The best thing you possess I will have for my costly draught! I must give you my own blood in it, so that the draught may be sharp as a two-edged sword.'

'But if you take away my voice,' said the little sea maid, 'what will remain to me?'

'Your beautiful form,' replied the witch, 'your graceful walk, and your eloquent eyes: with those you can take captive a human heart. Well, have you lost your courage? Put out your little tongue, and then I will cut it off for my payment, and then you shall have the strong draught.'

'Let it be so,' said the little sea maid.

And the witch put on her pot to brew the draught.

'Cleanliness is a good thing,' said she; and she cleaned out the pot with the snakes, which she tied up in a big knot; then she scratched herself, and let her black blood drop into it. The steam rose up in the strangest forms, enough to frighten the beholder. Every moment the witch threw something else into the pot; and when it boiled thoroughly, there was a sound like the weeping of a crocodile. At last the draught was ready. It looked like the purest water.

'There you have it,' said the witch.

And she cut off the little sea maid's tongue, so that now she was dumb, and could neither sing nor speak.

'If the polypes should lay hold of you when you are returning through my forest,' said the witch, 'just cast a single drop of this liquor upon them, and their arms and fingers will fly into a thousand pieces.' But the little sea maid had no need to do this: the polypes drew back in terror when they saw the shining liquor, that gleamed in her hand as if it were a twinkling star. In this way she soon passed through the forest, the moss, and the rushing whirlpools.

She could see her father's palace. The torches were extinguished in the great dancing-hall, and they were certainly sleeping within, but she did not dare to go to them, now that she was dumb and was about to quit them for ever. She felt as if her heart would burst with sorrow. She crept into the garden, took a flower from each of her sisters' flower-beds, blew a thousand kisses towards the palace, and rose up through the dark blue sea.

The sun had not yet risen when she beheld the prince's castle and mounted the splendid marble staircase. The moon shone beautifully clear. The little sea maid drank the burning sharp draught, and it seemed as if a two-edged sword went through her delicate body. She fell down in a swoon, and lay as if she were dead. When the sun shone out over the sea she awoke, and felt a sharp pain; but just before her stood the handsome young prince. He fixed his coal-black eyes upon her, so that she cast down her own, and then she perceived that her fishtail was gone, and that she had the prettiest pair of white feet a little girl could have. But she had no clothes, so she shrouded herself in her long hair. The prince asked who she was and how she had come there; and she looked at him mildly, but very mournfully, with her dark blue eyes, for she could not speak. Then he took her by the hand, and led her into the castle. Each step she took was, as the witch had told her, as if she had been treading on pointed needles and sharp knives, but she bore it gladly. At the prince's right hand she moved on, light as a soap-bubble, and he, like all the rest, was astonished at her graceful swaying movements.

She now received splendid clothes of silk and muslin. In the castle she was the most beautiful of all; but she was dumb, and could neither sing nor speak. Lovely slaves, dressed in silk and gold, stepped forward, and sang before the prince and his royal parents; one sang more charmingly than all the rest, and the prince smiled at her and clapped his hands. Then the little sea maid became sad; she knew that she herself had sung far more sweetly, and thought, 'Oh! if only he could know that I have given away my voice for ever to be with him.'

Now the slaves danced pretty waving dances to the loveliest music; then the little sea maid lifted her beautiful white arms, stood on the tips of her toes, and glided dancing over the floor as no one had yet danced. At each movement her beauty became more apparent, and her eyes spoke more directly to the heart than the songs of the slaves.

All were delighted, and especially the prince, who called her his little foundling; and she danced again and again, although every time she touched the earth it seemed as if she were treading upon sharp knives. The prince said that she should always remain with him, and she received permission to sleep on a velvet cushion before his door.

He had a page's dress made for her, that she might accompany him on horseback. They rode through the fragrant woods, where the green boughs swept their shoulders and the little birds sang in the fresh leaves. She climbed with the prince up the high mountains, and although her delicate feet bled so that even the others could see it, she laughed at it herself, and followed him until they saw the clouds sailing beneath them like a flock of birds travelling to distant lands.

At home in the prince's castle, when the others slept at night, she went out on to the broad marble steps. It cooled her burning feet to stand in the cold sea water, and then she thought of the dear ones in the deep.

Once, in the night-time, her sisters came arm in arm. Sadly they sang as they floated above the water; and she beckoned to them, and they recognised her, and told her how she had grieved them all. Then they visited her every night; and once she saw in the distance her old grandmother, who had not been above the surface for many years, and the sea king with his crown upon his head. They stretched out their hands towards her, but did not venture so near the land as her sisters.

Day by day the prince grew more fond of her. He loved her as one loves a dear good child, but it never came into his head to make her his wife; and yet she must become his wife, or she would not receive an immortal soul, and would have to become foam on the sea on his wedding morning.

'Do you not love me best of them all?' the eyes of the little sea maid seemed to say, when he took her in his arms and kissed her fair forehead.

'Yes, you are the dearest to me!' said the prince, 'for you have the best heart of them all. You are the most devoted to me, and are like a young girl whom I once saw, but whom I certainly shall not find again. I was on board a ship which was wrecked. The waves threw me ashore near a holy temple, where several young girls performed the service. The youngest of them found me by the shore and saved my life. I only saw her twice: she was the only one in the world I could love; but you chase her picture out of my mind, you are so like her. She belongs to the holy temple, and therefore my good fortune has sent you to me. We will never part!'

'Ah! he does not know that I saved his life,' thought the little sea maid. 'I carried him over the sea to the wood where the temple stands.

I sat there under the foam and looked to see if anyone would come. I saw the beautiful girl whom he loves better than me.' And the sea maid sighed deeply – she could not weep. 'The maiden belongs to the holy temple,' he has said, 'and will never come out into the world – they will meet no more. I am with him and see him every day; I will cherish him, love him, give up my life for him.'

But now they said that the prince was to marry, and that the beautiful daughter of a neighbouring king was to be his wife, and that was why such a beautiful ship was being prepared. The story was, that the prince travelled to visit the land of the neighbouring king, but it was done that he might see the king's daughter. A great company was to go with him. The little sea maid shook her head and smiled; she knew the prince's thoughts far better than any of the others.

'I must travel,' he had said to her; 'I must see the beautiful princess: my parents desire it, but they do not wish to compel me to bring her home as my bride. I cannot love her. She is not like the beautiful maiden in the temple, whom you resemble. If I were to choose a bride, I would rather choose you, my dear dumb foundling with the speaking eyes.'

And he kissed her red lips and played with her long hair, so that she dreamed of happiness and of an immortal soul.

'You are not afraid of the sea, my dumb child?' said he, when they stood on the superb ship which was to carry him to the country of the neighbouring king; and he told her of storm and calm, of strange fishes in the deep, and of what the divers had seen there. And she smiled at his tales, for she knew better than anyone what there was at the bottom of the sea.

In the moonlight night, when all were asleep, except the steersman who stood by the helm, she sat on the side of the ship gazing down through the clear water. She fancied she saw her father's palace. High on the battlements stood her old grandmother, with the silver crown on her head, and looking through the rushing tide up to the vessel's keel. Then her sisters came forth over the water, and looked mournfully at her and wrung their white hands. She beckoned to them, smiled, and wished to tell them that she was well and happy; but the cabin-boy approached her, and her sisters dived down, so that he thought the white objects he had seen were foam on the surface of the water.

The next morning the ship sailed into the harbour of the neighbouring king's splendid city. All the church bells sounded, and from the high towers the trumpets were blown, while the soldiers stood there with flying colours and flashing bayonets. Each day brought some festivity with it; balls and entertainments followed one another; but the princess was not yet there. People said she was being educated in a holy temple far away, where she was learning every royal virtue. At last she arrived.

The little sea maid was anxious to see the beauty of the princess, and was obliged to acknowledge it. A more lovely apparition she had never beheld. The princess's skin was pure and clear, and behind the long dark eyelashes there smiled a pair of faithful dark blue eyes.

'You are the lady who saved me when I lay like a corpse upon the shore!' said the prince; and he folded his blushing bride to his heart. 'Oh, I am too, too happy!' he cried to the little sea maid. 'The best hope I could have is fulfilled. You will rejoice at my happiness, for you are the most devoted to me of them all!'

And the little sea maid kissed his hand; and it seemed already to her as if her heart was broken, for his wedding morning was to bring death to her, and change her into foam on the sea.

All the church bells were ringing, and heralds rode about the streets announcing the betrothal. On every altar fragrant oil was burning in gorgeous lamps of silver. The priests swung their censers, and bride and bridegroom laid hand in hand, and received the bishop's blessing. The little sea maid was dressed in cloth of gold, and held up the bride's train; but her ears heard nothing of the festive music, her eye marked not the holy ceremony; she thought of the night of her death, and of all that she had lost in this world.

On the same evening the bride and bridegroom went on board the ship. The cannon roared, all the flags waved; in the midst of the ship a costly tent of gold and purple, with the most beautiful cushions, had been set up, and there the married pair were to sleep in the cool still night.

The sails swelled in the wind and the ship glided smoothly and lightly over the clear sea. When it grew dark, coloured lamps were lighted and the sailors danced merry dances on deck. The little sea maid thought of the first time when she had risen up out of the sea, and beheld a similar scene of splendour and joy; and she joined in the whirling dance, and flitted on as the swallow flits away when he is pursued; and all shouted and admired her, for she had danced so prettily. Her delicate feet were cut as if with knives, but she did not feel it, for her heart was wounded far more painfully. She knew this was the last evening on which she should see him for whom she had left her friends and her home, and had given up her beautiful voice, and had suffered unheard-of pains every day, while he was utterly unconscious of all. It was the last evening she should breathe the same air with him, and behold the starry sky and the deep sea; and everlasting night without thought or dream awaited her, for she had no soul, and could win none. And everything was merriment and gladness on the ship till past midnight, and she laughed and danced with thoughts of death in her heart. The prince kissed his beautiful bride, and she played with his raven hair, and hand in hand they went to rest in the splendid tent.

It became quiet on the ship; only the helmsman stood by the helm, and the little sea maid leaned her white arms upon the bulwark and gazed out towards the east for the morning dawn – the first ray, she knew, would kill her. Then she saw her sisters rising out of the flood; they were pale, like herself; their long beautiful hair no longer waved in the wind – it had been cut off.

'We have given it to the witch, that she might bring you help, so that you may not die tonight. She has given us a knife; here it is – look! how sharp! Before the sun rises you must thrust it into the heart of the prince, and when the warm blood falls upon your feet they will grow together again into a fishtail, and you will become a sea maid again, and come back to us, and live your three hundred years before you become dead salt sea foam. Make haste! He or you must die before the sun rises! Our old grandmother mourns so that her white hair has fallen off, as ours did under the witch's scissors. Kill the prince and come back! Make haste! Do you see that red streak in the sky? In a few minutes the sun will rise, and you must die!'

And they gave a very mournful sigh, and vanished beneath the waves.

The little sea maid drew back the purple curtain from the tent, and saw the beautiful bride lying with her head on the prince's breast; and she bent down and kissed his brow, and gazed up to the sky where the morning red was gleaming brighter and brighter; then she looked at the sharp knife, and again fixed her eyes upon the prince, who in his sleep murmured his bride's name. She only was in his thoughts, and the knife trembled in the sea maid's hands. But then she flung it far away into the waves – they gleamed red where it fell, and it seemed as if drops of blood spurted up out of the water. Once more she looked with half-extinguished eyes upon the prince; then she threw herself from the ship into the sea, and felt her frame dissolving into foam.

Now the sun rose up out of the sea. The rays fell mild and warm upon the cold sea foam, and the little sea maid felt nothing of death. She saw the bright sun, and over her head sailed hundreds of glorious ethereal beings – she could see them through the white sails of the ship and the red clouds of the sky; their speech was melody, but of such a spiritual kind that no human ear could hear it, just as no earthly eye could see them; without wings they floated through the air. The little sea maid found that she had a frame like these, and was rising more and more out of the foam.

'Whither am I going?' she asked; and her voice sounded like that of the other beings, so spiritual, that no earthly music could be compared to it.

'To the daughters of the air!' replied the others. 'A sea maid has no immortal soul, and can never gain one, except she win the love of a mortal. Her eternal existence depends upon the power of another. The daughters of the air have likewise no immortal soul, but they can make themselves one through good deeds. We fly to the hot countries, where the close pestilent air kills men, and there we bring coolness. We disperse the fragrance of the flowers through the air, and spread refreshment and health. After we have striven for three hundred years to accomplish all the good we can bring about, we receive an immortal soul and take part in the eternal happiness of men. You, poor little sea maid, have striven with your whole heart after the goal we pursue; you have suffered and endured: you have by good works raised yourself to the world of spirits, and can gain an immortal soul after three hundred years.'

And the little sea maid lifted her bright arms towards God's sun, and for the first time she felt tears. On the ship there was again life and noise. She saw the prince and his bride searching for her; then they looked mournfully at the pearly foam, as if they knew that she had thrown herself into the waves. Invisible, she kissed the forehead of the bride, smiled to the prince, and mounted with the other children of the air on the rosy cloud which floated through the ether.

'After three hundred years we shall thus float into Paradise!'

'And we may even get there sooner,' whispered one. 'Invisibly we float into the houses of men where children are, and for every day on which we find a good child that brings joy to its parents and deserves their love, our time of probation is shortened. The child does not know when we fly through the room; and when we smile with joy at the child's conduct, a year is counted off from the three hundred; but when we see a naughty or a wicked child, we shed tears of grief, and for every tear a day is added to our time of trial.'

The Emperor's New Clothes

MANY YEARS ago there lived an emperor, who cared so enormously for beautiful new clothes that he spent all his money upon them, that he might be very fine. He did not care about his soldiers, nor about the theatre, nor about driving in the park except to show his new clothes. He had a coat for every hour of the day; and just as they say of a king, 'He is in council,' one always said of him, 'The emperor is in the wardrobe.'

In the great city in which he lived it was always very merry; every day a number of strangers arrived there. One day two cheats came: they gave themselves out as weavers, and declared that they could weave the finest stuff anyone could imagine. Not only were their colours and patterns, they said, uncommonly beautiful, but the clothes made of the stuff possessed the wonderful quality that they became invisible to anyone who was unfit for the office he held, or was incorrigibly stupid.

'Those would be capital clothes!' thought the emperor. 'If I wore those, I should be able to find out what men in my empire are not fit for the places they have; I could distinguish the clever from the stupid. Yes, the stuff must be woven for me directly!'

And he gave the two cheats a great deal of cash in hand, that they might begin their work at once.

As for them, they put up two looms, and pretended to be working; but they had nothing at all on their looms. They at once demanded the finest silk and the costliest gold; this they put into their own pockets, and worked at the empty looms till late into the night.

'I should like to know how far they have got on with the stuff,' thought the emperor. But he felt quite uncomfortable when he thought that those who were not fit for their offices could not see it. He believed, indeed, that he had nothing to fear for himself, but yet he preferred first to send someone else to see how matters stood. All the people in the whole city knew what peculiar power the stuff possessed, and all were anxious to see how bad or how stupid their neighbours were.

'I will send my honest old minister to the weavers,' thought the emperor. 'He can judge best how the stuff looks, for he has sense, and no one discharges his office better than he.'

Now the good old minister went out into the hall where the two cheats sat working at the empty looms.

'Mercy preserve us!' thought the old minister, and he opened his eyes wide. 'I cannot see anything at all!' But he did not say this.

Both the cheats begged him to be kind enough to come nearer, and asked if he did not approve of the colours and the pattern. Then they pointed to the empty loom, and the poor old minister went on opening his eyes; but he could see nothing, for there was nothing to see.

'Mercy!' thought he, 'can I indeed be so stupid? I never thought that, and not a soul must know it. Am I not fit for my office? No, it will never do for me to tell that I could not see the stuff.'

'Do you say nothing to it?' said one of the weavers.

'Oh, it is charming – quite enchanting!' answered the old minister, as he peered through his spectacles. 'What a fine pattern, and what colours! Yes, I shall tell the emperor that I am very much pleased with it.'

'Well, we are glad of that,' said both the weavers; and then they named the colours, and explained the strange pattern. The old minister listened attentively, that he might be able to repeat it when he went back to the emperor. And he did so.

Now the cheats asked for more money, and more silk and gold, which they declared they wanted for weaving. They put all into their own pockets, and not a thread was put upon the loom; but they continued to work at the empty frames as before.

The emperor soon sent again, dispatching another honest states-man, to see how the weaving was going on, and if the stuff would soon be ready. He fared just like the first: he looked and looked, but, as there was nothing to be seen but the empty looms, he could see nothing.

'Is not that a pretty piece of stuff?' asked the two cheats; and they displayed and explained the handsome pattern which was not there at all.

'I am not stupid!' thought the man – 'it must be my good office, for which I am not fit. It is funny enough, but I must not let it be noticed.' And so he praised the stuff which he did not see, and expressed his pleasure at the beautiful colours and the charming pattern. 'Yes, it is enchanting,' he said to the emperor.

All the people in the town were talking of the gorgeous stuff. The emperor wished to see it himself while it was still upon the loom. With a whole crowd of chosen men, among whom were also the two honest statesmen who had already been there, he went to the two cunning cheats, who were now weaving with might and main without fibre or thread.

'Is that not splendid?' said the two old statesmen, who had already been there once. 'Does not your majesty remark the pattern and the colours?' And then they pointed to the empty loom, for they thought that the others could see the stuff.

'What's this?' thought the emperor. 'I can see nothing at all! That is terrible. Am I stupid? Am I not fit to be emperor? That would be the most dreadful thing that could happen to me. Oh, it is *very* pretty!' he said aloud. 'It has our exalted approbation.' And he nodded in a contented way, and gazed at the empty loom, for he would not say that he saw nothing. The whole suite whom he had with him looked and looked, and saw nothing, any more than the rest; but, like the emperor, they said, 'That *is* pretty!' and counselled him to wear these splendid new clothes for the first time at the great procession that was presently to take place. 'It is splendid, tasteful, excellent!' went from mouth to mouth. On all sides there seemed to be general rejoicing, and the emperor gave each of the cheats a cross to hang at his button-hole and the title of Imperial Court Weaver.

The whole night before the morning on which the procession was to take place the cheats were up, and had lighted more than sixteen candles. The people could see that they were hard at work, completing the emperor's new clothes. They pretended to take the stuff down from the loom; they made cuts in the air with great scissors; they sewed with needles without thread; and at last they said, 'Now the clothes are ready!'

The emperor came himself with his noblest cavaliers; and the two cheats lifted up one arm as if they were holding something, and said, 'See, here are the trousers! here is the coat! here is the cloak!' and so on. 'It is as light as a spider's web: one would think one had nothing on; but that is just the beauty of it.'

'Yes,' said all the cavaliers; but they could not see anything, for nothing was there.

'Does your imperial majesty please to condescend to undress?' said the cheats; 'then we will put you on the new clothes here in front of the great mirror.'

The emperor took off his clothes, and the cheats pretended to put on him each of the new garments, and they took him round the waist, and seemed to fasten on something; that was the train; and the emperor turned round and round before the mirror.

'Oh, how well they look! how capitally they fit!' said all. 'What a pattern! what colours! That *is* a splendid dress!'

'They are standing outside with the canopy which is to be borne above your majesty in the procession!' announced the head master of the ceremonies.

'Well, I am ready,' replied the emperor. 'Does it not suit me well?' And then he turned again to the mirror, for he wanted it to appear as if he contemplated his adornment with great interest.

The chamberlains, who were to carry the train, stooped down with their hands towards the floor, just as if they were picking up the

mantle; then they pretended to be holding something up in the air. They did not dare to let it be noticed that they saw nothing.

So the emperor went in procession under the rich canopy, and everyone in the streets said, 'How incomparable are the emperor's new clothes! what a train he has to his mantle! how it fits him!' No one would let it be perceived that he could see nothing, for that would have shown that he was not fit for his office, or was very stupid. No clothes of the emperor's had ever had such a success as these.

'But he has nothing on!' a little child cried out at last.

'Just hear what that innocent says!' said the father; and one whispered to another what the child had said. 'There is a little child that says he has nothing on.'

'But he has nothing on!' said the whole people at length. And the emperor shivered, for it seemed to him that they were right; but he thought within himself, 'I must go through with the procession.' And so he carried himself still more proudly, and the chamberlains held on tighter than ever, and carried the train which did not exist at all.

The Goloshes of Fortune

I

A Beginning

IT WAS in Copenhagen, in East Street, and in one of the houses not far from the King's New Market, that a large company had assembled, for one must occasionally give a party, in order to be invited in return. Half of the company already sat at the card-tables, the other half awaited the result of the hostess's question, 'What shall we do now?' They had progressed so far, and the conversation went as best it could. Among other subjects the conversation turned upon the Middle Ages. Some considered that period much more interesting than our own times: yes, Councillor Knap defended this view so zealously that the lady of the house went over at once to his side; and both loudly exclaimed against Oersted's treatise in the Almanac on old and modern times, in which the chief advantage is given to our own day. The councillor considered the times of the Danish King Hans as the noblest and happiest age.

While the conversation takes this turn, only interrupted for a moment by the arrival of a newspaper, which contains nothing worth reading, we will betake ourselves to the antechamber, where the cloaks, sticks, and goloshes had found a place. Here sat two maids – an old one and a young one. One would have thought they had come to escort their mistresses home; but, on looking at them more closely, the observer could see that they were not ordinary servants: their hands were too fine for that, their bearing and all their movements too majestic, and the cut of their dresses too uncommon. They were two fairies. The younger was not Fortune, but lady's-maid to one of her ladies of the bedchamber, who carry about the more trifling gifts of Fortune. The elder one looked somewhat more gloomy – she was Care, who always goes herself in her own exalted person to perform her business, for then she knows that it is well done.

They were telling each other where they had been that day. The messenger of Fortune had only transacted a few unimportant affairs, as, for instance, she had preserved a new bonnet from a shower of rain, had procured an honest man a bow from a titled Nobody, and so on; but what she had still to relate was something quite extraordinary.

'I can likewise tell,' said she, 'that today is my birthday; and in honour of it a pair of goloshes has been entrusted to me, which I am to bring to the human race. These goloshes have the property that everyone who puts them on is at once transported to the time and place in which he likes best to be – every wish in reference to time, place, and circumstance is at once fulfilled; and so for once man can be happy here below!'

'Believe me,' said Care, 'he will be very unhappy, and will bless the moment when he can get rid of the goloshes again.'

'What are you thinking of?' retorted the other. 'Now I shall put them at the door. Somebody will take them by mistake, and become the happy one!'

You see, that was the dialogue they held.

2

What Happened to the Councillor

It was late. Councillor Knap, lost in contemplation of the times of King Hans, wished to get home; and fate willed that instead of his own goloshes he should put on those of Fortune, and thus went out into East Street. But by the power of the goloshes he had been put back three hundred years – into the days of King Hans; and therefore he put his foot into mud and mire in the street, because in those days there was not any pavement.

'Why, this is horrible – how dirty it is here!' said the councillor. 'The good pavement is gone, and all the lamps are put out.'

The moon did not yet stand high enough to give much light, and the air was tolerably thick, so that all objects seemed to melt together in the darkness. At the next corner a lamp hung before a picture of the Madonna, but the light it gave was as good as none; he only noticed it when he stood just under it, and his eyes fell upon the painted figure of the mother and child.

'That is probably a museum of art,' he thought, 'where they have forgotten to take down the sign.'

A couple of men in the costume of those past days went by him.

'How they look!' he said. 'They must come from a masquerade.'

Suddenly there was a sound of drums and fifes, and torches gleamed brightly. The councillor started. And now he saw a strange procession go past. First came a whole troop of drummers, beating their instruments very dexterously; they were followed by men-at-arms, with longbows and crossbows. The chief man in the procession was a clerical lord. The astonished councillor asked what was the meaning of this, and who the man might be.

'That is the Bishop of Zealand.'

'What in the world has come to the bishop?' said the councillor, with a sigh, shaking his head. 'This could not possibly be the bishop!'

Ruminating on this, and without looking to the right or to the left, the councillor went through the East Street, and over the Highbridge Place. The bridge which led to the Palace Square was not to be found; he perceived the shore of a shallow water, and at length encountered two people, who sat in a boat.

'Do you wish to be ferried over to the Holm, sir?' they asked.

'To the Holm!' repeated the councillor, who did not know, you see, in what period he was. 'I want to go to Christian's Haven and to Little Turf Street.'

The men stared at him.

'Pray tell me where the bridge is?' said he. 'It is shameful that no lanterns are lighted here; and it is as muddy, too, as if one were walking in a marsh.' But the longer he talked with the boatmen the less could he understand them. 'I don't understand your Bornholm talk,' he at last cried, angrily, and turned his back upon them.

He could not find the bridge, nor was there any paling. 'It is quite scandalous how things look here!' he said – never had he thought his own times so miserable as this evening. 'I think it will be best if I take a cab,' thought he. But where were the cabs? not one was to be seen. 'I shall have to go back to the King's New Market, where there are many carriages standing, otherwise I shall never get as far as Christian's Haven.'

Now he went towards East Street, and had almost gone through it when the moon burst forth.

'What in the world have they been erecting here?' he exclaimed, when he saw the East Gate, which in those days stood at the end of East Street.

In the meantime, however, he found a passage open, and through this he came out upon our New Market; but it was a broad meadow. Single bushes stood forth, and across the meadow ran a great canal or stream. A few miserable wooden booths for skippers from Holland were erected on the opposite shore.

'Either I behold a *Fata Morgana*, or I am tipsy,' sighed the councillor. 'What can that be? what can that be?'

He turned back, in the full persuasion that he must be ill. In walking up the street he looked more closely at the houses; most of them were built of laths, and many were only thatched with straw.

'No, I don't feel well at all!' he lamented. 'And yet I only drank one glass of punch! But I cannot stand that; and besides, it was very foolish to give us punch and warm salmon. I shall mention that to our hostess – the agent's lady. Suppose I go back, and say how I feel? But that looks ridiculous, and it is a question if they will be up still.'

He looked for the house, but could not find it.

'That is dreadful!' he cried; 'I don't know East Street again. Not one shop is to be seen; old, miserable, tumbledown huts are all I see, as if I were at Roskilde or Ringstedt. Oh, I am ill! It's no use to make ceremony. But where in all the world is the agent's house? It is no longer the same; but within there are people up still. I certainly must be ill!'

He now reached a half-open door, where the light shone through a chink. It was a tavern of that date – a kind of beer-house. The room had the appearance of a farmhouse kitchen in Holstein; a number of people, consisting of seamen, citizens of Copenhagen, and a few scholars, sat in deep conversation over their jugs, and paid little attention to the newcomer.

'I beg pardon,' said the councillor to the hostess, 'but I feel very unwell; would you let them get me a fly to go to Christian's Haven?'

The woman looked at him and shook her head; then she spoke to him in German.

The councillor now supposed that she did not understand Danish, so he repeated his wish in the German language. This, and his costume, convinced the woman that he was a foreigner. She soon understood that he felt unwell, and therefore brought him a jug of water. It certainly tasted a little of sea water, though it had been taken from the spring outside.

The councillor leaned his head on his hand, drew a deep breath, and thought of all the strange things that were happening about him.

'Is that today's number of the *Day*?' he said, quite mechanically, for he saw that the woman was putting away a large sheet of paper.

She did not understand what he meant, but handed him the leaf: it was a woodcut representing a strange appearance in the air which had been seen in the city of Cologne.

'That is very old!' said the councillor, who became quite cheerful at sight of this antiquity. 'How did you come by this strange leaf? That is very interesting, although the whole thing is a fable. Nowadays these appearances are explained to be northern lights that have been seen; probably they arise from electricity.'

Those who sat nearest to him and heard his speech, looked at him in surprise, and one of them rose, took off his hat respectfully, and said, with a very grave face, 'You must certainly be a very learned man, sir!'

'Oh, no!' replied the councillor; 'I can only say a word or two about things one ought to understand.'

'*Modestia* is a beautiful virtue,' said the man. 'Moreover, I must say to your speech, *mihi secus videtur*; yet I will gladly suspend my *judicium*.'

'May I ask with whom I have the pleasure of speaking?' asked the councillor.

'I am a bachelor of theology,' replied the man.

This answer sufficed for the councillor; the title corresponded with the garb.

'Certainly,' he thought, 'this must be an old village schoolmaster, a queer character, such as one finds sometimes over in Jutland.'

'This is certainly not a *locus docendi*,' began the man; 'but I beg you to take the trouble to speak. You are doubtless well read in the ancients?'

'Oh, yes,' replied the councillor. 'I am fond of reading useful old books; and am fond of the modern ones, too, with the exception of the "Everyday Stories", of which we have enough, in all conscience.'

'Everyday Stories?' replied the bachelor, enquiringly.

'Yes, I mean the new romances we have now.'

'Oh!' said the man, with a smile, 'they are very witty, and are much read at court. The king is especially partial to the romance by Messieurs Iffven and Gaudian, which talks about King Arthur and his knights of the Round Table. He has jested about it with his noble lords.'

'That I have certainly not yet read,' said the councillor; 'that must be quite a new book published by Heiberg.'

'No,' retorted the man, 'it is not published by Heiberg, but by Godfrey von Gehmen.'*

'Indeed! is he the author?' asked the councillor. 'That is a very old name: was not that the name of about the first printer in Denmark?'

'Why, he *is* our first printer,' replied the man.

So far it had gone well. Now one of the men began to speak of a pestilence which he said had been raging a few years ago: he meant the plague of 1484. The councillor supposed that he meant the cholera, and so the conversation went on tolerably. The Freebooters' War of 1490 was so recent that it could not escape mention. The English pirates had taken ships from the very wharves, said the man; and the councillor, who was well acquainted with the events of 1801, joined in manfully against the English. The rest of the talk, however, did not pass over so well; every moment there was a contradiction. The good bachelor was terribly ignorant, and the simplest assertion

* The first printer and publisher in Denmark, under King Hans.

of the councillor seemed too bold or too fantastic. They looked at each other, and when it became too bad, the bachelor spoke Latin, in the hope that he would be better understood; but it was of no use.

'How are you now?' asked the hostess, and she plucked the councillor by the sleeve.

Now his recollection came back: in the course of the conversation he had forgotten everything that had happened.

'Good heavens! where am I?' he said, and he felt dizzy when he thought of it.

'We'll drink claret, mead, and Bremen beer,' cried one of the guests, 'and you shall drink with us.'

Two girls came in. One of them had on a cap of two colours. They poured out drink and bowed: the councillor felt a cold shudder running all down his back. 'What's that? what's that?' he cried; but he was obliged to drink with them. They took possession of the good man quite politely. He was in despair, and when one said that he was tipsy he felt not the slightest doubt regarding the truth of the statement, and only begged them to procure him a droshky. Now they thought he was speaking Muscovite.

Never had he been in such rude vulgar company.

'One would think the country was falling back into heathenism,' was his reflection. 'This is the most terrible moment of my life.'

But at the same time the idea occurred to him to bend down under the table, and then to creep to the door. He did so; but just as he had reached the entry the others discovered his intention. They seized him by the feet; and now the goloshes, to his great good fortune, came off, and – the whole enchantment vanished.

The councillor saw quite plainly, in front of him, a lamp burning, and behind it a great building; everything looked familiar and splendid. It was East Street, as we know it now. He lay with his legs turned towards a porch, and opposite to him sat the watchman asleep.

'Good heavens! have I been lying here in the street dreaming?' he exclaimed. 'Yes, this is East Street sure enough! how splendidly bright and gay! It is terrible what an effect that one glass of punch must have had on me!'

Two minutes afterwards he was sitting in a fly, which drove him out to Christian's Haven. He thought of the terror and anxiety he had undergone, and praised from his heart the happy present, our own time, which, with all its shortcomings, was far better than the period in which he had been placed a short time before.

3

The Watchman's Adventures

'On my word, yonder lies a pair o' goloshes!' said the watchman. 'They must certainly belong to the lieutenant who lives upstairs. They are lying close to the door.'

The honest man would gladly have rung the bell and delivered them, for upstairs there was a light still burning; but he did not wish to disturb the other people in the house, and so he let it alone.

'It must be very warm to have a pair of such things on,' said he. 'How nice and soft the leather is!' They fitted his feet very well. 'How droll it is in the world! Now, he might lie down in his warm bed, and yet he does not! There he is pacing up and down the room. He is a happy man! He has neither wife nor children, and every evening he is at a party. Oh, I wish I were he, then I should be a happy man!'

As he uttered the wish, the goloshes he had put on produced their effect, and the watchman was transported into the body and being of the lieutenant. Then he stood up in the room, and held a little pink paper in his fingers, on which was a poem, a poem written by the lieutenant himself. For who is there who has not once in his life had a poetic moment? and at such a moment, if one writes down one's thoughts, there is poetry.

Yes, people write poetry when they are in love; but a prudent man does not print such poems. The lieutenant was in love – and poor – that's a triangle, or, so to speak, the half of a broken square of happiness. The lieutenant felt that very keenly, and so he laid his head against the window-frame and sighed a deep sigh.

'The poor watchman in the street yonder is far happier than I. He does not know what I call want. He has a home, a wife, and children, who weep at his sorrow and rejoice at his joy. Oh! I should be happier than I am, if I could pass right over into him, for he is happier than I!'

In that same moment the watchman became a watchman again; for through the power of the goloshes of Fortune he had assumed the personality of the lieutenant; but then we know he felt far less content, and preferred to be what he really was. So the watchman became a watchman again.

'That was an ugly dream,' said he, 'but droll enough. It seemed to me that I was the lieutenant up yonder, and that it was not pleasant at all. I missed the wife and the boys, who are now ready to half stifle me with kisses.'

He sat down again and nodded. The dream would not go quite out of his thoughts. He had the goloshes still on his feet. A falling star glided down the sky.

'There went one,' said he, 'but for all that, there are enough left. I should like to look at those things a little nearer, especially the moon, for that won't vanish under one's hands. The student for whom my wife washes says that when we die we fly from one star to another. That's not true, but it would be very nice. If I could only make a little spring up there, then my body might lie here on the stairs for all I care.'

Now there are certain things we should be very cautious of uttering in this world, but doubly careful when we have goloshes of Fortune on our feet. Just hear what happened to the watchman.

So far as we are concerned, we all understand the rapidity of dispatch by steam; we have tried it either in railways, or in steamers across the sea. But this speed is as the crawling of the sloth or the march of the snail in comparison with the swiftness with which light travels. That flies nineteen million times quicker than the best racer, and yet electricity is still quicker. Death is an electric shock we receive in our hearts, and on the wings of electricity the liberated soul flies away. The sunlight requires eight minutes and a few seconds for a journey of more than ninety-five millions of miles; on the wings of electric power the soul requires only a few moments to accomplish the same flight. The space between the orbs of the universe is, for her, not greater than, for us, the distances between the houses of our friends dwelling in the same town and even living close together. Yet this electric shock costs us the life of the body here below, unless, like the watchman, we have the magic goloshes on.

In a few seconds the watchman had traversed the distance of two hundred and sixty thousand miles to the moon, which body, as we know, consists of a much lighter material than that of our earth, and is, as we should say, soft as new-fallen snow. He found himself on one of the many ring mountains with which we are familiar from Dr Mädler's great map of the moon. Within the ring a great bowl-shaped hollow went down to the depth of a couple of miles. At the base of the hollow lay a town, of whose appearance we can only form an idea by pouring the white of an egg into a glass of water: the substance here was just as soft as white of egg, and formed similar towers, and cupolas, and terraces like sails, transparent and floating in the thin air. Our earth hung over his head like a great fiery red ball.

He immediately became aware of a number of beings, who were certainly what we call 'men', but their appearance was very different from ours. They had also a language, but no one could expect that the soul of the watchman should understand it. But it did understand, nevertheless.

Thus the watchman's soul understood the language of the people in the moon very well. They disputed about this earth, and doubted if it could be inhabited; the air, they asserted, must be too thick for a sensible moon-man to live there. They considered that the moon alone was peopled; for that, they said, was the real body in which the old-world people dwelt. They also talked of politics.

But let us go down to the East Street, and see how it fared with the body of the watchman.

He sat lifeless upon the stairs. His pike had fallen out of his hand, and his eyes stared up at the moon, after his honest soul which was going about up there.

'What's o'clock, watchman?' asked a passer-by. But the man who didn't answer was the watchman. Then the passenger tweaked him quite gently by the nose, and then he lost his balance. There lay the body stretched out at full length – the man was dead. Great fear fell upon the man who had tweaked him; dead the watchman was, and dead he remained. It was reported, and it was discussed, and in the morning the body was carried out to the hospital.

That would be a pretty jest for the soul if it should chance to come back, and probably seek its body in the East Street, and not find it! Most likely it would go first to the police and afterwards to the address office, that enquiries might be made from thence respecting the missing goods; and then it would wander out to the hospital. But we may console ourselves with the idea that the soul is most clever when it acts upon its own account; it is the body that makes it stupid.

As we have said, the watchman's body was taken to the hospital, and brought into the washing-room; and naturally enough the first thing they did there was to pull off the goloshes; and then the soul had to come back. It took its way directly towards the body, and in a few seconds there was life in the man. He declared that this had been the most terrible night of his life; he would not have such feelings again, not for a shilling; but now it was past and over.

The same day he was allowed to leave; but the goloshes remained at the hospital.

4

A Great Moment – A Very Unusual Journey

Everyone who belongs to Copenhagen knows the look of the entrance to the Frederick's Hospital in Copenhagen; but as, perhaps, a few will read this story who do not belong to Copenhagen, it becomes necessary to give a short description of it.

The hospital is separated from the street by a tolerably high railing, in which the thick iron rails stand so far apart, that certain very thin inmates are said to have squeezed between them, and thus paid their little visits outside the premises. The part of the body most difficult to get through was the head; and here, as it often happens in the world, small heads were the most fortunate. This will be sufficient as an introduction.

One of the young volunteers, of whom one could only say in one sense that he had a great head, had the watch that evening. The rain was pouring down; but in spite of this obstacle he wanted to go out, only for a quarter of an hour. It was needless, he thought, to tell the porter of his wish, especially if he could slip through between the rails. There lay the goloshes which the watchman had forgotten. It never occurred to him in the least that they were goloshes of Fortune. They would do him very good service in this rainy weather, and he pulled them on. Now the question was whether he could squeeze through the bars; till now he had never tried it. There he stood.

'I wish to goodness I had my head outside!' cried he. And immediately, though his head was very thick and big, it glided easily and quickly through. The goloshes must have understood it well; but now the body was to slip through also, and that could not be done.

'I'm too fat,' said he. 'I thought my head would be the worst thing. I shan't get through.'

Now he wanted to pull his head back quickly, but he could not manage it: he could move his neck, but that was all. His first feeling was one of anger, and then his spirits sank down to zero. The goloshes of Fortune had placed him in this terrible condition, and, unfortunately, it never occurred to him to wish himself free. No: instead of wishing, he only strove, and could not stir from the spot. The rain poured down; not a creature was to be seen in the street; he could not reach the gate-bell, and how was he to get loose? He foresaw that he would have to remain here until the morning, and then they would have to send for a blacksmith, to file through the iron bars. But such a business is not to be done quickly. The whole charity school opposite would be upon its legs; the whole sailors' quarter close by would come up and see him standing in the pillory; and a fine crowd there would be.

'Ugh!' he cried, 'the blood's rising to my head, and I shall go mad! Yes, I'm going mad! O I wish I were free again, then most likely it would pass over.'

That's what he ought to have said a little sooner. The very moment he had uttered the thought his head was free; and now he rushed in, quite dazed with the fright the goloshes of Fortune had given him. But we must not think the whole affair was over; there was much worse to come yet.

The night passed away, and the following day too, and nobody sent for the goloshes. In the evening a representation was to take place in an amateur theatre in a distant street. The house was crammed; and among the audience was the volunteer from the hospital, who appeared to have forgotten his adventure of the previous evening. He had the goloshes on, for they had not been sent for; and as it was dirty in the streets, they might do him good service. A new piece was recited: it was called *My Aunt's Spectacles*. These were spectacles which, when anyone put them on in a great assembly of people, made all present look like cards, so that one could prophesy from them all that would happen in the coming year.

The idea struck him: he would have liked to possess such a pair of spectacles. If they were used rightly, they would enable the wearer to look into people's hearts; and that, he thought, would be more interesting than to see what was going to happen in the next year; for future events would be known in time, but the people's thoughts never.

'Now I'll look at the row of ladies and gentlemen on the first bench: if one could look directly into their hearts! yes, that must be a hollow, a sort of shop. How my eyes would wander about in that shop! In every lady's, yonder, I should doubtless find a great milliner's warehouse: with this one here the shop is empty, but it would do no harm to have it cleaned out. But there would also be substantial shops. Ah, yes!' he continued, sighing, 'I know one in which all the goods are first-rate, but there's a shopman in it already; that's the only drawback in the whole shop! From one and another the word would be "Please to step in!" Oh that I might only step in, like a neat little thought, and slip through their hearts!'

That was the word of command for the goloshes. The volunteer shrivelled up, and began to take a very remarkable journey through the hearts of the first row of spectators. The first heart through which he passed was that of a lady; but he immediately fancied himself in the Orthopaedic Institute, in the room where the plaster casts of deformed limbs are kept hanging against the walls; the only difference was, that these casts were formed in the institute when the patients came in, but here in the heart they were formed and preserved after the good persons had gone away. For they were casts of female friends, whose bodily and mental faults were preserved here.

Quickly he had passed into another female heart. But this seemed to him like a great holy church; the white dove of innocence fluttered over the high altar. Gladly would he have sunk down on his knees; but he was obliged to go away into the next heart. Still, however, he heard the tones of the organ, and it seemed to him that he himself had become another and a better man. He felt himself not unworthy to enter into the next sanctuary, which showed itself in the form of a poor garret, containing a sick mother. But through the window the warm sun streamed in, beautiful roses nodded from the little wooden box on the roof, and two sky-blue birds sang full of childlike joy, while the sick mother prayed for a blessing on her daughter.

Now he crept on his hands and knees through an overfilled butcher's shop. There was meat, and nothing but meat, wherever he went. It was the heart of a rich respectable man, whose name is certainly to be found in the directory.

Now he was in the heart of this man's wife: this heart was an old dilapidated pigeon-house. The husband's portrait was used as a mere weathercock: it stood in connection with the doors, and these doors opened and shut according as the husband turned.

Then he came into a cabinet of mirrors, such as we find in the castle of Rosenborg; but the mirrors magnified in a great degree. In the middle of the floor sat, like a Grand Lama, the insignificant *I* of the proprietor, astonished in the contemplation of his own greatness.

Then he fancied himself transported into a narrow needle-case full of pointed needles; and he thought, 'This must decidedly be the heart of an old maid!' But that was not the case. It was a young officer, wearing several orders, and of whom one said, 'He's a man of intellect and heart.'

Quite confused was the poor volunteer when he emerged from the heart of the last person in the first row. He could not arrange his thoughts, and fancied it must be his powerful imagination which had run away with him.

'Gracious powers!' he sighed, 'I must certainly have a great tendency to go mad. It is also unconscionably hot in here: the blood is rising to my head!'

And now he remembered the great event of the last evening, how his head had been caught between the iron rails of the hospital.

'That's where I must have caught it,' thought he. 'I must do something at once. A Russian bath might be very good. I wish I were already lying on the highest board in the bath-house.'

And there he lay on the highest board in the vapour bath; but he was lying there in all his clothes, in boots and goloshes, and the hot drops from the ceiling were falling on his face.

'Hi!' he cried, and jumped down to take a plunge bath.

The attendant uttered a loud cry on seeing a person there with all his clothes on. The volunteer had, however, enough presence of mind to whisper to him, 'It's for a wager!' But the first thing he did when he got into his own room was to put a big blister on the nape of his neck, and another on his back, that they might draw out his madness.

Next morning he had a very sore back; and that was all he had got by the goloshes of Fortune.

5

The Transformation of the Copying Clerk

The watchman, whom we assuredly have not yet forgotten, in the meantime thought of the goloshes, which he had found and brought to the hospital. He took them away; but as neither the lieutenant nor anyone in the street would own them, they were taken to the police office.

'They look exactly like my own goloshes,' said one of the copying gentlemen, as he looked at the unowned articles and put them beside his own. 'More than a shoemaker's eye is required to distinguish them from one another.'

'Mr Copying Clerk,' said a servant, coming in with some papers.

The copying clerk turned and spoke to the man: when he had done this, he turned to look at the goloshes again; he was in great doubt if the right-hand or the left-hand pair belonged to him.

'It must be those that are wet,' he thought. Now here he thought wrong, for these were the goloshes of Fortune; but why should not the police be sometimes mistaken? He put them on, thrust some papers into his pocket, and put a few manuscripts under his arm, for they were to be read at home, and abstracts to be made from them. But now it was Sunday morning, and the weather was fine. 'A walk to Fredericksberg would do me good,' said he; and he went out accordingly.

There could not be a quieter, steadier person than this young man. We grant him his little walk with all our hearts; it will certainly do him good after so much sitting. At first he only walked without thinking of anything, so the goloshes had no opportunity of displaying their magic power.

In the avenue he met an acquaintance, a young poet, who told him that he was going to start, next day, on a summer trip.

'Are you going away again already?' asked the copying clerk. 'What a happy, free man you are! You can fly wherever you like; we others have a chain to our foot.'

'But it is fastened to the bread tree!' replied the poet. 'You need not be anxious for the morrow; and when you grow old you get a pension.'

'But you are better off, after all,' said the copying clerk. 'It must be a pleasure to sit and write poetry. Everybody says agreeable things to you, and then you are your own master. Ah, you should just try it, poring over the frivolous affairs in the court.'

The poet shook his head; the copying clerk shook his head also: each retained his own opinions; and thus they parted.

'They are a strange race, these poets!' thought the copying clerk. 'I should like to try and enter into such a nature – to become a poet myself. I am certain I should not write such complaining verses as the rest. What a splendid spring day for a poet! The air is so remarkably clear, the clouds are so beautiful, and the green smells so sweet. For many years I have not felt as I feel at this moment.'

We already notice that he has become a poet. It was certainly not an obvious change, for it is a foolish fancy to imagine a poet different from other people, for among the latter there may be natures more poetical than those of many an acknowledged poet. The difference is only that the poet has a better spiritual memory: he can hold fast the feeling and the idea until they are embodied clearly and firmly in words; and the others cannot do that. But the transition from an everyday nature to that of a poet is always a transition, and as such it must be noticed in the copying clerk.

'What glorious fragrance!' he cried. 'How it reminds me of the violets at Aunt Laura's! Yes, that was when I was a little boy. I have not thought of that for a long time. The good old lady! She lived over there behind the Exchange. She always had a twig or a couple of green shoots in water, let the winter be as severe as it might. The violets bloomed, while I had to put warm farthings against the frozen window-panes to make peep-holes. That was a pretty view. Out in the canal the ships were frozen in, and deserted by the whole crew; a screaming crow was the only living creature left. Then, when the spring breezes blew, it all became lively: the ice was sawn asunder amid shouting and cheers, the ships were tarred and rigged, and then they sailed away to strange lands. I remained here, and must always remain, and sit at the police office, and let others take passports for abroad. That's my fate. Oh, yes!' and he sighed deeply. Suddenly he paused. 'Good heaven! what is come to me? I never thought or felt as I do now. It must be the spring air: it is both charming and agreeable!' He felt in his pockets for his papers. 'These will give me something else to think of,' said he, and let his eyes wander over the first leaf. There he read: '*Dame Sigbrith; an original tragedy in five acts*. What is that? And it is my own hand. Have I written this tragedy? *The Intrigue on the Promenade; or, the Day of Penance – Vaudeville*. But where did I get that from? It must have been put into my pocket. Here is a letter. Yes, it was from the manager of the theatre; the pieces were rejected, and the letter is not at all politely worded. H'm! H'm!' said the copying clerk, and he sat down upon a bench: his thoughts were so living, his heart so soft. Involuntarily he grasped one of the nearest flowers; it was a common little daisy. What the botanists require several lectures to explain to us, this flower told in a minute. It told the story of its birth; it told of the strength of the sunlight, which spread out the delicate leaves and made them give out fragrance. Then he thought of the battles of life, which likewise awaken feelings in our breasts. Air and light are the lovers of the flower, but light is the favoured one. Towards the light it turned, and only when the light vanished the flower rolled her leaves together and slept in the embrace of the air.

'It is light that adorns me!' said the flower.

'But the air allows you to breathe,' whispered the poet's voice.

Just by him stood a boy, knocking with his stick in a muddy ditch. The drops of water spurted up among the green twigs, and the copying clerk thought of the millions of invisible animals which were cast up on high with the drops, which was the same to them, in proportion to their size, as it would be to us if we were hurled high over the clouds. And the copying clerk thought of this, and of the great change which had taken place within him; he smiled. 'I sleep and dream! It is wonderful, though, how naturally one can dream, and yet know all the time that it is a dream. I should like to be able to remember it all clearly tomorrow when I wake. I seem to myself quite unusually excited. What a clear appreciation I have of everything, and how free I feel! But I am certain that if I remember anything of it tomorrow, it will be nonsense. That has often been so with me before. It is with all the clever famous things one says and hears in dreams, as with the money of the elves under the earth; when one receives it, it is rich and beautiful, but looked at by daylight, it is nothing but stones and dried leaves. Ah!' he sighed, quite plaintively, and gazed at the chirping birds, as they sprang merrily from bough to bough, 'they are much better off than I. Flying is a noble art. Happy he who is born with wings. Yes, if I could change myself into anything, it should be into a lark.'

In a moment his coat-tails and sleeves grew together and formed wings; his clothes became feathers, and his goloshes claws. He noticed it quite plainly, and laughed inwardly. 'Well, now I can see that I am dreaming, but I have never dreamed before so wildly.' And he flew up into the green boughs and sang; but there was no poetry in the song, for the poetic nature was gone. The goloshes, like everyone who wishes to do any business thoroughly, could only do one thing at a time. He wished to be a poet, and he became one. Then he wished to be a little bird, and, in changing thus, the former peculiarity was lost.

'That is very funny!' he said. 'In the daytime I sit in the police office among the driest of law papers; at night I can dream that I am flying about, as a lark in the Fredericksberg Garden. One could really write quite a popular comedy upon it.'

Now he flew down into the grass, turned his head in every direction, and beat with his beak upon the bending stalks of grass, which, in proportion to his size, seemed to him as long as palm branches of Northern Africa.

It was only for a moment, and then all around him became as the blackest night. It seemed to him that some immense substance was cast over him; it was a great cap, which a boy threw over the bird. A hand came in and seized the copying clerk by the back and wings in a way that made him chirp. In his first terror he cried aloud, 'You impudent rascal! I am copying clerk at the police office!' But that sounded to the boy only like 'piep! piep!' and he tapped the bird on the beak and wandered on with him.

In the alley the boy met with two other boys, who belonged to the educated classes, socially speaking; but, according to abilities, they ranked in the lowest class in the school. These bought the bird for threepence; and so the copying clerk was carried back to Copenhagen.

'It's a good thing that I am dreaming,' he said, 'or I should become really angry. First I was a poet, and now I'm a lark! Yes, it must have been the poetic nature which transformed me into that little creature. It is a miserable state of things, especially when one falls into the hands of boys. I should like to know what the end of it will be.'

The boys carried him into a very elegant room. A stout smiling lady received them. But she was not at all gratified to see the common field bird, as she called the lark, coming in too. Only for that day she would consent to it; but they must put the bird in the empty cage which stood by the window.

'Perhaps that will please Polly,' she added, and laughed at a great parrot swinging himself proudly in his ring in the handsome brass cage.

'It's Polly's birthday,' she said, fatuously, 'so the little field bird shall congratulate him.'

Polly did not answer a single word; he only swung proudly to and fro. But a pretty canary bird, who had been brought here last summer out of his warm fragrant fatherland, began to sing loudly.

'Screamer!' said the lady; and she threw a white handkerchief over the cage.

'Piep! piep!' sighed he; 'here's a terrible snowstorm. And thus sighing, he was silent.

The copying clerk or, as the lady called him, the field bird, was placed in a little cage close to the canary, and not far from the parrot. The only human words which Polly could say, and which often sounded very comically, were, '*Come, let's be men now!*' Everything else that he screamed out was just as unintelligible as the song of the canary bird, except for the copying clerk, who was now also a bird, and who understood his comrades very well.

'I flew under the green palm tree and the blossoming almond tree!' sang the canary. 'I flew with my brothers and sisters over the beautiful flowers and over the bright sea, where the plants waved in the depths. I also saw many beautiful parrots, who told the merriest stories.'

'Those were wild birds,' replied the parrot. 'They had no education. Let us be men now! Why don't you laugh? If the lady and all the strangers could laugh at it, so can you. It is a great fault to have no taste for what is humorous. No, let us be men now.'

'Do you remember the pretty girls who danced under the tents spread out beneath the blooming trees? Do you remember the sweet fruits and the cooling juice in the wild plants?'

'Oh, yes!' replied the parrot; 'but here I am far better off. I have good care and genteel treatment. I know I've a good head, and I don't ask for more. Let us be men now. You are what they call a poetic soul. I have thorough knowledge and wit. You have genius, but no prudence. You mount up into those high natural notes of yours, and then you get covered up. That is never done to me; no, no, for I cost them a little more. I make an impression with my beak, and can cast wit round me. Now let us be men!'

'O my warm flowery fatherland!' sang the canary. 'I will praise thy dark green trees and thy quiet bays, where the branches kiss the clear watery mirror; I'll sing of the joy of all my shining brothers and sisters, where the plants grow by the desert springs.'

'Now, pray leave off these dismal tones,' cried the parrot. 'Sing something at which one can laugh! Laughter is the sign of the highest mental development. Look if a dog or a horse can laugh! No: they can cry; but laughter – that is given to men alone. Ho! ho! ho!' screamed Polly, and finished the jest with 'Let us be men now.'

'You little grey Danish bird,' said the canary; 'so you have also become a prisoner. It is certainly cold in your woods, but still liberty is there. Fly out! they have forgotten to close your cage; the upper window is open. Fly! fly!'

Instinctively the copying clerk obeyed, and flew forth from his prison. At the same moment the half-opened door of the next room creaked, and stealthily, with fierce sparkling eyes, the house cat crept in, and made chase upon him. The canary fluttered in its cage, the parrot flapped its wings, and cried, 'Let us be men now.' The copying clerk felt mortally afraid, and flew through the window, away over the houses and streets; at last he was obliged to rest a little.

The house opposite had a homelike look: one of the windows stood open, and he flew in. It was his own room: he perched upon the table.

'Let us be men now,' he broke out, involuntarily imitating the parrot; and in the same moment he was restored to the form of the copying clerk; but he was sitting on the table.

'Heaven preserve me!' he cried. 'How could I have come here and fallen so soundly asleep? That was an unquiet dream, too, that I had. The whole thing was great nonsense.'

6

The Best that the Goloshes Brought

On the following day, quite early in the morning, as the clerk still lay in bed, there came a tapping at his door: it was his neighbour who lodged on the same floor, a young theologian; and he came in.

'Lend me your goloshes,' said he. 'It is very wet in the garden, but the sun shines gloriously, and I should like to smoke a pipe down there.'

He put on the goloshes, and was soon in the garden, which contained a plum tree and a pear tree. Even a little garden like this is highly prized in Copenhagen.

The student wandered up and down the path; it was only six o'clock, and a post-horn sounded out in the street.

'Oh, travelling! travelling!' he cried out, 'that's the greatest happiness in all the world. That's the highest goal of my wishes. Then this disquietude that I feel would be stilled. But it would have to be far away. I should like to see beautiful Switzerland, to travel through Italy, to – '

Yes, it was a good thing that the goloshes took effect immediately, for he might have gone too far even for himself, and for us others too. He was travelling; he was in the midst of Switzerland, packed tightly with eight others in the interior of a diligence. He had a headache and a weary feeling in his neck, and his feet had gone to sleep, for they were swollen by the heavy boots he had on. He was hovering in a condition between sleeping and waking. In his right-hand pocket he had his letter of credit, in his left-hand pocket his passport, and a few louis d'or

were sewn into a little bag he wore on his breast. Whenever he dozed off, he dreamed he had lost one or other of these possessions; and then he would start up in a feverish way, and the first movement his hand made was to describe a triangle from left to right, and towards his breast, to feel whether he still possessed them or not. Umbrellas, hats, and walking-sticks swung in the net over him, and almost took away the prospect, which was impressive enough: he glanced out at it, and his heart sang what one poet at least, whom we know, has sung in Switzerland, but has not yet printed:

> 'Tis a prospect as fine as heart can desire,
>   Before me Mont Blanc the rough:
> 'Tis pleasant to tarry here and admire,
>   If only you've money enough.

Great, grave, and dark was all nature around him. The pine woods looked like tufts of heather upon the high rocks, whose summits were lost in cloudy mists; and then it began to snow, and the wind blew cold.

'Ugh!' he sighed; 'if we were only on the other side of the Alps, then it would be summer, and I should have got money on my letter of credit: my anxiety about this prevents me from enjoying Switzerland. Oh, if I were only at the other side!'

And then he was on the other side, in the midst of Italy, between Florence and Rome. The lake Thrasymene lay spread out in the evening light, like flaming gold among the dark blue hills. Here, where Hannibal beat Flaminius, the grapevines held each other by their green fingers; pretty half-naked children were keeping a herd of coal-black pigs under a clump of fragrant laurels by the wayside. If we could reproduce this scene accurately, all would cry, 'Glorious Italy!' But neither the theologian nor any of his travelling companions in the carriage of the vetturino thought this.

Poisonous flies and gnats flew into the carriage by thousands. In vain they beat the air frantically with a myrtle branch – the flies stung them nevertheless. There was not one person in the carriage whose face was not swollen and covered with stings. The poor horses looked miserable, the flies tormented them woefully, and it only mended the matter for a moment when the coachman dismounted and scraped them clean from the insects that sat upon them in great swarms. Now the sun sank down; a short but icy coldness pervaded all nature; it was not at all agreeable, but all around the hills and clouds put on the most beautiful green colour, so clear, so shining – yes, go and see it in person, that is better than any description. It was a glorious spectacle; but the stomachs of all were empty and their bodies exhausted, and every wish of the heart turned towards a resting-place for the night; but how could that be won? To descry this resting-place all eyes were turned more eagerly to the road than towards the beauties of nature.

The way now led through an olive wood: he could have fancied himself passing between knotty willow trunks at home. Here, by the solitary inn, a dozen crippled beggars had taken up their positions: the quickest among them looked, to quote an expression of Marryat's, like the eldest son of Famine, who had just come of age. The others were either blind or had withered legs, so that they crept about on their hands, or they had withered arms with fingerless hands. This was misery in rags indeed. '*Eccellenza, miserabili!*' they sighed, and stretched forth their diseased limbs. The hostess herself, with bare feet, untidy hair, and dressed in a dirty blouse, received her guests. The doors were tied up with string; the floor of the room was of brick, and half of it was grubbed up; bats flew about under the roof, and the smell within –

'Yes, lay the table down in the stable,' said one of the travellers. 'There, at least, one knows what one is breathing.'

The windows were opened, so that a little fresh air might find its way in; but quicker than the air came the withered arms and the continual whining, '*Miserabili, Eccellenza!*' On the walls were many inscriptions; half of them were against '*La bella Italia.*'

The supper was served. It consisted of a watery soup, seasoned with pepper and rancid oil. This last dainty played a chief part in the salad; musty eggs and roasted cocks'-combs were the best dishes. Even the wine had a strange taste – it was a dreadful mixture.

At night the boxes were placed against the doors. One of the travellers kept watch while the rest slept. The theologian was the sentry. Oh, how close it was in there! The heat oppressed him, the gnats buzzed and stung, and the *miserabili* outside moaned in their dreams.

'Yes, travelling would be all very well,' said the theologian, 'if one had no body. If the body could rest, and the mind fly! Wherever I go, I find a want that oppresses my heart: it is something better than the present moment that I desire. Yes, something better – the best; but what is that, and where is it? In my own heart I know very well what I want: I want to attain to a happy goal, the happiest of all!'

And as soon as the word was spoken he found himself at home. The long white curtains hung down from the windows, and in the middle of the room stood a black coffin; in this he was lying in the quiet sleep of death: his wish was fulfilled – his body was at rest and his spirit roaming. 'Esteem no man happy who is not yet in his grave,' were the words of Solon; here their force was proved anew.

Every corpse is a sphinx of immortality; the sphinx here also in the black sarcophagus answered, what the living man had laid down two days before:

> Thou strong, stern Death! Thy silence waketh fear,
> Thou leavest mould'ring gravestones for thy traces.
> Shall not the soul see Jacob's ladder here?
> No resurrection type but churchyard grasses?

The deepest woes escape the world's dull eye:
Thou that alone on duty's path hast sped,
Heavier those duties on thy heart would lie
Than lies the earth now on thy coffined head.

Two forms were moving to and fro in the room. We know them both. They were the Fairy of Care and the Ambassadress of Happiness. They bent down over the dead man.

'Do you see?' said Care. 'What happiness have your goloshes brought to men?'

'They have at least brought a permanent benefit to him who slumbers here,' replied Happiness.

'Oh, no!' said Care. 'He went away of himself, he was not summoned. His spirit was not strong enough to lift the treasures which he had been destined to lift. I will do him a favour.'

And she drew the goloshes from his feet; then the sleep of death was ended, and the awakened man raised himself up. Care vanished, and with her the goloshes disappeared too: doubtless she looked upon them as her property.

The Daisy

NOW you shall hear! Out in the country, close by the roadside, there was a country house: you yourself have certainly once seen it. Before it is a little garden with flowers, and a paling which is painted. Close by it, by the ditch, in the midst of the most beautiful green grass, grew a little daisy. The sun shone as warmly and as brightly upon it as on the great splendid garden flowers, and so it grew from hour to hour. One morning it stood in full bloom, with its little shining white leaves spreading like rays round the little yellow sun in the centre. It never thought that no man would notice it down in the grass, and that it was a poor despised floweret; no, it was so well pleased, and turned to the warm sun, looked up at it, and listened to the lark carolling high in the air.

The little daisy was as happy as if it were a great holiday, and yet it was only a Monday. All the children were at school; and while they sat on their benches learning, it sat on its little green stalk, and learned also from the warm sun, and from all around, how good God is. And the daisy was very glad that everything it silently felt was sung so loudly and charmingly by the lark. And the daisy looked up with a kind of respect to the happy bird who could sing and fly; but it was not at all sorrowful because it could not fly and sing also.

'I can see and hear,' it thought: 'the sun shines on me, and the wind kisses me. Oh, how richly have I been gifted!'

Within the palings stood many stiff aristocratic flowers – the less scent they had the more they flaunted. The peonies blew themselves out to be greater than the roses, but size will not do it; the tulips had the most splendid colours, and they knew that, and held themselves bolt upright, that they might be seen more plainly. They did not notice the little daisy outside there, but the daisy looked at them the more, and thought, 'How rich and beautiful they are! Yes, the pretty bird will certainly fly down to them and visit them. I am glad that I stand so near them, for at any rate I can enjoy the sight of their splendour!' And just as she thought that – 'keevit!' – down came flying the lark, but not down to the peonies and tulips – no, down into the grass to the lowly daisy, which started so with joy that it did not know what to think.

The little bird danced round about it, and sang, 'Oh, how soft the grass is! and see what a lovely little flower, with gold in its heart and silver on its dress!'

For the yellow point in the daisy looked like gold, and the little leaves around it shone silvery white.

How happy was the little daisy – no one can conceive how happy! The bird kissed it with his beak, sang to it, and then flew up again into the blue air. A quarter of an hour passed, at least, before the daisy could recover itself. Half ashamed, and yet inwardly rejoiced, it looked at the other flowers in the garden; for they had seen the honour and happiness it had gained, and must understand what a joy it was. But the tulips stood up twice as stiff as before, and they looked quite peaky in the face and quite red, for they had been vexed. The peonies were quite wrong-headed: it was well they could not speak, or the daisy would have received a good scolding. The poor little flower could see very well that they were not in a good humour, and that hurt it sensibly. At this moment there came into the garden a girl with a great sharp shining knife; she went straight up to the tulips, and cut off one after another of them.

'Oh!' sighed the little daisy, 'this is dreadful; now it is all over with them.'

Then the girl went away with the tulips. The daisy was glad to stand out in the grass, and to be only a poor little flower; it felt very grateful; and when the sun went down it folded its leaves and went to sleep, and dreamed all night long about the sun and the pretty little bird.

Next morning, when the flower again happily stretched out all its white leaves, like little arms, towards the air and the light, it recognised the voice of the bird, but the song he was singing sounded mournfully. Yes, the poor lark had good reason to be sad: he was caught, and now sat in a cage close by the open window. He sang of free and happy roaming, sang of the young green corn in the fields, and of the glorious journey he might make on his wings high through the air. The poor lark was not in good spirits, for there he sat a prisoner in a cage.

The little daisy wished very much to help him. But what was it to do? Yes, that was difficult to make out. It quite forgot how everything was beautiful around, how warm the sun shone, and how splendidly white its own leaves were. Ah! it could think only of the imprisoned bird, and how it was powerless to do anything for him.

Just then two little boys came out of the garden. One of them carried in his hand a knife big and sharp like that which the girl had used to cut off the tulips. They went straight up to the little daisy, which could not at all make out what they wanted.

'Here we may cut a capital piece of turf for the lark,' said one of the boys; and he began to cut off a square patch round about the daisy, so that the flower remained standing in its piece of grass.

'Pull off the flower!' said the other boy.

And the daisy trembled with fear, for to be pulled off would be to lose its life; and now it wanted particularly to live, as it was to be given with the piece of turf to the captive lark.

'No, let it stay,' said the other boy; 'it makes such a nice ornament.'

And so it remained, and was put into the lark's cage. But the poor bird complained aloud of his lost liberty, and beat his wings against the wires of his prison; and the little daisy could not speak – could say no consoling word to him, gladly as it would have done so. And thus the whole morning passed.

'Here is no water,' said the captive lark. 'They are all gone out, and have forgotten to give me anything to drink. My throat is dry and burning. It is like fire and ice within me, and the air is so close. Oh, I must die! I must leave the warm sunshine, the fresh green, and all the splendour that God has created!'

And then he thrust his beak into the cool turf to refresh himself a little with it. Then the bird's eye fell upon the daisy, and he nodded to it, and kissed it with his beak, and said, 'You also must wither in here, you poor little flower. They have given you to me with the little patch of green grass on which you grow, instead of the whole world which was mine out there! Every little blade of grass shall be a green tree for me, and every one of your white leaves a fragrant flower. Ah, you only tell me how much I have lost!'

'If I could only comfort him!' thought the little daisy.

It could not stir a leaf; but the scent which streamed forth from its delicate leaves was far stronger than is generally found in these flowers; the bird also noticed that, and though he was fainting with thirst, and in his pain plucked up the green blades of grass, he did not touch the flower.

The evening came, and yet nobody appeared to bring the poor bird a drop of water. Then he stretched out his pretty wings and beat the air frantically with them; his song changed to a mournful piping, his little head sank down towards the flower, and the bird's heart broke with want and yearning. Then the flower could not fold its leaves, as it had done on the previous evening, and sleep; it drooped, sorrowful and sick, towards the earth.

Not till the next morning did the boys come; and when they found the bird dead they wept – wept many tears – and dug him a neat grave, which they adorned with leaves of flowers. The bird's corpse was put into a pretty red box, for he was to be royally buried – the poor bird! While he was alive and sang they forgot him, and let him sit in his cage and suffer want; but now that he was dead he had grandeur and many tears.

But the patch of turf with the daisy on it was thrown out into the high road: no one thought of the flower that had felt the most for the little bird, and would have been so glad to console him.

The Hardy Tin Soldier

THERE were once five and twenty tin soldiers; they were all brothers, for they had all been born of one old tin spoon. They shouldered their muskets, and looked straight before them: their uniform was red and blue, and very splendid. The first thing they had heard in the world, when the lid was taken off their box, had been the words 'Tin soldiers'! These words were uttered by a little boy, clapping his hands: the soldiers had been given to him, for it was his birthday; and now he put them upon the table. Each soldier was exactly like the rest only one of them was a little different, he had but one leg, for he had been cast last of all, and there had not been enough tin to finish him; but he stood as firmly upon his one leg as the others on their two; and it was just this soldier who became remarkable.

On the table on which they had been placed stood many other playthings, but the toy that attracted most attention was a neat castle of cardboard. Through the little windows one could see straight into the hall. Before the castle some little trees were placed round a little looking-glass, which was to represent a clear lake. Waxen swans swam on this lake, and were mirrored in it. This was all very pretty; but the prettiest of all was a little lady, who stood at the open door of the castle: she was also cut out in paper, but she had a dress of the clearest gauze, and a little narrow blue ribbon over her shoulders, that looked like a scarf; and in the middle of this ribbon was a shining tinsel rose as big as her whole face. The little lady stretched out both her arms, for she was a dancer; and then she lifted one leg so high that the tin soldier could not see it at all, and thought that, like himself, she had but one leg.

'That would be the wife for me,' thought he; 'but she is very grand. She lives in a castle, and I have only a box, and there are five and twenty of us in that. It is no place for her. But I must try to make acquaintance with her.'

And then he lay down at full length behind a snuff-box which was on the table; there he could easily watch the little dainty lady, who continued to stand on one leg without losing her balance.

When the evening came, all the other tin soldiers were put into their box, and the people in the house went to bed. Now the toys began to play at 'visiting,' and at 'war,' and 'giving balls.' The tin soldiers rattled in their box, for they wanted to join, but could not lift the lid. The nutcracker threw somersaults, and the pencil amused itself on the table: there was so much noise that the canary woke up, and began to speak too, and even in verse. The only two who did not stir from their places were the tin soldier and the dancing lady: she stood straight up on the point of one of her toes, and stretched out both her arms; and he was just as enduring on his one leg; and he never turned his eyes away from her.

Now the clock struck twelve – and, bounce! – the lid flew off the snuff-box; but there was not snuff in it, but a little black goblin: you see it was a trick.

'Tin soldier!' said the goblin, 'will you keep your eyes to yourself?'

But the tin soldier pretended not to hear him.

'Just you wait till tomorrow!' said the goblin.

But when the morning came, and the children got up, the tin soldier was placed in the window; and whether it was the goblin or the draught that did it, all at once the window flew open, and the soldier fell head over heels out of the third story. That was a terrible passage! He put his leg straight up, and stuck with his helmet downwards and his bayonet between the paving-stones.

The servant-maid and the little boy came down directly to look for him, but though they almost trod upon him they could not see him. If the soldier had cried out 'Here I am!' they would have found him; but he did not think it fitting to call out loudly, because he was in uniform.

Now it began to rain; the drops soon fell thicker, and at last it came down in a complete stream. When the rain was past, two street boys came by.

'Just look!' said one of them, 'there lies a tin soldier. He shall go out sailing.'

And they made a boat out of a newspaper, and put the tin soldier in the middle of it; and so he sailed down the gutter, and the two boys ran beside him and clapped their hands. Goodness preserve us! how the waves rose in that gutter, and how fast the stream ran! But then it had been a heavy rain. The paper boat rocked up and down, and sometimes turned round so rapidly that the tin soldier trembled; but he remained firm, and never changed countenance, but looked straight before him, and shouldered his musket.

All at once the boat went into a long drain, and it became as dark as if he had been in his box.

'Where am I going now?' he thought. 'Yes, yes, that's the goblin's fault. Ah! if the little lady only sat here with me in the boat, it might be twice as dark for what I should care.'

Suddenly there came a great water-rat, which lived under the drain. 'Have you a passport?' said the rat. 'Give me your passport.'

But the tin soldier kept silence, and held his musket tighter than ever.

The boat went on, but the rat came after it. Ugh! how he gnashed his teeth, and called out to the bits of straw and wood, 'Hold him! hold him! he hasn't paid toll – he hasn't shown his passport!'

But the stream became stronger and stronger. The tin soldier could see the bright daylight where the arch ended; but he heard a roaring noise, which might well frighten a bolder man. Only think – just where the tunnel ended, the drain ran into a great canal; and for him that would have been as dangerous as for us to be carried down a great waterfall.

Now he was already so near it that he could not stop. The boat was carried out, the poor tin soldier stiffening himself as much as he could, and no one could say that he moved an eyelid. The boat whirled round three or four times, and was full of water to the very edge – it must sink. The tin soldier stood up to his neck in water, and the boat sank deeper and deeper, and the paper was loosened more and more; and now the water closed over the soldier's head. Then he thought of the pretty little dancer, and how he should never see her again; and it sounded in the soldier's ears:

Farewell, farewell, thou warrior brave,
For this day thou must die!

And now the paper parted, and the tin soldier fell out; but at that moment he was snapped up by a great fish.

Oh, how dark it was in that fish's body! It was darker yet than in the drain tunnel; and then it was very narrow too. But the tin soldier remained unmoved, and lay at full length shouldering his musket.

The fish swam to and fro; he made the most wonderful movements, and then became quite still. At last something flashed through him like lightning. The daylight shone quite clear, and a voice said aloud, 'The tin soldier!' The fish had been caught, carried to market, bought, and taken into the kitchen, where the cook cut him open with a large knife.

She seized the soldier round the body with both her hands, and carried him into the room, where all were anxious to see the remarkable man who had travelled about in the inside of a fish; but the tin soldier was not at all proud. They placed him on the table, and there – no! What curious things may happen in the world! The tin soldier was in the very room in which he had been before! he saw the same children, and the same toys stood on the table; and there was the pretty castle with the graceful little dancer. She was still balancing herself on one leg, and held the other extended in the air. She was hardy too. That moved the tin soldier: he was very nearly weeping tin tears, but that would not have been proper. He looked at her and she at him, but they said nothing to each other.

Then one of the little boys took the tin soldier and flung him into the stove. He gave no reason for doing this. It must have been the fault of the goblin in the snuff-box.

The tin soldier stood there quite illuminated, and felt a heat that was terrible; but whether this heat proceeded from the real fire or from love he did not know. The colours had quite gone off from him; but whether that had happened on the journey, or had been caused by grief, no one could say. He looked at the little lady, she looked at him, and he felt that he was melting; but he still stood firm, shouldering his musket. Then suddenly the door flew open, and the draught of air caught the dancer, and she flew like a sylph just into the stove to the tin soldier, and flashed up in a flame, and she was gone. Then the tin soldier melted down into a lump, and when the servant-maid took the ashes out next day, she found him in the shape of a little tin heart. But of the dancer nothing remained but the tinsel rose, and that was burned as black as a coal.

The Wild Swans

FAR AWAY, where the swallows fly when our winter comes on, lived a King who had eleven sons, and one daughter named Eliza. The eleven brothers were Princes, and each went to school with a star on his breast and his sword by his side. They wrote with pencils of diamond upon slates of gold, and learned by heart just as well as they read; one could see directly that they were Princes. Their sister Eliza sat upon a little stool of plate glass, and had a picture-book which had been bought for the value of half a kingdom.

Oh, the children were particularly well off; but it was not always to remain so.

Their father, who was King of the whole country, married a bad Queen who did not love the poor children at all. On the very first day they could notice this. In the whole palace there was great feasting, and the children were playing at receiving guests: but instead of these children receiving, as they had been accustomed to do, all the spare cake and all the roasted apples, they only had some sand given them in a teacup, and were told that they might make believe that was something good.

The next week the Queen took the little sister Eliza into the country, to a peasant and his wife; and but a short time had elapsed before she told the King so many falsehoods about the poor Princes that he did not trouble himself any more about them.

'Fly out into the world and get your own living,' said the wicked Queen. 'Fly like great birds without a voice.'

But she could not make it so bad for them as she would have liked, for they became eleven magnificent wild swans. With a strange cry they flew out of the palace windows, far over the park and into the wood.

It was yet quite early morning when they came by the place where their sister Eliza lay asleep in the peasant's room. Here they hovered over the roof, turned their long necks, and flapped their wings; but no one heard or saw it. They were obliged to fly on, high up towards the clouds, far away into the wide world; there they flew into a great dark wood, which stretched away to the sea shore.

Poor little Eliza stood in the peasant's room and played with a green leaf, for she had no other playthings. And she pricked a hole in the leaf, and looked through it up at the sun, and it seemed to her that she saw her brothers' clear eyes; each time the warm sun shone upon her cheeks she thought of all the kisses they had given her.

Each day passed just like the rest. When the wind swept through the great rose hedges outside the house, it seemed to whisper to them, 'What can be more beautiful than you?' But the roses shook their heads and answered, 'Eliza!' And when the old woman sat in front of her door on Sunday and read in her hymn-book, the wind turned the leaves and said to the book, 'Who can be more pious than you?' and the hymn-book said, 'Eliza!' And what the rose bushes and the hymn-book said was the simple truth.

When she was fifteen years old she was to go home. And when the Queen saw how beautiful she was, she became spiteful and filled with hatred towards her. She would have been glad to change her into a wild swan, like her brothers, but she did not dare to do so at once, because the King wished to see his daughter.

Early in the morning the Queen went into the bath, which was built of white marble, and decked with soft cushions and the most splendid tapestry; and she took three toads and kissed them, and said to the first, 'Sit upon Eliza's head when she comes into the bath, that she may become as stupid as you. Seat yourself upon her forehead,' she said to the second, 'that she may become as ugly as you, and her father may not know her. Rest on her heart,' she whispered to the third, 'that she may receive an evil mind and suffer pain from it.'

Then she put the toads into the clear water, which at once assumed a green colour; and calling Eliza, caused her to undress and step into the water. And while Eliza dived, one of the toads sat upon her hair, and the second on her forehead, and the third on her heart; but she did not seem to notice it; and as soon as she rose, three red poppies were floating on the water. If the creatures had not been poisonous, and if the witch had not kissed them, they would have been changed into red roses. But at any rate they became flowers, because they had rested on the girl's head, and forehead, and heart. She was too good and innocent for sorcery to have power over her.

When the wicked Queen saw that, she rubbed Eliza with walnut juice, so that the girl became dark brown, and smeared an evil-smelling ointment on her face, and let her beautiful hair hang in confusion. It was quite impossible to recognise the pretty Eliza.

When her father saw her he was much shocked, and declared this was not his daughter. No one but the yard dog and the swallows would recognise her; but they were poor animals who had nothing to say in the matter.

Then poor Eliza wept, and thought of her eleven brothers who were all away. Sorrowfully she crept out of the castle, and walked all day over field and moor till she came into the great wood. She did not know whither she wished to go, only she felt very downcast and longed for her brothers: they had certainly been, like herself, thrust forth into the world, and she would seek for them and find them.

She had been only a short time in the wood when the night fell; she quite lost the path, therefore she lay down upon the soft moss, said her evening prayer, and leaned her head against the stump of a tree. Deep silence reigned around, the air was mild, and in the grass and in the moss gleamed like a green fire hundreds of glow-worms; when she lightly touched one of the twigs with her hand, the shining insects fell down upon her like shooting stars.

The whole night long she dreamed of her brothers. They were children again playing together, writing with their diamond pencils upon their golden slates, and looking at the beautiful picture-book which had cost half a kingdom. But on the slates they were not writing, as they had been accustomed to do, lines and letters, but the brave deeds they had done, and all they had seen and experienced; and in the picture-book everything was alive – the birds sang, and the people went out of the book and spoke with Eliza and her brothers. But when

the leaf was turned, they jumped back again directly, so that there should be no confusion.

When she awoke, the sun was already standing high. She could certainly not see it, for the lofty trees spread their branches far and wide above her. But the rays played above them like a gauzy veil, there was a fragrance from the fresh verdure, and the birds almost perched upon her shoulders. She heard the plashing of water; it was from a number of springs all flowing into a lake which had the most delightful sandy bottom. It was surrounded by thick growing bushes, but at one part the stags had made a large opening, and here Eliza went down to the water. The lake was so clear, that if the wind had not stirred the branches and the bushes, so that they moved, one would have thought they were painted upon the depths of the lake, so clearly was every leaf mirrored, whether the sun shone upon it or whether it lay in shadow.

When Eliza saw her own face she was terrified – so brown and ugly was she; but when she wetted her little hand and rubbed her eyes and her forehead, the white skin gleamed forth again. Then she undressed and went down into the fresh water: a more beautiful King's daughter than she was could not be found in the world. And when she had dressed herself again and plaited her long hair, she went to the bubbling spring, drank out of her hollow hand, and then wandered farther into the wood, not knowing whither she went. She thought of her dear brothers, and thought that Heaven would certainly not forsake her. It is God who lets the wild apples grow, to satisfy the hungry. He showed her a wild apple tree, with the boughs bending under the weight of the fruit. Here she took her midday meal, placed props under the boughs, and then went into the darkest part of the forest. There it was so still that she could hear her own footsteps, as well as the rustling of every dry leaf which bent under her feet. Not one bird was to be seen, not one ray of sunlight could find its way through the great dark boughs of the trees; the lofty trunks stood so close together that when she looked before her it appeared as though she were surrounded by sets of palings one behind the other. Oh, here was a solitude such as she had never before known!

The night came on quite dark. Not a single glow-worm now gleamed in the grass. Sorrowfully she lay down to sleep. Then it seemed to her as if the branches of the trees parted above her head, and mild eyes of angels looked down upon her from on high.

When the morning came, she did not know if it had really been so or if she had dreamed it.

She went a few steps forward, and then she met an old woman with berries in her basket, and the old woman gave her a few of them. Eliza asked the dame if she had not seen eleven Princes riding through the wood.

'No,' replied the old woman, 'but yesterday I saw eleven swans swimming in the river close by, with golden crowns on their heads.'

And she led Eliza a short distance farther, to a declivity, and at the foot of the slope a little river wound its way. The trees on its margin stretched their long leafy branches across towards each other, and where their natural growth would not allow them to come together, the roots had been torn out of the ground, and hung, intermingled with the branches, over the water.

Eliza said farewell to the old woman, and went beside the river to the place where the stream flowed out to the great open ocean.

The whole glorious sea lay before the young girl's eyes, but not one sail appeared on its surface, and not a boat was to be seen. How was she to proceed? She looked at the innumerable little pebbles on the shore; the water had worn them all round. Glass, ironstones, everything that was there had received its shape from the water, which was much softer than even her delicate hand.

'It rolls on unweariedly, and thus what is hard becomes smooth. I will be just as unwearied. Thanks for your lesson, you clear rolling waves; my heart tells me that one day you will lead me to my dear brothers.'

On the foam-covered sea grass lay eleven white swan feathers, which she collected into a bunch. Drops of water were upon them – whether they were dewdrops or tears nobody could tell. Solitary it was there on the strand, but she did not feel it, for the sea showed continual changes – more in a few hours than the lovely lakes can produce in a whole year. Then a great black cloud came. It seemed as if the sea would say, 'I can look angry, too;' and then the wind blew, and the waves turned their white side outward. But when the clouds gleamed red and the winds slept, the sea looked like a rose leaf; sometimes it became green, sometimes white. But however quietly it might rest, there was still a slight motion on the shore; the water rose gently like the breast of a sleeping child.

When the sun was just about to set, Eliza saw eleven wild swans, with crowns on their heads, flying towards the land: they swept along one after the other, so that they looked like a long white band. Then

Eliza ascended the slope and hid herself behind a bush. The swans alighted near her and flapped their great white wings.

As soon as the sun had disappeared beneath the water, the swans' feathers fell off, and eleven handsome Princes, Eliza's brothers, stood there. She uttered a loud cry, for although they were greatly altered, she knew and felt that it must be they. And she sprang into their arms and called them by their names; and the Princes felt supremely happy when they saw their little sister again; and they knew her, though she was now tall and beautiful. They smiled and wept; and soon they understood how cruel their stepmother had been to them all.

'We brothers,' said the eldest, 'fly about as wild swans as long as the sun is in the sky, but directly it sinks down we receive our human form again. Therefore we must always take care that we have a resting-place for our feet when the sun sets; for if at that moment we were flying up towards the clouds, we should sink down into the deep as men. We do not dwell here: there lies a land just as fair as this beyond the sea. But the way thither is long; we must cross the great sea, and on our path there is no island where we could pass the night, only a little rock stands forth in the midst of the waves; it is but just large enough that we can rest upon it close to each other. If the sea is rough, the foam spurts far over us, but we thank God for the rock. There we pass the night in our human form: but for this rock we could never visit our beloved native land, for we require two of the longest days in the year for our journey. Only once in each year is it granted to us to visit our home. For eleven days we may stay here and fly over the great wood, from whence we can see the palace in which we were born and in which our father lives, and the high church tower, beneath whose shade our mother lies buried. Here it seems to us as though the bushes and trees were our relatives; here the wild horses career across the steppe, as we have seen them do in our childhood; here the charcoal-burner sings the old songs to which we danced as children; here is our fatherland: hither we feel ourselves drawn, and here we have found you, our dear little sister. Two days more we may stay here; then we must away across the sea to a glorious land, but which is not our native land. How can we bear you away? for we have neither ship nor boat.'

'In what way can I release you?' asked the sister; and they conversed nearly the whole night, only slumbering for a few hours.

She was awakened by the rustling of the swans' wings above her head. Her brothers were again enchanted, and they flew in wide circles and at last far away; but one of them, the youngest, remained behind, and the swan laid his head in her lap, and she stroked his wings; and the whole day they remained together. Towards evening the others came back, and when the sun had gone down they stood there in their own shapes.

'Tomorrow we fly far away from here, and cannot come back until a whole year has gone by. But we cannot leave you thus! Have you courage to come with us? My arm is strong enough to carry you in the wood; and should not all our wings be strong enough to fly with you over the sea?'

'Yes, take me with you,' said Eliza.

The whole night they were occupied in weaving a net of the pliable willow bark and tough reeds; and it was great and strong. On this net Eliza lay down; and when the sun rose, and her brothers were changed into wild swans, they seized the net with their beaks, and flew with their beloved sister, who was still asleep, high up towards the clouds. The sunbeams fell exactly upon her face, so one of the swans flew over her head, that his broad wings might overshadow her.

They were far away from the shore when Eliza awoke: she was still dreaming, so strange did it appear to her to be carried high through the air and over the sea. By her side lay a branch with beautiful ripe berries and a bundle of sweet-tasting roots. The youngest of the brothers had collected them and placed them there for her. She smiled at him thankfully, for she recognised him; he it was who flew over her and shaded her with his wings.

They were so high that the first ship they descried beneath them seemed like a white seagull lying upon the waters. A great cloud stood behind them – it was a perfect mountain; and upon it Eliza saw her own shadow and those of the eleven swans; there they flew on, gigantic in size. Here was a picture, a more splendid one than she had ever yet seen. But as the sun rose higher and the cloud was left farther behind them, the floating shadowy images vanished away.

The whole day they flew onward through the air, like a whirring arrow, but their flight was slower than it was wont to be, for they had their sister to carry. Bad weather came on; the evening drew near; Eliza looked anxiously at the setting sun, for the lonely rock in the ocean could not be seen. It seemed to her as if the swans beat the air more strongly with their wings. Alas! she was the cause that they did not advance fast enough. When the sun went down, they must become men and fall into the sea and drown. Then she prayed a prayer from the depths of her heart; but still she could descry no rock. The dark clouds came nearer in a great black threatening body, rolling forward like a mass of lead, and the lightning burst forth, flash upon flash.

Now the sun just touched the margin of the sea. Eliza's heart trembled. Then the swans darted downwards, so swiftly that she thought they were falling, but they paused again. The sun was half-hidden below the water. And now for the first time she saw the little rock beneath her, and it looked no larger than a seal might look, thrusting his head forth from the water. The sun sank very fast; at last it appeared only like a star; and then her foot touched the firm land. The sun was extinguished like the last spark in a piece of burned paper; her brothers were standing around her, arm in arm, but there was not more than just enough room for her and for them. The sea beat against the rock and went over her like small rain; the sky glowed in continual fire, and peal on peal the thunder rolled; but sister and brothers held each other by the hand, and sang psalms, from which they gained comfort and courage.

In the morning twilight the air was pure and calm. As soon as the sun rose the swans flew away with Eliza from the island. The sea still ran high, and when they soared up aloft, the white foam looked like millions of white swans swimming upon the water.

When the sun mounted higher, Eliza saw before her, half-floating in the air, a mountainous country with shining masses of ice on its hills, and in the midst of it rose a castle, apparently a mile long, with row above row of elegant columns, while beneath waved the palm woods and bright flowers as large as mill-wheels. She asked if this was the country to which they were bound, but the swans shook their heads, for what she beheld was the gorgeous, ever-changing palace of Fata Morgana, and into this they might bring no human being. As Eliza gazed at it, mountains, woods, and castle fell down, and twenty proud churches, all nearly alike, with high towers and pointed windows, stood before them. She fancied she heard the organs sounding, but it was the sea she heard. When she was quite near the churches they changed to a fleet sailing beneath her, but when she looked down it was only a sea mist gliding over the ocean. Thus she had a continual change before her eyes, till at last she saw the real land to which they were bound. There arose the most glorious blue mountains, with cedar forests, cities, and palaces. Long before the sun went down she sat on the rock, in front of a great cave overgrown with delicate green trailing plants looking like embroidered carpets.

'Now we shall see what you will dream of here tonight,' said the youngest brother; and he showed her to her bedchamber.

'Heaven grant that I may dream of a way to release you,' she replied.

And this thought possessed her mightily, and she prayed ardently for help; yes, even in her sleep she continued to pray. Then it seemed to her as if she were flying high in the air to the cloudy palace of Fata Morgana; and the fairy came out to meet her, beautiful and radiant; and yet the fairy was quite like the old woman who had given her the berries in the wood, and had told her of the swans with golden crowns on their heads.

'Your brothers can be released,' said she. 'But have you courage and perseverance? Certainly, water is softer than your delicate hands, and yet it changes the shape of stones; but it feels not the pain that your fingers will feel; it has no heart, and does not suffer the agony and torment you will have to endure. Do you see the stinging-nettle which I hold in my hand? Many of the same kind grow around the cave in which you sleep: those only, and those that grow upon churchyard graves, are serviceable, remember that. Those you must pluck, though they will burn your hands into blisters. Break these nettles to pieces with your feet, and you will have flax; of this you must plait and weave eleven shirts of mail with long sleeves: throw these over the eleven swans, and the charm will be broken. But recollect well, from the moment you begin this work until it is finished, even though it should take years to accomplish, you must not speak. The first word you utter will pierce your brothers' hearts like a deadly dagger. Their lives hang on your tongue. Remember all this!'

And she touched her hand with the nettle; it was like a burning fire, and Eliza woke with the smart. It was broad daylight; and close by the spot where she had slept lay a nettle like the one she had seen in her dream. She fell upon her knees and prayed gratefully, and went forth from the cave to begin her work.

With her delicate hands she groped among the ugly nettles. These stung like fire, burning great blisters on her arms and hands; but she thought she would bear it gladly if she could only release her dear brothers. Then she bruised every nettle with her bare feet and plaited the green flax.

When the sun had set her brothers came, and they were frightened when they found her dumb. They thought it was some new sorcery of their wicked stepmother's; but when they saw her hands, they understood what she was doing for their sake, and the youngest brother wept. And where his tears dropped she felt no more pain, and the burning blisters vanished.

She passed the night at her work, for she could not sleep till she had delivered her dear brothers. The whole of the following day, while the swans were away, she sat in solitude, but never had time flown so quickly with her as now. One shirt of mail was already finished, and now she began the second.

Then a hunting horn sounded among the hills, and she was struck with fear. The noise came nearer and nearer; she heard the barking dogs, and timidly she fled into the cave, bound into a bundle the nettles she had collected and prepared, and sat upon the bundle.

Immediately a great dog came bounding out of the thicket, and then another, and another: they barked loudly, ran back, and then came again. Only a few minutes had gone before all the huntsmen stood before the cave, and the handsomest of them was the King of the country. He came forward to Eliza, for he had never seen a more beautiful maiden.

'How did you come hither, you delightful child?' he asked.

Eliza shook her head, for she might not speak – it would cost her brothers their deliverance and their lives. And she hid her hands under her apron, so that the King might not see what she was suffering.

'Come with me,' said he. 'You cannot stop here. If you are as good as you are beautiful, I will dress you in velvet and silk, and place the golden crown on your head, and you shall dwell in my richest castle, and rule.'

And then he lifted her on his horse. She wept and wrung her hands; but the King said, 'I only wish for your happiness: one day you will thank me for this.'

And then he galloped away among the mountains with her on his horse, and the hunters galloped at their heels.

When the sun went down, the fair regal city lay before them, with its churches and cupolas; and the King led her into the castle, where great fountains plashed in the lofty marble halls, and where walls and ceilings were covered with glorious pictures. But she had no eyes for all this – she only wept and mourned. Passively she let the women put royal robes upon her, and weave pearls in her hair, and draw dainty gloves over her blistered fingers.

When she stood there in full array, she was dazzlingly beautiful, so that the Court bowed deeper than ever. And the King chose her for his bride, although the archbishop shook his head and whispered that the beauteous forest maid was certainly a witch, who blinded the eyes and led astray the heart of the King.

But the King gave no ear to this, but ordered that the music should sound, and the costliest dishes should be served, and the most beautiful maidens should dance before them. And she was led through fragrant gardens into gorgeous halls; but never a smile came upon her lips or shone in her eyes: there she stood, a picture of grief. Then the King opened a little chamber close by, where she was to sleep. This chamber was decked with splendid green tapestry, and completely resembled the cave in which she had been. On the floor lay the bundle of flax which she had prepared from the nettles, and under the ceiling hung the shirt of mail she had completed. All these things one of the huntsmen had brought with him as curiosities.

'Here you may dream yourself back in your former home,' said the King. 'Here is the work which occupied you there, and now, in the midst of all your splendour, it will amuse you to think of that time.'

When Eliza saw this that lay so near her heart, a smile played round her mouth and the crimson blood came back into her cheeks. She thought of her brothers' deliverance, and kissed the King's hand; and he pressed her to his heart, and caused the marriage feast to be announced by all the church bells. The beautiful dumb girl out of the wood became the Queen of the country.

Then the archbishop whispered evil words into the King's ear, but they did not sink into the King's heart. The marriage was to take place; the archbishop himself was obliged to place the crown on her head, and with wicked spite he pressed the narrow circlet so tightly upon her brow that it pained her. But a heavier ring lay close around her heart – sorrow for her brothers; she did not feel the bodily pain. Her mouth was dumb, for a single word would cost her brothers their lives, but her eyes glowed with love for the kind, handsome King, who did everything to rejoice her. She loved him with her whole heart, more and more every day. Oh that she had been able to confide in him and to tell him of her grief! But she was compelled to be dumb, and to finish her work in silence. Therefore at night she crept away from his side, and went quietly into the little chamber which was decorated like the cave, and wove one shirt of mail after another. But when she began the seventh she had no flax left.

She knew that in the churchyard nettles were growing that she could use; but she must pluck them herself, and how was she to go out there?

'Oh, what is the pain in my fingers to the torment my heart endures?' thought she. 'I must venture it, and help will not be denied me!'

With a trembling heart, as though the deed she purposed doing had been evil, she crept into the garden in the moonlight night, and went through the long avenues and through the deserted streets to the churchyard. There, on one of the broadest tombstones, she saw sitting a circle of lamias. These hideous wretches took off their ragged garments, as if they were going to bathe; then with their skinny fingers they clawed open the fresh graves, and with fiendish greed they snatched up the corpses and ate the flesh. Eliza was obliged to pass close by them, and they fastened their evil glances upon her; but she prayed silently, and collected the burning nettles, and carried them into the castle.

Only one person had seen her, and that was the archbishop. He was awake while others slept. Now he felt sure his opinion was correct, that all was not as it should be with the Queen; she was a witch, and thus she had bewitched the King and the whole people.

In secret he told the King what he had seen and what he feared; and when the hard words came from his tongue, the pictures of saints in the cathedral shook their heads, as though they could have said, 'It is not so! Eliza is innocent!' But the archbishop interpreted this differently – he thought they were bearing witness against her, and shaking their heads at her sinfulness. Then two heavy tears rolled down the King's cheeks; he went home with doubt in his heart, and at night pretended to be asleep; but no quiet sleep came upon his eyes, for he noticed that Eliza got up. Every night she did this, and each time he followed her silently, and saw how she disappeared from her chamber.

From day to day his face became darker. Eliza saw it, but did not understand the reason; but it frightened her – and what did she not suffer in her heart for her brothers? Her hot tears flowed upon the royal velvet and purple; they lay there like sparkling diamonds, and all who saw the splendour wished they were Queens. In the meantime she had almost finished her work. Only one shirt of mail was still to be completed, but she had no flax left, and not a single nettle. Once more, for the last time, therefore, she must go to the churchyard, only to pluck a few handfuls. She thought with terror of this solitary wandering and of the horrible lamias, but her will was firm as her trust in Providence.

Eliza went on, but the King and the archbishop followed her. They saw her vanish into the churchyard through the wicket gate; and when they drew near, the lamias were sitting upon the gravestones as Eliza had seen them; and the King turned aside, for he fancied her among them, whose head had rested against his breast that very evening.

'The people must judge her,' said he.

And the people condemned her to suffer death by fire.

Out of the gorgeous regal halls she was led into a dark damp cell, where the wind whistled through the grated window; instead of velvet and silk they gave her the bundle of nettles which she had collected: on this she could lay her head; and the hard burning coats of mail which she had woven were to be her coverlet. But nothing could have been given her that she liked better. She resumed her work and prayed. Without, the street boys were singing jeering songs about her, and not a soul comforted her with a kind word.

But towards evening there came the whirring of swans' wings close by the grating – it was the youngest of her brothers. He had found his sister, and she sobbed aloud with joy, though she knew that the approaching night would probably be the last she had to live. But now the work was almost finished, and her brothers were here.

Now came the archbishop, to stay with her in her last hour, for he had promised the King to do so. But she shook her head, and with looks and gestures she begged him to depart, for in this night she must finish her work, or else all would be in vain, all her tears, her pain, and her sleepless nights. The archbishop withdrew uttering evil words against her; but poor Eliza knew she was innocent, and continued her work.

The little mice ran about on the floor, and dragged nettles to her feet in order to help her; and the thrush perched beside the bars of the window and sang all night as merrily as it could, so that she might not lose heart.

It was still twilight; not till an hour afterwards would the sun rise. And the eleven brothers stood at the castle gate, and demanded to be brought before the King. That could not be, they were told, for it was still almost night; the King was asleep, and might not be disturbed. They begged, they threatened, and the sentries came, yes, even the King himself came out, and asked what was the meaning of this. At that moment the sun rose, and no more were the brothers to be seen, but eleven wild swans flew away over the castle.

All the people came flocking out at the town gate, for they wanted to see the witch burned. An old horse drew the cart on which she sat.

They had put upon her a garment of coarse sackcloth. Her lovely hair hung loose about her beautiful head; her cheeks were as pale as death; and her lips moved silently, while her fingers were engaged with the green flax. Even on the way to death she did not interrupt the work she had begun; the ten shirts of mail lay at her feet, and she wrought at the eleventh. The mob derided her.

'Look at the witch, how she mutters! She has no hymn-book in her hand; no, there she sits with her ugly sorcery – tear it in a thousand pieces!'

And they all pressed upon her, and wanted to tear up the shirts of mail. Then eleven wild swans came flying up, and sat round about her on the cart, and beat with their wings; and the mob gave way before them, terrified.

'That is a sign from heaven! She is certainly innocent!' whispered many. But they did not dare to say it aloud.

Now the executioner seized her by the hand; then she hastily threw the eleven shirts over the swans, and immediately eleven handsome Princes stood there. But the youngest had a swan's wing instead of an arm, for a sleeve was wanting to his shirt – she had not quite finished it.

'Now I may speak!' she said. 'I am innocent!'

And the people who saw what happened bowed before her as before a saint; but she sank lifeless into her brothers' arms, such an effect had suspense, anguish, and pain had upon her.

'Yes, she is innocent,' said the eldest brother.

And now he told everything that had taken place; and while he spoke a fragrance arose as of millions of roses, for every piece of faggot in the pile had taken root and was sending forth shoots; and a fragrant hedge stood there, tall and great, covered with red roses, and at the top a flower, white and shining, gleaming like a star. This flower the King plucked and placed in Eliza's bosom; and she awoke with peace and happiness in her heart.

And all the church bells rang of themselves, and the birds came in great flocks. And back to the castle such a marriage procession took place as no King had ever seen.

The Garden of Paradise

THERE WAS once a King's son; no one had so many beautiful books as he: everything that had happened in this world he could read there, and could see represented in lovely pictures. Of every people and of every land he could get intelligence; but there was not a word to tell where the Garden of Paradise could be found, and it was just that of which he thought most.

His grandmother had told him, when he was quite little but was about to begin his schooling, that every flower in this Garden of Paradise was a delicate cake, and the pistils contained the choicest wine; on one of the flowers history was written, and on another geography or tables, so that one had only to eat cake, and one knew a lesson; and the more one ate, the more history, geography, or tables did one learn.

At that time he believed this. But when he became a bigger boy, and learned more and became wiser, he understood well that the splendour in the Garden of Paradise must be of quite a different kind.

'Oh, why did Eve pluck from the Tree of Knowledge? Why did Adam eat the forbidden fruit? If I had ben he it would never have happened – then sin would never have come into the world.'

That he said then, and he still said it when he was seventeen years old. The Garden of Paradise filled all his thoughts.

One day he walked in the wood. He was walking quite alone, for that was his greatest pleasure. The evening came, and the clouds gathered together; rain streamed down as if the sky were one single sluice from which the water was pouring; it was as dark as it usually is at night in the deepest well. Often he slipped on the smooth grass, often he fell over the smooth stones which stuck up out of the wet rocky ground. Everything was soaked with water, and there was not a dry thread on the poor Prince. He was obliged to climb over great blocks of stone, where the water oozed from the thick moss. He was nearly fainting. Then he heard a strange rushing, and saw before him a great illuminated cave. In the midst of it burned a fire, so large that a stag might have been roasted at it. And this was in fact being done. A glorious deer had been stuck, horns and all, upon a spit, and was turning slowly between two felled pine trunks. An elderly woman, large and strongly built, looking like a disguised man, sat by the fire, into which she threw one piece of wood after another.

'Come nearer!' said she. 'Sit down by the fire and dry your clothes.'

'There's a great draught here!' said the Prince; and he sat down on the ground.

'That will be worse when my sons come home,' replied the woman. 'You are here in the Cavern of the Winds, and my sons are the four winds of the world: can you understand that?'

'Where are your sons?' asked the Prince.

'It's difficult to answer when stupid questions are asked,' said the woman. 'My sons do business on their own account. They play at shuttlecock with the clouds up yonder in the great hall.'

And she pointed upwards.

'Oh, indeed!' said the Prince. 'But you speak rather gruffly, by the way, and are not so mild as the women I generally see about me.'

'Yes, they have most likely nothing else to do! I must be hard, if I want to keep my sons in order; but I can do it, though they are obstinate fellows. Do you see the four sacks hanging there by the wall? They are just as frightened of those as you used to be of the rod stuck behind the mirror. I can bend the lads together, I tell you, and then I pop them into the bag: we don't make any ceremony. There they sit, and may not wander about again until I think fit to allow them. But here comes one of them!'

It was the North Wind, who rushed in with piercing cold; great hailstones skipped about on the floor, and snowflakes fluttered about. He was dressed in a jacket and trousers of bearskin; a cap of sealskin was drawn down over his ears; long icicles hung on his beard, and one hailstone after another rolled from the collar of his jacket.

'Do not go so near the fire directly,' said the Prince, 'you might get your hands and face frost-bitten.'

'Frost-bitten?' repeated the North Wind, and he laughed aloud. 'Cold is exactly what rejoices me most! But what kind of little tailor art thou? How did you find your way into the Cavern of the Winds?'

'He is my guest,' interposed the old woman, 'and if you're not satisfied with this explanation you may go into the sack: do you understand me?'

You see, that was the right way; and now the North Wind told whence he came and where he had been for almost a month.

'I come from the Polar Sea,' said he; 'I have been in the bear's icy land with the Russian walrus hunters. I sat and slept on the helm when they sailed out from the North Cape, and when I awoke now and then, the storm-bird flew round my legs. That's a comical bird! He gives a sharp clap with his wings, and then holds them quite still and shoots along in full career.'

'Don't be too long-winded,' said the mother of the Winds. 'And so you came to the Bear's Island?'

'It is very beautiful there! There's a floor for dancing on, as flat as a plate. Half-thawed snow, with a little moss, sharp stones, and skeletons of walruses and polar bears lay around, they looked like gigantic arms and legs of a rusty green colour. One would have thought the sun had never shone there. I blew a little upon the mist, so that one could see the hut: it was a house built of wreck-wood and covered with walrus-skins – the fleshy side turned outwards. It was full of green and red, and on the roof sat a live polar bear who was growling. I went to the shore to look after birds' nests, and saw the unfledged nestlings screaming and opening their beaks; then I blew down into their thousand throats, and taught them to shut their mouths. Farther on the huge walruses were splashing like great maggots with pigs' heads and teeth an ell long!'

'You tell your story well, my son,' said the old lady. 'My mouth waters when I hear you!'

'Then the hunting began! The harpoon was hurled into the walrus's breast, so that a smoking stream of blood spurted like a fountain over the ice. When I thought of my sport, I blew, and let my sailing ships, the big icebergs, crush the boats between them. Oh, how the people whistled, and how they cried! but I whistled louder than they. They were obliged to throw the dead walruses and their chests and tackle out upon the ice. I shook the snowflakes over them, and let them drive south in their crushed boats with their booty to taste salt water. They'll never come to Bear's Island again!'

'Then you have done a wicked thing!' said the mother of the Winds.

'What good I have done others may tell,' replied he. 'But here comes a brother from the west. I like him best of all: he tastes of the sea and brings a delicious coolness with him.'

Is that little Zephyr?' asked the Prince.

'Yes, certainly, that is Zephyr,' replied the old woman. 'But he is not little. Years ago he was a pretty boy, but that's past now.'

He looked like a wild man, but he had a broad-brimmed hat on, to save his face. In his hand he held a club of mahogany, hewn in the American mahogany forests. It was no trifle.

'Where do you come from?' said his mother.

'Out of the forest wilderness,' said he, 'where the thorny creepers make a fence between every tree, where the water-snake lies in the wet grass, and people don't seem to be wanted.'

'What were you doing there?'

'I looked into the deepest river, and watched how it rushed down from the rocks, and turned to spray, and shot up towards the clouds to carry the rainbow. I saw the wild buffalo swimming in the stream, but the stream carried him away. He drifted with the flock of wild ducks that flew up where the water fell down in a cataract. The buffalo had to go down it! That pleased me, and I blew a storm, so that ancient trees were split up into splinters!'

'And have you done nothing else?' asked the old dame.

'I have thrown somersaults in the Savannahs: I have stroked the wild horses and shaken the coconut palms. Yes, yes, I have stories to tell! But one must not tell all one knows. You know that, old lady.'

And he kissed his mother so roughly that she almost tumbled over. He was a terribly wild young fellow!

Now came the South Wind, with a turban on and a flying Bedouin's cloak.

'It's terribly cold in here!' cried he, and threw some more wood on the fire. 'One can feel that the North Wind came first.'

'It's so hot that one could roast a Polar bear here,' said the North Wind.

'You're a Polar bear yourself,' retorted the South Wind.

'Do you want to be put in the sack?' asked the old dame. 'Sit upon the stone yonder and tell me where you have been.'

'In Africa, mother,' he answered. 'I was out hunting the lion with the Hottentots in the land of the Kaffirs. Grass grows there in the plains, green as an olive. There the ostrich ran races with me, but I am swifter than he. I came into the desert where the yellow sand lies: it looks there like the bottom of the sea. I met a caravan. The people were killing their last camel to get water to drink, but it was very little they got. The sun burned above and the sand below. The outspread deserts had no bounds. Then I rolled in the fine loose sand, and whirled it up in great pillars. That was a dance! You should have seen how dejected the dromedary stood there, and the merchant drew the caftan over his head. He threw himself down before me, as before Allah, his God. Now they are buried – a pyramid of sand covers them all. When I someday blow that away, the sun will bleach the white bones; then travellers may see that men have been there before them. Otherwise, one would not believe that, in the desert!'

'So you have done nothing but evil!' exclaimed the mother. 'March into the sack!'

And before he was aware, she had seized the South Wind round the body, and popped him into the bag. He rolled about on the floor; but she sat down on the sack, and then he had to keep quiet.

'Those are lively boys of yours,' said the Prince.

'Yes,' she replied, 'and I know how to punish them! Here comes the fourth!'

That was the East Wind, who came dressed like a Chinaman.

'Oh! do you come from that region?' said his mother. I thought you had been in the Garden of Paradise.'

'I don't fly there till tomorrow,' said the East Wind. 'It will be a hundred years tomorrow since I was there. I come from China now, where I danced around the porcelain tower till all the bells jingled again! In the streets the officials were being thrashed: the bamboos were broken upon their shoulders, yet they were high people, from the first to the ninth grade. They cried, "Many thanks, my paternal benefactor!" but it didn't come from their hearts. And I rang the bells and sang, "Tsing, tsang, tsu!" '

'You are foolish,' said the old dame. 'It is a good thing that you are going into the Garden of Paradise tomorrow: that always helps on your education. Drink bravely out of the spring of Wisdom, and bring home a little bottle-full for me.'

'That I will do,' said the East Wind. 'But why have you clapped my brother South in the bag? Out with him! He shall tell me about the Phoenix bird, for about that bird the Princess in the Garden of Paradise always wants to hear, when I pay my visit every hundredth year. Open the sack, then you shall be my sweetest of mothers, and I will give you two pocketfuls of tea, green and fresh as I plucked it at the place where it grew!'

'Well, for the sake of the tea, and because you are my darling boy, I will open the sack.'

She did so, and the South Wind crept out; but he looked quite downcast, because the strange Prince had seen his disgrace.

'There you have a palm leaf for the Princess,' said the South Wind. 'This palm leaf was given me by the Phoenix bird, the only one now in the world. With his beak he has scratched upon it a description of all the hundred years he has lived. Now she may read it all herself. I saw how the Phoenix bird set fire to her nest, and sat upon it, and was burned to death like a Hindu's widow. How the dry branches crackled! What a smoke and a perfume there was! At last everything burst into flame, and the old Phoenix turned to ashes, but her egg lay red-hot in the fire; it burst with a great bang, and the young one flew out. Now this young one is ruler over all the birds, and the only Phoenix in the world. It has bitten a hole in the palm leaf I have given you: that is a greeting to the Princess.'

'Let us have something to eat,' said the mother of the Winds.

And now they all sat down to eat of the roasted deer. The Prince sat beside the East Wind, and they soon became good friends.

'Just tell me,' said the Prince, 'what Princess is that about whom there is so much talk here? and where does the Garden of Paradise lie?'

'Ho, ho!' said the East Wind, 'do you want to go there? Well, then, fly tomorrow with me! But I must tell you, however, that no man has been there since the time of Adam and Eve. You have read of them in your Bible history?'

'Yes,' said the Prince.

'When they were driven away, the Garden of Paradise sank into the earth; but it kept its warm sunshine, its mild air, and all its splendour. The Queen of the Fairies lives there, and there lies the Island of Happiness, where death never comes, and where it is beautiful. Sit upon my back tomorrow, and I will take you with me: I think it can very well be done. But now leave off talking, for I want to sleep.'

And then they all went to rest.

In the early morning the Prince awoke, and was not a little astonished to find himself high above the clouds. He was sitting on the back of the East Wind, who was faithfully holding him: they were so high in the air, that the woods and fields, rivers and lakes, looked as if they were painted on a map below them.

'Good-morning!' said the East Wind. 'You might very well sleep a little longer, for there is not much to be seen on the flat country under us, unless you care to count the churches. They stand like dots of chalk on the green carpet.'

What he called green carpet was field and meadow.

'It was rude of me not to say goodbye to your mother and your brothers,' said the Prince.

'When one is asleep one must be excused,' replied the East Wind.

And then they flew on faster than ever. One could hear it in the tops of the trees, for when they passed over them the leaves and twigs rustled; one could hear it on the sea and on the lakes, for when they flew by the water rose higher, and the great ships bowed themselves towards the water like swimming swans.

Towards evening, when it became dark, the great towns looked charming, for lights were burning below, here and there; it was just as when one has lighted a piece of paper, and sees all the little sparks that vanish one after another. And the Prince clapped his hands; but the East Wind begged him not to do so, and rather to hold fast, otherwise he might easily fall down and get caught on a church spire.

The eagle in the dark woods flew easily, but the East Wind flew more easily still. The Cossack on his little horse skimmed swiftly over the steppes, but the Prince skimmed more swiftly still.

'Now you can see the Himalayas,' said the East Wind. 'That is the highest mountain range in Asia. Now we shall soon get to the Garden of Paradise.'

Then they turned more to the south, and soon the air was fragrant with flowers and spices; figs and pomegranates grew wild, and the wild vine bore clusters of red and purple grapes. Here both alighted and stretched themselves on the soft grass, where the flowers nodded to the wind, as though they would have said 'Welcome!'

'Are we now in the Garden of Paradise?' asked the Prince.

'Not at all,' replied the East Wind. 'But we shall soon get there. Do you see the rocky wall yonder, and the great cave, where the vines cluster like a broad green curtain? Through that we shall pass. Wrap yourself in your cloak. Here the sun scorches you, but a step farther it will be icy cold. The bird which hovers past the cave has one wing in the region of summer and the other in the wintry cold.'

'So this is the way to the Garden of Paradise?' observed the Prince.

They went into the cave. Ugh! but it was icy cold there, but this did not last long. The East Wind spread out his wings, and they gleamed like the brightest fire. What a cave was that! Great blocks of stone, from which the water dripped down, hung over them in the strangest shapes; sometimes it was so narrow that they had to creep on their hands and knees, sometimes as lofty and broad as in the open air. The place looked like a number of mortuary chapels, with dumb organ pipes, and petrified banners.

'We are going through the way of death to the Garden of Paradise, are we not?' enquired the Prince.

The East Wind answered not a syllable, but he pointed forward to where a lovely blue light gleamed upon them. The stone blocks over their heads became more and more like a mist, and at last looked like a white cloud in the moonlight. Now they were in a deliciously mild air, fresh as on the hills, fragrant as among the roses of the valley. There ran a river, clear as the air itself, and the fishes were like silver and gold; purple eels, flashing out blue sparks at every moment, played in the water below; and the broad water plant leaves shone in the colours of the rainbow; the flower itself was an orange-coloured burning flame, to which the water gave nourishment, as the oil to the burning lamp; a bridge of marble, strong, indeed, but so lightly built that it looked as if made of lace and glass beads, led them across the water to the Island of Happiness, where the Garden of Paradise bloomed.

The East Wind took the Prince in his arms and carried him over there. There flowers and leaves sang the loveliest songs from his childhood, but with such swelling music as no human voice can utter.

Were they palm trees that grew here, or gigantic waterplants? Such verdant mighty trees the Prince had never beheld; the most wonderful climbing plants hung there in long festoons, as one only sees them illuminated in gold and colours on the margins of old missal-books or twined among the initial letters. Here were the strangest groupings of birds, flowers, and twining lines. Close by, in the grass, stood a flock of peacocks with their shining starry trains outspread.

Yes, it was really so! But when the Prince touched these, he found they were not birds, but plants; they were great burdocks, which shone like the peacock's gorgeous train. The lion and the tiger sprang to and fro like agile cats among the green bushes, which were fragrant as the blossom of the olive tree; and the lion and the tiger were tame. The wild wood pigeon shone like the most beautiful pearl, and beat her wings against the lion's mane; and the antelope, usually so timid, stood by nodding its head, as if it wished to play too.

Now came the Fairy of Paradise. Her garb shone like the sun, and her countenance was cheerful like that of a happy mother when she is well pleased with her child. She was young and beautiful, and was followed by a number of pretty maidens, each with a gleaming star in her hair. The East Wind gave her the written leaf from the Phoenix

bird, and her eyes shone with pleasure.

She took the Prince by the hand and led him into her palace, where the walls had the colour of a splendid tulip leaf when it is held up in the sunlight. The ceiling was a great sparkling flower, and the more one looked up at it, the deeper did its cup appear. The Prince stepped to the window and looked through one of the panes. Here he saw the Tree of Knowledge, with the serpent, and Adam and Eve were standing close by.

'Were they not driven out?' he asked.

And the Fairy smiled, and explained to him that Time had burned in the picture upon that pane, but not as people are accustomed to see pictures. No, there was life in it: the leaves of the trees moved; men came and went as in a dissolving view. And he looked through another pane, and there was Jacob's dream, with the ladder reaching up into heaven, and the angels with great wings were ascending and descending. Yes, everything that had happened in the world lived and moved in the glass panes; such cunning pictures only Time could burn in.

The Fairy smiled, and led him into a great lofty hall, whose walls appeared transparent. Here were portraits, and each face looked fairer than the last. There were to be seen millions of happy ones who smiled and sang, so that it flowed together into a melody; the uppermost were so small that they looked like the smallest rosebud, when it is drawn as a point upon paper. And in the midst of the hall stood a great tree with rich pendent boughs; golden apples, great and small, hung like oranges among the leaves. That was the Tree of Knowledge, of whose fruit Adam and Eve had eaten. From each leaf fell a shining red dewdrop; it was as though the tree wept tears of blood.

'Let us now get into the boat,' said the Fairy, 'then we will enjoy some refreshment on the heaving waters. The boat rocks, yet does not quit its station; but all the lands of the earth will glide past in our sight.'

And it was wonderful to behold how the whole coast moved. There came the lofty snow-covered Alps, with clouds and black pine trees; the horn sounded with its melancholy note, and the shepherd trolled his merry song in the valley. Then the banana trees bent their long hanging branches over the boat; coal-black swans swam on the water, and the strangest animals and flowers showed themselves upon the shore. That was New Holland, the fifth great division of the world, which glided past with a background of blue hills. They heard the song of the priests, and saw the savages dancing to the sound of drums and of bone trumpets. Egypt's pyramids, towering aloft to the clouds, overturned pillars and sphinxes, half buried in the sand, sailed past likewise. The Northern Lights shone over the glaciers of the north – it was a firework that no one could imitate. The Prince was quite happy, and he saw a hundred times more than we can relate here.

'And can I always stay here?' asked he.

'That depends upon yourself,' answered the Fairy. 'If you do not, like Adam, yield to the temptation to do what is forbidden, you may always remain here.'

'I shall not touch the apples on the Tree of Knowledge!' said the Prince. 'Here are thousands of fruits just as beautiful as those.'

'Search your own heart, and if you are not strong enough, go away with the East Wind that brought you hither. He is going to fly back, and will not show himself here again for a hundred years: the time will pass for you in this place as if it were a hundred hours, but it is a long time for the temptation of sin. Every evening, when I leave you, I shall have to call to you, "Come with me!" and I shall have to beckon to you with my hand; but stay where you are: do not go with me, or your longing will become greater with every step. You will then come into the hall where the Tree of Knowledge grows; I sleep under its fragrant pendent boughs; you will bend over me, and I must smile; but if you press a kiss upon my mouth, the Paradise will sink deep into the earth and be lost to you. The keen wind of the desert will rush around you, the cold rain drop from your hair, and sorrow and woe will be your portion.'

'I shall stay here!' said the Prince.

And the East Wind kissed him on the forehead, and said, 'Be strong, and we shall meet here again in a hundred years. Farewell! farewell!'

And the East Wind spread out his broad wings, and they flashed like sheet lightning in harvest-time, or like the Northern Lights in the cold winter.

'Farewell! farewell!' sounded from among the flowers and the trees. Storks and pelicans flew away in rows like fluttering ribbons, and bore him company to the boundary of the garden.

'Now we will begin our dances!' cried the Fairy. 'At the end, when I dance with you, when the sun goes down, you will see me beckon to you; you will hear me call to you, "Come with me;" but do not obey. For a hundred years I must repeat this every evening; every time, when the trial is past, you will gain more strength; at last you will not think of it at all. This evening is the first time. Now I have warned you.'

And the Fairy led him into a great hall of white transparent lilies; the yellow stamens in each flower formed a little golden harp, which sounded both like a stringed instrument and a flute. The most beautiful maidens, floating and slender, clad in gauzy mist, glided by in the dance, and sang of the happiness of living, and declared that they would never die, and that the Garden of Paradise would bloom for ever.

And the sun went down. The whole sky shone like gold, which gave to the lilies the hue of the most glorious roses; and the Prince drank of the foaming wine which the maidens poured out for him, and felt a happiness he had never before known. He saw how the background of the hall opened, and the Tree of Knowledge stood in a glory which blinded his eyes; the singing there was soft and lovely as the voice of his dear mother, and it was as though she sang, 'My child! my beloved child!'

Then the Fairy beckoned to him, and called out persuasively, 'Come with me! come with me!'

And he rushed towards her, forgetting his promise, forgetting it the very first evening; and still she beckoned and smiled. The fragrance, the delicious fragrance around became stronger, the harps sounded far more lovely, and it seemed as though the millions of smiling heads in the hall, where the tree grew, nodded and sang, 'One must know everything – man is the lord of the earth.' And they were no longer drops of blood that the Tree of Knowledge wept; they were red shining stars which he seemed to see.

'Come! come!' the quivering voice still cried, and at every step the Prince's cheeks burned more hotly and his blood flowed more rapidly.

'I must!' said he. 'It is no sin, it cannot be one. Why not follow beauty and joy? I only want to see her asleep; there will be nothing lost if I only refrain from kissing her; and I will not kiss her: I am strong and have a resolute will!'

And the Fairy threw off her shining cloak and bent back the branches, and in another moment she was hidden among them.

'I have not yet sinned,' said the Prince, 'and I will not.'

And he pushed the boughs aside. There she slept already, beautiful as only a fairy in the Garden of Paradise can be. She smiled in her dreams, and he bent over her, and saw tears quivering beneath her eyelids!

'Do you weep for me?' he whispered. 'Weep not, thou glorious woman! Now only I understand the bliss of Paradise! It streams through my blood, through my thoughts; the power of the angel and of increasing life I feel in my mortal body! Let what will happen to me now; one moment like this is wealth enough!'

And he kissed the tears from her eyes – his mouth touched hers.

Then there resounded a clap of thunder so loud and dreadful that no one had ever heard the like, and everything fell down; and the beautiful Fairy and the charming Paradise sank down, deeper and deeper. The Prince saw it vanish into the black night; like a little bright star it gleamed out of the far distance. A deadly chill ran through his frame, and he closed his eyes and lay for a long time as one dead.

The cold rain fell upon his face, the keen wind roared round his head, and then his senses returned to him.

'What have I done?' he sighed. 'I have sinned like Adam – sinned so that Paradise has sunk deep down!'

And he opened his eyes, and the star in the distance – the star that gleamed like the Paradise that had sunk down, was the morning star in the sky.

He stood up, and found himself in the great forest, close by the Cave of the Winds, and the mother of the Winds sat by his side: she looked angry, and raised her arm in the air.

'The very first evening!' said she. 'I thought it would be so! Yes, if you were my son, you would have to go into the sack!'

'Yes, he shall go in there!' said Death. He was a strong old man, with a scythe in his hand, and with great black wings. 'Yes, he shall be laid in his coffin, but not yet: I only register him, and let him wander awhile in the world to expiate his sins and to grow better. But one day I shall come. When he least expects it, I shall clap him in the black coffin, put him on my head, and fly up towards the star. There, too, blooms the Garden of Paradise; and if he is good and pious he will go in there; but if his thoughts are evil, and his heart still full of sin, he will sink with his coffin deeper than Paradise has sunk, and only every thousandth year I shall fetch him, that he may sink deeper, or that he may attain to the star – the shining star up yonder!'

The Flying Trunk

THERE was once a merchant, who was so rich that he could pave the whole street with silver coins, and almost have enough left for a little lane. But he did not do that; he knew how to employ his money differently. When he spent a shilling he got back a crown, such a clever merchant was he; and this continued till he died.

His son now got all this money; and he lived merrily, going to the masquerade every evening, making kites out of dollar notes, and playing at ducks and drakes on the sea coast with gold pieces instead of pebbles. In this way the money might soon be spent, and indeed it was so. At last he had no more than four shillings left, and no clothes to wear but a pair of slippers and an old dressing-gown. Now his friends did not trouble themselves any more about him, as they could not walk with him in the street; but one of them, who was good-natured, sent him an old trunk, with the remark, 'Pack up!' Yes, that was all very well, but he had nothing to pack, therefore he seated himself in the trunk.

That was a wonderful trunk. So soon as anyone pressed the lock, the trunk could fly. This it now did; *whirr!* away it flew with him through the chimney and over the clouds, farther and farther away. But as often as the bottom of the trunk cracked a little he was in great fear lest it might go to pieces, and then he would have thrown a fine somersault! In that way he came to the land of the Turks. He hid the trunk in a wood under some dry leaves, and then went into the town. He could do that very well, for among the Turks all the people went dressed like himself in dressing-gown and slippers. Then he met a nurse with a little child.

'Here, you Turkish nurse,' he began, 'what kind of a great castle is that close by the town, in which the windows are so high up?'

'There dwells the Sultan's daughter,' replied she. 'It is prophesied that she will be very unhappy respecting a lover; and therefore nobody may go to her, unless the Sultan and Sultana are there too.'

'Thank you!' said the merchant's son; and he went out into the forest, seated himself in his trunk, flew on the roof, and crept through the window into the Princess's room.

She was lying asleep on the sofa, and she was so beautiful that the merchant's son was compelled to kiss her. Then she awoke, and was very much startled; but he said he was a Turkish angel who had come down to her through the air, and that pleased her.

They sat down side by side, and he told her stories about her eyes; he told her they were the most glorious dark lakes, and that thoughts were swimming about in them like mermaids. And he told her about her forehead; that it was a snowy mountain with the most splendid halls and pictures. And he told her about the stork who brings the lovely little children.

Yes, those were fine histories! Then he asked the Princess if she would marry him, and she said 'Yes,' directly.

'But you must come here on Saturday,' said she. 'Then the Sultan and the Sultana will be here to tea. They will be very proud that I am to marry a Turkish angel. But take care that you know a very pretty story, for both my parents are very fond indeed of stories. My mother likes them high-flown and moral, but my father likes them merry, so that one can laugh.'

'Yes, I shall bring no marriage gift but a story,' said he; and so they parted. But the Princess gave him a sabre, the sheath embroidered with gold pieces, and that was very useful to him.

Now he flew away, bought a new dressing-gown, and sat in the forest and made up a story; it was to be ready by Saturday, and that was not an easy thing.

By the time he had finished it Saturday had come. The Sultan and his wife and all the court were at the Princess's to tea. He was received very graciously.

'Will you tell us a story?' said the Sultana; 'one that is deep and edifying.'

'Yes, but one that we can laugh at,' said the Sultan.

'Certainly,' he replied; and began. And now listen well.

'There was once a bundle of Matches, and these Matches were particularly proud of their high descent. Their genealogical tree, that is to say, the great fir tree of which each of them was a little splinter, had been a great old tree out in the forest. The Matches now lay between a Tinder-Box and an old iron Pot; and they were telling about the days of their youth. "Yes, when we were upon the green boughs," they said, "then we really were upon the green boughs! Every morning and evening there was diamond tea for us, I mean dew; we had sunshine all day long whenever the sun shone, and all the little birds had to tell stories. We could see very well that we were rich, for the other trees were only dressed out in summer, while our family had the means to wear green dresses in the winter as well. But then the woodcutter came, like a great revolution, and our family was broken up. The head of the family got an appointment as mainmast in a first-rate ship, which could sail round the world if necessary; the other branches went to other places, and now we have the office of kindling a light for the vulgar herd. That's how we grand people came to be in the kitchen."

' "My fate was of a different kind," said the iron Pot which stood next to the Matches. "From the beginning, ever since I came into the world, there has been a great deal of scouring and cooking done in me. I look after the practical part, and am the first here in the house. My only pleasure is to sit in my place after dinner, very clean and neat, and to carry on a sensible conversation with my comrades. But except the Water Pot, which sometimes is taken down into the courtyard, we always live within our four walls. Our only newsmonger is the Market Basket; but he speaks very uneasily about the government and the people. Yes, the other day there was an old pot that fell down from fright, and burst. He's liberal, I can tell you!" "Now you're talking too much," the Tinder-Box interrupted, and the steel struck against the flint, so that sparks flew out. "Shall we not have a merry evening?"

' "Yes, let us talk about who is the grandest," said the Matches.

' "No, I don't like to talk about myself," retorted the Pot. "Let us get up an evening entertainment. I will begin. I will tell a story from real life, something that everyone has experienced, so that we can easily imagine the situation, and take pleasure in it. On the Baltic, by the Danish beech trees –"

' "That's a pretty beginning!" cried all the Plates. "That will be a story we shall like."

' "Yes, there I spent my youth in a quiet family where the furniture was polished, and the floors scoured, and new curtains were put up every fortnight."

' "What an interesting way you have of telling a story!" said the Carpet Broom. "One can tell directly that the narrator is a woman. There's something pure runs through it."

' "Yes, one feels that," said the Water Pot, and out of delight it gave a little hop, so that there was a splash on the floor.

'And the Pot went on telling her story, and the end was as good as the beginning.

'All the Plates rattled with joy, and the Carpet Broom brought some green parsley out of the dust hole, and put it like a wreath on the Pot, for he knew that it would vex the others. "If I crown her today," it thought, "she will crown me tomorrow."

' "Now I'll dance," said the Fire Tongs, and she danced. Preserve us! how that implement could lift up one leg! The old Chair Cushion burst to see it. "Shall I be crowned too?" thought the Tongs; and indeed a wreath was awarded.

' "They're only common people, after all!" thought the Matches.

Now the Tea Urn was to sing; but she said she had taken cold, and could not sing unless she felt boiling within. But that was only affectation; she did not want to sing, except when she was in the parlour with the grand people.

'In the window sat an old Quill Pen, with which the maid generally wrote: there was nothing remarkable about this pen, except that it had been dipped too deep into the ink, but she was proud of that. "If the Tea Urn won't sing," she said, "she may leave it alone. Outside hangs a nightingale in a cage, and he can sing. He hasn't had any education, but this evening we'll say nothing about that."

' "I think it very wrong," said the Tea Kettle – he was the kitchen singer, and half-brother to the Tea Urn – "that that rich and foreign bird should be listened to! Is that patriotic? Let the Market Basket decide."

' "I am vexed," said the Market Basket. "No one can imagine how much I am secretly vexed. Is that a proper way of spending the evening? Would it not be more sensible to put the house in order? Let each one go to his own place, and I would arrange the whole game. That would be quite another thing."

' "Yes, let us make a disturbance," cried they all. Then the door opened, and the maid came in, and they all stood still; not one stirred. But there was not one pot among them who did not know what he could do, and how grand he was. "Yes, if I had liked," each one thought, "it might have been a very merry evening."

'The servant girl took the Matches and lighted the fire with them. Mercy! how they sputtered and burst out into flame! "Now everyone can see," thought they, "that we are the first. How we shine! what a light!" – and they burned out.'

'That was a capital story,' said the Sultana. 'I feel myself quite carried away to the kitchen, to the Matches. Yes, now thou shalt marry our daughter.'

'Yes, certainly,' said the Sultan, 'thou shalt marry our daughter on Monday.'

And they called him *thou*, because he was to belong to the family.

The wedding was decided on, and on the evening before it the whole city was illuminated. Biscuits and cakes were thrown among the people, the street boys stood on their toes, called out 'Hurrah!' and whistled on their fingers. It was uncommonly splendid.

'Yes, I shall have to give something as a treat,' thought the merchant's son. So he bought rockets and crackers, and every imaginable sort of firework, put them all into his trunk, and flew up into the air.

'Crack!' how they went, and how they went off! All the Turks hopped up with such a start that their slippers flew about their ears; such a meteor they had never yet seen. Now they could understand that it must be a Turkish angel who was going to marry the Princess.

As soon as the merchant's son descended again into the forest with his trunk, he thought, 'I will go into the town now, and hear how it all looked.' And it was quite natural that he wanted to do so.

What stories people told! Everyone whom he asked about it had seen it in a separate way; but one and all thought it fine.

'I saw the Turkish angel himself,' said one. 'He had eyes like glowing stars, and a beard like foaming water.'

'He flew in a fiery mantle,' said another; 'the most lovely little cherub peeped forth from among the folds.'

Yes, they were wonderful things that he heard; and on the following day he was to be married.

Now he went back to the forest to rest himself in his trunk. But what had become of that? A spark from the fireworks had set fire to it, and the trunk was burned to ashes. He could not fly any more, and could not get to his bride.

She stood all day on the roof waiting; and most likely she is waiting still. But he wanders through the world telling fairy tales; but they are not so merry as that one he told about the Matches.

The Storks

ON THE last house in a little village stood a Stork's nest. The Mother Stork sat in it with her four young ones, who stretched out their heads with the pointed black beaks, for their beaks had not yet turned red. A little way off stood the Father-Stork, all alone on the ridge of the roof, quite upright and stiff; he had drawn up one of his legs, so as not to be quite idle while he stood sentry. One would have thought he had been carved out of wood, so still did he stand. He thought, 'It must look very grand, that my wife has a sentry standing by her nest. They can't tell that it is her husband. They certainly think I have been commanded to stand here. That looks so aristocratic!' And he went on standing on one leg.

Below in the street a whole crowd of children were playing; and when they caught sight of the Storks, one of the boldest of the boys, and afterwards all of them, sang the old verse about the Storks. But they only sang it just as he could remember it:

> Stork, stork, fly away;
> Go and stay at home today.
> Your wife is lying in the nest,
> With four young beneath her breast.
>
> The first he will be hanged,
> The second will be banged,
> The third he will be burned,
> And the fourth one will be turned
> Outside in!

'Just hear what those boys are singing!' said the little Stork-children. 'They say we're to be hanged and burned.'

'You're not to care for that!' said the Mother-Stork. 'Don't listen to it, and then it won't matter.'

But the boys went on singing, and pointed at the Storks mockingly with their fingers; only one boy, whose name was Peter, declared that it was a sin to make jest of animals, and he would not join in it at all.

The Mother-Stork comforted her children. 'Don't you mind it at all,' she said; 'see how quiet your father stands, though it's only on one leg.'

'We are very much afraid,' said the young Storks: and they drew their heads far back into the nest.

Now today, when the children came out again to play, and saw the Storks, they sang their song:

> The first he will be hanged,
> The second will be banged –

'Shall we be hanged and burned?' asked the young Storks.

'No, certainly not,' replied the mother. 'You shall learn to fly; I'll exercise you; then we shall fly out into the meadows and pay a visit to the frogs; they will bow before us in the water, and sing "Co-ax! co-ax!" and then we shall eat them up. That will be a real pleasure.'

'And what then?' asked the young Storks.

'Then all the Storks will assemble, all that are here in the whole country, and the autumn exercises begin: then one must fly well, for that is highly important, for whoever cannot fly properly will be thrust dead by the general's beak; so take care and learn well when the exercising begins.'

'But then we shall be killed, as the boys say: and only listen, now they're singing again.'

'Listen to me, and not to them,' said the Mother-Stork. 'After the great review we shall fly away to the warm countries, far away from here, over mountains and forests. We shall fly to Egypt, where there are three-cornered houses of stone, which run up to a point and tower above the clouds; they are called pyramids, and are older than a stork can imagine. There is a river in that country which runs out of its bed, and then all the land is turned to mud. One walks about in the mud, and eats frogs.'

'Oh!' cried all the young ones.

'Yes! It is glorious there! One does nothing all day long but eat; and while we are so comfortable over there, here there is not a green leaf on the trees; here it is so cold that the clouds freeze to pieces, and fall down in little white rags!'

It was the snow that she meant, but she could not explain it in any other way.

'And do the naughty boys freeze to pieces?' asked the young Storks.

'No, they do not freeze to pieces; but they are not far from it, and

must sit in the dark room and cower. You, on the other hand, can fly about in foreign lands, where there are flowers, and the sun shines warm.'

Now some time had elapsed, and the nestlings had grown so large that they could stand upright in the nest and look far around; and the Father-Stork came every day with delicious frogs, little snakes, and all kinds of stork-dainties as he found them. Oh! it looked funny when he performed feats before them! He laid his head quite back upon his tail, and clapped with his beak as if it had been a little clapper; and then he told them stories, all about the marshes.

'Listen! now you must learn to fly,' said the Mother-Stork one day; and all the four young ones had to go out on the ridge of the roof. Oh, how they tottered! how they balanced themselves with their wings, and yet they were nearly falling down.

'Only look at me,' said the mother. 'Thus you must hold your heads! Thus you must pitch your feet! One, two! one, two! That's what will help you on in the world.'

Then she flew a little way, and the young ones made a little clumsy leap. Bump! there they lay, for their bodies were too heavy.

'I will not fly!' said one of the young Storks, and crept back into the nest; 'I don't care about getting to the warm countries.'

'Do you want to freeze to death here, when the winter comes? Are the boys to come and hang you, and singe you, and roast you? Now I'll call them.'

'Oh, no!' cried the young Stork, and hopped out on to the roof again like the rest.

On the third day they could actually fly a little, and then they thought they could also soar and hover in the air. They tried it, but – bump! – down they tumbled, and they had to flap their wings again quickly enough. Now the boys came into the street again, and sang their song:

Stork, stork, fly away!

'Shall we fly down and pick their eyes out?' asked the young Storks.

'No,' replied the mother, 'let them alone. Only listen to me, that's far more important. One, two, three! now we fly round to the right. One, two, three! now to the left round the chimney! See, that was very good! the last flap with the wings was so neat and correct that you shall have permission tomorrow to fly with me to the marsh! Several nice stork families go there with their young: show them that mine are the nicest, and that you can stalk proudly; that looks well, and will get you consideration.'

'But are we not to take revenge on the rude boys?' asked the young Storks.

'Let them scream as much as they like. You will fly up to the clouds, and get to the land of the pyramids, when they will have to shiver, and not have a green leaf or a sweet apple.'

'Yes, we will revenge ourselves!' they whispered to one another; and then the exercising went on.

Among all the boys down in the street, the one most bent upon singing the teasing song was he who had begun it, and he was quite a little boy. He could hardly be more than six years old. The young Storks certainly thought he was a hundred, for he was much bigger than their mother and father; and how should they know what age children and grown-up people may be? Their revenge was to come upon this boy, for it was he who had begun, and he always kept on. The young Storks were very angry; and as they grew bigger they were less inclined to bear it: at last their mother had to promise them that they should be revenged, but not till the last day of their stay.

'We must first see how you behave at the grand review. It you get through badly, so that the general stabs you through the chest with his beak, the boys will be right, at least in one way. Let us see.'

'Yes, you shall see!' cried the young Storks; and then they took all imaginable pains. They practised every day, and flew so neatly and so lightly that it was a pleasure to see them.

Now the autumn came on; all the Storks began to assemble, to fly away to the warm countries while it is winter here. That *was* a review. They had to fly over forests and villages, to show how well they could soar, for it was a long journey they had before them. The young Storks did their part so well that they got as a mark, 'Remarkably well, with frogs and snakes.' That was the highest mark; and they might eat the frogs and snakes; and that is what they did.

'Now we will be revenged!' they said.

'Yes, certainly!' said the Mother-Stork. 'What I have thought of will be the best. I know the pond in which all the little mortals lie till the stork comes and brings them to their parents. The pretty little babies lie there and dream more sweetly than they ever dream afterwards. All parents are glad to have such a child, and all children want to have a sister or a brother. Now we will fly to the pond, and bring one for each

of the children who have not sung the naughty song and laughed at the storks.'

'But he who began to sing – that naughty, ugly boy!' screamed the young Storks; 'what shall we do with him?'

'There is a little dead child in the pond, one that has dreamed itself to death; we will bring that for him. Then he will cry because we have brought him a little dead brother. But that good boy – you have not forgotten him, the one who said, "It is wrong to laugh at animals!" for him we will bring a brother and a sister too. And as his name is Peter, all of you shall be called Peter too.'

And it was done as she said; all the storks were named Peter, and so they are all called even now.

The Metal Pig

IN THE CITY of Florence, not far from the *Piazza del Granduca*, there runs a little cross-street, I think it is called *Porta Rossa*. In this street, in front of a kind of market hall where vegetables are sold, there lies a Pig artistically fashioned of metal. The fresh clear water pours from the snout of the creature, which has become a blackish-green from age; only the snout shines as if it had been polished, and indeed it has been, by many hundreds of children and poor people, who seize it with their hands, and place their mouths close to the mouth of the animal, to drink. It is a perfect picture to see the well-shaped creature clasped by a half-naked boy, who lays his red lips against its snout.

Everyone who comes to Florence can easily find the place; he need only ask the first beggar he meets for the Metal Pig, and he will find it.

It was late on a winter evening. The mountains were covered with snow; but the moon shone, and moonlight in Italy is just as good as the light of a murky Northern winter's day; nay, it is better, for the air shines and lifts us up, while in the North the cold grey leaden covering seems to press us downwards to the earth – the cold damp earth, which will someday press down our coffin.

In the Grand Duke's palace garden, under a roof of pines, where a thousand roses bloom in winter, a little ragged boy had been sitting all day long, a boy who might serve as a type of Italy, pretty and smiling, and yet suffering. He was hungry and thirsty, but no one gave him anything; and when it became dark, and the garden was to be closed, the porter turned him out. Long he stood musing on the bridge that spans the Arno, and looked at the stars, whose light glittered in the water between him and the splendid marble bridge.

He took the way towards the Metal Pig, half knelt down, clasped his arms round it, put his mouth against its shining snout, and drank the fresh water in deep draughts. Close by lay a few leaves of salad and one or two chestnuts; these were his supper. No one was in the street but himself – it belonged to him alone, and so he boldly sat down on the Pig's back, bent forward, so that his curly head rested on the head of the animal, and before he was aware fell asleep.

It was midnight. The Metal Pig stirred, and he heard it say quite distinctly, 'You little boy, hold tight, for now I am going to run,' and away it ran with him. This was a wonderful ride. First they got to the *Piazza del Granduca*, and the metal horse which carries the Duke's statue neighed loudly, the painted coats of arms on the old council-house looked like transparent pictures, and Michelangelo's 'David' swung his sling: there was a strange life stirring among them. The metal groups representing Perseus, and the rape of the Sabines, stood there only too much alive: a cry of mortal fear escaped them, and resounded over the splendid lonely square.

By the *Palazzo degli Uffizi*, in the arcade, where the nobility assemble for the Carnival amusements, the Metal Pig stopped. 'Hold tight,' said the creature, 'for now we are going upstairs.' The little boy spoke not a word, for he was half frightened, half delighted.

They came into a long gallery where the boy had already been. The walls were adorned with pictures; here stood statues and busts, all in the most charming light, as if it had been broad day; but the most

beautiful of all was when the door of a side room opened: the little boy could remember the splendour that was there, but on this night everything shone in the most glorious colours.

Here stood a beautiful woman, as radiant in beauty as nature and the greatest master of sculpture could make her: she moved her graceful limbs, dolphins sprang at her feet, and immortality shone out of her eyes. The world calls her the Venus de Medici. By her side are statues in which the spirit of life had been breathed into the stone; they are handsome unclothed men. One was sharpening a sword, and was called the Grinder; the Wrestling Gladiators formed another group; and the sword was sharpened, and they strove for the goddess of beauty.

The boy was dazzled by all this pomp: the walls gleamed with bright colours, and everything was life and movement there. In twofold form was seen the image of Venus, the earthly Venus, full and glowing, as Titian had seen her. The pictures of two lovely women; their beautiful unveiled limbs were stretched out on the soft cushions; their bosoms heaved, and their heads moved, so that the rich locks fell down over the rounded shoulders, while their dark eyes uttered glowing thoughts. But not one of all the pictures dared to step quite out of its frame. The Goddess of Beauty herself, the Gladiators and the Grinder, remained in their places, for the glory that shone from the Madonna, Jesus, and St John, restrained them. The holy pictures were pictures no longer, they were the Holy Ones themselves.

What splendour, what beauty shone from hall to hall! and the little boy saw everything plainly, for the Metal Pig went step by step through all this scene of magnificence. Each fresh sight effaced the last. One picture only fixed itself firmly in his soul, especially through the very happy children introduced into it; the little boy had once nodded to these in the daylight.

Many persons pass by this picture with indifference, and yet it contains a treasure of poetry. It represents the Saviour descending into hell. But these are not the damned whom the spectator sees around him, they are the heathens. The Florentine Angiolo Bronzino painted this picture. Most beautiful is the expression on the faces of the children, the full confidence that they will get to heaven: two little beings are already embracing, and one little one stretches out his hand towards another who stands below him, and points to himself as if he were saying, 'I am going to heaven!' The older people stand uncertain, hoping, or bowing in humble adoration before the Lord Jesus. The boy's eyes rested longer on this picture than on any other. The Metal Pig stood still before it. A low sigh was heard: did it come from the picture or from the animal? The boy lifted up his hands towards the smiling children; then the Pig ran away with him, away through the open vestibule.

'Thanks and blessings to you, you dear thing!' said the little boy, and caressed the Metal Pig, as it sprang down the steps with him.

'Thanks and blessings to yourself,' replied the Metal Pig. 'I have helped you, and you have helped me, for only with an innocent child on my back do I receive power to run! Yes, you see, I may even step into the rays of the lamp in front of the picture of the Madonna, I can carry you everywhere, only I may not go into the church. But from without, when you are with me, I may look in through the open door. Do not get down from my back; if you do so, I shall lie dead as you see me in the daytime at the *Porta Rossa*.'

'I will stay with you, my dear creature!' cried the child.

So they went in hot haste through the streets of Florence, out into the place before the church of *Santa Croce*. The folding doors flew open, and lights gleamed out from the altar through the church into the deserted square.

A wonderful blaze of light streamed forth from a monument in the left aisle, and a thousand moving stars seemed to form a glory round it. A coat of arms shone upon the grave, a red ladder in a blue field seemed to glow like fire. It was the grave of Galileo. The monument is unadorned, but the red ladder is a significant emblem, as if it were that of art, for in art the way always leads up a burning ladder, towards heaven. The prophets of mind soar upwards towards heaven, like Elias of old.

To the right, in the aisle of the church, every statue on the richly carved sarcophagi seemed endowed with life. Here stood Michelangelo, there Dante with the laurel wreath round his brow, Alfieri and

Machiavelli; for here the great men, the pride of Italy, rest side by side. It is a glorious church, far more beautiful than the marble cathedral of Florence, though not so large.

It seemed as if the marble vestments stirred, as if the great forms raised their heads higher and looked up, amid song and music, to the bright altar glowing with colour, where the white-clad boys swing the golden censers; and the strong fragrance streamed out of the church into the open square.

The boy stretched forth his hand towards the gleaming light, and in a moment the Metal Pig resumed its headlong career: he was obliged to cling tightly; and the wind whistled about his ears; he heard the church door creak on its hinges as it closed; but at the same moment his senses seemed to desert him, he felt a cold shudder pass over him, and awoke.

It was morning, and he was still sitting on the Metal Pig, which stood where it always stood on the *Porta Rossa*, and he had slipped half off its back.

Fear and trembling filled the soul of the boy at the thought of her whom he called mother, and who had yesterday sent him forth to bring money; for he had none, and was hungry and thirsty. Once more he clasped his arms round the neck of his metal horse, kissed its lips, and nodded farewell to it. Then he wandered away into one of the narrowest streets, where there was scarcely room for a laden ass. A great iron-clamped door stood ajar; he passed through it, and climbed up a brick stair with dirty walls and a rope for a balustrade, till he came to an open gallery hung with rags; from here a flight of stairs led down into the court, where there was a fountain, and great iron wires led up to the different stories, and many water-buckets hung side by side, and at times the roller creaked, and one of the buckets would dance into the air, swaying so that the water splashed out of it down into the courtyard. A second ruinous brick staircase here led upwards. Two Russian sailors were running briskly down, and almost overturned the poor boy: they were going home from their nightly carouse. A strongly-built woman, no longer young, with coarse black hair, followed them.

'What do you bring home?' she asked the boy.

'Don't be angry,' he pleaded. 'I received nothing – nothing at all.' And he seized the mother's dress, and would have kissed it.

They went into the little room. I will not describe it, but only say that there stood in it an earthen pot with handles, made for holding fire, and called a *marito*. This pot she took in her arms, warmed her fingers, and pushed the boy with her elbow.

'Certainly you must have brought some money?' said she.

The boy wept, and she struck him with her foot, so that he cried aloud.

'Will you be silent, or I'll break your screaming head!'

And she brandished the fire-pot which she held in her hand. The boy crouched down to the earth with a scream of terror. Then a neighbour stepped in, also with a *marito* in her arms.

'Felicita,' she said, 'what are you doing to the child?'

'The child is mine,' retorted Felicita. 'I can murder him if I like, and you too, Giannina.'

And she swung her fire-pot. The other lifted up hers in self-defence, and the two pots clashed together with such fury that fragments, fire, and ashes flew about the room; but at the same moment the boy rushed out at the door, sped across the courtyard, and fled from the house. The poor child ran till he was quite out of breath. He stopped by the church, whose great doors had opened to him the previous night, and went in. Everything was radiant. The boy knelt down at the first grave on the right hand, the grave of Michelangelo, and soon he sobbed aloud. People came and went, and Mass was said; but no one noticed the boy, only an elderly citizen stood still, looked at him, and then went away like the rest.

Hunger and thirst tormented the child; he was quite faint and ill, and he crept into a corner between the wall and the marble monument, and went to sleep. Towards evening he was awakened by a tug at his sleeve; he started up, and the same citizen stood before him.

'Are you ill? Where do you live? Have you been here all day?' were three of the many questions the old man asked of him.

He answered, and the old man took him into his little house close by, in a back street. They came into a glover's workshop, where a

woman sat sewing busily. A little white Spitz dog, so closely shaven that his pink skin could be seen, frisked about on the table and gambolled before the boy.

'Innocent souls soon make acquaintance,' said the woman.

And she caressed the boy and the dog. The good people gave the child food and drink, and said he should be permitted to stay the night with them; and next day Father Guiseppe would speak to his mother. A little simple bed was assigned to him, but for him who had often slept on the hard stones it was a royal couch; and he slept sweetly, and dreamed of the splendid pictures and of the Metal Pig.

Father Guiseppe went out next morning: the poor child was not glad of this, for he knew that the object of the errand was to send him back to his mother. He wept, and kissed the merry little dog, and the woman nodded approvingly at both.

What news did Father Guiseppe bring home? He spoke a great deal with his wife, and she nodded and stroked the boy's cheek.

'He is a capital lad!' said she. 'He may become an accomplished glove-maker, like you; and look what delicate fingers he has! Madonna intended him for a glove-maker.'

And the boy stayed in the house, and the woman herself taught him to sew: he ate well, slept well, and became merry, and began to tease Bellissima, as the little dog was called; but the woman grew angry at this, and scolded and threatened him with her finger. This touched the boy's heart, and he sat thoughtful in his little chamber. This chamber looked upon the street, in which skins were dried; there were thick bars of iron before his window. He could not sleep, for the Metal Pig was always present in his thoughts, and suddenly he heard outside a pit-pat. That must be the Pig! He sprang to the window, but nothing was to be seen – it had passed by already.

'Help the gentleman to carry his box of colours,' said the woman next morning to the boy, when their young neighbour the artist passed by, carrying a paintbox and a large rolled canvas.

The boy took the box, and followed the painter; they betook themselves to the gallery, and mounted the same staircase which he remembered well from the night when he had ridden on the Metal Pig. He recognised the statues and pictures, the beautiful marble Venus, and the Venus that lived in the picture; and again he saw the Madonna, and the Saviour, and St John.

They stood still before the picture by Bronzino, in which Christ is descending into hell, and the children smiling around him in the sweet expectation of heaven. The poor child smiled too, for he felt as if his heaven were here.

'Go home now,' said the painter, when the boy had stood until the other had set up his easel.

'May I see you paint?' asked the boy. 'May I see you put the picture upon this white canvas?'

'I am not going to paint yet,' replied the man; and he brought out a piece of black crayon. His hand moved quickly; his eye measured the great picture, and though nothing appeared but a thin line, the figure of the Saviour stood there, as in the coloured picture.

'Why don't you go?' said the painter.

And the boy wandered home silently, and seated himself on the table and learned to sew gloves.

But all day long his thoughts were in the picture gallery; and so it came that he pricked his fingers, and was awkward; but he did not tease Bellissima. When evening came, and when the house door stood open, he crept out: it was cold but starlight, a bright beautiful evening. Away he went through the already deserted streets, and soon came to the Metal Pig. He bent down on it, kissed its shining mouth, and seated himself on its back.

'You happy creature!' he said; 'how I have longed for you! We must take a ride tonight.'

The Metal Pig lay motionless, and the fresh stream gushed forth from its mouth. The little boy sat astride on its back: then something tugged at his clothes. He looked down, and there was Bellissima – little smooth-shaven Bellissima – the dog had crept out of the house along with him, and had followed him without his noticing it. Bellissima barked as if she would have said, 'Here am I too: why are you sitting there?' A fiery dragon could not have terrified the boy so much as did the little dog in this place. Bellissima in the street, and not *dressed*, as the old lady called it! What would be the end of it? The dog never came out in winter, except attired in a little lambskin, which had been cut out and made into a coat for him; it was made to fasten with a red ribbon round the little dog's neck and body, and was adorned with bows and with bells. The dog looked almost like a little kid, when in winter he got permission to patter out with his mistress. Bellissima was outside, and not dressed! what would be the end of it? All his fancies were put to flight; yet the boy kissed the Metal Pig once more, and then took Bellissima on his arm: the little thing trembled with cold, therefore the boy ran as fast as he could.

'What are you running away with there?' asked two gendarmes whom he met, and at whom Bellissima barked. 'Where have you stolen that pretty dog?' they asked, and they took it away from him.

'Oh, give it back to me!' cried the boy despairingly.

'If you have not stolen him, you may say at home that the dog may be sent for to the watch-house.' And they told him where the watch-house was, and went away with Bellissima.

Here was a terrible calamity! The boy did not know whether he should jump into the Arno, or go home and confess everything; they would certainly kill him, he thought.

'But I will gladly be killed; then I shall die and get to heaven,' he reasoned. And he went home, principally with the idea of being killed.

The door was locked, and he could not reach the knocker; no one was in the street, but a stone lay there, and with this he thundered at the door.

'Who is there?' cried somebody from within.

'It is I,' said he. 'The dog is gone. Open the door, and then kill me!'

There was quite a panic. Madame was especially concerned for poor Bellissima. She immediately looked at the wall, where the dog's dress usually hung, and there was the little lambskin.

'Bellissima in the watch-house!' she cried aloud. 'You bad boy! How did you entice her out? She'll be frozen, the poor delicate little thing! among those rough soldiers.'

The father was at once sent off – the woman lamented and the boy wept. All the inhabitants of the house came together, and among the rest the painter: he took the boy between his knees and questioned him; and in broken sentences he heard the whole story about the Metal Pig and the gallery, which was certainly rather incomprehensible.

The painter consoled the little fellow, and tried to calm the old lady's anger; but she would not be pacified until the father came in with Bellissima, who had been among the soldiers; then there was great rejoicing; and the painter caressed the boy, and gave him a handful of pictures.

Oh, those were capital pieces – such funny heads! – and truly the Metal Pig was there among them, bodily. Oh, nothing could be more superb! By means of a few strokes it was made to stand there on the paper, and even the house that stood behind it was sketched in.

Oh, if one could only draw and paint! Then one could bring the whole world to oneself.

On the first leisure moment of the following day, the little fellow seized the pencil, and on the back of one of the pictures he attempted to copy the drawing of the Metal Pig, and he succeeded! it was certainly rather crooked, rather up and down, one leg thick and another thin; but still it was to be recognised, and he rejoiced himself at it. The pencil would not quite work as it should do, that he could well observe; but on the next day a second Metal Pig was drawn by the side of the first, and this looked a hundred times better; and the third was already so good that everyone could tell what it was meant for.

But the glove-making prospered little, and his errands in the town were executed but slowly; for the Metal Pig had taught him that all pictures may be drawn on paper; and Florence is a picture-book for anyone who chooses to turn over its pages. On the *Piazza del Trinitá* stands a slender pillar, and upon it the goddess of justice, blindfolded and with her scales in her hand. Soon she was placed on the paper, and it was the little glove-maker's boy who placed her there. The collection of pictures increased, but as yet it only contained representations of lifeless objects, when one day Bellissima came gambolling before him.

'Stand still!' said he, 'then you shall be made beautiful and put into my collection.'

But Bellissima would not stand still, so she had to be bound fast; her head and tail were tied, and she barked and jumped, and the string had to be pulled tight; and then the signora came in.

'You wicked boy! The poor creature!' was all she could utter.

And she pushed the boy aside, thrust him away with her foot, ordered him out of her house, and called him a most ungrateful good-for-nothing and a wicked boy; and then, weeping, she kissed her little half-strangled Bellissima.

At this very moment the painter came upstairs, and here is the turning-point of the story.

In the year 1834 there was an exhibition in the Academy of Arts at Florence. Two pictures, placed side by side, collected a number of spectators. The smaller of the two represented a merry little boy who sat drawing, with a little white Spitz dog, curiously shorn, for his model; but the animal would not stand still, and was therefore bound by a string fastened to its head and its tail. There was a truth and life in this picture that interested everyone. The painter was said to be a young Florentine, who had been found in the streets in his childhood, had been brought up by an old glove-maker, and had taught himself to draw. It was further said that a painter, now become famous, had discovered this talent just as the boy was to be sent away for tying up the favourite little dog of Madame, and using it as a model.

The glove-maker's boy had become a great painter: the picture proved this, and still more the larger picture that stood beside it. Here was represented only one figure, a handsome boy, clad in rags, asleep in the street, and leaning against the Metal Pig in the *Porta Rossa* street. All the spectators knew the spot. The child's arms rested upon the head of the Pig; the little fellow was fast asleep, and the lamp before the picture of the Madonna threw a strong effective light on the pale delicate face of the child – it was a beautiful picture! A great gilt frame surrounded it, and on one corner of the frame a laurel wreath had been hung; but a black band would among the green leaves, and a streamer of crape hung down from it. For within the last few days the young artist had – died!

The Bond of Friendship

WE HAVE lately taken a little journey together, and now we want to take a longer one. Whither? To Sparta, to Mycene, to Delphi? There are a hundred places at whose names the heart beats with the desire of travel. On horseback we go up the mountain paths, through brake and through brier. A single traveller makes an appearance like a whole caravan. He rides forward with his guide, a packhorse carries trunks, a tent, and provisions, and a few armed soldiers follow as a guard. No inn with warm beds awaits him at the end of his tiring day's journey: the tent is often his dwelling-place in the great wild region; the guide cooks him a pilau of rice, fowls, and curry for his supper. A thousand gnats swarm round the tent. It is a miserable night, and tomorrow the way will lead across swollen streams; sit fast on your horse that you may not be washed away!

What is your reward for undergoing these hardships? The fullest, richest reward. Nature manifests herself here in all her greatness; every spot is historical, and the eye and the thoughts are alike delighted. The poet may sing it, the painter portray it in rich pictures; but the air of reality which sinks deep into the soul of the spectator, and remains there, neither painter nor poet can reproduce.

The lonely herdsman yonder on the hills would, perhaps, by a simple recital of an event in his life, better enlighten you, who wish in a few features to behold the land of the Hellenes, than any writer of travel could do.

'Then,' says my Muse, 'let him speak.'

A custom, a good, peculiar custom, shall be the subject of the mountain shepherd's tale. It is called

The Bond of Friendship

Our rude house was put together of clay; but the doorposts were columns of fluted marble found near the spot where the house was erected. The roof reached almost down to the ground. It was now dark brown and ugly, but it had originally consisted of blooming olive and fresh laurel branches brought from beyond the mountain. Around our dwelling was a narrow gorge, whose walls of rock rose steeply upwards, and showed naked and black, and round their summits often hung clouds, like white living figures. Never did I hear a singing bird there, never did the men there dance to the sound of the bagpipe; but the spot was sacred from the old times: even its name reminded of this, for it was called Delphi! The dark solemn mountains were all covered with snow; the highest, which gleamed the longest in the red light of evening, was Parnassus; the brook which flowed from it near our house was once sacred also. Now the ass sullies it with its feet, but the stream rolls on and on, and becomes clear again. How I can remember every spot in the deep holy solitude! In the midst of the hut a fire was kindled, and when the hot ashes lay there red and glowing, the bread was baked in them. When the snow was piled so high around our hut as almost to hide it, my mother appeared most cheerful: then she would hold my head between her hands, kiss my forehead, and sing the songs she never sang at other times, for the Turks our masters would not allow it. She sang: 'On the summit of Olympus, in the forest of dwarf firs, lay an old stag. His eyes were heavy with tears; he wept red, green, and even pale blue tears; and there came a roebuck by, and said, "What ails thee, that thou weepest those blue, green, and red tears?" And the stag answered, "The Turk has come to our village: he has wild dogs for the chase, a goodly pack." "I will drive them away across the islands," cried the young roebuck, "I will drive them away across the islands into the deep sea!" But before evening sank down the roebuck was slain, and before night the stag was hunted and dead.'

And when my mother sang thus, her eyes became moist, and on the long eyelashes hung a tear; but she hid it, and baked our black bread in the ashes. Then I would clench my fist and cry, 'We will kill the Turks!'

But she repeated from the song the words, 'I will drive them across the islands into the deep sea. But before evening sank down the roebuck was slain, and before the night came the stag was hunted and dead.'

For several days and nights we had been lonely in our hut, when my father came home. I knew he would bring me shells from the Gulf of Lepanto, or perhaps even a bright gleaming knife. This time he brought us a child, a little half-naked girl, that he carried under his sheepskin cloak. It was wrapped in a fur, and all that the little creature possessed when this was taken off, and she lay in my mother's lap, were three silver coins, fastened in her dark hair. My father told us that the Turks had killed the child's parents; and he told so much about them that I dreamed of the Turks all night. He himself had been wounded, and my mother bound up his arm. The wound was deep, and the thick sheepskin was stiff with frozen blood. The little maiden was to be my sister. How radiantly beautiful she looked! Even my mother's eyes were not more gentle than hers. Anastasia, as she was called, was to be my sister, because her father had been united to mine by the old custom which we still keep. They had sworn brotherhood in their youth, and chosen the most beautiful and virtuous girl in the neighbourhood to consecrate their bond of friendship. I often heard of the strange good custom.

So now the little girl was my sister. She sat in my lap, and I brought her flowers and the feathers of the mountain birds: we drank together of the waters of Parnassus, and slept, cheek to cheek, under the laurel roof of the hut, while my mother sang winter after winter about the red, green, and pale blue tears. But as yet I did not understand that it was my own countrymen whose many sorrows were mirrored in those tears.

One day there came three Frankish men. Their dress was different from ours. They had tents and beds with them on their horses, and more than twenty Turks, all armed with swords and muskets, accompanied them; for they were friends of the pasha, and had letters from him commanding an escort for them. They only came to see our mountains, to ascend Parnassus amid the snow and the clouds, and to look at the strange black steep rocks near our hut. They could not find room in it, nor could they endure the smoke that rolled along the ceiling and found its way out at the low door; therefore they pitched their tents on the small space outside our dwelling, roasted lambs and birds, and poured out strong sweet wine, of which the Turks were not allowed to partake.

When they departed, I accompanied them for some distance, carrying my little sister Anastasia, wrapped in a goatskin, on my back. One of the Frankish gentlemen made me stand in front of a rock, and drew me, and her too, as we stood there, so that we looked like one creature. I never thought of it before, but Anastasia and I were really one. She was always sitting in my lap or riding in the goatskin at my back, and when I dreamed, she appeared in my dreams.

Two nights afterwards, other men, armed with knives and muskets, came into our tent. They were Albanians, brave men, my mother told me. They only stayed a short time. My sister Anastasia sat on the knee of one of them, and when they were gone she had not three, but only two silver coins in her hair. They wrapped tobacco in strips of paper and smoked it. I remember they were undecided as to the road they were to take.

But they had to make a choice. They went, and my father went with them. Soon afterwards we heard the sound of loud firing, soldiers rushed into our tent, and took my mother, and myself, and my sister Anastasia prisoners. They declared that the robbers had been entertained by us, and that my father had acted as the robbers' guide, and therefore we must go with them. Presently I saw the bodies of the robbers brought in; I saw my father's body too. I cried and cried till I fell asleep. When I awoke, we were in prison, but the room was not worse than ours in our own house. They gave me onions to eat, and musty wine poured from a tarry cask, but we had no better fare at home.

How long we were kept prisoners I do not know; but many days and nights went by. When we were set free it was the time of the holy Easter feast. I carried Anastasia on my back, for my mother was ill, and could only move slowly, and it was a long way till we came down to the sea, to the Gulf of Lepanto. We went into a church that gleamed with pictures painted on a golden ground. They were pictures of angels, and very beautiful; but it seemed to me that our little Anastasia was just as beautiful. In the middle of the floor stood a coffin filled with roses. 'The Lord Christ is pictured there in the form of a beautiful rose,' said my mother; and the priest announced, 'Christ is risen!' All the people kissed each other: each one had a burning taper in his hand, and I received one myself, and so did little Anastasia. The bagpipes sounded, men danced hand in hand from the church, and outside the women were roasting the Easter lamb. We were invited to partake, and I sat by the fire; a boy, older than myself, put his arms around my neck, kissed me, and said, 'Christ is risen!' and thus it was that for the first time I met Aphtanides.

My mother could make fishermen's nets, for which there was a good demand here in the bay, and we lived a long time by the side of the sea, the beautiful sea, that tasted like tears, and in its colours reminded me of the song of the stag that wept – for sometimes its waters were red, and sometimes green or blue.

Aphtanides knew how to manage a boat, and I often sat in it, with my little Anastasia, while it glided on through the water, swift as a bird flying through the air. Then, when the sun sank down, the mountains were tinted with a deeper and deeper blue, one range peeped over the other, and behind them all stood Parnassus with its snow-crowned summit. The mountain-top gleamed in the evening rays like glowing iron, and it seemed as though the light came from within it; for long after the sun had set, the mountain still shone through the clear blue air. The white water-birds touched the surface of the sea with their wings, otherwise all here was as calm and quiet as among the black rocks at Delphi. I lay on my back in the boat, Anastasia leaned against me, and the stars above us shone brighter than the lamps in our church. They were the same stars, and they stood exactly in the same positions above me, as when I had sat in front of our hut at Delphi; and at last I almost fancied I was back there. Suddenly there was a splash in the water, and the boat rocked violently. I cried out, for Anastasia had fallen into the water; but in a moment Aphtanides had sprung in after her, and was holding her up to me! We took off her clothes, wrung out the water, and then dressed her again; Aphtanides did the same for himself, and we remained on the water till they were dry; and no one knew what a fright we had had for our little adopted sister, in whose life Aphtanides now had a part.

The summer came. The sun burned so hot that the leaves turned yellow on the trees. I thought of our cool mountains, and of the fresh water they contained; my mother, too, longed for them; and one evening we wandered home. What peace, what silence! We walked on through the thick thyme, still fragrant though the sun had scorched its leaves. Not a single herdsman did we meet, not one solitary hut did we pass. Everything was quiet and deserted; but a shooting star announced that in heaven there was yet life. I know not if the clear blue air gleamed with light of its own, or if the radiance came from the stars; but we could see the outlines of the mountains quite plainly. My mother lighted a fire, roasted some roots she had brought with her, and I and my little sister slept among the thyme, without fear of the ugly Smidraki,* from whose throat fire spurts forth, or of the wolf and jackal; for my mother sat beside us, and I thought that was enough.

We reached our old home; but the hut was a heap of ruins, and a new one had to be built. A few women lent my mother their aid, and in a few days walls were raised, and covered with a new roof of oleander branches. My mother made many bottle-cases of bark and skins; I kept the priest's little flock,† and Anastasia and the little tortoises were my playmates.

Once we had a visit from our beloved Aphtanides, who said he had greatly longed to see us, and who stayed with us two whole happy days.

A month afterwards he came again, and told us that he was going in a ship to Corfu and Patras, but must bid us goodbye first; and he had brought a large fish for our mother. He had a great deal to tell, not only of the fishermen yonder in the Gulf of Lepanto, but also of Kings and heroes, who had once ruled in Greece, just as the Turks rule now.

I have seen a bud on a rose bush gradually unfold through days and weeks, till it became a rose, and hung there in its beauty, before I was

---

* According to the Greek superstition, this is a monster generated from the unopened entrails of slaughtered sheep, which are thrown away in the fields.
† A peasant who can read often becomes a priest; he is then called 'very holy Sir,' and the lower orders kiss the ground on which he has stepped.

aware how large and beautiful and red it had become; and the same thing I now saw in Anastasia. She was now a beautiful grown girl, and I had become a stout stripling. The wolfskins that covered my mother's and Anastasia's bed, I had myself taken from wolves that had fallen beneath my shots.

Years had gone by, when one evening Aphtanides came in, slender as a reed, strong and brown. He kissed us all, and had much to tell of the great ocean, of the fortifications of Malta, and of the marvellous sepulchres of Egypt. It sounded strange as a legend of the priests, and I looked up to him with a kind of veneration.

'How much you know!' I exclaimed; 'what wonders you can tell of!'

'But you have told me the finest thing, after all,' he replied. 'You told me of a thing that has never been out of my thoughts – of the good old custom of the bond of friendship, a custom I should like to follow. Brother, let you and I go to church, as your father and Anastasia's went before us: your sister Anastasia is the most beautiful and most innocent of girls; she shall consecrate us! No people has such grand old customs as we Greeks.'

Anastasia blushed like a young rose, and my mother kissed Aphtanides.

A couple of miles from our house, there where loose earth lies on the hill, and a few scattered trees give a shelter, stood the little church; a silver lamp hung in front of the altar.

I had put on my best clothes: the white fustanella fell in rich folds round my hips, the red jacket fitted tight and close, the tassel on my fez cap was silver, and in my girdle gleamed a knife and my pistols. Aphtanides was clad in the blue garb worn by Greek sailors; on his chest hung a silver plate with the figure of the Virgin Mary; his scarf was as costly as those worn by rich lords. Everyone could see that we were about to go through a solemn ceremony. We stepped into the little simple church, where the evening sunlight, streaming through the door, gleamed on the burning lamp and the pictures on golden ground. We knelt down on the altar steps, and Anastasia came before us. A long white garment hung loose over her graceful form; on her white neck and bosom hung a chain, covered with old and new coins, forming a kind of collar. Her black hair was fastened in a knot, and confined by a headdress made of silver and gold coins that had been found in the old temples. No Greek girl had more beautiful ornaments than she. Her countenance glowed, and her eyes were like two stars.

We all three prayed silently; and then she said to us, 'Will you be friends in life and in death?'

'Yes,' we replied.

'Will you, whatever may happen, remember this: my brother is a part of myself. My secrets are his, my happiness is his. Self-sacrifice, patience – everything in me belongs to him as to me?'

And we again answered, 'Yes.'

Then she joined our hands and kissed us on the forehead, and we again prayed silently. Then the priest came through the door near the altar, and blessed us all three; and a song, sung by the other holy men, sounded from behind the altar screen, and the bond of eternal friendship was concluded. When we rose, I saw my mother standing by the church door weeping heartily.

How cheerful it was now, in our little hut, and by the springs of Delphi! On the evening before his departure, Aphtanides sat thoughtful with me on the declivity of a mountain; his arm was flung round my waist, and mine was round his neck: we spoke of the sorrows of Greece, and of the men whom the country could trust. Every thought of our souls lay clear before each of us, and I seized his hand.

'One thing thou must still know, one thing that till now has been a secret between myself and Heaven. My whole soul is filled with love! with a love stronger than the love I bear to my mother and to thee!'

'And whom do you love?' asked Aphtanides, and his face and neck grew red as fire.

'I love Anastasia,' I replied – and his hand trembled in mine, and he became pale as a corpse. I saw it; I understood the cause; and I believe *my* hand trembled. I bent towards him, kissed his forehead, and whispered, 'I have never spoken of it to her, and perhaps she does not love me. Brother, think of this: I have seen her daily; she has grown up beside me, and has become a part of my soul!'

'And she shall be thine!' he exclaimed, 'thine! I may not deceive thee, nor will I do so. I also love her; but tomorrow I depart. In a year we shall see each other once more, and then you will be married, will you not? I have a little gold of my own: it shall be thine. Thou must, thou shalt take it.'

And we wandered home silently across the mountain. It was late in the evening when we stood at my mother's door.

Anastasia held the lamp upwards as we entered: my mother was not there. She gazed at Aphtanides with a strangely mournful gaze.

'Tomorrow you are going from us,' she said: 'I am very sorry for it.'

'Sorry!' he repeated, and in his voice there seemed a trouble as great as the grief I myself felt. I could not speak, but he seized her hand, and said, 'Our brother yonder loves you, and he is dear to you, is he not? His very silence is a proof of his affection.'

Anastasia trembled and burst into tears. Then I saw no one but her, thought of none but her, and threw my arms round her, and said, 'I love thee!' She pressed her lips to mine, and flung her arms round my neck; but the lamp had fallen to the ground, and all was dark around us – dark as in the heart of poor Aphtanides.

Before daybreak he rose, kissed us all, said farewell, and went away. He had given all his money to my mother for us. Anastasia was my betrothed, and a few days afterwards she became my wife.

A Rose from the Grave of Homer

ALL THE songs of the East tell of the love of the nightingale for the rose; in the silent starlit nights the winged songster serenades his fragrant flower. Not far from Smyrna, under the lofty plane trees, where the merchant drives his loaded camels, that proudly lift their long necks and tramp clumsily over the holy ground, I saw a hedge of roses. Wild pigeons flew among the branches of the high trees, and their wings glistened, while a sunbeam glided over them, as if they were of mother-o'-pearl.

The rose hedge bore a flower which was the most beautiful among all, and the nightingale sang to her of his woes; but the Rose was silent – not a dewdrop lay, like a tear of sympathy, upon her leaves: she bent down over a few great stones.

'Here rests the greatest singer of the world!' said the Rose: 'over his tomb will I pour out my fragrance, and on it I will let fall my leaves when the storm tears them off. He who sang of Troy became earth, and from that earth I have sprung. I, a rose from the grave of Homer, am too lofty to bloom for a poor nightingale!'

And the nightingale sang himself to death.

The camel driver came with his loaded camels and his black slaves: his little son found the dead bird, and buried the little songster in the grave of the great Homer. And the Rose trembled in the wind. The evening came, and the Rose wrapped her leaves more closely together, and dreamed thus:

'It was a fair sunshiny day; a crowd of strangers drew near, for they had undertaken a pilgrimage to the grave of Homer. Among the strangers was a singer from the North, the home of clouds and of the Northern Lights. He plucked the Rose, placed it in a book, and carried it away into another part of the world, to his distant father-land. The Rose faded with grief, and lay in the narrow book, which he opened in his home, saying, "Here is a rose from the grave of Homer." '

This the flower dreamed; and she awoke and trembled in the wind. A drop of dew fell from the leaves upon the singer's grave. The sun rose, the day became warm, and the Rose glowed more beauteous than before; she was in her own warm Asia. Then footsteps were heard, and Frankish strangers came, such as the Rose had seen in her dream; and among the strangers was a poet from the North: he plucked the Rose, pressed a kiss upon her fresh mouth, and carried her away to the home of the clouds and of the Northern Lights.

Like a mummy the flower corpse now rests in his *Iliad*, and, as in a dream, she hears him open the book and say, 'Here is a rose from the grave of Homer.'

Ole Luk-Oie

THERE'S nobody in the whole world who knows so many stories as Ole Luk-Oie. He can tell capital histories.

Well on in the evening, when the children still sit nicely at table, or upon their stools, Ole Luk-Oie comes. He comes up the stairs quite softly, for he walks in his socks: he opens the door noiselessly, and *whisk!* he squirts sweet milk in the children's eyes, a small, small stream, but enough to prevent them from keeping their eyes open; and thus they cannot see him. He creeps just among them, and blows softly upon their necks, and this makes their heads heavy. Yes, but it doesn't hurt them, for Ole Luk-Oie is very fond of the children; he only wants them to be quiet, and *that* they are not until they are taken to bed: they are to be quiet that he may tell them stories.

When the children sleep, Ole Luk-Oie sits down upon their bed. He is well dressed: his coat is of silk, but it is impossible to say of what colour, for it shines red, green, and blue, according as he turns. Under each arm he carries an umbrella: the one with pictures on it he spreads over the good children, and then they dream all night the most glorious stories; but on his other umbrella nothing at all is painted: this he spreads over the naughty children, and these sleep in a dull way, and when they awake in the morning they have not dreamed of anything.

Now we shall hear how Ole Luk-Oie, every evening through one whole week, came to a little boy named Hjalmar, and what he told him. There are seven stories, for there are seven days in the week.

Monday

'Listen,' said Ole Luk-Oie in the evening, when he had put Hjalmar to bed; 'now I'll decorate.'

And all the flowers in the flowerpots became great trees, stretching

out their long branches under the ceiling of the room and along the walls, so that the whole room looked like a beauteous bower; and all the twigs were covered with flowers, and each flower was more beautiful than a rose, and smelt so sweet that one wanted to eat it – it was sweeter than jam. The fruit gleamed like gold, and there were cakes bursting with raisins. It was incomparably beautiful. But at the same time a terrible wail sounded from the table drawer, where Hjalmar's school-book lay.

'Whatever can that be?' said Ole Luk-Oie; and he went to the table, and opened the drawer. It was the slate which was suffering from convulsions, for a wrong number had got into the sum, so that it was nearly falling in pieces; the slate pencil tugged and jumped at its string, as if it had been a little dog who wanted to help the sum; but he could not. And thus there was a great lamentation in Hjalmar's copy-book; it was quite terrible to hear. On each page the great letters stood in a row, one underneath the other, and each with a little one at its side; that was the copy; and next to these were a few more letters which thought they looked just like the first; and these Hjalmar had written; but they lay down just as if they had tumbled over the pencil lines on which they were to stand.

'See, this is how you should hold yourselves,' said the Copy. 'Look, sloping in this way, with a powerful swing!'

'Oh, we should be very glad to do that,' replied Hjalmar's Letters, 'but we cannot; we are too weakly.'

'Then you must take medicine,' said Ole Luk-Oie.

'Oh, no,' cried they; and they immediately stood up so gracefully that it was beautiful to behold.

'Yes, now we cannot tell any stories,' said Ole Luk-Oie; 'now I must exercise them. One, two! one, two!' and thus he exercised the Letters; and they stood quite slender, and as beautiful as any copy can be. But when Ole Luk-Oie went away, and Hjalmar looked at them next morning, they were as weak and miserable as ever.

Tuesday

As soon as Hjalmar was in bed, Ole Luk-Oie touched all the furniture in the room with his little magic squirt, and they immediately began to converse together, and each one spoke of itself, with the exception of the spittoon, which stood silent, and was vexed that they should be so vain as to speak only of themselves, and think only of themselves, without any regard for him who stood so modestly in the corner for everyone's use.

Over the chest of drawers hung a great picture in a gilt frame – it was a landscape. One saw therein large old trees, flowers in the grass, and a large lake with a river which flowed round about a forest, past many castles, and far out into the wide ocean.

Ole Luk-Oie touched the painting with his magic squirt, and the birds in it began to sing, the branches of the trees stirred, and the clouds began to move across it; one could see their shadows glide over the landscape.

Now Ole Luk-Oie lifted little Hjalmar up to the frame, and put the boy's feet into the picture, just in the high grass; and there he stood;

and the sun shone upon him through the branches of the trees. He ran to the water, and seated himself in a little boat which lay there; it was painted red and white, the sails gleamed like silver, and six swans, each with a gold circlet round its neck and a bright blue star on its forehead, drew the boat past the great wood, where the trees told of robbers and witches, and the flowers told of the graceful little elves, and of what the butterflies had told them.

Gorgeous fishes, with scales like silver and gold, swam after their boat; sometimes they gave a spring, so that it splashed in the water; and birds, blue and red, little and great, flew after them in two long rows; the gnats danced, and the cockchafers said, 'Boom! boom!' They all wanted to follow Hjalmar, and each one had a story to tell.

That *was* a pleasure voyage. Sometimes the forest was thick and dark, sometimes like a glorious garden full of sunlight and flowers; and there were great palaces of glass and of marble; on the balconies stood Princesses, and these were all little girls whom Hjalmar knew well – he had already played with them. Each one stretched forth her hand, and held out the prettiest sugar heart which ever a cake-woman could sell; and Hjalmar took hold of each sugar heart as he passed by, and the Princess held fast, so that each of them got a piece – she the smaller share, and Hjalmar the larger. At each palace little Princes stood sentry. They shouldered golden swords, and caused raisins and tin soldiers to shower down: one could see that they were real Princes. Sometimes Hjalmar sailed through forests, sometimes through great halls or through the midst of a town. He also came to the town where his nurse lived, who had carried him in her arms when he was quite a little boy, and who had always been so kind to him; and she nodded and beckoned, and sang the pretty verse she had made herself and had sent to Hjalmar.

> I've loved thee, and kissed thee, Hjalmar, dear boy;
> I've watched thee waking and sleeping;
> May the good Lord guard thee in sorrow, in joy,
> And have thee in His keeping.

And all the birds sang too, the flowers danced on their stalks, and the old trees nodded, just as if Ole Luk-Oie had been telling stories to *them*.

Wednesday

How the rain was streaming down without! Hjalmar could hear it in his sleep; and when Ole Luk-Oie opened a window, the water stood right up to the window-sill: there was quite a lake outside, and a noble ship lay close by the house.

'If thou wilt sail with me, little Hjalmar,' said Ole Luk-Oie, 'thou canst voyage tonight to foreign climes, and be back again tomorrow.'

And Hjalmar suddenly stood in his Sunday clothes upon the glorious ship, and immediately the weather became fine, and they sailed through the streets, and steered round by the church; and now everything was one great wild ocean. They sailed on until land was no longer to be seen, and they saw a number of storks, who also came from their home, and were travelling towards the hot countries: these storks flew in a row, one behind the other, and they had already flown far – far! One of them was so weary that his wings would scarcely carry him farther: he was the very last in the row, and soon remained a great way behind the rest; at last he sank, with outspread wings, deeper and deeper; he gave a few more strokes with his pinions, but it was of no use; now he touched the rigging of the ship with his feet, then he glided down from the sail, and – bump! – he stood upon the deck.

Now the cabin boy took him and put him into the hencoop with the Fowls, Ducks, and Turkeys; the poor Stork stood among them quite embarrassed.

'Just look at the fellow!' said all the Fowls.

And the Turkey-cock swelled himself up as much as ever he could, and asked the Stork who he was; and the Ducks walked backwards and quacked to each other, 'Quackery! quackery!'

And the Stork told them of hot Africa, of the pyramids, and of the ostrich, which runs like a wild horse through the desert; but the Ducks did not understand what he said, and they said to one another

'We're all of the same opinion, namely, that he's stupid.'

'Yes, certainly he's stupid,' said the Turkey-cock; and he gobbled.

Then the stork was quite silent, and thought of his Africa.

'Those are wonderful thin legs of yours,' said the Turkey-cock. 'Pray, how much do they cost a yard?'

'Quack! quack! quack!' grinned all the Ducks; but the Stork pretended not to hear it at all.

'You may just as well laugh too,' said the Turkey-cock to him, 'for that was very wittily said. Or was it, perhaps, too high for you? Yes, yes, he isn't very penetrating. Let us continue to be interesting among ourselves.'

And the Hens clucked, and the Ducks quacked, 'Gick! gack! gick! gack!' It was terrible how they made fun among themselves.

But Hjalmar went to the hencoop, opened the back door, and called to the Stork; and the Stork hopped out to him on to the deck. Now he had rested, and it seemed as if he nodded at Hjalmar, to thank him. Then he spread his wings, and flew away to the warm countries; but the Fowls clucked, and the Ducks quacked, and the Turkey-cock became fiery red in the face.

'Tomorrow we shall make soup of you,' said Hjalmar; and so saying he awoke, and was lying in his little bed. It was a wonderful journey that Ole Luk-Oie had caused him to take that night.

Thursday

'I tell you what,' said Ole Luk-Oie, 'you must not be frightened. Here you shall see a little Mouse,' and he held out his hand with the pretty little creature in it. 'It has come to invite you to a wedding. There are two little Mice here who are going to enter into the marriage state tonight. They live under the floor of your mother's store-closet: that is said to be a charming dwelling-place!'

'But how can I get through the little mouse-hole in the floor?' asked Hjalmar.

'Let me manage that,' said Ole Luk-Oie. 'I will make you small.'

And he touched Hjalmar with his magic squirt, and the boy began to shrink and shrink, until he was not so long as a finger.

'Now you may borrow the uniform of a tin soldier: I think it would fit you, and it looks well to wear a uniform when one is in society.'

'Yes, certainly,' said Hjalmar.

And in a moment he was dressed like the smartest of tin soldiers.

'Will you not be kind enough to take a seat in your mamma's thimble?' asked the Mouse. 'Then I shall have the honour of drawing you.'

'Will the young lady really take so much trouble?' cried Hjalmar.

And thus they drove to the mouse's wedding. First they came into a long passage beneath the boards, which was only just so high that they could drive through it in the thimble; and the whole passage was lit up with rotten wood.

'Is there not a delicious smell here?' observed the Mouse. 'The entire road has been greased with bacon rinds, and there can be nothing more exquisite.'

Now they came into the festive hall. On the right hand stood all the little lady mice; and they whispered and giggled as if they were making fun of each other; on the left stood all the gentlemen mice, stroking their whiskers with their fore paws; and in the centre of the hall the bridegroom and bride might be seen standing in a hollow cheese rind, and kissing each other terribly before all the guests; for of course they were engaged, and were just about to be married.

More and more strangers kept flocking in. One mouse was nearly treading another to death; and the happy couple had stationed themselves just in the doorway, so that one could neither come in nor go out. Like the passage, the room had been greased with bacon rinds, and that was the entire banquet; but for the dessert a pea was produced, in which a mouse belonging to the family had bitten the name of the betrothed pair – that is to say, the first letter of the name: that was something quite out of the common way.

All the mice said it was a beautiful wedding, and that the entertainment had been very agreeable. And then Hjalmar drove home again: he had really been in grand company; but he had been obliged to shrink in, to make himself little, and to put on a tin soldier's uniform.

Friday

'It is wonderful how many grown-up people there are who would be glad to have me!' said Ole Luk-Oie; 'especially those who have done something wrong. "Good little Ole," they say to me, "we cannot close our eyes, and so we lie all night and see our evil deeds, which sit on the bedstead like ugly little goblins, and throw hot water over us; will you not come and drive them away, so that we may have a good sleep?" – and then they sigh deeply – "we would really be glad to pay for it. Good-night, Ole; the money lies on the window sill." But I do nothing for money,' says Ole Luk-Oie.

'What shall we do this evening?' asked Hjalmar.

'I don't know if you care to go to another wedding tonight. It is of a different kind from that of yesterday. Your sister's great doll, that looks like a man, and is called Hermann, is going to marry the doll Bertha. Moreover, it is the doll's birthday, and therefore they will receive very many presents.'

'Yes, I know that,' replied Hjalmar. 'Whenever the dolls want new clothes my sister lets them either keep their birthday or celebrate a wedding; that has certainly happened a hundred times already.'

'Yes, but tonight is the hundred and first wedding; and when number one hundred and one is past, it is all over; and that is why it will be so splendid. Only look!'

And Hjalmar looked at the table. There stood the little cardboard house with the windows illuminated, and in front of it all the tin soldiers were presenting arms. The bride and bridegroom sat quite thoughtful, and with good reason, on the floor, leaning against a leg of the table. And Ole Luk-Oie, dressed up in the grandmother's black gown, married them to each other. When the ceremony was over, all the pieces of furniture struck up the following beautiful song, which the pencil had written for them. It was sung to the melody of the soldiers' tattoo.

> Let the song swell like the rushing wind,
> In honour of those who this day are joined,
> Although they stand here so stiff and blind,
> Because they are both of a leathery kind.
> Hurrah! hurrah! though they're deaf and blind,
> Let the song swell like the rushing wind.

And now they received presents – but they had declined to accept provisions of any kind, for they intended to live on love.

'Shall we now go into a summer lodging, or start on a journey?' asked the bridegroom.

And the Swallow, who was a great traveller, and the old yard Hen, who had brought up five broods of chickens, were consulted on the subject. And the Swallow told of the beautiful warm climes, where the grapes hung in ripe heavy clusters, where the air is mild, and the mountains glow with colours unknown here.

'But they have not our green colewort there!' objected the Hen. 'I was in the country, with my children one summer. There was a sand pit, in which we could walk about and scratch; and we had the *entrée* to a garden where green colewort grew: Oh, how green it was! I cannot imagine anything more beautiful.'

'But one cole plant looks just like another,' said the Swallow; 'and the weather here is often so bad.'

'One is accustomed to that,' said the Hen.

'But it is so cold here, it freezes.'

'That is good for the coleworts!' said the Hen. 'Besides, it can also be warm. Did we not, four years ago, have a summer which lasted five weeks? it was so hot here that one could scarcely breathe; and then we have not all the poisonous animals that infest these warm countries of yours, and we are free from robbers. He is a villain who does not consider our country the most beautiful – he certainly does not deserve to be here!' And then the Hen wept, and went on: 'I have also travelled. I rode in a coop above fifty miles; and there is no pleasure at all in travelling!'

'Yes, the Hen is a sensible woman!' said the doll Bertha. 'I don't think anything either of travelling among mountains, for you only have to go up, and then down again. No, we will go into the sand pit beyond the gate, and walk about in the colewort-patch.'

And so it was settled.

Saturday

'Am I to hear some stories now?' asked little Hjalmar, as soon as Ole Luk-Oie had got him into bed.

'This evening we have no time for that,' replied Ole; and he spread his fine umbrella over the lad. 'Only look at these Chinamen!'

And the whole umbrella looked like a great China dish, with blue trees and pointed bridges with little Chinamen upon them, who stood there nodding their heads.

'We must have the whole world prettily decked out for tomorrow morning,' said Ole, 'for that is a holiday – it is Sunday. I will go to the church steeples to see that the little church goblins are polishing the bells, that they may sound sweetly. I will go out into the field, and see if the breezes are blowing the dust from the grass and leaves; and, what is the greatest work of all, I will bring down all the stars, to polish them. I take them in my apron; but first each one must be numbered, and the holes in which they are fixed up there must be numbered likewise, so that they may be placed in the same holes again; otherwise they would not sit fast, and we should have too many shooting stars, for one after another would fall down.'

'Hark-ye! Do you know, Mr Luk-Oie,' said an old Portrait which hung on the wall where Hjalmar slept, 'I am Hjalmar's great-grand-father. I thank you for telling the boy stories; but you must not confuse his ideas. The stars cannot be taken down and polished! The stars are world-orbs, just like our own earth, and that is just the good thing about them.'

'I thank you, old great-grandfather,' said Ole Luk-Oie, 'I thank you! You are the head of the family. You are the ancestral head; but I am older than you! I am an old heathen: the Romans and Greeks called me the Dream God. I have been in the noblest houses, and am admitted there still! I know how to act with great people and with small. Now you may tell your own story!' And Ole Luk-Oie took his umbrella, and went away.

'Well, well! May one not even give an opinion nowadays?' grumbled the old Portrait. And Hjalmar awoke.

Sunday

'Good-evening!' said Ole Luk-Oie; and Hjalmar nodded, and then ran and turned his great-grandfather's Portrait against the wall, that it might not interrupt them, as it had done yesterday.

'Now you must tell me stories; about the five green peas that lived in one pod, and about the cock's foot that paid court to the hen's foot, and of the darning-needle who gave herself such airs because she thought herself a sewing needle.'

'There may be too much of a good thing!' said Ole Luk-Oie. 'You know that I prefer showing you something. I will show you my own brother. His name, like mine, is Ole Luk-Oie, but he never comes to anyone more than once; and he takes him to whom he comes upon his horse, and tells him stories. He only knows two. One of these is so exceedingly beautiful that no one in the world can imagine it, and the other so horrible and dreadful that it cannot be described.'

And then Ole Luk-Oie lifted little Hjalmar up to the window, and said, 'There you will see my brother, the other Ole Luk-Oie. They also call him Death! Do you see, he does not look so terrible as they make him in the picture-books, where he is only a skeleton. No, that is silver embroidery that he has on his coat; that is a splendid hussar's uniform; a mantle of black velvet flies behind him over the horse. See how he gallops along!'

And Hjalmar saw how this Ole Luk-Oie rode away, and took young people as well as old upon his horse. Some of them he put before him, and some behind; but he always asked first, 'How stands it with the mark-book?' 'Well,' they all replied. 'Yes, let me see it myself,' he said. And then each one had to show him the book; and those who had 'very well' and 'remarkably well' written in their books, were placed in front of his horse, and a lovely story was told to them; while those who had 'middling' or 'tolerably well,' had to sit up behind, and hear a very terrible story indeed. They trembled and wept, and wanted to jump off the horse, but this they could not do, for they had all, as it were, grown fast to it.

'But Death is a most splendid Ole Luk-Oie,' said Hjalmar. 'I am not afraid of him!'

'Nor need you be,' replied Ole Luk-Oie; 'but see that you have a good mark-book!'

'Yes, that is instructive!' muttered the great-grand-father's Picture. 'It is of some use after all giving one's opinion.' And now he was satisfied.

You see, that is the story of Ole Luk-Oie; and now he may tell you more himself, this evening!

The Rose-Elf

IN THE midst of a garden grew a rose bush, which was quite covered with roses; and in one of them, the most beautiful of all, there dwelt an elf. He was so tiny that no human eye could see him. Behind every leaf in the rose he had a bedroom. He was as well formed and beautiful as any child could be, and had wings that reached from his shoulders to his feet. Oh, what a fragrance there was in his rooms! and how clear and bright were the walls! They were made of the pale pink rose leaves.

The whole day he rejoiced in the warm sunshine, flew from flower to flower, danced on the wings of the flying butterfly, and measured how many steps he would have to take to pass along all the roads and crossroads that are marked out on a single linden leaf. What we call veins on the leaf were to him high roads and crossroads. Yes, those were long roads for him! Before he had finished his journey the sun went down, for he had begun his work too late!

It became very cold, the dew fell, and the wind blew: now the best thing to be done was to come home. He made what haste he could, but the rose had shut itself up, and he could not get in; not a single rose stood open. The poor little elf was very much frightened. He had never been out at night before; he had always slumbered sweetly and comfortably behind the warm rose leaves. Oh, it certainly would be the death of him.

At the other end of the garden there was, he knew, an arbour of fine honeysuckle. The flowers looked like great painted horns, and he wished to go down into one of them to sleep till the next day.

He flew thither. Silence! two people were in the arbour – a handsome young man and a young girl. They sat side by side, and wished that they need never part. They loved each other better than a good child loves its father and mother.

'Yet we must part!' said the young man. 'Your brother does not like us, therefore he sends me away on an errand so far over mountains and seas. Farewell, my sweet bride, for that you shall be!'

And they kissed each other, and the young girl wept, and gave him a rose. But, before she gave it him, she impressed a kiss so firmly and closely upon it that the flower opened. Then the little elf flew into it, and leaned his head against the delicate fragrant walls. But he could plainly hear them say 'Farewell! farewell!' and he felt that the rose was placed on the young man's heart. Oh, how that heart beat! the little elf could not go to sleep, it thumped so.

But not long did the rose rest undisturbed on that breast. The man took it out, and as he went lonely through the wood, he kissed the flower so often and so fervently that the little elf was almost crushed. He could feel through the leaf how the man's lips burned, and the rose itself had opened, as if under the hottest noonday sun.

Then came another man, gloomy and wicked; he was the bad brother of the pretty maiden. He drew out a sharp knife, and while the other kissed the rose, the bad man stabbed him to death, and then, cutting off his head, buried both head and body in the soft earth under the linden tree.

'Now he's forgotten and gone!' thought the wicked brother; 'he will never come back again. He was to have taken a long journey over mountains and seas. One can easily lose one's life, and he has lost his. He cannot come back again, and my sister dare not ask news of him from me.'

Then with his feet he shuffled dry leaves over the loose earth, and went home in the dark night. But he did not go alone, as he thought; the little elf accompanied him. The elf sat in a dry, rolled-up linden leaf that had fallen on the wicked man's hair as he dug the grave. The hat was now placed over the leaf, and it was very dark in the hat, and the elf trembled with fear and with anger at the evil deed.

In the morning hour the bad man got home; he took off his hat, and went into his sister's bedroom. There lay the beautiful blooming girl, dreaming of him whom she loved from her heart, and of whom she now believed that he was going across the mountains and through the forests. And the wicked brother bent over her, and laughed hideously, as only a fiend can laugh. Then the dry leaf fell out of his hair upon the coverlet; but he did not notice it, and he went out to sleep a little himself in the morning hour. But the elf slipped forth from the withered leaf, placed himself in the ear of the sleeping girl, and told her, as in a dream, the dreadful history of the murder; described to her the place where her brother had slain her lover and buried his body; told her of the blooming linden tree close by it, and said, 'That you may not think it is only a dream that I have told you, you will find on your bed a withered leaf.'

And she found it when she awoke. Oh, what bitter tears she wept, and to no one could she confide her sorrow. The window stood open the whole day: the little elf could easily get out to the roses and all the other flowers, but he could not find it in his heart to quit the afflicted maiden. In the window stood a plant, a monthly rose bush: he seated himself in one of the flowers, and looked at the poor girl. Her brother often came into the room, and, in spite of his wicked deed, he always seemed cheerful, but she dared not say a word of the grief that was in her heart.

As soon as the night came, she crept out of the house, went to the wood, to the place where the linden tree grew, removed the leaves from the ground, turned up the earth, and immediately found him who had been slain. Oh, how she wept, and prayed that she might die also!

Gladly would she have taken the body home with her, but that she could not do. Then she took the pale head with the closed eyes, kissed the cold mouth, and shook the earth out of the beautiful hair. 'That I will keep,' she said. And when she had laid earth upon the dead body, she took the head, and a little sprig of the jasmine that bloomed in the wood where he was buried, home with her.

As soon as she came into her room, she brought the greatest flower-pot she could find: in this she laid the dead man's head, strewed earth upon it and then planted the jasmine twig in the pot.

'Farewell! farewell!' whispered the little elf: he could endure it no longer to see all this pain, and therefore flew out to his rose in the garden. But the rose was faded; only a few pale leaves clung to the wild bush.

'Alas! how soon everything good and beautiful passes away!' sighed the elf.

At last he found another rose, and this became his house; behind its delicate fragrant leaves he could hide himself and dwell.

Every morning he flew to the window of the poor girl, and she was always standing weeping by the flowerpot. The bitter tears fell upon the jasmine spray, and every day, as the girl became paler and paler, the twig stood there fresher and greener, and one shoot after another sprouted forth, little white buds burst forth, and these she kissed. But the bad brother scolded his sister, and asked if she had gone mad. He could not bear it, and could not imagine why she was always weeping over the flowerpot. He did not know what closed eyes were there, what red lips had there faded into earth. And she bowed her head upon the flowerpot, and the little elf of the rose bush found her slumbering there. Then he seated himself in her ear, told her of the evening in the arbour, of the fragrance of the rose, and the love of the elves. And she dreamed a marvellously sweet dream, and while she dreamed her life passed away. She had died a quiet death, and she was in heaven with him whom she loved.

And the jasmine opened its great white bells. They smelt quite peculiarly sweet; it could not weep in any other way over the dead one.

But the wicked brother looked at the beautiful blooming plant, and took it for himself as an inheritance, and put it in his sleeping-room, close by his bed, for it was glorious to look upon and its fragrance was sweet and refreshing. The little Rose-elf followed, and went from flower to flower – for in each dwelt a little soul – and told of the murdered young man, whose head was now earth beneath the earth, and told of the evil brother and of the poor sister.

'We know it!' said each soul in the flowers, 'we know it: have we not sprung from the eyes and lips of the murdered man? We know it! we know it!'

And then they nodded in a strange fashion with their heads.

The Rose-elf could not at all understand how they could be so quiet, and he flew out to the bees that were gathering honey, and told them the story of the wicked brother. And the bees told it to their Queen, and the Queen commanded that they should all kill the murderer next morning. But in the night – it was the first night that followed upon the sister's death – when the brother was sleeping in his bed, close to the fragrant jasmine, each flower opened, and invisible, but armed with poisonous spears, the flower-souls came out and seated themselves in his ear, and told him bad dreams, and then flew across his lips and pricked his tongue with the poisonous spears.

'Now we have avenged the dead man!' they said, and flew back into the jasmine's white bells.

When the morning came and the windows of the bedchamber were opened, the Rose-elf and the Queen Bee and the whole swarm of bees rushed in to kill him.

But he was dead already. People stood around his bed, and said, 'The scent of the jasmine has killed him!' Then the Rose-elf understood the revenge of the flowers, and told it to the Queen and to the bees, and the Queen hummed with the whole swarm around the flowerpot. The bees were not to be driven away. Then a man carried away the flowerpot, and one of the bees stung him in the hand, so that he let the pot fall, and it broke in pieces.

Then they beheld the whitened skull, and knew that the dead man on the bed was a murderer.

And the Queen Bee hummed in the air, and sang of the revenge of the bees, and of the Rose-elf, and said that behind the smallest leaf there dwells One who can bring the evil to light, and repay it.

The Swineherd

THERE was once a poor Prince, who had a kingdom which was quite small, but still it was large enough that he could marry upon it, and that is what he wanted to do.

Now, it was certainly somewhat bold of him to say to the Emperor's daughter, 'Will you have me?' But he did venture it, for his name was famous far and wide: there were hundreds of Princesses who would have been glad to say yes; but did *she* say so? Well, we shall see.

On the grave of the Prince's father there grew a rose bush, a very beautiful rose bush. It bloomed only every fifth year, and even then it bore only a single rose, but what a rose that was! It was so sweet that whoever smelt at it forgot all sorrow and trouble. And then he had a nightingale, which could sing as if all possible melodies were collected in its little throat. This rose and this nightingale the Princess was to have, and therefore they were put into great silver cases and sent to her.

The Emperor caused the presents to be carried before him into the great hall where the Princess was playing at 'visiting' with her maids of honour (they did nothing else), and when she saw the great silver cases with the presents in them, she clapped her hands with joy.

'If it were only a little pussy-cat!' said she. But then came out the splendid rose.

'Oh, how pretty it is made!' said all the court ladies.

'It is more than pretty,' said the Emperor, 'it is charming.' But the Princess felt it, and then she almost began to cry.

'Fie, papa!' she said, 'it is not artificial, it's a *natural* rose!'

'Fie,' said all the court ladies, 'it's a natural one!'

'Let us first see what is in the other case before we get angry,' said the Emperor. And then the nightingale came out; it sang so beautifully that they did not at once know what to say against it.

Superbe! charmant!' said the maids of honour, for they all spoke French, the one worse than the other.

'How that bird reminds me of the late Empress's musical snuff-box,' said an old cavalier. 'Yes, it is the same tone, the same expression.'

'Yes,' said the Emperor; and then he wept like a little child.

'I really hope it is not a natural bird,' said the Princess.

'Yes, it is a natural bird,' said they who had brought it.

'Then let the bird fly away,' said the Princess; and she would by no means allow the Prince to come.

But the Prince was not at all dismayed. He stained his face brown and black, drew his hat down over his brows, and knocked at the door.

'Good-day, Emperor,' he said: 'could I not be employed here in the castle?'

'Well,' replied the Emperor, 'but there are so many who want places; but let me see, I want someone who can keep the pigs, for we have many of them.'

So the Prince was appointed the Emperor's swineherd. He received a miserable small room down by the pigsty, and here he was obliged to stay; but all day long he sat and worked, and when it was evening he had finished a neat little pot, with bells all round it, and when the pot boiled these bells rang out prettily and played the old melody –

> Oh, my darling Augustine,
> All is lost, all is lost.

But the cleverest thing about the whole arrangement was, that by holding one's finger in the steam from the pot, one could at once smell what food was being cooked at every hearth in the town. That was quite a different thing from the rose.

Now the Princess came with all her maids of honour, and when she heard the melody she stood still and looked quite pleased; for she, too, could play 'Oh, my darling Augustine.' It was the only thing she could play, but then she played it with one finger.

'Why, that is what I play!' she cried. 'He must be an educated swine-herd! Hark-ye: go down and ask the price of the instrument.'

So one of the maids of honour had to go down; but first she put on a pair of pattens.

'What do you want for the pot?' enquired the lady.

'I want ten kisses from the Princess,' replied the swineherd.

'Heaven preserve us!' exclaimed the maid of honour.

'Well, I won't sell it for less,' said the swineherd.

'Well, what did he say?' asked the Princess.

'I really can't repeat it, it is so shocking,' replied the lady.

'Well, you can whisper it in my ear.' And the lady whispered it to her. 'He is very rude,' declared the Princess; and she went away. But when she had gone a little way, the bells sounded so prettily:

> Oh, my darling Augustine,
> All is lost, all is lost.

'Hark-ye,' said the Princess: 'ask him if he will take ten kisses from my maids of honour.'

'No, thanks,' replied the swineherd: 'ten kisses from the Princess, or I shall keep my pot.'

'How tiresome that is!' cried the Princess. 'But at least you must stand round me, so that nobody sees it.'

And the maids of honour stood round her, and spread out their dresses, and then the swineherd received ten kisses, and she received the pot.

Then there was rejoicing! All the evening and all the day long the pot was kept boiling; there was not a kitchen hearth in the whole town of which they did not know what it had cooked, at the shoemaker's as well as the chamberlain's. The ladies danced with pleasure, and clapped their hands.

'We know who will have sweet soup and pancakes for dinner, and who has hasty pudding and cutlets; how interesting that is!'

'Very interesting!' said the head lady-superintendent.

'Yes, but keep counsel, for I'm the Emperor's daughter.'

'Yes, certainly,' said all.

The swineherd, that is to say, the Prince – but of course they did not know but that he was a real swineherd – let no day pass by without

doing something, and so he made a rattle; when any person swung this rattle, he could play all the waltzes, hops, and polkas that have been known since the creation of the world.

'But that is *superbe*!' cried the Princess, as she went past. 'I have never heard a finer composition. Hark-ye: go down and ask what the instrument costs; but I give no more kisses.'

'He demands a hundred kisses from the Princess,' said the maid of honour who had gone down to make the enquiry.

'I think he must be mad!' exclaimed the Princess; and she went away; but when she had gone a little distance she stood still. 'One must encourage art,' she observed. 'I am the Emperor's daughter! Tell him he shall receive ten kisses, like last time, and he may take the rest from my maids of honour.'

'Ah, but we don't like to do it!' said the maids of honour.

'That's all nonsense!' retorted the Princess, 'and if I can allow myself to be kissed, you can too; remember, I give you board and wages.'

And so the maids of honour had to go down to him again.

'A hundred kisses from the Princess,' said he, 'or each shall keep his own.'

'Stand round me,' said she then; and all the maids of honour stood round her while he kissed the Princess.

'What is that crowd down by the pigsty?' asked the Emperor, who had stepped out to the balcony. He rubbed his eyes, and put on his spectacles. 'Why, those are the maids of honour, at their tricks, yonder; I shall have to go down to them.'

And he pulled up his slippers behind, for they were shoes that he had trodden down at heel. Gracious mercy, how he hurried! So soon as he came down in the courtyard, he went quite softly, and the maids of honour were too busy counting the kisses, and seeing fair play, to notice the Emperor. Then he stood on tiptoe.

'What's that?' said he, when he saw that there was kissing going on; and he hit them on the head with his slipper, just as the swineherd was taking the eighty-sixth kiss.

'Be off!' said the Emperor, for he was angry.

And the Princess and the swineherd were both expelled from his dominions. So there she stood and cried, the rain streamed down, and the swineherd scolded.

'Oh, miserable wretch that I am!' said the Princess; 'if I had only taken the handsome Prince! Oh, how unhappy I am!'

Then the swineherd went behind a tree, washed the stains from his face, threw away the shabby clothes, and stepped forth in his princely attire, so handsome that the Princess was fain to bow before him.

'I have come to this, that I despise you,' said he. 'You would not have an honest Prince; you did not value the rose and the nightingale, but for a plaything you kissed the swineherd, and now you have your reward.'

And then he went into his kingdom and shut the door in her face, and put the bar on. So now she might stand outside and sing:

> Oh, my darling Augustine,
> All is lost, all is lost.

The Buckwheat

OFTEN, after a thunderstorm, when one passes a field in which Buckwheat is growing, it appears quite blackened and singed. It is just as if a flame of fire had passed across it; and then the countryman says, 'It got that from lightning.' But why has it received that? I will tell you what the Sparrow told me about it, and the Sparrow heard it from an old Willow Tree which stood by a Buckwheat field, and still stands there. It is quite a great venerable Willow Tree, but wrinkled and old: it is burst in the middle, and grass and brambles grow out of the cleft; the tree bends forward, and the branches hang quite down to the ground, as if they were long, green hair.

On all the fields round about corn was growing, not only rye and barley, but also oats, yes, the most capital oats, which when ripe look like a number of little yellow canary birds sitting upon a spray. The corn stood smiling, and the richer an ear was, the deeper did it bend in pious humility.

But there was also a field of Buckwheat, and this field was exactly opposite to the old Willow Tree. The Buckwheat did not bend at all, like the rest of the grain, but stood up proudly and stiffly.

'I'm as rich as any corn ear,' it said. 'Moreover, I'm very much handsomer: my flowers are beautiful as the blossoms of the apple tree: it's quite a delight to look upon me and mine. Do you know anything more splendid than we are, you old Willow Tree?'

And the Willow Tree nodded his head, just as if he would have said, 'Yes, certainly I do!'

But the Buckwheat spread itself out from mere vainglory, and said, 'The stupid tree! he's so old that the grass grows in his body.'

Now a terrible storm came on: all the field flowers folded their leaves together or bowed their little heads while the storm passed over them, but the Buckwheat stood erect in its pride.

'Bend your head like us,' said the Flowers.

'I've not the slightest cause to do so,' replied the Buckwheat.

'Bend your head as we do,' cried the corn. 'Now the angel of the storm comes flying on. He has wings that reach from the clouds just down to the earth, and he'll cut you right in two before you can cry for mercy.'

'Yes, but I won't bend,' quoth the Buckwheat.

'Shut up your flowers and bend your leaves,' said the old Willow Tree. 'Don't look up at the lightning when the cloud bursts: even men do not do that, for in the lightning one may look into heaven, but that sight dazzles even men; and what would happen to us, if we dared do so – we, the plants of the field, that are much less worthy than they?'

'Much less worthy!' cried the Buckwheat. 'Now I'll just look straight up into heaven.'

And it did so, in its pride and vainglory. It was as if the whole world were on fire, so vivid was the lightning.

When afterwards the bad weather had passed by, the flowers and the crops stood in the still, pure air, quite refreshed by the rain; but the Buckwheat was burned coal-black by the lightning, and it was now like a dead weed upon the field.

And the old Willow Tree waved its branches in the wind, and great drops of water fell down out of the green leaves just as if the tree wept.

And the Sparrows asked, 'Why do you weep? Here everything is so cheerful: see how the sun shines, see how the clouds sail on. Do you not breathe the scent of flowers and bushes? Why do you weep, Willow Tree?'

And the Willow Tree told them of the pride of the Buckwheat, of its vainglory, and of the punishment which always follows such sin.

I, who tell you this tale, have heard it from the Sparrows. They told it me one evening when I begged them to give me a story.

The Angel

WHENEVER a good child dies, an angel from heaven comes down to earth and takes the dead child in his arms, spreads out his great white wings, and flies away over all the places the child has loved, and picks quite a handful of flowers, which he carries up to the Almighty, that they may bloom in heaven more brightly than on earth. And the Father presses all the flowers to His heart; but He kisses the flower that pleases Him best, and the flower is then endowed with a voice, and can join in the great chorus of praise!

'See' – this is what an angel said, as he carried a dead child up to heaven, and the child heard, as if in a dream, and they went on over the regions of home where the little child had played, and they came through gardens with beautiful flowers – 'which of these shall we take with us to plant in heaven?' asked the angel.

Now there stood near them a slender, beautiful rose bush; but a wicked hand had broken the stem, so that all the branches, covered with half-opened buds, were hanging around, quite withered.

'The poor rose bush!' said the child. 'Take it, that it may bloom up yonder.'

And the angel took it, and kissed the child, and the little one half opened his eyes. They plucked some of the rich flowers, but also took with them the despised buttercup and the wild pansy.

'Now we have flowers,' said the child.

And the angel nodded, but he did not yet fly upwards to heaven. It was night and quite silent. They remained in the great city; they floated about there in one of the narrowest streets, where lay whole heaps of straw, ashes, and sweepings, for it had been removal-day. There lay fragments of plates, bits of plaster, rags, and old hats, and all this did not look well. And the angel pointed amid all this confusion to a few fragments of a flowerpot, and to a lump of earth which had fallen out, and which was kept together by the roots of a great dried field flower, which was of no use, and had therefore been thrown out into the street.

'We will take that with us,' said the angel. 'I will tell you why, as we fly onward.'

So they flew, and the angel related, 'Down yonder in the narrow lane, in the low cellar, lived a poor sick boy; from his childhood he had been bedridden. When he was at his best he could go up and down the room a few times, leaning on crutches; that was the utmost he could do. For a few days in summer the sunbeams would penetrate for a few hours to the front of the cellar, and when the poor boy sat there and the sun shone on him, and he looked at the red blood in his fine fingers, as he held them up before his face, they would say, "Yes, today he has been out!" He knew the forest with its beautiful vernal green only from the fact that the neighbour's son brought him the first green branch of a beech tree, and he held that up over his head, and dreamed he was in the beech wood where the sun shone and the birds sang. On a spring day the neighbour's boy also brought him field flowers, and among these was, by chance, one to which the root was hanging; and so it was planted in a flowerpot, and placed by the bed, close to the window. And the flower had been planted by a fortunate hand; and it grew, threw out new

shoots, and bore flowers every year. It became as a splendid flower garden to the sickly boy – his little treasure here on earth. He watered it, and tended it, and took care that it had the benefit of every ray of sunlight, down to the last that struggled in through the narrow window; and the flower itself was woven into his dreams, for it grew for him and gladdened his eyes, and spread its fragrance about him; and towards it he turned in death, when the Father called him. He has now been with the Almighty for a year; for a year the flower has stood forgotten in the window, and is withered; and thus, at the removal, it has been thrown out into the dust of the street. And this is the flower, the poor withered flower, which we have taken into our nosegay; for this flower has 'given more joy than the richest flower in a Queen's garden!'

'But how do you know all this?' asked the child which the angel was carrying to heaven.

'I know it,' said the angel, 'for I myself was that little boy who went on crutches! I know my flower well!'

And the child opened his eyes and looked into the glorious happy face of the angel; and at the same moment they entered the regions where there is peace and joy. And the Father pressed the dead child to His bosom, and then it received wings like the angel, and flew hand in hand with him. And the Almighty pressed all the flowers to His heart; but He kissed the dry withered field flower, and it received a voice and sang with all the angels hovering around – some near, and some in wider circles, and some in infinite distance, but all equally happy. And they all sang, little and great, the good happy child, and the poor field flower that had lain there withered, thrown among the dust, in the rubbish of the removal-day, in the narrow dark lane.

The Nightingale

I N CHINA, you must know, the Emperor is a Chinaman, and all whom he has about him are Chinamen too. It happened a good many years ago, but that's just why it's worth while to hear the story, before it is forgotten. The Emperor's palace was the most splendid in the world; it was made entirely of porcelain, very costly, but so delicate and brittle that one had to take care how one touched it. In the garden were to be seen the most wonderful flowers, and to the costliest of them silver bells were tied, which sounded, so that nobody should pass by without noticing the flowers. Yes, everything in the Emperor's garden was admirably arranged. And it extended so far, that the gardener himself did not know where the end was. If a man went on and on, he came into a glorious forest with high trees and deep lakes. The wood extended straight down to the sea, which was blue and deep; great ships could sail in beneath the branches of the trees; and in the trees lived a Nightingale, which sang so splendidly that even the poor fisherman, who had many other things to do, stopped still and listened, when he had gone out at night to take up his nets, and heard the Nightingale.

'How beautiful that is!' he said; but he was obliged to attend to his business, and thus forgot the bird. But when in the next night the bird sang again, and the fisherman heard it, he exclaimed again, 'How beautiful that is!'

From all the countries of the world travellers came to the city of the Emperor, and admired it, and the palace, and the garden, but when they heard the Nightingale, they said, 'That is the best of all!'

And the travellers told of it when they came home; and the learned men wrote many books about the town, the palace, and the garden. But they did not forget the Nightingale; that was placed highest of all; and those who were poets wrote most magnificent poems about the Nightingale in the wood by the deep lake.

The books went through all the world, and a few of them once came to the Emperor. He sat in his golden chair, and read, and read: every moment he nodded his head, for it pleased him to peruse the masterly descriptions of the city, the palace, and the garden. 'But the Nightingale is the best of all,' it stood written there.

'What's that?' exclaimed the Emperor. 'I don't know the Nightingale at all! Is there such a bird in my empire, and even in my garden? I've never heard of that. To think that I should have to learn such a thing for the first time from books!'

And hereupon he called his cavalier. This cavalier was so grand that if anyone lower in rank than himself dared to speak to him, or to ask him any question, he answered nothing but 'P!' – and that meant nothing.

'There is said to be a wonderful bird here called a Nightingale!' said the Emperor. 'They say it is the best thing in all my great empire. Why have I never heard anything about it?'

'I have never heard him named,' replied the cavalier. 'He has never been introduced at court.'

'I command that he shall appear this evening, and sing before me,' said the Emperor. 'All the world knows what I possess, and I do not know it myself!'

'I have never heard him mentioned,' said the cavalier. 'I will seek for him. I will find him.'

But where was he to be found? The cavalier ran up and down all the staircases, through halls and passages, but no one among all those whom he met had heard talk of the nightingale. And the cavalier ran back to the Emperor, and said that it must be a fable invented by the writers of books.

'Your Imperial Majesty cannot believe how much is written that is fiction, besides something that they call the black art.'

'But the book in which I read this,' said the Emperor, 'was sent to me by the high and mighty Emperor of Japan, and therefore it cannot be a falsehood. I *will* hear the Nightingale! It must be here this evening! It has my imperial favour; and if it does not come, all the court shall be trampled upon after the court has supped!'

'Tsing-pe!' said the cavalier; and again he ran up and down all the staircases, and through all the halls and corridors; and half the court ran with him, for the courtiers did not like being trampled upon.

Then there was a great enquiry after the wonderful Nightingale, which all the world knew excepting the people at court.

At last they met with a poor little girl in the kitchen, who said, 'The Nightingale? I know it well; yes, it can sing gloriously. Every evening I get leave to carry my poor sick mother the scraps from the table. She lives down by the strand, and when I get back and am tired, and rest in the wood, then I hear the Nightingale sing. And then the water comes into my eyes, and it is just as if my mother kissed me!'

'Little girl,' said the cavalier, 'I will get you a place in the kitchen, with permission to see the Emperor dine, if you will lead us to the Nightingale, for it is announced for this evening.'

So they all went out into the wood where the Nightingale was accustomed to sing; half the court went forth. When they were in the midst of their journey a cow began to low.

'Oh!' cried the court page, 'now we have it! That shows a wonderful power in so small a creature! I have certainly heard it before.'

'No, those are cows lowing!' said the little kitchen-girl. 'We are a long way from the place yet.'

Now the frogs began to croak in the marsh.

'Glorious!' said the Chinese court preacher. 'Now I hear it – it sounds just like little church bells.'

'No, those are frogs!' said the little kitchen-maid. 'But now I think we shall soon hear it.'

And then the Nightingale began to sing.

'That is it!' exclaimed the little girl. 'Listen, listen! and yonder it sits.'

And she pointed to a little grey bird up in the boughs.

'Is it possible?' cried the cavalier. 'I should never have thought it looked like that! How plain it looks! It must certainly have lost its colour at seeing such grand people around.'

'Little Nightingale!' called the little kitchen-maid, quite loudly, 'our gracious Emperor wishes you to sing before him.'

'With the greatest pleasure!' replied the Nightingale, and began to sing most delightfully.

'It sounds just like glass bells!' said the cavalier. 'And look at its little throat, how it's working! It's wonderful that we should never have heard it before. That bird will be a great success at court.'

'Shall I sing once more before the Emperor?' asked the Nightingale, for it thought the Emperor was present.

'My excellent little Nightingale,' said the cavalier, 'I have great pleasure in inviting you to a court festival this evening, when you shall charm his Imperial Majesty with your beautiful singing.'

'My song sounds best in the green wood!' replied the Nightingale; still it came willingly when it heard what the Emperor wished.

The palace was festively adorned. The walls and the flooring, which were of porcelain, gleamed in the rays of thousands of golden lamps. The most glorious flowers, which could ring clearly, had been placed in the passages. There was a running to and fro, and a thorough draught, and all the bells rang so loudly that one could not hear oneself speak.

In the midst of the great hall, where the Emperor sat, a golden perch had been placed, on which the Nightingale was to sit. The whole court was there, and the little kitchen-maid had got leave to stand behind the door, as she had now received the title of a real court cook. All were in full dress, and all looked at the little grey bird, to which the Emperor nodded.

And the Nightingale sang so gloriously that the tears came into the Emperor's eyes, and the tears ran down over his cheeks; and then the Nightingale sang still more sweetly, so that its song went straight to the heart. The Emperor was so much pleased that he said the Nightingale should have his golden slipper to wear round its neck. But the Nightingale declined this with thanks, saying it had already received a sufficient reward.

'I have seen tears in the Emperor's eyes – that is the real treasure to me. An Emperor's tears have a peculiar power. I am rewarded enough!' And then it sang again with a sweet glorious voice.

'That's the most amiable coquetry I ever saw!' said the ladies who stood round about, and then they took water in their mouths to gurgle when anyone spoke to them. They thought they should be nightingales too. And the lackeys and chambermaids reported that they were satisfied too; and that was saying a good deal, for they are the most difficult to please. In short, the Nightingale achieved a real success.

It was now to remain at court, to have its own cage, with liberty to go out twice every day and once at night. Twelve servants were appointed when the Nightingale went out, each of whom had a silken string fastened to the bird's leg, and which they held very tight. There was really no pleasure in an excursion of that kind.

The whole city spoke of the wonderful bird, and when two people met, one said nothing but 'Nightin', and the other said 'gale'; and then they sighed, and understood one another. Eleven pedlars' children were named after the bird, but not one of them could sing a note.

One day the Emperor received a large parcel, on which was written 'The Nightingale.'

'There we have a new book about this celebrated bird,' said the Emperor.

But it was not a book, but a little work of art, contained in a box, an artificial nightingale, which was to sing like the natural one, and was brilliantly ornamented with diamonds, rubies, and sapphires. So soon as the artificial bird was wound up, he could sing one of the pieces that the real one sang, and then his tail moved up and down, and shone with silver and gold. Round his neck hung a little ribbon, and on that was written, 'The Emperor of Japan's nightingale is poor compared to that of the Emperor of China.'

'That is capital!' said they all, and he who had brought the artificial bird immediately received the title, Imperial Head-Nightingale-Bringer.

'Now they must sing together; what a duet that will be!'

And so they had to sing together; but it did not sound very well, for the real Nightingale sang in its own way, and the artificial bird sang waltzes.

'That's not his fault,' said the playmaster; 'he's quite perfect, and very much in my style.'

Now the artificial bird was to sing alone. He had just as much success as the real one, and then it was much handsomer to look at – it shone like bracelets and breast-pins.

Three and thirty times over did it sing the same piece, and yet was not tired. The people would gladly have heard it again, but the Emperor said that the living Nightingale ought to sing something now. But where was it? No one had noticed that it had flown away out of the open window, back to the green wood.

'But what in all the world is this?' said the Emperor.

And all the courtiers abused the Nightingale, and declared that it was a very ungrateful creature.

'We have the best bird, after all,' said they.

And so the artificial bird had to sing again, and that was the thirty-fourth time that they listened to the same piece. For all that they did not know it quite by heart, for it was so very difficult. And the playmaster praised the bird particularly; yes, he declared that it was better than a nightingale, not only with regard to its plumage and the many beautiful diamonds, but inside as well.

'For you see, ladies and gentlemen, and above all, your Imperial Majesty, with a real nightingale one can never calculate what is coming, but in this artificial bird everything is settled. One can explain it; one can open it and make people understand where the waltzes come from, how they go, and how one follows up another.'

'Those are quite our own ideas,' they all said.

And the speaker received permission to show the bird to the people on the next Sunday. The people were to hear it sing too, the Emperor commanded; and they did hear it, and were as much pleased as if they had all got tipsy upon tea, for that's quite the Chinese fashion; and they all said, 'Oh!' and held up their forefingers and nodded. But the poor fisherman who had heard the real Nightingale, said, 'It sounds pretty enough, and the melodies resemble each other, but there's something wanting, though I know not what!'

The real Nightingale was banished from the country and empire. The artificial bird had its place on a silken cushion close to the Emperor's bed; all the presents it had received, gold and precious stones, were ranged about it; in title it had advanced to be the High Imperial Night-Singer, and in rank to number one on the left hand; for the Emperor considered that side the most important on which the heart is placed, and even in an Emperor the heart is on the left side; and the playmaster wrote a work of five-and-twenty volumes about the artificial bird; it was very learned and very long, full of the most difficult Chinese words; but yet all the people declared that they had read it and understood it, for fear of being considered stupid, and having their bodies trampled on.

So a whole year went by. The Emperor, the court, and all the other Chinese knew every little twitter in the artificial bird's song by heart. But just for that reason it pleased them best – they could sing with it themselves, and they did so. The street boys sang, 'Tsi-tsi-tsi-glug-glug!' and the Emperor himself sang it too. Yes, that was certainly famous.

But one evening, when the artificial bird was singing its best, and the Emperor lay in bed listening to it, something inside the bird said, 'Whizz!' Something cracked. 'Whir-r-r!' All the wheels ran round, and then the music stopped.

The Emperor immediately sprang out of bed, and caused his body physician to be called; but what could *he* do? Then they sent for a watchmaker, and after a good deal of talking and investigation, the bird was put into something like order; but the watchmaker said that the bird must be carefully treated, for the barrels were worn, and it would be impossible to put new ones in in such a manner that the music would go. There was a great lamentation; only once in a year was it permitted to let the bird sing, and that was almost too much. But then the playmaster made a little speech, full of hard words, and said this was just as good as before – and so of course it was as good as before.

Now five years had gone by, and a real grief came upon the whole nation. The Chinese were really fond of their Emperor, and now he was ill, and could not, it was said, live much longer. Already a new Emperor had been chosen, and the people stood out in the street and asked the cavalier how their old Emperor did.

'P!' said he, and shook his head.

Cold and pale lay the Emperor in his great gorgeous bed; the whole court thought him dead, and each one ran to pay homage to the new ruler. The chamberlains ran out to talk it over, and the ladies'-maids had a great coffee party. All about, in all the halls and passages, cloth had been laid down so that no footstep could be heard, and therefore it was quiet there, quite quiet. But the Emperor was not dead yet: stiff and pale he lay on the gorgeous bed with the long velvet curtains and the heavy gold tassels; high up, a window stood open, and the moon shone in upon the Emperor and the artificial bird.

The poor Emperor could scarcely breathe; it was just as if something lay upon his chest: he opened his eyes, and then he saw that it was Death who sat upon his chest, and had put on his golden crown, and held in one hand the Emperor's sword, and in the other his beautiful banner. And all around, from among the folds of the splendid velvet curtains, strange heads peered forth; a few very ugly, the rest quite lovely and mild. These were all the Emperor's bad and good deeds, that looked upon him now that Death sat upon his heart.

'Do you remember this?' whispered one after the other, 'Do you remember that?' and then they told him so much that the perspiration ran from his forehead.

'I did not know that!' said the Emperor. 'Music! music! the great Chinese drum!' he cried, 'so that I need not hear all they say!'

And they continued speaking, and Death nodded like a Chinaman to all they said.

'Music! music!' cried the Emperor. 'You little precious golden bird, sing, sing! I have given you gold and costly presents; I have even hung my golden slipper around your neck – sing now, sing!'

But the bird stood still; no one was there to wind him up, and he could not sing without that; but Death continued to stare at the Emperor with his great hollow eyes, and it was quiet, fearfully quiet.

Then there sounded from the window, suddenly, the most lovely song. It was the little live Nightingale, that sat outside on a spray. It had heard of the Emperor's sad plight, and had come to sing to him of comfort and hope. And as it sang the spectres grew paler and paler;

the blood ran quicker and more quickly through the Emperor's weak limbs; and even Death listened, and said, 'Go on, little Nightingale, go on!'

'But will you give me that splendid golden sword? Will you give me that rich banner? Will you give me the Emperor's crown?'

And Death gave up each of these treasures for a song. And the Nightingale sang on and on; and it sang of the quiet churchyard where the white roses grow, where the elder-blossom smells sweet, and where the fresh grass is moistened by the tears of survivors. Then Death felt a longing to see his garden, and floated out at the window in the form of a cold white mist.

'Thanks! thanks!' said the Emperor. 'You heavenly little bird! I know you well. I banished you from my country and empire, and yet you have charmed away the evil faces from my couch, and banished Death from my heart! How can I reward you?'

'You have rewarded me!' replied the Nightingale. 'I have drawn tears from your eyes, when I sang the first time – I shall never forget that. Those are the jewels that rejoice a singer's heart. But now sleep and grow fresh and strong again. I will sing you something.'

And it sang, and the Emperor fell into a sweet slumber. Ah! how mild and refreshing that sleep was! The sun shone upon him through the windows, when he awoke refreshed and restored: not one of his servants had yet returned, for they all thought he was dead; only the Nightingale still sat beside him and sang.

'You must always stay with me,' said the Emperor. You shall sing as you please; and I'll break the artificial bird into a thousand pieces.'

'Not so,' replied the Nightingale. 'It did well as long as it could; keep it as you have done till now. I cannot build my nest in the palace to dwell in it, but let me come when I feel the wish; then I will sit in the evening on the spray yonder by the window, and sing you something, so that you may be glad and thoughtful at once. I will sing of those who are happy and of those who suffer. I will sing of the good and the evil that remains hidden round about you. The little singing bird flies far around, to the poor fisherman, to the peasant's roof, to everyone who dwells far away from you and from your court. I love your heart more than your crown, and yet the crown has an air of sanctity about it. I will come and sing to you – but one thing you must promise me.'

'Everything!' said the Emperor; and he stood there in his imperial robes, which he had put on himself, and pressed the sword which was heavy with gold to his heart.

'One thing I beg of you: tell no one that you have a little bird who tells you everything. Then it will go all the better.'

And the Nightingale flew away.

The servants came in to look at their dead Emperor, and – yes, there they stood, and the Emperor said 'Good-morning!'

The Lovers

A WHIP-TOP and a Ball were together in a drawer among some other toys; and the Top said to the Ball, 'Shall we not be bridegroom and bride, as we live together in the same box?'

But the Ball, which had a coat of morocco leather, and was just as conceited as any fine lady, would make no answer to such a proposal.

Next day the little boy came to whom the toys belonged: he painted the top red and yellow, and hammered a brass nail into it; and it looked splendid when the top turned round!

'Look at me!' he cried to the Ball. 'What do you say now? Shall we not be engaged to each other? We suit one another so well! You jump and I dance! No one could be happier than we two should be.'

'Indeed? Do you think so?' replied the Ball. 'Perhaps you do not know that my papa and my mamma were morocco slippers, and that I have a cork inside me?'

'Yes, but I am made of mahogany,' said the Top; 'and the mayor himself turned me. He has a turning-lathe of his own, and it amuses him greatly.'

'Can I depend upon that?' asked the Ball.

'May I never be whipped again if it is not true!' replied the Top.

'You can speak well for yourself,' observed the Ball, 'but I cannot grant your request. I am as good as engaged to a swallow: every time I leap up into the air it puts its head out of its nest and says, "Will you?" And now I have silently said "Yes," and that is as good as half engaged; but I promise I will never forget you.'

'Yes, that will be much good!' said the Top.

And they spoke no more to each other.

Next day the Ball was taken out by the boy. The Top saw how it flew high into the air, like a bird; at last one could no longer see it. Each time it came back again, but gave a high leap when it touched the earth, and that was done either from its longing to mount up again, or because it had a cork in its body. But the ninth time the Ball remained absent, and did not come back again; and the boy sought and sought, but it was gone.

'I know very well where it is!' sighed the Top. 'It is in the swallow's nest, and has married the swallow!'

The more the Top thought of this, the more it longed for the Ball. Just because it could not get the Ball, its love increased; and the fact that the Ball had chosen another, formed a peculiar feature in the case. So the Top danced round and hummed, but always thought of the Ball, which became more and more beautiful in his fancy. Thus several years went by, and now it was an old love.

And the Top was no longer young! But one day he was gilt all over; never had he looked so handsome; he was now a golden Top, and sprang till he hummed again. Yes, that was something worth seeing! But all at once he sprang too high, and – he was gone!

They looked and looked, even in the cellar, but he was not to be found. Where could he be?

He had jumped into the dustbin, where all kinds of things were lying: cabbage stalks, sweepings, and dust that had fallen down from the roof.

'Here's a nice place to lie in! The gilding will soon leave me here. Among what a rabble have I alighted!'

And then he looked sideways at a long leafless cabbage stump, and at a curious round thing that looked like an old apple; but it was not an apple – it was an old Ball, which had lain for years in the gutter on the roof, and was quite saturated with water.

'Thank goodness, here comes one of us, with whom one can talk!' said the Ball, and looked at the gilt Top. 'I am real morocco, worked by maidens' hands, and have a cork within me; but no one would think it, to look at me. I was very nearly marrying a swallow, but I fell into the gutter on the roof, and have lain there full five years, and become quite wet through. You may believe me, that's a long time for a young girl.'

But the Top said nothing. He thought of his old love; and the more he heard, the clearer it became to him that this was she.

Then came the servant-girl, and wanted to turn out the dustbin. 'Aha! there's the gilt top!' she cried.

And so the Top was brought again to notice and honour, but nothing was heard of the Ball. And the Top spoke no more of his old love; for that dies away when the beloved object has lain for five years in a roof-gutter and got wet through; yes, one does not know her again when one meets her in the dustbin.

The Ugly Duckling

IT WAS glorious out in the country. It was summer, and the corn-fields were yellow, and the oats were green; the hay had been put up in stacks in the green meadows, and the stork went about on his long red legs, and chattered Egyptian, for this language he had learned from his mother. All around the fields and meadows were great forests, and in the midst of these forests lay deep lakes. Yes, it was really glorious out in the country. In the midst of the sunshine there lay an old manor, surrounded by deep canals, and from the wall down to the water grew great burdocks, so high that little children could stand upright under the loftiest of them. It was just as wild there as in the deepest wood. Here sat a Duck upon her nest, for she had to hatch her young ones; but she was almost tired out before the little ones came; and then she so seldom had visitors. The other ducks liked better to swim about in the canals than to run up to sit down under a burdock, and gossip with her.

At last one eggshell after another burst open. 'Piep! piep!' it cried, and in all the eggs there were little creatures that stuck out their heads.

'Rap! rap!' she said; and they all came rapping out as fast as they could, looking all round them under the green leaves; and the mother let them look as much as they chose, for green is good for the eyes.

'How wide the world is!' said the young ones, for they certainly had much more room now than when they were in the eggs.

'Do you think this is all the world?' asked the mother. 'That extends far across the other side of the garden, quite into the parson's field, but I have never been there yet. I hope you are all together,' she continued, and stood up. 'No, I have not all. The largest egg still lies there. How long is that to last? I am really tired of it.' And she sat down again.

'Well, how goes it?' asked an old Duck who had come to pay her a visit.

'It lasts a long time with that one egg,' said the Duck who sat there. 'It will not burst. Now, only look at the others; are they not the prettiest ducklings one could possibly see? They are all like their father: the bad fellow never comes to see me.'

'Let me see the egg which will not burst,' said the old visitor. 'Believe me, it is a turkey's egg. I was once cheated in that way, and had much anxiety and trouble with the young ones, for they are afraid of the water. I could not get them to venture in. I quacked and clucked, but it was no use. Let me see the egg. Yes, that's a turkey's egg! Let it lie there, and teach the other children to swim.'

'I think I will sit on it a little longer,' said the Duck. 'I've sat so long now that I can sit a few days more.'

'Just as you please,' said the old Duck; and she went away.

At last the great egg burst. 'Piep! piep!' said the little one, and crept forth. It was very large and very ugly. The Duck looked at it.

'It's a very large duckling,' said she; 'none of the others look like that: can it really be a turkey chick? Now we shall soon find it out. It must go into the water, even if I have to kick it in myself.'

The next day the weather was splendidly bright, and the sun shone on all the green burdocks. The Mother-Duck went down to the water with all her little ones. Splash, she jumped into the water. 'Quack! quack!' she said, and one duckling after another plunged in. The water closed over their heads, but they came up in an instant, and swam capitally; their legs went of themselves, and there they were all in the water. The ugly grey Duckling swam with them.

'No, it's not a turkey,' said she; 'look how well it can use its legs, and how upright it holds itself. It is my own child! On the whole it's quite pretty, if one looks at it rightly. Quack! quack! come with me, and I'll lead you out into the great world, and present you in the poultry-yard; but keep close to me, so that no one may tread on you, and take care of the cat!'

And so they came into the poultry-yard. There was a terrible riot going on there, for two families were quarrelling about an eel's head, and the cat got it after all.

'See, that's how it goes in the world!' said the Mother-Duck; and she whetted her beak, for she, too, wanted the eel's head. 'Only use your legs,' she said. 'See that you can bustle about, and bow your heads before the old Duck yonder. She's the grandest of all here; she's of Spanish blood – that's why she's so fat; and do you see, she has a red rag round her leg; that's something particularly fine, and the greatest distinction a duck can enjoy: it signifies that one does not want to lose her, and that she's to be recognised by man and beast. Shake yourselves – don't turn in your toes; a well-brought-up duck turns its toes quite out, just like father and mother, so! Now bend your necks and say "Rap!"'

And they did so; but the other ducks round about looked at them, and said quite boldly, 'Look there! now we're to have these hanging on as if there were not enough of us already! And – fie! – how that Duckling yonder looks; we won't stand him!' And one duck flew up immediately, and bit it in the neck.

'Let it alone,' said the mother; 'it does no harm to anyone.'

'Yes, but it's too large and peculiar,' said the Duck who had bitten it; 'and therefore it must be buffeted.'

'Those are pretty children that the mother has there,' said the old Duck with the rag round her leg. 'They're all pretty but that one; that was a failure. I wish she could alter it.'

'That cannot be done, my lady,' replied the Mother-Duck: 'it is not pretty, but it has a really good disposition, and swims as well as any other; I may even say it swims better. I think it will grow up pretty, and become smaller in time; it has lain too long in the egg, and therefore is not properly shaped.' And then she pinched it in the neck, and smoothed its feathers. 'Moreover, it is a drake,' she said, 'and therefore it is not of so much consequence. I think he will be very strong: he will make his way all right.'

'The other ducklings are graceful enough,' said the old Duck. 'Make yourself at home; and if you find an eel's head, you may bring it me.'

And now they were at home. But the poor Duckling which had crept last out of the egg, and looked so ugly, was bitten and pushed and jeered at, as much by the ducks as by the chickens.

'It is too big!' they all said. And the turkey-cock, who had been born with spurs, and therefore thought himself an emperor, blew himself up like a ship in full sail, and bore straight down upon it; then he gobbled, and grew quite red in the face. The poor Duckling did not know where it should stand or walk; it was quite melancholy because it looked ugly, and was scoffed at by the whole yard.

So it went on the first day; and afterwards it became worse and worse. The poor Duckling was hunted about by everyone; even its brothers and sisters were quite angry with it, and said, 'If the cat would only catch you, you ugly creature!' And the mother said, 'If you were only far away!' And the ducks bit it, and the chickens beat it, and the girl who had to feed the poultry kicked at it with her foot.

Then it ran and flew over the fence, and the little birds in the bushes flew up in fear.

'That is because I am so ugly!' thought the Duckling; and it shut its eyes, but flew on farther; thus it came out into the great moor, where the wild ducks lived. Here it lay the whole night long; and it was weary and downcast.

Towards morning the wild ducks flew up, and looked at their new companion.

'What sort of a one are you?' they asked; and the Duckling turned in every direction, and bowed as well as it could. 'You are remarkably ugly!' said the Wild Ducks. 'But that is very indifferent to us, so long as you do not marry into our family.'

Poor thing! it certainly did not think of marrying, and only hoped to obtain leave to lie among the reeds and drink some of the swamp water.

Thus it lay two whole days; then came thither two wild geese, or, properly speaking, two wild ganders. It was not long since each had crept out of an egg, and that's why they were so saucy.

'Listen, comrade,' said one of them. 'You're so ugly that I like you. Will you go with us, and become a bird of passage? Near here, in another moor, there are a few sweet lovely wild geese, all unmarried, and all able to say "Rap!" You've a chance of making your fortune, ugly as you are!'

'Piff! paff!' resounded through the air; and the two ganders fell down dead in the swamp, and the water became blood-red. 'Piff! paff!' it sounded again, and whole flocks of wild geese rose up from the reeds. And then there was another report. A great hunt was going on. The hunters were lying in wait all round the moor, and some were even sitting up in the branches of the trees, which spread far over the reeds. The blue smoke rose up like clouds among the dark trees, and was wafted far away across the water; and the hunting dogs came – splash, splash! – into the swamp, and the rushes and the reeds bent down on every side. That was a fright for the poor Duckling! It turned its head, and put it under its wing; but at that moment a frightful great dog stood close by the Duckling. His tongue hung far out of his mouth and his eyes gleamed horrible and ugly; he thrust out his nose close against the Duckling, showed his sharp teeth, and – splash, splash! – on he went, without seizing it.

'Oh, Heaven be thanked!' sighed the Duckling. 'I am so ugly, that even the dog does not like to bite me!'

And so it lay quite quiet, while the shots rattled through the reeds and gun after gun was fired. At last, late in the day, silence was restored; but the poor Duckling did not dare to rise up; it waited several hours before it looked round, and then hastened away out of the marsh as fast as it could. It ran on over field and meadow; there was such a storm raging that it was difficult to get from one place to another.

Towards evening the Duck came to a little miserable peasant's hut. This hut was so dilapidated that it did not know on which side it should fall; and that's why it remained standing. The storm whistled round the Duckling in such a way that the poor creature was obliged to sit down, to resist it; and the tempest grew worse and worse. Then the Duckling noticed that one of the hinges of the door had given way, and the door hung so slanting that the Duckling could slip through the opening into the room; and it did so.

Here lived an old woman, with her Tom Cat and her Hen. And the Tom Cat, whom she called Sonnie, could arch his back and purr, he could even give out sparks; but for that one had to stroke his fur the wrong way. The Hen had quite little short legs, and therefore she was called Chickabiddy-shortshanks; she laid good eggs, and the woman loved her as her own child.

In the morning the strange Duckling was at once noticed, and the Tom Cat began to purr, and the Hen to cluck.

'What's this?' said the woman, and looked all round; but she could not see well, and therefore she thought the Duckling was a fat duck that had strayed. 'This is a rare prize!' she said. 'Now I shall have duck's eggs. I hope it is not a drake. We must try that.'

And so the Duckling was admitted on trial for three weeks; but no eggs came. And the Tom Cat was master of the house, and the Hen was the lady, and always said 'We and the world!' for they thought they were half the world, and by far the better half. The Duckling thought one might have a different opinion, but the Hen would not allow it.

'Can you lay eggs?' she asked.

'No.'

'Then you'll have the goodness to hold your tongue.'

And the Tom Cat said, 'Can you curve your back, and purr, and give out sparks?'

'No.'

'Then you cannot have any opinion of your own when sensible people are speaking.'

And the Duckling sat in a corner and was melancholy; then the fresh air and the sunshine streamed in; and it was seized with such a strange longing to swim on the water, that it could not help telling the Hen of it.

'What are you thinking of?' cried the Hen. 'You have nothing to do, that's why you have these fancies. Purr or lay eggs, and they will pass over.'

'But it is so charming to swim on the water!' said the Duckling, 'so refreshing to let it close above one's head, and to dive down to the bottom.'

'Yes, that must be a mighty pleasure truly,' quoth the Hen. 'I fancy you must have gone crazy. Ask the Cat about it, he's the cleverest animal I know, ask him if he likes to swim on the water, or to dive down: I won't speak about myself. Ask our mistress, the old woman; no one in the world is cleverer than she. Do you think she has any desire to swim, and to let the water close above her head?'

'You don't understand me,' said the Duckling.

'We don't understand you? Then pray who is to understand you? You surely don't pretend to be cleverer than the Tom Cat and the woman – I won't say anything of myself. Don't be conceited, child, and be grateful for all the kindness you have received. Did you not get into a warm room, and have you not fallen into company from which you may learn something? But you are a chatterer, and it is not pleasant to associate with you. You may believe me, I speak for your good. I tell you disagreeable things, and by that one may always know one's true friends! Only take care that you learn to lay eggs, or to purr and give out sparks!'

'I think I will go out into the wide world,' said the Duckling.

'Yes, do go,' replied the Hen.

And the Duckling went away. It swam on the water, and dived, but it was slighted by every creature because of its ugliness.

Now came the autumn. The leaves in the forest turned yellow and brown; the wind caught them so that they danced about, and up in the air it was very cold. The clouds hung low, heavy with hail and snowflakes, and on the fence stood the raven, crying, 'Croak! croak!' for mere cold; yes, it was enough to make one feel cold to think of this. The poor little Duckling certainly had not a good time. One evening – the sun was just setting in his beauty – there came a whole flock of great handsome birds out of the bushes; the duckling had never before seen anything so beautiful; they were dazzlingly white, with long flexible necks; they were swans. They uttered a very peculiar cry, spread forth their glorious great wings, and flew away from that cold region to warmer lands, to open lakes. They mounted so high, so high! and the ugly little Duckling felt quite strangely as it watched them. It turned round and round in the water like a wheel, stretched out its neck towards them, and muttered such a strange loud cry as frightened itself. Oh! it could not forget those beautiful, happy birds; and so soon as it could see them no longer, it dived down to the very bottom, and when it came up again, it was quite beside itself. It knew not the name of those birds, and knew not whither they were flying; but it loved them more than it had ever loved anyone. It was not at all envious of them. How could it think of wishing to possess such loveliness as they had? It would have been glad if only the ducks would have endured its company – the poor ugly creature!

And the winter grew cold, very cold! The Duckling was forced to swim about in the water, to prevent the surface from freezing entirely; but every night the hole in which it swam about became smaller and smaller. It froze so hard that the icy covering crackled again; and the

Duckling was obliged to use its legs continually to prevent the hole from freezing up. At last it become exhausted, and lay quite still, and thus froze fast into the ice.

Early in the morning a peasant came by, and when he saw what had happened, he took his wooden shoe, broke the ice-crust to pieces, and carried the Duckling home to his wife. Then it came to itself again. The children wanted to play with it; but the Duckling thought they would do it an injury, and in its terror fluttered up into the milk-pan, so that the milk spurted down into the room. The woman screamed and clapped her hands, at which the Duckling flew down into the butter-tub, and then into the meal-barrel and out again. How it looked then! The woman screamed, and struck at it with the fire-tongs; the children tumbled over one another, in their efforts to catch the Duckling; and they laughed and screamed finely! Happily the door stood open, and the poor creature was able to slip out between the shrubs into the newly-fallen snow; and there it lay quite exhausted.

But it would be too melancholy if I were to tell all the misery and care which the Duckling had to endure in the hard winter. It lay out on the swamp among the reeds, when the sun began to shine again and the larks to sing: it was a beautiful spring.

Then all at once the Duckling raised its wings: they beat the air more strongly than before, and bore it strongly away; and before it well knew how all this happened, it found itself in a great garden, where the apple trees stood in blossom, where the lilac flowers smelt sweet, and hung their long green branches down to the winding canals. Oh, here it was so beautiful, such a gladness of spring! and from the thicket came three glorious white swans; they rustled their wings, and swam lightly on the water. The Duckling knew the splendid creatures, and felt oppressed by a peculiar sadness.

'I will fly away to them, to the royal birds! and they will kill me, because I, that am so ugly, dare to approach them. But it is of no consequence! Better to be killed by *them* than to be pursued by ducks, and beaten by fowls, and pushed about by the girl who takes care of the poultry-yard, and to suffer hunger in winter!' And it flew out into the water, and swam towards the beautiful swans: these looked at it, and came sailing down upon it with outspread wings. 'Kill me!' said the poor creature, and bent its head down upon the water, expecting nothing but death. But what was this that it saw in the clear water? It beheld its own image; and, lo! it was no longer a clumsy dark grey bird, ugly and hateful to look at, but – a swan!

It matters nothing if one is born in a duck-yard, if one has only lain in a swan's egg.

It felt quite glad at all the need and misfortune it had suffered, now it realised its happiness and all the splendour that surrounded it. And the great swans swam round it, and stroked it with their beaks.

Into the garden came little children, who threw bread and corn into the water; and the youngest cried, 'There is a new one!' and the other children shouted joyously, 'Yes, a new one has arrived!' And they clapped their hands and danced about, and ran to their father and mother; and bread and cake were thrown into the water; and they all said, 'The new one is the most beautiful of all! so young and handsome!' and the old swans bowed their heads before him.

Then he felt quite ashamed, and hid his head under his wings, for he did not know what to do; he was so happy, and yet not at all proud. He thought how he had been persecuted and despised; and now he heard them saying that he was the most beautiful of all birds. Even the elder tree bent its branches straight down into the water before him, and the sun shone warm and mild. Then his wings rustled, he lifted his slender neck, and cried rejoicingly from the depths of his heart, 'I never dreamed of so much happiness when I was still the ugly Duckling!'

The Fir Tree

OUT in the forest stood a pretty little Fir Tree. It had a good place; it could have sunlight, air there was in plenty, and all around grew many larger comrades – pines as well as firs. But the little Fir Tree was in such a hurry to grow. It did not care for the warm sun and the fresh air; it took no notice of the peasant children, who went about talking together, when they had come out to look for strawberries and raspberries. Often they came with a whole pot-full, or had strung berries on a straw; then they would sit down by the little Fir Tree and say, 'How pretty and small that one is!' and the Tree did not like to hear that at all.

Next year it had grown a great joint, and the following year it was longer still, for in fir trees one can always tell by the number of joints they have how many years they have been growing.

'Oh, if I were only as great a tree as the others!' sighed the little Fir, 'then I would spread my branches far around, and look out from my crown into the wide world. The birds would then build nests in my boughs, and when the wind blew I could nod just as grandly as the others yonder.'

It took no pleasure in the sunshine, in the birds, and in the red clouds that went sailing over it morning and evening.

When it was winter, and the snow lay all around, white and sparkling, a hare would often come jumping along, and spring right over the little Fir Tree. Oh! this made it so angry. But two winters went by, and when the third came the little Tree had grown so tall that the hare was obliged to run round it.

'Oh! to grow, to grow, and become old; that's the only fine thing in the world,' thought the Tree.

In the autumn woodcutters always came and felled a few of the largest trees; that happened every year, and the little Fir Tree, that was now quite well grown, shuddered with fear, for the great stately trees fell to the ground with a crash, and their branches were cut off, so that the trees looked quite naked, long, and slender – they could hardly be recognised. But then they were laid upon wagons, and horses dragged them away out of the wood. Where were they going? What destiny awaited them?

In the spring, when the Swallows and the Stork came, the Tree asked them, 'Do you know where they were taken? Did you not meet them?'

The Swallows knew nothing about it, but the Stork looked thoughtful, nodded his head, and said, 'Yes, I think so. I met many new ships when I flew out of Egypt; on the ships were stately masts; I fancy that these were the trees. They smelt like fir. I can assure you they're stately – very stately.'

'Oh that I were only big enough to go over the sea! What kind of thing is this sea, and how does it look?'

'It would take too long to explain all that,' said the Stork, and he went away.

'Rejoice in thy youth,' said the Sunbeams; 'rejoice in thy fresh growth, and in the young life that is within thee.'

And the wind kissed the Tree, and the dew wept tears upon it; but the Fir Tree did not understand that.

When Christmas-time approached, quite young trees were felled, sometimes trees which were neither so old nor so large as this Fir Tree, that never rested but always wanted to go away. These young trees, which were just the most beautiful, kept all their branches; they were put upon wagons, and horses dragged them away out of the wood.

'Where are they all going?' asked the Fir Tree. 'They are not greater than I – indeed, one of them was much smaller. Why do they keep all their branches? Whither are they taken?'

'We know that! We know that!' chirped the Sparrows. 'Yonder in the town we looked in at the windows. We know where they go. Oh! they are dressed up in the greatest pomp and splendour that can be imagined. We have looked in at the windows, and have perceived that they are planted in the middle of the warm room, and adorned with the most beautiful things – gilt apples, honey-cakes, playthings, and many hundreds of candles.'

'And then?' asked the Fir Tree, and trembled through all its branches. 'And then? What happens then?'

'Why, we have not seen anything more. But it was incomparable.'

'Perhaps I may be destined to tread this glorious path one day!' cried the Fir Tree rejoicingly. 'That is even better than travelling across the sea. How painfully I long for it! If it were only Christmas now! Now I am great and grown up, like the rest who were led away last year. Oh, if I were only on the carriage! If I were only in the warm room, among all the pomp and splendour! And then? Yes, then something even better will come, something far more charming, or else why should they adorn me so? There must be something grander, something greater still to come; but what? Oh! I'm suffering, I'm longing! I don't know myself what is the matter with me!'

'Rejoice in us,' said Air and Sunshine. 'Rejoice in thy fresh youth here in the woodland.'

But the Fir Tree did not rejoice at all, but it grew and grew; winter and summer it stood there, green, dark green. The people who saw it said, 'That's a handsome tree!' and at Christmas-time it was felled before any one of the others. The axe cut deep into its marrow, and the Tree fell to the ground with a sigh: it felt a pain, a sensation of faintness, and could not think at all of happiness, for it was sad at parting from its home, from the place where it had grown up: it knew that it should never again see the dear old companions, the little bushes and flowers all around – perhaps not even the birds. The parting was not at all agreeable.

The Tree only came to itself when it was unloaded in a yard, with other trees, and heard a man say, 'This one is famous; we only want this one!'

Now two servants came in gay liveries, and carried the Fir Tree into a large beautiful saloon. All around the walls hung pictures, and by the great stove stood large Chinese vases with lions on the covers; there were rocking-chairs, silken sofas, great tables covered with picture-books, and toys worth a hundred times a hundred dollars, at least the children said so. And the Fir Tree was put into a great tub filled with sand; but no one could see that it was a tub, for it was hung round with green cloth, and stood on a large many-coloured carpet. Oh, how the Tree trembled! What was to happen now? The servants, and the young ladies also, decked it out. On one branch they hung little nets, cut out of coloured paper; every net was filled with sweetmeats; golden apples and walnuts hung down as if they grew there, and more than a hundred little candles, red, white, and blue, were fastened to the different boughs. Dolls that looked exactly like real people – the Tree had never seen such before – swung among the foliage, and high on the summit of the Tree was fixed a tinsel star. It was splendid, particularly splendid.

'This evening,' said all, 'this evening it will shine.'

'Oh,' thought the Tree, 'that it were evening already! Oh that the lights may be soon lit up! What will happen then? I wonder if trees will come out of the forest to look at me? Will the sparrows fly against the panes? Shall I grow fast here, and stand adorned in summer and winter?'

Yes, it knew all about it. But it had a regular bark-ache from mere longing, and the bark-ache is just as bad for a Tree as the headache for a person.

At last the candles were lighted. What a brilliance, what splendour! The Tree trembled so in all its branches that one of the candles set fire to a green twig, and it was really painful.

'Heaven preserve us!' cried the young ladies; and they hastily put the fire out.

Now the Tree might not even tremble. Oh, that was terrible! It was so afraid of losing any of its ornaments, and it was quite bewildered with all the brilliance. And now the folding doors were thrown open, and a number of children rushed in as if they would have overturned the whole Tree; the older people followed more deliberately. The little ones stood quite silent, but only for a minute; then they shouted till the room rang: they danced gleefully round the Tree, and one present after another was plucked from it.

'What are they about?' thought the Tree. 'What's going to be done?'

And the candles burned down to the twigs, and as they burned down they were extinguished, and then the children received permission to plunder the Tree. Oh! they rushed in upon it, so that every branch cracked again: if it had not been fastened by the top and by the golden star to the ceiling, it would have fallen down.

The children danced about with their pretty toys. No one looked at the Tree except the old nursemaid, who came up and peeped among the branches, but only to see if a fig or an apple had not been forgotten.

'A story! a story!' shouted the children: and they drew a little fat man towards the Tree; and he sat down just beneath it, 'for then we shall be in the green wood,' said he, 'and the tree may have the advantage of listening to my tale. But I can only tell one. Will you hear the story of Ivede-Avede, or of Humpty-Dumpty, who fell downstairs, and still was raised up to honour and married the Princess?'

'Ivede-Avede!' cried some, 'Humpty-Dumpty!' cried others, and there was a great crying and shouting. Only the Fir Tree was quite silent, and thought, 'Shall I not be in it? shall I have nothing to do in it?' But it had been in the evening's amusement, and had done what was required of it.

And the fat man told about Humpty-Dumpty, who fell downstairs, and yet was raised to honour and married the Princess. And the children clapped their hands, and cried, 'Tell another! tell another!' for they wanted to hear about Ivede-Avede; but they only got the story of Humpty-Dumpty. The Fir Tree stood quite silent and thoughtful; never had the birds in the wood told such a story as that. Humpty-Dumpty fell downstairs, and yet came to honour and married the Princess!

'Yes, so it happens in the world!' thought the Fir Tree, and believed it must be true, because that was such a nice man who told it. 'Well, who can know? Perhaps I shall fall downstairs too, and marry a Princess!' And it looked forward with pleasure to being adorned again, the next evening, with candles and toys, gold and fruit. 'Tomorrow I shall not tremble,' it thought. 'I will rejoice in all my splendour. Tomorrow I shall hear the story of Humpty-Dumpty again, and, perhaps, that of Ivede-Avede too.'

And the Tree stood all night quiet and thoughtful.

In the morning the servants and the chambermaid came in.

'Now my splendour will begin afresh,' thought the Tree. But they dragged it out of the room, and upstairs to the garret, and here they put it in a dark corner where no daylight shone.

'What's the meaning of this?' thought the Tree. 'What am I to do here? What am I to get to know here?'

And he leaned against the wall, and thought, and thought. And he had time enough, for days and nights went by, and nobody came up; and when at length someone came, it was only to put some great boxes in a corner. Now the Tree stood quite hidden away, and one would think that it was quite forgotten.

'Now it's winter outside,' thought the Tree. 'The earth is hard and covered with snow, and people cannot plant me; therefore I suppose I'm to be sheltered here until spring comes. How considerate that is! How good people are! If it were only not so dark here, and so terribly solitary! not even a little hare! It was pretty out there in the wood, when the snow lay thick and the hare sprang past; yes, even when he jumped over me, although I did not like that at the time. It is terribly lonely up here!'

'Piep! piep!' said a little Mouse, and crept forward, and then came another little one. They smelt at the Fir Tree, and then slipped among the branches.

'It's horribly cold,' said the two little Mice, 'or else it would be comfortable here. Don't you think so, you old Fir Tree?'

'I'm not old at all,' said the Fir Tree. 'There are many much older than I.'

'Where do you come from?' asked the Mice. 'And what do you know?' They were dreadfully inquisitive. 'Tell us about the most beautiful spot on earth. Have you been there? Have you been in the store-room, where cheeses lie on the shelves, and hams hang from the ceiling, where one dances on tallow candles, and goes in thin and comes out fat?'

'I don't know that!' replied the Tree; 'but I know the wood, where the sun shines, and where the birds sing.'

And then it told all about its youth.

And the little Mice had never heard anything of the kind; and they listened and said, 'What a number of things you have seen! How happy you must have been!'

'I?' said the Fir Tree; and it thought about what it had told. 'Yes, those were really quite happy times.' But then it told of the Christmas-eve, when it had been hung with sweetmeats and candles.

'Oh!' said the little Mice, 'how happy you have been, you old Fir Tree!'

'I'm not old at all,' said the Tree. 'I only came out of the wood this winter. I'm in my very best years.'

'What splendid stories you can tell!' said the little Mice.

And next night they came with four other little Mice, to hear what the Tree had to relate; and the more it said, the more clearly did it remember everything, and thought, 'Those were quite merry days! But they may come again. Humpty-Dumpty fell downstairs, and yet he married the Princess. Perhaps I may marry a Princess too!' And then the Fir Tree thought of a pretty little birch tree that grew out in the forest: for the Fir Tree, that birch was a real Princess.

'Who's Humpty-Dumpty?' asked the little Mice.

And then the Fir Tree told the whole story. It could remember every single word; and the little Mice were ready to leap to the very top of the tree with pleasure. Next night a great many more Mice came, and on Sunday two Rats even appeared; but these thought the story was not pretty, and the little Mice were sorry for that, for now they also did not like it so much as before.

'Do you only know one story?' asked the Rats.

'Only that one,' replied the Tree. 'I heard that on the happiest evening of my life; I did not think then how happy I was.'

'That's an exceedingly poor story. Don't you know any about bacon and tallow candles – a store-room story?'

'No,' said the Tree.

'Then we'd rather not hear you,' said the Rats.

And they went back to their own people. The little Mice at last stayed away also; and then the Tree sighed and said, 'It was very nice when they sat round me, the merry little Mice, and listened when I spoke to them. Now that's past too. But I shall remember to be pleased when they take me out.'

But when did that happen? Why, it was one morning that people came and rummaged in the garret: the boxes were put away, and the Tree brought out; they certainly threw it rather roughly on the floor, but a servant dragged it away at once to the stairs, where the daylight shone.

'Now life is beginning again!' thought the Tree.

It felt the fresh air and the first sunbeams, and now it was out in the courtyard. Everything passed so quickly that the Tree quite forgot to look at itself, there was so much to look at all round. The courtyard was close to a garden, and here everything was blooming; the roses hung fresh and fragrant over the little paling, the linden trees were in blossom, and the swallows cried, 'Quirre-virre-vit! my husband's come!' But it was not the Fir Tree that they meant.

'Now I shall live!' said the Tree, rejoicingly, and spread its branches far out; but, alas! they were all withered and yellow; and it lay in the corner among nettles and weeds. The tinsel star was still upon it, and shone in the bright sunshine.

In the courtyard a couple of the merry children were playing, who had danced round the tree at Christmas-time, and had rejoiced over it. One of the youngest ran up and tore off the golden star.

'Look what is sticking to the ugly old fir tree,' said the child, and he trod upon the branches till they cracked again under his boots.

And the Tree looked at all the blooming flowers and the splendour of the garden, and then looked at itself, and wished it had remained in the dark corner of the garret; it thought of its fresh youth in the wood, of the merry Christmas-eve, and of the little Mice which had listened so pleasantly to the story of Humpty-Dumpty.

'Past! past!' said the poor Tree. 'Had I but rejoiced when I could have done so! Past! past!'

And the servant came and chopped the Tree into little pieces; a whole bundle lay there: it blazed brightly under the great brewing copper, and it sighed deeply, and each sigh was like a little shot: and the children who were at play there ran up and seated themselves at the fire, looked into it, and cried, 'Puff! puff!' But at each explosion, which was a deep sigh, the tree thought of a summer day in the woods, or of a winter night there, when the stars beamed; it thought of Christmas-eve and of Humpty-Dumpty, the only story it had ever heard or knew how to tell; and then the Tree was burned.

The boys played in the garden, and the youngest had on his breast a golden star, which the Tree had worn on its happiest evening. Now that was past, and the Tree's life was past, and the story is past too: past! past! and that's the way with all stories.

The Snow Queen

In Seven Stories

First Story

Which treats of the Mirror and Fragments

LOOK YOU, now we're going to begin. When we are at the end of the story we shall know more than we do now, for he was a bad goblin. He was one of the very worst, for he was the devil himself. One day he was in very high spirits, for he had made a mirror which had this peculiarity, that everything good and beautiful that was reflected in it shrank together into almost nothing, but that whatever was worthless and looked ugly became prominent and looked worse than ever. The most lovely landscapes seen in this mirror looked like boiled spinach, and the best people became hideous, or stood on their heads and had no stomachs; their faces were so distorted as to be unrecognisable, and a single freckle was shown spread out over nose and mouth. That was very amusing, the devil said. When a good pious thought passed through any person's mind, there came a grin in the mirror, so that the devil chuckled at his artistic invention. Those who went to the goblin school – for he kept a goblin school – declared everywhere that a wonder had been wrought. For now, they asserted, one could see, for the first time, how the world and the people in it really looked. They ran about with the mirror, and at last there was not a single country or person that had not been distorted in it. Now they wanted to fly up to heaven, to sneer and scoff at the angels themselves. The higher they flew with the mirror, the more it grinned; they could scarcely hold it fast. They flew higher and higher, and then the mirror trembled so terribly amid its grinning that it fell down out of their hands to the earth, where it was shattered into a hundred million million and more fragments. And now this mirror occasioned much more unhappiness than before; for some of the fragments were scarcely so large as a barleycorn, and these flew about in the world, and whenever they flew into anyone's eye they stuck there, and those people saw everything wrongly, or had only eyes for the bad side of a thing, for every little fragment of the mirror had retained the same power which the whole glass possessed. A few persons even got a fragment of the mirror into their hearts, and that was terrible indeed, for such a heart became a block of ice. A few fragments of the mirror were so large that they were used as window-panes, but it was a bad thing to look at one's friends through these panes; other pieces were made into spectacles, and then it went badly when people put on these spectacles to see rightly and to be just; and the demon laughed till his paunch shook, for it tickled him so. But without, some little fragments of glass still floated about in the air – and now we shall hear.

Second Story

A Little Boy and a Little Girl

In the great town, where there are many houses and so many people that there is not room enough for everyone to have a little garden, and where consequently most persons are compelled to be content with some flowers in flowerpots, were two poor children who possessed a garden somewhat larger than a flowerpot. They were not brother and sister, but they loved each other quite as much as if they had been. Their parents lived just opposite each other in two garrets, there where the roof of one neighbour's house joined that of another; and where the water-pipe ran between the two houses was a little window; one had only to step across the pipe to get from one window to the other.

The parents of each child had a great box, in which grew kitchen herbs that they used, and a little rose bush; there was one in each box, and they grew famously, Now, it occurred to the parents to place the boxes across the pipe, so that they reached from one window to another, and looked quite like two embankments of flowers. Pea plants hung down over the boxes, and the rose bushes shot forth long twigs, which clustered round the windows and bent down towards each other: it was almost like a triumphal arch of flowers and leaves. As the boxes were very high, and the children knew that they might not creep upon them, they often obtained permission to step out upon the roof behind the boxes, and to sit upon their little stools under the roses, and there they could play capitally.

In the winter there was an end of this amusement. The windows were sometimes quite frozen all over. But then they warmed copper farthings on the stove, and held the warm coins against the frozen pane; and this made a capital peep-hole, so round, so round! and behind it gleamed a pretty, mild eye at each window; and these eyes belonged to the little boy and the little girl. His name was Kay and the little girl's was Gerda.

In the summer they could get to one another at one bound; but in the winter they had to go down and up the long staircase, while the snow was pelting without.

'Those are the white bees swarming,' said the old grandmother.

'Have they a Queen-bee?' asked the little boy. For he knew that there is one among the real bees.

'Yes, they have one,' replied grandmamma. 'She always flies where they swarm thickest. She is the largest of them all, and never remains quiet upon the earth; she flies up again into the black cloud. Many a midnight she is flying through the streets of the town, and looks in at the windows, and then they freeze in such a strange way, and look like flowers.'

'Yes, I've seen that!' cried both the children; and now they knew that it was true.

'Can the Snow Queen come in here?' asked the little girl.

'Only let her come,' cried the boy; 'I'll set her upon the warm stove, and then she'll melt.'

But grandmother smoothed his hair, and told some other tales.

In the evening, when little Kay was at home and half undressed, he clambered upon the chair by the window, and looked through the little hole. A few flakes of snow were falling outside, and one of them, the largest of them all, remained lying on the edge of one of the flower-boxes. The snowflake grew larger and larger, and at last became a maiden clothed in the finest white gauze, made out of millions of starry flakes. She was beautiful and delicate, but of ice – of shining, glittering ice. Yet she was alive; her eyes flashed like two clear stars, but there was no peace or rest in them. She nodded towards the window, and beckoned with her hand. The little boy was frightened, and sprang down from the chair; then it seemed as if a great bird flew by outside, in front of the window.

Next day there was a clear frost, then there was a thaw, and then the spring came; the sun shone, the green sprouted forth, the swallows built nests, the windows were opened, and the little children again sat in their garden high up in the roof, over all the floors.

How splendidly the roses bloomed this summer! The little girl had learned a psalm, in which mention was made of roses; and, in speaking of roses, she thought of her own; and she sang it to the little boy, and he sang, too,

> The roses in the valleys grow
> Where we the infant Christ shall know.

And the little ones held each other by the hand, kissed the roses, looked at God's bright sunshine, and spoke to it, as if the Christ-child were there. What splendid summer days those were! How beautiful it was without, among the fresh rose bushes, which seemed as if they would never leave off blooming!

Kay and Gerda sat and looked at the picture-book of beasts and birds. Then it was, while the clock was just striking five on the church tower, that Kay said, 'Oh! something struck my heart and pricked me in the eye.'

The little girl fell upon his neck; he blinked his eyes. No, there was nothing at all to be seen.

'I think it is gone,' said he; but it was not gone. It was just one of those glass fragments which sprang from the mirror – the magic

mirror that we remember well, the ugly glass that made everything great and good which was mirrored in it to seem small and mean, but in which the mean and the wicked things were brought out in relief, and every fault was noticeable at once. Poor little Kay had also received a splinter just in his heart, and that will now soon become like a lump of ice. It did not hurt him now, but the splinter was still there.

'Why do you cry?' he asked. 'You look ugly like that. There's nothing the matter with me. Oh, fie!' he suddenly exclaimed, 'that rose is worm-eaten, and this one is quite crooked. After all, they're ugly roses. They're like the box in which they stand.'

And then he kicked the box with his foot, and tore both the roses off.

'Kay, what are you about?' cried the little girl.

And when he noticed her fright he tore off another rose, and then sprang in at his own window, away from pretty little Gerda.

When she afterwards came with her picture-book, he said it was only fit for babies in arms; and when grandmother told stories he always came in with a *but*; and when he could manage it, he would get behind her, put on a pair of spectacles, and talk just as she did; he could do that very cleverly, and the people laughed at him. Soon he could mimic the speech and the gait of everybody in the street. Everything that was peculiar or ugly about them Kay could imitate; and people said, 'That boy must certainly have a remarkable head.' But it was the glass he had got in his eye, the glass that stuck deep in his heart; so it happened that he even teased little Gerda, who loved him with all her heart.

His games now became quite different from what they were before; they became quite sensible. One winter's day when it snowed he came out with a great burning-glass, held up the blue tail of his coat, and let the snowflakes fall upon it.

'Now look at the glass, Gerda,' said he.

And every flake of snow was magnified, and looked like a splendid flower, or a star with ten points: it was beautiful to behold.

'See how clever that is,' said Kay. 'That's much more interesting than real flowers; and there is not a single fault in it – they're quite regular until they begin to melt.'

Soon after Kay came in thick gloves, and with his sledge upon his back. He called up to Gerda, 'I've got leave to go into the great square, where the other boys play,' and he was gone.

In the great square the boldest among the boys often tied their sledges to the country people's carts, and thus rode with them a good way. They went capitally. When they were in the midst of their playing there came a great sledge. It was painted quite white, and in it sat somebody wrapped in a rough white fur, and with a white rough cap on his head. The sledge drove twice round the square, and Kay bound his little sledge to it, and so he drove on with it. It went faster and faster, straight into the next street. The man who drove turned round and nodded in a friendly way to Kay; it was as if they knew one another: each time when Kay wanted to cast loose his little sledge, the stranger nodded again, and then Kay remained where he was, and thus they drove out at the town gate. Then the snow began to fall so rapidly that the boy could not see a hand's breadth before him, but still he drove on. Now he hastily dropped the cord, so as to get loose from the great sledge, but that was no use, for his sledge was fast bound to the other, and they went on like the wind. Then he called out quite loudly, but nobody heard him; and the snow beat down, and the sledge flew onward; every now and then it gave a jump, and they seemed to be flying over hedges and ditches. The boy was quite frightened. He wanted to say his prayers, but could remember nothing but the multiplication table.

The snowflakes became larger and larger, at last they looked like great white fowls. All at once they sprang aside and the great sledge stopped, and the person who had driven it rose up. The fur and the cap were made altogether of ice. It was *a lady*, tall and slender, and brilliantly white: it was the Snow Queen.

'We have driven well!' said she. 'But why do you tremble with cold? Creep into my fur.'

And she seated him beside her in her own sledge, and wrapped the fur round him, and he felt as if he sank into a snow-drift.

'Are you still cold?' asked she, and then she kissed him on the forehead.

Oh, that was colder than ice; it went quite through to his heart, half of which was already a lump of ice: he felt as if he were going to die; but only for a moment; for then he seemed quite well, and he did not notice the cold all about him.

'My sledge! don't forget my sledge.'

That was the first thing he thought of; and it was bound fast to one of the white chickens, and this chicken flew behind him with the sledge upon its back. The Snow Queen kissed Kay again, and then he had forgotten little Gerda, his grandmother, and all at home.

'Now you shall have no more kisses,' said she, 'for if you did I should kiss you to death.'

Kay looked at her. She was so beautiful, he could not imagine a more sensible or lovely face; she did not appear to him to be made of ice now as before, when she sat at the window and beckoned to him. In his eyes she was perfect; he did not feel at all afraid. He told her that he could do mental arithmetic as far as fractions, that he knew the number of square miles, and the number of inhabitants in the country. And she always smiled, and then it seemed to him that what he knew was not enough, and he looked up into the wide sky, and she flew with him high up upon the black cloud, and the storm blew and whistled; it seemed as though the wind sang old songs. They flew over woods and lakes, over sea and land: below them roared the cold wind, the wolves howled, the snow crackled; over them flew the black screaming crows; but above all the moon shone bright and clear, and Kay looked at the long, long winter night; by day he slept at the feet of the Queen.

Third Story

The Flower Garden of the Woman who could Conjure

But how did it fare with little Gerda when Kay did not return? What could have become of him? No one knew, no one could give information. The boys only told that they had seen him bind his sledge to another very large one, which had driven along the street and out at the town gate. Nobody knew what had become of him; many tears were shed, and little Gerda especially wept long and bitterly: then they said he was dead – he had been drowned in the river which flowed close by their town. Oh, those were very dark long winter days! But now spring came, with warmer sunshine.

'Kay is dead and gone,' said little Gerda.

'I don't believe it,' said the Sunshine.

'He is dead and gone,' said she to the Swallows.

'We don't believe it,' they replied; and at last little Gerda did not believe it herself.

'I will put on my new red shoes,' she said one morning, 'those that Kay has never seen; and then I will go down to the river, and ask for him.'

It was still very early; she kissed the old grandmother, who was still asleep, put on her red shoes, and went quite alone out of the town gate towards the river.

'Is it true that you have taken away my little playmate from me? I will give you my red shoes if you will give him back to me!'

And it seemed to her as if the waves nodded quite strangely; and then she took her red shoes, that she liked best of anything she possessed, and threw them both into the river; but they fell close to the shore, and the little wavelets carried them back to her, to the land. It seemed as if the river would not take from her the dearest things she possessed because it had not her little Kay; but she thought she had not thrown the shoes far enough out; so she crept into a boat that lay among the reeds; she went to the other end of the boat, and threw the shoes from thence into the water; but the boat was not bound fast, and at the movement she made it glided away from the shore. She noticed it, and hurried to get back, but before she reached the other end the boat was a yard from the bank, and it drifted away faster than before.

Then little Gerda was very much frightened, and began to cry; but no one heard her except the Sparrows, and they could not carry her to land; but they flew along by the shore, and sang, as if to console her, 'Here we are! here we are!' The boat drove on with the stream, and little Gerda sat quite still, with only her stockings on her feet; her little red shoes floated along behind her, but they could not come up to the boat, for that made more way.

It was very pretty on both shores. There were beautiful flowers, old trees, and slopes with sheep and cows; but not *one* person was to be seen.

'Perhaps the river will carry me to little Kay,' thought Gerda.

And then she became more cheerful, and rose up, and for many hours she watched the charming green banks; then she came to a great cherry orchard, in which stood a little house with remarkable blue and red windows; it had a thatched roof, and without stood two wooden soldiers, who presented arms to those who sailed past.

Gerda called to them, for she thought they were alive, but of course they did not answer. She came quite close to them; the river carried the boat towards the shore.

Gerda called still louder, and then there came out of the house an old, old woman leaning on a crutch: she had on a great sun-hat, painted over with the finest flowers.

'You poor little child!' said the old woman, 'how did you manage to come on the great rolling river, and to float thus far out into the world?'

And then the old woman went quite into the water, seized the boat with her crutch-stick, drew it to land, and lifted little Gerda out. And Gerda was glad to be on dry land again, though she felt a little afraid of the strange old woman.

'Come and tell me who you are, and how you came here,' said the old lady. And Gerda told her everything; and the old woman shook her head, and said, 'Hem! hem!' And when Gerda had told everything, and asked if she had not seen little Kay, the woman said that he had not yet come by, but that he probably would soon come. Gerda was not to be sorrowful, but to look at the flowers and taste the cherries, for they were better than any picture-book, for each one of them could tell a story. Then she took Gerda by the hand and led her into the little house, and the old woman locked the door.

The windows were very high, and the panes were red, blue, and yellow; the daylight shone in a remarkable way, with different colours. On the table stood the finest cherries, and Gerda ate as many of them as she liked, for she had leave to do so. While she was eating them, the old lady combed her hair with a golden comb, and the hair hung in ringlets of pretty yellow round the friendly little face, which looked as blooming as a rose.

'I have long wished for such a dear little girl as you,' said the old lady. 'Now you shall see how well we shall live with one another.'

And as the ancient dame combed her hair, Gerda forgot her adopted brother Kay more and more; for this old woman could conjure, but she was not a wicked witch. She only practised a little magic for her own amusement, and wanted to keep little Gerda. Therefore she went into the garden, stretched out her crutch towards all the rose bushes,

and, beautiful as they were, they all sank into the earth, and one could not tell where they had stood. The old woman was afraid that if the little girl saw roses, she would think of her own, and remember little Kay, and run away.

Now Gerda was led out into the flower-garden. What fragrance was there, and what loveliness! Every conceivable flower was there in full bloom; there were some for every season: no picture-book could be gayer and prettier. Gerda jumped high for joy, and played till the sun went down behind the high cherry trees; then she was put into a lovely bed with red silk pillows stuffed with blue violets, and she slept there, and dreamed as gloriously as a Queen on her wedding-day.

One day she played again with the flowers in the warm sunshine; and thus many days went by. Gerda knew every flower; but, as many as there were of them, it still seemed to her as if one were wanting, but which one she did not know. One day she sat looking at the old lady's hat with the painted flowers, and the prettiest of them all was a rose. The old lady had forgotten to take it out of her hat when she caused the others to disappear. But so it always is when one does not keep one's wits about one.

'What, are there no roses here?' cried Gerda.

And she went among the beds, and searched and searched, but there was not one to be found. Then she sat down and wept: her tears fell just upon a spot where a rose bush lay buried, and when the warm tears moistened the earth, the bush at once sprouted up as blooming as when it had sunk; and Gerda embraced it, and kissed the Roses, and thought of the beautiful roses at home, and also of little Kay.

'Oh, how I have been detained!' said the little girl. 'I wanted to seek for little Kay! Do you not know where he is?' she asked the Roses. 'Do you think he is dead?'

'He is not dead,' the Roses answered. 'We have been in the ground. All the dead people are there, but Kay is not there.'

'Thank you,' said little Gerda; and she went to the other flowers, looked into their cups, and asked, 'Do you not know where little Kay is?'

But every flower stood in the sun thinking only of her own story or fairy tale: Gerda heard many, many of them; but not one knew anything of Kay.

And what did the Tiger-Lily say?

'Do you hear the drum "Rub-dub"? There are only two notes, always "rub-dub!" Hear the morning song of the women, hear the call of the priests. The Hindu widow stands in her long red mantle on the funeral pile; the flames rise up around her and her dead husband; but the Hindu woman is thinking of the living one here in the circle, of him whose eyes burn hotter than flames, whose fiery glances have burned in her soul more ardently than the flames themselves, which are soon to burn her body to ashes. Can the flame of the heart die in the flame of the funeral pile?'

'I don't understand that at all!' said little Gerda.

'That's my story,' said the Lily.

What says the Convolvulus?

'Over the narrow road looms an old knightly castle: thickly the ivy grows over the crumbling red walls, leaf by leaf up to the balcony, and there stands a beautiful girl; she bends over the balustrade and looks down at the road. No rose on its branch is fresher than she; no apple blossom wafted onward by the wind floats more lightly along. How her costly silks rustle! "Comes he not yet?"'

'Is it Kay whom you mean?' asked little Gerda.

'I'm only speaking of my own story – my dream,' replied the Convolvulus.

What said the little Snowdrop?

'Between the trees a long board hangs by ropes; that is a swing. Two pretty little girls, with clothes white as snow and long green silk ribbons on their hats, are sitting upon it, swinging; their brother, who is greater than they, stands in the swing, and has slung his arm round the rope to hold himself, for in one hand he has a little saucer, and in the other a clay pipe; he is blowing bubbles. The swing flies, and the bubbles rise with beautiful changing colours; the last still hangs from the pipe-bowl, swaying in the wind. The swing flies on: the little black dog, light as the bubbles, stands up on his hind legs and wants to be taken into the swing; it flies on, and the dog falls, barks, and grows angry, for he is teased, and the bubble bursts. A swinging board and a bursting bubble – that is my song.'

'It may be very pretty, what you're telling, but you speak it so mournfully, and you don't mention little Kay at all.'

What do the Hyacinths say?

'There were three beautiful sisters, transparent and delicate. The dress of one was red, that of the second blue, and that of the third quite white; hand in hand they danced by the calm lake in the bright moon-light. They were not elves, they were human beings. It was so sweet and fragrant there! The girls disappeared in the forest, and the sweet fragrance became stronger: three coffins, with the three beautiful maidens lying in them, glided from the wood-thicket across the lake; the glow-worms flew gleaming about them like little hovering lights. Are the dancing girls sleeping, or are they dead? The flower-scent says they are dead and the evening bell tolls their knell.'

'You make me quite sorrowful,' said little Gerda. 'You scent so strongly, I cannot help thinking of the dead maidens. Ah! is little Kay really dead? The roses have been down in the earth, and they say no.'

'Kling! klang!' tolled the Hyacinth Bells. 'We are not tolling for little Kay – we don't know him; we only sing our song, the only one we know.'

And Gerda went to the Buttercup, gleaming forth from the green leaves.

'You are a little bright sun,' said Gerda. 'Tell me, if you know, where I may find my companion.'

And the Buttercup shone so gaily, and looked back at Gerda. What song might the Buttercup sing? It was not about Kay.

'In a little courtyard the clear sun shone warm on the first day of spring. The sunbeams glided down the white wall of the neighbouring house; close by grew the first yellow flower, glancing like gold in the bright sun's ray. The old grandmother sat out of doors in her chair; her granddaughter, a poor handsome maidservant, was coming home for a short visit: she kissed her grandmother. There was gold, heart's gold, in that blessed kiss, gold in the mouth, gold in the south, gold in the morning hour. See, that's my little story,' said the Buttercup.

'My poor old grandmother!' sighed Gerda. 'Yes, she is surely longing for me and grieving for me, just as she did for little Kay. But I shall soon go home and take Kay with me. There is no use of my asking the flowers, they only know their own song, and give me no information.' And then she tied her little frock round her, that she might run the faster; but the Jonquil struck against her leg as she sprang over it, and she stopped to look at the tall yellow flower, and asked, 'Do you, perhaps, know anything of little Kay?'

And she bent quite down to the flower, and what did it say?

'I can see myself! I can see myself!' said the Jonquil. 'Oh! oh! how I smell! Up in the little room in the gable stands a little dancing girl: she stands sometimes on one foot, sometimes on both; she seems to tread on all the world. She's nothing but an ocular delusion: she pours water out of a teapot on a bit of stuff – it is her bodice. "Cleanliness is a fine thing," she says; her white frock hangs on a hook; it has been washed in the teapot too, and dried on the roof: she puts it on and ties her saffron handkerchief round her neck, and the dress looks all the whiter. Point your toes! look how she seems to stand on a stalk. I can see myself! I can see myself!'

'I don't care at all about that,' said Gerda. 'That is nothing to tell me about.'

And then she ran to the end of the garden. The door was locked, but she pressed against the rusty lock, and it broke off, the door sprang open, and little Gerda ran with naked feet out into the wide world. She looked back three times, but no one was there to pursue her; at last she could run no longer, and seated herself on a great stone, and when she looked round the summer was over – it was late in autumn: one could not notice that in the beautiful garden, where there was always sunshine, and the flowers of every season always bloomed.

'Alas! how I have loitered!' said little Gerda. 'Autumn has come. I may not rest again.'

And she rose up to go on. Oh! how sore and tired her little feet were. All around it looked cold and bleak; the long willow leaves were quite yellow, and the mist dropped from them like water; one leaf after another dropped; only the sloe-thorn still bore fruit, but the sloes were sour, and set the teeth on edge. Oh! how grey and gloomy it looked, the wide world!

Fourth Story

The Prince and Princess

Gerda was compelled to rest again; then there came hopping across the snow, just opposite the spot where she was sitting, a great Crow. This Crow had long been sitting looking at her, nodding its head –

now it said, 'Krah! krah! Good-day! good-day!' It could not pronounce better, but it felt friendly towards the little girl, and asked where she was going all alone in the wide world. The word 'alone' Gerda understood very well, and felt how much it expressed; and she told the Crow the whole story of her life and fortunes, and asked if it had not seen Kay.

And the Crow nodded very gravely, and said, 'That may be! that may be!'

'What, do you think so?' cried the little girl, and nearly pressed the Crow to death, she kissed it so.

'Gently, gently!' said the Crow. 'I think I know: I believe it may be little Kay, but he has certainly forgotten you, with the Princess.'

'Does he live with a Princess?' asked Gerda.

'Yes; listen,' said the Crow. 'But it's so difficult for me to speak your language. If you know the Crows' language, I can tell it much better.'

'No, I never learned it,' said Gerda; 'but my grandmother understood it, and could speak the language too. I only wish I had learned it.'

'That doesn't matter,' said the Crow. 'I shall tell you as well as I can.'

And then the Crow told what it knew.

'In the country in which we now are, lives a Princess who is quite wonderfully clever, but then she has read all the newspapers in the world, and has forgotten them again, she is so clever. Lately she was sitting on the throne – and that's not so pleasant as is generally supposed – and she began to sing a song, and it was just this, "Why should I not marry now?" You see, there was something in that,' said the Crow. 'And so she wanted to marry, but she wished for a husband who could answer when he was spoken to, not one who only stood and looked handsome, for that is so tiresome. And so she had all her maids of honour summoned, and when they heard her intention they were very glad. "I like that," said they; "I thought the very same thing the other day." You may be sure that every word I am telling you is true,' added the Crow. 'I have a tame sweetheart who goes about freely in the castle, and she told me everything.'

Of course the sweetheart was a crow, for one crow always finds out another, and birds of a feather flock together.

'Newspapers were published directly, with a border of hearts and the Princess's initials. One could read in them that every young man who was good-looking might come to the castle and speak with the Princess, and him who spoke so that one could hear he was at home there, and who spoke best, the Princess would choose for her husband. Yes, yes,' said the Crow, 'you may believe me. It's as true as I sit here. Young men came flocking in; there was a great crowding and much running to and fro, but no one succeeded the first or second day. They could all speak well when they were out in the streets, but when they entered at the palace gates, and saw the guards standing in their silver lace, and went up the staircase, and saw the lackeys in their golden liveries, and the great lighted halls, they became confused. And when they stood before the throne itself, on which the Princess sat, they could do nothing but repeat the last word she had spoken, and she did not care to hear her own words again. It was just as if the people in there had taken some narcotic and fallen asleep, till they got into the street again, for not till then were they able to speak. There stood a whole row of them, from the town gate to the palace gate. I went in myself to see it,' said the Crow. 'They were hungry and thirsty, but in the palace they did not receive so much as a glass of lukewarm water. A few of the wisest had brought bread and butter with them, but they would not share with their neighbours, for they thought "Let him look hungry, and the Princess won't have him."'

'But Kay, little Kay?' asked Gerda. 'When did he come? Was he among the crowd?'

'Wait, wait! We're just coming to him. It was on the third day that there came a little personage, without horse or carriage, walking quite merrily up to the castle; his eyes sparkled like yours, he had fine long hair, but his clothes were shabby.'

'That was Kay!' cried Gerda, rejoicingly. 'Oh, then I have found him!' And she clapped her hands.

'He had a little knapsack on his back,' observed the Crow.

'No, that must certainly have been his sledge,' said Gerda, 'for he went away with a sledge.'

'That may well be,' said the Crow, 'for I did not look to it very closely. But this much I know from my tame sweetheart, that when he passed under the palace gate and saw the Life Guards in silver, and mounted the staircase and saw the lackeys in gold, he was not in the least embarrassed. He nodded, and said to them, "It must be tedious work standing on the stairs – I'd rather go in." The halls shone full of lights; privy councillors and Excellencies walked about with bare feet, and carried golden vessels; anyone might have become solemn; and his boots creaked most noisily, but he was not embarrassed.'

'That is certainly Kay!' cried Gerda. 'He had new boots on; I've heard them creak in grandmother's room.'

'Yes, certainly they creaked,' resumed the Crow. 'And he went boldly in to the Princess herself, who sat on a pearl that was as big as a spinning-wheel; and all the maids of honour with their attendants, and the attendants' attendants, and all the cavaliers with their followers, and the followers of their followers, who themselves kept a page apiece, were standing round; and the nearer they stood to the door, the prouder they looked. The followers' followers' pages, who always went in slippers, could hardly be looked at, so proudly did they stand in the doorway!'

'That must be terrible!' faltered little Gerda. 'And yet Kay won the Princess?'

'If I had not been a crow, I would have married her myself, notwithstanding that I am engaged. They say he spoke as well as I can when I speak the crows' language; I heard that from my tame sweetheart. He was merry and agreeable; he had not come to woo, but only to hear the wisdom of the Princess; and he approved of her, and she of him.'

'Yes, certainly that was Kay!' said Gerda. 'He was so clever, he could do mental arithmetic up to fractions. Oh! won't you lead me to the castle too?'

'That's easily said,' replied the Crow. 'But how are we to manage it? I'll talk it over with my tame sweetheart; she can probably advise us; for this I must tell you – a little girl like yourself will never get leave to go quite in.'

'Yes, I shall get leave,' said Gerda. 'When Kay hears that I'm there he'll come out directly, and bring me in.'

'Wait for me yonder at the stile,' said the Crow; and it wagged its head and flew away.

It was already late in the evening when the Crow came back.

'Rare! rare!' it said. 'I'm to greet you kindly from my sweetheart, and here's a little loaf for you. She took it from the kitchen. There's plenty of bread there, and you must be hungry. You can't possibly get into the palace, for you are barefoot, and the guards in silver and the lackeys in gold would not allow it. But don't cry; you shall go up. My sweetheart knows a little back staircase that leads up to the bedroom, and she knows where she can get the key.'

And they went into the garden, into the great avenue, where one leaf was falling down after another; and when the lights were extinguished in the palace one after the other, the Crow led Gerda to a back door, which stood ajar.

Oh, how Gerda's heart beat with fear and longing! It was just as if she had been going to do something wicked; and yet she only wanted to know if it was little Kay. Yes, it must be he. She thought so deeply of his clear eyes and his long hair, she could fancy she saw how he smiled as he had smiled at home when they sat among the roses. He would certainly be glad to see her; to hear what a long distance she had come for his sake; to know how sorry they had all been at home when he did not come back. Oh, what a fear and what a joy that was!

Now they were on the staircase. A little lamp was burning upon a cupboard, and in the middle of the floor stood the tame Crow turning her head on every side and looking at Gerda, who curtsied as her grandmother had taught her to do.

'My betrothed has spoken to me very favourably of you, my little lady,' said the tame Crow. 'Your history, as it may be called, is very moving. Will you take the lamp? then I will precede you. We will go the straight way, for we shall meet nobody.'

'I feel as if someone were coming after us,' said Gerda, as something rushed by her: it seemed like shadows on the wall; horses with flying manes and thin legs, hunters, and ladies and gentlemen on horseback.

'These are only dreams,' said the Crow; 'they are coming to carry the high masters' thoughts out hunting. That's all the better, for you may look at them the more closely, in bed. But I hope, when you come to honour and dignity, you will show a grateful heart.'

'Of that we may be sure!' observed the Crow from the wood.

Now they came into the first hall: it was hung with rose-coloured satin, and artificial flowers were worked on the walls; and here the dreams already came flitting by them, but they moved so quickly that Gerda could not see the high-born lords and ladies. Each hall was more splendid than the last; yes, one could almost become bewildered! Now they were in the bedchamber. Here the ceiling was like a great palm tree with leaves of glass, of costly glass, and in the middle of the floor two beds hung on a thick stalk of gold, and each of them looked like a lily. One of them was white, and in that lay the Princess; the other was red, and in that Gerda was to seek little Kay. She bent one of the red leaves aside, and then she saw a little brown neck. Oh, that was Kay! She called out his name quite loud, and held the lamp towards him. The dreams rushed into the room again on horseback – he awoke, turned his head, and – it was not little Kay!

The Prince was only like him in the neck; but he was young and good-looking, and the Princess looked up, blinking, from the white lily, and asked who was there. Then little Gerda wept, and told her whole history, and all that the Crows had done for her.

'You poor child!' said the Prince and Princess.

And they praised the Crows, and said that they were not angry with them at all, but the Crows were not to do it again. However, they should be rewarded.

'Will you fly out free?' asked the Princess, 'or will you have fixed positions as court crows, with the right to everything that is left in the kitchen?'

And the two Crows bowed, and begged for fixed positions, for they thought of their old age, and said, 'It is so good to have some provisions for one's old days,' as they called them.

And the Prince got up out of his bed, and let Gerda sleep in it, and he could not do more than that. She folded her little hands, and thought, 'How good men and animals are!' and then she shut her eyes and went quietly to sleep. All the dreams came flying in again, looking

like angels, and they drew a little sledge, on which Kay sat nodding;
but all this was only a dream, and therefore it was gone again as soon as
she awoke.

The next day she was clothed from head to foot in silk and velvet;
and an offer was made her that she should stay in the castle and enjoy
pleasant times; but she only begged for a little carriage, with a horse to
draw it, and a pair of little boots; then she would drive out into the
world and seek for Kay.

And she received not only boots, but a muff likewise, and was neatly
dressed; and when she was ready to depart a coach made of pure gold
stopped before the door. Upon it shone like a star the coat of arms of
the Prince and Princess; coachman, footmen, and outriders – for there
were outriders too – sat on horseback with gold crowns on their heads.
The Prince and Princess themselves helped her into the carriage, and
wished her all good fortune. The forest Crow, who was now married,
accompanied her the first three miles; he sat by Gerda's side, for he
could not bear riding backwards: the other Crow stood in the doorway
flapping her wings: she did not go with them, for she suffered from
headache, that had come on since she had obtained a fixed position and

was allowed to eat too much. The coach was lined with sugar-biscuits, and in the seat there were gingerbread-nuts and fruit.

'Farewell, farewell!' cried the Prince and Princess; and little Gerda wept, and the Crow wept. So they went on for the first three miles; and then the Crow said goodbye, and that was the heaviest parting of all. The Crow flew up on a tree, and beat his black wings as long as he could see the coach, which glittered like the bright sunshine.

Fifth Story

The Little Robber Girl

They drove on through the thick forest, but the coach gleamed like a torch, dazzling the robbers' eyes, so that they could not bear it.

'That is gold! that is gold!' cried they, and rushed forward, and seized the horses, killed the postilions, the coachman, and the footmen, and then pulled little Gerda out of the carriage.

'She is fat – she is pretty – she is fed with nut-kernels!' said the old robber woman, who had a very long stiff beard, and shaggy eyebrows that hung down over her eyes. 'She's as good as a little pet lamb; how I shall relish her!'

And she drew out her shining knife, that gleamed in a horrible way.

'Oh!' screamed the old woman at the same moment; for her own daughter who hung at her back bit her ear in a very naughty and spiteful manner. 'You ugly brat!' screamed the old woman; and she had not time to kill Gerda.

'She shall play with me!' said the little robber girl. 'She shall give me her muff and her pretty dress, and sleep with me in my bed!'

And then the girl gave another bite, so that the woman jumped high up, and turned right round, and all the robbers laughed, and said, 'Look how she dances with her calf.'

'I want to go into the carriage,' said the little robber girl.

And she would have her own way, for she was spoiled, and very obstinate; and she and Gerda sat in the carriage, and drove over stock and stone deep into the forest. The little robber girl was as big as

Gerda, but stronger and more broad-shouldered; and she had a brown skin; her eyes were quite black, and they looked almost mournful. She clasped little Gerda round the waist, and said, 'They shall not kill you as long as I am not angry with you. I suppose you are a Princess?'

'No,' replied Gerda. And she told all that had happened to her, and how fond she was of little Kay.

The robber girl looked at her seriously, nodded slightly, and said, 'They shall not kill you even if I do get angry with you, for then I will do it myself.'

And then she dried Gerda's eyes, and put her two hands into the beautiful muff that was so soft and warm.

Now the coach stopped, and they were in the courtyard of a robber castle. It had split from the top to the bottom; ravens and crows flew out of the great holes, and big bulldogs – each of which looked as if he could devour a man – jumped high up, but they did not bark, for that was forbidden.

In the great old smoky hall a bright fire burned upon the stone floor; the smoke passed along under the ceiling, and had to seek an exit for itself. A great cauldron of soup was boiling and hares and rabbits were roasting on the spit.

'You shall sleep tonight with me and all my little animals,' said the robber girl.

They got something to eat and drink, and then went to a corner, where straw and carpets were spread out. Above these sat on laths and perches more than a hundred pigeons, that all seemed asleep, but they turned a little when the two little girls came.

'All these belong to me,' said the little robber girl; and she quickly seized one of the nearest, held it by the feet, and shook it so that it flapped its wings. 'Kiss it!' she cried, and beat it in Gerda's face. 'There sit the wood rascals,' she continued, pointing to a number of laths that had been nailed in front of a hole in the wall. 'Those are wood rascals, those two; they fly away directly if one does not keep them well locked up. And here's my old sweetheart "Ba".' And she pulled out by the horn a Reindeer, that was tied up, and had a polished copper ring round its neck. 'We're obliged to keep him tight too, or he'd run away from us. Every evening I tickle his neck with a sharp knife, and he's very frightened at that.'

And the little girl drew a long knife from a cleft in the wall, and let it glide over the Reindeer's neck; the poor creature kicked out its legs, and the little robber girl laughed, and drew Gerda into bed with her.

'Do you keep the knife beside you while you're asleep?' asked Gerda, and looked at it in rather a frightened way.

'I always sleep with my knife,' replied the robber girl. 'One does not know what may happen. But now tell me again what you told me just now about little Kay, and why you came out into the wide world.'

And Gerda told it again from the beginning; and the Wood Pigeons cooed above them in their cage, and the other pigeons slept. The little robber girl put her arm round Gerda's neck, held her knife in the other hand, and slept so that one could hear her; but Gerda could not close her eyes at all – she did not know whether she was to live or die.

The robbers sat round the fire, singing and drinking, and the old robber woman tumbled about. It was quite terrible for a little girl to behold.

Then the Wood Pigeons said, 'Coo! coo! we have seen little Kay. A white hen was carrying his sledge: he sat in the Snow Queen's carriage, which drove close by the forest as we lay in our nests. She blew upon us young pigeons, and all died except us two. Coo! coo!'

'What are you saying there?' asked Gerda. 'Whither was the Snow Queen travelling? Do you know anything about it?'

'She was probably journeying to Lapland, for there they have always ice and snow. Ask the Reindeer that is tied up with the cord.'

'There is ice and snow yonder, and it is glorious and fine,' said the Reindeer. 'There one may run about free in great glittering plains. There the Snow Queen has her summer tent; but her strong castle is up towards the North Pole, on the island that's called Spitzbergen.'

'Oh, Kay, little Kay!' cried Gerda.

'You must lie still,' exclaimed the robber girl, 'or I shall thrust my knife into your body.'

In the morning Gerda told her all that the Wood Pigeons had said, and the robber girl looked quite serious, and nodded her head and said, 'That's all the same, that's all the same!'

'Do you know where Lapland is?' she asked the Reindeer.

'Who should know better than I?' the creature replied, and its eyes sparkled in its head. 'I was born and bred there; I ran about there in the snow-fields.'

'Listen!' said the robber girl to Gerda. 'You see all our men have gone away. Only mother is here still, and she'll stay; but towards noon she drinks out of the big bottle, and then she sleeps for a little while; then I'll do something for you.'

Then she sprang out of bed, and clasped her mother round the neck and pulled her beard, crying

'Good-morning, my own old nanny-goat.' And her mother filliped her nose till it was red and blue; but it was all done for pure love.

When the mother had drunk out of her bottle and had gone to sleep upon it, the robber girl went to the Reindeer, and said, 'I should like very much to tickle you a few times more with the knife, for you are very funny then; but it's all the same. I'll loosen your cord and help you out, so that you may run to Lapland; but you must use your legs well, and carry this little girl to the palace of the Snow Queen, where her playfellow is. You've heard what she told me, for she spoke loud enough, and you were listening.'

The Reindeer sprang up high for joy. The robber girl lifted little Gerda on its back, and had the forethought to tie her fast, and even to give her a little cushion as a saddle.

'There are your fur boots for you,' she said, 'for it's growing cold; but I shall keep the muff, for that's so very pretty. Still, you shall not be cold, for all that: here's my mother's big mufflers – they'll just reach up to your elbows. Now your hands look just like my ugly mother's.'

And Gerda wept for joy.

'I can't bear to see you whimper,' said the little robber girl. 'No, you just ought to look very glad. And here are two loaves and a ham for you, so you won't be hungry.'

These were tied on the Reindeer's back. The little robber girl opened the door, coaxed in all the big dogs, and then cut the rope with her sharp knife, and said to the Reindeer, 'Now run, but take good care of the little girl.'

And Gerda stretched out her hands with the big mufflers towards the little robber girl, and said, 'Farewell!'

And the Reindeer ran over stock and stone, away through the great forest, over marshes and steppes, as quick as it could go. The wolves howled and the ravens croaked. 'Hiss! hiss!' it went in the air. It seemed as if the sky were flashing fire.

'Those are my old Northern Lights,' said the Reindeer. 'Look how they glow!' And then it ran on faster than ever, day and night.

The loaves were eaten, and the ham as well, and then they were in Lapland.

Sixth Story

The Lapland Woman and the Finland Woman

At a little hut they stopped. It was very humble; the roof sloped down almost to the ground, and the door was so low that the family had to creep on their stomachs when they wanted to go in or out. No one was in the house but an old Lapland woman, cooking fish on a train-oil lamp; and the Reindeer told Gerda's whole history, but it related its own first, for this seemed to the Reindeer the more important of the two. Gerda was so exhausted by the cold that she could not speak.

'Oh, you poor things,' said the Lapland woman, 'you've a long way to run yet! You must go more than a hundred miles into Finmark, for the Snow Queen is there, staying in the country, and burning Bengal lights every evening. I'll write a few words on a dried cod, for I have no paper, and I'll give you that as a letter to the Finland woman; she can give you better information than I.'

And when Gerda had been warmed and refreshed with food and drink, the Lapland woman wrote a few words on a dried codfish, and telling Gerda to take care of it, tied her again on the Reindeer, and the Reindeer sprang away. Flash! flash! it went high in the air; the whole night long the most beautiful blue Northern Lights were burning.

And then they got to Finmark, and knocked at the chimney of the Finland woman, for she had not even a door.

There was such a heat in the chimney that the woman herself went about almost naked. She was little and very dirty. She at once loosened little Gerda's dress and took off the child's mufflers and boots; otherwise it would have been too hot for her to bear. Then she laid a piece of ice on the Reindeer's head, and read what was written on the codfish; she read it three times, and when she knew it by heart, she popped the fish into the soup-cauldron, for it was eatable, and she never wasted anything.

Now the Reindeer first told his own history, and then little Gerda's; and the Finland woman blinked with her clever eyes, but said nothing.

'You are very clever,' said the Reindeer: 'I know you can tie all the winds of the world together with a bit of twine: if the seaman unties one knot, he has a good wind; if he loosens the second, it blows hard; but if he unties the third and the fourth, there comes such a tempest that the forests are thrown down. Won't you give the little girl a draught, so that she may get twelve men's power, and overcome the Snow Queen?'

'Twelve men's power!' repeated the Finland woman. 'Great use that would be!'

And she went to a shelf, and brought out a great rolled-up fur, and unrolled it; wonderful characters were written upon it, and the Finland woman read until the water ran down over her forehead.

But the Reindeer again begged so hard for little Gerda, and Gerda looked at the Finland woman with such beseeching eyes full of tears, that she began to blink again with her own, and drew the Reindeer into a corner, and whispered to him, while she laid fresh ice upon his head, 'Little Kay is certainly at the Snow Queen's, and finds everything there to his taste and liking, and thinks it the best place in the world; but that is because he has a splinter of glass in his eye, and a little fragment in his heart; but these must be got out, or he will never be a human being again, and the Snow Queen will keep her power over him.'

'But cannot you give something to little Gerda, so as to give her power over all this?'

'I can give her no greater power than she possesses already: don't you see how great that is? Don't you see how men and animals are obliged to serve her, and how she gets on so well in the world, with her naked feet? She must not learn her power from us: it consists in this, that she is a dear innocent child. If she herself cannot penetrate to the Snow Queen and get the glass out of little Kay, we can be of no use! Two miles from here the Snow Queen's garden begins; you can carry the little girl thither: set her down by the great bush that stands with its red berries in the snow. Don't stand gossiping, but make haste, and get back here!'

And then the Finland woman lifted little Gerda on the Reindeer, which ran as fast as it could.

'Oh, I haven't my boots! I haven't my mufflers!' cried Gerda.

She soon noticed that in the cutting cold; but the Reindeer dare not stop: it ran till it came to the bush with the red berries; there it set Gerda down, and kissed her on the mouth, and great bright tears ran over the creature's cheeks; and then it ran back, as fast as it could. There stood poor Gerda without shoes, without gloves, in the midst of the terrible cold Finmark.

She ran forward as fast as possible; then came a whole regiment of snowflakes; but they did not fall down from the sky, for that was quite bright, and shone with the Northern Lights: the snowflakes ran along the ground, and the nearer they came the larger they grew. Gerda still remembered how large and beautiful the snowflakes had appeared when she looked at them through the burning-glass. But here they were certainly far longer and much more terrible – they were alive. They were the advanced posts of the Snow Queen, and had the strangest shapes. A few looked like ugly great porcupines; others like knots formed of snakes, which stretched forth their heads; and others like little fat bears, whose hair stood on end: all were brilliantly white, all were living snowflakes.

Then little Gerda said her prayer; and the cold was so great that she could see her own breath, which went forth out of her mouth like smoke. The breath became thicker and thicker, and formed itself into little angels, who grew and grew whenever they touched the earth; and all had helmets on their heads and shields and spears in their hands; their number increased more and more, and when Gerda had finished her prayer a whole legion stood round about her, and struck with their spears at the terrible snowflakes, so that these were shattered into a thousand pieces; and little Gerda could go forward afresh, with good courage. The angels stroked her hands and feet, and then she felt less how cold it was, and hastened on to the Snow Queen's palace.

But now we must see what Kay is doing. He certainly was not thinking of little Gerda, and least of all that she was standing in front of the palace.

Seventh Story

Of the Snow Queen's Castle, and what happened there at last

The walls of the palace were formed of the drifting snow, and the windows and doors of the cutting winds. There were more than a hundred halls, all blown together by the snow: the greatest of these extended for several miles; the strong Northern Lights illumined them all, and how great and empty, how icily cold and shining they all were! Never was merriment there, not even a little bears' ball, at which the storm could have played the music, while the bears walked about on their hind legs and showed off their pretty manners; never any little coffee gossip among the young lady white foxes. Empty, vast, and cold were the halls of the Snow Queen. The Northern Lights flamed so brightly that one could count them where they stood highest and lowest. In the midst of this immense empty snow hall was a frozen lake, which had burst into a thousand pieces; but each piece was like the rest, so that it was a perfect work of art; and in the middle of the lake sat the Snow Queen when she was at home, and then she said that she sat in the mirror of reason, and that this was the only one, and the best in the world.

Little Kay was quite blue with cold – indeed, almost black, but he did not notice it, for she had kissed the cold shudderings away from him; and his heart was like a lump of ice. He dragged a few sharp flat pieces of ice to and fro, joining them together in all kinds of ways, for he wanted to achieve something with them. It was just like when we have little tablets of wood, and lay them together to form figures – what we call the Chinese puzzle. Kay also went and laid figures, and, indeed, very artistic ones. That was the icy game of reason. In his eyes these figures were very remarkable and of the highest importance; that was because of the fragment of glass sticking in his eye. He laid out the figures so that they formed a word – but he could never manage to lay down the word as he wished to have it – the word 'Eternity'. And the Snow Queen had said, 'If you can find out this figure, you shall be your own master, and I will give you the whole world and a new pair of skates.'

But he could not.

'Now I'll hasten away to the warm lands,' said the Snow Queen. 'I will go and look into the black pots': these were the volcanoes, Etna and Vesuvius, as they are called. 'I shall make them a little white! That's necessary; that will do the grapes and lemons good.'

And the Snow Queen flew away, and Kay sat quite alone in the great icy hall that was miles in extent, and looked at his pieces of ice, and thought so deeply that cracks were heard inside him: he sat quite stiff and still, one would have thought that he was frozen to death.

Then it happened that little Gerda stepped through the great gate into the wide hall. Here reigned cutting winds, but she prayed a prayer, and the winds lay down as if they would have gone to sleep; and she stepped into the great empty cold halls, and beheld Kay; she knew him, and flew to him and embraced him, and held him fast, and called out, 'Kay, dear little Kay! at last I have found you!'

But he sat quite still, stiff and cold. Then little Gerda wept hot tears, that fell upon his breast; they penetrated into his heart, they thawed the lump of ice, and consumed the little piece of glass in it. He looked at her, and she sang:

> Roses bloom and roses decay,
> But we the Christ-child shall see one day.

Then Kay burst into tears; he wept so that the splinter of glass came out of his eye. Now he recognised her, and cried rejoicingly, 'Gerda, dear Gerda! where have you been all this time? And where have I been?' And he looked all around him. 'How cold it is here! how large and empty!'

And he clung to Gerda, and she laughed and wept for joy. It was so glorious that even the pieces of ice round about danced for joy; and when they were tired and lay down, they formed themselves just into the letters of which the Snow Queen had said that if he found them out he should be his own master, and she would give him the whole world and a new pair of skates.

And Gerda kissed his cheeks, and they became blooming; she kissed his eyes, and they shone like her own; she kissed his hands and feet, and he became well and merry. The Snow Queen might now come home; his letter of release stood written in shining characters of ice.

And they took one another by the hand, and wandered forth from the great palace of ice. They spoke of the grandmother, and of the roses on the roof; and where they went the winds rested and the sun burst forth; and when they came to the bush with the red berries, the Reindeer was standing there waiting: it had brought another young reindeer, which gave the children warm milk, and kissed them on the mouth. Then they carried Kay and Gerda, first to the Finnish woman, where they warmed themselves thoroughly in the hot room, and received instructions for their journey home, and then to the Lapland woman, who had made their new clothes and put their sledge in order.

The Reindeer and the young one sprang at their side, and followed them as far as the boundary of the country. There the first green sprouted forth, and there they took leave of the two reindeer and the Lapland woman. 'Farewell!' said all. And the first little birds began to twitter, the forest was decked with green buds, and out of it on a beautiful horse (which Gerda knew, for it was the same that had drawn her golden coach) a young girl came riding, with a shining red cap on her head and a pair of pistols in the holsters. This was the little robber girl, who had grown tired of staying at home, and wished to go first to the north, and if that did not suit her, to some other region. She knew Gerda at once, and Gerda knew her too; and it was a right merry meeting.

'You are a fine fellow to gad about!' she said to little Kay. 'I should like to know if you deserve that one should run to the end of the world after you?'

But Gerda patted her cheeks, and asked after the Prince and Princess.

'They've gone to foreign countries,' said the robber girl.

'But the Crow?' said Gerda.

'Why, the Crow is dead,' answered the other. 'The tame one has become a widow, and goes about with an end of black worsted thread round her leg. She complains most lamentably, but it's all talk. But now tell me how you have fared, and how you caught him.'

And Gerda and Kay told their story.

'Snip-snap-snurre-basse-lurre!' said the robber girl.

And she took them both by the hand, and promised that if she ever came through their town, she would come up and pay them a visit. And then she rode away into the wide world. But Gerda and Kay went hand in hand, and as they went it became beautiful spring, with green and with flowers. The church bells sounded, and they recognised the high steeples and the great town: it was the one in which they lived; and they went to the grandmother's door, and up the stairs, and into the room, where everything remained in its usual place. The big clock was going 'Tick! tack!' and the hands were turning; but as they went through the rooms they noticed that they had become grown-up people. The roses out on the roof gutter were blooming in at the open window, and there stood the little children's chairs, and Kay and Gerda sat each upon their own, and held each other by the hand. They had forgotten the cold empty splendour at the Snow Queen's like a heavy dream. The grandmother was sitting in God's bright sunshine, and read aloud out of the Bible, 'Except ye become as little children, ye shall in no wise enter into the kingdom of God.'

And Kay and Gerda looked into each other's eyes, and all at once they understood the old hymn –

> Roses bloom and roses decay,
> But we the Christ-child shall see one day.

There they both sat, grown up, and yet children – children in heart – and it was summer, warm, delightful summer.

The Elder Tree Mother

THERE was once a little boy who had caught cold; he had gone out and got wet feet; no one could imagine how it had happened, for it was quite dry weather. Now his mother undressed him, put him to bed, and had the tea-urn brought in to make him a good cup of elder tea, for that warms well. At the same time there also came in at the door the friendly old man who lived all alone at the top of the house, and was very solitary. He had neither wife nor children, but he was very fond of all children, and knew so many stories that it was quite delightful.

'Now you are to drink your tea,' said the mother, 'and then perhaps you will hear a story.'

'Ah! if one only could tell a new one!' said the old man, with a friendly nod. 'But where did the little man get his feet wet?' he asked.

'Yes,' replied the mother, 'no one can imagine how that came about.'

'Shall I have a story?' asked the boy.

'Yes, if you can tell me at all accurately – for I must know that first – how deep the gutter is in the little street through which you go to school.'

'Just halfway up to my knee,' answered the boy, 'that is, if I put my feet in the deep hole.'

'You see, that's how we get our feet wet,' said the old gentleman. 'Now I ought certainly to tell you a story; but I don't know any more.'

'You can make up one directly,' answered the little boy. 'Mother says that everything you look at can be turned into a story, and that you can make a tale of everything you touch.'

'Yes, but those stories and tales are worth nothing! No, the real ones come of themselves. They knock at my forehead, and say, "Here I am!"'

'Will there soon be a knock?' asked the little boy, and the mother laughed, and put elder tea in the pot, and poured hot water upon it.

'A story! a story!'

'Yes, if a story would come of itself; but that kind of thing is very grand; it only comes when it's in the humour. Wait!' he cried all at once; 'here we have it. Look you; there's one in the teapot now.'

And the little boy looked across at the teapot. The lid raised itself more and more, and the elder flowers came forth from it, white and fresh; they shot forth long fresh branches even out of the spout, they spread abroad in all directions, and became larger and larger; there was the most glorious elder bush – in fact, quite a great tree. It penetrated even to the bed, and thrust the curtains aside; how fragrant it was, and how it bloomed! And in the midst of the tree sat an old, pleasant-looking woman in a strange dress. It was quite green, like the leaves of the elder tree, and bordered with great white elder blossoms; one could not at once discern whether this border was of stuff or of living green and real flowers.

'What is the woman's name?' the little boy asked.

'The Romans and Greeks,' replied the old man, 'used to call her a Dryad; but we don't understand that: out in the sailors' quarter we have a better name for her; there she's called Elder Tree Mother, and it is to her you must pay attention: only listen, and look at that glorious elder tree.'

'Just such a great blooming tree stands out in the sailors' quarter; it grew there in the corner of a poor little yard, and under this tree two old people sat one afternoon in the brightest sunshine. It was an old, old sailor, and his old, old wife; they had great-grandchildren, and were soon to celebrate their golden wedding; but they could not quite make out the date, and the Elder Tree Mother sat in the tree and looked pleased, just as she does here. "I know very well when the golden wedding is to be," said she; but they did not hear it – they were talking of old times.

' "Yes, do you remember," said the old seaman, "when we were quite little, and ran about and played together! it was in the very same yard where we are sitting now, and we planted little twigs in the yard, and made a garden."

' "Yes," replied the old woman, "I remember it very well: we watered the twigs, and one of them was an elder twig; that struck root, shot out other green twigs, and has become the great tree, under which we old people sit."

' "Surely," said he; "and yonder in the corner stood a butt of water; there I swam my boat; I had cut it out myself. How it could sail! But I certainly soon had to sail in a different fashion myself."

' "But first we went to school and learned something," said she, "and then we were confirmed; we both cried, but in the afternoon we went hand in hand to the round tower, and looked out into the wide world, over Copenhagen and across the water; then we went out to Fredericksberg, where the King and Queen were sailing in their splendid boats upon the canals."

' "But I was obliged to sail in another fashion, and that for many years, far away on long voyages."

' "Yes, I often cried about you," she said. "I thought you were dead and gone, and lying down in the deep waters, rocked by the waves. Many a night I got up to look if the weathercock was turning. Yes, it turned indeed; but you did not come. I remember so clearly how the rain streamed down one day. The man with the cart who fetched away the dust came to the place where I was in service. I went down to him with the dustbin, and remained standing in the doorway. What wretched weather it was! And just as I stood there the postman came up and gave me a letter. It was from you! How that letter had travelled about! I tore it open and read; I laughed and wept at once, I was so glad. There it stood written that you were in the warm countries where the coffee-beans grow. What a delightful land that must be! You told me so much, and I read it all while the rain was streaming down, and I stood by the dustbin. Then somebody came and clasped me round the waist."

' "And you gave him a terrible box on the ear – one that sounded?"

' "I did not know that it was you. You had arrived just as quickly as your letter. And you were so handsome; but that you are still. You had a long yellow silk handkerchief in your pocket, and a shiny hat on your head. You were so handsome! And, gracious! what weather it was, and how the street looked!"

' "Then we were married," said he; "do you remember? And then when our first little boy came, and then Marie, and Neils, and Peter and Hans Christian?"

' "Yes; and how all of these have grown up to be respectable people, and everyone likes them."

' "And their children have had little ones in their turn,"

said the old sailor. "Yes, those are children's children! They're of the right sort. It was, if I don't mistake, at this very season of the year that we were married?"

' "Yes; this is the day of your golden wedding," said the Elder Tree Mother, putting out her head just between the two old people; and they thought it was a neighbour nodding to them, and they looked at each other, and took hold of one another's hands.

'Soon afterwards came their children and grandchildren; these knew very well that it was the golden wedding-day; they had already brought their congratulations in the morning, but the old people had forgotten it, while they remembered everything right well that had happened years and years ago.

'And the elder tree smelt so strong, and the sun that was just setting shone just in the faces of the old people, so that their cheeks looked quite red; and the youngest of their grandchildren danced about them, and cried out quite gleefully that there was to be a feast this evening, for they were to have hot potatoes; and the Elder Mother nodded in the tree, and called out "hurrah!" with all the rest.'

'But that was not a story,' said the little boy who had heard it told.

'Yes, if you could understand it,' replied the old man; 'but let us ask the Elder Mother about it.'

'That was not a story,' said the Elder Mother; 'but now it comes; but of truth the strangest stories are formed, otherwise my beautiful elder tree could not have sprouted forth out of the teapot.'

And then she took the little boy out of bed, and laid him upon her bosom, and the blossoming elder branches wound round them, so that they sat as it were in the thickest arbour, and this arbour flew with them through the air. It was indescribably beautiful. Elder Mother all at once became a pretty young girl; but her dress was still of the green stuff with the white blossoms that Elder Mother had worn; in her bosom she had a real elder blossom, and about her yellow curly hair a wreath of elder flowers; her eyes were so large and blue, they were beautiful to look at. She and the boy were of the same age, and they kissed each other and felt similar joys.

Hand in hand they went forth out of the arbour, and now they stood in the beauteous flower garden of home. The father's staff was tied up near the fresh grass-plot, and for the little boy there was life in that staff. As soon as they seated themselves upon it, the polished head turned into a noble neighing horse's head, with a flowing mane, and four slender legs shot forth; the creature was strong and spirited, and they rode at a gallop round the grass-plot – hurrah!

'Now we're going to ride many miles away,' said the boy; 'we'll ride to the nobleman's estate, where we went last year!'

And they rode round and round the grass-plot, and the little girl, who, as we know, was no one else but Elder Mother, kept crying out, 'Now we're in the country! Do you see the farmhouse, with the great baking-oven standing out of the wall like an enormous egg by the

wayside? The elder tree spreads its branches over it, and the cock walks about, scratching for his hens; look how he struts! Now we are near the church; it lies high up on the hill, among the great oak trees, one of which is half dead. Now we are at the forge, where the fire burns and the half-clad men beat with their hammers, so that the sparks fly far around. Away, away to the nobleman's splendid seat!'

And everything that the little maiden mentioned, as she sat on the stick behind him, flew past them, and the little boy saw it all, though they were only riding round and round the grass-plot. Then they played in the side walk, and scratched up the earth to make a little garden; and she took elder flowers out of her hair and planted them, and they grew just like those that the old people had planted when they were little, as has been already told. They went hand in hand just as the old people had done in their childhood; but not to the round tower, or to the Fredericksberg Garden. No, the little girl took hold of the boy round the body, and then they flew here and there over the whole of Denmark.

And it was spring, and summer came, and autumn, and winter, and thousands of pictures were mirrored in the boy's eyes and heart, and the little maiden was always singing to him.

He will never forget that; and throughout their whole journey the elder tree smelt so sweet, so fragrant: he noticed the roses and the fresh beech trees; but the elder tree smelt stronger than all, for its flowers hung round the little girl's heart, and he often leaned against them as they flew onward.

'How beautiful it is here in spring!' said the little girl.

And they stood in the new-leaved beech wood, where the green woodruff lay spread in fragrance at their feet, and the pale pink anemones looked glorious among the vivid green.

'Oh, that it were always spring in the fragrant Danish beech woods!'

'How beautiful it is here in summer!' said she.

And they passed by old castles of knightly days, castles whose red walls and pointed gables were mirrored in the canals, where swans swam about, and looked down the old shady avenues. In the fields the corn waved like a sea, in the ditches yellow and red flowers were growing, and in the hedges wild hops and blooming convolvulus. In the evening the moon rose round and large, and the haystacks in the meadows smelt sweet.

'How beautiful it is here in autumn!' said the little girl.

And the sky seemed twice as lofty and twice as blue as before, and the forest was decked in the most gorgeous tints of red, yellow, and green. The hunting dogs raced about; whole flocks of wild ducks flew screaming over the ancient grave-mound, on which bramble bushes twined over the old stones. The sea was dark blue, and covered with ships with white sails; and in the barns sat old women, girls, and children, picking hops into a large tub: the young people sang songs, and the older ones told tales of magicians and goblins. It could not be finer anywhere.

'How beautiful it is here in winter!' said the little girl.

And all the trees were covered with hoar frost, so that they looked like white trees of coral. The snow crackled beneath one's feet, as if everyone had new boots on; and one shooting star after another fell from the sky. In the room the Christmas tree was lighted up, and there were presents, and there was happiness. In the country people's farmhouses the violin sounded, and there were merry games for apples; and even the poorest child said, 'It is beautiful in winter!'

Yes, it was beautiful; and the little girl showed the boy everything; and still the blossoming tree smelt sweet, and still waved the red flag with the white cross, the flag under which the old seaman had sailed. The boy became a youth, and was to go out into the wide world, far away to the hot countries where the coffee grows. But when they were to part the little girl took an elder blossom from her breast, and gave it to him to keep. It was laid in his hymn-book, and in the foreign land, when he opened the book, it was always at the place where the flower of remembrance lay; and the more he looked at the flower the fresher it became, so that he seemed, as it were, to breathe the forest air of home; then he plainly saw the little girl looking out with her clear blue eyes from between the petals of the flower, and then she whispered, 'How beautiful it is here in spring, summer, autumn, and winter!' and hundreds of pictures glided through his thoughts.

Thus many years went by, and now he was an old man, and sat with his old wife under the blossoming elder tree: they were holding each other by the hand, just as the great-grandmother and great-grandfather had done before; and, like these, they spoke of old times and of the golden wedding. The little maiden with the blue eyes and with the elder blossoms in her hair sat up in the tree, and nodded to both of them, and said, 'Today is the golden wedding-day!' and then she took two flowers out of her hair and kissed them, and they gleamed first like silver and then like gold, and when she laid them on the heads of the old people each changed into a golden crown. There they both sat, like a King and a Queen, under the fragrant tree which looked quite like an elder bush, and he told his old wife of the story of the Elder Tree Mother, as it had been told to him when he was quite a little boy, and they both thought that there was so much in the story that resembled their own, and those parts they liked the best.

'Yes, thus it is!' said the little girl in the tree. 'Some call me Elder Tree Mother, others the Dryad, but my real name is Remembrance: it is I who sit in the tree that grows on and on, and I can think back and tell stories. Let me see if you have still your flower.'

And the old man opened his hymn-book; there lay the elder blossom as fresh as if it had only just been placed there; and Remembrance nodded, and the two old people with the golden crowns on their heads sat in the red evening sunlight, and they closed their eyes, and – and – the story was finished.

The little boy lay in his bed and did not know whether he had been dreaming or had heard a tale told; the teapot stood on the table, but no elder bush was growing out of it, and the old man who had told about it was just going out of the door, and indeed he went.

'How beautiful that was!' said the little boy. 'Mother, I have been in the hot countries.'

'Yes, I can imagine that!' replied his mother. 'When one drinks two cups of hot elder tea one very often gets into the hot countries!' And she covered him up well, that he might not take cold. 'You have slept well while I disputed with him as to whether it was a story or a fairy tale.'

'And where is the Elder Tree Mother?' asked the little lad.

'She's in the teapot,' replied his mother; 'and there she may stay.'

The Darning-Needle

THERE was once a Darning-Needle, who thought herself so fine, she imagined she was an embroidering-needle.

'Take care, and mind you hold me tight!' she said to the Fingers which took her out. 'Don't let me fall! If I fall on the ground I shall certainly never be found again, for I am so fine!'

'That's as it may be,' said the Fingers; and they grasped her round the body.

'See, I'm coming with a train!' said the Darning-Needle, and she drew a long thread after her, but there was no knot in the thread.

The Fingers pointed the needle just at the cook's slipper, in which the upper leather had burst, and was to be sewn together.

'That's vulgar work,' said the Darning-Needle. 'I shall never get through. I'm breaking! I'm breaking!' And she really broke. 'Did I not say so?' said the Darning-Needle; 'I'm too fine!'

'Now it's quite useless,' said the Fingers; but they were obliged to hold her fast, all the same; for the cook dropped some sealing-wax upon the needle, and pinned her handkerchief together with it in front.

'So, now I'm a breast-pin!' said the Darning-Needle. 'I knew very well that I should come to honour: when one is something, one always comes to something!'

And she laughed inwardly – for no one can ever see outwardly when a darning-needle laughs. There she sat, as proud as if she was in a state coach, and looked all about her.

'May I be permitted to ask if you are of gold?' she enquired of the pin, her neighbour. 'You have a very pretty appearance, and a head of your own, but it is only little. You must see that it grows, for it's not everyone that has sealing-wax dropped upon their end.'

And the Darning-Needle drew herself up so proudly that she fell out of the handkerchief right into the sink, which the cook was rinsing out.

'Now we're going on a journey,' said the Darning-Needle. 'If only I don't get lost!'

But she really was lost.

'I'm too fine for this world,' she observed, as she lay in the gutter. 'But I know who I am, and there's always something in that!'

So the Darning-Needle kept her proud behaviour, and did not lose her good humour. And things of many kinds swam over her, chips and straws and pieces of old newspapers.

'Only look how they sail!' said the Darning-Needle. 'They don't know what is under them! I'm here, I remain firmly here. See, there goes a chip thinking of nothing in the world but of himself – of a chip! There's a straw going by now. How he turns! how he twirls about! Don't think so much of yourself, you might easily run up against a stone. There swims a bit of newspaper. What's written upon it has long been forgotten, and yet it gives itself airs. I sit quietly and patiently here. I know who I am, and I shall remain what I am.'

One day something lay close beside her that glittered splendidly; then the Darning-Needle believed that it was a diamond; but it was a Bit of broken Bottle; and because it shone, the Darning-Needle spoke to it, introducing herself as a breast-pin.

'I suppose you are a diamond?' she observed.

'Why, yes, something of that kind.'

And then each believed the other to be a very valuable thing; and they began speaking about the world, and how very conceited it was.

'I have been in a lady's box,' said the Darning-Needle, 'and this lady was a cook. She had five fingers on each hand, and I never saw anything so conceited as those five fingers. And yet they were only there that they might take me out of the box and put me back into it.'

'Were they of good birth?' asked the Bit of Bottle.

'No, indeed,' replied the Darning-Needle, 'but very haughty. There were five brothers, all of the finger family. They kept very proudly together, though they were of different lengths: the outermost, the thumbling, was short and fat; he walked out in front of the ranks, and only had one joint in his back, and could only make a single bow; but he said that if he were hacked off from a man, that man was useless for service in war. Lick-pot, the second finger, thrust himself into sweet and sour, pointed to sun and moon, and he was the one who held the pen when they wrote. Longman, the third, looked over the heads of the others. Goldborder, the fourth, went about with a golden belt round his waist; and little Peter Playman did nothing at all, and was proud of it. There was nothing but bragging among them, and therefore I went away.'

'And now we sit here and glitter!' said the Bit of Bottle.

At that moment more water came into the gutter, so that it overflowed, and the Bit of Bottle was carried away.

'So, he is disposed of,' observed the Darning-Needle. 'I remain here, I am too fine. But that's my pride, and my pride is honourable.' And proudly she sat there, and had many great thoughts. 'I could almost believe I had been born of a sunbeam, I'm so fine! It really appears to me as if the sunbeams were always seeking for me under the water. Ah! I'm so fine that my mother cannot find me. If I had my old eye, which broke off, I think I should cry; but, no, I should not do that: it's not genteel to cry.'

One day a couple of street boys lay grubbing in the gutter, where they sometimes found old nails, farthings, and similar treasures. It was dirty work, but they took great delight in it.

'Oh!' cried one, who had pricked himself with the Darning-Needle, 'there's a fellow for you!'

'I'm not a fellow, I'm a young lady!' said the Darning-Needle.

But nobody listened to her. The sealing-wax had come off, and she had turned black; but black makes one look slender, and she thought herself finer even than before.

'Here comes an eggshell sailing along!' said the boys; and they stuck the Darning-Needle fast in the eggshell.

'White walls, and black myself! that looks well,' remarked the Darning-Needle. 'Now one can see me. I only hope I shall not be seasick!' But she was not seasick at all. 'It is good against seasickness, if one has a steel stomach, and does not forget that one is a little more than an ordinary person! Now my seasickness is over. The finer one is, the more one can bear.'

'Crack!' went the eggshell, for a handbarrow went over her.

'Good heavens, how it crushes one!' said the Darning-Needle. 'I'm getting seasick now, I'm quite sick.'

But she was not really sick, though the handbarrow went over her; she lay there at full length, and there she may lie.

The Bell

AT EVENING, in the narrow streets of the great city, when the sun went down and the clouds shone like gold among the chimneys, there was frequently heard, sometimes by one, and sometimes by another, a strange tone, like the sound of a church bell; but it was only heard for a moment at a time, for in the streets there was a continual rattle of carriages, and endless cries of men and women – and that is a sad interruption. Then people said, 'Now the evening bell sounds, now the sun is setting.'

Those who were walking outside the city, where the houses stood farther from each other, with gardens and little fields between, saw the evening sky looking still more glorious, and heard the sound of the bell far more clearly. It was as though the tones came from a church, deep in the still quiet fragrant wood, and people looked in that direction, and became quite meditative.

Now a certain time passed, and one said to another, 'Is there not a church out yonder in the wood? That bell has a peculiarly beautiful sound! Shall we not go out and look at it more closely?' And rich people drove out, and poor people walked; but the way seemed marvellously long to them; and when they came to a number of willow trees that grew on the margin of the forest, they sat down and looked up to the long branches, and thought they were now really in the green wood. The pastrycook from the town came there too, and pitched his tent; but another pastrycook came and hung up a bell just over his own tent, a bell, in fact, that had been tarred so as to resist the rain, but it had no clapper. And when the people went home again, they declared the whole affair had been very romantic, and that meant much more than merely that they had taken tea. Three persons declared that they had penetrated into the wood to where it ended, and that they had always heard the strange sound of bells, but it had appeared to them as

if it came from the town. One of the three wrote a song about it, and said that the sound was like the voice of a mother singing to a dear good child; no melody could be more beautiful than the sound of that bell.

The Emperor of that country was also informed of it, and promised that the person who could really find out whence the sound came should have the title of The World's Bell-ringer, even if it should turn out not to be a bell.

Many went to the forest, on account of the good entertainment there; but there was only one who came back with a kind of explanation. No one had penetrated deep enough into the wood, nor had he; but he said that the sound came from a very great owl in a hollow tree; it was an owl of wisdom, that kept knocking its head continually against the tree, but whether the sound came from the owl's head, or from the trunk of the tree, he could not say with certainty. He was invested with the title of The World's Bell-ringer, and every year wrote a short treatise upon the owl; and people were just as wise after reading his works as they were before.

On a certain day a confirmation was held. The old clergyman had spoken well and impressively, and the candidates for confirmation were quite moved. It was an important day for them; for from being children they became grown-up people, and the childish soul was as it were to be transformed to that of a more sensible person. The sun shone gloriously as the confirmed children marched out of the town, and from the wood the great mysterious bell sounded with peculiar strength. They at once wished to go out to it, and all felt this wish except three. One of these desired to go home, to try on her ball dress, for it was just on account of that dress and that ball that she was being confirmed at that time, otherwise she would not have been so; the second was a poor boy, who had borrowed the coat and boots in which he was confirmed from the son of his landlord, and he had to give them back at an appointed time; the third said he never went to a strange place unless his parents went with him, that he had always been an obedient son, and would continue to be so, even after he was confirmed, and they were not to laugh at him. But they did laugh at him, nevertheless.

So these three did not go, but the others trotted on. The sun shone, and the birds sang, and the young people sang too, and held each other by the hand, for they had not yet received any office, and were all alike before Heaven on that day. But two of the smallest soon became weary and returned to the town, and two little girls sat down to bind wreaths, and did not go with the rest. And when the others came to the willow trees where the pastrycook lived, they said, 'Well, now we are out here, the bell does not really exist – it is only an imaginary thing.'

Then suddenly the bell began to ring in the forest with such a deep and solemn sound that four or five determined to go still deeper into the wood. The leaves hung very close, and it was really difficult to get forward; woodruff and anemones grew almost too high to go, and blooming convolvulus and blackberry bushes stretched in long garlands from tree to tree, where the nightingales sang and the sunbeams played. It was splendid; but the path was not one for girls to go, they would have torn their clothes. There lay great blocks of stone covered with mosses of all colours; the fresh spring water bubbled forth, and it sounded strangely, almost like 'cluck, cluck.'

'Can that possibly be the bell?' said one of the party, and he laid himself down and listened. 'That should be properly studied!'

And he remained there, and let the others go on.

They came to a house built of the bark of trees and of twigs: a great tree laden with wild apples stretched out its branches over the dwelling, as though it would pour its whole blessing upon the roof, which was covered with blooming roses, the long branches turned about the gables. And from the gable hung a little bell. Could that be the bell they had heard? They all agreed that it was, except one; he said that the bell was far too small and too delicate to be heard at such a distance as they had heard it, and that they were quite different sounds that had so deeply moved the human heart. He who spoke thus was a King's son, and the others declared that a person of that kind always wanted to be wiser than everyone else.

Therefore they let him go alone, and as he went his mind was more and more impressed with the solitude of the forest, but still he heard the little bell, at which the others were rejoicing; and sometimes, when the wind carried towards him sounds from the pastrycook's abode, he could hear how the party there were singing at their tea. But the deep tones of the bell sounded louder still; sometimes it was as if an organ were playing to it; the sound came from the left, the side in which the heart is placed.

Now there was a rustling in the bushes, and a little boy stood before the Prince, a boy with wooden shoes, and such a short jacket that one could plainly see what long wrists he had. They knew one another. The boy was the youngster who had been confirmed that day, and had not been able to come with the rest because he had to go home and give up the borrowed coat and boots to his landlord's son. This he had done, and had then wandered away alone in his poor clothes and his wooden shoes, for the bell sounded so strongly and so deeply, he had been obliged to come out.

'We can go together,' said the Prince.

But the poor lad in the wooden shoes was quite embarrassed. He pulled at the short sleeves of his jacket, and said he was afraid he could not come quickly enough; besides, he thought the bell must be sought on the right hand, for there the place was great and glorious.

'But then we shall not meet at all,' said the Prince; and he nodded to the poor boy, who went away into the darkest, thickest part of the forest, where the thorns tore his shabby garments and scratched his face, his feet, and his hands. The Prince also had two or three brave rents, but the sun shone bright on his path; and it is he whom we will follow, for he was a brisk lad.

'I must and will find the bell,' said he, 'though I have to go to the end of the world.'

Ugly apes sat up in the trees, and grinned and showed their teeth.

'Shall we beat him?' said they. 'Shall we smash him? He's a King's son!'

But he went courageously farther and farther into the forest, where the most wonderful trees grew: there stood white star-lilies with blood-red stamens, sky-blue tulips that glittered in the breeze, and apple trees whose apples looked quite like great shining soap bubbles: only think how those trees must have gleamed in the sunbeams! All around lay the most beautiful green meadows, where hart and hind played in the grass, and noble oaks and beech trees grew there; and when the bark of any tree split, grass and long climbing plants grew out of the rifts; there were also great wooded tracts with quiet lakes on which white swans floated and flapped their wings. The Prince often stood still and listened; often he thought that the bell sounded upwards to him from one of the deep lakes; but soon he noticed that the sound did not come from thence, but that the bell was sounding deeper in the wood.

Now the sun went down. The sky shone red as fire; it became quite quiet in the forest, and he sank on his knees, sang his evening hymn, and said, 'I shall never find what I seek, now the sun is going down, and the night, the dark night, is coming. But perhaps I can once more see the round sun before he disappears beneath the horizon. I will climb upon the rocks, for they are higher than the highest trees.'

And he seized hold of roots and climbing plants, and clambered up the wet stones, where the water-snakes writhed and the toads seemed to be barking at him; but he managed to climb up before the sun, which he could see from this elevation, had quite set. Oh, what splendour! The sea, the great glorious sea, which rolled its long billows towards the shore, lay stretched out before him, and the sun stood aloft like a great flaming altar, there where the sea and sky met; everything melted together in glowing colours; the wood sang and the sea sang, and his heart sang too. All nature was a great holy church, in which trees and floating clouds were the pillars and beams, flowers and grass the velvet carpet, and the heavens themselves the vaulted roof. The red colours faded up there when the sun sank to rest; but millions of stars were lighted up and diamond lamps glittered, and the Prince stretched forth his arms towards heaven, towards the sea, and towards the forest. Suddenly there came from the right hand the poor lad who had been confirmed, with his short jacket and his wooden shoes: he had arrived here at the same time, and had come his own way. And they ran to meet each other, and each took the other's hand in the great temple of nature and of poetry. And above them sounded the holy invisible bell; and blessed spirits surrounded them and floated over them, singing a rejoicing song of praise!

Grandmother

GRANDMOTHER is very old; she has many wrinkles, and her hair is quite white; but her eyes, which shine like two stars, and even more beautifully, look at you mildly and pleasantly, and it does you good to look into them. And then she can tell the most wonderful stories; and she has a gown with great flowers worked in it, and it is of heavy silk, and it rustles. Grandmother knows a great deal, for she was alive long before father and mother, that's quite certain! Grandmother has a hymn-book with great silver clasps, and she often reads in that book; in the middle of the book lies a rose, quite flat and dry; it is not as pretty as the roses she has standing in the glass, and yet she smiles at it most pleasantly of all, and tears even come into her eyes. I wonder why Grandmother looks at the withered flower in the old book in that way? Do you know? Why, each time that Grandmother's tears fall upon the rose, its colours become fresh again; the rose swells and fills the whole room with its fragrance; the walls sink as if they were but mist, and all around her is the glorious green wood, where the sunlight streams through the leaves of the trees; and Grandmother – why, she is young again, a charming maid with yellow curls and full blooming cheeks, pretty and graceful, fresh as any rose; but the eyes, the mild blessed eyes, they have been left to Grandmother. At her side sits a young man, tall and strong: he gives the rose to her, and she smiles; Grandmother cannot smile thus now! yes, now she smiles! But now he has passed away, and many thoughts and many forms of the past; and the handsome young man is gone, and the rose lies in the hymn-book, and Grandmother sits there again, an old woman, and glances down at the withered rose that lies in the book.

Now Grandmother is dead. She had been sitting in her armchair, and telling a long, long lovely tale; and she said the tale was told now,

and she was tired; and she leaned her head back to sleep awhile. One could hear her breathing as she slept; but it became quieter and more quiet, and her countenance was full of happiness and peace: it seemed as if a sunshine spread over her features; and then the people said she was dead.

She was laid in the black coffin; and there she lay shrouded in the white linen folds, looking beautiful and mild, though her eyes were closed; but every wrinkle had vanished, and there was a smile around her mouth; her hair was silver-white and venerable; and we did not feel at all afraid to look on her who had been the dear good Grandmother. And the hymn-book was placed under her head, for she had wished it so, and the rose was still in the old book; and then they buried Grandmother.

On the grave, close by the churchyard wall, they planted a rose tree; and it was full of roses; and the nightingale sang over the flowers and over the grave. In the church the finest psalms sounded from the organ – the psalms that were written in the old book under the dead one's head. The moon shone down upon the grave, but the dead one was not there. Every child could go safely, even at night, and pluck a rose there by the churchyard wall. A dead person knows more than all we living ones. The dead know what a terror would come upon us, if the strange thing were to happen that they appeared among us: the dead are better than we all; the dead return no more. The earth has been heaped over the coffin, and it is earth that lies in the coffin; and the leaves of the hymn-book are dust, and the rose, with all its recollections, has returned to dust likewise. But above there bloom fresh roses; the nightingale sings and the organ sounds, and the remembrance lives of the old Grandmother with the mild eyes that always looked young. *Eyes can never die!* Ours will once again behold Grandmother young and beautiful, as when for the first time she kissed the fresh red rose that is now dust in the grave.

The Elf-Hill

A FEW great Lizards race nimbly about in the clefts of an old tree;
they could understand each other very well, for they spoke the
lizards' language.

'How it grumbles and growls in the old elf-hill!' said one Lizard.
'I've not been able to close my eyes for two nights, because of the
noise; I might just as well lie and have the toothache, for then I can't
sleep either.'

'There's something going on in there,' said the other Lizard. 'They
let the hill stand on four red posts till the cock crows at morn. It is
regularly aired, and the elf girls have learned new dances. There's
something going on.'

'Yes, I have spoken with an earthworm of my acquaintance,' said the
third Lizard. 'The earthworm came straight out of the hill, where he had
been grubbing in the ground night and day: he had heard much. He
can't see, the miserable creature, but he understands how to feel his
way about and listen. They expect some friends in the elf-hill – grand
strangers; but who they are the earthworm would not tell, or perhaps,
indeed, he did not know. All the Will-o'-the-wisps are ordered to hold a
torchlight procession, as it is called; and silver and gold, of which there is
enough in the elf-hill, is being polished and put out in the moonshine.'

'Who may these strangers be?' asked all the Lizards. 'What can be
going on there? Hark, how it hums! Hark, how it murmurs!'

At the same moment the elf-hill opened, and an old elf maid,[*]
hollow behind, but otherwise very respectably dressed, came tripping
out. She was the old Elf King's housekeeper. She was a distant relative
of the royal family, and wore an amber heart on her forehead. Her legs

---

[*] A prevailing superstition regarding the elf maid, or *elle maid*, is, that she is fair
    to look at in front, but behind she is hollow, like a mask.

moved so rapidly – trip, trip! Gracious! how she could trip! straight down to the moss, to the night Raven.

'You are invited to the elf-hill for this evening,' said she; 'but will you not first do us a great service and undertake the invitations? You must do something, as you don't keep any house yourself. We shall have some very distinguished friends, magicians who have something to say; and so the old Elf King wants to make a display.'

'Who's to be invited?' asked the night Raven.

'To the great ball the world may come, even men, if they can talk in their sleep, or do something that falls in our line. But at the first feast there's to be a strict selection; we will have only the most distinguished. I have had a dispute with the Elf King, for I declared that we could not even admit ghosts. The merman and his daughters must be invited first. They may not be very well pleased to come on the dry land, but they shall have a wet stone to sit upon, or something still better, and then I think they won't refuse for this time. All the old demons of the first class, with tails, and the river man and the goblins we must have; and then I think we may not leave out the grave pig, the death horse,* and the church lamb; they certainly belong to the clergy, and are not reckoned among our people. But that's only their office: they are closely related to us, and visit us diligently.'

'Bravo!' said the night Raven, and flew away to give the invitations.

The elf girls were already dancing on the elf-hill, and they danced with shawls which were woven of mist and moonshine; and that looks very pretty for those who like that sort of thing. In the midst, below the elf-hill, the great hall was splendidly decorated; the floor had been washed with moonshine, and the walls rubbed with witches' salve, so that they glowed like tulips in the light. In the kitchen, plenty of frogs were turning on the spit, snailskins with children's fingers in them and

---

* It is a popular superstition in Denmark, that under every church that is built, a living horse must be buried; the ghost of this horse is the death horse, that limps every night on three legs to the house where someone is to die. Under a few churches a living pig was buried, and the ghost of this was called the grave pig.

salads of mushroom spawn, damp mouse muzzles, and hemlock; beer brewed by the marsh witch, gleaming saltpetre wine from grave cellars: everything very grand; and rusty nails and church window glass among the sweets.

The old Elf King had one of his crowns polished with powdered slate pencil; it was slate pencil from the first form, and it's very difficult for the Elf King to get first form slate pencil! In the bedroom, curtains were hung up, and fastened with snail slime. Yes, there was a humming and murmuring there!

'Now we must burn horsehair and pigs' bristles as incense here,' said the Elf King, 'and then I think I shall have done my part.'

'Father dear!' said the youngest of the daughters, 'shall I hear now who the distinguished strangers are?'

'Well,' said he, 'I suppose I must tell it now. Two of my daughters must hold themselves prepared to be married; two will certainly be married. The old gnome from Norway yonder, he who lives in the Dovre mountain, and possesses many rock castles of granite, and a gold mine which is better than one thinks, is coming with his two sons, who want each to select a wife. The old gnome is a true old honest Norwegian veteran, merry and straightforward. I know him from old days, when we drank brotherhood with one another. He was down here to fetch his wife; now she is dead, she was a daughter of the King of the Chalk-rocks of Möen. He took his wife upon chalk, as the saying is. Oh, how I long to see the old Norwegian gnome! The lads, they say, are rather rude, forward lads; but perhaps they are belied, and they'll be right enough when they grow older. Let me see that you can teach them manners.'

'And when will they come?' asked one of the daughters.

'That depends on wind and weather,' said the Elf King. 'They travel economically: they come when there's a chance by a ship. I wanted them to go across Sweden, but the old one would not incline to that wish. He does not advance with the times, and I don't like that.'

Then two Will-o'-the-wisps came hopping up, one quicker than the other, and so one of them arrived first.

'They're coming! they're coming!' they cried.

'Give me my crown, and let me stand in the moonshine,' said the Elf King.

And the daughters lifted up their shawls and bowed down to the earth.

There stood the old gnome of Dovre, with the crown of hardened ice and polished fir cones; moreover, he wore a bearskin and great warm boots. His sons, on the contrary, went bare-necked, and with trousers without braces, for they were strong men.

'Is that a hillock?' asked the youngest of the lads; and he pointed to the elf-hill. 'In Norway yonder we should call it a hole.'

'Boys!' said the old man, 'holes go down, mounds go up. Have you no eyes in your heads?'

The only thing they wondered at down here, they said, was that they could understand the language without difficulty.

'Don't give yourselves airs,' said the old man. 'One would think you were home-nurtured.'

And then they went into the elf-hill, where the really grand company were assembled, and that in such haste that one might almost say they had been blown together. But for each it was nicely and prettily arranged. The sea folks sat at table in great washing tubs: they said it was just as if they were at home. All observed the ceremonies of the table except the two young Northern gnomes, and they put their legs up on the table; but they thought all that suited them well.

'Your feet off the tablecloth!' cried the old gnome.

And they obeyed, but not immediately. Their ladies they tickled with pine cones that they had brought with them, and then took off their boots for their own convenience, and gave them to the ladies to hold. But the father, the old Dovre gnome, was quite different from them: he told such fine stories of the proud Norwegian rocks, and of the waterfalls which rushed down with white foam and with a noise like thunder and the sound of organs; he told of the salmon that leaps up against the falling waters when Necken plays upon the golden harp; he told of shining winter nights, when the sledge bells sound, and the lads run with burning torches over the ice, which is so transparent that they see the fishes start beneath their feet. Yes! he could tell it so finely that one saw what he described: it was just as if the sawmills were going, as if the servants and maids were singing songs and dancing the Halling dance. Hurrah! all at once the old gnome gave the old elf girl a kiss: that *was* a kiss! and yet they were nothing to each other.

Now the elf maidens had to dance, both with plain and with stamping steps, and that suited them well; then came the artistic and solo dance. Wonderful how they could use their legs! one hardly knew where they began and where they ended, which were their arms and which their legs – they were all mingled together like wood-shavings; and then they whirled round till the death horse turned giddy and was obliged to leave the table.

'Prur!' said the old gnome; 'that's the way to use one's legs. But what can they do more than dance, stretch out their limbs, and make a whirlwind?'

'You shall soon know!' said the Elf King.

And then he called forward the youngest of his daughters. She was as light and graceful as moonshine; she was the most delicate of all the sisters. She took a white peg in her mouth, and then she was quite gone: that was her art.

But the old gnome said he should not like his wife to possess this art, and he did not think that his boys cared for it.

The other could walk beside herself, just as if she had a shadow, and the gnome people had none. The third daughter was of quite another kind; she had served in the brewhouse of the moor witch, and knew how to stuff elder tree knots with glow-worms.

'She will make a good housewife,' said the old gnome; and then he winked a health with his eyes, for he did not want to drink too much.

Now came the fourth: she had a great harp to play upon, and when she struck the first chord all lifted up their left feet, for the gnomes are left-legged; and when she struck the second chord, all were compelled to do as she wished.

'That's a dangerous woman!' said the old gnome; but both the sons went out of the hill, for they had had enough of it.

'And what can the next daughter do?' asked the old gnome.

'I have learned to love what is Norwegian,' said she, 'and I will never marry unless I can go to Norway.'

But the youngest sister whispered to the old King, 'That's only because she has heard in a Norwegian song, that when the world sinks down the cliffs of Norway will remain standing like monuments, and so she wants to get up there, because she is afraid of perishing.'

'Ho! ho!' said the old gnome, 'is that the reason? But what can the seventh and last do?'

'The sixth comes before the seventh!' said the Elf King, for he could count. But the sixth would not come out.

'I can only tell people the truth!' said she. 'Nobody cares for me, and I have enough to do to sew my shroud.'

Now came the seventh and last, and what could she do? Why, she could tell stories, as many as she wished.

'Here are all my five fingers,' said the old gnome; 'tell me one for each.'

And she took him by the wrist, and he laughed till it clucked within him; and when she came to the ring finger, which had a ring round its waist, just as if it knew there was to be a wedding, the old gnome said, 'Hold fast what you have: the hand is yours; I'll have you for my own wife.'

And the elf girl said that the story of the ring finger and of little Peter Playman, the fifth, were still wanting.

'We'll hear those in winter,' said the gnome, 'and we'll hear about the pine tree, and about the birch, and about the fairies' gifts, and about the biting frost. You shall tell your tales, for no one up there knows how to do that well; and then we'll sit in the stone chamber where the pine logs burn, and drink mead out of the horns of the old Norwegian Kings – Necken has given me a couple; and when we sit there, and the Brownie comes on a visit, he'll sing you all the songs of the milking-girls in the mountains. That will be merry. The salmon will spring in the waterfall, and beat against the stone walls, but he shall not come in.'

'Yes, it's very good living in Norway; but where are the lads?'

Yes, where were they? They were running about in the fields, and blowing out the Will-o'-the-wisps, which had come so good-naturedly for the torchlight procession.

'What romping about is that?' said the old gnome. 'I have taken a mother for you, and now you may take one of the aunts.'

But the lads said that they would rather make a speech and drink brotherhood – they did not care to marry; and they made speeches, and drank brotherhood, and tipped up their glasses on their nails, to show they had emptied them. Afterwards they took their coats off and lay down on the table to sleep, for they made no ceremony. But the old gnome danced about the room with his young bride, and he changed boots with her, for that's more fashionable than exchanging rings.

'Now the cock crows,' said the old elf girl who attended to the housekeeping. 'Now we must shut the shutters, so that the sun may not burn us.'

And the hill shut itself up. But outside, the Lizards ran up and down in the cleft tree, and one said to the other, 'Oh, how I like that old Norwegian gnome!'

'I like the lads better,' said the Earthworm. But he could not see, the miserable creature.

The Red Shoes

THERE was once a little girl; a very nice pretty little girl. But in summer she had to go barefoot, because she was poor, and in winter she wore thick wooden shoes, so that her little instep became quite red, altogether red.

In the middle of the village lived an old shoemaker's wife: she sat and sewed, as well as she could, a pair of little shoes, of old strips of red cloth; they were clumsy enough, but well meant, and the little girl was to have them. The little girl's name was Karen.

On the day when her mother was buried she received the red shoes and wore them for the first time. They were certainly not suited for mourning; but she had no others, and therefore thrust her little bare feet into them and walked behind the plain deal coffin.

Suddenly a great carriage came by, and in the carriage sat an old lady: she looked at the little girl and felt pity for her, and said to the clergyman, 'Give me the little girl, and I will provide for her.'

Karen thought this was for the sake of the shoes; but the old lady declared they were hideous; and they were burned. But Karen herself was clothed neatly and properly: she was taught to read and to sew, and the people said she was agreeable. But her mirror said, 'You are much more than agreeable; you are beautiful.'

Once the Queen travelled through the country, and had her little daughter with her; and the daughter was a Princess. And the people flocked towards the castle, and Karen too was among them; and the little Princess stood in a fine white dress at a window, and let herself be gazed at. She had neither train nor golden crown, but she wore splendid red morocco shoes; they were certainly far handsomer than those the shoemaker's wife had made for little Karen. Nothing in the world can compare with red shoes!

Now Karen was old enough to be confirmed: new clothes were made for her, and she was to have new shoes. The rich shoemaker in the town took the measure of her little feet; this was done in his own house, in his little room, and there stood great glass cases with neat shoes and shining boots. It had quite a charming appearance, but the old lady could not see well, and therefore took no pleasure in it. Among the shoes stood a red pair, just like those which the Princess had worn. How beautiful they were! The shoemaker also said they had been made for a Count's child, but they had not fitted.

'That must be patent leather,' observed the old lady, 'the shoes shine so!'

'Yes, they shine!' replied Karen; and they fitted her, and were bought. But the old lady did not know that they were red; for she would never have allowed Karen to go to her confirmation in red shoes; but that is what Karen did.

Everyone was looking at her shoes. And when she went up the floor of the church, towards the door of the choir, is seemed to her as if the old figures on the tombstones, the portraits of clergymen and clergymen's wives, in their stiff collars and long black garments, fixed their eyes upon her red shoes. And she thought of her shoes only, when the priest laid his hand upon her head and spoke holy words. And the organ pealed solemnly, the children sang with their fresh sweet voices, and the old precentor sang too; but Karen thought only of her red shoes.

In the afternoon the old lady was informed by everyone that the shoes were red; and she said it was naughty and unsuitable, and that when Karen went to church in future, she should always go in black shoes, even if they were old.

Next Sunday was Sacrament Sunday. And Karen looked at the black shoes, and looked at the red ones – looked at them again – and put on the red ones.

The sun shone gloriously; Karen and the old lady went along the footpath through the fields, and it was rather dusty.

By the church door stood an old invalid soldier with a crutch and a long beard; the beard was rather red than white, for it was red altogether; and he bowed down almost to the ground, and asked the old lady if he might dust her shoes. And Karen also stretched out her little foot.

'Look, what pretty dancing-shoes!' said the old soldier. 'Fit so tightly when you dance!'

And he tapped the soles with his hand. And the old lady gave the soldier an alms, and went into the church with Karen.

And everyone in the church looked at Karen's red shoes, and all the pictures looked at them. And while Karen knelt in the church she only thought of her red shoes; and she forgot to sing her psalm, and forgot to say her prayer.

Now all the people went out of church, and the old lady stepped into her carriage. Karen lifted up her foot to step in too; then the old soldier said, 'Look, what beautiful dancing-shoes!'

And Karen could not resist: she was obliged to dance a few steps; and when she once began, her legs went on dancing. It was just as though the shoes had obtained power over her. She danced round the corner of the church – she could not help it; the coachman was obliged to run behind her and seize her: he lifted her into the carriage, but her feet went on dancing, so that she kicked the good old lady violently. At last they took off her shoes, and her legs became quiet.

At home the shoes were put away in a cupboard; but Karen could not resist looking at them.

Now the old lady became very ill, and it was said she would not recover. She had to be nursed and waited on; and this was no one's duty so much as Karen's. But there was to be a great ball in the town, and Karen was invited. She looked at the old lady who could not recover; she looked at the red shoes, and thought there would be no harm in it. She put on the shoes, and that she might very well do; but then she went to the ball and began to dance.

But when she wished to go to the right hand, the shoes danced to the left, and when she wanted to go upstairs the shoes danced downwards, down into the street and out at the town gate. She danced, and was obliged to dance, straight out into the dark wood.

There was something glistening up among the trees, and she thought it was the moon, for she saw a face. But it was the old soldier with the red beard: he sat and nodded, and said, 'Look, what beautiful dancing-shoes!'

Then she was frightened, and wanted to throw away the red shoes; but they clung fast to her. And she tore off her stockings; but the shoes had grown fast to her feet. And she danced and was compelled to go dancing over field and meadow, in rain and sunshine, by night and by day; but it was most dreadful at night.

She danced into the open churchyard; but the dead there did not dance; they had something better to do. She wished to sit down on the poor man's grave, where the bitter tansy grows; but there was no peace nor rest for her. And when she danced towards the open church door, she saw there an angel in long white garments, with wings that reached from his shoulders to his feet; his countenance was serious and stern, and in his hand he held a sword that was broad and gleaming.

'Thou shalt dance!' he said – 'dance in thy red shoes, till thou art pale and cold, and till thy body shrivels to a skeleton. Thou shalt dance from door to door; and where proud, haughty children dwell, shalt thou knock, that they may hear thee, and be afraid of thee! Thou shalt dance, dance!'

'Mercy!' cried Karen.

But she did not hear what the angel answered, for the shoes carried her away – carried her through the gate on to the field, over stock and stone, and she was always obliged to dance.

One morning she danced past a door which she knew well. There was a sound of psalm-singing within and a coffin was carried out, adorned with flowers. Then she knew that the old lady was dead, and she felt that she was deserted by all, and condemned by the angel of God.

She danced, and was compelled to dance – to dance in the dark night. The shoes carried her on over thorn and brier; she scratched herself till she bled; she danced away across the heath to a little lonely house. Here she knew the executioner dwelt; and she tapped with her fingers on the panes, and called, 'Come out, come out! I cannot come in, for I must dance!'

And the executioner said, 'You probably don't know who I am? I cut off the bad people's heads with my axe, and mark how my axe rings!'

'Do not strike off my head,' said Karen, 'for if you do I cannot repent of my sin. But strike off my feet with the red shoes!'

And then she confessed all her sin, and the executioner cut off her feet with the red shoes; but the shoes danced away with the little feet over the fields and into the deep forest.

And he cut her a pair of wooden feet, with crutches, and taught her a psalm, which the criminals always sing; and she kissed the hand that had held the axe, and went away across the heath.

'Now I have suffered pain enough for the red shoes,' said she. 'Now I will go into the church, that they may see me.'

And she went quickly towards the church door; but when she came there the red shoes danced before her, so that she was frightened, and turned back.

The whole week through she was sorrowful, and wept many bitter tears; but when Sunday came, she said, 'Now I have suffered and striven enough! I think that I am just as good as many of those who sit in the church and carry their heads high.'

And then she went boldly on; but she did not get farther than the churchyard gate before she saw the red shoes dancing along before her: then she was seized with terror, and turned back, and repented of her sin right heartily.

And she went to the parsonage, and begged to be taken there as a servant. She promised to be industrious, and to do all she could; she did not care for wages, and only wished to be under a roof and with good people. The clergyman's wife pitied her, and took her into her service. And she was industrious and thoughtful. Silently she sat and listened when in the evening the pastor read the Bible aloud. All the little ones were very fond of her; but when they spoke of dress and splendour and beauty she would shake her head.

Next Sunday they all went to church, and she was asked if she wished to go too; but she looked sadly, with tears in her eyes, at her crutches. And then the others went to hear God's Word; but she went alone into her little room, which was only large enough to contain her bed and a chair. And here she sat with her hymn-book; and as she read it with a pious mind, the wind bore the notes of the organ over to her from the church; and she lifted up her face, wet with tears, and said, 'O Lord, help me!'

Then the sun shone so brightly; and before her stood the angel in white garments, the same she had seen that night at the church door. But he no longer grasped the sharp sword: he held a green branch covered with roses; and he touched the ceiling, and it rose up high, and wherever he touched it a golden star gleamed forth; and he touched the walls, and they spread forth widely, and she saw the organ which was pealing its rich sounds; and she saw the old pictures of clergymen and their wives; and the congregation sat in the decorated seats, and sang from their hymn-books. The church had come to the poor girl in her narrow room, or her chamber had become a church. She sat in the pew with the rest of the clergyman's people; and when they had finished the psalm, and looked up, they nodded and said, 'That was right, that you came here, Karen.'

'It was mercy!' said she.

And the organ sounded its glorious notes; and the children's voices singing in chorus sounded sweet and lovely; the clear sunshine streamed so warm through the window upon the chair in which Karen sat; and her heart became so filled with sunshine, peace, and joy, that it broke. Her soul flew on the sunbeams to heaven; and there was nobody who asked after the Red Shoes.

The Jumper

THE FLEA, the Grasshopper, and the Frog once wanted to see which of them could jump highest; and they invited the whole world, and whoever else would come, to see the grand sight. And there the three famous jumpers were met together in the room.

'Yes, I'll give my daughter to him who jumps highest,' said the King, 'for it would be mean to let these people jump for nothing.'

The Flea stepped out first. He had very pretty manners, and bowed in all directions, for he had young ladies' blood in his veins, and was accustomed to consort only with human beings; and that is of great consequence.

Then came the Grasshopper: he was certainly much heavier, but he had a good figure, and wore the green uniform that was born with him. This person, moreover, maintained that he belonged to a very old family in the land of Egypt, and that he was highly esteemed there. He had just come from the field, he said, and had been put into a card-house three stories high, and all made of picture cards with the figures turned inwards. There were doors and windows in the house, cut in the body of the Queen of Hearts.

'I sing so,' he said, 'that sixteen native crickets who have chirped from their youth up, and have never yet had a card-house of their own, have become even thinner than they were with envy at hearing me.'

Both of them, the Flea and the Grasshopper, took care to announce who they were, and that they considered themselves entitled to marry a Princess.

The Frog said nothing, but it was said of him that he thought all the more; and directly the Yard Dog had smelt at him he was ready to assert that the Frog was of good family. The old councillor, who had received three medals for holding his tongue, declared that he knew that the Frog possessed the gift of prophecy: one could tell by his backbone whether there would be a severe winter or a mild one; and that's more than one can always tell from the backbone of the man who writes the almanac.

'I shall not say anything more,' said the old King. 'I only go on quietly, and think my own thoughts.'

Now they were to take their jump. The Flea sprang so high that no one could see him; and then they asserted that he had not jumped at all. That was very mean. The grasshopper only sprang half as high, but he sprang straight into the King's face, and the King declared that was horribly rude. The Frog stood a long time considering; at last people thought that he could not jump at all.

'I only hope he's not become unwell,' said the Yard Dog, and then he smelt at him again.

'Tap!' He sprang with a little crooked jump just into the lap of the Princess, who sat on a low golden stool.

Then the King said, 'The highest leap was taken by him who jumped up to my daughter; for therein lies the point; but it requires head to achieve that, and the Frog has shown that he has a head.'

And so he had the Princess.

'I jumped highest, after all,' said the Flea. 'But it's all the same. Let her have the goose-bone with its lump of wax and bit of stick. I jumped the highest; but in this world a body is required if one wishes to be seen.'

And the Flea went into foreign military service, where it is said he was killed.

The Grasshopper seated himself out in the ditch, and thought and considered how things happened in the world. And he too said, 'Body is required! body is required!' And then he sang his own melancholy song, and from that we have gathered this story, which they say is not true, though it's in print.

The Shepherdess and the Chimney-Sweeper

HAVE you ever seen a very old wooden cupboard, quite black with age, and ornamented with carved foliage and arabesques? Just such a cupboard stood in a parlour: it had been a legacy from the great-grandmother, and was covered from top to bottom with carved roses and tulips. There were the quaintest flourishes upon it, and from among these peered forth little stags' heads with antlers. In the middle of the cupboard door an entire figure of a man had been cut out: he was certainly ridiculous to look at, and he grinned, for you could not call it laughing: he had goat's legs, little horns on his head, and a long beard. The children in the room always called him the Billygoat-legs-Lieutenant-and-Major-General-War-Commander-Sergeant; that was a difficult name to pronounce, and there are not many who obtain this title; but it was something to have cut him out. And there he was! He was always looking at the table under the mirror, for on this table stood a lovely little Shepherdess made of china. Her shoes were gilt, her dress was neatly caught up with a red rose, and besides this she had a golden hat and a shepherd's crook: she was very lovely. Close by her stood a little Chimney-Sweeper, black as a coal, but also made of porcelain: he was as clean and neat as any other man, for it was only make-believe that he was a sweep; the china-workers might just as well have made a prince of him, if they had been so minded.

There he stood very nattily with his ladder, and with a face as white and pink as a girl's; and that was really a fault, for he ought to have been a little black. He stood quite close to the Shepherdess: they had both been placed where they stood; but as they had been placed there they had become engaged to each other. They suited each other well. Both were young people, both made of the same kind of china, and both equally frail.

Close to them stood another figure, three times greater than they. This was an old Chinaman, who could nod. He was also of porcelain, and declared himself to be the grandfather of the little Shepherdess; but he could not prove his relationship. He declared he had authority over her, and that therefore he had nodded to Mr Billygoat-legs-Lieutenant-and-Major-General-War-Commander-Sergeant, who was wooing her for his wife.

'Then you will get a husband!' said the old Chinaman, 'a man who I verily believe is made of mahogany. He can make you Billygoat-legs-Lieutenant-and-Major-General-War-Commander-Sergeantess: he has the whole cupboard full of silver plate, besides what he hoards up in secret drawers.'

'I won't go into the dark cupboard!' said the little Shepherdess. 'I have heard tell that he has eleven porcelain wives in there.'

'Then you may become the twelfth,' cried the Chinaman. 'This night, so soon as it creaks in the old cupboard, you shall be married, as true as I am an old Chinaman!'

And with that he nodded his head and fell asleep. But the little Shepherdess wept and looked at her heart's beloved, the porcelain Chimney-Sweeper.

'I should like to beg of you,' said she, 'to go out with me into the wide world, for we cannot remain here.'

'I'll do whatever you like,' replied the little Chimney-Sweeper. 'Let us start directly! I think I can keep you by exercising my profession.'

'If we were only safely down from the table!' said she. 'I shall not be happy until we are out in the wide world.'

And he comforted her, and showed her how she must place her little foot upon the carved corners and the gilded foliage down the leg of the table; he brought his ladder, too, to help her, and they were soon together upon the floor. But when they looked up at the old cupboard there was great commotion within: all the carved stags were stretching out their heads, rearing up their antlers, and turning their necks; and the Billygoat-legs-Lieutenant-and-Major-General-War-Commander-Sergeant sprang high in the air, and called across to the old Chinaman, 'Now they're running away! now they're running away!'

Then they were a little frightened, and jumped quickly into the drawer of the window-seat. Here were three or four packs of cards which were not complete, and a little puppet-show, which had been built up as well as it could be done. There plays were acted, and all the ladies, diamonds, clubs, hearts, and spades, sat in the first row, fanning themselves with their tulips; and behind them stood all the knaves, showing that they had a head above and below, as is usual in playing-cards. The play was about two people who were not to be married to each other, and the Shepherdess wept, because it was just like her own history.

'I cannot bear this!' said she. 'I must go out of the drawer.'

But when they arrived on the floor, and looked up at the table, the old Chinaman was awake and was shaking over his whole body – for below he was all one lump.

'Now the old Chinaman's coming!' cried the little Shepherdess; and she fell down upon her porcelain knee, so startled was she.

'I have an idea,' said the Chimney-Sweeper. 'Shall we creep into the great *pot-pourri* vase which stands in the corner? Then we can lie on roses and lavender, and throw salt in his eyes if he comes.'

'That will be of no use,' she replied. 'Besides, I know that the old Chinaman and the *pot-pourri* vase were once engaged to each other, and a kind of liking always remains when people have stood in such a relation to each other. No, there's nothing left for us but to go out into the wide world.'

'Have you really courage to go into the wide world with me?' asked the Chimney-Sweeper. 'Have you considered how wide the world is, and that we can never come back here again?'

'I have,' replied she.

And the Chimney-Sweeper looked fondly at her, and said, 'My way is through the chimney. If you have really courage to creep with me through the stove – through the iron fire-box as well as up the pipe, then we can get out into the chimney, and I know how to find my way through there. We'll mount so high that they can't catch us, and quite at the top there's a hole that leads out into the wide world.'

And he led her to the door of the stove.

'It looks very black there,' said she; but still she went with him, through the box and through the pipe, where it was pitch-dark night.

'Now we are in the chimney,' said he; 'and look, look! up yonder a beautiful star is shining.'

And it was a real star in the sky, which shone straight down upon them, as if it would show them the way. And they clambered and crept: it was a frightful way, and terribly steep; but he supported her and helped her up; he held her, and showed her the best places where she could place her little porcelain feet; and thus they reached the edge of the chimney, and upon that they sat down, for they were desperately tired, as they well might be.

The sky with all its stars was high above, and all the roofs of the town deep below them. They looked far around – far, far out into the world. The poor Shepherdess had never thought of it as it really was: she leaned her little head against the Chimney-Sweeper, then she wept so bitterly that the gold ran down off her girdle.

That is too much,' she said. 'I cannot bear that. The world is too large! If I were only back upon the table below the mirror! I shall never be happy until I am there again. Now I have followed you out into the wide world, you may accompany me back again if you really love me.'

And the Chimney-Sweeper spoke sensibly to her – spoke of the old Chinaman and of the Billygoat-legs-Lieutenant-and-Major-General-War-Commander-Sergeant; but she sobbed bitterly and kissed her little Chimney-Sweeper, so that he could not help giving way to her, though it was foolish.

And so with much labour they climbed down the chimney again. And they crept through the pipe and the fire-box. That was not pleasant at all. And there they stood in the dark stove; there they listened behind the door, to find out what was going on in the room. Then it was quite quiet: they looked in – ah! there lay the old Chinaman in the middle of the floor! He had fallen down from the table as he was pursuing them, and now he lay broken into three pieces; his back had come off all in one piece, and his head had rolled into a corner. The Billygoat-legs-Lieutenant-and-Major-General-War-Commander-Sergeant stood where he had always stood, considering.

'That is terrible!' said the little Shepherdess. 'The old grandfather has fallen to pieces, and it is our fault. I shall never survive it!' And then she wrung her little hands.

'He can be mended! he can be mended!' said the Chimney-Sweeper. 'Don't be so violent. If they glue his back together and give him a good rivet in his neck he will be as good as new, and may say many a disagreeable thing to us yet.'

'Do you think so?' cried she.

So they climbed back upon the table where they used to stand.

'You see, we have come back to this,' said the Chimney-Sweeper: 'we might have saved ourselves all the trouble we have had.'

'If the old grandfather were only riveted!' said the Shepherdess. 'I wonder if that is dear?'

And he was really riveted. The family had his back cemented, and a great rivet was passed through his neck: he was as good as new, only he could no longer nod.

'It seems you have become proud since you fell to pieces,' said the Billygoat-legs-Lieutenant-and-Major-General-War-Commander-Sergeant. 'I don't think you have any reason to give yourself such airs. Am I to have her, or am I not?'

And the Chimney-Sweeper and the little Shepherdess looked at the old Chinaman most piteously, for they were afraid he might nod. But he could not do that, and it was irksome to him to tell a stranger that he always had a rivet in his neck. And so the porcelain people remained together, and they blessed Grandfather's rivet, and loved one another until they broke.

Holger the Dane

'IN DENMARK there lies an old castle named Kronborg. It lies close by the Öre Sound, where the great ships pass through by hundreds every day – English, Russian, and likewise Prussian ships. And they salute the old castle with cannons – "Boom!" And the castle answers again with cannons "Boom!" for that's what the cannons say instead of "Good-day" and "Thank you!" In winter no ships sail there, for the whole sea is covered with ice quite across to the Swedish coast; but it has quite the look of a high road. There wave the Danish flag and the Swedish flag, and Danes and Swedes say "Good-day" and "Thank you!" to each other, not with cannons, but with a friendly grasp of the hand; and one gets white bread and biscuits from the other – for strange fare tastes best. But the most beautiful of all is old Kronborg; and here it is that Holger the Dane sits in the deep dark cellar, where nobody goes. He is clad in iron and steel, and leans his head on his strong arm; his long beard hangs down over the marble table, and has grown into it. He sleeps and dreams, but in his dreams he sees everything that happens up here in Denmark. Every Christmas-eve comes an angel, and tells him that what he has dreamed is right, and that he may go to sleep in quiet, for that Denmark is not yet in any real danger; but when once such a danger comes, then old Holger the Dane will rouse himself, so that the table shall burst when he draws out his beard! Then he will come forth and strike, so that it shall be heard in all the countries in the world.'

An old grandfather sat and told his little grandson all this about Holger the Dane; and the little boy knew that what his grandfather told him was true. And while the old man sat and told his story, he carved an image which was to represent Holger the Dane, and to be fastened to the prow of a ship; for the old grandfather was a carver of figure-heads – that is, one who cuts out the figures fastened to the

front of ships, and from which every ship is named. And here he had cut out Holger the Dane, who stood there proudly with his long beard, and held the broad battlesword in one hand while with the other he leaned upon the Danish arms.

And the old grandfather told so much about famous Danish men and women, that it appeared at last to the little grandson as if he knew as much as Holger the Dane himself, who, after all, could only dream; and when the little fellow was in his bed, he thought so much of it, that he actually pressed his chin against the coverlet, and fancied he had a long beard that had grown fast to it.

But the old grandfather remained sitting at his work, and carved away at the last part of it; and this was the Danish coat of arms. When he had done, he looked at the whole, and thought of all he had read and heard, and that he had told this evening to the little boy; and he nodded, and wiped his spectacles, and put them on again, and said, 'Yes, Holger the Dane will probably not come in my time; but the boy in the bed yonder may get to see him, and be there when the push really comes.'

And the old grandfather nodded again: and the more he looked at his Holger the Dane the more plain did it become to him that it was a good image he had carved. It seemed really to gain colour, and the armour appeared to gleam like iron and steel; the hearts in the Danish arms became redder and redder, and the lions with the golden crowns on their heads leaped up.[*]

'That's the most beautiful coat of arms there is in the world!' said the old man. 'The lions are strength, and the heart is gentleness and love!'

And he looked at the uppermost lion, and thought of King Canute, who bound great England to the throne of Denmark; and he looked at the second lion, and thought of Waldemar, who united Denmark and conquered the Wendish lands; and he glanced at the third lion, and remembered Margaret, who united Denmark, Sweden, and Norway. But while he looked at the red hearts, they gleamed more brightly than before; they became flames which moved, and his heart followed each of them.

The first heart led him into a dark narrow prison: there sat a prisoner, a beautiful woman, the daughter of King Christian IV, Eleanor Ulfeld; and the flame, which was shaped like a rose, attached itself to her bosom and blossomed, so that it became one with the heart of her, the noblest and best of all Danish women. 'That is one of the hearts in the arms of Denmark,' said the old grandfather.

And his spirit followed the second flame, which led him out upon the sea, where the cannons thundered and the ships lay shrouded in smoke; and the flame fastened itself in the shape of a ribbon of honour on the breast of Hvitfeld, as he blew himself and his ship into the air, that he might save the fleet.

And the third flame led him to the wretched huts of Greenland, where the preacher Hans Egede wrought, with love in every word and deed: the flame was a star on his breast, another heart in the Danish arms.

And the spirit of the old grandfather flew on before the waving flames, for his spirit knew whither the flames desired to go. In the

---

[*] The Danish arms consist of three lions between nine hearts.

humble room of the peasant woman stood Frederick VI, writing his name with chalk on the beam. The flame trembled on his breast, and trembled in his heart; in the peasant's lowly room his heart too became a heart in the Danish arms. And the old grandfather dried his eyes, for he had known King Frederick with the silvery locks and the honest blue eyes, and had lived for him: he folded his hands, and looked in silence straight before him. Then came the daughter-in-law of the old grandfather, and said it was late, he ought now to rest; and the supper table was spread.

'But it is beautiful, what you have done, grandfather!' said she. 'Holger the Dane, and all our old coat of arms! It seems to me just as if I had seen that face before!'

'No, that can scarcely be,' replied the old grandfather; 'but I have seen it, and I have tried to carve it in wood as I have kept it in my memory. It was when the English lay in the roadstead, on the Danish second of April, when we showed that we were old Danes. In the *Denmark*, on board which I was, in Steen Bille's squadron, I had a man at my side – it seemed as if the bullets were afraid of him! Merrily he sang old songs, and shot and fought as if he were something more than a man. I remember his face yet; but whence he came, and whither he went, I know not – nobody knows. I have often thought he must have been old Holger the Dane himself, who had swum down from Kronborg, and aided us in the hour of danger: that was my idea, and there stands his picture.'

And the statue threw its great shadow up against the wall, and even over part of the ceiling; it looked as though the real Holger the Dane were standing behind it, for the shadow moved; but this might have been because the flame of the candle did not burn steadily. And the daughter-in-law kissed the old grandfather, and led him to the great armchair by the table; and she and her husband, who was the son of the old man, and father of the little boy in the bed, sat and ate their supper; and the grandfather spoke of the Danish lions and of the Danish hearts, of strength and of gentleness; and quite clearly did he explain that there was another strength besides the power that lies in the sword; and he pointed to the shelf on which were the old books, where

stood the plays of Holberg, which had been read so often, for they were very amusing; one could almost fancy one recognised the people of bygone days in them.

'See, he knew how to strike too,' said the grandfather: 'he scourged the foolishness and prejudice of the people as long as he could' – and the grandfather nodded at the mirror, above which stood the calendar, with the 'Round Tower' on it, and said, 'Tycho Brahe was also one who used the sword, not to cut into flesh and bone, but to build up a plainer way among all the stars of heaven. And then *he* whose father belonged to my calling, the son of the old figure-head carver, he whom we have ourselves seen with his silver hairs and his broad shoulders, he whose name is spoken of in all lands! Yes, *he* was a sculptor; *I* am only a carver. Yes, Holger the Dane may come in many forms, so that one hears in every country in the world of Denmark's strength. Shall we now drink the health of Thorwaldsen?'

But the little lad in the bed saw plainly the old Kronborg with the Öre Sound, the real Holger the Dane, who sat deep below, with his beard grown through the marble table, dreaming of all that happens up here. Holger the Dane also dreamed of the little humble room where the carver sat; he heard all that passed, and nodded in his sleep, and said, 'Yes, remember me, ye Danish folk; remember me. I shall come in the hour of need.'

And without by Kronborg shone the bright day, and the wind carried the notes of the hunting-horn over from the neighbouring land; the ships sailed past, and saluted – 'Boom! boom!' and from Kronborg came the reply, 'Boom! boom!' But Holger the Dane did not awake, however loudly they shot, for it was only 'Good-day' and 'Thank you!' There must be another kind of shooting before he awakes; but he will awake, for there is strength in Holger the Dane.

The Little Match Girl

I T WAS terribly cold; it snowed and was already almost dark, and evening came on, the last evening of the year. In the cold and gloom a poor little girl, bareheaded and barefoot, was walking through the streets. When she left her own house she certainly had had slippers on; but of what use were they? They were very big slippers, and her mother had used them till then, so big were they. The little maid lost them as she slipped across the road, where two carriages were rattling by terribly fast. One slipper was not to be found again, and a boy had seized the other, and run away with it. He said he could use it very well as a cradle, someday when he had children of his own. So now the little girl went with her little naked feet, which were quite red and blue with the cold. In an old apron she carried a number of matches, and a bundle of them in her hand. No one had bought anything of her all day, and no one had given her a farthing.

Shivering with cold and hunger she crept along, a picture of misery, poor little girl! The snowflakes covered her long fair hair, which fell in pretty curls over her neck; but she did not think of that now. In all the windows lights were shining, and there was a glorious smell of roast goose, for it was New Year's Eve. Yes, she thought of that!

In a corner formed by two houses, one of which projected beyond the other, she sat down, cowering. She had drawn up her little feet, but she was still colder, and she did not dare to go home, for she had sold no matches, and did not bring a farthing of money. From her father she would certainly receive a beating, and besides, it was cold at home, for they had nothing over them but a roof through which the wind whistled, though the largest rents had been stopped with straw and rags.

Her little hands were almost benumbed with the cold. Ah! a match might do her good, if she could only draw one from the bundle, and rub it against the wall, and warm her hands at it. She drew one out. R-r-atch! how it sputtered and burned! It was a warm, bright flame, like a little candle, when she held her hands over it; it was a wonderful little light! It really seemed to the little girl as if she sat before a great polished stove, with bright brass feet and a brass cover. How the fire burned! how comfortable it was! but the little flame went out, the stove vanished, and she had only the remains of the burned match in her hand.

A second was rubbed against the wall. It burned up, and when the light fell upon the wall it became transparent like a thin veil, and she could see through it into the room. On the table a snow-white cloth was spread; upon it stood a shining dinner service; the roast goose smoked gloriously, stuffed with apples and dried plums. And what was still more splendid to behold, the goose hopped down from the dish, and waddled along the floor, with a knife and fork in its breast, to the little girl. Then the match went out, and only the thick, damp, cold wall was before her. She lighted another match. Then she was sitting under a beautiful Christmas tree; it was greater and more ornamented than the one she had seen through the glass door last Christmas at the rich merchant's. Thousands of candles burned upon the green branches, and coloured pictures like those in the print shops looked down upon them. The little girl stretched forth her hand towards them; then the match went out. The Christmas lights mounted higher. She saw them now as stars in the sky: one of them fell down, forming a long line of fire.

'Now someone is dying,' thought the little girl, for her old grand-mother, the only person who had loved her, and who was now dead, had told her that when a star fell down a soul mounted up to God.

She rubbed another match against the wall; it became bright again, and in the brightness the old grandmother stood clear and shining, mild and lovely.

'Grandmother!' cried the child. 'Oh! take me with you! I know you will go when the match is burned out. You will vanish like the warm fire, the beautiful roast goose, and the great glorious Christmas tree!'

And she hastily rubbed the whole bundle of matches, for she wished to hold her grandmother fast. And the matches burned with such a glow that it became brighter than in the middle of the day; grandmother had never been so large or so beautiful. She took the little girl in her arms, and both flew in brightness and joy above the earth, very, very high, and up there was neither cold, nor hunger, nor care – they were with God!

But in the corner, leaning against the wall, sat in the cold morning hours the poor girl with red cheeks and smiling mouth, frozen to death on the last evening of the Old Year. The New Year's sun rose upon a little corpse! The child sat there, stiff and cold, with the matches of which one bundle was burned. 'She wanted to warm herself,' the people said. No one imagined what a beautiful thing she had seen, and in what glory she had gone in with her grandmother to the New Year's joy.

A Picture from the Fortress Wall

IT IS AUTUMN: we stand on the fortress wall, and look out over the sea; we look at the numerous ships, and at the Swedish coast on the other side of the Sound, which rises high in the evening glow; behind us the rampart goes steeply down; mighty trees surround us, the yellow leaves flutter down from the branches. Down there where the sentinel goes, stand gloomy houses fenced in with palisades; inside these it is very narrow and dismal, but still more dismal is it behind the grated loopholes in the wall, for there sit the prisoners, the worst criminals.

A ray of the sinking sun shoots into the bare cell of one of the captives. The sun shines upon the good and the evil. The dark stubborn criminal throws an impatient look at the cold ray. A little bird flies towards the grating. The bird twitters to the wicked as to the just.

He only utters his short 'tweet! tweet!' but he perches upon the grating, claps his wings, pecks a feather from one of them, puffs himself out, and sets his feathers on end on his neck and breast; and the bad chained man looks at him: a milder expression comes into the criminal's hard face; in his breast there swells up a thought – a thought he himself cannot rightly analyse; but the thought has to do with the sunbeam, with the scent of violets which grow luxuriantly in spring at the foot of the wall. Now the horns of the hunters sound merry and full. The little bird flies away from the prisoner's grating; the sunbeam vanishes, and again it is dark in the room, and dark in the heart of the bad man; but still the sun has shone into that heart, and the twittering of the bird has touched it!

Sound on, ye glorious strains of the hunting-horns! The evening is mild, the sea is smooth as a mirror and calm.

By the Almshouse Window

NEAR THE grass-covered rampart which encircles Copenhagen lies a great red house with many windows; in these grow balsams and plants of southernwood; the interior is sufficiently poverty-stricken; and poor and old are the people who inhabit it. The building is the Vartu Almshouse.

Look! at the window there leans an old maid: she plucks the withered leaf from the balsam, and looks at the grass-covered rampart, on which many children are playing. What is the old maid thinking of? A whole life-drama is unfolding itself before her mind.

'The poor little children, how happily they play! What red cheeks and what angels' eyes! but they have no shoes nor stockings. They dance on the green rampart, just on the place where, according to the old story, the ground always sank in, many years ago, and where an innocent child had been lured by means of flowers and toys, into an open grave, which was afterwards built up while the child played and ate; and from that moment the mound remained firm and fast, and was quickly covered with fine green turf. The little people who now play on that spot know nothing of the old tale, else would they fancy they heard the child crying deep below the earth, and the dewdrops on each blade of grass would be to them tears of woe. Nor do they know the story of the Danish King who, when the enemy lay outside, rode past here and took an oath that he would die here in his nest: then came women and men who poured boiling water down over the white-clad foes, who, in the snow, were crawling up the outer side of the rampart.

'No! the poor little ones are playing with light spirits. Play on, play on, thou little maiden! Soon the years will come – yes, those glorious years. The candidates for confirmation walk hand in hand: thou hast a white frock on – it has cost thy mother much labour, and yet it is only cut down for thee out of an old larger dress! You will also wear a red shawl; and what if it hang too far down? People will only see how large, how very large it is. You are thinking of your dress, and of the Giver of all good; so glorious is it to wander on the green rampart.

'And the years roll by with many dark days, but you have your cheerful young spirit, and you have gained *a friend*, you know not how. You meet, oh, how often! You walk together on the rampart in the fresh spring, when all the bells of the church steeples ring on the great Day of Intercession.

'Scarcely have the violets come forth, but outside Rosenborg there is a tree bright with the first green buds. There you stop. Every year this tree sends forth fresh green shoots. Alas! it is not so with the human heart! Dark mists, more in number than those that cover the northern skies, cloud the human heart. Poor child – thy friend's bridal chamber is a black coffin, and thou becomest an old maid. From the almshouse window behind the balsams thou shalt look on the merry children at play and shalt see thy own history renewed.'

And that is the life-drama that passes before the old maid while she looks out upon the rampart, where the children with their red cheeks and bare shoeless feet are rejoicing merrily, like the other birds of Heaven.

The Old Street Lamp

DID YOU ever hear the story of the old Street Lamp? It is not so remarkably entertaining, but it may be listened to for once in a way.

It was a very honest old Lamp, that had done its work for many, many years, but which was now to be pensioned off. It hung for the last time to its post, and gave light to the street. It felt as an old dancer at the theatre, who is dancing for the last time, and who tomorrow will sit forgotten in her garret. The Lamp was in great fear about the morrow, for it knew that it was to appear in the council-house, and to be inspected by the mayor and the council, to see if it were fit for further service or not.

And then it was to be decided whether it was to show its light in future for the inhabitants of some suburb, or in the country in some manufactory: perhaps it would have to go at once into an iron foundry to be melted down. In this last case anything might be made of it; but the question whether it would remember, in its new state, that it had been a Street Lamp, troubled it terribly. Whatever might happen, this much was certain, that it would be separated from the watchman and his wife, whom it had got to look upon as quite belonging to its family. It became a lamp when he became a watchman. The wife was a little proud in those days. Only in the evening, when she went by, she deigned to glance at the Lamp; in the daytime never. But now, in these latter years, when all three, the watchman, his wife, and the Lamp, had grown old, the wife had also tended it, cleaned it, and provided it with oil. The two old people were thoroughly honest; never had they cheated the Lamp of a single drop of the oil provided for it.

It was the Lamp's last night in the street, and tomorrow it was to go to the council-house; those were two dark thoughts! No wonder that it did not burn brightly. But many other thoughts passed through its brain. On what a number of events had it shone – how much it had seen! Perhaps as much as the mayor and the whole council had beheld. But it did not give utterance to these thoughts, for it was a good honest old Lamp, that would not willingly hurt anyone, and least of all those in authority. Many things passed through its mind, and at times its light flashed up. In such moments it had a feeling that it, too, would be remembered.

'There was that handsome young man – it is certainly a long while ago – he had a letter on pink paper with a gilt edge. It was so prettily written, as if by a lady's hand. Twice he read it, and kissed it, and looked up to me with eyes which said plainly, "I am the happiest of men!" Only he and I know what was written in this first letter from his true love. Yes, I remember another pair of eyes. It is wonderful how our thoughts fly about! There was a funeral procession in the street: the young beautiful lady lay in the decorated hearse, in a coffin adorned with flowers and wreaths; and a number of torches quite darkened my light. The people stood in crowds by the houses, and all followed the procession. But when the torches had passed from before my face, and I looked round, a single person stood leaning against my post, weeping. I shall never forget the mournful eyes that looked up to me!'

This and similar thoughts occupied the old Street Lantern, which shone tonight for the last time.

The sentry relieved from his post at least knows who is to succeed him, and may whisper a few words to him; but the Lamp did not know its successor; and yet it might have given a few useful hints with respect to rain and fog, and some information as to how far the rays of the moon lit up the pavement, and from what direction the wind usually came.

On the bridge of the gutter stood three persons who wished to introduce themselves to the Lamp, for they thought the Lamp itself could appoint its successor. The first was a herring's head, that could gleam with light in the darkness. He thought it would be a great saving of oil if they put him up on the post. Number two was a piece of rotten wood, which also glimmers in the dark, and always more than a piece of fish, it said to itself; besides, it was the last piece of a tree which had once been the pride of the forest. The third person was a glow-worm. Where this one had come from, the Lamp could not imagine; but there it was, and it could give light. But the rotten wood and the herring's head swore by all that was good that it only gave light at certain times, and could not be brought into competition with themselves.

The old Lamp declared that not one of them gave sufficient light to fill the office of a street lamp; but not one of them would believe this. When they heard that the Lamp had not the office to give away, they were very glad of it, and declared that the Lamp was too decrepit to make a good choice.

At the same moment the Wind came careering from the corner of the street, and blew through the air-holes of the old Street Lamp.

'What's this I hear?' he asked. 'Are you to go away tomorrow? Is this the last evening that I shall find you here? Then I must make you a present at parting. I will blow into your brain-box in such a way that you shall be able in future not only to remember everything you have seen and heard, but that you shall have such light within you as shall enable you to see all that is read of or spoken of in your presence.'

'Yes, that is really much, very much!' said the old Lamp. 'I thank you heartily. I only hope I shall not be melted down.'

'That is not likely to happen at once,' said the Wind. 'Now I will blow up your memory: if you receive several presents of this kind, you may pass your old days very agreeably.'

'If only I am not melted down!' said the Lamp again. 'Or should I retain my memory even in that case?'

'Be sensible, old Lamp,' said the Wind. And he blew, and at that moment the Moon stepped forth from behind the clouds.

'What will you give the old Lamp?' asked the Wind.

'I'll give nothing,' replied the Moon. 'I am on the wane, and the lamps never lighted me; but, on the contrary, I've often given light for the lamps.'

And with these words the Moon hid herself again behind the clouds, to be safe from further importunity.

A drop now fell upon the Lamp, as if from the roof; but the drop explained that it came from the clouds, and was a present – perhaps the best present possible.

'I shall penetrate you so completely that you shall receive the faculty, if you wish it, to turn into rust in one night, and to crumble into dust.'

The Lamp considered this a bad present, and the Wind thought so too.

'Does no one give more? does no one give more?' it blew as loud as it could.

Then a bright shooting star fell down, forming a long bright stripe.

'What was that?' cried the Herring's Head. 'Did not a star fall? I really think it went into the Lamp! Certainly if such high-born personages try for this office, we may say good-night and betake ourselves home.'

And so they did, all three. But the old Lamp shed a marvellous strong light around.

'That was a glorious present,' it said. 'The bright stars which I have always admired, and which shine as I could never shine though I shone with all my might, have noticed me, a poor old lamp, and have sent me a present, by giving me the faculty that all I remember and see as clearly as if it stood before me, shall also be seen by all whom I love. And in this lies the true pleasure; for joy that we cannot share with others is only half enjoyed.'

'That sentiment does honour to your heart,' said the Wind. 'But for that wax lights are necessary. If these are not lit up in you, your rare faculties will be of no use to others. Look you, the stars did not think of that; they take you and every other light for wax. But now I am tired and I will lie down.' And he lay down.

The next day – yes, it will be best that we pass over the next day. The next evening the Lamp was resting in a grandfather's chair. And guess where! In the watchman's dwelling. He had begged as a favour of the mayor and the council that he might keep the Street Lamp. They laughed at his request, but the Lamp was given to him, and now it lay in the great armchair by the warm stove. It seemed as if the Lamp had grown bigger, now that it occupied the chair all alone.

The old people sat at supper, and looked kindly at the old Lamp, to whom they would willingly have granted a place at their table.

Their dwelling was certainly only a cellar two yards below the footway, and one had to cross a stone passage to get into the room. But within it was very comfortable and warm, and strips of list had been nailed to the door. Everything looked clean and neat, and there were curtains round the bed and the little windows. On the window-sill stood two curious flowerpots, which sailor Christian had brought home from the East or West Indies. They were only of clay, and represented two elephants. The backs of these creatures were wanting; and instead of them there bloomed from within the earth with which one elephant was filled, some very excellent leeks, and that was the old folk's kitchen garden; out of the other grew a great geranium, and that was their flower garden. On the wall hung a great coloured print representing the Congress of Vienna. There you had all the Kings and Emperors at once. A Grandfather's clock with heavy weights went 'tick! tick!' and in fact it always went too fast; but the old people declared this was far better than if it went too slow. They ate their supper, and the Street Lamp lay, as I have said, in the armchair close beside the stove. It seemed to the Lamp as if the whole world had been turned round. But when the old watchman looked at it, and spoke of all that they two had gone through in rain and in fog, in the bright short nights of summer and in the long winter nights, when the snow beat down, and one longed to be at home in the cellar, then the old Lamp found its wits again. It saw everything as clearly as if it was happening then; yes, the Wind had kindled a capital light for it.

The old people were very active and industrious; not a single hour was wasted in idleness. On Sunday afternoon some book or other was brought out; generally a book of travels. And the old man read aloud about Africa, about the great woods, with elephants running about wild; and the old woman listened intently, and looked furtively at the clay elephants which served for flowerpots.

'I can almost imagine it to myself!' said she.

And the Lamp wished particularly that a wax candle had been there, and could be lighted up in it; for then the old woman would be able to see everything to the smallest detail, just as the Lamp saw it – the tall trees with great branches all entwined, the naked black men on horseback, and whole droves of elephants crashing through the reeds with their broad clumsy feet.

'Of what use are all my faculties if I can't obtain a wax light?' sighed the Lamp. 'They have only oil and tallow candles, and that's not enough.'

One day a great number of wax candle-ends came down into the cellar: the larger pieces were burned, and the smaller ones the old woman used for waxing her thread. So there were wax candles enough; but no one thought of putting a little piece into the Lamp.

'Here I stand with my rare faculties!' thought the Lamp. 'I carry everything within me, and cannot let them partake of it; they don't know that I am able to cover these white walls with the most gorgeous tapestry, to change them into noble forests, and all that they can possibly wish.'

The Lamp, however, was kept neat and clean, and stood all shining in a corner, where it caught the eyes of all. Strangers considered it a bit of old rubbish; but the old people did not care for that; they loved the Lamp.

One day – it was the old watchman's birthday – the old woman approached the Lantern, smiling to herself, and said, 'I'll make an illumination today, in honour of my old man!'

And the Lamp rattled its metal cover, for it thought, 'Well, at last there will be a light within me.' But only oil was produced, and no wax light appeared. The Lamp burned throughout the whole evening, but now understood, only too well, that the gift of the stars would be a hidden treasure for all its life. Then it had a dream: for one possessing its rare faculties, to dream was not difficult. It seemed as if the old people were dead, and that itself had been taken to the iron foundry to be melted down. It felt as much alarmed as on that day when it was to appear in the council-house to be inspected by the mayor and council. But though the power had been given to it to fall into rust and dust at will, it did not use this power. It was put into the furnace, and turned into an iron candlestick, as fair a candlestick as you would desire – one on which wax lights were to be burned. It had received the form of an angel holding a great nosegay; and the wax light was to be placed in the middle of the nosegay.

The candlestick had a place assigned to it on a green writing-table. The room was very comfortable; many books stood round about the walls, which were hung with beautiful pictures; it belonged to a poet. Everything that he wrote or composed showed itself round about him. The room was changed to thick dark forests, sometimes to beautiful meadows, where the storks strutted about, sometimes again to a ship sailing on the foaming ocean.

'What faculties lie hidden in me!' said the old Lamp, when it awoke. 'I could almost wish to be melted down! But no! that must not be so long as the old people live. They love me for myself; I am like a child to them; they have cleaned me and have given me oil. I am as well off now as the whole Congress.'

And from that time it enjoyed more inward peace; and the honest old Street Lamp had well deserved to enjoy it.

The Neighbouring Families

ONE WOULD really have thought that something important was going on by the duck-pond; but nothing was going on. All the ducks lying quietly upon the water, or standing on their heads in it – for they could do that – swam suddenly to the shore. One could see the traces of their feet on the wet clay, and their quacking sounded far and wide. The water, lately clear and bright as a mirror, was quite in a commotion. Before, every tree, every neighbouring bush, the old farmhouse with the holes in the roof and the swallow's nest, and especially the great rose bush covered with flowers, had been mirrored in it. This rose bush covered the wall and hung over the water, in which everything appeared as in a picture, only that everything stood on its head; but when the water was set in motion each thing ran into the other, and the picture was gone. Two feathers, which the fluttering ducks had lost, floated to and fro, and all at once they took a start, as if the wind were coming; but the wind did not come, so they had to be still, and the water became quiet and smooth again. One could see distinctly the gable, with the swallow's nest, and the rose bush. The Roses mirrored themselves in it again; they were beautiful, but they did not know it, for no one had told them. The sun shone among the delicate leaves; everything breathed in the sweet fragrance, and all felt as we feel when we are filled with the thought of our greatest happiness.

'How beautiful is life!' said each Rose. 'Only one thing I wish, that I were able to kiss the sun, because it is so bright and so warm. The roses, too, in the water yonder, our images, I should like to kiss, and the pretty birds in the nests. There are some up yonder too; they thrust out their heads and pipe quite feebly: they have no feathers like their father and mother. They are good neighbours, below and above. How beautiful is life!'

The young ones above and below – those below are certainly only shadows in the water – were Sparrows; their parents were Sparrows too; they had taken possession of the empty swallow's nest of last year, and kept house in it as if it had been their own.

'Are those ducks' children swimming yonder?' asked the young Sparrows, when they noticed the ducks' feathers upon the water.

'If you must ask questions, ask sensible ones,' replied their mother. 'Don't you see that they are feathers? living clothes, stuff like I wear and like you will wear; but ours is finer. I wish, by the way, we had those up here in our own nest, for they keep one warm. I wonder what the ducks were so frightened at; there must have been something in the water. Not at me, certainly, though I said "Piep" to you rather loudly. The thick-headed roses ought to know it, but they know nothing; they only look at one another and smell. I'm very tired of those neighbours.'

'Just listen to those darling birds up there,' said the Roses. 'They begin to want to sing, but are not able yet. But it will come in time. What a pleasure that must be! It's nice to have such merry neighbours.'

Suddenly two horses came galloping up to water. A peasant boy rode on one, and he had taken off all his clothes, except his big black hat which was so big and broad. The boy whistled like a bird, and rode into the pond where it was deepest, and when he came past the rose bush he plucked a rose, and put it upon his hat. And now he thought he looked very fine, and rode on. The other Roses looked after their sister, and said to each other, 'Whither may she be journeying?' but they did not know.

'I should like to go out into the world,' said the one to the other; 'but it's beautiful, too, here at home among the green leaves. All day the sun shines warm and bright, and in the night-time the sky is more beautiful still; we can see that through all the little holes in it.'

They meant the stars, but they knew no better.

'We make it lively about the house,' said the Mother-Sparrow; 'and "the swallow's nest brings luck", people say, so they're glad to see us. But the neighbours! Such a rose bush climbing up the wall causes damp. It will most likely be taken away; and then, at least, corn will perhaps grow here. The roses are fit for nothing but to be looked at and smelt, or at most one may be stuck on a hat. Every year, I know from my mother, they fall off. The farmer's wife preserves them, and puts salt among them; then they get a French name that I neither can nor will pronounce, and are put upon the fire to make a good smell. You see, *that*'s their life. They're only for the eye and the nose. Now you know it.'

When the evening came, and the gnats danced in the warm air and the red clouds, the Nightingale came and sang to the Roses, saying that the beautiful was like sunshine to the world, and that the beautiful lived for ever. But the Roses thought the Nightingale was singing of itself, and indeed one might easily have thought so; they never imagined that the song was about them. But they rejoiced greatly in it, and wondered whether all the little Sparrows might become nightingales.

'I understood the song of that bird very well,' said the young Sparrows, 'only one word was not clear. What is *the beautiful*?'

'That's nothing at all,' replied the Mother-Sparrow; 'that's only an outside affair. Yonder, at the nobleman's seat, where the pigeons have their own house, and have corn and peas strewn before them every day, I've been there myself, and dined with them; for tell me what company you keep, and I'll tell you who you are – yonder at the nobleman's seat there are two birds with green necks and a crest upon their head; they can spread out their tails like a great wheel, and then it plays with various colours, so that the sight makes one's eyes ache. These birds are called peacocks, and that's *the beautiful*. They should only be plucked a little, then they would look no better than all the rest of us. I should have plucked them myself if they had not been so large.'

'I'll pluck them,' piped the little Sparrow who had no feathers yet.

In the farmhouse dwelt two young married people; they loved each other well, were industrious and active, and everything in their home looked very pretty. On Sunday morning the young wife came out, plucked a handful of the most beautiful roses, and put them into a glass of water, which she put upon the cupboard.

'Now I see that it is Sunday,' said the husband, and he kissed his little wife.

They sat down, read their hymn-book, and held each other by the hand; and the sun shone on the fresh roses and the young couple.

'This sight is really too wearisome,' said the Mother-Sparrow, who could look from the nest into the room; and she flew away.

The same thing happened the next Sunday, for every Sunday fresh roses were placed in the glass; but the rose bush bloomed as beautiful as ever.

The young Sparrows had feathers now, and wanted to fly out too, but the mother would not allow it, and they were obliged to stay at home. She flew alone; but, however it may have happened, before she was aware of it, she was entangled in a noose of horsehair which some boys had fastened to the branches. The horsehair wound itself fast round her legs, as fast as if it would cut the leg through. What pain, what a fright she was in!

The boys came running up, and seized the bird; and indeed, roughly enough.

'It's only a Sparrow,' said they; but they did not let her go, but took her home with them. And whenever she cried, they tapped her on the beak.

In the farmhouse stood an old man, who understood making soap for shaving and washing, in cakes as well as in balls. He was a merry, wandering old man. When he saw the Sparrow, which the boys had brought, and for which they said they did not care, he said, 'Shall we make it very beautiful?'

The Mother-Sparrow felt an icy shudder pass through her.

Out of the box, in which were the most brilliant colours, the old man took a quantity of shining gold leaf, and the boys were sent for some white of egg, with which the Sparrow was completely smeared; the gold leaf was stuck upon that, and there was the Mother-Sparrow gilded all over. She did not think of the adornment, but trembled all over. And the soap-man tore off a fragment from the red lining of his old jacket, cut notches in it, so that it looked like a cock's comb, and stuck it on the bird's head.

'Now you shall see the gold bird fly,' said the old man; and he released the Sparrow, which flew away in deadly fear, with the sunlight shining upon her.

How it glittered! All the Sparrows, and even a Crow, a knowing old boy, were startled at the sight; but still they flew after her, to know what kind of strange bird this might be.

'From where, from where?' cried the Crow.

'Wait a bit, wait a bit!' said the Sparrows, but it would not wait.

Driven by fear and horror, she flew homeward; she was nearly sinking powerless to the earth; the flock of pursuing birds increased, and some even tried to peck at her.

'Look at her! look at her!' they all cried.

'Look at her! look at her!' cried the young ones, when the Mother-Sparrow approached the nest. 'That must be a young peacock. He glitters with all colours. It quite hurts one's eyes, as mother told us. Piep! that's *the beautiful*!'

And now they pecked at the bird with their little beaks, so that she could not possibly get into the nest; she was so much exhausted that she could not even say 'Piep!' much less 'I am your mother!'

The other birds also fell upon the Sparrow, and plucked off feather after feather till she fell bleeding into the rose bush.

'You poor creature!' said all the Roses: 'be quiet, and we will hide you. Lean your head against us.'

The Sparrow spread out her wings once more, then drew them tight to her body, and lay dead by the neighbouring family, the beautiful fresh Roses.

'Piep!' sounded from the nest. 'Where can our mother be? It's quite inexplicable. It cannot be a trick of hers, and mean that we're to shift for ourselves: she has left us the house as an inheritance, but to which of us shall it belong when we have families of our own?'

'Yes, it won't do for you to stay with me when I enlarge my establishment with a wife and children,' observed the smallest.

'I shall have more wives and children than you!' cried the second.

'But I am the eldest!' said the third.

Now they all became excited. They struck out with their wings, hacked with their beaks, and flump! one after another was thrust out of the nest. There they lay with their anger, holding their heads on one side, and blinking with the eye that looked upwards. That was their way of being sulky.

They could fly a little; by practice they improved, and at last they fixed upon a sign by which they should know each other when they met later in the world. This sign was to be the cry of 'Piep!' with a scratching of the left foot three times against the ground.

The young Sparrow that had remained behind in the nest made itself as broad as it possibly could, for it was the proprietor. But the proprietorship did not last long. In the night the red fire burst through the window, the flames seized upon the roof, the dry straw blazed brightly up, and the whole house was burned, and the young Sparrow too; but the others escaped with their lives.

When the sun rose again, and everything looked as much refreshed as if nature had had a quiet sleep, there remained of the farmhouse nothing but a few charred beams, leaning against the chimney that was now its own master. Thick smoke still rose from among the fragments, but without stood the rose bush quite unharmed, and every flower, every twig, was reflected in the clear water.

'How beautifully those roses bloom before the ruined house!' cried a passer-by. 'I cannot imagine a more agreeable picture: I must have that.'

And the traveller took out of his portfolio a little book with white leaves: he was a painter, and with his pencil he drew the smoking house, the charred beams, and the overhanging chimney, which bent more and more; quite in the foreground appeared the blooming rose bush, which presented a charming sight, and indeed for its sake the whole picture had been made.

Later in the day, the two Sparrows that had been born here came by.

'Where is the house?' asked they. 'Where is the nest? Piep! All is burned, and our strong brother is burned too. That's what he has got by keeping the nest to himself. The Roses have escaped well enough – there they stand yet, with their red cheeks. They certainly don't mourn at their neighbour's misfortune. I won't speak to them; it's so ugly here, that's my opinion.' And they flew up and away.

On a beautiful sunny autumn day, when one could almost have believed it was the middle of summer, there hopped about in the clean dry courtyard of the nobleman's seat, in front of the great steps, a number of pigeons, black, and white, and violet, all shining in the sunlight. The old Mother-Pigeons said to their young ones, 'Stand in groups, stand in groups, for that looks much better.'

'What are those little grey creatures, that run about among us?' asked an old Pigeon, with red and green in her eyes. 'Little grey ones, little grey ones!' she cried.

'They are sparrows, good creatures. We have always had the reputation of being kind, so we will allow them to pick up the corn with us. They don't interrupt conversation, and they scrape so nicely with the leg.'

Yes, they scraped three times each with the left leg, and said, 'Piep.' By that they recognised each other as the Sparrows from the nest by the burned house.

'Here's very good eating,' said the Sparrows.

The Pigeons strutted round one another, bulged out their chests mightily, and had their own opinions.

'Do you see that pouter-pigeon?' said one, speaking to the others. 'Do you see that one, swallowing the peas? She takes too many, and the best, moreover. Curoo! curoo! Do you see how bald she is getting on her crest, the ugly spiteful thing! Curoo! curoo!'

And all their eyes sparkled with spite.

'Stand in groups, stand in groups! Little grey ones, little grey ones! Curoo! curoo!'

So their beaks went on and on, and so they will go on when a thousand years are gone.

The Sparrows feasted bravely. They listened attentively, and even stood in the ranks of the Pigeons, but it did not suit them well. They were satisfied, and so they quitted the Pigeons, exchanged opinions concerning them, slipped under the garden railings, and when they found the door of the garden open, one of them, who was over-fed, and consequently valorous, hopped on the threshold.

'Piep!' said he, 'I may venture that.'

'Piep!' said the other, 'so can I, and something more too.'

And he hopped right into the room. No one was present; the third Sparrow saw that, and hopped still farther into the room, and said, 'Right in or not at all! By the way, this is a funny man's-nest; and what have they put up there? What's that?'

Just in front of the Sparrows the roses were blooming; they were mirrored in the water, and the charred beams leaned against the toppling chimney.

'Why, what is this? How came this in the room in the nobleman's house?'

And then these Sparrows wanted to fly over the chimney and the roses, but flew against a flat wall. It was all a picture, a great beautiful picture, that the painter had completed from a sketch.

'Piep!' said the Sparrows, 'it's nothing, it only looks like something. Piep! that's *the beautiful*! Can you understand it? *I* can't.'

And they flew away, for some people came into the room.

Days and years went by. The Pigeons had often cooed, not to say growled, the spiteful things; the Sparrows had suffered cold in winter, and lived riotously in summer; they were all betrothed or married, or whatever you like to call it. They had little ones, and of course each thought his own the handsomest and the cleverest: one flew this way, another that, and when they met they knew each other by their 'Piep!' and the three scrapes with the left leg. The eldest had remained a maiden Sparrow, with no nest and no young ones. Her great idea was to see a town, therefore she flew to Copenhagen.

There was to be seen a great house painted with many colours, close by the castle and by the canal, in which latter swam many ships laden with apples and pottery. The windows were broader below than at the top, and when the Sparrows looked through, every room appeared to them like a tulip with the most beautiful colours and shades. But in the middle of the tulip were white people, made of marble; a few certainly were made of plaster, but in the eyes of a sparrow that's all the same. Upon the roof stood a metal carriage, with metal horses harnessed to it, and the Goddess of Victory, also of bronze, driving. It was Thorwaldsen's Museum.

'How it shines! how it shines!' said the little maiden Sparrow. 'I suppose that's what they call *the beautiful*. Piep! But this is greater than the peacock!'

It still remembered what, in its days of childhood, the Mother-Sparrow had declared to be the greatest among the beautiful. The Sparrow flew down into the courtyard. There everything was very splendid: upon the walls palms and branches were painted; in the midst of the court stood a great blooming rose tree, spreading out its fresh branches, covered with many roses, over a grave. Thither the Sparrow flew, for there she saw many of her own kind. 'Piep!' and three scrapes with the left leg – that salutation it had often made throughout the summer, and nobody had replied, for friends who are once parted don't meet every day; and now this form of greeting had become quite a habit with it. But today two old Sparrows and a young one replied 'Piep!' and scraped three times each with the left leg.

'Ah! good-day! good-day!' They were three old ones from the nest, and a little one belonging to the family. 'Do we meet here again? It's a grand place, but there's not much to eat. This is *the beautiful*! Piep!'

And many people came out of the side chambers where the glorious marble statues stood, and approached the grave where slept the great master who had formed these marble images. All stood with radiant faces by Thorwaldsen's grave, and some gathered up the fallen rose leaves and kept them. They had come from afar: some from mighty England, others from Germany and France. The most beautiful among the ladies plucked one of the roses and hid it in her bosom. Then the Sparrows thought that the roses ruled here, and that the whole house had been built for their sake; that appeared to them to be too much; but as all the people showed their love for the roses, they would not be behindhand. 'Piep!' they said, and swept the ground with their tails, and glanced with one eye at the roses; and they had not looked long at the flowers before they recognised them as old neighbours. And so the roses really were. The painter who had sketched the rose bush by the ruined house had afterwards received permission to dig it up, and had given it to the architect, for nowhere could more beautiful roses be found. And the architect had planted it upon Thorwaldsen's grave, where it bloomed, an image of the beautiful, and gave its red fragrant petals to be carried into distant lands as mementoes.

'Have you found a situation here in the town?' asked the Sparrows.

And the Roses nodded; they recognised their grey neighbours, and were glad to see them again. 'How glorious it is to live and bloom, to see old faces again, and cheerful faces every day. Here it is as if every day was a great holiday.

Piep!' said the Sparrows. 'Yes, these are truly our old neighbours; we remember their origin by the pond. Piep! how they've got on! Yes, some people succeed while they're asleep, and what rarity there is in a red thing like that, I can't understand. Why, yonder is a withered leaf – I see it quite plainly!'

And they pecked at it till the leaf fell. But the tree stood there greener and fresher than ever; the Roses bloomed in the sunshine by Thorwaldsen's grave, and were associated with his immortal name.

Little Tuk

YES, THAT WAS little Tuk. His name was not really Tuk; but when he could not speak plainly, he used to call himself so. It was to mean 'Charley'; and it's a good thing to know that. Now, he was to take care of his little sister Gustava, who was much smaller than he, and at the same time he was to learn his lesson; but these two things would not go well together. The poor boy sat there with his little sister on his lap, and sang her all the songs that he knew, and every now and then he gave a glance at the geography-book that lay open before him; by tomorrow morning he was to know all the towns in Zealand by heart, and to know everything about them that one can well know.

Now his mother came home, for she had been out, and took little Gustava in her arms. Tuk ran to the window, and read so that he almost read his eyes out, for it became darker and darker; but his mother had no money to buy candles.

'There goes the old washerwoman out of the lane yonder,' said his mother, as she looked out of the window. 'The poor woman can hardly drag herself along, and now she has to carry the pail of water from the well. Be a good boy, Tuk, and run across, and help the old woman. Won't you?'

And Tuk ran across quickly, and helped her; but when he came back into the room it had become quite dark. There was no talk of a candle, and now he had to go to bed, and his bed was an old settle. There he lay, and thought of his geography lesson, and of Zealand, and of all the master had said. He ought certainly to have read it again, but he could not do that. So he put the geography-book under his pillow, because he had heard that this is a very good way to learn one's lesson; but one cannot depend upon it. There he lay, and thought and thought; and all at once he fancied someone kissed him upon his eyes and mouth. He slept, and yet he did not sleep; it was just as if the old washerwoman were looking at him with her kind eyes, and saying, 'It would be a great pity if you did not know your lesson tomorrow. You have helped me, therefore now I will help you; and Providence will help us both.'

All at once the book began to crawl, crawl about under Tuk's pillow.

'Kikeliki! Put! put!' It was a Hen that came crawling up, and she came from Kjöge. 'I'm a Kjöge hen!' she said.

And then she told him how many inhabitants were in the town, and about the battle that had been fought there, though that was really hardly worth mentioning.

'Kribli, kribli, plumps!' Something fell down: it was a wooden bird, the Parrot from the shooting match at Praestöe. He said that there were just as many inhabitants yonder as he had nails in his body; and he was very proud. 'Thorwaldsen lived close to me. Plumps! Here I lie very comfortably.'

But now little Tuk no longer lay in bed; on a sudden he was on horseback. Gallop, gallop! hop, hop! and so he went on. A splendidly-attired knight, with shining helmet and flowing plume, held him on the front of his saddle, and so they went riding on through the wood to the old town of Vordingborg, and that was a great and very busy town. On the King's castle rose high towers, and the radiance of lights streamed from every window; within was song and dancing, and King Waldemar and the young gaily-dressed maids of honour danced together. Now the morning came on, and so soon as the sun appeared the whole city and the King's castle suddenly sank down, one tower falling after another; and at last only one remained standing on the hill where the castle had formerly been; and the town was very small and poor, and the schoolboys came with their books under their arms, and said, 'Two thousand inhabitants'; but that was not true, for the town had not so many.

And little Tuk lay in his bed, as if he dreamed, and yet as if he did not dream; but someone stood close beside him.

'Little Tuk! little Tuk!' said the voice. It was a seaman, quite a little personage, as small as if he had been a cadet; but he was not a cadet. 'I'm to bring you a greeting from Korsör; that is a town which is just in good progress – a lively town that has steamers and mail coaches. In times past they used always to call it ugly, but that is now no longer true.

' "I lie by the sea-shore," said Korsör. "I have highroads and pleasure gardens; and I gave birth to a poet who was witty and entertaining, and that cannot be said of all of them. I wanted once to fit out a ship that was to sail round the world; but I did not do that, though I might have done it. But I smell deliciously, for close to my gates the loveliest roses bloom." '

Little Tuk looked, and it seemed red and green before his eyes; but when the confusion of colour had a little passed by, then there appeared a wooded declivity close by a bay, and high above it stood a glorious old church with two high pointed towers. Out of this hill flowed springs of water in thick columns, so that there was a continual splashing, and close by sat an old King with a golden crown upon his long hair: that was King Hroar of the springs, close by the town of Roskilde, as it is now called. And up the hill into the old church went all the Kings and Queens of Denmark, hand in hand, all with golden crowns; and the organ played, and the springs plashed. Little Tuk saw all and heard all.

'Don't forget the States of the realm,' said King Hroar.

At once everything had vanished, and whither? It seemed to him like turning a leaf in a book. And now stood there an old peasant woman. She was a weeding woman, who came from Soröe, where grass grows in the marketplace; she had an apron of grey cotton thrown over her head and shoulders, and the apron was very wet; it must have been raining.

'Yes, that it has!' said she; and she knew many amusing things out of Holberg's plays, and about Waldemar and Absalom. But all at once she cowered down, and wagged her head as if she were about to spring. 'Koax!' said she; 'it is wet! it is wet! There is a very agreeable death-silence in Soröe!' Now she changed all at once into a frog – 'Koax!' – and then she became an old woman again. 'One must dress according to the weather,' she said. 'It is wet! it is wet! My town is just like a bottle: one goes in at the cork, and must come out again at the cork. In old times I had capital fish, and now I've fresh red-cheeked boys in the bottom of the bottle, and they learn wisdom – Hebrew, Greek. Koax!'

That sounded just like the croak of the frogs, or the sound of someone marching across the moss in great boots; always the same note, so monotonous and wearisome that little Tuk fairly fell asleep, and that could not hurt him at all.

But even in this sleep came a dream, or whatever it was. His little sister Gustava with the blue eyes and the fair curly hair was all at once a tall slender maiden, and without having wings she could fly; and now they flew over Zealand, over the green forests and the blue lakes.

Do you hear the cock crow, little Tuk? Kikeliki! The fowls are flying up out of Kjöge! You shall have a poultry-yard – a great, great poultry-yard! You shall not suffer hunger nor need; and you shall shoot the popinjay, as the saying is; you shall become a rich and happy man. Your house shall rise up like King Waldemar's tower, and shall be richly adorned with marble statues, like those of Praetöe. You understand me well. Your name shall travel with fame round the whole world, like the ship that was to sail from Korsör.'

'Don't forget the States of the realm,' said King Hroar. 'You will speak well and sensibly, little Tuk; and when at last you descend to your grave, you shall sleep peacefully – '

'As if I lay in Soröe,' said Tuk, and he awoke. It was bright morning, and he could not remember the least bit of his dream. But that was not necessary, for one must not know what is to happen.

Now he sprang quickly out of his bed, and read his book, and all at once he knew his whole lesson. The old washerwoman, too, put her head in at the door, nodded to him in a friendly way, and said, 'Thank you, you good child, for your help. May your beautiful dreams come true!'

Little Tuk did not know at all what he had dreamed, but there was One above who knew it.

The Shadow

IN THE hot countries the sun burns very strongly; there the people become quite mahogany brown, and in the very hottest countries they are even burned into Negroes. But this time it was only to the hot countries that a learned man out of the cold regions had come. He thought he could roam about there just as he had been accustomed to do at home; but he soon altered his opinion. He and all sensible people had to remain at home, where the window-shutters and doors were shut all day long, and it looked as if all the inmates were asleep or had gone out. The narrow street with the high houses in which he lived was, however, built in such a way that the sun shone upon it from morning till evening; it was really quite unbearable! The learned man from the cold regions was a young man and a clever man: it seemed to him as if he was sitting in a glowing oven that exhausted him greatly, and he became quite thin; even his Shadow shrivelled up and became much smaller than it had been at home; the sun even told upon it, and it did not recover till the evening, when the sun went down. It was really a pleasure to see this. So soon as a light was brought into the room the Shadow stretched itself quite up the wall, farther even than the ceiling, so tall did it make itself; it was obliged to stretch to get strength again. The learned man went out into the balcony to stretch himself, and as soon as the stars came out in the beautiful clear sky, he felt himself reviving. On all the balconies in the streets – and in the hot countries there is a balcony to every window – people now appeared, for one must breathe fresh air, even if one has got used to being mahogany; then it became lively above and below; the shoemakers and tailors and everybody sat below in the street; then tables and chairs were brought out, and candles burned, yes, more than a thousand candles; one talked and another sang, and the people walked to and fro; carriages drove past, mules trotted, 'Kling-ling-ling!' for they had bells on their harness; dead people were buried with solemn songs; the church bells rang, and it was indeed very lively in the street. Only in one house, just opposite to that in which the learned man dwelt, it was quite quiet, and yet somebody lived there, for there were flowers upon the balcony, blooming beautifully in the hot sun, and they could not have done this if they had not been watered, so that someone must have watered them; therefore, there must be people in that house. Towards evening the door was half opened, but it was dark, at least in the front room; farther back, in the interior, music was heard. The strange learned man thought this music very lovely, but it was quite possible that he only imagined this, for out there in the hot countries he found everything exquisite, if only there had been no sun. The stranger's landlord said that he did not know who had taken the opposite house – one saw nobody there, and so far as the music was concerned, it seemed very monotonous to him.

'It was just,' he said, 'as if someone sat there, always practising a piece that he could not manage – always the same piece. He seemed to say, "I shall manage it, after all;" but he did not manage it, however long he played.'

The stranger was asleep one night. He slept with the balcony door open: the wind lifted up the curtain before it, and he fancied that a wonderful radiance came from the balcony of the house opposite; all the flowers appeared like flames of the most gorgeous colours, and in the midst, among the flowers, stood a beautiful slender maiden: it seemed as if a radiance came from her also. His eyes were quite dazzled; but he had only opened them too wide just when he awoke out of his sleep. With one leap he was out of bed; quite quietly he crept behind the curtain; but the maiden was gone, the splendour was gone, the flowers gleamed no longer, but stood there as beautiful as ever. The door was ajar, and from within sounded music, so lovely, so charming, that one fell into sweet thought at the sound. It was just like magic work. But who lived there? Where was the real entrance? for towards the street and towards the lane at the side the whole ground floor was shop by shop, and the people could not always run through there.

One evening the stranger sat up on his balcony; in the room just behind him a light was burning, and so it was quite natural that his Shadow fell upon the wall of the opposite house; yes, it sat just among the flowers on the balcony, and when the stranger moved his Shadow moved too.

'I think my Shadow is the only living thing we see yonder,' said the learned man. 'Look how gracefully it sits among the flowers. The door is only ajar, but the Shadow ought to be sensible enough to walk in and look round, and then come back and tell me what it has seen.

'Yes, you would thus make yourself very useful,' said he, in sport. 'Be so good as to slip in. Now, will you go?' And then he nodded at the Shadow, and the Shadow nodded back at him. 'Now go, but don't stay away altogether.'

And the stranger stood up, and the Shadow on the balcony opposite stood up too, and the stranger turned round, and the Shadow turned also, and if anyone had noticed closely he would have remarked how the Shadow went away in the same moment, straight through the half-opened door of the opposite house, as the stranger returned into his room and let the curtain fall.

Next morning the learned man went out to drink coffee and read the papers.

'What is this?' said he, when he came out into the sunshine. 'I have no Shadow! So it really went away yesterday evening, and did not come back: that's very tiresome.'

And that fretted him, but not so much because the Shadow was gone as because he knew that there was a story of a man without a shadow. All the people in the cold lands knew this story, and if the learned man came home and told his own history, they would say that it was only an imitation, and he did not choose that they should say this of him. So he would not speak of it at all, and that was a very sensible idea of his.

In the evening he again went out on his balcony: he had placed the light behind him, for he knew that a shadow always wants its master for a screen, but he could not coax it forth. He made himself little, he made himself long, but there was no shadow, and no shadow came. He said, 'Here, here!' but that did no good.

That was vexatious, but in the warm countries everything grows very quickly, and after the lapse of a week he remarked to his great joy that a new shadow was growing out of his legs when he went into the sunshine, so that the root must have remained behind. After three weeks he had quite a respectable shadow, which, when he started on his return to the North, grew more and more, so that at last it was so long and great that he could very well have parted with half of it.

When the learned man got home he wrote books about what is true in the world, and what is good, and what is pretty; and days went by, and years went by, many years.

He was one evening sitting in his room when there came a little quiet knock at the door. 'Come in!' said he; but nobody came. Then he opened the door, and there stood before him such a remarkably thin man that he felt quite uncomfortable. This man was, however, very respectably dressed; he looked like a man of standing.

'Whom have I the honour to address?' asked the professor.

'Ah!' replied the genteel man, 'I thought you would not know me; I have become so much a body that I have got real flesh and clothes. You never thought to see me in such a condition. Don't you know your old Shadow? You certainly never thought that I would come again. Things have gone remarkably well with me since I was with you last. I've become rich in every respect: if I want to buy myself free from servitude I can do it!'

And he rattled a number of valuable charms, which hung by his watch, and put his hand upon the thick gold chain he wore round his neck; and how the diamond rings glittered on his fingers! and everything was real!

'No, I cannot regain my self-possession at all!' said the learned man. 'What's the meaning of all this?'

'Nothing common,' said the Shadow. 'But you yourself don't belong to common folks; and I have, as you very well know, trodden in your footsteps from my childhood upwards. So soon as you thought that I was experienced enough to find my way through the world alone, I went away. I am in the most brilliant circumstances; but I was seized with a kind of longing to see you once more before you die, and I wanted to see these regions once more, for one always thinks much of one's fatherland. I know that you have got another shadow: have I anything to pay to it, or to you? You have only to tell me.'

'Is it really you?' said the learned man. 'Why, that is wonderful! I should never have thought that I should ever meet my old Shadow as a man!'

'Only tell me what I have to pay,' said the Shadow, 'for I don't like to be in anyone's debt.'

'How can you talk in that way?' said the learned man. 'Of what debt can there be a question here? You are as free as anyone! I am exceedingly pleased at your good fortune! Sit down, old friend, and tell me a little how it has happened, and what you saw in the warm countries, and in the house opposite ours.'

'Yes, that I will tell you,' said the Shadow; and it sat down. 'But then you must promise me never to tell anyone in this town, when you meet me, that I have been your Shadow! I have the intention of engaging myself to be married; I can do more than support a family.'

'Be quite easy,' replied the learned man; 'I will tell nobody who you really are. Here's my hand. I promise it, and my word's as good as my bond.'

'A Shadow's word in return!' said the Shadow, for he was obliged to talk in that way. But, by the way, it was quite wonderful how complete a man he had become. He was dressed all in black, and wore the very finest black cloth, polished boots, and a hat that could be crushed together till it was nothing but crown and rim, besides what we have already noticed of him, namely, the charms, the gold neck-chain, and the diamond rings. The Shadow was indeed wonderfully well clothed; and it was just this that made a complete man of him.

'Now I will tell you,' said the Shadow; and then he put down his polished boots as firmly as he could on the arm of the learned man's new shadow that lay like a poodle dog at his feet. This was done perhaps from pride, perhaps so that the new shadow might stick to his feet; but the prostrate shadow remained quite quiet, so that it might listen well, for it wanted to know how one could get free and work up to be one's own master.

'Do you know who lived in the house opposite to us?' asked the Shadow. 'That was the most glorious of all; it was Poetry! I was there for three weeks, and that was just as if one had lived there a thousand years, and could read all that has been written and composed. For this I say, and it is truth, I have seen everything, and I know everything!'

'Poetry!' cried the learned man. 'Yes, she often lives as a hermit in great cities. Poetry! Yes, I myself saw her for one single brief moment, but sleep was heavy on my eyes: she stood on the balcony, gleaming as the Northern Light gleams. Tell me! tell me! You were upon the balcony. You went through the door, and then –'

'Then I was in the ante-room,' said the Shadow. 'You sat opposite, and were always looking across at the ante-room. There was no light; a kind of twilight reigned there; but one door after another in a whole row of halls and rooms stood open, and there it was light; and the mass of light would have killed me if I had got as far as to where the maiden sat. But I was deliberate, I took my time; and that's what one must do.'

'And what didst thou see then?' asked the learned man.

'I saw everything, and I will tell you what; but – it is really not pride on my part – as a free man, and with the acquirements I possess, besides my good position and my remarkable fortune, I wish you would say *you* to me.'

'I beg your pardon,' said the learned man. 'This *thou* is an old habit, and old habits are difficult to alter. You are perfectly right, and I will remember it. But now tell me everything you saw.'

'Everything,' said the Shadow; 'for I saw everything, and I know everything.'

'How did things look in the inner room?' asked the learned man. 'Was it there as in the fresh wood? Was it there as in a holy temple? Were the chambers like the starry sky, when one stands on the high mountains?'

'Everything was there,' said the Shadow. 'I was certainly not quite inside; I remained in the front room, in the darkness; but I stood there remarkably well. I saw everything and know everything. I have been in the ante-room at the Court of Poetry.'

'But what did you see? Did all the gods of antiquity march through the halls? Did the old heroes fight there? Did lovely children play there, and relate their dreams?'

'I tell you that I have been there, and so you will easily understand that I saw everything that was to be seen. If *you* had got there you would not have become a man; but I became one, and at the same time I learned to understand my inner being and the relation in which I stood to Poetry. Yes, when I was with you I did not think of these things; but you know that whenever the sun rises or sets I am wonderfully great. In the moonshine I was almost more noticeable than you yourself. I did not then understand my inward being; in the ante-room it was revealed to me. I became a man! I came out ripe. But you were no longer in the warm countries. I was ashamed to go about as a man in the state I was then in: I required boots, clothes, and all this human varnish by which a man is known. I hid myself; yes, I can confide a secret to you – you will not put it into a book. I hid myself under the cake-woman's gown; the woman had no idea how much she concealed. Only in the evening did I go out: I ran about the streets by moonlight; I stretched myself quite long up the wall: that tickled my back quite agreeably. I ran up and down, looked through the highest windows into the halls and through the roof, where nobody could see, and I saw what nobody saw and what nobody ought to see. On the whole it is a despicable world: I would not be a man if it were not commonly supposed that it is something to be one. I saw the most incredible things going on among men, and women, and parents, and 'dear incomparable children'. I saw what no one else knows, but what they all would be very glad to know, namely, bad goings on at their neighbours'. If I had written a newspaper, how it would have been read! But I wrote directly to the persons interested, and there was terror in every town to which I came. They were so afraid of me that they were remarkably fond of me. The professor made me a professor; the tailor gave me new clothes (I am well provided); the mint-master coined money for me; the women declared I was handsome: and thus I became the man I am. And now, farewell! Here is my card; I live on the sunny side, and am always at home in rainy weather.'

And the Shadow went away.

'That was very remarkable,' said the learned man.

Years and days passed by, and the Shadow came again.

'How goes it?' he asked.

'Ah!' said the learned man, 'I'm writing about the true, the good, and the beautiful; but nobody cares to hear of anything of the kind: I am quite in despair, for I take that to heart.'

'That I do not,' said the Shadow. 'I'm becoming fat and hearty, and that's what one must try to become. You don't understand the world, and you're getting ill. You must travel. I'll make a journey this summer; will you go too? I should like to have a travelling companion; will you go with me as my shadow? I shall be very happy to take you, and I'll pay the expenses.'

'That's going a little too far,' said the learned man.

'As you take it,' replied the Shadow. 'A journey will do you a great deal of good. Will you be my shadow? then you shall have everything on the journey for nothing.'

'That's too strong!' said the learned man.

'But it's the way of the world,' said the Shadow, 'and so it will remain!' And he went away.

The learned man was not at all fortunate. Sorrow and care pursued him, and what he said of the true and the good and the beautiful was as little valued by most people as roses would be by a cow. At last he became quite ill.

'You really look like a shadow!' people said; and a shiver ran through him at these words, for he attached a peculiar meaning to them.

'You must go to a watering-place!' said the Shadow, who came to pay him a visit. 'There's no other help for you. I'll take you with me, for the sake of old acquaintance. I'll pay the expenses of the journey, and you shall make a description of it, and shorten time for me on the way. I want to visit a watering-place. My beard doesn't grow quite as it should, and that is a kind of illness; and a beard I must have. Now, be reasonable and accept my proposal: we shall travel like comrades.'

And they travelled. The Shadow was master now, and the master was shadow: they drove together, they rode together, and walked side by side, and before and behind each other, just as the sun happened to stand. The Shadow always knew when to take the place of honour. The learned man did not particularly notice this, for he had a very good heart, and was moreover particularly mild and friendly. Then one day the master said to the Shadow, 'As we have in this way become travelling companions, and have also from childhood's days grown up with one another, shall we not drink brotherhood? That sounds more confidential.'

'You're saying a thing there,' said the Shadow, who was now really the master, 'that is said in a very kind and straightforward way. I will be just as kind and straightforward. You, who are a learned gentleman, know very well how wonderful nature is. There are some men who cannot bear to touch brown paper, they become sick at it; others shudder to the marrow of their bones if one scratches with a nail upon a pane of glass; and I for my part have a similar feeling when anyone says "thou" to me; I feel myself, as I did in my first position with you, oppressed by it. You see that this is a feeling, not pride. I cannot let you say "thou"* to me, but I will gladly say "thou" to you; and thus your wish will be at any rate partly fulfilled.'

And now the Shadow addressed his former master as 'thou.'

'That's rather strong,' said the latter, 'that I am to say "you", while he says "thou".' But he was obliged to submit to it.

They came to a bathing-place, where many strangers were, and among them a beautiful young Princess, who had this disease, that she saw too sharply, which was very disquieting. She at once saw that the new arrival was a very different personage from all the rest.

'They say he is here to get his beard to grow; but I see the real reason – he can't throw a shadow.'

She had now become inquisitive, and therefore she at once began a conversation with the strange gentleman on the promenade. As a Princess, she was not obliged to use much ceremony, therefore she said outright to him at once, 'Your illness consists in this, that you can't throw a shadow.'

'Your Royal Highness must be much better,' replied the Shadow. 'I

* On the Continent, people who have 'drunk brotherhood' address each other as 'thou', in preference to the more ceremonious 'you'.

know your illness consists in this, that you see too sharply; but you
have got the better of that. I have a very unusual shadow: don't you
see the person who always accompanies me? Other people have a
common shadow, but I don't love what is common. One often gives
one's servants finer cloth for their liveries than one wears oneself, and
so I have let my shadow deck himself out like a separate person; yes,
you see I have even given him a shadow of his own. That cost very
much, but I like to have something peculiar.

'How!' said the Princess, 'can I really have been cured? This is the
best bathing-place in existence; water has wonderful power nowadays.
But I'm not going away from here yet, for now it begins to be amusing.
The stranger – pleases me remarkably well. I only hope his beard
won't grow, for if it does he'll go away.'

That evening the Princess and the Shadow danced together in the
great ballroom. She was light, but he was still lighter; never had she

seen such a dancer. She told him from what country she came, and he knew the country – he had been there, but just when she had been absent. He had looked through the windows of her castle, from below as well as from above; he had learned many circumstances, and could therefore make allusions, and give replies to the Princess, at which she marvelled greatly. She thought he must be the cleverest man in all the world, and was inspired with great respect for all his knowledge. And when she danced with him again, she fell in love with him, and the Shadow noticed that particularly, for she looked him almost through and through with her eyes. They danced together once more, and she was nearly telling him, but she was discreet: she thought of her country, and her kingdom, and of the many people over whom she was to rule.

'He is a clever man,' she said to herself, 'and that is well, and he dances capitally, and that is well too; but has he well-grounded knowledge? That is just as important, and he must be examined.'

And she immediately put such a difficult question to him, that she could not have answered it herself; and the Shadow made a wry face.

'You cannot answer me that,' said the Princess.

'I learned that in my childhood,' replied the Shadow, 'and I believe my very shadow, standing yonder by the door, could answer it.'

'Your shadow!' cried the Princess: 'that would be very remarkable.'

'I do not assert as quite certain that he can do so,' said the Shadow, 'but I am almost inclined to believe it, he has now accompanied me and listened for so many years. But your Royal Highness will allow me to remind you that he is so proud of passing for a man, that, if he is to be in a good humour, and he should be so to answer rightly, he must be treated just like a man.'

'I like that,' said the Princess.

And now she went to the learned man at the door; and she spoke with him of sun and moon, of people both inside and out, and the learned man answered very cleverly and very well.

'What a man that must be, who has such a clever shadow!' she thought. 'It would be a real blessing for my country and for my people if I chose him for my husband; and I'll do it!'

And they soon struck a bargain – the Princess and the Shadow; but no one was to know anything of it till she had returned to her kingdom.

'No one – not even my shadow,' said the Shadow; and for this he had especial reasons.

And they came to the country where the Princess ruled, and where was her home.

'Listen, my friend,' said the Shadow to the learned man. 'Now I am as lucky and powerful as anyone can become, I'll do something particular for you. You shall live with me in my palace, drive with me in the royal carriage, and have a hundred thousand dollars a year; but you must let yourself be called a shadow by everyone, and may never say that you were once a man; and once a year, when I sit on the balcony and show myself, you must lie at my feet as it becomes my shadow to do. For I will tell you I'm going to marry the Princess, and this evening the wedding will be held.'

'Now, that's too strong!' said the learned man. 'I won't do it; I won't have it. That would be cheating the whole country and the Princess too. I'll tell everything – that I'm the man and you are the Shadow, and that you are only dressed up!'

'No one would believe that,' said the Shadow. 'Be reasonable, or I'll call the watch.'

'I'll go straight to the Princess,' said the learned man.

'But I'll go first,' said the Shadow; 'and you shall go to prison.'

And that was so; for the sentinels obeyed him who they knew was to marry the Princess.

'You tremble,' said the Princess, when the Shadow came to her. 'Has anything happened? You must not be ill today, when we are to have our wedding.'

'I have experienced the most terrible thing that can happen,' said the Shadow. 'Only think! such a poor shallow brain cannot bear much – only think! my shadow has gone mad: he fancies he has become a man, and – only think! – that I am his shadow.'

'This is terrible!' said the Princess. 'He's locked up, I hope?'

'Certainly. I'm afraid he will never recover.'

'Poor shadow!' cried the Princess, 'he's very unfortunate. It would really be a good action to deliver him from his little bit of life. And when I think it over, properly, I believe it is quite necessary to put him quietly out of the way.'

'That's certainly very hard, for he was a faithful servant,' said the Shadow; and he pretended to sigh.

'You've a noble character,' said the Princess, and she bowed before him.

In the evening the whole town was illuminated, and cannon were fired – bang! – and the soldiers presented arms. That *was* a wedding! The Princess and the Shadow stepped out on the balcony to show themselves and receive another cheer.

The learned man heard nothing of all this festivity, for he had already been executed.

The Old House

DOWN YONDER, in the street, stood an old, old house. It was almost three hundred years old, for one could read as much on the beam, on which was carved the date of its erection, surrounded by tulips and trailing hops. There one could read entire verses in the characters of olden times, and over each window a face had been carved in the beam, and these made all kinds of strange grimaces. One story projected a long way above the other, and close under the roof was a leaden gutter with a dragon's head. The rain water was to run out of the dragon's mouth, but it ran out of the creature's body instead, for there was a hole in the pipe.

All the other houses in the street were still new and trim, with smooth walls and large window-panes. One could easily see that they would have nothing to do with the old house. They thought perhaps, 'How long is that old rubbish-heap to stand there, a scandal to the whole street? The parapet stands so far forward that no one can see out of our windows what is going on in that direction. The staircase is as broad as a castle staircase, and as steep as if it led to a church tower. The iron railing looks like the gate of a family vault, and there are brass bosses upon it. It's too ridiculous!'

Just opposite stood some more new neat houses that thought exactly like the rest; but here at the window sat a little boy, with fresh red cheeks, with clear sparkling eyes, and he was particularly fond of the old house, in sunshine as well as by moonlight. And when he looked down at the wall where the plaster had fallen off then he could sit and fancy all kinds of pictures – how the street must have appeared in old times, with stairs, balconies, and pointed gables; he could see soldiers with halberds, and roof-gutters running about in the form of dragons and griffins. It was just a good house to look at; and in it lived an old man who went about in leather knee-breeches, and wore a coat with

great brass buttons, and a wig which one could at once see was a real wig. Every morning an old man came to him, to clean his rooms and run on his errands. With this exception the old man in the leather knee-breeches was all alone in the old house. Sometimes he came to one of the windows and looked out, and the little boy nodded to him, and the old man nodded back, and thus they became acquainted and became friends, though they had never spoken to one another; but, indeed, that was not at all necessary.

The little boy heard his parents say, 'The old man opposite is very well off, but he is terribly lonely.'

Next Sunday the little boy wrapped something in a piece of paper, went with it to the house door, and said to the man who ran errands for the old gentleman, 'Hark-ye, will you take this to the old gentleman opposite for me? I have two tin soldiers; this is one of them, and he shall have it, because I know that he is terribly lonely.'

And the old attendant looked quite pleased, and nodded, and carried the Tin Soldier into the old house. Afterwards he was sent over, to ask if the little boy would not like to come himself and pay a visit. His parents gave him leave; and so it was that he came to the old house.

The brass bosses on the staircase shone much more brightly than usual; one would have thought they had been polished in honour of his visit. And it was just as if the carved trumpeters – for on the doors there were carved trumpeters, standing in tulips – were blowing with all their might; their cheeks looked much rounder than before. Yes, they blew 'Tan–ta–ra–ra! the little boy's coming! tan–ta–ra–ra!' and then the door opened. The whole of the hall was hung with old portraits of knights in armour and ladies in silk gowns; and the armour rattled and the silk dresses rustled; and then came a staircase that went up a great way and down a little way, and then one came to a balcony which was certainly in a very rickety state, with long cracks and great holes; but out of all these grew grass and leaves, for the whole balcony, the courtyard, and the wall, were overgrown with so much green that it looked like a garden, but it was only a balcony. Here stood old flowerpots that had faces with asses' ears; but the flowers grew just as they chose. In one pot pinks were growing over on all sides; that is to say, the green stalks, sprout upon sprout, and they said quite plainly, 'The air has caressed me and the sun has kissed me, and promised me a little flower for next Sunday, a little flower next Sunday!'

And then they came to a room where the walls were covered with pigskin, and golden flowers had been stamped on the leather.

'Flowers fade fast,
But pigskin will last,'

said the walls. And there stood chairs with quite high backs, with carved work and elbows on each side.

'Sit down!' said they. 'Oh, how it cracks inside me! Now I shall be sure to have the gout, like the old cupboard. Gout in my back, ugh!'

And then the little boy came to the room where the old man sat.

'Thank you for the Tin Soldier, my little friend,' said the old man, 'and thank you for coming over to me.'

'Thanks! thanks!' or 'Crick! crack!' said all the furniture; there were so many pieces that they almost stood in each other's way to see the little boy.

And in the middle, on the wall, hung a picture of a beautiful lady, young and cheerful in appearance, but dressed just like people of the old times, with powder in her hair and skirts that stuck out stiffly. She said neither 'Thanks' nor 'Crack', but looked down upon the little boy with her mild eyes; and he at once asked the old man, 'Where did you get her from?'

'From the dealer opposite,' replied the old man. 'Many pictures are always hanging there. No one knows them or troubles himself about them, for they are all buried. But many years ago I knew this lady, and now she's been dead and gone for half a century.'

And under the picture hung, behind glass, a nosegay of withered flowers; they were certainly also half a century old – at least they looked it; and the pendulum of the great clock went to and fro, and the hands turned round, and everything in the room grew older still, but no one noticed it.

'They say at home,' said the little boy, 'that you are always terribly solitary.'

'Oh,' answered the old man, 'old thoughts come, with all that they bring, to visit me; and now you come as well, I'm very well off.'

And then he took from a shelf a book with pictures: there were long processions of wonderful coaches, such as one never sees at the present day, soldiers like the knave of clubs, and citizens with waving flags. The tailors had a flag with shears on it held by two lions, and the shoemakers a flag, without boots, but with an eagle that had two heads; for among the shoemakers everything must be so arranged that they can say, 'There's a pair.' Yes, that was a picture-book! And the old man went into the other room, to fetch preserves, and apples, and nuts. It was really glorious in that old house.

'I can't stand it,' said the Tin Soldier, who stood upon the shelf. 'It is terribly lonely and dull here. When a person has been accustomed to family life, one cannot get accustomed to their existence here. I cannot stand it! The day is long enough, but the evening is longer still! Here it is not at all as it was in your house opposite, where your father and mother were always conversing cheerfully together, and you and all the other dear children made a famous noise. How solitary it is here at the old man's! Do you think he gets any kisses? Do you think he gets friendly looks, or a Christmas tree? He'll get nothing but a funeral! I cannot stand it!'

'You must not look at it from the sorrowful side,' said the little boy. 'To me it all appears remarkably pretty, and all the old thoughts, with all they bring with them, come to visit here.'

'Yes, but I don't see them, and don't know them,' objected the Tin Soldier. 'I can't bear it!'

'You must bear it,' said the little boy.

And the old man came with the pleasantest face and with the best of preserved fruits and apples and nuts; and then the little boy thought no more of the Tin Soldier. Happy and delighted, the youngster went home; and days went by, weeks went by, and there was much nodding from the boy's home across to the old house and back; and then the little boy went over there again.

And the carved trumpeters blew, 'Tan-ta-ra-ra! tan-ta-ra-ra! there's the little boy, tan-ta-ra-ra!' and the swords and armour on the old pictures rattled, and the silken dresses rustled, and the leather told tales, and the old chairs had the gout in their backs. Ugh! it was just like the first time, for over there one day or one hour was just like another.

'I can't stand it!' said the Tin Soldier. 'I've wept tears of tin. It's too dreary here. I had rather go to war and lose my arms and legs; at any rate, that's a change. I cannot stand it! Now I know what it means to have a visit from one's old thoughts and all they bring with them. I've had visits from my own, and you may believe me, that's no pleasure in the long run. I was very nearly jumping down from the shelf. I could see you all in the house opposite as plainly as if you had been here. It was Sunday morning, and you children were all standing round the table singing the psalm you sing every morning. You were standing reverently with folded hands, and your father and mother were just as solemn; then the door opened, and your little sister Maria, who is not two years old yet, and who always dances when she hears music or song, of whatever description they may be, was brought in. She was not to do it, but she immediately began to dance, though she could not get into right time, for the song was too slow, so she first stood on one leg and bent her head quite over in front, but it was not long enough. You all stood very quietly, though that was rather difficult; but I laughed inwardly, and so I fell down from the table and got a bruise which I have still; for it was not right of me to laugh. But all this, and all the rest that I have experienced, now passes before my mind's eye, and those must be the old thoughts with everything they bring with them. Tell me, do you still sing on Sundays? Tell me something about little Maria. And how is my comrade and brother Tin Soldier? Yes, he must be very happy. I can't stand it!'

'You have been given away,' said the little boy. 'You must stay where you are. Don't you see that?'

And the old man came with a box in which many things were to be seen: little rouge-pots and scent-boxes; and old cards, larger and more richly gilt than one ever sees them in these days; and many large drawers were opened, likewise the piano; and in this were painted landscapes, inside the lid. But the piano was quite hoarse when the old man played upon it, and then he hummed a song. 'Yes, she could sing that,' he said, and then he nodded to the picture that he had bought at the dealer's, and the old man's eyes shone quite brightly.

'I'll go to the war! I'll go to the war!' cried the Tin Soldier, as loud as he could; and he threw himself down on the floor.

Where had he gone? The old man searched, the little boy searched, but he was gone, and could not be found.

'I shall find him,' said the old man.

But he never found him: the flooring was so open and full of holes, that the Tin Soldier had fallen through a crack, and there he lay as in an open grave.

And the day passed away, and the little boy went home; and the week passed by, and many weeks passed by. The windows were quite frozen up, and the little boy had to sit and breathe upon the panes, to make a peep-hole to look at the old house; and snow had blown among all the carving and the inscriptions, and covered the whole staircase, as if no one were in the house at all. And, indeed, there *was* no one in the house, for the old man had died!

In the evening a carriage stopped at the door, and in that he was laid, in his coffin; he was to rest in a family vault in the country. So he was carried away; but no one followed him on his last journey, for all his friends were dead. And the little boy kissed his hand after the coffin as it rolled away.

A few days later, and there was an auction in the old house; and the little boy saw from his window how the old knights and ladies, the flowerpots with the long ears, the chairs and the cupboards, were carried away. One was taken here, and another there: *her* portrait, that had been bought from the dealer, went back into his shop, and there it was hung, for no one cared for the old picture.

In the spring the house itself was pulled down, for the people said it was old rubbish. One could look from the street straight into the room with the leather wall-covering, which was taken down, ragged and torn; and the green of the balcony hung straggling over the beams, that threatened to fall in altogether. And now a clearance was made.

'That is good!' said the neighbour houses.

And a capital house was built, with large windows and smooth white walls; but in front of the place where the old house had really stood, a little garden was planted, and by the neighbour's wall tall vine shoots clambered up. In front of the garden was placed a great iron railing with an iron door; and it had a stately look. The people stopped in front, and looked through. And the sparrows sat down in dozens upon the vine branches, and chattered all at once as loud as they could; but not about the old house, for they could not remember that, for many years had gone by – so many, that the little boy had grown to be a man, a thorough man, whose parents rejoiced in him. And he had just married, and was come with his wife to live in the house, in front of which was the garden; and here he stood next to her while she planted a field flower which she considered very pretty; she planted it with her little hand, pressing the earth close round it with her fingers. 'Ah, what was that?' She pricked herself. Out of the soft earth something pointed was sticking up. Only think! that was the Tin Soldier, the same that had been lost up in the old man's room, and had been hidden among old wood and rubbish for a long time, and had lain in the ground many a year. And the young wife first dried the Soldier in a green leaf, and then with her fine handkerchief, that smelt so deliciously. And the Tin Soldier felt just as if he were waking from a fainting fit.

'Let me see him,' said the young man. And then he smiled and shook his head. 'Ah! it can scarcely be the same; but it reminds me of an affair with a Tin Soldier which I had when I was a little boy.'

And then he told his wife about the old house, and the old man, and of the Tin Soldier he had sent across to the old man whom he had thought so lonely; and the tears came into the young wife's eyes for the old house and the old man.

'It is possible, after all, that it may be the same Tin Soldier,' said she. 'I will take care of him, and remember what you have told me; but you must show me the old man's grave.'

'I don't know where it is,' replied he, 'and no one knows. All his friends were dead; none tended his grave, and I was but a little boy.'

'Ah, how terribly lonely he must have been!' said she.

'Yes, horribly lonely,' said the Tin Soldier; 'but it is glorious not to be forgotten.'

'Glorious!' repeated a voice close to them.

But nobody except the Tin Soldier perceived that it came from a rag of the pig's-leather hangings, which was now devoid of all gilding. It looked like wet earth, but yet it had an opinion, which it expressed thus:

> 'Gilding fades fast,
> Pigskin will last!'

But the Tin Soldier did not believe that.

The Drop of Water

OF COURSE you know what is meant by a magnifying glass – one of those round spectacle-glasses that make everything look a hundred times bigger than it is? When anyone takes one of these and holds it to his eye, and looks at a drop of water from the pond yonder, he sees above a thousand wonderful creatures that are otherwise never discerned in the water. But they are there, and it is no delusion. It almost looks like a great plate-full of prawns jumping about in a crowd. And how fierce they are! They tear off each other's legs and arms and bodies, before and behind; and yet they are merry and joyful in their way.

Now, there was once an old man whom all the people called Cribble-Crabble, for that was his name. He always wanted the best of everything, and when he could not manage it otherwise, he did it by magic.

There he sat one day, and held his magnifying glass to his eye, and looked at a drop of water that had been taken out of a puddle in the ditch. But what a cribbling and crabbling was there! All the thousands of little creatures hopped and sprang and tugged at one another, and ate each other up.

'That is horrible!' said old Cribble-Crabble. 'Can one not persuade them to live in peace and quietness, so that each one may mind his own business?'

And he thought it over and over, but it would not do, and so he had recourse to magic.

'I must give them colour, that they may be seen more plainly,' said he; and he poured something like a little drop of red wine into the drop of water, but it was witches' blood, the finest kind, at a halfpenny a drop. And now the wonderful little creatures were pink all over: it looked like a little town of naked wild men.

'What have you there?' asked another old magician, who had no name – and that was the best thing about him.

'Ah! if you can guess what it is,' said Cribble-Crabble, 'I'll make you a present of it.'

But it is not so easy to find out if one does not know.

And the magician who had no name looked through the magnifying glass. It looked really like a great town reflected there, in which all the people were running about without clothes. It was terrible! But it was still more terrible to see how one beat and pushed the other, and bit and hacked, and tugged and mauled him. Those at the top were being pulled down, and those at the bottom were struggling upwards.

'Look! look! his leg is longer than mine! Bah! Away with it! There is one who has a little lump behind his ear. It hurts him, but it shall hurt him still more.'

And they hacked away at him, and they pulled at him, and ate him up, because of the little lump. And there was one sitting as still as any little maiden, and wishing only for peace and quietness. But now she had to come out, and they tugged at her, and pulled her about, and ate her up.

'That's remarkably funny!' said the magician.

'Yes, but what do you think it is?' said Cribble-Crabble. 'Can you find that out?'

'Why, one can see that easily enough,' said the other. 'That's Copenhagen, or some other great city, for they're all alike. It's a great city!'

'It's a drop of puddle water!' said Cribble-Crabble.

The Happy Family

THE BIGGEST leaf here in the country is certainly the burdock leaf. Put one in front of your waist and it's just like an apron, and if you lay it upon your head it is almost as good as an umbrella, for it is quite remarkably large. A burdock never grows alone; where there is one there are several more. It's splendid to behold! and all this splendour is snails' meat. The great white snails, which the grand people in old times used to have made into fricassees, and when they had eaten them they would say, 'H'm, how good that is!' for they had the idea that it tasted delicious. These snails lived on burdock leaves, and that's why burdocks were sown.

Now there was an old estate, on which people ate snails no longer. The snails had died out, but the burdocks had not. These latter grew and grew in all the walks and on all the beds – there was no stopping them; the place became a complete forest of burdocks. Here and there stood an apple or plum tree; but for this, nobody would have thought a garden had been there. Everything was burdock, and among the burdocks lived the two last ancient Snails.

They did not know themselves how old they were, but they could very well remember that there had been a great many more of them, that they had descended from a foreign family, and that the whole forest had been planted for them and theirs. They had never been away from home, but it was known to them that something existed in the world called the manor-house, and that there one was boiled, and one became black, and was laid upon a silver dish; but what was done afterwards they did not know. Moreover, they could not imagine what that might be, being boiled and laid upon a silver dish; but it was said to be fine, and particularly grand! Neither the cockchafer, nor the toad, nor the earthworm, whom they questioned about it, could give them any information, for none of their kind had ever been boiled and laid on silver dishes.

The old white Snails were the grandest in the world; they knew that! The forest was there for their sake, and the manor-house too, so that they might be boiled and laid on silver dishes.

They led a very retired and happy life, and as they themselves were childless, they had adopted a little common snail, which they brought up as their own child. But the little thing would not grow, for it was only a common snail, though the old people, and particularly the mother, declared one could easily see how he grew. And when the father could not see it, she requested him to feel the little snail's shell, and he felt it, and acknowledged that she was right.

One day it rained very hard.

'Listen, how it's drumming on the burdock leaves, rum-dum-dum! rum-dum-dum!' said the Father-Snail.

'That's what I call drops,' said the mother. 'It's coming straight down the stalks. You'll see it will be wet here directly. I'm only glad that we have our good houses, and that the little one has his own. There has been more done for us than for any other creature; one can see very plainly that we are the grand folks of the world! We have houses from our birth, and the burdock forest has been planted for us: I should like to know how far it extends, and what lies beyond it.'

'There's nothing outside of it,' said the Father-Snail, 'no place can be better than here at home; I have nothing at all to wish for.'

'Yes,' said the mother, 'I should like to be taken to the manor-house and boiled, and laid upon a silver dish; that has been done to all our ancestors, and you may be sure it's quite a distinguished honour.'

'The manor-house has perhaps fallen in,' said the Father-Snail, 'or the forest of burdocks may have grown over it, so that the people can't get out at all. You need not be in a hurry – but you always hurry so, and the little one is beginning just the same way. Has he not been creeping up that stalk these three days? My head quite aches when I look up at him.'

'You must not scold him,' said the Mother-Snail. 'He crawls very deliberately. We shall have much joy in him; and we old people have nothing else to live for. But have you ever thought where we shall get a wife for him? Don't you think that farther in the wood there may be some more of our kind?'

'There may be black snails there, I think,' said the old man, 'black snails without houses! but they're too vulgar. And they're conceited, for all that. But we can give the commission to the ants: they run to and fro, as if they had business; they're sure to know of a wife for our young gentleman.'

'I certainly know the most beautiful of brides,' said one of the Ants; 'but I fear she would not do, for she is the Queen!'

'That does not matter,' said the two old Snails. 'Has she a house?'

'She has a castle!' replied the Ant. 'The most beautiful ant's castle, with seven hundred passages.'

'Thank you,' said the Mother-Snail; 'our boy shall not go into an ant-hill. If you know of nothing better, we'll give the commission to the white gnats; they fly far about in rain and sunshine, and they know the burdock wood, inside and outside.'

'We have a wife for him,' said the Gnats. 'A hundred man-steps from here a little snail with a house is sitting on a gooseberry bush, she is quite alone, and old enough to marry. It's only a hundred man-steps from here.'

'Yes, let her come to him,' said the old people. 'He has a whole burdock forest, and she has only a bush.'

And so they brought the little maiden snail. Eight days passed before she arrived, but that was the rare circumstance about it, for by this one could see that she was of the right kind.

And then they had a wedding. Six glow-worms lighted as well as they could: with this exception it went very quietly, for the old snail people could not bear feasting and dissipation. But a capital speech was made by the Mother-Snail. The father could not speak, he was so much moved. Then they gave the young couple the whole burdock forest for an inheritance, and said, what they had always said, namely – that it was the best place in the world, and that the young people, if they lived honourably, and increased and multiplied, would someday be taken with their children to the manor-house, and boiled black, and laid upon a silver dish. And when the speech was finished, the old people crept into their houses and never came out again, for they slept.

The young snail pair now ruled in the forest, and had a numerous progeny. But as the young ones were never boiled and put into silver dishes, they concluded that the manor-house had fallen in, and that all the people in the world had died out. And as nobody contradicted them, they must have been right. And the rain fell down upon the burdock leaves to play the drum for them, and the sun shone to colour the burdock forest for them; and they were happy, very happy – the whole family was happy, uncommonly happy!

The Story of a Mother

A MOTHER sat by her little child: she was very sorrowful, fearing that it would die. Its little face was pale, and its eyes were closed. The child drew its breath with difficulty, and sometimes as deeply as if it were sighing; and then the mother looked more sorrowfully than before on the little creature.

There was a knock at the door, and a poor old man came in, wrapped up in something that looked like a great horse-cloth, for that keeps one warm; and he needed it, for it was cold winter. Without, everything was covered with ice and snow, and the wind blew so sharply that it cut one's face.

And as the old man trembled with cold, and the child was quiet for a moment, the mother went and put some beer on the stove in a little pot, to warm it for him. The old man sat down and rocked the cradle, and the mother seated herself on a chair by him, looked at her sick child that drew its breath so painfully, and lifted the little hand.

'You think I shall keep it, do you not?' she asked. 'The good God will not take it from me!'

And the old man – he was *Death* – nodded in such a strange way, that it might just as well mean *yes* as *no*. And the mother cast down her eyes, and tears rolled down her cheeks. Her head became heavy: for three days and three nights she had not closed her eyes; and now she slept, but only for a minute; then she started up and shivered with cold.

'What is that?' she asked, and looked round on all sides; but the old man was gone, and her little child was gone; he had taken it with him. And there in the corner the old clock was humming and whirring; the heavy leaden weight ran down to the floor – plum! – and the clock stopped.

But the poor mother rushed out of the house crying for her child.

Out in the snow sat a woman in long black garments, and she said,

'Death has been with you in your room; I saw him hasten away with your child: he strides faster than the wind, and never brings back what he has taken away.'

'Only tell me which way he has gone,' said the mother. 'Tell me the way, and I will find him.'

'I know him,' said the woman in the black garments; 'but before I tell you, you must sing me all the songs that you have sung to your child. I love those songs; I have heard them before. I am Night, and I saw your tears when you sang them.'

'I will sing them all, all!' said the mother. 'But do not detain me, that I may overtake him, and find my child.'

But Night sat dumb and still. Then the mother wrung her hands, and sang and wept. And there were many songs, but yet more tears, and then Night said, 'Go to the right into the dark fir wood; for I saw Death take that path with your little child.'

Deep in the forest there was a cross-road, and she did not know which way to take. There stood a thorn bush, with not a leaf nor a blossom upon it; for it was in the cold winter-time, and icicles hung from the twigs.

'Have you not seen Death go by, with my little child?'

'Yes,' replied the Bush, 'but I shall not tell you which way he went unless you warm me on your bosom. I'm freezing to death here, I'm turning to ice.'

And she pressed the thorn bush to her bosom, quite close, that it might be well warmed. And the thorns pierced into her flesh, and her blood oozed out in great drops. But the thorn shot out fresh green leaves, and blossomed in the dark winter night: so warm is the heart of a sorrowing mother! And the thorn bush told her the way that she should go.

Then she came to a great lake, on which there were neither ships nor boat. The lake was not frozen enough to carry her, nor sufficiently open to allow her to wade through, and yet she must cross it if she was to find her child. Then she laid herself down to drink the lake; and that was impossible for anyone to do. But the sorrowing mother thought that perhaps a miracle might be wrought.

'No, that can never succeed,' said the lake. 'Let us rather see how we can agree. I'm fond of collecting pearls, and your eyes are the two clearest I have ever seen: if you will weep them out into me I will carry you over into the great greenhouse, where Death lives and cultivates flowers and trees; each of these is a human life.'

'Oh, what would I not give to get to my child!' said the afflicted mother; and she wept yet more, and her eyes fell into the depths of the lake, and became two costly pearls. But the lake lifted her up, as if she sat in a swing, and she was wafted to the opposite shore, where stood a wonderful house, miles in length. One could not tell if it was a mountain containing forests and caves, or a place that had been built. But the poor mother could not see it, for she had wept her eyes out.

'Where shall I find Death, who went away with my little child?' she asked.

'He has not arrived here yet,' said the old grave-woman, who was going about and watching the hothouse of Death. 'How have you found your way here, and who helped you?'

'The good God has helped me,' she replied. 'He is merciful, and you will be merciful too. Where shall I find my little child?'

'I do not know it,' said the old woman, 'and you cannot see. Many flowers and trees have faded this night, and death will soon come and transplant them. You know very well that every human being has his tree of life, or his flower of life, just as each is arranged. They look like other plants, but their hearts beat. Children's hearts can beat too. Go by that. Perhaps you may recognise the beating of your child's heart. But what will you give me if I tell you what more you must do?'

'I have nothing more to give,' said the afflicted mother. 'But I will go for you to the ends of the earth.'

'I have nothing for you to do there,' said the old woman, 'but you can give me your long black hair. You must know yourself that it is beautiful, and it pleases me. You can take my white hair for it, and that is always something.'

'If you ask for nothing more,' said she, 'I will give you that gladly.' And she gave her beautiful hair, and received in exchange the old woman's white hair.

And then they went into the great hothouse of death, where flowers and trees were growing marvellously together. There stood the fine hyacinths under glass bells, and there stood large, sturdy peonies; there grew water plants, some quite fresh, others somewhat sickly; water-snakes were twining about them, and black crabs clung tightly to the stalks. There stood gallant palm trees, oaks, and plantains, and parsley and blooming thyme. Each tree and flower had its name; each was a human life: the people were still alive, one in China, another in Greenland, scattered about in the world. There were great trees thrust into little pots, so that they stood quite crowded, and were nearly bursting the pots; there was also many a little weakly flower in rich earth, with moss round about it, cared for and tended. But the sorrowful mother bent down over all the smallest plants, and heard the human heart beating in each, and out of millions she recognised that of her child.

'That is it!' she cried, and stretched out her hands over a little blue crocus flower, which hung down quite sick and pale.

'Do not touch the flower,' said the old dame; 'but place yourself here; and when Death comes – I expect him every minute – then don't let him pull up the plant, but threaten him that you will do the same to the other plants; then he'll be frightened. He has to account for them all; not one may be pulled up till he receives commission from Heaven.'

And all at once there was an icy cold rush through the hall, and the blind mother felt that Death was arriving.

'How did you find your way hither?' said he. 'How have you been able to come quicker than I?'

'I am a mother,' she answered.

And Death stretched out his long hands towards the little delicate flower; but she kept her hands tight about it, and held it fast; and yet she was full of anxious care lest she should touch one of the leaves. Then Death breathed upon her hands, and she felt that his breath was colder than the icy wind; and her hands sank down powerless.

'You can do nothing against me,' said Death.

'But the merciful God can,' she replied.

'I only do what He commands,' said Death. 'I am His gardener. I take all His trees and flowers, and transplant them into the great Paradise gardens, in the unknown land. But how they will flourish there, and how it is there, I may not tell you.'

'Give me back my child,' said the mother; and she implored and wept. All at once she grasped two pretty flowers with her two hands, and called to Death, 'I'll tear off all your flowers, for I am in despair.'

'Do not touch them,' said Death. 'You say you are so unhappy, and now you would make another mother just as unhappy!'

'Another mother?' said the poor woman; and she let the flowers go.

'There are your eyes for you,' said Death. 'I have fished them up out of the lake; they gleamed up quite brightly. I did not know that they were yours. Take them back – they are clearer now than before – and then look down into the deep well close by. I will tell you the names of the two flowers you wanted to pull up, and you will see their whole future, their whole human life; you will see what you were about to frustrate and destroy.'

And she looked down into the well, and it was a happiness to see how one of them became a blessing to the world, how much joy and gladness was diffused around her. And the woman looked at the life of the other, and it was made up of care and poverty, misery and woe.

'Both are the will of God,' said Death.

'Which of them is the flower of misfortune, and which the blessed one?' she asked.

'That I may not tell you,' answered Death; 'but this much you shall hear, that one of these two flowers is that of your child. It was the fate of your child that you saw – the future of your own child.'

Then the mother screamed aloud for terror.

'Which of them belongs to my child? Tell me that! Release the innocent child! Let my child free from all that misery! Rather carry it away! Carry it into God's kingdom! Forget my tears, forget my entreaties, and all that I have done!'

'I do not understand you,' said Death. 'Will you have your child back, or shall I carry it to that place that you know not?'

Then the mother wrung her hands, and fell on her knees, and prayed to the good God.

'Hear me not when I pray against Thy will, which is at all times the best! Hear me not! hear me not!' And she let her head sink down on her bosom.

And Death went away with her child into the unknown land.

The Shirt Collar

THERE WAS once a rich gentleman whose whole effects consisted of a Bootjack and a Hair-comb, but he had the finest Shirt Collar in the world, and about this Shirt Collar we will tell a story.

The Collar was now old enough to think of marrying, and it happened that he was sent to the wash together with a Garter.

'My word!' exclaimed the Shirt Collar. 'I have never seen anything so slender and delicate, so charming and genteel. May I ask your name?'

'I shall not tell you that,' said the Garter.

'Where is your home?' asked the Shirt Collar.

But the Garter was of rather a modest disposition, and it seemed such a strange question to answer.

'I presume you are a girdle?' said the Shirt Collar – 'a sort of under girdle? I see that you are useful as well as ornamental, my little lady.'

'You are not to speak to me,' said the Garter. 'I have not, I think, given you any occasion to do so.'

'Oh! when one is as beautiful as you are,' cried the Shirt Collar, 'that is occasion enough.'

'Go!' said the Garter; 'don't come so near me: you look to me quite like a man.'

'I am a fine gentleman, too,' said the Shirt Collar. 'I possess a bootjack and a hair-comb.'

And that was not true at all, for it was his master who owned these things, but he was boasting.

'Don't come too near me,' said the Garter; 'I'm not used to that.'

'Affectation!' cried the Shirt Collar.

And then they were taken out of the wash, and starched, and hung over a chair in the sunshine, and then laid on the ironing-board; and now came the hot Iron.

'Mrs Widow!' said the Shirt Collar, 'little Mrs Widow, I'm getting quite warm; I'm being quite changed; I'm losing all my creases; you're burning a hole in me! Ugh! I propose to you.'

'You old rag!' said the Iron, and rode proudly over the Shirt Collar, for it imagined that it was a steam boiler, and that it ought to be out on the railway, dragging carriages. 'You old rag!' said the Iron.

The Shirt Collar was a little frayed at the edges, therefore the Paper Scissors came to smooth away the frayed places.

'Ho, ho!' said the Shirt Collar; 'I presume you are a first-rate dancer. How you can point your toes! no one in the world can do that like you.'

'I know that,' said the Scissors.

'You deserve to be a countess,' said the Shirt Collar. 'All that I possess consists of a fine gentleman, a bootjack, and a comb. If I had only an estate!'

'What! do you want to marry?' cried the Scissors; and they were angry, and gave such a deep cut that the Collar had to be cashiered.

'I shall have to propose to the Hair-comb,' thought the Shirt Collar. 'It is wonderful how well you keep all your teeth, my little lady. Have you never thought of engaging yourself?'

'Yes, you can easily imagine that,' replied the Hair-comb. 'I am engaged to the Bootjack.'

'Engaged!' cried the Shirt Collar.

Now there was no one left to whom he could offer himself, and so he despised love-making.

A long time passed, and the Shirt Collar was put into the sack of a paper-miller. There was a terribly ragged company, and the fine ones kept to themselves, and the coarse ones to themselves, as is right. They all had much to tell, but the Shirt Collar had most of all, for he was a terrible Jack Brag.

'I have had a tremendous number of sweethearts,' said the Shirt Collar. 'They would not leave me alone; but I was a fine gentleman, a starched one. I had a bootjack and a hair-comb that I never used: you should only have seen me then, when I was turned down. I shall never forget my first love; it was a girdle; and how delicate, how charming, how genteel it was! And my first love threw herself into a washing-tub, and all for me! There was also a widow who became quite glowing, but I let her stand alone till she turned quite black. Then there was a dancer who gave me the wound from which I still suffer – she was very hot-tempered. My own hair-comb was in love with me, and lost all her teeth from neglected love. Yes, I've had many experiences of this kind; but I am most sorry for the Garter – I mean for the girdle, that jumped into the wash-tub for love of me. I've a great deal on my conscience. It's time I was turned into white paper.'

And to that the Shirt Collar came. All the rags were turned into white paper, but the Shirt Collar became the very piece of paper we see here, and upon which this story has been printed, and that was done because he boasted so dreadfully about things that were not at all true. And this we must remember, so that we may on no account do the same, for we cannot know at all whether we shall not be put into the rag bag and manufactured into white paper, on which our whole history, even the most secret, shall be printed, so that we shall be obliged to run about and tell it, as the Shirt Collar did.

The Flax

THE FLAX stood in blossom; it had pretty little blue flowers, smooth as a moth's wings, and even more delicate. The sun shone on the Flax, and the rain clouds moistened it, and this was just as good for it as it is for little children when they are washed, and afterwards get a kiss from their mother; they become much prettier, and so did the Flax.

'The people say that I stand uncommonly well,' said the Flax, 'and that I'm fine and long, and shall make a capital piece of linen. How happy I am! I'm certainly the happiest of beings. How well off I am! And I may come to something! How the sunshine gladdens, and the rain tastes good and refreshes me! I'm wonderfully happy; I'm the happiest of beings.'

'Yes, yes, yes!' said the Hedge-stake. 'You don't know the world, but we do, for we have knots in us;' and then it creaked out mournfully,

> 'Snip-snap-snurre,
> Basse-lurre!
> The song is done.'

'No, it is not done,' said the Flax. 'Tomorrow the sun will shine, or the rain will refresh us. I feel that I'm growing, I feel that I'm in blossom! I'm the happiest of beings.'

But one day the people came and took the Flax by the head and pulled it up by the root. That hurt; and it was laid in water as if they were going to drown it, and then put on the fire as if it was going to be roasted. It was quite fearful!

'One can't always have good times,' said the Flax. 'One must make one's experiences, and so one gets to know something.'

But bad times certainly came. The Flax was bruised and scutched, and broken and hackled. Yes, it did not even know what the operations

were called that they did with it. It was put on the spinning-wheel –
whirr! whirr! whirr! – it was not possible to collect one's thoughts.

'I have been uncommonly happy!' it thought in all its pain. 'One
must be content with the good one has enjoyed! Contented! contented!
Oh!' And it continued to say so even when it was put into the loom, and
till it became a large beautiful piece of linen. All the flax, to the last stalk,
was used in making one piece.

'But this is quite remarkable! I should never have believed it! How
favourable fortune is to me! The Hedge-stake was well informed,
truly, with its

> Snip-snap-snurre,
> Basse-lurre!

The song is not done by any means. Now it's beginning in earnest.
That's quite remarkable! If I've suffered something, I've been made into
something! I'm the happiest of all! How strong and fine I am, how white
and long! That's something different from being a mere plant, even if
one has a flower. One is not attended to, and only gets watered when it
rains. Now I'm attended to and cherished; the maid turns me over every
morning, and I get a shower bath from the watering-pot every evening.
Yes, the clergyman's wife has even made a speech about me, and says
I'm the best piece in the whole parish. I cannot be happier!'

Now the Linen was taken into the house, and put under the scissors:
how they cut and tore it, and then pricked it with needles! That was not
pleasant; but twelve pieces of body linen of a kind not often mentioned
by name, but indispensable to all people, were made of it – a whole
dozen!

'Just look! Now something has really been made of me! So, that was
my destiny. That's a real blessing. Now I shall be of some use in the
world, and that's right, that's a true pleasure! We've been made into
twelve things, but yet we're all one and the same; we're just a dozen:
how remarkably charming that is!'

Years rolled on, and now they would hold together no longer.

'It must be over one day,' said each piece. 'I would gladly have held
together a little longer, but one must not expect impossibilities.'

They were now torn into pieces and fragments. They thought it was all over now, for they were hacked to shreds, and softened and boiled; yes, they themselves did not know all that was done to them; and then they became beautiful white paper.

'Now, that is a surprise, and a glorious surprise!' said the Paper. 'Now I'm finer than before, and I shall be written on: that is remarkably good fortune.'

And really the most beautiful stories and verses were written upon it, and the people heard what was upon it; it was sensible and good, and made people much more sensible and good: there was a great blessing in the words that were on this Paper.

'That is more than I ever imagined when I was a little blue flower in the fields. How could I fancy that I should ever spread joy and knowledge among men? I can't yet understand it myself, but it is really so. I have done nothing myself but what I was obliged with my weak powers to do for my own preservation, and yet I have been promoted from one joy and honour to another. Each time when I think "the song is done," it begins again in a higher and better way. Now I shall certainly be sent about to journey through the world, so that all people may read me. That is the only probable thing. I've splendid thoughts, as many as I had pretty flowers in the old times. I'm the happiest of beings.'

But the Paper was not sent on its travels, it was sent to the printer, and everything that was written upon it was set up in type for a book, or rather for many hundreds of books, for in this way a very far greater number could derive pleasure and profit from the book than if the one paper on which it was written had run about the world, to be worn out before it had got halfway.

'Yes, that is certainly the wisest way,' thought the Written Paper. 'I really did not think of that. I shall stay at home, and be held in honour, just like an old grandfather. It was on me the writing was done; the words flowed from the pen right into me. I remain here and the books run about. Now something can really be done. I am the happiest of all.'

Then the Paper was tied together in a bundle, and put on a shelf.

'It's good resting after work,' said the Paper. 'It is very right that one

should collect one's thoughts. Now I'm able for the first time to think
of what is in me, and to know oneself is true progress. What will be
done with me now? At any rate I shall go forward again: I'm always
going forward.'

One day all the paper was laid on the hearth in order to be burnt,
for it must not be sold to the grocer to wrap up butter and sugar. And
all the children in the house stood round; they wanted to see it blaze,
they wanted to see among the ashes the many red sparks, which
seemed to dart off and go out, one after the other, so quickly. These
are the children going out of school, and the last spark of all is the
schoolmaster: one often thinks he has gone already, but he always
comes a little after all the others. All the old Paper, the whole bundle,
was laid upon the fire, and it was soon alight. 'Ugh!' it said, and burst
out into bright flame that mounted up higher than the Flax had ever
been able to lift its little blue flowers, and glittered as the white Linen
had never been able to glitter. All the written letters turned for a
moment quite red, and all the words and thoughts turned to flame.

'Now I'm mounting straight up to the sun,' said a voice in the flame; and it was as if a thousand voices said this in unison; and the flames mounted up through the chimney and out at the top, and more delicate than the flames, invisible to human eyes, little tiny beings floated there, as many as there had been blossoms on the Flax. They were lighter even than the flame from which they were born; and when the flame was extinguished, and nothing remained of the Paper but black ashes, they danced over it once more, and where they touched the black mass the little red sparks appeared. The children came out of school, and the schoolmaster was the last of all. That was fun! and the children sang over the dead ashes:

'Snip-snap-snurre,
Basse-lurre!
The song is done.'

But the little invisible beings all said, 'The song is never done, that is the best of all. I know it, and therefore I'm the happiest of all.'

But the children could neither hear that nor understand it, nor ought they, for children must not know everything.

The Phoenix Bird

IN THE Garden of Paradise, beneath the Tree of Knowledge, bloomed a rose bush. Here, in the first rose, a bird was born: his flight was like the flashing of light, his plumage was beauteous, and his song ravishing.

But when Eve plucked the fruit of the knowledge of good and evil, when she and Adam were driven from Paradise, there fell from the flaming sword of the cherub a spark into the nest of the bird, which blazed up forthwith. The bird perished in the flames; but from the red egg in the nest there fluttered aloft a new one – the one solitary Phoenix bird. The fable tells us that he dwells in Arabia, and that every hundred years he burns himself to death in his nest; but each time a new Phoenix, the only one in the world, rises up from the red egg.

The bird flutters round us, swift as light, beauteous in colour, charming in song. When a mother sits by her infant's cradle, he stands on the pillow, and, with his wings, forms a glory around the infant's head. He flies through the chamber of content, and brings sunshine into it, and the violets on the humble table smell doubly sweet.

But the Phoenix is not the bird of Arabia alone. He wings his way in the glimmer of the Northern Lights over the icy plains of Lapland, and hops among the yellow flowers in the short Greenland summer. Beneath the copper mountains of Fahlun and in England's coal mines, he flies, in the shape of a dusty moth, over the hymn-book that rests on the knees of the pious miner. On a lotus leaf he floats down the sacred waters of the Ganges, and the eye of the Hindu maid gleams bright when she beholds him.

The Phoenix bird, dost thou not know him? The Bird of Paradise, the holy swan of song! On the car of Thespis he sat in the guise of a chattering raven, and flapped his black wings, smeared with the lees of wine; over the sounding harp of Iceland swept the swan's red beak; on Shakespeare's shoulder he sat in the guise of Odin's raven, and whispered in his ear 'Immortality!' and at the minstrels' feast he fluttered through the halls of the Wartburg.

The Phoenix bird, dost thou not know him? He sang to thee the *Marseillaise*, and thou kissedst the feather that fell from his wing; he came in the radiance of Paradise, and perchance thou didst turn away from him towards the sparrow who sat with tinsel on his wings.

The Bird of Paradise – renewed each century – born in flame, ending in flame! Thy picture, in a golden frame, hangs in the halls of the rich, but thou thyself often fliest around, lonely and disregarded, a myth – 'The Phoenix of Arabia.'

In Paradise, when thou wert born in the first rose, beneath the Tree of Knowledge, thou receivedst a kiss, and thy right name was given thee – thy name, Poetry.

A Story

IN THE garden all the apple trees were in blossom. They had hurried up to get flowers before green leaves, and in the farmyard all the ducklings were out and the cat with them: he licked real sunshine, licked it from his own paws; and if one looked along to the field, the corn stood magnificently green, and there was a twittering and a chirping of all the little birds, as if it were a great festival, and indeed one might also say that it was so, for it was Sunday. The bells rang, and people in their best clothes went to church, and looked so well pleased; yes, there was something so pleasant about everything; it was certainly a day so warm and blessed, that one could say, 'Our Lord is really very good to His people!'

But inside the church, the priest stood in the pulpit and spoke very loudly and very angrily; he said that the people were so ungodly, and that God would punish them for it, and when they died, the wicked should go down to Hell, where they should burn for ever, and he said that their worm never died, and their fire was never quenched; and never did they get peace or rest. It was terrible to hear it, and he said it so positively; he described Hell to them as a stinking hole, where all the world's filthiness flowed together, there was no air except the hot sulphur-flame, there was no bottom, they sank and sank in an ever-lasting silence. It was gruesome merely to listen to it, but the priest said it from the heart, and all the people in the church were quite terrified.

But outside all the little birds sang so happily, and the sun shone so warmly, it seemed as if every little flower said, 'God is so very good to all of us.' Yes, outside it was certainly not as the preacher had said.

In the evening towards bedtime, the clergyman saw his wife sitting silent and thoughtful.

'What ails you?' he said to her.

'What ails me?' said she, 'I cannot collect my thoughts properly, I cannot get clearly into my head what you said, that there were so many ungodly, and that they should burn for ever; for ever, O, how long! I am only a sinful woman, but I could not bear to let even the worst sinner burn for ever; how then should our Lord be able to do it who is so infinitely good, and who knows how the evil comes both from without and from within? No, I cannot think it, even although you say it.'

It was autumn, the leaves fell from the trees; the severe, earnest priest sat by the deathbed of his wife.

'If anyone should get peace in the grave and mercy from God, it is you!' said the priest, and he folded her hands and read a psalm over her body.

And she was carried to her grave; two heavy tears rolled down over the cheeks of the earnest priest; and in his house it was quiet and lonely, the sunshine was extinguished; she had gone away.

It was night; a cold wind blew over the head of the priest, he opened his eyes, and it seemed as if the moon shone into his room, but the moon was not shining; it was a figure which stood before his bed; he saw the ghost of his dead wife; she looked at him sorrowfully, it seemed as if she wanted to say something.

And the man raised himself half up, and stretched out his arms to her: 'Have you not been granted eternal rest either? Do you suffer, you the best, the most pious?' And the departed one bowed her head for 'Yes', and laid her hands on her breast.

'And can I obtain rest for you in the grave?'

'Yes,' it answered him.

'And how?'

'Give me a hair, only a single hair, from the head of the sinner whose fire will never be quenched, the sinner whom God will thrust down into everlasting punishment.'

'Yes, so easily can you be set free, you pure and pious soul!'

'Then follow me!' said the departed. 'It is so vouchsafed to us. By my side you can float whither your thoughts will; unseen by men we stand in their most secret corners, but with steady hand you must point to the one consecrated to everlasting pain, and before cock-crow he must be found.'

And quickly, as if carried by thought, they were in the great town; and from the walls of the houses shone in letters of fire the names of the deadly sins: Pride, Avarice, Drunkenness, Self-indulgence, in short, the whole seven-hued rainbow of sin.

'Yes, in there, as I thought, as I knew,' said the priest, 'dwell those who are destined for eternal fire.' And they stood before the gorgeously lighted portal, where the broad stair was decorated with carpets and flowers, and dance-music sounded through the festive halls. The footman stood in silk and velvet with silver-mounted stick.

'Our ball can compare with that of the king,' said he, and he turned to the crowd on the street; from top to toe the thought shone out of him, 'Poor pack, who stare in at the portal, you are common people compared with me, all of you!'

'Pride,' said the departed one. 'Do you see him?'

'Yes, but he is a simpleton, only a fool, and will not be condemned to everlasting fire and pain!'

'Only a fool!' sounded through the whole house of Pride; they were all 'only fools' there.

And they flew within the four bare walls of Avarice, where, lean, chattering with cold, hungry and thirsty, the old one clung to his gold with all his thoughts; they saw how he sprang from his miserable couch, as in a fever, and took a loose stone out of the wall, where gold-money lay in a stocking-leg; he fingered his patched coat into which gold pieces were sewn, and the moist fingers trembled.

'He is ill, it is madness, a joyless madness, beset with fear and evil dreams.'

And they departed in haste, and stood by the couches of the criminals where they slept in long rows, side by side.

Like a wild animal, one of them started up out of his sleep, uttering a horrid shriek; he dug his pointed elbow into his comrade, who turned sleepily.

'Hold your tongue, you blockhead, and sleep! it is the same every night!'

'Every night,' he repeated, 'yes, every night he comes and howls and suffocates me. In passion have I done one thing and another, an angry mind was I born with; it has brought me here a second time; but if I have done wrong, then I have had my punishment. Only one thing have I not acknowledged. When I last came out of here and passed my master's farm, one thing and another boiled up in me, I scratched a sulphur match along the wall, it ran a little too near the thatch of the roof, everything burned. Passion came over it, as it comes over me. I helped to save the cattle and effects. Nothing living was burned but a flock of pigeons, which flew into the fire, and the watch-dog. I had not thought of it. One could hear it howling, and that howl I always hear still, when I want to sleep, and when I fall asleep, then comes the dog, so big and shaggy; he lays himself on me, howls, presses me, and suffocates me. Then listen to what I tell you; *you* can snore, snore the whole night, and I not a short quarter of an hour.' And the blood shone in his eyes, he threw himself over his comrade and hit him with clenched fist in the face.

'Angry Mads has gone mad again!' was the cry round about, and the other scoundrels caught hold of him, wrestled with him, and bent him so that his head sat between his legs where they bound it fast; the blood was almost springing out of his eyes and all his pores.

'You will kill him,' shouted the priest, 'the miserable one!' And whilst he, in order to hinder them, stretched out his hand over the sinner, who already in this world suffered too severely, the scene changed; they flew through rich halls, and through poor rooms; Self-indulgence, Envy, all the deadly sins marched past them; an angel of judgement read their sins, their defence; this was but weak before God, but God reads the hearts, He knows everything, the evil which comes from within and from without, He who is mercy and love. The hand of the priest trembled, he dared not stretch it forth to pull a hair from the sinner's head. And the tears streamed from his eyes, like the water of mercy and love, which quench the everlasting fires of Hell. And the cock crew.

'Merciful God! Thou will give her that rest in the grave, which I have not been able to obtain.'

'I have it now!' said the dead one, 'it was thy hard words, thy dark belief about God and His works, which drove me to thee! Learn to know men; even in the wicked there is something of God, something which will triumph, and quench the fire of Hell.'

A kiss was pressed on the mouth of the priest, light beamed round about him; God's clear sun shone into the chamber, where his wife, gentle and loving, wakened him from a dream sent by God.

The Dumb Book

BY THE HIGH ROAD in the forest lay a lonely farm; the road went right through the farmyard. The sun shone down, and all the windows were open. In the house was bustle and movement; but in the yard, in an arbour of blossoming lilac, stood an open coffin. A dead man had been carried out here, and he was to be buried this morning. Nobody stood by the coffin and looked sorrowfully at the dead man; no one shed a tear for him: his face was covered with a white cloth, and under his head lay a great thick book, whose leaves consisted of whole sheets of gray paper, and on each leaf lay a faded flower. It was a complete herbarium, gathered by him in various places; it was to be buried with him, for so he had wished it. With each flower a chapter in his life was associated.

'Who is the dead man?' we asked; and the answer was: 'The Old Student from Upsala. They say he was once a brisk lad, and studied the old languages, and sang, and even wrote poems. Then something happened to him that made him turn his thoughts to brandy, and take to it; and when at last he had ruined his health, he came out here into the country, where somebody paid for his board and lodging. He was as gentle as a child, except when the dark mood came upon him; but when it came he became like a giant, and then ran about in the woods like a hunted stag; but when we once got him home again, and prevailed with him so far that he opened the book with the dried plants, he often sat whole days, and looked sometimes at one plant and sometimes at another, and at times the tears rolled over his cheeks: Heaven knows what he was thinking of. But he begged us to put the book into the coffin, and now he lies there, and in a little while the lid will be nailed down, and he will have his quiet rest in the grave.'

The face-cloth was raised, and there was peace upon the features of the dead man, and a sunbeam played upon it; a swallow shot with arrowy flight into the arbour, and turned rapidly, and twittered over the dead man's head.

What a strange feeling it is – and we have doubtless all experienced it – that of turning over old letters of the days of our youth! a whole life seems to come up with them, with all its hopes and sorrows. How many persons with whom we were intimate in those days, are as it were dead to us! and yet they are alive, but for a long time we have not thought of them – of them whom we then thought to hold fast for ages, and with whom we were to share sorrow and joy.

Here the withered oak-leaf in the book reminded the owner of the friend, the schoolfellow, who was to be a friend for life: he fastened the green leaf in the student's cap in the green wood, when the bond was made 'for life': where does he live now? The leaf is preserved, but the friendship has perished! And here is a foreign hothouse plant, too delicate for the gardens of the North; the leaves almost seem to keep their fragrance still. She gave it to him, the young lady in the noble-man's garden. Here is the water-rose, which he plucked himself, and moistened with salt tears – the rose of the sweet waters. And here is a nettle – what tale may its leaves have to tell? What were his thoughts when he plucked it and kept it? Here is a lily of the valley from the solitudes of the forest. Here's an evergreen from the flowerpot of the tavern; and here's a sharp bare blade of grass.

The blooming lilac waves its fresh fragrant blossoms over the dead man's head, and the swallow flies past again. 'Pee-wit! pee-wit!' And now the men come with nails and hammers, and the lid is laid over the dead man, that his head may rest upon the dumb book – put away – forgotten!

'There is a Difference'

I T WAS in the month of May. The wind still blew cold, but bushes and trees, field and meadow, all alike said the spring had come. There was store of flowers even in the wild hedges; and there spring carried on his affairs, and preached from a little apple tree, where one branch hung fresh and blooming, covered with delicate pink blossoms that were just ready to open. The Apple Tree Branch knew well enough how beautiful he was, for the knowledge is inherent in the blade as well as in the blood; and consequently the Branch was not surprised when a nobleman's carriage stopped opposite to him on the road, and the young countess said that that apple branch was the loveliest thing one could behold, a very emblem of spring in its most charming form. And the Branch was broken off, and she held it in her delicate hand, and sheltered it with her silk parasol. Then they drove to the castle, where there were lofty halls and splendid apartments. Pure white curtains fluttered round the open windows, and beautiful flowers stood in shining transparent vases; and in one of these, which looked as if it had been cut out of fresh-fallen snow, the Apple Branch was placed among some fresh light twigs of beech. It was charming to behold. But the Branch became proud; and this was quite like human nature.

People of various kinds came through the room, and according to their rank they might express their admiration. A few said nothing at all, and others again said too much, and the Apple Tree Branch soon got to understand that there was a difference in human beings just as among plants.

'Some are created for beauty, and some for use; and there are some which one can do without altogether,' thought the Apple Branch.

And as he stood just in front of the open window, from whence he could see into the garden and across the fields, he had flowers and plants enough to contemplate and to think about, for there were rich plants and humble plants – some very humble indeed.

'Poor despised herbs!' said the Apple Branch. 'There is certainly a difference! And how unhappy they must feel, if indeed that kind *can* feel like myself and my equals. Certainly there is a difference, and distinctions must be made, or we should all be equal.'

And the Apple Branch looked down with a species of pity, especially upon a certain kind of flower of which great numbers are found in the fields and in ditches. No one bound them into a nosegay, they were too common; for they might be found even among the paving-stones, shooting up everywhere like the rankest weeds, and they had the ugly name of 'dandelion', or 'the devil's milk-pail'.

'Poor despised plants!' said the Apple Branch. 'It is not your fault that you are what you are, that you are so common, and that you received the ugly name you bear. But it is with plants as with men – there must be a difference!'

'A difference?' said the Sunbeam; and he kissed the blooming Apple Branch, but also kissed the yellow dandelions out in the field – all the brothers of the Sunbeam kissed them, the poor flowers as well as the rich.

Now the Apple Branch had never thought of the boundless beneficence of Providence in creation towards everything that lives and moves and has its being; he had never thought how much that is beautiful and good may be hidden, but not forgotten; but that, too, was quite like human nature.

The Sunbeam, the ray of light, knew better, and said, 'You don't see far and you don't see clearly. What is the despised plant that you especially pity?'

'The dandelion,' replied the Apple Branch. 'It is never received into a nosegay; it is trodden under foot. There are too many of them; and when they run to seed, they fly away like little pieces of wool over the roads, and hang and cling to people's dress. They are nothing but weeds – but it is right there should be weeds too. Oh, I'm really very thankful that I was not created one of those flowers.'

But there came across the fields a whole troop of children, the youngest of whom was so small that it was carried by the rest, and when it was set down in the grass among the yellow flowers it laughed aloud with glee, kicked out with its little legs, rolled about and plucked the yellow flowers, and kissed them in its pretty innocence. The elder children broke off the flowers with their hollow stalks, and bent the stalks round into one another, link by link, so that a whole chain was made; first a necklace, and then a scarf to hang over their shoulders and tie round their waists, and then a chaplet to wear on the head: it was quite a gala of green links and chains. The eldest children carefully gathered the stalks on which hung the white feathery ball, formed by the flower that had run to seed; and this loose, airy wool-flower, which is a beautiful object, looking like the finest snowy down, they held to their mouths, and tried to blow away the whole head at one breath; for their grandmother had said that whoever could do this would be sure to get new clothes before the year was out. So on this occasion the despised flower was a perfect prophet.

'Do you see?' said the Sunbeam. 'Do you see the beauty of those flowers? do you see their power?'

'Yes – over children,' replied the Apple Branch.

And now an old woman came into the field, and began to dig with a blunt shaftless knife round the root of the dandelion plant, and pulled it up out of the ground. With some of the roots she intended to make coffee for herself; others she was going to sell for money to the druggist.

'But beauty is a higher thing!' said the Apple Tree Branch. 'Only the chosen few can be admitted into the realm of beauty. There is a difference among plants, just as there is a difference among men.'

And then the Sunbeam spoke of the boundless love of the Creator, as manifested in the creation, and of the just distribution of things in time and in eternity.

'Yes, yes, that is your opinion,' the Apple Branch persisted.

But now some people came into the room, and the beautiful young countess appeared, the lady who had placed the Apple Branch in the transparent vase in the sunlight. She carried in her hand a flower, or something of the kind. The object, whatever it might be, was hidden by three or four great leaves, wrapped around it like a shield, that no draught or gust of wind should injure it; and it was carried more carefully than the Apple Bough had been. Very gently the large leaves were now removed, and lo, there appeared the fine feathery seed crown of the despised dandelion! This it was that the lady had plucked with the greatest care, and had carried home with every precaution, so that not one of the delicate feathery darts that form its downy ball should be blown away. She now produced it, quite uninjured, and admired its beautiful form, its peculiar construction, and its airy beauty, which was to be scattered by the wind.

'Look, with what singular beauty Providence has invested it,' she said. 'I will paint it, together with the Apple Branch, whose beauty all have admired; but this humble flower has received just as much from Heaven in a different way; and, various as they are, both are children of the kingdom of beauty.'

And the Sunbeam kissed the humble flower, and he kissed the blooming Apple Branch, whose leaves appeared to blush thereat.

The Old Gravestone

IN A LITTLE provincial town, in the house of a man who owned his own home, the whole family was sitting together in a circle one evening, in the time of the year when people say 'the evenings are drawing in'. The weather was still mild and warm. The lamp was lighted; the long curtains hung down in front of the windows, by which stood many flowerpots; and outside there was the most beautiful moonshine. But they were not talking about this. They were talking about the old great stone which lay below in the courtyard, close by the kitchen door, and on which the maids often laid the cleaned copper kitchen utensils that they might dry in the sun, and where the children were fond of playing. It was, in fact, an old gravestone.

'Yes,' said the master of the house, 'I believe the stone comes from the old convent church; for from the old convent church yonder, which was taken down, the pulpit, the memorial boards, and the gravestones were sold. My father bought several of the latter, and they were cut in two to be used as paving-stones; but that old stone was left over, and has been lying in the courtyard ever since.'

'One can very well see that it is a gravestone,' observed the eldest of the children; 'we can still see on it an hourglass and a piece of an angel; but the inscription which stood below it is almost quite effaced, except that you may read the name of *Preben*, and a great *S* close behind it, and a little farther down the name of *Martha*. But nothing more can be distinguished, and even that is only plain when it has been raining, or when we have washed the stone.'

'On my word, that must be the gravestone of Preben Svane and his wife!'

These words were spoken by an old man; so old, that he might well have been the grandfather of all who were present in the room.

'Yes, they were one of the last pairs that were buried in the old

churchyard of the convent. They were an honest old couple. I can remember them from the days of my boyhood. Everyone knew them, and everyone esteemed them. They were the oldest pair here in the town. The people declared that they had more than a tub-full of gold; and yet they went about very plainly dressed, in the coarsest stuffs, but always with splendidly clean linen. They were a fine old pair, Preben and Martha! When both of them sat on the bench at the top of the steep stone stairs in front of the house, with the old linden tree spreading its branches above them, and nodded at one in their kind gentle way, it seemed quite to do one good. They were very kind to the poor; they fed them and clothed them; and there was judgement in their benevolence and true Christianity. The old woman died first: that day is still quite clear before my mind. I was a little boy, and had accompanied my father over there, and we were just there when she fell asleep. The old man was very much moved, and wept like a child. The body lay in the room next to the one where we sat; and he spoke to my father and to a few neighbours who were there, and said how lonely it would be now in his house, and how good and faithful she (his dead wife) had been, how many years they had wandered together through life, and how it had come about that they came to know each other and to fall in love. I was, as I have told you, a boy, and only stood by and listened to what the others said; but it filled me with quite a strange emotion to listen to the old man, and to watch how his cheeks gradually flushed red when he spoke of the days of their courtship, and told how beautiful she was, and how many little innocent pretexts he had invented to meet her. And then he talked of the wedding-day, and his eyes gleamed; he seemed to talk himself back into that time of joy. And yet she was lying in the next room – dead – an old woman; and he was an old man, speaking of the past days of hope! Yes, yes, thus it is! Then I was but a child, and now I am old – as old as Preben Svane was then. Time passes away, and all things change. I can very well remember the day when she was buried, and how Preben Svane walked close behind the coffin. A few years before, the couple had caused their gravestone to be prepared, and their names to be engraved on it, with the inscription, all but the date. In the evening the stone was taken to the churchyard, and laid over the grave; and the year afterwards it was taken up, that old Preben might be laid to rest beside his wife. They did not leave behind them anything like the wealth people had attributed to them: what there was went to families distantly related to them – to people of whom, until then, one had known nothing. The old wooden house, with the seat at the top of the steps, beneath the lime tree, was taken down by the corporation; it was too old and rotten to be left standing. Afterwards, when the same fate befell the convent church, and the graveyard was levelled, Preben and Martha's tombstone was sold, like everything else, to anyone who would buy it; and now it has so happened that this stone was not broken in pieces and used, but that it still lies below in the yard as a scouring-bench for the maids and a plaything for the children. The high road now goes over the resting-place of old Preben and his wife. No one thinks of them any more.'

And the old man who had told all this shook his head mournfully.

'Forgotten! Everything will be forgotten!' he said.

And then they spoke in the room of other things; but the youngest child, a boy with great serious eyes, mounted up on a chair behind the window-curtains, and looked out into the yard, where the moon was pouring its radiance over the old stone – the old stone that had always appeared to him so empty and flat, but which lay there now like a great leaf out of a book of chronicles. All that the boy had heard about old Preben and his wife seemed to be in the stone; and he gazed at it, and looked at the pure bright moon and up into the clear air, and it seemed as though the countenance of the Creator was beaming over the world.

'Forgotten! Everything will be forgotten!' was repeated in the room.

But in that moment an invisible angel kissed the boy's forehead, and whispered to him:

'Preserve the seed-corn that has been entrusted to thee. Guard it well till the time of ripeness! Through thee, my child, the obliterated inscription on the old tombstone shall be chronicled in golden letters to future generations! The old pair shall wander again arm in arm through the streets, and smile, and sit with their fresh healthy faces under the lime tree on the bench by the steep stairs, and nod at rich and poor. The seed-corn of this hour shall ripen in the course of time to a blooming poem. The beautiful and the good shall not be forgotten; it shall live on in legend and in song.'

The Loveliest Rose in the World

ONCE THERE reigned a Queen, in whose garden were found the most glorious flowers at all seasons and from all the lands in the world; but especially she loved roses, and therefore she possessed the most various kinds of this flower, from the wild dog-rose, with the apple-scented green leaves, to the most splendid Provence rose. They grew against the castle walls, wound themselves round pillars and window-frames, into the passages, and all along the ceiling in all the halls. And the roses were various in fragrance, form, and colour.

But care and sorrow dwelt in these halls: the Queen lay upon a sick-bed, and the doctors declared that she must die.

'There is still one thing that can save her,' said the wisest of them. 'Bring her the loveliest rose in the world, the one which is the expression of the brightest and purest love; for if that is brought before her eyes ere they close, she will not die.'

And young and old came from every side with roses, the loveliest that bloomed in each garden; but they were not the right sort. The flower was to be brought out of the garden of Love; but what rose was it there that expressed the highest and purest love?

And the poets sang of the loveliest rose in the world, and each one named his own; and intelligence was sent far round the land to every heart that beat with love, to every class and condition, and to every age.

'No one has till now named the flower,' said the wise man. 'No one has pointed out the place where it bloomed in its splendour. They are not the roses from the coffin of Romeo and Juliet, or from the Walborg's grave, though these roses will be ever fragrant in song and story. They are not the roses that sprout forth from Winkelried's bloodstained lances, from the blood that flows in a sacred cause from the breast of the hero who dies for his country; though no death is sweeter than this, and no rose redder than the blood that flows then. Nor is it that wondrous flower, to cherish which man devotes, in a quiet chamber, many a sleepless night, and much of his fresh life – the magic flower of science.'

'I know where it blooms,' said a happy mother, who came with her tender child to the bedside of the Queen. 'I know where the loveliest rose of the world is found! The rose that is the expression of the highest and purest love springs from the blooming cheeks of my sweet child when, strengthened by sleep, it opens its eyes and smiles at me with all its affection!'

'Lovely is this rose; but there is still a lovelier,' said the wise man.

'Yes, a far lovelier one,' said one of the women. 'I have seen it, and a loftier, purer rose does not bloom, but it was pale like the petals of the tea-rose. I saw it on the cheeks of the Queen. She had taken off her royal crown, and in the long dreary night she was carrying her sick child in her arms: she wept, kissed it, and prayed for her child as a mother prays in the hour of her anguish.'

'Holy and wonderful in its might is the white rose of grief; but it is not the one we seek.'

'No, the loveliest rose of the world I saw at the altar of the Lord,' said the good old Bishop. 'I saw it shine as if an angel's face had appeared. The young maidens went to the Lord's Table, and renewed the promise made at their baptism, and roses were blushing, and pale roses shining on their fresh cheeks. A young girl stood there; she looked with all the purity and love of her young spirit up to heaven: that was the expression of the highest and the purest love.'

'May she be blessed!' said the wise man; 'but not one of you has yet named to me the loveliest rose of the world.'

Then there came into the room a child, the Queen's little son. Tears stood in his eyes and glistened on his cheeks: he carried a great open book, and the binding was of velvet, with great silver clasps.

'Mother!' cried the little boy, 'only hear what I have read.'

And the child sat by the bedside, and read from the book of Him who suffered death on the Cross to save men, and even those who were not yet born.

'Greater love there is not –'

And a roseate hue spread over the cheeks of the Queen, and her eyes gleamed, for she saw that from the leaves of the book there bloomed the loveliest rose, that sprang from the blood of Christ shed on the Cross.

'I see it!' she said: 'he who beholds this, the loveliest rose on earth, shall never die.'

The Story of the Year

I T WAS far in January, and a terrible fall of snow was pelting down. The snow eddied through the streets and lanes; the window-panes seemed plastered with snow on the outside; snow plumped down in masses from the roofs: and a sudden hurry had seized on the people, for they ran, and jostled, and fell into each other's arms, and as they clutched each other fast for a moment, they felt that they were safe at least for that length of time. Coaches and horses seemed frosted with sugar. The footmen stood with their backs against the carriages, so as to turn their faces from the wind. The foot passengers kept in the shelter of the carriages, which could only move slowly on in the deep snow; and when the storm at last abated, and a narrow path was swept clean alongside the houses, the people stood still in this path when they met, for none liked to take the first step aside into the deep snow to let the other pass him. Thus they stood silent and motionless, till, as if by tacit consent, each sacrificed one leg, and, stepping aside, buried it in the deep snow-heap.

Towards evening it grew calm. The sky looked as if it had been swept, and had become more lofty and transparent. The stars looked as if they were quite new, and some of them were amazingly bright and pure. It froze so hard that the snow creaked, and the upper rind of snow might well have grown hard enough to bear the Sparrows in the morning dawn. These little birds hopped up and down where the sweeping had been done; but they found very little food, and were not a little cold.

'Piep!' said one of them to another; 'they call this a new year, and it is worse than the last! We might just as well have kept the old one. I'm dissatisfied, and I've reason to be so.'

'Yes; and the people ran about and fired off shots to celebrate the New Year,' said a shivering little Sparrow; 'and they threw pans and pots against the doors, and were quite boisterous with joy because the Old Year was gone. I was glad of it too, because I hoped we should have had warm days; but that has come to nothing – it freezes much harder than before. People have made a mistake in reckoning the time!'

'That they have!' a third put in, who was old, and had a white poll: 'they've something they call the calendar – it's an invention of their own – and everything is to be arranged according to that; but it won't do. When spring comes, then the year begins – that is the course of nature.'

'But when will spring come?' the others enquired.

'It will come when the stork comes back. But his movements are very uncertain, and here in town no one knows anything about it: in the country they are better informed. Shall we fly out there and wait? There, at any rate, we shall be nearer to spring.'

'Yes, that may be all very well,' observed one of the Sparrows, who had been hopping about for a long time, chirping, without saying anything decided. 'I've found a few comforts here in town, which I am afraid I should miss out in the country. Near this neighbourhood, in a courtyard, there lives a family of people, who have taken the very sensible notion of placing three or four flowerpots against the wall, with their mouths all turned inwards, and the bottom of each pointing outwards. In each flowerpot a hole has been cut, big enough for me to fly in and out at it. I and my husband have built a nest in one of those pots, and have brought up our young family there. The family of people of course made the whole arrangement that they might have the pleasure of seeing us, or else they would not have done it. To please themselves they also strew crumbs of bread; and so we have food, and are in a manner provided for. So I think my husband and I will stay where we are, although we are very dissatisfied – but we shall stay.'

'And we will fly into the country to see if spring is not coming!'

And away they flew.

Out in the country it was hard winter, and the glass was a few degrees lower than in the town. The sharp winds swept across the snow-covered fields. The farmer, muffled in warm mittens, sat in his sledge, and beat his arms across his breast to warm himself, and the whip lay across his knees. The horses ran till they smoked again. The snow creaked, and the Sparrows hopped about in the ruts, and shivered, 'Piep! when will spring come? it is very long in coming!'

'Very long,' sounded from the next snow-covered hill, far over the field. It might be the echo which was heard; or perhaps the words were spoken by yonder wonderful old man, who sat in wind and weather high on the heap of snow. He was quite white, attired like a peasant in a coarse white coat of frieze; he had long white hair, and was quite pale, with big blue eyes.

'Who is that old man yonder?' asked the Sparrows.

'I know who he is,' quoth an old Raven, who sat on the fence-rail, and was condescending enough to acknowledge that we are all like little birds in the sight of Heaven, and therefore was not above speaking to the Sparrows, and giving them information. 'I know who the old man is. It is Winter, the old man of last year. He is not dead, as the calendar says, but is guardian to little Prince Spring, who is to come. Yes, Winter bears sway here. Ugh! the cold makes you shiver, does it not, you little ones?'

'Yes. Did I not tell the truth?' said the smallest Sparrow: 'the calendar is only an invention of man, and is not arranged according to nature! They ought to leave these things to us, who are born cleverer than they.'

And one week passed away, and two passed away. The forest was black, the frozen lake lay hard and stiff, looking like a sheet of lead, and damp icy mists lay brooding over the land; the great black crows flew about in long lines, but silently; and it seemed as if nature slept. Then a sunbeam glided along over the lake, and made it shine like burnished tin. The snowy covering on the field and on the hill did not glitter as it had done; but the white form, Winter himself, still sat there, his gaze fixed unswervingly upon the south. He did not notice that the snowy carpet seemed to sink as it were into the earth, and that here and there a little grass-green patch appeared, and that all these patches were crowded with Sparrows, which cried, 'Kee-wit! kee-wit! Is spring coming now?'

'Spring!' The cry resounded over field and meadow, and through the black-brown woods, where the moss still glimmered in bright green upon the tree trunks; and from the south the first two storks came flying through the air. On the back of each sat a pretty little child – one was a girl and the other a boy. They greeted the earth with a kiss, and wherever they set their feet, white flowers grew up from beneath the snow. Then they went hand in hand to the old ice man, Winter, clung to his breast embracing him, and in a moment they, and he, and all the region around were hidden in a thick damp mist, dark and heavy, that closed over all like a veil. Gradually the wind rose, and now it rushed roaring along, and drove away the mist, so that the sun shone warmly forth, and Winter himself vanished, and the beautiful children of Spring sat on the throne of the year.

'That's what I call New Year,' cried each of the Sparrows. 'Now we shall get our rights, and have amends for the stern winter.'

Wherever the two children turned, green buds burst forth on bushes and trees, the grass shot upwards, and the cornfields turned green and became more and more lovely. And the little maiden strewed flowers all around. Her apron, which she held up before her, was always full of them; they seemed to spring up there, for her lap continued full, however zealously she strewed the blossoms around; and in her eagerness she scattered a snow of blossoms over apple trees and peach trees, so that they stood in full beauty before their green leaves had fairly come forth.

And she clapped her hands, and the boy clapped his, and then flocks of birds came flying up, nobody knew whence, and they all twittered and sang, 'Spring has come.'

That was beautiful to behold. Many an old granny crept forth over the threshold into the sunshine, and tripped gleefully about, casting a glance at the yellow flowers which shone everywhere in the fields, just as they used to do when she was young. The world grew young again to her, and she said, 'It is a blessed day out here today!'

The forest still wore its brown-green dress, made of buds; but the woodruff was already there, fresh and fragrant; there were violets in plenty, anemones and primroses came forth, and there was sap and strength in every blade of grass. That was certainly a beautiful carpet to sit upon, and there accordingly the young spring pair sat hand in hand, and sang and smiled, and grew on.

A mild rain fell down upon them from the sky, but they did not notice it, for the raindrops were mingled with their own tears of joy. They kissed each other as bride and bridegroom, and in the same moment the verdure of the woods was unfolded, and when the sun rose, the forest stood there arrayed in green.

And hand in hand the betrothed pair wandered under the pendent roof of fresh leaves, where the rays of the sun gleamed through the green in lovely, ever-changing hues. What virgin purity, what refreshing balm in the delicate leaves! The brooks and streams rippled clearly and merrily among the green velvety rushes and over the coloured pebbles. All nature seemed to say, 'There is plenty, and there shall be plenty always!' And the cuckoo sang and the lark carolled: it was a charming spring; but the willows had woolly gloves over their blossoms; they were desperately careful, and that is tiresome.

And days went by and weeks went by, and the heat came as it were rolling down. Hot waves of air came through the corn, that became yellower and yellower. The white water-lily of the North spread its great green leaves over the glassy mirror of the woodland lakes, and the fishes sought out the shady spots beneath; and at the sheltered side of the wood, where the sun shone down upon the walls of the farmhouse, warming the blooming roses, and the cherry trees, which hung full of juicy black berries, almost hot with the fierce beams, there sat the lovely wife of Summer, the same being whom we have seen as a child and as a bride; and her glance was fixed upon the black gathering clouds, which in wavy outlines – blue-black and heavy – were piling themselves up, like mountains, higher and higher. They came from three sides, and growing like a petrified sea, they came swooping towards the forest, where every sound had been silenced as if by magic. Every breath of air was hushed, every bird was mute. There was a seriousness – a suspense throughout all nature; but in the highways and lanes, foot-passengers, and riders, and men in carriages, were hurrying on to get under shelter. Then suddenly there was a flashing of light, as if the sun were burst forth – flaming, burning, all-devouring! And the darkness returned amid a rolling crash. The rain poured down in streams, and there was alternate darkness and blinding light; alternate silence and deafening clamour. The young, brown, feathery reeds on the moor moved to and fro in long waves, the twigs of the woods were hidden in a mist of waters, and still came darkness and light, and still silence and roaring followed one another; the grass and corn lay beaten down and swamped, looking as though they could never raise themselves again. But soon the rain fell only in gentle drops, the sun peered through the clouds, the water-drops glittered like pearls on the leaves, the birds sang, the fishes leaped up from the surface of the lake, the gnats danced in the sunshine, and yonder on the rock, in the salt heaving sea-water, sat Summer himself – a strong man with sturdy limbs and long dripping hair – there he sat, strengthened by the cool bath, in the warm sunshine. All nature round about was renewed, everything stood luxuriant, strong, and beautiful; it was summer, warm, lovely summer.

And pleasant and sweet was the fragrance that streamed upwards from the rich clover-field, where the bees swarmed round the old ruined place of meeting: the bramble wound itself around the altar stone, which, washed by the rain, glittered in the sunshine; and thither flew the Queen-bee with her swarm, and prepared wax and honey. Only Summer saw it, he and his strong wife; for them the altar table stood covered with the offerings of nature.

And the evening sky shone like gold, shone as no church dome can shine; and in the interval between the evening and the morning red there was moonlight: it was summer.

And days went by, and weeks went by. The bright scythes of the reapers gleamed in the cornfields; the branches of the apple trees bent down, heavy with red-and-yellow fruit. The hops smelt sweetly, hanging in large clusters; and under the hazel bushes, where hung great bunches of nuts, rested a man and woman – Summer and his quiet consort.

'What wealth!' exclaimed the woman: 'all around a blessing is diffused, everywhere the scene looks homelike and good; and yet – I know not why – I long for peace and rest – I know not how to express it. Now they are already ploughing again in the field. The people want to gain more and more. See, the storks flock together, and follow at a little distance behind the plough – the bird of Egypt that carried us through the air. Do you remember how we came as children to this land of the North? We brought with us flowers, and pleasant sunshine, and green to the woods; the wind has treated them roughly, and they have become dark and brown like the trees of the South, but they do not, like them, bear golden fruit.'

'Do you wish to see the golden fruit?' said Summer: 'then rejoice.'

And he lifted his arm, and the leaves of the forest put on hues of red and gold, and beauteous tints spread over all the woodland. The rose bush gleamed with scarlet hips; the elder-branches hung down with great heavy bunches of dark berries; the wild chestnuts fell ripe from their dark husks; and in the depths of the forests the violets bloomed for the second time.

But the Queen of the Year became more and more silent, and paler and paler.

'It blows cold,' she said, 'and night brings damp mists. I long for the land of my childhood.'

And she saw the storks fly away, one and all; and she stretched forth her hands towards them. She looked up at the nests, which stood empty. In one of them the long-stalked cornflower was growing; in another, the yellow mustard-seed, as if the nest were only there for its protection; and the Sparrows were flying up into the storks' nests.

'Piep! where has the master gone? I suppose he can't bear it when the wind blows, and that therefore he has left the country. I wish him a pleasant journey!'

The forest leaves became more and more yellow, leaf fell down upon leaf, and the stormy winds of autumn howled. The year was now far advanced, and the Queen of the Year reclined upon the fallen yellow leaves, and looked with mild eyes at the gleaming star, and her husband stood by her. A gust swept through the leaves, it fell again, and the Queen was gone, but a butterfly, the last of the season, flew through the cold air.

The wet fogs came, an icy wind blew, and the long dark nights drew on apace. The Ruler of the Year stood there with locks white as snow, but he knew not it was his hair that gleamed so white – he thought snowflakes were falling from the clouds; and soon a thin covering of snow was spread over the fields.

And then the church bells rang for the Christmas-time.

'The bells ring for the new-born,' said the Ruler of the Year. 'Soon the new King and Queen will be born; and I shall go to rest, as my wife has done – to rest in the gleaming star.'

And in the fresh green fir-wood, where the snow lay, stood the Angel of Christmas, and consecrated the young trees that were to adorn his feast.

'May there be joy in the room and under the green boughs,' said the Ruler of the Year. In a few weeks he had become a very old man, white as snow. 'My time for rest draws near, and the young pair of the year shall now receive my crown and sceptre.'

'But the might is still thine,' said the Angel of Christmas; 'the might and not the rest. Let the snow lie warmly upon the young seed. Learn to bear it, that another receives homage while thou yet reignest. Learn to bear being forgotten while thou art yet alive. The hour of thy release will come when spring appears.'

'And when will spring come?' asked Winter.

'It will come when the stork returns.'

And with white locks and snowy beard, cold, bent, and hoary, but strong as the wintry storm and firm as ice, old Winter sat on the snowy drift on the hill, looking towards the south, as the Winter before had sat and gazed. The ice cracked, the snow creaked, the skaters skimmed to and fro on the smooth lakes, ravens and crows stood out well against the white ground, and not a breath of wind stirred. And in the quiet air old Winter clenched his fists, and the ice was fathoms thick between land and land.

Then the Sparrows came again out of the town, and asked, 'Who is that old man yonder?'

And the Raven sat there again, or a son of his, which comes to quite the same thing, and answered them and said, 'It is Winter, the old man of last year. He is not dead, as the almanac says, but he is the guardian of Spring, who is coming.'

'When will spring come?' asked the Sparrows. 'Then we shall have good times and a better rule. The old one was worth nothing.'

And Winter nodded in quiet thought at the leafless forest, where every tree showed the graceful form and bend of its twigs; and during the winter sleep the icy mists of the clouds came down, and the ruler dreamed of his youthful days, and of the time of his manhood; and towards the morning dawn the whole wood was clothed in glittering hoar frost. That was the summer dream of Winter, and the sun scattered the hoar frost from the boughs.

'When will spring come?' asked the Sparrows.

'The spring!' sounded like an echo from the hills on which the snow lay. The sun shone warmer, the snow melted, and the birds twittered, 'Spring is coming!'

And aloft through the air came the first stork, and the second followed him. A lovely child sat on the back of each, and they alighted on the field, kissed the earth, and kissed the old silent man, and he disappeared, shrouded in the cloudy mist. And the story of the year was done.

'That is all very well,' said the Sparrows; 'it is very beautiful too, but it is not according to the almanac, and therefore it is irregular.'

On the Last Day

THE MOST solemn day amongst all the days of our life is the day on which we die; it is the last day, the holy, great day of transformation. Have you really, seriously thought over this mighty, certain, last hour here on earth? There was a man, a strict believer, as he was called, a warrior of the Word, which was for him a law, a zealous servant of a zealous God. Death stood now by his bed, Death with the austere, heavenly countenance.

'The hour has come, you must follow me,' said Death, and with his ice-cold finger he touched his feet, and they turned cold as ice. Death touched his forehead, then his heart, and with that it burst, and the soul followed the Angel of Death. But in the few seconds before, between the consecration from foot to forehead and heart, all that life had brought and created went like great, heavy waves of the sea over the dying man.

In that way one sees with a single glance down into the giddy depths, and comprehends in a flash of thought the immeasurable way; thus one sees with a single glance, as a single whole, the countless myriads of stars, and discerns spheres and worlds in the vastness of space. In such a moment the terrified sinner trembles and has nothing to lean upon; it is as if he sank down into an emptiness without end. But the pious one leans his head on God and gives himself up, like a child, to 'Thy will be done'.

But this dying man had not the child-like mind, he felt he was a man; he did not tremble like the sinner, he knew he was a true believer. He had kept to the forms of religion in all their strictness; millions he knew must go the broad way to destruction; with sword and with fire he could have destroyed their bodies here, as their souls were already destroyed and always would be; his way was now towards Heaven, where Mercy opened the gate for him, the promised mercy.

And the soul went with the Angel of Death, but yet once he looked back to the couch where the earthly form lay in its white shroud, a strange image of its 'I' – and they flew, and they went – it seemed as in a vast hall and yet as in a wood: Nature was pruned, drawn out, tied up and set in rows, made artificial like the old French gardens; and here there was a masquerade.

'That is human life,' said the Angel of Death. All the figures were seen more or less masked; it was not altogether the noblest or mightiest who went dressed in velvet and gold; it was not quite the lowest and most insignificant who went in the cloak of poverty. It was a wonderful masquerade, and it was in particular quite strange to see how all of them concealed something carefully from each other under their clothing; but the one tugged at the other in order that this might be revealed, and then one saw the head of some animal sticking out: with one it was a grinning ape, with another an ugly goat, a clammy snake, or a flabby fish.

It was the animal which we all carry about, the animal which has grown fast in one, and it hopped and sprang and tried to come to light, and everyone held his clothes tight about it, but the others tore them aside and shouted, 'Look! look! there he is! There she is!' and the one laid bare the other's shame.

'And what was the animal in me?' asked the wandering soul, and the Angel of Death pointed to a haughty figure in front of them, around whose head appeared a many-coloured glory, but beside the man's heart the feet of the animal were concealed, the peacock's feet; the glory was only the many-coloured tail of the bird.

And as they wandered on, great birds screamed horridly from the branches of the trees; with distinct human voices they shrieked, 'Thou wanderer with Death, rememberest thou me?' These were all the evil thoughts and desires of his lifetime which shouted to him, 'Rememberest thou me?'

And the soul trembled for a moment, for it knew the voices of the wicked thoughts and desires, which came forward as witnesses.

'In our flesh, in our wicked nature lives nothing good!' said the soul, 'but with me the thoughts did not become deeds, the world has not seen the evil fruit!' and he hastened the more, to get quickly away from the horrid shrieks, but the great black birds hovered round him in circles, and shrieked and shrieked as if they meant to be heard over all the world; and he sprang like the hunted deer, and at every step he struck his feet on sharp flint stones, and they cut his feet and hurt him sorely. 'How come these sharp stones here? They lie like withered leaves over all the earth!'

'That is every incautious word you let fall, which wounded your neighbour's heart far deeper than the stones now wound your feet!'

'I did not think of that,' said the soul.

'Judge not, that ye be not judged!' sounded through the air.

'We have all sinned,' said the soul, and raised itself again. 'I have kept the law and the gospel; I have done what I could, I am not like the others!'

And they stood by the gate of Heaven, and the Angel that was the keeper of the gate asked, 'Who art thou? Tell me thy faith, and show it to me in thy works.'

'I have strictly fulfilled all the commandments. I have humbled myself before the eyes of the world. I have hated and persecuted wicked things and wicked men, those who go the broad way to everlasting destruction, and I would do it yet, with fire and with sword, if I had the power.'

'You are then one of Mohammed's followers?' said the Angel.

'I – never!'

'Who takes the sword shall perish with the sword, says the Son; His faith you have not! You are perhaps one of the sons of Israel, who say with Moses, "An eye for an eye, and a tooth for a tooth!" a son of Israel, whose zealous God is only the God of your people!'

'I am a Christian!'

'I discern it not in your faith and your works. The teaching of Christ is reconciliation, love, and mercy!'

'Mercy!' sounded again through endless space, and the gate of Heaven opened, and the soul floated towards the glory thus revealed. But the light which streamed out was so dazzling, so penetrating, that the soul drew back as before a drawn sword; and the music sounded so soft and touching, that no mortal tongue can declare it, and the soul trembled and bowed down lower and ever lower, but the heavenly clearness forced its way into it, and then it felt and understood what it had never thus felt before, the burden of its pride, its hardness, and its sin. All became so clear within it.

'Whatever good I have done in the world, I did because I could not do otherwise, but the evil – that was of myself!'

And the soul, feeling itself blinded with the clear heavenly light, sank powerless, as it seemed to it, deep down and rolled up in itself, weighed down, unripe for the Kingdom of Heaven; and at the thought of the austere, righteous God, it dared not stammer 'Mercy!'

And then Mercy appeared, the unexpected Mercy. God's Heaven was in all the infinite space, God's love streamed through it in inexhaustible fullness.

'Holy, happy, loving, and eternal be thou, O human soul,' was heard ringing and singing.

And all, all of us, on the last day of our lives, shall, like the soul here, shrink back before the brightness and glory of the Kingdom of Heaven, bow ourselves deeply, humbly sinking down, and yet, borne by His love and His mercy, be held up, hovering in new paths, purified, nobler, and better, coming nearer and nearer to the glory of the light, and, strengthened by Him, be enabled to enter into the everlasting brightness.

'It's Quite True!'

'THAT IS a terrible affair!' said a Hen; and she said it in a quarter of the town where the occurrence had not happened. 'That is a terrible affair in the poultry-house. I cannot sleep alone tonight! It is quite fortunate that there are many of us on the roost together!' And she told a tale at which the feathers of the other birds stood on end, and the cock's comb fell down flat. It's quite true!

But we will begin at the beginning; and that was in a poultry-house in another part of the town. The sun went down, and the fowls jumped up on their perch to roost. There was a Hen, with white feathers and short legs, who laid her right number of eggs, and was a respectable hen in every way; as she flew up on to the roost she pecked herself with her beak, and a little feather fell out.

'There it goes!' said she; 'the more I peck myself the handsomer I grow!' And she said it quite merrily, for she was a joker among the hens, though, as I have said, she was very respectable; and then she went to sleep.

It was dark all around; hen sat by hen, but the one that sat next to the merry Hen did not sleep: she heard and she didn't hear, as one should do in this world if one wishes to live in quiet; but she could not refrain from telling it to her next neighbour.

'Did you hear what was said here just now? I name no names; but here is a hen who wants to peck her feathers out to look well. If I were a cock I should despise her.'

And just above the Hens sat the Owl, with her husband and her little owlets; the family had sharp ears, and they all heard every word that the neighbouring Hen had spoken, and they rolled their eyes, and the Mother-Owl clapped her wings and said, 'Don't listen to it! But I suppose you heard what was said there? I heard it with my own ears, and one must hear much before one's ears fall off. There is one among the fowls who has so completely forgotten what is becoming conduct in a hen that she pulls out all her feathers, and then lets the cock see her.'

'*Prenez garde aux enfants*,' said the Father-Owl. 'That's not fit for the children to hear.'

'I'll tell it to the neighbour owl; she's a very proper owl to associate with.' And she flew away.

'Hoo! hoo! to-whoo!' they both hooted in front of the neighbour's dovecot to the doves within. 'Have you heard it? Have you heard it? Hoo! hoo! there's a hen who has pulled out all her feathers for the sake of the cock. She'll die with cold, if she's not dead already.'

'Coo! coo! Where, where?' cried the Pigeons.

'In the neighbour's poultry-yard. I've as good as seen it myself. It's hardly proper to repeat the story, but it's quite true!'

'Believe it! believe every single word of it!' cooed the Pigeons, and they cooed down into their own poultry-yard. 'There's a hen, and some say that there are two of them, that have plucked out all their feathers, that they may not look like the rest, and that they may attract the cock's attention. That's a bold game, for one may catch cold and die of a fever, and they are both dead.'

'Wake up! wake up!' crowed the Cock, and he flew up on to the fence; his eyes were still very heavy with sleep, but yet he crowed. 'Three hens have died of an unfortunate attachment to a cock. They have plucked out all their feathers. That's a terrible story. I won't keep it to myself; let it travel farther.'

'Let it travel farther!' piped the Bats; and the fowls clucked and the cocks crowed, 'Let it go farther! let it go farther!' And so the story travelled from poultry-yard to poultry-yard, and at last came back to the place from which it had gone forth.

'Five fowls,' it was told, 'have plucked out all their feathers to show which of them had become thinnest out of love to the cock; and then they have pecked each other and fallen down dead, to the shame and disgrace of their families, and to the great loss of the proprietor.'

And the Hen who had lost the little loose feather, of course did not know her own story again; and as she was a very respectable Hen, she said, 'I despise those fowls; but there are many of that sort. One ought not to hush up such a thing, and I shall do what I can that the story may get into the papers, and then it will be spread over all the country, and that will serve those fowls right, and their families too.'

It was put into the newspaper: it was printed; and it's quite true – *that one little feather may swell till it becomes five fowls.*

The Swan's Nest

BETWEEN THE Baltic and the North Sea there lies an old swan's nest, and it is called Denmark, wherein swans are born and have been born whose names shall never die.

In olden times a flock of swans flew over the Alps to the green plains around Milan, where it was delightful to dwell: this flight of swans men called *the Lombards*.

Another flock, with shining plumage and honest eyes, soared southward to Byzantium; the swans established themselves there close by the Emperor's throne, and spread their great white wings over him as shields to protect him. They received the name of *Varangians*.

On the coast of France there sounded a cry of fear, for the blood-stained swans that came from the North with fire under their wings; and the people prayed, 'Heaven deliver us from the wild *Northmen*.'

On the fresh sward of England stood the Danish swan by the open sea-shore, with the crown of three kingdoms on his head; and he stretched out his golden sceptre over the land. The heathens on the Pomeranian coast bent the knee, and the Danish swans came with the banner of the Cross and with the drawn sword.

'That was in the very old times,' you say.

In later days two mighty swans have been seen to fly from the nest. A light shone far through the air, far over the lands of the earth; the swan, with the strong beating of his wings, scattered the twilight mists, and the starry sky was more clearly seen, and it was as if it came nearer to the earth. That was the swan *Tycho Brahé*.

'Yes, at that time,' you say; 'but in our own days?'

We have seen swan after swan soar by in glorious flight. One let his pinions glide over the strings of the golden harp, and it resounded through the North: Norway's mountains seemed to rise higher in the sunlight of former days; there was a rustling among the pine trees and the birches; the gods of the North, the heroes, and the noble women showed themselves in the dark forest depths.

We have seen a swan beat with his wings upon the marble crag, so that it burst, and the forms of beauty imprisoned in the stone stepped out to the sunny day, and men in the lands round about lifted up their heads to behold these mighty forms.

We have seen a third swan spinning the thread of thought that is fastened from country to country round the world, so that the word may fly with lightning speed from land to land.

And our Lord loves the old swan's nest between the Baltic and the Northern Sea. And when the mighty birds come soaring through the air to destroy it, even the callow young stand round in a circle on the margin of the nest, and though their breasts may be struck so that their blood flows, they bear it, and strike with their wings and their claws.

Centuries will pass by, swans will fly forth from the nest, men will see them and hear them in the world, before it shall be said in spirit and in truth, 'This is the last swan – the last song from the swan's nest.'

Good Humour

MY FATHER left me the best inheritance; to wit – good humour. And who was my father? Why, that has nothing to do with the humour. He was lively and stout, round and fat; and his outer and inner man were in direct contradiction to his calling. And pray what was he by profession and calling in civil society? Ah, if this were to be written down and printed in the very beginning of a book, it is probable that many when they read it would lay the book aside, and say, 'It looks so uncomfortable; I don't like anything of that sort.' And yet my father was neither a horse-slaughterer nor an executioner; on the contrary, his office placed him at the head of the most respectable gentry of the town; and he held his place by right, for it was his right place. He had to go first, before the bishop even, and before the Princes of the Blood. He always went first – for he was the driver of the hearse!

There, now it's out! And I will confess that when people saw my father sitting perched up on the omnibus of death, dressed in his long, wide, black cloak, with his black-bordered three-cornered hat on his head – and then his face, exactly as the sun is drawn, round and jocund – it was difficult for them to think of the grave and of sorrow. The face said, 'It doesn't matter; it will be much better than one thinks.'

You see, I have inherited my good humour from him, and also the habit of going often to the churchyard, and that is an agreeable thing to do if it be done with good humour; and then I take in the *Intelligencer*, just as he used to do.

I am not quite young. I have neither wife, nor children, nor a library; but, as aforesaid, I take in the *Intelligencer*, and that's my favourite newspaper, as it was also my father's. It is very useful, and contains everything that a man needs to know – such as who preaches in the church and in the new books; where one can get houses, servants, clothes, and food; who is selling off, and who is going off himself. And

then what a lot of charity, and what a number of innocent, harmless verses are found in it! Advertisements for husbands and wives, and arrangements for meeting – all quite simple and natural. Certainly, one may live merrily and be contentedly buried if one takes in the *Intelligencer*. And then one has, by the end of his life, such a capital store of paper, that he may use it as a soft bed, unless he prefers to rest upon wood-shavings.

The newspaper and my walk to the churchyard were always my most exciting occupations – they were like bathing-places for my good humour.

The newspaper everyone can read for himself. But please come with me to the churchyard; let us wander there where the sun shines and the trees grow green, let us walk among the graves. Each of these is like a closed book, with the back placed uppermost, so that one can only read the title which tells what the book contains, and tells nothing more; but I know something of them. I heard it from my father, or found it out myself. I have it all down in my record that I wrote out for my own use and pleasure: all that lie here, and a few more, too, are chronicled in it.

Now we are in the churchyard.

Here, behind this white railing, where once a rose tree grew – it is gone now, but a little evergreen from the next grave stretches out its green fingers to make a show – there rests a very unhappy man; and yet, when he lived, he was in what they call a good position. He had enough to live upon, and something over; but worldly cares, or, to speak more correctly, his artistic taste, weighed heavily upon him. If in the evening he sat in the theatre to enjoy himself thoroughly, he would be quite put out if the machinist had put too strong a light into one side of the moon, or if the sky-pieces hung down over the scenes when they ought to have hung behind them, or when a palm tree was introduced into a scene representing Amager, or a cactus in a view of the Tyrol, or a beech tree in the far north of Norway. As if that was of any consequence. Is it not quite immaterial? Who would fidget about such a trifle? It's only make-believe, after all, and everyone is expected to be amused. Then sometimes the public applauded too much, and sometimes too little. 'They're like wet wood this evening,' he would say; 'they won't kindle at all!' And then he would look round to see what kind of people they were; and sometimes he would find them laughing at the wrong time, when they ought not to have laughed, and that vexed him; and he fretted, and was an unhappy man, and now he is in his grave.

Here rests a very happy man. That is to say, a very grand man. He was of high birth, and that was lucky for him, for otherwise he would never have been anything worth speaking of; and nature orders all that very wisely, so that it's quite charming when we think of it. He used to go about in a coat embroidered back and front, and appeared in the saloons of society just like one of those costly, pearl-embroidered bell-pulls which have always a good thick, serviceable cord behind them to do the work. He likewise had a good stout cord behind him, in the shape of a substitute, who did his duty, and who still continues to do it behind another embroidered bell-pull. Everything is so nicely managed, it's enough to put one into a good humour.

Here rests – well, it's a very mournful reflection – here rests a man who spent sixty-seven years considering how he should get a good idea. The object of his life was to say a good thing, and at last he felt convinced in his own mind that he had got one, and was so glad of it that he died of pure joy at having caught an idea at last. Nobody derived any benefit from it, for nobody even heard what the good thing was. Now, I can fancy that this same good thing won't let him lie quiet in his grave; for let us suppose that it is a good thing which can only be brought out at breakfast if it is to make an effect, and that he, according to the received opinion concerning ghosts, can only rise and walk at midnight. Why, then the good thing does not suit the time, no one laughs, and the man must carry his good idea down with him again. That is a melancholy grave.

Here rests a remarkably stingy woman. During her lifetime she used to get up at night and mew, so that the neighbours might think she kept a cat – she was so remarkably stingy.

Here lies a lady of good family; in company she always wanted to let her singing be heard, and then she sang 'mi manca la voce', that was the only true thing in her life.

Here is a maiden of another kind. When the canary bird of the heart begins to chirp, reason puts her fingers in her ears. The maiden was going to be married, but – well, it's an everyday story, and we will let the dead rest.

Here sleeps a widow who carried melody in her mouth and gall in her heart. She used to go out for prey in the families round about; and the prey she hunted was her neighbours' faults, and she was an indefatigable hunter.

Here's a family sepulchre. Every member of this family held so firmly to the opinions of the rest, that if all the world, and the newspapers into the bargain, said of a certain thing it is so and so, and the little boy came home from school and said, 'I've learned it thus and thus,' they declared his opinion to be the only true one, because he belonged to the family. And it is an acknowledged fact, that if the yard cock of the family crowed at midnight, they would declare it was morning, though the watchmen and all the clocks in the city were crying out that it was twelve o'clock at night.

The great poet Goethe concludes his 'Faust' with the words 'may be continued'; and our wanderings in the churchyard may be continued too. I come here often. If any of my friends, or my non-friends, go on too fast for me, I go out to my favourite spot, and select a mound, and bury him or her there – bury that person who is yet alive; and there those I bury must stay till they come back as new and improved characters. I inscribe their life and their deeds, looked at in my fashion, in my record; and that's what all people ought to do. They ought not to be vexed when anyone goes on ridiculously, but bury him directly, and maintain their good humour, and keep to the *Intelligencer*, which is usually a book written by people under competent guidance.

When the time comes for me to be bound with my history in the boards of the grave, I hope they will put up as my epitaph, 'A good humoured one.' And that's my story.

A Great Grief

THIS STORY really consists of two parts; the first part might be
left out, but it gives us a few particulars, and these are useful.
We were staying in the country at a gentleman's seat, where it
happened that the master and mistress were absent for a few days. In
the meantime there arrived from the next town a lady; she had a pug-
dog with her, and came, she said, to dispose of shares in her tan-yard.
She had her papers with her, and we advised her to put them in an
envelope, and to write thereon the address of the proprietor of the
estate, 'General War-Commissary Knight,' &c.

She listened to us attentively, seized the pen, paused, and begged us
to repeat the direction slowly. We complied, and she wrote; but in the
midst of the 'General War . . .' she stuck fast, sighed deeply, and said, 'I
am only a woman!' She had set the pug on the floor while she wrote,
and he growled, for he had been taken with her for his amusement and
for the sake of his health; and then one ought not to be set upon the
floor. His outward appearance was characterised by a snub nose and a
very fat back.

'He doesn't bite,' said the lady; 'he has no teeth. He is like one of the
family, faithful and grumpy, but that is because he is teased by my
grandchildren: they play at weddings, and want to give him the part of
the bridesmaid, and that's too much for him, poor old fellow.'

And she delivered her papers, and took Puggie upon her arm. And
this is the first part of the story, which might have been left out.

Puggie died!! That's the second part.

It was about a week afterwards we arrived in the town, and put up at
the inn. Our windows looked into the tanyard, which was divided into
two parts by a partition of planks; in one half were many skins and hides,
raw and tanned. Here was all the apparatus necessary to carry on a
tannery, and it belonged to the widow. Puggie had died in the morning,

and had been buried in this part of the yard: the grandchildren of the widow (that is, of the tanner's widow, for Puggie had never been married) filled up the grave, and it was a beautiful grave – it must have been quite pleasant to lie there.

The grave was bordered with pieces of flowerpots and strewn over with sand; quite at the top they had stuck up half a beer bottle, with the neck upwards, and that was not at all allegorical.

The children danced round the grave, and the eldest of the boys among them, a practical youngster of seven years, made the proposition that there should be an exhibition of Puggie's burial-place for all who lived in the lane; the price of admission was to be a trouser button, for every boy would be sure to have one, and each might also give one for a little girl. This proposal was adopted by acclamation.

And all the children out of the lane – yes, even out of the little lane at the back – flocked to the place, and each gave a button. Many were noticed to go about on that afternoon with only one brace; but then they had seen Puggie's grave, and the sight was worth as much as that.

But in front of the tan-yard, close to the entrance, stood a little girl clothed in rags, very pretty to look at, with curly hair, and eyes so blue and clear that it was a pleasure to look into them. The child said not a word, nor did she cry; but each time the little door was opened she gave a long, long look into the yard. She had not a button – that she knew right well, and therefore she remained standing sorrowfully outside, till all the others had seen the grave and had gone away; then she sat down, held her little brown hands before her eyes, and burst into tears: this girl alone had not seen Puggie's grave. It was a grief as great to her as any grown person can experience.

We saw this from above; and, looked at from above, how many a grief of our own and of others can make us smile! That is the story, and whoever does not understand it may go and purchase a share in the tan-yard of the widow.

Everything in its Right Place

I T WAS more than a hundred years ago.

Behind the wood, by the great lake, stood the old baronial mansion. Round about it lay a deep moat, in which grew reeds and grass. Close by the bridge, near the entrance gate, rose an old willow tree that bent over the reeds.

Up from the hollow lane sounded the clang of horns and the trampling of horses; therefore the little girl who kept the geese hastened to drive her charges away from the bridge, before the hunting company should come galloping by. They drew near with such speed that the girl was obliged to climb up in a hurry, and perch herself on the coping-stone of the bridge, lest she should be ridden down. She was still half a child, and had a pretty light figure, and a gentle expression in her face, with two clear blue eyes. The noble baron took no note of this, but as he galloped past the little goose-herd, he reversed the whip he held in his hand, and in rough sport gave her such a push in the chest with the butt-end that she fell backwards into the ditch.

'Everything in its place!' he cried; 'into the puddle with you!' And he laughed aloud, for this was intended for wit, and the company joined in his mirth: the whole party shouted and clamoured, and the dogs barked their loudest.

Fortunately for herself, the poor girl in falling seized one of the hanging branches of the willow tree, by means of which she kept herself suspended over the muddy water, and as soon as the baron and his company had disappeared through the castle gate, the girl tried to scramble up again; but the bough broke off at the top, and she would have fallen backward among the reeds, if a strong hand from above had not at that moment seized her. It was the hand of a pedlar, who had seen from a short distance what had happened, and who now hurried up to give aid.

'Everything in its right place!' he said, mimicking the gracious baron; and he drew the little maiden up to the firm ground. He would have restored the broken branch to the place from which it had been torn, but 'everything in its place' cannot always be managed, and therefore he stuck the piece in the ground. 'Grow and prosper till you can furnish a good flute for them up yonder,' he said; for he would have liked to play the 'rogue's march' for my lord the baron and my lord's whole family. And then he betook himself to the castle, but not into the ancestral hall, he was too humble for that! He went to the servants' quarters, and the men and maids turned over his stock of goods, and bargained with him; but from above, where the guests were at table, came a sound of roaring and screaming that was intended for song, and indeed they did their best. Loud laughter, mingled with the barking and howling of dogs resounded, for there was feasting and carousing up yonder. Wine and strong old ale foamed in the jugs and glasses, and the dogs sat with their masters and dined with them. They had the pedlar summoned upstairs, but only to make fun of him. The wine had mounted into their heads, and the sense had flown out. They poured ale into a stocking, that the pedlar might drink with them, but that he must drink quickly; that was considered a rare jest, and was a cause of fresh laughter. And then whole farms, with oxen and peasants too, were staked on a card, and lost and won.

'Everything in its right place!' said the pedlar, when he had at last made his escape out of what he called 'Sodom and Gomorrah.' 'The open high road is my right place,' he said; 'I did not feel at all happy there.'

And the little maiden who sat keeping the geese nodded at him from the gate of the field.

And days and weeks went by; and it became manifest that the willow branch which the pedlar had stuck into the ground by the castle moat remained fresh and green, and even brought forth new twigs. The little goose-girl saw that the branch must have taken root, and rejoiced greatly at the circumstance; for this tree, she thought, was now her tree.

The tree certainly came forward well; but everything else belonging

to the castle went very rapidly back, what with feasting and gambling –
for these two are like wheels, upon which no man can stand securely.

Six years had not passed away before the noble lord passed out of the
castle gate, a beggared man, and the mansion was bought by a rich
dealer; and this purchaser was the very man who had once been made
a jest of there, for whom ale had been poured into a stocking; but
honesty and industry are good winds to speed a vessel; and now the
dealer was possessor of the baronial estate. But from that hour no
more card-playing was permitted there.

'That is bad reading,' said he: 'when the Evil One saw a Bible for the
first time, he wanted to put a bad book against it, and invented card-
playing.'

The new proprietor took a wife, and who might that be but the
goose-girl, who had always been faithful and good, and looked as
beautiful and fine in her new clothes as if she had been born a great
lady. And how did all this come about? That is too long a story for our
busy time, but it really happened, and the most important part is to
come.

It was a good thing now to be in the old mansion. The mother
managed the domestic affairs, and the father superintended the estate,
and it seemed as if blessings were streaming down. Where prosperity
is, prosperity is sure to follow. The old house was cleaned and painted,
the ditches were cleared and fruit trees planted. Everything wore a
bright cheerful look, and the floors were as polished as a draught-
board. In the long winter evenings the lady sat at the spinning-wheel
with her maids, and every Sunday evening there was a reading from
the Bible by the Councillor of Justice himself – this title the dealer had
gained, though it was only in his old age. The children grew up – for
children had come – and they received the best education, though all
had not equal abilities, as we find indeed in all families.

In the meantime the willow branch at the castle gate had grown to
be a splendid tree, which stood there free and unpolled. 'That is our
family tree,' the old people said, and the tree was to be honoured and
respected – so they told all the children, even those who had not very
good heads.

And a hundred years rolled by.

It was in our own time. The lake had been converted to moorland, and the old mansion had almost disappeared. A pool of water and the ruins of some walls, this was all that was left of the old baronial castle, with its deep moat; and here stood also a magnificent old willow, with pendent boughs, which seemed to show how beautiful a tree may be if left to itself. The main stem was certainly split from the root to the crown, and the storm had bowed the noble tree a little; but it stood firm for all that, and from every cleft into which wind and weather had carried a portion of earth, grasses and flowers sprang forth: especially near the top, where the great branches parted, a sort of hanging garden had been formed of wild raspberry bush, and even a small quantity of rowan tree had taken root, and stood, slender and graceful, in the midst of the old willow which was mirrored in the dark water when the wind had driven the duck-meat away into a corner of the pool. A field-path led close by the old tree.

High by the forest hill, with a splendid prospect in every direction, stood the new hall, large and magnificent, with panes of glass so clearly transparent, that it looked as if there were no panes there at all. The grand flight of steps that led to the entrance looked like a bower of roses and broad-leaved plants. The lawn was as freshly green as if each separate blade of glass were cleaned morning and evening. In the hall hung costly pictures; silken chairs and sofas stood there, so easy that they looked almost as if they could run by themselves; there were tables of great marble slabs, and books bound in morocco and gold. Yes, truly, people of rank lived here: the baron with his family.

All things here corresponded with each other. The motto was still 'Everything in its right place'; and therefore all the pictures which had been put up in the old house for honour and glory, hung now in the passage that led to the servants' hall: they were considered as old lumber, and especially two old portraits, one representing a man in a pink coat and powdered wig, the other a lady with powdered hair and holding a rose in her hand, and each surrounded with a wreath of willow leaves. These two pictures were pierced with many holes, because the little barons were in the habit of setting up the old people as a mark for their crossbows. The pictures represented the Councillor of Justice and his lady, the founders of the present family.

'But they did not properly belong to our family,' said one of the little barons. 'He was a dealer, and she had kept the geese. They were not like papa and mamma.'

The pictures were pronounced to be worthless; and as the motto was 'Everything in its right place', the great-grandmother and great-grandfather were sent into the passage that led to the servants' hall.

The son of the neighbouring clergyman was tutor in the great house. One day he was out walking with his pupils, the little barons and their eldest sister, who had just been confirmed; they came along the field-path past the old willow, and as they walked on, the young lady bound a wreath of field flowers. 'Everything in its right place,' and the flowers formed a pretty whole. At the same time she heard every word that was spoken, and she liked to hear the clergyman's son talk of the powers of nature and of the great men and women in history. She had a good-hearted disposition, with true nobility of thought and soul, and a heart full of love for all that God hath created.

The party came to a halt at the old willow tree. The youngest baron insisted on having such a flute cut for him from it as he had had made of other willows. Accordingly the tutor broke off a branch.

'Oh, don't do that!' cried the young baroness; but it was done already. 'That is our famous old tree,' she continued, 'and I love it dearly. They laugh at me at home for this, but I don't mind. There is a story attached to this tree.'

And she told what we all know about the tree, about the old mansion, the pedlar and the goose-girl, who had met for the first time in this spot, and had afterwards become the founders of the noble family to which the young barons belonged.

'They would not be ennobled, the good old folks!' she said. 'They kept to the motto, "Everything in its right place"; and accordingly they thought it would be out of place for them to purchase a title with money. My grandfather, the first baron, was their son. He is said to have been a very learned man, very popular with princes and princesses, and a frequent guest at the court festivals. The others at home love him best; but, I don't know how, there seems to me something about that first pair that draws my heart towards them. How comfortable, how patriarchal it must have been in the old house, where the mistress sat at the spinning-wheel among her maids, and the old master read aloud from the Bible!'

'They were charming, sensible people,' said the clergyman's son.

And with this the conversation naturally fell upon nobles and citizens. The young man scarcely seemed to belong to the citizen class, so well did he speak of things belonging to nobility. He said, 'It is a great thing to belong to a family that has distinguished itself, and thus to have, as it were, in one's blood, a spur that urges one on to make progress in all that is good. It is delightful to have a name that serves as a card of admission into the highest circles. Nobility means that which is noble: it is a coin that has received a stamp to indicate what it is worth. It is the fallacy of the time, and many poets have frequently maintained this fallacy, that nobility of birth is accompanied by foolishness, and that the lower you go among the poor, the more does everything around you shine. But that is not my view, for I consider it entirely false. In the higher classes many beautiful and kindly traits are found. My mother told me one of this kind, and I could tell you many others.

'My mother was on a visit to a great family in town. My grandmother, I think, had been nurse to the lady there. The great nobleman and my mother were alone in the room, when the former noticed that an old woman came limping on crutches into the courtyard. Indeed, she was accustomed to come every Sunday, and carry away a gift with her. "Ah, there is the poor old lady," said the nobleman: "walking is a great toil to her;" and before my mother understood what he meant, he had gone out of the room and run down the stairs, to save the old woman the toilsome walk, by carrying to her the gift she had come to receive.

'Now, that was only a small circumstance, but, like the widow's two mites in the Scriptures, it has a sound that finds an echo in the depths of the heart in human nature; and these are the things the poet should show and point out; especially in these times should he sing of it, for that does good, and pacifies and unites men. But where a bit of mortality, because it has a genealogical tree and a coat of arms, rears up like an Arab horse, and prances in the street, and says in the room, "People from the street have been here," when a commoner has been present, *that* is nobility in decay and turned into a mere mask, a mask of the kind that Thespis created; and people are glad when such a one is made a subject of satire.'

This was the speech of the clergyman's son. It was certainly rather long, but then the flute was finished while he made it.

At the castle there was a great company. Many guests came from the neighbourhood and from the capital. Many ladies, some tastefully dressed and others dressed without taste, were there, and the great hall was quite full of people. The clergymen from the neighbourhood stood respectfully congregated in a corner, which made it look almost as if it was a burial. But it was not so, for this was a party of pleasure, only that the pleasure had not yet begun.

A great concert was to be performed, and consequently the little baron had brought in his willow flute; but he could not get a note out of it, nor could his papa, and therefore the flute was worth nothing. There was instrumental music and song, both of the kind that delight the performers most – quite charming!

'You are a performer?' said a fine gentleman – his father's son and nothing else – to the tutor. 'You play the flute and make it too – it is genius which commands, and should have the place of honour! Oh yes! I advance with the times, as everyone is obliged to do. Oh, you will enchant us with the little instrument, will you not?'

And with these words he handed to the clergyman's son the flute cut from the willow tree by the pool, and announced aloud that the tutor was about to perform a solo on that instrument.

Now, they only wanted to make fun of him, that was easily seen; and therefore the tutor would not play, though indeed he could do so very well; but they crowded round him and importuned him so strongly, that at last he took the flute and put it to his lips.

That was a wonderful flute! A sound, as sustained as that which is emitted by the whistle of a steam engine, and much stronger, echoed far over courtyard, garden, and wood, miles away into the country;

and simultaneously with the tone came a rushing wind that roared, 'Everything in its right place!' And papa flew as if carried by the wind straight out of the hall and into the shepherd's cot; and the shepherd flew, not into the hall, for there he could not come – no, but into the room of the servants, among the smart lackeys who strutted about there in silk stockings; and the proud servants were struck motionless with horror at the thought that such a personage dared to sit down to table with them.

But in the hall the young baroness flew up to the place of honour at the top of the table, where she was worthy to sit; and the young clergyman's son had a seat next to her; and there the two sat as if they were a newly-married pair. An old count of one of the most ancient families in the country remained untouched in his place of honour; for the flute was just, as men ought to be. The witty young gentleman, the son of his father and nothing else, who had been the cause of the flute-playing, flew head-over-heels into the poultry house – but not alone.

For a whole mile round about the sounds of the flute were heard, and singular events took place. A rich merchant's family, driving along in a coach and four, was blown quite out of the carriage, and could not even find a place on the footboard at the back. Two rich peasants who in our times had grown too high for their cornfields, were tumbled into the ditch. It was a dangerous flute, that: luckily, it burst at the first note; and that was a good thing, for then it was put back into the owner's pocket. 'Everything in its right place.'

The day afterwards not a word was said about this marvellous event; and thence has come the expression, 'pocketing the flute.' Everything was in its usual order, only that the two old portraits of the dealer and the goose-girl hung on the wall in the banqueting-hall. They had been blown up there, and as one of the real connoisseurs said they had been painted by a master's hand, they remained where they were, and were restored. One did not know before that they were any good, and how should it have been known? Now they hung in the place of honour: 'Everything in its right place.'

And to that it will come hereafter; for *hereafter* is long – longer than this story.

The Goblin and the Huckster

THERE WAS once a regular student: he lived in a garret, and nothing at all belonged to him; but there was also once a regular huckster: he lived on the ground floor, and the whole house was his; and the Goblin lodged with him, for here, every Christmas-eve, there was a dish of porridge, with a great piece of butter floating in the middle. The huckster could give that, and consequently the Goblin stuck to the huckster's shop, and that was very interesting.

One evening the student came through the back door to buy candles and cheese for himself. He had no one to send, and that's why he came himself. He procured what he wanted and paid for it, and the huckster and his wife both nodded a 'good-evening' to him; and the woman was one who could do more than merely nod – she had an immense power of tongue! And the student nodded too, and then suddenly stood still, reading the sheet of paper in which the cheese had been wrapped. It was a leaf torn out of an old book, a book that ought not to have been torn up, a book that was full of poetry.

'There lies more of it,' said the huckster: 'I gave an old woman a few coffee beans for it; give me three pence and you shall have the remainder.'

'Thanks,' said the student, 'give me the book instead of the cheese: I can eat my bread and butter without cheese. It would be a sin to tear the book up entirely. You are a capital man, a practical man, but you understand no more about poetry than does that cask yonder.'

Now, that was an impolite speech, especially towards the cask; but the huckster laughed and the student laughed, for it was only said in fun. But the Goblin was angry that anyone should dare to say such things to a huckster who lived in his own house and sold the best butter.

When it was night, and the shop was closed and all were in bed except the student, the Goblin came forth, went into the bedroom, and took away the good lady's tongue; for she did not want that while she was asleep; and whenever he put this tongue upon any object in the room, the said object acquired speech and language, and could express its thoughts and feelings as well as the lady herself could have done; but only one object could use it at a time, and that was a good thing, otherwise they would have interrupted each other.

And the Goblin laid the tongue upon the Cask in which the old newspapers were lying.

'Is it true,' he asked, 'that you don't know what poetry means?'

'Of course I know it,' replied the Cask: 'poetry is something that always stands at the foot of a column in the newspapers, and is sometimes cut out. I dare swear I have more of it in me than the student, and I'm only a poor tub compared to the huckster.'

Then the Goblin put the tongue upon the coffee-mill, and, mercy! how it began to go! And he put it upon the buttercask, and on the cashbox: they were all of the wastepaper Cask's opinion, and the opinion of the majority must be respected.

'Now I shall tell it to the student!'

And with these words the Goblin went quite quietly up the back stairs to the garret, where the student lived. The student had still a candle burning, and the Goblin peeped through the keyhole, and saw that he was reading in the torn book from downstairs.

But how light it was in his room! Out of the book shot a clear beam, expanding into a thick stem, and into a mighty tree, which grew upward and spread its branches far over the student. Each leaf was fresh, and every blossom was a beautiful girl's head, some with dark sparkling eyes, others with wonderfully clear blue orbs; every fruit was a gleaming star, and there was a glorious sound of song in the student's room.

Never had the little Goblin imagined such splendour, far less had he ever seen or heard anything like it. He stood still on tiptoe, and peeped in till the light went out in the student's garret. Probably the student blew it out, and went to bed; but the little Goblin remained standing there nevertheless, for the music still sounded on, soft and beautiful – a splendid cradle song for the student who had lain down to rest.

'This is an incomparable place,' said the Goblin: 'I never expected such a thing! I should like to stay here with the student.'

And then he thought it over – and thought sensibly; then he sighed, 'The student has no porridge!' And then he went down again to the huckster's shop: and it was a very good thing that he got down there again at last, for the Cask had almost worn out the good woman's tongue, for it had spoken out at one side everything that was contained in it, and was just about turning itself over, to give it out from the other side also, when the Goblin came in, and restored the tongue to its owner. But from that time forth the whole shop, from the cashbox down to the firewood, took its tone from the Cask, and paid him such respect, and thought so much of him, that when the huckster afterwards read the critical articles on theatricals and art in the newspaper, they were persuaded the information came from the Cask itself.

But the Goblin could no longer sit quietly and contentedly listening to all the wisdom down there: as soon as the light glimmered from the garret in the evening, he felt as if the rays were strong cables drawing him up, and he was obliged to go and peep through the keyhole; and there a feeling of greatness rolled around him, such as we feel beside the ever-heaving sea when the storm rushes over it, and he burst into tears! He did not know himself why he was weeping, but a peculiar feeling of pleasure mingled with his tears. How wonderfully glorious it must be to sit with the student under the same tree! But that might not be – he was obliged to be content with the view through the keyhole, and to be glad of that. There he stood on the cold landing-place, with the autumn wind blowing down from the loft-hole: it was cold, very cold; but the little mannikin only felt that when the light in the room was extinguished and the tones in the tree died away. Ha! then he shivered, and crept down again to his warm corner, where it was homely and comfortable.

And when Christmas came, and brought with it the porridge and the great lump of butter, why, then he thought the huckster the better man.

But in the middle of the night the Goblin was awakened by a terrible tumult and knocking against the window-shutters. People rapped noisily without, and the watchman blew his horn, for a great fire had broken out – the whole street was full of smoke and flame. Was it in the house itself or at a neighbour's? Where was it? Terror seized on all. The huckster's wife was so bewildered that she took her gold earrings out of her ears and put them in her pocket, that at any rate she might save something; the huckster ran up for his share-papers, and the maid for her black silk mantilla, for she had found means to purchase one. Each wanted to save the best thing they possessed; the Goblin wanted to do the same thing, and in a few leaps he was up the stairs and into the room of the student, who stood quite quietly at the open window, looking at the conflagration that was raging in the house of the neighbour opposite. The Goblin seized upon the wonderful book which lay upon the table, popped it into his red cap, and held the cap tight with both hands. The best treasure of the house was saved; and now he ran up and away, quite on to the roof of the house, on to the chimney. There he sat, illuminated by the flames of the burning house opposite, both hands pressed tightly over his cap, in which the treasure lay; and now he knew the real feelings of his heart, and knew to whom it really belonged. But when the fire was extinguished, and the Goblin could think calmly again, why, then . . .

'I must divide myself between the two,' he said; 'I can't quite give up the huckster, because of the porridge!'

Now, that was spoken quite like a human creature. We all of us visit the huckster for the sake of the porridge.

In a Thousand Years

YES, IN A thousand years people will fly on the wings of steam through the air, over the ocean! The young inhabitants of America will become visitors of old Europe. They will come over to see the monuments and the great cities, which will then be in ruins, just as we in our time make pilgrimages to the mouldering splendours of Southern Asia. In a thousand years they will come!

The Thames, the Danube, and the Rhine still roll their course, Mont Blanc stands firm with its snow-capped summit, and the Northern Lights gleam over the lands of the North; but generation after generation has become dust, whole rows of the mighty of the moment are forgotten, like those who already slumber under the grave-mound on which the rich trader whose ground it is has built a bench, on which he can sit and look out across his waving cornfields.

'To Europe!' cry the young sons of America; 'to the land of our ancestors, the glorious land of memories and fancy – to Europe!'

The ship of the air comes. It is crowded with passengers, for the transit is quicker than by sea. The electromagnetic wire under the ocean has already telegraphed the number of the aerial caravan. Europe is in sight: it is the coast of Ireland that they see, but the passengers are still asleep; they will not be called till they are exactly over England. There they will first step on European shore, in the land of Shakespeare as the educated call it; in the land of politics, the land of machinery, as it is called by others.

Here they stay a whole day. That is all the time the busy race can devote to the whole of England and Scotland. Then the journey is continued through the tunnel under the English Channel, to France, the land of Charlemagne and Napoleon. Molière is named: the learned men talk of a classical and romantic school of remote antiquity: there is rejoicing and shouting for the names of heroes, poets, and men of science, whom our time does not know, but who will be born after our time in Paris, the crater of Europe.

The air steamboat flies over the country whence Columbus went forth, where Cortez was born, and where Calderon sang dramas in sounding verse. Beautiful black-eyed women live still in the blooming valleys, and ancient songs speak of the Cid and the Alhambra.

Then through the air, over the sea, to Italy, where once lay old, everlasting Rome. It has vanished! The Campagna lies desert: a single ruined wall is shown as the remains of St Peter's, but there is a doubt if this ruin be genuine.

Next to Greece, to sleep a night in the grand hotel at the top of Mount Olympus, to say that they have been there; and the journey is continued to the Bosphorus, to rest there a few hours, and see the place where Byzantium lay; and where the legend tells that the harem stood in the time of the Turks, poor fishermen are now spreading their nets.

Over the remains of mighty cities on the broad Danube, cities which we in our time know not, the travellers pass; but here and there, on the rich sites of those that time shall bring forth, the caravan sometimes descends, and departs thence again.

Down below lies Germany, that was once covered with a close net of railways and canals, the region where Luther spoke, where Goethe sang, and Mozart once held the sceptre of harmony. Great names shone there, in science and in art, names that are unknown to us. One day devoted to seeing Germany, and one for the North, the country of Oersted and Linnaeus, and for Norway, the land of the old heroes and the young Normans. Iceland is visited on the journey home: Geyser boils no longer, Hecla is an extinct volcano, but the rocky island is still fixed in the midst of the foaming sea, a continual monument of legend and poetry.

'There is really a great deal to be seen in Europe,' says the young American, 'and we have seen it in a week, according to the directions of the great traveller' (and here he mentions the name of one of his contemporaries) 'in his celebrated work, "How to See all Europe in a Week."'

Under the Willow Tree

THE REGION round the little town of Kjöge is very bleak and bare. The town certainly lies by the sea-shore, which is always beautiful, but just there it might be more beautiful than it is: all around are flat fields, and it is a long way to the forest. But when one is really at home in a place, one always finds something beautiful, and something that one longs for in the most charming spot in the world that is strange to us. We confess that, by the utmost boundary of the little town, where some humble gardens skirt the streamlet that falls into the sea, it must be very pretty in summer; and this was the opinion of the two children from neighbouring houses, who were playing there, and forcing their way through the gooseberry bushes to get to one another. In one of the gardens stood an elder tree, and in the other an old willow, and under the latter especially the children were very fond of playing: they were allowed to play there, though, indeed, the tree stood close beside the stream, and they might easily have fallen into the water. But the eye of God watches over the little ones; if it did not, they would be badly off. And, moreover, they were very careful with respect to the water; in fact, the boy was so much afraid of it, that they could not lure him into the sea in summer, when the other children were splashing about in the waves. Accordingly, he was famously jeered and mocked at, and had to bear the jeering and mockery as best he could. But once Joanna, the neighbour's little girl, dreamed she was sailing in a boat, and Knud waded out to join her till the water rose, first to his neck, and afterwards closed right over his head. From the time when little Knud heard of this dream, he would no longer stand anyone saying that he was afraid of the water, but simply referred them to Joanna's dream; that was his pride, but into the water he did not go.

Their parents, who were poor people, often visited each other, and

Knud and Joanna played in the gardens and on the high road, where a row of willows had been planted beside the ditch; these trees, with their polled tops, certainly did not look beautiful, but they were not put there for ornament, but for use. The old willow tree in the garden was much handsomer, and therefore the children were fond of sitting under it. In the town itself there was a great market-place, and at the time of the fair this place was covered with whole streets of tents and booths, containing silk ribbons, boots, and everything that a person could wish for. There was great crowding, and generally the weather was rainy, and then one noticed the odour of the peasants' coats, but also the fragrance of the honey-cakes and the gingerbread, of which there was a booth quite full; and the best of it was, that the man who kept this booth came every year to lodge during the fair-time in the dwelling of little Knud's father. Consequently there came a present of a bit of gingerbread every now and then, and of course Joanna received her share of the gift. But perhaps the most charming thing of all was that the gingerbread dealer knew all sorts of tales, and could even relate histories about his own gingerbread cakes; and one evening, in particular, he told a story about them which made such a deep impression on the children that they never forgot it; and for that reason it is perhaps advisable that we should hear it too, more especially as the story is not long.

'On the shop-board,' he said, 'lay two gingerbread cakes, one in the shape of a man with a hat, the other of a maiden without a bonnet, but with a piece of gold-leaf on her head; both their faces were on the side that was uppermost, for they were to be looked at on that side, and not on the other; and, indeed, no one should be viewed from the wrong side. On the left side the man wore a bitter almond – that was his heart; but the maiden, on the other hand, was honey-cake all over. They were placed as samples on the shop-board, and remaining there a long time, at last they fell in love with one another, but neither told the other, as they should have done if they had expected anything to come of it.

' "He is a man, and therefore he must speak first," she thought; but she felt quite contented, for she knew her love was returned.

'His thoughts were far more extravagant, as is always the case with a

man. He dreamed that he was a real street boy, that he had four pennies of his own, and that he purchased the maiden and ate her up. So they lay on the shop-board for days and weeks, and grew dry and hard, but the thoughts of the maiden became ever more gentle and maidenly.

' "It is enough for me that I have lain on the same table with him," she said, and – crack! – she broke in two.

' "If she had only known of my love, she would have kept together a little longer," he thought.

'And that is the story, and here they are, both of them,' said the baker in conclusion. 'They are remarkable for their curious history, and for their silent love, which never came to anything. And there they are for you!' and, so saying, he gave Joanna the man who was yet entire, and Knud got the broken maiden; but the children had been so much impressed by the story that they could not summon courage to eat up the lovers.

On the following day they went out with them to the churchyard, and sat down by the church wall, which is covered, winter and summer, with the most luxuriant ivy as with a rich carpet. Here they stood the two cake figures up in the sunshine among the green leaves, and told the story to a group of other children; they told them of the silent love which led to nothing. It was called *love* because the story was so lovely, on that they all agreed. But when they turned to look again at the gingerbread pair, a big boy, out of mischief, had eaten up the broken maiden. The children cried about this, and afterwards – probably that the poor lover might not be left in the world lonely and desolate – they ate him up too; but they never forgot the story.

The children were always together by the elder tree and under the willow, and the little girl sang the most beautiful songs with a voice that was clear as a bell. Knud, on the other hand, had not a note of music in him, but he knew the words of the songs, and that is always something. The people of Kjöge, even to the rich wife of the ironmonger, stood still and listened when Joanna sang. 'She has a very sweet voice, that little girl,' she said.

Those were glorious days, but they could not last for ever. The neighbours were neighbours no longer. The little maiden's mother was dead, and the father intended to marry again, in the capital, where he had been promised a living as a messenger, which was to be a very lucrative office. And the neighbours separated regretfully, the children weeping heartily, but the parents promised that they should at least write to one another once a year.

And Knud was bound apprentice to a shoemaker, for the big boy could not be allowed to run wild any longer; and moreover he was confirmed.

Ah, how gladly on that day of celebration would he have been in Copenhagen, with little Joanna! but he remained in Kjöge, and had never yet been to Copenhagen, though the little town is only five Danish miles distant from the capital; but far across the bay, when the sky was clear, Knud had seen the towers in the distance, and on the day of his confirmation he could distinctly see the golden cross on the principal church glittering in the sun.

Ah, how often his thoughts were with Joanna! Did she think of him? Yes. Towards Christmas there came a letter from her father to the parents of Knud, to say that they were getting on very well in Copenhagen, and especially might Joanna look forward to a brilliant future on the strength of her fine voice. She had been engaged in the theatre in which people sing, and was already earning some money, out of which she sent her dear neighbours of Kjöge a dollar for the merry Christmas-eve. They were to drink her health, she had herself added in a postscript; and in the same postscript there stood further, 'A kind greeting to Knud.'

The whole family wept; and yet all this was very pleasant – those were joyful tears that they shed. Knud's thoughts had been occupied every day with Joanna; and now he knew that she also thought of him; and the nearer the time came when his apprenticeship would be over, the more clearly did it appear to him that he was very fond of Joanna, and that she must be his wife; and when he thought of this, a smile came upon his lips, and he drew the thread twice as fast as before, and pressed his foot hard against the knee-strap. He ran the awl far into his finger, but he did not care for that. He determined not to play the dumb lover, as the two gingerbread cakes had done: the story should teach him a lesson.

And now he was a journeyman, and his knapsack was packed ready for his journey: at length, for the first time in his life, he was to go to Copenhagen, where a master was already waiting for him. How glad Joanna would be! She was now seventeen years old, and he nineteen.

Already in Kjöge he had wanted to buy a gold ring for her; but he recollected that such things were to be had far better in Copenhagen. And now he took leave of his parents, and on a rainy day, late in the autumn, went forth on foot out of the town of his birth. The leaves were falling down from the trees, and he arrived at his new master's in

Copenhagen wet to the skin. Next Sunday he was to pay a visit to Joanna's father. The new journeyman's clothes were brought forth, and the new hat from Kjöge was put on, which became Knud very well, for till this time he had only worn a cap. And he found the house he sought, and mounted flight after flight of stairs until he became almost giddy. It was terrible to him to see how people lived piled up one over the other in the dreadful city.

Everything in the room had a prosperous look, and Joanna's father received him very kindly. To the new wife he was a stranger, but she shook hands with him, and gave him some coffee.

'Joanna will be glad to see you,' said the father: 'you have grown quite a nice young man. You shall see her presently. She is a girl who rejoices my heart, and, please God, she will rejoice it yet more. She has her own room now, and pays us rent for it.'

And the father knocked quite politely at the door, as if he were a visitor, and then they went in.

But how pretty everything was in that room! such an apartment was certainly not to be found in all Kjöge: the Queen herself could not be more charmingly lodged. There were carpets, there were window curtains quite down to the floor, and around were flowers and pictures, and a mirror into which there was almost danger that a visitor might step, for it was as large as a door; and there was even a velvet chair.

Knud saw all this at a glance; and yet he saw nothing but Joanna. She was a grown maiden, quite different from what Knud had fancied her, and much more beautiful. In all Kjöge there was not a girl like her. How graceful she was, and with what an odd unfamiliar glance she looked at Knud! But that was only for a moment, and then she rushed towards him as if she would have kissed him. She did not really do so, but she came very near it. Yes, she was certainly rejoiced at the arrival of the friend of her youth! The tears were actually in her eyes; and she had much to say, and many questions to put concerning all, from Knud's parents down to the elder tree and the willow, which she called Elder-mother and Willow-father, as if they had been human beings; and indeed they might pass as such, just as well as the gingerbread cakes; and of these she spoke too, and of their silent love, and how they had lain upon the shop-board and split in two – and then she laughed very heartily; but the blood mounted into Knud's cheeks, and his heart beat thick and fast. No, she had not grown proud at all. And it was through her – he noticed it well – that her parents invited him to stay the whole evening with them; and she poured out the tea and gave him a cup with her own hands; and afterwards she took a book and read aloud to them, and it seemed to Knud that what she read was all about himself and his love, for it matched so well with his thoughts; and then she sang a simple song, but through her singing, it became like a history, and seemed to be the outpouring of her very heart. Yes, certainly she was fond of Knud. The tears coursed down his cheeks – he could not restrain them, nor could he speak a single word: he thought himself very stupid; and yet she pressed his hand, and said.

'You have a good heart, Knud – remain always as you are now.'

That was an evening of matchless delight to Knud; to sleep after it was impossible, and accordingly Knud did not sleep.

At parting, Joanna's father had said, 'Now, you won't forget us altogether! Don't let the whole winter go by without once coming to see us again;' and therefore he could very well go again the next Sunday, and resolved to do so. But every evening when working hours were over – and they worked by candle-light there – Knud went out through the town: he went into the street in which Joanna lived, and looked up at her window; it was almost always lit up, and one evening he could see the shadow of her face quite plainly on the curtain – and that was a grand evening for him. His master's wife did not like his gallivanting abroad every evening, as she expressed it, and she shook her head; but the master only smiled.

'He is only a young fellow,' he said.

But Knud thought to himself: 'On Sunday I shall see her, and I shall tell her how completely she reigns in my thoughts, and that she must be my little wife. I know I am only a poor journeyman shoemaker, but I shall work and strive – yes, I shall tell her so. Nothing comes of silent love: I have learned that from the cakes.'

And Sunday came round, and Knud sallied forth; but, unluckily, they were all going out, and were obliged to tell him so. Joanna pressed his hand, and said, 'Have you ever been to the theatre? You must go once. I shall sing on Wednesday, and if you have time on that evening, I will send you a ticket; my father knows where your master lives.'

How kind that was of her! And on Wednesday at noon he received a sealed paper, with no words written in it; but the ticket was there, and in the evening Knud went to the theatre for the first time in his life. And what did he see? He saw Joanna, and how charming and how beautiful she looked! She was certainly married to a stranger, but that was all in the play – something that was only make-believe, as Knud knew very well. Otherwise, he thought, she would never have had the heart to send him a ticket that he might go and see it. And all the people shouted and applauded, and Knud cried out 'hurrah!'

Even the King smiled at Joanna, and seemed to delight in her. Ah, how small Knud felt! but then he loved her so dearly, and thought that she loved him too; but it was for the man to speak the first word, as the gingerbread maiden had thought; and there was a great deal for him in that story.

So soon as Sunday came, he went again. He felt as if he were going into a church. Joanna was alone, and received him – it could not have happened more fortunately.

'It is well that you are come,' she said. 'I had an idea of sending my father to you, only I felt a presentiment that you would be here this evening; for I must tell you that I start for France on Friday: I must do that so that I may really come to be something.'

It seemed to Knud as if the whole room turned round and as if his heart would burst; no tear rose to his eyes, but still it was easy to see how sorrowful he was.

Joanna saw it, and came near to crying.

'You honest, faithful soul!' she exclaimed.

And these words of hers loosened Knud's tongue. He told her how constantly he loved her, and that she must become his wife; and as he said this, he saw Joanna turn pale. She let his hand fall, and answered, seriously and mournfully, 'Knud, do not make yourself and me unhappy. I shall always be a good sister to you, one in whom you may trust, but I shall never be anything more.'

And she drew her white hand over his hot forehead.

'Heaven gives us strength for much,' she said, 'if we only endeavour to do our best.'

At that moment the stepmother came into the room; and Joanna said quickly, 'Knud is quite inconsolable because I am going away. Come, be a man,' she continued, and laid her hand upon his shoulder; and it seemed as if they had been talking of the journey, and nothing else. 'You are a child,' she added; 'but now you must be good and reasonable, as you used to be under the willow tree, when we were both children.'

But Knud felt as if a piece had gone out of the world, and his thoughts were like a loose thread fluttering to and fro in the wind. He stayed, though he could not remember if she had asked him to stay; and they were kind and good, and Joanna poured out his tea for him, and sang to him. It had not the old tone, and yet it was wonderfully beautiful, and made his heart feel ready to burst. And then they parted. Knud did not offer her his hand, but she seized it, and said, 'Surely you will shake hands with your sister at parting, old playfellow!'

And she smiled through the tears that were rolling over her cheeks, and she repeated the word 'brother' – as if that would help much! – and thus they parted.

She sailed to France, and Knud wandered about the muddy streets of Copenhagen. The other journeymen in the workshop asked him why he went about so gloomily, and told him he should go and amuse himself with them, for he was a young fellow.

And they went with him to the dancing-rooms. He saw many handsome girls there, but certainly not one like Joanna; and here, where he thought to forget her, she stood more vividly than ever in his thoughts. 'Heaven gives us strength for a great deal, if we only try to do our best,' she had said; and holy thoughts came into his mind, and he folded his hands. The violins played, and the girls danced round in a circle; and he was quite startled, for it seemed to him as if he were in a place to which he ought not to have brought Joanna – for she was there with him, in his heart; and accordingly he went out. He ran through the streets, and passed by the house where she had dwelt; it was dark there, dark everywhere, and empty, and lonely. The world went its way, and Knud went his.

The winter came, and the streams were frozen. Everything seemed to be preparing for a burial. But when spring returned, and the first steamer was to start, a longing seized him to go away, far, far into the world, but not too near to France. So he packed his knapsack, and wandered far into the German land, from city to city, without rest or peace; and it was not till he came to the glorious old city of Nuremberg that he could master his restless spirit; and in Nuremberg, therefore, he decided to remain.

Nuremberg is a wonderful old city, and looks as if it were cut out of an old picture-book. The streets lie just as they please. The houses do not like standing in regular ranks. Gables with little towers, arabesques, and pillars, start out over the pathway, and from the strange peaked roofs water-spouts, formed like dragons or great slim dogs, extend far over the street.

Here in the market-place stood Knud, with his knapsack on his back. He stood by one of the old fountains that are adorned with splendid bronze figures, scriptural and historical, rising up between the gushing jets of water. A pretty servant-maid was just filling her pails, and she gave Knud a refreshing draught; and as her hand was full of roses, she gave him one of the flowers, and he accepted it as a good omen.

From the neighbouring church the strains of the organ were sounding: they seemed to him as familiar as the tones of the organ at home at Kjöge; and he went into the great cathedral. The sunlight streamed in through the stained glass windows, between the lofty slender pillars. His spirit became prayerful, and peace returned to his soul.

And he sought and found a good master in Nuremberg, with whom he stayed, and learned the language.

The old moat round the town has been converted into a number of little kitchen gardens; but the high walls are standing yet, with their heavy towers. The ropemaker twists his ropes on a gallery or walk built of wood, inside the town wall, where elder bushes grow out of the clefts and cracks, spreading their green twigs over the little low houses that stand below; and in one of these dwelt the master with whom Knud worked; and over the little garret window where he slept the elder waved its branches.

Here he lived through a summer and a winter; but when the spring came again he could bear it no longer. The elder was in blossom, and its fragrance reminded him so of home, that he fancied himself back in the garden at Kjöge; and therefore Knud went away from his master, and dwelt with another, farther in the town, over whose house no elder bush grew.

His workshop was quite close to one of the old stone bridges, by a low water-mill, that rushed and foamed always. Without, rolled the roaring stream, hemmed in by houses, whose old decayed gables looked ready to topple down into the water. No elder grew here – there was not even a flowerpot with its little green plant; but just opposite the workshop stood a great old willow tree, that seemed to cling fast to the house, for fear of being carried away by the water, and which stretched forth its branches over the river, just as the willow at Kjöge spread its arms across the streamlet by the gardens there.

Yes, he had certainly gone from the 'Elder-mother' to the 'Willow-father'. The tree here had something, especially on moonlight evenings, that went straight to his heart – and that something was not in the moonlight, but in the old tree itself.

Nevertheless, he could not remain. Why not? Ask the willow tree, ask the blooming elder! And therefore he bade farewell to his master in Nuremberg, and journeyed onward.

To no one did he speak of Joanna – in his secret heart he hid his sorrow; and he thought of the deep meaning in the story of the two cakes. Now he understood why the man had a bitter almond in his breast – he himself felt the bitterness of it; and Joanna, who was always so gentle and kind, was typified by the honey-cake. The strap of his knapsack seemed so tight across his chest that he could scarcely breathe; he loosened it, but was not relieved. He saw but half the world around him; the other half he carried about him and within himself. And thus it stood with him.

Not till he came in sight of the high mountains did the world appear freer to him; and now his thoughts were turned without, and tears came into his eyes.

The Alps appeared to him as the folded wings of the earth; how if they were to unfold themselves, and display their variegated pictures of black woods, foaming waters, clouds, and masses of snow? At the last day, he thought, the world will lift up its great wings, and mount upwards towards the sky, and burst like a soap-bubble in the glance of the Highest!

'Ah,' sighed he, 'that the Last Day were come!'

Silently he wandered through the land, that seemed to him as an orchard covered with soft turf. From the wooden balconies of the houses the girls who sat busy with their lace-making nodded at him; the summits of the mountains glowed in the red sun of the evening; and when he saw the green lakes gleaming among the dark trees, he thought of the coast by the Bay of Kjöge, and there was a longing in his bosom, but it was pain no more.

There where the Rhine rolls onward like a great billow, and bursts, and is changed into snow-white, gleaming, cloud-like masses, as if clouds were being created there, with the rainbow fluttering like a loose ribbon above them; there he thought of the water-mill at Kjöge, with its rushing, foaming water.

Gladly would he have remained in the quiet Rhenish town, but here also were too many elder trees and willows, and therefore he journeyed on, over the high, mighty mountains, through shattered walls of rock, and on roads that clung like swallows' nests to the mountain-side. The waters foamed on in the depths, the clouds were below him, and he strode on over thistles, Alpine roses, and snow, in the warm summer sun; and saying farewell to the lands of the North, he passed on under the shade of chestnut trees, and through vineyards and fields of maize. The mountains were a wall between him and all his recollections; and he wished it to be so.

Before him lay a great glorious city which they called Milan, and here he found a German master who gave him work. They were an old pious couple, in whose workshop he now laboured. And the two old people became quite fond of the quiet journeyman, who said little, but worked all the more, and led a pious Christian life. To himself also it seemed as if Heaven had lifted the heavy burden from his heart.

His favourite pastime was to mount now and then upon the mighty marble church, which seemed to him to have been formed of the snow of his native land, fashioned into roofs, and pinnacles, and decorated open halls: from every corner and every point the white statues smiled upon him. Above him was the blue sky, below him the city and the widespreading Lombard plains, and towards the north the high mountains clad with perpetual snow; and he thought of the church at Kjöge, with its red ivy-covered walls, but he did not long to go thither: here, beyond the mountains, he would be buried.

He had dwelt here a year, and three years had passed away since he left his home, when one day his master took him into the city, not to the circus where riders exhibited, but to the opera, where was a hall worth seeing. There were seven stories, from each of which beautiful silken curtains hung down, and from the ground to the dizzy height of the roof sat elegant ladies, with bouquets of flowers in their hands, as if they were at a ball, and the gentlemen were in full dress, and many of them decorated with gold and silver. It was as bright there as in the brilliant sunshine, and the music rolled gloriously through the building. Everything was much more splendid than in the theatre at Copenhagen, but then Joanna had been there, while here – Yes, it was like magic – the curtain rose, and Joanna appeared, dressed in silk and gold, with a crown upon her head: she sang as he thought none but angels could sing, and came far forward, quite to the front of the stage, and smiled as only Joanna could smile, and looked straight down at Knud. Poor Knud seized his master's hand, and called out aloud, 'Joanna!' but it could not be heard, the musicians played so loudly, and the master nodded and said, 'Yes, yes, her name is Joanna.'

And he drew forth a printed playbill, and showed Knud her name – for the full name was printed there.

No, it was not a dream! All the people applauded and threw wreaths and flowers to her, and every time she went away they called her back, so that she was always going and coming.

In the street the people crowded round her carriage, and drew it away in triumph. Knud was in the foremost row, and gladdest of all; and when the carriage stopped before her brilliantly lighted house, Knud stood close beside the door of the carriage. It was opened, and she stepped out: the light fell upon her dear face, as she smiled, and made a kindly gesture of thanks, and appeared deeply moved. Knud looked straight into her face, and she looked into his, but she did not know him. A man with a star glittering on his breast gave her his arm – and it was whispered about that the two were engaged.

Then Knud went home and packed his knapsack. He was determined to go back to his own home, to the elder and willow trees – ah, under the willow tree!

The old couple begged him to remain, but no words could induce him to stay. It was in vain they told him that winter was coming, and pointed out that snow had already fallen in the mountains; he said he could march on, with his knapsack on his back, in the wake of the slow-moving carriage, for which they would have to clear a path.

So he went away towards the mountains, and marched up them and down them. His strength was giving way, but still he saw no village, no house; he marched on towards the north. The stars came out above him, his feet stumbled, and his head grew dizzy. Deep in the valley stars were shining too, and it seemed as if there were another sky below him. He felt he was ill. The stars below him became more and more numerous, and glowed brighter and brighter, and moved to and fro. It was a little town whose lights beamed there; and when he understood that, he exerted the remains of his strength, and at last reached a humble inn.

That night and the whole of the following day he remained there, for his body required rest and refreshment. It was thawing, and there was rain in the valley. But early on the second morning came a man with an organ, who played a tune of home; and now Knud could stay no longer. He continued his journey towards the north, marching onward for many days with haste and hurry, as if he were trying to get home before all were dead there; but to no one did he speak of his longing, for no one would have believed in the sorrow of his heart, the deepest a human heart can feel. Such a grief is not for the world, for it is not amusing; nor is it even for friends; and moreover he had no friends – a stranger, he wandered through strange lands towards his home in the North. In the only letter he had received from home, one that his parents had written more than a year before, were the words: 'You are not thoroughly Danish like the rest of us. You are fond only of foreign lands.' His parents could actually write that, yes, they knew him so well!

It was evening. He was walking on the public high road. The frost began to make itself felt, and the country soon became flatter, containing mere field and meadow. By the roadside grew a great willow tree. Everything reminded him of home, and he sat down under the tree: he felt very tired, his head began to nod, and his eyes closed in slumber, but still he was conscious that the tree lowered its branches towards him; the tree appeared to be an old, mighty man – it seemed as if the 'Willow-father' himself had taken up his tired son in his arms, and were carrying him back into the land of home, to the bare bleak shore of Kjöge, to the garden of his childhood. Yes, he dreamed it was the willow tree of Kjöge that had travelled out into the world to seek him, and that now had found him, and had led him back into the little garden by the streamlet, and there stood Joanna, in all her splendour, with the golden crown on her head, as he had seen her last, and she called out 'Welcome!' to him.

And before him stood two remarkable shapes, which looked much more human than they did in his childhood: they had changed also, but they were still the two cakes that turned the right side towards him, and looked very well.

'We thank you,' they said to Knud. 'You have loosened our tongues, and have taught us that thoughts should be spoken out freely, or nothing will come of them; and now something has indeed come of it – we are betrothed.'

Then they went hand in hand through the streets of Kjöge, and they looked very respectable in every way: there was no fault to find with *them*. And they went on, straight towards the church, and Knud and Joanna followed them; they also were walking hand in hand; and the church stood there as it had always stood, with its red walls, on which the green ivy grew; and the great door of the church flew open, and the organ sounded, and they walked up the long aisle of the church.

'Our master first,' said the cake couple, and made room for Joanna and Knud, who knelt by the altar, and she bent her head over him, and tears fell from her eyes, but they were icy cold, for it was the ice around her heart that was melting – melting by his strong love; and the tears fell upon his burning cheeks, and he awoke, and was sitting under the old willow tree in the strange land, in the cold wintry evening: an icy hail was falling from the clouds and beating on his face.

'That was the most delicious hour of my life!' he said, 'and it was but a dream. Oh, let me dream it over again!'

And he closed his eyes once more, and slept and dreamed.

Towards morning there was a great fall of snow. The wind drifted the snow over his feet, but he slept on. The villagers came forth to go to church, and by the roadside sat a journeyman. He was dead – frozen to death under the willow tree!

Five Out of One Pod

THERE WERE five peas in one pod: they were green, and the pod was green, and so they thought all the world was green; and that was just as it should be! The pod grew, and the peas grew; they accommodated themselves to circumstances, sitting all in a row. The sun shone without, and warmed the husk, and the rain made it clear and transparent; it was mild and agreeable during the clear day and dark during the night, just as it should be, and the peas as they sat there became bigger and bigger, and more and more thoughtful, for something they must do.

'Are we to sit here everlastingly?' asked one. 'I'm afraid we shall become hard by long sitting. It seems to me there must be something outside – I have a kind of inkling of it.'

And weeks went by. The peas became yellow, and the pod also.

'All the world's turning yellow,' said they; and they had a right to say it.

Suddenly they felt a tug at the pod. It was torn off, passed through human hands, and glided down into the pocket of a jacket, in company with other full pods.

'Now we shall soon be opened!' they said; and that is just what they were waiting for.

'I should like to know who of us will get farthest!' said the smallest of the five. 'Yes, now it will soon show itself.'

'What is to be will be,' said the biggest.

'Crack!' the pod burst, and all the five peas rolled out into the bright sunshine. There they lay in a child's hand. A little boy was clutching them, and said they were fine peas for his pea-shooter; and he put one in at once and shot it out.

'Now I'm flying out into the wide world, catch me if you can!' And he was gone.

'I,' said the second, 'I shall fly straight into the sun. That's a pod worth looking at, and one that exactly suits me.' And away he went.

'We sleep where we come,' said the two next, 'but we shall roll on all the same.' And so they rolled first on the floor before they got into the pea-shooter; but they were put in for all that. 'We shall go farthest,' said they.

'What is to happen will happen,' said the last, as he was shot forth out of the pea-shooter; and he flew up against the old board under the garret window, just into a crack which was filled up with moss and soft mould; and the moss closed round him; there he lay, a prisoner indeed, but not forgotten by our Lord.

'What is to happen will happen,' said he.

Within, in the little garret, lived a poor woman, who went out in the day to clean stoves, saw wood, and to do other hard work of the same kind, for she was strong and industrious too. But she always remained poor; and at home in the garret lay her half-grown only daughter, who was very delicate and weak; for a whole year she had kept her bed, and it seemed as if she could neither live nor die.

'She is going to her little sister,' the woman said. 'I had only the two children, and it was not an easy thing to provide for both, but the good God provided for one of them by taking her home to Himself; now I should be glad to keep the other that was left me; but I suppose they are not to remain separated, and she will go to her sister in heaven.'

But the sick girl remained where she was. She lay quiet and patient all day long while her mother went to earn money out of doors. It was spring, and early in the morning, just as the mother was about to go out to work, the sun shone mildly and pleasantly through the little window, and threw its rays across the floor; and the sick girl fixed her eyes on the lowest pane in the window.

'What may that green thing be that looks in at the window? It is moving in the wind.'

And the mother stepped to the window, and half opened it. 'Oh!' said she, 'on my word, it is a little pea which has taken root here, and is putting out its little leaves. How can it have got here into the crack? There you have a little garden to look at.'

504   THE COMPLETE FAIRY TALES

And the sick girl's bed was moved nearer to the window, so that she could always see the growing pea; and the mother went forth to her work.

'Mother, I think I shall get well,' said the sick child in the evening. 'The sun shone in upon me to day delightfully warm. The little pea is thriving famously, and I shall thrive too, and get up, and go out into the warm sunshine.'

'God grant it!' said the mother, but she did not believe it would be so; but she took care to prop with a little stick the green plant which had given her daughter the pleasant thoughts of life, so that it might not be broken by the wind; she tied a piece of string to the window-sill and to the upper part of the frame, so that the pea might have something round which it could twine, when it shot up: and it did shoot up indeed – one could see how it grew every day.

'Really, here is a flower coming!' said the woman one day; and now she began to cherish the hope that her sick daughter would recover. She remembered that lately the child had spoken much more cheerfully than before, that in the last few days she had risen up in bed of her own accord, and had sat upright, looking with delighted eyes at the little garden in which only one plant grew. A week afterwards the invalid for the first time sat up for a whole hour. Quite happy, she sat there in the warm sunshine; the window was opened, and in front of it outside stood a pink pea blossom, fully blown. The sick girl bent down and gently kissed the delicate leaves. This day was like a festival.

'The Heavenly Father Himself has planted that pea, and caused it to thrive, to be a joy to you, and to me also, my blessed child!' said the glad mother; and she smiled at the flower, as if it had been a good angel.

But about the other peas? Why, the one who flew out into the wide world and said, 'Catch me if you can,' fell into the gutter on the roof, and found a home in a pigeon's crop, and lay there like Jonah in the whale; the two lazy ones got just as far, for they, too, were eaten up by pigeons, and thus, at any rate, they were of some real use; but the fourth, who wanted to go up into the sun, fell into the gutter, and lay there in the dirty water for days and weeks, and swelled prodigiously.

'How beautifully fat I'm growing!' said the Pea. 'I shall burst at last; and I don't think any pea can do more than that. I'm the most remarkable of all the five that were in the pod.'

And the Gutter said he was right.

But the young girl at the garret window stood there with gleaming eyes, with the hue of health on her cheeks, and folded her thin hands over the pea blossom, and thanked Heaven for it.

'I,' said the Gutter, 'stand up for my own pea.'

A Leaf from the Sky

HIGH UP, in the thin clear air, flew an angel with a flower from the heavenly garden. As he was kissing the flower, a very little leaf fell down into the soft soil in the midst of the wood, and immediately took root, and sprouted, and sent forth shoots among the other plants.

'A funny kind of slip, that,' said the Plants.

And neither Thistle nor Stinging-Nettle would recognise the stranger.

'That must be a kind of garden plant,' said they.

And they sneered; and the plant was despised by them as being a thing out of the garden, but it grew and grew, like none of the others, and shot its branches far and wide.

'Where are you coming?' cried the lofty Thistles, whose leaves are all armed with thorns. 'You give yourself a good deal of space! That's all nonsense – we are not here to support you!'

And winter came, and snow covered the plant; but the plant imparted to the snowy covering a lustre as if the sun was shining upon it from below as from above. When spring came, the plant appeared as flourishing and more beautiful than any growth of the forest.

And now appeared on the scene the botanical professor, who could show what he was in black and white. He inspected the plant and tested it, but found it was not included in his botanical system; and he could not possibly find out to what class it belonged.

'It must be some subordinate species,' he said. 'I don't know it. It's not included in any system.'

'Not included in any system!' repeated the Thistles and the Nettles.

The great trees that stood round about heard what was said, and they also saw that it was not a tree of their kind; but they said not a word, good or bad, which is the wisest thing for people to do who are stupid.

There came through the forest a poor innocent girl. Her heart was pure, and her understanding was enlarged by faith. Her whole inheritance was an old Bible; but out of its pages a voice said to her, 'If people wish to do us evil, remember how it was said of Joseph: they imagined evil in their hearts, but God turned it to good. If we suffer wrong – if we are misunderstood and despised – then we may recall the words of Him Who was purity and goodness itself, and Who forgave and prayed for those who buffeted and nailed Him to the cross.'

The girl stood still in front of the wonderful plant, whose great leaves exhaled a sweet and refreshing fragrance, and whose flowers glittered like coloured flames in the sun; and from each flower there came a sound as though it concealed within itself a deep fount of melody that thousands of years could not exhaust. With pious gratitude the girl looked on this beautiful work of the Creator, and bent down one of the branches towards herself to breathe its sweetness; and a light arose in her soul. It seemed to do her heart good; and gladly would she have plucked a flower, but she could not make up her mind to break one off, for it would soon fade if she did so. Therefore the girl only took a single leaf, and laid it in her Bible at home; and it lay there quite fresh, always green, and never fading.

Among the pages of the Bible it was kept; and, with the Bible, it was laid under the young girl's head when, a few weeks afterwards, she lay in her coffin, with the solemn calm of death on her gentle face, as if the earthly remains bore the impress of the truth that she now stood before her Creator.

But the wonderful plant still bloomed without in the forest. Soon it was like a tree to look upon; and all the birds of passage bowed before it, especially the swallow and the stork.

'These are foreign airs now,' said the Thistles and the Burdocks; 'we never behave like that here.'

And the black snails actually spat at the flower.

Then came the swineherd. He was collecting thistles and shrubs, to burn them for the ashes. The wonderful plant was pulled up with all its roots and placed in his bundle.

'It shall be made useful,' he said; and so said, so done.

But for more than a year and a day, the King of the country was troubled with a terrible depression of spirits. He was busy and industrious, but that did him no good. They read him deep and learned books, and then they read from the very lightest that they could find; but it was of no use. Then one of the wise men of the world, to whom they had applied, sent a messenger to tell the King that there was one remedy to give him relief and to cure him. He said:

'In the King's own country there grows in a forest a plant of heavenly origin. Its appearance is thus and thus. It cannot be mistaken.' And here was added a drawing of the plant, which was easy to recognise. 'It remains green winter and summer. Take every evening a fresh leaf of it, and lay that on the King's forehead; then his thoughts will become clear, and during the night a beautiful dream will strengthen him for the coming day.'

This was all clear enough, and all the doctors and the professor of botany went out into the forest. Yes, but where was the plant?

'I fancy it was taken up in my bundle, and burned to ashes long ago,' said the swineherd; 'but I did not know any better.'

'You did not know any better!' said they all together. 'O ignorance, ignorance, how great thou art!'

And those words the swineherd might well take to himself, for they were meant for him, and for no one else.

Not another leaf was to be found; the only one lay in the coffin of the dead girl, and no one knew anything about that.

And the King himself, in his melancholy, wandered out to the spot in the wood.

'Here is where the plant stood,' he said; 'it is a sacred place.'

And the place was surrounded with a golden railing, and a sentry was posted there both by night and by day.

The botanical professor wrote a long treatise upon the heavenly plant. For this he was decorated, and that was a great delight to him, and the decoration suited him and his family very well. And indeed that was the most agreeable part of the whole story, for the plant was gone, and the King remained as low-spirited as before; but that he had always been, at least so the sentry said.

She was Good for Nothing

THE MAYOR stood at the open window. He was in his shirt-sleeves, with a breast-pin stuck in his frill, and was uncommonly smooth shaven – all his own work; certainly he had given himself a slight cut, but he had stuck a bit of newspaper on the place.

'Hark ye, youngster!' he cried.

The youngster in question was no other than the son of the poor washerwoman, who was just going past the house; and he pulled off his cap respectfully. The peak of the said cap was broken in the middle, for the cap was arranged so that it could be rolled up and crammed into his pocket. In his poor, but clean and well-mended attire, with heavy wooden shoes on his feet, the boy stood there, as humble as if he stood before the King himself.

'You're a good boy,' said Mr Mayor. 'You're a civil boy. I suppose your mother is rinsing clothes down in the river? I suppose you are to carry that thing to your mother that you have in your pocket? It's a bad affair with your mother. How much have you got there?'

'Half a quartern,' stammered the boy, in a frightened voice.

'And this morning she had just as much,' the mayor continued.

'No,' replied the boy, 'it was yesterday.'

'Two halves make a whole. She's good for nothing! It's a sad thing with that class of people! Tell your mother that she ought to be ashamed of herself; and mind you don't become a drunkard – but you will become one, though. Poor child – there, go!'

And the boy went. He kept his cap in his hand, and the wind played with his yellow hair, so that great locks of it stood up straight. He turned down by the street corner, into the little lane that led to the river, where his mother stood by the washing bench, beating the heavy linen with the mallet. The water rolled quickly along, for the floodgates at the mill had been drawn up, and the sheets were caught by the stream, and threatened to overturn the bench. The washerwoman was obliged to lean against the bench to support it.

'I was very near sailing away,' she said. 'It is a good thing that you are come, for I need to recruit my strength a little. It is cold out here in the water, and I have been standing here for six hours. Have you brought anything for me?'

The boy produced the bottle, and the mother put it to her mouth, and took a little.

'Ah, how that revives one!' said she: 'how it warms! It is as good as a hot meal, and not so dear. And you, my boy! you look quite pale. You are shivering in your thin clothes – to be sure it is autumn. Ugh! how cold the water is! I hope I shall not be ill. But no, I shall not be that! Give me a little more, and you may have a sip too, but only a little sip, for you must not accustom yourself to it, my poor dear child!'

And she stepped up to the bridge on which the boy stood, and came ashore. The water dripped from the straw matting she had wound round her, and from her gown.

'I work and toil as much as ever I can,' she said, 'but I do it willingly, if I can only manage to bring you up honestly and well, my boy.'

As she spoke, a somewhat older woman came towards them. She was poor enough to behold, lame of one leg, and with a large false curl hanging down over one of her eyes, which was a blind one. The curl was intended to cover the eye, but it only made the defect more striking. This was a friend of the laundress. She was called among the neighbours, 'Lame Martha with the curl.'

'Oh, you poor thing! How you work, standing there in the water!' cried the visitor. 'You really require something to warm you; and yet malicious folks cry out about the few drops you take!'

And in a few minutes' time the mayor's late speech was reported to the laundress; for Martha had heard it all, and she had been angry that a man could speak as he had done to a woman's own child, about the few drops the mother took; and she was the more angry, because the mayor on that very day was giving a great feast, at which wine was drunk by the bottle – good wine, strong wine.

'A good many will take more than they need – but that's not called drinking. *They* are good; but *you* are good for nothing!' cried Martha, indignantly.

'Ah, so he spoke to you, my child?' said the washerwoman; and her lips trembled as she spoke. 'So he says you have a mother who is good for nothing? Well, perhaps he's right, but he should not have said it to my child. Still, I have had much misfortune from that house.'

'You were in service there when the mayor's parents were alive, and lived in that house. That is many years ago: many bushels of salt have been eaten since then, and we may well be thirsty;' and Martha smiled. 'The mayor has a great dinner-party today. The guests were to have been put off, but it was too late, and the dinner was already cooked. The footman told me about it. A letter came a little while ago, to say that the younger brother had died in Copenhagen.'

'Died?' repeated the laundress – and she became pale as death.

'Yes, certainly,' said Martha. 'Do you take that so much to heart? Well, you must have known him years ago, when you were in service in the house.'

'Is he dead? He was such a good, worthy man! There are not many like him.' And the tears rolled down her cheeks. 'Good gracious!

everything is whirling around me – it was too much for me. I feel quite ill.' And she leaned against the plank.

'Good gracious, you are ill indeed!' exclaimed the other woman. 'Come, come, it will pass over presently. But no, you really look seriously ill. The best thing will be for me to lead you home.'

'But my linen yonder –'

'I will see to that. Come, give me your arm. The boy can stay here and take care of it, and I'll come back and finish the washing; it's only a trifle.'

The laundress's limbs shook under her. 'I have stood too long in the cold water,' she said faintly, 'and I have eaten and drunk nothing since this morning. The fever is in my bones. O kind Heaven, help me to get home! My poor child!' And she burst into tears.

The boy wept too, and soon he was sitting alone by the river, beside the damp linen. The two women could make only slow progress. The laundress dragged her weary limbs along, and tottered through the lane and round the corner into the street where stood the house of the mayor; and just in front of his mansion she sank down on the pavement. Many people assembled round her, and lame Martha ran into the house to get help. The mayor and his guests came to the window.

'That's the washerwoman!' he said. 'She has taken a glass too much. She is good for nothing. It's a pity for the pretty son she has. I really like the child very well; but the mother is good for nothing.'

Presently the laundress came to herself, and they led her into her poor dwelling, and put her to bed. Kind Martha heated a mug of beer for her, with butter and sugar, which she considered the best medicine; and then she hastened to the river, and rinsed the linen – badly enough, though her will was good. Strictly speaking, she drew it ashore, wet as it was, and laid it in a basket.

Towards evening she was sitting in the poor little room with the laundress. The mayor's cook had given her some roasted potatoes and a fine fat piece of ham for the sick woman, and Martha and the boy discussed these viands while the patient enjoyed the smell, which she pronounced very nourishing.

And presently the boy was put to bed, the same bed in which his mother lay; but he slept at her feet, covered with an old quilt made up of blue and white patches.

Soon the patient felt a little better. The warm beer had strengthened her, and the fragrance of the provisions also did her good.

'Thanks, you kind soul,' she said to Martha. 'I will tell you all when the boy is asleep. I think he has dropped off already. How gentle and good he looks, as he lies there with his eyes closed. He does not know what his mother has suffered, and Heaven grant he may never know it. I was in service at the councillor's, the father of the mayor. It happened that the youngest of the sons, the student, came home. I was young then, a wild girl, but honest, that I may declare in the face of Heaven. The student was merry and kind, good and brave. Every drop of blood in him was good and honest. I have not seen a better man on this earth. He was the son of the house, and I was only a maid, but we formed an attachment to each other, honestly and honourably. And he told his mother of it, for she was in his eyes as a deity on earth; and she was wise and gentle. He went away on a journey, but before he started he put his gold ring on my finger; and directly he was gone my mistress called me. With a firm yet gentle seriousness she spoke to me, and it seemed as if Wisdom itself were speaking. She showed me clearly, in spirit and in truth, the difference there was between him and me.

' "Now he is charmed with your pretty appearance," she said, "but your good looks will leave you. You have not been educated as he has. You are not equals in mind, and there is the misfortune. I respect the poor," she continued: "in the sight of God they may occupy a higher place than many a rich man can fill; but here on earth we must beware of entering a false track as we go onward, or our carriage is upset, and we are thrown into the road. I know that a worthy man wishes to marry you – an artisan – I mean Erich the glove-maker. He is a widower without children, and is well-to-do. Think it over."

'Every word she spoke cut into my heart like a knife, but I knew that my mistress was right, and that knowledge weighed heavily upon me. I kissed her hand, and wept bitter tears, and I wept still more when I went into my room and threw myself on my bed. It was a heavy night that I had to pass through. Heaven knows what I suffered and how I wrestled! The next Sunday I went to the Lord's house, to pray for strength and guidance. It seemed like a providence, that as I stepped out of church Erich came towards me. And now there was no longer a doubt in my mind. We were suited to each other in rank and in means, and he was even then a thriving man. Therefore I went up to him, took his hand, and said, "Are you still of the same mind towards me?" "Yes, ever and always," he replied. "Will you marry a girl who honours and respects, but who does not love you – though that may come later?" I asked him. "Yes, it will come!" he answered. And upon this we joined hands. I went home to my mistress. I wore the gold ring that her son had given me at my heart. I could not put it on my finger in the daytime, but only in the evening when I went to bed. I kissed the ring again and again, till my lips almost bled, and then I gave it to my mistress, and told her the banns were to be put up next week for me and the glove-maker. Then my mistress put her arms round me and kissed me. *She* did not say that I was good for nothing; but perhaps I was better then than I am now, for the misfortunes of life had not yet found me out. In a few weeks we were married; and for the first year the world went well with us: we had a journeyman and an apprentice, and you, Martha, lived with us as our servant.'

'Oh, you were a dear, good mistress,' cried Martha. 'Never shall I forget how kind you and your husband were!'

'Yes, those were our good years, when you were with us. We had not any children yet. The student I never saw again. Ah, yes, I saw him, but he did not see me. He was here at his mother's funeral. I saw him stand by the grave. He was pale as death, and very downcast, but that was for his mother; afterwards, when his father died, he was away in a foreign land, and did not come back here. I know that he never married; I believe he became a lawyer. He had forgotten me, and even if he had seen me again, he would not have known me, I look so ugly. And that is very fortunate.'

And then she spoke of her days of trial, and told how misfortune had come as it were swooping down upon them.

'We had five hundred dollars,' she said; 'and as there was a house in the street to be bought for two hundred, and it would pay to pull it down and build a new one, it was bought. The builder and carpenter calculated the expense, and the new house was to cost a thousand and twenty. Erich had credit, and borrowed the money in the chief town, but the captain who was to bring it was shipwrecked, and the money was lost with him.

'Just at that time my dear sweet boy who is sleeping yonder was born. My husband was struck down by a long heavy illness: for three-quarters of a year I was compelled to dress and undress him. We went back more and more, and fell into debt. All that we had was sold, and my husband died. I have worked, and toiled, and striven for the sake of the child, scrubbing staircases, washing linen, fine and coarse alike, but I was not to be better off, such was God's good will. But He will take me to Himself in His own good time, and will not forsake my boy.'

And she fell asleep.

Towards morning she felt much refreshed, and strong enough, as she thought, to go back to her work. She had just stepped again into the cold water, when a trembling and faintness seized her: she clutched at the air with her hand, took a step forward, and fell down. Her head rested on the bank, and her feet were still in the water; her wooden shoes, with a wisp of straw in each, which she had worn, floated down the stream, and thus Martha found her on coming to bring her some coffee.

In the meantime a messenger from the mayor's house had been dispatched to her poor lodging to tell her 'to come to the mayor immediately, for he had something to tell her.' It was too late! A barber-surgeon was brought to open a vein in her arm; but the poor woman was dead.

'She has drunk herself to death!' said the mayor.

In the letter that brought the news of his brother's death, the contents of the will had been mentioned, and it was a legacy of six hundred dollars to the glove-maker's widow, who had once been his mother's maid. The money was to be paid, according to the mayor's discretion, in larger or smaller sums, to her or to her child.

'There was some fuss between my brother and her,' said the mayor.

'It's a good thing that she is dead; for now the boy will have the whole, and I will get him into a house among respectable people. He may turn out a reputable working man.'

And Heaven gave its blessing to these words.

So the mayor sent for the boy, promised to take care of him, and added that it was a good thing the lad's mother was dead, inasmuch as she had been good for nothing.

They bore her to the churchyard, to the cemetery of the poor, and Martha planted a rose tree upon the grave, and the boy stood beside her.

'My dear mother!' he cried, as the tears fell fast. 'Is it true what they said, that she was good for nothing?'

'No, she was good for much!' replied the old servant, and she looked up indignantly. 'I knew it many a year ago, and more than all since last night. I tell you she was worth much, and the Lord in heaven knows it is true, let the world say, as much as it chooses, "She was good for nothing." '

The Last Pearl

IT WAS a rich, a happy house; all were cheerful and full of joy, master, servants, and friends of the family; for on this day an heir, a son, had been born, and mother and child were doing exceedingly well.

The lamp in the bedchamber had been partly shaded, and the windows were guarded by heavy curtains of some costly silken fabric. The carpet was thick and soft as a mossy lawn, and everything invited to slumber – was charmingly suggestive of repose; and the nurse found that, for she slept; and here she might sleep, for everything was good and blessed. The guardian spirit of the house leaned against the head of the bed; over the child at the mother's breast there spread as it were a net of shining stars in endless number, and each star was a pearl of happiness. All the good fairies of life had brought their gifts to the new-born one; here sparkled health, wealth, fortune, and love – in short, everything that man can wish for on earth.

'Everything has been presented here,' said the guardian spirit.

'No, not everything,' said a voice near him, the voice of the child's *good angel*. 'One fairy has not yet brought her gift; but she will do so someday; even if years should elapse first, she will bring her gift. The *last pearl* is yet wanting.'

'Wanting! here nothing should be wanting; but if it should be the case, let me go and seek the powerful fairy; let us betake ourselves to her!'

'She comes! she will come someday unsought! Her pearl must be there, so that the complete crown may be won.'

'Where is she to be found? Where does she dwell? Tell it me, and I will procure the pearl.'

'You will do that?' said the good angel of the child. 'I will lead you to her directly, wherever she may be. She has no abiding-place –

sometimes she comes to the Emperor's palace, sometimes you will find her in the peasant's humble cot; she goes by no person without leaving a trace: she brings her gift to all, be it a world or a trifle! To this child also she must come. You think the time is equally long, but not equally profitable. Well, then, let us go for this pearl, the last pearl in all this wealth.'

And hand in hand they floated towards the spot where the fairy was now lingering.

It was a great house, with dark windows and empty rooms, and a peculiar stillness reigned therein; a whole row of windows had been opened, so that the rough air could penetrate at its pleasure: the long white hanging curtains moved to and fro in the current of wind.

In the middle of the room was placed an open coffin, and in this rested the body of a woman, still in her best years. Fresh roses were scattered over her, so that only the delicate folded hands and the noble face, glorified in death by the solemn look of consecration and entrance to the better world, were visible.

Around the coffin stood the husband and the children, a whole troop: the youngest child rested on the father's arm, and all bade their mother the last farewell; the husband kissed her hand, the hand which now was as a withered leaf, but which a short time ago had been working and striving in diligent love for them all. Tears of sorrow fell in heavy drops to the floor; but not a word was spoken. The silence which reigned here expressed a world of grief. With silent footsteps and with many a sob they quitted the room.

A burning light stands in the room, and the long red wick peers out high above the flame that flickers in the current of air. Strange men come in, and lay the lid on the coffin over the dead one, and drive the nails firmly in, and the blows of the hammer resound through the house, and echo in the hearts that are bleeding.

'Whither art thou leading me?' asked the guardian spirit. 'Here dwells no fairy whose pearl might be counted among the best gifts for life!'

'Here she dwells; here in this sacred hour,' said the angel, and pointed to a corner of the room; and there, where in her lifetime the mother had taken her seat amid flowers and pictures; there, whence, like the beneficent fairy of the house, she had greeted husband, children, and friends; whence, like the sunbeams, she had spread joy and cheerfulness, and been the centre and the heart of all – there sat a strange woman, clad in long garments. It was Sorrow, now mistress and mother here in the dead lady's place. A hot tear rolled down into her lap, and formed itself into a pearl glowing with all the colours of the rainbow. The angel seized it, and the pearl shone like a star of sevenfold radiance.

The pearl of Sorrow, the last, which must not be wanting! it heightens the lustre and the power of the other pearls. Do you see the sheen of the rainbow – of the bow that unites heaven and earth? For each of our dear ones who dies and leaves us, we have one friend more in Heaven to long for. Through the earthly night we gaze upward to the stars, looking for perfection. Contemplate it, the pearl of Sorrow, for it hides within itself the wings that shall carry us to the better world.

Two Maidens

HAVE YOU ever seen a maiden? I mean what our paviours call a maiden, a thing with which they ram down paving-stones in the roads. A maiden of this kind is made altogether of wood, broad below, and girt round with iron rings; at the top she is narrow, and has a stick passed across through her waist; and this stick forms the arms of the maiden.

In the shed stood two Maidens of this kind. They had their place among shovels, hand-carts, wheelbarrows, and measuring tapes; and to all this company the news had come that the Maidens were no longer to be called 'maidens', but 'hand-rammers'; which word was the newest and the only correct designation among the paviours for the thing we all know from the old times by the name of 'the maiden'.

Now, there are among us human creatures certain individuals who are known as 'emancipated women'; as, for instance, principals of institutions, dancers who stand professionally on one leg, milliners, and sick nurses; and with this class of emancipated women the two maidens in the shed associated themselves. They were 'maidens' among the paviour folk, and determined not to give up this honourable appellation, and let themselves be miscalled rammers.

'Maiden is a human name, but rammer is a *thing*, and we won't be called *things* – that is insulting us.'

'My lover would be ready to give up his engagement,' said the youngest, who was betrothed to a pile-driver; and that is a large machine which drives great piles into the earth, and therefore does on a large scale what the maiden does on a small one. 'He wants to marry me as a Maiden, but whether he would have me, were I a rammer, is a question; so I won't have my name changed.'

'And I,' said the elder one, 'would rather have both my arms broken off.'

But the Wheelbarrow was of a different opinion; and the Wheelbarrow was looked upon as of some consequence, for he considered himself a quarter of a coach, because he went about upon one wheel.

'I must remark,' he said, 'that the name "maiden" is common enough, and not nearly so refined as "rammer", or "stamper", which latter has also been proposed, and through which you would be introduced into the category of seals; and only think of the great stamp of state, which impresses the royal seal that gives effect to the laws! No, in your case I would surrender my maiden name.'

'No, certainly not!' exclaimed the elder. 'I am too old for that.'

'I presume you have never heard of what is called "European necessity"?' observed the honest Measuring Tape. 'One must be able to adapt oneself to time and circumstances, and if there is a law that the "maiden" is to be called "rammer", why, she must be called "rammer", for everything has its measure.'

'No; if there must be a change,' said the younger, 'I should prefer to be called "Missy", for that reminds one a little of maidens.'

'But I would rather be chopped to bits,' said the elder.

At last they all went to work. The Maidens rode – that is, they were put in a wheelbarrow, and that was a distinction; but still they were called 'hand-rammers'.

'Mai – !' they said, as they were bumped upon the pavement. 'Mai – !' and they were very nearly pronouncing the whole word 'maiden'; but they broke off short, and swallowed the last syllable; for they considered it beneath their dignity to protest. But they always called each other 'maiden', and praised the good old days in which everything had been called by its right name, and those who were maidens were called maidens. And they remained as they were; for the pile-driver really broke off his engagement with the younger one, for he would have nothing to do with a rammer.

In the Uttermost Parts of the Sea

SOME GREAT ships had been sent up towards the North Pole, to explore the most distant coasts, and to try how far men might penetrate up there. For more than a year they had already been pushing their way among ice and mist, and had endured many hardships; and now the winter was begun, and the sun had disappeared. For many many weeks there would now be a long night. All around was a single field of ice; the ships had been made fast to it, and the snow had piled itself up in great masses, and out of these, huts had been built in the form of beehives, some of them large as our old grave-mounds, others only containing room enough for two or four men. But it was not dark, for the Northern Lights flamed red and blue, like great continual fireworks; and the snow glistened, so that the night here was one long, flaming twilight hour. When the gleam was brightest, the natives came in crowds, wonderful to behold in their hairy fur dresses; and they rode in sledges formed of blocks of ice, and brought with them furs in great bundles, so that the snow houses were furnished with warm carpets; and, in turn, the furs also served for coverlets when the sailors went to bed under their roofs of snow, while outside it froze in far different fashion than in the hardest winter here with us. In our regions it was still the late autumn-time; and they thought of that up there, and thought of the sunshine at home, and of the yellow and red leaves on the trees. The clock showed that it was evening, and time to go to sleep; and in one of the huts two men had already stretched themselves out to rest. The younger of these had his best, dearest treasure, that he had brought from home – the Bible which his grandmother had given him on his departure. Every night it lay beneath his head, and he knew from his childish years what was written in it. Every day he read in the book, and often the holy words came into his mind where it is written, 'If I take the wings of the morning, and flee into the uttermost parts of the sea, even there Thou art with me, and Thy right hand shall uphold me'; and, under the influence of these words of truth and in faith, he closed his eyes, and sleep came upon him, and dreams – the manifestation of Providence to the spirit. The soul lived and was working while the body was enjoying its rest: he felt this life, and it seemed to him as if dear old well-known melodies were sounding, as if the mild breezes of summer were playing around him; and over his bed he beheld a brightness, as if something were shining in through the roof of snow. He lifted up his head, and behold, the bright gleam was neither wall nor roof, but came from the mighty pinions of an angel, into whose beaming face he was gazing. As if from the cup of a lily the angel arose from among the leaves of the Bible, and on his stretching out his arm, the walls of the snow hut sank down around, as though they had been a light airy veil of mist; the green meadows and hillocks of home, and its russet woods, lay spread around him in the quiet sunshine of a beauteous autumn day; the nest of the stork was empty, but ripe fruit still clung to the wild apple tree, although the leaves had fallen; the red hips gleamed, and the magpie whistled in the green cage over the window of the peasant's cottage that was his home; the magpie whistled the tune that had been taught him, and the grand-mother hung green food around the cage, as he, the grandson, had been accustomed to do; and the daughter of the blacksmith, very young and fair, stood by the well drawing water, and nodded to the grand-dame, and the old woman nodded to her, and showed her a letter that had come from a long way off. That very morning the letter had arrived from the cold regions of the North – there where the grandson was resting in the hand of God. And they smiled and wept; and he, far away among the ice and snow, under the pinions of the angel, he, too, smiled and wept with them in spirit, for he saw them and heard them. And from the letter they read aloud the words of Holy Writ, that in the uttermost parts of the sea His right hand would be a stay and a safety. And the sound of a beauteous hymn welled up all around; and the angel spread his wings like a veil over the sleeping youth. The vision had fled, and it grew dark in the snow hut; but the Bible rested beneath his head, and faith and hope dwelt in his soul. God was with him; and he carried *home* about with him in his heart, even in the uttermost parts of the sea.

The Money-Pig

IN THE nursery a number of toys lay strewn about: high up, on the wardrobe, stood the Money-box, it was of clay in the shape of a little pig; of course the pig had a slit in its back, and this slit had been so enlarged with a knife that whole dollar-pieces could slip through; and, indeed, two such had slipped into the box, besides a number of pence. The Money-pig was stuffed so full that it could no longer rattle, and that is the highest point a Money-pig can attain. There it stood upon the cupboard, high and lofty, looking down upon everything else in the room. It knew very well that what it had in its stomach would have bought all the toys, and that's what we call having self-respect.

The others thought of that too, even if they did not exactly express it, for there were many other things to speak of. One of the drawers was half pulled out, and there lay a great handsome Doll, though she was somewhat old, and her neck had been mended. She looked out and said, 'Shall we now play at men and women, for that is always something?'

And now there was a general uproar, and even the framed prints on the walls turned round and showed that there was a wrong side to them; but they did not do it to protest against the proposal.

It was late at night; the moon shone through the window-frames and gave free light. Now the game was about to begin, and all, even the children's Go-Cart, which certainly belonged to the coarser playthings, were invited to take part in the sport.

'Each one has his own peculiar value,' said the Go-Cart: 'we cannot all be noblemen. There must be some who do the work, as the saying is.'

The Money-pig was the only one who received a written invitation, for he was of high standing, and they were afraid he would not accept a verbal message. Indeed, he did not answer to say whether he would come, nor did he come: if he was to take a part, he must enjoy the sport from his own home; they were to arrange accordingly, and so they did.

The little toy theatre was now put up in such a way that the Money-pig could look directly in. They wanted to begin with a comedy, and afterwards there was to be a tea party and a discussion for mental improvement, and with this latter part they began immediately. The Rocking-Horse spoke of training and race, the Go-Cart of railways and steam power, for all this belonged to their profession, and it was something they could talk about. The Clock talked politics – ticks – ticks – and knew what was the time of day, though it was whispered he did not go correctly; the Bamboo Cane stood there, stiff and proud, for he was conceited about his brass ferrule and his silver top, for being thus bound above and below; and on the sofa lay two worked Cushions, pretty and stupid. And now the play began.

All sat and looked on, and it was requested that the audience should applaud and crack and stamp according as they were gratified. But the Riding-Whip said he never cracked for old people, only for young ones who were not yet married.

'I crack for everything,' said the Cracker.

And these were the thoughts they had while the play went on. The piece was worthless, but it was well played; all the characters turned their painted side to the audience, for they were so made that they should only be looked at from that side, and not from the other; and all played wonderfully well, coming out quite beyond the lamps, because the wires were a little too long, but that only made them come out the more. The mended Doll was so affected that she burst at the mended place in her neck, and the Money-pig was so enchanted in his way that he formed the resolution to do something for one of the players, and to remember him in his will as the one who should be buried with him in the family vault when matters were so far advanced.

It was true enjoyment, so that they quite gave up the thoughts of tea, and only carried out the idea of mental recreation. That's what they called playing at men and women; and there was no malice in it, for they were only playing; and each one thought of himself and of what the Money-pig might think; and the Money-pig thought farthest of all, for he thought of making his will and of his burial. And when might this come to pass? Certainly far sooner than was expected. Crack! it fell down from the cupboard – fell on the ground, and was broken to pieces; and the pennies hopped and danced: the little ones turned round like tops, and the bigger ones rolled away, particularly the one great Silver Dollar who wanted to go out into the world. And he came out into the world, and they all succeeded in doing so. The pieces of the Money-pig were put into the dustbin; but the next day a new Money-pig was standing on the cupboard: it had not yet a farthing in its stomach, and therefore could not rattle, and in this it was like the other. But that was a beginning – and with that we will make an end.

Ib and Christine

NOT FAR from the stream Gudenaa, in the forest of Silkeborg, a great ridge of land rises and stretches along like a wall. By this ridge, westward, stands a farmhouse, surrounded by poor land; the sandy soil is seen through the spare rye and wheat that grow upon it. Some years have elapsed since the time of which we speak. The people who lived here cultivated the fields, and moreover kept three sheep, a pig, and two oxen; in fact, they supported themselves quite comfortably, for they had enough to live on if they took things as they came. Indeed, they could have managed to save enough to keep two horses; but, like the other peasants of the neighbourhood, they said, 'The horse eats itself up' – that is to say, it eats as much as it earns. Jeppe-Jens cultivated his field in summer. In the winter he made wooden shoes, and then he had an assistant, a journeyman, who understood how to make the wooden shoes strong, and light, and graceful. They carved shoes and spoons, and that brought in money. It would have been wronging the Jeppe-Jenses to call them poor people.

Little Ib, a boy seven years old, the only child of the family, would sit by, looking at the workmen, cutting at a stick, and occasionally cutting his finger. But one day he had cut two pieces of wood, so that they looked like little wooden shoes; and these he wanted to give to little Christine. She was the boatman's daughter, and was graceful and delicate as a gentleman's child; had she been differently dressed, no one would have imagined that she came out of the hut on the neighbouring heath. There lived her father, who was a widower, and supported himself by carrying firewood in his great boat out of the forest down to the eel-weir of Silkeborg, and sometimes even to the distant town of Randers. He had no one who could take care of little Christine, who was a year younger than Ib, and therefore the child was almost always with him in his boat, or in the forest among the heath plants and barberry bushes. When he had to go as far as Randers, he would bring little Christine to stay at the Jeppe-Jenses'.

Ib and Christine agreed very well in every particular: they dug in the ground together for treasures, and they ran and crept, and one day they ventured together up the high ridge, and a long way into the forest; they found a few snipe's eggs there, and that was a great event for them.

Ib had never been on the heath, nor had he ever been on the river. But even this was to happen; for Christine's father once invited him to go with them, and on the evening before the excursion, Ib went home with him.

Next morning early, the two children were sitting high up on the pile of firewood in the boat, eating bread and raspberries. Christine's father and his assistant propelled the boat with staves. They had the current with them, and swiftly they glided down the stream, through the lakes which sometimes seemed shut in by woods and reeds. But there was always room for them to pass, even if the old trees bent quite forward over the water, and the old oaks bent down their bare branches, as if they had turned up their sleeves, and wanted to show their knotty naked arms. Old alder trees, which the stream had washed away from the bank, clung with their roots to the bottom of the stream, and looked like little wooded islands. The water-lilies rocked themselves on the river. It was a splendid excursion; and at last they came to the great eel-weir, where the water rushed through the floodgates; that was something for Ib and Christine to see!

In those days there was no manufactory there, nor was there any town: only the old farmyard, and the stock there was not large; and the rushing of the water through the weir and the cry of the wild ducks were the only signs of life in Silkeborg. After the firewood had been unloaded, the father of Christine bought a whole bundle of eels and a slaughtered sucking-pig, and all was put into a basket and placed in the stern of the boat. Then they went back again up the stream; but the wind was favourable, and when the sails were hoisted it was as good as if two horses had been harnessed to the boat.

When they had arrived at a point in the stream where the assistant-boatman dwelt, a little way from the bank, the boat was moored, and the two men landed, after exhorting the children to sit still. But the children did not do that very long. They must be peeping into the basket in which the eels and the sucking-pig had been placed, and they must needs pull the sucking-pig out, and take it in their hands; and as both wanted to hold it at the same time, it came to pass that they let it fall into the water, and the sucking-pig drifted away with the stream – and here was a terrible event!

Ib jumped ashore, and ran a little distance along the bank, and Christine sprang after him.

'Take me with you!' she cried.

And in a few minutes they were deep in the thicket, and could no longer see either the boat or the bank. They ran on a little farther, and then Christine fell down on the ground and began to cry; but Ib picked her up.

'Follow me!' he cried. 'The house lies over there.'

But the house was not there. They wandered on and on, over the withered leaves, and over dry fallen branches that crackled beneath their feet. Soon they heard a loud piercing scream. They stood still and listened, and presently the scream of an eagle again sounded through the wood. It was an ugly scream, and they were frightened at it; but before them, in the thick wood, the most beautiful blueberries grew in wonderful profusion. They were so inviting that the children could not do otherwise than stop; and they lingered for some time, eating the blueberries till they had quite blue mouths and blue cheeks. Now again they heard the cry they had heard before.

'We shall get into trouble about the pig,' said Christine.

'Come, let us go to our house,' said Ib; 'it is here in the wood.'

And they went forward. They presently came to a road, but it did not lead them home; and darkness came on, and they were afraid. The wonderful stillness that reigned around was interrupted now and then by the shrill cries of the great horned owl and of the birds that were strange to them. At last they both lost themselves in a thicket. Christine cried, and Ib cried too; and after they had cried for a time, they threw themselves down on the dry leaves, and went fast asleep.

The sun was high in the heavens when the two children awoke. They were cold; but on the hillock close at hand the sun shone through the trees, and there they thought they would warm themselves; and from there Ib fancied they would be able to see his parents' house. But they were far away from that, in quite another part of the forest. They clambered to the top of the rising ground, and found themselves on the summit of a slope running down to the margin of a transparent lake. They could see fish in great numbers in the pure water illumined by the sun's rays. This spectacle was quite a sudden surprise for them; close beside them grew a nut tree covered with the finest nuts; and now they picked the nuts and cracked them, and ate the delicate young kernels, which had only just begun to form. But there was another surprise and another fright in store for them. Out of the thicket stepped a tall old woman: her face was quite brown, and her hair was deep black and shining. The whites of her eyes gleamed like a Negro's; on her back she carried a bundle, and in her hand she bore a knotted stick. She was a gypsy. The children did not at once understand what she said. She brought three nuts out of her pocket, and told them that in these nuts the most beautiful, the loveliest things were hidden, for they were wishing-nuts.

Ib looked at her, and she seemed so friendly that he plucked up courage and asked her if she would give him the nuts; and the woman gave them to him, and gathered some more for herself, a whole pocketful, from the nut tree.

And Ib and Christine looked at the wishing-nuts with great eyes.

'Is there a carriage with a pair of horses in this nut?' he asked.

'Yes, there's a golden carriage with golden horses,' answered the woman.

'Then give me the nut,' said little Christine.

And Ib gave it to her, and the strange woman tied it in her pocket-handkerchief for her.

'Is there in this nut a pretty little neckerchief, like the one Christine wears round her neck?' enquired Ib.

'There are ten neckerchiefs in it,' answered the woman. 'There are beautiful dresses in it, and stockings, and a hat.'

'Then I will have that one too,' cried little Christine.

And Ib gave her the second nut also. The third was a little black thing.

'That one you can keep,' said Christine; 'and it is a pretty one too.'

'What is in it?' enquired Ib.

'The best of all things for you,' replied the gypsy woman.

And Ib held the nut very tight. The woman promised to lead the children into the right path, so that they might find their way home; and now they went forward, certainly in quite a different direction from the path they should have followed. But that is no reason why we should suspect the gypsy woman of wanting to steal the children. In the wild wood-path they met the forest bailiff, who knew Ib; and by his help, Ib and Christine both arrived at home, where their friends had been very anxious about them. They were pardoned and forgiven, although they had indeed both deserved to get into trouble; firstly, because they had let the sucking-pig fall into the water, and secondly, because they had run away.

Christine was taken back to her father on the heath, and Ib remained in the farmhouse by the wood. The first thing he did in the evening was to bring forth out of his pocket the nut, in which 'the best thing of all' was said to be enclosed. He placed it carefully between the door and the doorframe, and then shut the door so as to break the nut; but there was not much kernel in it. The nut looked as if it were filled with snuff or black rich earth; it was what we call hollow, or worm-eaten.

'Yes, that's exactly what I thought,' said Ib. 'How could the very best thing be contained in this little nut? And Christine will get just as little out of her two nuts, and will have neither fine clothes nor golden carriage.'

And winter came on, and the new year began; indeed, several years went by.

Ib was now to be confirmed, and the clergyman lived a long way off. About this time the boatman one day visited Ib's parents, and told them that Christine was now going into service, and that she had been really fortunate in getting a remarkably good place, and falling into worthy hands.

'Only think!' he said; 'she is going to the rich innkeeper's, in the inn at Herning, far towards the west. She is to assist the hostess in keeping the house; and afterwards, if she takes to it well, and stays to be confirmed there, the people are going to keep her with them.'

And Ib and Christine took leave of one another. People called them sweethearts; and at parting, the girl showed Ib that she had still the two nuts which he had given her long ago, during their wanderings in the forest; and she told him, moreover, that in a drawer she had carefully kept the little wooden shoes which he had carved as a present for her in their childish days. And thereupon they parted.

Ib was confirmed. But he remained in his mother's house, for he had become a clever maker of wooden shoes, and in summer he looked after the field. His mother had no one else to do this, for his father was dead.

Only seldom he got news of Christine from some passing postilion or eel-fisher. But she was well off at the rich innkeeper's; and after she had been confirmed, she wrote a letter to her father, and sent a kind message to Ib and his mother; and in the letter there was mention made of six new shifts and a fine new gown, which Christine had received from her master and mistress. This was certainly good news.

Next spring, there was a knock one day at the door of our Ib's old mother, and behold, the boatman and Christine stepped into the room. She had come on a visit to spend a day: a carriage had to come from the Herning Inn to the next village, and she had taken the opportunity to see her friends once again. She looked as handsome as a real lady, and she had a pretty gown on, which had been well sewn, and made expressly for her. There she stood, in grand array, and Ib was in his working clothes. He could not utter a word: he certainly seized her hand, and held it fast in his own, and was heartily glad; but he could not get his tongue to obey him. Christine was not embarrassed, however, for she went on talking and talking, and, moreover, kissed Ib on his mouth in the heartiest manner.

'Do you really not know me?' she asked; but even afterwards, when they were left quite by themselves, and he stood there still holding her hand in his, he could only say, 'You look quite like a real lady, and I am so uncouth. How often I have thought of you, Christine, and of the old times!'

And arm in arm they sauntered up the great ridge, and looked across the stream towards the heath, towards the great heather banks. It was perfectly silent; but by the time they parted it had grown quite clear to him that Christine must be his wife. Had they not, even in their childhood, been called sweethearts? To him they seemed to be really engaged to each other, though neither of them had spoken a word on the subject. Only for a few more hours could they remain together, for Christine was obliged to go back into the next village, from whence the carriage was to start early next morning for Herning. Her father and Ib escorted her as far as the village. It was a fair moonlight evening, and when they reached their destination, and Ib still held Christine's hand in his own, he could not let it go. His eyes brightened, but still the words came halting over his lips. Yet they came from the depths of his heart, when he said, 'If you have not become too grand, Christine, and if you can make up your mind to live with me in my mother's house as my wife, we must become a wedded pair someday; but we can wait a while yet.'

'Yes, let us wait for a time, Ib,' she replied; and she pressed his hand, and he kissed her lips. 'I trust in you, Ib,' said Christine; 'and I think that I love you – but I will sleep upon it.'

And with that they parted. And on the way home Ib told the boatman that he and Christine were as good as betrothed; and the boatman declared he had always expected it would turn out so; and he went home with Ib, and remained that night in the young man's house; but nothing further was said of the betrothal.

A year passed by, in the course of which two letters were exchanged between Ib and Christine. The signature was prefaced by the words, 'Faithful till death!' One silent of late; indeed, he had become very pensive, and thus the three nuts came into his mind which the gypsy woman had given him long ago, and of which he had given two to Christine. Yes, it seemed right – in one of hers lay a golden carriage with horses, and in the other very elegant clothes; all those luxuries would now be Christine's in the capital. Her part had thus come true. And to him, Ib, the nut had offered only black earth. The gypsy woman had said this was 'the best of all for him'. Yes, it was right – that also was coming true. The black earth was the best for him. Now he understood clearly what had been the woman's meaning. In the black earth, in the dark grave, would be the best happiness for him.

And once again years passed by, not very many, but they seemed long years to Ib. The old innkeeper and his wife died, and the whole of their property, many thousands of dollars, came to the son. Yes, now Christine could have the golden carriage and plenty of fine clothes.

During the two long years that followed, no letter came from Christine; and when her father at length received one from her, it was not written in prosperity, by any means. Poor Christine! neither she nor her husband had understood how to keep the money together, and there seemed to be no blessing with it, because they had not sought it.

And again the heather bloomed and faded. The snow had swept for many winters across the heath, and over the ridge beneath which Ib dwelt, sheltered from the rough winds. The spring sun shone bright, and Ib guided the plough across his field, when one day it glided over what appeared to be a flint stone. Something like a great black shaving came out of the ground, and when Ib took it up it proved to be a piece of metal; and where the plough had cut into it, it gleamed brightly. It was a great heavy armlet of gold from heathen times. A grave-mound had been levelled here and its precious treasure found. Ib showed what he had found to the clergyman, who explained its value to him, and then he betook himself to the local judge, who reported the discovery to Copenhagen, and recommended Ib to deliver up the treasure in person. day the boatman came in to Ib, and brought him a greeting from Christine. What he had further to say was brought out in somewhat hesitating fashion, but it was to the effect that Christine was almost more than prosperous, for she was a pretty girl, courted and loved. The son of the host had been home on a visit; he was employed in the office of some great institution in Copenhagen; and he was very much pleased with Christine, and she had taken a fancy to him: his parents were not unwilling, but it lay very much on Christine's mind that Ib had such a fancy for her; 'and so she had thought of refusing this great piece of good fortune,' said the boatman.

At first Ib said not a word, but he became as white as the wall, and slightly shook his head. Then he said slowly, 'Christine must not thrust her good fortune away.'

'Then do you write a few words to her,' said the boatman.

And Ib sat down to write; but he could not manage it well: the words would not come as he wished them; and first he altered, and then he tore up the page; but the next morning a letter lay ready to be sent to Christine, and here it is:

I have read the letter you have sent to your father, and gather from it that you are prospering in all things, and that there is a prospect of higher fortune for you. Ask your heart, Christine, and think well over what you are going into, if you take me for your husband; what I possess is but little. Do not think of me, or my position, but think of your own welfare. You are bound to me by no promise, and if in your heart you have given me one, I release you from it. May all the joy of the world be yours, Christine. Heaven will have comfort for my heart.

Ever your sincere friend, Ib

And the letter was dispatched, and Christine duly received it.

In the course of that November her banns were published in the church on the heath, and in Copenhagen, where her bridegroom lived; and to Copenhagen she travelled, with her mistress, because the bridegroom could not undertake the journey into Jutland on account of his various occupations. On the journey, Christine met her father in a certain village, and here the two took leave of one another. A few words were mentioned concerning this fact, but Ib made no remark upon it: his mother said he had grown very

'You have found in the earth the best thing you could find,' said the judge.

'The best thing!' thought Ib. 'The very best thing for me, and found in the earth! Well, if that is the best, the gypsy woman was correct in what she prophesied to me.'

So Ib travelled with the boat from Aarhus to Copenhagen. To him, who had only crossed Gudenaa, it was like a voyage across the ocean. And he arrived in Copenhagen.

The value of the gold he had found was paid over to him; it was a large sum – six hundred dollars. And Ib of the heath wandered about in the great capital.

On the day on which he had settled to go back with the captain, Ib lost his way in the streets, and took quite a different direction from the one he intended to follow. He had wandered into the suburb of Christianshaven, into a poor little street. Not a human being was to be seen. At last a very little girl came out of a wretched house. Ib enquired of the little one the way to the street which he wanted; but she looked shyly at him, and began to cry bitterly. He asked her what ailed her, but could not understand what she said in reply. But as they were both under a lamp, and the light fell on the girl's face, he felt quite strange, for Christine stood bodily before him, just as he remembered her from the days of his childhood.

And he went with the little maiden into the wretched house, and ascended the narrow, crazy staircase, which led to a little attic chamber in the roof. The air in this chamber was heavy and almost suffocating: no light was burning; but there was heavy sighing and moaning in one corner. Ib struck a light with the help of a match. It was the mother of the child who lay on the miserable bed.

'Can I be of any service to you?' asked Ib. 'This little girl has brought me up here, but I am a stranger in this city. Are there no neighbours or friends whom I could call to you?' And he raised the sick woman's head.

It was Christine of the heath!

For years her name had not been mentioned at home in Jutland, for it would have disturbed Ib's peace of mind, and rumour had told nothing good concerning her. The wealth which her husband had inherited from his parents had made him proud and arrogant. He had given up his certain appointment, had travelled for half a year in foreign lands, and on his return had incurred debts, and yet lived in an expensive fashion. His carriage had bent over more and more, so to speak, until at last it turned over completely. The many merry companions and table-friends he had entertained declared it served him right, for he had kept house like a madman; and one morning his body was found in the canal.

The hand of death was already on Christine. Her youngest child, only a few weeks old, expected in prosperity and born in misery, was already in its grave, and it had come to this with Christine herself, that she lay sick to death and forsaken, in a miserable room, amid a poverty that she might well have borne in her childish days, but which now oppressed her painfully, since she had been accustomed to better things. It was her eldest child, also a little Christine, that here suffered hunger and poverty with her, and who had conducted Ib there.

'I am afraid I shall die and leave the poor child here alone,' she said. 'Where in the world will she go then?' And not a word more could she utter.

And Ib brought out another match, and lighted up a piece of candle he found in the room, and the flame illumined the wretched dwelling. And Ib looked at the little girl, and thought how Christine had looked when she was young; and he felt that for her sake he would be good to this child, which was as yet a stranger to him. The dying woman gazed at him, and her eyes opened wider and wider – did she recognise him? He never knew, for no further word passed over her lips.

And it was in the forest by the river Gudenaa, in the region of the heath. The air was grey, and there were no blossoms on the heath plant; but the autumn tempests whirled the yellow leaves from the wood into the stream, and out over the heath towards the hut of the boatman, in which strangers now dwelt; but beneath the ridge, safe beneath the protection of the high trees, stood the little farm, trimly whitewashed and painted, and within it the turf blazed up cheerily in the chimney; for within was sunlight, the beaming sunlight of a child's two eyes; and the tones of the spring birds sounded in the words that came from the child's rosy lips: she sat on Ib's knee, and Ib was to her both father and mother, for her own parents were dead, and had vanished from her as a dream vanishes alike from children and grown men. Ib sat in the pretty neat house, for he was a prosperous man, while the mother of the little girl rested in the churchyard at Copenhagen, where she had died in poverty.

Ib had money, and was said to have provided for the future. He had won gold out of the black earth, and he had a Christine for his own, after all.

Jack the Dullard

OUT IN the country lay an old mansion, and in it lived an old proprietor, who had two sons, which two young men thought themselves too clever by half. They wanted to go out and woo the King's daughter; for the maiden in question had publicly announced that she would choose for her husband that one that she thought could best speak for himself.

So these two prepared themselves a full week for the wooing – this was the longest time that could be granted them; but it was enough, for they had previous accomplishments, and these are useful. One of them knew the whole Latin dictionary by heart, and three whole years of the daily paper of the little town, and that either backwards or forwards. The other was deeply read in the corporation laws, and knew by heart what every alderman ought to know; and accordingly he thought he could talk of affairs of state. And he knew one thing more: he could embroider braces, for he was a tasty, light-fingered fellow.

'I shall win the Princess!' So cried both of them. Therefore their father gave to each a handsome horse. The youth who knew the dictionary and newspaper by heart had a black horse, and he who knew all about the corporation laws received a milk-white steed. Then they rubbed the corners of their mouths with fish-oil, so that they might become very smooth and glib. All the servants stood below in the courtyard, and looked on while they mounted their horses; and just by chance the third son came up. For there were three of them, though nobody counted the third with his brothers, because he was not so learned as they, and indeed he was generally known as 'Jack the Dullard'.

'Hallo!' said he, 'where are you going since you have put on your best clothes?'

'We're going to the King's court, as suitors to the King's daughter.

Don't you know the announcement that has been made all through the country?' And they told him all about it.

'My word! I'll be in it too!' cried Jack the Dullard; and his two brothers burst out laughing at him, and rode away.

'Father,' said Jack, 'I must have a horse too. I do feel so desperately inclined to marry! If she accepts me, she accepts me; and if she won't have me, I'll have her all the same!'

'Don't talk nonsense,' said the father. 'You shall have no horse from me. You don't know how to speak. Your brothers are very different fellows from you.'

'Well,' quoth Jack the Dullard, 'if I can't have a horse, I'll take the billy-goat, who belongs to me, and he can carry me very well!'

And so he mounted the billy-goat, pressed his heels into its sides, and galloped off along the highway.

'Hei, houp! that was a ride! Here I come!' shouted Jack the Dullard, and he sang till his voice echoed far and wide.

But his brothers rode slowly on in advance of him. They spoke not a word, for they were thinking all about the fine ideas they would have to bring out, and these had to be cleverly prepared beforehand.

'Hallo!' shouted Jack the Dullard. 'Here am I! Look what I have found on the high road.' And he showed them a dead crow which he had found.

'Dullard!' exclaimed the brothers, 'what are you going to do with that?'

'I am going to give it to the Princess.'

'Yes, do so,' said they; and they laughed, and rode on.

'Hallo, here I am again! Just see what I have found now: you don't find that on the high road every day!'

And the brothers turned round to see what he could have found now.

'Dullard!' they cried, 'that is only an old wooden shoe, and the upper part is missing into the bargain; are you going to give that also to the Princess?'

'Most certainly I shall,' replied Jack the Dullard; and again the brothers laughed and rode on, and thus they got far in advance of him; but – 'Hallo!' and there was Jack the Dullard again. 'It is getting better and better,' he cried. 'Hurrah! it is quite famous.'

'Why, what have you found this time?' enquired the brothers.

'Oh,' said Jack the Dullard, 'I can hardly tell you. How glad the Princess will be!'

'Bah!' said the brothers; 'that is nothing but clay out of the ditch.'

'Yes, certainly it is,' said Jack the Dullard; 'and clay of the finest sort. See, it is so wet, it runs through one's fingers.' And he filled his pocket with the clay.

But his brothers galloped on as hard as the harness could stand, and consequently they arrived a full hour earlier at the town gate than could Jack. Now at the gate each suitor was provided with a number, and all were placed in rows, six in each row, and so closely packed together that they could not move their arms; and that was a prudent arrangement, for they would certainly have come to blows, had they been able, merely because one of them stood before the other.

All the inhabitants of the country round about stood in great crowds around the castle, almost under the very windows, to see the Princess receive the suitors; and as each stepped into the hall, his power of speech seemed to desert him. Then the Princess would say, 'He is of no use! away with him!'

At last the turn came for that brother who knew the dictionary by heart; but he had absolutely forgotten it; and the boards seemed to re-echo with his footsteps, and the ceiling of the hall was made of looking-glass, so that he saw himself standing on his head; and at the window stood three clerks and a head clerk, and every one of them was writing down every single word that was uttered, so that it might be printed in the newspapers, and sold for a penny at the street corners. It was a terrible ordeal, and they had moreover made such a fire in the stove, that the stove-pipe was quite red hot.

'It is dreadfully hot here!' observed the first brother.

'Yes,' replied the Princess, 'my father is going to roast young pullets today.'

Baa! there he stood. He had not been prepared for a speech of this kind, and had not a word to say, though he intended to say something witty. Baa!

'He is of no use!' said the Princess. 'Away with him!'

And he was obliged to go accordingly. And now the second brother came in.

'It is terribly warm here!' he observed.

'Yes, we're roasting pullets today,' replied the Princess.

'What – what were you – were you pleased to ob –' stammered he – and all the clerks wrote down, 'pleased to ob –'

'He is of no use!' said the Princess. 'Away with him!'

Now came the turn of Jack the Dullard. He rode into the hall on his goat.

'Well, it's most desperately hot here.'

'Yes, because I'm roasting young pullets,' replied the Princess.

'Ah, that's lucky!' exclaimed Jack the Dullard, 'then I suppose I can get a crow roasted?'

'With the greatest pleasure,' said the Princess. 'But have you anything you can roast it in? for I have neither pot nor pan.'

'Certainly I have!' said Jack. 'Here's a cooking utensil with a tin handle.'

And he brought out the old wooden shoe, and put the crow into it.

'Well, that *is* a famous dish!' said the Princess. 'But what shall we do for sauce?'

'Oh, I have that in my pocket,' said Jack: 'I have so much of it that I can afford to throw some away;' and he poured some of the clay out of his pocket.

'I like that!' said the Princess. 'You can give an answer, and you have something to say for yourself, and so you shall be my husband. But are you aware that every word we speak is being taken down, and will be published in the paper tomorrow? You will see in every window three clerks and a head clerk; and the old head clerk is the worst of all, for he can't understand anything.'

But she only said this to frighten him; and the clerks gave a great shout of delight, and each one spurted a blot out of his pen on to the floor.

'Oh, those are the gentlemen, are they?' said Jack; 'then I will give the best I have to the head clerk.' And he turned out his pockets, and flung the wet clay full in the head clerk's face.

'That was very cleverly done,' observed the Princess. 'I could not have done that; but I shall learn in time.'

And accordingly Jack the Dullard was made a king, and received a crown and a wife, and sat upon a throne. And this report we have straight from the newspaper of the head clerk – but it is not to be depended upon!

The Thorny Road of Honour

THERE IS an old story called 'The Thorny Road of Honour',
trod by a marksman named Bryde, who indeed came to great
honour and dignity, but only after long and great adversity and
peril of life. Many a one of us has certainly heard the tale as a child, and
perhaps when older has read it, and thought of his own unregarded
thorny road and 'great adversity'. Romance is very closely akin to
reality; but romance has its harmonious explanation here on earth,
while reality often points beyond this earthly life to the regions of
eternity. The history of the world is like a magic lantern that displays
to us, in light pictures upon the dark ground of the present, how the
benefactors of mankind, the martyrs of genius, wandered along the
thorny road of honour.

From all periods, and from every country, these shining pictures
display themselves to us: each only appears for a few moments, but
each represents a whole life, sometimes a whole age, with its conflicts
and victories. Let us contemplate here and there one of the company
of martyrs – the company which will receive new members until the
world itself shall pass away.

We look down upon a crowded amphitheatre. Out of the 'Clouds'
of Aristophanes, satire and humour are pouring down in streams upon
the audience; on the stage Socrates, the most remarkable man in
Athens, he who had been the shield and defence of the people against
the thirty tyrants, is held up mentally and bodily to ridicule – Socrates,
who saved Alcibiades and Xenophon in the turmoil of battle, and
whose genius soared far above the gods of the ancients. He himself is
present; he has risen from the spectators' bench, and has stepped
forward, that the laughing Athenians might see what likeness there
was between himself and the caricature on the stage: there he stands
before them, towering high above them all.

Thou juicy, green, poisonous hemlock, throw thy shadow over Athens and not the olive tree!

Seven cities contended for the honour of giving birth to Homer – that is to say, after his death! Let us look at him as he was in his lifetime. He wanders on foot through the cities, and recites his verses for a livelihood; the thought for the morrow turns his hair grey! He, the great seer, is blind and lonely – the sharp thorn tears the mantle of the king of poets. His songs yet live, and through them alone live all the heroes and gods of antiquity.

One picture after another springs up from the east, from the west, far removed from each other in time and place, and yet each one forming a portion of the thorny road of honour, on which the thistle indeed displays a flower, but only to adorn the grave.

The camels pass along under the palm trees; they are richly laden with indigo and other treasures of price, sent by the ruler of the land to him whose songs are the delight of the people, the fame of the country: he whom envy and falsehood have driven into exile has been found, and the caravan approaches the little town in which he has taken refuge. A poor corpse is carried out of the town gate, and the funeral procession causes the caravan to halt. The dead man is he whom they have been sent to seek – Firdusi – who has wandered the thorny road of honour even to the end.

The African, with blunt features, thick lips, and woolly hair, sits on the marble steps of the palace in the capital of Portugal, and begs: he is the faithful slave of Camoens, and but for him, and for the copper coins thrown to him by the passers-by, his master, the poet of the 'Lusiad', would die of hunger. Now, a costly monument marks the grave of Camoens.

There is a new picture.

Behind the iron grating a man appears, pale as death, with long unkempt beard.

'I have made a discovery,' he says, 'the greatest that has been made for centuries; and they have kept me locked up here for more than twenty years!'

Who is the man?

'A madman,' replies the keeper of the madhouse. 'What whimsical ideas these lunatics have! He imagines that one can propel things by means of steam.'

It is Salomon de Caus, the discoverer of the power of steam, whose theory, expressed in dark words, was not understood by Richelieu – and he dies in the madhouse!

Here stands Columbus, whom the street boys used once to follow and jeer, because he wanted to discover a new world – and he *has* discovered it. The clash of bells sounds to celebrate his triumphant return; but the clash of the bells of envy soon drowns the others. The discoverer of a world, he who lifted the American gold land from the sea, and gave it to his King – he is rewarded with iron chains. He wishes that these chains may be placed in his coffin, for they witness to the world of the way in which a man's contemporaries reward good service.

One picture after another comes crowding on; the thorny path of honour and of fame is over-filled.

Here in dark night sits the man who measured the mountains in the moon; he who forced his way out into the endless space, among stars and planets; he, the mighty man who understood the spirit of nature, and felt the earth moving beneath his feet – Galileo. Blind and deaf he sits – an old man thrust through with the spear of suffering, and amid the torments of neglect, scarcely able to lift his foot – that foot with which, in the anguish of his soul, when men denied the truth, he stamped upon the ground with the exclamation, '*Yet* it moves!'

Here stands a woman of childlike mind, yet full of faith and inspiration; she carries the banner in front of the combating army, and brings victory and salvation to her fatherland. The sound of shouting arises, and the pile flames up: they are burning the witch, Joan of Arc. Yes, and a future century jeers at the White Lily. Voltaire, the satyr of human intellect, writes '*La Pucelle*'.

At the *Thing* or Assembly at Viborg, the Danish nobles burn the laws of the King – they flame up high, illuminating the period and the law-giver, and throw a glory into the dark prison tower, where an old man is growing grey and bent. With his finger he marks out a groove in the stone table. It is the popular King who sits there, once the ruler of three kingdoms, the friend of the citizen and the peasant: it is Christian the Second. Enemies wrote his history. Let us remember his imprisonment of seven-and-twenty years, if we cannot forget his crime.

A ship sails away from Denmark; a man leans against the mast, casting a last glance towards the Island Hveen. It is Tycho Brahe. He raised the name of Denmark to the stars, and was rewarded with injury, loss, and sorrow. He is going to a strange country.

'The sky is everywhere,' he says, 'and what do I want more?'

And away sails the famous Dane, the astronomer, to live honoured and free in a strange land.

'Aye, free, if only from the unbearable sufferings of the body!' comes in a sigh through time, and strikes upon our ear. What a picture! Griffenfeldt, a Danish Prometheus, bound to the rocky island of Munkholm.

We are in America, on the margin of one of the largest rivers; an innumerable crowd has gathered, for it is said that a ship is to sail against wind and weather, bidding defiance to the elements; the man who thinks he can do this is named Robert Fulton. The ship begins its passage, but suddenly it stops. The crowd begins to laugh and whistle and hiss – the very father of the man whistles with the rest.

'Conceit! Foolery!' is the cry. 'It has happened just as he deserved: put the crack-brain under lock and key!'

Then suddenly a little nail breaks, which had stopped the machine for a few moments; and now the wheels turn again, the floats break the force of the waters, and the ship continues its course – and the beam of the steam engine shortens the distance between far lands from hours into minutes.

O human race, canst thou grasp the happiness of such a minute of consciousness, this penetration of the soul by its mission, the moment in which all dejection, and every wound – even those caused by one's own fault – is changed into health and strength and clearness – when discord is converted to harmony – the minute in which men seem to recognise the manifestation of the heavenly grace in one man, and feel how this one imparts it to all?

Thus the thorny path of honour shows itself as a glory, surrounding the earth: thrice happy he who is chosen to be a wanderer there, and, without merit of his own, to be placed among the builders of the bridge, between Providence and the human race!

On mighty wings the spirit of history floats through the ages, and shows – giving courage and comfort, and awakening gentle thoughts – on the dark nightly background, but in gleaming pictures, the thorny path of honour; which does not, like a fairy tale, end in brilliancy and joy here on earth, but points out beyond all time, even into eternity!

The Jewish Girl

AMONG THE other children in a charity school sat a little Jewish girl. She was a good, intelligent child, the quickest in all the school; but she had to be excluded from one lesson, for she was not allowed to take part in the Scripture lesson, for it was a Christian school.

In that hour the girl was allowed to open the geography book, or to do her sum for the next day; but that was soon done; and when she had mastered her lesson in geography, the book indeed remained open before her, but the little one read no more in it: she sat and listened, and the teacher soon became aware that she was listening more intently than almost any of the other children.

'Read your book,' the teacher said, in mild reproof; but her dark beaming eye remained fixed upon him; and once when he addressed a question to her, she knew how to answer better than any of the others could have done. She had heard, understood, and remembered.

When her father, a poor honest man, first brought the girl to the school, he had stipulated that she should be excluded from the lessons on the Christian faith. But it would have caused disturbance, and perhaps might have awakened discontent in the minds of the others, if she had been sent from the room during the hours in question, and consequently she stayed; but this could not go on any longer.

The teacher betook himself to her father, and exhorted him either to remove his daughter from the school, or to consent that Sara should become a Christian.

'I can no longer bear to see these gleaming eyes of the child, and her deep and earnest longing for the words of the Gospel,' said the teacher.

Then the father burst into tears.

'I know but little of our own religion,' he said; 'but her mother was a daughter of Israel, firm and steadfast in the faith, and I vowed to her as she lay dying that our child should never be baptised. I must keep my vow, for it is even as a covenant with God Himself.'

And accordingly the little Jewish maiden quitted the Christian school.

Years have rolled on.

In one of the smallest provincial towns there dwelt, as a servant in a humble household, a maiden who held the Mosaic faith. Her hair was black as ebony, her eye so dark, and yet full of splendour and light, as is usual with the daughters of the East. It was Sara. The expression in the countenance of the now grown-up maiden was still that of the child sitting upon the schoolroom bench and listening with thoughtful eyes.

Every Sunday there pealed from the church the sounds of the organ and the song of the congregation. The strains penetrated into the house where the Jewish girl, industrious and faithful in all things, stood at her work.

'Thou shalt keep holy the Sabbath-day,' said a voice within her, the voice of the Law; but her Sabbath-day was a working day among the Christians, and she could keep it holy only in her heart, which she did not think was sufficient. But then the thought arose in her soul: 'Doth God reckon by days and hours?' And on the Sunday of the Christians the hour of prayer remained undisturbed; and when the sound of the organ and the songs of the congregation sounded across to her as she stood in the kitchen at her work, then even that place seemed to become a sacred one to her. Then she would read in the Old Testament, the treasure and possession of her people, and it was only in this one she could read; for she kept faithfully in the depths of her heart the words her father had said to herself and the teacher when she was taken away from the school, and the promise given to her dying mother, that she should never receive Christian baptism, or desert the faith of her ancestors. The New Testament was to be a sealed book to her; and yet she knew much of it, and the Gospel echoed faintly among the recollections of her youth.

One evening she was sitting in a corner of the living-room. Her master was reading aloud; and she might listen to him, for it was not the Gospel that he read, but an old story-book, therefore she might stay. The book told of a Hungarian knight who was taken prisoner by a Turkish pasha, who caused him to be yoked with his oxen to the plough, and driven with blows of the whip till he almost sank under the pain and ignominy he endured. The wife of the knight at home parted with all her jewels, and pledged castle and land. The knight's friends contributed large sums, for the ransom demanded was almost unattainably high; but it was collected at last, and the knight was freed from servitude and misery. Sick and exhausted, he reached his home. But soon another summons came to war against the foes of Christianity: the sick knight heard the call, and had neither peace nor rest. He caused himself to be lifted on his war-horse; and the blood came back to his cheek, his strength appeared to return, and he went forth to battle and to victory. The very same pasha who had yoked him to the plough became his prisoner, and was dragged to his castle. But not an hour had passed when the knight stood before the captive pasha, and said to him, 'What dost thou suppose awaiteth thee?'

'I know it,' replied the Turk. 'Retribution.'

'Yes, the retribution of the Christian!' resumed the knight. 'The doctrine of Christ commands us to forgive our enemies, and to love our fellow man, for God is love. Depart in peace to thy home and to thy dear ones; but in future be mild and merciful to all who are unfortunate.'

Then the prisoner broke out into tears, and exclaimed, 'How could I believe in the possibility of such mercy? Misery and torment seemed to me inevitable; therefore I took poison, which in a few hours will kill me. I must die – there is no remedy! But before I die, do thou expound to me the teaching which includes so great a measure of love and mercy, for it is great and godlike! Grant me to hear this teaching, and to die a Christian!' And his prayer was fulfilled.

That was the legend, the story that was read. It was heard and followed by them all; but Sara, the Jewish girl, sitting alone in her corner, listened with a burning heart; great tears came into her gleaming black eyes, and she sat there with a gentle and lowly spirit as she had once sat on the school bench, and felt the grandeur of the

Gospel; and the tears rolled down over her cheeks.

But again the dying words of her mother rose up within her:

'Let not my daughter become a Christian,' the voice cried; and together with it arose the words of the Law: 'Thou shalt honour thy father and thy mother.'

'I am not baptised,' she said; 'they call me a Jewish girl – our neighbour's boys hooted me last Sunday, when I stood at the open church door, and looked in at the flaming candles on the altar, and listened to the song of the congregation. Ever since I sat upon the school bench I have felt the force of Christianity, a force like that of a sunbeam, which streams into my soul, however firmly I may shut my eyes against it. But I will not pain thee in thy grave, O my mother, I will not be unfaithful to the oath of my father, I will not read the Bible of the Christians. I have the God of my fathers to lean upon!'

And years rolled on again.

The master died. His widow fell into poverty; and the servant girl was to be dismissed. But Sara refused to leave the house: she became the staff in time of trouble, and kept the household together, working till late in the night to earn the daily bread through the labour of her hands; for no relative came forward to assist the family, and the widow became weaker every day, and lay for months together on a bed of sickness. Sara worked hard, and in the intervals sat kindly ministering by the sick-bed: she was gentle and pious, an angel of blessing in the poverty-stricken house.

'Yonder on the table lies the Bible,' said the sick woman to Sara. 'Read me something from it this long evening: my soul thirsts for the word of the Lord.'

And Sara bowed her head. Her hands folded over the Bible themselves, which she opened and read to the sick woman. Tears stood in her eyes, which gleamed and shone with ecstasy, and light shone in her heart.

'O my mother,' she whispered to herself; 'thy child may not receive the baptism of the Christians, or be admitted into the congregation – thou hast willed it so, and I shall respect thy command: we will remain in union together here on earth; but beyond this earth there is a higher union, even union in God! He will be at our side, and lead us through the valley of death. It is He that descendeth upon the earth when it is athirst, and covers it with fruitfulness. I understand it – I know not how I came to learn the truth; but it is through Him, through Christ!'

And she started as she pronounced the sacred name, and there came upon her a baptism as of flames of fire, and her frame shook, and her limbs tottered so that she sank down fainting, weaker even than the sick woman by whose couch she had watched.

Poor Sara!' said the people; 'she is overcome with night watching and toil!'

They carried her out into the hospital for the sick poor. There she died; and from thence they carried her to the grave, but not to the churchyard of the Christians, for yonder was no room for the Jewish girl; outside, by the wall, her grave was dug.

But God's sun, that shines upon the graves of the Christians, throws its beams also upon the grave of the Jewish girl beyond the wall; and when the psalms are sung in the churchyard of the Christians, they echo likewise over her lonely resting-place; and she who sleeps beneath is included in the call to the resurrection, in the name of Him who spake to His disciples:

'John baptised you with water, but I will baptise you with the Holy Ghost!'

The Bottle-Neck

IN A NARROW crooked street, among other abodes of poverty, stood an especially narrow and tall house built of timber, which had given way in every direction. The house was inhabited by poor people, and the deepest poverty was in the garret-lodging in the gable, where, in front of the only window, hung an old bent birdcage, which had not even a proper water-glass, but only a Bottle-neck reversed, with a cork stuck in the mouth, and filled with water. An old maid stood by the window: she had hung the cage with green chickweed; and a little chaffinch hopped from perch to perch, and sang and twittered merrily enough.

'Yes, it's all very well for you to sing,' said the Bottle-neck; that is to say, it did not pronounce the words as we can speak them, for a bottle-neck can't speak; but that's what he thought to himself in his own mind, as when we people talk quietly to ourselves. 'Yes, it's all very well for you to sing, you that have all your limbs uninjured. You ought to feel what it's like to lose one's body, and to have only mouth and neck left, and that with a cork into the bargain, as in my case; and then I'm sure you would not sing. But after all it is well that there should be somebody at least who is merry. I've no reason to sing, and, moreover, I can't sing. Yes, when I was a whole bottle, I sang out well if they rubbed me with a cork. They used to call me a perfect lark, a magnificent lark! Ah, when I was out at a picnic with the tanner's family, and his daughter was betrothed! Yes, I remember it as if it had happened only yesterday. I have gone through a great deal, when I come to recollect. I've been in the fire and the water, have been deep in the black earth, and have mounted higher than most of the others; and now I'm hanging here, outside the birdcage, in the air and the sunshine! Oh, it would be quite worth while to hear my history; but I don't speak aloud of it, because I can't.'

And now the Bottle-neck told its story, which was sufficiently remarkable. It told the story to itself, or only thought it in its own mind; and the little bird sang his song merrily, and down in the street there was driving and hurrying, and everyone thought of his own affairs, or perhaps of nothing at all; but the Bottle-neck did think. It thought of the flaming furnace in the manufactory, where it had been blown into life; it still remembered that it had been quite warm, that it had glanced into the hissing furnace, the home of its origin, and had felt a great desire to leap directly back again; but that gradually it had become cooler, and had been very comfortable in the place to which it was taken. It had stood in a rank with a whole regiment of brothers and sisters, all out of the same furnace; some of them had certainly been blown into champagne bottles, and others into beer bottles, and that makes a difference. Later, out in the world, it may well happen that a beer bottle may contain the most precious wine, and a champagne bottle be filled with blacking; but even in decay there is always something left by which people can see what one has been – nobility is nobility, even when filled with blacking.

All the bottles were packed up, and our bottle was among them. At that time it did not think to finish its career as a bottle-neck, or that it should work its way up to be a bird's glass, which is always an honourable thing, for one is of some consequence, after all. The bottle did not again behold the light of day till it was unpacked with the other bottles in the cellar of the wine merchant, and rinsed out for the first time; and that was a strange sensation. There it lay, empty and without a cork, and felt strangely unwell, as if it wanted something, it could not tell what. At last it was filled with good costly wine, and was provided with a cork, and sealed down. A ticket was placed on it marked 'first quality'; and it felt as if it had carried off the first prize at an examination; for, you see, the wine was good and the bottle was good. When one is young, that's the time for poetry! There was a singing and sounding within it, of things which it could not understand – of green sunny mountains, whereon the grape grows, where many vine dressers, men and women, sing and dance and rejoice. 'Ah, how beautiful is life!' There was a singing and sounding of all this in the bottle, as in a young poet's brain; and many a young poet does not understand the meaning of the song that is within him.

One morning the bottle was bought, for the tanner's apprentice was dispatched for a bottle of wine – 'of the best.' And now it was put in the provision basket, with ham and cheese and sausages; the finest butter and the best bread were put into the basket too – the tanner's daughter herself packed it. She was young and very pretty; her brown eyes laughed, and round her mouth played a smile which said just as much as her eyes. She had delicate hands, beautifully white, and her neck was whiter still; you saw at once that she was one of the most beautiful girls in the town: and still she was not engaged.

The provision basket was in the lap of the young girl when the family drove out into the forest. The Bottle-neck looked out from the folds of the white napkin. There was red wax upon the cork, and the bottle looked straight into the girl's face. It also looked at the young sailor who sat next to the girl. He was a friend of old days, the son of the portrait painter. Quite lately he had passed with honour through his examination as mate, and tomorrow he was to sail away in a ship, far off to a distant land. There had been much talk of this while the basket was being packed; and certainly the eyes and mouth of the tanner's pretty daughter did not wear a very joyous expression just then.

The young people sauntered through the greenwood, and talked to one another. What were they talking of? No, the bottle could not hear that, for it was in the provision basket. A long time passed before it was drawn forth; but when that happened, there had been pleasant things going on, for all were laughing, and the tanner's daughter laughed too; but she spoke less than before, and her cheeks glowed like two roses.

The father took the full bottle and the corkscrew in his hand. Yes, it's a strange thing to be drawn thus, the first time! The Bottle-neck could never afterwards forget that impressive moment; and indeed there was quite a convulsion within him when the cork flew out, and a great throbbing as the wine poured forth into the glasses.

'Health to the betrothed pair!' cried the papa. And every glass was emptied to the bottom, and the young mate kissed his beautiful bride.

'Happiness and blessing!' said the two old people. And the young man filled the glasses again.

'Safe return, and a wedding this day next year!' he cried; and when the glasses were emptied, he took the bottle, raised it on high, and said, 'Thou hast been present at the happiest day of my life, thou shalt never serve another!'

And so saying, he hurled it high into the air. The tanner's daughter did not then think that she should see the bottle fly again; and yet it was to be so. It then fell into the thick reeds on the margin of a little woodland lake; and the Bottle-neck could remember quite plainly how it lay there for some time.

'I gave them wine, and they give me marsh water,' he said; 'but it is well meant.'

He could no longer see the betrothed couple and the cheerful old people; but for a long time he could hear them rejoicing and singing. Then at last came two peasant boys, and looked into the reeds; they spied out the bottle, and took it up; and now it was provided for.

At their home, in the wooden cottage, the eldest of three brothers, who was a sailor, and about to start on a long voyage, had been the day before to take leave. The mother was just engaged in packing up various things he was to take with him upon his journey, and which the father was going to carry into the town that evening to see his son once more, to give him a farewell greeting from the lad's mother and himself, and a little bottle of medicated brandy had already been wrapped up in a parcel, when the boys came in with the larger and stronger bottle which they had found. This bottle would hold more than the little one, and they pronounced that the brandy would be capital for a bad digestion, inasmuch as it was mixed with medical herbs. The draught that was poured into the bottle was not so good as the red wine with which it had once been filled; these were bitter thoughts, but even these are sometimes good. The new big bottle was to go, and not the little one; and so the bottle went travelling again. It was taken on board for Peter Jensen, in the very same ship in which the young mate sailed. But he did not see the bottle; and, indeed, he would not have known it, or thought it was the same one out of which had been drunk a health to the betrothed pair and to his own happy return.

Certainly it had no longer wine to give, but still it contained something that was just as good. Accordingly, whenever Peter Jensen brought it out, it was dubbed by his messmates The Apothecary. It contained the best medicine, medicine that strengthened the weak, and it gave liberally so long as it had a drop left. That was a pleasant time, and the bottle sang when it was rubbed with the cork; and it was called the Great Lark, 'Peter Jensen's Lark.'

Long days and months rolled on, and the bottle already stood empty in a corner, when it happened – whether on the passage out or home the bottle could not tell, for it had never been ashore – that a storm arose; great waves came careering along, darkly and heavily, and lifted and tossed the ship to and fro. The mainmast was shivered, and a wave started one of the planks, and the pumps became useless. It was black night. The ship sank; but at the last moment the young mate wrote on a leaf of paper, 'God's will be done! We are sinking!' He wrote the name of his betrothed, and his own name, and that of the ship, and put the leaf in an empty bottle that happened to be at hand: he corked it firmly down, and threw it out into the foaming sea. He knew not that it was the very bottle from which the goblet of joy and hope had once been filled for him and for her; and now it was tossing on the waves with his last greeting and the message of death.

The ship sank, and the crew sank with her. The bottle sped on like a bird, for it bore a heart, a loving letter, within itself. And the sun rose and set; and the bottle felt as at the time when it first came into being in the red gleaming oven – it felt a strong desire to leap back into the light.

It experienced calms and fresh storms; but it was hurled against no rock, and was devoured by no shark; and thus it drifted on for a year and a day, sometimes towards the north, sometimes towards the south, just as the current carried it. Beyond this it was its own master, but one may grow tired even of that.

The written page, the last farewell of the sweetheart to his betrothed, would only bring sorrow if it came into her hands; but where were the hands, so white and delicate, which had once spread the cloth on the fresh grass in the greenwood, on the betrothal day? Where was the tanner's daughter? Yes, where was the land, and which land might be nearest to her dwelling? The bottle knew not; it drove onward and onward, and was at last tired of wandering, because that was not in its way; but yet it had to travel until at last it came to land – to a strange land. It understood not a word of what was spoken here, for this was not the language it had heard spoken before; and one loses a good deal if one does not understand the language.

The bottle was fished out and examined. The leaf of paper within it was discovered, and taken out, and turned over and over, but the people did not understand what was written thereon. They saw that the bottle must have been thrown overboard, and that something about this was written on the paper, but what were the words? That question remained unanswered, and the paper was put back into the bottle, and the latter was deposited in a great cupboard in a great room in a great house.

Whenever strangers came, the paper was brought out and turned over and over, so that the inscription, which was only written in pencil, became more and more illegible, so that at last no one could see that there were letters on it. And for a whole year more the bottle remained standing in the cupboard; and then it was put into the loft, where it became covered with dust and cobwebs. Then it thought of the better days, the times when it had poured forth red wine in the greenwood, when it had been rocked on the waves of the sea, and when it had carried a secret, a letter, a parting sigh.

For full twenty years it stood up in the loft; and it might have remained there longer, but that the house was to be rebuilt. The roof was taken off, and then the bottle was noticed, and they spoke about it, but it did not understand their language; for one cannot learn a language by being shut up in a loft, even if one stays there twenty years.

'If I had been down in the room,' thought the Bottle, 'I might have learned it.'

It was now washed and rinsed, and indeed this was requisite. It felt quite transparent and fresh, and as if its youth had been renewed in this its old age; but the paper it had carried so faithfully had been destroyed in the washing.

The bottle was filled with seeds, it did not know the kind. It was corked and well wrapped up. It saw neither lantern nor candle, to say nothing of sun or moon; and yet, it thought, when one goes on a journey one ought to see something; but though it saw nothing, it did what was most important – it travelled to the place of its destination, and was there unpacked.

'What trouble they have taken over yonder with that bottle!' it heard people say; 'and yet it is most likely broken.' But it was not broken.

The bottle understood every word that was now said; this was the language it had heard at the furnace, and at the wine merchant's, and in the forest, and in the ship, the only good old language it understood: it had come back home, and the language was as a salutation of welcome to it. For very joy it felt ready to jump out of people's hands; hardly did it notice that its cork had been drawn, and that it had been emptied and carried into the cellar, to be placed there and forgotten. There's no place like home, even if it's in a cellar! It never occurred to the bottle to think how long it lay there, for it felt comfortable, and accordingly lay there for years. At last people came down into the cellar to carry off all the bottles, and ours among the rest.

Out in the garden there was a great festival. Flaming lamps hung like garlands, and paper lanterns shone transparent, like great tulips. The evening was lovely, the weather still and clear, the stars twinkled; it was the time of the new moon, but in reality the whole moon could be seen as a bluish-grey disk with a golden rim round half its surface, which was a very beautiful sight for those who had good eyes.

The illumination extended even to the most retired of the garden walks; at least, so much of it that one could find one's way there. Among the leaves of the hedges stood bottles, with a light in each; and among them was also the bottle we know, and which was destined one day to finish its career as a bottle-neck, a bird's drinking-glass. Everything here appeared lovely to our bottle, for it was once more in the greenwood, amid joy and feasting, and heard song and music, and the noise and murmur of a crowd, especially in that part of the garden where the lamps blazed and the paper lanterns displayed their many colours. Thus it stood, in a distant walk certainly, but that made it the more important; for it bore its light, and was at once ornamental and useful, and that is as it should be: in such an hour one forgets twenty years spent in a loft, and it is right one should do so.

There passed close to it a pair, like the pair who had walked together long ago in the wood, the sailor and the tanner's daughter; the bottle seemed to experience all that over again. In the garden were walking not only the guests, but other people who were allowed to view all the splendour; and among these latter came an old maid without kindred, but not without friends. She was just thinking, like the bottle, of the greenwood, and of a young betrothed pair – of a pair which concerned her very nearly, a pair in which she had an interest, and of which she had been a part in that happiest hour of her life – the hour one never forgets, if one should become ever so old a maid. But she did not know the bottle, and it did not know her: it is thus we pass each other in the world, meeting again and again, as these two met, now that they were together again in the same town.

From the garden the bottle was dispatched once more to the wine merchant's, where it was filled with wine and sold to the aeronaut, who was to make an ascent in his balloon on the following Sunday. A great crowd had assembled to witness the sight; military music had been provided, and many other preparations had been made. The bottle saw everything from a basket in which it lay next to a live rabbit, which latter was quite bewildered because he knew he was to be taken up into the air, and let down again in a parachute; but the bottle knew nothing of the 'up' or the 'down'; it only saw the balloon swelling up bigger and bigger, and at last, when it could swell no more, beginning to rise, and to grow more and more restless. The ropes that held it were cut, and the huge machine floated aloft with the aeronaut and the basket containing the bottle and the rabbit, and the music sounded, and all the people cried, 'Hurrah!'

'This is a wonderful passage, up into the air!' thought the Bottle;

'this is a new way of sailing: at any rate, up here we cannot strike upon anything.'

Thousands of people gazed up at the balloon, and the old maid looked up at it also; she stood at the open window of the garret, in which hung the cage, with the little chaffinch, who had no water-glass as yet, but was obliged to be content with an old cup. In the window stood a myrtle in a pot; and it had been put a little aside that it might not fall out, for the old maid was leaning out of the window to look, and she distinctly saw the aeronaut in the balloon, and how he let down the rabbit in the parachute, and then drank to the health of all the spectators, and at length hurled the bottle high in the air; she never thought that this was the identical bottle which she had already once seen thrown aloft in honour of her and of her friend on the day of rejoicing in the greenwood, in the time of her youth.

The bottle had no time for thought, for it was quite startled at thus suddenly reaching the highest point in its career. Steeples and roofs lay far, far beneath, and the people looked like mites.

But now it began to descend with a much more rapid fall than that of the rabbit; the bottle threw somersaults in the air, and felt quite young, and quite free and unfettered; and yet it was half full of wine, though it did not remain so for long. What a journey! The sun shone on the bottle, all the people were looking at it; the balloon was already far away, and soon the bottle was far away too, for it fell upon a roof and broke; but the pieces had got such an impetus that they could not stop themselves, but went jumping and rolling on till they came down into the courtyard and lay there in smaller pieces yet; only the Bottle-neck managed to keep whole, and that was cut off as if it had been done with a diamond.

'That would do capitally for a bird-glass,' said the cellarman; but he had neither a bird nor a cage; and to expect him to provide both because they had found a bottle-neck that might be made available for a glass, would have been expecting too much; but the old maid in the garret, perhaps it might be useful to her; and now the Bottle-neck was taken up to her, and was provided with a cork. The part that had been uppermost was now turned downwards, as often happens when changes take place; fresh water was poured into it, and it was fastened to the cage of the little bird, which sang and twittered right merrily.

'Yes, it's very well for you to sing,' said the Bottle-neck.

And it was considered remarkable for having been in the balloon – for that was all they knew of its history. Now it hung there as a bird-glass, and heard the murmuring and noise of the people in the street below, and also the words of the old maid in the room within. An old friend had just come to visit her, and they talked – not of the Bottle-neck, but about the myrtle in the window.

'No, you certainly must not spend two dollars for your daughter's bridal wreath,' said the old maid. 'You shall have a beautiful little nosegay from me, full of blossoms. Do you see how splendidly that tree has come on? yes, that has been raised from a spray of the myrtle you gave me on the day after my betrothal, and from which I was to have made my own wreath when the year was past; but that day never came! The eyes closed that were to have been my joy and delight through life. In the depths of the sea he sleeps sweetly, my dear one! The myrtle has become an old tree, and I have become a yet older woman; and when it faded at last, I took the last green shoot, and planted it in the ground, and it has become a great tree; and now at length the myrtle will serve at the wedding – as a wreath for your daughter.'

There were tears in the eyes of the old maid. She spoke of the beloved of her youth, of their betrothal in the wood; many thoughts came to her, but the thought never came that, quite close to her, before the very window, was a remembrance of those times – the neck of the bottle which had shouted for joy when the cork flew out with a bang on the betrothal day. But the Bottle-neck did not recognise her either, for he was not listening to what she said – partly because it only thought about itself.

The Stone of the Wise Men

OF COURSE you know the story of Holger the Dane; we are not going to tell you that, but will ask if you remember from it that 'Holger the Dane won the great land of India, east as far as the world's end, even to the tree which is called the Tree of the Sun,' as Christian Pedersen puts it. Do you know Christian Pedersen? it doesn't matter if you don't. Holger the Dane gave Prester John power and authority over the land of India. Do you know Prester John? it doesn't matter either if you don't know him, for he doesn't come into this story at all. You are to hear about the Tree of the Sun 'in India, east as far as the world's end', and it was then understood by men who had not learned geography as we have: but that also does not matter at the present time.

The Tree of the Sun was a noble tree, such as we have never seen and such as you will never see either. The crown stretched out several miles around; it was really an entire wood; each of its smallest branches formed, in its turn, a whole tree. Palms, beech trees, pines, plane trees, and various other kinds grew here, which are found scattered in all other parts of the world: they shot out like small branches from the great boughs, and these large boughs with their windings and knots formed, as it were, valleys and hills, clothed with velvety green and covered with flowers. Every branch was like a wide, blooming meadow, or like the most charming garden. The sun shone down on it with delightful rays, for it was the tree of the sun, and the birds from all quarters of the world assembled together – birds from the primaeval forests of America, the rose gardens of Damascus, from the deserts of Africa, in which the elephant and the lion boast of being the only rulers. The Polar birds came flying hither, and of course the stork and the swallow were not absent; but the birds were not the only living beings: the stag, the squirrel, the antelope, and a hundred other beautiful and light-footed animals were at home. The crown of the tree was a widespread fragrant garden, and in the midst of it, where the great boughs raised themselves like green hillocks, there stood a castle of crystal, with a view of all the lands of the world. Each tower was reared in the form of a lily. Through the stem one could ascend, for within it was a winding stair; one could step out upon the leaves as upon balconies; and up in the calyx of the flower itself was the most beautiful, sparkling round hall, above which no other roof rose but the blue firmament with sun and stars.

Just as much splendour, though in another way, appeared below, in the wide halls of the castle. Here, on the walls, the whole world around was reflected. One saw everything that was done, so that there was no necessity for reading any papers, and indeed there were no papers there. Everything was to be seen in living pictures, if one only wished to see it; for too much is still too much even for the wisest man; and this man dwelt here. His name is very difficult – you will not be able to pronounce it, and therefore it may remain unmentioned. He knew everything that a man on earth can know or can get to know; every invention which had already been or which was yet to be made was known to him; but nothing more, for everything in the world has its limits. The wise King Solomon was only half as wise as he, and yet he was very wise, and governed the powers of nature, and held sway over potent spirits: yea, Death itself was obliged to give him every morning a list of those who were to die during the day. But King Solomon himself was obliged to die too; and this thought it was which often in the deepest manner employed the enquirer, the mighty lord in the castle on the Tree of the Sun. He also, however high he might tower above men in wisdom, must die one day. He knew that he and his children also must fade away like the leaves of the forest, and become dust. He saw the human race fade away like the leaves on the tree; saw new men come to fill their places; but the leaves that fell off never sprouted forth again – they fell to dust or were transformed into other parts of plants.

'What happens to man,' the wise man asked himself, 'when the angel of death touches him? What may death be? The body is dissolved. And the soul? Yes, what is the soul? whither doth it go? To eternal life, says the comforting voice of religion; but what is the transition? where does one live and how? Above, in heaven, says the pious man, thither we go. Thither?' repeated the wise man, and fixed his eyes upon the sun and the stars; 'up yonder?'

But he saw, from the earthly ball, that up and down were one and the same, according as one stood here or there on the rolling globe; and even if he mounted as high as the loftiest mountains of earth rear their heads, to the air which we below call clear and transparent – the pure heaven – a black darkness spread abroad like a cloth, and the sun had a coppery glow and sent forth no rays, and our earth lay wrapped in an orange-coloured mist. How narrow were the limits of the bodily eye, and how little the eye of the soul could see! how little did even the wisest know of that which is the most important to us all!

In the most secret chamber of the castle lay the greatest treasure of the earth: the Book of Truth. Leaf for leaf, the wise man read it through: every man may read in this book, but only by fragments. To many an eye the characters seem to tremble, so that the words cannot be put together; on certain pages the writing often seems so pale, so faded, that only a blank leaf appears. The wiser a man becomes, the more he can read; and the wisest read most. For that purpose he knew how to unite the sunlight and the starlight with the light of reason and of hidden powers; and through this stronger light many things came clearly before him from the page. But in the division of the book whose title is 'Life after Death' not even one point was to be distinctly seen. That pained him. Should he not be able here upon earth to obtain a light by which everything should become clear to him that stood written in the Book of Truth?

Like the wise King Solomon, he understood the language of the animals, and could interpret their talk and their songs. But that made him none the wiser. He found out the forces of plants and metals – the forces to be used for the cure of diseases, for delaying death – but none that could destroy death. In all created things that were within his reach he sought the light that should shine upon the certainty of an eternal life; but he found it not. The Book of Truth lay before him with leaves that appeared blank. Christianity showed him in the Bible words of promise of an eternal life; but he wanted to read it in *his* book, and in that he saw nothing.

He had five children – four sons, educated as well as the children of the wisest father could be, and a daughter, fair, mild, and clever, but blind; yet this appeared no loss to her – her father and brothers were eyes to her, and the vividness of her feelings saw for her.

Never had the sons gone farther from the castle than the branches of the tree extended, still less the sister. They were happy children in the land of childhood – in the beautiful fragrant Tree of the Sun. Like all children, they were very glad when any story was related to them; and the father told them many things that other children would not have understood; but these were just as clever as most grown-up people are among us. He explained to them what they saw in living pictures on the castle walls – the doings of men and the march of events in all the lands of the earth; and often the sons expressed the wish that they could be present at all the great deeds and take part in them; and their father then told them that out in the world it was difficult and toilsome – that the world was not quite what it appeared to them from their beauteous home. He spoke to them of the true, the beautiful, and the good, and told them that these three things held the world together, and that under the pressure they had to endure they became hardened into a precious stone, clearer than the water of the diamond – a jewel whose splendour had value with God, and whose brightness outshone everything, and which was called the 'Stone of the Wise'. He told them that just as one through created things could attain to the knowledge of God, so through men themselves one could attain to the certainty that such a jewel as the 'Stone of the Wise' existed. He could not tell them any more about it, for he knew no more. This narration would have exceeded the perception of other children, but these children understood it, and at length other children, too, will learn to comprehend its meaning.

They questioned their father concerning the true, the beautiful, and the good; and he explained it to them, told them many things, and told them also that God, when He made man out of the dust of the earth, gave five kisses to His work – fiery kisses, heart kisses – which we now call the five senses. Through these the true, the beautiful, and the good is seen, perceived, and understood; through these it is valued, protected, and furthered. Five senses have been given bodily and mentally, inwardly and outwardly, to body and soul.

The children reflected deeply upon all these things; they meditated upon them by day and night. Then the eldest of the brothers dreamed a splendid dream. Strangely enough, the second brother had the same dream, and the third, and the fourth brother likewise; all of them dreamed exactly the same thing – namely, that each went out into the world and found the 'Stone of the Wise', which gleamed like a beaming light on his forehead when, in the morning dawn, he rode back on his swift horse over the velvety green meadows of his home into the castle of his father; and the jewel threw such a heavenly light and radiance upon the leaves of the book, that everything was illuminated that stood written concerning the life beyond the grave. But the sister dreamed nothing about going out into the wide world: it never entered her mind. Her world was her father's house.

'I shall ride forth into the wide world,' said the eldest brother. 'I must try what life is like there, and go to and fro among men. I will practise only the good and the true; with these I will protect the beautiful. Much shall change for the better when I am there.'

Now his thoughts were bold and great, as our thoughts generally are at home in the corner of the hearth, before we have gone forth into the world and have encountered wind and rain, and thorns and thistles.

In him and in all his brothers the five senses were highly developed, inwardly and outwardly; but each of them had *one* sense which in keenness and development surpassed the other four. In the case of the eldest this was Sight. This was to do him especial service. He said he had eyes for all time, eyes for all nations, eyes that could look into the depths of the earth, where the treasures lie hidden, and deep into the hearts of men, as though nothing but a pane of glass were placed before them: he could read more than we can see on the cheek that blushes or grows pale, in the eye that weeps or smiles. Stags and antelopes escorted him to the boundary of his home towards the west, and there the wild swans received him and flew north-west. He followed them. And now he had gone far out into the world – far from the land of his father, that extended eastward to the end of the earth.

But how he opened his eyes in astonishment! Many things were here to be seen; and many things appear very different, when a man beholds them with his own eyes, from when he merely sees them in a picture, as the son had done in his father's house, however faithful the picture may be. At the outset he nearly lost his eyes in astonishment at all the rubbish and all the masquerading stuff put forward to represent the beautiful; but he did not quite lose them, he had other use for them. He wished to go thoroughly and honestly to work in the understanding of the beautiful, the true, and the good. But how were these represented in the world? He saw that often the garland that belonged to the beautiful was given to the hideous; that the good was often passed by without notice, while mediocrity was applauded when it should have been hissed off. People looked to the dress, and not to the wearer; asked for a name, and not for desert; and went more by reputation than by service. It was the same thing everywhere.

'I see I must attack these things vigorously,' he said, and attacked them with vigour accordingly.

But while he was looking for the truth, came the Evil One, the father of lies. Gladly would the fiend have plucked out the eyes of this Seer; but that would have been too direct: the devil works in a more cunning way. He let him see and seek the true and the good; but while the young man was contemplating them, the Evil Spirit blew one mote after another into each of his eyes; and such a proceeding would be hurtful even to the best sight. Then the fiend blew upon the motes, so that they became beams; and the eyes were destroyed, and the Seer stood like a blind man in the wide world, and had no faith in it: he lost his good opinion of it and himself; and when a man gives up the world and himself, all is over with him.

'Over!' said the wild swans, who flew across the sea towards the east. 'Over!' twittered the swallows, who likewise flew eastward, towards the Tree of the Sun. That was no good news for those at home.

'I fancy the *Seer* must have fared badly,' said the second brother; 'but the *Hearer* may have better fortune.' For this one possessed the sense of hearing in an eminent degree: he could hear the grass grow, so quick was he to hear.

He took a hearty leave of all at home, and rode away, provided with good abilities and good intentions. The swallows escorted him, and he followed the swans; and he stood far from his home in the wide world.

But he experienced the fact that one may have too much of a good thing. His hearing was *too* fine. He not only heard the grass grow, but could hear every man's heart beat, in sorrow and in joy. The whole world was to him like a great clockmaker's workshop, wherein all the clocks were going 'tick, tick!' and all the turret clocks striking 'ding dong'. It was unbearable. For a long time his ears held out, but at last all the noise and screaming became too much for one man. There came blackguard boys of sixty years old – for it is not age that does it; they roared and shouted in a way that one could laugh at; but then came gossip, which whispered through all houses, lanes, and streets, right out to the highway. Falsehood thrust itself forward and played the master; the bells on the fool's cap jangled and declared they were church bells; and the noise became too bad for the Hearer, and he thrust his fingers into both ears; but still he could hear false singing and bad sounds, gossip and idle words, scandal and slander, groaning and moaning without and within. Heaven help us! He thrust his fingers deeper and deeper into his ears, but at last the drums burst. Now he could hear nothing at all of the good, the true, and the beautiful, for his hearing was to have been the bridge by which he crossed. He became silent and suspicious, trusted no one at last, not even himself, and that is very unfortunate, and, no longer hoping to find and bring home the costly jewel, he gave it up, and gave himself up; and that was the worst of all. The birds who winged their flight towards the east brought tidings of this, till the news reached the castle in the Tree of the Sun.

'*I* will try now!' said the third brother. 'I have a sharp *nose*!'

Now that was not said in very good taste; but it was his way, and one must take him as he was. He had a happy temper, and was a poet, a real poet: he could sing many things that he could not say, and many things struck him far earlier than they occurred to others. 'I can smell fire!' he said; and he attributed to the sense of smelling, which he possessed in a very high degree, a great power in the region of the beautiful.

'Every fragrant spot in the realm of the beautiful has its frequenters,' he said. 'One man feels at home in the atmosphere of the tavern, among the flaring tallow candles, where the smell of spirits mingles with the fumes of bad tobacco. Another prefers sitting among the overpowering scent of jessamine, or scenting himself with strong clove oil. This man seeks out the fresh sea breeze, while that one climbs to the highest mountain-top and looks down upon the busy little life beneath.'

Thus he spake. It seemed to him as if he had already been out in the world, as if he had already associated with men and known them. But this experience arose from within himself: it was the poet within him, the gift of Heaven, and bestowed on him in his cradle.

He bade farewell to his paternal roof in the Tree of the Sun, and departed on foot through the pleasant scenery of home. Arrived at its confines, he mounted on the back of an ostrich, which runs faster than a horse; and afterwards, when he fell in with the wild swans, he swung himself on the strongest of them, for he loved change; and away he flew over the sea to distant lands with great forests, deep lakes, mighty mountains, and proud cities; and wherever he came it seemed as if sunshine travelled with him across the fields, for every flower, every bush, every tree exhaled a new fragrance, in the consciousness that a friend and protector was in the neighbourhood, who understood them and knew their value. The crippled rose bush reared up its twigs, unfolded its leaves, and bore the most beautiful roses; everyone could see it, and even the black damp Wood Snail noticed its beauty.

'I will give my seal to the flower,' said the Snail; 'I have spit on it, and I can do no more for it.'

'Thus it always fares with the beautiful in this world!' said the poet.

And he sang a song concerning it, sang it in his own way; but nobody listened. Then he gave the drummer twopence and a peacock's feather, and set the song for the drum, and had it drummed in all the streets of the town; and the people heard it, and said that they understood it, it was so deep. Then the poet sang several songs of the beautiful, the true, and the good. His songs were listened to in the tavern, where the tallow candles smoked, in the fresh meadow, in the forest, and on the high seas. It appeared as if this brother was to have better fortune than the two others. But the Evil Spirit was angry at this, and accordingly he set to work with incense powder and incense smoke, which he can prepare so artfully as to confuse an angel, and how much more therefore a poor poet! The Evil One knows how to take that kind of people! He surrounded the poet so completely with incense, that the man lost his head, and forgot his mission and his home, and at last himself – and ended in smoke.

But when the little birds heard of this they mourned, and for three days they sang not one song. The black Wood Snail became blacker still, not for grief, but for envy.

'They should have strewed incense for me,' she said, 'for it was I who gave him his idea of the most famous of his songs, the drum song of "The Way of the World"; it was I who spat upon the rose! I can bring witness to the fact.'

But no tidings of all this penetrated to the poet's home in India, for all the birds were silent for three days; and when the time of mourning was over, their grief had been so deep that they had forgotten for whom they wept. That's the usual way!

'Now I shall have to go out into the world, to disappear like the rest,' said the fourth brother.

He had just as good a humour as the third, but he was no poet, and so he had good reason to have good humour. Those two had filled the castle with cheerfulness, and now the last cheerfulness was going away. Sight and hearing have always been looked upon as the two chief senses of men, and as the two that it is most desirable to sharpen; the other senses are looked upon as of less consequence. But that was not the opinion of this son, as he had especially cultivated his *taste* in every respect, and taste is very powerful. It holds sway over what goes into the mouth, and also over what penetrates into the mind; and consequently this brother tasted everything that was stored up in bottles and pots, saying that this was the rough work of his office. Every man was to him a vessel in which something was seething, every country an enormous kitchen, a kitchen of the mind.

'That was the fine work,' he said; and he wanted to go out and try what was delicate. 'Perhaps fortune may be more favourable to me than it was to my brothers,' he said. 'I shall start on my travels. But what conveyance shall I choose? Are air balloons invented yet?' he asked his father, who knew of all inventions that had been made or that were to be made. But air balloons had not yet been invented, nor steamships, nor railways. 'Good: then I shall choose an air balloon,' he said; 'my father knows how they are made and guided. Nobody has invented them yet, and consequently the people will believe that it is an aerial phantom. When I have used the balloon I will burn it, and for this purpose you must give me a few pieces of the invention that will be made next – I mean chemical matches.'

And he obtained what he wanted, and flew away. The birds accompanied him farther than they had flown with the other brothers. They were curious to know what would be the result of the flight, and more of them came sweeping up: they thought he was some new bird; and he soon had a goodly following. The air became black with birds, they came on like a cloud – like the cloud of locusts over the land of Egypt.

Now he was out in the wide world.

'I have had a good friend and helper in the East Wind,' he said.

'The East and the West Wind, you mean,' said the winds. 'We have been both at work, otherwise you would not have come north-west.'

But he did not hear what the winds said, and it does not matter either. The birds had also ceased to accompany him. When they were most numerous, a few of them became tired of the journey. Too much was made of this kind of thing, they said. He had got fancies into his head. 'There is nothing at all to fly after; there is nothing; it's quite stupid;' and so they stayed behind, the whole flock of them.

The air balloon descended over one of the greatest cities, and the aeronaut took up his station on the highest point, on the church steeple. The balloon rose again, which it ought not to have done: where it went to is not known, but that was not a matter of consequence, for it was not yet invented. Then he sat on the church steeple. The birds no longer hovered around him, they had got tired of him, and he was tired of them.

All the chimneys in the town were smoking merrily.

'Those are altars erected to thy honour!' said the Wind, who wished to say something agreeable to him.

He sat boldly up there, and looked down upon the people in the street. There was one stepping along, proud of his purse, another of the key he carried at his girdle, though he had nothing to unlock; one proud of his motheaten coat, another of his wasted body.

'Vanity! I must hasten downward, dip my finger in the pot, and taste!' he said. 'But for a while I will still sit here, for the wind blows so pleasantly against my back. I'll sit here as long as the wind blows. I'll enjoy a slight rest. "It is good to sleep long in the morning, when one has much to do," says the lazy man, but laziness is the root of all evil, and there is no evil in our family. I'll stop here as long as this wind blows, for it pleases me.'

And there he sat, but he was sitting upon the weathercock of the steeple, which kept turning round and round with him, so that he thought that the same wind still blew; so he might stay up there a goodly while.

But in India, in the castle in the Tree of the Sun, it was solitary and still, since the brothers had gone away one after the other.

'It goes not well with them,' said the father; 'they will never bring the gleaming jewel home; it is not made for me: they are gone, they are dead!'

And he bent down over the Book of Truth, and gazed at the page on which he should read of life after death; but for him nothing was to be seen or learned upon it.

The blind daughter was his consolation and joy; she attached herself with sincere affection to him, and for the sake of his peace and joy she wished the costly jewel might be found and brought home. With sorrow and longing she thought of her brothers. Where were they? Where did they live? She wished sincerely that she might dream of them, but it was strange, not even in dreams could she approach them. But at length, one night she dreamed that the voices of her brothers sounded across to her, calling to her from the wide world, and she could not refrain, but went far far out, and yet it seemed in her dream that she was still in her father's house. She did not meet her brothers, but she felt, as it were, a fire burning in her hand, but it did not hurt her, for it was the jewel she was bringing to her father. When she awoke, she thought for a moment that she still held the stone, but it was the knob of her distaff that she was grasping. During the long nights she had spun incessantly, and round the distaff was turned a thread, finer than the finest web of the spider; human eyes were unable to distinguish the separate threads. She had wetted them with her tears, and the twist was strong as a cable. She rose, and her resolution was taken: the dream must be made a reality. It was night, and her father slept. She pressed a kiss upon his hand, and then took her distaff, and fastened the end of the thread to her father's house. But for this, blind as she was, she would never have found her way home; to the thread she must hold fast, and trust not to herself or to others. From the Tree of the Sun she broke four leaves; these she would confide to wind and weather, that they might fly to her brothers as a letter and a greeting, in case she did not meet them in the wide world. How would she fare out there, she, the poor blind child? But she had the invisible thread to which she could hold fast. She possessed a gift which all the others lacked. This was *thoroughness*; and in virtue of this it seemed as if she had eyes at the tips of her fingers and ears down in her very heart.

And quietly she went forth into the noisy, whirling, wonderful world, and wherever she went the sky grew bright – she felt the warm ray – the rainbow spread itself out from the dark cloud through the blue air. She heard the song of the birds, and smelt the scent of orange groves and apple orchards so strongly that she seemed to taste it. Soft tones and charming songs reached her ear, but also howling and roaring, and thoughts and opinions sounded in strange contradiction to each other. Into the innermost depths of her heart penetrated the echoes of human thoughts and feelings. One chorus sounded darkly –

> The life of earth is a shadow vain,
> A night created for sorrow!

but then came another strain –

> The life of earth is the scent of the rose,
> With its sunshine and its pleasure.

And if one strophe sounded painfully –

> Each mortal thinks of himself alone,
> This truth has been shown, how often!

on the other side the answer pealed forth –

> A mighty stream of warmest love
> All through the world shall bear us.

She heard, indeed, the words –

> In the little petty whirl here below,
> Each thing shows mean and paltry;

but then came also the comfort –

> Many things great and good are achieved,
> That the ear of man heareth never.

And if sometimes the mocking strain sounded around her –

> Join in the common cry; with a jest
> Destroy the good gifts of the Giver,

in the blind girl's heart a stronger voice repeated –

> To trust in thyself and in God is best;
> *His will* be done for ever.

And whenever she entered the circle of human kind, and appeared among young or old, the knowledge of the true, the good, and the beautiful beamed into their hearts. Whether she entered the study of the artist, or the festive decorated hall, or the crowded factory, with its whirring wheels, it seemed as though a sunbeam were stealing in – as if the sweet string sounded, the flower exhaled its perfume, and a living dewdrop fell upon the exhausted leaf.

But the Evil Spirit could not see this and be content. He has more cunning than ten thousand men, and he found out a way to compass his end. He betook himself to the marsh, collected little bubbles of the stagnant water, and passed over them a sevenfold echo of lying words to give them strength. Then he pounded up paid-for eulogies and lying epitaphs, as many as he could get, boiled them in tears that envy had shed, put upon them rouge he had scraped from faded cheeks, and of these he composed a maiden, with the aspect and gait of the blessed blind girl, the angel of thoroughness; and then the Evil One's plot was in full progress. The world knew not which of the two was the true one; and, indeed, how should the world know?

'To trust in thyself and in God is best;
His good will be done for ever,'

sang the blind girl, in full faith. She entrusted the four green leaves from the Tree of the Sun to the winds, as a letter and a greeting to her brothers, and had full confidence that they would reach their destination, and that the jewel would be found which outshines all the glories of the world. From the forehead of humanity it would gleam even to the castle of her father.

'Even to my father's house,' she repeated. 'Yes, the place of the jewel is on earth, and I shall bring more than the promise of it with me. I feel its glow, it swells more and more in my closed hand. Every grain of truth, were it never so fine, which the sharp wind carried up and whirled towards me, I took up and treasured; I let it be penetrated by the fragrance of the beautiful, of which there is so much in the world, even for the blind. I took the sound of the beating heart engaged in what is good, and added it to the first. All that I bring is but dust, but still it is the dust of the jewel we seek, and in plenty. I have my whole hand full of it.'

And she stretched forth her hand towards her father. She was soon at home – she had travelled thither in the flight of thoughts, never having quitted her hold of the invisible thread from the paternal home.

The evil powers rushed with hurricane fury over the Tree of the Sun, pressed with a wind-blast against the open doors, and into the sanctuary.

'It will be blown away by the wind!' said the father, and he seized the hand she had opened.

'No,' she replied, with quiet confidence, 'it cannot be blown away; I feel the beam warming my very soul.'

And the father became aware of a glancing flame, there where the shining dust poured out of her hand over the Book of Truth, that was to tell of the certainty of an everlasting life; and on it stood one shining word – one only word – 'Faith.'

And with the father and daughter were again the four brothers. When the green leaf fell upon the bosom of each, a longing for home had seized them and led them back. They had arrived. The birds of passage, and the stag, the antelope, and all the creatures of the forest followed them, for all wished to have a part in their joy.

We have often seen, where a sunbeam bursts through a crack in the door into the dusty room, how a whirling column of dust seems circling round; but this was not poor and insignificant like common dust, for even the rainbow is dead in colour compared with the beauty which showed itself. Thus, from the leaf of the book with the beaming word 'Faith', arose every grain of truth, decked with the charms of *the beautiful* and *the good*, burning brighter than the mighty pillar of flame that led Moses and the children of Israel through the desert; and from the word '*Faith*' went the bridge of *Hope* the Infinite.

Soup on a Sausage-Peg

I

'THAT WAS a remarkably fine dinner yesterday,' observed an old Mouse of the female sex to another who had not been at the festive gathering. 'I sat number twenty-one from the old Mouse King, so that I was not badly placed. Should you like to hear the order of the banquet? The courses were very well arranged – mouldy bread, bacon rind, tallow candle, and sausage – and then the same dishes over again from the beginning: it was just as good as having two banquets on end. There was as much joviality and agreeable jesting as in the family circle. Nothing was left but the pegs at the ends of the sausages. And the discourse turned upon these; and at last the expression, "Soup on a sausage-peg," was mentioned. Everyone had heard the proverb, but no one had ever tasted the sausage-peg soup, much less knew how to prepare it. A capital toast was drunk to the inventor of the soup, and it was said he deserved to be a relieving officer. Was not that witty? And the old Mouse King stood up, and promised that the young mouse who could best prepare that soup should be his queen; and a year was allowed for the trial.'

'That was not at all bad,' said the other Mouse; 'but how does one prepare this soup?'

'Ah, how is it prepared? That is just what all the young female mice, and the old ones too, are asking. They would all very much like to be queen; but they don't want to take the trouble to go out into the world to learn how to prepare the soup, and that they would certainly have to do. But everyone has not the gift of leaving the family circle and the chimney corner. Away from home one can't get cheese rinds and bacon every day. No, one must bear hunger, and perhaps be eaten up alive by a cat.'

Such were no doubt the thoughts by which most of them were

scared from going out to gain information. Only four Mice announced themselves ready to depart. They were young and brisk, but poor. Each of them would go to one of the four quarters of the globe, and then it was a question which of them was favoured by fortune. Everyone took a sausage-peg, so as to keep in mind the object of the journey. This was to be their pilgrim's staff.

It was at the beginning of May that they set out, and they did not return till the May of the following year; and then only three of them appeared. The fourth did not report herself, nor was there any intelligence of her, though the day of trial was close at hand.

'Yes, there's always some drawback in even the pleasantest affair,' said the Mouse King.

And then he gave orders that all mice within a circuit of many miles should be invited. They were to assemble in the kitchen, the three travelled Mice stood in a row by themselves, while a sausage-peg, shrouded in crape, was set up as a memento of the fourth, who was missing. No one was to proclaim his opinion before the three had spoken and the Mouse King had settled what was to be said further. And now let us hear.

2

What the First little Mouse had seen and learned in her Travels

'When I went out into the wide world,' said the little Mouse, 'I thought, as many think at my age, that I had already learned everything; but that was not the case. Years must pass before one gets so far. I went to sea at once. I went in a ship that steered towards the north. They had told me that the ship's cook must know how to manage things at sea; but it is easy enough to manage things when one has plenty of sides of bacon, and whole tubs of salt pork, and mouldy flour. One has delicate living on board; but one does not learn to prepare soup on a sausage-peg. We sailed along for many days and nights; the ship rocked fearfully, and we did not get off without a wetting. When we at last reached the port to which we were bound, I left the ship; and it was high up in the far north.

'It is a wonderful thing, to go out of one's own corner at home, and sail in a ship, where one has a sort of corner too, and then suddenly to find oneself hundreds of miles away in a strange land. I saw great pathless forests of pine and birch, which smelt so strong that I sneezed, and thought of sausage. There were great lakes there too. When I came close to them the waters were quite clear, but from a distance they looked black as ink. White swans floated upon them: I thought at first they were spots of foam, they lay so still; but then I saw them walk and fly, and I recognised them. They belong to the goose family – one can see that by their walk; for no one can deny his parentage. I kept with my own kind. I associated with the forest and field mice, who, by the way, know very little, especially as regards cookery, though this was the very thing that had brought me abroad. The thought that soup might be boiled on a sausage-peg was such a startling idea to them, that it flew at once from mouth to mouth through the whole forest. They declared the problem could never be solved; and little did I think that there, on the very first night, I should be initiated into the method of its preparation. It was in the height of summer, and that, the mice said, was the reason why the wood smelt so strongly, and why the herbs were so fragrant, and the lakes so clear and yet so dark, with the white swans on them.

'On the margin of the wood, among three or four houses, a pole as tall as the mainmast of a ship had been erected, and from its summit hung wreaths and ribbons: this was called a maypole. Men and maids danced round the tree, and sang as loudly as they could, to the violin of the fiddler. There were merry doings at sundown and in the moonlight, but I took no part in them – what has a little mouse to do with a May dance? I sat in the soft moss and held my sausage-peg fast. The moon shone especially upon one spot, where a tree stood, covered with moss so fine that I may almost venture to say it was as fine as the skin of the Mouse King; but it was of a green colour, so that it was a great relief to the eye.

'All at once, the most charming little people came marching forth. They were only tall enough to reach to my knee. They looked like men, but were better proportioned: they called themselves elves, and had delicate clothes on, of flower leaves trimmed with the wings of flies and gnats, which had a very good appearance. Directly they appeared, they seemed to be seeking for something – I knew not what; but at last some of them came towards me, and the chief pointed to my sausage-peg, and said, "That is just such a one as we want – it is pointed – it is capital!" and the longer he looked at my pilgrim's staff the more delighted he became.

' "I will lend it," I said, "but not to keep."

' "Not to keep!" they all repeated; and they seized the sausage-peg, which I gave up to them, and danced away to the spot where the fine moss grew; and here they set up the peg in the midst of the green. They wanted to have a maypole of their own, and the one they now had, seemed cut out for them; and they decorated it so that it was beautiful to behold.

'First, little spiders spun it round with gold thread, and hung it all over with fluttering veils and flags, so finely woven, bleached so snowy white in the moonshine, that they dazzled my eyes. They took colours from the butterfly's wing, and strewed these over the white linen, and flowers and diamonds gleamed upon it, so that I did not know my sausage-peg again: there is not in all the world such a maypole as they had made of it. And now came the real great party of elves. They were quite without clothes, and looked as dainty as possible; and they invited me to be present; but I was to keep at a distance, for I was too large for them.

'And now began such music! It sounded like thousands of glass bells, so full, so rich, that I thought the swans were singing. I fancied also that I heard the voice of the cuckoo and the blackbird, and at last the whole forest seemed to join in. I heard children's voices, the sound of bells, and the song of birds; the most glorious melodies – and all came from the elves' maypole, namely, my sausage-peg. I should never have believed that so much could come out of it; but that depends very much upon the hands into which it falls. I was quite touched. I wept, as a little mouse may weep, with pure pleasure.

'The night was far too short; but it is not longer up yonder at that season. In the morning dawn the breeze began to blow, the mirror of the forest lake was covered with ripples, and all the delicate veils and flags fluttered away in the air. The waving garlands of spiders' web, the hanging bridges and balustrades, and whatever else they are called, flew away as if they were nothing at all. Six elves brought me back my sausage-peg, and asked me at the same time if I had any wish that they could gratify; so I asked them if they could tell me how soup was made on a sausage-peg.

' "How *we* do it?" asked the chief of the elves, with a smile. "Why, you have just seen it. I fancy you hardly knew your sausage-peg again?"

' "You only mean that as a joke," I replied. And then I told them in so many words, why I had undertaken a journey, and what hopes were founded on it at home. "What advantage," I asked, "can it be to our Mouse King, and to our whole powerful state, from the fact of my having witnessed all this festivity? I cannot shake it out of the sausage-peg, and say, 'Look, here is the peg, now the soup will come.' That would be a dish that could only be offered when the guests had dined."

'Then the elf dipped his little finger into the cup of a blue violet, and said to me, ' "See here! I will anoint your pilgrim's staff; and when you go back home to the castle of the Mouse King, you have but to touch his warm breast with the staff, and violets will spring forth and cover its whole staff, even in the coldest winter-time. And so I think I've given you something to carry home, and a little more than something!"'

But before the little Mouse said what this 'something more' was, she stretched her staff out towards the King's breast, and in very truth the most beautiful bunch of violets burst forth; and the scent was so powerful that the Mouse King incontinently ordered the mice who stood nearest the chimney to thrust their tails into the fire and create a smell of burning, for the odour of the violets was not to be borne, and was not of the kind he liked.

'But what was the "something more", of which you spoke?' asked the Mouse King.

'Why,' the little Mouse answered, 'I think it is what they call effect!' and herewith she turned the staff round, and lo! there was not a single flower to be seen upon it; she only held the naked skewer, and lifted this up like a music *bâton*. ' "Violets," the elf said to me, "are for sight, and smell, and touch. Therefore it yet remains to provide for hearing and taste!" '

And now the little Mouse began to beat time; and music was heard, not such as sounded in the forest among the elves, but such as is heard in the kitchen. There was a bubbling sound of boiling and roasting; and all at once it seemed as if the sound were rushing through every chimney, and pots or kettles were boiling over. The fire-shovel hammered upon the brass kettle, and then, on a sudden, all was quiet again. They heard the quiet subdued song of the tea-kettle, and it was wonderful to hear – they could not quite tell if the kettle were beginning to sing or leaving off; and the little pot simmered, and the big pot simmered, and neither cared for the other: there seemed to be no reason at all in the pots. And the little Mouse flourished her *bâton* more and more wildly; the pots foamed, threw up large bubbles, boiled over, and the wind roared and whistled through the chimney. Oh! it became so terrible that the little Mouse lost her stick at last.

'That was a heavy soup!' said the Mouse King. 'Shall we not soon hear about the preparation?'

'That was all,' said the little Mouse, with a bow.

'That all! Then we should be glad to hear what the next has to relate,' said the Mouse King.

3

What the Second little Mouse had to tell

'I was born in the palace library,' said the second Mouse. 'I and several members of our family never knew the happiness of getting into the dining-room, much less into the store-room; on my journey, and here today, are the only times I have seen a kitchen. We have indeed often been compelled to suffer hunger in the library, but we got a good deal of knowledge. The rumour penetrated even to us, of the royal prize offered to those who could cook soup upon a sausage-peg; and it was my old grandmother who thereupon ferreted out a manuscript, which she certainly could not read, but which she had heard read out, and in which it was written: "Those who are poets can boil soup upon a sausage-peg." She asked me if I were a poet. I felt quite innocent of that, and then she told me I must go out, and manage to become one. I again asked what was required for that, for it was as difficult for me to find that out as to prepare the soup; but grandmother had heard a good deal of reading, and she said that three things were especially necessary: "Understanding, imagination, feeling – if you can go and get these into you, you are a poet, and the sausage-peg affair will be quite easy to you."

'And I went forth, and marched towards the west, away into the wide world, to become a poet.

'Understanding is the most important thing in every affair. I knew that, for the two other things are not held in half such respect, and consequently I went out first to seek understanding. Yes, where does that dwell? "Go to the ant and be wise," said the great King of the Jews; I knew that from the library; and I never stopped till I came to the first great ant-hill, and there I placed myself on the watch, to become wise.

'The ants are a respectable people. They are understanding itself. Everything with them is like a well-worked sum, that comes right. To work and to lay eggs, they say, is to live while you live, and to provide for posterity; and accordingly that is what they do. They were divided into the clean and the dirty ants. The rank of each is indicated by a number, and the ant queen is number one; and her view is the only correct one, she has absorbed all wisdom; and that was important for me to know. She spoke so much, and it was all so clever, that it sounded to me like nonsense. She declared her ant-hill was the loftiest thing in the world; though close by it grew a tree, which was certainly loftier, much loftier, that could not be denied, and therefore it was never mentioned. One evening an ant had lost herself upon the tree; she had crept up the stem – not up to the crown, but higher than any ant had climbed until then; and when she turned, and came back home, she talked of something far higher than the ant-hill that she had found; but the other ants considered that an insult to the whole community, and consequently she was condemned to wear a muzzle, and to continual solitary confinement. But a short time afterwards another ant got on the tree, and made the same journey and the same discovery: and this one spoke about it with caution and indefiniteness, as they said; and as, moreover, she was one of the pure ants and very much respected, they believed her; and when she died they erected an eggshell as a memorial of her, for they had a great respect for the sciences. I saw,' continued the little Mouse, 'that the ants are always running to and fro with their eggs on their backs. One of them once dropped her egg; she exerted herself greatly to pick it up again, but she could not succeed. Then two others came up, and helped her with all their might, insomuch that they nearly dropped their own eggs over it; but then they stopped helping at once, for each should think of himself first – the ant queen had declared that by so doing they exhibited at once heart and understanding.

' "These two qualities," she said, "place us ants on the highest step among all reasoning beings. Understanding must and shall be the predominant thing, and I have the greatest share of understanding." And so saying, she raised herself on her hind legs, so that she was easily to be recognised. I could not be mistaken, and I ate her up. Go to the ant and be wise – and I had got the queen!

'I now proceeded nearer to the before-mentioned lofty tree. It was an oak, and had a great trunk and a far-spreading top, and was very old. I knew that a living being dwelt here, a Dryad as it is called, who is born with the tree, and dies with it. I had heard about this in the library; and now I saw an oak tree and an oak girl. She uttered a piercing cry when she saw me so near. Like all females, she was very much afraid of mice; and she had more ground for fear than others, for I might have gnawed through the stem of the tree on which her life depended. I spoke to her in a friendly and intimate way, and bade her take courage. And she took me up in her delicate hand; and when I had told her my reason for coming out into the wide world, she promised me that perhaps on that very evening I should have one of the two treasures of which I was still in quest. She told me that Phantasy was her very good friend, that he was beautiful as the god of love, and that he rested many an hour under the leafy boughs of the tree, which then rustled more strongly than ever over the pair of them. He called her his Dryad, she said, and the tree his tree, for the grand gnarled oak was just to his taste, with its root burrowing so deep in the earth and the stem and crown rising so high out in the fresh air, and knowing the beating snow, and the sharp wind, and the warm sunshine, as they deserve to be known. "Yes," the Dryad continued, "the birds sing aloft there and tell of strange countries; and on the only dead bough the stork has built a nest which is highly ornamental, and, moreover, one gets to hear something of the land of the pyramids. All that is very pleasing to Phantasy; but it is not enough for him: I myself must tell him of life in the woods, when I was little, and the tree such a delicate thing that a stinging-nettle overshadowed it – and I have to tell everything, till now that the tree is great and strong. Sit you down under the green woodruff, and pay attention; and when Phantasy comes, I shall find an opportunity to pinch his wings, and to pull out a little feather. Take that – no better is given to any poet – and it will be enough for you!"

'And when Phantasy came the feather was plucked, and I seized it,' said the little Mouse. 'I held it in water, till it grew soft. It was very hard to digest, but I nibbled it up at last. It is not at all easy to gnaw oneself into being a poet, there are so many things one must take into oneself. Now I had these two things, imagination and understanding, and through these I knew that the third was to be found in the library; for a great man has said and written that there are romances whose sole and single use is that they relieve people of their superfluous tears, and that they are, in fact, like sponges sucking up human emotion. I remembered a few of these old books, which had always looked especially palatable, and were much thumbed and very greasy, having evidently absorbed a great deal of feeling into themselves.

'I betook myself back to the library, and devoured nearly a whole novel – that is, the essence of it, the soft part, for I left the crust or binding. When I had digested this, and a second one in addition, I felt a stirring within me, and I ate a bit of a third romance, and now I was a poet. I said so to myself, and told the others also. I had headache, and stomach-ache, and I can't tell what aches besides. I began thinking what kind of stories could be made to refer to a sausage-peg; and many pegs came into my mind – the ant queen must have had a particularly fine understanding. I remembered the man who took a white peg in his mouth, and then both he and the peg were invisible. I thought of being screwed up a peg, of standing on one's own pegs, and of driving a peg into one's own coffin. All my thoughts ran upon pegs; and when one is a poet (and I am a poet, for I have worked most terribly hard to become one) a person can make poetry on these subjects. I shall therefore be able to wait upon you every day with a poem or a history – and that's the soup I have to offer.'

'Let us hear what the third has to say,' said the Mouse King.

'Peep! peep!' was heard at the kitchen door, and a little Mouse – it was the fourth of them, the one whom they looked upon as dead – shot in like an arrow. She toppled the sausage-peg with the crape covering over. She had been running day and night, and had travelled on the railway, in the goods train, having watched her opportunity, and yet she had almost come too late. She pressed forward, looking very much rumpled, and she had lost her sausage-peg, but not her voice, for she at once took up the word, as if they had been waiting only for her, and wanted to hear none but her, and as if everything else in the world were of no consequence. She spoke at once, and spoke fully: she had appeared so suddenly that no one found time to object to her speech or to her, while she was speaking. And now let us hear her.

4

What the Fourth Mouse, who spoke before the Third had spoken, had to tell

'I went immediately to the largest town,' she said; 'the name has escaped me – I have a bad memory for names. From the railway I was carried, with some confiscated goods, to the council-house, and there I ran into the dwelling of the jailer. The jailer was talking of his prisoners, and especially of one, who had spoken unconsidered words. These words had given rise to others, and these latter had been written down and recorded.

' "The whole thing is soup on a sausage-peg," said the jailer; "but the soup may cost him his neck."

'Now, this gave me an interest in the prisoner,' continued the Mouse, 'and I watched my opportunity and slipped into his prison – for there's a mouse-hole to be found behind every locked door. The prisoner looked pale, and had a great beard and bright sparkling eyes. The lamp smoked, but the walls were so accustomed to that, that they grew none the blacker for it. The prisoner scratched pictures and verses in white upon the black ground, but I did not read them. I think he found it tedious, and I was a welcome guest. He lured me with bread crumbs, with whistling, and with friendly words: he was glad to see me, and I got to trust him, and we became friends. He shared with me his bread and water, gave me cheese and sausage; I lived well, but I must say that it was especially the good society that kept me there. He let me run upon his hand, his arm, and into his sleeve; he let me creep about in his beard, and called me his little friend. I really got to love him, for these things are reciprocal. I forgot my mission in the wide world, forgot my sausage-peg in a crack in the floor – it's lying there still. I wished to stay where I was, for if I went away the poor prisoner would have no one at all, and that's having *too* little, in this world. *I* stayed, but *he* did not stay. He spoke to me very mournfully the last time, gave me twice as much bread and cheese as usual, and kissed his hand to me; then he went away, and never came back. I don't know his history.

' "Soup on a sausage-peg!" said the jailer, to whom I now went; but I should not have trusted him. He took me in his hand, certainly, but he popped me into a cage, a treadmill. That's a horrible engine, in which you go round and round without getting any farther; and people laugh at you into the bargain.

'The jailer's granddaughter was a charming little thing, with a mass of curly hair that shone like gold, and such merry eyes, and such a smiling mouth!

' "You poor little mouse," she said, as she peeped into my ugly cage; and she drew out the iron rod, and forth I jumped to the window board, and from thence to the roof spout. Free! free! I thought only of that, and not of the goal of my journey.

'It was dark, and night was coming on. I took up my quarters in an old tower, where dwelt a watchman and an owl. I trusted neither of them, and the owl least. That is a creature like a cat, who has the great failing that she eats mice. But one may be mistaken, and so was I, for this was a very respectable, well-educated old owl: she knew more than the watchman, and as much as I. The young owls were always making a racket; but "Do not make soup on a sausage-peg" were the hardest words she could prevail on herself to utter, she was so fondly attached to her family. Her conduct inspired me with so much confidence, that from the crack in which I was crouching I called out "Peep!" to her. This confidence of mine pleased her hugely, and she assured me I should be under her protection, and that no creature should be allowed to do me wrong; she would reserve me for herself, for the winter, when there would be short commons.

'She was in every respect a clever woman, and explained to me how the watchman could only "whoop" with the horn that hung at his side, adding, "He is terribly conceited about it, and imagines he's an owl in the tower. Wants to do great things, but is very small – soup on a sausage-peg!"

'I begged the owl to give me the recipe for this soup, and then she explained the matter to me.

' "Soup on a sausage-peg," she said, "was only a human proverb, and was understood in different ways: Each thinks his own way the best, but the whole really signifies nothing."

' "Nothing!" I exclaimed. I was quite struck. Truth is not always agreeable, but truth is above everything; and that's what the old owl said. I now thought about it, and readily perceived that if I brought what was *above everything* I brought something far beyond soup on a sausage-peg. So I hastened away, that I might get home in time, and bring the highest and best, that is above everything – namely, *the truth*. The mice are an enlightened people, and the King is above them all. He is capable of making me Queen, for the sake of truth.'

'Your truth is a falsehood,' said the Mouse who had not yet spoken. 'I can prepare the soup, and I mean to prepare it.'

5

How it was prepared

'I did not travel,' the third Mouse said. 'I remained in my country – that's the right thing to do. There's no necessity for travelling; one can get everything as good here. I stayed at home. I've not learned what I know from supernatural beings, or gobbled it up, or held converse with owls. I have what I know through my own reflections. Will you just put that kettle upon the fire and get water poured in up to the brim! Now make up the fire, that the water may boil – it must boil over and over! Now throw the peg in. Will the King now be pleased to dip his tail in the boiling water, and to stir it round? The longer the King stirs it, the more powerful will the soup become. It costs nothing at all – no further materials are necessary, only stir it round!'

'Cannot anyone else do that?' asked the Mouse King.

'No,' replied the Mouse. 'The power is contained only in the tail of the Mouse King.'

And the water boiled and bubbled, and the Mouse King stood close beside the kettle – there was almost danger in it – and he put forth his tail, as the mice do in the dairy, when they skim the cream from a pan of milk, and afterwards lick the tail; but he only got his into the hot steam, and then he sprang hastily down from the hearth.

'Of course – certainly you are my Queen,' he said. 'We'll wait for the soup till our golden wedding, so that the poor of my subjects may have something to which they can look forward with pleasure for a long time.'

And soon the wedding was held. But many of the mice said, as they were returning home, that it could not be really called soup on a sausage-peg, but rather soup on a mouse's tail. They said that some of the stories had been very cleverly told; but the whole thing might have been different. '*I* should have told it so – and so – and so!'

Thus said the critics, who are always wise – after the fact.

And this story went round the world; and opinions varied concerning it, but the story remained as it was. And that's the best in great things and in small, so also with regard to soup on a sausage-peg – not to expect any thanks for it.

The Old Bachelor's Nightcap

THERE IS a street in Copenhagen that has this strange name – 'Hysken Straede'. Whence comes this name and what is its meaning? It is said to be German; but injustice has been done to the Germans in this matter, for it would have to be 'Häuschen', and that means little houses. For here stood, once upon a time, and indeed for a great many years, a few little houses, which were little more than wooden booths, just as we see now in the market-places at fair-time. They were, perhaps, a little larger, and had windows; but the panes were of horn or bladder, for glass was then too expensive to be used in every house. But then we are speaking of a long time ago – so long since, that grandfather's grandfather, when he talked about it, used to speak of it as 'the old times' – in fact, it is several centuries ago.

The rich merchants in Bremen and Lübeck carried on trade with Copenhagen. They did not come here themselves, but sent their clerks, who lived in the wooden booths in the street of the small houses, and sold beer and spices. The German beer was good, and there were many kinds of it – Bremen, and Pryssing, Emser, and even Brunswick mumm; and quantities of spices were sold – saffron, and aniseed, and ginger, and especially pepper. Yes, pepper was the chief article here; and so it happened that the German clerks got the nickname, 'pepper gentry'; and there was a condition which they had to enter into at home, that they would not marry at Copenhagen, and many of them became very old. They had to care for themselves, and to look after their own comforts, and to put out their own fire – when they had any; and some of them became very solitary old boys, with eccentric ideas and eccentric habits. From them, all unmarried men who have attained a certain age are called in Denmark 'pepper gentry'; and this must be understood by all who wish to comprehend this history.

The 'pepper gentleman' becomes a butt for ridicule, and is told that he ought to put on his nightcap, draw it down over his eyes, and go to bed. The boys sing –

> 'Cut, cut wood,
> Poor bachelor's a sorry elf;
> A nightcap goes with him to bed,
> And he must light his fire himself.'

Yes, that's what they sing about the 'pepperer' – thus they make game of the poor bachelor and his nightcap, just because they know very little about either. Ah, that kind of nightcap no one should wish to earn! And why not? We shall hear.

In the old times the street of the small houses was not paved, and the people stumbled out of one hole into another, as in a neglected byway; and it was narrow too. The booths leaned side by side, and stood so close together that in the summer-time a sail was often stretched from one booth to its opposite neighbour, on which occasion the fragrance of pepper, saffron, and ginger became doubly powerful. Behind the counters young men were seldom seen. The clerks were generally old boys; but they did not look like what we should fancy them, namely, with wig, and nightcap, and plush small-clothes, and with waistcoat and coat buttoned up to the chin. No, grandfather's great-grandfather may look like that, and has been thus portrayed, but the 'pepper gentry' did not have the means to have their portraits taken; though, indeed, it would be interesting now to have a picture of one of them, as he stood behind the counter or went to church on holy days. His hat was high-crowned and broad-brimmed, and sometimes one of the youngest clerks would mount a feather. The woollen shirt was hidden behind a broad clean collar, the close jacket was buttoned up to the chin, and the cloak hung loose over it; and the trousers were tucked into the broad-toed shoes, for the clerks did not wear stockings. In their girdles they carried a dinner-knife and spoon, and a larger knife was placed there also for the defence of the owner; and this weapon was often very necessary. Just so was Anthony, one of the oldest clerks, clad on high days and holy days, except that, instead of a high-crowned hat, he wore a low bonnet, and under it a knitted cap (a regular nightcap), to which he had grown so accustomed that it was always on his head; and he had two of them. The old fellow was a subject for a painter. He was as thin as a lath, had wrinkles about his eyes and mouth, and long bony fingers, and bushy grey eyebrows; over the left eye hung quite a tuft of hair, and that did not look very handsome, though it made him very noticeable. People knew that he came from Bremen; but that was not his native place, though his master lived there. His own native place was in Thuringia, the town of Eisenach, close by the Wartburg. Old Anthony did not speak much of this, but he thought of it all the more.

The old clerks in the street did not often come together. Each one remained in his booth, which was closed early in the evening; and then it looked dark enough in the street: only a faint glimmer of light forced its way through the little horn-pane in the roof; and in the booth sat, generally on his bed, the old bachelor, his German hymn-book in his hand, singing an evening psalm; or he went about in the booth till late into the night, and busied himself about all sorts of things. It was certainly not an amusing life. To be a stranger in a strange land is a bitter lot: nobody cares for you, unless you happen to get in anybody's way.

Often when it was dark night outside, with snow and rain, the place looked very gloomy and lonely. No lamps were to be seen, with the exception of one solitary light hanging before the picture of the Virgin that was fastened against the wall. The plash of the water against the neighbouring rampart at the castle wharf could be plainly heard. Such evenings are long and dreary, unless people devise some employment for themselves. There is not always packing or unpacking to do, nor can the scales be polished or paper bags be made continually; and, failing these, people should devise other employment for themselves. And that is just what old Anthony did; for he used to mend his clothes and put pieces on his boots. When he at last sought his couch he used from habit to keep his nightcap on. He drew it down a little closer; but soon he would push it up again, to see if the light had been properly extinguished. He would touch it, press the wick together, and then lie down on the other side, and draw his nightcap down again; but then a doubt would come upon him, if every coal in the little fire-pan below had been properly deadened and put out – a tiny spark might have been left burning, and might set fire to something and cause damage. And therefore he rose from his bed, and crept down the ladder, for it could scarcely be called a stair. And when he came to the fire-pan not a spark was to be discovered, and he might just go back again. But often, when he had gone half of the way back, it would occur to him that the shutters might not be securely fastened; yes, then his thin legs must carry him downstairs once more. He was cold, and his teeth chattered in his mouth when he crept back again to bed; for the cold seems to become doubly severe when it knows it cannot stay much longer. He drew up the coverlet closer around him, and pulled down the nightcap lower over his brows, and turned his thoughts away from trade and from the labours of the day. But that did not procure him agreeable entertainment; for now old thoughts came and put up their curtains, and these curtains have sometimes pins in them, with which one pricks oneself, and one cries out 'Oh!' and they prick into one's flesh and burn so, that the tears sometimes come into one's eyes; and that often happened to old Anthony – hot tears. The largest pearls streamed forth, and fell on the coverlet or on the floor, and then they sounded as if one of his heart-strings had broken. Sometimes again they seemed to rise up in flame, illuminating a picture of life that never faded out of his heart. If he then dried his eyes with his nightcap, the tear and the picture were indeed crushed, but the source of the tears remained, it lay in his heart. The pictures did not come up in the order in which the scenes had occurred in reality, for very often the most painful would come together; then again the most joyful would come, but these had the deepest shadows of all.

The beech woods of Denmark are beautiful, but the woods of Thuringia arose far more beautiful in the eyes of Anthony. More mighty and more venerable seemed to him the old oaks around the proud knightly castle, where the creeping plants hung down over the stony blocks of the rock; sweeter there bloomed the flowers of the apple tree than in the Danish land. This he remembered very vividly.

A glittering tear rolled down over his cheek; and in this tear he could plainly see two children playing – a boy and a girl. The boy had red cheeks, and yellow curling hair, and honest blue eyes. He was the son of the rich merchant, little Anthony – himself. The little girl had brown eyes and black hair, and had a bright clever look. She was the burgomaster's daughter Molly. The two were playing with an apple. They shook the apple, and heard the pips rattling in it. Then they cut the apple in two, and each of them took a half; they divided even the pips, and ate them all but one, which the little girl proposed that they should lay in the earth.

'Then you shall see,' she said, 'what will come out. It will be something you don't at all expect. A whole apple tree will come out, but not directly.'

And she put the pip in a flowerpot, and both were very busy and eager about it. The boy made a hole in the earth with his finger, and the little girl dropped the pip in it, and they both covered it with earth.

'Now, you must not take it out tomorrow to see if it has struck root,' said Molly. 'That won't do at all. I did it with my flowers; but only twice. I wanted to see if they were growing – I didn't know any better then – and the plants withered.'

Anthony took away the flowerpot, and every morning, the whole winter through, he looked at it; but nothing was to be seen but the black earth. At length, however, the spring came, and the sun shone warm again; and two little green leaves came up out of the pot.

'Those are for me and Molly,' said the boy. 'That's beautiful – that's marvellously beautiful!'

Soon a third leaf made its appearance. Whom did that represent? Yes, and there came another, and yet another. Day by day and week by week they grew larger, and the plant began to take the form of a real tree. And all this was now mirrored in a single tear, which was wiped away and disappeared; but it might come again from its source in the heart of old Anthony.

In the neighbourhood of Eisenach a row of stony mountains rises up. One of these mountains is round in outline, naked and without tree, bush, or grass. It is called the Venus Mount. In this mountain dwells Lady Venus, one of the deities of the heathen times. She is also called Lady Holle; and every child in and around Eisenach has heard about her. She it was who lured Tannhäuser, the noble knight and minstrel, from the circle of the singers of the Wartburg into her mountain.

Little Molly and Anthony often stood by this mountain; and once Molly said, 'Dare you knock and say, "Lady Holle, open the door – Tannhäuser is here"?'

But Anthony did not dare. Molly, however, did it, though she only said the words 'Lady Holle, Lady Holle!' aloud and distinctly; the rest she muttered so indistinctly that Anthony felt convinced she had not really said anything; and yet she looked as bold and saucy as possible – as saucy as when she sometimes came round him with other little girls in the garden, and all wanted to kiss him because he did not like to be kissed and tried to keep them off; and she was the only one who dared to kiss him.

'*I* may kiss him!' she would say proudly.

That was her vanity; and Anthony submitted, and thought no more about it.

How charming and how teasing Molly was! It was said that Lady Holle in the mountain was beautiful also, but that her beauty was like that of a tempting fiend. The greatest beauty and grace was possessed by Saint Elizabeth, the patron saint of the country, the pious Princess of Thuringia, whose good actions have been immortalised in many places in legends and stories. In the chapel her picture was hanging, surrounded by silver lamps; but it was not in the least like Molly.

The apple tree which the two children had planted grew year by year, and became so tall, that it had to be transplanted into the garden, into the fresh air, where the dew fell and the sun shone warm. And the tree developed itself strongly, so that it could resist the winter. And it seemed as if, after the rigour of the cold season was past, it put forth blossoms in spring for very joy. In the autumn it brought two apples – one for Molly and one for Anthony. It could not well have produced less.

The tree had grown apace, and Molly grew like the tree. She was as fresh as an apple-blossom: but Anthony was not long to behold this flower. All things change! Molly's father left his old home, and Molly went with him, far away. Yes, in our time steam has made the journey they took a matter of a few hours, but then more than a day and a night were necessary to go so far eastward from Eisenach to the farthest border of Thuringia, to the city which is still called Weimar.

And Molly wept, and Anthony wept; but all their tears now melted into one, and this tear had the rosy, charming hue of joy. For Molly told him she loved him – loved him more than all the splendours of Weimar.

One, two, three years went by, and during this period two letters were received. One came by a carrier, and a traveller brought the other. The way was long and difficult, and passed through many windings by towns and villages.

Often had Molly and Anthony heard of Tristram and Iseult, and often had the boy applied the story to himself and Molly, though the name Tristram was said to mean 'born in tribulation', and that did not apply to Anthony, nor would he ever be able to think, like Tristram, 'She has forgotten me.' But, indeed, Iseult did not forget her faithful knight; and when both were laid to rest in the earth, one on each side of the church, the linden trees grew from their graves over the church roof, and there met each other in bloom. Anthony thought that was beautiful, but mournful, but it could not become mournful between him and Molly; and he whistled a song of the old minnesinger, Walter of the Vogelweide –

> Under the lindens
> Upon the heath.

And especially that passage appeared charming to him –

> From the forest, down in the vale,
> Sang her sweet song the nightingale.

This song was often in his mouth, and he sang and whistled it in the moonlight night, when he rode along the deep hollow way on horseback to get to Weimar and visit Molly. He wished to come unexpectedly, and he came unexpectedly.

He was made welcome with full goblets of wine, with jovial company, fine company, and a pretty room and a good bed were provided for him; and yet his reception was not what he had dreamed and fancied it would be. He could not understand himself – he could not understand the others; but *we* can understand it. One may be admitted into a house and associate with a family without becoming one of them. One may converse together as one would converse in a post-carriage, and know one another as people know each other on a journey, each incommoding the other and wishing that either oneself or the good neighbour were away. Yes, that was the kind of thing Anthony felt.

'I am an honest girl,' said Molly, 'and I myself will tell you what it is. Much has changed since we were children together – changed inwardly and outwardly. Habit and will have no power over our hearts. Anthony, I should not like to have an enemy in you, now that I shall soon be far away from here. Believe me, I entertain the best wishes for you; but to feel for you what I know now one may feel for a man, has never been the case with me. You must reconcile yourself to this. Farewell, Anthony!'

And Anthony bade her farewell. No tear came into his eye, but he felt that he was no longer Molly's friend. Hot iron and cold iron alike take the skin from our lips, and we have the same feeling when we kiss it: and he kissed himself into hatred as into love.

Within twenty-four hours Anthony was back in Eisenach, though certainly the horse on which he rode was ruined.

'What matter!' he said: 'I am ruined too; and I will destroy everything that can remind me of her, or of Lady Holle, or Venus the heathen woman! I will break down the apple tree and tear it up by the roots, so that it shall never bear flower or fruit more!'

But the apple tree was not broken down, though he himself was broken down, and bound on a couch by fever. What could raise him up again? A medicine was presented to him which had strength to do this – the bitterest of medicines, that shakes up body and spirit together. Anthony's father ceased to be the richest of merchants. Heavy days – days of trial – were at the door; misfortune came rolling into the house like great waves of the sea. The father became a poor man. Sorrow and suffering took away his strength. Then Anthony had to think of something else besides nursing his love-sorrows and his anger against Molly. He had to take his father's place – to give orders, to help, to act energetically, and at last to go out into the world and earn his bread.

Anthony went to Bremen. There he learned what poverty and hard living meant; and these sometimes make the heart hard, and sometimes soften it, even too much.

How different the world was, and how different the people were from what he had supposed them to be in his childhood! What were the minnesinger's songs to him now? an echo, a vanishing sound! Yes, that is what he thought sometimes; but again the songs would sound in his soul, and his heart became gentle.

'God's will is best!' he would say then. 'It was well that I was not permitted to keep Molly's heart – that she did not remain true to me. What would it have led to now, when fortune has turned away from me? She quitted me before she knew of this loss of prosperity, or had any notion of what awaited me. That was a mercy of Providence towards me. Everything has happened for the best. It was not her fault – and I have been so bitter, and have shown so much rancour towards her!'

And years went by. Anthony's father was dead, and strangers lived in the old house. But Anthony was destined to see it again. His rich employer sent him on commercial journeys, and his duty led him into his native town of Eisenach. The old Wartburg stood unchanged on the mountain, with 'the monk and the nun' hewn out in stone. The great oaks gave to the scene the outlines it had possessed in his childish days. The Venus Mount glimmered grey and naked over the valley. He would have been glad to cry, 'Lady Holle, Lady Holle, unlock the door, and I shall enter and remain in my native earth!'

That was a sinful thought, and he blessed himself to drive it away. Then a little bird out of the thicket sang clearly, and the old minnesong came into his mind:

From the forest, down in the vale,
Sang her sweet song the nightingale.

And here in the town of his childhood, which he thus saw again through tears, much came back into his remembrance. His father's house stood as in the old times; but the garden was altered, and a field-path led over a portion of the old ground, and the apple tree that he had not broken down stood there, but outside the garden, on the farther side of the path. But the sun threw its rays on the apple tree as in the old days, the dew descended gently upon it as then, and it bore such a burden of fruit that the branches were bent down towards the earth.

'That flourishes!' he said. 'The tree can grow!'

Nevertheless, one of the branches of the tree was broken. Mischievous hands had torn it down towards the ground; for now the tree stood by the public way.

'They break its blossoms off without a feeling of thankfulness – they steal its fruit and break the branches. One might say of the tree as has been said of some men – "It was not sung at his cradle that it should come thus." How brightly its history began, and what has it come to? Forsaken and forgotten – a garden tree by the hedge, in the field, and on the public way! There it stands unprotected, plundered, and broken! It has certainly not died, but in the course of years the number of blossoms will diminish; at last the fruit will cease altogether; and at last – at last all will be over!'

Such were Anthony's thoughts under the tree; such were his thoughts during many a night in the lonely chamber of the wooden house in the distant land – in the street of the small houses in Copenhagen, whither his rich employer, the Bremen merchant, had sent him, first making it a condition that he should not marry.

'Marry! Ha, ha!' he laughed bitterly to himself.

Winter had set in early; it was freezing hard. Without, a snowstorm was raging, so that everyone who could do so remained at home; thus, too, it happened that those who lived opposite to Anthony did not notice that for two days his house had not been unlocked, and that he did not show himself; for who would go out unnecessarily in such weather?

They were grey, gloomy days; and in the house, whose windows were not of glass, twilight only alternated with dark night. Old Anthony had not left his bed during the two days, for he had not the strength to rise; he had for a long time felt in his limbs the hardness of the weather. Forsaken by all lay the old bachelor, unable to help himself. He could scarcely reach the water-jug that he had placed by his bedside, and the last drop it contained had been consumed. It was not fever, nor sickness, but old age that had struck him down. Up there, where his couch was placed, he was overshadowed, as it were, by continual night. A little spider, which, however, he could not see, busily and cheerfully span its web around him, as if it were weaving a little crape banner that should wave when the old man closed his eyes.

The time was very slow, and long, and dreary. Tears he had none to shed, nor did he feel pain. The thought of Molly never came into his mind. He felt as if the world and its noise concerned him no longer – as if he were lying outside the world, and no one were thinking of him. For a moment he felt a sensation of hunger – of thirst. Yes, he felt them both. But nobody came to tend him – nobody. He thought of those who had once suffered want; of Saint Elizabeth, as she had once wandered on earth; of her, the saint of his home and of his childhood, the noble Duchess of Thuringia, the benevolent lady who had been accustomed to visit the lowliest cottages, bringing to the inmates refreshment and comfort. Her pious deeds shone bright upon his soul. He thought of her as she had come to distribute words of comfort, binding up the wounds of the afflicted and giving meat to the hungry, though her stern husband had chidden her for it. He thought of the legend told of her, how she had been carrying the full basket containing food and wine, when her husband, who watched her footsteps, came forth and asked angrily what she was carrying, whereupon she answered, in fear and trembling, that the basket contained roses which she had plucked in the garden; how he had torn away the white cloth from the basket, and a miracle had been performed for the pious lady; for bread and wine, and everything in the basket, had been transformed into roses!

Thus the saint's memory dwelt in Anthony's quiet mind; thus she stood bodily before his downcast face, before his warehouse in the simple booth in the Danish land. He uncovered his head, and looked into her gentle eyes, and everything around him was beautiful and roseate. Yes, the roses seemed to unfold themselves in fragrance. There came to him a sweet, peculiar odour of apples, and he saw a blossoming apple tree, which spread its branches above him – it was the tree which Molly and he had planted together.

And the tree strewed down its fragrant leaves upon him, cooling his burning brow. The leaves fell upon his parched lips, and were like strengthening bread and wine; and they fell upon his breast, and he felt calm, and inclined to sleep peacefully.

'Now I shall sleep,' he whispered to himself. 'Sleep is refreshing. Tomorrow I shall be upon my feet again, and strong and well – glorious, wonderful! That apple tree, planted in true affection, now stands before me in heavenly radiance –'

And he slept.

The day afterwards – it was the third day that his shop had remained closed – the snowstorm had ceased, and a neighbour from the opposite house came over towards the booth where dwelt old Anthony, who had not yet shown himself. Anthony lay stretched upon his bed – dead – with his old cap clutched tightly in his two hands! They did not put that cap on his head in his coffin, for he had a new white one.

Where were now the tears that he had wept? What had become of the pearls? They remained in the nightcap – and the true ones do not come out in the wash – they were preserved in the nightcap, and in time forgotten; but the old thoughts and the old dreams still remained in the 'bachelor's nightcap'. Don't wish for such a cap for yourself. It would make your forehead very hot, would make your pulse beat feverishly, and conjure up dreams which appear like reality. The first who wore that cap afterwards felt all that, though it was half a century afterwards; and that man was the burgomaster himself, who had a wife and eleven children, and was very well off. He was immediately seized with dreams of unfortunate love, of bankruptcy, and of heavy times.

'Hallo! how the nightcap warms!' he cried, and tore it from his head.

And a pearl rolled out, and another, and another, and they sounded and glittered.

'This must be gout,' said the burgomaster. 'Something dazzles my eyes!'

They were tears, shed half a century before by old Anthony from Eisenach.

Everyone who afterwards put that nightcap upon his head had visions and dreams. His own history was changed into that of Anthony, and became a story; in fact, many stories. But someone else may tell *them*. We have told the first. And our last word is – don't wish for 'the Old Bachelor's Nightcap'.

Something

'I WANT TO be something!' said the eldest of five brothers. 'I want to be of use in the world. I don't care how humble my position may be in society, if I only effect some good, for that will really be something. I'll make bricks, for they are quite indispensable things, and then I shall truly have done something.'

'But that *something* will not be enough!' quoth the second brother. 'What you intend doing is just as much as nothing at all. It is journey-man's work, and can be done by a machine. No, I would rather be a bricklayer at once, for that *is* something real; and that's what I will be. That brings rank: as a bricklayer one belongs to a guild, and is a citizen, and has one's own flag and one's own house of call. Yes, and if all goes well, I will keep journeymen. I shall become a master bricklayer, and my wife will be a master's wife – that is what *I* call something.'

'That's nothing at all!' said the third. 'That is outside of the classes, and there are many of those in a town that stand far above the mere master artisan. You may be an honest man; but as a "master" you will after all only belong to those who are ranked among common men. I know something better than that. I will be an architect, and will thus enter into the territory of art and speculation. I shall be reckoned among those who stand high in point of intellect. I must begin at the bottom – I may as well say it straight out; so I must begin as a carpenter's apprentice, and must go about with a cap, though I am accustomed to wear a silk hat. I shall have to fetch beer and spirits for the common journeymen, and they will call me "thou", and that is insulting! But I shall imagine to myself that the whole thing is only acting, and a kind of masquerade. Tomorrow – that is to say, when I have served my time – I shall go my own way, and the others will be nothing to me. I shall go to the academy, and get instructions in drawing, and shall be called an architect. *That's something!* I may get to be called "sir", and even "worshipful sir", or even get a handle at the front or at the back of my name, and shall go on building and building, just as those before me have built. That will always be a thing to remember, and that's what *I* call something!'

'But I don't care at all for *that* something,' said the fourth. '*I* won't sail in the wake of others, and be a copyist. I will be a genius, and will stand up greater than all the rest of you together. I shall be the creator of a new style, and will give the plan of a building suitable to the climate and the material of the country, for the nationality of the people, for the development of the age – and an additional story for my own genius.'

'But supposing the climate and the material are bad,' said the fifth, 'that would be a disastrous circumstance, for these two exert a great influence! Nationality, moreover, may expand itself until it becomes affectation, and the development of the century may run wild with your work, as youth often runs wild. I can quite well see that none of you will be anything real, however much you may believe in yourselves. But, do what you like, I will not resemble you: I shall keep on the outside of things, and criticise whatever you produce. To every work there is attached something that is not right; and I will ferret that out and find fault with it; and *that* will be doing *something*!'

And he kept his word; and everybody said concerning this fifth brother, 'There is certainly something in him; he has a good head, but he does nothing.' And by that very means they thought *something* of him!

Now, you see, this is only a little story; but it will never end so long as the world lasts.

But did nothing further come of the five brothers? For this was *nothing* at all.

Listen, it is a story in itself.

The eldest brother, who made bricks, became aware that every brick, when it was finished, produced for him a little coin, only of copper; but many copper pennies laid one upon the other can become a shining dollar; and wherever one knocks with such a dollar in one's hand, whether at the baker's, or the butcher's, or the tailor's – wherever it may be, the door flies open, and one gets what one wants. You see, that is what comes of bricks. Some certainly went to pieces, or broke in two, but there was a use even for these.

On the sea-dyke, Margaret, the poor woman, wished to build herself a little house. All the faulty bricks were given to her, and a few perfect ones into the bargain, for the eldest brother was a good-natured man, though he certainly did not achieve anything beyond the manufacture of bricks. The poor woman put together the house for herself. It was little and narrow, and the single window was quite crooked. The door was too low, and the thatched roof might have shown better workmanship. But after all it was a shelter; and from the little house you could look far across the sea, whose waves broke vainly against the dyke. The salt billows spurted their spray over the whole house, which was still standing when he who had given the bricks was dead and gone.

The second brother knew better how to build a wall, for he had served an apprenticeship to it. When he had served his time and passed his examination, he packed his knapsack and sang the journeyman's song:

> While I am young I'll wander, from place to place I'll roam,
> And everywhere build houses, until I come back home;
> And youth will give me courage, and my true love won't forget:
> Hurrah then for a workman's life! I'll be a master yet!

And he carried his idea into effect. When he had come home and become a master, he built one house after another in the town. He built a whole street; and when the street was finished and had become an ornament to the place, the houses built a house for him in return, that was to be his own. But how can houses build a house? If you ask them they will not answer you, but people will answer, and say, 'Certainly, it was the street that built his house for him.' It was little, and the floor was covered with clay; but when he danced with his bride upon this clay floor, it became polished oak; and from every stone in the wall sprang forth a flower, and the room was gay, as if with the costliest paperhanger's work. It was a pretty house, and in it lived a happy pair. The flag of the guild fluttered before the house, and the journeymen and apprentices shouted hurrah! Yes, *that was something*! And at last he died; and *that* was something too.

Now came the architect, the third brother, who had been at first a carpenter's apprentice, had worn a cap, and served as an errand boy, but had afterwards gone to the academy, and risen to become an architect, and to be called 'honoured sir'. Yes, if the houses of the street had built a house for the brother who had become a bricklayer, the street now received its name from the architect, and the handsomest house in it became his. *That* was something, and *he* was something; and he had a long title before and after his name. His children were called *genteel* children, and when he died his widow was 'a widow of rank', and *that* is something! and his name always remained at the corner of the street, and lived on in the mouth of everyone as the street's name – and *that* was something!

Now came the genius, the fourth brother, who wanted to invent something new and original, and an additional story on the top of it. But the top story tumbled down, and he came tumbling down with it, and broke his neck. Nevertheless he had a splendid funeral, with guild flags and music, poems in the papers, and flowers strewn on the paving-stones in the street; and three funeral orations were held over him, each one longer than the last, which would have rejoiced him greatly, for he was always fond of being talked about; a monument also was erected over his grave. It was only one story high, but *that* is always *something*.

Now he was dead, like the three other brothers; but the last, the one who was a critic, outlived them all: and that was quite right, for by this means he got the last word, and it was of great importance to him to have the last word. The people always said he had a good head of his own. At last his hour came, and he died, and came to the gates of Paradise. Souls always enter there two and two, and he came up with another soul that wanted to get into Paradise too; and who should this be but old Dame Margaret from the house upon the sea wall.

'I suppose this is done for the sake of contrast, that I and this wretched soul should arrive here at exactly the same time,' said the critic. 'Pray, who are you, my good woman?' he asked. 'Do you want to get in here too?'

And the old woman curtsied as well as she could: she thought it must be St Peter himself talking to her.

'I'm a poor old woman of a very humble family,' she replied. 'I'm old Margaret that lived in the house on the sea wall.'

'Well, and what have you done? What have you accomplished down there?'

'I have really accomplished nothing at all in the world: nothing that can open the door for me here. It would be a real mercy to allow me to slip in through the gate.'

'In what manner did you leave the world?' asked he, just for the sake of saying something; for it was wearisome work standing there and waiting.

'Why, I really don't know how I left it. I was sick and poorly during my last years, and could not well bear creeping out of bed, and going out suddenly into the frost and cold. It was a hard winter, but I have got out of it all now. For a few days the weather was quite calm, but very cold, as your honour must very well know. The sea was covered with ice as far as one could look. All the people from the town walked out upon the ice, and I think they said there was a dance there, and skating. There was beautiful music and a great feast there too; the sound came into my poor little room, where I lay ill. And it was towards evening; the moon had risen, but was not yet in its full splendour; I looked from my bed out over the wide sea, and far off, just where the sea and sky join, a strange white cloud came up. I lay looking at the cloud, and I saw a little black spot in the middle of it, that grew larger and larger; and now I knew what it meant, for I am old and experienced, though this token is not often seen. I knew it, and a shuddering came upon me. Twice in my life I have seen the same thing; and I knew there would be an awful tempest, and a spring flood, which would overwhelm the poor people who were now drinking and dancing and rejoicing – young and old, the whole town had issued forth: who was to warn them, if no one saw what was coming yonder, or knew, as I did, what it meant? I was dreadfully alarmed, and felt more lively than I had done for a long time.

I crept out of bed, and got to the window, but could not crawl farther, I was so exhausted. But I managed to open the window. I saw the people outside running and jumping about on the ice; I could see the beautiful flags that waved in the wind. I heard the boys shouting "hurrah!" and the servant men and maids singing. There were all kinds of merriment going on. But the white cloud with the black spot rose higher and higher! I cried out as loud as I could, but no one heard me; I was too far from the people. Soon the storm would burst, and the ice would break, and all who were upon it would be lost without remedy. They could not hear me, and I could not come out to them. Oh, if I could only bring them ashore! Then kind Heaven inspired me with the thought of setting fire to my bed, and rather to let the house burn down, than that all those people should perish so miserably. I succeeded in lighting up a beacon for them. The red flame blazed up on high, and I escaped out of the door, but fell down exhausted on the threshold, and could get no farther. The flames rushed out towards me, flickered through the window, and rose high above the roof. All the people on the ice yonder beheld it, and ran as fast as they could, to give aid to a poor old woman who, they thought, was being burned to death. Not one remained behind. I heard them coming; but I also became aware of a rushing sound in the air; I heard a rumbling like the sound of heavy artillery; the spring flood was lifting the covering of ice, which broke in pieces. But the people succeeded in reaching the sea wall where the sparks were flying over me – I saved them all! But I fancy I could not bear the cold and the fright, and so I came up here to the gates of Paradise. I am told they are opened to poor creatures like me – and now I have no house left down upon the dyke: not that I think this will give me admission here.'

Then the gates of heaven were opened, and the angel led the old woman in. She left a straw behind her, a straw that had been in her bed when she set it on fire to save the lives of many; and this straw had been changed into the purest gold – into gold that grew and grew, and spread out into beauteous leaves and flowers.

'Look, this is what the poor woman brought,' said the angel to the critic. 'What dost *thou* bring? I know that thou hast accomplished nothing – thou hast not made so much as a single brick. Ah, if thou couldst only return, and effect at least as much as that! Probably the brick, when thou hadst made it, would not be worth much; but if it were made with a good will, it would at least be *something*. But thou canst not go back, and I can do nothing for thee!'

Then the poor soul, the old dame who had lived on the dyke, put in a petition for him. She said, 'His brother gave me the bricks and the pieces out of which I built up my house, and that was a great deal for a poor woman like me. Could not all those bricks and pieces be counted as a single brick in his favour? It was an act of mercy. He wants it now; and is not this the very fountain of mercy?'

Then the angel said, 'Thy brother, him whom thou hast regarded as the least among you all, he whose honest industry seemed to thee as the most humble, hath given thee this heavenly gift. Thou shalt not be turned away. It shall be vouchsafed to thee to stand here without the gate, and to reflect, and repent of thy life down yonder; but thou shalt not be admitted until thou hast in earnest accomplished *something*.'

'I could have said that in better words!' thought the critic, but he did not find fault aloud; and for him, that was already 'something!'

The Last Dream of the Old Oak Tree

A Christmas Tale

IN THE forest, high up on the steep shore, hard by the open sea coast, stood a very old Oak Tree. It was exactly three hundred and sixty-five years old, but that long time was not more for the Tree than just as many days would be to us men. We wake by day and sleep through the night, and then we have our dreams: it is different with the Tree, which keeps awake through three seasons of the year, and does not get its sleep till winter comes. Winter is its time for rest, its night after the long day which is called spring, summer, and autumn.

On many a warm summer day the Ephemera, the fly that lives but for a day, had danced around his crown – had lived, enjoyed, and felt happy; and then the tiny creature had rested for a moment in quiet bliss on one of the great fresh Oak leaves; and then the Tree always said, 'Poor little thing! Your whole life is but a single day! How very short! It's quite melancholy.'

'Melancholy! Why do you say that?' the Ephemera would then always reply. 'It's wonderfully bright, warm, and beautiful all around me, and that makes me rejoice.'

'But only one day, and then it's all done!'

'Done!' repeated the Ephemera. 'What's the meaning of *done*? Are you *done*, too?'

'No; I shall perhaps live for thousands of your days, and my day is whole seasons long! It's something so long, that you can't at all manage to reckon it out.'

'No? then I don't understand you. You say you have thousands of my days; but I have thousands of moments, in which I can be merry and happy. Does all the beauty of this world cease when you die?'

'No,' replied the Tree; 'it will certainly last much longer – far longer than I can possibly think.'

'Well, then, we have the same time, only that we reckon differently.'

And the Ephemera danced and floated in the air, and rejoiced in her delicate wings of gauze and velvet, and rejoiced in the balmy breezes laden with the fragrance of the meadows and of wild roses and elder flowers, of the garden hedges, wild thyme, and mint, and daisies; the scent of these was all so strong that the Ephemera was almost intoxicated. The day was long and beautiful, full of joy and of sweet feeling, and when the sun sank low the little fly felt very agreeably tired of all its happiness and enjoyment. The delicate wings would not carry it any more, and quietly and slowly it glided down upon the soft grass-blade, nodded its head as well as it could nod, and went quietly to sleep – and was dead.

'Poor little Ephemera!' said the Oak. 'That was a terribly short life!'

And on every summer day the same dance was repeated, the same question and answer, and the same sleep. The same thing was repeated through whole generations of Ephemerae, and all of them felt equally merry and equally happy.

The Oak stood there awake through the spring morning, the noon of summer, and the evening of autumn; and its time of rest, its night, was coming on apace. Winter was approaching.

Already the storms were singing their 'good-night! good-night!' Here fell a leaf, and there fell a leaf.

'We pull! See if you can sleep! We sing you to sleep, we shake you to sleep, but it does you good in your old twigs, does it not? They seem to crack for very joy. Sleep sweetly! sleep sweetly! It's your three hundred and sixty-fifth night. Properly speaking, you're only a year old yet! Sleep sweetly! The clouds strew down snow, there will be quite a coverlet, warm and protecting, around your feet. Sweet sleep to you, and pleasant dreams!'

And the old Oak Tree stood there, stripped of all its leaves, to sleep through the long winter, and to dream many a dream, always about something that had happened to it, just as in the dreams of men.

The great Oak Tree had once been small – indeed, an acorn had been its cradle. According to human computation, it was now in its fourth century. It was the greatest and best tree in the forest; its crown towered far above all the other trees, and could be descried from afar across the sea, so that it served as a landmark to the sailors: the Tree had no idea how many eyes were in the habit of seeking it. High up in its green summit the wood-pigeon built her nest, and the cuckoo sat in its boughs and sang his song; and in autumn, when the leaves looked like thin plates of copper, the birds of passage came and rested there, before they flew away across the sea; but now it was winter, and the Tree stood there leafless, so that everyone could see how gnarled and crooked the branches were that shot forth from its trunk. Crows and rooks came and took their seat by turns in the boughs, and spoke of the hard times which were beginning, and of the difficulty of getting a living in winter.

It was just at the holy Christmas-time, when the Tree dreamed its most glorious dream.

The Tree had a distinct feeling of the festive time, and fancied he heard the bells ringing from the churches all around; and yet it seemed as if it were a fine summer's day, mild and warm. Fresh and green he spread out his mighty crown; the sunbeams played among the twigs and the leaves; the air was full of the fragrance of herbs and blossoms; gay butterflies chased each other to and fro. The ephemeral insects danced as if all the world were created merely for them to dance and be merry in. All that the Tree had experienced for years and years, and that had happened around him, seemed to pass by him again, as in a festive pageant. He saw the knights of ancient days ride by with their noble dames on gallant steeds, with plumes waving in their bonnets and falcons on their wrists. The hunting horn sounded, and the dogs barked. He saw hostile warriors in coloured jerkins and with shining weapons, with spear and halberd, pitching their tents and striking them again. The watchfires flamed up anew, and men sang and slept under the branches of the Tree. He saw loving couples meeting near his trunk, happily, in the moonshine; and they cut the initials of their names in the grey-green bark of his stem. Once – but long years had rolled by since then – citherns and Aeolian harps had been hung up on his boughs by merry wanderers; now they hung there again, and once again they sounded in tones of marvellous sweetness. The wood-pigeons cooed, as if they were telling what the Tree felt in all this, and the cuckoo called out to tell him how many summer days he had yet to live.

Then it appeared to him as if new life were rippling down into the remotest fibre of his root, and mounting up into his highest branches, to the tops of the leaves. The Tree felt that he was stretching and spreading himself, and through his root he felt that there was life and warmth even in the ground itself. He felt his strength increase, he grew higher, his stem shot up unceasingly, and he grew more and more, his crown became fuller and spread out; and in proportion as the Tree grew, he felt his happiness increase, and his joyous hope that he should reach even higher – quite up to the warm brilliant sun.

Already had he grown high up above the clouds, which floated past beneath his crown like dark troops of passage-birds, or like great white swans. And every leaf of the Tree had the gift of sight, as if it had eyes wherewith to see: the stars became visible in broad daylight, great and sparkling; each of them sparkled like a pair of eyes, mild and clear. They recalled to his memory well-known gentle eyes, eyes of children, eyes of lovers, who had met beneath his boughs.

It was a marvellous spectacle, and one full of happiness and joy! And yet amid all this happiness the Tree felt a longing, a yearning desire that all other trees of the wood beneath him, and all the bushes, and herbs, and flowers, might be able to rise with him, that they too might see this splendour and experience this joy. The great majestic Oak was not quite happy in his happiness, while he had not them all, great and little, about him; and this feeling of yearning trembled through his every twig, through his every leaf, warmly and fervently as through a human heart.

The crown of the Tree waved to and fro, as if he sought something in his silent longing, and he looked down. Then he felt the fragrance of woodruff, and soon afterwards the more powerful scent of honeysuckle and violets; and he fancied he heard the cuckoo answering him.

Yes, through the clouds the green summits of the forest came peering up, and under himself the Oak saw the other trees, as they grew and raised themselves aloft. Bushes and herbs shot up high, and some tore themselves up bodily by the roots to rise the quicker. The birch was the quickest of all. Like a white streak of lightning, its slender stem shot upwards in a zigzag line, and the branches spread around it like green gauze and like banners; the whole woodland natives, even to the brown-plumed rushes, grew up with the rest, and the birds came too, and sang; and on the grass-blade that fluttered aloft like a long silken ribbon into the air, sat the grasshopper cleaning his wings with his leg; the May beetles hummed, and the bees murmured, and every bird sang in his appointed manner; all was song and sound of gladness up into the high heaven.

'But the little blue flower by the waterside, where is that?' said the Oak; 'and the purple bell-flower and the daisy?' for, you see, the old Oak Tree wanted to have them all about him.

'We are here! we are here!' was shouted and sung in reply.

'But the beautiful woodruff of last summer – and in the last year there was certainly a place here covered with lilies of the valley! and the wild apple tree that blossomed so splendidly! and all the glory of the wood that came year by year – if that had only lived and remained till now, then it might have been here now!'

'We are here! we are here!' replied voices still higher in the air. It seemed as if they had flown on before.

'Why, that is beautiful, indescribably beautiful!' exclaimed the old Oak Tree, rejoicingly. 'I have them all around me, great and small; not one has been forgotten! How can so much happiness be imagined? How can it be possible?'

'In heaven it can be imagined, and it is possible!' the reply sounded through the air.

And the old Tree, who grew on and on, felt how his roots were tearing themselves free from the ground.

'That's best of all!' said the Tree. 'Now no fetters hold me! I can fly up now, to the very highest, in glory and in light! And all my beloved ones are with me, great and small – all of them, all!'

That was the dream of the old Oak Tree; and while he dreamed thus a mighty storm came rushing over land and sea – at the holy Christmastide. The sea rolled great billows towards the shore, and there was a cracking and crashing in the tree – his root was torn out of the ground in the very moment while he was dreaming that his root freed itself from the earth. He fell. His three hundred and sixty-five years were now as the single day of the Ephemera.

On the morning of the Christmas festival, when the sun rose, the storm had subsided. From all the churches sounded the festive bells, and from every hearth, even from the smallest hut, arose the smoke in blue clouds, like the smoke from the altars of the Druids of old at the feast of thank-offerings. The sea became gradually calm, and on board a great ship in the offing, that had fought successfully with the tempest, all the flags were displayed, as a token of joy suitable to the festive day.

'The Tree is down – the old Oak Tree, our landmark on the coast!' said the sailors. 'It fell in the storm of last night. Who can replace it? No one can.'

This was the funeral oration, short but well meant, that was given to the Tree, which lay stretched on the snowy covering on the sea-shore; and over its prostrate form sounded the notes of a song from the ship, a carol of the joys of Christmas, and of the redemption of the soul of man by the blood of Christ, and of eternal life.

> Sing, sing aloud, this blessed morn –
> It is fulfilled – and He is born,
> Oh, joy without compare!
> Hallelujah! Hallelujah!

Thus sounded the old psalm tune, and everyone on board the ship felt lifted up in his own way, through the song and the prayer, just as the old Tree had felt lifted up in its last, its most beauteous, dream in the Christmas night.

The ABC Book

THERE WAS a man who had written some new verses for the ABC book; two lines for every letter, as in the old ABC books; he thought that one ought to have something new, the old verses were so stale, and he always thought so well of his own. The new ABC book was as yet only in manuscript, and it was placed beside the old printed one in the big bookcase, in which stood so many learned and interesting books; but the old ABC book would not be a neighbour to the new one, and so it had sprung from the shelf, and at the same time had given the new one a push, so that it also lay upon the floor with all its loose leaves scattered round about. The old ABC book was open at the first page, and it is the most important: all the letters stand there, the big and the little. That page contains everything that all the other books live upon, the alphabet, the letters, which really rule the world; they have a terrible power! it entirely depends on how they are commanded to stand; they can give life, put to death, gladden, and afflict. Placed separately they signify nothing, but placed in ranks – ah! when our Lord caused them to be placed under His thoughts, we learned more than we had strength to bear, we bowed ourselves deeply, but the letters had the strength to bear it.

There the books lay now, facing upwards! and the cock in the capital A shone with red, blue, and green feathers; he thrust out his chest, for he knew what the letters meant, and knew that he was the only living thing amongst them.

When the old ABC book fell on the floor, he flapped his wings, flew out, and set himself on the edge of the bookcase, preened his feathers and crowed, so that echo rang with it. Every book in the bookcase, which at other times stood day and night as in a doze when not in use, heard the trumpet-call – and then the cock talked clearly and distinctly about the injustice which had been done to the worthy old ABC book.

'Everything must now be new, be different,' he said, 'everything must be so advanced! Children are so clever, that they can now read before they know the letters.

"They shall have something new," said he who wrote the new ABC verses, which lie there scattered on the floor. I know them! more than ten times have I heard him read them aloud to himself! it was such a pleasure to him. No, may I beg to have my own verses, the good old ones with Xanthus, and the pictures which belong to them; these will I fight for, these will I crow for! Every book in the bookcase knows them well. Now I shall read the new ones he has written, read them with all calmness, and then let us agree that they are no good!'

A — *Ayah*
An Ayah has an Eastern air
And others' children are her care.

B — *Boor*
A Boor in former days but toiled;
Now he's somewhat proud and spoiled.

'That verse, now, I think wonderfully flat!' said the cock, 'but I will read on!'

C — *Columbus*
Columbus sailed across the main,
And earth became as large again.

D — *Denmark*
Of Denmark's kingdom it is told,
God over it His hand will hold.

'Many will think that beautiful!' said the cock, 'but I don't! I find nothing beautiful here! Let us read on!'

E ⁓ *Elephant*

The Elephant, though young it be,
Can tread but heavily, we see.

F ⁓ *Flood*

When rain makes rivers rise in Flood,
It may do harm, but also good.

G ⁓ *Goose*

A Goose, though ne'er so wisely taught,
Is always slow in learning aught.

H. *Hurrah*

Hurrah is used to mark applause,
And often for but trifling cause.

'How's a child to understand that now?' said the cock, 'there certainly stands on the title-page "A.B.C. book for big and little", but the big ones have other things to do than read A.B.C. verses, and the little ones cannot possibly understand it! There is limit to everything! Let us go on!'

I ⁓ *Island*

Our earth an Island is in space,
And we but atoms on its face.

K ⁓ *Kine*

The Kine are kindred to the bull,
And with their calves the fields are full.

'How can one explain to children the relationship of these to each other?'

L ⁓ *Lion*

In deserts wild the Lions roam,
But we have other lions at home.

M ～ Morning Sun

The Morning sun its beams has shown,
But not because the cock has crown.

'Now I am being insulted!' said the cock, 'but I am in good company, in company with the sun. Let's go on!'

N ～ Negro

Black is the Negro past all hope,
One cannot wash him white with soap.

O ～ Olive

The Olive leaf of Noah's dove
Must rank all other leaves above.

P ～ Post

The Post conveys from land to land
The work of many a head and hand.

Q ～ Quey

A Quey will one day be a cow,
And so is worth the having now.

R ～ Round-tower

One may as stout as Round-tower stand,
And yet have neither name nor land

S ～ Swine

Be not too proud, though all the Swine
That in the forest feed are thine

'Allow me to crow now!' said the cock, 'it tries one's strength to read so much! one must take a breath!' and he crowed, so that it rang like a brass trumpet, and it was a great delight to hear it – for the cock.

T ~ Tea-kettle
Though lowly the Tea-kettle's place,
It sings with all a Tea-urn's grace.

U ~ Uranus
Though far as Uranus we fly,
Beyond is still the endless sky.

W ~ Washerwoman
A Washerwoman may wash so long
That things will tear, however strong.

X ~ Xanthippe

'Here he hasn't been able to invent anything new.'

A stormy cliff in wedlock's seas
Xanthippe proved to Socrates.

'He had to take Xanthippe; but Xanthus is better.'

Y ~ Ygdrasil
'Neath Ygdrasil the gods did dwell;
The tree is dead, and the gods as well.

Z ~ Zephyr
The Danish Zephyr from the west
Can blow through fur-lined coat and vest.

'There it ended! but it is not done with! now it is to be printed! and then it is to be read! it is to be offered instead of the worthy old letter-verses in my book! What says the meeting, learned and unlearned, single and collected works? What says the bookcase? I have spoken – now the others can act!'

And the books stood and the bookcase stood, but the cock flew down again into his capital A, and looked about him proudly. 'I talked well, I crowed well! that the new ABC book cannot do after me! it will certainly die! it is dead already! it has no cock!'

The Marsh King's Daughter

THE STORKS tell their little ones very many stories, all of the swamp and the marsh. These stories are generally adapted to the age and capacity of the hearers. The youngest are content if they are told 'Cribble-crabble, plurry-murry' as a story, and find it charming; but the older ones want something with a deeper meaning, or at any rate something relating to the family. Of the two oldest and longest stories that have been preserved among the storks we all know the one, namely, that of Moses, who was exposed by his mother on the banks of the Nile, and whom the King's daughter found, and who afterwards became a great man and the place of whose burial is unknown. That story is very well known.

The second is not known yet, perhaps because it is quite an inland story. It has been handed down from stork-mamma to stork-mamma, for thousands of years, and each of them has told it better and better; and now *we*'ll tell it best of all.

The first Stork pair who told the story had their summer residence on the wooden house of the Viking, which lay by the wild moor in Wendsyssel: that is to say, if we are to speak out of the abundance of our knowledge, hard by the great moor in the circle of Hjörring, high up by Skagen, the most northern point of Jutland. The wilderness there is still a great wild moss, about which we can read in the official description of the district. It is said that in old times there was here a sea, whose bottom was upheaved; now the moss extends for miles on all sides, surrounded by damp meadows, and unsteady shaking swamp, and turfy moor, with blueberries and stunted trees. Mists are almost always hovering over this region, which seventy years ago was still inhabited by the wolves. It is certainly rightly called the 'wild moss'; and one can easily think how dreary and lonely it must have been, and how much marsh and lake there was here a thousand years ago. Yes, in detail, exactly the same things were seen then that may yet be beheld. The reeds had the same height, and bore the same kind of long leaves and bluish-brown feathery plumes that they bear now; the birch stood there, with its white bark and its fine loosely-hanging leaves, just as now; and as regards the living creatures that dwelt here – why, the fly wore its gauzy dress of the same cut that it wears now, and the favourite colours of the stork were white picked out with black, and red stockings. The people certainly wore coats of a different cut from those they now wear; but whoever stepped out on the shaking moss, be he huntsman or follower, master or servant, met with the same fate a thousand years ago that he would meet with today. He sank and went down to the Marsh King, as they called him, who ruled below in the great empire of the moss. They also called him Quagmire King; but we like the name Marsh King better, and by that name the storks also called him. Very little is known of the Marsh King's rule; but perhaps that is a good thing.

In the neighbourhood of the moss, close by Limfjorden, lay the wooden house of the Viking, with its stone watertight cellars, with its tower and its three projecting stories. On the roof the Stork had built his nest, and Stork-mamma there hatched the eggs, and felt sure that her hatching would come to something.

One evening Stork-papa stayed out very late, and when he came home he looked very bustling and important.

'I've something very terrible to tell you,' he said to the Stork-mamma.

'Let that be,' she replied. 'Remember that I'm hatching the eggs, and you might agitate me, and I might do them a mischief.'

'You must know it,' he continued. 'She has arrived here – the daughter of our host in Egypt – she has dared to undertake the journey here – and she's gone!'

'She who came from the race of the fairies? Oh, tell me all about it! You know I can't bear to be kept long in suspense when I'm hatching eggs.'

'You see, mother, she believed in what the doctor said, and you told me true. She believed that the moss flowers would bring healing to her sick father, and she has flown here in swan's plumage, in company with the other Swan Princesses, who come to the North every year to renew their youth. She has come here, and she is gone!'

'You are much too long-winded!' exclaimed the Stork-mamma, 'and the eggs might catch cold. I can't bear being kept in such suspense!'

'I have kept watch,' said the Stork-papa; 'and tonight, when I went into the reeds – there where the marsh ground will bear me – three swans came. Something in their flight seemed to say to me, "Look out! That's not altogether swan; it's only swan's feathers!" Yes, mother, you have a feeling of intuition just as I have; you can tell whether a thing is right or wrong.'

'Yes, certainly,' she replied; 'but tell me about the Princess. I'm sick of hearing of the swan's feathers.'

'Well, you know that in the middle of the moss there is something like a lake,' continued Stork-papa. 'You can see one corner of it if you raise yourself a little. There, by the reeds and the green mud, lay a great elder stump, and on this the three swans sat, flapping their wings and looking about them. One of them threw off her plumage, and I immediately recognised her as our own Princess from Egypt! There she sat, with no covering but her long black hair. I heard her tell the others to pay good heed to the swan's plumage, while she dived down into the water to pluck the flowers which she fancied she saw growing there. The others nodded, and picked up the empty feather dress and took care of it. "I wonder what they will do with it?" thought I; and perhaps she asked herself the same question. If so, she got an answer, for the two rose up and flew away with her swan's plumage. "Do thou dive down!" they cried; "thou shalt never fly more in swan's form, thou shalt never see Egypt again! Remain thou there in the moss!" And so saying, they tore the swan's plumage into a hundred pieces, so that the feathers whirled about like a snowstorm; and away they flew – the two faithless Princesses!'

'Why, that is terrible!' said Stork-mamma. 'I can't bear to hear it. But now tell me what happened next.'

'The Princess wept and lamented. Her tears fell fast on the elder stump, and the latter moved, for it was the Marsh King himself – he who lives in the moss! I myself saw it – how the stump of the tree turned round, and ceased to be a tree stump; long thin branches grew forth from it like arms. Then the poor child was terribly frightened, and sprang away on to the green slimy ground; but that cannot even carry me, much less her. She sank immediately, and the elder stump dived down too; and it was he who drew her down. Great black bubbles rose up, and there was no more trace of them. Now the Princess is buried in the wild moss, and never more will she bear away a flower to Egypt. Your heart would have burst, mother, if you had seen it.'

'You ought not to tell me anything of the kind at such a time as this,' said Stork-mamma; 'the eggs might suffer by it. The Princess will find some way of escape; someone will come to help her. If it had been you or I, or one of our people, it would certainly have been all over with us.'

'But I shall go and look every day to see if anything happens,' said Stork-papa.

And he was as good as his word.

A long time had passed, when at last he saw a green stalk shooting up out of the deep moss. When it reached the surface a leaf spread out and unfolded itself broader and broader; close by it, a bud came out. And one morning, when the Stork flew over the stalk, the bud opened through the power of the strong sunbeams, and in the cup of the flower lay a beautiful child – a little girl – looking just as if she had risen out of the bath. The little one so closely resembled the Princess from Egypt, that at the first moment the Stork thought it must be the Princess herself; but, on second thoughts, it appeared more probable that it must be the daughter of the Princess and of the Marsh King; and that also explained her being placed in the cup of the water-lily.

'But she cannot possibly be left lying there,' thought the Stork; 'and in my nest there are so many already. But stay, I have a thought. The wife of the Viking has no children, and how often has she not wished for a little one! People always say, "The stork has brought a little one;" and I will do so in earnest this time. I shall fly with the child to the Viking's wife. What rejoicing there will be there!'

And the Stork lifted the little girl, flew to the wooden house, picked a hole with his beak in the bladder-covered window, laid the child on the bosom of the Viking's wife, and then hurried up to the Stork-mamma, and told her what he had seen and done; and the little Storks listened to the story, for they were big enough to do so now.

'So you see,' he concluded, 'the Princess is not dead, for she must have sent the little one up here; and now that is provided for too.'

'Ah, I said it would be so from the very beginning!' said the Stork-mamma; 'but now think a little of your own family. Our travelling time is drawing on; sometimes I feel quite restless in my wings already. The cuckoo and the nightingale have started, and I heard the quails saying that they were going too, as soon as the wind was favourable. Our young ones will behave well at the exercising, or I am much deceived in them.'

The Viking's wife was extremely glad when she woke next morning and found the charming infant lying in her arms. She kissed and caressed it, but it cried violently, and struggled with its arms and legs, and did not seem rejoiced at all. At length it cried itself to sleep, and as it lay there it looked exceedingly beautiful. The Viking's wife was in high glee: she felt light in body and soul; her heart leapt within her; and it seemed to her as if her husband and his warriors, who were absent, must return quite as suddenly and unexpectedly as the little one had come.

Therefore she and the whole household had enough to do in preparing everything for the reception of her lord. The long coloured curtains of tapestry, which she and her maids had worked, and on which they had woven pictures of their idols, Odin, Thor, and Freia, were hung up; the slaves polished the old shields that served as ornaments; and cushions were placed on the benches, and dry wood laid on the fireplace in the midst of the hall, so that the fire could be lighted at a moment's notice. The Viking's wife herself assisted in the work, so that towards evening she was very tired, and slept well.

When she awoke towards morning, she was violently alarmed, for the infant had vanished! She sprang from her couch, lighted a pine torch, and searched all round about; and, behold, in the part of the bed where she had stretched her feet, lay, not the child, but a great ugly frog! She was horror-struck at the sight, and seized a heavy stick to kill the frog; but the creature looked at her with such strange mournful eyes, that she was not able to strike the blow. Once more she looked round the room – the frog uttered a low, wailing croak, and she started, sprang from the couch, and ran to the window and opened it. At that moment the sun shone forth, and flung its beams through the window on the couch and on the great frog; and suddenly it appeared as though the frog's great mouth contracted and became small and red, and its limbs moved and stretched and became beautifully symmetrical, and it was no longer an ugly frog which lay there, but her pretty child!

'What is this?' she said. 'Have I had a bad dream? Is it not my own lovely cherub lying there?'

And she kissed and hugged it; but the child struggled and fought like a little wild cat.

Not on this day nor on the morrow did the Viking return, although he was on his way home; but the wind was against him, for it blew towards the south, favourably for the storks. A good wind for one is a contrary wind for another.

When one or two more days and nights had gone, the Viking's wife clearly understood how the case was with her child, that a terrible power of sorcery was upon it. By day it was charming as an angel of light, though it had a wild, savage temper; but at night it became an ugly frog, quiet and mournful, with sorrowful eyes. Here were two natures changing inwardly as well as outwardly with the sunlight. The reason of this was that by day the child had the form of its mother, but the disposition of its father; while, on the contrary, at night the paternal descent became manifest in its bodily appearance, though the mind and heart of the mother then became dominant in the child. Who might be able to loosen this charm that wicked sorcery had worked?

The wife of the Viking lived in care and sorrow about it; and yet her heart yearned towards the little creature, of whose condition she felt she should not dare tell her husband on his return, for he would probably, according to the custom which then prevailed, expose the child on the public highway, and let whoever listed take it away. The good Viking woman could not find it in her heart to allow this, and she therefore determined that the Viking should never see the child except by daylight.

One morning the wings of storks were heard rushing over the roof; more than a hundred pairs of those birds had rested from their exercise during the previous night, and now they soared aloft, to travel southwards.

'All males here, and ready,' they cried; 'and the wives and children too.'

'How light we feel!' screamed the young Storks in chorus: 'it seems to be creeping all over us, down into our very toes, as if we were filled with living frogs. Ah, how charming it is, travelling to foreign lands!'

'Mind you keep close to us during your flight,' said papa and mamma. 'Don't use your beaks too much, for that tires the chest.'

And the Storks flew away.

At the same time the sound of the trumpets rolled across the heath, for the Viking had landed with his warriors; they were returning home, richly laden with spoil, from the Gallic coast, where the people, as in the land of the Britons, sang in their terror:

'Deliver us from the wild Northmen!'

And life and tumultuous joy came with them into the Viking's castle on the moorland. The great mead-tub was brought into the hall, the pile of wood was set ablaze, horses were killed, and a great feast was to begin. The officiating priest sprinkled the slaves with the warm blood; the fire crackled, the smoke rolled along beneath the roof, soot dropped from the beams, but they were accustomed to that. Guests were invited, and received handsome gifts: all feuds and all malice were forgotten. And the company drank deep, and threw the bones of the feast in each other's faces, and this was considered a sign of good humour. The bard, a kind of minstrel, who was also a warrior and had been on the expedition with the rest, sang them a song in which they heard all their warlike deeds praised, and everything remarkable was specially noticed. Every verse ended with the burden:

Goods and gold, friends and foes will die; every man must one day die; But a famous name will never die!

And with that they beat upon their shields, and hammered the table with bones and knives.

The Viking's wife sat upon the crossbench in the open hall. She wore a silken dress and golden armlets, and great amber beads: she was in her costliest garb. And the bard mentioned her in his song, and sang of the rich treasure she had brought her rich husband. The latter was delighted with the beautiful child, which he had seen in the daytime in all its loveliness; and the savage ways of the little creature pleased him especially. He declared that the girl might grow up to be a stately heroine, strong and determined as a man. She would not wink her eyes when a practised hand cut off her eyebrows with a sword by way of a jest.

The full mead-barrel was emptied, and a fresh one brought in, for these were people who liked to enjoy all things plentifully. The old proverb was indeed well known, which says, 'The cattle know when they should quit the pasture, but a foolish man knoweth not the measure of his own appetite.' Yes, they knew it well enough; but one *knows* one thing, and one *does* another. They also knew that 'even the welcome guest becomes wearisome when he sitteth long in the house'; but for all that they sat still, for pork and mead are good things; and there was high carousing, and at night the bondmen slept among the warm ashes, and dipped their fingers in the fat grease and licked them. Those were glorious times!

Once more in the year the Viking sallied forth, though the storms of autumn already began to roar: he went with his warriors to the shores of Britain, for he declared that was but an excursion across the water; and his wife stayed at home with the little girl. And thus much is certain, that the foster-mother soon got to love the frog with its gentle eyes and its sorrowful sighs, almost better than the pretty child that bit and beat all around her.

The rough damp mist of autumn, which devours the leaves of the forest, had already descended upon thicket and heath. 'Birds featherless,' as they called the snow, flew in thick masses, and the winter was coming on fast. The sparrows took possession of the storks' nests, and talked about the absent proprietors according to their fashion; but these – the Stork-pair, with all the young ones – what had become of them?

The Storks were now in the land of Egypt, where the sun sent forth warm rays, as it does here on a fine midsummer day. Tamarinds and acacias bloomed in the country all around; the crescent of Mohammed glittered from the cupolas of the temples, and on the slender towers sat many a stork-pair resting after the long journey. Great troops divided the nests, built close together on venerable pillars and in fallen temple arches of forgotten cities. The date-palm lifted up its screen as if it would be a sunshade; the greyish-white pyramids stood like masses of shadow in the clear air of the far desert, where the ostrich ran his swift career, and the lion gazed with his great grave eyes at the marble

Sphinx which lay half buried in the sand. The waters of the Nile had fallen, and the whole river bed was crowded with frogs; and that was, for the Stork family, the finest spectacle in the country. The young Storks thought it was optical illusion, they found everything so glorious.

'Yes, it's delightful here; and it's always like this in our warm country,' said the Stork-mamma.

And the young ones felt quite frisky on the strength of it.

'Is there anything more to be seen?' they asked. 'Are we to go much farther into the country?'

'There's nothing further to be seen,' answered Stork-mamma. 'Behind this delightful region there are only wild forests, whose branches are interlaced with one another, while prickly climbing plants close up the paths – only the elephant can force a way for himself with his great feet; and the snakes are too big and the lizards too quick for us. If you go into the desert, you'll get your eyes full of sand when there's a light breeze, but when it blows great guns you may get into the middle of a pillar of sand. It is best to stay here, where there are frogs and locusts. I shall stay here, and you shall stay too.'

And there they remained. The parents sat in the nest on the slender minaret, and rested, and yet were busily employed smoothing their feathers, and whetting their beaks against their red stockings. Now and then they stretched out their necks, and bowed gravely, and lifted their heads, with their high foreheads and fine smooth feathers, and looked very clever with their brown eyes. The female young ones strutted about in the juicy reeds, looked slyly at the other young storks, made acquaintances, and swallowed a frog at every third step, or rolled a little snake to and fro in their bills, which they thought became them well, and, moreover, tasted nice. The male young ones began a quarrel, beat each other with their wings, struck with their beaks, and even pricked each other till the blood came. And in this way sometimes one couple was betrothed, and sometimes another, of the young ladies and gentlemen, and that was just what they lived for: then they took to a new nest, and began new quarrels, for in hot countries people are generally hot tempered and passionate. But it was pleasant for all that, and the old people especially were much rejoiced, for all that young people do seems to suit them well. There was sunshine every day, and every day plenty to eat, and nothing to think of but pleasure. But in the rich castle at the Egyptian host's, as they called him, there was no pleasure to be found.

The rich mighty lord reclined on his divan, in the midst of the great hall of the many-coloured walls, looking as if he were sitting in a tulip; but he was stiff and powerless in all his limbs, and lay stretched out like a mummy. His family and servants surrounded him, for he was not dead, though one could not exactly say that he was alive. The healing moss flower from the North, which was to have been found and brought home by her who loved him best, never appeared. His beauteous young daughter, who had flown in the swan's plumage over sea and land to the far North, was never to come back. 'She is dead!' the two returning Swan-maidens had said, and they had made up a complete story, which ran as follows:

'We three together flew high in the air: a hunter saw us, and shot his arrow at us; it struck our young companion and friend, and slowly, singing her farewell song, she sank down, a dying swan, into the woodland lake. By the shore of the lake, under a weeping birch tree, we buried her. But we had our revenge. We bound fire under the wings of the swallow who had her nest beneath the huntsman's thatch; the house burst into flames, the huntsman was burned in the house, and the glare shone over the sea as far as the hanging birch beneath which she sleeps. Never will she return to the land of Egypt.'

And then the two wept. And when Stork-papa heard the story, he clapped with his beak so that it could be heard a long way off.

'Falsehood and lies!' he cried. 'I should like to run my beak deep into their chests.'

'And perhaps break it off,' interposed the Stork-mamma: 'and then you would look well. Think first of yourself, and then of your family, and all the rest does not concern you.'

'But tomorrow I shall seat myself at the edge of the open cupola, when the wise and learned men assemble to consult on the sick man's state: perhaps they may come a little nearer the truth.'

And the learned and wise men came together and spoke a great deal, out of which the Stork could make no sense – and it had no result, either for the sick man or for the daughter in the swampy waste. But for all that we may listen to what the people said, for we have to listen to a great deal of talk in the world.

But then it will be an advantage to hear what went before, and in this case we are well informed, for we know just as much about it as Stork-papa.

'Love gives life! the highest love gives the highest life! Only through love can his life be preserved.'

That is what they all said, and the learned men said it was very cleverly and beautifully spoken.

'That is a beautiful thought!' Stork-papa said immediately.

'I don't quite understand it,' Stork-mamma replied; 'and that's not my fault, but the fault of the thought. But let it be as it will, I've something else to think of.'

And now the learned men had spoken of the love to this one and that one, and of the difference between the love of one's neighbour and love between parents and children, of the love of plants for the light, when the sunbeam kisses the ground and the germ springs forth from it, everything was so fully and elaborately explained that it was quite impossible for Stork-papa to take it in, much less to repeat it. He felt quite weighed down with thought, and half shut his eyes, and the whole of the following day he stood thoughtfully upon one leg: it was quite heavy for him to carry, all that learning.

But one thing Stork-papa understood. All, high and low, had spoken out of their inmost hearts, and said that it was a great misfortune for thousands of people, yes, for the whole country, that this man was lying sick, and could not get well, and that it would spread joy and pleasure abroad if he should recover. But where grew the flower that could restore him to health? They had all searched for it, consulted learned books, the twinkling stars, the weather and the wind; they had made enquiries in every byway of which they could think; and at length the wise men and the learned men had said, as we have already told, that 'Love begets life – will restore a father's life'; and on this occasion they said more than they understood. They repeated it, and wrote down as a recipe, 'Love begets life.' But how was the thing to be prepared according to the recipe? that was a difficulty they could not get over. At last they were decided upon the point that help must come by means of the Princess, who loved her father with her whole soul; and at last a method had been devised whereby help could be procured. Yes, it was already more than a year ago since the Princess was to go forth by night, when the brief rays of the new moon were waning: she was to go out to the marble Sphinx, to shake the dust from her sandals, and to go onward through the long passage which leads into the midst of one of the great pyramids, where one of the mighty Kings of antiquity, surrounded by pomp and treasure, lay swathed in mummy cloths. There she was to incline her ear to the dead King, and then it would be revealed to her where she might find life and health for her father. She had fulfilled all this, and had seen in a vision that she was to bring home from the deep moss up in the Danish land – the very place had been accurately described to her – the lotus flower which grows in the depths of the waters, and then her father would regain health and strength. And therefore she had gone forth in the swan's plumage out of the land of Egypt up to the wild moss. And the Stork-papa and Stork-mamma knew all this; and now we also know it more accurately than we knew it before. We know that the Marsh King had drawn her down to himself, and know that to those at home she is dead for ever. Only the wisest of them said, as the Stork-mamma said too, 'She will manage to help herself;' and they resolved to wait and see what would happen, for they knew of nothing better that they could do.

'I should like to take away the swans' feathers from the two faithless Princesses,' said the Stork-papa; 'then at any rate, they will not be able to fly up again to the wild moss and do mischief. I'll hide the two swan-feather suits up there, till somebody has occasion for them.'

'But where do you intend to hide them?' asked Stork-mamma.

'Up in our nest in the moss,' answered he. 'I and our young ones will take turns in carrying them up yonder on our return, and if that should prove too difficult for us, there are places enough on the way where we can conceal them till our next journey. Certainly, one suit of swan's feathers would be enough for the Princess, but two are always better. In those northern countries no one can have too many wraps.'

'No one will thank you for it,' quoth Stork-mamma; 'but you're the master. Except at breeding-time, I have nothing to say.'

In the Viking's castle by the wild moss, whither the Storks bent their flight when the spring approached, they had given the little girl the name of Helga; but this name was too soft for a temper like that which went with her beauteous form. Month by month this temper showed itself more and more; and in the course of years – during which the Storks made the same journey over and over again, in autumn to the Nile, in spring back to the moorland lake – the child grew to be a big girl; and before people were aware of it, she was a beautiful maiden in her sixteenth year. The shell was splendid, but the kernel was harsh and hard; harder even than most in those dark, gloomy times. It was a pleasure to her to splash about with her white hands in the blood of the horse that had been slain in sacrifice. In her wild mood she bit off the neck of the black cock the priest was about to offer up; and to her foster-father she said in perfect seriousness, 'If thy enemy should pull down the roof of thy house, while thou wert sleeping, I would not wake thee even if I had the power. I should never hear it, for my ears still tingle with the blow that thou gavest me years ago – thou! I have never forgotten it.'

But the Viking took her words in jest; for, like all others, he was bewitched with her beauty, and he knew not how temper and form changed in Helga. Without a saddle she sat upon a horse, as if she were part of it, while it rushed along in full career; nor would she spring from the horse when it quarrelled and fought with other horses. Often she would throw herself, in her clothes, from the high shore into the sea, and swim to meet the Viking when his boat steered near home; and she cut her longest lock of hair, and twisted it into a string for her bow.

'Self-made is well-made,' she said.

The Viking's wife was strong of character and of will, according to the custom of the times; but, compared to her daughter, she appeared as a feeble, timid woman; moreover, she knew that an evil charm weighed heavily upon the unfortunate child.

It seemed as if, out of mere malice, when her mother stood on the threshold or came out into the yard, Helga would often seat herself on the margin of the well, and wave her arms in the air; then suddenly she would dive into the deep well, where her frog nature enabled her to dive and rise, down and up, until she climbed forth again like a cat, and came back into the hall dripping with water, so that the green leaves strewn upon the ground turned about in the stream.

But there was one thing that imposed a check upon Helga, and that was the evening twilight. When that came she was quiet and thoughtful, and would listen to reproof and advice; and then a secret feeling seemed to draw her towards her mother. And when the sun sank, and the usual transformation of body and spirit took place in her, she would sit quiet and mournful, shrunk to the shape of the frog, her body indeed much larger than that of the animal, and for that reason much more hideous to behold, for she looked like a wretched dwarf with a frog's head and webbed fingers. Her eyes then had a very melancholy expression. She had no voice, and could only utter a hollow croaking that sounded like the stifled sob of a dreaming child. Then the Viking's wife took her on her lap, and forgot the ugly form as she looked into the mournful eyes, and said, 'I could almost wish that thou wert always my poor dumb frog-child; for thou art only the more terrible to look at when thy beauty is on the outside.'

And she wrote Runes against sorcery and sickness, and threw them over the wretched child; but she could not see that they worked any good.

'One can scarcely believe that she was ever so small that she could lie in the cup of a water-lily,' said Stork-papa, 'now she's grown up the image of her Egyptian mother. *Her* we shall never see again! She did not know how to help herself, as you and the learned physicians said. Year after year I have flown to and fro, across and across the great moss, and she has never once given a sign that she was still alive. Yes, I may as well tell you, that every year, when I came here a few days before you, to repair the nest and attend to various matters, I spent a whole night in flying to and fro over the lake, as if I had been an owl or a bat, but every time in vain. The two suits of swan feathers which I and the young ones dragged up here out of the land of the Nile have consequently not been used: we had trouble enough with them to bring them hither in three journeys; and now they have lain for many years at the bottom of the nest, and if it should happen that a fire broke out, and the wooden house were burned, they would be destroyed.'

'And our good nest would be destroyed too,' said Stork-mamma; 'but you think less of that than of your plumage stuff and of your Moor Princess. You'd best go down into the mud and stay there with her. You're a bad father to your own children, as I told you when I hatched our first brood. I only hope neither we nor our children will get an arrow in our wings through that wild girl. Helga doesn't know in the least what she does. I wish she would only remember that we have lived here longer than she, and that we have never forgotten our duty, and have given our toll every year, a feather, an egg, and a young one, as it was right we should do. Do you think I can now wander about in the courtyard and everywhere, as I used to in former days, and as I still do in Egypt, where I am almost the playfellow of the people, and that I can press into pot and kettle as I can yonder? No, I sit up here and am angry at her, the stupid chit! And I am angry at you too. You should have just left her lying in the water-lily, and she would have been dead long ago.'

'You are much better than your words,' said Stork-papa. 'I know you better than you know yourself.'

And with that he gave a hop, and flapped his wings heavily twice, stretched out his legs behind him, and flew away, or rather sailed away, without moving his wings. He had already gone some distance when he gave a great *flap!* The sun shone upon the white feathers, and his head and neck were stretched forth proudly. There was power in it, and dash!

'After all, he's handsomer than any of them,' said Stork-mamma to herself; 'but I don't tell him so.'

Early in that autumn the Viking came home, laden with booty, and bringing prisoners with him. Among these was a young Christian priest, one of those who contemned the gods of the North.

Often in those later times there had been a talk, in hall and chamber, of the new faith that was spreading far and wide in the South, and which, by means of Saint Ansgar, had penetrated as far as Hedeby on the Slie. Even Helga had heard of this belief in the White Christ who, from love to men and for their redemption, had sacrificed His life; but with her all this had, as the saying is, gone in at one ear and come out at the other. It seemed as if she only understood the meaning of the word 'love' when she crouched in a corner of the chamber in the form of a miserable frog; but the Viking's wife had listened, and had felt strangely moved by the stories and tales which were told in the South about the one only true Word.

On their return from their last voyage, the men told of the splendid temples built of hewn stones, raised for the worship of Him whose message is love. Some massive vessels of gold, made with cunning art, had been brought home among the booty, and each one had a peculiar fragrance; for they were incense vessels, which had been swung by Christian priests before the altar.

In the deep cellars of the Viking's house the young priest had been immured, his hands and feet bound with strips of bark. The Viking's wife declared that he was beautiful as Balder to behold, and his misfortune touched her heart; but Helga declared that it would be right to tie ropes to his heels and fasten him to the tails of wild oxen. And she exclaimed, 'Then I would let loose the dogs – hurrah! over the moor and across the swamp! That would be a spectacle! And yet finer would it be to follow him in his career.'

But the Viking would not suffer him to die such a death: he purposed to sacrifice the priest on the morrow, on the death-stone in the grove, as a despiser and foe of the high gods.

For the first time a man was to be sacrificed here.

Helga begged, as a boon, that she might sprinkle the image of the god and the assembled multitude with the blood of the victim. She sharpened her glittering knife, and when one of the great savage dogs, of whom a number were running about near the Viking's abode, ran by her, she thrust the knife into his side, 'merely to try its sharpness,' as she said. And the Viking's wife looked mournfully at the wild, evil-disposed girl; and when night came on and the maiden exchanged beauty of form for gentleness of soul, she spoke in eloquent words to Helga of the sorrow that was deep in her heart.

The ugly frog, in its monstrous form, stood before her, and fixed its brown eyes upon her face, listening to her words, and seeming to comprehend them with human intelligence.

'Never, not even to my husband, have I allowed my lips to utter a word concerning the sufferings I have to undergo through thee,' said the Viking's wife; 'my heart is full of more compassion for thee than I myself believed: great is the love of a mother! But love never entered into thy heart – thy heart that is like the wet, cold moorland plants. From whence have you come into my house?'

Then the miserable form trembled, and it was as though these words touched an invisible bond between body and soul, and great tears came into her eyes.

'Thy hard time will come,' said the Viking's wife; 'and it will be terrible to me too. It had been better if thou hadst been set out by the high road, and the night wind had lulled thee to sleep.'

And the Viking's wife wept bitter tears, and went away full of wrath and bitterness of spirit, disappearing behind the curtain of furs that hung over the beam and divided the hall.

The wrinkled frog crouched in the corner alone. A deep silence reigned all around, but at intervals a half-stifled sigh escaped from its breast, from the breast of Helga. It seemed as though a painful new life were arising in her inmost heart. She came forward and listened; and, stepping forward again, grasped with her clumsy hands the heavy pole that was laid across before the door. Silently she pushed back the pole, silently drew back the bolt, and took up the flickering lamp which stood in the antechamber of the hall. It seemed as if a strong will gave her strength. She drew back the iron bolt from the closed cellar door, and crept in to the captive. He was asleep; she touched him with her cold, clammy hand, and when he awoke and saw the hideous form, he shuddered as though he had beheld a wicked apparition. She drew her knife, cut his bonds, and beckoned him to follow her.

He uttered some holy names and made the sign of the cross; and when the form remained unchanged, he said, 'Who art thou? Whence this animal shape that thou bearest, while yet thou art full of gentle mercy?'

The frog-woman beckoned him to follow, and led him through passages shrouded with curtains, into the stables, and there pointed to a horse. He mounted on its back, and she also sprang up before him, holding fast by the horse's mane. The prisoner understood her meaning, and in a rapid trot they rode on a way which he would never have found, out on to the open heath.

He thought not of her hideous form, but felt how the mercy and loving-kindness of the Almighty were working by means of this monster apparition; he prayed pious prayers and sang songs of praise. Then she trembled. Was it the power of song and of prayer that worked in her, or was she shuddering at the cold morning twilight that was approaching? What were her feelings? She raised herself up, and wanted to stop the horse and to alight; but the Christian priest held her back with all his strength, and sang a psalm, as if that would have the power to loosen the charm that turned her into the hideous semblance of a frog. And the horse galloped on more wildly than ever; the sky turned red, the first sunbeam pierced through the clouds, and as the flood of light came streaming down, the frog changed its nature. Helga was again the beautiful maiden with the wicked, demoniac spirit. He held a beautiful maiden in his arms, but was horrified at the sight: he swung himself from the horse, and compelled it to stand. This seemed to him a new and terrible sorcery; but Helga likewise leaped from the saddle, and stood on the ground. The child's short garment reached only to her knee. She plucked the sharp knife from her girdle, and rushed in upon the astonished priest.

'Let me get at thee!' she screamed; 'let me get at thee, and plunge this knife in thy body! Thou art pale as straw, thou beardless slave!'

She pressed in upon him. They struggled together in a hard strife, but an invisible power seemed given to the Christian captive. He held her fast; and the old oak tree beneath which they stood came to his assistance; for its roots, which projected over the ground, held fast the maiden's feet that had become entangled in it. Quite close to them gushed a spring; and he sprinkled Helga's face and neck with the fresh water, and commanded the unclean spirit to come forth, and blessed her in the Christian fashion; but the water of faith has no power when the well-spring of faith flows not from within.

And yet the Christian showed his power even now, and opposed more than the mere might of a man against the evil that struggled within the girl. His holy action seemed to overpower her: she dropped her hands, and gazed with astonished eyes and pale cheeks upon him who appeared to her a mighty magician learned in secret arts; he seemed to her to speak in a dark Runic tongue, and to be making magic signs in the air. She would not have winked had he swung a sharp knife or a glittering axe against her; but she trembled when he signed her with the sign of the cross on her brow and her bosom, and she sat there like a tame bird with bowed head.

Then he spoke to her in gentle words of the kindly deed she had done for him in the past night, when she came to him in the form of the hideous frog, to loosen his bonds and to lead him out to life and light; and he told her that she too was bound in closer bonds than those that had confined him, and that she should be released by his means. He would take her to Hedeby, to the holy Ansgar, and there in the Christian city the spell that bound her would be loosed. But he would not let her sit before him on the horse, though of her own accord she offered to do so.

'Thou must sit behind me, not before me,' he said. 'Thy magic beauty hath a power that comes of evil, and I fear it; and yet I feel that the victory is sure to him who hath faith.'

And he knelt down and prayed fervently. It seemed as though the woodland scenes were consecrated as a holy church by his prayer. The birds sang as though they belonged to the new congregation, the wild flowers smelt sweet as incense; and while he spoke the horse that had carried them both in headlong career stood still before the tall bramble bushes, and plucked at them, so that the ripe juicy berries fell down upon Helga's hands, offering themselves for her refreshment.

Patiently she suffered the priest to lift her on the horse, and sat like a somnambulist, neither completely asleep nor wholly awake. The Christian bound two branches together with bark, in the form of a cross, which he held up high as they rode through the forest. The wood became thicker as they went on, and at last became a trackless wilderness.

The wild sloe grew across the way, so that they had to ride round the bushes. The spring became not a stream but a standing marsh, round which likewise they were obliged to ride. There was strength and refreshment in the cool forest breeze; and no small power lay in the gentle words which were spoken in faith and in Christian love, from a strong inward yearning to lead the poor lost one into the way of light and life.

They say the raindrops can hollow the hard stone, and the waves of the sea can smooth and round the sharp edges of the rocks. Thus did the dew of mercy, that dropped upon Helga, smooth what was rough and penetrate what was hard in her. The effects did not yet appear, nor was she aware of them herself; but doth the seed in the bosom of earth know, when the refreshing dew and the quickening sunbeams fall upon it, that it hath within itself the power of growth and blossoming? As the song of the mother penetrates into the heart of the child, and it babbles the words after her, without understanding their import, until they afterwards engender thought, and come forward in due time clearer and more clearly, so here also did the Word take effect, that is powerful to create.

They rode forth from the dense forest, across the heath, and then again through pathless woods; and towards evening they encountered a band of robbers.

'Where hast thou stolen that beauteous maiden?' cried the robbers; and they seized the horse's bridle and dragged the two riders from its back. The priest had no weapon save the knife he had taken from Helga, and with this he tried to defend himself. One of the robbers lifted his axe, but the young priest sprang aside, otherwise he would have been struck, and now the edge of the axe went deep into the horse's neck, so that the blood spurted forth, and the creature sank down on the ground. Then Helga seemed suddenly to wake up from her long reverie, and threw herself hastily upon the gasping animal. The priest stood before her to protect and defend her, but one of the robbers swung his iron hammer over the Christian's head, and brought it down with such a crash that blood and brains were scattered around, and the priest sank to the earth, dead.

Then the robbers seized little Helga by her white arms; but the sun went down, and its last ray disappeared at that moment, and she was changed into the form of a frog. A white-green mouth spread over half her face, her arms became thin and slimy, and broad hands with webbed fingers spread out upon them like fans. Then the robbers were seized with terror, and let her go. She stood, a hideous monster, among them; and as it is the nature of the frog to do, she hopped up high, and disappeared in the thicket. Then the robbers saw that this must be a bad prank of the spirit Loke, or the evil power of magic, and in great affright they hurried away from the spot.

The full moon was already rising. Presently it shone with splendid radiance over the earth, and poor Helga crept forth from the thicket in the wretched frog's shape. She stood still beside the corpse of the priest and the carcass of the slain horse. She looked at them with eyes that appeared to weep, and from the frog-mouth came forth a croaking like the voice of a child bursting into tears. She leaned first over the one, then over the other, brought water in her hand, which had become larger and more hollow by the webbed skin, and poured it over them; but dead they were, and dead they would remain, she at last understood. Soon the wild beasts would come and tear their dead bodies; but no, that must not be! so she dug up the earth as well as she could, in the endeavour to prepare a grave for them. She had nothing to work with but a stake and her two hands encumbered with the webbed skin that grew between the fingers, and which was torn by the labour, so that the blood flowed. At last she saw that her endeavours would not succeed. Then she brought water and washed the dead man's face, and covered it with fresh green leaves; she brought large boughs and laid them upon him, scattering dead leaves in the spaces between. Then she brought the heaviest stones she could carry and laid them over the dead body, stopping up the openings with moss. And now she thought the grave-hill would be strong and secure. The night had passed away in this difficult work – the sun broke through the clouds, and beautiful Helga stood there in all her loveliness, with bleeding hands, and for the first time with tears on her blushing maiden cheeks.

Then in this transformation it seemed as if two natures were striving within her. Her whole frame trembled, and she looked around, as if she had just awoke from a troubled dream. Then she ran towards the slender tree, clung to it for support, and in another moment she had climbed to the summit of the tree, and held fast. There she sat like a startled squirrel, and remained the whole day long in the silent solitude of the wood, where everything is quiet, and, as they say, dead. Butterflies fluttered around in sport, and in the neighbourhood were several ant-hills, each with its hundreds of busy little occupants moving briskly to and fro. In the air danced innumerable gnats, swarm upon swarm, and hosts of buzzing flies, ladybirds, gold beetles, and other little winged creatures; the worm crept forth from the damp ground, the moles came out; but except these all was silent around – silent, and, as people say, dead. No one noticed Helga, but some flocks of jays, that flew screaming about the top of the tree on which she sat: the birds hopped close up to her on the twigs with pert curiosity; but when the glance of her eye fell upon them, it was a signal for their flight. But they could not understand her – nor, indeed, could she understand herself.

When the evening twilight came on, and the sun was sinking, the time of her transformation roused her to fresh activity. She glided down from the tree, and as the last sunbeam vanished she stood in the wrinkled form of the frog, with the torn webbed skin on her hands; but her eyes now gleamed with a splendour of beauty that had scarcely been theirs when she wore her garb of loveliness, for they were a pair of pure, pious, maidenly eyes that shone out of the frog-face. They bore witness of depth of feeling, of the gentle human heart; and the beauteous eyes overflowed in tears, weeping precious drops that lightened the heart.

On the sepulchral mound she had raised there yet lay the cross of boughs, the last work of him who slept beneath. Helga lifted up the cross, in pursuance of a sudden thought that came upon her. She planted it between the stones, over the priest and the dead horse. The sorrowful remembrance of him called fresh tears into her eyes; and in this tender frame of mind she marked the same sign in the earth around the grave; and as she wrote the sign with both her hands, the webbed skin fell from them like a torn glove; and when she washed her hands in the woodland spring, and gazed in wonder at her fine white hands, she again made the holy sign in the air between herself and the dead man; then her lips trembled, the holy name that had been preached to her during the ride from the forest came to her mouth, and she pronounced it audibly.

Then the frogskin fell from her, and she was once more the beauteous maiden. But her head sank wearily, her tired limbs required rest, and she slept.

Her sleep, however, was short. Towards midnight she awoke. Before her stood the dead horse, beaming and full of life, which gleamed forth from his eyes and from his wounded neck; close beside the creature stood the murdered Christian priest, 'more beautiful than Balder,' the Viking woman would have said; and yet he seemed to stand in a flame of fire.

Such gravity, such an air of justice, such a piercing look shone out of his great mild eyes, that their glance seemed to penetrate every corner of her heart. Little Helga trembled at the look, and her remembrance awoke as though she stood before the tribunal of judgement. Every good deed that had been done for her, every loving word that had been spoken, seemed endowed with life: she understood that it had been love that kept her here during the days of trial, during which the creature formed of dust and spirit, soul and earth, combats and struggles; she acknowledged that she had only followed the leading of temper, and had done nothing for herself; everything had been given her, everything had been guided by Providence. She bowed herself humbly, confessing her own deep imperfection in the presence of the Power that can read every thought of the heart – and then the priest spoke.

'Thou daughter of the moss,' he said, 'out of the earth, out of the moor, thou camest; but from the earth thou shalt arise. The sunbeam in you, which comes not from the sun, but from God, will go back to its origin, conscious of the body it has inhabited. No soul shall be lost, but time is long; it is the course of life through eternity. I come from the land of the dead. Thou, too, shalt pass through the deep valleys into the beaming mountain region, where dwell mercy and complete-ness. I cannot lead thee to Hedeby, to receive Christian baptism; for, first, thou must burst the veil of waters over the deep moss, and draw forth the living source of thy being and of thy birth; thou must exercise thy faculties in deeds before the consecration can be given thee.'

And he lifted her upon the horse, and gave her a golden censer similar to the one she had seen in the Viking's castle. The open wound in the forehead of the slain Christian shone like a diadem. He took the cross from the grave and held it aloft. And now they rode through the air, over the rustling wood, over the mounds where the old heroes lay buried, each on his dead war-horse; and the mighty figures rose up and galloped forth, and stationed themselves on the summits of the mounds. The golden hoop on the forehead of each gleamed in the moonlight and their mantles floated in the night breeze. The dragon that guards buried treasures likewise lifted up his head and gazed after the riders. The gnomes and wood spirits peeped forth from beneath the hills and from between the furrows of the fields, and flitted to and fro with red, blue, and green torches, like the sparks in the ashes of a burned paper.

Over woodland and heath, over river and marsh they fled away, up to the wild moss; and over this they hovered in wide circles. The Christian priest held the cross aloft: it gleamed like gold; and from his lips dropped pious prayers. Beautiful Helga joined in the hymns he sang, like a child joining in its mother's song. She swung the censer, and a wondrous fragrance of incense streamed forth thence, so that the reeds and grass of the moss burst forth into blossom. Every germ came forth from the deep ground. All that had life lifted itself up. A veil of water-lilies spread itself forth like a carpet of wrought flowers, and upon this carpet lay a sleeping woman, young and beautiful. Helga thought it was her own likeness she saw upon the mirror of the calm waters. But it was her mother whom she beheld, the Marsh King's wife, the Princess from the banks of the Nile.

The dead priest commanded that the slumbering woman should be lifted upon the horse; but the horse sank under the burden, as though its body had been a cloth fluttering in the wind. But the holy sign gave strength to the airy phantom, and then the three rode from the moss to the firm land.

Then the cock crowed in the Viking's castle, and the phantom shapes dissolved and floated away in air; but mother and daughter stood opposite each other.

'Is it myself that I see in the deep waters?' asked the mother.

'Is it myself that I see reflected on the clear mirror?' exclaimed the daughter.

And they approached one another and embraced. The heart of the mother beat quickest, and she understood it.

'My child! thou flower of my own heart! my lotus flower of the deep waters!'

And she embraced her child anew, and wept; and the tears were as a new baptism of life and love to Helga.

'In the swan's plumage came I hither,' said the mother, 'and threw it off. I sank through the shaking mud, far down into the black slime, which closed like a wall around me. But soon I felt a fresher stream; a power drew me down, deeper and ever deeper. I felt the weight of sleep upon my eyelids; I slumbered, and dreams hovered round me. It seemed to me that I was again in the pyramid in Egypt, and yet the waving alder trunk that had frightened me up in the moss was ever before me. I looked at the clefts and wrinkles in the stem, and they shone forth in colours and took the form of hieroglyphics: it was the case of the mummy at which I was gazing; the case burst, and forth stepped the thousand-year old King, the mummied form, black as pitch, shining black as the wood snail or the fat mud of the swamp: whether it was the Marsh King or the mummy of the pyramids I knew not. He seized me in his arms, and I felt as if I must die. When I returned to consciousness a little bird was sitting on my bosom, beating with its wings, and twittering and singing. The bird flew away from me up towards the heavy, dark covering, but a long green band still fastened him to me. I heard and understood his longing tones: "Freedom! Sunlight! To my father!" Then I thought of my father and the sunny land of my birth, my life, and my love; and I loosened the band and let the bird soar away home to the father. Since that hour I have dreamed no more. I have slept a sleep, a long and heavy sleep, till in this hour harmony and incense awoke me and set me free.'

The green band from the heart of the mother to the bird's wings, where did it flutter now? whither had it been wafted? Only the Stork had seen it. The band was the green stalk, the bow at the end, the beauteous flower, the cradle of the child that had now bloomed into beauty and was once more resting on its mother's heart.

And while the two were locked in each other's embrace, the old Stork flew around them in circles, and at length shot away towards his nest, whence he brought out the swan-feather suits he had preserved there for years, throwing one to each of them, and the feathers closed around them, so that they soared up from the earth in the semblance of two white swans.

'And now we will speak with one another,' quoth Stork-papa, 'now we understand each other, though the beak of one bird is differently shaped from that of another. It happens more than fortunately that you came tonight. Tomorrow we should have been gone – mother, myself, and the young ones, for we are flying southward. Yes, only look at me! I am an old friend from the land of the Nile, and mother has a heart larger than her beak. She always declared the Princess would find a way to help herself; and I and the young ones carried the swans' feathers up here. But how glad I am! and how fortunate that I'm here still! At dawn of day we shall move hence, a great company of storks. We'll fly first, and do you follow us; thus you cannot miss your way; moreover, I and the youngsters will keep a sharp eye upon you.'

'And the lotus flower which I was to bring with me,' said the Egyptian Princess, 'she is flying by my side in the swans' plumage! I bring with me the flower of my heart; and thus the riddle has been read. Homeward! homeward!'

But Helga declared she could not quit the Danish land before she had once more seen her foster-mother, the affectionate Viking woman. Every beautiful recollection, every kind word, every tear that her foster-mother had wept for her, rose up in her memory, and in that moment she almost felt as if she loved the Viking woman best of all.

'Yes, we must go to the Viking's castle,' said Stork-papa; 'mother and the youngsters are waiting for us there. How they will turn up their eyes and flap their wings! Yes, you see, mother doesn't speak much – she's short and dry, but she means all the better. I'll begin clapping at once, that they may know we're coming.'

And Stork-papa clapped in first-rate style, and they all flew away towards the Viking's castle.

In the castle everyone was sunk in deep sleep. The Viking's wife had not retired to rest until it was late. She was anxious about Helga, who had vanished with the Christian priest three days before: she must have assisted him in his flight, for it was the girl's horse that had been missed from the stables; but how all this had been effected was a mystery to her. The Viking woman had heard of the miracles told of the White Christ, and by those who believed in His words and followed Him. Her passing thoughts formed themselves into a dream, and it seemed to her that she was still lying awake on her couch, and that deep darkness reigned without. The storm drew near: she heard the sea roaring and rolling to the east and to the west, like the waves of the North Sea and the Cattegat. The immense snake which was believed to surround the span of the earth in the depths of the ocean was trembling in convulsions; she dreamed that the night of the fall of the gods had come – Ragnarok, as the heathen called the last day, when everything was to pass away, even the great gods themselves. The war-trumpet sounded, and the gods rode over the rainbow, clad in steel, to fight the last battle. The winged Valkyries rode before them, and the dead warriors closed the train. The whole firmament was ablaze with Northern Lights, and yet the darkness seemed to predominate. It was a terrible hour.

And, close by the terrified Viking woman, Helga seemed to be crouching on the floor in the hideous frog-form, trembling and pressing close to her foster-mother, who took her on her lap and embraced her affectionately, hideous though she was. The air resounded with the blows of clubs and swords, and with the hissing of arrows, as if a hailstorm were passing across it. The hour was come when earth and sky were to burst, the stars to fall, and all things to be swallowed up in Surt's sea of fire; but she knew that there would be a new heaven and a new earth, that the cornfields then would wave where now the ocean rolled over the desolate tracts of sand, and that the unutterable God would reign; and up to Him rose Balder the gentle, the affectionate, delivered from the kingdom of the dead: he came; the Viking woman saw him and recognised his countenance; it was that of the captive Christian priest. 'White Christ!' she cried aloud, and with these words she pressed a kiss upon the forehead of the hideous frog-child. Then the frogskin fell off, and Helga stood revealed in all her beauty, lovely and gentle as she had never appeared, and with beaming eyes. She kissed her foster-mother's hands, blessed her for all the care and affection lavished during the days of bitterness and trial, for the thought she had awakened and cherished in her, for naming the name, which she repeated, 'White Christ;' and beauteous Helga arose in the form of a mighty swan, and spread her white wings with a rushing like the sound of a troop of birds of passage winging their way through the air.

The Viking woman awoke, and she heard the same noise without still continuing. She knew it was the time for the storks to depart, and that it must be those birds whose wings she heard. She wished to see them once more, and to bid them farewell as they set forth on their journey. Therefore she rose from her couch and stepped out upon the threshold, and on the top of the gable she saw stork ranged behind stork, and around the castle, over the high trees, flew bands of storks wheeling in wide circles; but opposite her, by the well where Helga had often sat and alarmed her with her wildness, sat two white swans gazing at her with intelligent eyes. And she remembered her dream, which still filled her soul as if it were reality. She thought of Helga in the shape of a swan, and of the Christian priest: and suddenly she felt her heart rejoice within her.

The swans flapped their wings and arched their necks, as if they would send her a greeting, and the Viking's wife spread out her arms towards them, as if she understood it, and smiled through her tears, and then stood sunk in deep thought.

Then all the storks arose, flapping their wings and clapping with their beaks, to start on their voyage towards the South.

'We will not wait for the swans,' said Stork-mamma: 'if they want to go with us they had better come. We can't sit here till the plovers start. It is a fine thing, after all, to travel in this way, in families, not like the finches and partridges, where the male and female birds fly in separate bodies, which appears to me a very unbecoming thing. What are yonder swans flapping their wings for?'

'Everyone flies in his own fashion,' said Stork-papa: 'the swans in an oblique line, the cranes in a triangle, and the plovers in a snake's line.'

'Don't talk about snakes while we are flying up here,' said Stork-mamma. 'It only puts ideas into the children's heads which can't be gratified.'

'Are those the high mountains of which I have heard tell?' asked Helga, in the swan's plumage.

'They are storm clouds driving on beneath us,' replied her mother.

'What are yonder white clouds that rise so high?' asked Helga again.

'Those are the mountains covered with perpetual snow which you see yonder,' replied her mother.

And they flew across the lofty Alps towards the blue Mediterranean.

'Africa's land! Egypt's strand!' sang, rejoicingly, in her swan's plumage, the daughter of the Nile, as from the lofty air she saw her native land in the form of a yellowish wavy stripe of shore.

And all the birds caught sight of it, and hastened their flight.

'I can scent the Nile mud and wet frogs,' said Stork-mamma; 'I begin to feel quite hungry. Yes; now you shall taste something nice; and you will see the marabou bird, the crane, and the ibis. They all belong to our family, though they are not nearly so beautiful as we. They give themselves great airs, especially the ibis. He has been quite spoiled by the Egyptians, for they make a mummy of him and stuff him with spices. I would rather be stuffed with live frogs, and so would you, and so you shall. Better have something in one's inside while one is alive than to be made a fuss of after one is dead. That's my opinion, and I am always right.'

'Now the storks are come,' said the people in the rich house on the banks of the Nile, where the royal lord lay in the open hall on the downy cushions, covered with a leopardskin, not alive and yet not dead, but waiting and hoping for the lotus flower from the deep moss in the far North. Friends and servants stood around his couch.

And into the hall flew two beauteous swans. They had come with the storks. They threw off their dazzling white plumage, and two lovely female forms were revealed, as like each other as two dewdrops. They bent over the old, pale, sick man, they put back their long hair, and while Helga bent over her grandfather, his white cheeks reddened, his eyes brightened, and life came back to his wasted limbs. The old man rose up cheerful and well, and daughter and granddaughter embraced him joyfully, as if they were giving him a morning greeting after a long heavy dream.

And joy reigned through the whole house, and likewise in the Stork's nest, though there the chief cause was certainly the good food, especially the numberless frogs; and while the learned men wrote down hastily, in flying characters, a sketch of the history of the two Princesses, and of the flower of health that had been a source of joy for the home and the land, the Stork-pair told the story to their family in their own fashion, but not till all had eaten their fill, otherwise they would have found something more interesting to do than to listen to stories.

'Now, at last, you will become something,' whispered Stork-mamma, 'there's no doubt about that.'

'What should I become?' asked Stork-papa. 'What have I done? Nothing at all!'

'You have done more than the rest! But for you and the youngsters the two Princesses would never have seen Egypt again, or have effected the old man's cure. You will turn out something! They must certainly give you a doctor's degree, and our youngsters will inherit it, and so will their children after them, and so on. You already look like an Egyptian doctor – at least in my eyes.'

The learned and wise men developed the ground-thought, as they called it, which went through the whole affair. 'Love begets life;' this maxim they explained in various ways. 'The warm sunbeam was the Egyptian Princess; she descended to the Marsh King, and from their meeting arose the flower –'

'I cannot quite repeat the words as they were spoken,' said Stork-papa, who had listened from the roof, and was now telling it again to his own family. 'What they said was so involved, it was so wise and learned, that they immediately received rank and presents: even the head cook received an especial mark of distinction – probably for the soup.'

'And what did you receive?' asked Stork-mamma. 'Surely they ought not to forget the most important person of all, and you are certainly he! The learned men have done nothing throughout the whole affair but used their tongues; but you will doubtless receive what is due to you.'

Late in the night, when the gentle peace of sleep rested upon the now happy house, there was one who still watched. It was not Stork-papa, though he stood upon one leg and slept on guard – it was Helga who watched. She bowed herself forward over the balcony, and looked into the clear air, gazed at the great gleaming stars, greater and purer in their lustre than she had ever seen them in the North, and yet the same orbs. She thought of the Viking woman in the wild moorland, of the gentle eyes of her foster-mother, and of the tears which the kind soul had wept over the poor frog-child that now lived in splendour under the gleaming stars, in the beauteous spring air on the banks of the Nile. She thought of the love that dwelt in the breast of the heathen woman, the love that had been shown to a wretched creature, hateful in human form, and hideous in its transformation. She looked at the gleaming stars, and thought of the glory that had shone upon the forehead of the dead man, when she flew with him through the forest and across the moorland; sounds passed through her memory, words she had heard pronounced as they rode onward, and when she was borne wondering and trembling through the air, words from the great Fountain of love that embraces all human kind.

Yes, great things had been achieved and won! Day and night beautiful Helga was absorbed in the contemplation of the great sum of her happiness, and stood in the contemplation of it like a child that turns hurriedly from the giver to gaze on the splendours of the gifts it has received. She seemed to lose herself in the increasing happiness, in contemplation of what might come, of what would come. Had she not been borne by miracle to greater and greater bliss? And in this idea she one day lost herself so completely, that she thought no more of the Giver. It was the exuberance of youthful courage, unfolding its wings for a bold flight! Her eyes were gleaming with courage, when suddenly a loud noise in the courtyard below recalled her thoughts from their wandering flight. There she saw two great ostriches running round rapidly in a narrow circle. Never before had she seen such creatures – great clumsy things they were, with wings that looked as if they had been clipped, and the birds themselves looking as if they had suffered violence of some kind; and now for the first time she heard the legend which the Egyptians tell of the ostrich.

Once, they say, the ostriches were a beautiful, glorious race of birds, with strong large wings; and one evening the larger birds of the forest said to the ostrich, 'Brother, shall we fly tomorrow, God willing, to the river to drink?' And the ostrich answered, 'I will.' At daybreak, accordingly, they winged their flight from thence, flying first up on high, towards the sun, that gleamed like the eye of God – higher and higher, the ostrich far in advance of all the other birds. Proudly the ostrich flew straight towards the light, boasting of his strength, and not thinking of the Giver, or saying, 'God willing!' Then suddenly the avenging angel drew aside the veil from the flaming ocean of sunlight, and in a moment the wings of the proud bird were scorched and shrivelled up, and he sank miserably to the ground. Since that time the ostrich has never again been able to raise himself in the air, but flees timidly along the ground, and runs round in a narrow circle. And this is a warning for us men, that in all our thoughts and schemes, in all our doings and devices, we should say, 'God willing.' And Helga bowed her head thoughtfully, and looked at the circling ostrich, noticing its timid fear, and its stupid pleasure at sight of its own great shadow cast upon the white sunlit wall. And seriousness struck its roots deep into her mind and heart. A rich life in present and future happiness was given and won; and what was yet to come? the best of all, 'God willing.'

In early spring, when the storks flew again towards the North, beautiful Helga took off her golden bracelet and scratched her name upon it; and beckoning to the Stork-papa, she placed the golden hoop around his neck, and begged him to deliver it to the Viking woman, so that the latter might see that her adopted daughter was well, and had not forgotten her.

'That's heavy to carry,' thought the Stork-papa, when he had the golden ring round his neck; 'but gold and honour are not to be flung on the highway. The stork brings good fortune; they'll be obliged to acknowledge that up there.'

'You lay gold and I lay eggs,' said the Stork-mamma. 'But with you it's only once in a way, whereas I lay eggs every year; but neither of us is appreciated – that's very disheartening.'

'Still one has one's inward consciousness, mother,' replied Stork-papa.

'But you can't hang that round your neck,' Stork-mamma retorted, 'and it won't give you a good wind or a good meal.'

The little nightingale, singing in the tamarind tree, would soon be going north too. Helga the fair had often heard the sweet bird sing up yonder by the wild moss; now she wanted to give it a message to carry, for she had learned the language of birds when she flew in the swan's plumage; she had often conversed with stork and with swallow, and she knew the nightingale would understand her. So she begged the little bird to fly to the beech-wood on the peninsula of Jutland, where the grave-mound had been reared with stones and branches and asked the nightingale to beg all other little birds to build their nests around the grave, and sing their song there again and again. And the nightingale flew away – and time flew away.

In autumn the eagle stood upon the pyramid, and saw a stately train of richly laden camels approaching, and richly attired armed men on snorting Arab steeds, shining white as silver, with pink trembling nostrils, and great thick manes hanging down almost over their slender legs. Wealthy guests, a royal Prince of Arabia, handsome as a Prince should be, came into the proud mansion on whose roof the storks' nests now stood empty; those who had inhabited the nest were away in the far North, but they would soon return. And, indeed, they returned on that very day that was so rich in joy and gladness. Here a marriage was celebrated, and fair Helga was the bride, shining in jewels and silk. The bridegroom was the young Arab Prince, and bride and bridegroom sat together at the upper end of the table, between mother and grandfather.

But her gaze was not fixed upon the bridegroom, with his manly sun-browned cheeks, round which a black beard curled; she gazed not at his dark fiery eyes that were fixed upon her – but far away at a gleaming star that shone down from the sky.

Then strong wings were heard beating the air. The storks were coming home, and however tired the old Stork-pair might be from the journey, and however much they needed repose, they did not fail to come down at once to the balustrades of the verandah, for they knew what feast was being celebrated. Already on the frontier of the land they had heard that Helga had caused their figures to be painted on the wall – for did they not belong to her history?

'That's very pretty and suggestive,' said Stork-papa.

'But it's very little,' observed Stork-mamma. 'They could not possibly have done less.'

And when Helga saw them, she rose and came on to the verandah, to stroke the backs of the Storks. The old pair bowed their necks, and even the youngest among the young ones felt highly honoured by the reception.

And Helga looked up to the gleaming star, which seemed to glow purer and purer; and between the star and herself there floated a form, purer than the air, and visible through it: it floated quite close to her. It was the spirit of the dead Christian priest; he too was coming to her wedding feast – coming from heaven.

'The glory and brightness yonder outshines everything that is known on earth!' he said.

And fair Helga begged so fervently, so beseechingly, as she had never yet prayed, that it might be permitted her to gaze in there for one single moment, that she might be allowed to cast but a single glance into the brightness that beamed in the kingdom of heaven.

Then he bore her up amid splendour and glory. Not only around her, but within her, sounded voices and beamed a brightness that words cannot express.

'Now we must go back; thou wilt be missed,' he said.

'Only one more look!' she begged. 'But one short minute more!'

'We must go back to the earth. The guests will all depart.'

'Only one more look – the last.'

And Helga stood again in the verandah; but the marriage lights without had vanished, and the lamps in the hall were extinguished, and the storks were gone – nowhere a guest to be seen – no bridegroom – all seemed to have been swept away in those few short minutes!

Then a great dread came upon her. Alone she went through the empty great hall into the next chamber. Strange warriors slept yonder. She opened a side door which led into her own chamber, and, as she thought to step in there, she suddenly found herself in the garden; but yet it had not looked thus here before – the sky gleamed red – the morning dawn was come.

Three minutes only in heaven and a whole night on earth had passed away!

Then she saw the Storks again. She called to them and spoke their language; and Stork-papa turned his head towards her, listened to her words, and drew near.

'You speak our language,' he said; 'what do you wish? Why do you appear here – you, a strange woman?'

'It is I – it is Helga – dost thou not know me? Three minutes ago we were speaking together yonder in the verandah!'

'That's a mistake,' said the Stork; 'you must have dreamed that!'

'No, no!' she persisted. And she reminded him of the Viking's castle, and of the wild moss, and of the journey hither.

Then Stork-papa winked with his eyes, and said, 'That's an old story, which I heard from the time of my great-great-grandmother. There certainly was here in Egypt a Princess of that kind from the

Danish land, but she vanished on the evening of her wedding-day, many hundred years ago, and never came back! You may read about it yourself yonder on the monument in the garden; there you'll find swans and storks sculptured, and at the top you yourself are cut in white marble!'

And thus it was. Helga saw it, and understood it, and sank on her knees.

The sun burst forth in glory; and as, in time of yore, the frog-shape had vanished in its beams, and the beautiful form had stood displayed, so now in the light a beauteous form, clearer, purer than air – a beam of brightness – flew up into heaven!

The body crumbled to dust, and a faded lotus flower lay on the spot where Helga had stood.

'Well, that's a new ending to the story,' said Stork-papa. 'I had certainly not expected it. But I like it very well.'

'But what will the young ones say to it?' said Stork-mamma.

'Yes, certainly, that's the important point,' replied he.

The Racers

A PRIZE, or rather two prizes, had been announced – a big one and a little one – for the greatest swiftness, not in a single race, but for swiftness throughout an entire year.

'I got the first prize!' said the Hare; 'there must be justice when relations and good friends are among the prize committee; but that the Snail should have received the second prize, I consider almost an insult to myself.'

'No!' declared the Fence-rail, who had been witness at the distribution of prizes, 'reference must also be had to industry and perseverance. Many respectable people said so, and I understood it well. The Snail certainly took half a year to get across the threshold; but has broken his thigh-bone in the haste he was compelled to make. He devoted himself entirely to his work, and he ran with his house on his back! All that is very praiseworthy, and that's how he got the second prize.'

'I might certainly have been considered too,' said the Swallow. 'I should think that no one appeared swifter in flying and soaring than myself, and how far I have been around – far – far – far!'

'Yes, that's just your misfortune,' said the Fence-rail. 'You're too fond of fluttering. You must always be journeying about into far countries when it begins to be cold here. You've no love of fatherland in you. You cannot be taken into account.'

'But if I lay in the swamp all through the winter?' said the Swallow. 'Suppose I slept through the whole time; should I be taken into account then?'

'Bring a certificate from the old swamp-wife that you have slept away half the time in your fatherland, and you shall be taken into account.'

'I deserved the first prize, and not the second,' said the Snail. 'I know so much at least, that the Hare only ran from cowardice, because he thought each time there was danger in delay. I, on the other hand, made my running the business of my life, and have become a cripple in the service. If anyone was to have the first prize, I should have had it; but I make no fuss, I despise it!'

And so he spat.

'I am able to depose with word and oath that each prize, at least my vote for each, was given after proper consideration,' observed the old Boundary-post in the wood, who had been a member of the body of judges. 'I always go on with due consideration, with order, and calculation. Seven times before I have had the honour to be present at the distribution of prizes, but not till today have I carried out my will. At each distribution I have started from a fixed principle. I always went to the first prize from the beginning of the alphabet, and to the second from the end. And if you will now take notice, when one starts from the beginning, the eighth letter from A is H, and there we have the Hare, and so I awarded him the first prize; the eighth letter from the end of the alphabet is S, and therefore the Snail received the second prize. Next time, I will have its turn for the first prize, and R for the second: there must be due order in everything! One must have a certain starting-point!'

'I should certainly have voted for myself, if I had not been among the judges,' said the Mule, who had been one of the committee. 'One must not only consider the rapidity of advance, but every other quality also that is found – as, for example, how much a candidate is able to draw; but I would not have put that prominently forward this time, nor the sagacity of the Hare in his flight, or the cunning with which he suddenly takes a leap to one side to bring people on a false track, so that they may not know where he has hidden himself. No! there is something else on which many lay great stress, and which one may not leave out of the calculation. I mean what is called the beautiful. On the beautiful I particularly fixed my eyes; I looked at the beautiful well-grown ears of the Hare: it's quite a pleasure to see how long they are; it almost seemed to me as if I saw myself in the days of my childhood. And so I voted for the Hare.'

'But,' said the Fly, 'I'm not going to talk, I'm only going to say something. I know that I have overtaken more than one hare. Quite lately I crushed the hind legs of one. I was sitting on the engine in front of a railway train – I often do that, for thus one can best notice one's own swiftness. A young hare ran for a long time in front of the engine; he had no idea that I was present; but at last he was obliged to give in and spring aside – and then the engine crushed his hind legs, for I was upon it. The hare lay there, but I rode on. That certainly was conquering him! But I don't count upon getting the prize!'

'It certainly appears to me,' thought the Wild Rose – but she did not say it, for it is not her nature to give her opinion, though it would have been quite as well if she had done so – 'it certainly appears to me that the sunbeam ought to have had the first prize and the second too. The sunbeam flies in a moment along the enormous path from the sun to ourselves, and arrives in such strength that all nature awakes at it; such beauty does it possess that all we roses blush and exhale fragrance in its presence. Our worshipful judges do not appear to have noticed this at all. If I were the sunbeam, I would give each of them a sunstroke – but that would only make them mad, and that they may become as things stand. I say nothing,' thought the Wild Rose. 'May peace reign in the forest! It is glorious to blossom, to scent, and to refresh – to live in song and legend. The sunbeam will outlive us all.'

'What's the first prize?' asked the Earthworm, who had overslept the time, and only came up now.

'It consists in a free admission to a cabbage garden,' replied the Mule. 'I proposed that as the prize. The Hare was decided to have won it, and therefore I, as an active and reflective member, took especial notice of the advantage of him who was to get it: now the Hare is provided for. The Snail may sit upon the fence and lick up moss and sunshine, and has further been appointed one of the first umpires in the racing. It is so good to have a professional in the thing men call a committee. I must say I expect much from the future – we have made so good a beginning.'

The Bell-Deep

'DING–DONG! ding–dong!' It sounds up from the 'bell-deep' in the Odense River. What river is that? Every child in the town of Odense knows that it runs at the bottom of the gardens and flows on under the wooden bridges from the dam to the water-mill. In the river grow the yellow water-lilies and brown feathery reeds; the dark velvety reed-mace grows there, high and thick; old and decayed willows, slanting and tottering, hang far out over the stream beside the monks' meadow and by the bleaching ground; but opposite there are gardens upon gardens, each different from the rest, some with pretty flowers and bowers like little dolls' pleasure grounds, others displaying only cabbage and other kitchen plants; and here and there the gardens cannot be seen at all, for the great elder trees that spread themselves out by the bank, and hang far out over the streaming waters, which are deeper here and there than an oar can fathom. Opposite the old nunnery is the deepest place, which is called the 'bell-deep', and there dwells the 'River-man'. He sleeps through the day while the sun shines down upon the water; but in starry and moonlit nights he shows himself. He is very old: grandmother says that she has heard her own grandmother tell of him; he is said to lead a solitary life, and to have nobody with whom he can converse save the great old church Bell. Once the Bell hung in the church tower; but now there is no trace left of the tower or of the church, which was called St Alban's.

'Ding–dong! ding–dong!' sounded the Bell, when the tower still stood there; and one evening, while the sun was setting, and the Bell was swinging away bravely, it broke loose and came flying down through the air, the brilliant metal shining in the ruddy beam.

'Ding–dong! ding–dong! Now I'm going to bed!' sang the Bell, and flew down into the Odense River where it is deepest; and that is why the place is called the 'bell-deep'.

But the Bell got neither rest nor sleep. Down in the River-man's haunt it sounds and rings, so that the tones sometimes pierce upward through the waters; and many people maintain that its strains forebode the death of someone; but that is not true, for then the Bell is only talking with the River-man, who is now no longer alone.

And what is the Bell telling? It is old, very old, the story goes; it was there long before grandmother's grandmother was born; and yet it is but a child in comparison with the River-man, who is an old quiet personage, an oddity, with his hose of eelskin, and his scaly jacket with the yellow lilies for buttons, and a wreath of reed in his hair and duckweed in his beard, and that is not very pretty.

What the Bell tells? To repeat it all would require years and days; for year by year it is telling the old stories, sometimes short ones, sometimes long ones, according to its whim; it tells of old times, of the dark hard times, thus: 'In the church of St Alban, the monk mounted up into the tower where the bell hung. He was young and handsome, but thoughtful exceedingly. He looked through the loophole out upon the Odense River, when the bed of the water was yet broad and the monks' meadow was still a lake: he looked out over it, and over the rampart, and over the nuns' hill opposite, where the convent lay, and the light gleamed forth from the nun's cell; he had known the nun right well, and he thought of her, and his heart beat quicker as he thought. Ding–dong! ding–dong!'

Yes, that is how the Bell told the story.

'Into the tower came also the silly manservant of the bishop; and when I, the Bell, who am made of metal, rang hard and loud, and swung to and fro, I might have beaten out his brains. He sat down close under me, and played with two little sticks as if they had been a stringed instrument; and he sang to it. "Now I may sing it out aloud, though at other times I may not whisper it. I may sing of everything that is kept concealed behind lock and bars. There it is cold and wet. The rats are eating them up alive! Nobody knows of it! Nobody hears of it! Not even now, for the Bell is ringing and singing its loud Ding– dong! ding–dong!"

'There was a King; they called him Canute. He bowed himself before bishop and monk; but when he offended the free peasants with heavy taxes and hard words, they seized their weapons and put him to flight like a wild beast. He sought shelter in the church, and shut gate and door behind him. The violent band surrounded the church; I heard tell of it. The crows, ravens, and magpies started up in terror at the yelling and shouting that sounded around. They flew into the tower and out again, they looked down upon the throng below, and they also looked into the windows of the church, and screamed out aloud what they saw there. King Canute knelt before the altar in prayer, his brothers Eric and Benedict stood by him as a guard with drawn swords; but the King's servant, the treacherous Blake, betrayed his master; the throng in front of the church knew where they could hit the King, and one of them flung a stone through a pane of glass, and the King lay there dead! The cries and screams of the savage horde and of the birds sounded through the air, and I joined in it also; for I sang "Ding–dong! ding–dong!"

'The church bell hangs high and looks far around, gets visits from the birds and understands their language; the wind roars in upon it through windows and loopholes; and the wind knows everything, for he gets it from the air, which encircles all living things; the air makes its way into men's lungs, it knows everything that finds utterance there, every word and every sigh. The air knows it, the wind tells it, and the church Bell understands his tongue, and rings it out into the world, "Ding–dong! ding–dong!"

'But it was too much for me to hear and to know; I was not able to ring it out. I became so tired, so heavy, that the beam broke, and I flew out into the shining air down where the water is deepest, and where the Riverman lives, solitary and alone; and year by year I tell him what I have heard and what I know. "Ding–dong! ding–dong!" '

Thus it sounds out of the bell-deep in the Odense River: that is what grandmother told us.

But our schoolmaster says that there is no bell that rings down there, for it can't do so; and that no Riverman dwells there, for there are no River-men! And when all the other church bells are sounding sweetly, he says that it is not really the bells that are sounding, but that it is the air itself which sends forth the notes; and grandmother said to us that the Bell itself said it was the air who told it him, consequently they are agreed on that point, and this much is sure.

'Be cautious, cautious, and take good heed to thyself,' they both say.

The air knows everything. It is around us, it is in us, it talks of our thoughts and of our deeds, and it speaks longer of them than does the Bell down in the depths of the Odense River where the River-man dwells; it rings it out into the vault of heaven, far, far out, for ever and ever, till the heaven bells sound 'Ding–dong! ding–dong!'

The Wicked Prince

THERE WAS once a wicked and arrogant Prince. His whole ambition was to conquer all the countries in the world, and to inspire all men with fear. He went about with fire and sword, and his soldiers trampled down the corn in the fields, and set fire to the peasants' houses, so that the red flames licked the leaves from the trees, and the fruit hung burned on the black charred branches. With her naked baby in her arms, many a poor mother took refuge behind the still smoking walls of her burned house; and the soldiers sought for her, and if they found her, it was new food for their demoniac fury: evil spirits could not have raged worse than did these soldiers; but the Prince thought their deeds were right, and that it must be so. Every day his power increased; his name was feared by all, and fortune accompanied him in all his actions. From conquered towns he brought vast treasures home, and in his capital was heaped an amount of wealth unequalled in any other place. And he caused gorgeous palaces, churches, and halls to be built, and everyone who saw all this grandeur, said, 'What a great Prince!' They thought not of the misery he had brought upon other lands; they heard not all the sighs and all the moanings that arose from among the demolished towns.

The Prince looked upon his gold, and upon his mighty buildings, and his thoughts were like those of the crowd.

'What a great Prince! But, I must have more, far more! No power may be equal to mine, much less exceed it!'

And he made war upon all his neighbours, and overcame them all. The conquered Kings he caused to be bound with fetters of gold to his chariot when he drove through the streets of his capital; when he banqueted, those Kings were compelled to kneel at his feet, and at the feet of his courtiers, and receive the broken pieces which were thrown to them from the table.

At last the Prince caused his own statue to be set up in the open squares and in the royal palaces, and he even wished to place it in the churches before the altars; but the priests said, 'Prince, thou art mighty, but Heaven is mightier, and we dare not do it.'

'Good: then,' said the Prince, 'I will vanquish Heaven likewise.'

And in his pride and impious haughtiness he caused an ingenious ship to be built, in which he could sail through the air: it was gay to behold, like the tail of a peacock, and seemed to be studded with thousands of eyes; but each eye was the muzzle of a gun. The Prince sat in the midst of the ship, and needed only to press on a spring, and a thousand bullets flew out on all sides, while the gun barrels were reloaded immediately. Hundreds of eagles were harnessed in front of the ship, and in this way he now flew towards the sun. Deep lay the earth below him! With its mountains and forests, it seemed but a ploughed field where the green peeps out from the overturned grass turf; soon it appeared only like a flat map; and at last it lay completely hidden in mist and cloud. Ever higher flew the eagles, up into the air; then one of the innumerable angels appeared. The wicked Prince hurled thousands of bullets against him; but the bullets sprang back from the angel's shining pinions, and fell down like hailstones; but a drop of blood, one single drop, fell from one of the white wing-feathers, and this drop fell upon the ship in which the Prince sat, and burned its way deep into the ship, and weighing like a thousand hundredweight of lead, dragged down the ship in headlong fall towards the earth; the strongest pinions of the eagles broke; the wind roared round the Prince's head, and the clouds – formed from the smoke of burned cities – drew themselves together in threatening shapes, like huge sea-crabs stretching forth their claws and nippers towards him, like rolling masses of rock and fire-vomiting dragons, till the Prince lay half dead in the ship, which at last remained hanging in the thick branches of a forest.

'I will conquer Heaven!' said the Prince. 'I have sworn it, and my will *must* be done!'

And for seven years he caused his men to work at making ships for sailing through the air, and had thunderbolts made of the hardest steel,

for he wished to storm the fortress of Heaven; out of all his dominions he gathered armies together, so that when they were drawn up in rank and file they covered a space of several miles. The armies went on board the ships, and the Prince approached his own vessel. Then there was sent out against him a swarm of gnats, a single swarm of little gnats. The swarm buzzed round the Prince, and stung his face and hands: raging with anger, he drew his sword and struck all round him; but he only struck the empty air, for he could not hit the gnats. Then he commanded his people to bring costly hangings, and to wrap them around him, so that no gnat might further sting him; and the servants did as he commanded them. But a single gnat had attached itself to the inner side of the hangings, and crept into the ear of the Prince, and stung him there. It burned like fire, and the poison penetrated to his brain: like a madman he tore the hangings from his body, tore his clothes and danced about naked before the eyes of his rude, savage soldiers, who now jeered at the mad Prince who wanted to overcome Heaven, and who himself was conquered by one single little gnat.

The Wind Tells about Waldemar Daa
and his Daughters

WHEN THE wind sweeps across the grass, the field has a ripple like a pond, and when it sweeps across the corn the field waves to and fro like a sea. That is called the wind's dance; but hear it tell stories; it sings them out, and how different it sounds in the tree-tops in the forest, and through the loopholes and clefts and cracks in walls! Do you see how the wind drives the clouds up yonder, like a flock of sheep? Do you hear how the wind howls down here through the open gate, like a watchman blowing his horn? With wonderful tones he whistles and screams down the chimney and into the fire-place! The fire crackles and flares up, and shines far into the room, and the little place is warm and snug, and it is pleasant to sit there listening to the sounds. Let the Wind speak, for he knows plenty of stories and fairy tales, many more than are known to any of us. Just hear what the Wind can tell.

'Huh – uh – ush! roar along!' That is the burden of the song.

'By the shores of the Great Belt lies an old mansion with thick red walls,' says the Wind. 'I know every stone in it; I saw it when it still belonged to the castle of Marsk Stig on the promontory. But it had to be pulled down, and the stone was used again for the walls of a new mansion in another place, the baronial mansion of Borreby, which still stands by the coast.

'I knew them, the noble lords and ladies, the changing races that dwelt there, and now I'm going to tell about Waldemar Daa and his daughters. How proudly he carried himself – he was of royal blood! He could do more than merely hunt the stag and empty the wine-can. "It *shall* be done," he was accustomed to say.

'His wife walked proudly in gold-embroidered garments over the polished marble floors. The tapestries were gorgeous, the furniture was expensive and artistically carved. She had brought gold and silver plate with her into the house, and there was German beer in the cellar. Black fiery horses neighed in the stables. There was a wealthy look about the house of Borreby at that time, when wealth was still at home there.

'Children dwelt there also; three dainty maidens, Ida, Joanna, and Anna Dorothea: I have never forgotten their names.'

'They were rich people, noble people, born in affluence, nurtured in affluence.

'Huh – sh! roar along!' sang the Wind; and then he continued:

'I did not see here, as in other great noble houses, the high-born lady sitting among her women in the great hall turning the spinning-wheel: she played on the sounding lute, and sang to the sound, but not always old Danish melodies, but songs of a strange land. Here was life and hospitality: distinguished guests came from far and near, the music sounded, the goblets clashed, and I was not able to drown the noise,' said the Wind. 'Ostentation, and haughtiness, and splendour, and display, and rule were there, but the fear of the Lord was not there.

'And it was just on the evening of the first day of May,' the Wind continued. 'I came from the west, and had seen how the ships were being crushed by the waves, on the west coast of Jutland. I had hurried across the heath, and the wood-girt coast, and over the Island of Fyen, and now I drove over the Great Belt, groaning and sighing.

'Then I lay down to rest on the shore of Zealand, in the neighbour-hood of the great house of Borreby, where the forest, the splendid oak forest, still rose.

'The young menservants of the neighbourhood were collecting branches and brushwood under the oak trees; the largest and driest they could find they carried into the village, and piled them up in a heap, and set them on fire; and men and maids danced, singing in a circle round the blazing pile.

'I lay quite quiet,' continued the Wind; 'but I quietly touched a branch, which had been brought by the handsomest of the men-servants, and the wood blazed up brightly, blazed up higher than all the rest; and now he was the chosen one, and bore the name of Street-goat, and might choose his Street-lamb first from among the maids; and there was mirth and rejoicing, greater than there was in the rich mansion of Borreby.

'And the noble lady drove towards the mansion, with her three daughters, in a gilded carriage drawn by six horses. The daughters were young and fair – three charming blossoms, rose, lily, and pale hyacinth. The mother was a proud tulip, and never acknowledged the salutation of one of the men or maids who paused in their sport to do her honour: the gracious lady seemed a flower that was rather stiff in the stalk.

'Rose, lily, and pale hyacinth; yes, I saw them all three! Whose lambkins will they one day become? thought I; their Street-goat will be a gallant knight, perhaps a Prince. Huh – sh! hurry along! hurry along!

'Yes, the carriage rolled on with them, and the peasant people resumed their dancing. They rode that summer through all the villages round about. But in the night, when I rose again,' said the Wind, 'the very noble lady lay down, to rise again no more: that thing came upon her which comes upon all – there is nothing new in that.

'Waldemar Daa stood for a space silent and thoughtful. "The proudest tree can be bowed without being broken," said a voice within him. His daughters wept, and all the people in the mansion wiped their eyes; but Lady Daa had driven away – and I drove away too, and rushed along, huh – sh!' said the Wind.

I returned again; I often returned again over the Island of Fyen and the shores of the Belt, and I sat down by Borreby, by the splendid oak wood; there the heron made his nest, and wood-pigeons haunted the place, and blue ravens, and even the black stork. It was still spring; some of them were yet sitting on their eggs, others had already hatched their young. But how they flew up, how they cried! The axe sounded, blow upon blow: the wood was to be felled. Waldemar Daa wanted to build a noble ship, a man-of-war, a three-decker, which the King would be sure to buy; and therefore the wood must be felled, the landmark of the seamen, the refuge of the birds. The hawk started up and flew away, for its nest was destroyed; the heron and all the birds of the forest became homeless, and flew about in fear and in anger: I could well understand how they felt. Crows and jackdaws croaked aloud as if in scorn. "From the nest! from the nest, far, far!"

'Far in the interior of the wood, where the swarm of labourers were working, stood Waldemar Daa and his three daughters; and all laughed at the wild cries of the birds; only one, the youngest, Anna Dorothea, felt grieved in her heart; and when they made preparations to fell a tree that was almost dead, and on whose naked branches the black stork had built his nest, whence the little storks were stretching out their heads, she begged for mercy for the little things, and tears came into her eyes. Therefore the tree with the black stork's nest was left standing. The tree was not worth speaking of

'There was a great hewing and sawing, and a three-decker was built. The architect was of low origin, but of great pride; his eyes and forehead told how clever he was, and Waldemar Daa was fond of listening to him, and so was Waldemar's daughter Ida, the eldest, who was now fifteen years old; and while he built a ship for the father, he was building for himself a castle in the air, into which he and Ida were to go as a married couple – which might indeed have happened, if the castle had been of stone walls, and ramparts, and moats with forest and garden. But in spite of his wise head, the architect remained but a poor bird; and, indeed, what business has a sparrow to take part in a dance of cranes? Huh – sh! I careered away, and he careered away too, for he was not allowed to stay; and little Ida got over it, because she was obliged to get over it.

'The proud black horses were neighing in the stable; they were worth looking at, and they *were* looked at. The admiral, who had been sent by the King himself to inspect the new ship and take measures for its purchase, spoke loudly in admiration of the beautiful horses.

'I heard all that,' said the Wind. 'I accompanied the gentlemen through the open door, and strewed blades of straw like bars of gold before their feet. Waldemar Daa wanted to have gold, and the admiral wished for the black horses, and that is why he praised them so much;

but the hint was not taken, and consequently the ship was not bought. It remained on the shore covered over with boards, a Noah's ark that never got to the water – Huh – sh! rush away! away! – and that was a pity.

'In the winter, when the fields were covered with snow, and the water with large blocks of ice that I blew up on to the coast,' continued the Wind, 'crows and ravens came, all as black as might be, great flocks of them, and alighted on the dead, deserted, lonely ship by the shore, and croaked in hoarse accents of the wood that was no more, of the many pretty birds' nests destroyed, and the old and young ones left without a home; and all for the sake of that great bit of lumber, that proud ship that never sailed forth.

'I made the snowflakes whirl, and the snow lay like great waves high around the ship, and drifted over it. I let it hear my voice, that it might know what a storm has to say. Certainly I did my part towards teaching it seamanship. Huh – sh! push along!

'And the winter passed away; winter and summer, both passed away, and they are still passing away, even as I pass away; as the snow whirls along, and the apple-blossom whirls along, and the leaves fall – away! away! away! – and men are passing away too!

'But the daughters were still young, and little Ida was a rose, as fair to look upon as on the day when the architect saw her. I often seized her long brown hair, when she stood in the garden by the apple tree, musing, and not heeding how I strewed blossoms on her hair, and loosened it, while she was gazing at the red sun and the golden sky, through the dark underwood and the trees of the garden.

'Her sister was bright and slender as a lily. Joanna had height and stateliness, but was like her mother, rather stiff in the stalk. She was very fond of walking through the great hall, where hung the portraits of her ancestors. The women were painted in dresses of silk and velvet, with a tiny little hat, embroidered with pearls, on their plaited hair. They were handsome women. Their husbands were in steel, or in costly cloaks lined with squirrel's skin; they wore little ruffs, and swords at their sides, but not buckled to their hips. Where would Joanna's picture find its place on that wall someday? and how would *he* look, her noble lord and husband? This is what she thought of, and of this she spoke softly to herself. I heard it as I swept into the long hall and turned round to come out again.

'Anna Dorothea, the pale hyacinth, a child of fourteen, was quiet and thoughtful; her great deep-blue eyes had a musing look, but the childlike smile still played around her lips: I was not able to blow it away, nor did I wish to do so.

'We met in the garden, in the hollow lane, in the field and meadow; she gathered herbs and flowers which she knew would be useful to her father in concocting the drinks and drops he distilled. Waldemar Daa was arrogant and proud, but he was also a learned man, and knew a great deal. That was no secret, and many opinions were expressed concerning it. In his chimney there was fire even in summer-time. He would lock the door of his room, and for days the fire would be poked and raked; but of this he did not talk much – the forces of nature must be conquered in silence; and soon he would discover the art of making the best thing of all – the red gold.

'That is why the chimney was always smoking, therefore the flames crackled so frequently. Yes, I was there too,' said the Wind. ' "Let it go," I sang down through the chimney: "it will end in smoke, air, coals and ashes! You will burn yourself! Hu-uh-ush! drive away! drive away!" But Waldemar Daa did *not* drive it away.

'The splendid black horses in the stable – what became of them? what became of the old gold and silver vessels in cupboards and chests, the cows in the fields, and the houses and home itself? Yes, they may melt, may melt in the golden crucible, and yet yield no gold.

'Empty grew the barns and store-rooms, the cellars and magazines. The servants decreased, and the mice multiplied. Then a window broke, and then another, and I could get in elsewhere besides at the door,' said the Wind. ' "Where the chimney smokes the meal is being cooked," the proverb says. But here the chimney smoked that devoured all the meals, for the sake of the red gold.

'I blew through the courtyard gate like a watchman blowing his horn,' the Wind went on, 'but no watchman was there. I twirled the weathercock round on the summit of the tower, and it creaked like the snoring of the warder, but no warder was there; only mice and rats were there. Poverty laid the tablecloth; poverty sat in the wardrobe and in the larder; the door fell off its hinges, cracks and fissures made their appearance, and I went in and out at pleasure; and that is how I know all about it.

'Amid smoke and ashes, amid sorrow and sleepless nights, the hair became grey, in his beard and around his temples; his skin turned pale and yellow, as his eyes looked greedily for the gold, the desired gold.

'I blew the smoke and ashes into his face and beard: debt came instead of gold. I sang through the broken window-panes and the yawning clefts in the walls. I blew into the chests of drawers belonging to the daughters, wherein lay the clothes that had become faded and threadbare from being worn over and over again. That was not the song that had been sung at the children's cradle. The lordly life had changed to a life of penury. I was the only one who sang aloud in that castle,' said the Wind. 'I snowed them up, and they say snow keeps people warm. They had no wood, and the forest from which they might have brought it was cut down. It was a biting frost. I rushed in through loopholes and passages, over gables and roofs, that I might be brisk. They were lying in bed because of the cold, the three high-born daughters, and their father was crouching under his leathern coverlet. Nothing to bite, nothing to burn – there was a life for highborn people! Huh-sh! let it go! But that is what my Lord Daa could *not* do – he could *not* let it go.

' "After winter comes spring," he said. "After want, good times will come, but they must be waited for! Now my house and lands are mortgaged, it is indeed high time; and the gold will soon come. At Easter!"

'I heard how he spoke thus, looking at a spider's web. "Thou diligent little weaver, thou dost teach me perseverance. Let them tear thy web, and thou wilt begin it again and complete it. Let them destroy it again, and thou wilt resolutely begin to work again – again! That is what we must do, and that will repay itself at last."

'It was the morning of Easter-day. The bells and the sun seemed to rejoice in the sky. The master had watched through the night in feverish excitement, and had been melting and cooling, distilling and mixing. I heard him sighing like a soul in despair; I heard him praying, and I noticed how he held his breath. The lamp was burned out, but he did not notice it. I blew at the fire of coals, and it threw its red glow upon his ghastly white face, lighting it up with a glare, and his sunken eyes looked forth wildly out of their deep sockets – but they became larger and larger, as though they would burst.

'Look at the alchemic glass! It glows in the crucible, red-hot, and pure and heavy! He lifted it with a trembling hand, and cried with a trembling voice, "Gold! gold!"

'He was quite dizzy – I could have blown him down,' said the Wind; 'but I only fanned the glowing coals, and accompanied him through the door to where his daughters sat shivering. His coat was powdered with ashes, and there were ashes in his beard and in his tangled hair. He stood straight up, and held his costly treasure on high, in the brittle glass. "Found, found! – Gold, gold!" he shouted, and again held aloft the glass to let it flash in the sunshine; but his hand trembled, and the alchemic glass fell clattering to the ground, and broke into a thousand pieces; and the last bubble of his happiness had burst! Hu-uh-ush! rushing away! – and I rushed away from the gold-maker's house.

'Late in autumn, when the days are short, and the mist comes and strews cold drops upon the berries and leafless branches, I came back in fresh spirits, rushed through the air, swept the sky clear, and snapped the dry twigs – which is certainly no great labour, but yet it must be done. Then there was another kind of sweeping clean at Waldemar Daa's, in the mansion of Borreby. His enemy, Ove Ramel, of Basnäs, was there with the mortgage of the house and everything it contained in his pocket. I drummed against the broken window-panes, beat against the old rotten doors, and whistled through cracks and rifts – huh-sh! Ove Ramel was not to be encouraged to stay there. Ida and Anna Dorothea wept bitterly; Joanna stood pale and proud, and bit her thumb till it bled – but what could that avail? Ove Ramel offered to allow Waldemar Daa to remain in the mansion till the end of his life, but no thanks were given him for his offer. I listened to hear what occurred. I saw the ruined gentleman lift his head and throw it back prouder than ever, and I rushed against the house and the old lime trees with such force, that one of the thickest branches broke, one that was not decayed; and the branch remained lying at the entrance as a broom when anyone wanted to sweep the place out: and a grand sweeping out there was – I thought it would be so.

'It was hard on that day to preserve one's composure; but their will was as hard as their fortune.

'There was nothing they could call their own except the clothes they wore: yes, there was one thing more – the alchemist's glass, a new one that had lately been bought, and filled with what had been gathered up from the ground, the treasure which promised so much but never kept its promise. Waldemar Daa hid the glass in his bosom, and taking his stick in his hand, the once rich gentleman passed with his daughters out of the house of Borreby. I blew cold upon his heated cheeks, I stroked his grey beard and his long white hair, and I sang as well as I could, "Huh-sh! gone away! gone away!" And that was the end of the wealth and splendour.

'Ida walked on one side of the old man, and Anna Dorothea on the other. Joanna turned round at the entrance – why? Fortune would not turn because she did so. She looked at the old walls of what had once been the castle of Marsk Stig, and perhaps she thought of his daughters:

> The eldest gave the youngest her hand,
> And forth they went to the far-off land.

Was she thinking of this old song? Here were three of them, and their father was with them too. They walked along the road on which they had once driven in their splendid carriage – they walked forth as beggars, with their father, and wandered out into the open field, and into a mud hut, which they rented for ten marks a year – into their new house with the empty rooms and empty vessels. Crows and jackdaws fluttered above them, and cried, as if in contempt, "From the nest! from the nest! far! far!" as they had done in the wood at Borreby when the trees were felled.

'Daa and his daughters could not help hearing it. I blew about their ears for what use would it be that they should listen?

'And they went to live in the mud hut on the open field, and I wandered away over moor and field, through bare bushes and leafless forests, to the open waters, to other lands – huh-uh-ush! away, away! – year after year!'

And how did Waldemar Daa and his daughters prosper? The Wind tells us:

'The one I saw last, yes, for the last time, was Anna Dorothea, the pale hyacinth: then she was old and bent, for it was fifty years afterwards. She lived longer than the rest; she knew all.

'Yonder on the heath, by the town of Wiborg, stood the fine new house of the Dean, built of red bricks with projecting gables; the smoke came up thickly from the chimney. The Dean's gentle lady and her beautiful daughters sat in the bay window, and looked over the hawthorn hedge of the garden towards the brown heath. What were they looking at? They looked on the stork's nest out there, on the hut, which was almost falling in; the roof consisted of moss and house-leek, in so far as a roof existed there at all – the stork's nest covered the greater part of it, and that alone was in proper condition, for it was kept in order by the stork himself.

'That is a house to be looked at, but not to be touched: I must deal gently with it,' said the Wind. 'For the sake of the stork's nest the hut has been allowed to stand, though it was a blot upon the landscape. They did not like to drive the stork away, therefore the old shed was left standing, and the poor woman who dwelt in it was allowed to stay: she had the Egyptian bird to thank for that; or was it perchance her reward, because she had once interceded for the nest of its black brother in the forest of Borreby? At that time she, the poor woman, was a young child, a pale hyacinth in the rich garden. She remembered all that right well, did Anna Dorothea.

' "Oh! oh!" Yes, people can sigh like the wind moaning in the rushes and reeds. "Oh! oh!" she sighed, "no bells sounded at thy burial, Waldemar Daa! The poor schoolboys did not even sing a psalm when the former lord of Borreby was laid in the earth to rest! Oh, everything has an end, even misery. Sister Ida became the wife of a peasant. That was the hardest trial that befell our father, that the husband of a daughter of his should be a miserable serf, whom the proprietor could mount on the wooden horse for punishment! I suppose he is under the ground now. And thou, Ida? Alas, alas! it is not ended yet, wretch that I am! Grant me that I may die, kind Heaven!"

'That was Anna Dorothea's prayer in the wretched hut which was left standing for the sake of the stork.

'I took pity on the fairest of the sisters,' said the Wind. 'Her courage was like that of a man, and in man's clothes she took service as a sailor on board a ship. She was sparing of words, and of a dark countenance, but willing at her work. But she did not know how to climb; so I blew her overboard before anybody found out that she was a woman, and that was well done of me!' said the Wind.

'On such an Easter morning as that on which Waldemar Daa had fancied that he had found the red gold, I heard the tones of a psalm under the stork's nest, among the crumbling walls – it was Anna Dorothea's last song.

'There was no window, only a hole in the wall. The sun rose up like a mass of gold, and looked through. What a splendour he diffused! Her eyes and her heart were breaking – but that they would have done, even if the sun had not shone that morning on her.

'The stork covered her hut till her death. I sang at her grave!' said the Wind. 'I sang at her father's grave; I know where his grave is, and where hers is, and nobody else knows it.

'New times, changed times! The old high road now runs through cultivated fields; the new road winds among the trim ditches, and soon the railway will come with its train of carriages, and rush over the graves which are forgotten like the names – hu-ush! passed away! passed away!

'That is the story of Waldemar Daa and his daughters. Tell it better, any of you, if you know how,' said the Wind, and turned away – and he was gone.

The Girl Who Trod on the Loaf

THE STORY of the girl who trod on the loaf to avoid soiling her shoes, and of the misfortune that befell this girl, is well known. It has been written, and even printed.

She was a poor child, but proud and presumptuous; there was a bad foundation in her, as the saying is. When she was quite a little child, it was her delight to catch flies and tear off their wings, so as to make them into creeping things. She would take cockchafers and beetles, and spit them on pins. Then she pushed a green leaf or a little scrap of paper towards their feet, and the poor creatures seized it, and held it fast, and turned it over and over, struggling to get free from the pin.

'The cockchafer is reading,' said little Inger. 'See how he turns the leaf!'

With years she grew worse rather than better; but she was pretty, and that was her misfortune; otherwise she would have been more sharply reproved than she was.

'Your headstrong will requires something strong to break it!' her own mother often said. 'As a little child, you used to trample on my apron; but I fear you will one day trample on my heart.'

And that is what she really did.

She was sent into the country, into service in the house of rich people, who treated her as their own child, and dressed her accordingly. She looked well, and her presumption increased.

When she had been there about a year, her mistress said to her, 'You ought now to visit your parents, Inger.'

And she went too, but it was only to show herself, that they might see how grand she had become; but when she came to the entrance of the village, and the young husbandmen and maids stood there chatting, and her own mother appeared among them, sitting on a stone to rest, and with a faggot of sticks before her that she had picked

up in the wood, then Inger turned back, for she felt ashamed that she, who was so finely dressed, should have for a mother a ragged woman, who picked up wood in the forest. She did not in the least feel sorry for having turned back, she was only annoyed.

And another half-year went by, and her mistress said again, 'You ought to go to your home, and visit your old parents, Inger. I'll make you a present of a great wheaten loaf that you may give to them: they will certainly be glad to see you again.'

And Inger put on her best clothes, and her new shoes, and drew her skirts around her, and set out, stepping very carefully, that she might be clean and neat about the feet; and there was no harm in that. But when she came to the place where the footway led across the marsh, and where there was mud and puddles, she threw the loaf into the mud, and trod upon it to pass over without wetting her feet. But as she stood there with one foot upon the loaf and the other uplifted to step farther, the loaf sank with her, deeper and deeper, till she disappeared altogether, and only a great puddle, from which the bubbles rose, remained where she had been.

And that's the story.

But whither did Inger go? She went down to the marsh woman, who is always brewing there. The marsh woman is cousin to the elf maidens, who are well enough known, of whom songs are sung, and of whom pictures are painted; but concerning the marsh woman it is only known that when the meadows steam in summer- time it is because she is brewing. Into the marsh woman's brewery did Inger sink down; and no one can endure that place long. A box of mud is a palace compared with the marsh woman's brewery. Every barrel there had an odour that almost takes away one's senses; and the barrels stand close to each other; and wherever there is a little opening among them, through which one might push one's way, then one cannot get through for the number of damp toads and fat snakes who are all in a tangle there. Among this company did Inger fall; and all the horrible mass of living creeping things was so icy cold, that she shuddered in all her limbs, and became stark and stiff. She continued fastened to the loaf, and the loaf drew her down as an amber button draws a fragment of straw.

The marsh woman was at home, and on that day the Devil and his grandmother had come to inspect the brewery; and she is a venomous old woman, who is never idle: she never rides out to pay a visit without taking her work with her; she also had it here. She sewed gadding leather to be worked into men's shoes, and that makes them wander about unable to settle anywhere. She wove webs of lies, and strung together hastily-spoken words that had fallen to the ground; and all this was done for the injury and ruin of mankind. Yes, indeed, she knew how to sew, to weave, and to string, did this old grandmother!

Catching sight of Inger, she put up her double eyeglass, and took another look at the girl.

'That's a girl who has ability!' she observed, 'and I beg you will give me the little one as a memento of my visit here. She'll make a capital statue to stand in my grandson's antechamber.'

And Inger was given up to her, and this is how Inger came into Hell. People don't always go there by the direct path, but they can get there by roundabout routes if they have a tendency in that direction.

That was a never-ending antechamber. The visitor became giddy who looked forward, and doubly giddy when he looked back, and saw a whole crowd of people, almost utterly exhausted, waiting till the gate of mercy should be opened to them – they had to wait a long time! Great fat waddling spiders spun webs of a thousand years over their feet, and these webs cut like wire, and bound them like bronze fetters; and, moreover, there was an eternal unrest working in every heart – a miserable unrest. The miser stood there, and had forgotten the key of his strong box, and he knew the key was sticking in the lock. It would take too long to describe the various sorts of torture that were found there together. Inger felt a terrible pain while she had to stand there as a statue, for she was tied fast to the loaf.

'That's the fruit of wishing to keep one's feet neat and tidy,' she said to herself. 'Just look how they're all staring at me!'

Yes, certainly, the eyes of all were fixed upon her, and their evil thoughts gleamed forth from their eyes, and they spoke to one another, moving their lips, from which no sound whatever came forth: they were very horrible to behold.

'It must be a great pleasure to look at me!' thought Inger, 'and indeed I have a pretty face and fine clothes.' And she turned her eyes; her neck was too stiff to turn. But she had not considered how her clothes had been soiled in the marsh woman's brewhouse. Her garments were covered with mud; a snake had fastened in her hair, and dangled down her back; and out of each fold of her frock a great toad looked forth, croaking like an asthmatic poodle. That was very unpleasant. 'But all the rest of them down here also look horrible,' she observed to herself, and derived consolation from the thought.

The worst of all was the terrible hunger that tormented her. But could she not stoop and break off a piece of the loaf on which she stood? No, her back was too stiff, her hands and arms were benumbed, and her whole body was like a pillar of stone; she was only able to turn her eyes in her head, to turn them quite round, so that she could see backwards: it was an ugly sight. And then the flies came up, and crept to and fro over her eyes, and she blinked her eyes, but the flies would not go away, for they could not fly: their wings had been pulled out, so that they were converted into creeping insects: it was horrible torment added to the hunger, for she felt empty, quite, entirely empty.

'If this lasts much longer,' she said, 'I shall not be able to bear it.'

But she had to bear it, and it lasted on and on.

Then a hot tear fell down upon her head, rolled over her face and neck, down on to the loaf on which she stood; and then another tear rolled down, followed by many more. Who might be weeping for Inger? Had she not still a mother in the world? The tears of sorrow which a mother weeps for her child always make their way to the child; but they do not relieve it, they only increase its torment. And now to bear this unendurable hunger, and yet not to be able to touch the loaf on which she stood! She felt as if she had been feeding on herself, and had become like a thin hollow reed that takes in every sound, for she heard everything that was said of her up in the world, and all that she heard was hard and evil. Her mother, indeed, wept much and sorrowed for her, but for all that she said, 'A haughty spirit goes before a fall. That was thy ruin, Inger. Thou hast sorely grieved thy mother.'

Her mother and all on earth knew of the sin she had committed; knew that she had trodden upon the loaf, and had sunk and disappeared; for the cowherd had seen it from the hill beside the marsh.

'Greatly hast thou grieved thy mother, Inger,' said the mother; 'yes, yes, I thought it would be thus.'

'Oh that I had never been born!' thought Inger; 'it would have been far better. But what use is my mother's weeping now?'

And she heard how her master and mistress, who had kept and cherished her like kind parents, now said she was a sinful child, and did not value the gifts of God, but trampled them under her feet, and that the gates of mercy would only open slowly to her.

'They should have punished me,' thought Inger, 'and have driven out the whims I had in my head.'

She heard how a complete song was made about her, a song of the proud girl who trod upon the loaf to keep her shoes clean, and she heard how the song was sung everywhere.

'That I should have to bear so much evil for that!' thought Inger; 'the others ought to be punished, too, for their sins. Yes, then there would be plenty of punishing to do. Ah, how I'm being tortured!'

And her heart became harder than her outward form.

'Here in this company one can't even become better,' she said, 'and I don't want to become better! Look, how they're all staring at me!' And her heart was full of anger and malice against all men. 'Now they've something to talk about at last up yonder. Ah, how I'm being tortured!'

And then she heard how her story was told to the little children, and the little ones called her the godless Inger, and said she was so naughty and ugly that she must be well punished

Thus even the children's mouths spoke hard words of her.

But one day, while grief and hunger gnawed her hollow frame, and she heard her name mentioned and her story told to an innocent child, a little girl, she became aware that the little one burst into tears at the tale of the haughty, vain Inger.

'But will Inger never come up here again?' asked the little girl.

And the reply was, 'She will never come up again.'

'But if she were to beg for forgiveness, and say she would never do so again?'

'But she will not beg for forgiveness,' was the reply.

'I should be *so* glad if she would,' said the little girl; and she was quite inconsolable. 'I'll give my doll and all my playthings if she may only come up. It's too dreadful – poor Inger!'

And these words penetrated to Inger's heart, and seemed to do her good. It was the first time anyone had said, 'Poor Inger,' without adding anything about her faults: a little innocent child was weeping and praying for her. It made her feel quite strangely, and she herself would gladly have wept, but she could not weep, and that was a torment in itself.

While years were passing above her, for where she was there was no change, she heard herself spoken of more and more seldom. At last one day a sigh struck on her ear: 'Inger, Inger, how you have grieved me! I said how it would be!' It was the last sigh of her dying mother.

Occasionally she heard her name spoken by her former employers, and they were pleasant words when the woman said, 'Shall I ever see thee again, Inger? One knows not what may happen.'

But Inger knew right well that her good mistress would never come to the place where she was.

And again time went on – a long, bitter time. Then Inger heard her name pronounced once more, and saw two bright stars that seemed gleaming above her. They were two gentle eyes closing upon earth. So many years had gone by since the little girl had been inconsolable and wept about 'poor Inger', that the child had become an old woman, who was now to be called home to heaven; and in the last hour of existence, when the events of the whole life stand at once before us, the old woman remembered how as a child she had cried heartily at the story of Inger. That time and that impression came so clearly before the old woman in her last hour, that she called out quite loud: 'Have not I also, like Inger, often trod upon the gifts of heaven without thinking? have not I also gone about with pride at my heart? Yet Thou in Thy mercy hast not let me sink, but hast held me up. Leave me not in my last hour!'

And the eyes of the old woman closed, and the eye of her soul was opened to look upon the hidden things. She, in whose last thoughts Inger had been present so vividly, saw how deeply the poor girl had sunk, and burst into tears at the sight; in heaven she stood like a child, and wept for poor Inger. And her tears and prayers sounded like an echo in the dark empty space that surrounded the tormented captive soul, and the unhoped-for love from above conquered her, for an angel was weeping for her. Why was this vouchsafed to her? The tormented soul seemed to gather in her thoughts every deed she had done on earth, and she, Inger, trembled and wept such tears as she had never yet wept. She was filled with sorrow about herself: it seemed as though the gate of mercy could never open to her; and while in deep penitence she acknowledged this, a beam of light shot radiantly down into the depths to her, with a greater force than that of the sunbeam which melts the snow man the boys have built up; and quicker than the snowflake melts, and becomes a drop of water that falls on the warm lips of a child, the stony form of Inger was changed to mist, and a little bird soared with the speed of lightning upward into the world of men. But the bird was timid and shy towards all things around; it was ashamed of itself, ashamed to encounter any living thing, and hurriedly sought to conceal itself in a dark hole in an old crumbling wall; there it sat cowering, trembling through its whole frame, and unable to utter a sound, for it had no voice. Long it sat there before it could rightly see all the beauty around it; for beauty there was. The air was fresh and mild, the moon shone so clear; trees and bushes exhaled fragrance, and it was right pleasant where it sat, and its coat of feathers was clean and pure. How all creation seemed to speak of beneficence and love! The bird wanted to sing of the thoughts that stirred in its breast, but it could not; gladly would it have sung as the cuckoo and the nightingale sang in spring-time. But Heaven, that hears the mute song of praise of the worm, could hear the notes of praise which now trembled in the breast of the bird, as David's psalms were heard before they had fashioned themselves into words and song.

For weeks these toneless songs stirred within the bird; at last, the holy Christmas-time approached. The peasant who dwelt near set up a pole by the old wall, with some ears of corn bound to the top, that the birds of heaven might have a good meal, and rejoice in the happy, blessed time.

And on Christmas morning the sun arose and shone upon the ears of corn, which were surrounded by a number of twittering birds. Then out of the hole in the wall streamed forth the voice of another bird, and the bird soared forth from its hiding-place; and in heaven it was well known what bird this was.

It was a hard winter. The ponds were covered with ice, and the beasts of the field and the birds of the air were stinted for food. Our little bird flew away over the high road, and in the ruts of the sledges it found here and there a grain of corn, and at the halting-places some crumbs. Of these it ate only a few, but it called all the other hungry sparrows around it, that they, too, might have some food. It flew into the towns, and looked round about; and wherever a kind hand had strewn bread on the window-sill for the birds, it only ate a single crumb itself, and gave all the rest to the other birds.

In the course of the winter, the bird had collected so many bread crumbs, and given them to the other birds, that they equalled the weight of the loaf on which Inger had trod to keep her shoes clean; and when the last bread crumb had been found and given, the grey wings of the bird became white, and spread far out.

'Yonder is a sea-swallow, flying away across the water,' said the children when they saw the white bird. Now it dived into the sea, and now it rose again into the clear sunlight. It gleamed white; but no one could tell whither it went, though some asserted that it flew straight into the sun.

Ole the Tower-Keeper

'IN THE world it's always going up and down – and now I can't go up any higher!' So said Ole the tower-keeper. 'Most people have to try both the ups and the downs; and, rightly considered, we all get to be watchmen at last, and look down upon life from a height.'

Such was the speech of Ole, my friend, the old tower-keeper, an amusing talkative old fellow, who seemed to speak out everything that came into his head, and who for all that had many a serious thought deep in his heart. Yes, he was the child of respectable people, and there were even some who said that he was the son of a privy councillor, or that he might have been; he had studied too, and had been assistant teacher and deputy clerk; but of what service was all that to him? In those days he lived in the dean's house, and was to have everything in the house, to be at free quarters, as the saying is; but he was still, so to speak, a fine young gentleman. He wanted to have his boots cleaned with patent blacking, and the dean would only give ordinary grease; and upon that point they split – one spoke of stinginess, the other of vanity, and the blacking became the black cause of enmity between them, and at last they parted.

But what he demanded from the dean he also demanded from the world – namely, patent blacking – and he got nothing but grease. Accordingly he at last drew back from all men, and became a hermit; but the church tower is the only place in a great city where hermitage, office, and bread can be found together. So he betook himself up thither, and smoked his pipe on his solitary rounds. He looked upward and downward, and had his own thoughts, and told in his way of what he saw and did not see, of what he read in books and in himself. I often lent him books, good books; and you may know a man by the company he keeps. He loved neither the English governess novels, nor the French ones, which he called a mixture of empty wind and raisin-stalks: he wanted biographies and descriptions of the wonders of the world. I visited him at least once a year, generally directly after New Year's Day, and then he always spoke of this and that which the change of the year had put into his head.

I will tell the story of two of these visits, and will give his own words if I can do so.

First Visit

Among the books which I had lately lent Ole, was one about cobble-stones, which had greatly rejoiced and occupied him.

'Yes, they're rare old fellows, those cobble-stones!' he said; 'and to think that we should pass them without noticing them! I have often done that myself in the fields and on the beach, where they lie in great numbers. And over the street pavement, those fragments of the oldest remains of antiquity, one walks without ever thinking about them. I have done the very thing myself. But now I look respectfully at every paving-stone. Many thanks for the book! It has filled me with thought, has pushed old thoughts and habits aside, and has made me long to read more on the subject. The romance of the earth is, after all, the most wonderful of all romances. It's a pity one can't read the first volumes of it, because they're written in a language that we don't understand. One must read in the different strata, in the pebble-stones, for each separate period. And it is only in the sixth volume that the human personages first appear, Adam and Eve; that is a little too late for some readers, they would like to have them at once, but it is all the same to me. Yes, it is a romance, a very wonderful romance, and we all have our place in it. We grope and ferret about, and yet remain where we are, but the ball keeps turning, without emptying the ocean over us; the crust we walk upon holds together, and does not let us through. And then it's a story that has been acting for millions of years, with constant progress. My best thanks for the book about the cobblestones. Those are fellows indeed! they could tell us something worth hearing, if they only knew how to talk. It's really a pleasure, now and then to become a mere nothing, especially when a man is as highly placed as I am. And then to think that we all, even with patent lacquer, are nothing more than insects of a moment on that anthill the earth, though we may be insects with stars and garters, places and offices! One feels quite a novice beside these venerable million-year-old cobble-stones. On last New Year's Eve I was reading the book, and had lost myself in it so completely, that I forgot my usual New Year's diversion, namely, the wild hunt to Amager. Ah, you don't know what that is!

'The journey of the witches on broomsticks is well enough known – that journey is taken on St John's Eve, to the Brocken; but we have a wild journey also, which is national and modern, and that is the journey to Amager on the eve of the New Year. All indifferent poets and poetesses, musicians, newspaper writers, and artistic notabilities, I mean those who are no good, ride in the New Year's Eve through the air to Amager. They sit astride on their painting brushes or quill pens, for steel pens won't bear them, they're too stiff. As I told you, I see it every New Year's Eve, and could mention most of them by name, but I should not like to draw their enmity upon myself, for they don't like people to talk about their ride to Amager on quill pens. I've a kind of niece, who is a fishwife, and who, as she tells me, supplies three respectable newspapers with the terms of abuse they use, and she has herself been there as an invited guest; but she was carried out thither, for she does not own a quill pen, nor can she ride. She has told me all about it. Half of what she says is not true, but the half is quite enough. When she was out there, the festivities began with a song: each of the guests had written his own song, and each one sang his own song, for he thought that the best, and it was all one, all the same melody. Then those came marching up, in little bands, who are only busy with their mouths. There were ringing bells that sang alternately; and then came the little drummers that beat their tattoo in the family circle; and acquaintance was made with those who write without putting their names, which here means as much as using grease instead of patent blacking; and then there was the hangman with his boy, and the boy was the smartest, otherwise he would not be noticed; then too there was the good street-sweeper with his cart, who turns over the dustbin, and calls it "good, very good, remarkably good." And in the midst of the pleasure there shot up out of the great dirt-heap a stem, a tree, an immense flower, a great mushroom, a perfect roof, which formed a sort of storehouse for the worthy company, for in it hung everything they had given to the world during the Old Year. Out of the tree poured sparks like flames of fire; these were the ideas and thoughts, borrowed from others, which they had used, and which now got free and rushed away like so many fireworks. They played at "the fuse burns", and the young poets played at "heartburns", and the witlings played off their jests, and the jests rolled away with a thundering sound, as if empty pots were being shattered against doors. "It was very amusing!" my niece said; in fact, she said many things that were very malicious but very amusing, but I won't mention them, for a man must be good-natured and not a carping critic. But you will easily perceive that when a man once knows the rights of the festival out there, as I know them, it's quite natural that on the New Year's Eve one should look out to see the wild chase go by. If in the New Year I miss certain persons who used to be there, I am sure to notice others who are new arrivals; but this year I omitted taking my look at the guests. I bowled away on the cobble-stones, rolled back through millions of years, and saw the stones break loose high up in the North, saw them drifting about on icebergs, long before Noah's ark was constructed, saw them sink down to the bottom of the sea, and reappear again on a sandbank, the one that stuck up out of the water and said, "This shall be Zealand!" I saw them become the dwelling-place of birds that are unknown to us, and then became the seat of wild chiefs of whom we know nothing, until with their axes they cut their Runic signs into a few of these stones, which then came into the calendar of time. But as for me, I had quite gone out of it, and had become a nothing. Then three or four beautiful falling stars came down, which cleared the air, and gave my thoughts another direction. You know what a falling star is, do you not? The learned men are not at all clear about it. I have my own ideas about shooting stars, and my idea is this: How often are silent thanksgivings offered up for one who has done a good and noble action! the thanks are often speechless, but they are not lost for all that. I think these thanks are caught up, and the sunbeams bring the silent, hidden thankfulness over the head of the benefactor; and if it be a whole people that has been expressing its gratitude through a long lapse of time, the thankfulness appears as a nosegay of flowers, and falls in the form of a shooting star over the good man's grave. I am always very much pleased when I see a shooting star, especially in the New Year's Eve, and then find out for whom the gift of gratitude was intended. Lately a gleaming star fell in the southwest, as a tribute of thanksgiving to many, many! "For whom was that star intended?" thought I. It fell, no doubt, on the hill by the Bay of Flensborg, where the Danebrog waves over the graves of Schleppegrell, Laessöe, and their comrades. One star also fell in the midst of the land, fell upon Sorö, a flower on the grave of Holberg, the thanks of the year from a great many – thanks for his charming plays!

'It is a great and pleasant thought to know that a shooting star falls upon our graves: on mine certainly none will fall – no sunbeam brings thanks to me, for here there is nothing worthy of thanks. I shall not get the patent lacquer,' said Ole; 'for my fate on earth is only grease, after all.'

Second Visit

It was New Year's Day, and I went up the tower. Ole spoke of the toasts that were drunk at the passing of the Old Year into the New. And he told me a story about the glasses, and this story had a very deep meaning. It was this:

'When on the New Year's Eve the clock strikes twelve, the people at the table rise up, with full glasses in their hands, and drink success to the New Year. They begin the year with the glass in their hands; that is a good beginning for topers. They begin the New Year by going to bed, and that's a good beginning for drones. Sleep is sure to play a great part in the course of the year, and the glass likewise. Do you know what dwells in the glass?' asked Ole. 'There dwell in the glass, health, pleasure, and the wildest delight; and misfortune and the bitterest woe dwell there also. Now suppose we count the glasses – of course I count the different degrees in the glasses for different people.

'You see, the *first glass*, that's the glass of health, and in that the herb of health is found growing; put it up on the beam in the ceiling, and at the end of the year you may be sitting in the arbour of health.

'If you take the *second glass* – from this a little bird soars upwards, twittering in guileless cheerfulness, so that a man may listen to his song and perhaps join in, "Fair is life! no downcast looks! Take courage and march onward!"

'Out of the *third glass* rises a little winged urchin, who cannot certainly be called an angel-child, for there is goblin blood in his veins, and he has the spirit of a goblin; not wishing to hurt or harm you, indeed, but very ready to play off tricks upon you. He'll sit at your ear and whisper merry thoughts to you; he'll creep into your heart and warm you, so that you grow very merry and become a wit, so far as the wits of the others can judge.

'In the *fourth glass* is neither herb, bird, nor urchin: in that glass is the pause drawn by reason, and one may never go beyond that sign.

'Take the *fifth glass*, and you will weep at yourself, you will feel such a deep emotion; or it will affect you in a different way. Out of the glass there will spring with a bang Prince Carnival, impertinent and extravagantly merry: he'll draw you away with him, you'll forget your dignity, if you have any, and you'll forget more than you should or ought to forget. All is dance, song, and sound; the masks will carry you away with them, and the daughters of vanity, clad in silk and satin, will come with loose hair and alluring charms; tear yourself away if you can!

'The *sixth glass*! Yes, in that glass sits a demon, in the form of a little, well-dressed, attractive and very fascinating man, who thoroughly understands you, agrees with you in everything, and becomes quite a second self to you. He has a lantern with him, to give you light as he accompanies you home. There is an old legend about a saint who was allowed to choose one of the seven deadly sins, and who accordingly chose drunkenness, which appeared to him the least, but which led him to commit all the other six. The man's blood is mingled with that of the demon – it is the sixth glass, and with that the germ of all evil shoots up within us; and each one grows up with a strength like that of the grains of mustard seed, and shoots up into a tree, and spreads over the whole world; and most people have no choice but to go into the oven, to be recast in a new form.

'That's the history of the glasses,' said the towerkeeper Ole, 'and it can be told with lacquer or only with grease; but I give it you with both!'

That was my second visit to Ole, and if you want to hear about more of them, then the visits must be – continued.

Anne Lisbeth

ANNE LISBETH had a colour like milk and blood; young and merry, she looked beautiful, with gleaming white teeth and clear eyes; her footstep was light in the dance, and her mind was lighter still. And what came of it all? Her son was an ugly brat! Yes, he was not pretty; so he was put out to be nursed by the labourer's wife. Anne Lisbeth was taken into the count's castle, and sat there in the splendid room arrayed in silks and velvets; not a breath of wind might blow upon her, and no one was allowed to speak a harsh word to her. No, that might not be, for she was nurse to the count's child, who was delicate and fair as a prince, and beautiful as an angel; and how she loved this child! Her own boy was provided for at the labourer's, where the mouth boiled over more frequently than the pot, and where, in general, no one was at home. Then he would cry; but what nobody knows, that nobody cares for; and he would cry till he was tired, and then he fell asleep; and in sleep one feels neither hunger nor thirst. A capital invention is sleep.

With years, just as weeds shoot up, Anne Lisbeth's child grew, but yet they said his growth was stunted; but he had quite become a member of the family in which he dwelt; they had received money to keep him. Anne Lisbeth was rid of him for good. She had become a town lady, and had a comfortable home of her own; and out of doors she wore a bonnet when she went out for a walk; but she never walked out to see the labourer – that was too far from the town; and indeed she had nothing to go for: the boy belonged to the labouring people, and she said he could eat his food, and he should do something to earn his food, and consequently he kept Mads Jensen's red cow. He could already tend cattle and make himself useful.

The big dog, by the yard gate of the nobleman's mansion, sits proudly in the sunshine on the top of the kennel, and barks at everyone who goes by; if it rains he creeps into his house, and there he is warm and dry. Anne Lisbeth's boy sat in the sunshine on the fence of the field, and cut out a tether-peg. In the spring he knew of three strawberry plants that were in blossom, and would certainly bear fruit, and that was his most hopeful thought; but they came to nothing. He sat out in the rain in foul weather, and was wet to the skin, and afterwards the cold wind dried the clothes on his back. When he came to the farmyard he was hustled and cuffed, for the men and maids declared he was horribly ugly; but he was used to that – loved by nobody!

That was how it went with Anne Lisbeth's boy; and how could it go otherwise? It was, once for all, his fate to be loved by nobody.

From the land he was thrown overboard. He went to sea in a wretched vessel, and sat by the helm, while the skipper drank. He was dirty and ugly, half frozen and half starved: one would have thought he had never had enough; and that really was the case.

It was late in autumn: rough, wet, windy weather; the wind cut cold through the thickest clothing, especially at sea; and out to sea went a wretched boat, with only two men on board, or, properly speaking, with only a man and a half, the skipper and his boy. It had only been a kind of twilight all day, and now it became dark, and it was bitterly cold. The skipper drank a dram, which was to warm him from within. The bottle was old, and the glass too; it was whole at the top, but the foot was broken off, and therefore it stood upon a little carved block of wood painted blue. 'A dram comforts one, and two are better still,' thought the skipper. The boy sat at the helm, which he held fast in his hard tarry hands: he was ugly, and his hair was matted, and he looked crippled and stunted; he was the field-labourer's boy, though in the church register he was entered as Anne Lisbeth's son.

The wind cut its way through the rigging, and the boat cut through the sea. The sail blew out, filled by the wind, and they drove on in wild career. It was rough and wet around and above, and it might come worse still. Hold! what was that? what struck there? what burst? what seized the boat? It heeled, and lay on its beam ends! Was it a waterspout? Was it a heavy sea coming suddenly down? The boy at the helm cried out aloud, 'Heaven help us!' The boat had struck on a great rock standing up from the depths of the sea, and it sank like an old shoe in a puddle; it sank 'with man and mouse,' as the saying is; and there were mice on board, but only one man and a half, the skipper and the labourer's boy. No one saw it but the screaming seagulls, and the fishes down below, and even they did not see it rightly, for they started back in terror when the water rushed into the ship, and it sank. There it lay scarce a fathom below the surface, and those two were provided for, buried and forgotten! Only the glass with the foot of blue wood did not sink, for the wood kept it up; the glass drifted away, to be broken and cast upon the shore – where and when? But, indeed, that is of no consequence. It had served its time, and it had been loved, which Anne Lisbeth's boy had not been. But in Heaven no soul will be able to say, 'Never loved!'

Anne Lisbeth had lived in the city for many years. She was called Madam, and felt her dignity, when she remembered the old 'noble' days in which she had driven in the carriage, and had associated with countesses and baronesses. Her beautiful noble-child was the dearest angel, the kindest heart; he had loved her so much, and she had loved him in return; they had kissed and loved each other, and the boy had been her joy, her second life. Now he was so tall, and was fourteen years old, handsome and clever: she had not seen him since she carried him in her arms; for many years she had not been in the count's palace, for indeed it was quite a journey thither.

'I must once make an effort and go,' said Anne Lisbeth. 'I must go to my darling, to my sweet count's child. Yes, he certainly must long to see me too; he thinks of me and loves me as in those days when he flung his angel arms round my neck and cried, "Anne Liz!" It sounded like music. Yes, I must make an effort and see him again.'

She drove across the country in a grazier's cart, and then got out and continued her journey on foot, and thus reached the count's castle. It was great and magnificent, as it had always been, and the garden looked the same as ever; but all the people there were strangers to her; not one of them knew Anne Lisbeth, and they did not know of what consequence she had once been there, but she felt sure the countess would let them know it, and her darling boy too. How she longed to see him!

Now Anne Lisbeth was at her journey's end. She was kept waiting a considerable time, and for those who wait time passes slowly. But before the great people went to table she was called in, and accosted very graciously. She was to see her sweet boy after dinner, and then she was to be called in again.

How tall and slender and thin he had grown! But he had still his beautiful eyes and the angel-sweet mouth! He looked at her, but he said not a word: certainly he did not know her. He turned round, and was about to go away, but she seized his hand and pressed it to her mouth.

'Good, good!' said he; and with that he went out of the room – he who filled her every thought – he whom she had loved best, and who was her whole earthly pride.

Anne Lisbeth went out of the castle into the open highway, and she felt very mournful: he had been so cold and strange to her, had not a word nor a thought for her, he whom she had once carried day and night, and whom she still carried in her dreams.

A great black raven shot down in front of her on to the high road, and croaked and croaked again.

'Ha!' she said, 'what bird of ill omen art thou?'

She came past the hut of the labourer; the wife stood at the door, and the two women spoke to one another.

'You look well,' said the woman. 'You are plump and fat; you're well off.'

'Oh, yes,' answered Anne Lisbeth.

'The boat went down with them,' continued the woman. 'The skipper and the boy were both drowned. There's an end of them. I always thought the boy would be able to help me out with a few dollars He'll never cost *you* anything more, Anne Lisbeth.'

'So they were drowned?' Anne Lisbeth repeated; and then nothing more was said on the subject.

Anne Lisbeth was very low-spirited because her countchild had shown no disposition to talk with her who loved him so well, and who had journeyed all that way to get a sight of him; and the journey had cost money too, though the pleasure she had derived from it was not great. Still she said not a word about this. She would not relieve her heart by telling the labourer's wife about it, lest the latter should think she did not enjoy her former position at the castle. Then the raven screamed again, and flew past over her once more.

'The black wretch!' said Anne Lisbeth; 'he'll end by frightening me today.'

She had brought coffee and chicory with her, for she thought it would be a charity to the poor woman to give them to her to boil a cup of coffee, and then she herself would take a cup too. The woman prepared the coffee, and in the meantime Anne Lisbeth sat down upon a chair and fell asleep. There she dreamed of something she had never dreamed before: singularly enough, she dreamed of her own child that had wept and hungered there in the labourer's hut, had been hustled about in heat and in cold, and was now lying in the depths of the sea, Heaven knows where. She dreamed she was sitting in the hut, where the woman was busy preparing the coffee – she could smell the coffee-beans roasting. But suddenly it seemed to her that there stood on the threshold a beautiful young form, as beautiful as the count's child; and this apparition said to her, 'The world is passing away! Hold fast to me, for you are my mother after all. You have an angel in heaven. Hold me fast!'

And he stretched out his hand to her; and there was a terrible crash, for the world was going to pieces, and the angel was raising himself above the earth, and holding her by the sleeve so tightly, it seemed to her, that she was lifted up from the ground; but, on the other hand, something heavy hung at her feet and dragged her down, and it seemed to her that hundreds of women clung to her, and cried, 'If thou art to be saved, we must be saved too! Hold fast! hold fast!'

And then they all hung on to her; but there were too many of them, and – *ritsch! ratsch!* – the sleeve tore, and Anne Lisbeth fell down in horror – and awoke. And, indeed, she was on the point of falling over with the chair on which she sat; she was so startled and alarmed that she could not recollect what it was she had dreamed, but she remembered that it had been something dreadful.

The coffee was taken, and they had a chat together; and then Anne

Lisbeth went away towards the little town where she was to meet the
carrier, and to drive back with him to her own home. But when she
came to speak to him, he said he should not be ready to start before the
evening of the next day. She began to think about the expense and the
length of the way, and when she considered that the route by the sea-
shore was shorter by two miles than the other, and that the weather
was clear and the moon shone, she determined to make her way on
foot, that she might be at home by next day.

The sun had set, and the evening bells were still ringing; but no, it
was not the bells, but the cry of the frogs in the marshes. Now they
were silent, and all around was still; not a bird was heard, for they were
all gone to rest; and even the owl seemed to be at home: deep silence
reigned on the margin of the forest and by the sea-shore. As Anne
Lisbeth walked on she could hear her own footsteps on the sand; there
was no sound of waves in the sea; everything out in the deep waters had
sunk to silence. All was quiet there, the living and the dead.

Anne Lisbeth walked on 'thinking of nothing at all,' as the saying is,
or rather, her thoughts wandered; but her thoughts had not wandered
away from her, for they are never absent from us, they only slumber,
both those which have been alive but have gone to rest again, and
those which have not yet stirred. But the thoughts come forth at their
time, and begin to stir sometimes in the heart and sometimes in the
head, or seem to come upon us from above.

It is written that a good deed bears its fruit of blessing, and it is also
written that sin is death. Much has been written and much has been
said which one does not know or think of; and thus it was with Anne
Lisbeth. But it may happen that a light arises within one; it is quite
possible.

All virtues and all vices lie in our hearts. They are in mine and in
thine; they lie there like little invisible grains of seed; and then from
without comes a ray of sunshine or the touch of an evil hand, or maybe
you turn the corner and go to the right or to the left, and that may be
decisive; for the little seed-corn perhaps is stirred, and it swells and
shoots up, and it bursts, and pours its sap into all your blood, and then
your career has commenced. There are tormenting thoughts, which

one does not feel when one walks on with slumbering senses, but they are there, fermenting in the heart. Anne Lisbeth walked on thus with her senses half in slumber, but the thoughts were fermenting within her. From one Shrove Tuesday to the next there comes much that weighs upon the heart – the reckoning of a whole year: much is forgotten, sins against Heaven in word and in thought, against our neighbour, and against our own conscience. We don't think of these things, and Anne Lisbeth did not think of them. She had committed no crime against the law of the land, she was very respectable, an honoured and well-placed person, *that* she knew. And as she walked along by the margin of the sea, what was it she saw lying there? An old hat, a man's hat. Now, where might that have been washed overboard? She came nearer, and stopped to look at the hat. Ha! what was lying there? She shuddered; but it was nothing save a heap of sea-grass and tangle flung across a long stone; but it looked just like a real person; it was only sea-grass and tangle, and yet she was frightened at it, and as she turned away to walk on much came into her mind that she had heard in her childhood – old superstitions of spectres by the sea-shore, of the ghosts of drowned but unburied people who have been washed up on the desert shore. The body, she had heard, could do harm to none, but the spirit could pursue the lonely wanderer, and attach itself to him, and demand to be carried to the churchyard that it might rest in consecrated ground. 'Hold fast! hold fast!' it cried; and while Anne Lisbeth murmured the words to herself, her whole dream suddenly stood before her just as she had dreamed it, when the mothers clung to her and had repeated this word amid the crash of the world, when her sleeve was torn and she slipped out of the grasp of her child, who wanted to hold her up in that terrible hour. Her child, her own child, whom she had never loved, now lay buried in the sea, and might rise up like a spectre from the waters, and cry, 'Hold fast! carry me to consecrated earth.' And as these thoughts passed through her mind, fear gave speed to her feet, so that she walked on faster and faster; fear came upon her like the touch of a cold wet hand that was laid upon her heart, so that she almost fainted; and as she looked out across the sea, all there grew thicker and darker; a heavy mist came rolling onward, and clung round bush and tree, twisting them into fantastic shapes. She turned round, and glanced up at the moon, which had risen behind her. It looked like a pale, rayless surface; and a deadly weight appeared to cling to her limbs. 'Hold fast!' thought she; and when she turned round a second time and looked at the moon, its white face seemed quite close to her, and the mist hung like a pale garment from her shoulders. 'Hold fast! carry me to consecrated earth!' sounded in her ears in strange hollow tones. The sound did not come from the frogs in the pond, or from ravens or crows; she saw no sign of any such creatures. 'A grave! dig me a grave!' was repeated quite loud. Yes, it was the spectre of her child, the child that lay in the ocean, and whose spirit could have no rest until it was carried to the churchyard, and until a grave had been dug for it in consecrated ground. Thither she would go, and there she would dig; and she went on in the direction of the church, and the weight on her heart seemed to grow lighter, and even to vanish altogether; but when she turned to go home by the shortest way, it returned. 'Hold fast! hold fast!' and the words came quite clear, though they were like the croak of a frog or the wail of a bird, 'A grave! dig me a grave!'

The mist was cold and damp; her hands and face were cold and damp with horror; a heavy weight again seized her and clung to her, and in her mind a great space opened for thoughts that had never before been there.

Here in the North the beech wood often buds in a single night, and in the morning sunlight it appears in its full glory of youthful green; and thus in a single instant can the consciousness unfold itself of the sin that has been contained in the thoughts, words, and works of our past life. It springs up and unfolds itself in a single second when once the conscience is awakened; and God wakens it when we least expect it. Then we find no excuse for ourselves – the deed is there, and bears witness against us; the thoughts seem to become words, and to sound far out into the world. We are horrified at the thought of what we have carried within us, and have not stifled what we have sown in our thoughtlessness and pride. The heart hides within itself all the virtues and likewise all the vices, and they grow even in the barrenest ground.

Anne Lisbeth now experienced all the thoughts we have clothed in words. She was overpowered by them, and sank down, and crept along for some distance on the ground. 'A grave! dig me a grave!' it sounded again in her ears; and she would gladly have buried herself if in the grave there had been forgetfulness of every deed. It was the first hour of her awakening – full of anguish and horror. Superstition alternately made her shudder with cold and made her blood burn with the heat of fever. Many things of which she had never liked to speak came into her mind. Silent as the cloud-shadows in the bright moonshine, a spectral apparition flitted by her: she had heard of it before. Close by her galloped four snorting steeds, with fire spurting from their eyes and nostrils; they dragged a red-hot coach, and within it sat the wicked proprietor who had ruled here a hundred years ago. The legend said that every night at twelve o'clock he drove into his castle yard and out again. He was not pale, as dead men are said to be, but black as a coal. He nodded at Anne Lisbeth and beckoned to her. 'Hold fast! hold fast! then you may ride again in a nobleman's carriage, and forget your own child!'

She gathered herself up, and hastened to the churchyard; but the black crosses and the black ravens danced in confusion before her eyes. The ravens croaked, as the raven had done that she saw in the daytime, but now she understood what they said. 'I am the raven-mother! I am the raven-mother!' each raven croaked, and Anne Lisbeth now understood that the name also applied to her; and she fancied she should be transformed into a black bird, and be obliged to cry what they cried, if she did not dig the grave.

And she threw herself on the earth, and with her hands dug a grave in the hard ground, so that the blood ran from her fingers.

'A grave! dig me a grave!' it still sounded; she was fearful that the cock might crow, and the first red streak appear in the east, before she had finished her work, and then she would be lost.

And the cock crowed, and day dawned in the east, and the grave was only half dug. An icy hand passed over her head and face and down towards her heart.

'Only half a grave!' a voice wailed, and floated away down to the bottom of the sea.

It was the ocean spectre; and exhausted and overpowered, Anne Lisbeth sank to the ground, and her senses forsook her.

It was bright day when she came to herself, and two men were raising her up; but she was not lying in the churchyard, but on the sea-shore, where she had dug a deep hole in the sand, and cut her hand against a broken glass, whose sharp stem was stuck in a little painted block of wood. Anne Lisbeth was in a fever. Conscience had shuffled the cards of superstition, and had laid out these cards, and she fancied she had only half a soul, and that her child had taken the other half down into the sea. Never would she be able to swing herself aloft to the mercy of Heaven till she had recovered this other half, which was now held fast in the deep water. Anne Lisbeth got back to her former home, but was no longer the woman she had been her thoughts were confused like a tangled skein; only one thread, only one thought she had disentangled, namely, that she must carry the spectre of the sea-shore to the churchyard, and dig a grave for him, that thus she might win back her soul.

Many a night she was missed from her home; and she was always found on the sea-shore, waiting for the spectre. In this way a whole year passed by; and then one night she vanished again, and was not to be found; the whole of the next day was wasted in fruitless search.

Towards evening, when the clerk came into the church to toll the vesper bell, he saw, by the altar, Anne Lisbeth, who had spent the whole day there. Her strength was almost exhausted, but her eyes gleamed brightly, and her cheeks had a rosy flush. The last rays of the sun shone upon her, and gleamed over the altar on the bright clasps of the Bible which lay there, opened at the words of the prophet Joel: 'Rend your hearts, and not your garments, and turn unto the Lord!' That was just a chance, the people said, as many things happen by chance.

In the face of Anne Lisbeth, illumined by the sun, peace and rest were to be seen. She said she was happy, for now she had conquered. Last night the spectre of the shore, her own child, had come to her, and had said to her, 'Thou hast dug me only half a grave, but thou hast now, for a year and a day, buried me altogether in thy heart, and it is there that a mother can best hide her child!'

And then he gave her her lost half soul back again, and brought her here into the church.

'Now I am in the house of God,' she said, 'and in that house we are happy.'

And when the sun had set, Anne Lisbeth's soul had risen to that region where there is no more anguish, and Anne Lisbeth's troubles were over.

Children's Prattle

AT THE rich merchant's there was a children's party; rich people's children and grand people's children were there. The merchant was a learned man: he had once gone through the college examination, for his honest father had kept him to this, his father who had at first only been a cattle dealer, but always an honest and industrious man. The trade had brought money, and the merchant had managed to increase the store. Clever he was, and he had also a heart, but there was less said of his heart than of his money. At the merchant's, grand people went in and out – people of blood, as it is called, and people of intellect, and people who had both of these, and people who had neither. Now there was a children's party there, and children's prattle, and children speak frankly from the heart. Among the rest there was a beautiful little girl, and the little one was terribly proud. However, the servants had taught her that, not her parents, who were far too sensible people. Her father was a groom of the bedchamber, and that is a very grand office, and she knew it.

'I am a child of the bedchamber,' she said.

Now she might just as well have been a child of the cellar, for nobody can help his birth; and then she told the other children that she was 'well born', and said that no one who was not well born could get on far in the world: it was of no use to read and be industrious; if one was not well born one could not achieve anything.

'And those whose names end with "sen",' said she, 'they cannot be anything at all. One must put one's arms akimbo, and keep them at a great distance, these "sen"!'

And she stuck out her pretty little arms, and made the elbows quite pointed, to show how it was to be done and her little arms were very pretty. She was sweet.

But the little daughter of the merchant became very angry at this

speech, for her father's name was Madsen, and she knew that the name ended in 'sen'; and therefore she said, as proudly as ever she could, 'But my papa can buy a hundred dollars' worth of bon-bons, and throw them to the children! Can your papa do that?'

'Yes, but my papa,' said an author's little daughter, 'can put your papa and everybody's papa into the newspaper. All people are afraid of him, my mamma says, for it is my father who rules in the paper.'

And the little maiden looked exceedingly proud, as though she had been a real Princess, who is expected to look proud.

But outside at the door, which was ajar, stood a poor boy, peeping through the crack. He was of such lowly station that he was not even allowed to enter the room. He had turned the spit for the cook, and she had allowed him to stand behind the door, and to look at the well-dressed children who were making a merry day within, and for him that was a great deal.

'Oh, to be one of them!' thought he; and then he heard what was said, which was certainly calculated to make him very unhappy. His parents at home had not a penny to spare to buy a newspaper, much less could they write one; and what was worst of all, his father's name, and consequently his own, was a common one, ending in "son", and so he could not turn out well. That was terrible. But, after all, he had been born, and very well born as it seemed to him; there was no getting over that.

And that is what was done on that evening.

Many years have elapsed since then, and in the course of years children become grown-up persons.

In the town stood a splendid house; it was filled with all kinds of beautiful objects and treasures, and all people wished to see it; even people who dwelt out of town came in to see it. Which of the children of whom we have told might call this house his own? To know that is very easy. No, no; it is not so very easy. The house belonged to the poor little boy – he had become something great, although his name ended in 'sen,' – Thorwaldsen.

And the three other children? the children of *blood* and of money, and of spiritual pride? Well, they had nothing wherewith to reproach each other – they turned out well enough, for they had been well dowered by nature; and what they had thought and spoken on that evening was mere *children's prattle*.

A String of Pearls

T HE RAILWAY in Denmark extends as yet only from Copenhagen to Korsör; it is a string of pearls, such as Europe has abundance of; the most costly beads there are called Paris, London, Vienna and Naples. Yet many a one does not point to these great cities as his loveliest pearl, but on the contrary to a little, unimportant town; there is the home of homes, there his dear ones live! Yes, often it is only a single farm, a little house, hidden amongst green hedges, a mere point which disappears as the train flashes past it.

How many pearls are there on the string from Copenhagen to Korsör? We will consider six, which most people must take notice of; old memories and poetry itself give these pearls a lustre, so that they shine in our thoughts.

Close by the hill where the castle of Frederick the Sixth lies, the home of Oehlenschläger's childhood, one of the pearls glitters in the shelter of Söndermarken's woods; it was called 'The Cottage of Philemon and Baucis,' that is to say, the home of a lovable old couple. Here lived Rahbek with his wife Emma; here, under their hospitable roof, for a whole generation several men of genius came together from busy Copenhagen; here was a home of intellect, and now! Say not: 'Alas, how changed!' – no, it is still a home of intellect, a conservatory for pining plants! The flower-bud which is not strong enough to unfold itself yet contains, concealed, all the germs for leaf and seed. Here the sun of intellect shines into a carefully guarded home of intellect, enlivening and giving life. The world round about shines through the eyes into the unfathomable depths of the soul. The idiots' home, encompassed with human love, is a holy place, a conservatory for the pining plants, which shall at sometime be transplanted and bloom in the garden of God. Here the weakest in intellect are now assembled, where at one time the greatest and most powerful minds met, exchanged ideas, and were lifted upward – and the soul's flame still mounts upwards in 'The Cottage of Philemon and Baucis.'

The town of the royal tombs beside Hroar's well, the old Roskilde, lies before us! The slender spires of the cathedral towers soar above the low-built town, and mirror themselves in Isefiord. One grave only will we search for here, and regard it in the sheen of the pearl; it is not that of the great Queen Margaret – no, within the churchyard, close to whose white wall we fly past, is the grave; a common stone is laid over it; the master of the organ, the reviver of Danish romance, lies here. The old traditions became melodies in our soul; we learned that where 'The clear waves rolled,' 'there dwelt a king in Leire!' Roskilde, the burial place of kings! in thy pearl will we look at the simple grave, where on the stone is carved a lyre and the name of Weyse.

Now we come to Sigersted near the town of Ringsted; the river-bed lies low; the golden corn grows where Hagbarth's boat put in to the bank, not far from the maiden-bower of Signe. Who does not know the story of Hagbarth, who was hanged in the oak, and Little Signe's bower which stood in flames; the legend of strong love!

'Lovely Sorö surrounded by woods!' the quiet cloister-town peeps out between the moss-grown trees; with the glance of youth it looks out from the academy over the lake to the world's highway, and hears the engine's dragon puff whilst it flies through the wood. Sorö, thou pearl of poetry, which preserves the dust of Holberg. Like a great white swan beside the deep woodland lake lies thy palace of learning, and near to it shines, like the white star-wort in the woods, a little house to which our eyes turn; from it pious psalms sound through the land, words are uttered in it, even the peasant listens to them and learns of vanished times in Denmark. The green wood and the song of the birds go together; so also do the names of Sorö and Ingemann.

On to the town of Slagelse! what is reflected here in the sheen of the pearl? Vanished is the cloister of Antvorskov, vanished the rich halls of the castle, and even its solitary deserted wing; still one old relic remains, renewed and again renewed, a wooden cross on the hill over there, where in legendary times, St Andrew, the priest of Slagelse, wakened up, borne hither in one night from Jerusalem.

Korsör – here wert thou born, who gave us

> Jest with earnest blended
> In songs of Knud the voyager.

Thou master of words and wit! the decaying old ramparts of the forsaken fortress are now the last visible witness of the home of thy childhood; when the sun sets, their shadows point to where thy birth-place stood; from these ramparts, looking towards the height of Sprogö, thou sawest, when thou wast small, 'the moon glide down behind the isle,' and sang of it in immortal strains, as thou since hast sung of the mountains of Switzerland; thou, who didst wander about in the labyrinth of the world and found that

> Nowhere is the rose so red,
> And nowhere are the thorns so few,
> And nowhere is the couch so soft
> As those our simple childhood knew.

Thou lively singer of wit! we weave thee a garland of woodruff, and cast it in the lake, and the waves will bear it to Kielerfiord, on whose coast thy dust is laid; it brings a greeting from the young generation, a greeting from the town of thy birth, Korsör – where the string of pearls is broken.

'It is indeed a string of pearls from Copenhagen to Korsör,' said Grandmother, who had heard what we have just read. 'It is a string of pearls for me, and it had already come to be that for me more than forty years ago,' said she. 'We had no steam-engines then; we spent days on the way, where you now only spend hours. It was in 1815; I was twenty-one then – it is a delightful age! And yet up in the sixties is also a delightful age, so full of blessings! In my young days it was a greater event than now to get to Copenhagen, the town of all towns, as we considered it. My parents wished, after twenty years, once again to pay a visit to it, and I was to accompany them. We had talked of the journey for years, and now it was really to take place; I thought that quite a new life would begin, and, in a way, a new life really began for me.

There was such sewing and packing, and when it was time to depart, how many good friends came to bid us goodbye! It was a big journey we had before us! It was in the forenoon that we drove out of Odense in my parents' carriage; acquaintances nodded from the windows all the way up the street, almost until we were out of St George's Gate. The weather was lovely, the birds sang, all was delightful; one forgot that it was a long, difficult road to Nyborg. Towards evening we came there. The post did not arrive until late in the night, and the boat did not leave before that, but we went on board. The great water lay before us, as far as we could see, so smooth and still. We lay down in our clothes and slept. When I wakened and came on deck in the morning, nothing could be seen on either side, there was such a fog. I heard the cocks crowing, observed that the sun had risen, and heard the bells ringing. Where could we be? The fog lifted, and we actually were still lying just out from Nyborg. During the day a slight wind blew, but dead against us; we tacked and tacked, and finally we were fortunate enough to get to Korsör a little after eleven in the evening, after we had spent twenty-two hours in traversing the eighteen miles.

'It was nice to get on land, but it was dark; the lamps burned badly, and everything was so perfectly strange to me, who had never been in any town except Odense.

' "Look," said my father, "here Baggesen was born, and here Birckner lived." Then it seemed to me that the old town with the little houses grew at once brighter and larger; we also felt so glad to have firm land under us. I could not sleep that night for thinking of all that I had already seen and experienced since I left home the day before last.

'We had to rise early next morning, as we had before us a bad road with very steep hills and many holes, until we came to Slagelse, and beyond, on the other side of Slagelse, it was not much better, and we wished to arrive early at the "Crab", so that we might walk into Sorö by daylight and visit the miller's Emil, as we called him; yes, it was your grandfather, my late husband, the dean; he was a student at Sorö, and had just passed his second examination.

'We came to the "Crab" in the afternoon; it was a fashionable place at that time, the best inn on the whole of the journey, and the most charming district; yes, you must all allow it is still that. She was an active hostess, Mrs Plambek; everything in the house was like a well-scoured table. On the wall hung Baggesen's letter to her, framed and under glass, and well worth seeing; to me it was something very notable. Then we went up to Sorö, and there met Emil. You may suppose that he was glad to see us, and we to see him, and he was so good and attentive. With him we saw the church with Absalon's grave and Holberg's coffin; we saw the old monkish inscriptions, and we sailed over the lake to "Parnassus"; the most beautiful evening I can remember! It seemed to me that if one could make poetry anywhere in the world, it must be at Sorö, in this peace and beauty of nature. Then in the moonlight we went along the "Philosopher's Walk", as they call it, the lovely, lonely path by the lake and the stream, out towards the high-road leading to the "Crab". Emil stayed to supper with us; Father and Mother thought he had grown so sensible and looked so well. He promised us that he would be in Copenhagen in five days, at his own home and together with us, for Whitsuntide. These hours in Sorö and the "Crab" belong to my life's loveliest pearls.

'Next morning we set out very early, for we had a long way to go before we reached Roskilde, and we must get there betimes, so that the cathedral might be seen, and in the evening father could have time to visit an old school friend. This was duly carried out, and then we spent the night in Roskilde, and next day, but only by dinnertime, for it was the worst and most cut-up road that we had yet to travel, we arrived in Copenhagen. We had spent about three days from Korsör to Copenhagen; now the same distance is done in three hours. The beads have not become more precious, they could not be that; but the string is new and marvellous. I stayed with my parents in Copenhagen for three weeks. Emil was with us the whole time, and when we travelled back to Fyen, he accompanied us all the way from Copenhagen to Korsör; there we became engaged before we parted! So now you can understand that I also call from Copenhagen to Korsör a string of pearls.

'Afterwards, when Emil was called to Assens, we were married. We often talked of the journey to Copenhagen, and about doing it once again, but then first came your mother, and after that she got brothers and sisters, and there was much to look after and to take care of, and when father was promoted and became dean, of course everything was a pleasure and a joy, but to Copenhagen we never got. I never was there again, however often we thought and talked about it, and now I am too old, I have not the strength to travel on the railway; but I am glad of the railways. It is a blessing that we have them! With them you come all the quicker to me! Now Odense is not much farther from Copenhagen than it was from Nyborg in my young days. You can now fly to Italy as quickly as we travelled to Copenhagen! Yes, that is something! – all the same I shall sit still, and let others travel, let them come to me! But you ought not to laugh either, because I sit so still! I have a great journey before me quite different from yours, one that is much quicker than by the railway. When our Father wills it, I shall go to join your grandfather, and when you have completed your work, and enjoyed yourselves here in this dear world, I know that you will come up to us, and if we talk there about our earthly days, believe me, children, I shall also say there as now, "from Copenhagen to Korsör is indeed a string of pearls!" '

The Pen and Inkstand

IN THE room of a poet, where his Inkstand stood upon the table, it was said, 'It is wonderful what can come out of an inkstand. What will the next thing be? It is wonderful!'

'Yes, certainly,' said the Inkstand. 'It's inconceivable – that's what I always say,' he exclaimed to the Pen and to the other articles on the table that were near enough to hear. 'It is wonderful what a number of things can come out of me. It's quite incredible. And I really don't myself know what will be the next thing, when that man begins to dip into me. One drop out of me is enough for half a page of paper; and what cannot be contained in half a page? From me all the works of the poet go forth – all these living men, whom people can imagine they have met – all the deep feeling, the humour, the vivid pictures of nature. I myself don't understand how it is, for I am not acquainted with nature, but it certainly is in me. From me all these things have gone forth, and from me proceed the troops of charming maidens, and of brave knights on prancing steeds, and all the lame and the blind, and I don't know what more – I assure you I don't think of anything.'

'There you are right,' said the Pen; 'you don't think at all, for if you did, you would comprehend that you only furnish the fluid. You give the fluid, that I may exhibit upon the paper what dwells in me, and what I would bring to the day. It is the pen that writes. No man doubts that; and, indeed, most people have about as much insight into poetry as an old inkstand.'

'You have but little experience,' replied the Inkstand. 'You've hardly been in service a week, and are already half worn out. Do you fancy you are the poet? You are only a servant; and before you came I knew many of your sort, some of the goose family, and others of English manufacture. I know the quill as well as the steel pen. Many have been in my service, and I shall have many more when *he* comes – the man

who goes through the motions for me, and writes down what he derives from me. I should like to know what will be the next thing he'll take out of me.'

'Inkpot!' exclaimed the Pen.

Late in the evening the poet came home. He had been to a concert, where he had heard a famous violinist, with whose admirable performances he was quite enchanted. The player had drawn a wonderful wealth of tone from the instrument: sometimes it had sounded like tinkling water-drops, like rolling pearls, sometimes like birds twittering in chorus, and then again it went swelling on like the wind through the fir trees. The poet thought he heard his own heart weeping, but weeping melodiously, like the sound of a woman's voice. It seemed as though not only the strings sounded, but every part of the instrument. It was a wonderful performance; and difficult as the piece was, the bow seemed to glide easily to and fro over the strings, and it looked as though anyone might do it. The violin seemed to sound of itself, and the bow to move of itself – those two appeared to do everything; and the audience forgot the master who guided them and breathed soul and spirit into them. The master was forgotten; but the poet remembered him, and named him, and wrote down his thoughts concerning the subject.

'How foolish it would be of the violin and the bow to boast of their achievements! And yet we men often commit this folly – the poet, the artist, the inventor in the domain of science, the general – we all do it. We are only the instruments which the Almighty uses: to Him alone be the honour! We have nothing of which we should be proud.'

Yes, that is what the poet wrote down. He wrote it in the form of a parable, which he called 'The Master and the Instruments.'

'That is what you get, madam,' said the Pen to the Inkstand, when the two were alone again. 'Did you not hear him read aloud what I have written down!'

'Yes, what I gave you to write,' retorted the Inkstand. 'That was a cut at you, because of your conceit. That you should not even have understood that you were being quizzed! I gave you a cut from within me – surely I must know my own satire!'

'Ink-pipkin!' cried the Pen.

'Writing-stick!' cried the Inkstand.

And each of them felt a conviction that he had answered well; and it is a pleasing conviction to feel that one has given a good answer – a conviction on which one can sleep; and accordingly they slept upon it. But the poet did not sleep. Thoughts welled up from within him, like the tones from the violin, falling like pearls, rushing like the stormwind through the forests. He felt his own heart in these thoughts, and caught a ray from the Eternal Master.

To *Him* be all the honour!

The Child in the Grave

THERE WAS sorrow in the house, sorrow in every heart. The youngest child, a boy four years old, the joy and hope of his parents, had died. There still remained to them two daughters, the elder of whom was about to be confirmed – good, charming girls both; but the child that one has lost always seems the dearest; and here it was the youngest, and a son. It was a heavy trial. The sisters mourned as young hearts can, and were especially moved at the sight of their parents' sorrow. The father was bowed down, and the mother completely overpowered by the great grief. Day and night she had been busy about the sick child, and had tended, lifted, and carried it; she had felt how it was a part of herself. She could not realise that the child was dead, and that it must be laid in a coffin and sleep in the ground. She thought God *could not* take this child from her; and when it was so, nevertheless, and there could be no more doubt on the subject, she said in her feverish pain, 'God did not know it. He has heartless servants here on earth, who do according to their own liking, and hear not the prayers of a mother.'

In her grief she fell away from God, and then there came dark thoughts, thoughts of death, of everlasting death – that man was but dust in the dust, and that with this life all was ended. But these thoughts gave her no stay, nothing on which she could take hold; and she sank into the fathomless abyss of despair.

In her heaviest hours she could weep no more, and she thought not of the young daughters who were still left to her. The tears of her husband fell upon her forehead, but she did not look at him. Her thoughts were with the dead child; her whole thought and being were fixed upon it, to call back every remembrance of the little one, every innocent childish word it had uttered.

The day of the funeral came. For nights before, the mother had not slept; but in the morning twilight she now slept, overcome by weariness; and in the meantime the coffin was carried into a distant room, and there nailed down, that she might not hear the blows of the hammer.

When she awoke, and wanted to see her child, the husband said, 'We have nailed down the coffin. It was necessary to do so.'

'When God is hard towards me, how should men be better?' she said, with sobs and groans.

The coffin was carried to the grave. The inconsolable mother sat with her young daughters. She looked at her daughters, and yet did not see them, for her thoughts were no longer busied with home. She gave herself up to her grief, and grief tossed her to and fro as the sea tosses a ship without compass or rudder. So the day of the funeral passed away, and similar days followed, of dark, wearying pain. With moist eyes and mournful glances, the sorrowing daughters and the afflicted husband looked upon her who would not hear their words of comfort; and, indeed, what words of comfort could they speak to her, when they themselves were heavily bowed down?

It seemed as though she knew sleep no more; and yet he would now have been her best friend, who would have strengthened her body, and poured peace into her soul. They persuaded her to seek her couch, and she lay still there, like one who slept. One night her husband was listening to her breathing, and fully believed that she had now found rest and relief. He folded his arms and prayed, and soon sank into a deep healthy sleep; and thus he did not notice that his wife arose, threw on her clothes, and silently glided from the house, to go where her thoughts always lingered – to the grave which held her child. She stepped through the garden of the house, and over the fields, where a path led to the churchyard. No one saw her and she saw no one.

It was a lovely starlight night; the air was still mild; it was in the beginning of September. She entered the churchyard, and stood by the little grave, which looked like a great nosegay of fragrant flowers. She sat down, and bowed her head low over the grave, as if she could have seen her child through the earth, her little boy, whose smile rose so vividly before her – the gentle expression of whose eyes, even on his sick bed, she could never forget. How eloquent had that glance been, when she had bent over him and seized his delicate hand, which he had no longer strength to raise! As she had sat by his crib, so she now sat by his grave, but here her tears had free course, and fell thick upon the grave.

'Thou wouldst gladly go down and be with thy child,' said a voice quite close to her, a voice that sounded so clear and deep, it went straight to her heart.

She looked up, and near her stood a man wrapped in a black cloak, with a hood drawn closely down over his face. But she glanced keenly up, and saw his face under his hood. It was stern, but yet awakened confidence, and his eyes beamed with the radiance of youth.

'Down to my child!' she repeated; and a despairing supplication spoke out of her words.

'Darest thou follow me?' asked the form. 'I am Death.'

And she bowed her head in assent. Then suddenly it seemed as though all the stars were shining with the radiance of the full moon; she saw the varied colours of the flowers on the grave, and the covering of earth was gradually withdrawn like a floating drapery; and she sank down, and the apparition covered her with his black cloak; night closed around her, the night of death, and she sank deeper than the sexton's spade can penetrate, and the churchyard was as a roof over her head.

A corner of the cloak was removed, and she stood in a great hall which spread wide and pleasantly around. It was twilight. But in a moment her child appeared, and was pressed to her heart, smiling at her in greater beauty than he had ever possessed. She uttered a cry, but it was inaudible, for a glorious swelling strain of music sounded close to her, and then in the distance, and then again close at hand: never had such tones fallen on her ear; they came from beyond the great dark curtain which separated the hall from the great land of eternity beyond.

'My sweet darling mother,' she heard her child say.

It was the well-known, much-loved voice, and kiss followed kiss in boundless felicity; and the child pointed to the dark curtain.

'It is not so beautiful on earth. Do you see, mother – do you see them all? Oh, that is happiness!'

But the mother saw nothing which the child pointed out – nothing but the dark night. She looked with earthly eyes, and could not see as the child saw, whom God had called to Himself. She could hear the sounds of the music, but not the word – *the Word* in which she was to believe.

'Now I can fly, mother – I can fly with all the other happy children into the presence of the Almighty. I would fain fly; but, if you weep as you are weeping now, I might be lost to you – and yet I would go so gladly. May I not fly? And you will come to me soon – will you not, dear mother?'

'Oh, stay! stay!' entreated the mother. 'Only one moment more – only once more I should wish to look at thee, and kiss thee, and press thee in my arms.'

And she kissed and fondled the child. Then her name was called from above – called in a plaintive voice. What might this mean?

'Hearest thou?' asked the child. 'It is my father who calls thee.'

And in a few moments deep sighs were heard, as of weeping children.

'They are my sisters,' said the child. 'Mother, you surely have not forgotten them?'

And then she remembered those she had left behind. A great terror came upon her. She looked out into the night, and above her dim forms were flitting past. She seemed to recognise a few more of these. They floated through the Hall of Death towards the dark curtain, and there they vanished. Would her husband and her daughters thus flit past? No, their sighs and lamentations still sounded from above: and she had been nearly forgetting them for the sake of him who was dead!

'Mother, now the bells of heaven are ringing,' said the child. 'Mother, now the sun is going to rise.'

And an overpowering light streamed in upon her. The child had vanished, and she was borne upwards. It became cold round about her, and she lifted up her head, and saw that she was lying in the churchyard, on the grave of her child.

But the Lord had been a stay unto her feet, in a dream, and a light to her spirit; and she bowed her knees and prayed for forgiveness that she had wished to keep back a soul from its immortal flight, and that she had forgotten her duties towards the living who were left to her.

And when she had spoken those words, it was as if her heart were lightened. Then the sun burst forth, and over her head a little bird sang out, and the church bells sounded for early service. Everything was holy around her, and her heart was chastened. She acknowledged the goodness of God, acknowledged the duties she had to perform, and eagerly she went home. She bent over her husband, who still slept; her warm devoted kiss awakened him, and heartfelt words of love came from the lips of both. And she was gentle and strong as a wife can be; and from her came the consoling words, God's will is always the best.

Then her husband asked her, 'From whence hast thou all at once derived this strength – this feeling of consolation?'

And she kissed him, and kissed her children, and said, 'They came from God, through the child in the grave.'

The Farm-Yard Cock and Weathercock

THERE WERE two Cocks – one on the dunghill, the other on the roof. Both were conceited; but which of the two effected most? Tell us your opinion; but we shall keep our own nevertheless.

The poultry-yard was divided by a wooden fence from another yard, in which lay a manure-heap, whereon grew a great Cucumber, which was fully conscious of being a forcing-bed plant.

'That's a privilege of birth,' the Cucumber said to herself. 'Not all can be born cucumbers; there must be other kinds too. The fowls, the ducks, and all the cattle in the neighbouring yard are creatures too. I now look up to the Yard Cock on the fence. He certainly is of much greater consequence than the Weathercock, who is so highly placed, and who can't even creak, much less crow; and he has neither hens nor chickens, and thinks only of himself, and perspires verdigris. But the Yard Cock – he's something like a cock! His gait is like a dance, his crowing is music; and wherever he comes, one hears directly what a trumpeter he is! If he would only come in here! Even if he were to eat me up, stalk and all, it would be quite a blissful death,' said the Cucumber.

In the night the weather became very bad. Hens, chickens, and even the Cock himself sought shelter. The wind blew down the fence between the two yards with a crash; the tiles came tumbling down, but the Weathercock sat firm. He did not even turn round; he could not turn round, and yet he was young and newly cast, but steady and sedate. He had been 'born old', and did not at all resemble the fluttering birds of heaven, such as the sparrows and the swallows. He despised those, considering them piping birds of trifling stature – ordinary song birds. The pigeons, he allowed, were big and shining, and gleamed like mother-o'-pearl, and looked like a kind of weather-cocks; but then they were fat and stupid, and their whole endeavour was to fill themselves with food.

'Moreover, they are tedious things to converse with,' said the Weathercock.

The birds of passage had also paid a visit to the Weathercock, and told him tales of foreign lands, of airy caravans, and exciting robber stories; of encounters with birds of prey; and that was interesting for the first time, but the Weathercock knew that afterwards they always repeated themselves, and that was tedious.

'They are tedious, and all is tedious,' he said. 'No one is fit to associate with, and one and all of them are wearisome and stupid. The world is worth nothing,' he cried. 'The whole thing is a stupidity.'

The Weathercock was what is called 'used up'; and that quality would certainly have made him interesting in the eyes of the Cucumber if she had known it; but she had only eyes for the Yard Cock, who had now actually come into her own yard.

The wind had blown down the fence, but the storm had passed over.

'What do you think of *that* crowing?' the Yard Cock enquired of his hens and chickens. 'It was a little rough – the elegance was wanting.'

And hens and chickens stepped upon the muck-heap, and the Cock came along like a knight.

'Garden plant!' he cried out to the Cucumber; and in this one word she perceived all his extensive breeding, and forgot that he was pecking at her and eating her up – a happy death!

And the hens came, and the chickens came, and when one of them runs the rest run also; and they clucked and chirped, and looked at the Cock, and were proud that he was of their kind.

'Cock-a-doodle-doo!' he crowed. 'The chickens will grow up large fowls if I make a noise in the poultry-yard of the world.'

And hens and chickens clucked and chirped, and the Cock told them a great piece of news:

'A cock can lay an egg; and do you know what there is in that egg? In that egg lies a basilisk. No one can stand the sight of a basilisk. Men know that, and now you know it too – you know what is in me, and what a Cock of the world I am.'

And with this the Yard Cock flapped his wings, and made his comb swell up, and crowed again; and all of them shuddered – all the hens and the chickens; but they were proud that one of their people should be such a cock of the world. They clucked and chirped, so that the Weathercock might hear it; and he heard it, but he never stirred.

'It's all stupid stuff!' said a voice within the Weathercock. 'The Yard Cock does not lay eggs, and I am too lazy to lay any. If I liked, I could lay a wind-egg; but the world is not worth a wind-egg. And now I don't like even to sit here any longer.'

And with this the Weathercock broke off; but he did not kill the Yard Cock, though he intended to do so, as the hens declared. And what does the moral say? 'Better to crow than to be "used up" and break off.'

Charming

ALFRED THE sculptor – you know him? We all know him: he won the gold medal, went to Italy, and then came home again. He was young in those days, and indeed he is young yet, though he is ten years older than he was then.

After his return he visited one of the little provincial towns on the island of Zealand. The whole town knew who the stranger was, and one of the richest persons gave a party in honour of him, and all who were of any consequence, or possessed any property, were invited. It was quite an event, and all the town knew of it without its being announced by beat of drum. Apprentice boys, and children of poor people, and even some of the poor people themselves, stood in front of the house, and looked at the lighted curtain; and the watchman could fancy that *he* was giving a party, so many people were in the streets. There was quite an air of festivity about, and in the house was festivity also, for Mr Alfred the sculptor was there.

He talked, and told anecdotes, and all listened to him with pleasure and a certain kind of awe; but none felt such respect for him as did the elderly widow of an official: she seemed, so far as Mr Alfred was concerned, like a fresh piece of blotting paper, that absorbed all that was spoken, and asked for more. She was very receptive and incredibly ignorant – a kind of female Caspar Hauser.

'I should like to see Rome,' she said. 'It must be a lovely city, with all the strangers who are continually arriving there. Now, do give us a description of Rome. How does the city look when you come in by the gate?'

'I cannot very well describe it,' replied the sculptor. 'A great open place, and in the midst of it an obelisk, which is four thousand years old.'

'An organist!' exclaimed the lady, who had never met with the word *obelisk*.

A few of the guests could hardly keep from laughing, nor could the sculptor quite keep his countenance; but the smile that rose to his lips faded away, for he saw, close by the inquisitive dame, a pair of dark-blue eyes – they belonged to the daughter of the speaker, and anyone who has such a daughter cannot be silly! The mother was like a fountain of questions, and the daughter, who listened but never spoke, might pass for the beautiful Naiad of the fountain. How charming she was! She was a study for the sculptor to contemplate, but not to converse with; and, indeed, she did not speak, or only very seldom.

'Has the Pope a large family?' asked the lady.

And the young man answered, as if the question could have been better put, 'No, he does not come of a great family.'

'That's not what I mean,' the widow persisted. 'I mean, has he a wife and children?'

'The Pope is not allowed to marry,' said the gentleman.

'I don't like that,' was the lady's comment.

She certainly might have put more sensible questions; but if she had not spoken in just the manner she used, would her daughter have leaned so gracefully upon her shoulder, looking straight out with the almost mournful smile upon her face?

Then Mr Alfred spoke again, and told of the glory of colour in Italy, of the purple hills, the blue Mediterranean, the azure sky of the South, whose brightness and glory was only to be surpassed in the North by a maiden's deep blue eyes. And this he said with a peculiar application; but she who should have understood his meaning, looked as if she were quite unconscious of it, and that again was charming!

'Italy!' sighed a few of the guests.

'Oh, to travel!' sighed others.

'Charming! charming!'

'Yes, if I win fifty thousand dollars in the lottery,' said the head tax-collector's lady, 'then we will travel. I and my daughter, and you, Mr Alfred; you must be our guide. We'll all three travel together, and one or two good friends more.' And she nodded in such a friendly way at the company, that each one might imagine he or she was the person who was to be taken to Italy. 'Yes, we will go to Italy! but not to those parts where there are robbers – we'll keep to Rome, and to the great high roads where one is safe.'

And the daughter sighed very quietly. And how much may lie in one little sigh, or be placed in it! The young man placed a great deal in it. The two blue eyes, lit up that evening in honour of him, must conceal treasures – treasures of the heart and mind – richer than all the glories of Rome; and when he left the party that night he had lost *his* heart – lost it completely, to the young lady.

The house of the widow was now the one which Mr Alfred the sculptor frequented; and it was understood that his visits were not intended for that lady, though he and she were the people who kept up the conversation: he came for the daughter's sake. They called her Kala. Her name was really Karen Malena, and these two names had been contracted into the one name, Kala. She was beautiful; but a few said she was rather dull, and slept late of a morning.

'She has always been accustomed to that,' her mother said. 'She's a beauty, and they always are easily tired. She sleeps rather late, but that makes her eyes so clear.'

What a power lay in those bright eyes! 'Still waters run deep.' The young man felt the truth of this proverb, and his heart had sunk into the depths. He spoke and told his adventures, and the mamma was as simple and eager in her questioning as on the first evening of their meeting.

It was a pleasure to hear Alfred describe anything. He spoke of Naples, of excursions to Mount Vesuvius, and showed coloured prints of several of the eruptions. And the widow had never heard of them before, or taken time to consider the question

'Good heavens!' she exclaimed. 'So that is a burning mountain! But is it not dangerous to the people round about?'

'Whole cities have been destroyed,' he answered; 'for instance, Pompeii and Herculaneum.'

'But the poor people! – And you saw all that with your own eyes?'

'No, I did not see any of the eruptions represented in these pictures, but I will show you a picture of my own of an eruption I saw.'

He laid a pencil sketch upon the table, and mamma, who had been absorbed in the contemplation of the highly coloured prints, threw a glance at the pale drawing, and cried in astonishment, 'Did you see it throw up white fire?'

For a moment Alfred's respect for Kala's mamma suffered a sudden diminution; but, dazzled by the light that illumined Kala, he soon found it quite natural that the old lady should have no eye for colour. After all, it was of no consequence, for Kala's mamma had the best of all things – namely, Kala herself.

And Alfred and Kala were betrothed, which was natural enough, and the betrothal was announced in the little newspaper of the town. Mamma purchased thirty copies of the paper, that she might cut out the paragraph and send it to their friends and acquaintances. And the betrothed pair were happy, and the mother-in-law elect was happy too, for it seemed like connecting herself with Thorwaldsen.

'For you are a continuation of Thorwaldsen,' she said to Alfred.

And it seemed to Alfred that mamma had in this instance said a clever thing. Kala said nothing; but her eyes shone, her lips smiled, her every movement was graceful. Yes, she was beautiful; that cannot be too often repeated.

Alfred undertook to make a bust of Kala and of his mother-in-law. They sat to him accordingly, and saw how he moulded and smoothed the soft clay with his fingers.

'I suppose it's only on our account,' said mamma-in-law, 'that you undertake this commonplace work, and don't leave your servant to do all that sticking together?'

'It is necessary that I should mould the clay myself,' he replied.

'Ah, yes, you are so very polite, retorted mamma; and Kala silently pressed his hand, still soiled by the clay.

And he unfolded to both of them the loveliness of nature in creation, how the living stood above the dead, the plant above the mineral, the animal above the plant, and man above the animal. How mind and beauty become manifest in outward form, and how the sculptor gave that beauty its manifestation in his works.

Kala stood silent, and nodded approbation of the expressed thought, while mamma-in-law made the following confession: 'It's difficult to follow all that. But I manage to hobble after you with my thoughts, though they whirl round and round, but I contrive to hold them fast.'

And Kala's beauty held Alfred fast, filled his whole soul, and seized and mastered him. Beauty gleamed forth from Kala's every feature – from her look, from the corners of her mouth, and in every movement of her fingers. Alfred the sculptor saw this: he spoke only of her, thought only of her, and the two became one; and thus it may be said that she spoke much, for he spoke very much.

Such was the betrothal; and now came the wedding, with bridesmaids and wedding presents, all duly mentioned in the wedding speech.

Mamma-in-law had set up Thorwaldsen's bust at the end of the table, attired in a dressing-gown, for he was to be a guest; such was her whim. Songs were sung and cheers were given, for it was a gay wedding, and they were a handsome pair. 'Pygmalion received his Galatea,' so one of the songs said.

'Ah, that's your mythology,' said mamma-in-law.

Next day the youthful pair started for Copenhagen, where they were to live. Mamma-in-law accompanied them, 'to take care of the commonplace,' as she said, meaning the domestic economy. Kala was like a doll in a doll's house, all was so bright, so new, and so fine. There they sat, all three; and as for Alfred, to use a proverb that will describe his position, we may say that he sat like the friar in the goose-yard.

The magic of form had enchanted him. He had looked at the case, and cared not to enquire what the case contained, and that omission brings unhappiness, much unhappiness, into married life; for the case may be broken and the gilt may come off, and then the purchaser may repent his bargain. In a large party it is very disagreeable to observe that one's buttons are giving way, and that there are no buckles to fall back upon; but it is worse still in a great company to become aware that wife and mother-in-law are talking nonsense and that one cannot depend upon oneself for a happy piece of wit to carry off the stupidity of the thing.

The young married pair often sat hand in hand, he speaking and she letting fall a word here and there – the same melody, the same two or three tones of the bell. It was a mental relief when Sophy, one of her friends, came to pay a visit.

Sophy was not pretty. She was certainly free from bodily deformity, though Kala always asserted she was a little crooked; but no eye save a friend's would have remarked it. She was a very sensible girl, and it never occurred to her that she might become at all dangerous here. Her appearance was like a pleasant breath of air in the doll's house; and air was certainly required there, as they all acknowledged. They felt they wanted airing, and consequently they came out into the air, and mamma-in-law and the young couple travelled to Italy.

'Thank Heaven that we are in our own four walls again,' was the exclamation of mother and daughter when they came home a year after.

'There's no pleasure in travelling,' said mamma-in-law. 'To tell the truth, it's very wearisome – I beg pardon for saying so. I found the time hang heavily, although I had my children with me; and it's expensive work, travelling, very expensive! And all those galleries one has to see, and the quantity of things you are obliged to run after! You must do it for decency's sake, for you're sure to be asked when you come back; and then you're sure to be told that you've omitted to see what was best worth seeing. I got tired at last of those endless Madonnas: one seemed to be turning a Madonna oneself!'

'And what bad living you get!' said Kala.

'Yes,' replied mamma, 'no such thing as an honest meat soup. It's miserable trash, their cookery.'

And the travelling fatigued Kala: she was always fatigued, that was the worst of it. Sophy was taken into the house, and she did good there.

Mamma-in-law acknowledged that Sophy understood both house-wifery and art, though a knowledge of the latter could not be expected from a person of her limited means; and she was, moreover, an honest, faithful girl: she showed that thoroughly while Kala lay ill – fading away.

Where the case is everything, the case should be strong, or else all is over. And all *was* over with the case – Kala died.

'She was beautiful,' said mamma; 'she was quite different from the antiques, for they are so damaged. Kala was whole, and a beauty should be whole.'

Alfred wept, and mamma wept, and both of them wore mourning. The black dress suited mamma very well, and she wore mourning the longest. Moreover, she had soon to experience another grief in seeing Alfred marry again – marry Sophy, who had no appearance at all.

'He's gone to the very extreme,' cried mamma-in-law; 'he has gone from the most beautiful to the ugliest, and has forgotten his first wife. Men have no constancy. My husband was of a different stamp, and he died before me.'

'Pygmalion received his Galatea,' said Alfred: 'yes, that's what they said in the wedding song. I had once really fallen in love with the beautiful statue, which awoke to life in my arms; but the kindred soul which Heaven sends down to us, the angel who can feel and sympathise with and elevate us, I have not found and won till now. You came, Sophy, not in the glory of outward beauty, though you are fair, fairer than is needful. The chief thing remains the chief. You came to teach the sculptor that his work is but clay and dust, only an outward form in a fabric that passes away, and that we must seek the essence, the eternal spirit. Poor Kala! ours was but wayfarers' life. Yonder, where we shall know each other by sympathy, we shall be half strangers.'

'That was not lovingly spoken,' said Sophy, 'not spoken like a true Christian. Yonder, where there is no giving in marriage, but where, as you say, souls attract each other by sympathy; there where everything beautiful develops itself and is elevated, her soul may acquire such completeness that it may sound more harmoniously than mine; and you will then once more utter the first rapturous exclamation of your love, "Beautiful – most beautiful!" '

A Story from the Sand-Dunes

THIS IS a story from the sand-dunes of Jutland; though it does not begin in Jutland, but far away in the south, in Spain. The ocean is the high road between the nations – transport thyself thither in thought to Spain. There it is warm and beautiful, there the fiery pomegranate blossoms flourish among the dark laurels; from the mountains a cool refreshing wind blows down, upon, and over the orange gardens, over the gorgeous Moorish halls with their golden cupolas and coloured walls: through the streets go children in procession, with candles and with waving flags, and over them, lofty and clear, rises the sky with its gleaming stars. There is a sound of song and of castanets, and youths and maidens join in the dance under the blooming acacias, while the beggar sits upon the hewn marble stone, refreshing himself with the juicy melon, and dreamily enjoying life. The whole is like a glorious dream. And there was a newly married couple who completely gave themselves up to its charm; moreover, they possessed the good things of this life, health and cheerfulness of soul, riches and honour.

'We are as happy as it is possible to be,' exclaimed the young couple, from the depths of their hearts. They had indeed but one step more to mount in the ladder of happiness in the hope that God would give them a child – a son like them in form and in spirit.

The happy child would be welcomed with rejoicing, would be tended with all care and love, and enjoy every advantage that wealth and ease possessed by an influential family could give.

And the days went by like a glad festival.

'Life is a gracious gift of Providence, an almost inappreciable gift!' said the young wife, 'and yet they tell us that fullness of joy is found only in the future life, for ever and ever. I cannot compass the thought.'

'And perhaps the thought arises from the arrogance of men,' said the husband. 'It seems a great pride to believe that we shall live for ever, that we shall be as gods. Were these not the words of the serpent, the origin of falsehood?'

'Surely you do not doubt the future life?' exclaimed the young wife; and it seemed as if one of the first shadows flitted over the sunny heaven of her thoughts.

'Faith promises it, and the priests tell us so!' replied the man; 'but amid all my happiness, I feel that it is arrogance to demand a continued happiness, another life after this. Has not so much been given us in this state of existence, that we ought to be, that we *must* be, contented with it?'

'Yes, it has been given to *us*,' said the young wife, 'but to how many thousands is not this life one scene of hard trial? How many have been thrown into this world, as if only to suffer poverty and shame and sickness and misfortune? If there were no life after this, everything on earth would be too unequally distributed, and the Almighty would not be justice itself.'

'Yonder beggar,' replied the man, 'has his joys which are just as great for him as the King has in his rich palace. And then, do you not think that the beast of burden, which suffers blows and hunger, and works itself to death, suffers from its heavy fate? It might likewise demand a future life, and declare the decree unjust that does not admit it into a higher place of creation.'

'He has said, "In my Father's house are many mansions," ' replied the young wife: 'heaven is immeasurable, as the love of our Maker is immeasurable. Even the dumb beast is His creature; and I firmly believe that no life will be lost, but that each will receive that amount of happiness which he can enjoy, and which is sufficient for him.'

'This world is sufficient for me!' said the man, and he threw his arms round his beautiful, amiable wife, and then smoked his cigarette on the open balcony, where the cool air was filled with the fragrance of oranges and pinks. The sound of music and the clatter of castanets came up from the road, the stars gleamed above, and two eyes full of affection, the eyes of his wife, looked on him with the undying glance of love.

'Such a moment,' he said, 'makes it worth while to be born, to enjoy, and to disappear!' and he smiled.

The young wife raised her hand in mild reproach, and the shadow passed away from her world, and they were happy – quite happy.

Everything seemed to work together for them. They advanced in honour, in prosperity, and in joy. There was a change, indeed, but only a change of place; not in enjoyment of life and of happiness. The young man was sent by his sovereign as ambassador to the Court of Russia. This was an honourable office, and his birth and his acquirements gave him a title to be thus honoured. He possessed a great fortune, and his wife had brought him wealth equal to his own, for she was the daughter of a rich and respected merchant. One of this merchant's largest and finest ships was to be dispatched during that year to Stockholm, and it was arranged that the dear young people, the daughter and the son-in-law, should travel in it to St Petersburg. And all the arrangements on board were princely – rich carpets for the feet, and silk and luxury on all sides.

There is an old ballad, which every Dane knows – it is called, 'The King's Son of England.' He also sailed in a gallant ship, and the anchor was gilded with ruddy gold, and each rope was woven through with silk.

And this ship one must think of on seeing the one from Spain, for here was the same pomp, and the same parting thought arose – the thought:

> God grant that we all in joy
> Once more may meet again.

And the wind blew fairly seaward from the Spanish shore, and the parting was to be but a brief one, for in a few weeks the voyagers would reach their destination; but when they came out upon the high seas, the wind sank, the sea became calm and shining, the stars of heaven gleamed brightly, and they were festive evenings that were spent in the sumptuous cabin.

At length the voyagers began to wish for wind, for a favouring breeze; but the breeze would not blow, or, if it did arise, it was contrary. Thus weeks passed away, two full months; and then at last the fair wind blew – it blew from the south-west. The ship sailed on the high seas between Scotland and Jutland, and the wind increased just as in the old song of 'The King's Son of England'.

And it blew a storm, and the clouds were dark,
And they found neither land nor shelter,
Then forth they threw their anchor so true,
But the wind blew them east towards Denmark.

This all happened a long, long while ago. King Christian VII then sat on the Danish throne, and he was still a young man. Much has happened since that time, much has changed or has been changed. Sea and moorland have been converted into green meadows, heath has become arable land, and in the shelter of the West Jute huts grow apple trees and rose bushes, though they certainly require to be sought for, as they bend beneath the sharp west wind. In Western Jutland one may go back in thought to the old times, farther back than the days when Christian VII bore rule. As it did then, in Jutland, the brown heath now also extends for miles, with its 'Grave-mounds', its mirages, and its crossing, sandy, uneven roads; westward, where large rivulets run into the bays, extend marshes and meadow land, girdled with lofty sand-hills, which, like a row of Alps raise their peaked summits towards the ocean, only broken by the high clayey ridges, from which the waves year by year bite out huge mouthfuls, so that the impending shores fall down as if by the shock of an earthquake. Thus it is there today, and thus it was many, many years ago, when the happy pair were sailing in the gorgeous ship.

It was in the last days of September, a Sunday, and sunny weather; the chiming of the church bells in the Bay of Nissum was wafted along like a chain of sounds. The churches there are erected almost entirely of hewn boulder stones, each like a piece of rock; the North Sea might foam over them, and they would not be overthrown. Most of them are without steeples, and the bells are hung between two beams in the open air. The service was over, and the congregation thronged out into the churchyard, where then, as now, not a tree nor a bush was to be seen; not a single flower had been planted there, nor had a wreath been laid upon the graves. Rough mounds show where the dead have been buried, and rank grass, tossed by the wind, grows thickly over the whole churchyard. Here and there a grave had a monument to show, in the shape of a half-decayed block of wood rudely shaped into the form of a coffin, the said block having been brought from the forest of West Jutland; but the forest of West Jutland is the wild sea itself, where the inhabitants find the hewn beams and planks and fragments which the breakers cast ashore. The wind and the sea fog soon destroy the wood. One of these blocks had been placed on a child's grave, and one of the women, who had come out of the church, stepped towards it. She stood still, and let her glance rest on the discoloured memorial. A few moments afterwards her husband stepped up to her. Neither of them spoke a word, but he took her hand, and they wandered across the brown heath, over moor and meadow, towards the sand-hills; for a long time they thus walked silently.

'That was a good sermon today,' the man said at length. 'If we had not God to look to, we should have nothing!'

'Yes,' observed the woman, 'He sends joy and sorrow, and He has a right to send them. Tomorrow our little boy would have been five years old, if we had been allowed to keep him.'

'You will gain nothing by fretting, wife,' said the man. 'The boy is well provided for. He is there whither we pray to go.'

And they said nothing more, but went forward to their house among the sand-hills. Suddenly, in front of one of the houses, where the sea grass did not keep the sand down, there arose what appeared to be a column of smoke; it was a gust of wind which swept in among the hills, whirling the particles of sand high in the air. Another, and the strings of fish hung up to dry flapped and beat violently against the wall of the hut; and then all was still again, and the sun shone down hotly.

Man and wife stepped into the house. They had soon taken off their Sunday clothes, and then hurried away over the dunes, which stood there like huge waves of sand suddenly arrested in their course, while the sand-weeds and the dune grass with its bluish stalks spread a changing colour over them. A few neighbours came up and helped one another to draw the boats higher up on the sand. The wind blew more sharply; it was cutting and cold: and when they went back over the sand-hills, sand and little pointed stones blew into their faces. The waves reared themselves up with their white crowns of foam, and the wind cut off their crests, flinging the foam far around.

The evening came on. In the air was a swelling roar, moaning and complaining like a troop of despairing spirits, that sounded above the hoarse rolling of the sea, although the fisher's little hut was on the very margin. The sand rattled against the window-panes, and every now and then came a violent gust of wind, that shook the house to its foundations. It was dark, but towards midnight the moon would rise.

The air became clearer, but the storm swept in all its force over the perturbed sea. The fisher people had long gone to bed, but in such weather there was no chance of closing an eye. Presently there was a knocking at the window, and the door was opened, and a voice said:

'There's a great ship fast stranded on the outermost reef.'

In a moment the fisher people had sprung from their beds and hastily arrayed themselves.

The moon had risen, and it was light enough to make the surrounding objects visible to those who could open their eyes for the blinding clouds of sand. The violence of the wind was terrible, and only by creeping forward between the gusts was it possible to pass among the sandhills; and now the salt spray flew up from the sea like down, while the ocean foamed like a roaring cataract towards the beach. It required a practised eye to descry the vessel out in the offing. The vessel was a noble brig. The billows now lifted it over the reef, three or four cables' length out of the usual channel. It drove towards the land, struck against the second reef, and remained fixed.

To render assistance was impossible; the sea rolled fairly in upon the vessel, making a clean breach over her. Those on shore fancied they heard the cries for help from on board, and could plainly descry the busy useless efforts made by the stranded crew. Now a wave came rolling onward, falling like a rock upon the bowsprit and tearing it from the brig. The stern was lifted high above the flood. Two people sprang together into the sea; in a moment more, and one of the largest waves that rolled towards the sand-hills threw a body upon the shore. It was a woman, and appeared quite dead; but some women thought they discerned signs of life in her, and the stranger was carried across the sand-hills into the fisherman's hut. How beautiful and fair she was! certainly she must be a great lady. They laid her upon the humble bed that boasted not a yard of linen; but there was a woollen coverlet to wrap her in, and that would keep her warm.

Life returned to her, but she was delirious, and knew nothing of what had happened or where she was; and it was better so, for everything she loved and valued lay buried in the sea. It was with her ship as with the vessel in the song of 'The King's Son of England':

> Alas! it was a grief to see
> How the gallant ship sank speedily.

Portions of wreck and fragments of wood drifted ashore, she was the only living thing among them all. The wind still drove howling over the coast. For a few moments the strange lady seemed to rest; but she awoke in pain, and cries of anguish and fear came from her lips. She opened her wonderfully beautiful eyes, and spoke a few words, but none understood her.

And behold, as a reward for the pain and sorrow she had undergone, she held in her arms a new-born child, the child that was to have rested upon a gorgeous couch, surrounded by silken curtains, in the sumptuous home. It was to have been welcomed with joy to a life rich in all the goods of the earth; and now Providence had caused it to be born in this humble corner, and not even a kiss did it receive from its mother.

The fisher's wife laid the child upon the mother's bosom, and it rested on a heart that beat no more, for she was dead. The child who was to be nursed by wealth and fortune, was cast into the world, washed by the sea among the sand-hills, to partake the fate and heavy days of the poor. And here again comes into our mind the old song of the English King's son, in which mention is made of the customs prevalent at that time, when knights and squires plundered those who had been saved from shipwreck.

The ship had been stranded some distance south of Nissum Bay. The hard inhuman days, in which, as people say, the inhabitants of the Jutland shores did evil to the shipwrecked, were long past. Affection and sympathy and self-sacrifice for the unfortunate were to be found, as they are to be found in our own time, in many a brilliant example. The dying mother and the unfortunate child would have found succour and help wherever the wind blew them; but nowhere could they have found more earnest care than in the hut of the poor fisherwife, who had stood but yesterday, with a heavy heart, beside the grave which covered her child, which would have been five years old that day if God had spared it to her.

No one knew who the dead stranger was, or where she came from. The pieces of wreck said nothing on the subject.

To the rich house in Spain no tidings penetrated of the fate of the daughter and the son-in-law. They had not arrived at their destined port, and violent storms had raged during the past weeks. At last the verdict was given, 'Foundered at sea – all lost.'

But on the sand-hills near Husby, in the fisherman's hut, they now had a little boy.

Where Heaven sends food for two, a third can manage to make a meal, and in the depths of the sea is many a dish of fish for the hungry.

And they called the boy Jürgen.

'It must certainly be a Jewish child,' the people said, 'it looks so swarthy.'

'It might be an Italian or a Spaniard,' observed the clergyman.

But to the fisherwoman these three nations seemed the same, and she consoled herself with the idea that the child was baptised as a Christian.

The boy throve. The noble blood in his veins was warm, and he became strong on his homely fare. He grew apace in the humble house, and the Danish dialect spoken by the West Jutes became his language. The pomegranate seed from Spanish soil became a hardy plant on the coast of West Jutland. Such may be a man's fate! To this home he clung with the roots of his whole being. He was to have experience of cold and hunger, and the misfortunes and hardships that surrounded the humble, but he tasted also of the poor man's joys.

Childhood has sunny heights for all, whose memory gleams through the whole of later life. The boy had many opportunities for pleasure and play. The whole coast, for miles and miles, was full of playthings, for it was a mosaic of pebbles, red as coral, yellow as amber, and others again white and rounded like birds' eggs, and all smoothed and prepared by the sea. Even the bleached fish skeletons, the water plants dried by the wind, seaweed, white, gleaming, and long linen-like bands, waving among the stones, all these seemed made to give pleasure and amusement to the eye and the thoughts; and the boy had an intelligent mind – many and great faculties lay dormant in him. How readily he retained in his mind the stories and songs he heard, and how neat-handed he was! With stones and mussel shells he could put together pictures and ships with which one could decorate the room; and he could cut out his thoughts wonderfully on a stick, his foster-mother said, though the boy was still so young and little! His voice sounded sweetly; every melody flowed at once from his lips. Many chords were attuned in his heart which might have sounded out into the world, if he had been placed elsewhere than in the fisherman's hut by the North Sea.

One day another ship was stranded there. Among other things, a chest of rare flower bulbs floated ashore. Some were put into the cooking pots, for they were thought to be eatable, and others lay and shrivelled in the sand, but they did not accomplish their purpose or unfold the richness of colour whose germ was within them. Would it be better with Jürgen? The flower bulbs had soon played their part, but he had still years of apprenticeship before him.

Neither he nor his friends remarked in what a solitary and uniform way one day succeeded another, for there was plenty to do and to see. The sea itself was a great lesson-book, unfolding a new leaf every day, such as calm and breakers, breeze and storm. Shipwrecks were great events. The visits to the church were festal visits. But among the festal visits in the fisherman's house, one was particularly distinguished. It was repeated twice in the year, and was, in fact, the visit of the brother of Jürgen's foster-mother, the eel breeder from Fjaltring, upon the neighbourhood of the 'Bow Hill'. He used to come in a cart painted red and filled with eels. The cart was covered and locked like a box, and painted all over with blue and white tulips. It was drawn by two dun oxen, and Jürgen was allowed to guide them.

The eel breeder was a witty fellow, a merry guest, and brought a measure of brandy with him. Everyone received a small glassful or a cupful when there was a scarcity of glasses: even Jürgen had as much as a large thimbleful, that he might digest the fat eel, the eel breeder said, who always told the same story over again, and when his hearers laughed he immediately told it over again to the same audience. As, during his childhood, and even later, Jürgen used many expressions from this story of the eel breeder's, and made use of it in various ways, it is as well that we should listen to it too. Here it is:

'The eels went out in the river; and the mother-eel said to her daughters, who begged leave to go a little way up the river, "Don't go too far: the ugly eel spearer might come and snap you all up." But they went too far; and of eight daughters only three came back to the eel-mother, and these wept and said, "We only went a little way before the door, and the ugly eel spearer came directly, and stabbed our five sisters to death." "They'll come again," said the mother-eel. "Oh, no," exclaimed the daughters, "for he skinned them, and cut them in two, and fried them." "Oh, they'll come again," the mother-eel persisted. "No," replied the daughters, "for he ate them all up." "They'll come again," repeated the mother-eel. "But he drank brandy after them," continued the daughters. "Ah, then they'll never come back," said the mother, and she burst out crying, "It's the brandy that buries the eels."

'And therefore,' said the eel breeder, 'it is always right to take brandy after eating eels.'

And this story was the tinsel thread, the most humorous recollection of Jürgen's life. *He* likewise wanted to go a little way outside the door and up the river – that is to say, out into the world in a ship; and his mother said, like the eel-mother, 'There are so many bad people – eel spearers!' But he wished to go a little way past the sand-hills, a little way into the dunes; and he succeeded in doing so. Four merry days, the happiest of his childhood, unrolled themselves, and the whole beauty and splendour of Jutland, all the joy and sunshine of his home, were concentrated in these. He was to go to a festival – though it was certainly a burial feast.

A wealthy relative of the fisherman's family had died. The farm lay deep in the country, eastward, and a point towards the north, as the saying is. Jürgen's foster-parents were to go, and he was to accompany them. From the dunes across heath and moor, they came to the green meadows where the river Skaerum rolls its course, the river of many eels, where mother-eels dwell with their daughters, who are caught and eaten up by wicked people. But men were said sometimes to have acted no better towards their own fellow men; for had not the knight, Sir Bugge, been murdered by wicked people? and though he was well spoken of, had he not wanted to kill the architect, who had built for him the castle with the thick walls and tower, where Jürgen and his parents now stood, and where the river falls into the bay? The wall on the ramparts still remained, and red crumbling fragments lay strewn around. Here it was that Sir Bugge, after the architect had left him, said to one of his men, 'Go thou after him, and say, "Master, the tower leans." If he turns round, you are to kill him, and take from him the money I paid him; but if he does not turn round let him depart in peace.' The man obeyed, and the architect answered, 'The tower does not lean, but one day there will come a man from the west, in a blue cloak, who will cause it to lean!' And so it chanced, a hundred years later; for the North Sea broke in, and the tower was cast down, but the man who then possessed the castle, Prebjörn Gyldenstjerne, built a new castle higher up, at the end of the meadow, and that stands to this day, and is called Nörre Vosborg.

Past this castle went Jürgen and his foster-parents. They had told him its story during the long winter evenings, and now he saw the lordly castle, with its double moat, and trees, and bushes; the wall, covered with ferns, rose within the moat; but most beautiful of all were the lofty lime trees, which grew up to the highest windows and filled the air with sweet fragrance. In a corner of the garden towards the north-west stood a great bush full of blossom like winter snow amid the summer's green: it was an elder bush, the first that Jürgen had seen thus in bloom. He never forgot it, nor the lime tree: the child's soul treasured up these remembrances of beauty and fragrance to gladden the old man.

From Nörre Vosborg, where the elder blossomed, the way went more easily, for they encountered other guests who were also bound for the burial, and were riding in wagons. Our travellers had to sit all together on a little box at the back of the wagon, but even this was preferable to walking, they thought. So they pursued their journey in the wagon across the rugged heath. The oxen which drew the vehicle slipped every now and then, where a patch of fresh grass appeared amid the heather. The sun shone warm, and it was wonderful to behold how in the far distance something like smoke seemed to be rising; and yet this smoke was clearer than the mist; it was transparent and looked like rays of light rolling and dancing afar over the heath.

'That is Lokeman driving his sheep,' said someone; and this was enough to excite the fancy of Jürgen. It seemed to him as if they were now going to enter fairyland, though everything was still real.

How quiet it was! Far and wide the heath extended around them like a beautiful carpet. The heather bloomed and the juniper bushes and the vigorous oak sapling stood up like nosegays from the earth. An inviting place for a frolic, if it were not for the number of poisonous adders of which the travellers spoke, as they did also of the wolves which formerly infested the place, from which circumstance the region was still called the Wolfborg region. The old man who guided the oxen related how, in the lifetime of his father, the horses had to sustain many a hard fight with the wild beasts that were now extinct; and how he himself, when he went out one morning, had found one of the horses standing with its forefeet on a wolf it had killed, but the flesh was quite off the legs of the horse.

The journey over the heath and the deep sand was only too quickly accomplished. They stopped before the house of mourning, where they found plenty of guests within and without. Wagon after wagon stood ranged in a row, and horses and oxen went out to crop the scanty pasture. Great sand-hills, like those at home by the North Sea, rose behind the house and extended far and wide. How had they come here, miles into the interior of the land, and as large and high as those on the coast? The wind had lifted and carried them hither, and to them also a history was attached.

Psalms were sung, and a few of the old people shed tears; beyond this, the guests were cheerful enough, as it appeared to Jürgen, and there was plenty to eat and drink. Eels there were of the fattest, upon which brandy should be poured to bury them, as the eel breeder said; and certainly his maxim was here carried out.

Jürgen went to and fro in the house. On the third day he felt quite at home, just as in the fisherman's hut on the sand-hills where he had passed his early days. Here on the heath there was certainly an unheard-of wealth, for the flowers and blackberries and bilberries were to be found in plenty, so large and sweet, that when they were crushed beneath the tread of the passers-by, the heath was coloured with their red juice.

Here was a grave-mound, and yonder another. Columns of smoke rose into the still air: it was a heath-fire, he was told, that shone so splendidly in the dark evening.

Now came the fourth day, and the funeral festivities were to conclude, and they were to go back from the land-dunes to the sand-dunes.

'Ours are the best,' said the old fisherman, Jürgen's foster-father; 'these have no strength.'

And they spoke of the way in which the sand-dunes had come into the country, and it seemed all very intelligible.

A corpse had been found on the coast, and the peasants had buried it in the churchyard; and from that time the sand began to fly and the sea broke in violently. A wise man in the parish advised them to open the grave and to look if the buried man was not lying sucking his thumb; for if so, he was a man of the sea, and the sea would not rest until it had got him back. So the grave was opened, and he really was found with his thumb in his mouth. So they laid him upon a cart and harnessed two oxen before it; and as if stung by a gadfly, the oxen ran away with the man of the sea over heath and moorland to the ocean; and then the sand ceased flying inland, but the hills that had been heaped up still remained there. All this Jürgen heard and treasured in his memory from the happiest days of his childhood, the days of the burial feast. How glorious it was to get out into strange regions and to see strange people! And he was to go farther still. He was not yet fourteen years old when he went out in a ship to see what the world could show him: bad weather, heavy seas, malice, and hard men – these were his experiences, for he became a ship boy. There were cold nights, and bad living, and blows to be endured; then it was as if his noble Spanish blood boiled within him, and bitter wicked words seethed up to his lips; but it was better to gulp them down, though he felt as the eel must feel when it is flayed and cut up and put into the frying-pan.

'I shall come again!' said a voice within him. He saw the Spanish coast, the native land of his parents. He even saw the town where they had lived in happiness and prosperity; but he knew nothing of his home or race, and his race knew just as little about him.

The poor ship boy was not allowed to land; but on the last day of their stay he managed to get ashore. There were several purchases to be made, and he was to carry them on board.

There stood Jürgen in his shabby clothes, which looked as if they had been washed in the ditch and dried in the chimney: for the first time he, the inhabitant of the dunes, saw a great city. How lofty the houses seemed, and how full of people were the streets! some pushing this way, some that – a perfect maelstrom of citizens and peasants, monks and soldiers – a calling and shouting, and jingling of bell-harnessed asses and mules, and the church bells chiming between song and sound, hammering and knocking, all going on at once. Every handicraft had its workshop in the doorway or on the pavement; and the sun shone so hotly, and the air was so close, that one seemed to be in an oven full of beetles, cockchafers, bees, and flies, all humming and buzzing together. Jürgen hardly knew where he was or which way he went. Then he saw just in front of him the mighty portal of the cathedral; the lights were gleaming in the dark aisles, and a fragrance of incense was wafted towards him. Even the poorest beggar ventured up the steps into the temple. The sailor with whom Jürgen went took his way through the church, and Jürgen stood in the sanctuary. Coloured pictures gleamed from their golden ground. On the altar stood the figure of the Virgin with the Child Jesus, surrounded by lights and flowers; priests in festive garb were chanting, and choir boys, beautifully attired, swung the silver censer. What splendour, what magnificence did he see here! It streamed through his soul and overpowered him; the church and the faith of his parents surrounded him, and touched a chord in his soul, so that the tears overflowed his eyes.

From the church they went to the market-place. Here a quantity of provisions were given him to carry. The way to the harbour was long, and, tired, he rested for a few moments before a splendid house, with marble pillars, statues, and broad staircases. Here he leaned his burden against the wall. Then a liveried porter came out, lifted up a silver-headed cane, and drove him away – him, the grandson of the house. But no one there knew that, and he just as little as anyone. And afterwards he went on board again, and there were hard words and cuffs, little sleep and much work; such were his experiences. They say that it is well to suffer in youth, yes, when age brings something to make up for it.

His time of service had expired, and the vessel lay once more at Ringkjöbing, in Jutland: he came ashore and went home to the sand-dunes by Husby; but his foster-mother had died while he was away on his voyage

A hard winter followed that summer. Snowstorms swept over land and sea, and there was a difficulty in getting about. How variously things appeared to be distributed in the world! here biting cold and snowstorms, while in the Spanish land there was burning sunshine and oppressive heat. And yet, when here at home there came a clear frosty day, and Jürgen saw the swans flying in numbers from the sea towards the land, and across to Vosborg, it appeared to him that people could breathe most freely here; and here too was a splendid summer! In imagination he saw the heath bloom and grow purple with rich juicy berries, and saw the elder trees and the lime trees at Vosborg in full blossom. He determined to go there once more.

Spring came on, and the fishery began. Jürgen helped with this; he had grown in the last year, and was quick at work. He was full of life, he understood how to swim; to tread water, to turn over and tumble in the flood. They often warned him to beware of the shoals of mackerel which could seize the best swimmer, and draw him down and devour him; but such was not Jürgen's fate.

At the neighbour's on the dune was a boy named Martin, with whom Jürgen was very friendly, and the two took service in the same ship to Norway, and also went together to Holland; and they had never had any quarrel; but a quarrel can easily come, for when a person is hot by nature he often uses strong expressions, and that is what Jürgen did one day on board when they had a quarrel about nothing at all. They were sitting behind the cabin door, eating out of an earthenware plate which they had placed between them. Jürgen held his pocket-knife in his hand, and lifted it against Martin, and at the same time became ashy pale in the face, and his eyes had an ugly look. Martin only said, 'Ah! ha! so you're one of that sort who are fond of using the knife!'

Hardly were the words spoken when Jürgen's hand sank down. He answered not a syllable, but went on eating, and afterwards walked away to his work. When they were resting again, he stepped up to Martin, and said, 'You may hit me in the face! I have deserved it. But I feel as if I had a pot in me that boiled over.'

'There let the thing rest,' replied Martin.

And after that they were almost doubly as good friends as before; and when afterwards they got back to the dunes and began telling their adventures, this was told among the rest; and Martin said that Jürgen was certainly passionate, but a good fellow for all that.

They were both young and strong, well grown and stalwart; but Jürgen was the cleverer of the two.

In Norway the peasants go up to the mountains, and lead out the cattle there to pasture. On the west coast of Jutland, huts have been erected among the sand-hills; they are built of pieces of wreck, and roofed with turf and heather. There are sleeping-places around the walls, and here the fisher people live and sleep during the early spring. Every fisherman has his female helper, whose work consists in baiting the hooks, handing the warm beer to the fishermen when they come ashore, and getting their dinners cooked when they come back into the hut tired and hungry. Moreover, the girls bring up the fish from the boats cut them open, and have generally a great deal to do.

Jürgen, his father, and several other fishermen and their helpers inhabited the same hut; Martin lived in the next one.

One of the girls, Elsie by name, had been known to Jürgen from childhood: they got on well with each other, and in many things were of the same mind; but in outward appearance they were entirely opposite, for he was brown, whereas she was pale and had flaxen hair, and eyes as blue as the sea in sunshine.

One day as they were walking together, and Jürgen held her hand in his very firmly and warmly, she said to him, 'Jürgen, I have something weighing upon my heart! Let me be your helper, for you are like a brother to me, whereas Martin, who has engaged me – he and I are lovers; but you need not tell that to the rest.'

And it seemed to Jürgen as if the loose sand were giving way under his feet. He spoke not a word, but only nodded his head, which signified 'yes'. More was not required; but suddenly he felt in his heart that he detested Martin; and the longer he considered of this – for he had never thought of Elsie in this way before – the more did it become clear to him that Martin had stolen from him the only being he loved; and now it was all at once plain to him that Elsie was that one.

When the sea is somewhat disturbed, and the fishermen come home in their great boats, it is a sight to behold how they cross the reefs. One of the men stands upright in the bow of the boat, and the others watch him, sitting with oars in their hands. Outside the reef they appear to be rowing not towards the land, but backing out to sea, till the man standing in the boat gives them the sign that the great wave is coming which is to float them across the reef; and accordingly the boat is lifted – lifted high in the air, so that its keel is seen from the shore; and in the next minute the whole boat is hidden from the eye – neither mast nor keel nor people can be seen, as though the sea had devoured them; but in a few moments they emerge like a great sea animal climbing up the waves, and the oars move as if the creature had legs. The second and the third reef are passed in the same manner; and now the fishermen jump into the water; every wave helps them, and pushes the boat well forward, till at length they have drawn it beyond the range of the breakers.

A wrong order given in front of the reef – the slightest hesitation – and the boat must founder.

'Then it would be all over with me, and Martin too!' This thought struck Jürgen while they were out at sea, where his foster-father had been taken alarmingly ill. The fever had seized him. They were only a few oars' strokes from the reef, and Jürgen sprang from his seat and stood up in the bow.

'Father – let me come!' he said; and his eye glanced towards Martin and across the waves; but while every oar bent with the exertions of the rowers, as the great wave came towering towards them, he beheld the pale face of his father, and dared not obey the evil impulse that had seized him. The boat came safely across the reef to land, but the evil thought remained in his blood, and roused up every little fibre of bitterness which had remained in his memory since he and Martin had been comrades. But he could not weave the fibres together, nor did he endeavour to do so. He felt that Martin had despoiled him, and this was enough to make him detest his former friend. Several of the fisher-men noticed this, but not Martin, who continued to be obliging and talkative – indeed, a little too talkative.

Jürgen's adopted father had to keep his bed, which became his deathbed, for in the next week he died; and now Jürgen was installed as heir in the little house behind the sand-hills. It was but a little house, certainly, but still it was something, and Martin had nothing of the kind.

'You will not take sea service again, Jürgen?' observed one of the old fishermen. 'You will always stay with us, now.'

But this was not Jürgen's intention, for he was just thinking of looking about him a little in the world. The eel breeder of Fjaltring had an uncle in Old Skagen, who was a fisherman, but at the same time a prosperous merchant who had ships upon the sea; he was said to be a good old man, and it would not be amiss to enter his service. Old Skagen lies in the extreme north of Jutland, as far removed from the

Husby dunes as one can travel in that country; and this is just what pleased Jürgen, for he did not want to remain till the wedding of Martin and Elsie, which was to be celebrated in a few weeks.

The old fisherman asserted that it was foolish now to quit the neighbourhood, since Jürgen had a home, and Elsie would probably be inclined to take him rather than Martin.

Jürgen answered so much at random, that it was not easy to understand what he meant; but the old man brought Elsie to him, and she said, 'You have a home now; that ought to be well considered.'

And Jürgen thought of many things. The sea has heavy waves, but there are heavier waves in the human heart. Many thoughts, strong and weak, thronged through Jürgen's brain; and he said to Elsie, 'If Martin had a house like mine, whom would you rather have?'

'But Martin has no house, and cannot get one.'

'But let us suppose he had one.'

'Why, then I would certainly take Martin, for that's what my heart tells me; but one can't live upon that.'

And Jürgen thought of these things all night through. Something was working within him, he could not understand what it was, but he had a thought that was stronger than his love for Elsie; and so he went to Martin, and what he said and did there was well considered. He let the house to Martin on the most liberal terms, saying that he wished to go to sea again, because it pleased him to do so. And Elsie kissed him on the mouth when she heard that, for she loved Martin best.

In the early morning Jürgen purposed to start. On the evening before his departure when it was already growing late, he felt a wish to visit Martin once more; he started, and among the dunes the old fisher met him, who was angry at his going. The old man made jokes about Martin, and declared there must be some magic about that fellow, 'of whom all the girls were so fond.' Jürgen paid no heed to this speech, but said farewell to the old man, and went on towards the house where Martin dwelt. He heard loud talking within. Martin was not alone, and this made Jürgen waver in his determination, for he did not wish to encounter Elsie; and on second consideration, he thought it better not to hear Martin thank him again, and therefore he turned back.

On the following morning, before break of day, he fastened his knapsack, took his wooden provision-box in his hand, and went away among the sand-hills towards the coast path. That way was easier to traverse than the heavy sand road, and moreover shorter; for he intended to go in the first instance to Fjaltring, by Bowberg, where the eel breeder lived, to whom he had promised a visit.

The sea lay pure and blue before him, and mussel shells and sea pebbles, the playthings of his youth crunched under his feet. While he was thus marching on, his nose suddenly began to bleed: it was a trifling incident, but little things can have great significance. A few large drops of blood fell upon one of his sleeves. He wiped them off and stopped the bleeding, and it seemed to him as if this had cleared and lightened his brain. In the sand the sea eringo was blooming here and there. He broke off a stalk and stuck it in his hat; he determined to be merry and of good cheer, for he was going into the wide world – 'a little way out of the door and up the river,' as the young eels had said. 'Beware of bad people, who will catch you and flay you, cut you in two, and put you in the frying-pan!' he repeated in his mind, and smiled, for he thought he should find his way through the world – good courage is a strong weapon!

The sun already stood high when he approached the narrow entrance to Nissum Bay. He looked back, and saw a couple of horsemen galloping a long distance behind him, and they were accompanied by other people. But this concerned him nothing.

The ferry was on the opposite side of the bay. Jürgen called to the ferryman, and when the latter came over with the boat, Jürgen stepped in; but before they had gone halfway across, the men whom he had seen riding so hastily behind him hailed the ferryman and summoned him to return in the name of the law. Jürgen did not understand the reason of this, but he thought it would be best to turn back, and therefore himself took an oar and returned. The moment the boat touched the shore, the men sprang on board, and, before he was aware, they had bound his hands with a rope.

'Thy wicked deed will cost thee thy life,' they said. 'It is well that we caught thee.'

He was accused of nothing less than murder! Martin had been found dead, with a knife thrust through his neck. One of the fishermen had (late on the previous evening) met Jürgen going towards Martin's house; and this was not the first time Jürgen had raised his knife against Martin, they knew; so he must be the murderer, and it was necessary to get him into safe custody. The town in which the prison was built was a long way off, and the wind was contrary for going there; but not half an hour would be required to get across the bay, and a quarter of an hour would bring them from thence to Nörre Vosborg, a great building with walls and ditches. One of Jürgen's captors was a fisherman, a brother of the keeper of the castle, and he declared it might be managed that Jürgen should for the present be put into the dungeon at Vosborg, where Long Margaret the gypsy had been shut up till her execution.

No attention was paid to the defence made by Jürgen; the few drops of blood upon his shirt-sleeve bore heavy witness against him. But Jürgen was conscious of his innocence, and as there was no chance of immediately righting himself, he submitted to his fate.

The party landed just at the spot where Sir Bugge's castle had stood and where Jürgen had walked with his foster-parents after the burial feast, during the four happiest days of his childhood. He was led by the old path over the meadow to Vosborg; and again the elder blossomed and the lofty limes smelt sweet, and it seemed but yesterday that he had left the spot.

In the west wing of the castle a staircase leads down to a spot below the entrance, and from thence there is access to a low vaulted cellar. Here Long Margaret had been imprisoned, and hence she had been led away to the scaffold. She had eaten the hearts of five children, and had been under the delusion that if she could obtain two more, she would be able to fly, and to make herself invisible. In the cellar wall was a little narrow air-hole, but no window. The blooming lindens could not waft a breath of comforting fragrance into that abode, where all was dark and mouldy. Only a rough bench stood in the prison; but 'a good conscience is a soft pillow', and consequently Jürgen could sleep well.

The thick oaken door was locked, and secured on the outside by an iron bar; but the goblin of superstition can creep through a keyhole in the baron's castle just as into the fisherman's hut; and wherefore should he not creep in here, where Jürgen sat thinking of Long Margaret and her evil deeds? Her last thought on the night before her execution had filled this space; and all the magic came into Jürgen's mind which tradition asserted to have been practised there in the old times, when Sir Svanwedel dwelt there. It was well known that the watch-dog, which had its place on the drawbridge, was found every morning hanged in its own chain over the railing. All this passed through Jürgen's mind, and made him shudder; but a sunbeam from without penetrated his heart even here: it was the remembrance of the blooming elder and the fragrant lime trees

He was not left there long. They carried him off to the town of Ringkjöbing, where his imprisonment was just as hard.

Those times were not like ours. Hard measure was dealt out to the 'common' people; and it was just after the days when farms were converted into knights' estates, on which occasions coachmen and servants were often made magistrates, and had it in their power to sentence a poor man, for a small offence, to lose his property and to corporal punishment. Judges of this kind were still to be found; and in Jutland, far from the capital and from the enlightened well-meaning government, the law was still sometimes very loosely administered; and the smallest grievance that Jürgen had was that his case was protracted.

Cold and cheerless was his abode – and when would this state of things end? He had innocently sunk into misfortune and sorrow – that was his fate. He had leisure now to ponder on the difference of fortune on earth, and to wonder why this fate had been allotted to him; and he felt sure that the question would be answered in the next life – the existence that awaits us when this is over. This faith had grown strong in him in the poor fisherman's hut; that which had never shone into his father's mind, in all the richness and sunshine of Spain, was vouchsafed as a light of comfort to him in cold and darkness – a sign of mercy from God, who never deceives.

The spring storms began to blow. The rolling and moaning of the

North Sea could be heard for miles inland when the wind was lulled, for then it sounded like the rushing of a thousand wagons over a hard road with a mine beneath. Jürgen, in his prison, heard these sounds, and it was a relief to him. No melody could have appealed so directly to his heart as did these sounds of the sea – the rolling sea, the boundless sea, on which a man can be borne across the world before the wind, carrying his own house with him wherever he is driven, just as the snail carries his; one stood always on one's own ground, on the soil of home, even in a strange land.

How he listened to the deep moaning, and how the thought arose in him – 'Free! free! How happy to be free, even without shoes and in ragged clothes!' Sometimes, when such thoughts crossed his mind, the fiery nature rose within him, and he beat the wall with his clenched fists.

Weeks, months, a whole year had gone by, when a vagabond – Niels, the thief, called also the horse couper – was arrested; and now the better times came, and it was seen what wrong Jürgen had endured.

In the neighbourhood of Ringkjöbing, at a beer-house, Niels, the thief, had met Martin on the afternoon before Jürgen's departure from home and before the murder. A few glasses were drunk – not enough to cloud anyone's brain, but yet enough to loosen Martin's tongue; and he began to boast, and to say that he had obtained a house, and intended to marry; and when Niels asked where he intended to get the money, Martin slapped his pocket proudly, and said, 'The money is here, where it ought to be.'

This boast cost him his life, for when he went home, Niels went after him, and thrust a knife through his throat, to take the money from him.

This was circumstantially explained; but for us it is enough to know that Jürgen was set at liberty. But what amends did he get for having been imprisoned a whole year, and shut out from all communion with men? They told him he was fortunate in being proved innocent, and that he might go. The burgomaster gave him ten marks for travelling expenses, and many citizens offered him provisions and beer – there were still some good men, not all 'grind and flay'. But the best of all was, that the merchant Brönne of Skagen, the same into whose service Jürgen had intended to go a year since, was just at that time on business in the town of Ringkjöbing. Brönne heard the whole story; and the man had a good heart, and understood what Jürgen must have felt and suffered. He therefore made up his mind to make amends to the poor lad, and convince him that there were still kind folks in the world.

So Jürgen went forth from the prison as if to Paradise, to find freedom, affection, and trust. He was to travel this road now; for no goblet of life is all bitterness: no good man would pour out such measure to his fellow man, and how should God do it, who is love itself?

'Let all that be buried and forgotten,' said Brönne the merchant. 'Let us draw a thick line through last year; and we will even burn the calendar. And in two days we'll start for dear, friendly, peaceful Skagen. They call it an out-of-the-way corner; but it's a good warm chimney-corner, and its windows open towards every part of the world.'

That was a journey! – it was like taking fresh breath – out of the cold dungeon air into the warm sunshine! The heath stood blooming in its greatest pride, and the herd-boy sat on the grave-mound and blew his pipe, which he had carved for himself out of the sheep's bone. Fata Morgana, the beautiful aerial phenomenon of the desert, showed itself with hanging gardens and swaying forests; and the wonderful trembling of the air, called here the 'Lokeman driving his flock', was seen likewise.

Up through the land of the Wendels, up towards Skagen, they went, from whence the men with the long beards (the Longobardi, or Lombards) had emigrated in the days when, in the reign of King Snio, all the children and the old people were to have been killed, till the noble Dame Gambaruk proposed that the younger people had better leave the country. All this was known to Jürgen – thus much knowledge he had; and even if he did not know the land of the Lombards beyond the high Alps, he had an idea how it must be there, for in his boyhood he had been in the south, in Spain. He thought of the southern fruits piled up there; of the red pomegranate blossoms; of the humming, murmuring, and toiling, in the great beehive of a city he had seen; but, after all, home is best; and Jürgen's home was Denmark.

At length they reached 'Wendelskage,' as Skagen is called in the old Norwegian and Icelandic writings. Then already Old Skagen, with Vesterby and Österby, extended for miles, with sand-hills and arable land, as far as the lighthouse near the Fork of Skagen. Then, as now, houses and farms were strewn among the wind-raised sand-hills – a desert where the wind sports with the sand, and where the voices of the seamews and the wild swans strike harshly on the ear. In the south-west, a mile from the sea, lies Old Skagen; and here dwelt merchant Brönne, and here Jürgen was henceforth to dwell. The great house was painted with tar; the smaller buildings had each an overturned boat for a roof; the pigsty had been put together of pieces of wreck. There was no fence here, for indeed there was nothing to fence in; but long rows of fishes were hung upon lines, one above the other, to dry in the wind. The whole coast was strewn with spoiled herrings, for there were so many of those fish, that a net was scarcely thrown into the sea before they were caught by cartloads; there were so many, that often they were thrown back into the sea or left to lie and rot.

The old man's wife and daughter, and his servants too, came rejoicingly to meet him. There was a great pressing of hands, and talking, and questioning. And the daughter, what a lovely face and bright eyes she had!

The interior of the house was roomy and comfortable. Plates of fish were set on the table, plaice that a King would have called a splendid dish; and there was wine from the vineyard of Skagen – that is, the sea; for there the grapes come ashore ready pressed and prepared in barrels and in bottles.

When the mother and daughter heard who Jürgen was, and how innocently he had suffered, they looked at him in a still more friendly way; and the eyes of the charming Clara were the friendliest of all. Jürgen found a happy home in Old Skagen. It did his heart good; and his heart had been sorely tried, and had drunk the bitter goblet of love, which softens or hardens according to circumstances. Jürgen's heart was still soft – it was young, and there was still room in it; and therefore it was well that Clara was going in three weeks in her father's ship to Christiansand, in Norway, to visit an aunt and to stay there the whole winter.

On the Sunday before her departure they all went to church, to the Holy Communion. The church was large and handsome, and had been built centuries before by Scotchmen and Hollanders; it lay at a little distance from the town. It was certainly somewhat ruinous, and the road to it was heavy, through the deep sand; but the people gladly went through the difficulties to get to the house of God, to sing psalms and hear the sermon. The sand had heaped itself up round the walls of the church, but the graves were kept free from it.

It was the largest church north of the Limfjord. The Virgin Mary, with the golden crown on her head and the Child Jesus in her arms, stood lifelike upon the altar; the holy Apostles had been carved in the choir; and on the walls hung portraits of the old burgomasters and councillors of Skagen; the pulpit was of carved work. The sun shone brightly into the church, and its radiance fell on the polished brass chandelier and on the little ship that hung from the vaulted roof.

Jürgen felt as if overcome by a holy, childlike feeling, like that which possessed him when, as a boy, he had stood in the splendid Spanish cathedral; but here the feeling was different, for he felt conscious of being one of the congregation.

After the sermon followed the Holy Communion. He partook of the bread and wine, and it happened that he knelt beside Clara; but his thoughts were so fixed upon Heaven and the holy service, that he did not notice his neighbour until he rose from his knees, and then he saw tears rolling down her cheeks.

Two days later she left Skagen and went to Norway. He stayed behind, and made himself useful in the house and in the business. He went out fishing, and at that time fish were more plentiful than now. Every Sunday when he sat in the church, and his eye rested on the statue of the Virgin on the altar, his glance rested for a time on the spot where Clara had knelt beside him, and he thought of her, how pleasant and kind she had been to him.

And so the autumn and the winter time passed away. There was wealth here, and a real family life; even down to the domestic animals, who were all well kept. The kitchen glittered with copper and tin and white plates, and from the roof hung hams and beef and winter stores in plenty. All this is still to be seen in many rich farms of the west coast of Jutland: plenty to eat and drink, clean decorated rooms, clever heads, happy tempers, and hospitality, prevail there as in an Arab tent.

Never since the famous burial feast had Jürgen spent such a happy time; and yet Clara was absent, except in the thoughts and memory of all.

In April a ship was to start for Norway, and Jürgen was to sail in it. He was full of life and spirits, and looked so stout and jovial that Dame Brönne declared it did her good to see him.

'And it's a pleasure to see you too,' said the old merchant. 'Jürgen has brought life into our winter evenings, and into you too, mother. You look younger this year, and you seem well and bonny. But then you were once the prettiest girl in Wiborg, and that's saying a great deal, for I have always found the Wiborg girls the prettiest of any.'

Jürgen said nothing to this, but he thought of a certain maiden of Skagen; and he sailed to visit that maiden, for the ship steered to Christiansand in Norway, and a favouring wind took him there in half a day.

One morning merchant Brönne went out to the lighthouse that stands far away from Old Skagen: the coal fire had long gone out and the sun was already high when he mounted the tower. The sandbanks extend under the water a whole mile from the shore. Outside these banks many ships were seen that day; and with the help of his telescope the old man thought he descried his own vessel, the *Karen Brönne*.

Yes, surely, there she was; and the ship was sailing up with Jürgen and Clara on board. The church and the lighthouse appeared to them as a heron and a swan rising from the blue waters. Clara sat on deck, and saw the sandhills gradually looming forth: if the wind held she might reach her home in about an hour – so near were they to home and its joys – so near were they to death and its terrors. For a plank in the ship gave way, and the water rushed in. The crew flew to the pumps and attempted to stop the leak, and a signal of distress was hoisted; but they were still a full mile from the shore. Fishing-boats were in sight, but they were still far distant. The wind blew shoreward, and the tide was in their favour too; but all was insufficient, for the ship sank. Jürgen threw his right arm about Clara.

With what a look she gazed in his face! As he threw himself in God's name into the water with her, she uttered a cry; but still she felt safe, certain that he would not let her sink.

And now, in the hour of terror and danger, Jürgen experienced what the old song told:

> And written it stood, how the brave King's son
> Embraced the bride his valour had won.

How rejoiced he felt that he was a good swimmer! He worked his way onward with his feet and with one hand, while with the other he tightly held the young girl. He rested upon the waves, he trod the water, he practised all the arts he knew, so as to reserve strength enough to reach the shore. He heard how Clara uttered a sigh, and felt a convulsive shudder pass through her, and he pressed her to him closer than ever. Now and then a wave rolled over them; and he was still a few cables' length from the land, when help came in the shape of an approaching boat. But under the water – he could see it clearly – stood a white form gazing at him; a wave lifted him up, and the form approached him: he felt a shock, and it grew dark, and everything vanished from his gaze.

On the sand-reef lay the wreck of a ship, which the sea washed over; the white figure-head leaned against an anchor, the sharp iron of which extended just to the surface. Jürgen had come in contact with this, and the tide had driven him against it with double force. He sank down fainting with his load, but the next wave lifted him and the young girl aloft again.

The fishermen grasped them and lifted them into the boat. The blood streamed down over Jürgen's face; he seemed dead, but he still clutched the girl so tightly that they were obliged to loosen her by force from his grasp. And Clara lay pale and lifeless in the boat, that now made for the shore.

All means were tried to restore Clara to life; but she was dead! For some time he had been swimming onward with a corpse, and had exerted himself to exhaustion for one who was dead.

Jürgen was still breathing. The fishermen carried him into the nearest house upon the sand-hills. A kind of surgeon who lived there, and who was at the same time a smith and a general dealer, bound up Jürgen's wounds, till a physician could be got next day from the nearest town.

The brain of the sick man was affected. In delirium he uttered wild cries; but on the third day he lay quiet and exhausted on his couch, and his life seemed to hang by a thread, and the physician said it would be best if this string snapped.

'Let us pray that God may take him to Himself; he will never be a sane man again!'

But life would not depart from him – the thread would not snap; but the thread of memory broke: the thread of all his mental power had been cut through; and, what was most terrible, a body remained – a living healthy body.

Jürgen remained in the house of the merchant Brönne.

'He contracted his illness in his endeavour to save our child,' said the old man, 'and now he is our son.'

People called Jürgen imbecile; but that was not the right expression. He was like an instrument in which the strings are loose and will sound no more; only at times for a few minutes they regained their power, and then they sounded anew: old melodies were heard, snatches of song; pictures unrolled themselves, and then disappeared again in the mist, and once more he sat staring before him, without a thought. We may believe that he did not suffer, but his dark eyes lost their brightness, and looked only like black clouded glass.

'Poor imbecile Jürgen!' said the people.

He it was whose life was to have been so pleasant that it would be 'presumption and pride' to expect or believe in a higher existence hereafter. All his great mental faculties had been lost; only hard days, pain, and disappointment had been his lot. He was like a rare plant torn from its native soil, and thrown upon the sand, to wither there.

And was the image, fashioned in God's likeness, to have no better destination? Was it to be merely the sport of chance? No. The all-loving God would certainly repay him, in the life to come, for what he had suffered and lost here. 'The Lord is good to all, and His mercy is over all His works.' These words from the Psalms of David, the old pious wife of the merchant repeated in patience and hope, and the prayer of her heart was that Jürgen might soon be summoned to enter into the life eternal.

In the churchyard where the sand blows across the walls, Clara lay buried. It seemed as if Jürgen knew nothing of this – it did not come within the compass of his thoughts, which comprised only fragments of a past time. Every Sunday he went with the old people to church, and sat silent there with vacant gaze. One day, while the Psalms were being sung, he uttered a deep sigh, and his eyes gleamed: they were fixed upon the altar, upon the place where he had knelt with his friend who was dead. He uttered her name, and became pale as death, and tears rolled over his cheeks.

They led him out of the church, and he said to the bystanders that he was well, and had never been ill: he, the heavily afflicted, the waif cast upon the world, remembered nothing of his sufferings. And the Lord our Creator is wise and full of loving-kindness – who can doubt it? Our heart and our understanding acknowledge it, and the Bible confirms it: 'His mercy is over all His works.'

In Spain, where the warm breezes blow over the Moorish cupolas, among the orange trees and laurels, where song and the sound of castanets are heard, sat in the sumptuous house a childless old man, the richest merchant in the place, while children marched in procession through the streets, with waving flags and lighted tapers. How much of his wealth would the old man not have given to have his children again! his daughter, or her child, that had perhaps never seen the light in this world.

'Poor child!'

Yes, poor child – a child still, and yet more than thirty years old; for to that age Jürgen had attained in Old Skagen.

The drifting sand had covered the graves in the churchyard quite up to the walls of the church; but yet the dead must be buried among their relations and loved ones who had gone before them. Merchant Brönne and his wife now rested here with their children, under the white sand.

It was spring-time, the season of storms. The sand-hills whirled up in clouds, and the sea ran high, and flocks of birds flew like clouds in the storms, shrieking across the dunes; and shipwreck followed shipwreck on the reefs from Skagen as far as the Husby dunes. One evening Jürgen was sitting alone in the room. Suddenly his mind seemed to become clearer, and a feeling of unrest came upon him, which in his younger years had often driven him forth upon the heath and the sand-hills.

'Home! home!' he exclaimed.

No one heard him. He went out of the house towards the dunes. Sand and stones blew into his face and whirled around him. He went on towards the church: the sand lay high around the walls, half over the windows, but the heap had been shovelled away from the door, and the entrance was free and easy to open; and Jürgen went into the church.

The storm went howling over the town of Skagen. Within the memory of man no one could remember such a terrible tempest! but Jürgen was in the temple of God, and while black night reigned without, a light arose in his soul, a light that was never to be extinguished; he felt the heavy stone which seemed to weigh upon his head burst asunder. He thought he heard the sound of the organ, but it was the storm and the roaring of the sea. He sat down on one of the seats; and behold, the candles were lighted up one by one; a richness was displayed such as he had seen only in the church in Spain; and all the pictures of the old councillors were endued with life, and stepped forth from the walls against which they had stood for centuries, and seated themselves in the choir. The gates and doors flew open, and in came all the dead people, festively clad, and sat down to the sound of beautiful music, and filled the seats in the church. Then the psalm tune rolled forth like a sounding sea; and his old foster-parents from the Husby dunes were here, and the old merchant Brönne and his wife; and at their side, close to Jürgen, sat their friendly, lovely daughter

Clara, who gave her hand to Jürgen, and they both went to the altar, where they had once knelt together, and the priest joined their hands and knit them together for life. Then the sound of music was heard again, wonderful, like a child's voice full of joy and expectation, and it swelled on to an organ's sound, to a tempest of full, noble sounds, lovely and elevating to hear, and yet strong enough to burst the stone tombs.

And the little ship that hung down from the roof of the choir came down, and became wonderfully large and beautiful, with silken sails and golden yards, the anchors were of red gold, 'and every rope wrought through with silk,' as the old song said. The married pair went on board, and the whole congregation with them, for there was room and joyfulness for all. And the walls and arches of the church bloomed like the elder and the fragrant lime trees, and the leaves and branches waved and distributed coolness; then they bent and parted, and the ship sailed through the midst of them, through the sea, and through the air; and every church taper became a star, and the wind sang a psalm tune, and all sang with the wind:

'In love, to glory – no life shall be lost. Full of blessedness and joy. Hallelujah!'

And these words were the last that Jürgen spoke in this world. The thread snapped that bound the immortal soul, and nothing but a dead body lay in the dark church, around which the storm raged, covering it with loose sand.

The next morning was Sunday, and the congregation and their pastor came to the service. The road to church had been heavy; the sand made the way almost impassable; and now, when they at last reached their goal, a great hill of sand was piled up before the entrance, and the church itself was buried. The priest spoke a short prayer, and said that God had closed the door of this house, and the congregation must go and build a new one for Him elsewhere.

So they sang a psalm, and went back to their homes.

Jürgen was nowhere to be found in the town of Skagen, or in the dunes, however much they sought for him. It was thought that the waves, which had rolled far up on the sand, had swept him away.

His body lay buried in a great sepulchre, in the church itself. In the storm the Lord's hand had thrown earth on his coffin; and the heavy mound of sand lay upon it, and lies there to this day.

The whirling sand had covered the high vaulted passages; white-thorn and wild rose trees grow over the church, over which the wanderer now walks; while the tower, standing forth like a gigantic tombstone over a grave, is to be seen for miles around: no King has a more splendid tombstone. No one disturbs the rest of the dead; no one knew of this before now: the storm sang the tale to me among the sand-hills.

The Puppet Showman

ON BOARD the steamer was an elderly man with such a merry face that, if it did not belie him, he must have been the happiest fellow in creation. And, indeed, he declared he was the happiest man; I heard it out of his own mouth. He was a Dane, a countryman of mine, and a travelling theatre director. He had all his company with him in a large box, for he was proprietor of a puppet-show. His inborn cheerfulness, he said, had been *purified* by a Polytechnic candidate, and the experiment had made him completely happy. I did not at first understand all this, but afterwards he explained the whole story to me, and here it is:

'It was in the little town of Slagelse I gave a performance in the hall of the post-house, and had a brilliant audience, entirely a juvenile one, with the exception of two old ladies. All at once a person in black, of student-like appearance, came into the room and sat down; he laughed aloud at the telling parts, and applauded quite appropriately. That was quite an unusual spectator for me! I felt anxious to know who he was, and I heard he was a candidate from the Polytechnic Institution in Copenhagen, who had been sent out to instruct the folks in the provinces. At eight o'clock my performance closed; for children must go early to bed, and a manager must consult the convenience of his public. At nine o'clock the candidate commenced his lecture, with experiments, and now I formed part of *his* audience. It was wonderful to hear and to see. The greater part of it went over my head and into the clergyman's, as one says; but still it made me think that if we men can find out so much, we must be surely intended to last longer than the little span until we are hidden away in the earth. They were quite miracles in a small way that he showed, and yet altogether genuine, straight out of nature! At the time of Moses and the prophets such a man would have been received among the sages of the land; in the

Middle Ages they would have burned him at a stake. All night long I could not go to sleep. And the next evening, when I gave another performance, and the candidate was again present, I felt fairly overflowing with humour. I once heard from a player that when he acted a lover he always thought of one particular lady among the audience; he only played for her, and forgot all the rest of the house; and now the Polytechnic candidate was my "she," my only spectator, for whom alone I played. And when the performance was over, all the puppets were called before the curtain, and the Polytechnic candidate invited me into his room to take a glass of wine; and he spoke of my comedies, and I of his science; and I believe we were both equally pleased. But I had the best of it, for there was much in what he did of which he could not always give me an explanation. For instance, that a piece of iron that falls through a spiral should become magnetic. Now, how does that happen? The spirit comes upon it; but whence does it come? It is as with people in this world; they are made to tumble through the spiral of the time, and the spirit comes upon them, and there stands a Napoleon, or a Luther, or a person of that kind. "The whole world is a series of miracles," said the candidate; "but we are so accustomed to them that we call them everyday matters." And he went on explaining things to me until my skull seemed lifted up over my brain, and I declared that if I were not an old fellow I would at once go to the Polytechnic Institution, that I might learn to look at the seamy side of the world, though I am one of the happiest of men. "One of the happiest!" said the candidate, and he seemed to take real pleasure in it. "Are you happy?" "Yes," I replied, 'and they welcome me in all the towns where I come with my company; but I certainly have *one* wish, which sometimes comes over me, like a nightmare, and rides upon my good humour: I should like to become a real theatrical manager, the director of a real troupe of men and women!" "I see," he said, "you would like to have life breathed into your puppets, so that they might be real actors, and you their director; and would you then be quite happy?" He did not believe it; but I believed it, and we talked it over all manner of ways without coming any nearer to an agreement; but we clinked our glasses together, and the wine was excellent. There was

some magic in it, or I should certainly have become tipsy. But that did
not happen; I retained my clear view of things, and somehow there was
sunshine in the room, and sunshine beamed out of the eyes of the
Polytechnic candidate. It made me think of the old gods, in their
eternal youth, when they still wandered upon earth; and I said so to
him, and he smiled, and I could have sworn he was one of the ancient
gods in disguise, or one of the family! and certainly he must have been
something of the kind, for my highest wish was to be fulfilled, the
puppets were to be gifted with life, and I was to be director of a real
company. We drank to my success and clinked our glasses. He packed
all my dolls into a box, bound the box on my back, and then let me fall
through a spiral. I can still hear how I dumped down, and then I was
lying on the floor – I know that quite well – and the whole company
sprang out of the box. The spirit had come upon all of us: all the
puppets had become distinguished artists, so they said themselves, and
I was the director. All was ready for the first performance; the whole
company wanted to speak to me, and the public also. The dancing lady
said the house would fall down if she did not stand on one leg; for she
was the great genius, and begged to be treated as such. The lady who
acted the queen wished to be treated off the stage as a queen, or else
she should get out of practice. The man who was only employed to
deliver a letter gave himself just as many airs as the first lover, for he
declared the little ones were just as important as the great ones, and all
were of equal consequence, considered in an artistic whole. The hero
would only play parts composed of nothing but points; for those
brought down the applause. The prima donna would only play in a red
light; for she declared that a blue one did not suit her complexion. It
was like a company of flies in a bottle; and I was in the bottle with
them, for I was the director. My breath stopped and my head whirled
round; I was as miserable as a man can be. It was quite a novel kind of
men among whom I now found myself. I only wished I had them all in
the box again, and that I had never been a director at all; so I told them
roundly that after all they were nothing but puppets; and then they
killed me. I found myself lying on my bed in my room; and how I got
there, and how I got away at all from the Polytechnic candidate, he

may perhaps know, for I don't. The moon shone upon the floor where the box lay open, and the dolls all in a confusion together – great and small all scattered about; but I was not slow. Out of bed I jumped, and into the box they all had to go, some on their heads, some on their feet, and I shut down the lid and seated myself upon the box. "Now you'll just have to stay there," said I, "and I shall beware how I wish you flesh and blood again." I felt quite light; my good humour had come back, and I was the happiest of mortals. The Polytechnic student had fully purified me. I sat as happy as a king, and went to sleep on the box. The next morning – strictly speaking it was noon, for I slept wonderfully late that day – I was still sitting there, happy and conscious that my former wish had been a foolish one. I enquired for the Polytechnic candidate, but he was gone, like the Greek and Roman gods; and from that time I've been the happiest of men. I am a happy director: none of my company ever grumble, nor my public either, for they are always merry. I can put my pieces together just as I please. I take out of every comedy what pleases me best, and no one is angry at it. Pieces that are neglected nowadays at the great theatres, but which the public used to run after thirty years ago, and at which it used to cry till the tears ran down its cheeks, these pieces I now take up: I put them before the little ones, and the little ones cry just as papa and mamma used to cry; but I shorten them, for the youngsters don't like a long palaver of a love story; what they want is something mournful, but quick. Now I have travelled through all Denmark in every manner of way; I know all people and am known in return; now I am on my way to Sweden, and if I am successful there, and make money out of it, I shall be a zealous Scandinavian – not otherwise; I tell you that because you are my countryman.'

And I, being his countryman, of course immediately tell it again, just for the pleasure of telling it.

Two Brothers

ON ONE of the Danish islands where the old places of assembly are found in the fields, and great trees tower in the beech woods, there lies a little town, whose low houses are covered with red tiles. In one of these houses wondrous things were brewed over glowing coals on the open hearth; there was a boiling in glasses, a mixing and a distilling, and herbs were being bruised in mortars, and an elderly man attended to all this.

'One must only do the right thing,' said he; 'yes, the right thing. One must learn the truth about every created particle, and keep close to this truth.'

In the room with the good housewife sat her two sons, still small, but with grown-up thoughts. The mother had always spoken to them of right and justice, and had exhorted them to hold truth fast, declaring that it was as the countenance of the Almighty in this world.

The elder of the boys looked roguish and enterprising. It was his delight to read of the forces of nature, of the sun and of the stars; no fairy tale pleased him so much as these. Oh! how glorious it must be, to go out on voyages of discovery, or to find out how the wings of birds could be imitated, and then to fly through the air! yes, to find that out would be the right thing: father was right, and mother was right – truth keeps the world together.

The younger brother was quieter, and quite lost himself in books. When he read of Jacob clothing himself in sheepskins, to be like Esau and to cheat his brother of his birthright, his little fist would clench in anger against the deceiver: when he read of tyrants, and of all the wickedness and wrong that is in the world, the tears stood in his eyes, and he was quite filled with the thoughts of the right and truth which must and will at last be triumphant. One evening he already lay in bed, but the curtains were not yet drawn close, and the light streamed in upon him: he had taken the book with him to bed, because he wanted to finish reading the story of Solon.

And his thoughts lifted and carried him away marvellously, and it seemed to him that his bed became a ship, under full sail. Did he dream? or what was happening to him? It glided onward over the rolling waters and the great ocean of time, and he heard the voice of Solon. In a strange tongue, and yet intelligible to him, he heard the Danish motto, 'With law the land is ruled.'

And the Genius of the human race stood in the humble room, and bent down over the bed, and printed a kiss on the boy's forehead.

'Be thou strong in fame, and strong in the battle of life! With the truth in thy breast, fly thou towards the land of truth!'

The elder brother was not yet in bed; he stood at the window gazing out at the mists that rose from the meadows. They were not elves dancing there, as the old nurse had told him; he knew better: they were vapours, warmer than the air, and consequently they mounted. A shooting star gleamed athwart the sky, and the thoughts of the boy were roused from the mists of the earth to the shining meteor. The stars of heaven twinkled, and golden threads seemed to hang from them down upon the earth.

'Fly with me!' it sang and sounded in the boy's heart; and the mighty genius, swifter than the bird, than the arrow, than anything that flies with earthly means, carried him out into space where rays stretching from star to star bind the heavenly bodies to each other; our earth revolved in the thin air; its cities seemed quite close together; and through the sphere it sounded, 'What is near, what is far to men, when the mighty genius of mind lifts them up?'

And again the boy stood at the window and gazed forth, and the younger brother lay in his bed, and their mother called them by their names, 'Anders' and 'Hans Christian.'

Denmark knows them, and the world knows the two brothers – Oersted.

The Old Church Bell

I N THE German land of Würtemberg, where the acacias bloom by the high road, and the apple trees and pear trees bend in autumn under their burden of ripe fruit, lies the little town of Marbach. Although this place can only be ranked among the smaller towns, it is charmingly situated on the Neckar stream, that flows on and on, hurrying past villages and old castles and green vineyards, to pour its waters into the proud Rhine.

It was late in autumn. The leaves still clung to the grape-vine, but they were already tinged with red. Rain showers fell, and the cold wind increased. It was no pleasant time for poor folk.

The days became dark, and it was darker still in the little old-fashioned houses. One of these houses was built with its gable end towards the street, with low windows, humble and poor enough in appearance; the family was poor, too, that inhabited the little house, but good and industrious, and rich in piety, in the treasury of the heart. And they expected that God would soon give them another child: the hour had come, and the mother lay in pain and sorrow. Then from the church tower the deep rich sound of the bell came to her. It was a solemn hour, and the sound of the bell filled the heart of the praying woman with trustfulness and faith; the thoughts of her inmost heart soared upward towards the Almighty, and in the same hour she gave birth to a son. Then she was filled with a great joy, and the bell in the tower seemed to be ringing to spread the news of her happiness over town and country. The clear child-eyes looked at her, and the infant's hair gleamed like gold. Thus was the little one ushered into the world with the ringing of the church bell on the dark November day. The mother and father kissed it, and wrote in their Bible: 'On the 10th of November, 1759, God gave us a son;' and soon afterwards the fact was added that the child had been baptised under the name of 'Johann Christoph Friedrich'.

And what became of the little fellow, the poor boy from the little town of Marbach? Ah, at that time no one knew what would become of him, not even the old church bell that had sung at his birth, hanging so high in the tower, over him who was one day himself to sing the beautiful 'Lay of the Bell'.

Well, the boy grew older, and the world grew older with him. His parents removed to another town, but they had left dear friends in little Marbach; and therefore it was that mother and son one day went there on a visit. The lad was only six years old, but he already knew many things out of the Bible, and many a pious psalm; and many an evening he had sat on his little stool, listening while his father read aloud from 'Gellert's Fables', and the poem about the Messiah; and he and his sister, who was his senior by two years, had wept hot tears of pity for Him who died on the cross to redeem us all.

At the time of this first visit to Marbach the little town had not greatly changed; and indeed they had not long left it. The houses stood, as before, with their pointed gables, projecting walls, and low windows; but there were new graves in the churchyard; and there, in the grass, hard by the wall, lay the old bell. It had fallen from its position, and had received a crack and could ring no more, and accordingly a new bell had been put in its place.

Mother and son went into the churchyard. They stopped where the old bell lay, and the mother told the boy how for centuries this had been a very useful bell, and had rung at christenings, at weddings, and at burials; how it had spoken about feasts and rejoicings, and alarms of fire; and how it had, in fact, sung the whole life of man. And the boy never forgot what his mother told him. It echoed in his heart, until, when he was grown a man, he was compelled to sing it. The mother told him also how the bell had rung of joy and comfort to her in the time of her peril, that it had rung and sung at the time when he, her little son, was born. And the boy gazed, almost with a feeling of devotion, at the great old bell; and he bent over it and kissed it, as it lay all rusty and broken among the long grass and nettles.

The old bell was held in remembrance by the boy, who grew up in poverty, tall and thin, with reddish hair and freckled face; yes, that's how he looked; but he had a pair of eyes, clear and deep as the deepest water. And what fortune had he? Why, good fortune, enviable fortune. We find him graciously received into the military school, and even in the department where sons of people in society were taught, and that was honour and fortune. He went about with boots, a stiff collar, and a powdered wig, and they educated him to the words of command, 'Halt! march! front!' and on such a system much might be expected.

The old church bell would no doubt find its way into the melting furnace, and what would become of it then? It was impossible to say, and equally impossible to tell what would come from the bell within that young heart; but that bell was of bronze, and kept sounding so loud that it must at last be heard out in the wide world; and the more cramped the space within the school walls, and the more deafening the shout of 'March! halt! front!' the louder did the sound ring through the youth's breast; and he sang it in the circle of his companions, and the sound was heard beyond the boundaries of the land. But it was not for this he had got his schooling, board, and clothing. Had he not been already numbered and destined to be a certain wheel in the great watchwork to which we all belong as pieces of practical machinery? How imperfectly do we understand ourselves! and how, then, shall others, even the best men, understand us? But it is the pressure that forms the precious stone. There was pressure enough here; but would the world be able, someday, to recognise the jewel?

In the capital of the prince of the country, a great festival was being celebrated. Thousands of lamps gleamed, and rockets glittered. The splendour of that day yet lives through him, who was trying in sorrow and tears to escape unperceived from the land: he was compelled to leave all – mother, native country, those he loved – or perish in the stream of commonplace things.

The old bell was well off; it stood sheltered beside the church-wall of Marbach. The wind whistled over it, and might have told about him at whose birth the bell had sounded, and over whom the wind had but now blown cold in the forest of a neighbouring land, where he had sunk down, exhausted by fatigue, with his whole wealth, his only hope for the future, the written pages of his tragedy 'Fiesco': the wind might have told of the youth's only patrons, men who were artists, and who yet slunk away to amuse themselves at skittles while his play was being read: the wind could have told of the pale fugitive, who lived for weary weeks and months in the wretched tavern, where the host brawled and drank, and coarse merriment was going on while he sang of the ideal. Heavy days, dark days! The heart must suffer and endure for itself the trials it is to sing.

Dark days and cold nights also passed over the old bell. It did not feel them, but the bell within the heart of man is affected by gloomy times. How fared it with the young man? How fared it with the old bell? The bell was carried far away, farther than its sound could have been heard from the lofty tower in which it had once hung. And the youth? The bell in his heart sounded farther than his eye should ever see or his foot should ever wander; it sounded and is sounding on, over the ocean, round the whole earth. But let us first speak of the belfry bell. It was carried away from Marbach, was sold for old metal, and destined for the melting furnace in Bavaria. But when and how did this happen? Well, the bell itself must tell about that, if it can; it is not a matter of great importance, but certain it is that it came to the capital of Bavaria; many years had passed since the bell had fallen from the tower, and now it was to be melted down, to be used in the manufacture of a memorial in honour of one of the great ones of the German people and land. And behold how suitable this was – how strangely and wonderfully things happen in the world! In Denmark, on one of those green islands where the beech tree grows, and the many grave-mounds are to be seen, there was quite a poor boy. He had been accustomed to walk about in wooden shoes, and to carry a dinner wrapped in an old handkerchief to his father, who carved figure-heads on the shipbuilders' wharves; but this poor lad had become the pride of his country. He carved marble blocks into such glorious shapes as made the whole world wonder, and to him had been awarded the honourable commission that he should fashion of clay a noble form that was to be cast in bronze – a statue of him whose name the father in Marbach had inscribed in the old Bible as Johann Christoph Friedrich.

And the glowing metal flowed into the mould. The old church bell –

of whose home and of whose vanished sounds no one thought – the bell flowed into the mould, and formed the head and bust of the figure that was soon to be unveiled, which now stands in Stuttgart, before the old palace – a representation of him who once walked to and fro there, striving and suffering, harassed by the world without – he, the boy of Marbach, the pupil of the 'Karlschule', the fugitive, Germany's great immortal poet, who sang of the liberator of Switzerland and of the Heaven-inspired Maid of Orleans.

It was a beautiful sunny day; flags were waving from roofs and steeples in the royal city of Stuttgart; the bells rang for joy and festivity; one bell alone was silent, but it gleamed in another form in the bright sunshine – it gleamed from the head and breast of the statue of honour. On that day, exactly one hundred years had elapsed since the day on which the bell at Marbach had rung comfort and peace to the suffering mother, when she bore her son, in poverty, in the humble cottage – him who was afterwards to become the rich man, whose treasures enriched the world, the poet who sang of the noble virtues of woman, who sang of all that was great and glorious – Johann Christoph Friedrich Schiller.

Twelve by the Mail

I T WAS bitterly cold; the sky gleamed with stars, and not a breeze was stirring.

Bump! an old pot was thrown at the neighbours' house doors. Bang! bang! went the gun; for they were welcoming the New Year. It was New Year's Eve! The church clock was striking twelve!

Tan–ta–ra–ra! the mail came in. The great carriage stopped at the gate of the town. There were twelve persons in it; all the places were taken.

'Hurrah! hurrah!' sang the people in the houses of the town, for the New Year was being welcomed, and they had just risen with the filled glass in their hand, to drink success to the new year.

'Happy New Year!' was the cry. 'A pretty wife, plenty of money, and no sorrow or care!'

This wish was passed round, and then glasses were clashed together till they rang again, and in front of the town gate the post-carriage stopped with the strange guests, the twelve travellers.

And who were these strangers? Each of them had his passport and his luggage with him; they even brought presents for me and for you and for all the people of the little town. Who are they? What did they want? and what did they bring with them?

'Good-morning!' they cried to the sentry at the town gate.

'Good-morning!' replied the sentry, for the clock struck twelve.

'Your name and profession?' the sentry enquired of the one who alighted first from the carriage.

'See yourself, in the passport,' replied the man. 'I am myself!' And a capital fellow he looked, arrayed in a bearskin and fur boots. 'I am the man on whom many persons fix their hopes. Come to me tomorrow, and I'll give you a New Year's present. I throw pence and dollars among the people, I even give balls, thirty-one balls; but I cannot devote more than thirty-one nights to this. My ships are frozen in, but in my office it is warm and comfortable. I'm a merchant. My name is January, and I only carry accounts with me.'

Now the second alighted. He was a merry companion; he was a theatre director, manager of the masque balls, and all the amusements one can imagine. His luggage consisted of a great tub.

'We'll knock more than the cat out of the tub at the Shrovetide sports,' said he. 'I'll prepare a merry tune for you and for myself too. I have the shortest lifetime of my whole family, for I only become twenty-eight. Sometimes they pop me in an extra day, but I trouble myself very little about that. Hurrah!'

'You must not shout so!' said the sentry.

'Certainly, I may shout!' retorted the man. 'I'm Prince Carnival, travelling under the name of February!'

The third now got out. He looked like Fasting itself, but carried his nose very high, for he was related to the 'Forty Knights', and was a weather prophet. But that's not a profitable office, and that's why he praised fasting. In his buttonhole he had a little bunch of violets, but they were very small.

'March! March!' the fourth called after him, and slapped him on the shoulder. 'Into the guardroom; there is punch! I can smell it.'

But it was not true; he only wanted to make an April fool of him; for with that the fourth began his career in the town. He looked very jovial, did little work, but had the more holidays.

'Up and down it goes with one's humour!' said he; 'now rain, now sunshine. I am a kind of house and office-letting agent, also a manager of funerals. I can both laugh and cry, according to circumstances. Here in this box I have my summer wardrobe, but it would be very foolish to put it on. Here I am now! On Sundays I go out walking in shoes and silk stockings, and with a muff!'

After him, a lady came out of the carriage. She called herself Miss May. She wore a summer costume and overshoes, a light green dress, and anemones in her hair, and she was so scented with woodruff that the sentry had to sneeze.

'God bless you!' she said, and that was her salutation.

How pretty she was! and she was a singer, not a theatre singer, but a singer of the woods, for she roamed through the gay green forest, and sang there for her own amusement.

'Now comes the young dame!' said those in the carriage.

And the young dame stepped out, delicate, proud, and pretty. It was easy to see that she was Mistress June, accustomed to be served by drowsy marmots. She gave a great feast on the longest day of the year, that the guests might have time to partake of the many dishes at her table. She, indeed, kept her own carriage; but still she travelled in the mail with the rest, because she wanted to show that she was not high-minded. But she was not without protection; her elder brother July was with her.

He was a plump young fellow, clad in summer garments, and with a Panama hat. He had but little baggage with him, because it was cumbersome in the great heat; therefore he had only swimming-drawers, and those are not much.

Then came the mother herself, Madam August, wholesale dealer in fruit, proprietress of a large number of fishponds, and land cultivator, in a great crinoline; she was fat and hot, could use her hands well, and would herself carry out beer to the workmen in the fields.

'In the sweat of thy face shalt thou eat bread,' said she: 'that is written in the Book. Afterwards one can have dancing in the greenwood, and the harvest feasts!'

She was a thorough housewife.

After her, a man came out of the coach, a painter, Mr Master-colourer. The forest had to receive him; the leaves were to change their colours, but how beautifully! when he wished it; soon the wood gleamed with red, yellow, and brown. The master whistled like the black magpie, was a quick workman, and wound the brown green hop plants round his beer-jug. That was an ornament for the jug, and he had a good idea of ornament. There he stood with his colour pot, and that was his whole luggage.

A landed proprietor followed him, one who cared for the ploughing and preparing of the land, and also for field sports. He brought his dog and his gun with him, and had nuts in his game-bag. 'Crack! crack!' He had much baggage, even an English plough; and he spoke of farming, but one could scarcely hear what he said, for the coughing and gasping of his neighbour.

It was November who came. He was very much plagued by a cold, a violent cold, so that he used a sheet and not a pocket-handkerchief, and yet, he said, he was obliged to accompany the servant girls to their new winter places. He said he should get rid of his cold when he went out woodcutting, and had to saw and split wood, for he was master-sawyer to the firewood guild. He spent his evenings cutting the wooden soles for skates, for he knew, he said, that in a few weeks there would be occasion to use these amusing shoes.

At length appeared the last passenger, the old Mother with her fire-stool. The old lady was cold, but her eyes glistened like two bright stars. She carried a flowerpot with a little fir tree.

'This tree I will guard and cherish, that it may grow large by Christmas Eve, and may reach from the ground to the ceiling, and may rear itself upward with flaming candles, golden apples, and little carved figures. The fire-stool warms like a stove. I bring the story-book out of my pocket and read aloud, so that all the children in the room become quite quiet; but the little figures on the trees become lively, and the little waxen angel on the top spreads out his wings of gold leaf, flies down from his green perch, and kisses great and small in the room, yes, even the poor children who stand outside, singing the carol about the Star of Bethlehem.'

'Well, now the coach may drive away!' said the sentry: 'we have the whole twelve. Let a new chaise drive up.'

'First let all the twelve come in to me,' said the captain on duty, 'one after the other. The passports I will keep here. Each of them is available for a month; when that has passed, I shall write their behaviour on each passport. Mr January, have the goodness to come here.'

And Mr January stepped forward.

When a year is passed I think I shall be able to tell you what the twelve have brought to me, and to you, and to all of us. Now I do not know it, and they don't know it themselves, probably, for we live in strange times.

The Beetle

THE EMPEROR'S horse was shod with gold. It had a golden shoe on each of its feet.

And why was this?

He was a beautiful creature, with delicate legs, bright intelligent eyes, and a mane that hung down over his neck like a veil. He had carried his master through the fire and smoke of battle, and heard the bullets whistling around him, had kicked, bitten, and taken part in the fight when the enemy advanced, and had sprung with his master on his back over the fallen enemy's horse, and had saved the crown of red gold, and the life of the Emperor, which was more valuable than the red gold; and that is why the Emperor's horse had golden shoes.

And a Beetle came creeping forth.

'First the great ones,' said he, 'and then the little ones; but it's not size that does it.' And so saying, he stretched out his thin legs.

'What do you want?' asked the smith.

'Golden shoes,' replied the Beetle.

'Why, you must be out of your senses,' cried the smith. 'Do you want to have golden shoes too?'

'Golden shoes!' said the Beetle. 'Am I not just as good as that big creature, that is waited on, and brushed, and has meat and drink put before him? Don't I belong to the imperial stable?'

'But *why* is the horse to have golden shoes? Don't you understand that?' asked the smith.

'Understand? I understand that it is a slight to me,' cried the Beetle. 'It is an insult, and therefore I am now going into the wide world.'

'Go along!' said the smith.

'You're a rude fellow!' cried the Beetle; and then he went out of the stable, flew a little way, and soon afterwards found himself in a beautiful flower garden, all fragrant with roses and lavender.

'Is it not beautiful here?' asked one of the little Ladybirds that flew
about, with black spots on their red shield-like wings. 'How sweet it
smells here – how beautiful it is!'

'I'm accustomed to better things,' said the Beetle. 'Do you call *this*
beautiful? Why, there is not so much as a dung-heap.'

Then he went on, under the shadow of a great stock, and found a
Caterpillar crawling along.

'How beautiful the world is!' said the Caterpillar: 'the sun is so
warm, and everything so enjoyable! And when I go to sleep, and die, as
they call it, I shall wake up as a butterfly.'

'How conceited you are!' exclaimed the Beetle. '*You* fly about as a
butterfly, indeed! I've come out of the stable of the Emperor, and no
one there, not even the Emperor's favourite horse, that wears my cast-

off golden shoes, has any such idea. To have wings to fly! why, we can fly now;' and he spread his wings and flew away. 'I don't want to be annoyed, and yet I am annoyed,' he said, as he flew off.

Soon afterwards he fell down upon a great lawn. Here he lay for a little, and then he fell asleep.

Suddenly a heavy shower of rain came falling from the clouds. The Beetle woke up at the noise, and wanted to escape into the earth, but could not. He was tumbled over and over: sometimes he was swimming on his stomach, sometimes on his back, and as for flying, that was out of the question; he doubted whether he should escape from the place with his life. He therefore remained lying where he was.

When the weather had moderated a little, and the Beetle had blinked the water out of his eyes, he saw something white. It was linen that had been placed there to bleach. He managed to make his way up to it, and crept into a fold of the damp linen. Certainly the place was not so comfortable to lie in as the warm stable; but there was no better to be had, and therefore he remained lying there for a whole day and a whole night, and the rain kept on during all the time. Towards morning he crept forth: he was very much out of temper because of the climate.

On the linen two Frogs were sitting. Their bright eyes absolutely gleamed with pleasure.

'Wonderful weather this!' one of them cried. 'How refreshing! And the linen keeps the water together so beautifully. My hind legs seem to quiver as if I were going to swim.'

'I should like to know,' said the second, 'if the swallow, who flies so far round in her many journeys in foreign lands, ever meets with a better climate than this. What delicious dampness! It is really as if one were lying in a wet ditch. Whoever does not rejoice in this, certainly does not love his fatherland.'

'Have you then never been in the Emperor's stable?' asked the Beetle; 'there the dampness is warm and refreshing. That's the climate for me; but I cannot take it with me on my journey. Is there never a muck-heap, here in the garden, where a person of rank, like myself, can feel himself at home, and take up his quarters?'

But the Frogs either did not or would not understand him.

'I never ask a question twice!' said the Beetle, after he had already asked this one three times without receiving any answer.

Then he went a little farther, and stumbled against a fragment of pottery, that certainly ought not to have been lying there; but since it was there, it gave a good shelter against wind and weather. Here dwelt several families of Earwigs; and these did not require much house-room, but only companionship. The females are specially gifted with maternal affection, and accordingly each one considered her own child the most beautiful and cleverest of all.

'Our son has engaged himself,' said one mother. 'Dear, innocent boy! His greatest hope is that he may creep one day into a clergyman's ear. That is very artless and lovable; and being engaged will keep him steady. What joy for a mother!'

'Our son,' said another mother, 'had scarcely crept out of the egg, when he was already off on his travels. He's all life and spirits; he'll run his horns off! What joy that is for a mother! Is it not so, Mr Beetle?' for she knew the stranger by his shape.

'You are both quite right,' said he; so they begged him to walk in; that is to say, to come as far as he could under the bit of pottery.

'Now, you also see *my* little earwig,' observed a third mother and a fourth; 'they are lovely little things, and highly amusing. They are never ill-behaved, except when they are uncomfortable in their inside; but one is very subject to that at their age.'

Thus each mother spoke about her young ones; and the young ones also talked, and made use of the little nippers they have in their tails to nip the beard of the Beetle.

'Yes, they are always busy about something, the little rogues!' said the mothers; and they quite beamed with maternal pride; but the Beetle felt bored by it all, and therefore he enquired how far it was to the nearest muck-heap.

'That is quite out in the big world, on the other side of the ditch,' answered an Earwig. 'I hope none of my children will go so far away, for it would be the death of me.'

'But I shall try to get so far,' said the Beetle; and he went off without taking formal leave; for that is considered the polite thing to do. And by the ditch he met several friends; Beetles, all of them.

'Here we live,' they said. 'We are very comfortable here. Might we ask you to step down into this rich mud? You must be fatigued after your journey.'

'Certainly,' replied the Beetle. 'I have been exposed to the rain, and have had to lie upon linen, and cleanliness is a thing that greatly exhausts me. I have also pains in one of my wings, from standing in a draught under a fragment of pottery. It is really quite refreshing to be among one's companions once more.'

'Perhaps you come from a muck-heap?' observed the oldest of them.

'From higher up,' replied the Beetle. 'I come from the Emperor's stable, where I was born with golden shoes on my feet. I am travelling on a secret embassy. You must not ask any questions, for I may tell you nothing.'

With this the Beetle stepped down into the rich mud. There sat three young maiden Beetles; and they tittered, because they did not know what to say.

'Not one of them is engaged yet,' said their mother; and the Beetle maidens tittered again, this time from embarrassment.

'I have never seen greater beauties in the royal stables,' exclaimed the travelling Beetle.

'Don't spoil my girls,' said the mother; 'and don't talk to them, please, unless you have serious intentions. But of course your intentions are serious, and therefore I give you my blessing.'

'Hurrah!' cried all the other Beetles together; and our friend was engaged. Immediately after the betrothal came the marriage, for there was no reason for delay.

The following day passed very pleasantly, and the next in tolerable comfort; but on the third it was time to think of food for the wife, and perhaps also for children.

'I have allowed myself to be taken in,' said our Beetle to himself. 'So I must just take *them* in, in turn.'

So said, so done. Away he went, and he stayed away all day, and stayed away all night; and his wife sat there, a forsaken widow.

'Oh,' said the other Beetles, 'this fellow whom we received into our family is nothing more than a thorough vagabond. He has gone away, and has left his wife a burden upon our hands.'

'Well, then, she shall be unmarried again, and sit here among my daughters,' said the mother. 'Fie on the villain who forsook her!'

In the meantime the Beetle had been journeying on, and had sailed across the ditch on a cabbage leaf. In the morning two persons came to the ditch. When they saw him, they took him up, and turned him over and over; they were very learned, especially one of them – a boy.

'Allah sees the black beetle in the black stone and in the black rock. Is not that written in the Koran?' Then he translated the Beetle's name into Latin, and enlarged upon the creature's nature and history. The older scholar voted against carrying him home. He said they had just as good specimens; and this seemed an uncivil speech to our Beetle, and in consequence he flew suddenly out of the speaker's hand. As he had now dry wings, he flew a considerable distance, and reached a hothouse, where a sash of the glass roof was partly open, so he quietly slipped in and buried himself in the warm earth.

'Very comfortable it is here,' said he.

Soon after he went to sleep, and dreamed that the Emperor's horse had fallen, and that Mr Beetle had got its golden shoes, with the promise that he should have two more.

That was all very charming. When the Beetle woke up, he crept forth and looked around him. What splendour was in the hothouse! Great palm trees growing up on high; the sun made them look transparent; and beneath them what a luxuriance of green, and of beaming flowers, red as fire, yellow as amber, or white as fresh-fallen snow!

'This is an incomparable show of plants,' cried the Beetle. 'How good they will taste when they are decayed! A capital store-room this! There must certainly be relations of mine living here. I will just see if I can find anyone with whom I may associate. I'm proud, certainly, and I'm proud of being so.'

And so he prowled about in the earth, and thought what a pleasant dream that was about the dead horse, and the golden shoes he had inherited.

Suddenly a hand seized the Beetle, and pressed him, and turned him round and round.

The gardener's little son and a companion were in the hothouse, had espied the Beetle, and wanted to have their fun with him. First he was wrapped in a vine leaf, and then put into a warm trousers-pocket. He crept and crawled; but he got a good pressing from the boy's hand for this. Then the boy went rapidly towards the great lake that lay at the end of the garden. Here the Beetle was put in an old broken wooden shoe, on which a little stick was placed upright for a mast, and to this mast the Beetle was bound with a woollen thread. Now he was a sailor, and had to sail away.

The lake was very large, to the Beetle it seemed an ocean; and he was so astonished, that he fell over on his back and kicked out with his legs.

The little ship sailed away. The current of the water seized it; but whenever it went too far from the shore, one of the boys turned up his trousers and went in after it, and brought it back to the land. But at length, just as it went merrily out again, the two boys were called away, and very urgently, so that they hurried away, and left the wooden shoe to its fate. Thus it drove away from the shore, farther and farther into the open sea: it was terrible work for the Beetle, for he could not get away, in consequence of being bound to the mast.

Then a Fly came and paid him a visit.

'What beautiful weather!' said the Fly. 'I'll rest here, and sun myself. You have an agreeable time of it.'

'You speak according to your intelligence,' replied the Beetle. 'Don't you see that I'm a prisoner?'

'Ah! but I'm not a prisoner,' observed the Fly; and he flew away accordingly.

'Well, now I know the world,' said the Beetle to himself. 'It is an abominable world. I'm the only honest person in it. First, they refuse me my golden shoes; then I have to lie on wet linen, and to stand in the draught; and, to crown all, they fasten a wife upon me. Then, when I've taken a quick step out into the world, and found out how one can have it there, and how I wished to have it, one of those human whelps comes and ties me up, and leaves me to the mercy of the wild waves, while the Emperor's horse prances about proudly in golden shoes. That is what annoys me more than all. But one must not look for sympathy in this world! My career has been very interesting; but what's the use of that, if nobody knows it? The world does not deserve to know it either, otherwise it would have given me golden shoes, in the Emperor's stable, when his favourite horse stretched out its legs and was shod. If I had received golden shoes, I should have become an ornament to the stable. Now the stable has lost me, and the world has lost me. It is all over!'

But all was not over yet. There came a boat, with some young girls.

'There sails a wooden shoe,' said one of the girls.

'There's a little creature bound fast to it,' said another.

The boat came quite close to our Beetle's ship, and the young girls fished him out of the water. One of them drew a small pair of scissors from her pocket, and cut the woollen thread, without hurting the Beetle; and when she stepped on shore, she put him down on the grass.

'Creep, creep – fly, fly – if thou canst,' she said. 'Liberty is a splendid thing.'

And the Beetle flew up, and straight through the open window of a great building; there he sank down, tired and exhausted, exactly on the fine, soft, long mane of the Emperor's favourite horse, who stood in the stable where he and the Beetle had their home. The Beetle clung fast to the mane, and sat there a short time to recover himself.

'Here I'm sitting on the Emperor's favourite horse – sitting like a knight!' he cried. 'What is that I am saying? Now it becomes clear to me. That's a good thought, and quite correct. The smith asked me why the golden shoes were given to the horse. Now I'm quite clear about the answer. They were given to the horse on *my* account.'

And now the Beetle was in a good temper again.

'One becomes clear-headed by travelling,' said he.

The sun shone very beautifully upon him.

'The world is not so bad, upon the whole,' said the Beetle; 'but one must just know how to take it.' The world was beautiful, for the Emperor's horse had got golden shoes, because the Beetle was to be its rider.

'Now I shall go down to the other beetles and tell them how much has been done for me. I shall tell them about all the advantages I have enjoyed in my foreign travels; and I shall say, that now I am going to stay at home until the horse has worn out his golden shoes.'

What the Old Man does is Right

I WILL TELL you a story which was told to me when I was a little boy. Every time I thought of the story, it seemed to me to become more and more charming; for it is with stories as it is with many people – they become better as they grow older.

I take it for granted that you have been in the country, and seen a very old farmhouse with a thatched roof, and mosses and small plants growing wild upon the thatch. There is a stork's nest on the summit of the gable; for we can't do without the stork. The walls of the house are sloping, and the windows are low, and only one of the latter is made so that it will open. The baking-oven sticks out of the wall like a little fat body. The elder tree hangs over the paling, where there is a little pool of water with a duck or ducklings, right under the gnarled willow tree. There is a yard dog too, who barks at all comers.

Just such a farmhouse stood out in the country; and in this house dwelt an old couple – a peasant and his wife. Small as was their property, there was one article among it that they could do without – a horse, which made a living out of the grass it found by the side of the high road. The old peasant rode into the town on this horse; and often his neighbours borrowed it from him, and rendered the old couple some service in return for the loan of it. But they thought it would be best if they sold the horse, or exchanged it for something that might be more useful to them. But what might this *something* be?

'You'll know that best, old man,' said the wife. 'It is fair-day today, so ride into town, and get rid of the horse for money, or make a good exchange: whichever you do will be right to me. Ride off to the fair.'

And she fastened his neckerchief for him, for she could do that better than he could; and she tied it in a double bow, for she could do that very prettily. Then she brushed his hat round and round with the palm of her hand, and gave him a kiss. So he rode away upon the horse that was to be sold or to be bartered for something else. Yes, the old man knew what he was about.

The sun shone hot, and not a cloud was to be seen in the sky. The road was very dusty, for many people who were all bound for the fair were driving, or riding, or walking upon it. There was no shelter anywhere from the sunbeams.

Among the rest, a man was trudging along, and driving a cow to the fair. The cow was as beautiful a creature as any cow can be.

'She gives good milk, I'm sure,' said the peasant. 'That would be a very good exchange – the cow for the horse.'

'Hallo, you there with the cow!' he said. 'Shall we two not talk a little together? I tell you what – I fancy a horse costs more than a cow, but I don't mind that; a cow would be more useful to me. If you like, we'll exchange.'

'To be sure I will,' said the man; and they exchanged accordingly.

So that was settled, and the peasant might have turned back, for he had done the business he came to do; but as he had once made up his mind to go to the fair, he determined to proceed, merely to have a look at it; and so he went on to the town with his cow.

Leading the animal, he strode sturdily on; and after a short time, he overtook a man who was driving a sheep. It was a good fat sheep, with a fine fleece on its back.

'I should like to have that fellow,' said our peasant to himself. 'He would find plenty of grass by our palings, and in the winter we could keep him in the room with us. Perhaps it would be more practical to have a sheep instead of a cow. Shall we exchange?'

The man with the sheep was quite ready, and the bargain was struck. So our peasant went on in the high road with his sheep.

Beside a stile he saw another man, carrying a great goose under his arm.

'That's a heavy thing you have there. It has plenty of feathers and plenty of fat, and would look well tied to a string, and paddling in the water at our place. That would be something for my old woman to collect peelings for. How often she has said, "If we only had a goose!" Now she can have one; and it shall be hers. Shall we exchange? I'll give you my sheep for your goose, and thank you into the bargain.'

The other man had not the least objection; and accordingly they exchanged, and our peasant got the goose.

By this time he was very near the town. The crowd on the high road became greater and greater; there was quite a crush of men and cattle. They walked in the road, and close by the ditch; and at the barrier they even walked into the toll-man's potato-field, where his own fowl was strutting about with a string to its leg, lest it should take fright at the crowd, and stray away, and so be lost. This fowl had short tail-feathers, and winked with both its eyes, and looked very well. 'Cluck, cluck!' said the fowl. What it thought when it said this I cannot tell you; but directly our good man saw it, he thought, 'That's the finest fowl I've ever seen in my life! Why, it's finer than our parson's brood hen. On my word, I should like to have that fowl. A fowl can always find a grain or two, and can almost keep itself. I think it would be a good exchange if I could get that for my goose.'

'Shall we exchange?' he asked the toll-taker.

'Exchange!' repeated the man; 'well, that would not be a bad thing.'

And so they exchanged; the toll-man at the barrier kept the goose, and the peasant carried away the fowl.

Now, he had done a good deal of business on his way to the fair, and he was hot and tired. He wanted something to eat, and a glass of brandy to drink; and soon he was in front of the inn. He was just about to step in, when the ostler came out, so they met at the door. The ostler was carrying a sack.

'What have you in that sack?' asked the peasant.

'Rotten apples,' answered the ostler; 'a whole sackful for the pigs.'

'Why, that's a terrible quantity! I should like my old woman at home to see that sight. Last year the old tree by the turf-house only bore a single apple, and we kept it in the cupboard till it was quite rotten and spoiled. "It was always property," my old woman said; but here she could see a quantity of property. Yes, I shall be glad to show them to her.'

'What will you give me for the sackful?' asked the ostler.

'What will I give? I will give my fowl in exchange.

And he gave the fowl accordingly, and received the apples, which he carried into the guest-room. He leaned the sack carefully by the stove, and then went to the table. But the stove was hot: he had not thought of that. Many guests were present – horse-dealers, cattle-dealers, and two Englishmen – and they are so rich that their pockets are bursting with gold coins; and they could bet, too, as you shall hear.

Hiss-s-s! hiss-s-s! What was that by the stove? The apples were beginning to roast!

'What is that?'

Well, they soon got to know that, and the whole story of the horse that he had changed for a cow, and all the rest of it, down to the apples.

'Well, your old woman will give it you well when you get home!' said one of the two Englishmen. 'There will be a disturbance.'

'I will get a kiss and not a pounding,' said the peasant. 'My wife will say, "What the old man does is always right." '

'Shall we wager?' said the Englishman. 'We'll wager coined gold by the bushel – a hundred pounds to the hundredweight!'

'A bushel will be enough,' replied the peasant. 'I can only set the bushel of apples against it; and I'll throw myself and my old woman into the bargain – and I fancy that's piling up the measure.'

'Done – taken!'

And the bet was made. The host's carriage came up, and the Englishmen got in, and the peasant got in; away they went, and soon they stopped before the peasant's hut.

'Good-evening, old woman.'

'Good-evening, old man.'

'I've made the exchange.'

'Yes, you understand what you're about,' said the woman.

And she embraced him, and forgot both the sack and the strangers.

'I got a cow in exchange for the horse,' said he.

'Heaven be thanked for the milk!' said she. 'Now we shall have milk-food, and butter and cheese on the table! That was a most capital exchange!'

'Yes, but I changed the cow for a sheep.'

'Ah, that's better still!' cried the wife. 'You always think of everything:

we have just pasture enough for a sheep. Ewe's milk and cheese, and woollen jackets and stockings! The cow cannot give those, and her hairs will only come off. How you think of everything!'

'But I changed away the sheep for a goose.'

'Then this year we shall really have a Martinmas goose to eat, my dear old man. You are always thinking of something to give me pleasure. How charming that is! We can let the goose walk about with a string to her leg, and she'll grow fatter still before Martinmas.'

But I gave away the goose for a fowl,' said the man.

'A fowl? That *was* a good exchange!' replied the woman. 'The fowl will lay eggs and hatch them, and we shall have chickens: we shall have a whole poultry-yard! Oh, that's just what I was wishing for.'

'Yes, but I exchanged the fowl for a sack of rotten apples.'

'What! I must positively kiss you for that,' exclaimed the wife. 'My dear, good husband! Now I'll tell you something. Do you know, you

had hardly left me this morning before I began thinking how I could give you something very nice this evening. I thought it should be pancakes with savoury herbs. I had the eggs; but I wanted herbs. So I went over to the schoolmaster's – they have herbs there, I know – but the schoolmistress is a mean woman. I begged her to lend me a handful of herbs. "Lend!" she answered me; "nothing at all grows in our garden, not even a rotten apple. I could not even lend you that." But now *I* can lend *her* ten, or a whole sackful; that makes me laugh!' And with that she gave him a sounding kiss.

'I like that!' exclaimed both the Englishmen together. 'Always going downhill, and always merry; that's worth the money.'

So they paid a hundredweight of gold to the peasant, who was not scolded, but kissed.

Yes, it always pays, when the wife sees and always asserts that her husband knows best, and that whatever he does is right.

You see, that is my story. I heard it when I was a child; and now you have heard it too, and know that 'What the old man does is always right'.

The Snow Man

'IT'S SO beautifully cold that my whole body crackles!' said the Snow Man. 'This is a kind of wind that can blow life into one; and how the gleaming one up yonder is staring at me.' He meant the sun, which was just about to set. 'It shall not make *me* wink – I shall manage to keep the pieces.'

He had two triangular pieces of tile in his head instead of eyes. His mouth was made of an old rake, and consequently was furnished with teeth.

He had been born amid the joyous shouts of the boys, and welcomed by the sound of sledge bells and the slashing of whips.

The sun went down, and the full moon rose, round, large, clear, and beautiful in the blue air.

'There it comes again from the other side,' said the Snow Man. He intended to say the sun is showing himself again. 'Ah! I have cured him of staring. Now let him hang up there and shine, that I may see myself. If I only knew how I could manage to move from this place, I should like so much to move. If I could, I would slide along yonder on the ice, just as I see the boys slide; but I don't know how to run.'

'Off! Off!' barked the old Yard Dog. He was somewhat hoarse. He had got the hoarseness from the time when he was an indoor dog, and lay by the fire. 'The sun will teach you to run! I saw that last winter in your predecessor, and before that in *his* predecessor. Off! Off! and they all go.'

'I don't understand you, comrade,' said the Snow Man. 'That thing up yonder is to teach me to run?' He meant the moon. 'Yes, it was running itself, when I looked hard at it a little while ago, and now it comes creeping from the other side.'

'You know nothing at all,' retorted the Yard Dog. 'But then you've only just been patched up. What you see yonder is the moon, and the one that went before was the sun. It will come again tomorrow, and will teach you to run down into the ditch by the wall. We shall soon have a change of weather; I can feel that in my left hind leg, for it pricks and pains me: the weather is going to change.'

'I don't understand him,' said the Snow Man; 'but I have a feeling that he's talking about something disagreeable. The one who stared so just now, and whom he called the sun, is not my friend. I can feel that.'

'Off! Off!' barked the Yard Dog; and he turned round three times, and then crept into his kennel to sleep.

The weather really changed. Towards morning, a thick damp fog lay over the whole region; later there came a wind, an icy wind. The cold seemed quite to seize upon one; but when the sun rose, what splendour! Trees and bushes were covered with hoar-frost, and looked like a complete forest of coral, and every twig seemed covered with gleaming white buds. The many delicate ramifications, concealed in summer by the wreath of leaves, now made their appearance: it seemed like a lacework, gleaming white. A snowy radiance sprang from every twig. The birch waved in the wind – it had life, like the trees in summer. It was wonderfully beautiful. And when the sun shone, how it all gleamed and sparkled, as if diamond dust had been strewn everywhere, and big diamonds had been dropped on the snowy carpet of the earth! or one could imagine that countless little lights were gleaming, whiter than even the snow itself.

'That is wonderfully beautiful,' said a young girl, who came with a young man into the garden. They both stood still near the Snow Man, and contemplated the glittering trees. 'Summer cannot show a more beautiful sight,' said she; and her eyes sparkled.

'And we can't have such a fellow as this in summer-time,' replied the young man, and he pointed to the Snow Man. 'He is capital.'

The girl laughed, nodded at the Snow Man, and then danced away over the snow with her friend – over the snow that cracked and crackled under her tread as if she were walking on starch.

'Who were those two?' the Snow Man enquired of the Yard Dog. 'You've been longer in the yard than I. Do you know them?'

'Of course I know them,' replied the Yard Dog. 'She has stroked

me, and he has thrown me a meat bone. I don't bite those two.'

'But what are they?' asked the Snow Man.

'Lovers!' replied the Yard Dog. 'They will go to live in the same kennel, and gnaw at the same bone. Off! Off!'

'Are they of as much consequence as you and I?' asked the Snow Man.

'Why, they belong to the master,' retorted the Yard Dog. 'People certainly know very little who were only born yesterday. I can see that in you. I have age and information. I know everyone here in the house, and I know a time when I did not lie out here in the cold, fastened to a chain. Off! Off!'

'The cold is charming,' said the Snow Man. 'Tell me, tell me. But you must not clank with your chain, for it jars within me when you do that.'

'Off! Off!' barked the Yard Dog. 'They told me I was a pretty little fellow: then I used to lie in a chair covered with velvet, up in master's house, and sit in the lap of the mistress of all. They used to kiss my nose, and wipe my paws with an embroidered handkerchief. I was called "Ami – dear Ami – sweet Ami". But afterwards I grew too big for them, and they gave me away to the housekeeper. So I came to live in the basement story. You can look into that from where you are standing, and you can see into the room where I was master; for I was master at the housekeeper's. It was certainly a smaller place than up-stairs, but I was more comfortable, and was not continually taken hold of and pulled about by children as I had been. I received just as good food as ever, and much more. I had my own cushion, and there was a stove, the finest thing in the world at this season. I went under the stove, and could lie down quite beneath it. Ah! I still dream of that stove. Off! Off!'

'Does a stove look so beautiful?' asked the Snow Man. 'Is it at all like me?'

'It's just the reverse of you. It's as black as a crow, and has a long neck and a brazen drum. It eats firewood, so that the fire spurts out of its mouth. One must keep at its side, or under it, and there one is very comfortable. You can see it through the window from where you stand.'

And the Snow Man looked and saw a bright polished thing with a brazen drum, and the fire gleamed from the lower part of it. The Snow Man felt quite strangely: an odd emotion came over him, he knew not what it meant, and could not account for it; but all people who are not snow men know the feeling.

'And why did you leave her?' asked the Snow Man, for it seemed to him that the stove must be of the female sex. 'How could you quit such a comfortable place?'

'I was obliged,' replied the Yard Dog. 'They turned me out of doors, and chained me up here. I had bitten the youngest young master in the leg, because he kicked away the bone I was gnawing. "Bone for bone," I thought. They took that very much amiss, and from that time I have been fastened to a chain and have lost my voice. Don't you hear how hoarse I am? Off! Off! that was the end of the affair.'

But the Snow Man was no longer listening to him. He was looking in at the housekeeper's basement lodging, into the room where the stove stood on its four iron legs, just the same size as the Snow Man himself.

'What a strange crackling within me!' he said. 'Shall I ever get in there? It is an innocent wish, and our innocent wishes are certain to be fulfilled. It is my highest wish, my only wish, and it would be almost an injustice if it were not satisfied. I must go in there and lean against her, even if I have to break through the window.'

'You will never get in there,' said the Yard Dog; 'and if you approach the stove then you are off! off!'

'I am as good as gone,' replied the Snow Man. 'I think I am breaking up.'

The whole day the Snow Man stood looking in through the window. In the twilight hour the room became still more inviting: from the stove came a mild gleam, not like the sun nor like the moon; no, it was only as the stove can glow when he has something to eat. When the room door opened, the flame started out of his mouth; this was a habit the stove had. The flame fell distinctly on the white face of the Snow Man, and gleamed red upon his bosom.

'I can endure it no longer,' said he; 'how beautiful it looks when it stretches out its tongue!'

The night was long; but it did not appear long to the Snow Man, who stood there lost in his own charming reflections, crackling with the cold.

In the morning the window-panes of the basement lodging were covered with ice. They bore the most beautiful ice-flowers that any snow man could desire; but they concealed the stove. The window-panes would not thaw; he could not see her. It crackled and whistled in him and around him; it was just the kind of frosty weather a snow man must thoroughly enjoy. But he did not enjoy it; and, indeed, how could he enjoy himself when he was stove-sick?

'That's a terrible disease for a Snow Man,' said the Yard Dog. 'I have suffered from it myself, but I got over it. Off! Off!' he barked; and he added, 'the weather is going to change.'

And the weather did change; it began to thaw.

The warmth increased, and the Snow Man decreased. He said nothing and made no complaint – and that's an infallible sign.

One morning he broke down. And, behold, where he had stood, something like a broomstick remained sticking up out of the ground. It was the pole round which the boys had built him up.

'Ah! now I can understand why he had such an intense longing,' said the Yard Dog. 'The Snow Man has had a stove-rake in his body, and that's what moved within him. Now he has got over that too. Off! Off!'

And soon they had got over the winter.

'Off! Off!' barked the Yard Dog; but the little girls in the house sang:

> 'Spring out, green woodruff, fresh and fair;
> Thy woolly gloves, O willow, bear.
> Come, lark and cuckoo, come and sing,
> Already now we greet the Spring.
> I sing as well: twit-twit! cuckoo!
> Come, darling Sun, and greet us too.'

And nobody thought any more of the Snow Man.

In the Duck-Yard

A DUCK arrived from Portugal. Some said from Spain, but that's all the same. She was called the Portuguese, and laid eggs, and was killed and cooked, and that was *her* career. But the ducklings which crept forth from her eggs were afterwards also called Portuguese, and there is something in that. Now, of the whole family there was only one left in the duck-yard, a yard to which the chickens had access likewise, and where the cock strutted about with infinite pride.

'He annoys me with his loud crowing!' observed the Portuguese Duck. 'But he is a handsome bird, there's no denying that, though he is not a drake. He ought to moderate himself, but that's an art which shows superior breeding, like that possessed by the little singing birds over in the lime trees in the neighbour's garden. How charmingly they sing! There's something quite pretty in their warbling. I call it Portugal. If I had only such a little singing bird, I'd be a mother to him, kind and good, for that's in my blood, my Portuguese blood!'

And while she was still speaking, a little Singing Bird came head over heels from the roof into the yard. The cat was behind him, but the Bird escaped with a broken wing, and came tumbling into the yard.

'That's just like the cat, the villain!' said the Portuguese Duck. 'I remember him when I had children of my own. That such a creature should be allowed to live, and to wander about upon the roofs! I don't think they do such things in Portugal!'

And she pitied the little Singing Bird, and the other Ducks who were not of Portuguese descent pitied him too.

'Poor little creature!' they said, as one after another came up. 'We certainly can't sing,' they said, 'but we have an internal feeling for song, or something of the kind, within us; we can feel that, though we don't talk of it.'

'But I can talk of it,' said the Portuguese Duck; 'and I'll do something for the little fellow, for that's my duty!' And she stepped into the water-trough, and beat her wings upon the water so heartily, that the little Singing Bird was almost drowned by the bath he got, but the Duck meant it kindly. 'That's a good deed,' she said: 'the others may take example by it.'

'Piep!' said the little Bird: one of his wings was broken, and he found it difficult to shake himself; but he quite understood that the bath was kindly meant. 'You are very kind-hearted, madam,' he said; but he did not wish for a second bath.

'I have never thought about my heart,' continued the Portuguese Duck, 'but I know this much, that I love all my fellow creatures except the cat; but nobody can expect me to love him, for he ate up two of my ducklings. But pray make yourself at home, for one can make oneself comfortable. I myself am from a strange country, as you may see from my bearing and from my feathery dress. My drake is a native of these parts, he's not of my race; but for all that I'm not proud! If anyone here in the yard can understand you, I may assert that *I* am that person.'

'She's quite full of Portulak,' said a little common Duck, who was witty; and all the other common Ducks considered the word *Portulak* quite a good joke, for it sounded like Portugal; and they nudged each other and said 'Rapp!' It was too witty! And all the other Ducks now began to notice the little Singing Bird.

'The Portuguese has certainly a greater command of language,' they said. 'For our part, we don't care to fill our beaks with such long words, but our sympathy is just as great. If we don't do anything for you, we do not say anything about it; and we think that the best thing we can do.'

'You have a lovely voice,' said one of the oldest. 'It must be a great satisfaction to be able to give so much pleasure as you are able to impart. I certainly am no great judge of your song, and consequently I keep my beak shut; and even that is better than talking nonsense to you, as others do.'

'Don't plague him so,' interposed the Portuguese Duck: 'he requires rest and nursing. Little Singing Bird, shall I splash you again?'

'Oh, no! pray let me be dry!' he begged.

'The water cure is the only thing that helps me,' quoth the Portuguese. 'Amusement is beneficial too. The neighbouring fowls will soon come to pay their visit. There are two Cochin-Chinas among them. They wear feathers on their legs, are well educated, and have been brought from afar, that raises them in my regard.'

And the Fowls came, and the Cock came; today he was polite enough to abstain from being rude.

'You are a true Singing Bird,' he said, 'and you do as much with your little voice as can possibly be done with it. But one requires a little more shrillness, that every hearer may hear that one is a male.'

The two Chinese stood quite enchanted with the appearance of the Singing Bird. He looked very much rumpled after his bath, so that he seemed to them to have quite the appearance of a little Cochin-China fowl.

'He's charming,' they cried, and began a conversation with him, speaking in whispers, and using the most aristocratic Chinese dialect.

'We are of your race,' they continued. 'The Ducks, even the Portuguese, are swimming birds, as you cannot fail to have noticed. You do not know us yet; very few know us, or give themselves the trouble to make our acquaintance – not even any of the fowls, though we are born to sit on a higher perch than most of the rest. But that does not disturb us: we quietly pursue our path amid the others, whose principles are certainly not ours; but we look at things on the favourable side, and only speak of what is good, though it is difficult sometimes to find something when nothing exists. Except us two and the Cock, there's no one in the whole poultry-yard who is at once talented and polite. It cannot even be said of the inhabitants of the duck-yard. We warn you, little Singing Bird: don't trust that one yonder with the short tail-feathers, for she's cunning. The pied one there, with the crooked stripes on her wings, is a strife-seeker, and lets nobody have the last word, though she's always in the wrong. The fat duck yonder speaks evil of everyone, and that's against our principles; if we have nothing good to tell, we should hold our beaks. The Portuguese is the only one who has any education, and with whom one can associate, but she is passionate, and talks too much about Portugal.'

'What a lot those two Chinese have to whisper,' whispered one Duck to her friend. 'They annoy me – I have never spoken to them.'

Now the Drake came up. He thought the little Singing Bird was a sparrow.

'Well, I don't understand the difference,' he said; 'and indeed it's all the same thing. He's only a plaything, and if one has them, why, one has them.'

'Don't attach any value to what he says,' the Portuguese whispered. 'He's very respectable in business matters; and with him business takes precedence of everything. But now I shall lie down for a rest. One owes that to oneself, that one may be nice and fat when one is to be embalmed with apples and prunes.'

And accordingly she lay down in the sun, and winked with one eye; and she lay very comfortably, and she felt very comfortable, and she slept very comfortably.

The little Singing Bird busied himself with his broken wing. At last he lay down too, close to his protectress: the sun shone warm and bright, and he had found a very good place.

But the neighbour's fowls went about scratching up the earth; and, to tell the truth, they had paid the visit simply and solely to find food for themselves. The Chinese were the first to leave the duck-yard, and the other fowls soon followed them. The witty little Duck said of the Portuguese that the old lady would soon be in her second duckling-hood. At this the other Ducks laughed and cackled aloud. 'Second ducklinghood,' they said; 'that's too witty!' and then they repeated the former joke about Portulak, and declared that it was vastly amusing. And then they lay down.

They had been lying asleep for some time, when suddenly something was thrown into the yard for them to eat. It came down with such a thwack, that the whole company started up from sleep and clapped their wings. The Portuguese awoke too, and threw herself over on the other side, pressing the little Singing Bird very hard as she did so.

'Piep!' he cried; 'you trod very hard upon me, madam.'

'Well, why do you lie in my way?' the Duck retorted. 'You must not be so touchy. I have nerves of my own, but yet I never called out "Piep!" '

'Don't be angry,' said the little Bird; 'the "piep" came out of my beak unawares.'

The Portuguese did not listen to him, but began eating as fast as she could, and made a good meal. When this was ended, and she lay down again, the little Bird came up, and wanted to be amiable, and sang:

> Tilly-lilly lee,
> Of your dear heart
> I'll sing so oft
> As far and wide I flee.'

'Now I want to rest after my dinner,' said the Portuguese. 'You must conform to the rules of the house while you're here. I want to sleep now.'

The little Singing Bird was quite taken aback, for he had meant it kindly. When Madam afterwards awoke, he stood before her again with a little corn that he had found, and laid it at her feet; but as she had not slept well, she was naturally in a very bad humour.

'Give that to a chicken!' she said, 'and don't be always standing in my way.'

'Why are you angry with me?' replied the little Singing Bird. 'What have I done?'

'Done!' repeated the Portuguese Duck: 'your mode of expression is not exactly genteel; a fact to which I must call your attention.'

'Yesterday it was sunshine here,' said the little Bird, 'but today it's cloudy and grey.'

'You don't know much about the weather, I fancy,' retorted the Portuguese. 'The day is not done yet. Don't stand there looking so stupid.'

'But you are looking at me just as the wicked eyes looked when I fell into the yard yesterday.'

'Impertinent creature!' exclaimed the Portuguese Duck, 'would you compare me with the cat, that beast of prey? There's not a drop of malicious blood in me. I've taken your part, and will teach you good manners.'

And so saying, she bit off the Singing Bird's head, and he lay dead on the ground.

'Now, what's the meaning of this?' she said, 'could he not bear even that? Then certainly he was not made for this world. I've been like a mother to him, I know that, for I've a good heart.'

Then the neighbour's Cock stuck his head into the yard, and crowed with steam-engine power.

'You'll kill me with your crowing!' she cried. 'It's all your fault. He's lost his head, and I am very near losing mine.'

'There's not much lying where he fell!' observed the Cock.

'Speak of him with respect,' retorted the Portuguese Duck, 'for he had song, manners, and education. He was affectionate and soft, and that's as good in animals as in your so called human beings.'

And all the Ducks came crowding round the little dead Singing Bird. Ducks have strong passions, whether they feel envy or pity; and as there was nothing here to envy, pity manifested itself, even in the two Chinese.

'We shall never get such a singing bird again; he was almost a Chinese,' they whispered; and they wept with a mighty clucking sound, and all the fowls clucked too, but the Ducks went about with the redder eyes.

'We've hearts of our own,' they said; 'nobody can deny that.'

'Hearts!' repeated the Portuguese, 'yes, that we have, almost as much as in Portugal.'

'Let us think of getting something to satisfy our hunger,' said the Drake, 'for that's the most important point. If one of our toys is broken, why, we have plenty more!'

The Muse of the New Century

The Muse of the New Century, as our children's children, perhaps even a more distant generation, though not we, shall know her, when will she reveal herself? In what form will she appear? What will she sing? What chords of the soul will she touch? To what elevation will she lift the age she lives in?

So many questions in our busy time! a time in which Poetry stands almost solitary and alone, and in which one knows with certainty that much of the 'immortal' verse, written by poets of the present day, will perhaps in the future exist only in charcoal inscriptions on prison walls, seen and read by a few inquisitive souls.

Poetry must join in the bustle too, at least take some share in the war of parties, where blood or ink flows.

'That is a one-sided opinion,' many will say; 'Poetry is not forgotten in our time.'

No, there are still people, who on their free days feel a desire for Poetry and, when they perceive this spiritual grumbling in the nobler part of their being, certainly do send to the bookseller and buy a whole threepennyworth of poetry, of the kind that is most recommended. Some are quite content with as much as they can get for nothing, or are satisfied with reading a fragment on the paper bag from the grocer's; that is a cheaper way, and in our busy time some regard must be paid to cheapness. The desire is felt for what we have, and that is enough! The poetry of the future, like the music of the future, belongs to the stories of Don Quixote; to speak about it is just like talking about voyages of discovery in Uranus.

The time is too short and valuable for the play of fancy; and if we are to speak quite sensibly, what *is* Poetry? These rhymed outpourings of feelings and thoughts are merely the movements and vibrations of the nerves. All enthusiasm, joy, pain, even the material striving, are – the learned tell us – vibrations of the nerves. Each of us is – a stringed instrument.

But who touches these strings? Who makes them vibrate and tremble? The Spirit, the invisible divine Spirit, which lets *its* emotion, *its* feeling, sound through them, and that is understood by the other stringed instruments, so that they also sound in harmonious tones or in the strong dissonances of opposition. So it has been, and so it will be, in the progress which humanity makes in the consciousness of freedom.

Every century, every thousand years, one may say, finds in Poetry the expression of its greatness; born in the period that is closing, it steps forward and rules in the period that is coming.

In the midst of our busy time, noisy with machinery, she is thus already born, the Muse of the New Century. We send her our greeting. Let her hear it, or read it someday, perhaps among the charcoal inscriptions we spoke of above.

The rockers of her cradle stretched from the farthest point which human foot had trod on North Polar expeditions to the utmost limit of human vision in the 'black coal-sack' of the Polar sky. We did not hear the sound of the cradle for the clattering of machines, the whistling of railway engines, the blasting of real rocks and of the old fetters of the mind.

She has been born in the great factory of the present age, where steam exerts its power, where 'Master Bloodless' and his workmen toil by day and night.

She has in her possession the great loving heart of woman, with the Vestal's flame and the fire of passion. She received the lightning flash of intellect, endowed with all the colours of the prism, changing from century to century, and estimated according to the colour most in fashion at the time. The glorious swan-plumage of fancy is her ornament and strength; science wove it, and primitive forces gave it power to soar.

She is the child of the people on the father's side, sound in mind and thought, with seriousness in her eye and humour on her lips. Her mother is the nobly-born, highly educated daughter of the French refugee with recollections of the gilded rococo period. The Muse of the New Century has blood and soul in her from both of these.

Splendid christening gifts were laid upon her cradle. Like bonbons were strewed there in abundance the hidden riddles of Nature, and their answers; from the diver's bell were shaken marvellous trinkets from the depths of ocean. As a coverlet there was spread over her a copy of the map of the heavens, that suspended ocean with its myriads of islands, each of them a world. The sun paints pictures for her; photography supplies her with playthings.

Her nurse has sung to her of Eyvind Skalda-spiller and Firdusi, of the Minnesingers and of what Heine in youthful wantonness sang of his own poetic soul. Much, too much, her nurse has told her; she knows the old ancestral mother Edda's horror-waking sagas, where curses sweep along with blood-stained wings. All the Arabian Nights she has heard in a quarter of an hour.

The Muse of the New Century is still a child, yet she has leaped out of her cradle; she is full of will, without knowing what she desires.

She still plays in her great nursery, which is full of art-treasures and rococo. Greek Tragedy, and Roman Comedy, stand there, hewn in marble; the popular songs of the nations hang like dried plants on the walls; print a kiss on them, and they swell again into freshness and fragrance. She is surrounded by eternal harmonies from the thoughts of Beethoven, Gluck, Mozart, and all the great masters, expressed in melody. On her bookshelf are laid away many who in their time were immortal, and there is still room for many more, whose names we hear sounding along the telegraph-wire of immortality.

A terrible amount she has read, far too much, for she has been born in our time; much must be forgotten again, and the Muse will know how to forget.

She thinks not of her song, which will live on into a new millennium, as the books of Moses live, and Bidpai's fable of the fox's craft and success. She thinks not of her mission, of her great future; she is still at play, amid the strife of nations which shakes the air, which produces sound-figures with the pen and with the cannon, runes that are hard to read.

She wears a Garibaldi hat, yet reads her Shakespeare, and thinks for a moment, 'He can still be acted when I am grown up! Let Calderon rest in the sarcophagus of his works, with his inscription of fame.' As for Holberg, the Muse is cosmopolitan, she has bound him up in one volume with Molière, Plautus, and Aristophanes, but reads Molière most.

She is free from the restlessness which drives the chamois of the Alps, yet her soul longs for the salt of life as the chamois does for that of the mountain. There dwells in her heart a restfulness, as in the legends of Hebrew antiquity, that voice from the nomad on the green plains in the still starry nights; and yet in song her heart swells more strongly than that of the inspired warrior from the Thessalian mountains in the days of ancient Greece.

How is it with her Christian faith? She has learned the great and little table of Philosophy; the elementary substances have broken one of her milk-teeth, but she has got a new set now. In her cradle she bit into the fruit of knowledge, ate it and became wise, so that Immortality flashed upon her as the most inspired idea of the human mind.

When will the new century of Poetry arise? When will the Muse be recognised? When will she be heard?

One beautiful morning in spring she will come rushing on her dragon, the locomotive, through tunnels and over viaducts, or over the soft strong sea on the snorting dolphin, or through the air on the great bird Roc, and will descend in the land from which her divine voice will first hail the human race. Where? Is it from the land of Columbus, the land of freedom, where the natives became hunted game and the Africans beasts of burden, the land from which we heard the song of Hiawatha? Is it from the Antipodes, the gold nugget in the South Seas – the land of contraries, where our night is day, and black swans sing in the mimosa forests? Or from the land where Memnon's pillar rang and still rings, though we understood not the song of the sphinx in the desert? Is it from the coal-island, where Shakespeare is the ruler from the times of Elizabeth? Is it from the land of Tycho Brahe, where he was not allowed to remain, or from the fairy-land of California, where the Wellingtonia rears its head as king of the forests of the world.

When will the star shine, the star on the forehead of the Muse – the flower on whose leaves are inscribed the century's expression of the beautiful in form, in colour, and in fragrance?

'What is the programme of the new Muse?' say the skilled parliamentarians of our time. 'What does she want to do?'

Rather ask what she does not want to do!

She will not come forward as the ghost of the age that is past. She will not construct dramas out of the cast-off glories of the stage, nor will she conceal defects in dramatic architecture by means of specious draperies of lyric verse. Her flight before our eyes will be like passing from the car of Thespis to the amphitheatre of marble. She will not break honest human talk in pieces, and patch it together again like an artificial chime of bells with ingratiating tinkles borrowed from the contests of the troubadours. She will not set up verse as a nobleman and prose as a plebeian; they stand equal in melody, in fullness, and in strength. She will not sculpture the old gods out of Iceland's saga-blocks; they are dead, there is no feeling for them in the new age, no kinship with them. She will not invite the men of her time to lodge their thoughts in the taverns of French novels; she will not deaden them with the chloroform of commonplace tales. She will bring an elixir of life; her song in verse and in prose will be short, clear, and rich. The heartbeats of the nations are each but one letter in the great alphabet of evolution, but she will with equal affection take hold of each letter, form them into words, and link the words into rhythms for her hymn of the present time.

And when will the fullness of time have come?

It is long for us, who are still behind here; it is short for those, who flew on ahead.

Soon the Chinese Wall will fall, the railways of Europe reach the secluded cultures of Asia – the two streams of culture meet. Then perhaps the waterfall will foam with its deep resounding roar; we old men of the present will shake at the mighty tones, and hear in them a Ragnarök, the fall of the ancient gods; we forget that times and races here below must disappear, and only a slight image of each, enclosed in the capsule of a word, will swim like a lotus-flower on the stream of eternity, and tell us that they all are and were flesh of our flesh, though in different raiment. The image of the Jews shines out from the Bible, that of the Greeks from the Iliad and Odyssey, and ours? Ask the Muse of the New Century, at Ragnarök, when the new Grimlè arises glorified and made intelligible.

All the power of steam, all the forces of the present, were levers. Master Bloodless and his busy workmen, who seem to be the powerful rulers of our time, are only servants, black slaves who adorn the palace-hall, bring forth the treasures, lay the tables for the great feast at which the Muse, with the innocence of a child, the enthusiasm of a maid, and the calmness and knowledge of a matron, raises the marvellous lamp of Poetry, the rich, full heart of man with the flame of God in it.

Hail to thee, Muse of the new century of Poetry. Our greeting soars up and is heard, even as the worm's hymn of gratitude is heard, the worm which is cut asunder by the ploughshare when a new spring dawns and the plough cleaves the furrows, cutting us worms asunder, so that blessing may grow for the new generation that is to come.

Hail to thee, Muse of the New Century!

The Ice Maiden

Little Rudy

LET US visit Switzerland, and wander through the glorious land of mountains, where the forests cling to the steep walls of rock; let us mount up to the dazzling snowfields, and then descend into the green valleys through which rivers and brooks are rushing, hurrying on as if they could not reach the sea and disappear there quickly enough. The sun looks hotly down upon the deep valley, and it glares likewise upon the heavy masses of snow, so that they harden in the course of centuries into gleaming blocks of ice, or form themselves into falling avalanches, or become piled up into glaciers. Two such glaciers lie in the broad rocky gorges under the 'Schreckhorn' and the 'Wetterhorn', by the little mountain town of Grindelwald: they are wonderful to behold, and therefore in the summertime many strangers come from all parts of the world to see them. The strangers come across the lofty snow-covered mountains, they come through the deep valleys; and in this latter case they must climb for several hours, and, as they climb, the valley seems to be descending behind them, deeper and deeper, and they look down upon it as out of a balloon. Above them the clouds often hang like thick heavy veils of smoke over the mountain-tops, while a sunbeam still penetrates into the valley, through which the many brown wooden houses lie scattered, making one particular spot stand forth in shining transparent green. Down there the water hums and gushes, while above, it purls and ripples and looks like silver bands fluttering down the mountain.

On both sides of the road that leads uphill, stand wooden houses. Each has its potato patch; and this is a necessity, for there are many little mouths in those cottages – plenty of children are there, who can eat up their share right heartily. They peep forth everywhere, and gather round the traveller, whether he be on foot or in a carriage. All the children here carry on a trade: the little people offer carved houses for sale, models of those that are built here in the mountains. In rain or in sunshine, there are the children offering their wares.

About twenty years ago, a little boy might often be seen standing there, anxious to carry on his trade, but always standing a short distance away from the rest. He would stand there with a very grave face, holding his little box with the carved toys so firmly in both hands that it seemed as if he would not let it go on any account. This appearance of earnestness, together with the fact of his being such a little fellow, often attracted the notice of strangers; so that he was very frequently beckoned forward, and relieved of a great part of his stock, without himself knowing why this preference was shown him. A couple of miles away, in the mountains, lived his grandfather, who carved the pretty little houses; and in the old man's room stood a wooden cupboard filled with things of that kind – carved toys in abundance, nutcrackers, knives and forks, boxes adorned with carved leaves and with jumping chamois, all kinds of things that delight children's eyes; but the boy, Rudy was his name, looked with greater longing at an old rifle that hung from the beam under the ceiling, for his grandfather had promised him that it should be his one day, when he should have grown tall and strong enough to manage it properly.

Young as the boy was, he had to keep the goats; and if ability to climb with his flock makes a good goat-herd, then Rudy was certainly an efficient one, for he even climbed a little higher than the goats could mount, and loved to take the birds' nests from the high trees. A bold and courageous child he was, but he was never seen to smile, save when he stood by the foaming waterfall or heard an avalanche crashing down the mountain-side. He never played with the other children, and only came in contact with them when his grandfather sent him down the mountain to deal in carved toys; and this was a business Rudy did not exactly like. He preferred clambering about alone among the mountains, or sitting beside his grandfather and hearing the old man tell stories of the old times, or of the people in the neighbouring town of Meiringen, his birthplace. The old man said that the people who dwelt in that place had not been there from the beginning: they had come into the land from the far north, where their ancestors dwelt, who were called Swedes. And Rudy was very proud of knowing this. But he had others who taught him something, and these others were companions of his belonging to the animal creation. There was a great dog, whose name was Ajola, and who had belonged to Rudy's father; and a Tom Cat was there too; this Tom Cat had a special significance for Rudy, for it was Pussy who had taught him to climb.

'Come with me out on the roof,' the Cat had said, quite distinctly and plainly, to Rudy; for, you see, children who cannot talk yet, can understand the language of fowls and ducks right well, and cats and dogs speak to them quite as plainly as Father and Mother can do; but that is only when the children are very little, and then, even Grand-father's stick will become a perfect horse to them, and can neigh, and, in their eyes, is furnished with head and legs and tail. With some children this period ends later than with others, and of such we are accustomed to say that they are very backward, and that they have remained children a long time. People are in the habit of saying many strange things.

'Come out with me on to the roof,' was perhaps the first thing the Cat had said and that Rudy had understood. 'What people say about falling down is all fancy: one does not fall down if one is not afraid. Just you come, and put one of your paws thus and the other thus. Feel your way with your forepaws. You must have eyes in your head and nimble limbs; and if an empty space comes, jump over, and then hold tight as I do.'

And Rudy did so too; consequently he was often found seated on the top of the roof by the Cat; and afterwards he sat with him in the tree-tops, and at last was even seen seated on the edge of the cliff, whither Puss did not go.

'Higher up!' said Tree and Bush. 'Don't you see how we climb? How high we reach, and how tight we cling, even to the narrowest, loftiest ridge of rock!'

And Rudy climbed to the very summit of the mountain, frequently reaching the top before the sun touched it, and there he drank his morning draught of fresh mountain air, the draught that the bountiful Creator above can prepare, and the recipe for making which, according to the reading of men, consists in mingling the fragrant aroma of the mountain herbs with the scent of the wild thyme and mint of the valley. All that is heavy is absorbed by the brooding clouds, and then the wind drives them along, and rubs them against the tree-tops, and the spirit of fragrance is infused into the air to make it lighter and fresher, ever fresher. And this was Rudy's morning draught.

The sunbeams, the blessing-laden daughters of the sun, kissed his cheeks, and Giddiness, who stood lurking by, never ventured to approach him; but the swallows, who had no less than seven nests on his grandfather's roof, flew round about him and his goats, and sang, 'We and ye! we and ye!' They brought him a greeting from home, even from the two fowls, the only birds in the house, but with whom Rudy never became at all intimate.

Small as he was, he had been a traveller, and for such a little fellow he had made no mean journey. He had been born over in the Canton of Wallis, and had been carried across the high mountains to his present dwelling. Not long ago he had made a pilgrimage on foot to the 'Staubbach' or 'Dust Fountain', which flutters through the air like a silver tissue before the snow-covered dazzling white mountain called the 'Jungfrau' or 'Maiden'. He had also been in the Grindelwald, at the great glacier; but that was a sad story. His mother had met her death there; and there, said Grandfather, little Rudy had lost his childlike cheerfulness. When the boy was not a year old his mother had written concerning him that he laughed more than he cried, but from the time when he sat in the ice cleft, another spirit came upon him. His grandfather seldom talked of it, but the people through the whole mountain region knew the story.

Rudy's father had been a postilion. The great dog that lay in grandfather's room had always followed him in his journeys over the Simplon down to the Lake of Geneva. In the valley of the Rhone, in the Canton of Wallis, lived some relatives of Rudy on the father's side. His uncle was a first-rate chamois hunter and a well-known guide. Rudy was only a year old when he lost his father, and the mother now longed to return with her child to her relatives in the Oberland of Berne. Her father lived a few miles from Grindelwald; he was a wood-carver, and earned enough to live on. Thus, in the month of June, carrying her child, and accompanied by two chamois hunters, she set out on her journey home, across the Gemmi towards Grindelwald. They had already gone the greater part of the way, had crossed the high ridge as far as the snow-field, and already caught sight of the valley of home, with all the well-known wooden houses, and had only one great glacier to cross. The snow had fallen freshly, and concealed a cleft which did not indeed reach to the deep ground where the water gushed, but was still more than six feet deep. The young mother, with her child in her arms, stumbled, slipped over the edge, and vanished. No cry was heard, no sigh, but they could hear the crying of the little child. More than an hour elapsed before ropes and poles could be brought up from the nearest house for the purpose of giving help, and after much exertion what appeared to be two corpses were brought forth from the icy cleft. Every means was tried; and the child, but not the mother, was recalled to life; and thus the old grandfather had a daughter's son brought into his house, an orphan, the boy who had laughed more than he cried; but it seemed that a great change had taken place in him, and this change must have been wrought in the glacier cleft, in the cold wondrous ice world, in which, according to the Swiss peasants' belief, the souls of the wicked are shut up until the last day.

The glacier lies stretched out, a foaming body of water stiffened into ice, and as it were pressed together into green blocks, one huge lump piled upon another; from beneath it the rushing stream of melted ice and snow thunders down into the valley, and deep caverns and great clefts extend below. It is a wondrous glass palace, and within dwells the Ice Maiden, the Glacier Queen. She, the death-dealing, the crushing one, is partly a child of air, partly the mighty ruler of the river; thus she is also able to raise herself to the summit of the snow mountain, where the bold climbers are obliged to hew steps in the ice before they can mount; she sails on the slender fir twig down the rushing stream, and springs from one block to another, with her long snow-white hair and her blue-green garment fluttering around her and glittering like the water in the deep Swiss lakes.

'To crush and to hold, mine is the power!' she says. 'They have stolen a beautiful boy from me, a boy whom I have kissed, but not kissed to death. He is again among men: he keeps the goats on the mountains, and climbs upward, ever higher, far away from the others, but not from me. He is mine, and I will have him!'

And she bade Giddiness do her errand, for it was too hot for the Ice Maiden, in summer, in the green woods where the wild mint grows; and Giddiness raised herself and came down; and her sisters went with her, for she has many sisters, a whole troop of them; and the Ice Maiden chose the strongest of the many who hover without and within. These spirits sit on the staircase railing and upon the railing at the summit of the tower; they run like squirrels along the rocky ridge, they spring over railing and path, and tread the air as a swimmer treads the water, luring their victims forth, and hurling them down into the abyss. Giddiness and the Ice Maiden both grasp at a man as a polypus grasps at everything that comes near it. And now Giddiness was to seize upon Rudy.

'Yes, but to seize *him*,' said Giddiness, 'is more than I can do. The cat, that wretched creature, has taught him her tricks. That child has a particular power which thrusts me away; I am not able to seize him, this boy, when he hangs by a bough over the abyss. How gladly would I tickle the soles of his feet, or thrust him head over heels into the air! But I am not able to do it.'

'We shall manage to do it,' said the Ice Maiden. 'Thou or I – I shall do it – I!'

'No, no!' sounded a voice around her, like the echo of the church bells among the mountains; but it was a song; it was the melting chorus of other spirits of nature – of good affectionate spirits – the Daughters of the Sunshine. These hover every evening in a wreath about the summits of the mountains; there they spread forth their roseate wings, which become more and more fiery as the sun sinks, and gleam above the high mountains. The people call this the 'Alpine glow'. And then, when the sun has set, they retire into the mountain summits, into the white snow, and slumber there until the sun rises again, when they appear once more. They are especially fond of flowers, butterflies, and human beings; and among these latter they had chosen Rudy as an especial favourite.

'You shall not catch him – you shall not have him,' they said.

'I have caught them larger and stronger than he,' said the Ice Maiden.

Then the Daughters of the Sun sang a song of the wanderer whose mantle the storm carried away.

'The wind took the covering, but not the man. Ye can seize him, but not hold him, ye children of strength. He is stronger, he is more spiritual than even we are. He will mount higher than the sun, our parent. He possesses the magic word that binds wind and water, so that they must serve him and obey him. You will but loosen the heavy oppressive weight that holds him down, and he will rise all the higher.'

Gloriously swelled the chorus that sounded like the ringing of the church bells.

And every morning the sunbeams pierced through the one little window into the grandfather's house, and shone upon the quiet child. The Daughters of the Sunbeams kissed the boy; they wanted to thaw and remove the icy kisses which the royal maiden of the glaciers had given him when he lay in the lap of his dead mother in the deep ice cleft, from whence he had been saved as if by a miracle.

2

The Journey to the New Home

Rudy was now eight years old. His uncle, who dwelt beyond the mountains in the Rhone valley, wished that the boy should come to him to learn something and get on in the world; the grandfather saw the justice of this, and let the lad go.

Accordingly Rudy said goodbye. There were others besides his grandfather to whom he had to say farewell; and foremost came Ajola, the old dog.

'Your father was the postilion and I was the post dog,' said Ajola; 'we went to and fro together; and I know some dogs from beyond the mountains, and some people too. I was never much of a talker; but now that we most likely shall not be able to talk much longer together, I will tell you a little more than usual. I will tell you a story that I have kept to myself and ruminated on for a long while. I don't understand it, and you won't understand it, but that does not signify: this much at least I have made out, that things are not quite equally divided in the world, either for dogs or for men. Not all are destined to sit on a lady's lap and to drink milk: I've not been accustomed to it, but I've seen one of those little lap dogs, driving in the coach, and taking up a passenger's place in it; the lady, who was its mistress, or whose master it was, had a little bottle of milk with her, out of which she gave the dog a drink; and she offered him sweetmeats, but he only sniffed at them, and would not even accept them, and then she ate them up herself. I was running along in the mud beside the carriage, as hungry as a dog can be, chewing my own thoughts, that this could not be quite right; but they say a good many things are going on that are not quite right. Should you like to sit in a lady's lap and ride in a coach? I should be glad if you did. But one can't manage that for oneself. I never could manage it, either by barking or howling.'

These were Ajola's words; and Rudy embraced him and kissed him heartily on his wet nose; then the lad took the Cat in his arms, but Puss struggled, saying, 'You're too strong for me, and I don't like to use my claws against you! Clamber away over the mountains, for I have taught you how to climb. Don't think that you can fall, and then you will be sure to maintain your hold.'

And so saying the Cat ran away, not wishing Rudy to see that the tears were in his eyes.

The Fowls were strutting about in the room. One of them had lost its tail. A traveller who wanted to be a sportsman had shot the Fowl's tail away, looking upon the bird as a bird of prey.

'Rudy wants to go across the mountains,' said one of the Fowls.

'He's always in a hurry,' said the other, 'and I don't like saying goodbye.'

And with this they both tripped away.

To the Goats he also said farewell; and they bleated 'Meek! meek!' which made him feel very sorrowful.

Two brave guides from the neighbourhood, who wanted to go across the mountains to the other side of the Gemmi, took him with them, and he followed them on foot. It was a tough march for such a little fellow, but Rudy was a strong boy, and his courage never gave way.

The Swallows flew with them for a little distance. 'We and ye! we and ye!' sang they. The road led across the foaming Lütschine, which pours forth in many little streams from the black cleft of the Grindelwald glacier and fallen trunks of trees and blocks of stone serve for a bridge. When they had reached the forest opposite, they began to ascend the slope where the glacier had slipped away from the mountain, and now they strode across and around ice blocks over the glacier. Rudy sometimes had alternately to crawl and to walk for some distance: his eyes gleamed with delight, and he trod so firmly in his spiked climbing-shoes that it seemed as if he wished to leave a trace behind him at every footstep. The black earth which the mountain stream had strewn over the glacier gave the great mass a swarthy look, but the bluish-green glassy ice nevertheless peered through. They had to make circuits round the numerous little lakes which had formed among the great blocks of ice, and now and then they passed close to a great stone that lay tottering on the edge of a crack in the ice, and sometimes the stone would overbalance, and roll crashing down, and a hollow echo sounded forth from the deep dark fissures in the glacier.

Thus they continued climbing. The glacier itself extended upwards like a mighty river of piled-up ice masses, shut in by steep rocks. Rudy thought for a moment of the tale they had told him, how he and his mother had lain in one of these deep, cold-breathing fissures; but soon all such thoughts vanished from him, and the tale seemed to him only like many others of the same kind which he had heard. Now and then, when the men thought the way too toilsome for the little lad, they would reach him a hand; but he did not grow tired, and stood on the smooth ice as safely as a chamois. Now they stepped on the face of the rock, and strode on among the rugged stones; sometimes, again, they marched among the pine trees, and then over the pasture grounds, ever seeing new and changing landscapes. Around them rose snow-clad mountains, whose names the 'Jungfrau', the 'Mönch', the 'Eiger', were known to every child, and consequently to Rudy too. Rudy had never yet been so high; he had never yet stepped on the outspread sea of snow: here it lay with its motionless snowy billows, from which the wind every now and then blew off a flake, as it blows the foam from the waves of the sea. The glaciers stand here, so to speak hand in hand; each one is a glass palace for the Ice Maiden, whose might and whose desire it is to catch and to bury. The sun shone warm, the snow was dazzlingly white and seemed strewn with bluish sparkling diamonds. Numberless insects, especially butterflies and bees, lay dead upon the snow; they had ventured too high, or the wind had carried them up until they perished in the frosty air. Above the Wetterhorn hung, like a bundle of fine black wool, a threatening cloud; it bowed down, teeming with the weight it bore, the weight of a whirlwind, irresistible when once it bursts forth. The impressions of this whole journey – the night encampment in these lofty regions, the further walk, the deep rocky chasms, where the water has pierced through the blocks of stone by a labour, at the thought of whose duration the mind stands still – all this was indelibly impressed upon Rudy's recollection.

A deserted stone building beyond the snow sea offered them a shelter for the night. Here they found fuel and pine branches, and soon a fire was kindled, and the bed arranged for the night as comfortably as possible. Then the men seated themselves round the fire, smoked their pipes, and drank the warm refreshing drink they had prepared for themselves. Rudy received his share of the supper; and then the men began telling stories of the mysterious beings of the Alpine land: of the strange gigantic serpents that lay coiled in the deep lakes; of the marvellous company of spirits that had been known to carry sleeping men by night through the air to the wonderful floating city, Venice; of the wild shepherd who drove his black sheep across the mountain pastures, and how, though no man had seen him, the sound of the bell and the ghostly bleating of the flock had been heard by many. Rudy listened attentively, but without any feeling of fear, for he knew not what fear meant; and while he listened he seemed to hear the hollow, unearthly bleating and lowing; and it became more and more audible, so that presently the men heard it too, and stopped in their talk to listen, and told Rudy he must not go to sleep.

It was a 'Föhn', the mighty whirlwind that hurls itself from the mountains into the valley, cracking the trees in its strength as if they were feeble reeds, and carrying the wooden houses from one bank of a river to the other as we move the figures on a chessboard.

After the lapse of about an hour, they told Rudy it was all over, and he might go to sleep; and tired out with his long march, he went to sleep as at the word of command.

Very early next morning they resumed their journey. This day the sun shone on new mountains for Rudy, on fresh glaciers and new fields of snow: they had entered the Canton of Wallis, and had proceeded beyond the ridge which could be seen from the Grindelwald; but they were still far from the new home. Other chasms came in view, new valleys, forests, and mountain paths, and new houses also came into view, and other people. But what strange-looking people were these! They were deformed, and had fat, sallow faces; and from their necks hung heavy, ugly lumps of flesh, like bags: they were *crétins*, dragging themselves languidly along, and looking at the strangers with stupid eyes; the women especially were hideous in appearance. Were the people in his new home like these?

3

Uncle

Thank Heaven! the people in the house of Rudy's uncle, where the boy was now to live, looked like those he had been accustomed to see; only one of them was a *crétin*, a poor idiotic lad, one of those pitiable creatures who wander in their loneliness from house to house in the Canton of Wallis, staying a couple of months with each family. Poor Saperli happened to be at Rudy's uncle's when the boy arrived.

Uncle was still a stalwart huntsman, and, moreover, understood the craft of tub-making; his wife was a little lively woman with a face like a bird's. She had eyes like an eagle, and her neck was covered with a fluffy down.

Everything here was new to Rudy – costume, manners, and habits, and even the language; but to the latter the child's ear would soon adapt itself. There was an appearance of wealth here, compared with grandfather's dwelling. The room was larger, the walls were ornamented with chamois horns, among which hung polished rifles, and over the door was a picture of the Madonna, with fresh Alpine roses and a lamp burning in front of it.

As already stated, uncle was one of the best chamois hunters in the whole country, and one of the most trusted guides. In this household Rudy was now to become the pet child. There was one pet here already in the person of an old blind and deaf hound, who no longer went out hunting as he had been used to do; but his good qualities of former days had not been forgotten, and therefore he was looked upon as one of the family and carefully tended. Rudy stroked the dog, who, however, was not willing to make acquaintance with a stranger; but Rudy did not long remain a stranger in that house.

'It is not bad living, here in the Canton of Wallis,' said Uncle; 'and we have chamois here, who don't die out so quickly as the steinbock; and it is much better here now than in former days. They may say what they like in honour of the old times, but ours are better, after all: the bag has been opened, and a fresh wind blows through our sequestered valley. Something better always comes up when the old is worn out,' he continued. And when uncle was in a very communicative mood, he would tell of his youthful years, and of still earlier times, the strong times of his father, when Wallis was, as he expressed it, a closed bag, full of sick people and miserable *crétins*. 'But the French soldiers came in,' he said, 'and they were the proper doctors, for they killed the disease at once, and they killed the people who had it too. They knew all about fighting, did the French, and they could fight in more than one way. Their girls could make conquests too,' and then uncle would laugh and nod to his wife, who was a Frenchwoman by birth.

'The French hammered away at our stones in famous style! They hammered the Simplon road through the rocks – such a road that I can now say to a child of three years, "Go to Italy, only keep to the high road," and the child will arrive safely in Italy if it does not stray from the road.'

And then uncle would sing a French song, and cry 'Hurrah for Napoleon Bonaparte!'

Here Rudy for the first time heard them tell of France and Lyons, the great town on the Rhone, where his uncle had been.

Not many years were to elapse before Rudy should become an expert chamois hunter; his uncle said he had the stuff for it in him, and accordingly taught him to handle a rifle, to take aim, and shoot; and in the hunting season he took the lad with him into the mountains and let him drink the warm blood of the chamois, which cures the huntsman of giddiness; he also taught him to judge of the various times when the avalanches would roll down the mountains, at noon or at evening, according as the sunbeams had shone upon the place; he taught him to notice the way the chamois sprang, that Rudy might learn to come down firmly on his feet; and told him that where the rocky cleft gave no support for the foot, a man must cling by his elbows, hips, and legs, and that even the neck could be used as a support in case of need. The chamois were clever, he said – they posted sentinels; but the hunter should be more clever still – keep out of the line of scent, and lead them astray; and one day when Rudy was out hunting with uncle, the latter hung his coat and hat on the alpenstock, and the chamois took the coat for a man.

The rocky path was narrow; it was, properly speaking, not a path at all, but merely a narrow shelf beside the yawning abyss. The snow that lay here was half thawed, the stone crumbled beneath the tread, and therefore uncle laid himself down and crept forward. Every fragment that crumbled away from the rock fell down, jumping and rolling from one ledge of rock to another until it was lost to sight in the darkness below. About a hundred paces behind his uncle, stood Rudy, on a firm projecting point of rock; and from this station he saw a great vulture circling in the air and hovering over uncle, whom it evidently intended to hurl into the abyss with a blow of its wings, that it might make a prey of him. Uncle's whole attention was absorbed by the chamois, which was to be seen, with its young one, on the other side of the cleft. Rudy kept his eyes on the bird. He knew what the vulture intended to do, and accordingly stood with his rifle ready to fire; when suddenly the chamois leaped up: uncle fired, and the creature fell pierced by the deadly bullet; but the young one sprang away as if it had been accustomed all its life to flee from danger. Startled by the sound of the rifle, the great bird soared away in another direction, and uncle knew nothing of the danger in which he had stood until Rudy informed him of it.

As they were returning homeward, in the best spirits, uncle whistling one of the songs of his youth, they suddenly heard a peculiar noise not far from them; they looked around, and there on the declivity of the mountain, the snowy covering suddenly rose, and began to heave up and down, like a piece of linen stretched on a field when the wind passes beneath it. The snow waves, which had been smooth and hard as marble slabs, now broke to pieces, and the roar of waters sounded like rumbling thunder. An avalanche was falling, not over Rudy and uncle, but near where they stood, not at all far from them.

'Hold fast, Rudy!' cried uncle, 'hold fast with all your strength.'

And Rudy clung to the trunk of the nearest tree. Uncle clambered up above him, and the avalanche rolled past, many feet from them; but the concussion of the air, the stormy wings of the avalanche, broke trees and shrubs all around as if they had been frail reeds, and scattered the fragments headlong down. Rudy lay crouched upon the earth, the trunk of the tree to which he clung was split through, and the crown hurled far away; and there among the broken branches lay uncle, with his head shattered: his hand was still warm, but his face could no longer be recognised. Rudy stood by him pale and trembling; it was the first fright of his life – the first time he felt a shudder run through him.

Late at night he brought the sorrowful news into his home, which was now a house of mourning. The wife could find no words, no tears for her grief; at last, when the corpse was brought home, her sorrow found utterance. The poor *crétin* crept into his bed, and was not seen during the whole of the next day; but at last, towards evening, he stole up to Rudy.

'Write a letter for me,' he said. 'Saperli can't write, but Saperli can carry the letter to the post.'

'A letter from you?' asked Rudy. 'And to whom?'

'To the Lord.'

'To *whom* do you say?'

And the simpleton, as they called the *crétin*, looked at Rudy with a moving glance, folded his hands, and said solemnly and slowly, 'To the Saviour! Saperli will send Him a letter, and beg that Saperli may lie dead, and not the man in the house here.'

Rudy pressed his hand, and said, 'The letter would not arrive, and it cannot restore him to us.'

But it was very difficult to make poor Saperli believe that this was impossible.

'Now thou art the prop of this house,' said the widow; and Rudy became that.

4

Babette

Who is the best marksman in the Canton of Wallis? The chamois knew well enough, and said to each other, 'Beware of Rudy.' Who is the handsomest marksman? 'Why, Rudy,' said the girls; but *they* did not add, 'Beware of Rudy.' Nor did even the grave mothers pronounce such a warning, for Rudy nodded at them just as kindly as at the young maidens. How quick and merry he was! His cheeks were browned, his teeth regular and white, and his eyes black and shining; he was a handsome lad, and only twenty years old. The icy water could not harm him when he swam; he could turn and twist in the water like a fish, and climb better than any man in the mountains; he could cling like a snail to the rocky ledge, for he had good sinews and muscles of his own; and he showed that in his power of jumping, an art he had learned first from the Cat and afterwards from the goats. Rudy was the safest guide to whom any man could trust himself, and might have amassed a fortune in that calling; his uncle had also taught him the craft of tub-making; but he did not take to that occupation, preferring chamois hunting, which also brought in money. Rudy was what might be called a good match, if he did not look higher than his station. And he was such a dancer that the girls dreamed of him, and indeed more than one of them carried the thought of him into her waking hours.

'He kissed me once at the dance!' said the schoolmaster's daughter Annette to her dearest girl-friend; but she should not have said that, even to her dearest friend. A secret of that kind is hard to keep – it is like sand in a sieve, sure to run out; and soon it was known that Rudy, honest lad though he was, kissed his partner in the dance; and yet he had not kissed the one whom he would have liked best of all to kiss.

'Yes,' said an old hunter, 'he has kissed Annette. He has begun with A, and will kiss his way through the whole alphabet.'

A kiss at the dance was all that the busy tongues could say against him until now: he had certainly kissed Annette, but she was not the beloved one of his heart.

Down in the valley near Bex, among the great walnut trees, by a little brawling mountain stream, lived the rich miller. The dwelling-house was a great building, three stories high, with little towers, roofed with planks and covered with plates of metal that shone in the sunlight and in the moonlight; the principal tower was surmounted by a weather-vane, a flashing arrow that had pierced an apple – an emblem of Tell's famous feat. The mill looked pleasant and comfortable, and could be easily drawn and described; but the miller's daughter could neither be drawn nor described – so, at least, Rudy would have said; and yet she was portrayed in his heart, where her eyes gleamed so brightly that they had lighted up a fire. This had burst out quite suddenly, as other fires break forth; and the strangest thing of all was, that the miller's daughter, pretty Babette, had no idea of the conquest she had made, for she and Rudy had never exchanged a word together.

The miller was rich, and this wealth of his made Babette very difficult to get at. But nothing is so high that it may not be reached if a man will but climb; and he will not fall, if he is not afraid of falling. That was a lesson Rudy had brought from his first home.

Now it happened that on one occasion Rudy had some business to do in Bex. It was quite a journey thither, for in those days the railway had not yet been completed. From the Rhone glacier, along the foot of the Simplon, away among many changing mountain heights, the proud valley of Wallis extends, with its mighty river the Rhone, which often overflows its banks and rushes across the fields and high roads, carrying destruction with it. Between the little towns of Sion and St Maurice the valley makes a bend, like an elbow, and becomes so narrow below St Maurice that it only affords room for the bed of the river and a narrow road. An old tower here stands as a sentinel at the boundary of the Canton of Wallis, which ends here. The tower looks across over the stone bridge at the toll-house on the opposite side. There commences the Canton of Waud, and at a little distance is the first town of that Canton, Bex. At every step the signs of fertility and plenty increase, and the traveller seems to be journeying through a garden of walnut trees and chestnuts; here and there cypresses appear, and blooming pomegranates; and the climate has the southern warmth of Italy.

Rudy duly arrived in Bex, and concluded his business there; then he took a turn in the town; but not even a miller's lad, much less Babette, did he see there. That was not as it should be.

Evening came on; the air was full of the fragrance of the wild thyme and of the blooming lime trees; a gleaming bluish veil seemed to hang over the green mountains; far around reigned a silence – not the silence of sleep or of death, but a stillness as if all nature held its breath, as if it were waiting to have its picture photographed upon the blue sky. Here and there among the trees on the green meadows stood long poles, supporting the telegraph wires that had been drawn through the quiet valley; against one of these leaned an object, so motionless that it might have been taken for the trunk of a tree; but it was Rudy, who stood as quiet and motionless as all nature around him. He did not sleep, nor was he dead by any means; but just as the records of great events sometimes fly along the telegraph – messages of vital importance to those whom they concern, while the wire gives no sign, by sound or movement, of what is passing over it – so there was passing through the mind of Rudy a thought which was to be the happiness of his whole life and his one absorbing idea from that moment. His eyes were fixed on one point – on a light that gleamed out among the trees from the chamber of the miller where Babette dwelt. So motionless did Rudy stand here, one might have thought he was taking aim at a chamois, a creature which sometimes stands as if carved out of the rock, till suddenly, if a stone should roll down, it springs away in a headlong career. And something of this kind happened to Rudy – suddenly a thought rolled into his mind.

'Never falter!' he cried. 'Pay a visit to the mill, say good-evening to the miller and good-evening to Babette. He does not fall who is not afraid of falling. Babette must see me, sooner or later, if I am to be her husband.'

And Rudy laughed, for he was of good courage, and he strode away towards the mill. He knew what he wanted; he wanted to have Babette.

The river, with its yellowish bed, foamed along, and the willows and lime trees hung over the hurrying waters; Rudy strode along the path. But, as the children's song has it:

> Nobody was at home to greet him,
> Only the house cat came to meet him.

The house cat stood on the step and said 'Miaou', and arched her back; but Rudy paid no attention to this address. He knocked, but no one heard him, no one opened the door to him. 'Miaou!' said the cat. If Rudy had been still a child, he would have understood her language, and have known that the cat was saying, 'There's nobody at home here!' but now he must fain go over to the mill to make enquiries, and there he heard the news that the miller had gone far away to Interlaken, and Babette with him: a great shooting match was to come off there; it would begin tomorrow, and last a full week, and people from all the German Cantons were to be present at it.

Poor Rudy! he might be said to have chosen an unlucky day for his visit to Bex, and now he might go home. He turned about accordingly, and marched over St Maurice and Sion towards his own valley and the mountains of his home; but he was not discouraged. When the sun rose next morning his good humour already stood high, for it had never set.

'Babette is at Interlaken, many days' journey from here,' he said to himself. 'It is a long way thither if a man travels along the broad high road, but it is not so far if one takes the short cut across the mountains, and the chamois hunter's path is straight forward. I've been that way already: yonder is my early home, where I lived as a child in grandfather's house, and there's a shooting match at Interlaken. I'll be there too, and be the best shot; and I'll be with Babette too, when once I have made her acquaintance.'

With a light knapsack containing his Sunday clothes on his back, and his gun and hunting bag across his shoulder, Rudy mounted the hill by the short cut, which was, nevertheless, tolerably long; but the shooting match had only begun that day, and was to last a week or more; and they had told him that the miller and Babette would pass the whole time with their friends at Interlaken. Rudy marched across the Gemmi, intending to descend at Grindelwald.

Fresh and merry, he walked on in the strengthening light mountain air. The valley sank deeper and deeper behind him, and his horizon became more and more extended; here a snowy peak appeared, and there another, and presently the whole gleaming white chain of the Alps could be seen. Rudy knew every peak, and he made straight towards the Schreckhorn, that raised its white-powdered, stony finger up into the blue air.

At last he had crossed the ridge. The grassy pastures sloped down towards the valley of his old home. The air was light and his spirits were light. Mountain and valley bloomed fair with verdure and with flowers, and his heart was filled with the feeling of youth, that recks not of coming age or of death. To live, to conquer, to enjoy, free as a bird! and light as a bird he felt. And the swallows flew past him, and sang, as they had sang in his childhood, 'We and ye! we and ye!' and all seemed joy and rapid motion.

Below lay the summer-green meadow, studded with brown wooden houses, with the Lütschine rushing and humming among them. He saw the glacier with the grass-green borders and the clouded snow; he looked into the deep crevasses, and beheld the upper and the lower glacier. The church bells sounded across to him, as if they were ringing to welcome him into the valley of home; and his heart beat stronger, and swelled so, that for a moment Babette entirely disappeared, so large did his heart become, and so full of recollections.

He went along again, up on the mountain where he had stood as a child with other little children, offering carved houses for sale. There among the pine trees stood the house of his grandfather; but strangers inhabited it now. Children came running along the road towards him to sell their wares, and one of them offered him an Alpine rose, which Rudy looked upon as a good omen, and thought of Babette. Soon he had crossed the bridge where the two branches of the Lütschine join; the woods became thicker here and the walnut trees gave a friendly shade. Now he saw the waving flags, the flags with the white cross in a red field, the national emblem of the Switzer and the Dane, and Interlaken lay before him.

This was certainly a town without equal, according to Rudy's estimate. It was a little Swiss town in its Sunday dress. It did not look like other places, a heavy mass of stone houses, dismal and pretentious; no, here the wooden houses looked as if they had run down into the valley from the hills, and placed themselves in a row beside the clear river that ran so gaily by; they were a little out of order, but nevertheless they formed a kind of street; and the prettiest of all the streets was one that had grown up since Rudy had been here in his boyish days; and it looked to him as if it had been built of all the natty little houses his grandfather had carved, and which used to be kept in the cupboard of the old house. A whole row of such houses seemed to have grown up here like strong chestnut trees; each of them was called an hotel, and had carved work on the windows and doors, and a projecting roof, prettily and tastefully built, and in front of each was a garden separating it from the broad macadamised road. The houses only stood on one side of the road, so that they did not hide the fresh green pastures, in which the cows were walking about with bells round their necks like those which sound upon the lofty Alps. The pasture was surrounded by high mountains, which seemed to have stepped aside in the middle, so that the sparkling snow-covered mountain, the 'Jungfrau', the most beautiful of all the Swiss peaks, could be plainly seen.

What a number of richly dressed ladies and gentlemen from foreign lands! what a crowd of people from the various Cantons! Every marksman wore his number displayed in a wreath round his hat. There was music and singing, barrel organs and trumpets, bustle and noise. Houses and bridges were adorned with verses and emblems; flags and banners were waving; the rifles cracked merrily now and again; and in Rudy's ears the sound of the shots was the sweetest music; and in the bustle and tumult he had quite forgotten Babette, for whose sake he had come.

And now the marksmen went crowding to shoot at the target. Rudy soon took up his station among them, and proved to be the most skilful and the most fortunate of all – each time his bullet struck the black spot in the centre of the target.

'Who may that stranger, that young marksman be?' asked many of the bystanders. 'He speaks the French they talk in the Canton of Wallis.'

'He can also make himself well understood in our German,' said others.

'They say he lived as a child in the neighbourhood of Grindelwald,' observed one of the marksmen.

And he was full of life, this stranger youth. His eyes gleamed, and his glance and his arm were sure, and that is why he hit the mark so well. Fortune gives courage, but Rudy had courage enough of his own. He had soon assembled a circle of friends round him, who paid him honour, and showed respect for him; and Babette was almost forgotten for the moment. Then suddenly a heavy hand clapped him on the shoulder, and a deep voice addressed him in the French tongue:

'You're from the Canton of Wallis?'

Rudy turned round, and saw a red good-humoured face, belonging to a portly person. The speaker was the rich miller of Bex; and his broad body almost eclipsed the pretty delicate Babette, who, however, soon peeped forth from behind him with her bright dark eyes. It pleased the rich miller that a marksman from his Canton should have shot best, and have won respect from all present. Well, Rudy was certainly a fortunate youth, for the person for whose sake he had come, but whom he had forgotten after his arrival, now came to seek him out.

When fellow countrymen meet at a long distance from home, they are certain to converse and to make acquaintance with one another. By virtue of his good shooting, Rudy had become the first at the marksmen's meeting, just as the miller was the first at home in Bex on the strength of his money and his good mill; and so the two men shook hands, a thing they had never done before; Babette also held out her hand frankly to Rudy, who pressed it so warmly and gave her such an earnest look that she blushed crimson to the roots of her hair.

The miller talked of the long distance they had come, and of the many huge towns they had seen; according to his idea, they had made quite a long journey of it, having travelled by railway, steamboat, and diligence.

'I came the shortest way,' observed Rudy. 'I walked across the mountains. No road is so high but a man may get over it.'

'And break his neck,' quoth the miller. 'You look just the fellow to break your neck one of these days, so bold as you are, too.'

'Oh, a man does not fall unless he is afraid of falling,' observed Rudy.

The relatives of the miller in Interlaken, at whose house he and Babette were staying, invited Rudy to visit them, since he belonged to the same Canton as the rich miller. That was a good offer for Rudy. Fortune was favourable to him, as she always is to anyone who seeks to win by his own energy, and remembers that 'Providence provides us with nuts, but leaves us to crack them'.

Rudy sat among the miller's relatives like one of the family. A glass was emptied to the health of the best marksman, and Babette clinked her glass with the rest, and Rudy returned thanks for the toast.

Towards evening they all took a walk on the pretty road by the prosperous hotels under the old walnut trees, and so many people were there, and there was so much pushing, that Rudy was obliged to offer his arm to Babette. He declared he was very glad to have met people from Waud, for Waud and Wallis were good neighbour Cantons. He expressed his joy so heartily, that Babette could not help giving him a grateful pressure of the hand. They walked on together as if they had been old friends, and she talked and chattered away; and Rudy thought how charmingly she pointed out the ridiculous and absurd points in the costumes and manners of the foreign ladies; not that she did it to make game of them, for they might be very good honourable people, as Babette well knew, for was not her own god-mother one of these grand English ladies? Eighteen years ago, when Babette was christened, this lady had been residing in Bex, and had given Babette the costly brooch the girl now wore on her neck. Twice the lady had written, and this year Babette had expected to meet her and her two daughters at Interlaken. 'The daughters were old maids, nearly thirty years old,' added Babette; but then she herself was only eighteen.

The sweet little mouth never rested for a moment; and everything that Babette said, sounded in Rudy's ears like a matter of the utmost importance; and he, on his part, told all he had to tell – how often he had been at Bex, how well he knew the mill, and how often he had seen Babette, though she had probably never noticed him; and how, when he had lately called at the mill, full of thoughts that he could not express, she and her father had been absent – had gone far away, but not so far that a man might not climb over the wall that made the way so long.

He said all that and a great deal more. He said how fond he was of her, and that he had come hither on her account, and not for the sake of the marksmen's meeting.

Babette was quite still while he said all this; it almost seemed to her as if he entrusted her with too great a secret.

And as they wandered on, the sun sank down behind the high rocky wall. The 'Jungfrau' stood there in full beauty and splendour, surrounded by the green wreath of the forest-clad hills. Everyone stood still to enjoy the glorious sight, and Rudy and Babette rejoiced in it too.

'It is nowhere more beautiful than here!' said Babette.

'Nowhere!' cried Rudy, and he looked at Babette. 'Tomorrow I must return home,' he said, after a silence of a few moments.

'Come and see us at Bex,' whispered Babette; 'it will please my father.'

5

On the Way Home

Oh, what a load Rudy had to carry when he went homeward across the mountains on the following day! Yes, he had three silver goblets, two handsome rifles, and a silver coffee-pot. The coffee-pot would be useful when he set up housekeeping. But that was not all he had to carry: he bore something mightier and weightier, or rather it bore him, carrying him homewards across the high mountains. The weather was rough, grey, rainy, and heavy; the clouds floated down upon the mountain heights like funereal crape, concealing the sparkling summits. From the woodland valleys the last strokes of the axe sounded upward, and down the declivities of the mountains rolled trunks of trees, which looked like thin sticks from above, but were in reality thick enough to serve as masts for the largest ships. The Lütschine foamed along with its monotonous song, the wind whistled, the clouds sailed onward. Then suddenly a young girl appeared, walking beside Rudy: he had not noticed her till now that she was quite close to him. She wanted, like himself, to cross the mountain. The maiden's eyes had a peculiar power: you were obliged to look at them, and they were strange to behold, clear as glass, and deep, unfathomable.

'Have you a sweetheart?' asked Rudy, for his thoughts all ran on that subject.

'I have none,' replied the girl, with a laugh; but she did not seem to be speaking a true word. 'Don't let us make a circuit,' she said. 'We must keep more to the left, then the way will be shorter.'

'Yes, and we shall fall into an ice cleft,' said Rudy. 'You want to be a guide, and you don't know the way better than that!'

'I know the way well,' the girl replied, 'and my thoughts are not wandering. Yours are down in the valley, but up here one ought to think of the Ice Maiden: she does not love the human race – so people say.'

'I'm not afraid of her,' cried Rudy. 'She was obliged to give me up when I was still a child, and I shall not give myself up to her now that I am older.'

And the darkness increased, the rain fell, and the snow came, and dazzled and blinded.

'Reach me your hand,' said the girl to Rudy; 'I will help you to climb.'

And he felt the touch of her fingers icy cold upon him.

'*You* help me!' cried Rudy. 'I don't want a woman's help to show me how to climb.'

And he went on faster, away from her. The driving snow closed round him like a mantle, the wind whistled, and behind him he heard the girl laughing and singing in a strange way. He felt sure she was a phantom in the service of the Ice Maiden. Rudy had heard tell of such apparitions when he passed the night on the mountains in his boyish days, during his journey from his grandfather's house.

The snowfall abated, and the cloud was now below him. He looked back, but nobody was to be seen; but he could hear laughter and whooping that did not seem to proceed from a human voice.

When Rudy at last reached the highest mountain plateau, whence the path led downward into the Rhone valley, he saw in the direction of Chamonix, in a strip of pure blue sky, two bright stars which glittered and twinkled; and he thought of Babette, of himself, and of his good fortune, and the thought made him quite warm.

6

The Visit to the Mill

'What magnificent things you have brought home!' exclaimed the old aunt; and her strange eagle's eyes flashed, and her thin neck waved to and fro faster than ever in strange contortions. 'You have luck, Rudy! I must kiss you, my darling boy!'

And Rudy allowed himself to be kissed, but with an expression in his face which told that he submitted to it as a necessary evil, a little domestic infliction.

'How handsome you are, Rudy!' said the old woman.

'Don't put nonsense into my head,' replied Rudy, with a laugh; but still he was pleased to hear her say it.

'I repeat it,' she cried. 'Good luck attends upon you!'

'Perhaps you are right,' he observed; and he thought of Babette.

Never had he felt such a longing to go down into the deep valley.

'They must have returned,' he said to himself. 'It is two days beyond the time when they were to have been back. I must go to Bex.'

Accordingly Rudy journeyed to Bex, and the people of the mill were at home. He was well received, and the people at Interlaken had sent a kind message of remembrance to him. Babette did not say much: she had grown very silent, but her eyes spoke, and that was quite enough for Rudy. It seemed as if the miller, who was accustomed to lead the conversation, and who always expected his hearers to laugh at his ideas and jokes because he was the rich miller – it seemed as if he would never tire of hearing Rudy's hunting adventures; and Rudy spoke of the dangers and difficulties the chamois hunters have to encounter on the high mountains, how they have to cling, how they have to clamber over the frail ledges of snow, that are, as it were, glued to the mountain-side by frost and cold, and to clamber across the bridges of snow that stretch across rocky chasms. And the eyes of the brave Rudy flashed while he told of the hunter's life, of the cunning of the chamois and its perilous leaps, of the mighty whirlwind and the rushing avalanches. He noticed clearly enough, that with every fresh narrative he enlisted the miller more and more in his favour; and the old man felt especially interested in what the young hunter told about the vultures and the royal eagles.

Not far off, in the Canton of Wallis, there was an eagle's nest built very cleverly under a steep overhanging rock, and in the nest was an eaglet which could not be captured. An Englishman had a few days before offered Rudy a handful of gold pieces if he could procure him the eaglet alive.

'But there is a limit in all things,' said Rudy: 'that eaglet is not to be taken; it would be folly to make the attempt.'

And the wine flowed and conversation flowed; but the evening appeared far too short for Rudy, although it was past midnight when he set out to go home after his first visit to the mill.

The lights still gleamed for a short time through the windows of the mill among the green trees, and the Parlour Cat came forth from the open loophole in the roof, and met the Kitchen Cat walking along the rain-spout.

'Do you know the news in the mill?' asked the Parlour Cat. 'There's a silent engagement going on in the house. Father knows nothing about it. Rudy and Babette were treading on each other's paws under the table all the evening. They trod upon me twice, but I would not mew for fear of exciting attention.'

'*I* should have mewed,' said the Kitchen Cat.

'What will pass in the kitchen would never do for the parlour,' retorted the other Cat; 'but I'm curious to know what the miller will think about it when he hears of the affair.'

Yes, indeed, what would the miller say? That is what Rudy would have liked to know too; and, moreover, he could not bear to remain long in suspense without knowing it. Accordingly, a few days afterwards, when the omnibus rattled across the Rhone bridge between Wallis and Waud, Rudy sat in the vehicle, in good spirits as usual, and already basking in the sunny prospect of the consent he hoped to gain that very evening.

And when the evening came, and the omnibus was making its way back, Rudy once more sat in it as a passenger; but in the mill the Parlour Cat had some important news to tell.

'Do you know it, you there out of the kitchen? The miller has been told all about it. There was a fine end to it all. Rudy came here towards evening, and he and Babette had much to whisper and to tell each other, standing in the passage outside the miller's room. I was lying at their feet, but they had neither eyes nor thoughts for me. "I shall go to your father without more ado," said Rudy; "that's the honest way to do it." "Shall I go with you?" asked Babette; "it will give you courage."

"I've courage enough," replied Rudy; "but if you are present he must be kind, whether he likes it or not." And they went in together. Rudy trod upon my tail most horribly. He's a very awkward fellow, is Rudy. I called out, but neither he nor Babette had ears to hear me. They opened the door, and both went in, and I went on before them; but I sprang up on the back of a chair, for I could not know where Rudy would kick. But it was the miller who kicked this time, and it was a good kick too! out at the door and up to the mountain among the chamois; and he may take aim at them now, may Rudy, and not at our Babette.'

'But what did they say?' asked the Kitchen Cat.

'What did they say? Why, they said everything that people are accustomed to say when they come a-wooing. "I love her and she loves me, and if there's milk enough in the pail for one, there's enough for two." "But she's perched too high for you," said the miller. "She's perched on grist, on golden grist, as you very well know, and you can't reach up to her." "Nothing is so high that a man can't reach it, if he has the will," said Rudy, for he is a bold fellow. "But you can't reach the eaglet, you said so yourself the other day, and Babette is higher than that." "I shall take both of them," exclaimed Rudy. "I'll give you Babette when you give me the young eaglet alive," said the miller, and he laughed till the tears ran down his cheeks. "But now I must thank you for your visit. Call again tomorrow, and you'll find nobody at home. Goodbye to you, Rudy." And Babette said goodbye too, as pitifully as a little kitten that can't see its mother yet. "Your word is your bond," cried Rudy. "Don't cry, Babette: I'll bring you the eaglet!" "You'll break your neck first, I hope," said the miller, "and then we shall be rid of your dangling here!" That's what I call a capital kick!

'And now Rudy is gone, and Babette sits and weeps, but the miller sings German songs that he has learned on his late journey. I don't like to be downhearted about it, for that can do no good!'

'Well, after all, there's some prospect for him still,' observed the Kitchen Cat.

The Eagle's Nest

Down from the rocky path sounded a fresh song, merry and strong, indicating courage and good spirits; and the singer was Rudy, who came to seek his friend Vesinand.

'You must help me! We will have Ragli with us. I want to take the eaglet out of the nest on the rock,'

'Would you not like to take the black spots out of the moon first?' replied Vesinand. 'That would be just as easy. You seem to be in a merry mood.'

'Certainly I am, for I hope to be married soon. But let us speak seriously, and I will tell you what it is all about.'

And soon Vesinand and Ragli knew what Rudy wanted.

'You're a headstrong fellow,' they said. 'It can't be done: you will break your neck over it.'

'A man does not fall who's not afraid of falling,' Rudy persisted.

At midnight they set out with poles, ladders, and ropes; their way led through forest and thicket, over loose rolling stones, ever upward, upward, through the dark night. The water rushed beneath them, water dripped down from above, and heavy clouds careered through the air. The hunters reached the steep wall of rock. Here it was darker than ever. The opposite sides of the chasm almost touched, and the sky could only be seen through a small cleft above them, and around them and beneath them was the great abyss with its foaming waters. The three sat on the rock waiting for the dawn, when the eagle should fly forth, for the old bird must be shot before they could think of capturing the young one. Rudy sat on the ground, as silent as if he were a piece of the stone on which he crouched; his rifle he held before him ready cocked; his eyes were fixed on the upper cleft beneath which the eagle's nest lay concealed against the rock. And a long time those three hunters had to wait!

Now there was a rushing, whirring sound above them, and a great soaring object darkened the air. Two guns were pointed, as the black form of the eagle arose from the nest. A shot rang sharply out, for a moment the outstretched wings continued to move, and then the bird sank slowly down, and it seemed with its outstretched wings to fill up the chasm, and threatened to bear down the hunters in its fall. Then the eagle sank down into the abyss, breaking off twigs of trees and bushes in its descent.

And now the hunters began operations. Three of the longest ladders were bound together – those would reach high enough; they were reared on end on the last firm foothold on the margin of the abyss; but they did not reach far enough; and higher up, where the nest lay concealed under the shelter of the projecting crag, the rock was as smooth as a wall. After a short council the men determined that two ladders should be tied together and let down from above into the cleft, and that these should be attached to the three that had been fastened together below. With great labour the two ladders were dragged up and the rope made fast above; then the ladders were passed over the margin of the projecting rock, so that they hung dangling above the abyss. Rudy had already taken his place on the lowest step. It was an icy-cold morning; misty clouds were rising from the dark chasm. Rudy sat as a fly sits on a waving wheat-straw which some nest-building bird has deposited on the edge of a factory chimney; only the fly can spread its wings and escape if the wheat-straw gives way, while Rudy had nothing for it, in such a case, but to break his neck. The wind whistled about him, and below in the abyss thundered the waters from the melting glacier, the palace of the Ice Maiden.

Now he imparted a swaying motion to the ladders, just as a spider sways itself to and fro, when, hanging at the end of its thread, it wishes to seize upon an object; and when Rudy for the fourth time touched the top of the ladder, the highest of the three that had been bound together, he seized it and held it firmly. Then he bound the other two ladders with a strong hand to the first three, but they still rattled and swayed as if they had loose hinges.

The five long ladders thus bound together, and standing perpendicularly against the rocky wall, looked like a long swaying reed; and now

came the most dangerous part of the business. There was climbing to be done as the cat climbs; but Rudy had learned to climb, and it was the Cat who had taught him. He knew nothing of the Spirit of Giddiness who stood treading the air behind him, and stretching out long arms towards him like the feelers of a polypus. Now he stood upon the highest step of the topmost ladder, and perceived that after all it was not high enough to let him look into the nest: he could only reach up into it with his hand. He felt about to test the firmness of the thick plaited branches that formed the lower part of the nest, and when he had secured a thick steady piece he swung himself up by it from the ladder, and leaned against the branch, so that his head and shoulders were above the level of the nest. A stifling stench of carrion streamed towards him, for in the nest lay chamois, birds, and lambs, in a putrid state. The Spirit of Giddiness, that had no power over him, blew the poisonous vapour into his face, to make him sick and trouble his senses; and below, in the black yawning gulf, on the rushing waters, sat the Ice Maiden herself, with her long whitish-green hair, and stared at him with cold deathlike eyes.

'Now I shall catch you!' she thought.

In a corner of the nest he saw the young one, which was not yet fledged, sitting large and stately. Rudy fixed his eyes upon it, held himself fast with all the strength of one hand, while with the other he threw the noose over the young eagle. It was caught – caught alive! Its legs were entangled in the tough noose, and Rudy threw the cord and the bird across his shoulder, so that the creature hung some distance beneath him, while he held fast by a rope they had lowered down to assist him, till his feet touched the topmost round of the ladder.

'Hold fast! Don't fancy you're going to fall, and you won't fall!' It was the old maxim, and he followed it; he held fast and climbed, was convinced that he should not fall, and accordingly he did not fall.

And now a whoop resounded, strong and jubilant, and Rudy stood safe and sound on the firm rock with the captured eaglet.

8

What News the Parlour Cat had to Tell

'Here is what you wished for!' said Rudy, as he entered the house of the miller at Bex.

He set down a great basket on the ground, and lifted the cloth that covered it. Two yellow eyes bordered with black stared forth; they seemed to shoot forth sparks, and gleamed burning and savage, as if they would burn and bite all they looked at. The short strong beak was open, ready to snap, and the neck was red and downy.

'The young eagle!' cried the miller.

Babette screamed aloud and started back, but she could not turn her eyes from Rudy or from the eagle.

'You're not to be frightened off,' observed the miller.

'And you always keep your word,' answered Rudy. 'Every man has his own character.'

'But why did you not break your neck?' asked the miller.

'Because I held fast,' replied Rudy; 'and I do that still. I hold Babette fast!'

'First see that you get her,' said the miller; and he laughed. But his laughter was a good sign, and Babette knew it.

'We must have him out of the basket; his staring is enough to drive one mad. But how did you contrive to get at him?'

And Rudy had to relate the adventure, at which the miller opened his eyes wider and wider.

'With your courage and good fortune you may gain a living for three wives,' cried the miller at last.

'Thank you!' said Rudy.

'Still, you have not Babette yet,' continued the miller; and he slapped the young huntsman playfully on the shoulder.

'Do you know the latest news from the mill?' the Parlour Cat enquired of the Kitchen Cat. 'Rudy has brought us the eaglet, and is going to take Babette away in exchange. They have kissed each other, and let the old man see it. That's as good as a betrothal. The old man didn't kick; he drew in his claws, and took his nap, and let the two young ones sit together and purr. They've so much to tell each other that they won't have done till Christmas.'

And they had not done till Christmas. The wind tossed up the brown leaves; the snow whirled through the valley and over the high mountains; the Ice Maiden sat in her proud castle, which increases in size during the winter; the rocky walls were covered with a coating of ice, and icicles thick as pine trunks and heavy as elephants hung down, where in the summer the mountain stream spread its misty veil; garlands of ice of whimsical forms hung sparkling on the snow-powdered fir trees. The Ice Maiden rode on the rushing wind over the deepest valleys. The snowy covering reached almost down to Bex, and the Ice Maiden came thither also, and saw Rudy sitting in the mill: this winter he sat much more indoors than was his custom – he sat by Babette. The wedding was to be next summer; their ears often buzzed, their friends spoke so much about it. In the mill there was sunshine – the loveliest Alpine rose bloomed there, the cheerful smiling Babette, beautiful as the spring, the spring that makes all the birds sing of summer and of marriage feasts.

'How those two are always sitting together – close together!' said the Parlour Cat. 'I've heard enough of their mewing.'

9

The Ice Maiden

Spring had unfolded its fresh green garland on the walnut and chestnut trees extending from the bridge at St Maurice to the shore of the Lake of Geneva, along the Rhone that rushes along with headlong speed from its source beneath the green glacier, the ice palace where the Ice Maiden dwells, and whence she soars on the sharp wind up to the loftiest snow-field, there to rest upon her snowy couch: there she sat, and gazed with far-seeing glance into the deep valleys, where the men ran busily to and fro, like ants on the stone that glitters in the sun.

'Ye spirit powers, as the Children of the Sun call you,' said the Ice Maiden, 'ye are but worms. Let a snowball roll from the mountain, and you and your houses and towns are crushed and swept away!'

And higher she lifted her haughty head, and gazed out far and wide with deadly flashing eyes.

But from the valley there arose a rumbling sound. They were blasting the rocks. Human work was going on. Roads and tunnels for railways were being constructed.

'They're playing like moles!' she said. 'They're digging passages under the earth, and thence come these sounds like the firing of guns. When I remove one of my castles, it sounds louder than the thunder's roar.'

Out of the valley rose a smoke which moved forward like a fluttering veil: it was the waving steam plume of the engine, which on the lately opened road dragged the train, the curling snake, each of whose joints is a carriage. Away it shot, swift as an arrow.

'They're playing at being masters down yonder, the spirit powers,' said the Ice Maiden, 'but the power of the forces of nature is greater than theirs.'

And she laughed and sang till the valley echoed.

'Yonder rolls an avalanche!' said the people.

But the Children of the Sun sang louder still of human thought, the powerful agent that places barriers against the sea, and levels mountains, and fills up valleys – of human thought, that is master of the powers of nature. And at this time there marched across the snow-field where the Ice Maiden rules, a company of travellers. The men had bound themselves to one another with ropes, that they might, as it were, form a heavier body here on the slippery surface of ice on the margin of the deep chasms.

'Insects that you are!' cried the Ice Maiden. '*You* the rulers of the powers of nature!'

And she turned away from the company, and looked contemptuously down into the deep valley, where the long train of carriages was rushing along.

'There they sit, those thoughts! there they sit, in the power of the forces of nature! I see them, each and all of them! One of them sits alone, proud as a King, and yonder they sit in a crowd. Half of them are asleep. And when the steam dragon stops, they alight and go their ways. The thoughts go abroad into the world.'

And she laughed again.

'There rolls another avalanche!' said the people in the valley.

'It will not reach us,' said two who sat behind the steam dragon. 'Two hearts that beat like one,' as the song has it. These two were Babette and Rudy; and the miller was with them too.

'I go as baggage!' he said. 'I am here as a necessary appendage.'

'There those two sit,' said the Ice Maiden. 'Many a chamois have I crushed, millions of Alpine roses have I broken to pieces, not even sparing the roots. I'll wipe them out, these thoughts – these spirit powers.'

And she laughed again.

'There rolls another avalanche!' said the people in the valley below.

10

Babette's Godmother

At Montreux, the first of the towns which with Clarens, Vernex, and Crin form a garland round the north-eastern portion of the Lake of Geneva, lived Babette's godmother, a high-born English lady, with her daughters and a young male relative. They had only lately arrived, but the miller had already waited upon them to tell them of Babette's betrothal, and the story of Rudy and the eaglet, and of his visit to Interlaken – in short, the whole story. And the visitors were much pleased to hear it, and showed themselves very friendly towards Rudy, Babette, and the miller, who were all three urgently invited to come and see them, and came accordingly. Babette was to see her god-mother, and the lady to make acquaintance with Babette.

By the little town of Villeneuve, at the extremity of the Lake of Geneva, lay the steamship which in a half-hour's trip goes from there to Vernex just below Montreux. The coast here has been sung by poets; here, under the walnut trees, by the deep bluish-green lake, sat Byron, and wrote his melodious verses of the prisoner in the gloomy rocky fortress of Chillon. Yonder, where the weeping willows of Clarens are clearly mirrored in the water, Rousseau wandered, dreaming of Héloïse. The Rhone rolls onward among the lofty snow-clad mountains of Savoy: here, not far from its mouth, lies in the lake a little island, so small that seen from the coast it appears like a ship upon the waters. It is a rock which, about a century ago, a lady caused to be walled round with stone and coated with earth, wherein three acacia trees were planted, which now overshadow the whole island.

Babette was quite delighted with this spot, which seemed to her the prettiest point of all their journey, and she declared that they must land, for it must be charming there. But the steamer glided past, and was moored according to custom, at Vernex.

The little party wandered from here among the white sunny walls which surround the vineyards of Montreux, where the fig tree casts its shadow over the peasants' huts, and laurels and cypresses grow in the gardens. Halfway up the hill was situated the hotel in which the English lady was staying.

The reception was very hearty. The English lady was very friendly, with a round smiling face: in her childhood her head must have been like one of Raphael's angels; but she had an old angel's head now, surrounded by curls of silvery white. The daughters were tall, slender, good-looking, lady-like girls. The young cousin whom they had brought with them was dressed in white from head to foot. He had yellow hair, and enough of yellow whisker to have been shared among three or four gentlemen. He immediately showed the very greatest attention to Babette.

Richly bound volumes, music-books, and drawings lay strewn about upon the large table; the balcony door stood open, and they could look out upon the beautiful far-spreading lake, which lay so shining and still that the mountains of Savoy, with their towns, forests, and snowy peaks, were most accurately reproduced on its surface.

Rudy, who was generally frank, cheerful, and ready, felt very uncomfortable here, and he moved as if he were walking on peas spread over a smooth surface. How long and wearisome the time seemed to him! He could have fancied himself on a treadmill! And now they even went out to walk together; that was just as slow and wearisome as the rest. Rudy might have taken one step backward to every two he made forward, and yet have kept up with the others. They went down to Chillon, the old gloomy castle on the rocky island, to see the instruments of torture, the deadly dungeons, the rusty chains fastened to the walls, the stone benches on which men condemned to death had sat, the trap-door through which the unhappy wretches were hurled down to be impaled below upon tipped iron stakes in the water. They called it a pleasure to see all this. It was a place of execution that had been lifted by Byron's song into the domain of poetry. Rudy only associated the prison feeling with it. He leaned against one of the great stone window-frames, and looked out into the deep bluish-green water and over at the little island with the three acacias; thither he wished himself transported, to be free from the whole chattering company. But Babette was in unusually good spirits. She declared she had enjoyed herself immensely, and told Rudy she considered the young cousin a complete gentleman.

'A complete booby!' cried Rudy.

And it was the first time he had said anything she did not like. The Englishman had given her a little book in remembrance of Chillon. It was Byron's poem, 'The Prisoner of Chillon,' translated into French, so that Babette could read it.

'The book may be good,' said Rudy, 'but I don't like the combed and curled fellow who gave it you.'

'He looked to me like a flour-sack without any flour,' said the miller; and he laughed at his own joke.

Rudy laughed too, and said that was just his own opinion.

II

The Cousin

A few days after these events, when Rudy went to pay a visit at the mill, he found the young Englishman there, and Babette was just about to offer her visitor some boiled trout – which she certainly must have decorated with parsley with her own hands, so tempting did they look, a thing that was not at all necessary. What did the Englishman want here? And what business had Babette to treat him and pet him? Rudy was jealous; and that pleased Babette, for she liked to become acquainted with all the points of his character, the weak as well as the strong. Love was still only a game to her, and she played with Rudy's whole heart; yet he was, we must confess, her happiness, her whole life, her constant thought, the best and most precious possession she had on earth; but, for all that, the darker his glance became, the more did her eyes laugh, and she would have liked to kiss the fair Englishman with the yellow beard, if her doing this would have made Rudy wild and sent him raging away; for that would show how much he loved her. Now, this was not right of Babette; but she was only nineteen years old. She did not think much, and least of all did she think that her conduct might be misinterpreted by the young Englishman into something very unworthy of the respectable affianced miller's daughter.

The mill stood just where the high road from Bex leads down under the snow-covered mountain height, which in the language of the country is called 'Diablerets'. It was not far from a rushing mountain stream, whose waters were whitish-grey, like foaming soapsuds: it was not this stream that worked the mill; a smaller stream drove round the great wheel – one which fell from the rock some way beyond the main river, and whose power and fall were increased by a stone dam, and by a long wooden trough, which carried it over the level of the great stream. This trough was so full that the water poured over its margin; this wooden margin offered a narrow slippery path for those who chose to walk along it, that they might get to the mill by the shortest cut; and to whom, of all people, should the idea of reaching the mill by this road occur, but to the young Englishman! Dressed in white, like a miller's man, he climbed over at night, guided by the light that shone from Babette's chamber window; but he had not learned how to climb like Rudy, and consequently was near upon falling headlong into the stream below, but he escaped with a pair of wet coat-sleeves and soiled trousers; and thus, wet and bespattered with mud, he came below

Babette's window. Here he climbed into the old elm tree, and began to imitate the voice of the owl, the only bird whose cry he could manage. Babette heard the noise, and looked out of her window through the thin curtain; but when she saw the white form, and conjectured who it was, her heart beat with fear and with anger also. She put out the light in a hurry, saw that all the bolts of the windows were well secured, and then let him whoop and tu-whoo to his heart's content.

It would be dreadful if Rudy were in the mill just now! But Rudy was not in the mill; no – what was worse still, he stood just under the elm tree. Presently there were loud and angry voices, and there might be a fight there, and even murder. Babette opened the window in a fright, and called Rudy by name, begging him to go, and declaring that she would not allow him to remain.

'You won't allow me to remain?' he shouted. 'Then it's a planned thing! You expect good friends, better men than I! For shame, Babette!'

'You are odious!' cried Babette. 'I hate you! Go, go!'

'I have not deserved this,' he said, and went away, his face burning like fire, and his heart burning as fiercely.

Babette threw herself on her bed and wept.

'So dearly as I love you, Rudy! And that you should think evil of me!'

Then she broke out in anger; and that was good for her, for otherwise she would have suffered too much from her grief; and now she could sleep – could sleep the strengthening sleep of health and youth.

12

Evil Powers

Rudy quitted Bex and took the way towards his home; he went up the mountain, into the fresh cool air, where the snow lay on the ground, where the Ice Maiden ruled. The leafy trees stood far below him and looked like field plants; the pines and bushes all looked tiny from here; the Alpine roses grew beside the snow, that lay in long patches like linen lying to bleach. A blue gentian that stood by his path he crushed with a blow of his riflestock.

Higher up still two chamois came in view. Rudy's eyes brightened and his thoughts took a new direction; but he was not near enough to be sure of his aim, so he mounted higher, where nothing but scanty grass grew among the blocks of stone. The chamois were straying quietly along on the snow-field. He hastened his steps till the veil of clouds began to encompass him, and suddenly he found himself in front of a steep wall of rock; and now the rain began to pour down.

He felt a burning thirst, his head was hot, his limbs were cold. He took his hunting flask, but it was empty – he had not thought of filling it when he rushed out upon the mountains. He had never been ill in his life, but now he had warnings of such a condition, for he was weary, and had an inclination to lie down, a longing to go to sleep, though the rain was pouring all around. He tried to collect his faculties, but all objects danced and trembled strangely before his eyes. Then suddenly he beheld what he had never seen in that spot before – a new low-browed house, that leaned against the rock. At the door stood a young girl, and she almost appeared to him like the schoolmaster's daughter Annette, whom he had once kissed at the dance; but it was not Annette, though he felt certain he had seen this girl before; perhaps at Grindelwald on that evening when he returned from the marksmen's feast at Interlaken.

'Whence do you come?' he asked.

'I am at home here. I am keeping my flock,' was the reply.

'Your flock! Where does it graze? Here there is only snow and rocks.'

'Much you know about what is here,' retorted the girl, with a laugh. 'Behind us, lower down, is a glorious pasture: my goats graze there. I tend them carefully. Not one of them do I lose, and what is once mine remains mine.'

'You are bold,' said Rudy.

'And you too,' replied the girl.

'If you have any milk in the house, pray give me some to drink; I am insufferably thirsty.'

'I've something better than milk,' said the girl, 'and I will give you that. Yesterday some travellers were here with their guide, who forgot a bottle of wine of a kind you have probably never tasted. They will not come back to take it away, and I do not drink it, therefore you must drink it.'

And the girl brought the wine, and poured it into a wooden cup, which she gave to Rudy.

'That *is* good wine,' said he. 'I've never tasted any so strong or so fiery!'

And his eyes glistened, and a glowing, lifelike feeling streamed through him, as if every care, every pressure, had melted into air, and the fresh bubbling human nature stirred within him.

'Why, this must be Annette!' he cried. 'Give me a kiss.'

'Then give me the beautiful ring that you wear on your finger.'

'My betrothal ring?'

'Yes, that very one,' said the girl.

And again she poured wine in the cup, and she put it to his lips, and he drank. The joy of life streamed into his blood: the whole world seemed to be his, and why should he mourn? Everything is made for us to enjoy, that it may make us happy. The stream of life is the stream of enjoyment, and to be carried along by it is happiness. He looked at the young girl – it was Annette, and yet not Annette; still less did it seem like the phantom, the goblin as he called it, which had met him at Grindelwald. The girl here on the mountain looked fresh as the white snow, blooming as an Alpine rose, and swift-footed as a kid; but still she looked as much a mortal as Rudy himself. And he looked in her wonderfully clear eyes, only for a moment he looked into them, and – who shall describe it? – in that moment, whether it was the life of the spirit or death that filled him, he was borne upward, or else he sank into the deep and deadly ice cleft, lower and lower. He saw the icy walls gleaming like blue-green glass, fathomless abysses yawned around, and the water dropped tinkling down like shining bells, clear as pearls, glowing with pale blue flames. The Ice Maiden kissed him – a kiss which sent a shudder from neck to brow; a cry of pain escaped from him; he tore himself away, staggered, and – it was night before his eyes; but soon he opened them again. Evil powers had been playing their sport with him.

Vanished was the Alpine girl, vanished the sheltering hut; the water poured down the naked rocky wall, and snow lay all around. Rudy trembled with cold: he was wet to the skin, and his ring was gone – the betrothal ring which Babette had given him. His rifle lay near him in the snow: he took it up and tried to fire it, but it missed. Damp clouds hovered like masses of snow over the abyss, and Giddiness was there, lying in wait for the powerless prey; and below, in the deep abyss, there was a sound as if a block of stone were falling, crushing in its descent everything that tried to arrest its progress.

But Babette sat in the mill and wept. Rudy had not been there for six days – he who was in the wrong, and who ought to come and beg her pardon, and whom she loved with her whole heart.

13

In the Mill

'What a strange thing it is with those people!' said the Parlour Cat to the Kitchen Cat. 'They're parted now, Babette and Rudy. She's weeping; and he, I suppose, does not think any more about her.'

'I don't like that,' said the Kitchen Cat.

'Nor do I,' observed the Parlour Cat; 'but I won't take it to heart. Babette may betroth herself to the red-beard. But he has not been here either since that night when he wanted to climb on the roof.'

Evil powers sport with us and in us: Rudy had experienced that, and had thought much of it. What was all that which had happened to him and around him on the summit of the mountain? Were they spirits he had seen, or had he had a feverish vision? Never until now had he suffered from fever or any other illness. But in judging Babette, he had looked into his own heart also. He had traced the wild whirlwind, the hot wind that had raged there. Would he be able to confess to Babette every thought he had had – thoughts that might become actions in the hour of temptation? He had lost her ring, and through this loss she had won him again. Would she be able to confess to him? He felt as if his heart would burst when he thought of her. What a number of recollections arose within him! He saw her, as if she were standing bodily before him, laughing like a wayward child. Many a sweet word she had spoken out of the fullness of her heart now crept into his breast like a sunbeam, and soon there was nothing but sunshine within him when he thought of Babette.

Yes, she would be able to confess to him, and she should do so. Accordingly he went to the mill, and the confession began with a kiss, and ended in the fact that Rudy was declared to be the sinner. His great fault had been that he had doubted Babette's fidelity – it was quite wicked of him. Such distrust, such headlong anger, might bring sorrow upon them both. Yes, certainly they could; and accordingly Babette read him a short lecture, to her own great contentment, and with charming grace. But in one point she agreed with Rudy: the nephew of her godmother was a booby, and she would burn the book he had given her, for she would not keep the slightest thing that reminded her of him.

'That's all past and gone,' said the Parlour Cat. 'Rudy is here again, and they understand one another, and that's the greatest happiness, they say.'

'I heard from the rats last night,' observed the Kitchen Cat, 'that the greatest happiness was to eat tallow candles and to have plenty of rancid bacon. Now, whom is one to believe, the rats or the lovers?'

'Neither,' said the Parlour Cat; 'that's always the safest way.'

The greatest happiness of Rudy and Babette – the fairest day, as they called it – the wedding day, now approached rapidly.

But the wedding was not to be celebrated at the church at Bex and in the mill. Babette's godmother wished her godchild to be married from her house, and the service was to be read in the beautiful little church at Montreux. The miller insisted upon having his way in this matter. He alone knew what were the English lady's intentions with respect to her godchild, and declared that the lady intended making such a wedding present that they were bound to show some sense of obligation. The day was fixed. On the evening before it, they were to travel to Villeneuve, so that they might drive over early to Montreux, that the young English ladies might dress the bride.

'I suppose there will be a wedding feast here in the house?' said the Parlour Cat: 'if not, I wouldn't give a mew for the whole affair.'

'Of course there will be a feast here,' replied the Kitchen Cat. 'Ducks and pigeons have been killed, and a whole buck is hanging against the wall. My mouth waters when I think of it. Tomorrow the journey will begin.'

Yes, tomorrow. And on this evening Rudy and Babette sat for the last time together in the mill as a betrothed pair.

Without, the Alps were glowing, the evening bells sounded, and the Daughters of the Sunbeams sang, 'Let that happen which is best.'

14

Visions of the Night

The sun had gone down and the clouds lowered among the high mountains in the Rhone valley; the wind blew from the south – a wind from Africa was passing over the lofty Alps, a whirlwind that tore the clouds asunder; and when it had passed by, all was still for a moment; the rent clouds hung in fantastic forms among the forest-clad mountains and over the hurrying Rhone; they hung in shapes like those of the sea monsters of the primaeval world, like the soaring eagles of the air, like the leaping frogs of the marshes; they came down towards the rushing stream, sailing upon it, and yet suspended in air. The river carried down with it an uprooted pine tree, and bubbling eddies rushed on in front of the mass; they were Spirits of Giddiness, more than one of them, that whirled along over the foaming stream. The moon lit up the snow on the mountain-tops, the dark woods, and the wonderful white clouds – the nightly visions, the spirits of the powers of nature. The dwellers in the mountains saw them through the window-panes sailing on in troops in front of the Ice Maiden, who came out of her glacier palace, and sat on the frail ship, the uprooted pine tree: she was carried by the glacier water down the river into the open sea.

'The wedding guests are coming!' she said; and she sang the news to the air and to the water.

Visions without, visions within. Babette was dreaming a wonderful dream.

It seemed to her as if she were married to Rudy, and had been his wife for many years. He was absent, chamois hunting, but she was sitting at home in her dwelling, and the young Englishman, he with the yellow beard, was sitting by her. His eyes were so eloquent, his words had such magic power, that when he stretched out his hand to her, she was forced to follow him. They went away together from her home. On they went, ever downwards; and it seemed to Babette as though there lay on her heart a weight that grew heavier and heavier, and this weight was a sin against Heaven and a sin against Rudy. And suddenly she stood forsaken, and her dress was torn by the thorns, and her head had turned grey: she looked upwards in her misery, and on the edge of the rock she caught sight of Rudy: she stretched out her arms to him, but did not dare to call or to beseech him to help her; and, indeed, that would have availed her nothing, for soon she saw that it was not he, but only his hunting coat and his hat, hanging up on the alpenstock in the fashion adopted by the hunters to deceive the chamois. And in her boundless agony Babette moaned out, 'Oh that I had died on my wedding day, the happiest day of my life! That would have been a mercy, a great happiness! Then all would have happened for the best! the best that could happen to me and to Rudy; for no one knows what the future will bring!'

And in her God-forsaken despair she threw herself into the abyss, and a string seemed to burst, and a sorrowful note resounded through the mountains!

Babette awoke: the dream was past and effaced from her mind, but she knew that she had dreamed something terrible, and that it was about the young Englishman, whom she had not seen, whom she had not even thought of, for months past. Could he be in Montreux? Should she see him at her wedding? A light shade passed over her delicate mouth and her eyebrows contracted to a frown, but soon there was a smile on her lips and beams of gladness shot from her eyes; for, without, the sun was shining brightly, and it was morning, and she was to be married to Rudy.

Rudy was already in the sitting-room when she entered it, and now they started for Villeneuve. They were both supremely happy, and so was the miller likewise. He laughed, and his face beamed with good humour. A kind father he was, and an honest man.

'Now we are the masters of the house!' said the Parlour Cat.

15

Conclusion

It was not yet evening when the three happy people entered Villeneuve, where they dined. Thereupon the miller sat in the armchair, smoked his pipe, and took a short nap. The betrothed pair went arm in arm out of the town: they walked along the road, under the green-clad rocks, beside the deep blue-green lake; the grey walls and heavy towers of gloomy Chillon were mirrored in the clear flood; the little island of the three acacias lay still nearer to them, looking like a nosegay in the lake.

'It must be charming there!' said Babette.

She felt the greatest desire to go there; and this wish might be immediately fulfilled, for by the shore lay a boat, and it was an easy matter to loosen the rope by which it was fastened. No one was to be seen of whom permission could be asked, and so they borrowed the boat without ceremony, for Rudy was an expert rower.

The oars cut like fins into the yielding water – the water that is so pliant and yet so strong – that has a back to bear burdens and a mouth to devour – that can smile, the very picture of mildness, and yet can terrify and crush. The water glistened in the wake of the boat, which in a few minutes had carried the two over to the island, where they stepped ashore. There was not more room on the spot than two persons would require for a dance.

Rudy danced round it twice or thrice with Babette; then they sat down, hand in hand, upon the bench under the drooping acacias, looked into each other's eyes; and everything glowed in the radiance of the setting sun. The pine woods on the mountains were bathed in a lilac tint, like that of the blooming heather; and where the trees ended and the naked rock was shown, it glowed as if the stone had been transparent; the clouds in the sky were like red fire, and the whole lake lay like a fresh blushing rose leaf. Gradually the shadows crept up the snow-covered mountains of Savoy, painting them blue-black; but the highest summit gleamed like red lava, and seemed to give a picture from the early history of the mountains' formation, when these masses rose glowing from the depths of the earth and had not yet cooled. Rudy and Babette declared they had never yet beheld such a sunset in the Alps. The snow-covered Dent du Midi was tipped with a radiance like that of the full moon when she first rises above the horizon.

'So much beauty! So much happiness!' they both exclaimed.

'This earth has nothing more to give,' said Rudy. 'An evening like this seems to comprise a whole life! How often have I felt my happiness as I feel it now, and have thought, "If everything were to end this moment, how happily I should have lived! How glorious is this world!" And then the day would end, and another began, and the new day seemed more beautiful to me than the last! How immeasurably good is God, Babette!'

'I am happy from the very depth of my heart!' she said.

'This earth can offer me nothing more,' said Rudy.

And the evening bells began to sound from the mountains of Savoy and from the Swiss hills, and in the west rose the black Jura range, crowned with a wreath of gold.

'May Heaven grant to thee what is happiest and best!' murmured Babette.

'It will,' replied Rudy. 'Tomorrow I shall have it. Tomorrow you will be mine entirely. My own sweet wife!'

'The boat!' exclaimed Babette, suddenly.

The little skiff in which they were to return had broken loose and was drifting away from the island.

'I will bring it back,' said Rudy.

And he threw aside his coat, pulled off his boots, jumped into the lake, and swam with powerful strokes towards the boat.

Cold and deep was the clear blue-green ice water from the glacier of the mountain. Rudy looked down into its depths – one glance – and it seemed to him that he saw a golden ring, rolling, shining, sparkling: he thought of his ring of betrothal – and the ring grew larger, and widened into a sparkling circle into which the gleaming glacier shone: deep abysses yawned around, and the water-drops rang like the chiming of bells, and glittered with white flames. In a moment he beheld all this that it has taken many words to describe. Young hunters and young girls, men and women who had at different times sunk down into the crevasses among the glaciers, stood here living, with smiling mouths, and deep below them sounded the church bells of sunken cities. The congregation knelt beneath the church roof, the organ pipes were formed of great icicles, and beneath all the Ice Maiden sat on the clear transparent ground. She raised herself towards Rudy and kissed his feet; then a cold death-like numbness poured through his limbs, and an electric shock – ice and fire mingled! There is no difference to be felt between a sudden touch of these two.

'Mine! mine!' sounded around him and within him. 'I kissed thee when thou wert little, kissed thee on thy mouth. Now I kiss thy feet, and thou art mine altogether!'

And he disappeared beneath the clear blue water.

All was silent; the chime of the church bells ceased, the last echoes died away with the last ruddy tints of the evening clouds.

'Thou art mine!' sounded from the depths. 'Thou art mine!' sounded from the heights, from the regions of the Infinite.

Glorious! from love to love – to fly from earth to heaven!

A chord broke, a sound of mourning was heard; the icy kiss of Death conquered that which was to pass away; the prologue ended that the true drama of life might begin, and discord was blended into harmony.

Do you call that a sorrowful story?

But poor Babette. Her anguish was unspeakable. The boat drifted farther and farther away. No one on the mainland knew that the betrothed pair had gone over to the little island. The sun went down and it became dark. She stood alone, weeping – despairing. A storm came on: flash after flash lit up the Jura mountains, Switzerland and Savoy; flash upon flash on all sides, the rolling thunderclap mingling with clap for minutes together. The gleams of lightning were some-times bright as the sun, showing every separate vine as at noonday, and the next moment all would be shrouded in darkness. The flashes were forked, ring-shaped, wavy; they darted into the lake and glittered on every side, while the rolling of the thunder was redoubled by the echo. On the mainland, people drew the boats high up on the shore; everything that had life hastened to get under shelter; and now the rain came pouring down.

'Where can Rudy and Babette be in this tempest?' said the miller.

Babette sat with folded hands, her head on her knees, speechless with grief; she no longer moaned or wept.

'In the deep waters!' was the one thought in her mind. 'He is far down in the lakes as if under the glacier.'

And then arose in her the remembrance of what Rudy had told concerning the death of his mother and his own rescue; how he had been borne forth, like a corpse, from the depths of the glacier.

'The Ice Maiden has got him again!'

And a flash of lightning glared like sunshine over the white snow. Babette started up. The whole lake was at this moment like a shining glacier; and there stood the Ice Maiden, majestic, with a bluish-white light upon her, and at her feet lay Rudy's corpse.

'Mine!' she said.

And again there was darkness all around, and the crash of falling waters.

'How cruel!' groaned Babette. 'Why must he die when the day of our happiness was about to dawn? O Lord, enlighten my understanding! Send Thy light into my heart! I understand not Thy ways. I grope in darkness, amid the behests of Thy power and Thy wisdom!'

And the light for which she prayed was given to her. A gleam of thought, a ray of light, her dream of the past night in its living reality, flashed through her. She remembered the words, the wish she had uttered, concerning what would be 'the best' for her and for Rudy.

'Woe is me! Was it the germ of sin within my heart? Was my dream a vision of a future life, whose strings must be snapped asunder that I might be saved? Wretched that I am!'

And she sat there in the dark night, lamenting. Through the thick darkness Rudy's words seemed to sound, the last words he had spoken on earth, 'The earth has nothing more to give me!' They had sounded in the fullness of joy; they echoed now through the depths of distress.

And years have flown by since that time. The lake smiles and its shores smile; the grape-vine is covered with swelling branches; steamboats with waving flags glide along; pleasure-boats with full sails flit across the mirror of waters like white butterflies; the railway has been opened past Chillon, and leads deep into the valley of the Rhone. At every station strangers alight, with red-bound guidebooks in their hands, and they read of the sights they have come to see. They visit Chillon, and in the lake they behold the little island with three acacias, and in the book they read about the betrothed pair who, on an evening of the year 1856, sailed across thither, and of the death of the bridegroom, and how the despairing cries of the bride were not heard on the shore till the next morning.

But the guidebook has nothing to tell concerning the quiet life of Babette in her father's house – not in the mill, for other people live there now, but in the beautiful house near the station, from whose windows she looks on many an evening across over the chestnut trees towards the snowy mountains on which Rudy once wandered; in the evening she marks the Alpine glow – the Children of the Sun recline on the lofty mountains, and renew the song of the wanderer whose cloak the whirlwind once tore away, taking the garment but not the man.

There is a rosy gleam on the snow of the mountains, a rosy gleam in every heart in which dwells the thought, 'God lets that happen which is best for us!' But the cause is not always revealed to us, as it was revealed to Babette in her dream.

The Butterfly

THE BUTTERFLY wished for a bride; naturally, he wanted a very pretty one from among the flowers; so he looked at them, and found that every flower sat quietly and demurely on her stalk, just as amaiden ought to sit before she is engaged; but there were a great many of them, and the choice threatened to become wearisome. The Butterfly did not care to take much trouble, and so he flew off to the daisy. The French call this floweret 'Marguerite', and they know that Marguerite can prophesy, when lovers pluck off its leaves, and ask of every leaf they pluck some question concerning their lovers. 'Heartily? Painfully? Loves me much? A little? Not at all?' and so on. Everyone asks in his own language. The Butterfly also came to enquire; but he did not pluck off her leaves: he kissed each of them, for he considered that most is to be done with kindness.

'Darling Marguerite daisy!' he said to her, 'you are the wisest woman among the flowers. Pray, pray tell me, shall I get this one or that? Which will be my bride? When I know that, I will directly fly to her and propose for her.'

But Marguerite did not answer him. She was angry that he had called her a 'woman', when she was yet a girl; and there is a great difference. He asked for the second and for the third time, and when she remained dumb, and answered him not a word, he would wait no longer, but flew away to begin his wooing at once.

It was in the beginning of spring; the crocus and the snowdrop were blooming around.

'They are very pretty,' thought the Butterfly. 'Charming little lasses, but a little too much of the schoolgirl about them.' Like all young lads, he looked out for the elder girls.

Then he flew off to the anemones. These were a little too bitter for his taste; the violet somewhat too sentimental; the tulips too showy;

the eastern lilies too plebeian; the lime blossoms were too small, and, moreover, they had too many relations; the apple blossoms – they looked like roses, but they bloomed today, to fall off tomorrow, to fall beneath the first wind that blew; and he thought that a marriage with them would last too short a time. The Pease Blossom pleased him best of all: she was white and red, and graceful and delicate, and belonged to the domestic maidens who look well, and at the same time are useful in the kitchen. He was just about to make his offer, when close by the maiden he saw a pod at whose end hung a withered flower.

'Who is that?' he asked.

'That is my sister,' replied the Pease Blossom.

'Oh, indeed; and you will get to look like her!' he said.

And away he flew, for he felt quite shocked.

The honeysuckle hung forth blooming from the hedge, but there were a number of girls like that, with long faces and sallow complexions. No, he did not like her.

But which one did he like?

The spring went by, and the summer drew towards its close; it was autumn, but he was still undecided.

And now the flowers appeared in their most gorgeous robes, but in vain – they had lost the fresh fragrant air of youth. But the heart demands fragrance, even when it is no longer young, and there is very little of that to be found among the dahlias and dry chrysanthemums, therefore the Butterfly turned to the Mint on the ground.

This plant has no blossom; but indeed it is blossom all over, full of fragrance from head to foot, with flower scent in every leaf.

'I shall take her,' said the Butterfly.

And he made an offer to her.

But the Mint stood silent and stiff, listening to him. At last she said, 'Friendship, but nothing more. I am old, and you are old, we may very well live for one another; but as to marrying – no – don't let us appear ridiculous at our age.'

And thus it happened that the Butterfly had no wife at all. He had been too long choosing, and that is a bad plan. So the Butterfly became what we call an old bachelor.

It was late in autumn, with rain and cloudy weather. The wind blew cold over the backs of the old willow trees, so that they creaked again. It was no weather to be flying about in summer clothes, nor, indeed, was the Butterfly in the open air. He had got under shelter by chance, where there was fire in the stove and the heat of summer. He could live well enough, but he said, 'It's not enough, merely to live. One must have freedom, sunshine, and a little flower.'

And he flew against the window-frame, and was seen and admired, and then stuck upon a pin and placed in the box of curiosities; they could not do more for him.

'Now I am perched on a stalk, like the flowers,' said the Butterfly. 'It certainly is not very pleasant. It must be something like being married, for one is stuck fast.'

And he consoled himself with that thought.

'That's very poor comfort,' said the potted Plants in the room.

'But,' thought the Butterfly, 'one cannot well trust these potted Plants. They've had too much to do with mankind.'

The Psyche

IN THE fresh morning dawn there gleams in the rosy air a great Star, the brightest Star of the morning. His rays tremble on the white wall, as if he wished to write down on it what he can tell, what he has seen there and elsewhere during thousands of years of our rolling world. Let us hear one of his stories.

'A short time ago' – the Star's 'short time ago' is called among men 'centuries ago' – 'my rays followed a young artist. It was in the city of the Popes, in the world-city Rome. Much has been changed there in the course of time, but the changes have not come so quickly as the change from youth to old age. Then already the palace of the Caesars was a ruin, as it is now; fig trees and laurels grew among the fallen marble columns, and in the desolate bathing-halls, where the gilding still clings to the wall; the Coliseum was a ruin; the church bells sounded, the incense sent up its fragrant cloud, and through the streets marched processions with flaming tapers and glowing canopies. Holy Church was there, and art was held as a high and holy thing. In Rome lived the greatest painter in the world, Raphael; there also dwelt the first of sculptors, Michael Angelo. Even the Pope paid homage to these two, and honoured them with a visit: art was recognised and honoured, and was rewarded also. But, for all that, everything great and splendid was not seen and known.

'In a narrow lane stood an old house. Once it had been a temple; a young sculptor now dwelt there. He was young and quite unknown. He certainly had friends, young artists, like himself, young in spirit, young in hopes and thoughts; they told him he was rich in talent, and an artist, but that he was foolish for having no faith in his own power; for he always broke what he had fashioned out of clay, and never completed anything; and a work must be completed if it is to be seen and to bring money.

' "You are a dreamer," they went on to say to him, "and that's your misfortune. But the reason of this is, that you have never lived, you have never tasted life, you have never enjoyed it in great wholesome draughts, as it ought to be enjoyed. In youth one must mingle one's own personality with life, that they may become one. Look at the great master Raphael, whom the Pope honours and the world admires: he's no despiser of wine and bread."

' "And he even appreciates the baker's daughter, the pretty *Fornarina*," added Angelo, one of the merriest of the young friends.

'Yes, they said a good many things of the kind, according to their age and intelligence. They wanted to draw the young artist out with them into the merry wild life, the mad life as it might be called; and at certain times he felt an inclination for it. He had warm blood, a strong imagination, and could take part in the merry chat, and laugh aloud with the rest; but what they called "Raphael's merry life" disappeared before him like a vapour when he saw the divine radiance that beamed forth from the pictures of the great master; and when he stood in the Vatican, before the forms of beauty which the masters had hewn out of marble, thousands of years since, his breast swelled, and he felt within himself something high, something holy, something elevating, great, and good, and he wished that he could produce similar forms from the blocks of marble. He wished to make a picture of that which was within him, stirring upward from his heart to the realms of the infinite; but how, and in what form? The soft clay was fashioned under his fingers into forms of beauty, but the next day he broke what he had fashioned, according to his wont.

'One day he walked past one of those rich palaces of which Rome has many to show. He stopped before the great open portal, and beheld a garden surrounded by cloistered walks. The garden bloomed with a goodly show of the fairest roses. Great white lilies with green juicy leaves shot upward from the marble basin in which the clear water was splashing; and a form glided past, a young girl, the daughter of the princely house, graceful, delicate, and wonderfully fair. Such a form of female loveliness he had never before beheld – yet, stay: he had seen it, painted by Raphael, painted as a Psyche, in one of the

Roman palaces. Yes, there she was painted; but here she walked alive.

'The remembrance lived in his thoughts, in his heart. He went home to his humble room, and modelled a Psyche of clay. It was the rich young Roman girl, the noble maiden; and for the first time he looked at his work with satisfaction. It had a meaning for him, for it was *she*. And the friends who saw his work shouted aloud for joy; they declared that this work was a manifestation of his artistic power, of which they had long been aware, and that now the world should be made aware of it too.

'The clay figure was lifelike and beautiful, but it had not the whiteness or the durability of marble. So they declared that the Psyche must henceforth live in marble. He already possessed a costly block of that stone. It had been lying for years, the property of his parents, in the courtyard. Fragments of glass, fennel tops, and remains of artichokes had gathered about it and sullied its purity; but under the surface the block was as white as the mountain snow; and from this block the Psyche was to arise.'

Now, it happened one morning – the bright Star tells nothing about this, but we know it occurred – that a noble Roman company came into the narrow lane. The carriage stopped a little way off, the company came to inspect the young sculptor's work, for they had heard it spoken of by chance. And who were these distinguished guests? Poor young man! or fortunate young man he might be called. The young girl stood in the room and smiled radiantly when her father said to her, 'It is your living image.' That smile could not be copied, any more than the look could be reproduced, the wonderful look which she cast upon the young artist. It was a look that seemed at once to elevate and to crush him.

'The Psyche must be executed in marble,' said the wealthy patrician. And those were words of life for the dead clay and the heavy block of marble, and words of life likewise for the deeply-moved artist. 'When the work is finished I will purchase it,' continued the rich noble.

A new era seemed to have arisen in the poor studio. Life and cheerfulness gleamed there, and busy industry plied its work. The beaming Morning Star beheld how the work progressed. The clay itself seemed inspired since *she* had been there, and moulded itself, in heightened beauty, to a likeness of the well-known features.

'Now I know what life is,' cried the artist rejoicingly; 'it is Love! It is the lofty abandonment of self for the dawning of the beautiful in the soul! What my friends call life and enjoyment is a passing shadow; it is like bubbles among seething dregs, not the pure heavenly wine that consecrates us to life.'

The marble block was reared in its place. The chisel struck great fragments from it; the measurements were taken, points and lines were made, the mechanical part was executed, till gradually the stone assumed a human female form, a shape of beauty, and became converted into the Psyche, fair and glorious – a divine being in human shape. The heavy stone appeared as a gliding, dancing, airy Psyche, with the heavenly innocent smile – the smile that had mirrored itself in the soul of the young artist.

The Star of the roseate dawn beheld and understood what was stirring within the young man, and could read the meaning of the changing colour of his cheek, of the light that flashed from his eye, as he stood busily working, reproducing what had been put into his soul from above.

'Thou art a master like those masters among the ancient Greeks,' exclaimed his delighted friends: 'soon shall the whole world admire thy Psyche.'

'*My* Psyche!' he repeated. 'Yes, mine. She must be mine. I, too, am an artist, like those great men who are gone. Providence has granted me the boon, and has made me the equal of that lady of noble birth.'

And he knelt down and breathed a prayer of thankfulness to Heaven, and then he forgot Heaven for her sake – for the sake of her picture in stone – for the Psyche which stood there as if formed of snow, blushing in the morning dawn.

He was to see her in reality, the living graceful Psyche, whose words sounded like music in his ears. He could now carry the news into the rich palace that the marble Psyche was finished. He betook himself thither, strode through the open courtyard where the waters ran splashing from the dolphin's jaws into the marble basins, where the snowy lilies and the fresh roses bloomed in abundance. He stepped into the great lofty hall, whose walls and ceilings shone with gilding and bright colours and heraldic devices. Gaily dressed serving-men, adorned with trappings like sleigh horses, walked to and fro, and some reclined at their ease upon the carved oak seats, as if they were the masters of the house. He told them his errand, and was conducted up the shining marble staircase, covered with soft carpets and adorned with many a statue. Then he went on through richly furnished chambers, over mosaic floors, amid gorgeous pictures. All this pomp and luxury seemed to weary him; but soon he felt relieved, for the princely old master of the house received him most graciously, almost heartily; and when he took his leave he was requested to step into the Signora's apartment, for she, too, wished to see him. The servants led him through more luxurious halls and chambers into her room, where she appeared the chief and leading ornament.

She spoke to him. No hymn of supplication, no holy chant could melt his soul like the sound of her voice. He took her hand and lifted it to his lips: no rose was softer, but a fire thrilled through him from this rose – a feeling of power came upon him, and words poured from his tongue – he knew not what he said. Does the crater of the volcano know that glowing lava is pouring from it? He confessed what he felt for her. She stood before him astonished, offended, proud, with contempt in her face, an expression as if she had suddenly touched a wet, clammy frog; her cheeks reddened, her lips grew white, and her eyes flashed fire, though they were dark as the blackness of night

'Madman!' she cried, 'away! begone!'

And she turned her back upon him. Her beautiful face wore an expression like that of the stony countenance with the snaky locks.

Like a stricken, fainting man, he tottered down the stair and out into the street. Like a man walking in his sleep, he found his way back to his dwelling. Then he woke up to madness and agony, and seized his hammer, swung it high in the air, and rushed forward to shatter the beautiful marble image. But, in his pain, he had not noticed that his friend Angelo stood beside him; and Angelo held back his arm with a strong grasp, crying, 'Are you mad? What are you about?'

They struggled together. Angelo was the stronger; and with a deep sigh of exhaustion, the young artist threw himself into a chair.

'What has happened?' asked Angelo. 'Command yourself. Speak!'

But what could he say? How could he explain? And as Angelo could make no sense of his friend's incoherent words, he forbore to question him further, and merely said, 'Your blood grows thick from your eternal dreaming. Be a man, as all others are, and don't go on living in ideals for that is what drives men crazy. A jovial feast will make you sleep quietly and happily. Believe me, the time will come when you will be old, and your sinews will shrink, and then, on some fine sunshiny day, when everything is laughing and rejoicing, you will lie there a faded plant, that will grow no more. I do not live in dreams, but in reality. Come with me: be a man!'

And he drew the artist away with him. At this moment he was able to do so, for a fire ran in the blood of the young sculptor; a change had taken place in his soul; he felt a longing to tear himself away from the old, the accustomed – to forget, if possible, his own individuality; and therefore it was that he followed Angelo.

In an out-of-the-way suburb of Rome lay a tavern much visited by artists. It was built on the ruins of some ancient baths. The great yellow citrons hung down among the dark shining leaves and covered a part of the old reddish-yellow walls. The tavern consisted of a vaulted chamber, almost like a cavern, in the ruins. A lamp burned there before the picture of the Madonna. A great fire gleamed on the hearth, and roasting and boiling was going on there; without, under the citron trees and laurels, stood a few covered tables.

The two artists were received by their friends with shouts of welcome. Little was eaten, but much was drunk, and the spirits of the company rose. Songs were sung and ditties were played on the guitar; presently the *Saltarello* sounded, and the merry dance began. Two young Roman girls, who sat as models to the artists, took part in the dance and in the festivity. Two charming Bacchantes were they; certainly not Psyches – not delicate beautiful roses, but fresh, hearty, glowing carnations.

How hot it was on that day! Even after sundown it was hot: there was fire in the blood, fire in every glance, fire everywhere. The air gleamed with gold and roses, and life seemed like gold and roses.

'At last you have joined us, for once,' said his friends. 'Now let yourself be carried by the waves within and around you.'

'Never yet have I felt so well, so merry!' cried the young artist. 'You are right, you are all of you right. I was a fool, a dreamer – man belongs to reality, and not to fancy.'

With song and with sounding guitars the young people returned that evening from the tavern, through the narrow streets; the two glowing carnations, daughters of the Campagna, went with them.

In Angelo's room, among a litter of coloured sketches, studies, and glowing pictures, the voices sounded mellower but not less merrily. On the ground lay many a sketch that resembled the daughters of the Campagna, in their fresh comeliness, but the two originals were far handsomer than their portraits. All the burners of the six-armed lamp flared and flamed; and the *human* flamed up from within, and appeared in the glare as if it were divine.

'Apollo! Jupiter! I feel myself raised to your heaven, to your glory! I feel as if the blossom of life were unfolding itself in my veins at this moment!'

Yes, the blossom unfolded itself, and then burst and fell, and an evil vapour arose from it, blinding the sight, leading astray the fancy – the firework of the senses went out, and it became dark.

He was again in his own room; there he sat down on his bed and collected his thoughts.

'Fie on thee!' – these were the words that sounded out of his mouth from the depths of his heart. 'Wretched man, go, begone!' And a deep painful sigh burst from his bosom.

'Away! begone!' These, her words, the words of the living Psyche, echoed through his heart, escaped from his lips. He buried his head in the pillows, his thoughts grew confused, and he fell asleep.

In the morning dawn he started up, and collected his thoughts anew. What had happened? Had all the past been a dream? The visit to *her*, the feast at the tavern, the evening with the purple carnations of the Campagna? No, it was all real – a reality he had never before experienced.

In the purple air gleamed the bright Star, and its beams fell upon him and upon the marble Psyche. He trembled as he looked at the picture of immortality, and his glance seemed impure to him. He threw the cloth over the statue, and then touched it once more to unveil the form – but he was not able to look again at his own work.

Gloomy, quiet, absorbed in his own thoughts, he sat there through the long day; he heard nothing of what was going on around him, and no man guessed what was passing in this human soul.

And days and weeks went by, but the nights passed more slowly than the days. The flashing Star beheld him one morning as he rose, pale and trembling with fever, from his sad couch; then he stepped towards the statue, threw back the covering, took one long sorrowful gaze at his work, and then, almost sinking beneath the burden, he dragged the statue out into the garden. In that place was an old dry well, now nothing but a hole: into this he cast the Psyche, threw earth in above her, and covered up the spot with twigs and nettles.

'Away! begone!' Such was the short epitaph he spoke.

The Star beheld all this from the pink morning sky, and its beam trembled upon two great tears on the pale feverish cheeks of the young man; and soon it was said that he was sick unto death, and he lay stretched upon a bed of pain.

The monk Ignatius visited him as a physician and a friend, and brought him words of comfort, of religion, and spoke to him of the peace and happiness of the Church, of the sinfulness of man, of rest and mercy to be found in heaven.

And the words fell like warm sunbeams upon a teeming soil. The soil smoked and sent up clouds of mist, fantastic pictures, pictures in which there was reality; and from these floating islands he looked across at human life. He found it vanity and delusion – and vanity and delusion it had been to him. They told him that art was a sorcerer, betraying us to vanity and to earthly lusts; that we are false to ourselves, unfaithful to our friends, unfaithful towards Heaven; and that the serpent was always repeating within us, 'Eat, and thou shalt become as God.'

And it appeared to him as if now, for the first time, he knew himself, and had found the way that leads to truth and to peace. In the Church was the light and the brightness of God – in the monk's cell he should find the rest through which the tree of human life might grow on into eternity.

Brother Ignatius strengthened his longings, and the determination became firm within him. A child of the world became a servant of the Church – the young artist renounced the world, and retired into the cloister.

The brothers came forward affectionately to welcome him, and his inauguration was as a Sunday feast. Heaven seemed to him to dwell in the sunshine of the church, and to beam upon him from the holy pictures and from the cross. And when, in the evening, at the sunset hour, he stood in his little cell, and, opening the window, looked out upon old Rome, upon the desolated temples, and the great dead Coliseum – when he saw all this in its spring garb, when the acacias bloomed, and the ivy was fresh, and roses burst forth everywhere, and the citron and orange were in the height of their beauty, and the palm trees waved their branches – then he felt a deeper emotion than had ever yet thrilled through him. The quiet open Campagna spread itself forth towards the blue snow-covered mountains, which seemed to be painted in the air; all the outlines melting into each other, breathing peace and beauty, floating, dreaming – and all appearing like a dream!

Yes, this world was a dream, and the dream lasts for hours, and may return for hours; but convent life is a life of years – long years, and many years.

From within comes much that renders men impure. He felt the truth of this. What flames arose in him at times! What a source of evil, of that which he would not, welled up continually! He mortified his body, but the evil came from within.

One day, after the lapse of many years, he met Angelo, who recognised him.

'Man!' exclaimed Angelo. 'Yes, it is thou! Art thou happy now? Thou hast sinned against God, and cast away His boon from thee – hast neglected thy mission in this world! Read the parable of the talents! The Master, who spoke that parable, spoke truth! What hast thou gained? what hast thou found? Dost thou not fashion for thyself a religion and a dreamy life after thine own idea, as almost all do? Suppose all this is a dream, a fair delusion!'

'Get thee away from me, Satan!' said the monk; and he quitted Angelo.

'There is a devil, a personal devil! This day I have seen him!' said the monk to himself. 'Once I extended a finger to him, and he took my whole hand. But no,' he sighed, 'the evil is within me, and it is in yonder man; but it does not bow him down: he goes abroad with head erect, and enjoys his comfort; and I grasped at comfort in the consolations of religion. If it were nothing but a consolation? Supposing everything here were, like the world I have quitted, only a beautiful fancy, a delusion like the beauty of the evening clouds, like the misty blue of the distant hills! when you approach them, they are very different! O eternity! Thou actest like the great calm ocean, that beckons us, and fills us with expectation – and when we embark upon thee, we sink, disappear, and cease to be. Delusion! away with it! begone!'

And tearless, but sunk in bitter reflection, he sat upon his hard couch, and then knelt down – before whom? Before the stone cross fastened to the wall? – No, it was only habit that made him take this position.

The more deeply he looked into his own heart the blacker did the darkness seem. 'Nothing within, nothing without – this life squandered and cast away!' And this thought rolled and grew like a snowball, until it seemed to crush him.

'I can confide my griefs to none. I may speak to none of the gnawing worm within. My secret is my prisoner; if I let the captive escape, I shall be his!'

And the godlike power that dwelt within him suffered and strove.

'O Lord, my Lord!' he cried in his despair, 'be merciful, and grant me faith. I threw away the gift thou hadst vouchsafed to me, I left my mission unfulfilled. I lacked strength, and strength thou didst not give me. Immortality – the Psyche in my breast – away with it! it shall be buried like that Psyche, the best gleam of my life; never will it arise out of its grave!'

The Star glowed in the roseate air, the Star that shall surely be extinguished and pass away while the soul still lives on; its trembling beam fell upon the white wall, but it wrote nothing there upon being made perfect in God, nothing of the hope of mercy, of the reliance on the divine love that thrills through the heart of the believer.

'The Psyche within can never die. Shall it live in consciousness? Can the incomprehensible happen? Yes, yes. My being is incomprehensible. Thou art unfathomable, O Lord. Thy whole world is incomprehensible – a wonder-work of power, of glory, and of love.'

His eyes gleamed, and then closed in death. The tolling of the church bell was the last sound that echoed above him, above the dead man; and they buried him, covering him with earth that had been brought from Jerusalem, and in which was mingled the dust of many of the pious dead.

When years had gone by his skeleton was dug up, as the skeletons of the monks who had died before him had been: it was clad in a brown frock, a rosary was put into the bony hand, and the form was placed among the ranks of other skeletons in the cloisters of the convent. And the sun shone without, while within the censers were waved and the Mass was celebrated.

And years rolled by.

The bones fell asunder and became mingled with others. Skulls were piled up till they formed an outer wall around the church; and there lay also *his* head in the burning sun, for many dead were there, and no one knew their names, and his name was forgotten also. And see, something was moving in the sunshine, in the sightless cavernous eyes! What might that be? A sparkling lizard moved about in the skull, gliding in and out through the sightless holes. The lizard now represented all the life left in that head, in which, once, great thoughts, bright dreams, the love of art and of the glorious had arisen, whence hot tears had rolled down, where hope and immortality had had their being. The lizard sprang away and disappeared, and the skull itself crumbled to pieces and became dust among dust. Centuries passed away. The bright Star gleamed unaltered, radiant and large, as it had gleamed for thousands of years, and the air glowed red with tints fresh as roses, crimson like blood.

There, where once had stood the narrow lane containing the ruins of the temple, a nunnery was now built; a grave was being dug in the convent garden, for a young nun had died, and was to be laid in the earth this morning. The spade struck against a stone that shone dazzling white. A block of marble soon appeared, a rounded shoulder was laid bare, and now the spade was plied with a more careful hand, and presently a female head was seen, and butterflies' wings. Out of the grave in which the young nun was to be laid they lifted, in the rosy morning, a wonderful statue of a Psyche carved in white marble.

'How beautiful, how perfect it is!' cried the spectators. 'A relic of the best period of art.'

And who could the sculptor have been? No one knew, no one remembered him, except the bright Star that had gleamed for thousands of years. The Star had seen the course of that life on earth, and knew of the man's trials, of his weakness – in fact, that he had been but human. The man's life had passed away, his dust had been scattered abroad as dust is destined to be; but the result of his noblest striving, the glorious work that gave token of the divine element within him – the Psyche that never dies, that lives beyond posterity – the brightness even of this earthly Psyche remained here after him, and was seen and acknowledged and appreciated.

The bright Morning Star in the roseate air threw its glancing ray downward upon the Psyche, and upon the radiant countenances of the admiring spectators, who here beheld the *image of the soul* portrayed in marble.

What is earthly will pass away and be forgotten, and the Star in the vast firmament knows it. What is heavenly will shine brightly through posterity; and when the ages of posterity are past, the Psyche – the soul – will still live on!

The Snail and the Rose Tree

AROUND THE garden ran a hedge of hazels; beyond this hedge lay fields and meadows, with cows and sheep; but in the midst of the garden stood a blooming Rose Tree; and under it lived a Snail, who had a good deal in his shell – namely, himself.

'Wait till my time comes!' he said: 'I shall do something more than produce roses and bear nuts; or give milk, like the cows and the sheep!'

'I expect a great deal of you,' said the Rose Tree. 'But may I ask when it will appear?'

'I take my time,' replied the Snail. '*You*'re always in such a hurry. You don't rouse people's interest by suspense.'

Next year the Snail lay almost in the same spot, in the sunshine under the Rose Tree, which again bore buds that bloomed into roses, always fresh, always new. And the Snail crept halfway out, put out its horns and then drew them in again.

'Everything looks just like last year. There has been no progress. The Rose Tree sticks to roses; it gets no farther.'

The summer passed, the autumn came; the Rose Tree had always flowers and buds, until the snow fell and the weather became raw and cold; then the Rose Tree bowed its head and the Snail crept into the ground.

A new year began; and the roses came out, and the Snail came out also.

'You're an old Rose Tree now!' said the Snail. 'You must make haste and come to an end, for you have given the world all that was in you: whether it was of any use is a question that I have had no time to consider; but so much is clear and plain, that you have done nothing at all for your own development, or you would have produced something else. How can you answer for that? In a little time you will be nothing at all but a stick. Do you understand what I say?'

'You alarm me!' replied the Rose Tree. 'I never thought of that at all.'

'No, you have not taken the trouble to consider anything. Have you ever given an account to yourself, why you bloomed, and how it is that your blooming comes about – why it is thus, and not otherwise?'

'No,' answered the Rose Tree. 'I bloomed in gladness, because I could not do anything else. The sun was so warm, and the air so refreshing. I drank the pure dew and the fresh rain, and I lived, I breathed. Out of the earth there arose a power within me, from above there came down a strength: I perceived a new ever-increasing happiness, and consequently I was obliged to bloom over and over again; that was my life; I could not do otherwise.'

'You have led a very pleasant life,' observed the Snail.

'Certainly. Everything was given to me,' said the Rose Tree. 'But more still was given to you. You are one of those deep thoughtful characters, one of those highly gifted spirits, which will cause the world to marvel.'

'I've no intention of doing anything of the kind,' cried the Snail. 'The world is nothing to me. What have I to do with the world? I have enough of myself and in myself.'

'But must we not all, here on earth, give to others the best that we have, and offer what lies in our power? Certainly I have only given roses. But you – you who have been so richly gifted – what have you given to the world? what do you intend to give?'

'What have I given – what do I intend to give? I spit at it. It's worth nothing. It's no business of mine. Continue to give your roses, if you like: you can't do anything better. Let the hazel bush bear nuts, and the cows and ewes give milk: they have their public; but I have mine within myself – I retire within myself, and there I remain. The world is nothing to me.'

And so the Snail retired into his house, and closed up the entrance after him.

'That is very sad!' said the Rose Tree. 'I cannot creep into myself, even if I wish it – I must continue to produce roses. They drop their leaves, and are blown away by the wind. But I saw how a rose was laid in the matron's hymn-book, and one of my roses had a place on the bosom of a fair young girl, and another was kissed by the lips of a child in the full joy of life. That did me good; it was a real blessing. That's my remembrance – my life!'

And the Rose Tree went on blooming in innocence, while the Snail lay idly in his house – the world did not concern him.

And years rolled by.

The Snail had become dust in the dust, and the Rose Tree was earth in the earth; the rose of remembrance in the hymn-book was faded, but in the garden bloomed fresh rose trees, in the garden grew new snails; and these still crept into their houses, and spat at the world, for it did not concern them.

Suppose we begin the story again, and read it right through. It will never alter.

'The Will-O'-The-Wisps are in the Town,'
says the Moor-Woman

THERE WAS a man who once knew many stories, but they had slipped away from him – so he said; the Story that used to visit him of its own accord no longer came and knocked at his door: and why did it come no longer? It is true enough that for days and years the man had not thought of it, had not expected it to come and knock; but it certainly had not been there either, for outside there was war, and within was the care and sorrow that war brings with it.

The stork and the swallows came back from their long journey, for they thought of no danger; and, behold, when they arrived, the nest was burnt, the habitations of men were burnt, the gates were all in disorder, and even quite gone, and the enemy's horses trampled on the old graves. Those were hard, gloomy times, but they came to an end.

And now they were past and gone, so people said; and yet no Story came and knocked at the door, or gave any tidings of its presence.

'I suppose it must be dead, or gone away with many other things,' said the man.

But the Story never dies. And more than a whole year went by, and he longed – oh, so very much! – for the Story.

'I wonder if the Story will ever come back again, and knock?'

And he remembered it so well in all the various forms in which it had come to him, sometimes young and charming, like spring itself, sometimes as a beautiful maiden, with a wreath of woodruff in her hair, and a beechen branch in her hand, and with eyes that gleamed like deep woodland lakes in the bright sunshine.

Sometimes it had come to him in the guise of a pedlar, and had opened its pack and let silver ribbon come fluttering out, with verses and inscriptions of old remembrances.

But it was most charming of all when it came as an old grandmother, with silvery hair, and such large sensible eyes: she knew so well how to tell about the oldest times, long before the Princesses span with the golden spindles, and the dragons lay outside the castles, guarding them. She told with such an air of truth, that black spots danced before the eyes of all who heard her, and the floor became black with human blood; terrible to see and to hear, and yet so entertaining, because such a long time had passed since it all happened.

'Will she ever knock at my door again?' said the man; and he gazed at the door, so that black spots came before his eyes and upon the floor; he did not know if it was blood, or mourning crape from the dark heavy days.

And as he sat thus, the thought came upon him, whether the Story might not have hidden itself, like the Princess in the old tale? And he would now go in search of it: if he found it, it would beam in new splendour, lovelier than ever.

'Who knows? Perhaps it has hidden itself in the straw that balances on the margin of the well. Carefully, carefully! Perhaps it lies hidden in a withered flower – that flower in one of the great books on the bookshelf.'

And the man went and opened one of the newest books, to gain information on this point; but there was no flower to be found. There he read about Holger the Dane; and the man read that the whole tale had been invented and put together by a monk in France, that it was a romance, 'translated into Danish and printed in that language'; that Holger the Dane had never really lived, and consequently could never come again, as we have sung, and would have so much liked to believe. It was just the same with Holger the Dane as with William Tell, mere idle legend, not to be depended on, and all this was written in the book, with great learning.

'Well, I shall believe what I believe!' said the man; 'there grows no plantain where no foot has trod.'

And he closed the book and put it back in its place, and went to the fresh flowers at the window: perhaps the Story might have hidden itself in the red tulips, with the golden yellow edges, or in the fresh rose, or in the strongly-coloured camellia. The sunshine lay among the flowers, but no Story.

The flowers which had been here in the dark troublous time had been much more beautiful; but they had been cut off, one after another, to be woven into wreaths and placed in coffins, and the flag had waved over them! Perhaps the Story had been buried with the flowers; but then the flowers would have known of it, and the coffin would have heard it, and every little blade of grass that shot forth would have told of it. The Story never dies.

Perhaps it has been here once, and has knocked – but who had eyes or ears for it in those times? People looked darkly, gloomily, and almost angrily at the sunshine of spring, at the twittering birds, and all the cheerful green; the tongue could not even bear the old, merry, popular songs, and they were laid in the coffin with so much that our heart held dear. The Story may have knocked without obtaining a hearing; there was none to bid it welcome, and so it may have gone away.

'I will go forth and seek it! Out in the country! out in the wood! and on the open sea beach!'

Out in the country lies an old manor house, with red walls, pointed gables, and a flag that floats on the tower. The nightingale sings among the finely-fringed beech-leaves, looking at the blooming apple trees of the garden, and thinking that they bear roses. Here the bees are busy in the summer-time, and hover round their queen with their humming song. The autumn has much to tell of the wild chase, of the leaves of the trees, and of the races of men that are passing away together. The wild swans sing at Christmas-time on the open water, while in the old hall the guests by the fireside gladly listen to songs and to old legends.

Down into the old part of the garden, where the great avenue of wild chestnut trees lures the wanderer to tread its shades, went the man who was in search of the Story; for here the wind had once murmured something to him of 'Waldemar Daa and his Daughters'. The Dryad in the tree, who was the Story-mother herself, had here told him the 'Last Dream of the old Oak Tree'. Here, in grand-mother's time, had stood clipped hedges, out now only ferns and stinging-nettles grew there, hiding the scattered fragments of old sculptured figures; the moss is growing in their eyes, but they could see as well as ever, which was more than the man could do who was in search of the Story, for he could not find it. Where could it be?

The crows flew over him by hundreds across the old trees, and screamed, 'Krah! da! Krah! da!'

And he went out of the garden, and over the grass-plot of the yard, into the alder grove; there stood a little sixsided house, with a poultry-yard and a duck-yard. In the middle of the room sat the old woman who had the management of the whole, and who knew accurately about every egg that was laid, and about every chicken that could creep out of an egg. But she was not the Story of which the man was in search; that she could attest with a certificate of Christian baptism and of vaccination that lay in her drawer.

Without, not far from the house, is a mound covered with red-thorn and laburnum: here lies an old gravestone, which was brought many years ago from the churchyard of the provincial town, a remembrance of one of the most honoured councillors of the place; his wife and his five daughters, all with folded hands and stiff ruffs, stand round him. One could look at them so long, that it had an effect upon the thoughts, and these reacted upon the stone, so that it told of old times; at least it had been so with the man who was in search of the Story.

As he came nearer, he noticed a living butterfly sitting on the forehead of the sculptured councillor. The butterfly flapped its wings, and flew a little bit farther, and settled again close by the gravestone, as if to point out what grew there. Four-leaved clover grew there; there were seven of them. When fortune comes, it comes in a heap. He plucked the clover leaves, and put them in his pocket.

'Fortune is as good as ready money, but a new, charming story would be better still,' thought the man; but he could not find it here.

And the sun went down, red and large; the meadow was covered with vapour: the Moor-woman was at her brewing.

It was evening: he stood alone in his room, and looked out upon the sea, over the meadow, over moor and coast. The moon shone bright, a mist was over the meadow, making it look like a great lake; and, indeed, it was once so, as the legend tells – and in the moonlight there was evidence of the truth of the story.

Then the man thought of what he had been reading in the town, that William Tell and Holger the Dane never really lived, but yet live in popular story, like the lake yonder, a living evidence for such myths. Yes, Holger the Dane will return again!

As he stood thus and thought, something beat quite strongly against the window. Was it a bird, a bat, or an owl? Those are not let in, even when they knock. The window flew open of itself, and an old woman looked in at the man.

'What's your pleasure?' said he. 'Who are you? You're looking in at the first floor window. Are you standing on a ladder?'

'You have a four-leaved clover in your pocket,' she replied. 'Indeed, you have seven, and one of them is a six-leaved one.'

'Who are you?' asked the man again.

'The Moor-woman,' she replied. 'The Moor-woman who brews. I was at it. The bung was in the cask, but one of the little moor-imps pulled it out in his mischief, and flung it up into the yard, where it beat against the window; and now the beer's running out of the cask, and that won't do good to anybody.'

'Pray tell me some more!' said the man.

'Ah, wait a little,' answered the Moor-woman. 'I've something else to do just now.' And she was gone.

The man was going to shut the window, when the woman stood before him again.

'Now it's done,' she said; 'but I shall have half the beer to brew over again tomorrow, if the weather is suitable. Well, what have you to ask me? I've come back, for I always keep my word, and you have seven four-leaved clovers in your pocket, and one of them is a six-leaved one. That inspires respect, for that's a decoration that grows beside the highway; but everyone does not find it. What have you to ask me? Don't stand there like a ridiculous oaf, for I must go back again directly to my bung and my cask.'

And the man asked about the Story, and enquired if the Moor-woman had met it in her journeyings.

'By the big brewing-vat!' exclaimed the woman, 'haven't you got stories enough? I really believe that most people have enough of them. Here are other things to take notice of, other things to look after. Even the children have gone beyond that. Give the little boy a cigar, and the little girl a new crinoline; they like that much better. To listen to stories! No, indeed, there are more important things to be done here, and other things to attend to!'

'What do you mean by that?' asked the man, 'and what do you know of the world? You don't see anything but frogs and will-o'-the-wisps!'

'Yes, beware of the will-o'-the-wisps,' said the Moor-woman, 'for they're out – they're let loose – that's what we must talk about! Come to me in the moor, where my presence is necessary, and I will tell you all about it; but you must make haste, and come while your seven four-leaved clovers, of which one has six leaves, are still fresh, and the moon stands high!'

And the Moor-woman was gone.

It struck twelve on the church-clock, and before the last stroke had died away, the man was out in the yard, out in the garden, and stood in the meadow. The mist had vanished, and the Moor-woman stopped her brewing.

'You've been a long time coming!' said the Moor-woman. 'Witches get forward faster than men, and I'm glad that I belong to the witch folk!'

'What have you to say to me now?' asked the man. 'Is it anything about the Story?'

'Can you never get beyond asking about that?' retorted the woman.

'Can you tell me anything about the poetry of the future?' resumed the man.

'Don't get on your stilts,' said the crone, 'and I'll answer you. You think of nothing but poetry, and only ask about that Story, as if she were the lady of the whole troop. She's the oldest of us all, but she always passes for the youngest. I know her well. I've been young, too, and she's no chicken now. I was once quite a pretty elfmaiden, and have danced in my time with the others in the moonlight, and have heard the nightingale, and have gone into the forest and met the

Story-maiden, who was always to be found out there, running about. Sometimes she took up her night's lodging in a half-blown tulip, or in a field flower; sometimes she would slip into the church, and wrap herself in the mourning crape that hung down from the candles on the altar.'

'You are capitally well informed,' said the man.

'I ought at least to know as much as you,' answered the Moor-woman. 'Stories and poetry – yes, they're like two yards of the same piece of stuff: they can go and lie down where they like, and one can brew all their prattle, and have it all the better and cheaper. You shall have it from me for nothing. I have a whole cupboardful of poetry in bottles. It makes essences; and that's the best of it – bitter and sweet herbs. I have everything that people want of poetry, in bottles, so that I can put a little on my handkerchief, on holidays, to smell.'

'Why, these are wonderful things that you're telling!' said the man. 'You have poetry in bottles?'

'More than you can stand,' said the woman. 'I suppose you know the history of "the Girl who trod on the Loaf, so that she might not soil her new Shoes"? That has been written, and printed too.'

'I told that story myself,' said the man.

'Yes, then you must know it; and you must know also that the girl sank into the earth directly, to the Moor-woman, just as Old Bogey's grandmother was paying her morning visit to inspect the brewery. She saw the girl gliding down, and asked to have her as a remembrance of her visit, and got her too; while I received a present that's of no use to me – a travelling druggist's shop – a whole cupboardful of poetry in bottles. Grandmother told me where the cupboard was to be placed, and there it's standing still. Just look! You've your seven four-leaved clovers in your pocket, one of which is a six-leaved one, and so you will be able to see it.'

And really in the midst of the moor lay something like a great knotted block of alder, and that was the old grandmother's cupboard. The Moor-woman said that this was always open to her and to every-one in all lands and at all times, if they only knew where the cupboard stood. It could be opened either at the front or at the back, and at every side and corner – a perfect work of art, and yet only an old alder stump in appearance. The poets of all lands, and especially those of our own country, had been arranged here; the spirit of them had been extracted, refined, criticised and renovated, and then stored up in bottles. With what may be called great aptitude, if it was not genius, the grandmother had taken as it were the flavour of this and of that poet, and had added a little devilry, and then corked up the bottles for use during all future times.

'Pray let me see,' said the man.

'Yes, but there are more important things to hear,' replied the Moor-woman.

'But now we are at the cupboard!' said the man. And he looked in. 'Here are bottles of all sizes. What is in this one? and what in that one yonder?'

'Here is what they call may-balm,' replied the woman: 'I have not tried it myself, but I know that if one sprinkles ever so little of it on the floor, there immediately appears a beautiful woodland lake, with water-lilies, and calla and wild mint. One need only pour two drops on an old exercise-book, even one from the lowest class at school, and the book becomes a whole drama of perfume, which one may very well perform and fall asleep over, the scent of it is so powerful. It is intended as a compliment to me that the label on the flask bears the words, 'The Moorwoman's Brewing'.

Here stands the Scandal-Bottle. It looks as if there were only dirty water in it, and it is dirty water, but with an effervescing power of town-gossip, three ounces of lies and two grains of truth, stirred about with a birch-twig, not one that has been steeped in brine and used on a criminal's back, nor yet a piece of a schoolmaster's birchrod, but one taken direct from the broom with which the gutter has been swept.

Here stands the bottle with pious poetry, written to psalm-tunes. Each drop has a terrifying ring about it, and it is made from the blood and sweat of punishment. Some say it is only dove's gall; but doves are most innocent creatures, and have no gall; so say those who do not know natural history.

Here stood the greatest bottle of all; it occupied half of the cupboard, the bottle of Everyday Stories. Its mouth was covered both with bladder and with pigskin, so that it might lose none of its strength. Each nation could get its own soup here; it came according as one turned about the bottle. Here was old German blood-soup with robber-dumplings in it; also thin peasant-soup with real privy councillors swimming in it. There was English governess-soup and French *potage à la Kock*, made from cocks' legs and sparrows' eggs; but the best soup of all was the Copenhagen. So the family said.

Here stood Tragedy in a champagne bottle; it could pop, and so it ought. Comedy looked like fine sand to throw in people's eyes – that is to say, the finer Comedy; the coarser was also in a bottle, but consisted only of theatre-bills, on which the name of the piece was the strongest item.

The man fell quite into a reverie over this, but the Moor-woman looked farther ahead, and wished to make an end of the matter.

'Now you have seen quite enough of the old cupboard,' she said, 'and know what is in it; but the more important matter which you ought to know, you do not know yet. The Will-o'-the-Wisps are in the town! That's of much more consequence than poetry and stories. I ought, indeed, to hold my tongue; but there must be a necessity – a fate – a something that sticks in my throat, and that wants to come out. Take care, you mortals!'

'I don't understand a word of all this!' cried the man.

'Be kind enough to seat yourself on that cupboard,' she retorted, 'but take care you don't fall through and break the bottles – you know what's inside them. I must tell of the great event. It occurred no longer ago than yesterday. It did not happen earlier. It has now three hundred and sixty-four days to run about. I suppose you know how many days there are in a year?'

And this is what the Moor-woman told: 'There was a great commotion yesterday out here in the marsh! There was a christening feast! A little Will-o'-the-Wisp was born here – in fact, twelve of them were born all together; and they have permission, if they choose to use it, to go abroad among men, and to move about and command among them, just as if they were born mortals. That was a great event in the marsh, and accordingly all the Will-o'-the-Wisps went dancing like little lights across the moor, both male and female, for there are some of them of the female sex, though they are not usually spoken about. I sat there on the cupboard, and had all the twelve little new-born Will-o'-the-Wisps upon my lap: they shone like glow-worms; they already began to hop, and increased in size every moment, so that before a quarter of an hour had elapsed, each of them looked just as large as his father or his uncle. Now, it's an old-established regulation and privilege, that when the moon stands just as it did yesterday, and the wind blows just as it blew then, it is allowed and accorded to all Will-o'-the-Wisps – that is, to all those who are born at that minute of time – to become mortals, and individually to exert their power for the space of one year.

'The Will-o'-the-Wisp may run about in the country and through the world, if it is not afraid of falling into the sea, or of being blown out by a heavy storm. It can enter into a person and speak for him, and make all the movements it pleases. The Will-o'-the-Wisp may take whatever form he likes, of man or woman, and can act in their spirit and in their disguise in such a way that he can effect whatever he wishes to do. But he must manage, in the course of the year, to lead three hundred and sixty-five people into a wrong way, and in a grand style, too: to lead them away from the right and the truth; and then he reaches the highest point that a Will-o'-the-Wisp can attain – to become a runner before the devil's state coach; and then he'll wear clothes of fiery yellow, and breathe forth flames out of his throat. That's enough to make a simple Will-o'-the-Wisp smack his lips. But there's some danger in this, and a great deal of work for a Will-o'-the-Wisp who aspires to play so distinguished a part. If the eyes of the man are opened to what he is, and if the man can then blow him away, it's all over with him, and he must come back into the marsh; or if, before the year is up, the Will-o'-the-Wisp is seized with a longing to see his family, and so returns to it and gives the matter up, it is over with him likewise, and he can no longer burn clear, and soon becomes extinguished, and cannot be lit up again; and when the year has elapsed, and he has not led three hundred and sixty-five people away from the truth and from all that is grand and noble, he is condemned to be imprisoned in decayed wood, and to lie glimmering there without being able to move; and that's the most terrible punishment that can be inflicted on a lively Will-o'-the-Wisp.

'Now, all this I knew, and all this I told to the twelve little Will-o'-the-Wisps whom I had on my lap, and who seemed quite crazy with joy.

'I told them that the safest and most convenient course was to give up the honour, and do nothing at all; but the little flames would not agree to this, and already fancied themselves clad in fiery yellow clothes, breathing flames from their throats.

' "Stay with us," said some of the older ones.

' "Carry on your sport with mortals," said the others.

' "The mortals are drying up our meadows; they've taken to draining. What will our successors do?"

' "We want to flame; we will flame – flame!" cried the new-born Will-o'-the-Wisps.

'And thus the affair was settled.

'And now a ball was given, a minute long; it could not well be shorter. The little elf-maidens whirled round three times with the rest, that they might not appear proud, but they prefer dancing with one another.

'And now the sponsors' gifts were presented, and presents were thrown them. These presents flew like pebbles across the swamp-water. Each of the elf-maidens gave a little piece of her veil.

' "Take that," they said, "and then you'll know the higher dance, the most difficult turns and twists – that is to say, if you should find them necessary. You'll know the proper deportment, and then you can show yourself in the very pick of society."

'The night raven taught each of the young Will-o'-the-Wisps to say, "Goo – goo – good," and to say it in the right place; and that's a great gift, which brings its own reward.

'The owl and the stork also made some remarks – but they said it was not worth mentioning, and so we won't mention it.

'*King Waldemar's wild chase* was just then rushing over the moor, and when the great lords heard of the festivities that were going on, they sent as a present a couple of handsome dogs, which hunt with the speed of the wind, and can well bear two or three of the Will-o'-the-Wisps. A couple of old Nightmares, spirits who support themselves with riding, were also at the feast; and from these the young Will-o'-the-Wisps learned the art of slipping through every keyhole, as if the door stood open before them. These offered to carry the youngsters to the town, with which they were well acquainted. They usually rode through the air on their own back hair, which is fastened into a knot, for they love a hard seat; but now they sat astride on the wild hunting dogs, took the young Will-o'-the-Wisps in their laps, who wanted to go into the town to mislead and entice mortals, and, whisk! away they were. Now, this is what happened last night. Today the Will-o'-the-Wisps are in the town, and have taken the matter in hand – but where and how? Ah, can you tell me that? Still, I've a lightning-conductor in my great toe, and that will always tell me something.'

'Why, this is a complete story,' exclaimed the man.

'Yes, but it is only the beginning,' replied the woman.

Can you tell me how the Will-o'-the-Wisps deport themselves, and how they behave? and in what shapes they have appeared in order to lead people into crooked paths?'

'I believe,' replied the man, 'that one could tell quite a romance about the Will-o'-the-Wisps, in twelve parts; or, better still, one might make quite a popular play of them.'

'You might write that,' said the woman, 'but it's best let alone.'

'Yes, that's better and more agreeable,' the man replied, 'for then we shall escape from the newspapers, and not be tied up by them, which is just as uncomfortable as for a Will-o'-the-Wisp to lie in decaying wood, to have to gleam, and not be able to stir.'

'I don't care about it either way,' cried the woman. 'Let the rest write, those who can, and those who cannot likewise. I'll give you an old tap from my cask that will open the cupboard where poetry is kept in bottles, and you may take from that whatever may be wanting. But you, my good man, seem to have blackened your hands sufficiently with ink, and to have come to that age of sedateness, that you need not be running about every year for stories, especially as there are much more important things to be done. You must have understood what is going on?'

'The Will-o'-the-Wisps are in the town,' said the man. 'I've heard it, and I have understood it. But what do you think I ought to do? I should be thrashed if I were to go to the people and say, "Look, yonder goes a Will-o'-the-Wisp in his best clothes!"'

'They also go in undress,' replied the woman. 'The Will-o'-the-Wisp can assume all kinds of forms, and appear in every place. He goes into the church, but not for the sake of the service; and perhaps he may enter into one or other of the priests. He speaks at the elections, not for the benefit of the country, but only for himself. He's an artist with the colour-pot as well as in the theatre; but when he gets all the power into his own hands, then the pot's empty! I chatter and chatter, but it must come out, what's sticking in my throat, to the disadvantage of my own family. But I must now be the woman that will save a good many people. It is not done with my goodwill, or for the sake of a medal. I do the most insane things I possibly can, and then I tell a poet about it, and thus the whole town gets to know of it directly.'

'The town will not take that to heart,' observed the man; 'that will not disturb a single person; for they will all think I'm only telling them a story when I say with the greatest seriousness, "The Will-o'-the-Wisps are in the town, says the Moor-woman. Take care of yourselves!"'

The Windmill

A WINDMILL stood upon the hill, proud to look at, and it was proud too.

'I am not proud at all,' it said, 'but I am very much enlightened without and within. I have sun and moon for my outward use, and for inward use too; and into the bargain I have stearine candles, train oil lamps, and tallow candles; I may well say that I'm enlightened. I am a thinking being, and so well constructed that it's quite delightful. I have a good set of millstones in my chest, and I have four wings that are placed outside my head, just beneath my hat; the birds have only two wings, and are obliged to carry them on their backs. I am a Dutchman by birth, that may be seen by my figure – a flying Dutchman. They are considered supernatural beings, I know, and yet I am quite natural. I have a gallery round my chest, and house-room beneath it; that's where my thoughts dwell. My strongest thought, who rules and reigns, is called by the others "the man in the mill". He knows what he wants, and is lord over the meal and the bran; but he has his companion too, and she is called "Mother". She is the very heart of me. She does not run about stupidly and awkwardly, for she knows what she wants, she knows what she can do, she's as soft as a zephyr and as strong as a storm; she knows how to begin a thing carefully, and to have her own way. She is my soft temper, and the father is my hard one: they are two, and yet one; they each call the other "My half". These two have some little boys, young thoughts, that can grow. The little ones keep everything stirring. When, lately, in my wisdom, I let the father and the boys examine the millstones and the wheels in my chest, to see what was going on there – for something in me was out of order, and it's well to examine oneself – the little ones made a tremendous noise, which is not a becoming thing when one stands on a hill as I do; there one must remember that one stands in a strong light – that of public opinion. Well, as I was saying, the young ones made a terrible noise. The youngest jumped up into my hat, and shouted there so that it tickled me. The little thoughts may grow; I know that very well; and out in the world thoughts come too, and not only of my kind, for as far as I can see I cannot discern anything like myself; but the wingless houses, whose throats make no noise, have thoughts too, and these come to my thoughts, and make love to them, as it is called. It's wonderful enough – yes, there are many wonderful things. Something has come over me, or into me, something has changed in the mill-work: it seems as if the one-half, the father, had altered, and had received a better temper and a more affectionate helpmate – so young and good, and yet the same, only more gentle and good through the course of time. What was bitter has passed away, and the whole is much more comfortable.

'The days go on, and the days come nearer and nearer to clearness and to joy; and then a day will come when it will be over with me; but not over altogether. I must be pulled down that I may be built up again; I shall cease, but yet shall live on. To become quite a different being, and yet remain the same! That's difficult for me to understand, however enlightened I may be with sun, moon, stearine, train oil, and tallow. My old woodwork and my old brickwork will rise again from the dust!

'I will hope that I may keep my old thoughts, the father in the mill, and the mother, great ones and little ones – the family; for I call them all, great and little, the *company of thoughts*, because I must, and cannot refrain from it.

'And I must also remain "myself", with my throat in my chest, my wings on my head, the gallery round my body; else I should not know myself, nor could the others know me, and say, "There's the mill on the hill, proud to look at, and yet not proud at all." '

That is what the mill said. Indeed, it said much more, but that is the most important part.

And the days came, and the days went, and yesterday was the last day.

Then the mill caught fire. The flames rose up high, and beat out and in, and bit at the beams and planks, and ate them up. The mill fell, and nothing remained of it but a heap of ashes. The smoke drove across the scene of the conflagration, and the wind carried it away.

Whatever had been alive in the mill remained, and lost nothing by that event; it actually gained by it.

The miller's family – one soul, many thoughts, and yet only one – built a new, a splendid mill, which answered its purpose. It was quite like the old one, and people said, 'Why, yonder is the mill on the hill, proud to look at!' But this mill was better arranged, more up to date than the last, so that progress might be made. The old beams had became worm-eaten and spongy – they lay in dust and ashes. The body of the mill did not rise out of the dust as they had believed it would do: they had taken the words literally, and all things are *not* to be taken literally.

The Silver Shilling

THERE WAS once a Shilling. He came out quite bright from the Mint, and sprang up, and rang out, 'Hurrah! now I'm off into the wide world.' And into the wide world he went.

The child held him with warm hands, and the miser with cold clammy hands; the old man turned it over and over many times, while youth rolled him lightly away. The Shilling was of silver, and had very little copper about him: he had been now a whole year in the world – that is to say, in the country in which he had been struck. But one day he started on his foreign travels; he was the last native coin in the purse borne by his travelling master. The gentleman was himself not aware that he still had this coin until it came among his fingers.

'Why, here's a shilling from home left to me,' he said. 'Well, he can make the journey with me.'

And the Shilling rattled and jumped for joy as it was thrust back into the purse. So here it lay among strange companions, who came and went, each making room for a successor; but the Shilling from home always remained in the bag; which was a distinction for it.

Several weeks had gone by, and the Shilling had travelled far out into the world without exactly knowing where he was, though he learned from the other coins that they were French or Italian. One said they were in such and such a town, another that they had reached such and such a spot; but the Shilling could form no idea of all this. He who has his head in a bag sees nothing; and this was the case with the Shilling. But one day, as he lay there, he noticed that the purse was not shut, and so he crept forward to the opening, to take a look around. He ought not to have done so; but he was inquisitive, and people often have to pay for that. He slipped out into the fob: and when the purse was taken out at night the Shilling remained behind, and was sent out into the passage with the clothes. There he fell upon the floor: no one heard it, no one saw it.

Next morning the clothes were carried back into the room; the gentleman put them on, and continued his journey, while the Shilling remained behind. The coin was found, and was required to go into service again, so he was sent out with three other coins.

'It is a pleasant thing to look about one in the world,' thought the Shilling, 'and to get to know other people and other customs.'

'What sort of a shilling is that?' was said at the same moment; 'that is not a coin of the country, it is false, it's of no use.'

And now begins the history of the Shilling, as told by himself.

' "Away with him, he's bad – no use." These words went through and through me,' said the Shilling. 'I knew I was of good silver, sounded well and had been properly coined. The people were certainly mistaken. They could not mean me! but, yes, they did mean me. I was the one of whom they said, "He's bad – he's no good." "I must get rid of that fellow in the dark," said the man who had received me; and I was passed at night, and abused in the daytime. "Bad – no good!" was the cry: "we must make haste and get rid of him."

And I trembled in the fingers of the holder each time I was to be secretly passed on as a coin of the country.

'What a miserable shilling I am! Of what use is my silver to me, my value, my coinage, if all these things are looked on as worthless? In the eyes of the world one has only the value the world chooses to put upon one. It must be terrible indeed to have a bad conscience, and to creep along on evil ways, if I, who am quite innocent, can feel so badly because I am only thought guilty.

'Each time I was brought out I shuddered at the thought of the eyes that would look at me, for I knew that I should be rejected and flung back upon the table, like an impostor and a cheat. Once I came into the hands of a poor old woman, to whom I was paid for a hard day's work, and she could not get rid of me at all. No one would accept me, and I was a perfect worry to the old dame.

' "I shall certainly be forced to deceive someone with this shilling," she said; "for I cannot afford to hoard up a false shilling. The rich baker shall have him; he will be able to bear the loss – but it's wrong in me to do it, after all."

' "And I must lie heavy on that woman's conscience too," sighed I. "Am I really so much changed in my old age?"

'And the woman went her way to the rich baker; but he knew too well what kind of shillings were current, and he threw me back at the woman, who got no bread for me. And I felt miserably low to think that I should be the cause of distress to others – I who had been in my young days so proudly conscious of my value and of the correctness of my mintage. I became as miserable as a poor shilling can be whom no one will accept; but the woman took me home again, and looked at me with a friendly, hearty face, and said, "No, I will not deceive anyone with thee. I will bore a hole through thee, that everyone may see thou art a false thing. And yet – it just occurs to me – perhaps this is a lucky shilling; and the thought comes so strongly upon me that I am sure it must be true! I will make a hole through the shilling, and pass a string through the hole, and hang the coin round the neck of my neighbour's little boy for a lucky shilling."

'So she bored a hole through me. It is certainly not agreeable to have a hole bored through one; but many things can be borne when the intention is good. A thread was passed through the hole, and I became a kind of medal, and was hung round the neck of the little child; and the child smiled at me, and kissed me, and I slept all night on its warm, innocent neck.

'When the morning came, the child's mother took me up in her fingers and looked at me, and she had her own thoughts about me, I could feel that very well. She brought out a pair of scissors, and cut the string through.

' "A lucky shilling!" she said. "Well, we shall soon see that."

'And she laid me in vinegar, so that I turned quite green. Then she plugged up the hole, rubbed me a little, and carried me, in the evening twilight, to the lottery collector, to buy a lottery ticket that should bring her luck.

'How miserably wretched I felt! There was a heavy feeling in me, as if I should break in two. I knew that I should be called false and thrown down – and before a crowd of shillings and other coins, too, who lay there with an image and superscription of which they might be proud. But I escaped, for there were many people in the collector's room – he had a great deal to do, and I went rattling down into the box among the other coins. Whether my ticket won anything or not I don't know; but this I do know, that the very next morning I was recognised as a bad shilling, and was sent out to deceive and deceive again. That is a very trying thing to bear when one knows one has a good character, and of that I *am* conscious.

'For a year and a day I thus wandered from house to house and from hand to hand, always abused, always unwelcome; no one trusted me; and I lost confidence in the world and in myself. It was a heavy time. At last, one day a traveller, a strange gentleman, arrived, and I was passed to him, and he was innocent enough to accept me for current coin; but he wanted to pass me on, and again I heard the cry, "No use – false!"

' "I received it as a good coin," said the man, and he looked closely at me: suddenly he smiled all over his face; and I had never seen that expression before on any face that looked at me. "Why, whatever is that?" he said. "That's one of our own country coins, a good honest shilling from my home, and they've bored a hole through him, and they call him false. Now, this is a curious circumstance. I must keep him and take him home with me."

'A glow of joy thrilled through me when I heard myself called a good honest shilling; and now I was to be taken home, where each and everyone would know me, and be sure that I was real silver and properly coined. I could have thrown out sparks for very gladness; but, after all, it's not in my nature to throw out sparks, for that's the property of steel, not of silver.

'I was wrapped up in clean white paper, so that I should not be confounded with the other coins, and spent; and on festive occasions, when fellow countrymen met together, I was shown about, and they spoke very well of me: they said I was interesting – and it is wonderful how interesting one can be without saying a single word.

'And at last I got home again. All my troubles were ended, joy came back to me, for I was of good silver, and had the right stamp, and I had no more disagreeables to endure, though a hole had been bored through me, as through a false coin; but that does not matter if one is not really false. One must wait for the end, and one will be righted at last – that's my belief,' said the Shilling.

The Bishop of Börglum and his Kinsmen

NOW WE are up in Jutland, quite beyond the 'wild moor'. We hear what is called the 'Western wow-wow' – the roar of the North Sea as it breaks against the western coast of Jutland – and we are quite near to it, but before us rises a great mound of sand – a mountain we have long seen, and towards which we are wending our way, driving slowly along through the deep sand. On this mountain of sand is a lofty old building – the convent of Börglum. In one of its wings (the larger one) there is still a church. And at this we arrive in the late evening hour; but the weather is clear in the bright June night around us, and the eye can range far, far over field and moor to the Bay of Aalborg, over heath and meadow, and far across the sea.

Now we are there, and roll past between barns and other farm buildings; and at the left of the gate we turn aside to the old Castle Farm, where the lime trees stand in lines along the walls, and, sheltered from the wind and weather, grow so luxuriantly that their twigs and leaves almost conceal the windows.

We mount the winding staircase of stone, and march through the long passages under the heavy roof-beams. The wind moans very strangely here, both within and without. It is hardly known how, but the people say – yes, people say a great many things when they are frightened or want to frighten others – they say that the old dead canons glide silently past us into the church, where mass is sung. They can be heard in the rushing of the storm, and their singing brings up strange thoughts in the hearers – thoughts of the old times into which we are carried back.

On the coast a ship is stranded; and the bishop's warriors are there, and spare not those whom the sea has spared. The sea washes away the blood that has flowed from the cloven skulls. The stranded goods belong to the bishop, and there is a store of goods here. The sea casts

up casks and barrels filled with costly wine for the convent cellar, and in the convent is already good store of beer and mead. There is plenty in the kitchen – dead game and poultry, hams and sausages; and fat fish swim in the ponds without.

The Bishop of Börglum is a mighty lord. He has great possessions, but still he longs for more – everything must bow before the mighty Olaf Glob. His rich cousin at Thyland is dead. 'Kinsman is worst to kinsman': his widow will find this saying true. Her husband has possessed all Thyland, with the exception of the Church property. Her son was not at home. In his boyhood he had already been sent abroad to learn foreign customs, as it was his wish to do. For years there had been no news of him. Perhaps he had long been laid in the grave, and would never come back to his home, to rule where his mother then ruled.

'What has a woman to do with rule?' said the bishop.

He summoned the widow before a law court; but what did he gain thereby? The widow had never been disobedient to the law, and was strong in her just rights.

Bishop Olaf of Börglum, what dost thou purpose? What writest thou on yonder smooth parchment, sealing it with thy seal, and entrusting it to the horsemen and servants, who ride away – far away – to the city of the Pope?

It is the time of falling leaves and of stranded ships, and soon icy winter will come.

Twice had icy winter returned before the bishop welcomed the horsemen and servants back to their home. They came from Rome with a papal decree – a ban, or bull, against the widow who had dared to offend the pious bishop. 'Cursed be she and all that belongs to her. Let her be expelled from the congregation and the Church. Let no man stretch forth a helping hand to her, and let friends and relations avoid her as a plague and a pestilence!'

'What will not bend must break,' said the Bishop of Börglum.

And all forsake the widow; but she holds fast to her God. He is her helper and defender.

One servant only – an old maid – remained faithful to her; and, with the old servant, the widow herself followed the plough; and the crop grew, although the land had been cursed by the Pope and by the bishop.

'Thou child of perdition, I will yet carry out my purpose!' cried the Bishop of Börglum. 'Now will I lay the hand of the Pope upon thee, to summon thee before the tribunal that shall condemn thee!'

Then did the widow yoke the two last oxen that remained to her to a wagon, and mounted up on the wagon, with her old servant, and travelled away across the heath out of the Danish land. As a stranger she came into a foreign country, where a strange tongue was spoken and where new customs prevailed. Farther and farther she journeyed, to where green hills rise into mountains, and the vine clothes their sides. Strange merchants drive by her, and they look anxiously after their wagons laden with merchandise. They fear an attack from the armed followers of the robberknights. The two poor women, in their humble vehicle drawn by two black oxen, travel fearlessly through the dangerous sunken road and through the darksome forest. And now they were in France. And there met them a stalwart knight, with a train of twelve armed followers. He paused, gazed at the strange vehicle, and questioned the women as to the goal of their journey and the place whence they came. Then one of them mentioned Thyland in Denmark, and spoke of her sorrows – of her woes – which were soon to cease, for so Divine Providence had willed it. For the stranger knight is the widow's son! He seized her hand, he embraced her, and the mother wept. For years she had not been able to weep, but had only bitten her lips till the blood started.

It is the time of falling leaves and of stranded ships.

The sea rolled wine-casks to the shore for the bishop's cellar. In the kitchen the deer roasted on the spit before the fire. At Börglum it was warm and cheerful in the heated rooms, while cold winter raged without, when a piece of news was brought to the bishop: 'Jens Glob, of Thyland, has come back, and his mother with him.' Jens Glob laid a complaint against the bishop, and summoned him before the temporal and the spiritual court.

'That will avail him little,' said the bishop. 'Best leave off thy efforts, knight Jens.'

Again it is the time of falling leaves, of stranded ships – icy winter comes again, and the 'white bees' are swarming, and sting the traveller's face till they melt.

'Keen weather today!' say the people, as they step in.

Jens Glob stands by the fire, so deeply wrapped in thought that he singes the skirt of his long garment.

'Thou Börglum bishop,' he exclaims, 'I shall subdue thee after all! Under the shield of the Pope, the law cannot reach thee; but Jens Glob shall reach thee!'

Then he writes a letter to his brother-in-law, Olaf Hase, in Sallingland, and prays that knight to meet him on Christmas-eve, at matins, in the church at Widberg. The bishop himself is to say the mass, and consequently will journey from Börglum to Thyland; and this is known to Jens Glob.

Moorland and meadow are covered with ice and snow. The marsh will bear horse and rider, the bishop with his priests and armed men. They ride the shortest way, through the brittle reeds, where the wind moans sadly.

Blow thy brazen trumpet, thou trumpeter clad in foxskin! it sounds merrily in the clear air. So they ride on over heath and moorland – over what is the garden of Fata Morgana in the hot summer, towards the church of Widberg.

The wind is blowing his trumpet too – blowing it harder and harder. He blows up a storm – a terrible storm – that increases more and more. Towards the church they ride, as fast as they may through the storm. The church stands firm, but the storm careers on over field and moorland, over land and sea.

Börglum's bishop reaches the church; but Olaf Hase will scarce do so, hard as he may ride. He journeys with his warriors on the farther side of the bay, to help Jens Glob, now that the bishop is to be summoned before the judgement seat of the Highest.

The church is the judgement hall; the altar is the council table. The lights burn clear in the heavy brass candelabra. The storm reads out the accusation and the sentence, resounding in the air over moor and heath, and over the rolling waters. No ferry-boat can sail over the bay in such weather as this.

Olaf Hase makes halt at Ottesund. There he dismisses his warriors, presents them with their horses and harness, and gives them leave to ride home and greet his wife. He intends to risk his life alone in the roaring waters; but they are to bear witness for him that it is not his fault if Jens Glob stands without reinforcement in the church at Widberg. The faithful warriors will not leave him, but follow him out into the deep waters. Ten of them are carried away; but Olaf Hase and two of the youngest men reach the farther side. They have still four miles to ride.

It is past midnight. It is Christmas. The wind has abated. The church is lighted up; the gleaming radiance shines through the window-panes, and pours out over meadow and heath. The mass has long been finished, silence reigns in the church, and the wax is heard dropping from the candles to the stone pavement. And now Olaf Hase arrives.

In the forecourt Jens Glob greets him kindly, and says, 'I have just made an agreement with the bishop.'

'Sayest thou so?' replied Olaf Hase. 'Then neither thou nor the bishop shall quit this church alive.'

And the sword leaps from the scabbard, and Olaf Hase deals a blow that makes the panel of the church door, which Jens Glob hastily closes between them, fly in fragments.

'Hold, brother! First hear what the agreement was that I made. I have slain the bishop and his warriors and priests. They will have no word more to say in the matter, nor will I speak again of all the wrong that my mother has endured.'

The long wicks of the altar lights glimmer red; but there is a redder gleam upon the pavement, where the bishop lies with cloven skull, and his dead warriors around him in the quiet of the holy Christmas night.

And four days afterwards the bells toll for a funeral in the convent of Börglum. The murdered bishop and the slain warriors and priests are displayed under a black canopy, surrounded by candelabra decked with crape. There lies the dead man, in the black cloak wrought with silver; the crosier in the powerless hand that was once so mighty. The incense rises in clouds, and the monks chant the funeral hymn. It sounds like a wail – it sounds like a sentence of wrath and condemnation that must be heard far over the land, carried by the wind – sung by the wind – the wail that sometimes is silent, but never dies; for ever again it rises in song, singing even into our own time this legend of the Bishop of Börglum and his hard nephew. It is heard in the dark night by the frightened husbandman, driving by in the heavy sandy road past the convent of Börglum. It is heard by the sleepless listener in the thickly-walled rooms at Börglum. And not only to the ear of superstition is the sighing and the tread of hurrying feet audible in the long echoing passages leading to the convent door that has long been locked. The door still seems to open, and the lights seem to flame in the brazen candlesticks; the fragrance of incense arises; the church gleams in its ancient splendour; and the monks sing and say the mass over the slain bishop, who lies there in the black silver-embroidered mantle, with the crosier in his powerless hand; and on his pale proud forehead gleams the red wound like fire, and there burn the worldly mind and the wicked thoughts . . .

Sink down into his grave – into oblivion – ye terrible shapes of the times of old!

Hark to the raging of the angry wind, sounding above the rolling sea! Outside a storm approaches, calling aloud for human lives. The sea has not put on a new mind with the new time. This night it is a horrible pit to devour up lives, and tomorrow, perhaps, it may be a glassy mirror – even as in the old time that we have buried. Sleep sweetly, if thou canst sleep!

Now it is morning.

The new time flings sunshine into the room. The wind still keeps up mightily. A wreck is announced – as in the old time.

During the night, down yonder by Lökken, the little fishing village with the red-tiled roofs – we can see it up here from the window – a ship has come ashore. It has struck, and is fast embedded in the sand; but the rocket apparatus has thrown a rope on board, and formed a bridge from the wreck to the mainland; and all on board are saved, and reach the land, and are wrapped in warm blankets; and today they are invited to the farm at the convent of Börglum. In comfortable rooms they encounter hospitality and friendly faces. They are addressed in the language of their country, and the piano sounds for them with melodies of their native land; and before these have died away, the chord has been struck, the wire of thought that reaches to the land of the sufferers announces that they are rescued. Then their anxieties are dispelled; and in the evening they join in the dance, at the feast given in the great hall at Börglum. Waltzes and other dances will be danced, and songs will be sung of Denmark and of 'The Gallant Soldier' of the present day.

Blessed be thou, new time! Speak thou of summer and of purer gales! Send thy sunbeams gleaming into our hearts and thoughts! On thy glowing canvas let them be painted – the dark legends of the rough hard times that are past!

In the Nursery

FATHER, and mother, and brothers, and sisters, were gone to the play; only little Anna and her godfather were left at home. 'We'll have a play too,' he said; 'and it may begin immediately.'

'But we have no theatre,' cried little Anna, 'and we have no one to act for us: my old doll cannot, for she is a fright, and my new one cannot, for she must not rumple her new clothes.'

'One can always get actors if one makes use of what one has,' observed Godfather.

'Now we build the theatre. Here we will put up a book, there another, and there a third, in a sloping row. Now three on the other side; so, now we have the side-scenes. The old box that lies yonder may be the background; and we'll turn the bottom outwards. The stage represents a room, as everyone may see. Now we want the actors. Let us see what we can find in the play-box. First the personages, and then we will get the play ready: one after the other, that will be capital! Here's a pipe-head, and yonder an odd glove; they will do very well for father and daughter.'

'But those are only two characters,' said little Anna. 'Here's my brother's old waistcoat – could not that play in our piece, too?'

'It's big enough, certainly,' replied Godfather. 'It shall be the lover. There's nothing in the pockets, and that's very interesting, for that's half of an unfortunate attachment. And here we have the nutcrackers' boots, with spurs to them. Row, dow, dow! how they can stamp and strut! They shall represent the unwelcome wooer, whom the lady does not like. What kind of play will you have now? Shall it be a tragedy, or a domestic drama?'

'A domestic drama, please,' said little Anna; 'for the others are so fond of that. Do you know one?'

'I know a hundred,' said Godfather. 'Those that are most in favour are from the French, but they are not good for little girls. In the meantime, we may take one of the prettiest, for inside they're all very much alike. Now I shake the pen! Cock-a-lorum! So now, here's the play, brin-bran-span new! Now listen to the play-bill.'

And Godfather took a newspaper, and read as if he were reading from it:

The Pipe-Head and the Good Head
A Family Drama in one Act

CHARACTERS

Mr Pipe-head, *a father*.	Mr Waistcoat, *a lover*.
Miss Glove, *a daughter*.	Mr de Boots, *a suitor*.

'And now we're going to begin. The curtain rises: we have no curtain, so it has risen already. All the characters are there, and so we have them at hand. Now I speak as Papa Pipe-head! he's angry today. One can see that he's a coloured meerschaum.

' "Snip-snap-snurre, bassellurre! I'm master in my own house! I'm the father of my daughter! Will you hear what I have to say? Mr de Boots is a person in whom one may see one's face; his upper part is of morocco, and he has spurs into the bargain. Snip-snap-snurre! He shall have my daughter!"

'Now listen to what the Waistcoat says, little Anna,' said Godfather. 'Now the Waistcoat's speaking. The Waistcoat has a lie-down collar, and is very modest; but he knows his own value, and has quite a right to say what he says: "I haven't a spot on me! Goodness of material ought to be appreciated. I am of real silk, and have strings to me." '

' " – On the wedding day, but no longer; you don't keep your colour in the wash." This is Mr Pipe-head who is speaking. "Mr de Boots is watertight, of strong leather, and yet very delicate; he can creak, and clank with his spurs, and has an Italian physiognomy –" '

'But they ought to speak in verse,' said Anna, 'for I've heard that's the most charming way of all.'

'They can do that too,' replied Godfather; 'and as the public demands, so one talks. Just look at little Miss Glove, how she's pointing her fingers!

Rather live and wait,
A glove without a mate!
Ah!
If I from him must part,
I'm sure 'twill break my heart!
'Bah!'

That last word was spoken by Mr Pipe-head; and now it's Mr Waistcoat's turn:

O Glove, my own dear,
Though it cost thee a tear,
Thou must be mine,
For Holger the Dane has sworn it!

'Mr de Boots, hearing this, kicks up, jingles his spurs, and knocks down three of the side-scenes.'

'That's exceedingly charming!' cried little Anna.

'Silence! silence!' said Godfather. 'Silent approbation will show that you are the educated public in the stalls. Now Miss Glove sings her great song with startling effects:

I cannot talk, heigho!
And therefore I will crow!
Kikkeriki, in the lofty hall!

'Now comes the exciting part, little Anna. This is the most important in all the play. Mr Waistcoat undoes himself, and addresses his speech to you, that you may applaud; but leave it alone, that's considered more genteel.

' "I am driven to extremities! Take care of yourself! Now comes the plot! You are the Pipe-head, and I am the good head – snap! there you go!"

'Do you notice this, little Anna?' asked Godfather. 'That's a most charming scene and comedy. Mr Waistcoat seized the old Pipe-head, and put him in his pocket; there he lies, and the Waistcoat says: "You are in my pocket; you can't come out till you promise to unite me to your daughter Glove on the left: I hold out my right hand." '

'That's awfully pretty,' said little Anna.

'And now the old Pipe-head replies:

> My head's in a hum,
> So confused I've become;
> Where's my humour? Gone, I fear,
> And I feel my hollow stick's not here.
> Ah! never, my dear,
> Did I feel so queer.
> Oh! take out my head
> From your pocket, I pray;
> And my daughter and you
> May be married today.

'Is the play over already?' asked little Anna.

'By no means,' replied Godfather. 'It's only all over with Mr de Boots. Now the lovers kneel down, and one of them sings:

> Father!

and the other,

> Take back your head again,
> And bless your son and daughter.

And they receive his blessing, and celebrate their wedding, and all the pieces of furniture sing in chorus,

> Clink! clanks!
> A thousand thanks;
> And now the play is over!

'And now we'll applaud,' said Godfather. 'We'll call them all out, and the pieces of furniture too, for they are of mahogany.'

'And is our play just as good as those which the others have in the real theatre?'

'Our play is much better,' said Godfather. 'It is shorter, it has been given free, and it has passed away the hour before tea-time.'

The Golden Treasure

THE DRUMMER'S wife went into the church. She saw the new altar with the painted pictures and the carved angels: they were so beautiful, both those upon the canvas, in colours and with haloes, and those that were carved in wood, and painted and gilt into the bargain. Their hair gleamed golden in the sunshine, lovely to behold; but the real sunshine was more beautiful still. It shone redder, clearer through the dark trees, when the sun went down. It was lovely thus to look at the sunshine of heaven. And she looked at the red sun, and she thought about it so deeply, and thought of the little one whom the stork was to bring; and the wife of the drummer was very cheerful, and looked and looked, and wished that the child might have a gleam of sunshine given to it, so that it might at last become like one of the shining angels over the altar.

And when she really had the little child in her arms, and held it up to its father, then it was like one of the angels in the church to behold, with hair like gold – the gleam of the setting sun was upon it.

'My golden treasure, my riches, my sunshine!' said the mother; and she kissed the shining locks, and it sounded like music and song in the room of the drummer; and there was joy, and life, and movement. The drummer beat a roll – a roll of joy. And the Drum, the Fire-drum, that was beaten when there was a fire in the town, said:

'Red hair! the little fellow has red hair! Believe the drum, and not what your mother says! Rub–a–dub, rub–a–dub!'

And the town repeated what the Fire-drum had said.

The boy was taken to church; the boy was christened. There was nothing much to be said about his name; he was called Peter. The whole town, and the Drum too, called him 'Peter the drummer's boy with the red hair'; but his mother kissed his red hair, and called him her golden treasure.

In the hollow way in the clayey bank, many had scratched their names as a remembrance.

'Celebrity is always something!' said the drummer; and so he scratched his own name there, and his little son's name likewise.

And the swallows came: they had, on their long journey, seen more durable characters engraven on rocks, and on the walls of the temples in Hindustan, mighty deeds of great kings, immortal names, so old that no one now could read or speak them. Remarkable celebrity!

In the clayey bank the martins built their nest: they bored holes in the deep declivity, and the splashing rain and the thin mist came and crumbled and washed the names away, and the drummer's name also, and that of his little son.

'Peter's name remained, however, a year and a half!' said the father.

'Fool!' thought the Fire-drum; but it only said, 'Dub, dub, dub, rub– a–dub!'

He was a boy full of life and gladness, this drummer's son with the red hair. He had a lovely voice: he could sing, and he sang like a bird in the woodland. There was melody, and yet no melody.

'He must become a choirboy,' said his mother. 'He shall sing in the church, and stand under the beautiful gilded angels who are like him!'

'Fiery cat!' said some of the witty ones of the town.

The Drum heard that from the neighbours' wives.

'Don't go home, Peter,' cried the street boys. 'If you sleep in the garret, there'll be a fire in the house, and the fire-drum will have to be beaten.'

'Look out for the drumsticks,' replied Peter; and, small as he was, he ran up boldly, and gave the foremost such a punch in the body with his fist that the fellow lost his legs and tumbled over, and the others took their legs off with themselves very rapidly.

The town musician was very genteel and fine. He was the son of the royal plate-washer. He was very fond of Peter, and would sometimes take him to his home, and he gave him a violin, and taught him to play it. It seemed as if the whole art lay in the boy's fingers; and he wanted to be more than a drummer – he wanted to become musician to the town.

'I'll be a soldier,' said Peter; for he was still quite a little lad, and it seemed to him the finest thing in the world to carry a gun, and to be able to march 'left, right, left, right,' and to wear a uniform and a sword.

'Ah, you must learn to obey the drum-skin, drum, dum, dum!' said the Drum.

'Yes, if he could only march his way up to be a general!' observed his father; 'but before he can do that there must be war.'

'Heaven forbid!' said his mother.

'We have nothing to lose,' remarked the father.

'Yes, we have my boy,' she retorted.

'But suppose he came back a general!' said the father.

'Without arms and legs!' cried the mother. 'No, I would rather keep my golden treasure whole.'

'Drum, dum, dum!' The Fire-drum and all the other drums were beating, for war had come. The soldiers all set out, and the son of the drummer followed them. 'Red-head. Golden treasure!'

The mother wept; the father in fancy saw him 'famous'; the town musician was of opinion that he ought not to go to war, but should stay at home and learn music.

'Red-head,' said the soldiers, and little Peter laughed; but when one of them sometimes said to another, 'Foxey,' he would bite his teeth together and look another way – into the wide world: he did not care for the nickname.

The boy was active, pleasant of speech, and good humoured; and these qualities are the best canteen, said his elder comrades.

And many a night he had to sleep under the open sky, wet through with the driving rain or the falling mist; but his good humour never forsook him. The drumsticks sounded, 'Rub–a–dub, all up, all up!' Yes, he was certainly born to be a drummer.

The day of battle dawned. The sun had not yet risen, but the morning was come. The air was cold, the battle was hot, there was mist in the air, but still more gunpowder-smoke. The bullets and shells flew over the soldiers' heads, and into their heads, into their bodies and limbs; but still they pressed forward. Here or there one or other of them would sink on his knees, with bleeding temples and a face as white as chalk. The little drummer still kept his healthy colour; he had suffered no damage; he looked cheerfully at the dog of the regiment, which was jumping along as merrily as if the whole thing had been got up for his amusement, and as if the bullets were only flying about that he might have a game of play with them.

'March! Forward! March!' These were the words of command for the drum, and they were words not to be taken back; but they may be taken back at times, and there may be wisdom in doing so; and now at last the word 'Retire' was given; but our little drummer beat 'Forward! march!' for so he had understood the command, and the soldiers obeyed the sound of the drum. That was a good roll, and proved the summons to victory for the men, who had already begun to give way.

Life and limb were lost in the battle. Bombshells tore away the flesh in red strips; bombshells lit up into a terrible glow the straw-heaps to which the wounded had dragged themselves, to lie untended for many hours, perhaps for all the hours they had to live.

It's no use thinking of it; and yet one cannot help thinking of it, even far away in the peaceful town. The drummer and his wife also thought of it, for Peter was at the war.

'Now, I'm tired of these complaints,' said the Fire-drum.

Again the day of battle dawned; the sun had not yet risen, but it was morning. The drummer and his wife were asleep, which they had not been nearly all night: they had been talking about their son, who was out yonder, in God's hand. And the father dreamt that the war was over, that the soldiers had returned home, and that Peter wore a silver cross on his breast. But the mother dreamt that she had gone into the church, and had seen the painted pictures and the carved angels with the gilded hair, and her own dear boy, the golden treasure of her heart, who was standing among the angels in white robes, singing so sweetly, as surely only the angels can sing; and that he had soared up with them into the sunshine, and nodded so kindly at his mother.

'My golden treasure!' she cried out; and she awoke. 'Now the good God has taken him to Himself!' She folded her hands, and hid her face in the cotton curtains of the bed, and wept. 'Where does he rest now? among the many in the big grave that they have dug for the dead?

Perhaps he's in the water in the marsh! Nobody knows his grave; no holy words have been read over it!' And the Lord's Prayer went inaudibly over her lips; she bowed her head, and was so weary that she went to sleep.

And the days went by, in life and in dreams!

It was evening: over the battlefield a rainbow spread, which touched the forest and the deep marsh.

It has been said, and is preserved in popular belief, that where the rainbow touches the earth a treasure lies buried, a golden treasure; and here there was one. No one but his mother thought of the little drummer, and therefore she dreamt of him.

And the days went by, in life and in dreams!

Not a hair of his head had been hurt, not a golden hair.

'Drum–ma–rum! drum–ma–rum! there he is!' the Drum might have said, and his mother might have sung, if she had seen or dreamt it.

With hurrah and song, adorned with green wreaths of victory, they came home, as the war was at an end, and peace had been signed. The dog of the regiment sprang on in front with large bounds, and made the way three times as long for himself as it really was.

And days and weeks went by, and Peter came into his parents' room: he was as brown as a wild man, and his eyes were bright, and his face beamed like sunshine. And his mother held him in her arms; she kissed his lips, his eyes, his red hair. She had her boy back again; he had not a silver cross on his breast, as his father had dreamt, but he had sound limbs, a thing the mother had not dreamt. And what a rejoicing was there! They laughed and they wept; and Peter embraced the old Fire-drum.

'There stands the old skeleton still!' he said.

And the father beat a roll upon it.

'One would think that a great fire had broken out here,' said the Fire-drum. 'Bright day! fire in the heart! golden treasure! skrat! skr–r–at! skr–r–r–r–at!'

And what then? What then? Ask the town musician.

'Peter's far outgrowing the drum,' he said. 'Peter will be greater than I.'

And yet he was the son of a royal plate-washer; but all that he had learned in half a lifetime, Peter learned in half a year.

There was something so merry about him, something so truly kind-hearted. His eyes gleamed, and his hair gleamed too – there was no denying that!

'He ought to have his hair dyed,' said the neighbour's wife. 'That answered capitally with the policeman's daughter, and she got a husband.'

'But her hair turned as green as duckweed, and was always having to be coloured up.'

'She can afford that,' said the neighbours, 'and so can Peter. He goes to the most genteel houses, even to the burgomaster's, where he gives Miss Charlotte pianoforte lessons.'

He *could* play! He could play, fresh out of his heart, the most charming pieces, that had never been put upon music-paper. He played in the bright nights, and in the dark nights too. The neighbours declared it was unbearable, and the Fire-drum was of the same opinion.

He played until his thoughts scared up, and burst forth in great plans for the future:

'To be famous!'

And Burgomaster's Charlotte sat at the piano. Her delicate fingers danced over the keys, and made them ring into Peter's heart. It seemed too much for him to bear; and this happened not once, but many times; and at last one day he seized the delicate fingers and the white hand, and kissed it, and looked into her great brown eyes. Heaven knows what he said; but we may be allowed to guess at it. Charlotte blushed to guess at it. She reddened from brow to neck, and answered not a single word; and then strangers came into the room, and one of them was the state councillor's son: he had a lofty white forehead, and carried it so high that it seemed to go back into his neck. And Peter sat with them a long time, and she looked at him with gentle eyes.

At home that evening he spoke of travel in the wide world, and of the golden treasure that lay hidden for him in his violin.

'To be famous!'

'Tum–me–lum, tum–me–lum, tum–me–lum!' said the Fire-drum. 'Peter has gone clean out of his wits. I think there must be a fire in the house.'

Next day the mother went to market.

'Shall I tell you news, Peter?' she asked when she came home. 'A capital piece of news. Burgomaster's Charlotte has engaged herself to the state councillor's son; the betrothal took place yesterday evening.'

'No!' cried Peter, and he sprang up from his chair. But his mother persisted in saying 'Yes'. She had heard it from the barber's wife, whose husband had it from the burgomaster's own mouth.

And Peter became as pale as death, and sat down again.

'Good Heaven! what's the matter with you?' asked his mother.

'Nothing, nothing; only leave me to myself,' he answered, but the tears were running down his cheeks.

'My sweet child, my golden treasure!' cried the mother, and she wept; but the Fire-drum sang – not out loud, but inwardly, 'Charlotte's gone! Charlotte's gone! and now the song is done.'

But the song was not done; there were many more verses in it, long verses, the most beautiful verses, the golden treasures of a life.

'She behaves like a mad woman,' said the neighbour's wife. 'All the world is to see the letters she gets from her golden treasure, and to read the words that are written in the papers about his violin-playing. And he sends her money too, and that's very useful to her since she has been a widow.'

'He plays before emperors and kings,' said the town musician. 'I never had that fortune; but he's my pupil, and he does not forget his old master.'

And his mother said, 'His father dreamt that Peter came home from the war with a silver cross. He did not gain one in the war; but it is still more difficult to gain one in this way. Now he has the cross of honour. If his father had only lived to see it!'

'He's grown famous!' said the Fire-drum; and all his native town said the same thing, for the drummer's son, Peter with the red hair – Peter whom they had known as a little boy, running about in wooden shoes, and then as a drummer, playing for the dancers – was become famous!

'He played at our house before he played in the presence of kings,' said the burgomaster's wife. 'At that time he was quite smitten with Charlotte. He was always of an aspiring turn. At that time he was saucy and an enthusiast. My husband laughed when he heard of the foolish affair, and now our Charlotte's a state councillor's wife.'

A golden treasure had been hidden in the heart and soul of the poor child, who had beaten the roll as a drummer – a roll of victory for those who had been ready to retreat. There was a golden treasure in his bosom, the power of sound: it burst forth on his violin as if the instrument had been a complete organ, and as if all the elves of a midsummer night were dancing across the strings. In its sounds were heard the piping of the thrush and the full clear note of the human voice; therefore the sound brought rapture to every heart, and carried his name triumphant through the land. That was a great firebrand – the firebrand of inspiration.

'And then he looks so splendid!' said the young ladies and the old ladies too; and the oldest of all procured an album for famous locks of hair, wholly and solely that she might beg a lock of his rich splendid hair, that treasure, that golden treasure.

And the son came into the poor room of the drummer, elegant as a prince, happier than a king. His eyes were as clear and his face as radiant as sunshine; and he held his mother in his arms, and she kissed his mouth, and wept as blissfully as anyone can weep for joy; and he nodded at every old piece of furniture in the room, at the cupboard with the teacups, and at the flower-vase. He nodded at the sleeping-bench, where he had slept as a little boy; but the old Fire-drum he brought out, and dragged it into the middle of the room, and said to it and to his mother:

'My father would have beaten a famous roll this evening. Now I must do it!'

And he beat a thundering roll-call on the instrument, and the Drum felt so highly honoured that the parchment burst with exultation.

'He has a splendid touch!' said the Drum. 'I've a remembrance of him now that will last. I expect that the same thing will happen to his mother, from pure joy over her golden treasure.'

And this is the story of the Golden Treasure.

The Storm Shifts the Signs

IN THE old days, when Grandpapa was quite a little boy, and ran about in little red breeches and a red coat, a sash round his waist, and a feather in his cap – for that's the costume the little boys wore in his time when they were dressed in their best – many things were very different from what they are now: there was often a good deal of show in the streets – show that we don't see nowadays, because it has been abolished as too old-fashioned: still, it is very interesting to hear Grandfather tell about it.

It must really have been a gorgeous sight to behold, in those days, when the shoemakers shifted their sign, when they changed their guild-hall. The silken flag waved, on it a double-headed eagle was displayed, and a big boot; the youngest lads carried the welcome cup, and the chest of the guild, and their shirt-sleeves were adorned with red and white ribbons; the elder ones carried drawn swords, each with a lemon stuck on its point. There was a full band of music, and the most splendid of all the instruments was the 'bird', as Grandfather called the big stick with the crescent at the top, and all manner of dingle-dangles hanging to it, a perfect Turkish clatter of music. The stick was lifted high in the air, and swung up and down till it jingled again, and quite dazzled one's eyes when the sun shone on all its glory of gold, and silver, and brass.

In front of the procession ran the Harlequin, dressed in clothes made of all kinds of coloured patches artfully sewn together, with a black face, and bells on his head like a sledge horse: he beat the people with his bat, which made a great clattering without hurting them, and the people pushed each other in order to move back or move forward the next moment. Little boys and girls fell over their own toes into the gutter, old women dispensed digs with their elbows, and looked sour, and scolded. One laughed, another chatted; the people thronged the

windows and doorsteps, and even all the roofs. The sun shone; and although they had a little rain too, that was good for the farmer; and when they got wetted thoroughly, they only thought what a blessing it was for the country.

And what stories Grandpapa could tell! As a little boy he had seen all these fine doings in their greatest pomp. The oldest member of the guild used to make a speech from the platform on which the shield was hung up, and the speech was in verses, as if it had been made by a poet, as, indeed, it had; for three people had concocted it together, and they had first drunk a good bowl of punch, so that the speech might turn out well.

And the people gave a cheer for the speech, but they shouted much louder for the Harlequin, when he appeared in front of the platform, and made a grimace at them.

The fool played the fool most admirably, and drank mead out of spirit-glasses, which he then flung among the crowd, by whom they were caught up. Grandfather was the possessor of one of these glasses, which had been given him by a plasterer, who had managed to catch it. Such a scene was really very pleasant; and the shield on the new guild-house was hung with flowers and green wreaths.

'One never forgets a display like that, however old one may grow,' said Grandfather. Nor did he forget it, though he saw many other grand spectacles in his time, and could tell about them too; but it was most pleasant of all to hear him tell about shifting the signs in the great town itself.

Once, when he was a little boy, Grandpapa had gone there with his parents. He had never yet been in the metropolis of the country. There were so many people in the streets, that he thought that the signs were being moved; and there were many signs to move here; a hundred rooms might have been filled with them, if they had been hung up inside, and not outside. At the tailor's were pictures of all kinds of clothing, to show that he could stitch up people from the coarsest to the finest; at the tobacco manufacturer's were pictures of the most charming little boys, smoking cigars, just as they do in reality; there were signs with painted butter and herrings, clerical collars, and coffins, and inscriptions and announcements into the bargain. A person could walk up and down for a whole day through the streets, and tire himself out with looking at the pictures; and then he would know all about what people lived in the houses, for they had hung out their signs; and, as Grandfather said, it was a very instructive thing, in a great town, to know at once who the inhabitants were.

And this is what happened with these signs, when Grandpapa came to the town. He told it me himself, and he hadn't a 'rogue on his back', as mother used to tell me he had when he wanted to make me believe something outrageous, for now he looked quite trustworthy.

The first night after he came to the town, there was the most terrible gale ever recorded in the newspapers, a gale such as none of the inhabitants had ever before experienced. The air was filled with flying tiles; old woodwork crashed and fell; and a wheelbarrow ran up the street all alone, only to get out of the way. There was a groaning in the air, and a howling and a shrieking, and altogether it was a terrible storm. The water in the canal rose over the banks, for it did not know where to run. The storm swept over the town, carrying plenty of chimneys with it, and more than one proud old church spire had to bend, and has never got over it from that time.

There was a kind of sentry-box, where dwelt the venerable old superintendent of the fire brigade, who always arrived with the last engine. The storm would not leave this little sentry-box alone, but must needs tear it from its fastenings, and roll it down the street; and, wonderfully enough, it rose up and stopped opposite to the door of the humble carpenter, who had saved three lives at the last fire, but the sentry-box thought nothing of that.

The barber's sign, the great brazen dish, was carried away, and hurled straight into the embrasure of the councillor of justice; and the whole neighbourhood said this looked almost like malice, inasmuch as even her most intimate friends used to call the councillor's lady 'the Razor'; for she was so sharp that she knew more about other people's business than they knew about it themselves.

A sign with a dried salt fish painted on it flew exactly in front of the door of a house where dwelt a man who wrote a newspaper. That was a very poor joke of the gale, which did not remember that a man who writes in a paper is not to be joked with; for he is a king in his own newspaper, and likewise in his own opinion.

The weathercock flew to the opposite house, where he perched, looking the picture of malice – so the neighbours said.

The cooper's tub stuck itself up under the head of 'ladies' costumes'.

The eating-house keeper's bill of fare, which had hung at his door in a heavy frame, was posted by the storm over the entrance to the theatre, where nobody went: it was a ridiculous list – 'Horseradish soup, and stuffed cabbage'. And now people came in plenty.

The fox's skin, the honourable sign of the furrier, was found fastened to the bell-pull of a young man who always went to early lecture, and looked like a furled umbrella, and said he was striving after truth, and was considered by his aunt 'a model and an example'.

The inscription 'Institute for Higher Education' was found over the billiard club, and the Institute itself got the sign 'Children brought up by hand'. Now, this was not at all witty, merely naughty; but the storm had done it, and no one has any control over that.

It was a terrible night, and in the morning – only think! – nearly all the signs had changed places: in some places the inscriptions were so malicious, that Grandfather would not speak of them at all; but I saw that he was chuckling secretly, and it is possible he was keeping something to himself.

The poor people in the town, and still more the strangers, were continually making mistakes in the people they wanted to see; nor was this to be avoided, when they went according to the signs. Thus, for instance, some who wanted to go to a very grave assembly of elderly men, where important affairs were to be discussed, found themselves in a noisy boys' school, where all the company were leaping over the chairs and tables.

There were also people who made a mistake between the church and the theatre, and that was terrible indeed!

Such a storm we have never witnessed in our day; for that only happened in Grandpapa's time, when he was quite a little boy. Perhaps we shall never experience a storm of the kind, but our grandchildren may; and we can only hope and pray that all may *stay at home while the storm is shifting the signs.*

The Teapot

THERE WAS a proud teapot, proud of its porcelain, proud of its long spout, proud of its broad handle; it had something both before and behind, the spout before and the handle behind, and it talked about it; but it did not talk about its lid; that was cracked, it was riveted, it had a defect, and one does not willingly talk of one's defects; others do that sufficiently. The cups, the creampot, and the sugar-basin, the whole of the tea-service would remember more about the frailty of the lid and talk about it, than about the good handle and the splendid spout; the teapot knew that.

'I know them!' it said to itself, 'I know also my defect and I admit it; therein lies my humility, my modesty; we all have defects, but one has also merits. The cups have a handle, the sugar-basin a lid, I have both of these and another thing besides, which they never have, I have a spout, and that makes me the queen of the tea-table. To the sugar-basin and the cream-pot it is granted to be the servants of sweet taste, but I am the giver, the ruler of all; I disseminate blessing among thirsty humanity; in my inside the Chinese leaves are prepared in the boiling, tasteless water.

The teapot said all this in its undaunted youth. It stood on the table laid for tea, and it was lifted by the finest hand; but the finest hand was clumsy, the teapot fell, the spout broke off, the handle broke off, the lid is not worth talking about, for enough has been said about it. The teapot lay in a faint on the floor; the boiling water ran out of it. That was a hard blow it got, and the hardest of all was that they laughed; they laughed at it, and not at the awkward hand.

'I shall never get that experience out of my mind,' said the teapot, when it afterwards related its career to itself, 'I was called an invalid and set in a corner, and the day after, presented to a woman who begged kitchen-refuse. I came down into poverty, stood speechless both out and in; but there, as I stood, my better life began; one is one thing, and becomes something quite different. Earth was put into me; for a teapot, that is the same as to be buried, but in the earth was put a bulb; who laid it there, who gave it, I know not, but given it was, a compensation for the Chinese leaves and the boiling water, a compensation for the broken-off handle and spout. And the bulb lay in the earth, the bulb lay in me, it became my heart, my living heart, and such a thing I had never had before. There was life in me, there was strength and vigour. The pulse beat, the bulb sprouted, it was bursting with thoughts and feelings; then it broke out in flower; I saw it, I carried it, I forgot myself in its loveliness; it is a blessed thing to forget oneself in others! It did not thank me; it did not think about me: it was admired and praised. I was so glad about it; how glad must it have been then! One day I heard it said that it deserved a better pot. They broke me through the middle; it was frightfully painful; but the flower was put in a better pot, and I was thrown out into the yard; I lie there like an old potsherd, but I have the remembrance, that I cannot lose.

The Bird of Popular Song

IT IS winter-time. The earth wears a snowy garment, and looks like marble hewn out of the rock; the air is bright and clear; the wind is sharp as a well-tempered sword, and the trees stand like branches of white coral or blooming almond twigs, and here it is keen as on the lofty Alps.

The night is splendid with the gleam of the Northern Lights, and with the glitter of innumerable twinkling stars.

The storms come; the clouds arise and shake out their swan's-down; the snowflakes fly; they cover road and house, open fields and closed-in streets. But we sit in the warm room, by the hot stove, and talk about the old times. And we listen to this story:

By the open sea was a grave-mound; and on it sat at midnight the spirit of the buried hero, who had been a king. The golden circlet gleamed on his brow, his hair fluttered in the wind, and he was clad in steel and iron. He bent his head mournfully, and sighed in deep sorrow, as an unquiet spirit might sigh.

And a ship came sailing by. The sailors lowered the anchor, and landed. Among them was a singer, and he approached the royal spirit, and said, 'Why mournest thou, and wherefore dost thou suffer thus?'

And the dead man answered, 'No one hath sung the deeds of my life; they are dead and forgotten: song doth not carry them forth over the lands, nor into the hearts of men; therefore I have no rest and no peace.'

And he spoke of his works, and of his warlike deeds, which his contemporaries had known, but which had not been sung, because there was no singer among his companions.

Then the old bard struck the strings of his harp, and sang of the youthful courage of the hero, of the strength of the man, and of the greatness of his good deeds. Then the face of the dead gleamed like the margin of the cloud in the moonlight. Gladly and of good courage, the form arose in splendour and in majesty, and vanished like the glancing of the Northern Lights. Naught was to be seen but the green turfy mound, with the stones on which no Runic record has been graven; but at the last sound of the harp there soared over the hill, as though he had fluttered from the harp, a little bird, a charming singing-bird, with the ringing voice of the thrush, with the moving pathos of the human heart, with a voice that told of home, like the voice that is heard by the bird of passage. The singing-bird soared away, over mountain and valley, over field and wood – he was the Bird of Popular Song, who never dies.

We hear his song – we hear it now in the room on a winter's evening while the 'white bees' are swarming without, and the storm takes firm hold. The bird sings not alone the praise of heroes; he sings also sweet gentle songs of love, so many and so warm, of Northern fidelity and truth. He has stories in words and in tones; he has proverbs and snatches of proverb; songs which, like Runes laid under a dead man's tongue, force him to speak; and thus Popular Song tells of the land of his birth.

In the old heathen days, in the times of the Vikings, its nest was in the harp of the bard.

In the days of knightly castles, when the strong fist held the scales of justice, when only might was right, and a peasant and a dog were of equal importance, where did the Bird of Song find shelter and protection? Neither violence nor stupidity gave him a thought.

But in the gabled window of the knightly castle, the lady of the castle sat with the parchment roll before her, and wrote down the old recollections in song and legend, while near her stood the old woman from the wood, and the travelling pedlar who went wandering through the country. As these told their tales, there fluttered around them, with twittering and song, the Bird of Popular Song, who never dies so long as the earth has a hillock upon which his foot may rest.

And now he looks in upon us and sings. Without are the night and the snowstorm: he lays the Runes beneath our tongues, and we know the land of our home. Heaven speaks to us in our native tongue, in the voice of the Bird of Popular Song: the old remembrances awake, the faded colours glow with a fresh lustre, and story and song pour us a blessed draught which lifts up our minds and our thoughts, so that the evening becomes as a Christmas festival.

The snowflakes chase each other, the ice cracks, the storm rules without, for he has the might, he is lord – but not the Lord of all.

It is winter-time. The wind is sharp as a two-edged sword, the snowflakes chase each other: it seemed as though it had been snowing for days and weeks, and the snow lies like a great mountain over the whole town, like a heavy dream of the winter night. Everything on the earth is hidden away, only the golden cross of the church, the symbol of faith, arises over the snow grave, and gleams in the blue air and in the bright sunshine.

And over the buried town fly the birds of heaven, the small and the great; they twitter and they sing as best they may, each bird with his own beak.

First comes the band of sparrows: they pipe at every trifle in the streets and lanes, in the nests and the houses; they have stories to tell about the front buildings and the back buildings.

'We know the buried town,' they say; 'everything living in it is piep! piep! piep!'

The black ravens and crows flew on over the white snow.

'Grub, grub!' they cried. 'There's something to be got down there; something to swallow, and that's most important. That's the opinion of most of them down there and the opinion is goo – goo – good!'

The wild swans come flying on whirring pinions, and sing of the noble and the great, that will still sprout in the hearts of men, down in the town which is resting beneath its snowy veil.

No death is there – life reigns yonder; we hear it on the notes that swell onward like the tones of the church organ, which seize us like sounds from the elf-hill, like the songs of Ossian, like the rushing swoop of the War-maidens' wings. What harmony! That harmony speaks to our hearts, and lifts up our souls! – It is the Bird of Popular Song whom we hear.

And at this moment the warm breath of heaven blows down from the sky. There are gaps in the snowy mountains, the sun shines into the clefts; spring is coming, the birds are returning, and new races are coming with the same home sounds in their hearts.

Hear the story of the year: 'The might of the snowstorm, the heavy dream of the winter night, all shall be dissolved, all shall rise again in the beauteous notes of the Bird of Popular Song who never dies!'

The Little Green Ones

IN THE window stood a rose tree, lately blooming with youth, but now it looked sickly; something ailed it.

It had got a company quartered on it which ate it up: otherwise, a very respectable company in green uniform. I spoke with one of them, he was only three days old, and already a great-grandfather. Do you know what he said? It was true what he said; he spoke of himself and the whole company.

'We are the most remarkable regiment among all the creatures of earth. In the warm season, we bear living young ones; the weather is good then, and we betroth ourselves at once, and celebrate the wedding. Towards the cold season, we lay eggs and the little ones lie snug in them. That wisest of animals, the ant – we have a great respect for it – studies us and values us. It does not eat us at once, it takes our eggs, lays them in the common ant-hill of the family, on the ground floor, lays us marked and numbered, side by side, layer on layer, so that every day a fresh one can spring out of the egg; then they set us in stalls, stroke us over the hind legs and milk us, so that we die. That is extremely comfortable! Among them we have the most charming name, "Sweet little milk cow!" All the animals with the understanding of the ant call us so; only human beings – and it is a great insult to us, it is enough to lose one's sweetness over, can you not write against it, can you not reprimand them, these human beings? – they look at us so stupidly, look sullen because we eat a rose-leaf, while they themselves eat all living things, everything which is green and grows. They call us the most contemptuous name, the most disgusting name; I will not name it, ugh! it turns me sick! I cannot say it, at least in uniform, and I am always in uniform.

'I was born on a rose tree leaf; I and the whole regiment live on the rose tree, but it lives again in us, who belong to the higher order of creation. Men cannot tolerate us; they come and murder us with soap-suds; it is a nasty drink! I think I smell it! It is frightful to be washed, when one is born not to be washed.

'Man! thou who lookest upon me with severe, soap-suddy eyes; think of our place in nature, our ingenious equipment for laying eggs and producing young! We received the blessing, "Increase and multiply!" We are born in roses, we die in roses; the whole of our life is poetry. Fix not upon us the name thou deemest most horrid and ugly, the name, I cannot say it, cannot name it; call us the milk-cow of the ants, the regiment of the rose tree, the little green ones.'

And I, the human being, stood and looked at the tree, and at the little green ones, whose name I shall not name, nor offend a rose-citizen, a great family with eggs and living young. The soap-suds I meant to wash them with (for I had come with soap-suds, and wicked intentions), I will now whip up and blow into froth, blow soap-bubbles and gaze on their beauty. Perhaps a story lies in every one of them. And the bubble grew so big with glittering colours, and in it there lay, as it were, a silver pearl at the bottom. The bubble floated and soared, flew against the door and burst; but the door flew open, and there stood Mother Fairy Tale herself.

'Yes, now she can tell better than I can about – I will not say the name! – the little green ones.' 'Plant-lice,' said Mother Fairy Tale. 'One should call everything by its right name; and if one dares not do it as a usual thing, one can do it in a fairy tale.'

Brownie and the Dame

YOU KNOW the brownie, but do you know the dame, the gardener's dame? She had learning, knew verses by heart, could even write them herself with ease; only the rhymes, 'clinchings', she called them, caused her a little trouble. She had the gift of writing, and of talking; she might very well have been a pastor, or at least a pastor's wife. 'The earth is lovely in its Sunday gown,' said she, and this thought she had put into words and 'clinching', and had set it in a poem, so long and beautiful. The student, Mr Kisserup (the name has nothing to do with the story), was a nephew, and on a visit to the gardener; he heard the dame's poem, and it did him good, he said – ever so much good. 'You have soul, madam,' said he.

'Stuff and nonsense,' said the gardener, 'don't be putting such ideas into her head! a woman should be a body, a decent body, and look after her pot, so that the porridge may not be burned.'

'I will take away that burnt taste with a piece of burning charcoal,' said the dame, 'and then I will take the burnt taste from you with a little kiss. One would think that you only thought of cabbages and potatoes, and yet you love the flowers!' and so she kissed him. 'The flowers are the soul,' said she.

'Look after your pot,' said he, and went into the garden: that was his pot, and he looked after it. But the student sat and talked with the dame. Her beautiful words, 'The earth is lovely', he made quite a sermon about, in his own way.

'The earth is lovely, make it subject unto you! was said, and we became its rulers. Some are so with the mind, some with the body; one is sent into the world like an exclamation mark, another like a printer's dash, so that one may well ask, "What is he doing here?" One becomes a bishop, another only a poor schoolmaster, but all is wisely ordered. The earth is lovely, and always in its Sunday dress!

That was a thought-stirring poem, dame, full of feeling and geography.'

'You have soul, Mr Kisserup,' said the dame, 'much soul, I assure you! One gets clearness in oneself, when one talks with you.'

And so they went on talking, as beautifully and as well; but out in the kitchen, there was also one who talked, and that was the brownie, the little brownie dressed in grey with a red cap. You know him! Brownie sat in the kitchen, and was the pot-watcher; he talked, but no one heard him except the big black pussy cat, 'Cream-thief', as the dame called him.

The brownie was so angry with her, because she did not believe in his existence, he knew; she had certainly never seen him, but still she must, with all her learning, know that he did exist, and might have shown him a little attention. It never occurred to her on Christmas Eve, to set so much as a spoonful of porridge down for him; all his ancestors had got that, and had got it from dames who had absolutely no learning; the porridge had been swimming in butter and cream. It made the cat's mouth water to hear of it.

'She calls me an idea!' said the brownie, 'that is beyond all *my* ideas. She actually denies me! That I have listened to, and now I have listened again; she sits and wheezes to that boy-whacker, the student. I say with the goodman, "Mind your pot!" that she doesn't do; now I shall make it boil over!' And Brownie puffed at the fire, which blazed and burned. 'Hubble-bubble-hish,' – the pot boiled over. 'Now I shall go in and make holes in the goodman's socks!' said Brownie, 'I will unravel a big hole in the toe and the heel, so there will be something to darn, unless she must go and make poetry. Dame poetess, darn the goodman's stockings!'

The cat sneezed at that; he had a cold, although he always wore furs.

'I have opened the dining-room door,' said Brownie, 'there is clotted cream there, as thick as gruel. If *you* won't lick it, *I* shall.'

'If I shall have the blame and the blows,' said the cat, 'let me also lick the cream.'

'First the cream, then the licking,' said the brownie. 'But now I shall go into the student's room, hang his braces on the looking-glass, and put his socks in the waterjug; then he will think that the punch has been too strong, and that he is giddy in the head. Last night I sat on the wood-stack beside the dog-kennel; I take a great pleasure in teasing the watch-dog; I let my legs hang down and dangle. The dog could not reach them, however high he jumped; that made him angry; he barked and barked, I dingled and dangled; it *was* a racket. The student woke up with it and got up three times to look out; but he did not see me, although he had spectacles on; he always sleeps with spectacles.'

'Say *mew*, when the dame is coming,' said the cat. 'I am rather deaf; I am not well today!'

'You are licking-sick,' said Brownie, 'lick away, lick the sickness away! but dry your whiskers, so that the cream may not hang there. Now I will go and listen.'

And Brownie stood by the door, and the door stood ajar; there was no one in the room except the dame and the student; they talked about what the student so finely called 'that which one ought to set above all pots and pans in every household; the gifts of the soul!'

'Mr Kisserup,' said the dame, 'now I shall show you something in this connection, which I have never yet shown to any earthly soul, least of all to a man, my little poems; some are rather long, however. I have called them "Clinchings by a gentlewoman".'

And she took out of the drawer a writing-book with a light-green cover and two blots of ink on it. 'There is much that is earnest in this book,' said she. 'I have the strongest feeling for what is sorrowful. Here now is "The Sigh in the Night", "My Evening-Red", and "When I got Klemmensen", my husband. You can pass over that, although it has feeling and thought. "The Housewife's Duties" is the best piece! all very melancholy, in that lies my strength. Only one piece is jocular; it contains some lively thoughts, such as one may also have, thoughts about, you must not laugh at me – about being a poetess! It is only known to myself and my drawer, and now also to you, Mr Kisserup! I am very fond of poetry, it comes over me, it teases, and rules, and reigns over me. I have expressed it in the title, "Little Brownie." You know the old peasant belief in the brownie, who is always playing tricks in the house. I have imagined that I myself was the house, and that poetry, the feeling within me, was the brownie, the spirit which rules in me. His power and greatness I have sung in "The little Brownie", but you must promise me with hand and mouth, never to disclose it to my husband or anyone. Read it aloud, so that I can hear if you understand my writing!'

And the student read, and the dame listened, and the little brownie listened too; he was eavesdropping, you know, and had just come when the title 'The little Brownie' was read.

'That concerns me,' said he; 'what can she have written about me? Oh! I shall pinch her, pinch her eggs, pinch her chickens, hound the fat off her fat calf. What a dame!'

And he listened with pursed-up mouth and long ears, but as he heard about Brownie's glory and power, and his lordship over the dame (it was Poetry, you know, that she meant, but the brownie took it literally) the little fellow smiled more and more, his eyes sparkled with joy, there came something of a superior air into the corners of his mouth, he lifted his heels and stood on his toes, and became a whole inch taller than before; he was delighted with what was said about the little brownie.

'The dame has soul and great breeding! I have done the woman great injustice. She has set me in her "Clinchings", which will be printed and read. Now, the cat will not get leave to drink her cream, I will do that myself! One drinks less than two, that is always a saving, and that I will introduce, and respect and honour the dame.'

'What a human creature he is, the brownie,' said the old cat; 'only a sweet *mew* from the dame, a *mew* about himself, and he at once changes his mind. The dame is sly.'

But she was not sly; it was the brownie who was a human being.

If you cannot understand this story, then ask, but you must not ask the brownie, nor the dame, either.

Peter, Pete, and Peterkin

I
T IS INCREDIBLE what children know nowadays. One is almost at a loss to say what there is that they do not know.

That the stork has fetched them out of the well or out of the mill-dam, and brought them as little children to their father and mother, is now such an old story, that they don't believe it, and yet it is the only true one.

But how do the children come to be in the mill-dam and the well? Ah, everyone does not know that, but still some do. Have you ever really looked at the sky, on a clear starry night, and seen the many shooting-stars? It is as if a star fell and vanished. The most learned cannot explain what they do not know themselves! but it can be explained when one knows it. It is just as if a little Christmas candle fell from the sky and was extinguished; it is a soul-spark from Our Father, which travels down towards the earth, and when it comes into our closer, heavier atmosphere the brightness vanishes, and there remains only what our eyes have not the power to see, for it is something much finer than our air, it is a heavenchild which is sent, a little angel, but without wings, for the little one shall become a man. Quietly it glides through the air, and the wind carries it into a flower, it may be a violet, a dandelion, a rose or a ragged robin, there it lies and makes itself strong. It is light and airy; a fly might fly away with it, or at any rate a bee, and they come by turns to search for the sweetness in the flower. If now the air-child should lie in their way, they do not whisk it out, they have not the heart to do that; they lay it in the sun, on a water-lily leaf, and from there it crawls and creeps down into the water, where it sleeps and grows, till the stork can see it, and fetches it to a human family, which wishes for such a sweet little one; but whether it is sweet or not, depends on whether the little one has drunk of the clear spring, or has swallowed mud or duckweed the wrong way: that makes it so earthy. The stork takes the first he sees, without making any choice. One comes into a good house to matchless parents; another comes to hard people in great poverty; it would have been much better to stay in the mill-dam.

The little ones do not remember at all what they dreamt about under the water-lily leaf, where in the evening the frogs sang to them, 'Croak, croak, creek, creek,' – which means in the language of men, 'Will you see now, if you can sleep and dream!' They cannot remember either in which flower they first lay, or how it smelt, and yet there is something in them, when they grow up, which says, 'This is the flower we like best,' and that is the one they lay in as air-children.

The stork becomes a very old bird, and always pays attention to how things go with the little ones he has brought, and how they behave in the world. He cannot really do anything for them, or change their lot, as he has his own family to care for, but he never lets them slip out of his thoughts.

I know an old, very honest stork, who has a great deal of knowledge, and has brought many little ones, and knows their stories, in which there is always a little mud and duckweed from the mill-dam. I begged him to give a little life-sketch of one of them, and so he said that I should get three for one from Peterson's house.

It was a particularly nice family, Peterson's. The man was one of the town's two and thirty men, and that was a distinction: he lived for the two and thirty, and went with the two and thirty. The stork came there, and brought a little Peter, for so the child was called. Next year the stork came again with another one; him they called Pete, and when the third was brought, he got the name of Peterkin, for in the names Peter, Pete, and Peterkin, lies the name Peterson.

There were thus three brothers, three shooting-stars cradled each in his own flower, laid under the water-lily leaf in the mill-dam, and brought from there to the family Peterson, whose house is at the corner, as you know.

They grew up both in body and soul, and then they wished to be something still greater than the two and thirty men.

Peter said that he would be a robber. He had seen the play of 'Fra

Diavolo', and made up his mind for the robber-business as the most delightful in the world.

Pete would be a rattle-man, and Peterkin, who was such a good, sweet child, round and plump, but who bit his nails (that was his only fault), Peterkin would be 'Father'. That is what each of them said when anyone asked what they wanted to be in the world.

And then they went to school. One became dux, and one became dunce, and one was betwixt and between; but for all that they might be equally good and equally clever, and that they were, said their very clear-sighted parents.

They went to children's balls; they smoked cigars when no one saw them; they grew in learning and knowledge.

Peter was stubborn from his earliest days, as of course a robber must be; he was a very naughty boy, but his mother said that was because he suffered from worms; naughty children have always worms; mud in the stomach. His self-will and stubbornness one day spent themselves on his mother's new silk dress.

'Don't push the coffee-table, my lamb,' she had said; 'you might upset the cream-jug, and I should get a stain on my new silk dress.' And the 'lamb' took the cream-jug with a firm hand, and emptied it right into mother's lap, who could not help saying, 'My lamb, my lamb, that was not considerate of you, my lamb!' But the child had a will, she must admit. Will shows character, and that is so promising for a mother. He might certainly have become a robber, but he did not become it literally; he only came to look like a robber; went about with a soft hat, bare neck, and long, loose hair; he was going to be an artist, but only got into the clothes of one, and also looked like a hollyhock; all the people he drew, looked like hollyhocks, they were so long and lanky. He was very fond of that flower; he had in fact lain in a hollyhock, the stork said.

Pete had lain in a buttercup. He looked so buttery round the corners of his mouth, and was yellow-skinned; one might believe that if he was cut in the cheek, butter would come out. He seemed born to be a butter-man, and might have been his own sign-board, but inwardly he was a 'rattle-man'; he was the musical portion of the Peterson family, 'but enough for all of them together,' said the neighbours. He composed seventeen new polkas in a week, and made an opera out of them with trumpet and rattle. Oh, how lovely it was!

Peterkin was white and red, little and common-looking; he had lain in a daisy. He never hit out when the other boys struck him; he said that he was the most sensible, and the most sensible always gives way. He collected first slate-pencils, then seals, then he got a little cabinet of natural curiosities, in which was the skeleton of a stickleback, three blind young rats in spirits, and a stuffed mole. Peterkin had a taste for the scientific and an eye for nature, and that was delightful for the parents, and for Peterkin too. He would rather go into the woods than the school, and preferred nature to discipline. His brothers were already engaged to be married, while he still lived only to complete his collection of the eggs of water-fowls. He very soon knew more about beasts than about human beings, and even thought that we could not approach the beasts in that which we set highest – 'love.' He saw that when the hen-nightingale sat hatching her eggs, the father nightingale sat and sang the whole night to his little wife, 'Cluck, cluck, jug, jug, jug.' Peterkin could never have done that, nor devoted himself to the task. When the mother stork lay in the nest with the young ones, the father stork stood on the roof the whole night on one leg: Peterkin could not have stood like that for one hour. And when he one day observed the spider's web and what was in it, he quite gave up all thought of matrimony. Mr Spider weaves to catch thoughtless flies, young and old, blood-filled and wind-dried; he lives to weave and nourish his family, but Mrs Spider lives for Father alone. She eats him up from sheer love; she eats his heart, his head, his stomach, only his long thin legs remain behind in the web, where he sat with the task of supporting the whole family. That is the simple truth, straight out of natural history. Peterkin saw that and thought it over; 'to be loved by one's wife like that, to be eaten by her in violent love. No; no human being goes as far as that; and would it be desirable?'

Peter determined never to marry! never to give or to take a kiss; that might look like the first step towards matrimony. But still he got one kiss, the one we all get, the great hearty kiss of Death. When we have lived long enough, Death gets the order 'Kiss away!' and so the person is gone. There flashes from our Lord a sun-blink, so strong that one is almost blinded. The soul of man, which came like a meteor, flies hence again like a meteor, but not to rest in a flower or to dream under a water-lily leaf. It has more important things before it, it flies into the great land of Eternity, but how things are there, or what it looks like, no one can tell. No one has seen into it, not even the stork, however far he can see, and however much he may know. Nor did he know any more about Peterkin, though he did about Peter and Pete; but I have heard enough about them, and so have you; so I said 'Thanks' to the stork for this time; but now he demands for this common little story three frogs and a young snake; he takes his payment in victuals. Will you pay? I won't! I have neither frogs nor young snakes.

Hidden is not Forgotten

THERE WAS once an old manor-house with muddy ditches and a drawbridge, which was more often up than down; for not all guests who come are good. Under the eaves were holes for shooting from, and pouring boiling water, and even melted lead, down over the enemy if he came too near. Inside it was high to the rafters, and that was good for the smoke which came from the hearth, where the great damp logs lay. There hung on the walls pictures of men in armour, and proud ladies in heavy clothes, but the stateliest of them all was living here still; she was called Metta Mogens; she was the lady of the manor. One evening robbers came there; they killed three of her men, and the watch-dog besides, and then they chained Lady Metta to the kennel with the dog-chain, and sat themselves down in the hall, and drank the wine from her cellar, and all the good ale. Lady Metta stood chained up like a dog, but she could not even bark.

Then the robber's boy came to her; he sneaked along quietly, so that he might not be noticed; otherwise they would have killed him.

'Lady Metta Mogens,' said the boy, 'can you remember when my father had to ride on the wooden horse in your husband's time? You begged mercy for him then, but it had no effect; he had to sit till he was crippled; but you slipped down, as I do now, and you placed a little stone under each of his feet, so that he could get some ease. No one saw it, or they pretended not to; you were the young, gracious lady. My father has told me this, and I have kept it to myself, but have not forgotten it! now I will set you free, Lady Metta Mogens.' Then they took horses from the stable, and rode in rain and in wind, and got friendly help.

'That was a good return for the little bit of service to the old man,' said Metta Mogens.

'Hidden is not forgotten!' said the boy.

The robbers were hanged.

There stood another old mansion, it stands there still; it was not Lady Metta Mogens'; it belonged to another noble family.

It is in our own days. The sun shines on the gilt spire of the tower, little wooded islands lie like bouquets on the water, and round about them swim the wild swans. Roses grow in the garden. The lady of the house is herself the finest rose-leaf, shining in gladness, the gladness of good deeds, not out in the wide world, but inwardly in the heart, where they are hidden, but not forgotten.

She now goes from the house to an outlying cottage in the fields. In it lives a poor, pain-ridden girl. The window in the little room looked to the north, and the sun did not come there, she had only a view over a little bit of a field which is shut in by a high dyke. But today there is sunshine. Our Lord's lovely warm sun is inside; it comes from the south, through the new window, where there was only a wall before.

The invalid sits in the warm sunshine, sees the wood and shore; the world has become so big and so lovely, and that at a single word from the kind lady up at the house.

'The word was so easy, the service so small,' says she, 'and the joy I gained was unspeakably great and blessed!'

And so she does many good deeds, thinks of all the poor people in the cottages, and in the rich houses, where there are also afflicted ones. It is concealed and hidden, but it is not forgotten by our Lord.

There was another old house; it was in the great busy town. In the house were rooms and halls; but we will not go into them; we will stay in the kitchen, it is snug and bright there, it is clean and neat. The copper things shine, the table looks polished, the sink is like a newly-scrubbed larding-board. It has all been done by one maid-of-all-work, and yet she has had time to dress herself as if she were going to church. She has ribbons in her cap – black ribbons – that means mourning. Yet she has no one to mourn for, neither father nor mother, neither relative nor sweetheart; she is a poor girl. Once she was engaged to a poor young fellow; they thought much of each other. One day he came to her. 'We two have nothing!' said he, 'and the rich widow downstairs has spoken warm words to me; she will put me into a good position, but you are in my heart. What do you advise me to do?'

'Whatever you think is for your happiness!' said the girl. 'Be good and kind to her, but remember, that from the moment we part, we two cannot see each other again!'

And so some years passed; then she met her former friend and sweetheart on the street; he looked ill and miserable; then she could not forbear, she must ask, 'How are you getting on?'

'Very well in every way,' said he. 'My wife is honest and good, but you are in my heart. I have fought my fight; it will soon be finished! We shall not see each other now until we meet in Heaven.' A week has passed. Yesterday morning she read in the paper that he was dead: that is why she wears mourning. Her sweetheart is dead, leaving a widow and three stepchildren, the paper said.

The black ribbon betokens mourning: the girl's face betokens it still more! it is hidden in the heart, but will never be forgotten!

See, there are three stories; three leaves on one stalk. Do you wish for more clover-leaves? There are many in the book of the heart – hidden but not forgotten!

The Porter's Son

THE GENERAL'S family lived on the first floor; the Porter's lived in the cellar; there was a great distance between the two families – the whole of the ground-floor, and the difference in rank; but they lived under the same roof, and had the same outlook to the street and the yard. In the yard there was a grass-plot with a flowering acacia tree – when it *did* flower; and under it sat sometimes the smartly-dressed nurse, with the still more smartly-dressed child, the General's, 'Little Emily.' Before them the Porter's little boy, with the brown eyes and dark hair, used to dance on his bare feet, and the child laughed, and stretched out her little hands to him, and when the General saw it from his window, he nodded down to them, and said, 'Charming!' The General's lady, who was so young that she could almost have been his daughter by an earlier marriage, never looked out to the yard, but had given orders that the cellar-folks' little boy might play for the child, but must not touch it. The nurse kept strictly to the lady's orders.

And the sun shone in upon the people in the first floor, and upon those in the cellar; the acacia tree put forth its blossoms, they fell off, and new ones came again next year; the tree bloomed, and the Porter's little boy bloomed, he looked like a fresh tulip. The General's daughter grew delicate and pale, like the pink leaf of the acacia flower. She seldom came down now under the tree; she took her fresh air in the carriage. She drove out with Mamma, and she always nodded to the Porter's little George, even kissed her fingers to him, until her mother told her that she was now too big for that.

One forenoon he went up to the General's with the letters and papers which had been left in the Porter's lodge in the morning. As he went upstairs, past the door of the sand-hole, he heard something whimpering inside; he thought it was a chicken chirping there, but instead it was the General's little daughter in muslin and lace.

'Don't tell Papa and Mamma, for they will be angry!'

'What is the matter, little miss?' asked George.

'It is all burning!' said she. 'It is burning and blazing!'

George opened the door to the little nursery: the window curtain was almost all burned, the curtain rod was glowing and in flames. George sprang up, pulled it down, and called to the people. But for him there would have been a house on fire. The General and his lady questioned little Emily. 'I only took one single match,' said she, 'that burned at once, and the curtain burned at once. I spat to put it out, I spat as hard as I could, but I could not spit enough, and so I ran out and hid myself, for Papa and Mamma would be so angry.' 'Spit!' said the General, 'what kind of a word is that? When did you hear Papa or Mamma say "spit"? You have got that from downstairs.'

But little George got a penny. This did not go to the baker, it went into the savings box; and soon there were so many shillings, that he could buy himself a paintbox to paint his drawings; and of these he had many. They seemed to come out of his pencil and his finger-ends. He presented his first paintings to little Emily.

'Charming!' said the General; the lady herself admitted that one could distinctly see what the little one had meant. 'He has Genius!'

These were the words that the Porter's wife brought down into the cellar.

The General and his wife were people of rank: they had two coats of arms on their carriage; one for each of them. The lady had hers on every piece of clothing, outside and inside, on her nightcap, and nightdress bag. Hers was an expensive one, bought by her father for shining dollars; for he had not been born with it, nor she either; she had come too early, seven years before the coat of arms. Most people could remember that, but not the family. The General's coat of arms was old and big: it might well make one's bones crack to carry it, to say nothing of two such coats, and her ladyship's bones cracked when, stiff and stately, she drove to a court-ball.

The General was old and grey, but looked well on horseback. He knew that, and he rode out every day with a groom at a respectful distance behind him. When he came to a party, it was as if he came riding on his high horse, and he had so many orders that it was inconceivable; but that was not his fault at all. When quite a young man he had served in the army, had been at the great autumn manoeuvres, which then were held by the troops in the days of peace. About that time he had an anecdote, the only one he had to tell. His under-officer cut off and took prisoner one of the princes; and the Prince with his little troop of captured soldiers, himself a prisoner, had to ride into the town behind the General. It was an event not to be forgotten, which always, through all the years, was retold by the General, with just the same memorable words which he had used when he returned the Prince's sabre to him, 'Only my subaltern could have taken your Highness prisoner, I never!' and the Prince answered, 'You are incomparable!' The General had never been in a real war; when that went through the land, he went on the diplomatic path, through three foreign courts. He spoke the French language, so that he almost forgot his own; he danced well, he rode well, orders grew on his coat in profusion; sentinels presented arms to him, and one of the most beautiful young girls presented herself to him and became his wife, and they had a charming baby, which seemed to have fallen down from Heaven, it was so lovely, and the Porter's son danced in the yard for her, as soon as she could take notice, and gave her all his coloured pictures, and she looked at them, and was delighted with them, and tore them to pieces. She was so fine and so charming!

'My rose-leaf,' said the General's lady, 'you are born for a Prince!'

The Prince already stood outside the door; but they did not know it. People cannot see very far beyond the doorstep.

'The other day, our boy shared his bread and butter with her,' said the Porter's wife; 'there was neither cheese nor meat on it, but she enjoyed it as if it had been roast beef.' The General's people would have brought the house down if they had seen that feast, but they didn't see it.

George had shared his bread and butter with little Emily; he would willingly have shared his heart with her, if it would have pleased her. He was a good boy, he was clever and sprightly, he now went to the evening class at the Academy, to learn to draw properly. Little Emily also made progress in learning; she talked French with her nurse, and had a dancing-master.

'George will be confirmed at Easter,' said the Porter's wife. George was now so far advanced.

'It would be sensible to put him to a trade,' said the father – 'a nice trade it should be, of course, and so we should have him out of the house.'

'He will have to sleep at home at night,' said the mother; 'it is not easy to find a master who has room for him to sleep; clothes, too, we must give him; the little bit of food he eats is easily got, he is quite happy with one or two boiled potatoes; he has free education too. Just let him go his own way, you will see that he will be a pleasure to us; the Professor said so.'

The confirmation clothes were ready. The mother herself had sewed them, but they were cut out by the jobbing tailor, and he cut well. If he had only been in a better position, and had been able to have a workshop and workmen, said the Porter's wife, he might very well have been court-tailor.

The confirmation clothes were ready, and the confirmant was

ready. On the confirmation day George got a large pinchbeck watch from his godfather, the flax-dealer's old workman, the richest of George's godfathers. The watch was old and tried; it always went fast, but that is better than going slow. It was a costly present; and from the General's came a Psalm-book, bound in morocco, sent from the little lady to whom George had presented his pictures. In the front of the book stood his name and her name and 'earnest well-wishes'. It was written from the dictation of the General's lady, and the General had read it through and said, 'Charming!'

'It was really a great attention from such grand gentlefolk,' said the Porter's wife; and George had to go up in his confirmation clothes and with the Psalm-book, to show himself and return thanks.

The General's lady was much wrapped up, and had one of her bad headaches, which she always had when she was tired of things. She looked kindly at George, and wished him everything good and never to have her headaches. The General was in his dressing-gown, and wore a tasselled cap and red-topped Russian boots. He went up and down the floor three times in thoughts and memories of his own, stood still, and said, 'So little George is now a Christian man? Let him be also an honest man, and honour his superiors. Someday, as an old man, you can say that the General taught you that sentence!'

This was a longer speech than he usually made, and he returned again to his meditation and looked dignified. But of all that George heard or saw up there, he kept most clearly in his thoughts the little Miss Emily; how charming she was, how gentle, how light, and how fragile! If she was to be painted, it must be in a soap-bubble. There was a fragrance about her clothes, about her curly, golden hair, as if she was a fresh-blossomed rose tree; and with her he had once shared his bread and butter! She had eaten it with a hearty appetite, and nodded to him at every other mouthful. Could she remember it still? Yes, certainly; she had given him the beautiful Psalmbook 'in memory' of it; and then the first time the New Year's new moon was seen, he went outside with bread and a farthing, and opened the book to see what Psalm he would light upon. It was a psalm of praise and thanksgiving; and he opened it again to see what would be granted to little Emily. He took care not to dip into the book where the funeral hymns were, and yet he opened it between Death and the Grave. This was nothing to put faith in, and yet he was frightened when the dainty little girl was soon laid up in bed, and the doctor's carriage stopped outside the gate every noon.

'They won't keep her!' said the Porter's wife; 'our Lord knows well whom He will have!'

But they did keep her; and George drew pictures and sent them to her; he drew the Castle of the Tsar, the old Kremlin in Moscow, exactly as it stood, with towers and cupolas; they looked like gigantic green and golden cucumbers, at least in George's drawings. They pleased little Emily so much, and therefore, in the course of a week, George sent a few more pictures, all of them buildings, because with them she could imagine so much inside the doors and windows. He drew a Chinese house, with bells throughout all the sixteen stories; he drew two Greek temples, with slender marble pillars, and steps round about; he drew a Norwegian church; one could see that it was made entirely of timber, carved and wonderfully set up, every story looked as if it were on cradle-rockers. Most beautiful of all, however, was one drawing, a castle, which he called 'Little Emily's'. In such a one should she live; George had completely thought it out, and had taken for that castle everything that he thought most beautiful in the other buildings. It had carved beams like the Norwegian church, marble pillars like the Greek temple, bells in every story, and at the top of all, cupolas, green and gilded, like those on the Tsar's Kremlin. It was a real child's castle, and under each window was written what the room or hall was to be used for: 'Here Emily sleeps.' 'Here Emily dances,' and 'Here Emily plays at receiving visitors.' It was amusing to see, and it was looked at too.

'Charming!' said the General.

But the old Count, for there was an old Count, who was still more dignified than the General, and himself had a castle and an estate, said nothing; he heard that it was designed and drawn by the Porter's little son. He was not so little, however, seeing that he was confirmed. The old Count looked at the pictures, and had his own quiet thoughts about them.

One day, when the weather was downright grey, wet, and horrid, was one of the brightest and best for little George. The Professor of the Academy of Art called him in.

'Listen, my friend,' said he, 'let us have some talk together! God has been very good to you with abilities; He is also good to you with good people. The old Count at the corner has spoken to me about you; I have also seen your pictures; we will draw the pencil over them; in them there is much to correct! Now you can come twice a week to the drawing school, and you will be able to do better afterwards. I believe there is more in you to make an architect than a painter; you can have time to consider that yourself; but today you must go up to the old Count at the corner, and thank our Lord for such a man!'

It was a great house at the corner; round the windows were carved elephants and dromedaries, all from olden times; but the old Count thought most of the new times with what good they brought, whether it came from the first floor, the cellar, or the garret.

'I believe,' said the Porter's wife, 'that the more folks are really grand, the less stuck-up they are! How charming and straightforward the old Count is! And he speaks just like you and me! the General's people can't do that. Was George not quite wild with delight yesterday, over the delightful treatment he got from the Count; and today I am the same after having spoken with the great man. Is it not a good thing now, that we did not apprentice George to a trade? He has abilities.'

'But they must have help from outside,' said the father.

'He has got that now,' said the mother, 'the Count said it clearly and distinctly.'

'It is from the General's, though, that it was all set going!' said the father. 'We must also thank them.'

'That we can well do,' said the mother, 'but I don't believe there is much to thank them for; I will thank our Lord, and I will also thank Him because the little Emily is coming to herself again!' Emily kept getting on, and George kept getting on; in the course of the year he got the little silver medal, and afterwards the bigger one.

'It would have been better if he had been put to a trade,' said the mother, and wept; 'then we should have kept him! What shall he do in Rome? I shall never see him again, even if he comes home, but he won't do that, the sweet child!'

'But it is his good fortune and his glory!' said the father.

'Yes, thank you, my friend,' said the mother, 'but you don't mean what you say! You are as much distressed as I am!'

And it was true, both about the grief and the going away. Everybody said it was great good fortune for the young fellow!

And parting visits were paid, including one to the General's; but the lady did not show herself, she had one of her headaches. By way of farewell the General told his only anecdote, about what he had said to the Prince, and what the Prince said to him, You are incomparable!' Then he gave George his hand – his flabby hand; Emily also gave George her hand and looked almost distressed, but George was the most distressed of all.

Time goes when one is doing something; it goes also when one is doing nothing. The time is equally long, but not equally profitable. For George it was profitable, and not at all long, except when he thought about those at home. How were they getting on upstairs and downstairs? Well, he got news of them; and one can put so much in a letter, both the bright sunshine, and the dark, heavy days. They lay in the letter, which told that the father was dead, and only the mother was left behind. Emily had been like an angel of comfort; she had come down to her, the mother wrote, and added that she herself had got leave to keep the employment at the gate.

The General's lady kept a diary; in it was recorded every party, every ball, she had gone to, and all the visitors she had received. The diary was illustrated with the visiting cards of diplomats and the highest nobility. She was proud of her diary; it grew for many a day, during many big headaches, and also during many brilliant nights, that is to say, court-balls.

Emily had been at a court-ball for the first time. The mother was dressed in pink with black lace; Spanish! The daughter in white, so clear, so fine! green ribbons fluttered like leaves of sedge amongst her curly, golden hair, which bore a crown of water-lilies. Her eyes were so blue and so clear, her mouth so small and red, she looked like a little mermaid, as lovely as can be imagined. Three princes danced with her, that is to say, first one and then another; the General's lady did not have a headache for a week.

But the first ball was not the last one; it was all too much for Emily, and it was a good thing that the summer came with its rest and fresh air. The family was invited to the old Count's castle. It was a castle with a garden worth seeing. One part of it was quite as in olden days, with stiff, green hedges, where one seemed to go between green screens, in which there were peep-holes. Box trees and yew trees were clipped into stars and pyramids; water sprang from great grottoes, set with cockle-shells: round about stood stone figures of the very heaviest stone, one could see that by the clothes and the faces; every flowerbed had its shape of a fish, shield, or monogram; that was the French part of the garden. From there one came, as it were, into the fresh open wood, where the trees dared to grow as they would, and were therefore so big and so beautiful. The grass was green, and good for walking on; it was rolled, mowed, and well kept; that was the English part of the garden.

'Olden times and modern times,' said the Count, 'here they glide well into each other! In about two years the house itself will get its proper appearance. It will undergo a complete change to something better and more beautiful. I shall show you the plans, and I shall show you the architect. He is here today for dinner!'

'Charming!' said the General.

'It is like Paradise here! said her ladyship, 'and there you have a baronial castle!'

'That is my hen-house,' said the Count. 'The pigeons live in the tower, the turkeys on the first floor, but on the ground floor old Dame Elsie rules. She has guest-chambers on all sides: the sitting-hens by themselves, the hen with chickens by herself, and the ducks have their own outlet to the water!'

'Charming!' repeated the General, and they all went to see this fine show.

Old Elsie stood in the middle of the room, and by the side of her was George, the architect; he and little Emily met after many years, met in the hen-house. Yes, there he stood, and he was nice enough to look at; his face open and decided, with black glossy hair, and on his lips a smile which said, 'There sits a rogue behind my ear who knows you outside and in.' Old Elsie had taken her wooden shoes off, and stood on her stocking soles, in honour of the distinguished guests. And the hens cackled, and the cock crew, and the ducks waddled away with 'quack, quack!' But the pale, slender girl, the friend of his childhood, the General's daughter, stood there with a rosy tinge on the otherwise pale cheeks; her eyes became so big, and her mouth spoke without saying a single word, and the greeting he got was the prettiest any young man could wish for from a young lady, if they were not related or had never danced much together; she and the architect had never danced with each other.

The Count shook hands with him, and presented him: 'Our young friend, Mr George, is not quite a stranger.'

Her ladyship curtsied, the daughter was about to give him her hand, but she did not give it. 'Our little Mr George!' said the General, 'old house-friends; charming!'

'You have become quite an Italian,' said her ladyship, and you talk the language like a native, I suppose.'

Her ladyship sang Italian, but did not speak it, the General said.

At the dinner-table George sat at Emily's right hand The General had taken her in, the Count had taken in her ladyship.

Mr George talked and told anecdotes, and he told them well; he was the life and soul of the party, although the old Count could have been that too. Emily sat silent; her ears heard, and her eyes shone, but she said nothing. Afterwards she and George stood in the verandah amongst the flowers; a hedge of roses hid them. George was again the first to speak.

'Thank you for your kindness to my old mother!' said he; 'I know that the night my father died, you came down to her, and stayed with her till his eyes were closed. Thanks!' He caught Emily's hand and kissed it; he might do that on this occasion. She blushed rosy-red, but pressed his hand again and looked at him with her tender blue eyes.

'Your mother was a loving soul! how fond she was of you! And she let me read all your letters; I believe I almost know you! how kind you were to me when I was little; you gave me pictures –'

'Which you tore in pieces!' said George.

'No! I have still my castle, the drawing of it.'

'And now I must build it in reality!' said George, and grew quite hot with what he said.

The General and her ladyship talked in their own room about the Porter's son; he knew how to comport himself, and could express himself with knowledge and intelligence. 'He could be a tutor!' said the General.

'Genius!' said her ladyship, and she said no more.

Often in the lovely summer-time Mr George came to the castle of the Count. He was missed when he did not come.

'How much more God has given to you than to us other poor creatures!' said Emily to him. 'Do you realise that properly?'

It flattered George that the lovely young girl looked up to him, and he thought her uncommonly gifted. And the General felt himself more and more convinced that Mr George could not possibly be a child of the cellar.

'The mother was, however, a very honest woman,' said he; 'I owe that to her memory.'

The summer went and the winter came, and there was more talk about Mr George; he had been received with favour in the highest places. The General had met him at a court-ball. And now there was to be a ball in the house for little Emily. Could Mr George be invited?

'Whom the King invites, the General can invite,' said the General, and lifted himself a whole inch from the floor.

Mr George was invited, and he came; and princes and counts came, and the one danced better than the other; but Emily could only dance the first dance. In it she sprained her foot, not badly, but enough to feel it; so she had to be careful, stop dancing, and look at the others; and she sat and looked, and the architect stood by her side: 'You are surely giving her the whole of St Peter's!' said the General, as he went past, and smiled like benevolence itself.

With the same benevolent smile he received Mr George some days after. The young man certainly came to call after the ball, what else? Yes, the most astounding, the most astonishing thing; he came with insane words; the General could not believe his own ears; a perfectly incredible proposal, Mr George asked for little Emily as his wife!

'Man!' said the General, and began to boil. 'I don't understand you in the least! What do you say? What do you want? I don't know you! Sir! Fellow! it comes into your head to come like this into my house! am I to be here, or am I not to be here?' and he went backwards into his bedroom and locked the door, leaving George standing alone. He stood for some minutes, and then turned about to go. In the corridor stood Emily.

'My father answered – ?' she asked, and her voice trembled.

George pressed her hand. 'He ran from me! there is a better time coming!'

There were tears in Emily's eyes; in those of the young man were courage and confidence; and the sun shone in upon the two and gave them his blessing. In his room sat the General, perfectly boiling; in fact he boiled over and sputtered out, 'Madness! Porter's madness!' –

Before an hour had passed, the General's lady got it from the General's own mouth, and she called for Emily and sat alone with her.

'You poor child! to insult you so! to insult us! You have tears in your eyes, but it suits you! You are charming in tears! You resemble me on my wedding-day. Cry away, little Emily!'

'Yes, that I must,' said Emily, 'if you and father don't say "Yes!" '

'Child!' cried her ladyship, 'you are ill! you talk in delirium, and I am getting my frightful headache! to think of all the unhappiness which comes to our house! Do not be your mother's death, Emily. Then you will have no mother!'

And her ladyship's eyes grew wet; she could not bear to think of her own death.

In the newspaper one read amongst the appointments: 'Mr George, appointed Professor.'

'It is a pity his parents are in their grave and cannot read it!' said the new porter-folk, who now lived in the cellar, under the General's; they knew that the Professor had been born and brought up within their four walls.

'Now he will come in for paying the tax on titles,' said the man.

'Yes, is it not a great deal for a poor child,' said the wife.

'Forty shillings in the year!' said the man, 'yes, that is a lot of money!'

'No, I mean the position!' said the wife. 'Do you suppose he will trouble himself about the money; he can earn that many times over; and he will, no doubt, get a rich wife besides. If we had children, they should also be architects and professors.'

George was well spoken of in the cellar, he was well spoken of on the first floor; even the old Count condescended to do so.

It was the pictures from his childhood days which gave occasion for it. But why were they mentioned? They were talking about Russia, and about Moscow, and so of course they came to the Kremlin, which little George had once drawn for little Emily; he had drawn so many pictures! but one in particular, the Count remembered: 'little Emily's castle,' where she slept, where she danced, and played at 'receiving visitors'. The Professor had much ability; he would certainly die an old Privy-Councillor, it was not impossible, and before that he might have built a castle for the young lady; why not?

'That was a curious flight of fancy!' observed her ladyship, when the Count had departed. The General shook his head thoughtfully, rode out with his groom at a respectful distance, and sat more proudly than ever on his high horse.

It was little Emily's birthday; flowers and books, letters and cards, were brought; her ladyship kissed her on the mouth, the General on the forehead; they were affectionate parents, and both she and they had distinguished visitors – two of the Princes. There was talk about balls and theatres, about diplomatic embassies, the government of kingdoms and countries. There was talk of talent, native talent, and with that, the young Professor was brought into the conversation – Mr George, the architect.

'He builds for immortality!' it was said, 'he will certainly build himself into one of the first families, too!'

'One of the first families?' repeated the General to his lady afterwards; 'which one of our first families?'

'I know which was meant,' said her ladyship, 'but I will say nothing about it! I will not even think it! God ordains! but I will be astonished!'

'Let me also be astonished!' said the General, 'I have not an idea in my head,' and he sank into a reverie.

There is a power, an unspeakable power, in the fountain of favour from above, the favour of the court, or the favour of God; and all that gracious favour little George had. But we forget the birthday.

Emily's room was fragrant with flowers from friends of both sexes, on the table lay lovely presents of greeting and remembrance, but not a single one from George; that could not come, but it was not needed either, the whole house was a remembrance of him. Even from the sand-hole under the stair a memorial flower peeped; there Emily had hidden when the curtain was burnt, and George came as first fire-engine. A glance out of the window, and the acacia tree reminded her of childhood's days. Flowers and leaves had fallen off, but the tree stood in the hoar-frost, as if it were a monster branch of coral, and the moon shone big and clear amongst the branches, unchanged in all its changing, as when George shared his bread and butter with little Emily. From a drawer she took out the drawings of the Tsar's castle, with her own castle, keepsakes from George. They were looked at and mused upon, and many thoughts arose; she remembered the day, when, unobserved by her father and mother, she went down to the Porter's wife, who was lying at the point of death. She sat beside her and held her hand, and heard her last words, 'Blessing – George!' The mother thought of her son. Now Emily put her own meaning into the words. Yes, George was with her on her birthday, really with her!

The next day, it so happened, there was again a birthday in the house – the General's birthday; he was born the day after his daughter, but of course at an earlier date, many years earlier. Again there came presents, and amongst them a saddle, of distinguished appearance, comfortable and costly; there was only one of the princes who had its equal. Who could it be from? The General was delighted. A little card came with it. If it had said, 'Thanks for yesterday,' we could have guessed from whom it came; but on it was written, 'From one whom the General does not know!'

'Who in the world do I not know?' said the General. 'I know everybody!' and his thoughts went into society; he knew everyone there. 'It is from my wife,' he said at last, 'she is making fun of me! Charming!'

But she was not making fun of him; that time had gone past.

And now there was a festival again, but not at the General's; a costume ball at the house of one of the princes. Masks were also allowed.

The General went as Rubens, in a Spanish costume with a little ruff, a sword and stately bearing; her ladyship as Madame Rubens, in black velvet, high-necked, frightfully warm, with a millstone round her neck – that is to say, a huge ruff, quite in accordance with a Dutch painting which the General possessed, and in which the hands in particular were much admired – they were quite like her ladyship's. Emily was Psyche in muslin and lace. She was like a floating tuft of swan's-down: she had no need of wings, she only wore them as a sign of Psyche. There was splendour, magnificence, lights, and flowers, richness, and taste; there was so much to see, that no one noticed Madame Rubens's beautiful hands.

A black domino, with acacia-blossoms in the hat, danced with Psyche.

'Who is he?' asked her ladyship.

'His Royal Highness!' said the General; 'I am quite sure of it, I knew him at once by his handshake.'

Her ladyship doubted.

General Rubens had no doubts; he approached the black domino, and wrote royal initials on his hand; they were denied, but a hint was given; 'The motto of the saddle! One whom the General does not know!'

'But I do know you, then!' said the General. 'You have sent me the saddle.'

The domino lifted his hand, and disappeared amongst the others.

'Who is the black domino you were dancing with, Emily?' asked the General's wife.

'I have not asked his name,' she answered.

'Because you knew it! It is the Professor! Your Professor is here, Count,' she continued, turning to the Count, who stood close by. 'Black domino, with acacia-blossom!'

'Very possibly, my dear madam,' answered he; 'but one of the princes is also wearing the same costume.'

'I know the handshake!' said the General. 'The Prince sent me the saddle. I am so certain of it, that I shall invite him to dinner.'

'Do so! if it is the Prince, he will be sure to come,' said the Count.

'And if it is the other, he will not come!' said the General, and approached the black domino, who was just then talking with the King. The General delivered a very respectful invitation, 'so that they might get to know each other.' The General smiled in full confidence and certainty of whom he was inviting; he spoke loudly and distinctly.

The Domino raised his mask: it was George.

'Does the General repeat the invitation?' asked he. The General drew himself an inch higher, assumed a stiffer bearing, took two steps backwards, and one step forwards, as if in a minuet; and there was gravity and expression, as much of the General as could be expressed in his aristocratic face.

'I never take back my word; the Professor is invited,' and he bowed with a glance at the King, who could certainly have heard the whole.

And so there was a dinner at the General's, only the Count and his protégé were invited.

'The foot under the table,' thought George, 'then the foundation-stone is laid!' and the foundation-stone was really laid with great solemnity, by the General and her ladyship.

The person had come, and as the General knew and recognised, had talked quite like a man of good society, had been most interesting; the General had been obliged many times to say his 'Charming!' Her ladyship talked of her dinner-party, talked of it even to one of the court ladies; and she, who was one of the most gifted, begged for an invitation the next time the Professor came. So he had to be invited again, and he was invited and came, and was again charming; he could even play chess.

'He is not from the cellar!' said the General, 'he is quite certainly of a good family! there are many of good family, and the young man is not to blame for that.'

The Professor, who was admitted to the house of the King, might well be allowed to enter the General's; but to take root in it, there was no talk of that, except in the whole town.

He grew. The dew of grace fell from above!

It was therefore no surprise, that when the Professor became a Privy Councillor, Emily became a Privy Councillor's wife.

'Life is either a tragedy or a comedy,' said the General. 'In tragedy they die, in comedy they marry each other.'

Here they had each other. And they also had three strong boys, but not all at once.

The sweet children rode hobby-horses through the rooms and halls, when they were at Grandfather's and Grandmother's, and the General also rode on a hobby-horse behind them 'as groom for the little Privy-Councillors!'

Her ladyship sat on the sofa and smiled, even if she had her bad headache.

So far had George got on, and much farther too, else it would not have been worth while telling about the Porter's son.

Removing-Day

YOU REMEMBER Ole the watchman in the tower! I have told of two visits to him, now I shall tell about a third one, but that is not the last.

It is usually at New Year time that I go up to him; now on the contrary it was on removing-day, for then it is not very pleasant down in the streets of the town; they are so heaped-up with sweepings and rubbish of all kinds, not to speak of cast-out bed-straw, which one must wade through. I came by just now, and saw that in this great collection of rubbish several children were playing; they played at going to bed; it was so inviting for this game, they thought; they snuggled down in the straw, and pulled an old ragged piece of wall-paper over them for a coverlet. 'It was so lovely!' they said; it was too much for me, and so I had to run off up to Ole.

'It is removing-day!' said he, 'The streets and lanes serve as an ash-box, an enormous ash-box. A cart-load is enough for me. I can get something out of that, and I did get something shortly after Christmas. I came down into the street, which was raw, wet, dirty, and enough to give one a cold. The dustman stopped with his cart, which was full, a kind of sample of the streets of Copenhagen on a removing-day. In the back of the cart was a fir tree, still quite green and with gold-tinsel on the branches; it had been used for a Christmas tree and was now thrown out into the street, and the dustman had stuck it up at the back of the heap. It was pleasant to look at, or something to weep over; yes, one can say either, according to how one thinks about it, and I thought about it, and so did one and another of the things which lay in the cart, or they might have thought, which is about one and the same thing. A lady's torn glove lay there; what did it think about? Shall I tell you? It lay and pointed with the little finger at the fir tree. "That tree concerns me," it thought; "I have also been at a party where there were chandeliers! my real life was one ball-night; a hand-clasp, and I split! there my recollection stops; I have nothing more to live for!" That is what the glove thought, or could have thought. "How silly the fir tree is!" said the potsherd. Broken crockery thinks everything foolish. "If one is on the dust-cart," they said, "one should not put on airs and wear tinsel! I know that I have been of use in this world, of more use than a green branch like that." That was also an opinion such as many people may have; but the fir tree looked well, it was a little poetry on the pile of rubbish, and there is plenty of *that* about in the streets on removing-day! The way got heavy and troublesome for me down there, and I became eager to come away, up into the tower again, and to stay up here: here I sit and look down with good humour.

'The good people down there play at changing houses! they drag and toil with their belongings; and the brownie sits in the tub and removes with them. House rubbish, family troubles, sorrows and afflictions remove from the old to the new dwelling, and so what do they and we get out of the whole? Yes, it is already written down long ago in the good, old verse in the newspaper: "Think of Death's great removing-day!" It is a serious thought, but I suppose it is not unpleasant for you to hear about it. Death is, and remains, the most trustworthy official, in spite of his many small occupations. Have you never thought over this?

'Death is the omnibus conductor, he is the passport-writer, he puts his name to our character book, and he is the director of the great savings bank of life. Can you understand it? All the deeds of our earthly life, great and small, we put in the savings bank, and when Death comes with his removing-day omnibus, and we must go into it and drive to the land of eternity, then at the boundary he gives us our character-book as a passport. For pocket-money on the journey he takes out of the savings bank one or other of the deeds we have done, the one that most shows our worth. That may be delightful, but it may also be terrible.

'No one has escaped yet from the omnibus drive. They certainly tell about one who was not allowed to go with it – the shoemaker of Jerusalem, he had to run behind; if he had got leave to come into the omnibus, then he would have escaped being a subject for the poets. Peep just once with your thoughts into the great omnibus of the removing-day! It is a mixed company! The king and the beggar sit side by side, the genius and the idiot; they must set off, without goods or gold, only with their character-book and the savings bank pocket-money; but which of one's deeds will be brought forward and sent with one? Perhaps a very little one, as small as a pea, but the pea can send out a blossoming plant.

'The poor outcast, who sat on the low stool in the corner, and got blows and hard words, will perhaps get his worn-out stool with him as a token and a help. The stool becomes a sedan-chair to carry him into the land of eternity; it raises itself there to a throne, shining like gold, and flowering like an arbour.

'One, who in this life always went about and tippled pleasure's spicy drink to forget other mischief he had done, gets his wooden keg with him and must drink from it on the omnibus journey; and the drink is pure and clear, so that the thoughts are cleared; all good and noble feelings are awakened, he sees and feels what he did not care to see before, or could not see, and so he has his punishment in himself, "the gnawing worm, which dies not for ages and ages." If there was written on the glass "Oblivion", there is written on the keg "Remembrance".

'If I read a good book, an historical writing, I must always think of the person I read about as coming into Death's omnibus at last; I must think about which of his deeds Death took out of the savings bank for him, what pocket-money he took into the land of eternity.

'There was once a French king, I have forgotten his name; the names of good things are forgotten sometimes, even by me, but they are sure to come back again. It was a king who in time of famine became his people's benefactor, and the people raised a monument of snow to him, with this inscription: "Quicker than this melts, you helped!" I can imagine, that Death gave him, in allusion to this monument, a single snowflake which never melts, and that it flew like a white snow-bird over his royal head into the land of immortality.

'There was also Louis the Eleventh; yes, I remember his name, one always remembers bad things well. A trait of him comes often into my mind; I wish that one could say the story was untrue. He ordered his constable to be beheaded; he could do that, whether it was just or unjust; but the constable's innocent children, the one eight years old, the other seven, he ordered to be stationed at the place of execution and to be sprinkled with their father's blood; then to be taken to the Bastille and put in an iron cage, where they did not even get a blanket to cover them; and King Louis sent the executioners to them every week and had a tooth pulled from each of them, so that they should not have too good a time; and the eldest said: "My mother would die of sorrow, if she knew that my little brother suffered so much; pull out two of my teeth, and let him go free!" The tears came to the executioner's eyes at that, but the King's will was stronger than the tears, and every week two children's teeth were brought to the king on a silver salver; he had demanded them, and he got them. These two teeth, I imagine, Death took out of life's savings bank for King Louis XI, and gave him them to take with him on his journey into the great land of immortality; they fly, like two flames of fire, before him; they shine, they burn, they pinch him, these innocent children's teeth.

'Yes, it is a serious journey, the omnibus drive on the great removing-day; and when will it come?

'That is the serious thing about it, that any day, any hour, any minute, one may expect the omnibus. Which of our deeds will Death take out of the savings bank and give to us? Let us think about it; that removing-day is not to be found in the Almanac.'

The Snowdrop, or Summer-Geck

IT WAS winter-time; the air was cold, the wind sharp; but indoors it was snug and warm. Indoors lay the flower; it lay in its bulb under the earth and the snow.

One day rain fell; the drops trickled through the snow-coverlet, down into the ground, touched the flower-bulb, and told about the bright world up above; soon a sunbeam, fine and pointed, pierced its way through the snow, down to the bulb, and tapped on it.

'Come in!' said the flower.

'I can't,' said the sunbeam, 'I am not strong enough to open the door; I shall be strong when summer comes.'

'When will it be summer?' asked the flower, and repeated it every time a new sunbeam pierced down to it. But it was a long time till summer: the snow still lay on the ground, and every night ice formed on the water.

'How long it is in coming! How long it is!' said the flower; 'I feel a prickling and tingling, I must stretch myself, I must stir myself, I must open up, I must get out and nod good-morning to the summer; that will be a happy time!'

And the flower stretched itself and strained itself inside against the thin shell, which the water outside had softened, which the snow and the earth had warmed, and the sunbeam had tapped upon; it shot out under the snow, with its whitey-green bud on its green stalk, with narrow, thick leaves, which seemed trying to shelter it. The snow was cold, but permeated with light and easy to push through; and here the sunbeams came with greater strength than before.

'Welcome! welcome!' sang every sunbeam, and the flower raised itself above the snow, out into the world of light. The sunbeams patted and kissed it, so that it opened itself completely, white as snow, and adorned with green stripes. It bowed its head in gladness and humility.

'Beautiful flower,' sang the sunbeams, 'how fresh and pure thou art! Thou art the first; thou art the only one! Thou art our darling! Thou ringest in summer, lovely summer, over town and field! All the snow shall melt! the cold winds shall be chased away! we shall rule! Everything will become green! And then thou wilt have company, lilacs, and laburnum, and last of all the roses; but thou art the first, so fine and pure!'

It was a great delight. It seemed as if the air was music, as if the beams of light penetrated into its leaves and stalk. There it stood, so fine and fragile, and yet so strong, in its young beauty; it stood there in its white kirtle with green ribbons, and praised the summer. But it was far from summer-time, clouds hid the sun, and sharp winds blew upon the flowers.

'Thou art come a little too early,' said Wind and Weather; 'we still have power, and that thou shalt feel and submit to. Thou shouldst have kept indoors, not run out to make a show. It is not time yet!'

It was biting cold! The days which came, brought not a single sunbeam; it was weather to freeze to pieces in, for such a little delicate flower. But there was more strength in it than it knew of; it was strong in joy and faith in the summer, which must come, which was foretold to it by its own deep longing, and confirmed by the warm sunshine; and so it stood with confident hope, in its white dress, in the white snow, bowing its head, when the snowflakes fell heavy and thick, whilst the icy winds swept over it.

'Thou wilt be broken!' said they, 'wither and freeze: what didst thou seek out here! Why wert thou lured abroad! the sunbeam has fooled thee! Now canst thou enjoy thyself, thou summer-geck?'

'Summer-geck!' echoed in the cold morning hours.

'Summer-geck!' shouted some children who came down into the garden, 'there stands one so pretty, so beautiful, the first, the only one!'

And these words did the flower so much good; they were words like warm sunbeams. The flower did not even notice in its gladness that it was being plucked: it lay in a child's hand, was kissed by a child's lips, was brought into a warm room, gazed at by kind eyes, and put in water, so strengthening, so enlivening. The flower believed that it was come right into summer, all at once.

The daughter of the house, a pretty little girl, was just confirmed; she had a dear friend, and he was also just confirmed. 'He shall be my summer-geck,' said she; so she took the fragile little flower, laid it in a piece of scented paper, on which were written verses, verses about the flower. Yes, it was all in the verses, and it was made up as a letter; the flower was laid inside, and it was all dark about it, as dark as when it lay in the bulb. The flower went on a journey, lay in the post-bag, was pressed and squeezed, and that was not pleasant, but it came to an end at last.

The journey was over, the letter was opened and read by the dear friend; he was so delighted he kissed the flower, and laid it, with the verses around it, in a drawer, in which were many delightful letters, but all without a flower; this was the first, the only one, as the sunbeams had called it, and that was very pleasant to think about. It got a long time to think about it, it thought whilst the summer passed, and the long winter passed, and it was summer once more; then it was brought out again. But this time the young man was not at all delighted; he gripped the paper hard and threw away the verses, so that the flower fell on the floor; it had become flat and withered, but it should not have been thrown on the floor for all that; still it was better lying there than on the fire, where the letter and verses were blazing. What had happened? What so often happens. The flower had fooled him; it was a jest, the maiden had fooled him, and that was no jest; she had chosen another sweetheart in midsummer. In the morning, the sun shone in on the little flattened summer-geck, which looked as if it were painted on the floor. The girl who was sweeping took it up and put it in one of the books on the table; she thought it had fallen out, when she was clearing up and putting things in order. And so the flower lay again amongst verses, printed verses, and they are grander than written ones; at least more is spent upon them.

Years passed away, and the book stood on the shelf. At length it was taken down, opened and read; it was a good book, songs and poems by the Danish poet, Ambrosius Stub, who is well worth knowing. And the man who read the book, turned the page. 'Here is a flower!' said he, 'a summer-geck! not without some meaning does it lie here. Poor Ambrosius Stub! he was also a summer-geck, a befooled poet! he was too early in his time; and so he got sleet and sharp winds, and went his rounds amongst the gentlemen of Fyen, like the flower in the flower-glass, the flower in the verses. A summer-geck, a winter-fool, all jest and foolery, and yet the first, the only, the youthfully fresh Danish poet. Yes, lie as a mark in the book, little summer-geck! Thou art laid there with some meaning.'

And so the summer-geck was laid in the book again, and felt itself both honoured and delighted with the knowledge that it was a mark in the lovely song-book, and that the one who had first sung and written about it, had also been a summer-geck, had been befooled in the winter. Of course the flower understood this in its own way, just as we understand anything in our own way.

This is the story of the summer-geck.

Auntie

YOU SHOULD have known Auntie! She was charming! that is to say, she was not at all charming in the usual sense of the word, but she was sweet and nice, and funny in her own way, just the thing to talk about, when someone is to be talked about and made merry over. She was fit to be put in a play, and that simply and solely because she lived for the play-house and all that goes on in it. She was so very respectable, but Agent Fab, whom Auntie called Flab, called her theatre-mad.

'The theatre is my schoolroom,' said she, 'my fountain of knowledge; from it I have freshened up my Bible history; "Moses", "Joseph and his brethren", these are operas! From the theatre I have my general history, geography and knowledge of mankind! From the French plays I know the life of Paris – naughty, but highly interesting! How I have wept over "The Riquebourg Family"; to think that the husband should drink himself to death, so that his wife should get her young sweetheart! Yes, how many tears I have shed in the fifty years I have been a "regular ticket-holder".'

Auntie knew every piece, every bit of scenery, every person who came on, or had ever come on. She really lived only in the nine theatrical months. The summer-time, without a play, was a time which made her old, whilst a play-night which lasted till past midnight was a lengthening of life. She did not say like other people, 'Now spring is coming, the stork has arrived!' or 'There is mention in the papers of the first strawberry'. On the contrary, she announced the coming of autumn: 'Have you seen that the theatre seats are being taken; now the performances will begin!'

She reckoned the worth of a house and its situation by how near it lay to the theatre. It was a grief to her to leave the little lane behind the theatre and remove to the bigger street a little farther off, and there live in a house where she had no opposite neighbours.

'At home my window has to be my theatre-box! one can't sit and think only of oneself; one must see people. But now I live as if I had removed right out into the country. If I wish to see people, I must go out into my kitchen and climb on to the sink; only there have I opposite neighbours. Now, when I lived in my lane, I could see right into the flax-dealer's, and then I had only three steps to the theatre; now I have three thousand lifeguard's steps.'

Auntie might be ill, but however bad she was, she never neglected the theatre. One evening her doctor ordered her to have poultices on her feet; she did as he directed, but drove to the theatre, and sat there with her feet in poultices. If she had died there, it would have delighted her. Thorwaldsen died in the theatre, and she called that 'a happy death'.

She certainly could not imagine a heavenly kingdom without a theatre. It certainly had not been promised to us, but it was to be supposed that the many celebrated actors and actresses, who had gone before, must have a continued sphere of activity.

Auntie had her electric wire from the theatre to her room; the telegram came every Sunday to coffee. Her electric wire was Mr Sivertson of the stage-machinery department, the man who gave the signals for the scenery and curtains to go up and down, in and out.

From him she got in advance a short and pithy review of the pieces. Shakespeare's 'Tempest', he called 'wretched stuff! there is so much to set up, and then it begins with water up to the first side-scene!' that is to say, the rolling waves went so far forward. On the other hand, if one and the same room-decoration remained through all five acts, he said that it was a sensible and well-written, restful piece, which played itself without setting up.

In earlier times, as Auntie called the times some thirty and odd years ago, she and the above-named Mr Sivertson were younger; he was already in the 'machinery', and, as she called him, her 'benefactor'. At that time, it was the custom at the evening performance, in the great and only theatre of the town, to admit spectators to the flies; every stage-carpenter had one or two places to dispose of. It was often chock-full, and that with very select company; it was said that the wives both of generals and aldermen had been there; it was so interesting to look down behind the scenes, and know how the performers stood and moved when the curtain was down. Auntie had been there many times, both at tragedies and ballets, for the pieces with the greatest number of performers were the most interesting from the flies.

One sat pretty much in the dark up there, and most of the people brought supper with them. Once three apples and a slice of bread and butter, with sausage on it, fell right down into Ugolino's prison, where he was just about to die of hunger. At that there was a general laugh. The sausage was one of the important reasons why the directors ordered the public to be excluded from the flies.

'But I was there thirty-seven times,' said Auntie, 'and I shall never forget it, Mr Sivertson.'

It was just the very last night that the flies were open to the public that they played 'The Judgement of Solomon'. Auntie remembered it so well. She had, through her benefactor, Mr Sivertson, procured a ticket for Agent Fab, although he did not deserve it, as he was always making fun of the theatre, and teasing her about it; but still she had got him a place up there. He wanted to see the theatre-things upside-down; these were his own words – and just like him, said Auntie.

And he saw 'The Judgement of Solomon', from above, and fell asleep; one would really have thought that he had just come from a big dinner with many toasts. He slept and was locked in, sat and slept through the dark night in the theatre, and when he awoke he told a story; but Auntie did not believe him. The play was finished, all the lamps and candles were out, all the people were out, upstairs and downstairs; but then began the real play, the after-piece – the best of all, the agent said. Life came into the properties! it was not 'The Judgement of Solomon' that was played; no, it was 'The Judgement Day at the Theatre'. And all this Agent Fab had the impudence to try to make Auntie believe; that was her thanks for getting him admission to the flies.

What the agent told was, no doubt, comical enough to hear but malice and mockery lay at the bottom of it.

'It was dark up there,' said the agent, 'but then the demon-show began, the great spectacle, 'The Judgement Day at the Theatre.' Checktakers stood at the doors, and every spectator had to show a certificate as to his character, to settle whether he was to enter with hands free or fettered, with muzzle or without. Gentlefolks who came too late, when the performance had already begun, as well as young men who were given to wasting their time, were tethered outside, and got felt-soles under their feet, to go in with at the beginning of the next act, besides being muzzled; and then began 'The Judgement Day at the Theatre'.

'Mere spite, which Our Lord knows nothing of,' said Auntie.

The scene-painter, if he wished to get into Heaven, had to go up a stair which he had painted himself, but which no man could walk up. That was only a sin against perspective, however. All the plants and buildings, which the stage-carpenter had with great trouble placed in countries to which they did not belong, the poor man had to move to their right places, and that before cock-crow, if he wished to get into Heaven. Mr Fab had better see that he himself got in there; and what he now told about the actors, both in comedy and tragedy, in song and in dance, was the worst of all. He did not deserve to get into the flies; Auntie would not repeat his words. He had said that the whole account was written down, and would be printed after he was dead and gone – not before; he did not want to be skinned alive.

Auntie had only once been in anguish and terror in her temple of happiness, the theatre. It was one winter's day, one of the days when we have two hours' daylight and that only grey. It was cold and snowy, but Auntie must go to the theatre. They were playing 'Herman von Unna,' besides a little opera and a great ballet, a prologue and an epilogue; it would last right into the night. Auntie must go there; her lodger had lent her a pair of sledging-boots with fur both outside and inside; they came high up on the legs.

She came into the theatre, and into her box; the boots were warm, so she kept them on. All at once a cry of 'Fire' was raised. Smoke came from one of the wings, smoke came from the flies; there was a frightful commotion; people rushed out; Auntie was the last in the box – 'the second tier to the left – the decorations look best from there,' she said, 'they are placed always to look most beautiful from the royal side' – Auntie wished to get out, but those in front of her, had thoughtlessly slammed the door in their terror. There sat Auntie; she could not get out, nor in either, that is to say into the next box, the partition was too high. She shouted, no one heard; she looked down into the tier underneath, it was empty, it was low, and it was near. Auntie, in her fear, felt herself so young and active; she would jump down; she got one leg over the balustrade and the other off the bench. There she sat astride, beautifully draped with her flowered skirt, with one long leg dangling out, a leg with a monster sledging-boot. That was a sight to see! and when it was seen, Auntie was also heard, and saved from burning, for the theatre was not burnt after all.

That was the most memorable evening of her life, she said, and she was glad that she had not been able to see herself; for then she would have died of shame.

Her benefactor, Mr Sivertson, came constantly to her every Sunday, but it was a long time from Sunday to Sunday. Latterly, therefore, in the middle of the week she had a little child for 'the leavings', that is to say, to enjoy what had been left over from dinner-time. This was a little child from the ballet, who was in need of food. The little one appeared on the stage both as a page and a fairy; her hardest part was that of hind-legs for the lion in 'The Enchanted Whistle', but she grew to be forelegs in the lion. She only got a shilling for this, whereas for the backlegs she got two; but there she had to go about stooping, and missed the fresh air. It was very interesting to know all this, Auntie thought.

She had deserved to live as long as the theatre lasted, but she was not able to do that; she did not die there either, but respectably and quietly in her own bed. Her last words were full of meaning; she asked, 'What are they playing tomorrow?'

She left behind her about five hundred rix-dollars: we infer that from the interest, which is twenty rix-dollars. Auntie had assigned these as a legacy for a worthy old maid without relatives; they should be applied yearly to pay for a seat in the second tier, left side, and on Saturdays, for then they gave the best pieces. There was only one condition for the person who profited by the legacy; every Saturday in the theatre, she must think of Auntie, who lay in her grave.

That was Auntie's religion.

The Toad

THE WELL was deep, and so the rope was long; the windlass had barely room to turn, when one came to lift the bucket full of water over the edge of the well. The sun could never get down to reflect itself in the water, however clear it was; but so far as it managed to shine down, green plants grew between the stones.

A family of the toad-race lived there. They were immigrants, who had really come down there head-foremost with the old mother-toad, who still lived. The green frogs, who swarm in the water, and had been there much earlier, acknowledged relationship and called them 'the well-guests'. These quite intended to remain there; they lived very comfortably on the dry land, as they called the wet stones.

The mother-frog had once travelled, had been in the bucket when it went up, but the light became too strong for her, and she got a pain in her eyes; luckily she got out of the bucket. She fell with a frightful splash into the water, and lay three days afterwards with a pain in her back. She could not tell very much about the world up above, but she knew, and they all knew, that the well was not the whole world. Mother Toad should have been able to tell one or two things, but she never answered when she was asked, and so one did not ask.

'Thick and ugly, horrid and fat she is!' said the young green frogs. 'Her children will be just as ugly!'

'That may be so,' said Mother Toad, 'but one of them has a jewel in its head, or I have it myself!'

And the green frogs heard, and they stared; and as they didn't like it, they made faces, and went to the bottom. But the young toads stretched their hind legs with sheer pride; each of them believed that he had the jewel, and so they sat and kept their heads very still, but finally they asked what they were so proud of, and what a jewel really was.

'It is something so splendid and precious,' said Mother Toad, 'that I cannot describe it! it is something that one goes about with for one's own pleasure, and which the others go about and fret over. But don't ask, I won't answer!'

'Well, I have not got the jewel,' said the smallest toad; it was just as ugly as it could be. 'Why should I have such a grand thing? And if it vexes others, it cannot give me pleasure! No, I only wish that I might come up to the edge of the well sometime to look out. It must be charming there!'

'Better remain where you are!' said the old one. 'You know what you are doing then. Take care of the bucket, it may squash you; and if you get safely into it, you may fall out; not all fall so luckily as I did, and keep their limbs and eggs whole.'

'Quack!' said the little one, and it was just as when we mortals say 'Alack!'

It had such a desire to get up to the edge of the well and look out; it felt such a longing after the green things up there; and when next morning the bucket, filled with water, was being drawn up, and accidentally stopped for a moment just by the stone, on which the toad sat, the little creature quivered and sprang into the full bucket, and sank to the bottom of the water, which then came up and was emptied out.

'Ugh, confound it!' said the man, who saw it. 'It is the ugliest thing I have seen,' and he made a kick with his wooden shoe at the toad, which came near to being crippled, but escaped by getting in amongst the high stinging-nettles. It saw stalk by stalk, and it looked upwards too. The sun shone on the leaves, they were quite transparent; it was for it, as it is for us when we come all at once into a great wood, where the sun shines through the leaves and branches.

'It is much lovelier here than down in the well! One could wish to stay here all one's life!' said the little toad. It lay there one hour, it lay there two! 'Now, I wonder what can be outside? As I have come so far, I may as well go farther!' And it crawled as fast as it could, and came out on to the road, where the sun shone on it, and the dust powdered it whilst it marched across the high road.

'Here one is really on dry land,' said the toad; 'I am getting almost too much of a good thing; it tickles right into me!'

Now it came to the ditch; the forget-me-nots grew here and the meadow-sweet; there was a hedge close by, with hawthorn and elder bushes; and the white-flowered convolvulus climbed over it. Here were colours to be seen; and yonder flew a butterfly; the toad thought it was a flower which had broken loose, the better to look about the world; it was such a natural thing to do.

'If one could only get along like that,' said the toad. 'Ah! ah! how delightful!'

It stayed in the ditch for eight days and nights, and had no want of food. The ninth day it thought, 'Farther on now!' – but what more beautiful could be found? Perhaps a little toad, or some green frogs. During the past night, it had sounded in the wind as if there were cousins in the neighbourhood. 'It is lovely to live! to come up out of the well; to lie among stinging-nettles; to crawl along a dusty road, and to rest in the wet ditch! but forward still! let us find frogs or a little toad; one cannot do without that; Nature is not enough for one!' And so it set out again on its wanderings. It came into the field, to a big pond with sedges round it, and it made its way into these.

'It is too wet for you here, isn't it?' said the frogs, 'but you are very welcome! Are you a he or a she? It does not matter, you are welcome all the same.'

And so it was invited to a concert in the evening, a family concert; great enthusiasm and thin voices, we all know that kind. There were no refreshments, except free drinks, the whole pond if they liked.

'Now I shall travel farther!' said the little toad. It was always craving after something better. It saw the stars twinkle, so big and so clear; it saw the new moon shine, it saw the sun rise, higher and higher.

'I am still in the well, in a bigger well; I must get higher up! I have a restlessness and a longing.'

And when the moon was full and round, the poor creature thought, 'Can that be the bucket, which is let down, and which I can jump into, to come higher up! or is the sun the big bucket? how big it is, and how beaming; it could hold all of us together. I must watch for my chance! Oh, what a brightness there is in my head! I don't believe the jewel can shine better! but I haven't got it, and I don't weep for it. No; higher up in brightness and gladness! I have an assurance, and yet a fear – it is a hard step to take! but one must take it! forwards! right out on the highway!'

And it stepped out, as well as such a crawling creature can, and then it was on the highway where people lived; there were both flower-gardens and kitchen-gardens. It rested beside a kitchen-garden.

'How many different beings there are, which I have never known! and how big and blessed the world is! But one must also look about in it, and not remain sitting in one place,' and so it hopped into the kitchen-garden. 'How green it is! how lovely it is here!'

'I know that well enough!' said the caterpillar on the leaf. 'My leaf is the biggest one here! it hides half the world, but I can do without that.'

'Cluck, cluck,' was heard, and fowls came tripping into the garden.

The foremost hen was long-sighted; she saw the caterpillar on the curly leaf, and pecked at it, so that it fell to the ground, where it wriggled and twisted itself. The hen looked first with one eye and then with the other, for it did not know what was to be the end of this wriggling.

'It does not do that with any good intent,' thought the hen, and lifted its head to peck at it. The toad became so frightened, that it crawled right up towards the hen.

'So it has friends to help it!' said the hen, 'look at that crawler!' and it turned away. 'I don't care a bit about the little green mouthful: it only tickles one's throat!' The other fowls were of the same opinion, and so they went away.

'I wriggled myself away from it!' said the caterpillar, 'it is a good thing to have presence of mind; but the hardest task remains, to get back on to my cabbage leaf. Where is it?'

And the little toad came and expressed its sympathy. It was glad that it had frightened the hens with its ugliness.

'What do you mean by that?' asked the caterpillar. 'I wriggled myself away from them. You are very unpleasant to look at! May I be allowed to occupy my own place? Now I smell cabbage! Now I am close to my leaf! There is nothing so nice as one's own! But I must get higher up!'

'Yes, higher up!' said the little toad, 'higher up! it feels as I do! but it is not in a good humour today; that comes from the fright. We all wish to get higher up!' And it looked up as high as it could.

The stork sat in his nest on the farmer's roof; he chattered, and the mother-stork chattered.

'How high up they live!' thought the toad; 'if one could only get up there!'

In the farmhouse lived two young students. The one was a poet, the other a naturalist; the one sang and wrote in gladness about all that God had made, and as it was reflected in his heart; he sang it out, short, clear, and rich in melodious verse. The other took hold of the thing itself; aye, split it up, if necessary. He took our Lord's creation as a vast sum in arithmetic, subtracted, multiplied, wanted to know it out and in and to talk with understanding about it; and it was perfect understanding, and he talked in gladness and with wisdom about it. They were good, happy fellows, both of them.

'There sits a good specimen of a toad,' said the naturalist. 'I must have it in spirit.'

'You have two others already,' said the poet; 'let it sit in peace, and enjoy itself!'

'But it is so beautifully ugly,' said the other.

'Yes, if we could find the jewel in its head!' said the poet, 'I myself would help to split it up.'

'The jewel!' said the other; 'you are good at natural history!'

'But is there not something very beautiful in the common belief that the toad, the very ugliest of animals, often carries hidden in its head the most precious jewel? Is it not the same with men? What a jewel had not Aesop, and Socrates!' – The toad heard no more, and it did not understand the half of it. The two friends went on, and it escaped being put in spirit.

'They also talked about the jewel!' said the toad. 'It is a good thing that I have not got it; otherwise I should have got into trouble.'

There was a chattering on the farmer's roof; the father-stork was delivering a lecture to his family, and they looked down askance at the two young men in the kitchen-garden.

'Man is the most conceited creature!' said the stork. 'Listen how they chatter! and yet they can't give a single decent croak. They are vain of their oratorical powers and their language! And it is a rare language! It becomes unintelligible every day's journey that we do. The one doesn't understand the other. Our language we can talk over the whole world, both in Denmark and in Egypt. And men can't fly at all! they fly along by means of an invention which they call a railway, but they often break their necks with that. I get shivers in my bill, when I think of it; the world can exist without men. We can do without them. Let us only keep frogs and rain-worms!'

'That was a grand speech!' thought the little toad. 'What a big man he is, and how high he sits, higher than I have ever seen anyone before! and how he can swim!' it exclaimed, when the stork with outspread wings flew through the air.

And the mother-stork spoke in the nest, and told about the land of Egypt, about the water of the Nile, and about all the splendid mud which was in foreign lands; it sounded quite new and charming to the little toad.

'I must go to Egypt,' it said, 'if only the stork would take me with it; or one of the young ones. I would do it a service in return on its wedding-day. Yes, I am sure I shall get to Egypt, for I am so lucky. All the longing and desire which I have is much better than having a jewel in one's head.'

And it just had the jewel; the eternal longing and desire, upwards, always upwards! it shone within it, shone in gladness, and beamed with desire.

At that moment came the stork; it had seen the toad in the grass, and he swooped down, and took hold of the little creature, not altogether gently. The bill pinched, the wind whistled; it was not pleasant, but upwards it went – up to Egypt, it knew; and so its eyes shone, as if a spark flew out of them. 'Quack! ack!'

The body was dead, the toad was killed. But the spark from his eyes, what became of it?

The sunbeam took it, the sunbeam bore the jewel from the head of the toad. Whither?

You must not ask the naturalist, rather ask the poet; he will tell it you as a story; and the caterpillar is in it, and the stork-family is in it. Think! the caterpillar is transformed, and becomes a lovely butterfly! The stork-family flies over mountains and seas, to distant Africa, and yet finds the shortest way home again to Denmark, to the same place, the same roof! Yes, it is really almost too like a fairy tale, and yet it is true! You may quite well ask the naturalist about it; he must admit it, and you yourself know it too, for you have seen it.

But the jewel in the head of the toad?

Look for it in the sun, see it there if you can. The splendour there is too strong. We have not yet got the eyes to look into all the glories which God has created, but someday we shall get them, and that will be the loveliest story, for we shall be in it ourselves!

Godfather's Picture-Book

GODFATHER could tell stories, ever so many and ever so long; he could cut out paper figures and draw pictures, and when it came near Christmas, he would bring out a copy-book, with clean white pages; on this he pasted pictures, taken out of books and newspapers; if he had not enough for the story he wished to tell, he drew them himself. When I was little, I got several such picture-books, but the loveliest of them all was the one from 'the memorable year when Copenhagen got gas in place of the old oil-lamps', and that was set down on the first page.

'Great care must be taken of this book,' said Father and Mother; 'it must only be brought out on grand occasions.'

Yet Godfather had written on the cover:

Though the book be torn, it is hardly a crime;

Other young friends have done worse in their time.

Most delightful it was when Godfather himself showed the book, read the verses and the other inscriptions, and told so many things besides; then the story became a real story.

On the first page there was a picture cut out of 'The Flying Post', in which one saw Copenhagen with its Round Tower, and Our Lady's Church; to the left of this was pasted an old lantern, on which was written 'Train-oil', to the right was a chandelier – on it was written 'Gas'. 'See, that is the placard,' said Godfather; 'that is the prologue to the story you are going to hear. It could also be given as a whole play, if one could have acted it: "Train-oil and Gas, or the Life and Doings of Copenhagen." That is a very good title! At the foot of the page there is still another little picture; it is not so easy to understand, so I shall explain it. That is a Death-horse. He ought to have come only at the end of the book, but he has run on ahead to say, that neither the beginning, the middle, nor the end is any good; he could have done it better himself – if he could have done it at all. The Death-horse, I must tell you, stands during the day tethered to the newspaper; but in the evening he slips out and posts himself outside the poet's door and neighs, so that the man inside may die instantly; but he does not die if there is any real life in him. The Death-horse is nearly always a poor creature who cannot understand himself, and cannot get a livelihood; he must get air and food by going about and neighing. I am convinced that he thinks nothing of Godfather's picture-book, but for all that it may well be worth the paper it is written on.

'Now, that is the first page of the book; that is the placard.

'It was just the last evening on which the old oil-lamps were lighted; the town had got gas, and it shone so that the old lamps seemed to be quite lost in it.

'I was in the street myself that evening,' said Godfather. 'The people walked up and down to look at the old and the new lighting. There were many people, and twice as many legs as heads. The watchmen stood about gloomily; they did not know when they might be dismissed, like the lamps; these themselves thought so far back – they dared not think forward. They remembered so much from the quiet evenings and the dark nights. I leaned up against a lamp-post,' said Godfather; 'there was a sputtering in the oil and the wick; I could hear what the lamp said, and you shall also hear it.

' "We have done what we could," said the lamp, "we have been sufficient for our time, have lighted up for joy and for sorrow; we have lived through many remarkable things; we have, so to speak, been the night-eyes of Copenhagen. Let new lights now take our place and undertake our office; but how many years they may shine, and what they may light up, remains to be seen! They certainly shine a little stronger than we old ones, but that is nothing, when one is made like a gas-chandelier, and has such connections, as they have, the one pours into the other! They have pipes in all directions and can get new strength in the town and outside of the town! But each one of us oil-lamps shines by what he has in himself and not by family relationship. We and our forefathers have shone for Copenhagen from immeasurably ancient times, far far back. But as this is now the last evening that we stand and shine in the second rank, so to speak, here in the street along with you, ye shining comrades, we will not sulk and be envious; no, far from it, we will be glad and good-natured. We are the old sentinels, who are relieved by new-fashioned guards in better uniforms than ours. We will tell you what our family, right up to the great-great-great-grandmother lantern, has seen and experienced – the whole of Copenhagen's history. May you and your successors, right down to the last gas-chandelier, experience and be able to tell as remarkable things as we, when one day you get your discharge! and you will get it, you may be prepared for that. Men are sure to find a stronger light than gas. I have heard a student say that it is hinted that they will yet burn sea-water!" The wick sputtered when the lamp said these words; just as if it had water in it already.'

Godfather listened closely, thought it over and considered that it was an excellent idea of the old lantern, on this evening of transition from oil to gas, to recount and display the whole of the history of Copenhagen. 'A good idea must not be let slip,' said Godfather; 'I seized it directly, went home and made this picture-book for you, it goes still farther back in time than the lamps could go.

'Here is the book; here is the history:

COPENHAGEN'S LIFE AND DOINGS

It begins with pitch-darkness, a coal-black page – that is the Dark Ages.

'Now we shall turn the page!' said Godfather. 'Do you see the pictures? Only the wild sea and the blustering north-east wind; it is driving heavy ice-floes along; there is no one out to sail on them except great stone-blocks, which rolled down on to the ice from the mountains of Norway. The north wind blows the ice away; he means to show the German mountains what boulders are found up in the north. The ice-fleet is already down in the Sound, off the coast of Zealand, where Copenhagen now lies; but there was no Copenhagen at that time. There were great sandbanks under the water, against one of these the ice-floes with the big boulders struck; the whole of the ice-fleet stuck fast, the north-east wind could not float them again, and so he grew as mad as he could be, and pronounced a curse upon the sandbank, "the thieves' ground," as he called it; and he swore that if it ever lifted itself above the surface of the sea, thieves and robbers should come there, gallows and wheel should be raised on it.

'But whilst he cursed and swore in this manner, the sun broke forth, and in its beams there swayed and swung bright and gentle spirits, children of light; they danced along over the chilling ice-floes, and melted them, and the great boulders sank down to the sandy bottom.

' "Sun-vermin!" said the north wind, "is that comradeship and kinship? I shall remember and revenge that. Now I pronounce a curse!"

' "We pronounce a blessing!" sang the children of light. "The sandbank shall rise and we will protect it! Truth and goodness and beauty shall dwell there!"

' "Stuff and nonsense!" said the north-east wind.

'Of all this the lantern had nothing to tell,' said Godfather, 'but I knew it, and it is of great importance for the life and doings of Copenhagen.

'Now we shall turn the page!' said Godfather. 'Years have passed, the sandbank has lifted itself; a sea-bird has settled on the biggest stone, which jutted out of the water. You can see it in the picture. Years and years have passed. The sea threw up dead fish on the sand. The tough lymegrass sprang up, withered, rotted, and enriched the ground; then came several different kinds of grasses and plants; the bank became a green island. The Vikings landed there. There was level ground for fighting, and good anchorage beside the island off the coast of Zealand.

'The first oil-lamp was kindled, I believe, to cook fish over, and there were fish in plenty. The herrings swam in great shoals through the Sound; it was hard to push a boat through them; they flashed in the water as if there was lightning down there, they shone in the depths like the Northern Lights. The Sound had wealth of fish, and so houses were built on the coast of Zealand; the walls were of oak and the roofs of bark; there were trees enough for the purpose. Ships came into the harbour; the oil-lantern hung from the swaying ropes; the north-east wind blew and sang – "U-hu-u." If a lantern shone on the island, it was a thieves' lantern. Smugglers and thieves exercised their trade on "Thieves' Island".

' "I believe that all the evil that I wished will grow," said the north-east wind. "Soon will come the tree, of which I can shake the fruit."

'And here stands the tree,' said Godfather. 'Do you see the gallows on Thieves' Island? Robbers and murderers hang there in iron chains, exactly as they hung at that time. The wind blew so that the long skeletons rattled, but the moon shone down on them very serenely, as it now shines on a rustic dance. The sun also shone down serenely, crumbling away the dangling skeletons, and from the sunbeams the children of light sang; "We know it! we know it! it shall yet be beautiful here in the time to come! Here it will be good and splendid!"

' "Cackle! cackle!" said the north-east wind.

'Now we turn over the page!' said Godfather.

'The bells were ringing in the town of Roskilde, where Bishop Absalon lived; he could both read his Bible and swing his sword; he had power and will; the busy fishermen at the harbour whose town was growing and was now a market-place, Absalon wished to protect these from assault. He sprinkled the unhallowed ground with holy water; Thieves' Island got a mark of honour. Masons and carpenters set to work on it; a building grew up at the Bishop's command. The sunbeams kissed the red walls as they rose. There stood Axel's house:

> The castle with its towers high in air,
> Its balconies and many a noble stair.
>> Boo! hoo!
> The north-east wind in fury blew,
> But the stronghold stood unyielding all the same.

And outside it stood "The Haven", the merchants' harbour:

> Mermaid's bower 'mid gleaming lakes,
> Built in groves of green.

'The foreigners came there and bought the wealth of fish, built booths and houses, with bladders for windowpanes – glass was too dear; then came warehouses with gables and windlasses. Look! inside the shops sit the old bachelors; they dare not marry; they trade in ginger and pepper, the pepper-lads.

'The north-east wind blows through the streets and lanes, sends the dust flying, and tears a thatched roof off. Cows and pigs walk about in the street-ditch.

' "I shall cow and subdue them," says the north-east wind; "whistle round the houses and round Axel's house! I cannot miss it! They call it 'Gallows' Castle on Thieves' Island'." '

And Godfather showed a picture of it, which he himself had drawn. On the walls were stake after stake, and on everyone sat the head of a captured pirate, and showed the teeth.

'That really happened,' said Godfather; 'and it is worth knowing about.

'Bishop Absalon was in his bathroom, and heard through the thin walls the arrival of a ship of freebooters. At once he sprang out of the bath and into his ship, blew his horn, and his crew came. The arrows flew into the backs of the robbers, who rowed hard to get away. The arrows fastened themselves in their hands, and there was no time to tear them out. Bishop Absalon caught every living soul and cut his head off, and every head was set up on the outer wall of the castle. The north-east wind blew with swollen cheeks – with bad weather in his jaw, as the sailors say.

' "Here I will stretch myself out," said the wind; "here I will lie down and look at the whole affair."

'It rested for hours, it blew for days; years went past.

'The watchman came out on the castle tower; he looked to the east, to the west, to the south, and the north. There you have it in the picture,' said Godfather, and showed it. 'You see him there, but what he saw I shall tell you.

'From Steileborg's wall there is open water right out to Köge Bay, and broad is the channel over to Zealand's coast. In front of Serritslev and Solberg commons, where the large villages lie, grows up more and more the new town with gabled timber houses. There are whole streets for shoemakers and tailors, for grocers and ale-sellers; there is a market-place, there is a guild-hall, and close by the shore, where once there was an island, stands the splendid Church of St Nicholas. It has a tower and a spire, immensely high; how it reflects itself in the clear water! Not far from this stands the Church of Our Lady, where masses are said and sung, incense gives out its odour, and wax-tapers burn. The merchants' haven is now the Bishop's town; the Bishop of Roskilde rules and reigns there.

'Bishop Erlandsen sits in Axel's house. There is cooking in the kitchen, there is serving of ale and claret, there is the sound of fiddles and kettledrums. Candles and lamps burn, the castle shines, as if it were a lantern for the whole country and kingdom. The north-east wind blows round the tower and walls, but they stand firm enough. The north-east wind blows round the western fortifications of the town – only an old wooden barricade, but it holds out well. Outside of it stands Christopher the First, the King of Denmark. The rebels have beaten him at Skelskör; he seeks shelter in the Bishop's town.

'The wind whistles, and says like the Bishop, "Keep outside! keep outside! The gate is shut for thee!"

'It is a time of trouble; these are dismal days; every man will have his own way. The Holstein banner waves from the castle tower. There is want and woe; it is the night of anguish. Strife is in the land, and the Black Death; pitch-dark night – but then came Waldemar. The Bishop's town is now the King's town; it has gabled houses and narrow streets; it has watchmen, and a town-hall; it has a fixed gallows by the west-port. None but townsmen can be hanged on it: one must be a citizen to be able to dangle there, to come up so high as to see Köge and the hens of Köge.

' "That is a lovely gallows," says the north-east wind; "the beautiful grows!" and so it whistled and blew. From Germany blew trouble and want.

'The Hansa merchants came,' said Godfather; 'they came from warehouse and counter, the rich traders from Rostock, Lübeck, and Bremen; they wanted to snatch up more than the golden goose from

Waldemar's Tower; they had more power in the town of the Danish King than the Danish King himself; they came with armed ships, and no one was prepared. King Eric had no mind either to fight with his German kinsfolk; they were so many and so strong. So King Eric and all his courtiers hurried out at the west-port to the town of Sorö, to the quiet lake and the green woods, to the song of love and the goblet's clang.

'But one remained behind in Copenhagen, a kingly heart, a kingly mind. Do you see the picture here, the young woman, so fine and tender, with sea-blue eyes and flaxen hair? it is Denmark's Queen, Philippa, the English Princess. She stayed in the distracted city, where in the narrow lanes and streets with the steep stairs, sheds, and lath-and-plaster shops, townspeople swarmed and knew not what to do. She has the heart and courage of a man. She summons burghers and peasants, inspires and encourages them. They rig the ships and garrison the blockhouses; they bang away with the carbines; there is fire and smoke, there is lightness of heart; our Lord will not give up Denmark! and the sun shines into all hearts, it beams out of all eyes in the gladness of victory. Blessed be Philippa! and blessed she is in the hut and in the house, and in the castle of the King, where she looks after the wounded and the sick. I have cut a wreath and put it round the picture here,' said Godfather. 'Blessed be Queen Philippa!'

'Now we spring years forward!' said Godfather, 'and Copenhagen springs with us. King Christian the First has been in Rome, has been blessed by the Pope, and greeted with honour and homage on the long journey. He is building here a hall of red brick; learning shall grow there, and display itself in Latin. The poor man's children from the plough or workshop can come there too, can live upon alms, can attain to the long black gown and sing before the citizens' doors.

'Close to the hall of learning, where all is in Latin, lies a little house; in it Danish rules, both in language and in customs. There is ale-porridge for breakfast, and dinner is at ten o'clock in the forenoon. The sun shines in through the small panes on cupboards and book-cases; in the latter lie written treasures, Master Mikkel's "Rosary" and

"Godly Comedies", Henrik Harpestreng's "Leech-book", and Denmark's "Rhyming Chronicle" by Brother Niels of Sorö. "Every man of breeding ought to know these," says the master of the house, and he is the man to make them known. He is Denmark's first printer, the Dutchman, Gotfred van Gehmen. He practises the blessed black art of book-printing.

'And books come into the King's castle, and into the houses of the burghers. Proverbs and songs get eternal life. Things which men dare not say in sorrow and pleasure are sung by the Bird of Popular Song, darkly and yet clearly; it flies so free, it flies so wide, through the common sitting-room, through the knightly castle; it sits like a falcon on the hand of the noble lady and twitters; it steals in like a little mouse, and squeaks in the dungeon to the enslaved peasant.

' "It is all mere words!" says the sharp north-east wind.

' "It is spring-time!" say the sunbeams. "See how the green buds are peeping!"

'Now we will go forward in our picture-book!' said Godfather.

'How Copenhagen glitters! There are tournaments and sports; there are splendid processions; look at the gallant knights in armour, at the noble ladies in silk and gold! King Hans is giving his daughter Elizabeth to the Elector of Brandenburg; how young she is, and how happy! she treads on velvet; there is a future in her thoughts, a life of household happiness. Close beside her stands her royal brother, Prince Christian, with the melancholy eyes and the hot, surging blood. He is dear to the townsfolk; he knows their burdens; he has the poor man's future in his thoughts. God alone decides our fortunes!

'Now we will go on with the picture-book,' said Godfather. 'Sharp blows the wind, and sings about the sharp sword, about the heavy time of unrest.

'It is an icy-cold day in the middle of April. Why is the crowd thronging outside the castle, and in front of the old tollbooth, where the King's ship lies with its sails and flags? There are people in the windows and on the roofs. There is sorrow and affliction, expectancy, and anxiety. They look towards the castle, where formerly there were torch-dances in the gilded halls, now so still and empty; they look at the window-balcony, from which King Christian so often looked out over the drawbridge, and along the narrow street, to his Dovelet, the little Dutch girl he brought from the town of Bergen. The shutters are closed, the crowd looks towards the castle; now the gate is opening, the drawbridge is being let down. King Christian comes with his faithful wife Elizabeth; she will not forsake her royal lord, now when he is so hard beset.

'There was fire in his blood, there was fire in his thoughts; he wished to break with the olden times, to break the peasants' yoke, to be good to the burghers, to cut the wings of "the greedy hawks"; but they were too many for him. He departs from his country and kingdom, to win friends and kinsfolk for himself abroad. His wife and faithful men go with him; every eye is wet now in the hour of parting.

'Voices blend themselves in the song of time, against him and for him; a threefold choir. Hear the words of the nobles; they are written and printed:

' "Woe to thee, Christian the Bad! the blood poured out on Stockholm's market-place cries aloud and curses thee!"

'And the monk's shout utters the same sentence:

' "Be thou cast off by God and by us! Thou hast called hither the Lutheran doctrine; thou hast given it church and pulpit, and let the tongue of the Devil speak. Woe to thee, Christian the Bad!"

'But peasants and burghers weep so bitterly. "Christian, beloved of the people! No longer shall the peasant be sold like cattle, no longer be bartered away for a hound! That law is thy witness!"

'But the words of the poor man are like chaff before the wind.

'Now the ship sails past the castle, and the burghers run upon the ramparts, so that they may once more see the royal galley sail.

' "The time is long, the time is hard; trust not in friends or kinsmen."

'Uncle Frederick in the Castle of Kiel would like to be King of Denmark. King Frederick lies before Copenhagen; do you see the picture here, "the faithful Copenhagen?" Round about it are coal-black clouds, with picture on picture; only look at each of them! It is a resounding picture; it still resounds in song and story: the heavy, hard, and bitter time in the course of the years.

'How went it with King Christian, that wandering bird? The birds have sung about it, and they fly far, over land and sea. The stork came early in the spring, from the south over the German lands; it has seen what will now be told.

' "I saw the fugitive King Christian driving on a heathergrown moor; there met him a wretched car, drawn by one horse; in it sat a woman, King Christian's sister, the Margravine of Brandenburg – faithful to the Lutheran religion, she had been driven away by her husband. On the dark heath met the exiled children of a king. The time is hard, the time is long; trust not in friend or in kin."

'The swallow came from Sönderborg Castle with a doleful song: "King Christian is betrayed. He sits there in the dungeon-tower deep as a well; his heavy steps wear tracks in the stone floor, his fingers leave their marks in the hard marble."

> What sorrow ever found such vent
> As in that furrowed stone?

'The fish-eagle came from the rolling sea! it is open and free; a ship flies over it; it is the brave Sören Norby from Fyn. Fortune is with him – but fortune is changeful, like wind and weather.

'In Jutland and Fyn the ravens and crows scream: "We are out for spoil. It is grand; it is grand! Here lie bodies of horses, and of men as well." It is a time of trouble; it is the Count of Oldenburg's war. The peasant seized his club and the townsman his knife, and shouted loudly: "We shall kill the wolves and leave no cub of them alive." Clouds of smoke rise from the burning towns.

'King Christian is a prisoner in Sönderborg Castle; he cannot escape, or see Copenhagen and its bitter distress. On the North Common stands Christian III, where his father stood before. In the town is despair; famine is there, and plague.

'Up against the church wall sits an emaciated woman in rags; she is a corpse; two living children lie on her lap and suck blood from the dead breast.

'Courage has fallen, resistance falls. Oh, thou faithful Copenhagen!'

'Fanfares are blown. Listen to the drums and trumpets! In rich dresses of silk and velvet, and with waving plumes, come the noble lords on gold-caparisoned horses; they ride to the old market. Is there a joust or tournament after the usual custom? Burghers and peasants in their best array are flocking thither. What is there to see? Has a bonfire been made to burn popish images? or does the hangman stand there, as he stood at Slaghoek's death fire? The King, the ruler of the land, is Lutheran, and this shall now be solemnly proclaimed.

'High and mighty ladies and noble maidens sit with high collars and pearls in their caps, behind the open windows, and see all the show. On an outspread carpet, under a canopy, sit the councillors of state in antique dress, near the King's throne. The King is silent. Now his will is proclaimed in the Danish tongue, the will of the statecouncil. Burghers and peasants receive words of stern rebuke for the opposition they have shown to the high nobility. The burgher is humbled; the peasant becomes a thrall. Now words of condemnation are uttered against the bishops of the land. Their power is past. All the property of the church and cloisters is transferred to the King and the nobles.

'Haughtiness and hate are there, pomp and misery.

'The time of change has heavy clouds, but also sunshine; it shone now in the hall of learning, in the student's home, and names shine out from it right on to our time. Hans Tausen, the son of a poor smith in Fyn:

> It was the little lad from Birkendè who came,
> His name flew over Denmark, so widely spread his fame;
> A Danish Martin Luther, who drew the Gospel sword,
> And gained a victory for truth and for the Word.

'There also shines the name of Petrus Palladius; so it is in Latin, but in Danish it is Peter Plade, the Bishop of Roskilde, also the son of a poor smith in Jutland. Among the names of noblemen shines that of Hans Friis, the Chancellor of the kingdom. He seated the students at his table, and looked after their wants, and those of the schoolboys too. And one name before all others is greeted with hurrahs and song:

> While but a single student here
> At learning's desk is seated,
> So long shall good King Christian's name
> With loud Hurrahs be greeted.

'Sunbeams came amongst the heavy clouds in that time of change.

'Now we turn the page.

'What whistles and sings in "The Great Belt" under the coast of Samsö? From the sea rises a mermaid, with seagreen hair; she tells the future to the peasant. A prince shall be born, who will become a king, great and powerful.

'In the fields, under the blossoming white-thorn, he was born. His name now blooms in song and story, in the knightly halls and castles round about. The exchange sprang up with tower and spire; Rosenborg lifted itself and looked far out over the ramparts; the students themselves got a house of their own, and close beside it stood and still points to Heaven the "Round Tower", which looks toward the island of Hveen where Uranienborg once stood. Its golden domes glittered in the moonlight, and mermaids sang of the master there whom kings and sages visited, the sage of noble blood, Tycho Brahe. He raised the name of Denmark so high, that along with the stars of heaven it was known in all the cultured lands of the world. And Denmark spurned him away from her.

'He sang for comfort in his grief:

> "Is not Heaven everywhere?
> What more then do I require!"

'His song lives in the hearts of the people, like the mermaid's song about Christian the Fourth.

'Now comes a page which you must look at in earnest,' said Godfather; 'there is picture after picture, as there is verse after verse in the old ballads. It is a song, so joyful in its beginning, so sorrowful in its ending.

'A king's child dances in the castle of the King; how charming she is to see! She sits on the lap of Christian the Fourth, his beloved daughter Eleonora. She grows in womanly virtues and graces. The foremost man amongst the nobles, Corfitz Ulfeldt, is her bridegroom. She is still a child, and still gets whippings from her stern governess; she complains to her sweetheart, and with good right too. How clever she is, and cultured and learned; she knows Latin and Greek, sings Italian to her lute, and is able to talk about the Pope and Luther.

'King Christian lies in the chapel-vault in Roskilde Cathedral, and Eleonora's brother is King. There is pomp and show in the palace in Copenhagen, there is beauty and wit; foremost is the Queen herself, Sophia Amalia of Lyneborg. Who can guide her horse so well as she? Who dances with such dignity as she? Who talks with such knowledge and cleverness as Denmark's Queen? "Eleonora Christina Ulfeldt!" – these words were spoken by the French Ambassador – "in beauty and cleverness she surpasses all."

'From the polished dancing-floor of the palace grew the burdock of envy; it hung fast, it worked itself in and twisted around itself, the scorn of contempt. "The baseborn creature! her carriage shall stop at the castle-bridge: where the Queen drives, the lady must walk." There is a perfect storm of gossip, slander, and lies.

'And Ulfeldt takes his wife by the hand in the quietness of the night. He has the keys of the town gates; he opens one of them, horses wait outside. They ride along the shore, and then sail away to Sweden.

'Now we turn the page, even as fortune turns itself for these two.

'It is autumn; the day is short, the night is long; it is grey and damp, the wind so cold, and rising in strength. It whistles in the leaves of the trees on the rampart, the leaves fly into Peter Oxe's courtyard, which stands empty and forsaken by its owners. The wind sweeps out over Christianshaven, round Kai Lykke's mansion, now a common jail. He himself has been hunted from honour and home; his scutcheon is broken, his effigy hanged on the highest gallows. Thus is he punished for his wanton thoughtless words about the honoured Queen of the land. Shrilly pipes the wind, and rushes over the open place where the mansion of the Lord High Steward has stood; only one stone of it is now left – "that I drove as a boulder down here on the floating ice," whoops the wind. "The stone stranded where Thieves' Island has since grown, under my curse, and so it came into the mansion of Lord Ulfeldt, where the lady sang to the sounding lute, read Greek and Latin, and bore herself proudly: now only the stone stands up here with its inscription:

To the Eternal Shame and Disgrace of the Traitor
Corfitz Ulfeldt

' "But where is she now, the stately lady? Hoo-ee! hoo-ee!" pipes the wind with ear-splitting voice. In the Blue Tower, behind the palace, where the sea-water beats against the slimy walls, there she has already sat for many years. There is more smoke than warmth in the chamber; the little window is high up under the ceiling. Christian the Fourth's petted child, the daintiest of maids and matrons, in what discomfort and misery she sits. Memory hangs curtains and tapestries on the smoke-blackened walls of her prison. She remembers the lovely time of her childhood, her father's soft and beaming features; she remembers her splendid wedding; the days of her pride, her hours of hardship in Holland, in England, and in Bornholm.

> Naught seems too hard for wedded love to bear,
> And faithfulness is not a cause for shame.

'Still, he was with her then; now she is alone, alone for ever. She knows not his grave, no one knows it.

> Her faithfulness to him was all her crime.

'She sat there for years, long and many, whilst life went on outside. It never stands still, but we will do that for a moment here, and think of her, and the words of the song:

> I keep my promise to my husband still
> In want and great necessity.

'Do you see the picture here?' said Godfather. 'It is winter-time; the frost makes a bridge between Lolland and Fyn, a bridge for Carl

Gustav, who is pushing on irresistibly. There is plundering and burning, fear and want, in the whole land.

'The Swedes are lying before Copenhagen. It is biting cold and a blinding snow; but true to their king, and true to themselves, men and women stand ready for the fight. Every tradesman, shopman, student, and schoolmaster is up on the ramparts to defend and guard. There is no fear of the red-hot balls. King Frederick swore he would die in his nest. He rides up there and the queen with him. Courage, discipline, and patriotic zeal are there. Only let the Swede put on his grave-clothes, and crawl forward in the white snow, and try to storm! Beams and stones are rolled down on him; yea, the women come with brewing cauldrons and pour boiling pitch and tar over the storming enemy.

'This night king and commoner are one united power. And there is rescue and there is victory. The bells ring; songs of thanksgiving resound. Burgherfolk, here you won your knightly spurs!

'What follows now? See the picture here. Bishop Svane's wife comes in a closed carriage. Only the high and mighty nobility may do that. The proud young gentlemen break the carriage down; the bishop's wife must walk to the bishop's house.

'Is that the whole story? – Something much bigger shall be broken next – the power of pride.

'Burgomaster Hans Nansen and Bishop Svane grasp hands for the work, in the name of the Lord. They talk with wisdom and honesty; it is heard in the church and in the burgher's house.

'One hand-grip of fellowship, and the haven is blocked, the gates are locked, the alarm bell rings.

'The power is given to the king alone, he who remained in his nest in the hour of danger; he governs, he rules over great and small. It is the time of absolute monarchy.

'Now we turn the page and the time with it.

' "Hallo, hallo, hallo!" The plough is laid aside, the heather gets leave to grow, but the hunting is good. "Hallo, hallo!" Listen to the ringing horn, and the baying hounds! See the huntsmen, see the king himself, King Christian V: he is young and gay. There is merriment in palace and in town. In the halls are wax-lights, in the courtyards are torches, and the streets of the town have got lamps. Everything shines so new! The new nobility, called in from Germany, barons and counts, get favours and gifts. Nothing passes current now except titles and rank, and the German language.

'Then sounds a voice that is thoroughly Danish; it is the weaver's son who is now a bishop; it is the voice of Kingo; he sings his lovely psalms.

'There is another burgher's son, a vintner's son; his thoughts shine forth in law and justice; his law-book became gold-ground for the king's name; it will stand for times to come. That burgher's son, the mightiest man in the land, gets a coat of arms and enemies with it, and so the sword of the executioner is raised over the head of Griffenfeldt. Then grace is granted, with imprisonment for life. They send him to a rocky islet off the coast of Trondhjem,

Munkholm – Denmark's St Helena.

But the dance goes merrily in the palace hall; splendour and pomp are there; there is lively music, and courtiers and ladies dance there.

'Now comes the time of Frederick IV!

'See the proud ships with the flag of victory! See the rolling sea! it can tell of great exploits, of the glories of Denmark. We remember the names, the victorious Sehested and Gyldenlöwe! We remember Hvitfeldt, who, to save the Danish fleet, blew up his ship, and flew to Heaven with the Danish flag. We think of the time, and the struggle of those days, and the hero who sprang from the Norwegian mountains to the defence of Denmark, Peter Tordenskjold. From the glorious surging sea, his name thunders from coast to coast.

> There flashed a lightning through the powder-dust,
> A thunder rumbled through the whispering age;
> A tailor-lad sprang from the tailor's board,

From Norway's coast sailed out a little sloop,
And over Northern seas there flew again
The Viking spirit, youthful, girt with steel.

'Then there came a fresh breeze from Greenland's coast, a fragrance as from the land of Bethlehem; it bore tidings of the Gospel light kindled by Hans Egede and his wife.

'The half leaf here has therefore a gold ground; the other half, which betokens sorrow, is ashen-grey with black specks, as if from fire sparks, as if from disease and pestilence.

'In Copenhagen the plague is raging. The streets are empty; the doors are barred, and round about are crosses marked with chalk; inside is the plague, but where the cross is black, all are dead.

'In the night the bodies are carried away, without the tolling-bell; they take the half-dead from the streets with them; the army wagons rumble, they are filled with corpses. But from the alehouses sound the horrid songs of the drunkard and wild shrieks. In drink they seek to forget their bitter distress; they would forget, and end – end! Everything comes to an end. Here the page ends with the second time of distress and trial for Copenhagen.

'King Frederick IV is still alive; his hair has grown grey in the course of the years. From the window of the palace he looks out upon the stormy weather; it is late in the year.

'In a little house by the Westgate a boy plays with his ball; it flies up into the garret. The little one takes a tallow-candle and goes up to search for it; he sets fire to the little house, and so to the whole street. It flares in the air, so that the clouds shine. The flames increase! There is food for the fire; there is hay and straw, bacon and tar, there are piles of firewood for the winter-time, and everything burns. There is weeping and shrieking and great confusion. In the tumult rides the old king, encouraging and commanding. There is blowing up with powder, and pulling down of houses. Now there is fire also in the north quarter, and the churches are burning, St Peter's and Our Lady's. Listen to the bells playing their last tune: "Turn away thy wrath, Lord God of Mercy!"

'Only the "Round Tower" and the castle are left standing; round about them are smoking ruins. King Frederick is good to the people; he comforts and feeds them; he is with them; he is the friend of the homeless. Blessed be Frederick IV!

'See this page now!

'See the gilded carriage with footmen round it, with armed riders before and behind it, coming from the castle, where an iron chain is stretched to prevent the people from coming too near. Every plebeian man must go over the square with bare head; because of this not many are seen there, they avoid the place. There comes one now with downcast eyes, with hat in hand, and he is just the man of that time, whom we name with pride:

> His words like a cleansing storm-wind rang
>   For sunshine in days yet to come;
> And smuggled-in fashions like grasshoppers sprang
>   In haste to escape and get home.

It is wit and humour in person; it is Ludwig Holberg. The Danish theatre, the scene of his greatness, has been closed, as if it were the dwelling-place of infamy. All merriment is coffined; dance, song, and music are forbidden and banished. The dark side of religion is now in power.

' "The Danish prince!" as his mother called him; now comes his time with sunshiny weather, with the song of birds, with gladness and gaiety, and true Danish ways. King Frederick V is king. And the chain is taken away from the square beside the castle; the Danish theatre is opened again; there is laughter and pleasure and good humour. And the peasants hold their summer festival. It is a time of gaiety after the time of fast and oppression. The beautiful thrives, blossoming and bearing fruit in sound, in colour, and in creative art. Hearken to Gretry's music! Watch the acting of Londemann! And Denmark's queen loves what is Danish. Louisa of England, beautiful and gentle; God in his Heaven, bless you! The sunbeams sing in lively chorus about the queens in the Danish land – Philippa, Elizabeth, Louisa!

'The earthly parts have long been buried, but the souls live, and the names live. Again, England sends a royal bride, Matilda, so young, and so soon forsaken! Poets will sing of thee in times to come, of thy youthful heart and time of trial. And song has power, an indescribable power through times and peoples. See the burning of the castle, King Christian's castle! They try to save the best they can find. See, the dockyard men are dragging away a basket with silver plate and precious things. It is a great treasure; but suddenly they see through the open door, where the flames are bright, a bronze bust of King Christian IV. Then they cast away the treasure they are carrying; his image is much more to them! that must be saved, however heavy it may be to carry. They know him from Ewald's song, from Hartmann's lovely melody.

'There is power in the words and the song, and it shall sound even twice as strong for the poor Queen Matilda.

'Now we shall turn farther on in our picture-book.

'On Ulfeldt's Place stood the stone of shame; where is there one on the earth like it? By the Westgate a column was raised; how many are there like it on the earth?

'The sunbeams kissed the boulder, which is the foundation under the "Column of Freedom". All the church bells rang, and the flags waved; the people hurrahed for the Crown-Prince Frederick. In the hearts and on the lips of old and young were the names of Bernstorff, Reventlow, Colbjörnson. With beaming eyes and thankful hearts they read the blessed inscription on the column:

' "The King has decreed it: Serfdom shall cease; the agrarian laws shall be set in order and put in force, that the free yeoman may become brave and enlightened, diligent and good, a worthy citizen, and happy!"

'What a day of sunshine! What "a Summer festival"!

'The spirits of light sang: "The good grows! The beautiful grows! Soon the stone on Ulfeldt's Place will fall, but Freedom's column shall stand in sunshine, blessed by God, the king, and the people."

> We have a highway old and wide
> And to the ends of earth it goes.

'The open sea, open for friend or foe; and the foe was there. It sailed up, the mighty English fleet; a great power came against a little one. The fight was hard, but the people were brave.

> Each stood firm with dauntless breath,
> Stood and fought and met his death.

'They won the admiration of the foe, and inspired the poets of Denmark. That day of battle is still commemorated with waving flags – Denmark's glorious second of April, the battle-day at the Roadstead.

'Years passed. A fleet was seen in Öre Sound. Was it bound for Russia or Denmark? No one knew, not even on board.

'There is a legend in the mouth of the people, that that morning in Öre Sound, when the sealed orders were broken open and read, and instructions given to take the Danish fleet, a young captain stepped forward to his chief, a son of Britain, noble in word and deed: "I swore," was his word, "that to my death I would fight for England's flag in open and honourable fight, but not to overpower the weak." And with that he sprang overboard!

> And so to Copenhagen sailed the fleet.
> While far from where they fought the battle stark,
> Lay he, the Captain – no one knows his name –
> A corpse sea-cold, hidden by waters dark,
> Until he drifted shorewards, and the Swedes,
> Beneath the starry sky who cast their nets,
> Found him, and bore him in their boat to land,
> And – cast the dice to win his epaulettes!

'The enemy made for Copenhagen; the town went up in flames, and we lost our fleet, but not our courage and our faith in God; He casteth down, but He raiseth up again. Our wounds were healed as in the battles of Valhalla. Copenhagen's history is rich in consolation.

Our faith has been from times of old
That God is ever Denmark's friend,
If we hold firm, He too will hold,
And still the sun shine in the end.

'And soon the sun shone on the rebuilt city, on the rich cornfields, on the workers' skill and art; a blessed summer day of peace, where poetry raised her Fata Morgana so rich in colour, with the coming of Oehlenschläger.

'And in science a discovery was made, far greater than that of a goldhorn in olden days, a bridge of gold was found:

A bridge for thought to dart
At all times into other lands and nations.

'Hans Christian Oersted wrote his name there. And see! beside the church by the castle was raised a building to which the poorest man and woman gave gladly their mite.

'You remember from the first part of the picture-book,' said God-father, 'the old stone-blocks, which rolled down from the mountains of Norway, and were carried down here on the ice; they are lifted again from the sandy bottom at Thorwaldsen's bidding, in marble beauty, lovely to see! Remember what I have shown you and what I have told you! The sandbank in the sea raised itself up and became a breakwater for the harbour, bore Axel's house, bore the bishop's mansion and the king's castle, and now it bears the temple of the beautiful. The words of the curse have blown away, but what the children of the sunlight sang in their gladness, about the coming time, has been fulfilled. So many storms have gone past, but may come again and will again pass. The true and the good and the beautiful have the victory.

'And with this the picture-book is finished; but not the history of Copenhagen – far from it. Who knows what you yourself may yet live to see! It has often looked black and blown a gale, but the sunshine is not yet blown away – that remains; and stronger yet than the strongest sunshine is God! Our Lord reigns over more than Copenhagen.'

So said Godfather, and gave me the book. His eyes shone, he was so certain of the thing. And I took the book so gladly, so proudly, and so carefully, just as I lately carried my little sister for the first time.

And Godfather said: 'You are quite welcome to show your picture-book to one or another; you may also say that I have made, pasted, and drawn the whole work. But it is a matter of life or death, that they know at once from where I have got the idea of it. You know it, so tell it them! The idea is due to the old oil-lamps, who just, on the last evening they burned, showed for the town's gaslights like a Fata Morgana, all that had been seen from the time the first lamp was lighted at the harbour, till this evening when Copenhagen was lighted both with oil and gas.

'You may show the book to whom you please, that is to say, to people with kind eyes and friendly hearts; but if a death-horse should come, then close Godfather's Picture-book.'

The Rags

OUTSIDE the factory lay heaps of clouts piled up in stacks, gathered together from far and wide; every rag had its story, everyone was telling his own tale, but one cannot listen to them altogether. Some rags were native, others came from foreign countries. Here a Danish rag lay close to a Norwegian rag; real Danish was the one, and thoroughly Norwegian the other, and that was the amusing thing about the two of them, every sensible Norwegian and Dane will say.

They knew each other by their speech, although each of these, said the Norwegian, was as different as French and Hebrew. 'We do our best to get ours raw and original, while the Dane makes his sickly-sweet flavourless language for himself.'

The rags talked, and a rag is a rag in every country; they only count for something in the cloth-heap.

'I am Norwegian,' said the Norwegian rag, 'and when I say I am Norwegian, I think I have said enough! I am of firm stuff, like the ancient hills in old Norway, the country which has a constitution like free America! It tickles me in my threads, to think what I am, and to let my thoughts ring out in granite words.'

'But we have a literature,' said the Danish rag. 'Do you understand what that is?'

'Understand!' repeated the Norwegian. 'Inhabitant of a flat land, shall I lift him to the mountains and let the Northern Lights shine on him, rag that he is! When the ice melts before the Norwegian sun, then Danish fruitboats come up to us with butter and cheese, very appetising wares! and there comes as ballast Danish literature. We do not need it! one prefers to dispense with flat ale where the fresh spring bubbles, and here it is a well which is not bored, not gossiped into European fame by newspapers and authors' travels in foreign countries. I speak freely from the lungs, and the Dane must accustom himself to the free sound, and that he will do in his Scandinavian clinging to our proud, rocky country, the primaeval clump of the world.'

'A Danish rag could never talk like that,' said the Danish rag. 'It is not our nature. I know myself, and all our rags are like me; we are so good-natured, so modest; we have too little confidence in ourselves, and one gains nothing by that, but I like it all the same, I think it so charming! As a matter of fact, I can assure you I know to the full my own good qualities, but I do not talk about them, no one shall be able to blame me for such a mistake. I am soft and tractable, bear with everything, envy none, speak good of all, although there is not much good to be said of most of the others, but let that be their affair. I only laugh at it all, being so gifted as I am.'

'Don't speak that flat-land's soft pasty language to me, it makes me sick,' said the Norwegian rag, and lifted itself in the wind from the heap and went over into another one.

Both of them were made into paper, and as chance would have it, the Norwegian rag became paper, on which a Norwegian wrote a faithful love-letter to a Danish girl, and the Danish rag became the manuscript for a Danish ode in praise of Norway's strength and grandeur.

Something good can come even out of rags, when they have been on the clothes-heap and the transformation into truth and beauty has taken place; then they shine in good understanding, and in that there is blessing.

That is the story; it is quite enjoyable, and need offend no one except – the rags.

Vaenöe and Glaenöe

ONCE UPON a time, there lay off the coast of Zealand, out from Holsteinborg, two wooded islands, Vaenöe and Glaenöe, with hamlets and farms on them; they lay near the coast, they lay near each other, and now there is only one island.

One night it was dreadful weather; the sea rose as it had not risen within the memory of man; the storm grew worse; it was Doomsday weather; it sounded as if the earth were splitting, the church bells began to swing and rang without the aid of man.

That night Vaenöe vanished in the depths of the sea; it was as if the island had never been. But many a summer night since then, with still, clear low-water, when the fisher was out spearing eels with a torch burning in the bows of his boat, he saw, with his sharp sight, deep down under him, Vaenöe with its white church-tower and the high church wall; 'Vaenöe is waiting for Glaenöe,' says the legend; he saw the island, he heard the church bells ringing down there; but he made a mistake in that, it was assuredly the sound made by the many wild swans, which often lie on the water here; they make sobbing and wailing sounds like a distant peal of bells.

There was a time when many old people on Glaenöe still remembered so well that stormy night, and that they themselves, when children, had at low tide driven between the two islands, as one at the present day drives over to Glaenöe from the coast of Zealand, not far from Holsteinborg; the water only comes halfway up the wheels. 'Vaenöe is waiting for Glaenöe,' was the saying, and it became a settled tradition.

Many a little boy and girl lay on stormy nights and thought, 'Tonight will come the hour when Vaenöe fetches Glaenöe.' They said their Lord's Prayer in fear and trembling, fell asleep, and dreamt sweet dreams, and next morning Glaenöe was still there with its woods and cornfields, its friendly farmhouses, and hop-gardens; the birds sang, the deer sprang; the mole smelt no sea-water, as far as he could burrow.

And yet Glaenöe's days are numbered; we cannot say how many they are, but they are numbered: one fine morning the island will have vanished.

You were perhaps, only yesterday, down there on the beach, and saw the wild swans floating on the water between Zealand and Glaenöe, a sailing boat with out-spread sails glided past the woodland; you yourself drove over the shallow ford, there was no other way; the horses trampled in the water and it splashed about the wheels of the wagon. You have gone away, and perhaps travelled a little out into the wide world, and come back again after some years. You see the wood here encircling a big green stretch of meadow, where the hay smells sweet in front of tidy farmhouses. Where are you? Holsteinborg still stands proudly here with its gilt spires, but not close to the fjord, it lies higher up on the land. You go through the wood, along over the field, and down to the shore, where is Glaenöe? You see no wooded island in front of you, you see the open water. Has Vaenöe fetched Glaenöe, that it waited for so long? When was the stormy night on which it happened, when the earth quaked, so that old Holsteinborg was moved many thousand cock-strides up into the country?

It was no stormy night, it was on a bright sunshiny day. The skill of man raised a dam against the sea; the skill of man blew the pent-up waters away, and bound Glaenöe to the mainland. The firth has become a meadow with luxuriant grass, Glaenöe has grown fast to Zealand. The old farm lies where it always lay. It was not Vaenöe which fetched Glaenöe, it was Zealand, which with long dike-arms seized it, and blew with the breath of pumps and read the magic words, the words of wedlock, and Zealand got many acres of land as a wedding gift. This is a true statement, it has been duly proclaimed, you have the fact before your eyes. The island Glaenöe has vanished.

Who was the Luckiest?

'WHAT LOVELY roses!' said the sunshine. 'And every bud will unfold, and be equally beautiful. They are my children! I have kissed them into life!'

'They are my children!' said the dew. 'I have suckled them with my tears.'

'I should think that I am their mother!' said the rose-hedge. 'You others are only godparents, who gave christening gifts, according to your means and good will.'

'My lovely rose-children!' said all three of them, and wished every blossom the greatest luck, but only one could be the luckiest, and one must be also the least lucky; but which of them?'

'That I shall find out!' said the wind. 'I travel far and wide, force myself through the narrowest chink; I know about everything outside and inside.'

Every blossomed rose heard what had been said, every swelling bud caught it.

Then there came through the garden a sorrowful, loving mother, dressed in black; she plucked one of the roses, which was just half-blown, fresh and full; it seemed to her to be the most beautiful of them all. She took the blossom into the quiet, silent chamber, where only a few days ago the young, happy daughter had romped about, but now lay there, like a sleeping marble figure, stretched out in the black coffin. The mother kissed the dead child, then kissed the half-blown rose, and laid it on the breast of the young girl, as if it by its freshness and a mother's kiss could make the heart beat again.

It was as if the rose were swelling; every leaf quivered with delight at the thought, 'What a career of love was granted to me! I become like a child of man, receive a mother's kiss and words of blessing, and go into the unknown kingdom, dreaming on the breast of the dead!

Assuredly I am the luckiest among all my sisters!'

In the garden, where the rose tree stood, walked the old weeding-woman; she also gazed at the glory of the tree, and fixed her eyes on the biggest full-blown rose. One drop of dew, and one warm day more, and the leaves would fall; the woman saw that, and thought that as it had fulfilled its mission of beauty, now it should serve its purpose of usefulness. And so she plucked it, and put it in a newspaper; it was to go home with her to other leaf-stripped roses, and be preserved with them and become pot-pourri, to be mixed with the little blue boys which are called lavender, and be embalmed with salt. Only roses and kings are embalmed.

'I am the most honoured!' said the rose, as the woman took it. 'I am the luckiest! I shall be embalmed!'

There came into the garden two young men, one was a painter, the other a poet; each of them plucked a rose, beautiful to behold. And the painter made a picture of the rose on canvas, so that it thought it saw itself in a mirror.

'In that way', said the painter, 'it shall live for many generations, during which many millions and millions of roses will wither and die!'

'I have been the most favoured! I have won the greatest happiness!'

The poet gazed at his rose, and wrote a poem about it, a whole mystery, all that he read, leaf by leaf, in the rose. 'Love's Picture-book;' it was an immortal poem.

'I am immortal with that,' said the rose, 'I am the luckiest!'

There was yet, amongst the display of roses, one which was almost hidden by the others; accidentally, fortunately perhaps, it had a blemish, it did not sit straight on its stalk, and the leaves on one side did not match those on the other; and in the middle of the rose itself, grew a little, deformed, green leaf; that happens with roses!

'Poor child!' said the wind, and kissed it on the cheek.

The rose thought it was a greeting, a homage; it had a feeling that it was a little differently formed from the other roses, that there grew a green leaf out of its interior, and it looked upon that as a distinction. A butterfly flew down upon it, and kissed its leaves. This was a wooer; she let him fly away again. There came an immensely big grasshopper;

he sat himself certainly upon another rose, and rubbed his shin-bone in amorous mood – that is the sign of love with grasshoppers. The rose he sat on did not understand it, but the rose with the distinction did, for the grasshopper looked at her with eyes which said, 'I could eat you up out of sheer love!' and no farther can love ever go; then the one is absorbed by the other! But the rose would not be absorbed by the jumper. The nightingale sang in the clear starry night.

'It is for me alone!' said the rose with the blemish or distinction. 'Why should I thus in every respect be distinguished above all my sisters? Why did I get this peculiarity, which makes me the luckiest?'

Then two gentlemen smoking cigars came into the garden; they talked about roses and about tobacco; roses, it was said, could not stand smoke, they lose their colour and become green; it was worth trying. They had not the heart to take one of the very finest roses, they took the one with the blemish.

'What a new distinction!' it said, 'I am exceedingly lucky! The very luckiest!'

And it became green with self-consciousness and tobacco smoke.

One rose, still half-blown, perhaps the finest on the tree, got the place of honour in the gardener's tastefully arranged bouquet; it was brought to the young, lordly master of the house, and drove with him in the carriage; it sat as a flower of beauty among other flowers and lovely green leaves; it went to a splendid gathering, where men and women sat in fine attire illuminated by a thousand lamps; music sounded; it was in the sea of light which filled the theatre; and when amidst the storm of applause the celebrated young dancer fluttered forward on the stage, bouquet after bouquet flew like a rain of flowers before her feet. There fell the bouquet in which the lovely rose sat like a gem. It felt the fullness of its indescribable good fortune, the honour and splendour into which it floated; and as it touched the floor, it danced too, it sprang, and flew along the boards, breaking its stalk as it fell. It did not come into the hands of the favourite, it rolled behind the scenes, where a scene-shifter took it up, saw how beautiful it was, how full of fragrance it was, but there was no stalk on it. So he put it in his pocket, and when he went home in the evening it was in a dram-glass, and lay there in water the whole night. Early in the morning it was set before the grandmother, who sat in her armchair, old and frail. She looked at the lovely broken rose, and rejoiced in its beauty and its scent.

'Yes, you did not go to the rich and fine lady's table, but to the poor old woman; but here you are like a whole rose tree; how lovely you are!'

And she looked with childlike delight at the flower, and thought, no doubt, of her own long-past youthful days.

'There was a hole in the pane,' said the wind, 'I easily got in, and saw the old woman's eyes, youthfully shining, and the lovely, broken rose in the dram-glass. The luckiest of all! I know it! I can tell it!'

Each rose on the tree had its story. Each rose believed and thought itself to be the luckiest, and faith makes blessed. The last rose, however, was the luckiest of all, in its own opinion.

'I outlived them all! I am the last, the only one, mother's dearest child!'

'And I am the mother of them!' said the rose-hedge.

'I am that!' said the sunshine.

'And I,' said wind and weather.

'Each has a share in them!' said the wind, 'and each shall get a share in them!' and so the wind strewed the leaves out over the hedge, where the dewdrops lay, where the sun shone. 'I, also, will get my share,' said the wind. 'I got all the stories of all the roses, which I will tell out in the wide world! Tell me now, which was the luckiest of them all? Yes, you must say that; I have said enough!'

The Dryad

WE ARE travelling to the Paris Exhibition.

Now we are there! it was a flight, a rush, but quite without witchcraft; we came by steam, in a ship and on a high road.

Our time is the fairy-tale time.

We are in the midst of Paris, in a great hotel, all the staircase is decorated with flowers, and soft carpets cover the steps.

Our room is comfortable, the balcony door is standing open to a big square. Down there the spring lives. It has driven to Paris, arriving at the same time as we; it has come in the shape of a big, young chestnut tree, with fine, newly-opened leaves. How it is clothed in all the glory of spring, far beyond all the other trees in the square! One of these has gone out of the number of the living trees, and lies prostrate on the ground, torn up by the roots. There, where it stood, the new chestnut tree shall be planted and grow.

As yet it stands high up in the heavy cart which brought it to Paris this morning from the country, several miles away. There it had stood for years, close beside a mighty oak, under which sat often the kindly old priest, who told stories to the listening children. The young chestnut tree listened with them: the Dryad inside it, who was still a child, could remember the time when the tree was so small that it only reached a little higher than the ferns and long blades of grass. They were then as big as they could be, but the tree grew and increased every year, drank air and sunshine, received dew and rain, and was shaken and lashed by the rough winds: this is necessary for education.

The Dryad rejoiced in her life and experiences, in the sunshine and the song of birds, but happy most of all at the voices of men; she understood their language quite as well as she understood that of animals.

Butterflies, dragon-flies, and common flies – everything that could fly, paid her a visit; they all gossiped together; told about the village, the vineyard, the wood, the old castle with the park, in which were canals and dams; down there in the water, dwelt also living things, which in their own way could also fly from place to place under the water, beings with thought and knowledge; they said nothing, so wise were they.

And the swallow, which had dipped down into the water, told about the lovely goldfish, about the fat bream, the thick tench, and the old, moss-grown carp. The swallow gave a very good description, 'but one can see better for oneself,' she said; but how should the Dryad ever get to see these beings? She must content herself with being able to look out over the beautiful landscape and see the busy activity of men. That was lovely, but most lovely of all, when the old priest stood here under the oak, and told about France, and about the great deeds of men and women, whose names are named with admiration throughout all times. The Dryad heard of the shepherdess Joan of Arc, of Charlotte Corday; she heard of olden times, of the times of Henry IV, and of Napoleon I, and of greatness and talent, right up to the present day. She heard names, each of which rang in the hearts of the people. France is a worldwide land; a soil of intellect with a crater of freedom.

The village children listened devoutly, and the Dryad not less so; she was a schoolchild like the others. She saw in the forms of the sailing clouds picture after picture of what she had heard told. The cloudy sky was her picturebook.

She felt herself so happy in the lovely France; but had still a feeling that the birds, and every animal which could fly, were much more favoured than she. Even the fly could look about himself, far and wide, much farther than the Dryad's horizon.

France was so extensive and so glorious, but she could only see a little bit of it; like a world, the country stretched out with vineyards, woods, and great towns, and of all of these Paris was the mightiest, and the most brilliant; thither the birds could go, but never she.

Amongst the village children was a little girl, so poor and so ragged, but lovely to look at; she was always laughing and singing, and wreathing red flowers in her black hair.

'Do not go to Paris!' said the old priest. 'Poor child! if you go there, it will be your ruin!'

And yet she went.

The Dryad often thought about her, for they had both the same desire and longing for the great city. Spring came, summer, autumn, winter; two or three years passed.

The Dryad's tree bore its first chestnut blossoms, the birds twittered about it in the lovely sunshine. Then there came along the road a grand carriage with a stately lady; she, herself, drove the beautiful prancing horses; a smart little groom sat behind her. The Dryad knew her again, the old priest knew her again, shook his head, and said sorrowfully, 'You did go there! it was your ruin! Poor Marie!'

'She poor!' thought the Dryad. 'Why, what a change! she is dressed like a duchess! she became like this in the city of enchantment. Oh, if I were only there in all the splendour and glory! it even throws a light up into the clouds at night, when I look in the direction where I know the city is.'

Yes, thither, towards that quarter, the Dryad looked every evening, every night. She saw the glimmering mist on the horizon; she missed it in the bright, moonlight nights; she missed the floating clouds which showed her pictures of the city and of history.

The child grasps at its picture-book; the Dryad grasped at the cloud world, her book of thoughts.

The warm summer sky, free from clouds, was for her a blank page, and now for several days she had seen such a sky.

It was the warm summer-time, with sultry days without a breath of air. Every leaf, every flower, lay as in a doze, and men were like that too. Then clouds arose, and that in the quarter where at night the glimmering mist announced, 'Here is Paris.'

The clouds arose, forming themselves like a whole mountain range, and scudded through the air, out over the whole landscape as far as the Dryad could see.

The clouds lay like enormous purple rocks, layer on layer, high up in the sky. Flashes of lightning darted forth; 'they also are servants of God the Lord,' the old priest had said. And there came a bluish dazzling flash, a blaze as if the sun itself had burst the purple rocks, and the lightning came down, and splintered the mighty old oak tree to the roots; its crown was rent, its trunk was rent, it fell split asunder as if it spread itself out to embrace the messenger of light. No metal cannon can boom through the air and over the land at the birth of a royal child, as the thunder rumbled here at the death of the old oak tree. The rain streamed down: a refreshing breeze blew, the storm was past, and a Sunday calm fell on everything. The village people gathered round the fallen old oak; the venerable priest spoke words in its praise, and an artist made a sketch of the tree itself as a lasting memorial.

'Everything passes away!' said the Dryad, 'passes away like the clouds, and returns no more.' The old priest came there no more; the school roof had fallen, and the teachers' chair was gone. The children came no more, but the autumn came, winter came, and the spring came too, and in all the changing seasons the Dryad gazed towards the quarter where every evening and night, far away on the horizon, Paris shone like a shimmering mist. Out from it sped engine after engine, the one train after the other, rushing and roaring, at all hours; in the evening and at midnight, in the morning, and through the whole of the daytime came the trains, and from everyone and into everyone crowded people from all the countries in the world; a new wonder of the world had called them to Paris. How did this wonder reveal itself?

'A splendid flower of art and industry,' they said, 'has sprung up on the barren soil of the Field of Mars; a gigantic sunflower, from whose leaves one can learn geography and statistics, get the learning of a guild-master, be elevated in art and poetry, and learn the size and greatness of different countries.'

'A fairy-blossom,' said others, 'a many-coloured lotus plant, which spreads its green leaves over the sand, like a velvet carpet, which has sprung forth in the early spring. The summer shall see it in all its glory; the autumn storms will sweep it away; neither root nor leaf shall be left.'

Outside the military school stretches the arena of war in times of peace; the field without grass and stalk, a piece of sandy plain cut out of the African desert, where Fata Morgana shows her strange castles in the air and hanging gardens; on the Field of Mars they now stand more brilliant and more wonderful, because genius had made them real.

'The present-day Palace of Aladdin is reared,' it was said. Day by day, and hour by hour, it unfolds its rich splendour more and more. Marble and colours adorn its endless halls. 'Master Bloodless' here moves his steel and iron limbs in the great machinery-hall. Works of art in metal, in stone, in weaving, proclaim the mental life which is stirring in all the countries of the world. Picture-galleries, masses of flowers, everything that intellect and hand can create in the workshops of the craftsman is here displayed to view. Even relics of ancient days from old castles and peat-mosses have met here.

The overwhelmingly great and varied sight must be reduced and condensed to a toy in order to be reproduced, understood, and seen as a whole.

The Field of Mars, like a great Christmas table, had on it an Aladdin's Palace of industry and art, and round about it were little articles from all countries; every nation found something to remind it of home. Here stood the Egyptian royal palace, here the caravanserai of the desert; the Bedouin coming from his sunny land swung past on his camel; here extended Russian stables with magnificent fiery steeds from the steppes. The little thatched farmhouse from Denmark stood with its 'Dannebrog' flag beside Gustav Vasa's beautifully carved wooden house from Dalarne in Sweden; American huts; English cottages, French pavilions, kiosks, churches, and theatres lay oddly strewn about, and amidst all that, the fresh green turf, the clear, running water, flowering shrubs, rare trees, glass-houses where one could imagine oneself in a tropical forest; whole rose-gardens, as if brought from Damascus, bloomed under the roof; what colours, what fragrance! Stalactite caves, artificially made, enclosing fresh and salt lakes, gave an exhibition from the kingdom of fish. One stood down on the bottom of the sea among fish and polypi.

All this, they said, the Field of Mars now bears and presents to view, and over this great richly-decked table moves, like a busy swarm of ants, the whole crowd of people, either on foot or drawn in little carriages; all legs cannot stand such an exhausting promenade.'

They come here from early morning until late in the evening.

Steamer after steamer, full of people, glides down the Seine. The number of carriages is constantly increasing, the crowds of people both on foot and on horseback are increasing, omnibuses and tramcars are stuffed and filled and covered with people, all these streams move to one goal, 'The Paris Exhibition!' All the entrances are decorated with the French flag; round about the bazaar-buildings wave the flags of all nations; from the machinery-hall there is a whirring and humming; the bells chime in melody from the towers; the organs play inside the churches; hoarse, snuffling songs from the Oriental cafés mingle with the music. It is like the kingdom of Babel, the language of Babel, a Wonder of the World. It was such indeed – so the reports about it said; who did not hear them? The Dryad knew everything that has been said here about the 'new wonder' in the city of cities.

'Fly, ye birds! fly thither to look, come again and tell!' was the prayer of the Dryad.

The longing swelled to a wish, and became a life's thought; and then one still silent night, when the full moon was shining, there flew out from its disk – the Dryad saw it – a spark, which fell glittering like a meteor; and before the tree, whose branches shook as in a blast of wind, stood a mighty, radiant figure. It spoke in tones so soft and yet as strong as the trump of the Last Day, which kisses to life and calls to judgement.

'Thou shalt enter that place of enchantment, thou shalt there take root, feel the rushing currents, the air and the sunshine there. But thy lifetime shall be shortened, the series of years which awaited thee out here in the open, will shrink there to a small number of seasons. Poor Dryad; it will be thy ruin! thy longing will grow, thy yearning and thy craving will become stronger! The tree itself will become a prison for thee; thou wilt forsake thy dwelling, forsake thy nature, and fly away and mix with human beings, and then thy years will dwindle down to half the lifetime of the ephemeral fly, only a single night; thy life shall be extinguished, the leaves of the tree shall wither and be blown away, to return no more.'

Thus it sounded, thus it sang, and the brightness vanished, but not the longing and desire of the Dryad; she trembled with expectation, in a fever of wild anticipation.

'I shall go to the city of cities!' she exultingly cried. 'Life begins, gathers like the cloud, and no one knows where it goes.'

In the grey dawn, when the moon grew pale and the clouds red, the hour of fulfilment struck, and the promise was redeemed.

People came with spades and poles; they dug round the roots of the tree, deep down, right under it. Then a cart was brought up, drawn by horses, the tree, with the roots and clods of earth hanging to them, was lifted, wrapped in matting which made a warm foot-bag for it, then it was placed on the cart and bound fast. It was to go on a journey to Paris, to grow and remain there in the grandest city of France – the city of cities.

The leaves and branches of the chestnut tree trembled in the first moment of motion; the Dryad trembled in the delight of expectation.

'Away! away!' rang in every pulse-beat. 'Away! away!' came the echo in trembling, fluttering words. The Dryad forgot to say 'Farewell' to her native place, to the waving grasses and the innocent daisies, which had looked up to her as to a great lady in our Lord's garden, a young Princess who played the shepherdess out in the country.

The chestnut tree was on the cart, it nodded with its branches 'Farewell', or 'Away', the Dryad knew not which; she thought and dreamt of the wonderful, new, and yet so familiar scenes which should be unfolded before her. No childish heart in innocent delight, no passion-filled soul, has ever begun its journey to Paris more full of thought than she. 'Farewell!' became 'Away! away!'

The wheels of the cart went round, the distant became near and was left behind; the country changed, as the clouds change; new vineyards, forests, villages, villas, and gardens sprang up, came in sight, and rolled away again. The chestnut tree moved forward, the Dryad forward with it, engine after engine rushed close past each other and crossed each other; the engines sent out clouds, which formed figures that told of the Paris they came from, and to which the Dryad was bound.

Everything round about knew and must understand whither her way led; she thought that every tree she went past stretched out its branches to her, and begged: 'Take me with you! take me with you!' In every tree there was also a Dryad full of longing. What changes! What a journey! It seemed as if houses shot up out of the earth, more and more, closer and closer. Chimneys rose like flowerpots, placed above each other and side by side along the roofs; great inscriptions with letters a yard long, painted figures on the walls from the ground-floor to the cornice shone forth.

'Where does Paris begin, and when shall I be in it?' the Dryad asked herself. The crowds of people increased, the noise and bustle grew greater, carriage followed carriage, men on foot followed men on horse, and all round was shop upon shop, music and song, screaming and talking.

The Dryad in her tree was in the midst of Paris.

The great, heavy cart stopped in a little square, planted with trees, surrounded by high houses, where every window had its balcony. People looked down from there upon the young, fresh chestnut tree which was driven up, and which was now to be planted here, in place of the worn-out, uprooted tree, which lay stretched along the ground. People stood still in the square, and looked at the spring verdure, smiling and delighted; the older trees, still only in bud, greeted her with rustling branches, 'Welcome! welcome!' and the fountain which threw its jets of water into the air, letting them splash again into the broad basin, allowed the wind to carry drops over to the newly-arrived tree, as if it would offer it a cup of welcome.

The Dryad felt that its tree was lifted from the cart and placed in its future position. The tree's roots were hidden in the earth, fresh turf was laid over them; blossoming shrubs and pots of flowers were planted like the tree; here was a whole garden plot right in the middle of the square. The dead, uprooted tree, killed by gas-fumes, kitchen fumes, and all the plant-killing vapours of a town, was laid on the cart and driven away. The crowd looked on, children and old people sat on benches on the grass, and looked up among the leaves of the newly-planted tree. And we, who tell about it, stood on the balcony, looked down on the young spring verdure just come from the fresh country air, and said, as the old priest would have said: 'Poor Dryad!'

'How happy I am!' said the Dryad, 'and yet I cannot quite realise it, nor quite express what I feel; everything is as I expected it! and yet not quite as I expected!'

The houses were so high, and so close: the sun shone properly only upon one wall, and it was pasted over with posters and placards, before which the people stood and made the place crowded. Vehicles went past, light and heavy; omnibuses, those over-filled houses on wheels, rolled along, riders trotted ahead, carts and carriages claimed the right to do the same. The Dryad wondered whether the tall houses, which stood so close, would also flit away, change their shapes like the clouds and glide aside, so that she could see into Paris, and out over it. Notre-Dame must show itself, and the Vendôme Column, and the Wonder which had called and was calling so many strangers hither. But the houses did not move.

It was still day, when the lamps were lighted, the gas-rays shone out from the shops and up among the branches of the tree; it was like summer sunshine. The stars came out overhead, the same ones the Dryad had seen in her native place; she thought she felt a breeze from there, so pure and mild. She felt herself elevated and strengthened, and found she had the power of seeing right out through all the leaves of the tree, and had feeling to the farthest tips of the roots. She felt herself in the living human world, looked at with kindly eyes; round about were bustle and music, colours and lights.

From a side street sounded wind-instruments, and the dance-inspiring tunes of the barrel-organ. Yes, to the dance, to the dance! it sounded – to gladness and the pleasure of life.

It was a music that must set men, horses, carriages, trees, and houses dancing, if they could dance. An intoxicating joy arose in the Dryad's breast.

'How delightful and beautiful!' she cried joyfully, 'I am in Paris!'

The day which came, the night which followed, and again the next day, offered the same sights, the same stir, the same life, changing and yet always the same.

'Now I know every tree and every flower in the square here! I know every house, balcony and shop here, where I am placed in this

little cramped corner which hides the great, mighty town from me.
Where are the triumphal arches, the boulevards, and the Wonder of
the World? None of all these do I see! I am imprisoned as in a cage
amongst the tall houses, which I now know by heart, with their
placards, and posters, and sign-boards, all these plaster sweetmeats,
which I have no taste for any longer. Where is all that I heard about,
know about, longed for, and for the sake of which I wished to come
here? What have I grasped, won, or found! I am longing as before, I
see a life which I must grasp and live in! I must enter the ranks of the
living! I must revel there, fly like the birds, see and understand,
become wholly human, seize half a day of that in place of years of life
in everyday fatigue and tediousness, in which I sicken and droop, and
vanish like the mist on the meadow. I must shine like the cloud, shine
in the sunlight of life, look out over everything like the cloud, and
pass away like it, no one knows whither!'

This was the Dryad's sigh, which lifted itself in prayer.

'Take my lifetime, and give me the half of the Ephemera's life! Free
me from my imprisonment, give me human life, human joy for a short
space, only this single night, if it must be so, and punish me thus for my
presumptuous spirit, my longing for life! Annihilate me; let the fresh,
young tree that encloses me then wither and fall, become ashes, and be
scattered to the winds.'

A rustling passed through the branches of the tree; there came a
titillating feeling, a trembling in every leaf, as if fire ran through it or
out of it, a blast went through the crown of the tree, and in the midst of
it arose a woman's form, the Dryad herself. In the same instant she sat
under the gas-illumined, leafy branches, young and beautiful, like poor
Marie, to whom it was said, 'The great city will be thy ruin!'

The Dryad sat by the foot of the tree, by the door of her house, which
she had locked and of which she had thrown away the key. So young,
so beautiful! The stars saw her and twinkled. The gas-lamps saw her
and beamed and beckoned! How slender she was and yet strong, a
child and yet a full-grown maiden. Her clothes were fine as silk, and
green as the fresh, newly-unfolded leaves in the crown of the tree; in

her nut-brown hair hung a half-blown chestnut blossom; she looked like the goddess of Spring.

Only a short minute she sat motionless and still, then she sprang up, and ran like a gazelle from the place, and disappeared round the corner. She ran, she sprang like the light from a mirror which is carried in the sunshine, the light which with every motion is cast now here and now there; and if one had looked closely, and been able to see what there was to see, how wonderful! At every place where she stopped for a moment, her clothes and her figure were changed according to the character of the place, or the house whose lamp shone upon her.

She reached the Boulevards; a sea of light streamed from the gas in the lamps, shops, and cafés. Young and slender trees stood here in rows; each one hid its Dryad from the beams of the artificial sunlight. The whole of the long, never-ending pavement was like one great assembly room; tables stood spread with refreshments of all kinds, from champagne and chartreuse down to coffee and beer. There was a display of flowers, of pictures, statues, books, and many-coloured fabrics. From the throng under the tall houses she looked out over the alarming stream under the rows of trees: there rushed a tide of rolling carriages, cabriolets, coaches, omnibuses, and cabs, gentlemen on horseback, and marching regiments, it was risking life and limb to cross over to the opposite side. Now shone a blue light, then the gaslights were supreme, and suddenly a rocket shot up; whence and whither? Certainly, it was the highway of the great city of the world.

Here sounded soft Italian melodies, there Spanish songs, accompanied by the beating of castanets, but strongest, and swelling above all, sounded the musical-box melodies of the moment, the tickling can-can music, unknown to Orpheus, and never heard by beautiful Helen; even the wheelbarrow must have danced on its one wheel if it could have danced. The Dryad danced, floated, flew, changing in colour like the honey-bird in the sunshine; each house and the world within it gave fresh tints to her. As the gleaming lotus-flower, torn from its root, is borne by the stream on its eddies, she drifted; and wherever she stood, she was again a new shape, therefore no one could follow her, recognise and watch her.

Like cloud-pictures everything flew past her, face after face, but not a single one did she know; she saw no form from her own home. There shone in her thoughts two bright eyes, and she thought of Marie, poor Marie! the happy, ragged child with the red flower in her black hair. She was in the city of the world, rich, and dazzling, as when she drove past the priest's house, the Dryad's tree, and the old oak. She was here, no doubt, in the deafening noise; perhaps she had just got out of that magnificent coach waiting yonder; splendid carriages stood here with laced coachmen, and silk-stockinged footmen. The grand people alighting were all women, richly dressed ladies. They went through the open lattice-door, up the high, broad stairs, which led to a building with white marble columns. Was this perhaps the 'Wonder of the World'? Then certainly Marie was there!

'Sancta Maria!' they sang within; the clouds of incense floated under the lofty painted and gilded arches, where twilight reigned. It was the Church of the Madeleine. Dressed in black, in costly materials made after the latest fashion, ladies of the highest society glided over the polished floor. Coats of arms were on the silver clasps of the prayerbooks bound in velvet, and on the fine, strongly-scented handkerchiefs trimmed with costly Brussels lace. Some of the ladies knelt in silent prayer before the altars, others sought the confessionals. The Dryad felt a restlessness, a fear, as if she had entered a place where she ought not to have set foot. Here was the home of silence, the palace of secrets; all was whispered and confided without a sound being heard.

The Dryad saw herself disguised in silk and veil, resembling in form the other rich and high-born ladies; was each of them a child of longing like herself?

There sounded a sigh, so painfully deep; did it come from the confessional corner, or from the breast of the Dryad? She drew her veil closer round her. She breathed the incense and not the fresh air. Here was no place for her longing.

Away! away! in flight without rest! The Ephemera has no rest; its flight is its life!

She was again outside under the blazing gas-lamps by the splendid fountain. 'All the streams of water will not be able to wash away the innocent blood which has been shed here.' So it has been said.

Foreigners stood here and talked loudly and with animation, as no one dared to do in the High Court of Mystery, from which the Dryad came.

A large stone-slab was turned and lifted up; she did not understand this; she saw an open entrance to the depths of the earth; into this people descended from the starlit sky, from the sunshiny gas-flames, from all the stirring life.

'I am afraid of this!' said one of the women who stood there; 'I dare not go down; I don't care either about seeing the sight! Stay with me!'

'And go back home,' said the man, 'go from Paris without having seen the most remarkable thing, the real wonder of the present time, called into being by the talent and will of a single man!'

'I shall not go down there,' was the answer.

'The wonder of the present age,' they said. The Dryad heard and understood it; the goal of her greatest longing was reached, and here was the entrance, down in the depths under Paris; she had not thought of this, but when she heard it now, and saw the foreigners going down, she followed them. The spiral staircase was of cast iron, broad and commodious. A lamp gleamed down there, and another one still farther down.

They stood in a labyrinth of endlessly long intersecting halls and arched passages; all the streets and lanes of Paris were to be seen here, as in a dim mirror, the names could be read, every house above had its number here, its root, which struck down under the empty, macadamised footway, which ran along by a broad canal with a stream of rolling mud. Higher up, along the arches, was led the fresh running water, and above all hung, like a net, gas-pipes and telegraph wires. Lamps shone in the distance, like reflected images from the metropolis above. Now and then was heard a noisy rumbling overhead; it was the heavy wagons which drove over the bridges above.

Where was the Dryad?

You have heard of the catacombs; they are but the faintest of outlines compared to this new subterranean world, the wonder of the present day, the drains of Paris. Here stood the Dryad and not out in the world's exhibition on the Field of Mars. She heard exclamations of astonishment, admiration and appreciation.

'From down here,' they said, 'health and years of life are growing for thousands and thousands up above! Our time is the time of progress with all its blessings.'

That was the opinion and the talk of the people, but not of the creatures who lived and dwelt and had been born here, the rats; they squeaked from the rifts in a piece of old wall, so clearly, distinctly and intelligibly to the Dryad.

A big old he-rat, with his tail bitten off, piercingly squeaked his feelings, his discomfort, and his honest opinion, and the family gave him support for every word.

'I am disgusted with this nonsense, this human nonsense, this ignorant talk! Oh yes, it is very fine here now with gas and petroleum! I don't eat that kind of thing! It has become so fine and bright here that one is ashamed of oneself, and does not know why. If we only lived in the time of tallow-candles! it isn't so far back either! That was a romantic time, as they call it!'

'What is that you are talking about?' said the Dryad. 'I did not see you before. What are you talking about?'

'The good old days,' said the rat, 'the happy days of great-grandfather and great-grandmother rats! In those days it was something to come down here. It was a rat's nest different from the whole of Paris! Mother Plague lived down here; she killed people, but never rats. Robbers and smugglers breathed freely down here. Here was the place of refuge for the most interesting personages, who are now only seen in melodramas in the theatre up above. The time of romance is gone in our rat's nest too; we have got fresh air and petroleum down here.'

So squeaked the rat! squeaked against the new times in favour of the old days with Mother Plague.

A carriage stood there, a kind of open omnibus with swift, little horses; the party got into it, and rushed along the Boulevard Sebastopol, the subterranean one: right above stretched the well-known Parisian one full of people.

The carriage disappeared in the dim light; the Dryad also vanished, rose up into the gaslight and the fresh free air; there, and not down in the crossing arches and their suffocating air, could the wonder be found, the Wonder of the World, that which she sought in her short night of life; it must shine stronger than all the gaslights up here, stronger than the moon which now glided forth. Yes, certainly! and she saw it yonder, it beamed before her, it twinkled and glittered like the star of Venus in the sky.

She saw a shining gate, opening into a little garden, full of light and dancing melodies. Gas-jets shone here as borders round little quiet lakes and pools, where artificial water plants, cut out of tin-plate bent and painted, glittered in the light, and threw jets of water yard-high out of their chalices. Beautiful weeping-willows, real weeping-willows of the spring-time, drooped their fresh branches like a green transparent yet concealing veil.

Here, amongst the bushes, blazed a bonfire; its red glow shone over small, half-dark, silent arbours, permeated with tones, with a music thrilling to the ear, captivating, alluring, chasing the blood through the veins.

She saw young women, beautiful in festal attire, with trusting smiles, and the light laughing spirit of youth, a 'Marie', with a rose in the hair, but without carriage and footmen. How they floated, how they whirled in the wild dance! As if bitten by the Tarantella, they sprang and laughed and smiled, blissfully happy, ready to embrace the whole world.

The Dryad felt herself carried away in the dance. About her slender little foot fitted the silken shoe, chestnut-brown, like the ribbon which floated from her hair over her uncovered shoulders. The green silk garment waved in great folds, but did not conceal the beautifully formed limb with the pretty foot, which seemed as if it wished to describe magic circles in the air. Was she in the enchanted garden of Armida? What was the place called? The name shone outside in gas-jets,

Mabille

Sounds of music and clapping of hands, rockets, and murmuring water, popping of champagne corks mingled here. The dance was wildly bacchanalian, and over the whole sailed the moon, with a rather wry face, no doubt. The sky was cloudless, clear and serene; it seemed as if one could see straight into Heaven from 'Mabille'.

A consuming desire of life thrilled through the Dryad; it was like an opium trance.

Her eyes spoke, her lips spoke, but the words were not heard for the sound of flutes and violins. Her partner whispered words in her ear, they trembled in time to the music of the can-can; she did not understand them, we do not understand them either. He stretched his arms out towards her and about her, and only embraced the transparent, gas-filled air.

The Dryad was carried away by the stream of air, as the wind bears a rose-leaf. On high before her she saw a flame, a flashing light, high up on a tower. The light shone from the goal of her longing, from the red lighthouse on the 'Fata Morgana' of the Field of Mars. She fluttered about the tower; the workmen thought it was a butterfly which they saw dropping down to die in its all too early arrival.

The moon shone, gaslights and lamps shone in the great halls and in the scattered buildings of all lands, shone over the undulating greensward, and the rocks made by the ingenuity of men, where the waterfall poured down by the strength of 'Mr Bloodless'. The depths of the ocean and of the fresh water, the realms of the fishes were opened here; one was at the bottom of the deep pool, one was down in the ocean, in a diving-bell. The water pressed against the thick glass walls above and around. The polypi, fathom-long, flexible, winding, quivering, living arms, clutched, heaved, and grew fast to the bottom of the sea.

A great flounder lay thoughtfully close by, stretched itself out in comfort and ease: the crab crawled like an enormous spider over it, whilst shrimps darted about with a haste, a swiftness, as if they were the moths and butterflies of the sea.

In the fresh water grew water-lilies, sedges, and rushes. The gold-fishes had placed themselves in rows, like red cows in the field, all with the heads in the same direction, so as to get the current in their mouths. Thick fat tench stared with stupid eyes towards the glass walls; they knew that they were at the Paris Exhibition; they knew that they had made the somewhat difficult journey hither, in barrels filled with water, and had been land-sick on the railway, just as people are seasick on the sea. They had come to see the Exhibition, and so they saw it from their own fresh or salt water box, saw the throng of men which moved past from morning to night. All the countries of the world had sent and exhibited their natives, so that the old tench and bream, the nimble perch and the moss-grown carp should see these beings and give their opinions upon the species.

'They are shellfish!' said a muddy little bleak. 'They change their shells two or three times in the day, and make sounds with their mouths – talking, they call it. We don't change, and we make ourselves understood in an easier way; movements with the corners of the mouth, and a stare with the eyes! We have many points of superiority over mankind!'

'They have learnt swimming, though,' said a little freshwater fish. 'I am from the big lake; men go into the water in the hot season there, but first they put off their shells, and then they swim. The frogs have taught them that, they push with the hind-legs, and paddle with the forelegs; they can't keep it up long. They would like to imitate us, but they don't get near it. Poor men!'

And the fishes stared; they imagined that the whole crowd of people they had seen in the strong daylight was still moving here; yes, they were convinced that they still saw the same forms which, so to speak, first struck their nerves of apprehension.

A little perch, with beautifully striped skin, and an enviable round back, asserted that the 'human mud' was there still; he saw it.

'I also see it; it is so distinct!' said a jaundice-yellow tench. 'I see plainly the beautiful well-shaped human figure, "high-legged lady" or whatever it was they called her; she had our mouth and staring eyes, two balloons behind, and an umbrella let down in front, a great quantity of hanging duckweed dingling and dangling. She should put it all off, go like us in the guise of nature, and she would look like a respectable tench, as far as human beings can do so!'

'What became of him – he on the string, the male – they dragged?'

'He rode in a bath-chair, sat with paper, pen and ink, and wrote everything down. What was he doing? They called him a reporter.'

'He is riding about there still,' said a moss-grown maiden carp, with the trials of the world in her throat, so that she was hoarse with it; she had once swallowed a fish-hook, and still swam patiently about with it in her throat.

'A reporter,' she said, 'that is, speaking plainly and fishily, a kind of cuttlefish among men.'

So the fishes talked in their own manner. But in the midst of the artificial grotto sounded the blows of hammers and the songs of the work-people; they must work at night, so that everything might be finished as soon as possible. They sang in the Dryad's summer night's dream, she herself stood there, ready to fly and vanish.

'They are goldfish!' said she, and nodded to them. 'So I have managed to see you after all! I know you! I have known you a long time! The swallow has told me about you in my home country. How pretty you are, how glittering and charming! I could kiss each and all of you! I know the others also! That is certainly the fat tench; that one there, the dainty bream; and here, the old moss-grown carp! I know you! but you don't know me!'

The fish stared and did not understand a single word; they stared out into the dim light. The Dryad was there no longer, she stood out in the open air, where the world's 'wonder-blossoms' from the different countries gave out their fragrance, from the land of rye-bread, from the coast of the stock-fish, the empire of russia leather, the river-banks of Eau-de-Cologne, and from the eastern land of the essence of roses.

When, after a ball, we drive home, half-asleep, the tunes we have heard still sound distinctly in our ears; we could sing each and all of them. And as in the eye of a murdered man, the last thing the glance rested on is said to remain photographed on it for a time, so here in the night the bustle and glare of the day was not extinguished. The Dryad felt it and knew that it would roll on in the same way through the coming day. The Dryad stood amongst the fragrant roses, thinking that she recognised them from her home, roses from the park of the castle and from the priest's garden. She also saw the red pomegranate flower here; Marie had worn one like it in her coal-black hair.

Memories from the home of her childhood out in the country flashed through her mind; she drank in the sights round about her with greedy eyes, whilst feverish restlessness possessed her, and carried her through the wonderful halls.

She felt tired, and this tiredness increased. She had a longing to rest upon the soft Eastern cushions and carpets spread around, or to lean against the weeping-willow down by the clear water, and plunge herself into that.

But the Ephemera has no rest. The day was only a few minutes from the end.

Her thoughts trembled, her limbs trembled, she sank down on the grass, by the rippling water.

'Thou springest from the earth with lasting life!' said she; 'cool my tongue, give me refreshment!'

'I am not the living fountain!' answered the water. 'I flow by machinery!'

'Give me of thy freshness, thou green grass,' begged the Dryad. 'Give me one of the fragrant flowers!'

'We die when we are broken off!' answered the grass and flowers.

'Kiss me, thou fresh breeze! only one single kiss of life!'

'Soon the sun will kiss the clouds red!' said the wind, 'and then wilt thou be amongst the dead, passed away, as all the splendour here will pass away, before the year is gone, and I can again play with the light, loose sand in the square here, and blow the dust along over the ground, dust in the air, dust! all dust!'

The Dryad felt a dread, like that of the woman who in the bath has cut an artery and is bleeding to death, but while bleeding wishes still to live. She raised herself, came some steps forward, and again sank down in front of a little church. The door stood open, candles burned on the altar, and the organ pealed.

What music! such tones the Dryad had never heard, and yet she seemed to hear in them well-known voices. They came from the depths of the heart of the whole creation. She thought she heard the rustling of the old oak tree, she thought she heard the old priest talking about great deeds, and about famous names, and of what God's creatures had power to give as a gift to future times, and must give it in order to win, by that means, eternal life for itself.

The tones of the organ swelled and pealed, and spoke in song: 'Thy longing and desire uprooted thee from thy God-given place. It became thy ruin, poor Dryad!'

The organ tones, soft and mild, sounded as if weeping, dying away in tears.

The clouds shone red in the sky. The wind whistled and sang, 'Pass away, ye Dead, the sun is rising!'

The first beam fell on the Dryad. Her form shone in changing colours, like the soap-bubble when it breaks, vanishes and becomes a drop, a tear which falls to the ground and disappears.

Poor Dryad! a dewdrop, only a tear, shed, vanished!

The sun shone over the 'Fata Morgana' on the Field of Mars, shone over the Great Paris, over the little square with the trees and the splashing fountain, amongst the tall houses, where the chestnut tree stood, but with drooping branches, withered leaves, the tree which only yesterday lifted itself as fresh and full of life as the spring itself. Now it was dead, they said. The Dryad had gone, passed away like the cloud, no one knew whither.

There lay on the ground a withered, broken chestnut flower; the holy water of the Church had no power to call it to life. The foot of man soon trod it down into the dust.

The whole of this actually happened, we saw it ourselves at the Paris Exhibition in 1867, in our own time, in the great, wonderful, time of fairy-tale.

Poultry Meg's Family

POULTRY MEG was the only human occupant in the handsome new house which was built for the fowls and ducks on the estate. It stood where the old baronial mansion had stood, with its tower, crow-step gable, moat, and drawbridge. Close by was a wilderness of trees and bushes; the garden had been here and had stretched down to a big lake, which was now a bog. Rooks, crows, and jackdaws flew screaming and cawing over the old trees, a perfect swarm of birds. They did not seem to decrease, but rather to increase, although one shot amongst them. One could hear them inside the poultry-house, where Poultry Meg sat with the ducklings running about over her wooden shoes. She knew every fowl, and every duck, from the time it crept out of the egg; she was proud of her fowls and ducks, and proud of the splendid house which had been built for them.

Her own little room was clean and neat, that was the wish of the lady to whom the poultry-house belonged; she often came there with distinguished guests and showed them the 'barracks of the hens and ducks', as she called it.

Here was both a wardrobe and an easy-chair, and even a chest of drawers, and on it was a brightly polished brass plate on which was engraved the word 'Grubbe', which was the name of the old, noble family who had lived here in the mansion. The brass plate was found when they were digging here, and the parish clerk had said that it had no other value except as an old relic. The clerk knew all about the place and the old time, for he had knowledge from books; there were so many manuscripts in his table-drawer. He had great knowledge of the old times; but the oldest of the crows knew more perhaps, and screamed about it in his own language, but it was crow-language, which the clerk did not understand, clever as he might be. The bog could steam after a warm summer day so that it seemed as if a lake lay behind the old trees, where the crows, rooks, and jackdaws flew; so it had appeared when the Knight Grubbe had lived here, and the old manor-house stood with its thick, red walls. The dog's chain used to reach quite past the gateway in those days; through the tower, one went into a stone-paved passage which led to the rooms; the windows were narrow and the panes small, even in the great hall, where the dancing took place, but in the time of the last Grubbe there was no dancing as far back as one could remember, and yet there lay there an old kettledrum which had served as part of the music. Here stood a curious carved cupboard, in which rare flower bulbs were kept, for Lady Grubbe was fond of gardening, and cultivated trees and plants; her husband preferred riding out to shoot wolves and wild boars, and his little daughter Marie always went with him. When she was only five years old, she sat proudly on her horse, and looked round bravely with her big black eyes. It was her delight to hit out with her whip amongst the hounds; her father would have preferred to see her hit out amongst the peasant boys who came to look at the company.

The peasant in the clay house close to the manor had a son called Sören, the same age as the little noble lady. He knew how to climb, and had always to go up and get the bird's nests for her. The birds screamed as loud as they could scream, and one of the biggest of them cut him over the eye, so that the blood poured out. It was thought at first that the eye had been destroyed; but it was very little damaged after all. Marie Grubbe called him *her* Sören – that was a great favour, and it was a good thing for his father, poor John; he had committed a fault one day, and was to be punished by riding the wooden horse. It stood in the yard, with four poles for legs, and a single narrow plank for a back; on this John had to ride astride, and have some heavy bricks fastened to his legs, so that he might not sit too comfortably; he made horrible grimaces, and Sören wept and implored little Marie to interfere; immediately she ordered that Sören's father should be taken down, and when they did not obey her she stamped on the stone pavement, and pulled her father's coat sleeve till it was torn. She would have her way, and she got it, and Sören's father was taken down.

The Lady Grubbe, who now came up, stroked her little daughter's hair, and looked at her affectionately; Marie did not understand why. She would go to the hounds, and not with her mother, who went into the garden, down to the lake, where the white and yellow water-lilies bloomed, and the bulrushes nodded amongst the reeds. She looked at all this luxuriance and freshness. 'How pleasant!' said she. There stood in the garden a rare tree which she herself had planted; it was called a 'copper-beech', a kind of blackamoor amongst the other trees, so dark brown were the leaves; it must have strong sunshine, otherwise in continual shade it would become green like the other trees and so lose its distinctive character. In the high chestnut trees were many birds' nests, as well as in the bushes and the grassy meadows. It seemed as if the birds knew that they were protected here, for here no one dared to fire a gun.

The little Marie came here with Sören; he could climb, as we know, and he fetched both eggs and young downy birds. The birds flew about in terror and anguish, little ones and big ones! Peewits from the field, rooks, crows, and jackdaws from the high trees, screamed and shrieked; it was a shriek exactly the same as their descendants shriek in our own day.

'What are you doing, children?' cried the gentle lady. 'This is ungodly work!'

Sören stood ashamed, and even the high-born little girl looked a little abashed, but then she said, shortly and sulkily, 'My father lets me do it!'

'Afar! afar!' screamed the great blackbirds, and flew off, but they came again next day, for their home was here.

But the quiet, gentle lady did not stay long at home here; our Lord called her to Himself, with Him she was more at home than in the mansion, and the church bells tolled solemnly when her body was carried to the church. Poor men's eyes were wet, for she had been good to them. When she was gone, no one cared for her plants, and the garden ran to waste.

Sir Grubbe was a hard man, they said, but his daughter, although she was so young, could manage him; he had to laugh, and she got her way. She was now twelve years old, and strongly built; she looked through and through people, with her big black eyes, rode her horse like a man, and shot her gun like a practised hunter.

One day there came great visitors to the neighbourhood, the very greatest, the young king and his half-brother and comrade Lord Ulrik Frederick Gyldenlöwe; they wanted to hunt the wild boar there, and would stay some days at Sir Grubbe's castle.

Gyldenlöwe sat next Marie at table; he took her round the neck and gave her a kiss, as if they had been relations, but she gave him a slap on the mouth and said that she could not bear him. At that there was great laughter, as if it was an amusing thing.

And it may have been amusing too, for five years after, when Marie had completed her seventeenth year, a messenger came with a letter; Lord Gyldenlöwe proposed for the hand of the noble lady; that was something!

'He is the grandest and most gallant gentleman in the kingdom!' said Sir Grubbe. 'That is not to be despised.'

'I don't care much about him!' said Marie Grubbe, but she did not reject the grandest man in the country, who sat by the king's side.

Silver plate, woollen and linen went with a ship to Copenhagen; she travelled overland in ten days. The outfit had contrary winds, or no wind at all; four months passed before it arrived, and when it did come Lady Gyldenlöwe had departed.

'I would rather lie on coarse sacking, than in his silken bed!' said she; 'I'd rather walk on my bare feet than drive with him in a carriage!'

Late one evening in November, two women came riding into the town of Aarhus; it was Lady Gyldenlöwe and her maid: they came from Veile, where they had arrived from Copenhagen by ship. They rode up to Sir Grubbe's stone mansion. He was not delighted with the visit. She got hard words, but she got a bedroom as well; got nice food for breakfast, but not nice words, for the evil in her father was roused against her, and she was not accustomed to that. She was not of a gentle temper, and as one is spoken to, so one answers. She certainly did answer, and spoke with bitterness and hate about her husband, with whom she would not live; she was too honourable for that.

So a year went past, but it did not pass pleasantly. There were evil words between father and daughter, and that there should never be. Evil words have evil fruit. What could be the end of this?

'We two cannot remain under the same roof,' said the father one day. 'Go away from here to our old manor-house, but rather bite your tongue out than set lies going!'

So these two separated; she went with her maid to the old manor-house, where she had been born and brought up, and where the gentle pious lady, her mother, lay in the church vault; an old cowherd lived in the house, and that was the whole establishment. Cobwebs hung in the rooms, dark and heavy with dust; in the garden everything was growing wild. Hops and other climbing plants twisted a net between the trees and bushes; and hemlock and nettles grew larger and stronger. The copper beech was overgrown by the others and now stood in shade, its leaves were now as green as the other common trees, and its glory had departed. Rooks, crows, and daws flew in thick swarms over the high chestnut trees, and there was a cawing and screaming, as if they had some important news to tell each other: now she is here again, the little one who had caused their eggs and their young ones to be stolen from them. The thief himself, who had fetched them, now climbed on a leafless tree, sat on the high mast, and got good blows from the rope's end if he did not behave himself.

The clerk told all this in our own time; he had collected it and put it together from books and manuscripts; it lay with many more manuscripts in the table-drawer.

'Up and down is the way of the world!' said he, 'it is strange to hear!' And we shall hear how it went with Marie Grubbe, but we will not forget Poultry Meg, who sits in her grand hen-house in our time; Marie Grubbe sat there in her time, but not with the same spirit as old Poultry Meg.

The winter passed, spring and summer passed, and then again came the stormy autumn-time, with the cold, wet sea-fogs. It was a lonely life, a wearisome life there in the old manor-house. So Marie Grubbe took her gun and went out on the moors, and shot hares and foxes, and whatever birds she came across. Out there she met oftener than once noble Sir Palle Dyre from Nörrebaek, who was also wandering about with his gun and his dogs. He was big and strong, and boasted about it when they talked together. He could have dared to measure himself with the late Mr Brockenhus of Egeskov, of whose strength there were still stories. Palle Dyre had, following his example, caused an iron chain with a hunting-horn to be hung at his gate, and when he rode home he caught the chain, and lifted himself with the horse from the ground, and blew the horn.

'Come yourself and see it, Dame Marie!' said he, 'there is fresh air blowing at Nörrebaek!'

When she went to his house is not recorded, but on the candlesticks in Nörrebaek Church one can read that they were given by Palle Dyre and Marie Grubbe of Nörrebaek Castle.

Bodily strength had Palle Dyre: he drank like a sponge; he was like a tub that could never be filled; he snored like a whole pigsty, and he looked red and bloated.

'He is piggish and rude!' said Dame Palle Dyre, Grubbe's daughter. Soon she was tired of the life, but that did not make it any better. One day the table was laid, and the food was getting cold; Palle Dyre was fox-hunting and the lady was not to be found. Palle Dyre came home at midnight, Dame Dyre came neither at midnight nor in the morning, she had turned her back on Nörrebaek had ridden away without greeting or farewell.

It was grey wet weather; the wind blew cold, and a flock of black screaming birds flew over her, they were not so homeless as she.

First she went south, quite up to Germany; a couple of gold rings with precious stones were turned into money; then she went east, and then turned again to the west; she had no goal before her eyes, and was angry with everyone, even with the good God Himself, so wretched was her mind; soon her whole body became wretched too, and she could scarcely put one foot before another. The peewit flew up from its tussock when she fell over it: the bird screamed as it always does, 'You thief! You thief!' She had never stolen her neighbour's goods, but birds' eggs and young birds she had had brought to her when she was a little girl; she thought of that now.

From where she lay she could see the sand-hills by the shore;

fishermen lived there, but she could not get so far, she was so ill. The great white sea-mews came flying above her and screamed as the rooks and crows screamed over the garden at home. The birds flew very near her, and at last she imagined that they were coal-black, but then it became night before her eyes. When she again opened her eyes she was being carried; a big, strong fellow had taken her in his arms. She looked straight into his bearded face; he had a scar over his eye, so that the eyebrow appeared to be divided in two. He carried her, miserable as she was, to the ship, where he got a rating from the captain for it.

The day following, the ship sailed; Marie Grubbe was not put ashore, so she went with it. But she came back again, no doubt? Yes, but when and where?

The clerk could also tell about this, and it was not a story which he himself had put together. He had the whole strange story from a trustworthy old book; we ourselves can take it out and read it.

The Danish historian, Ludwig Holberg, who has written so many useful books and the amusing comedies from which we can get to know his time and people, tells in his letters of Marie Grubbe, where and how he met her; it is well worth hearing about, but we will not forget Poultry Meg, who sits so glad and comfortable in her grand hen-house.

The ship sailed away with Marie Grubbe; it was there we left off.

Years and years went past.

The plague was raging in Copenhagen; it was in the year 1711. The Queen of Denmark went away to her German home, the king quitted the capital, everyone who could, hastened away. The students, even if they had board and lodging free, left the city. One of them, the last who still remained at the so-called Borch's College, close by Regensen, also went away. It was two o'clock in the morning; he came with his knapsack, which was filled more with books and manuscripts than with clothes. A damp, clammy mist hung over the town; not a creature was to be seen in the whole street; round about on the doors and gates crosses were marked to show that the plague was inside, or that the people were dead. No one was to be seen either in the broader, winding Butcher's Row, as the street was called which led from the Round Tower to the King's Castle. A big ammunition wagon rumbled past; the driver swung his whip and the horses went off at a gallop, the wagon was full of dead bodies. The young student held his hand before his face, and smelt at some strong spirits which he had on a sponge in a brass box.

From a tavern in one of the streets came the sound of singing and unpleasant laughter, from people who drank the night through, to forget that the plague stood before the door and would have them to accompany him in the wagon with the other corpses. The student turned his steps towards the castle bridge, where one or two small ships lay; one of them was weighing anchor to get away from the plague-stricken city.

'If God spares our lives and we get wind for it, we are going to Grönsund in Falster,' said the skipper, and asked the name of the student who wished to go with him.

'Ludwig Holberg,' said the student, and the name sounded like any other name; now the sound is one of the proudest names in Denmark; at that time he was only a young, unknown student.

The ship glided past the castle. It was not yet clear morning when they came out into the open water. A light breeze came along, and the sails swelled, the young student set himself with his face to the wind, and fell asleep, and that was not quite the wisest thing to do. Already on the third morning the ship lay off Falster.

'Do you know anyone in this place, with whom I could live cheaply?' Holberg asked the captain.

'I believe that you would do well to go to the ferry-woman in Borrehouse,' said he. 'If you want to be very polite, her name is Mother Sören Sörensen Möller! yet it may happen that she will fly into a rage if you are too polite to her! Her husband is in custody for a crime; she herself manages the ferry-boat, she has fists of her own!'

The student took his knapsack and went to the ferry-house. The door was not locked, he lifted the latch, and went into a room with a brick-laid floor, where a bench with a big leather coverlet was the chief article of furniture. A white hen with chickens was fastened to the bench, and had upset the water-dish, and the water had run across the floor. No one was here, or in the next room, only a cradle with a child in it. The ferry-boat came back with only one person in it, whether man or woman was not easy to say. The person was wrapped in a great cloak, and wore a fur cap like a hood on the head. The boat lay to.

It was a woman who got out and came into the room. She looked very imposing when she straightened her back; two proud eyes sat under the black eyebrows. It was Mother Sören, the ferry-woman; rooks, crows, and daws would scream out another name which we know better.

She looked morose, and did not seem to care to talk, but so much was said and settled, that the student arranged for board and lodging for an indefinite time, whilst things were so bad in Copenhagen. One or other honest citizen from the neighbouring town came regularly out to the ferry-house. Frank the cutler and Sivert the excise-man came there; they drank a glass of ale and talked with the student. He was a clever young man, who knew his 'Practica', as they called it; he read Greek and Latin, and was well up in learned subjects.

'The less one knows, the less one is burdened with it,' said Mother Sören.

'You have to work hard!' said Holberg, one day when she soaked her clothes in the sharp lye, and herself chopped the tree-roots for firewood.

'That's my affair!' said she.

'Have you always from childhood been obliged to work and toil?'

'You can see that in my hands!' said she, and showed him two small but strong, hard hands with bitten nails. 'You have learning and can read.'

At Christmas it began to snow heavily. The cold came on, the wind blew sharply, as if it had vitriol to wash people's faces with. Mother Sören did not let that disturb her. She drew her cloak around her, and pulled her hood down over her head. It was dark in the house, early in the afternoon. She laid wood and turf on the fire, and set herself down to darn her stockings, there was no one else to do it. Towards evening she talked more to the student than was her custom. She spoke about her husband.

'He has by accident killed a skipper of Dragör, and for that he must work three years in irons. He is only a common sailor, and so the law must take its course.'

'The law applies also to people of higher position,' said Holberg.

'Do you think so?' said Mother Sören, and looked into the fire, but then she began again, 'Have you heard of Kai Lykke, who caused one of his churches to be pulled down, and when the priest thundered from the pulpit about it, he caused the priest to be laid in irons, appointed a court, and adjudged him to have forfeited his head, which was accordingly struck off; that was not an accident, and yet Kai Lykke went free that time!'

'He was in the right according to the times!' said Holberg, 'now we are past that!'

'You can try to make fools believe that,' said Mother Sören as she rose and went into the room where the child lay, eased it and laid it down again, and then arranged the student's bed; he had the leather covering, for he felt the cold more than she did, and yet he had been born in Norway.

On New Year's morning it was a real bright sunshiny day; the frost had been and still was so strong that the drifted snow lay frozen hard, so that one could walk upon it. The bells in the town rang for church, and the student Holberg took his woollen cloak about him and would go to the town.

Over the ferry-house the crows and rooks were flying with loud cries, one could scarcely hear the church bells for their noise. Mother Sören stood outside, filling a brass kettle with snow, which she was going to put on the fire to get drinking-water. She looked up to the swarm of birds, and had her own thoughts about it.

The student Holberg went to church; on the way there and back he passed Sivert the tax-collector's house, by the town gate; there he was invited in for a glass of warm ale with syrup and ginger. The conversation turned on Mother Sören, but the tax-collector did not know much about her – indeed, few people did. She did not belong to

Falster, he said; she had possessed a little property at one time; her husband was a common sailor with a violent temper, who had murdered a skipper of Dragör. 'He beats his wife, and yet she takes his part.'

'I could not stand such treatment!' said the tax-collector's wife. 'I am also come of better people; my father was stocking-weaver to the Court!'

'Consequently you have married a Government official,' said Holberg, and made a bow to her and the tax-collector.

It was Twelfth Night, the evening of the festival of the Three Kings. Mother Sören lighted for Holberg a three-king candle – that is to say, a tallow-candle with three branches, which she herself had dipped.

'A candle for each man!' said Holberg.

'Each man?' said the woman, and looked sharply at him.

'Each of the wise men from the east!' said Holberg.

'That way!' said she, and was silent for a long time. But on the evening of the Three Kings he learned more about her than he did before.

'You have an affectionate mind to your husband,' said Holberg, 'and yet people say that he treats you badly.'

'That is no one's business but mine!' she answered. 'The blows could have done me good as a child; now I get them for my sin's sake! I know what good he has done me,' and she rose up. 'When I lay ill on the open heath, and no one cared to come in contact with me, except perhaps the crows and the rooks to peck at me, he carried me in his arms and got hard words for the catch he brought on board. I am not used to be ill, and so I recovered. Everyone has his own way, Sören has his, and one should not judge a horse by the halter! With him I have lived more comfortably than with the one they called the most gallant and noble of all the king's subjects. I have been married to the Stadtholder Gyldenlöwe, the half-brother of the king; later on I took Palle Dyre! Right or wrong, each has his own way, and I have mine. That was a long story, but now you know it!' And she went out of the room.

It was Marie Grubbe! so strange had been the rolling ball of her fortune. She did not live to see many more anniversaries of the festival of the Three Kings; Holberg has recorded that she died in 1716, but he has not recorded, for he did not know it, that when Mother Sören, as she was called, lay a corpse in the ferry-house, a number of big blackbirds flew over the place. They did not scream, as if they knew that silence belonged to a burial. As soon as she was laid in the earth the birds disappeared, but the same evening over at the old manor in Jutland an enormous number of crows and rooks were seen; they all screamed as loud as they could, as if they had something to announce, perhaps about him who as a little boy took their eggs and young ones, the farmer's son who had to wear a garter of iron, and the noble lady who ended her life as a ferry-woman at Grönsund.

'Brave! brave!' they screamed.

And the whole family screamed 'Brave! brave!' when the old manor-house was pulled down. 'They still cry, and there is no more to cry about!' said the clerk, when he told the story. 'The family is extinct, the house pulled down, and where it stood, now stands the grand hen-house with the gilded weathercock and with old Poultry Meg. She is so delighted with her charming dwelling; if she had not come here, she would have been in the workhouse.'

The pigeons cooed over her, the turkeys gobbled round about her, and the ducks quacked.

'No one knew her!' they said. 'She has no relations. It is an act of grace that she is here. She has neither a drake father nor a hen mother, and no descendants!'

Still she had relations, although she did not know it, nor the clerk either, however much manuscript he had in the table-drawer, but one of the old crows knew about it, and told about it. From its mother and grandmother it had heard about Poultry Meg's mother and her grandmother, whom we also know from the time she was a child and rode over the bridge looking about her proudly, as if the whole world and its birds' nests belonged to her; we saw her out on the heath by the sand-dunes, and last of all in the ferry-house. The grandchild, the last of the race, had come home again where the old house had stood, where the wild birds screamed, but she sat among the tame birds, known by them and known along with them. Poultry Meg had no more to wish for, she was glad to die, and old enough to die.

'Grave! grave!' screamed the crows.

And Poultry Meg got a good grave, which no one knew except the old crow, if he is not dead also.

And now we know the story of the old manor, the old race, and the whole of Poultry Meg's family.

The Thistle's Experiences

BESIDE the lordly manor-house lay a lovely, well-kept garden with rare trees and flowers; the guests of the house expressed their admiration of it; the people of the district, from town and country, came on Sundays and holidays and begged permission to see the garden, even whole schools came to visit it.

Outside the garden, close to the palings beside the field-path, stood a huge thistle; it was very big and spread from the root in several branches, so that it might be called a thistle bush. No one looked at it except the old ass which drew the milk-cart. It stretched out its neck to the thistle, and said, 'You are lovely! I could eat you!' but the halter was not long enough for the ass to get near enough to eat it.

There was a great deal of company at the manor-house – some very noble people from the capital, young pretty girls, and amongst them a young lady who came from a distance; she came from Scotland, was of high birth, rich in lands and gold, a bride worth winning, more than one young gentleman said, and their mothers said the same thing.

The young people amused themselves on the lawn and played croquet; they walked about amongst the flowers, and each of the young girls picked a flower and put it in the buttonhole of one of the young gentlemen. But the young Scottish lady looked round for a long time, rejecting one after the other; none of the flowers seemed to please her; then she looked over the paling, outside stood the great thistle bush with its strong, purple flowers; she saw it, she smiled and begged the son of the house to pick one of them for her.

'It is the flower of Scotland!' said she, 'it blooms in the scutcheon of the country, give it to me!'

And he brought her the most beautiful of the thistles, and pricked his fingers, as if it were the most prickly rose bush that it grew on.

She fastened the thistle-flower in the buttonhole of the young man, and he felt himself highly honoured. Each of the other young men would willingly have given his own beautiful flower to have worn the one given by the Scottish girl's fair hand. And if the son of the house felt himself honoured, what did not the thistle bush feel? It seemed as if the dew and the sunshine were going through it.

'I am something more than I thought!' it said to itself. 'I really belong inside the paling and not outside! One is strangely placed in the world! but now I have one of mine over the paling, and even in a buttonhole!'

Every bud which came forth and unfolded was told of this event, and not many days went past before the thistle bush heard, not from people, nor from the twittering of the birds, but from the air itself, which preserves and carries sound, from the most retired walks of the garden and the rooms of the house, where the doors and windows stood open, that the young gentleman who got the thistle-flower from the fair Scottish girl's hand, had now got her hand and heart as well. They were a handsome pair – it was a good match.

'I have brought that about!' thought the thistle bush, and thought of the flower it had given for a buttonhole. Each flower that opened heard of this occurrence.

'I shall certainly be planted in the garden!' thought the thistle; 'perhaps put in a pot which pinches: that is the greatest honour of all!'

And the thistle thought of this so strongly that it said with full conviction, 'I shall be put in a pot!'

It promised every little thistle-flower which opened that it also should be put in a pot, perhaps in a buttonhole – the highest honour that was to be attained; but none of them was put in a pot, to say nothing of a buttonhole; they drank in the air and the light, licked the sunshine by day and the dew by night, bloomed, were visited by bees and hornets which searched for the dowry, the honey in the flowers, and they took the honey and left the flower standing. 'The thieving pack!' said the thistle, 'if I could only stab them! But I cannot!'

The flowers hung their heads and faded, but new ones came again.

'You come in good time!' said the thistle, 'every minute I expect to get across the fence.'

A few innocent daisies and narrow-leaved plantains stood and listened with deep admiration, and believed everything that was said.

The old ass of the milk-cart looked along from the wayside to the thistle bush, but the halter was too short to reach it.

And the thistle thought so long of the Scottish thistle to whose family it thought it belonged, that at last it believed it came from Scotland and that its parents had been put into the national scutcheon. It was a great thought, but great thistles can have great thoughts!

'One is often of such a noble family, that one dare not know it!' said the nettle, which grew close by; it also had an idea that it might turn into nettle-cloth if it were properly handled. And the summer passed and the autumn passed; the leaves fell off the trees, the flowers got strong colours and less scent. The gardener's apprentice sang in the garden, across the fence:

> 'Up the hill and down the hill,
> That is all the story still.'

The young fir trees in the wood began to long for Christmas, but it was a long time to Christmas.

'Here I stand still!' said the thistle. 'It seems as if no one thought about me, and yet *I* have made the match; they were betrothed, and they held their wedding eight days ago. I won't take a step, for I cannot.'

Some more weeks went past; the thistle stood with its last single flower, big and full, it had shot up close by the root. The wind blew cold over it, the colours went, the splendour vanished, the calyx of the flower, big as that of an artichoke bloom, looked like a silver sunflower. Then the young couple, now man and wife, came into the garden; they went along by the paling, and the young wife looked across it.

'There stands the big thistle yet!' said she; 'now it has no more flowers!'

'Yes, there is the ghost of the last one!' said he, and pointed to the silvery remains of the flower, itself a flower.

'It is lovely!' said she, 'such a one must be carved round about the frame of our picture!'

And the young man had to climb the paling again to break off the calyx of the thistle. It pricked him in the fingers, he had called it a 'ghost'. And it came into the garden, into the house, and into the drawing-room; there stood a picture – 'the young couple'. In the bridegroom's buttonhole was painted a thistle. They talked about this and about the thistle-flower they brought, the last thistle-flower now gleaming like silver, a copy of which was to be carved on the frame.

And the breeze carried what was said, away, far away.

'What one can experience!' said the thistle bush. 'My firstborn was put in a buttonhole, my last in a frame! Where shall *I* go?'

And the ass stood by the roadside and looked long at the thistle.

'Come to me, my kitchen-love! I cannot come to you, the halter is not long enough!'

But the thistle did not answer; it became more and more thoughtful; it thought, and it thought, right up to Christmas-time, and then the thought came into flower:

'If one's children have got inside, a mother can be content to stand outside the fence!'

'That is an honourable thought!' said the sunbeam. 'You shall also get a good place!'

'In a pot or in a frame?' asked the thistle.

'In a story!' said the sunbeam. And here it is!

What One Can Invent

THERE WAS once a young man who was studying to be a poet. He wanted to become one by Easter, to marry, and to live by poetry. To write poems, he knew, was only to invent something, but he could not invent anything. He had been born too late, everything had been taken up before he came into the world, everything had been written and told about.

'Happy people who were born thousands of years ago!' said he. 'They could easily become immortal! Happy even, those who were born hundreds of years ago, for then there was still something to make a poem about; how the world is written out, and what can I write poetry about?'

He worried about that till he became sick and ill. Wretched man! no doctor could help him, but perhaps the wise woman could! She lived in the little house beside the field gate, which she opened for those riding and driving: she could open up more than the gate, she was wiser than the doctor, who drives in his own carriage and pays taxes for his rank.

'I must go out to her!' said the young man. The house she lived in was small and neat, but dreary to behold; there was neither tree nor flower; a beehive, which was very useful, stood outside the door; there was a small potato patch, also very useful; and a ditch with sloe bushes which had flowered and now bore berries, which draw the mouth together if one tastes them before they have got frost.

'That is a true picture of our unpoetic time, I see here!' thought the young man, and it was always a thought, a grain of gold, that he found by the wise woman's door.

'Write it down!' said she. 'Crumbs are also bread! I know why you come here; you cannot invent anything, and yet you want to be a poet by Easter!'

'Everything has been written down!' said he; 'our time is not the old time!'

'No!' said the woman, 'in olden times the wise women were burned, and poets went about with empty stomachs and holes in their elbows. The time is good, it is the very best! but you have not the right outlook on the thing. You have not sharpened your hearing, and you do not say the Lord's Prayer at night. There is quite a lot of all kinds of things to write poems about and tell of, if one *can* tell. You can glean it from the plants and fruits of the earth, draw it from the running and the still waters, but you must understand it, understand how to catch a sun-beam. Now try my spectacles, put my ear-trumpet in your ear, pray to our Father, and leave off thinking of yourself!'

The last thing was very difficult, more than a wise woman ought to ask.

He got the spectacles and the ear-trumpet and was placed in the middle of the potato-patch; she gave him a big potato in his hand; sounds came from it; there came a song with words, the story of the potato, interesting – an everyday story in ten parts; ten lines were enough. And what did the potato sing?

It sang about itself and its family; the coming of the potatoes to Europe, the misjudgement they had experienced and suffered, before they stood acknowledged as a greater blessing than a lump of gold.

'We were distributed by royal command from the council-houses in all towns; notification of our great importance was given, but people did not believe in it, and did not even understand how to plant us. One dug a hole and threw the whole of his bushel of potatoes into it; another stuck one potato here, one there, in the earth and expected that they would each shoot up a perfect tree, from which one could shake potatoes. There came growth, flowers, and watery fruit, but it all withered away. No one thought of what lay at the root, the blessing, the potatoes.

'Yes, we have experienced and suffered – that is to say, our ancestors, they and we, it is all the same thing! What a story!'

'Yes, now that will do!' said the woman. 'Now look at the sloe bush!'

'We have also,' said the sloe, 'near relations in the home of the potatoes, farther north than they grow. Northmen came there from Norway; they steered west through fog and storms to an unknown land, where, behind ice and snow, they found plants and vegetables, bushes with blue-black grapes – the sloe-berries; the grapes were ripened by the frost, just as we are. And the country was called "wine-land", "green-land", "sloe-land"!'

'That is quite a romantic story!' said the young man.

'Yes. Now come with me!' said the wise woman, and led him to the beehive. He looked into it. What life and stir! Bees stood in all the passages and waved their wings, so that there might be fresh draughts of air in the whole factory: that was their business. Now came from outside, bees born with baskets on their legs; they brought pollendust, which was shaken out, sorted and made into honey and wax. They flew in and out. The queen-bee wanted to fly too, but they must all go with her; it was not yet time for that: but still she wished to fly; so they bit the wings off her Majesty, and so she had to remain.

'Now get up on the earth-bank!' said the woman, 'Come and look out over the highway, where people are to be seen!'

'What a crowd it is!' said the young man. 'Story after story! it whirls and whirls! I get quite confused. I shall fall backwards!'

'No, go forward,' said the woman, 'go right into the crowd, have an eye for it, an ear for it, and a heart as well! then you will soon invent something; but before you go, I must have my spectacles and my ear-trumpet,' and so saying she took them both.

'Now I can't see the least thing!' said the young man, 'now I hear nothing more!'

'Well, then, you can't become a poet before Easter,' said the wise woman.

'But when, then?' he asked.

'Neither by Easter, nor by Whitsuntide! You will not learn how to invent anything.'

'What shall I do, then, to earn my bread by poetry?'

'You can join in the Shrove-Tuesday sports, and knock the poets out of the barrel! To hit at their writings is as good as hitting themselves. Only don't let yourself be abashed; strike boldly, and so you will get dumplings with which you can feed both your wife and yourself.'

'What one can invent!' said the young man, and so he knocked down every other poet, because he could not be a poet himself.

We have it from the wise woman; she knows what one can invent.

Good Luck Can Lie in a Pin

NOW I shall tell a story about good luck. We all know good luck: some see it from year's end to year's end, others only at certain seasons, on a certain day; there are even people who only see it once in their lives, but see it we all do.

Now I need not tell you, for everyone knows it, that God sends the little child and lays it in a mother's lap, it may be in the rich castle, and in the well-to-do house, but it may also be in the open field where the cold wind blows. Everyone does not know, however, but it is true all the same, that God, when He brings the child, brings also a lucky gift for it: but it is not laid openly by its side; it is laid in some place in the world where one would least expect to find it, and yet it always *is* found: that is the best of it. It may be laid in an apple; it was so for a learned man who was called Newton: the apple fell, and so he found his good luck. If you do not know the story, then ask someone who knows it to tell it you. I have another story to tell, and that is a story about a pear.

Once upon a time there was a man who was born in poverty, had grown up in poverty, and in poverty he had married. He was a turner by trade and made, especially, umbrella handles and rings; but he only lived from hand to mouth. 'I never find good luck,' he said. This is a story that really happened, and one could name the country and the place where the man lived, but that doesn't matter.

The red, sour rowan-berries grew in richest profusion about his house and garden. In the garden there was also a pear tree, but it did not bear a single pear, and yet the good luck was laid in that pear tree, laid in the invisible pears.

One night the wind blew a terrible storm. They told in the newspapers that the big stage-coach was lifted off the road and thrown aside like a rag. It could very well happen then that a great branch was broken off the pear tree.

The branch was put into the workshop, and the man, as a joke, made a big pear out of it, and then another big one, then a smaller one, and then some very little ones. 'The tree must sometime or other have pears,' the man said, and he gave them to the children to play with.

One of the necessities of life in a wet country is an umbrella. The whole house had only one for common use; if the wind blew too strongly, the umbrella turned insideout; it also snapped two or three times, but the man soon put it right again. The most provoking thing, however, was that the button which held it together when it was down, too often jumped off, or the ring which was round it broke in two.

One day the button flew off; the man searched for it on the floor, and there got hold of one of the smallest of the wooden pears which the children had got to play with. 'The button is not to be found,' said the man, 'but this little thing will serve the same purpose.' So he bored a hole in it, pulled a string through it, and the little pear fitted very well into the broken ring. It was assuredly the very best fastener the umbrella had ever had.

Next year when the man was sending umbrella handles to the town, as he regularly did, he also sent some of the little wooden pears, and begged that they might be tried, and so they came to America. There they very soon noticed that the little pears held much better than any other button, and now they demanded of the merchant that all the umbrellas which were sent after that should be fastened with a little pear.

Now, there was something to do! Pears in thousands! Wooden pears on all umbrellas! The man must set to work. He turned and turned. The whole pear tree was cut up into little pears! It brought in pennies, it brought in shillings!

'My good luck was laid in the pear tree,' said the man. He now got a big workshop with workmen and boys. He was always in a good humour, and said, 'Good luck can lie in a pin!'

I also, who tell the story, say so. People have a saying, 'Take a white pin in your mouth and you will be invisible,' but it must be the right pin, the one which was given us as a lucky gift by our Lord. I got that, and I also, like the man, can catch chinking gold, gleaming gold, the very best, that kind which shines from children's eyes, the kind that sounds from children's mouths, and from father and mother too. They read the stories, and I stand among them in the middle of the room, but invisible, for I have the white pin in my mouth. If I see that they are delighted with what I tell them, then I also say, 'Good luck can lie in a pin!'

The Comet

THE COMET came, shone with its core of fire, and threatened with its rod; they looked at it from the rich palace, and the poor cottage; the crowd on the street looked at it, and the lonely one who went his way over the pathless heath; everyone had his thoughts about it.

'Come and look at the sign in the heavens! come and look at the splendid sight,' they said, and all hastened to look.

But in the room there sat a little boy with his mother; the tallow candle was burning, and the mother thought that there was a shroud in the candle; the tallow stood up in a point and curled over; that meant, she believed, that the little boy must soon die, the shroud turned towards him. It was an old superstition, and she believed it.

The little boy was really destined to live many years on the earth, to live and see the comet, when it reappeared more than sixty years later.

He did not see the shroud in the candle, and had no thought for the comet, which for the first time in his life shone from the heavens. He sat with a mended slop-basin in front of him; in it were some soap-suds, and he dipped the head of a clay-pipe down into it, put the stem in his mouth and blew soap-bubbles, great and small; they swayed and floated with the most lovely colours, which changed from yellow to red, lilac and blue, and then became green, like the leaves of the forest when the sun shines through them.

'God grant thee as many years here on the earth as the bubbles thou blowest!'

'So many, so many,' said the little one, 'the soap-suds can never be all used up!' and the little one blew bubble after bubble.

'There flies a year! there flies a year! see how they fly!' said he, with every bubble which got free and flew off. One or two went right into his eyes; they smarted and burned, and the tears came into his eyes. In every bubble he saw a vision of the future, shining and glittering.

'Now you can see the comet!' cried the neighbours. 'Come out; don't sit inside there!'

And the mother took the little boy by the hand; he was obliged to lay aside the clay-pipe, and stop playing with the soap-bubbles; the comet was there.

And the little boy saw the shining ball of fire, with the radiant tail; some people said that it was three yards long, others that it was millions of yards long; people see so differently. 'Children and grandchildren may be dead before it appears again!' people said.

Most of those who said it were really dead and gone before it reappeared; but the little boy for whom the shroud stood in the candle, and of whom the mother thought 'He will die soon!' still lived, old and white-haired. 'White hair is the flower of age!' the proverb says, and he had many of the flowers; he was now an old schoolmaster. The schoolchildren said he was very wise, and knew so much; knew history, and geography, and everything that is known about the heavenly bodies.

'Everything comes round again!' said he; 'only take notice of people and events, and you will find that they always come again, in another dress, in another country.'

The schoolmaster had just told about William Tell, who had to shoot an apple off his son's head, but before he shot the arrow, he hid in his breast another arrow with which to shoot the wicked Gesler in the heart. It was in Switzerland that that happened, but many years before, the same thing had happened in Denmark with Palnatoke; he also had to shoot an apple off his son's head, and hid, like Tell, an arrow to avenge himself with; and more than a thousand years farther back, the same story was recorded as having taken place in Egypt. The same things come again like the comet, they pass away, disappear, and come again.

And he talked about the comet which was expected, the comet he had seen as a little boy. The schoolmaster knew the heavenly bodies, and thought over them, but did not forget history and geography because of them.

He had laid out his garden in the shape of the map of Denmark. The plants and flowers were arranged according as they grow best in the different parts of the country. 'Bring me some peas!' said he, and one went to the bed which represented Lolland. 'Fetch me some buckwheat,' and one went to Langeland. The lovely blue gentian and sweet-willow were to be found up in Skagen, the glistening holly over at Silkeborg. The towns themselves were marked with stone figures. Here stood St Canute with the dragon, that signified Odense; Absalon with a bishop's staff signified Sorö; the little boat with the oars was the mark that here lay the town of Aarhus. From the schoolmaster's garden, one could learn the map of Denmark very well; but one must first be instructed by him, and that was so pleasant.

The comet was expected now, and he told what the people had said and thought about it, in the old days when it was here last. 'The comet-year is a good wine-year,' he said; 'one can dilute the wine with water, and it will not be noticed. The wine-sellers should think much of the comet-year.'

The sky was full of clouds for fourteen days and nights. The comet could not be seen, but it was there.

The old schoolmaster sat in his little room, close by the schoolroom. The grandfather's clock, which had belonged to his parents, stood in the corner; the heavy leaden weights neither rose nor fell, the pendulum did not move. The little cuckoo, which used to come forward to cuckoo the hour, had for several years sat silent behind closed doors: all was quiet and silent there, the clock went no more. But the old piano close by, which had also belonged to his parents, still had life, and the strings could sound, though certainly a little hoarse, the melodies of a whole generation. The old man remembered so many of them, both joyful and sorrowful, in the years from the time when he was a little boy and saw the comet, till now when it was here again. He remembered what his mother said about the shroud in the candle, he remembered the lovely soap-bubbles he blew; everyone was a year of life, he had said, how radiant, how rich in colour! everything lovely and joyful he saw there; childish games and youthful pleasure, the whole of the wide world open in the sunshine, and he should go out in it! that was the bubble of the future. As an old man he heard melodies of the vanished times from the strings of the piano: the bubbles of remembrance with memory's colour tints; there sounded Grandmother's knitting song:

> 'Twas certainly no Amazon
> That knitted first a stocking.

There sounded the song which the old servant had sung for him as a child:

> There are so many dangers
> Wherein the young may fall,
> Who are of years but tender
> And understanding small.

Now sounded the melodies from the first ball, a minuet and Polish dance; now sounded soft, sorrowful tones, which brought tears into the eyes of the old man; now rushed a battle-march, now a psalm tune, now gay tones, bubble on bubble, just as when he, as a little boy, blew them of soap-suds.

His eyes were fastened on the window, a cloud in the sky glided away and he saw in the clear air the comet, its shining heart, its bright misty veil.

It seemed as if he had seen it yesterday evening, and yet there lay a whole lifetime between that time and now; at that time he was a child, and saw the future in the bubbles, now the bubbles pointed backward; he felt the childish mind and childish faith, his eyes shone, his hand sank down on the keys – it sounded as if a string broke.

'Come and see, the comet is here,' cried the neighbours, the sky is so beautifully clear! come and see!'

The old schoolmaster did not answer, he was gone to see in reality; his soul had gone on a longer course, in a wider space than the comet flies through. The comet was again seen from the rich castle, from the poor cottage, by the crowd in the street, and by the lonely one on the trackless heath. His soul was seen by God and by the dear ones who had gone before – those he had longed for.

The Days of the Week

THE DAYS of the Week once resolved to get free from work, meet together, and have a social party. Every day, however, was so occupied, that all the year round they had no free time at their disposal; they must have a whole day to themselves, and this they really had every fourth year, the day that is put into February to keep the reckoning of time correct.

On that day therefore they decided to have their meeting; and as Shrove Tuesday falls in February, they would come in carnival dress, each according to his taste and usual character; they would eat well, drink well, make speeches, and say pleasant and unpleasant things to each other in the most unconstrained good fellowship. The heroes of old times, when at their meals, threw at each other's heads the bones from which they had gnawed the beef, but the Days of the Week would overwhelm each other with showers of wit and satire – all in innocent Shrove Tuesday merry-making.

So the extra day came, and they all met together.

Sunday, the leader of the days, appeared in a black silk gown; pious people would have supposed that he was dressed as a clergyman about to go to church, but the children of the world saw that he was in domino in order to go and enjoy himself, and that the blushing carnation he had in his buttonhole was the little red lantern at the theatre, which announced 'All tickets sold; see that you enjoy yourselves.'

Monday, a young fellow, a relative of Sunday and especially given to enjoyment, came next. He left the workshop, he said, when the guard-parade took place. 'I must go out and hear Offenbach's music. It does not affect my head nor my heart, but it tickles the muscles of my legs. I must dance and enjoy myself, get a black eye, and begin work again next day. I am the new-moon of the week.'

Tuesday takes its name from Tiw, the old god of strength and power. 'Yes, I am the day of that,' said Tuesday. 'I set to work, fasten the wings of Mercury to the boots of the merchant, and see whether the factory wheels are oiled and spinning properly; I insist that the tailor shall be on his board and the paviour on the street. Let each attend to his own work: I keep an eye on the whole.'

'Now I come,' said Wednesday. 'I stand in the middle of the week. The Germans call me Mr Midweek. I stand like the shopman in the shop, like a flower in the midst of all the other respected days of the week. If we all march together, I have three days before and three behind, like a guard of honour. I must suppose that I am the most distinguished day in the week.'

Thursday came dressed as a coppersmith with a hammer and a copper kettle; these were the marks of his nobility. 'I am of the highest birth,' he said, 'heathen and divine. In the northern lands I am named after Thor, and in the southern after Jupiter, who both knew how to thunder and lighten. That has remained in the family.' And then he beat on the copper kettle and demonstrated his high birth.

Friday was dressed like a young girl, and called herself Freia, and by way of change also Venus; it depended on the language of the country in which she appeared. She was usually of a quiet happy nature, she said, but today she was dashing and free, for it was leap-year's day, and that brings freedom to woman; by old custom she may then woo for herself, and need not wait to be wooed.

Saturday appeared as an old housekeeper with broom and cleaning-things. Her favourite dish was a broth made of the week's bread-crusts, but she did not demand that on this festive occasion it should be set on the table for all of them, but only that she herself might have it; and she got it.

And so the Days of the Week took their places at the table.

Here they are now described, all the seven, ready for use in tableaux for the family circle. In these they might be presented in the most amusing manner possible; we give them here only as a playful jest for February, the only month that gets an extra day given to it.

Sunshine's Stories

'NOW *I* shall tell a story,' said the Wind.

'No, excuse me,' said the Rain, 'now it is *my* turn! You have stood long enough at the street corner and howled all that you could howl!'

'Is that your thanks,' said the Wind, 'for my having, in your honour, turned many an umbrella outside in; yes, even broken them, when people would have nothing to do with you!'

'*I* am going to tell one,' said the Sunshine, 'be quiet;' and it was said with dignity and majesty, so that the Wind laid itself down all its length, but the Rain drizzled in the Wind, and said, 'Must we stand this! She always breaks through, this Madam Sunshine. We shall not listen to her! it is not worth the trouble to listen!'

And the Sunshine said:

'There flew a swan over the rolling sea: every feather on it shone like gold; one feather fell down on the big merchant ship which glided past under full sail. The feather fell on the curly hair of the young man who had charge of the cargo, the "Super-cargo" they called him. The feather of the bird of Fortune touched his forehead, and became a pen in his hand, and he soon became a rich merchant, who could easily buy himself spurs of gold, and change gold plate into a nobleman's shield. I have shone upon it,' said the Sunshine.

'The swan flew away over the green meadow, where the little shepherd, a boy of seven years old, had laid himself to rest under the shadow of the single old tree there. And the swan in its flight kissed a leaf of the tree; it fell into the boy's hand, and the one leaf became three, then ten, then a whole book, and he read in it about the wonders of nature, about his mother-tongue, and about faith and knowledge. At bedtime he laid the book under his head, so that he should not forget what he had read, and the book took him to the school bench and the desk of learning. I have read his name among those of the learned!' said the Sunshine.

'The swan flew into the loneliness of the forest, rested there on the still, dark lakes, where the water-lilies and the wild apples grow, where the cuckoo and the wood-pigeon have their homes.

'A poor woman gathered fallen branches for firewood, and carried them on her back; she bore her child in her arms, and was on her way home. She saw the golden swan, the swan of Fortune, fly up from the rush-grown bank. What shone there? A golden egg; she laid it in her bosom, and the warmth remained; there was certainly life in the egg. Yes, there was a tapping inside the shell; she noticed it, and thought it was the beating of her own heart.

'At home in her poor room she took out the golden egg. "Tick, tick," it said, as if it were a valuable gold watch, but it was an egg with living life. The egg burst, and a little cygnet, feathered like pure gold, stuck its head out; it had four rings round its neck, and as the poor woman had just four boys, three at home, and the fourth which she had carried with her in the forest, she understood at once that here was a ring for each of the children; and just as she understood it, the little golden bird flew away.

'She kissed each ring, and let each of the children kiss one of the rings, laid it on the child's heart, and placed it on the child's finger.

'I saw it!' said the Sunshine, 'I saw what followed this!

'The one boy seated himself in the clay pit, took a lump of clay in his hand, turned it with the fingers, and it became a figure of Jason, who fetched the golden fleece.

'The second boy ran out at once into the meadow where the flowers stood with all the colours one could think of: he plucked a handful, clutched them so firmly that the sap sprang into his eyes and wetted the ring; there came life and movement into his thoughts and into his hand, and after a year and a day, the great town talked of the great painter.

'The third of the boys held the ring so fast in his mouth that it gave out a sound, an echo from the bottom of his heart. Thoughts and feelings lifted themselves in melody, lifted themselves like singing swans, dived like swans down into the deep sea, the deep sea of thought. He became the great master of melody. Every country may now think "He belongs to me!"

'The fourth little one; ah, he was the outcast. They said he "had the pip", and ought to have pepper and butter, like the sick chickens! "Pepper and bootter," was how they said it, and he got that; but from me he got a sunshine kiss,' said the Sunshine, 'he got ten kisses for one. He had a poet's nature and got both knocks and kisses; but he had the ring of Fortune from Fortune's golden swan. His thoughts flew out like a golden butterfly, the symbol of immortality!'

'That was a long story!' said the Wind.

'And tiresome!' said the Rain; 'blow on me so that I may come to myself again.'

And the Wind blew, and the Sunshine went on: 'The swan of Fortune flew away over the deep bay, where the fishers had spread their nets. The poorest of them had thought of getting married, and so he got married.

'The swan brought a piece of amber to him; amber attracts to itself, it drew hearts to the house. Amber is the loveliest incense. There came a fragrance as from the church; there came a fragrance from God's nature. They felt truly the happiness of home, content with their lowly condition, and so their life became a real sunshine story.'

'Shall we stop now?' said the Wind. 'Sunshine has talked long enough now. I am tired of it!'

'I also,' said the Rain.

What do we others, who have heard the stories, say? We say ... now they are finished.

Great-Grandfather

GREAT-GRANDFATHER was so very nice and wise and good that we all looked up to him. He was really called, as far back as I can remember, 'Grandfather,' but when my brother's little son, Frederick, came into the family, he was advanced to 'Great-grandfather'; higher up he could not get! He thought so much of all of us, but he seemed not to think so much of our times. 'Old times were the best times,' he said, 'they were steady and solid: now there is such a rush and such a turning up and down of everything. Youth leads the talk, and speaks of royalty itself as if they were its equal. Every person from the street can dip his rag in dirty water and wring it out on the head of a gentleman.'

With such talk Great-grandfather got very red in the face, but a little time after, his friendly smile reappeared, and then the words, 'Well, well, perhaps I am a little mistaken! I stand in old times and cannot get a proper foothold in the new. May our Father lead and guide them!'

When Great-grandfather talked about old times it was just as if I had them before me. In thought I drove in a golden chariot with attendants in livery, saw the guilds carrying their signs in procession with music and flags, and took part in the delightful Christmas parties, with forfeits and mumming.

There was certainly, also, in those times much that was horrible and nasty; the stake, the wheel, and the shedding of blood, but all the horrible had something alluring and exciting about it. I learned about the Danish noblemen who gave the peasants their freedom, and Denmark's Crown Prince who abolished the slave-trade. It was delightful to hear Great-grandfather tell about all this, and to hear about the days of his youth. Still the time before that was the very best, so strong and so great.

'Rough it was,' said brother Frederick, 'God be praised that we are out of it,' and he said this straight out to Great-grandfather. It was not nice to say that, but yet I had great respect for Frederick; he was my eldest brother, and he could have been my father, he said. He said so many funny things. He was a very successful student, and so diligent in my father's office that he would soon be able to go into the business. He was the one that Great-grandfather was most familiar with, but they always ended in disputing about something. These two did not understand each other, and never would, the family said; but little as I was, I soon noticed that these two could not do without each other.

Great-grandfather listened with shining eyes when Frederick spoke or read about progress in science, about the discoveries of the powers of nature, and about all the remarkable things of our time.

'People become wiser, but not better,' he said; 'they invent the most terrible weapons of destruction against each other.'

'The quicker will war be past,' said Frederick; 'one will not have to wait seven years for the blessings of peace! The world is full-blooded and must occasionally be bled; it is necessary.'

One day Frederick told him something which had really happened in our time in a little town.

The Mayor's clock, the big one on the town-hall, set the time for the town and the people. The clock did not go quite correctly, but all the same the town ordered itself by it. By and by the railways came, and they are connected with all other countries, and so one must know the time exactly, or there will be collisions. The railway got a clock which was set by the sun and so kept good time; and now the whole of the townspeople settled everything by the railway clock.

I laughed and thought it was a funny story, but Great-grandfather didn't laugh; he became quite serious.

'There is a great deal in that story of yours,' he said, 'and I also understand your idea in telling it to me. There is instruction in your clockwork. It makes me think of another instance, my parents' simple old grandfather's clock, with its leaden weights; it was their and my childhood's chronometer: it did not go quite correctly, but it went, and we looked at the hands; we believed in them and did not think of the wheels inside. So also was it with the machinery of the state at that time; one looked at it with confidence and believed in the hands. Now the state machine has become like a glass clock, where one can look right into the machinery and see the wheels turn and whirl. One gets quite afraid for this pivot and that wheel! I wonder how it will go with the striking, and I have no longer my childhood's faith. That is the weakness of the present time!'

And so Great-grandfather talked himself quite angry. He and Frederick could not agree, but they could not separate either, just like the old and the new time! They learned that, both of them and all the family, when Frederick had to start on a long journey, far away to America. It was on the business of the house that the journey had to be made. It was a terrible separation for Great-grandfather, and the journey was so long, right across the ocean to another part of the globe.

'Every fortnight you will have a letter from me,' said Frederick, 'and quicker than all the letters, you will be able to hear from me by telegraph; the days become hours, and the hours minutes!'

Over the telegraph wires came a message from England, when Frederick went on board. Quicker than a letter, even if the flying clouds had been the postman, came a message from America when Frederick landed. It was only a few hours since he had done so.

'It is a divine thought which is granted to our time,' said Great-grandfather; 'a blessing for mankind.'

'Yes, and Frederick has told me that it was in our country that these powers of Nature were first understood and made known.'

'Yes,' said Great-grandfather, and kissed me. 'Yes, and I have looked into the two mild eyes which first saw and understood this power of Nature; they were childish eyes, like yours! and I have shaken hands with him!' And he kissed me again.

More than a month had gone, when we had a letter from Frederick with the news that he was engaged to a charming young girl, whom the whole family would assuredly be delighted with. Her photograph was sent, and was examined with the naked eye and with a magnifying glass, for that is the charm of these pictures, that they can stand examination with the sharpest glass, and that the likeness becomes even clearer in that way. No painter has ever been capable of that, not even the greatest of the old times.

'If one had only known the discovery in those times,' said Great-grandfather, 'we should have been able to see the world's great men and benefactors face to face. How good and sweet this young girl looks,' he said, and gazed through the glass; 'I shall know her now when she comes in at the door.'

But it was very near not happening: fortunately we at home scarcely knew of the danger until it was past.

The young newly-married couple arrived in England in joy and good health; from there they proceeded with the steamer to Copenhagen. They saw the Danish coast, the white sand-hills of Jutland: then a great storm arose, and the ship grounded on one of the sand-banks and stuck fast. The sea rose high and seemed as if it would wreck the ship; no lifeboat could work. The night came, but in the middle of the darkness a rocket was thrown from the shore over the stranded ship. The rocket carried a rope over it, a connection was made between those out there and those on the shore, and soon a beautiful young lady was drawn through the heavy rolling waves in a cradle, and glad and happy was she when her young husband stood by her side on dry land. All on board were saved, and it was not daylight yet.

We lay sleeping soundly in Copenhagen, thinking neither of sorrow nor danger. As we assembled for breakfast, there came a rumour, brought by a telegram, that an English steamer had gone down on the west coast. We were in great anxiety, but just then came a telegram from Frederick and his young wife, who had been saved and would soon be with us.

They all wept together; I wept too, and Great-grandfather wept, folded his hands, and – I am certain of it – blessed the new times.

That day Great-grandfather gave twenty pounds for the monument to Hans Christian Oersted, the electrician.

When Frederick came home with his young wife and heard it, he said, 'That was right, Great-grandfather! now I shall read to you what Oersted many years ago said about the old and new times!'

'He was of your opinion, no doubt?' said Great-grandfather.

'Yes, you may be sure of that,' said Frederick; 'and you are too, since you have subscribed for the monument to him!'

The Candles

THERE WAS once a big wax-candle which knew its own importance quite well.

'I am born of wax and moulded in a shape,' it said; 'I give better light and burn longer than other candles; my place is in a chandelier or on a silver candlestick!'

'That must be a lovely existence!' said the tallow-candle. 'I am only made of tallow, but I comfort myself with the thought that it is always a little better than being a farthing dip: that is only dipped twice, and I am dipped eight times to get my proper thickness. I am content! it is certainly finer and more fortunate to be born of wax instead of tallow, but one does not settle one's own place in this world. You are placed in the big room in the glass chandelier, I remain in the kitchen, but that is also a good place; from there the whole house gets its food.'

'But there is something which is more important than food,' said the wax-candle. 'Society! to see it shine, and to shine oneself! There is a ball this evening, and soon I and all my family will be fetched.'

Scarcely was the word spoken, when all the wax-candles were fetched, but the tallow-candle also went with them. The lady herself took it in her dainty hand, and carried it out to the kitchen: a little boy stood there with a basket, which was filled with potatoes; two or three apples also found their way there. The good lady gave all this to the poor boy.

'There is a candle for you as well, my little friend,' said she. 'Your mother sits and works till late in the night; she can use it!'

The little daughter of the house stood close by, and when she heard the words 'late in the night', she said with great delight, 'I also shall stay up till late in the night! We shall have a ball, and I shall wear my big red sash!' How her face shone! that was with joy! No wax-candle can shine like two childish eyes!

'That is a blessing to see,' thought the tallow-candle; 'I shall never forget it, and I shall certainly never see it again.'

And so it was laid in the basket, under the lid, and the boy went away with it.

'Where shall I go now?' thought the candle; 'I shall go to poor people, and perhaps not even get a brass candlestick, while the wax-candle sits in silver and sees all the grand people. How lovely it must be to shine for the grand people! but it was my lot to be tallow and not wax!'

And so the candle came to poor people, a widow with three children, in a little, low room, right opposite the rich house.

'God bless the good lady for her gifts,' said the mother, 'what a lovely candle that is! it can burn till late in the night.'

And then the candle was lighted.

'Fut, foi,' it said, 'what a horrid-smelling match that was she lighted me with! the wax-candle over in the rich house would not have such treatment offered to it.'

There also the candles were lighted: they shone out across the street; the carriages rolled up with the elegant ball-guests and the music played.

'Now they begin across there,' the tallow-candle noticed, and thought of the beaming face of the rich little girl, more sparkling than all the wax-lights. 'That sight I shall never see again!'

Then the smallest of the children in the poor house, a little girl, came and took her brother and sister round the neck: she had something very important to tell them, and it must be whispered. 'Tonight we shall have – just think! – Tonight we shall have hot potatoes!'

And her face shone with happiness: the tallow-candle shone right into it, and it saw a gladness, a happiness as great as over in the rich house, where the little girl said, 'We shall have a ball tonight, and I shall wear my big red sash!'

'It is just as much to get hot potatoes,' thought the candle. 'Here there is just as much joy amongst the children.' And it sneezed at that; that is to say, it sputtered; a tallow-candle can do no more.

The table was laid, and the potatoes eaten. Oh, how good they tasted! it was a perfect feast, and each one got an apple besides, and the smallest child said the little verse:

> 'Thou good God, I give thanks to Thee
> That Thou again hast nourished me.
> Amen!

'Was that not nicely said, Mother?' broke out the little one.

'You must not ask that again,' said the mother; 'you must think only of the good God who has fed you.'

The little ones went to bed, got a kiss and fell asleep at once, and the mother sat and sewed late into the night to get the means of support for them and for herself. And over from the big house the lights shone and the music sounded. The stars shone over all the houses, over the rich and over the poor, equally clear and blessed.

'This has really been a delightful evening!' thought the tallow-candle. 'I wonder if the wax-candles had it any better in the silver candlestick? I would like to know that before I am burned out.'

And it thought of the two happy ones, the one lighted by the wax-candle, and the other by the tallow-candle.

Yes, that is the whole story!

The Most Incredible Thing

THE ONE who could do the most incredible thing should have the king's daughter and the half of his kingdom.

The young men, and even the old ones, strained all their thoughts, sinews, and muscles; two ate themselves to death, and one drank until he died, to do the most incredible thing according to their own taste, but it was not in this way it was to be done. Little boys in the streets practised spitting on their own backs, they considered that the most incredible thing.

On a certain day an exhibition was to be held of what each had to show as the most incredible. The judges who were chosen were children from three years old to people up in the sixties. There was a whole exhibition of incredible things, but all soon agreed that the most incredible was a huge clock in a case marvellously designed inside and out.

On the stroke of every hour living figures came out, which showed what hour was striking: there were twelve representations in all, with moving figures and with music and conversation.

'That was the most incredible thing,' the people said.

The clock struck one, and Moses stood on the mountain and wrote down on the tables of the law the first commandment, 'There is only one true God.'

The clock struck two, and the garden of Eden appeared, where Adam and Eve met, happy both of them, without having so much as a wardrobe; they did not need one either.

On the stroke of three, the three kings from the East were shown; one of them was coal-black, but he could not help that, the sun had blackened him. They came with incense and treasures.

On the stroke of four came the four seasons: spring with a cuckoo on a budding beech-bough; summer with a grasshopper on a stalk of ripe corn; autumn with an empty stork's nest – the birds were flown; winter with an old crow which could tell stories in the chimney-corner, old memories.

When the clock struck five, the five senses appeared – sight as a spectacle-maker, hearing as a coppersmith, smell sold violets and woodruff, taste was cook, and feeling was an undertaker with crape down to his heels.

The clock struck six; and there sat a gambler who threw the dice, and the highest side was turned up and showed six.

Then came the seven days of the week, or the seven deadly sins, people were not certain which; they belonged to each other and were not easily distinguished.

Then came a choir of monks and sang the eight o'clock service.

On the stroke of nine came the nine muses; one was busy with astronomy; one with historical archives; the others belonged to the theatre.

On the stroke of ten, Moses again came forward with the tables of the law, on which stood all God's commandments, and they were ten.

The clock struck again; then little boys and girls danced and hopped about. They played a game, and sang, 'Two and two and seven, the clock has struck eleven.'

When twelve struck the watchman appeared with his fur cap and halberd: he sang the old watch verse:

> ' 'Twas at the midnight hour
> Our saviour He was born.'

And while he sang, roses grew and changed into angelheads borne on rainbow-coloured wings.

It was charming to hear, and lovely to see. The whole was a matchless work of art – the most incredible thing, everyone said.

The designer of it was a young man, good-hearted and happy as a child, a true friend, and good to his old parents; he deserved the Princess and the half of the kingdom.

The day of decision arrived; the whole of the town had a holiday, and the Princess sat on the throne, which had got new horsehair, but which was not any more comfortable. The judges round about looked very knowingly at the one who was to win, and he stood glad and confident; his good fortune was certain, he had made the most incredible thing.

'No, I shall do that now!' shouted just then a long bony fellow. 'I am the man for the most incredible thing,' and he swung a great axe at the work of art.

'Crash, crash!' and there lay the whole of it. Wheels and springs flew in all directions; everything was destroyed.

'That *I* could do!' said the man. 'My work has overcome his and overcome all of you. I have done the most incredible thing.'

'To destroy such a work of art!' said the judges. 'Yes, certainly that is the most incredible thing.'

All the people said the same, and so he was to have the Princess and the half of the kingdom, for a promise is a promise, even if it is of the most incredible kind.

It was announced with trumpet-blast from the ramparts and from all the towers that the marriage should be celebrated. The Princess was not quite pleased about it, but she looked charming and was gorgeously dressed. The church shone with candles; it shows best late in the evening. The noble maidens of the town sang and led the bride forward; the knights sang and accompanied the bridegroom. He strutted as if he could never be broken.

Now the singing stopped and one could have heard a pin fall, but in the midst of the silence the great church door flew open with a crash and clatter, and boom! boom! the whole of the clockwork came marching up the passage and planted itself between the bride and bridegroom. Dead men cannot walk again, we know that very well, but a work of art can walk again; the body was knocked to pieces, but not the spirit; the spirit of the work walked, and that in deadly earnest.

The work of art stood there precisely as if it were whole and untouched. The hours struck, the one after the other, up to twelve, and the figures swarmed forward; first Moses: flames of fire seemed to flash from his forehead; he threw the heavy stone tables down on the feet of the bridegroom and pinned them to the church floor.

'I cannot lift them again,' said Moses, 'you have knocked my arm off! Stand as you stand now!'

Then came Adam and Eve, the wise men from the East, and the four Seasons; each of these told him unpleasant truths, and said 'For shame!'

But he was not in the least ashamed.

All the figures which each stroke of the clock had to exhibit came out of it, and all increased to a terrible size; there seemed scarcely to be room for the real people; and when at the stroke of twelve the watchman appeared with his fur cap and halberd, there was a wonderful commotion; the watchman walked straight up to the bridegroom and struck him on the forehead with his halberd.

'Lie there,' he said, 'like for like! we are avenged and our master as well! we vanish!'

And so the whole work disappeared; but the candles round about in the church became great bouquets, and the gilded stars on the ceiling of the church sent out long, clear beams, and the organ played of itself. All the people said it was the most incredible thing they had ever experienced.

'Will you then summon the right one!' said the Princess, 'the one who made the work of art; let him be my lord and husband.'

And he stood in the church with the whole of the people for his retinue. All were glad and all blessed him; there was not one who was jealous – and that was the most incredible thing of all.

What the Whole Family Said

WHAT DID the whole family say? Well, listen first to what little Mary said.

It was little Mary's birthday, the loveliest of all days, she thought. All her little friends came to play with her, and she wore the most beautiful dress; she had got it from her Grandmother, who was now with the good God, but Grandmother herself had cut and sewed it before she went up into the bright, beautiful heaven. The table in Mary's room shone with presents; there was the neatest little kitchen, with all that belongs to a kitchen, and a doll which could roll its eyes and say 'Au', when one pressed its stomach; there was also a picture-book with the loveliest stories to read, if one could read! But was nicer even than all the stories to live through many birthdays.

'Yes, it is lovely to live,' said little Mary. Godfather added that it was the loveliest fairy tale.

In the room close by were Mary's two brothers; they were big boys, the one nine years old, the other eleven. They also thought it was lovely to be alive, to live in their way, not to be a child like Mary, but to be smart schoolboys, to have 'excellent' in the character book, and to be able to enjoy a fight with their companions, to skate in winter, and to ride velocipedes in summer, to read about castles, drawbridges, and prisons, and to hear about discoveries in the heart of Africa. One of the boys had, however, one anxiety, that everything would be discovered before he grew up; he wanted to go in quest of adventures then. Life is the most lovely story of adventure, Godfather said, and one takes part in it oneself.

It was on the ground floor that these children lived and played; up above lived another branch of the family, also with children, but these were grown up: the one son was seventeen years old, the second twenty, but the third was very old, little Mary said – he was twenty-five and engaged.

They were all happily situated, had good parents, good clothes, good abilities, and they knew what they wanted. 'Forward! away with all the old barricades! a free view into all the world; that is the most lovely thing we know. Godfather is right: life is the loveliest fairy tale!'

Father and Mother, both elderly people – naturally they must be older than the children – said with a smile on their lips, with a smile in their eyes and hearts: 'How young they are, the young people! things do not go quite as they think in the world, but they do go. Life is a strange, lovely fairy tale.'

Overhead, a little nearer heaven, as one says, when people live in the garret, lived Godfather. He was old, but so young in spirit, always in good humour, and he could also tell stories, many and long. He had travelled widely in the world, and lovely things from all the countries in the world stood in his room. There were pictures from floor to ceiling, and some of the window-panes were of red and some of yellow glass: if one looked through them, the whole world lay in sunshine, however grey the weather was outside. In a big glass case grew green plants, and in a part of it goldfish swam about: they looked as if they knew so much that they would not talk about it. It always smelt of flowers here, even in winter, and then a big fire burned in the stove; it was so nice to sit and look into it and hear how it crackled and sputtered. 'It repeats old memories to me,' said Godfather, and to little Mary it seemed as if many pictures showed themselves in the fire.

But in the big bookcase close by, stood the real books: one of these Godfather read very often, and he called it the Book of books; it was the Bible. There, in pictures was shown the whole history of man and of the world, the creation, the flood, the kings and the King of kings.

'All that has happened and will happen stands in this book!' said Godfather. 'So infinitely much in a little book! think of it! Everything that a man has to pray for, is said and put in few words in the Lord's Prayer. It is a drop of grace, a pearl of comfort from God. It is laid as a gift on the cradle of the child, at the child's heart. Little child, keep it carefully! never lose it, however big you grow, and then you will not be left alone on the changing paths! it will shine in on you and you will not be lost.'

Godfather's eyes shone at that; they beamed with joy. Once in earlier days they had wept, 'and that was also good,' he said, 'it was a time of trial when things looked grey. Now I have sunshine about me and in me. The older one grows, the better one sees both in prosperity and adversity, that our Father is always with us, that life is the loveliest fairy tale, and only He can give us that, and it lasts into eternity.'

'It is lovely to live,' said little Mary.

The little and the big boys said so too; Father and Mother and the whole family said it, but above all Godfather, and he had experience, he was the oldest of them all, he knew all the stories, all the fairy tales, and he said, and that right out of his heart, 'Life is the loveliest fairy tale!'

The Great Sea-Serpent

THERE WAS a little sea-fish of good family; the name I cannot remember, you must get that from the learned. The little fish had eighteen hundred brothers and sisters all of the same age; they did not know either their father or their mother; they had just to take care of themselves at once and swim about, but that was a great delight to them.

They had plenty of water to drink – the whole of the sea; they did not think about food – that would come of itself; everyone would do just as he liked, everyone would have his own story – but none of them thought about that either. The sun shone down into the water, and lighted it up round about them; it was so clear, it was a world with the most wonderful creatures, and some frightfully big, with enormous mouths which could have swallowed the eighteen hundred brothers and sisters; but they did not think of that either, for none of them had been swallowed yet.

The little ones swam about together, close up to each other, as herring and mackerel swim; but as they swam about in the water, doing their very best and thinking of nothing, there sank from above right into the middle of them, with a frightful noise, a long, heavy thing that would not stop coming; longer and longer it stretched itself, and every one of the little fishes which it struck, was squashed or got a blow which it could never get over. All the little fishes, and the big ones too, right from the surface of the sea down to the bottom, swam away in alarm: the heavy, monstrous thing sank deeper and deeper, and became longer and longer, miles in length – throughout the whole sea.

Fishes and snails, everything that swims, everything which crawls or drifts with the currents, noticed this frightful thing, this immense, unknown sea-eel, which had suddenly come down from above.

What kind of a thing was it? We know what it was! It was the great league-long telegraph wire, which was being laid down between Europe and America.

There was a scare and a great commotion among the lawful inhabitants of the sea where the wire was sunk. The flying-fish sprang into the air above the sea, as high as it could; the gurnard flew the length of a gunshot above the water; other fish sought the bottom of the sea, and fled so quickly that they arrived there long before the telegraph wire had even been sighted: they frightened both the codfish and the flounder, which were swimming about peacefully in the depths of the sea and eating their fellow creatures.

A pair of sea-cucumbers were so scared that they vomited their stomachs out; but they still lived, for they can do that. Many lobsters and crabs came out of their good harness, and had to leave their legs behind them.

Among all this fright and commotion, the eighteen hundred brothers and sisters got separated from each other, and never met again, or knew each other; only about a dozen remained in the same place, and when they had kept quiet for an hour or two, they began to get over their fright and become inquisitive. They looked round about, they looked up, and they looked down, and there in the depths they thought they saw the terrible thing which had frightened them, frightened both big and little. The thing lay along the bottom of the sea as far as they could spy; it was very thin, but they did not know how thick it could make itself, or how strong it was. It lay very still; but this, they thought, might be its cunning.

'Let it lie where it is! It does not concern us,' said the most cautious of the little fishes, but the very smallest of them would not give up getting to know what the thing could be. It came down from above; up above would therefore be the best place to get news about it, and so they swam up to the surface of the sea. The weather was quite calm.

There they met a dolphin, a kind of acrobat, a vagrant of the sea who can turn somersaults on the surface of the water; it had eyes to see with, and it must have seen and would know all about it. They enquired of it, but it had only thought of itself and its somersaults, had seen nothing, could give no answer, and so was silent and looked haughty.

Thereupon they addressed themselves to a seal who just then dived; it was more polite, although it ate little fishes; but today it was full. It knew a little more than the dolphin.

'I have, many a night, lain on a wet stone and looked towards the land, miles away from here. There are clumsy creatures there, who in their language are called men; they hunt after us, but oftenest we escape from them. I have known how to do that, and so has the sea-eel you now ask about. It has been in their power, been upon the land, no doubt from time immemorial; from there they have taken it on board a ship to convey it over the sea to another distant land. I saw what trouble they had, but they managed it; it had become so weak with being on shore. They laid it in coils and twists; I heard how it rattled and clattered as they laid it; but it escaped from them, escaped out here. They held it with all their might, many hands held fast, but it slipped from them and got to the bottom; it lies there, I think, till later on!'

'It is rather thin,' said the little fishes.

'They have starved it,' said the seal, 'but it will soon come to itself, and get its old thickness and bigness. I imagine it is the great sea-serpent, which men are so afraid of and talk so much about. I have never seen it before, and never believed in it; now, I believe that this is it,' and so the seal dived.

'How much he knew! How much he talked!' said the little fishes, 'I have never been so wise before! If only it is not a lie!'

'We could swim down and investigate!' said the smallest one; 'on the way we may hear others' opinions.'

'I won't make a single stroke with my fins, to get to know anything,' the others said, and turned about.

'But I will!' said the smallest, and set off into deep water; but it was far from the place where 'the long sunken thing' lay. The little fish looked and searched about on all sides down in the deep.

It had never noticed before how big the world was. The herring went in great shoals, shining like big silver boats; the mackerel followed, and looked even more magnificent. There came fish of all shapes and with markings of all colours. Jellyfishes, like half-transparent flowers, allowed themselves to be carried to and fro by the currents. Great plants grew from the bottom of the sea, fathom-high grass and palm-shaped trees, every leaf adorned with shining shells.

At last the little fish spied a long dark stripe and made towards it, but it was neither fish nor cable – it was the railing of a big sunken ship, whose upper and lower decks were broken in two by the pressure of the sea. The little fish swam into the cabin where so many people had perished when the ship sank, and were now all washed away except two: a young woman lay stretched out there with a little child in her arms. The water lifted them and seemed to rock them; they looked as if they were asleep. The little fish was very frightened; it did not know that they would never waken again. Water plants hung like foliage over the railing and over the lovely bodies of mother and child. It was so still and lonely. The little fish hurried away as quickly as it could, out where the water was clearer and where there were fishes to be seen. It had not gone very far before it met a young whale, so frightfully big.

'Don't swallow me,' said the little fish, 'I am not even a taste, I am so little, and it is a great pleasure to me to be alive!'

'What are you doing down here, where your kind does not come?' asked the whale. And so the little fish told about the long, wonderful eel, or whatever the thing was, which had come down from above and frightened even the most courageous inhabitants of the deep.

'Ho, ho!' said the whale, and sucked in so much water that it had to send out a huge spout of it when it came up to the surface to draw breath. 'Ho, ho!' it said 'so it was that thing which tickled me on the back as I turned myself! I thought it was a ship's mast which I could use as a clawing-pin! But it was not at this spot. No, the thing lies much farther out. I will investigate it; I have nothing else to do!'

And so it swam forward and the little fish behind, not too near, for there came a tearing current where the big whale shot through the water.

They met a shark and an old sawfish; they also had heard about the strange sea-eel, so long and so thin; they had not seen it, but they wanted to. Now there came a catfish.

'I will go with you,' it said; it was going the same way. 'If the great sea-serpent is no thicker than an anchor-rope, I shall bite it through in one bite,' and it opened its jaws and showed its six rows of teeth. 'I can bite a mark in a ship's anchor, so I can surely bite through that stalk.'

'There it is,' said the big whale, 'I see it!'

He thought he saw better than the others. 'Look how it lifts itself, look how it sways, bends, and curves itself!'

It was not it, however, but an immensely big conger-eel, several yards long, which approached.

'I have seen that one before,' said the sawfish; 'it has never made a great noise in the sea, or frightened any big fish.'

And so they spoke to it about the new eel, and asked if it would go with them to discover it.

'Is that eel longer than me?' said the conger; 'then there will be trouble!'

'That there will be!' said the others. 'We are strong enough and won't stand it,' and so they hastened forward.

But just then something came in the way, a wonderful monster, bigger than all of them put together. It looked like a floating island, which could not keep itself up.

It was a very old whale. Its head was overgrown with sea plants; its back was thickly set with creeping things and so many oysters and mussels, that its black skin was quite covered with white spots.

'Come with us, old one,' said they; 'a new fish has come here, which is not to be tolerated.'

'I would rather lie where I am,' said the old whale. 'Leave me alone! Let me lie! Oh, yes, yes, yes. I suffer from a serious illness! I get relief by going up to the surface and getting my back above it! then the big sea-birds come and pick me. It is so nice, if only they don't put their beaks too far in; they often go right into my blubber. Just look! The whole skeleton of a bird is still sitting on my back, it stuck its claws too far in and could not get loose, when I went to the bottom! Now the little fishes have picked him. See how he looks, and how I look! I have an illness!'

'It is only imagination!' said the young whale; 'I am never ill. No fish is ill!'

'Excuse me,' said the old whale, 'the eel has a skin-disease, the carp is said to have smallpox, and we all suffer from worms.'

'Rubbish,' said the shark; he could not be bothered listening to any more, nor the others either, they had other things to think about.

At last they came to the place where the telegraph cable lay. It had a long lair on the bottom of the sea, from Europe to America, right over the sandbanks and sea-mud, rocky bottoms and wildernesses of plants and whole forests of coral. Down there the currents are ever changing, whirlpools turn and eddy, fish swarm in greater numbers than the countless flocks of birds which we see at the time of their migration. There is a movement, a splashing, a buzzing, and a humming; the humming still echoes a little in the big empty sea-shells, when we hold them to our ears. Now they came to the place.

'There lies the beast,' said the big fish, and the little one said the same thing. They saw the cable, whose beginning and end lay beyond the range of their vision.

Sponges, polypi and gorgons swayed about from the bottom of the sea, sank and bent down over it, so that it was seen and hidden alternately. Sea-urchins, snails, and worms crawled about it; gigantic spiders, with a whole crew of creeping things upon them, stalked along the cable. Dark-blue sea-cucumbers (or whatever the creatures are called – they eat with the whole of their body) lay and seemed to snuff at the new animal which laid itself along the bottom of the sea. Flounders and codfish turned round in the water so as to listen on all sides. The starfish, which always bores itself into the mud and only leaves the two long stalks with eyes sticking out, lay and stared to see what the result of all the commotion would be.

The cable lay without moving, but life and thought were in it all the same. The thoughts of men went through it.

'The thing is cunning!' said the whale. 'It is quite capable of hitting me in the stomach, and that is my tender spot!'

'Let us feel our way!' said the polypus. 'I have long arms, I have supple fingers! I have touched it, I will now take hold a little more firmly.'

And it stretched its supple, longest arm down to the cable and round about it.

'It has no scales,' said the polypus, 'it has no skin.'

The sea-eel laid itself down beside the cable, and stretched itself out as far as it could.

'The thing is longer than I!' it said, 'but it is not the length that matters, one must have skin, stomach, and suppleness.'

The whale, the strong young whale, dropped itself down deeper than it had ever been before.

'Are you fish or plant?' he asked, 'or are you only something from above which cannot thrive down here amongst us?'

But the cable answered nothing: that is not its way of doing. Thoughts went through it; the thoughts of men; they ran in a second, many hundreds of miles from land to land.

'Will you answer or will you be snapped?' asked the ferocious shark, and all the other big fishes asked the same. 'Will you answer or be snapped?'

The cable paid no attention, it had its own thoughts; it is full of thoughts.

'Only let them snap me, and I shall be pulled up and put right again; that has happened to others of my kind in lesser channels.'

And so it answered nothing, it had other things to do; it telegraphed and lay in lawful occupation at the bottom of the sea.

Up above the sun set, as men say; it looked like the reddest fire, and all the clouds in the sky shone like fire, the one more magnificent than the other.

'Now we will get the red light!' said the polypus, 'and so the thing will perhaps be seen better, if that is necessary.'

'On it, on it!' shouted the catfish, and showed all his teeth.

'On it, on it,' said the swordfish, the whale, and the sea-eel.

They hurled themselves forward, the catfish first, but just as they were going to bite the cable, the sawfish drove his saw with great force into the back of the catfish: that was a great mistake, and the cat had no strength to bite.

There was a commotion down there in the mud; big fishes and little fishes, sea-cucumbers and snails ran into each other, ate each other, mashed each other and squashed each other. The cable lay still and did its work as it ought to do. Dark night brooded above the sea, but the millions and millions of living sea animals gave out light. Crabs, not so big as pin-heads, gave out light. It is very wonderful, but so it is. The sea animals gazed at the cable.

'What is the thing, and what is it not?'

Yes, that was the question.

Then came an old sea-cow. Men call that kind, mermaids or mermen. This one – a she – had a tail, and two short arms to paddle with, hanging breast, and seaweed and creeping things in her head, and she was very proud of that.

'Will you have knowledge and information?' said she; 'then I am the only one who can give it to you; but I demand for it, free grazing on the bottom of the sea for me and mine. I am a fish like you, and I am also a reptile by practice. I am the wisest in the sea; I know about everything that moves down here, and about all that is above as well. That thing there which you are puzzling about is from above, and whatever is dumped down from up there is dead or becomes dead and powerless; let it alone for what it is; it is only an invention of man!'

'I believe there is something more than that about it,' said the little sea-fish.

'Hold your tongue, mackerel,' said the big sea-cow.

'Stickleback,' said the others, and there were still more insulting things said.

And the sea-cow explained to them that the whole cause of alarm, which did not say a single word itself, was only an invention from the dry land. And it held a little discourse over the tiresomeness of men.

'They want to get hold of us,' it said, 'it is the only thing they live for; they stretch out nets and come with bait on a hook to catch us. That thing there is a kind of big line which they think we will bite, they are so stupid! We are not that! Don't touch it and it will crumble to pieces, the whole of it. What comes from up there has cracks and flaws, and is fit for nothing!'

'Fit for nothing,' said all the fishes, and adopted the sea-cow's opinion, so as to have an opinion.

The little sea-fish had its own thoughts. 'The enormous, long, thin serpent is perhaps the most marvellous fish in the sea. I have a feeling like that.'

'The most marvellous,' we men say also, and say it with knowledge and assurance.

It is the great sea-serpent talked about long before, in song and story. It is conceived and born, sprung from man's ingenuity and laid at the bottom of the sea, stretching itself from the eastern to the western lands, bearing messages as quickly as beams of light from the sun to our earth. It grows, grows in power and extent, grows from year to year, through all the seas, round the earth, under the stormy waters and under the glass-clear water, where the skipper looks down as if he sailed through transparent air, and sees fish swarming like a whole firework show of colours. Farthest down the serpent stretches itself, a world-serpent of blessing, which bites its tail as it encircles the earth. Fish and reptiles run against it with their heads, they do not yet understand the thing from above, the serpent of the knowledge of good and evil, filled with human thoughts and declaring them in all languages, yet silent itself, the most marvellous of the marvels of the deep, the great sea-serpent of our time.

The Gardener and the Family

FOUR OR five miles from the capital stood an old manor, with thick walls, tower, and pointed gables.

Here lived, but only in the summer-time, a noble family: this manor was the best and most beautiful of all the estates they possessed: outside, it looked as if it were newly built, and inside was very comfortable and cosy. The family coat of arms was carved in stone over the door, lovely roses twined themselves over the coat of arms and over the balcony, and a beautiful lawn stretched out before the house: there were red thorns and white thorns, and rare flowers even outside of the hot-house. The family had a very good gardener; it was a treat to see the flower garden, the fruit and kitchen gardens. Up to this time there was still a part of the original old garden, with some box hedges, cut in the shapes of crowns and pyramids. Behind these stood two old trees: they were nearly always leafless, and one could easily believe that a wind storm or a water-spout had strewn them over with great clumps of manure, but every clump was a bird's nest.

Here from time immemorial a swarm of screaming crows and rooks had built their nests. It was a whole bird town and the birds were the proprietors, the eldest branch of the family, the real masters of the estate. None of the people down there concerned them, but they tolerated these low walking creatures, although they sometimes shot with guns, so that it gave the birds shivers along the spine, and every bird flew up in a fright and shrieked 'Rak! Rak!' The gardener talked often to his master about cutting down the old trees, they did not look well, and if they were taken away, one would most probably be free from the screaming birds – they would search for another place then. But the master would neither be free from the trees nor the swarms of birds – it was something which the estate could not lose, it was something from the old times, and one ought not to wipe that out entirely.

'The trees are now the birds' inheritance, let them keep it, my good Larsen!'

The gardener was called Larsen, but that is of no further importance.

'Have you, little Larsen, not enough room for working – the whole of the flower garden, the greenhouses, the fruit and kitchen gardens?'

These he had, and nursed them, loved them, and cared for them with earnestness and capability, and the family knew that, but they did not hide from him that when visiting they often ate fruit and saw flowers which excelled what they had in their own garden, and that distressed the gardener, for he wished to do his best and he did his best. He was good of heart, and good in his work.

One day the master called him and said in all mildness and dignity that the day before, when with distinguished friends, they had got a variety of apples and pears, so juicy and so well flavoured that all the guests had exclaimed in admiration. The fruit was certainly not native, but it ought to be brought in and made at home here if the climate allowed it. One knew that it had been bought in town at the principal fruiterer's: the gardener should ride in and get to know where these apples and pears came from and order cuttings.

The gardener knew the fruiterer very well, for it was to him that he sold, on the proprietor's account, the surplus of the fruit which was grown in the gardens of the estate.

And the gardener went to town and asked the fruiterer where he got these highly prized apples and pears.

'They are from your own garden!' said the fruiterer, and showed him both apples and pears, which he knew again.

How delighted the gardener was! He hurried home and told the family that both the apples and pears were from their own garden.

The family could not believe that. 'That is impossible, Larsen! Can you get a written assurance from the fruiterer?'

And that he could, and so he brought a written assurance.

'That is extraordinary!' said the master.

Every day now great dishes of these lovely apples and pears from their own garden were brought to the table, baskets and barrels of these fruits were sent to friends in the town and country and even to other countries. It was a great joy! It must be said, however, that these had been two remarkable summers for fruit trees; over all the country these had succeeded well.

Time passed; the family one day dined with the court. The day after, the gardener was sent for by his master. They had at dinner got melons from His Majesty's greenhouse which were so juicy and so full of flavour.

'You must go to His Majesty's gardener, good Larsen, and get for us some of the seeds of these precious melons.'

'But His Majesty's gardener has got the seeds from us!' said the gardener, quite delighted.

'Then the man has known how to bring them to a higher development,' answered the master; 'every melon was excellent!'

'Yes, then I may be proud!' said the gardener. 'I may tell your lordship that the court gardener this year has not been successful with his melons, and when he saw how lovely ours were, and tasted them, he ordered three of them to be sent up to the castle.'

'Larsen! don't imagine that they were the melons from our garden!'

'I believe it!' said the gardener, and he went to the court gardener and got from him a written assurance that the melons at the king's table had come from the gardens of the manor.

It was really a great surprise for the family, and they did not keep the story a secret; they showed the assurance, and they sent melon seeds far and wide, just as they had sent cuttings before.

About these they got news that they caught on and set quite excellent fruit, and it was called after the family's estate, so that the name could now be read in English, German, and French. They had never thought of that before.

'If only the gardener won't get too great an opinion of himself!' said the family.

But he took it in another manner: he would only strive now to bring forward his name as one of the best gardeners in the country, and tried every year to bring out something excellent in the gardening line, and did it; but often he heard that the very first fruits he had brought, the apples and pears, were really the best, all later kinds stood far below.

The melons had really been very good, but that was quite another thing; the strawberries could also be called excellent, but still no better than those on other estates; and when the radishes one year were a failure, they only talked about the unfortunate radishes and not about any other good thing which he had produced.

It was almost as if the family felt a relief in saying, 'It didn't succeed this year, little Larsen!' They were very glad to be able to say, 'It didn't succeed this year!'

Twice a week the gardener brought fresh flowers for the rooms, always so beautifully arranged; the colours came as it were into a stronger light with the contrasts.

'You have taste, Larsen,' said the family; 'it is a gift which is given to you from our Father, not of yourself!'

One day he came with a big crystal bowl in which lay a water-lily leaf; on it was laid, with its long, thick stalk down in the water, a brilliant blue flower, as big as a sunflower.

'The lotus flower of India,' exclaimed the family. They had never seen such a flower; and it was placed in the sunshine by day and in the evening in a reflex light. Everyone who saw it found it both remarkable and rare, yes, even the highest young lady of the land, and she was the princess; she was both wise and good.

The family did itself the honour of presenting it to the princess, and it went with her up to the castle.

Now the master went down into the garden to pluck for himself a flower of the same kind, if such a one could be found, but there was not such a thing. So he called the gardener and asked him where he got the blue lotus from.

'We have sought in vain,' said he; 'we have been in the greenhouse and all round about!'

'No, it is certainly not there!' said the gardener; 'it is only a common flower from the kitchen-garden! but, indeed, isn't it lovely! it looks like a blue cactus, and yet it is only the flower of the artichoke.'

'You should have told us that at once!' said the master. 'We imagined that it was a strange, rare flower. You have made fools of us before the princess! She saw the flower and thought it beautiful, but did not know it, and she is well up in botany, but that science has nothing to do with vegetables. How could it have entered your head, good Larsen, to send such a flower up to the house? It will make us look ridiculous!'

And the lovely blue flower which was brought from the kitchen-garden was put out of the drawing-room, where it was not at home. The master made an apology to the princess and told her that the flower was only a vegetable which the gardener had taken the idea to present, but for which he had been given a good scolding.

'That was a sin and a shame!' said the princess. 'He has opened our eyes to a beautiful flower we had not noticed, he has shown us beauty where we did not expect to find it! The court gardener shall bring one up to my room every day, so long as the artichoke is in flower!'

And so it was done.

The family then told the gardener that he could again bring them a fresh artichoke flower.

'It is really beautiful!' they said, and praised the gardener.

'Larsen likes that,' said the family. 'He is a spoilt child.'

In the autumn there was a terrible storm. It got so violent during the night that many of the big trees in the outskirts of the wood were torn up by the roots, and to the great sorrow of the family, but to the joy of the gardener, the two big trees with all the birds' nests were blown down. During the storm one heard the screaming of the rooks and the crows; they beat the windows with their wings, the people in the house said.

'Now you are glad, Larsen,' said the master, 'the storm has blown down the trees and the birds have gone to the woods. There are no more signs of old times; every sign and every allusion has gone; it has troubled us!'

The gardener said nothing, but he thought of what he had long intended to do – to use the lovely sunshiny place which formerly he had no control over. It should become the pride of the garden and the delight of the family. The great trees had crushed and broken the old box-hedges with all their cut shapes. He raised here a thicket of plants, home plants from field and forest.

What no other gardener had thought of planting in the flower-garden, he set here in the kind of soil each should have, and in shade or sunshine as every kind required. He tended it in love, and it grew in magnificence.

Snow-berry bushes from the heath in Jutland, in form and colour like Italian cypress; the smooth, prickly holly, always green, in winter's cold and summer's sun, stood there lovely to look at. In front grew ferns, many different kinds, some looked as if they were the children of palm trees, and some as if they were the parents of the fine, lovely plant we call Venus's hair. Here stood the slighted burdock, which in its freshness is so beautiful that it can be put in a bouquet. The burdock stood on dry ground, but lower down in the damper soil grew the colt's-foot, also a despised plant, and yet with its fine height and huge leaves so picturesquely beautiful. Fathom high, with flower above flower, like a huge, many-armed candelabrum, the cow's lung-wort lifted itself. Here stood the wood-ruff, the marsh-marigold, and the lily of the valley, the wild calla, and the fine three-leaved wood-sorrel. It was a delight to see.

In front, supported on wire fences, little French pear trees grew in rows; they got sun and good care, and very soon they bore big, juicy fruit, as in the country they came from.

In place of the two leafless trees, there was a big flagstaff on which waved the Danish flag, and close beside it a pole, on which in summer and autumn hops with their sweet-smelling clusters twined themselves, but where in the winter, according to old custom, a sheaf of oats was raised that the birds of the air could have their meal at the joyous Christmas time.

'The good Larsen is growing sentimental in his old age,' said the family; 'but he is faithful and devoted to us.'

At New Year time, one of the illustrated papers of the capital had a picture of the old manor; one saw the flagstaff and the sheaf of oats for the birds, and it was spoken of as a beautiful thought that an old custom should be brought into recognition and honour; so distinctive for the old manor.

'All that Larsen does,' said the family, 'they beat the drum for. He is a lucky man! we must almost be proud that we have him!'

But they were not proud of it! They felt that they were the owners, they could give Larsen his dismissal; but they did not do that, they were good people, and there are so many good people of their class, that it is a good thing for every Larsen.

Yes, that is the story of 'The Gardener and the Family.' Now you can think it over!

The Flea and the Professor

ONCE UPON a time there was a balloonist with whom things went badly; the balloon burst, and the man came down and was dashed to pieces. He had sent his boy down with the parachute two minutes before: that was lucky for the boy. He was unhurt, and went about with great abilities for becoming a balloonist, but he had no balloon, and no means of getting one.

Live he must, and so he laid himself out to acquire the art of legerdemain, and to be able to talk with his stomach, which is called being a ventriloquist.

He was young and good-looking, and when he got a moustache, and was dressed in good clothes, he might have been taken for a nobleman's son. The ladies thought him beautiful: one young lady was so enchanted with his beauty and his cleverness, that she accompanied him to strange towns and countries; there he called himself Professor; less it could not be.

His constant thought was to get a balloon and fly in the air with his little wife, but as yet they had not the means.

'They will come,' said he.

'If only they would,' said she.

'We are young people! and now I am a Professor. Even crumbs are bread!'

She helped him faithfully, sat by the door and sold tickets for the performance, and that was a cold entertainment in winter. She helped him also in one trick. He put his wife in a table-drawer, a big table-drawer; she crept into the back drawer, and so was not to be seen from the front; it was like an optical illusion.

But one evening, when he pulled the drawer out, she had gone; she was not in the front drawer, nor in the back drawer, nor in the whole house – not to be seen, not to be heard. It was *her* clever trick. She never came back. She was tired of it, and *he* became tired of it, lost his good humour, could not talk or play tricks any more, and so nobody came; the profits became poor, his clothes became poor; he owned at last only a huge flea, an inheritance from his wife, and therefore he thought so much of it. So he trained it, taught it to do clever tricks, taught it to present arms, and fire a cannon.

The Professor was proud of the flea, and it was proud of itself; it had learnt something and had human blood in it, and had been in the biggest towns, had been seen by princes and princesses, and had won their high admiration. It appeared printed in the newspapers and on placards. It knew that it was famous, and could maintain a Professor, yes, even a whole family.

Proud and famous it was, and yet, when it and the Professor travelled, they went fourth class on the railway; that travels just as quickly as the first. There was a tacit promise that they would never separate, never marry, the flea would remain a bachelor, and the Professor a widower. It comes to the same thing.

'Where one has the greatest success,' said the Professor, 'one should not come twice.' He was a judge of character, and that is also an art.

At last he had travelled in all countries except savage countries, and so he decided to go there; there, indeed, they ate Christian men, the Professor knew, but he was not really a Christian, and the flea was not really a man, so he imagined that they might venture to travel there and have good fortune.

They travelled by steamship and sailing ship; the flea went through his tricks, and so they travelled free on the way and came to the country of the savages.

Here reigned a little Princess; she was only eight years old, but she reigned. She had taken the power from her father and mother, for she had a will and was exceptionally charming and naughty. As soon as the flea had presented arms and fired the cannon, she was so enchanted with it, that she said, 'Him, or no one!' She became quite wild with love, and was already wild before that. 'Sweet little sensible child!' said her father, 'if one could first make a man of it!'

'Leave that to me, old man!' said she, and it was not nicely said by a little princess, who talks to her father, but she was wild.

She set the flea on her little hand. 'Now you are a man ruling with me, but you shall do what I wish, or I shall kill you and eat the Professor.'

The Professor got a big room to live in. The walls were made of sugar-cane – he could go and lick them, but he had not a sweet tooth. He got a hammock to sleep in. It was as if he lay in a balloon such as he had always wished for, and which was his constant thought.

The flea stayed with the Princess, sat on her little hand and on her smooth neck. She had taken a hair from her head, and the Professor had to tie it to the leg of the flea, and so she kept it tied to the great piece of coral which she wore in her ear.

It was a delightful time for the Princess, also for the flea, she thought; but the Professor was not quite at his ease; he was a traveller, and liked to go from town to town, and to read in the newspapers about his perseverance and cleverness in teaching a flea all human actions. Day in and day out he lay in his hammock, dozed, and got good food – fresh eggs, elephants' eyes, and giraffe steak; cannibals do not live only on human flesh, *that* is a delicacy. 'Child's shoulder with sharp sauce,' said the mother of the Princess, 'is the most delicate!'

The Professor was wearied, and wished to get away from the savage country, but he must have the flea with him, it was his prodigy and breadwinner. How could he get it? That was not so easy. He strained all his powers of thought, and then he said, 'Now I have it!'

'Princess-father; vouchsafe me something to do! May I exercise the inhabitants of this country in presentations, or introductions; that is what one calls culture in the greatest countries of the world.'

'And what can you teach me?' said the father of the Princess.

'My greatest art,' said the Professor – 'to fire a cannon, so that the whole earth trembles, and all the nicest birds of the air fall down cooked! That makes a noise!'

'Come with the cannon!' said the Princess-father.

But in the whole country there was no cannon, except the one the flea had brought, and that was too little.

'I will make a bigger one,' said the Professor; 'give me only the materials; I must have fine silk, needle and thread, rope and cord, together with stomach drops for the balloon – they puff up, make lighter and lift up; they make the explosion in the stomach of the cannon.'

All that he demanded he got.

The whole country came together to see the big cannon. The Professor did not call before he had the balloon quite ready to fill up and to ascend.

The flea sat on the Princess's hand and looked on. The balloon was filled up, it bulged out and could scarcely be held, it was so wild.

'I must take it up into the air, so that it may be cooled,' said the Professor, and took his seat in the basket which hung under it. 'But I cannot manage to steer it alone. I must have an experienced companion with me to help me. There is no one here but the flea who can do that!'

'I am not willing to allow it!' said the Princess, but passed the flea to the Professor, who set it on his hand.

'Let go the ropes and cords!' said he. 'Now the balloon goes off!'

They thought he said, 'Cannon!'

And so the balloon went higher and higher, up over the clouds, away from the savage land. The little Princess, with her father and mother and all the people, stood and waited. They wait still, and if you don't believe it, go to the savage land, where every child talks about the flea and the Professor, and believes that they will come again when the cannon is cooled, but they come not, they are at home with us, they are in their fatherland, ride on the railway, first class, not fourth; they have good fortune and a huge balloon. No one asks how they have got the balloon, or from where they have it; they are well-to-do and honourable people, the flea and the Professor.

What Old Johanna Told

THE WIND moans in the old willow tree!

It is as if one heard a song; the wind sings it, the tree tells it. If you don't understand it, then ask Johanna in the almshouse; she knows, she was born here in the district.

Years ago, when the highway still lay here, the tree was already big and remarkable. It stood where it yet stands, outside the tailor's whitened framework house, close to the pool, which at that time was so big that the cattle were watered there, and there in the warm summer the little children ran about naked and splashed about in the water. Close up under the tree was a milestone; it has fallen down now, and bramble branches grow over it.

On the other side of the rich squire's farm the new high road was made, the old road became the field road, the pool a puddle, over-grown with duckweed; when a frog jumped down, the green was separated and one saw the black water; round about it grew, and still grow, the buckbean and gold irises.

The tailor's house became old and crooked, the roof a hot-bed for moss and house-leek; the dovecote fell in and the starlings built there, the swallows hung nest after nest on the gable of the house and under the roof, just as if it was a lucky dwelling-place. That was here at one time; now it has become lonely and silent. Alone and weak-willed, 'Poor Rasmus', as they called him, lived here; he had been born here, he had played here, he had sprung over the fields and the hedges, splashed as a little child in the open pool, clambered up in the old tree.

It lifted its great branches with pomp and beauty, as it lifts them still, but the storm had already twisted the trunk a little, and time had given it a crack; now wind and weather have laid earth in the crack, where grass and green things grow, yes, even a little rowan tree has planted itself there.

When the swallows came in the spring, they flew about the tree and the roof, they plastered and mended their old nests, but poor Rasmus let his nest stand and fall as it liked; he neither mended nor propped it. 'What is the use!' was his adage, and it was also his father's.

He remained in his home, the swallows flew away from it, but they came again, the faithful creatures. The starling flew away, but it came again and whistled its song; once Rasmus knew how to whistle in competition with it; now he neither whistled nor sang.

The wind moaned in the old willow tree – it still moans, it is as if one heard a song; the wind sings it, the tree tells it; if you do not understand it, then ask old Johanna in the almshouse; she knows, she is wise in old affairs, she is like a chronicle book, with legends and old memories.

When the house was new and good, the village tailor Ivar Olse moved into it with his wife Maren; respectable, industrious people, both of them. Old Johanna was at that time a child, she was the daughter of the maker of wooden shoes, one of the poorest in the neighbourhood. Many a nice piece of bread and butter she got from Maren, who had no lack of food. Maren stood well with the squire's wife; she was always laughing and glad, she never allowed herself to be disheartened, she used her tongue, but also her hands; she wielded her needle as well as her tongue, and looked after her house and her children; there were eleven of them.

'Poor people have always a nest full of young ones!' grumbled the squire; 'if one could drown them like kittens, and only keep one or two of the strongest, there would be less misfortune!'

'God bless me!' said the tailor's wife, 'children are a blessing of God; they are a joy in the house, each child is another Lord's Prayer! if things are straitened, and one has many mouths to feed, then one strives all the harder, finds ways and means in all respectability. Our Father does not let go, if we do not let go!'

The squire's lady gave her her countenance, bowed in a friendly way, and patted Maren on the cheek: she had done that many times, even kissed her, but that was when she was little, and Maren her nursemaid. They had thought much of each other, and still did so.

Every year at Christmas, came winter supplies from the big house to the tailor's house; a barrel of meal, a pig, two geese, a stone of butter, cheese and apples. It was a help to the larder. Ivar Olse looked quite contented then, but soon came his old adage, 'What is the use!' Everything was clean and neat in the house, curtains at the windows, and flowers, both carnations and balsams. A sampler hung in a picture frame, and close beside it a composition in rhyme: Maren Olse herself had composed it; she knew how rhymes ought to go. She was almost a little proud of the family name 'Oise'. It was the only word in the Danish language that rhymed with 'Polse' (sausage). 'That is always something in which one is superior to other people,' she said, and laughed. She always kept her good humour, and never said like her husband, 'What is the use!' Her adage was, 'Hold to yourself and our Father!' She did that, and it kept everything together. The children throve, grew too big for the nest, went far, and behaved themselves well. Rasmus was the youngest; he was such a lovely child, and one of the great artists in the town borrowed him for a model, and that as naked as when he came into this world. The picture hung now in the king's palace, where the squire's lady had seen it and recognised little Rasmus, although he had no clothes on.

But now bad times came. The tailor had pains, got rheumatism in both hands, great knots came into them, and no doctor could help him, not even the wise Stine who 'doctored'.

'One must not be disheartened!' said Maren. 'It is no use to hang the head! now that we no longer have father's two hands to help, I must see about using mine the quicker. Little Rasmus also can use the needle!'

He already sat on the board, whistling and singing; he was a happy boy.

The mother said that he must not sit there all day; it was a sin against the child; he must also run about and play.

The shoemaker's little Johanna was his best playmate; she belonged to still poorer people than Rasmus. She was not beautiful; she was bare-legged; her clothes hung in tatters, she had no one to look after them, and it never occurred to her to do it herself; she was a child, and as glad as a bird in our Lord's sunshine.

Rasmus and Johanna played beside the milestone and the big willow tree.

He had high thoughts; he meant to be a fine tailor someday and live in the town, where there were masters who had ten men on the board; he had heard that from his father; there he would be a man, and there he would be a master, and then Johanna could come and visit him, and if she knew how to cook, she could make the food for them all and have her own big room.

Johanna dared not really believe this, but Rasmus believed that it really would happen. So they sat under the old tree and the wind moaned in the leaves and the branches: it was as if the wind sang and the tree spoke.

In the autumn every single leaf fell and the rain dripped from the bare branches.

'They will grow green again!' said Mother Olse.

'What is the use!' said the man. 'New year, new care for a living!'

'The larder is full!' said the wife. 'We have to thank our good lady for that. I am healthy and have good strength. It is sinful of us to complain!'

The squire's family were at their country home for Christmas, but the week after the New Year they went to town, where they spent the winter in enjoying themselves: they went to balls and festivals with the king himself.

The lady had got two expensive dresses from France; they were of such stuff, and such cut and sewing that the tailor's Maren had never seen the like before. She asked the lady if she might come up to the house and bring her husband also, to see the dresses. Such things had never been seen by a country tailor.

He saw them and had never a word to say, before he came home, and what he said, was only what he always said, 'What is the use!' and this time his word was true.

The family went to town; balls and parties had begun there, but in the midst of the enjoyment the squire died, and the lady could not wear the lovely dresses. She was so sorrowful, and dressed from head to foot in black mourning clothes; not so much as a white strip was to be seen; all the servants were in black, even the state coach was draped with fine black cloth.

It was a bitter, frosty night, the snow glittered and the stars shone. The heavy gun-carriage came from the town with the body to the private chapel, where it was to be placed in the family vault. The steward and the parish beadle sat on horseback with torches before the churchyard gate. The church was lighted up, and the priest stood in the open church door to receive the body. The coffin was carried up into the choir, and all the people followed it. The priest made a speech and a psalm was sung. The lady was in the church, she had driven there in the black-draped state carriage; it was black inside and out, and the like had never been seen in the district before.

They talked the whole winter about the squire's funeral.

'One saw there what this man signified!' said the country people. 'He was nobly born and he was nobly buried!'

'What is the use of that!' said the tailor. 'Now he has neither life nor property. We have still one of these!'

'Don't say such things!' said Maren, 'he has everlasting life in the heavenly kingdom!'

'Who has told you that, Maren?' said the tailor. 'Dead men are good manure! but this man was too superior to make profit to the earth, he must lie in a chapel vault!'

'Don't talk so unChristian-like!' said Maren. 'I tell you again, he has everlasting life!'

'Who has told you that, Maren?' repeated the tailor. And Maren threw her apron over little Rasmus so that he might not hear the conversation. She carried him over to the turf-house and wept.

'The talk you heard over there, little Rasmus, was not your father's; it was the wicked one who went through the room, and took your father's voice! Say "Our Father". We will both say it!' She folded the child's hands.

'Now I am glad again!' she said; 'hold fast by yourself and our Father!'

The year of mourning was ended, the widow was dressed in half-mourning, and she was quite light-hearted. There were rumours that she had a wooer and already thought of a second marriage. Maren knew something of it, and the priest knew a little more.

On Palm Sunday, after the service, the banns were published for the marriage of the widow and her betrothed. He was a sculptor, the name of his occupation was not well known; at that time Thorwaldsen and his art were not yet in the mouths of the people. The new squire was not of noble birth, but yet a very splendid man; he was one who was something no one understood, they said; he carved statues, was clever in his work, young and good-looking.

'What use is that!' said the tailor Olse.

On Palm Sunday the banns were published from the pulpit, and then followed psalm-singing and communion. The tailor, his wife, and little Rasmus were in the church; the parents went to the communion, Rasmus sat in the pew – he was not confirmed yet. There had been a lack of clothes lately in the tailor's house. The old ones they had, had been turned again and again, sewed and patched; now all three were in new clothes, but black, as if for a funeral; they were dressed in the covering from the mourning-coach. The man had got a coat and trousers from it, Maren a high-necked dress, and Rasmus a whole suit to grow in till his confirmation. Both the inside and outside covering of the mourning-coach had been used. No one need know what it had been used for before, but people got to know it very quickly; the wise woman Stine, and others just as wise, who did not live by their wisdom, said that the clothes would bring sickness into the house. 'One dares not dress oneself in the trappings of a hearse except to drive to the grave.'

The shoemaker's Johanna wept when she heard that talk; and when it happened that the tailor grew worse from day to day, it would assuredly appear who was to be the victim.

And it showed itself.

The first Sunday after Trinity, tailor Olse died, and now Maren was alone to keep the whole thing together; she held to that, to herself, and to our Father.

The following year Rasmus was confirmed; then he went to town as apprentice to a big tailor, not with twelve men on the board, but with one: little Rasmus could be counted as a half: he was glad and looked contented, but little Johanna wept; she thought more of him than she herself knew. The tailor's wife remained in the old house and carried on the business.

It was just at that time that the new high road was opened; the old one, past the willow tree and the tailor's house, became the field way, the pond became overgrown, duckweed covered the little pool of water that remained, the milestone fell down – it had nothing to stand up for, but the tree held itself up, strong and beautiful; the wind whistled in the leaves and branches. The swallows flew away, the starlings flew away, but they came again in the spring, and when they came back for the fourth time, Rasmus came back to his home. He had finished his apprenticeship, was a good-looking but slender young fellow; now he would tie up his knapsack and go to see foreign lands; his mind was bent on that. But his mother hung on to him; home was best! all the other children were scattered, he was the youngest, the house should be his. He could get plenty of work if he would stay in the district and be a travelling tailor, sew fourteen days at one farm, and fourteen days at another. That was also travelling. And Rasmus followed his mother's advice. So he slept again under the roof of his birthplace, and sat again under the old willow tree, and heard it moan.

He was good-looking, and could whistle like a bird, and sing both new and old songs. He was in favour at all the big farms, particularly at Klaus Hansen's, who was the second richest farmer in the district.

His daughter Elsie was like the loveliest flower, and she was always laughing; there were people who were so ill-natured as to say that she only laughed to show her pretty teeth.

She was ready to laugh, and always in the humour to play pranks.

They fell in love with each other, but neither of them said it in so many words.

So he went about and became heavy-hearted; he had more of his father's than his mother's disposition. The humour only came when Elsie came, then they both laughed, joked, and played tricks, but although there was good opportunity, he said never a word of his love. 'What is the use!' was his thought. 'Her parents look for riches for her, and that I have not got; it were wisest to go away from here!' But he could not go away from the farm; it was as if Elsie had bound him with a thread: he was like a trained bird for her, he sang and whistled for her pleasure and after her will.

Johanna, the shoemaker's daughter, was servant on the farm there, engaged in menial work; she drove the milkcart out to the field, where she, with the other girls, milked the cows; she had even to drive the manure when that was wanted. She never went up to the big room, and so did not see much of Rasmus or Elsie, but she heard that they were as good as engaged.

'Rasmus comes into prosperity,' said she, 'I cannot grudge him that!' And her eyes became wet, although there was nothing to cry for.

It was market day in town. Klaus Hansen drove into it and Rasmus was with him; he sat by the side of Elsie both going and coming. He was overwhelmed with love, but said never a word about it.

'He might say something to me about the thing!' thought the girl, and she was right. 'If he will not speak, then I will give him a fright!'

And soon people were saying on the farm that the richest farmer in the neighbourhood had made love to Elsie, and so he had, but no one knew what answer she had given him.

Thoughts buzzed about in Rasmus's head.

One evening Elsie put a gold ring on her finger and asked Rasmus what it meant.

'Engagement,' said he.

'And with whom, do you think?' asked she.

'With the rich farmer,' said he.

'You have hit it!' said she, nodded, and slipped away.

But he also slipped away, came home to his mother's house like a madman, and packed his knapsack. Out into the wide world would he go; his mother wept, but it was of no use. He cut himself a stick from the old willow, he whistled as if he were in a good humour, he was going out to see the grandeur of the world.

'It is a great trial for me!' said the mother. 'But for you it is, no doubt, the best thing to go away, and so I must just submit to it. Hold to yourself and our Lord, and so I will get you home glad and contented again!'

He went by the new high road, and there he saw Johanna driving a load of manure. She had not noticed him, and he did not want her to see him, so he sat himself behind the hedge, and hid there – and Johanna drove past.

Out into the world he went, and no one knew where; his mother thought he would come home again before the year was finished: 'He has now something new to see and to think about, but he will get back into the old folds again, which cannot be ironed out with any pressing-iron. He has a little too much of his father's disposition. I would rather he had mine, the poor child! but he will come home, he cannot give the old house and me the slip.'

The mother would wait a year and a day; Elsie waited only a month, then she went secretly to the wise woman Stine, who could 'doctor', read fortunes in cards and coffee, and knew more than her Lord's Prayer. She knew also where Rasmus was. She could read that in the coffee-grounds. He was in a foreign town, but she could not read the name of it. There were in that town soldiers and pretty girls. He thought either of taking a musket or one of the girls.

Elsie could not bear to hear that. She would willingly give her savings to buy him off, but no one must know that she had done it.

And old Stine promised that he would come back; she knew an art, a dangerous art for the person concerned, but it was the last resource. She would set the pot on to boil for him, and then he must come away from the place where he happened to be; he must come home, where the pot boiled and his dearest one waited: months might pass before he came, but come he must, if there was life in him.

Without resting, night and day he must travel, over lake and mountain, be the weather mild or hard, however tired he was. He *should* come home, he *must* come home.

The moon was in the first quarter; it must be so for the exercise of that art, said old Stine. It was stormy weather, the old willow tree cracked: Stine cut off a twig, and tied it into a knot, it would help to draw Rasmus home to his mother's house. Moss and house-leek were taken from the roof of the house, put into the pot, which was set on the fire. Elsie must now tear a leaf out of a psalm-book; she accidentally tore out the last one, the one with the list of misprints. 'It will do quite as well!' said Stine, and threw it in the pot.

Many kinds of things must go into the gruel, which must boil and constantly boil until Rasmus came home. The black cock in Stine's room must lose its red comb, it was put in the pot. Elsie's thick gold ring must also go in, and she would never get it again, Stine told her beforehand. Stine was so wise. Many things which we do not know the names of went into the pot; it stood constantly on the fire, or on glowing embers, or hot ashes. Only she and Elsie knew about it.

The moon waxed and waned; and always Elsie came and asked, 'Do you not see him coming?'

'Much I know,' said Stine, 'and much I see, but the length of the way for him I cannot see. Now he is over the first mountain! now he is on the sea in bad weather! The way is long through the great woods, he has blisters on his feet, he has fever in his body, but he must go on!'

'No! no!' said Elsie, 'I am sorry for him!'

'He cannot be stopped now! for if we do that he will drop dead on the highway!'

A year and a day had gone. The moon shone round and big, the wind moaned in the old tree, a rainbow in the moonshine was seen in the sky.

'That is the sign of confirmation!' said Stine. 'Now Rasmus is coming.'

But he came not.

'The waiting-time is long!' said Stine.

'Now I am tired of it!' said Elsie. She came less often to Stine and brought her no new gifts. Her heart became lighter, and one fine morning everybody in the neighbourhood knew that Elsie had said 'Yes' to the richest farmer.

She went to look at the farm and the fields, the cattle and the furniture. Everything was in good order, there was nothing to delay the wedding for.

It was held with great festivity for three days. There was dancing to flute and violin. Everyone in the neighbourhood was invited. Mother Olse was there also; and when the gaiety was at an end, and the guests had said 'Thanks', and the musicians had gone, she went home with the remnants of the feast.

She had only fastened the door with a pin; that was taken off, the door stood open, and there stood Rasmus. He had come home, come at this hour. Lord, how he looked! skin and bone only, pale and yellow was he!

'Rasmus!' said the mother, 'is it you, I see? How poorly you look! but I am glad in my heart that I have you!'

And she gave him of the good food she had brought home from the feast – a piece of steak, and a wedding tart.

He had, in these last days, he said, thought often of his mother, his homestead, and the old willow tree. It was wonderful how often in his dreams he had seen the tree and the bare-legged Johanna. Elsie he did not even name. He was ill and must go to bed; but we do not believe that the pot was the cause of this, or that it had exercised any power over him; only old Stine and Elsie believed that, but they spoke to no one about it.

Rasmus lay in a fever; it was infectious, so no one sought the tailor's house except Johanna, the shoemaker's daughter. She wept to see how miserable Rasmus was.

The doctor wrote out a prescription for him; he would not take the medicine, 'What is the use?' said he.

'Yes, then you will be yourself again,' said the mother. 'Hold fast to yourself and our Lord! If I could only see you put on flesh again, hear you whistle and sing, I would willingly lay down my life.'

And Rasmus got better of his illness, but his mother took it; our Lord called her and not him.

It was lonely in the house, and it grew poorer. 'He is worn out,' said the neighbours. 'Poor Rasmus!' A wild life had he led on his travels, that, and not the black pot which boiled, had sapped his strength and given him unrest in his body. His hair became thin and grey; he did not care to do anything properly.

'What good can that do?' said he. He sought the public-house rather than the church.

One autumn evening, in wind and rain, he struggled along the dirty road from the public-house to his home: his mother had long ago been laid in her grave. The swallows and the starling had also gone, the faithful creatures; Johanna the shoemaker's daughter had not gone; she overtook him on the way and accompanied him a little bit.

'Pull yourself together, Rasmus!'

'What good can that do?' said he.

'That is a bad motto you have!' said she. 'Remember your mother's words: "Hold to yourself and our Lord!" You don't do that, Rasmus! that one *ought*, and that one *shall*. Never say "What good can that do?" for then you pull up the root of all your actions.'

She accompanied him to the door of his house, and there she left him. He did not stay inside, but went and sat himself on part of the fallen milestone.

The wind moaned in the branches of the tree, it was like a song, it was like a talk. Rasmus answered it; he talked aloud, but no one heard it, except the tree and the moaning wind.

'I am getting cold! It is time to go to bed. Sleep! sleep!'

And he went, not towards the house but to the pool, where he stumbled and fell. The rain poured down, the wind was icy cold, but he did not notice it: but when the sun rose, and the crows flew over the pool, he wakened, half-dead. If he had laid his head where his feet lay, he would never have got up again, the green duckweed would have been his shroud.

Later in the day Johanna came to the tailor's house; she was his help; she got him taken to the hospital.

'We have known each other from childhood,' said she; 'your mother has given me both meat and drink, I can never repay her for it! You will get your health again, you will be able to live yet.'

And our Lord willed it that he should live, but it was up and down with the health and the mind. The swallows and the starlings came and went and came again; Rasmus became old before his time. Lonely he sat in the house, which became more and more dilapidated. He was poor, poorer now than Johanna.

'You have no faith,' said she, 'and if we have not our Lord, what have we? You should go to communion! you have not been there since your confirmation.'

'Well, what good can that do?' said he.

'If you say that and believe it, so let it be! Unwilling guests the Lord will not see at His Table. Think, however, of your mother and your childhood's days! You were at that time a good, God-fearing boy. May I read a psalm for you?'

'What good can that do?' said he.

'It always comforts me,' said she.

'Johanna, you have become one of the holy ones!' and he looked at her with heavy, tired eyes. And Johanna read the psalm, but not from the book – she did not have one, she knew it by heart.

'Those were beautiful words,' said he, 'but I could not quite follow. It is so heavy in my head!'

Rasmus had become an old man, but Elsie was no longer young either, if we are to mention her; Rasmus never did. She was a grandmother; a little flippant girl was her grandchild, the little one played with the other children in the village. Rasmus came, leaning on his stick; he stood still, looked at the children's play, smiled to them, old times shone into his thoughts. Elsie's grandchild pointed at him. 'Poor Rasmus!' she shouted; the other children followed her example and shouted 'Poor Rasmus!' and followed the old man with shrieks.

It was a grey, heavy day, and several like it followed, but after grey and heavy days there comes a sunshiny one.

It was a lovely Whitsuntide, the church was decorated with green birch branches, there was the smell of the woods, and the sun shone over the church pews. The big altar candles were lighted, it was communion; Johanna was amongst those kneeling there, but Rasmus was not amongst them. Just that morning our Lord had called him. With God are compassion and mercy.

Many years have passed since then; the tailor's house stands there still, but no one lives there, it may fall with the first storm. The pool is covered with reeds and buckbean. The wind moans in the old tree, it is as if one heard a song; the wind sings it, the tree tells it; if you don't understand it, then ask old Johanna in the almshouse.

She lives there, she sings her psalm, the one she sang for Rasmus; she thinks of him, prays to our Lord for him, the faithful soul that she is. She can tell about the past times, the memories, which moan in the old tree.

The Door-Key

EVERY KEY has its story, and there are many keys; the chamberlain's key, the clock-key, St Peter's key; we could tell about all the keys, but now we shall only tell about the chamberlain's door-key.

It came into being at a locksmith's, but it could well believe that it was at a blacksmith's, it was hammered and filed so much. It was too big for the trousers pocket, so it had to be carried in the coat pocket. Here it lay for the most part in the dark, but it also had its appointed place on the wall, by the side of the chamberlain's portrait from childhood's days, in which he looked like a force-meat ball with a frill on.

They say that every person has in his character and conduct something of the constellation he was born under, the bull, the virgin, or the scorpion, as they are called in the almanac. The chamberlain's wife named none of these, but said her husband was born under the 'sign of the wheelbarrow', because he had always to be shoved forward.

His father pushed him into an office, his mother pushed him into marriage, and his wife pushed him up to be chamberlain, but she did not say so, she was an excellent discreet woman, who was silent in the right place, and talked and pushed in the right place.

Now he was up in years, 'well proportioned,' as he said himself, a man with education, good humour, and a knowledge of keys as well, something which we shall understand better presently.

He was always in a good humour, everyone thought much of him and liked to talk with him. If he went into the town, it was difficult to get him home again if mother was not with him to push him along. He must talk with every acquaintance he met. He had many acquaintances, and the result was bad for the dinner.

His wife watched from the window. 'Now he is coming!' said she to the servant, 'put on the pot! Now he is stopping to talk to someone, so take off the pot, or the food will be cooked too much! Now he is coming! Yes, put the pot on again!' But he did not come for all that.

He would stand right under the window and nod up to her, but if an acquaintance came past, then he could not help it, he must say a word or two to him; if another one came past while he talked with the first, he held the first one by the buttonhole and seized the other one by the hand, whilst he shouted to another one who was passing.

It was a trial of patience for his wife. 'Chamberlain! Chamberlain!' she shouted then. 'Yes, the man is born under the sign of the wheel-barrow, he cannot come away unless he is pushed!'

He liked very much to go into the bookshops, to look at the books and papers. He gave the bookseller a little present, to be allowed to take the new books home to read – that is to say, to have leave to cut the books up the long way, but not along the top, because then they could not be sold as new. He was a living journal of etiquette, knew everything about engagements, weddings, literary talk and town gossip; he threw out mysterious allusions about knowing things which nobody knew. He got it from the door-key.

As young newly married people the chamberlain and his wife had lived on their own estate, and from that time they had the same door-key, but then they did not know its wonderful power – they only got to know that later on.

It was in the time of Frederick VI. Copenhagen at that time had no gas; it had oil lamps; it had no Tivoli or Casino, no tramways and no railways. There were not many amusements compared to what there are now. On Sunday people went out of the town on an excursion to the churchyard, read the inscriptions on the graves, sat in the grass and ate and drank, or they went to Fredericksberg, where the band played before the castle, and many people watched the royal family rowing about on the little, narrow canals where the old king steered the boat, and he and the queen bowed to all the people without making any distinctions. Prosperous families came out there from the town and drank their evening tea. They could get hot water at a peasant's little house, outside the garden, but they had to bring the other things with them.

The chamberlain's family went there one sunny Sunday afternoon;

the servant went on first with the tea-basket, and a basket with eatables. 'Take the door-key!' said the wife, 'so that we can slip in ourselves when we come back; you know they lock up at dusk, and the bell-wire was broken yesterday! We shall be late in coming home! After we leave Fredericksberg we shall go to the theatre to see the pantomime.'

And so they went to Fredericksberg, heard the music, saw the royal boat with the waving flag, saw the old king, and the white swans. After they had had a good tea, they hurried off, but did not come in time to the theatre.

The rope-dance was over and the stilt-dance was past and the pantomime begun: they were too late, as usual, and it was the chamberlain's fault; every minute he stood and talked to some acquaintance on the way; in the theatre he also found good friends, and when the performance was over, he and his wife must necessarily go in with a family, to enjoy a glass of punch: it would only take about ten minutes, but they dragged on to an hour. They talked and talked. Particularly entertaining was a Swedish Baron, or was he a German? the chamberlain did not exactly remember, but on the contrary, the trick he taught him with the key he remembered for all time. It was extraordinarily interesting! he could get the key to answer everything he asked it about, even the most secret things.

The chamberlain's key was peculiarly fitted for this, it was heavy in the wards, and it must hang down. The Baron let the handle of the key rest on the first finger of his right hand. Loose and easy it hung there, every pulsebeat in the finger point could set it in motion, so that it turned, and if that did not happen, then the Baron knew how to make it turn as he wished without being noticed.

Every turning was a letter, from A, and as far down the alphabet as one wished. When the first letter was found, the key turned to the opposite side, and then one sought for the next letter, and so one got the whole word, then whole sentences; the answer to the question. It was all fabrication, but always entertaining. That was also the chamberlain's first idea, but he did not stick to it.

'Man! Man!' shouted his wife. 'The west gate is shut at twelve o'clock! we will not get in, we have only a quarter of an hour.'

They had to hurry themselves; several people who wished to get into the town went quickly past them. As they approached the last guardhouse, the clock struck twelve, and the gate banged to: many people stood shut out, and amongst them the chamberlain and his wife and the girl with the tea-basket. Some stood there in great terror, others in vexation: each took it in his own way. What was to be done?

Fortunately, it had been settled lately that one of the town gates should not be locked, and through the guardhouse there, foot-passengers could slip into the town.

The way was not very short, but the weather was beautiful, the sky clear and starry, frogs croaked in ditch and pond. The party began to sing, one song after another, but the chamberlain neither sang nor looked at the stars, nor even at his own feet, so he fell all his length, along by the ditch; one might have thought that he had been drinking too much, but it was not the punch, it was the key, which had gone to his head and was turning about there.

Finally they got to the guardhouse, slipped over the bridge and into the town.

'Now I am glad again,' said the wife. 'Here is our door!'

'But where is the door-key?' said the chamberlain. It was neither in the back pocket, nor the side pocket.

'Merciful God!' shouted his wife. 'Have you not got the key? You have lost it with your key-tricks with the Baron. How can we get in now? The bell-wire was broken yesterday, and the policeman has no key for the house. We are in despair!'

The servant girl began to sob, the chamberlain was the only one who had any self-possession.

'We must break one of the chandler's window-panes,' said he; 'get him up and then slip in.'

He broke one pane, he broke two. 'Petersen!' he shouted, and stuck his umbrella handle through the panes; the cellar-man's daughter inside screamed. The cellar-man threw open the shop door and shouted 'Police!' and before he had seen the chamberlain's family, recognised and let them in; the policeman whistled, and in the next street another policeman answered with a whistle. People ran to the windows. 'Where is the fire? Where is the disturbance?' they asked, and were still asking when the chamberlain was already in his room; there he took his coat off, and in it lay the door-key – not in the pocket, but in the lining; it had slipped down through a hole, which should not have been in the pocket.

From that evening the door-key had a particularly great significance, not only when they went out in the evening, but when they sat at home, and the chamberlain showed his cleverness and let the key give answers to questions. He himself thought of the most likely answer, and so he let the key give it, till at last he believed in it himself; but the apothecary – a young man closely related to the chamberlain – did not believe. The apothecary had a good critical head; he had, from his schooldays, written criticisms on books and theatres, but without signing his name, that does so much. He was what one calls a wit, but did not believe in spirits, and least of all in key-spirits.

'Yes, I believe, I believe,' said he, 'dear chamberlain, I believe in the door-key and all key-spirits, as firmly as I believe in the new science which is beginning to be known, table-turning and spirits in old and new furniture. Have you heard about it? I have! I have doubted, you know I am a sceptic, but I have become converted by reading in a quite trustworthy foreign paper, a terrible story. Can you imagine, chamberlain – I give you the story as I have it. Two clever children had seen their parents waken the spirit in a big dining-table. The little ones were alone and would now try in the same way to rub life into an old bureau. The life came, the spirit awoke, but it would not tolerate the command of the children; it raised itself, a crash sounded, it shot out its drawers and laid each of the children in a drawer and ran with them out of the open door, down the stair and into the street, along to the canal, into which it rushed and drowned both of them. The little ones were buried in Christian ground, but the bureau was brought into the council room, tried for child murder, and burnt alive in the market.

'I have read it!' said the apothecary, 'read it in a foreign paper, it is not something that I have invented myself. It is, the key take me, true! now I swear a solemn oath!'

The chamberlain thought that such a tale was too rude a jest. These two could never talk about the key, the apothecary was stupid on the subject of keys.

The chamberlain made progress in the knowledge of keys; the key was his amusement and his hobby.

One evening the chamberlain was just about to go to bed – he stood half undressed, and then he heard a knocking on the door out in the passage; it was the cellar-man who came so late; he also was half undressed, but he had, he said, suddenly got a thought which he was afraid he could not keep over the night.

'It is my daughter, Lotte-Lena, I must speak about. She is a pretty girl, and she is confirmed, and now I would like to see her well placed.'

'I am not yet a widower,' said the chamberlain, and smiled, 'and I have no son I can offer her!'

'You understand me, I suppose, Chamberlain,' said the cellar-man. 'She can play the piano, and sing; you might be able to hear her up here in the house. You don't know all that that girl can hit upon. She can imitate everybody in speaking and walking. She is made for comedy, and that is a good way for pretty girls of good family, they might be able to marry a count, but that is not the thought with me or Lotte-Lena. She can sing and she can play the piano! so I went with her the other day up to the music school. She sang, but she has not the finest kind of voice for a woman; she has not the canary-shriek in the highest notes which one demands in lady singers, and so they advised her against that career. Then, I thought, if she cannot be a singer, she can at any rate be an actress, which only requires speech. Today I spoke to the instructor, as they call him. "Has she education?" he asked. "No," said I, "absolutely none!" "Education is necessary for an artist!" said he. She can get that yet, I thought, and so I went home. She can go into a lending library and read what is there. But as I sat this evening, undressing, it occurred to me, why hire books when one can borrow them? The chamberlain is full up with books, let her read them; that is education enough, and she can have that free!'

'Lotte-Lena is a nice girl!' said the chamberlain, 'a pretty girl! She shall have books for her education. But has she that which one calls "go" in her brain – genius? And has she, what is of as much importance – luck?'

'She has twice won a prize in the lottery,' said the cellar-man, 'once she won a wardrobe, and once six pairs of sheets; I call that luck, and she has that!'

'I will ask the key!' said the chamberlain. And he placed the key upon his forefinger and on the cellar-man's forefinger, let it turn itself and give letter by letter.

The key said, 'Victory and Fortune!' and so Lotte-Lena's future was settled.

The chamberlain at once gave her two books to read: the play of 'Dyveke' and Knigge's 'Intercourse with People'. From that evening a kind of closer acquaintanceship between Lotte-Lena and the chamberlain's family began. She came up into the family, and the chamberlain thought that she was an intelligent girl; she believed in him and in the key. The chamberlain's wife saw, in the boldness with which she every moment showed her great ignorance, something childish and innocent. The couple, each in their own way, thought much of her, and she of them.

'There is such a nice smell upstairs,' said Lotte-Lena. There was a smell, a scent of apples in the passage, where the wife had laid out a whole barrel of 'greystone' apples. There was also an incense smell of roses and lavender through all the rooms.

'It is something lovely,' said Lotte-Lena. Her eyes were delighted with the many lovely flowers, which the chamberlain's wife always had here; yes, even in winter the lilac and cherry branches flowered here. The leafless branches were cut off and put in water, and in the warm room they soon bore leaves and flowers.

'One might believe that the bare branches were dead, but, look! how they rise up from the dead.'

'That has never occurred to me before,' said Lotte-Lena. 'Nature is charming!'

And the chamberlain let her see his 'Key-book' where he had written the remarkable things the key had said, even about half of an apple cake which had disappeared from the cupboard just the evening when the servant girl had a visit from her sweetheart. The chamberlain asked his key, 'Who has eaten the apple cake – the cat or the sweetheart?' and the door-key answered, 'The sweetheart!' The chamberlain knew it before he asked, and the servant girl confessed: the cursed key knew everything.

'Yes, is it not remarkable?' said the chamberlain. 'The key! the key! and about Lotte-Lena it predicted "Victory and Fortune!" – We shall see that yet – I answer for it!'

'That is delightful,' said Lotte-Lena.

The chamberlain's wife was not so confident, but she did not express her doubt when her husband could hear it, but confided to Lotte-Lena that the chamberlain, when he was a young man, had been quite given up to the theatre. If anyone at that time had pushed him, he would certainly have been trained as an actor, but the family pushed the other way. He insisted on going on the stage, and to get there he wrote a comedy.

'It is a great secret I confide to you, little Lotte-Lena. The comedy was not bad, it was accepted at the Royal Theatre and hissed off the stage, so that it has never been heard of since, and I am glad of it. I am his wife and know him. Now, you will go the same way; I wish you everything good, but I don't believe it will happen, I do not believe in the key!'

Lotte-Lena believed in it; and the chamberlain agreed with her. Their hearts understood each other in all virtue and honour. The girl had several abilities which the chamberlain appreciated. Lotte-Lena knew how to make starch from potatoes, to make silk gloves from old silk stockings, and to cover her silk dancing-shoes, although she had had the means to buy everything new. She had what the chandler called 'money in the table-drawer, and bonds in the bank'. The chamberlain's wife thought she would make a good wife for the apothecary, but she did not say so and did not let the key say it either. The apothecary was going to settle down soon, and have his own business in one of the nearest and biggest provincial towns.

Lotte-Lena constantly read the books she had borrowed from the chamberlain. She kept them for two years, but by that time she knew by heart all the parts of 'Dyveke', but she only wished to appear in one of them, that of Dyveke herself, and not in the capital where there was so much jealousy, and where they would not have her. She would begin her artistic career (as the chamberlain called it) in one of the bigger provincial towns.

Now it was quite miraculous, that it was just the very same place where the young apothecary had settled himself as the town's youngest, if not the only, apothecary.

The long-looked-for evening came when Lotte-Lena should make her first appearance and win victory and fortune, as the key had said. The chamberlain was not there, he was ill in bed and his wife nursed him; he had to have warm bandages and camomile tea; the bandages *on* the stomach and the tea *in* the stomach.

The couple were not present themselves at the performance of 'Dyveke', but the apothecary was there and wrote a letter about it to his relative the chamberlain's wife.

'If the chamberlain's key had been in my pocket,' he wrote, 'I would have taken it out and whistled in it; she deserved that, and the door-key deserved it, which had so shamefully lied to her with its "Victory and Fortune".'

The chamberlain read the letter. The whole thing was malice, said he – hatred of the key – which vented itself on the innocent girl.

And as soon as he rose from his bed, and was himself again, he sent a short but venomous letter to the apothecary, who answered it as if he had not found anything but jest and good humour in the whole epistle.

He thanked him for that as for every future, benevolent contribution to the publication of the key's incomparable worth and importance. Next, he confided to the chamberlain, that he, besides his work as apothecary, was writing a great key romance, in which all the characters were keys; without exception, keys. 'The door-key' was naturally the leading person, and the chamberlain's door-key was the model for him, endowed with prophetic vision and divination. All the other keys must revolve round it; the old chamberlain's key, which knew the splendour and festivities of the court; the clock-key, little, fine, and elegant, costing three-pence at the ironmonger's; the key of the pulpit, which reckons itself among the clergy, and has, by sitting through the night in the keyhole, seen ghosts. The dining-room, the wood-house and the wine-cellar keys all appear, curtsy, and revolve around the door-key. The sunbeams light it up like silver; the wind, the spirit of the universe, rushes in on it, so that it whistles. It is the key of all keys, it was the chamberlain's door-key, now it is the key of the gate of Heaven, it is the Pope's key, it is 'infallible'.

'Malice,' said the chamberlain, 'colossal malice!

He and the apothecary did not see each other again except at the funeral of the chamberlain's wife.

She died first.

There was sorrow and regret in the house. Even the branches of cherry tree, which had sent out fresh shoots and flowers, sorrowed and withered; they stood forgotten, she cared for them no more.

The chamberlain and the apothecary followed her coffin, side by side, as the two nearest relations; here was no time or inclination for wrangling.

Lotte-Lena sewed the mourning-band round the chamberlain's hat. She was here in the house, come back long ago without victory and fortune in her artistic career. But it would come; Lotte-Lena had a future. The key had said it, and the chamberlain had said it.

She came up to him. They talked of the dead, and they wept, Lotte-Lena was tender; they talked of art, and Lotte-Lena was strong.

'The theatre life is charming!' said she, 'but there is so much quarrelling and jealousy! I would rather go my own way. First myself, then art!'

Knigge had spoken truly in his chapter about actors; she saw that the key had not spoken truly, but she did not speak about that to the chamberlain; she thought too much of him.

The door-key was his comfort and consolation all the year of mourning. He asked it questions and it gave answers. And when the year was ended, and he and Lotte-Lena sat together one evening, he asked the key, 'Shall I marry, and whom shall I marry?'

There was no one to push him, he pushed the key, and it said 'Lotte-Lena'. So it was said, and Lotte-Lena became the chamberlain's wife.

'Victory and Fortune!' These words had been said beforehand – by the door-key.

The Cripple

THERE WAS an old country-house which belonged to young, wealthy people. They had riches and blessings, they liked to enjoy themselves, but they did good as well, they wished to make everybody as happy as they were themselves.

On Christmas Eve a beautifully decorated Christmas tree stood in the old hall, where the fire burned in the chimney, and fir branches were hung round the old pictures. Here were assembled the family and their guests, and there was dancing and singing.

Earlier in the evening there had been Christmas gaiety in the servants' hall. Here also was a great fir tree with red and white candles, small Danish flags, swans and fishing-nets, cut out of coloured paper, and filled with 'goodies'. The poor children from the neighbourhood were invited, everyone had his mother with him. The mothers did not look much at the Christmas tree, but at the Christmas table, where there lay linen and woollen cloth – stuff for gowns and stuff for trousers. They and the bigger children looked there, only the very little ones stretched out their hands to the candles, and the tinsel and flags.

The whole party came early in the afternoon and got Christmas porridge and roast goose with red cabbage. Then when the Christmas tree was seen and the gifts distributed, each got a little glass of punch with apple fritters. Then they went back to their own poor homes and talked of the good living, that is to say good things to eat; and the gifts were once more inspected. There were now Garden Kirsten and Garden Ole. They were married, and had their house and daily bread for weeding and digging in the garden of the big house. Every Christmas festival they got a good share of the gifts; they had five children, and all of them were clothed by the family.

'They are generous people, our master and mistress!' said they, 'but they have the means to be so, and they have pleasure in doing it.'

'Here are good clothes for the four children to wear,' said Ole; 'but why is there nothing for the "cripple"? They used to think about him too, although he was not at the festival.'

It was the eldest of the children they called 'The Cripple', he was called Hans otherwise.

As a little boy, he was the smartest and liveliest child, but he became all at once 'loose in the legs', as they call it, he could neither walk nor stand, and now he had been lying in bed for five years.

'Yes, I got something for him too,' said the mother, 'but it is nothing much, it is only a book to read.'

'He won't get fat on that,' said the father.

But Hans was glad of it. He was a very clever boy who liked to read, but used his time also for working, so far as one who must always lie in bed could be useful. He was very handy, and knitted woollen stockings, and even bedcovers. The lady at the big house had praised and bought them. It was a story-book Hans had got; in it there was much to read and much to think about.

'It is not of any kind of use here in the house,' said his parents, 'but let him read, it passes the time, he cannot always be knitting stockings!'

The spring came; flowers and green leaves began to sprout – the weeds also, as one may call the nettles, although the psalm speaks so nicely of them:

> Though kings in all their power and might
> Came forth in splendid row,
> They could not make the smallest leaf
> Upon a nettle grow.

There was much to do in the garden, not only for the gardener and his apprentice, but also for Kirsten and Ole.

'It is perfect drudgery,' said they. 'We have no sooner raked the paths and made them nice, than they are just trodden down again. There is such a run of visitors up at the house. How much it must cost! But the family are rich people!'

'Things are badly divided,' said Ole; 'the priest says we are all our Father's children, why the difference then?'

'It comes from the Fall!' said Kirsten.

They talked about it again in the evening, where cripple Hans lay with his story-book.

Straitened circumstances, work, and drudgery, had made the parents not only hard in the hands, but also in their opinions and judgements; they could not grasp it, could not explain it, and made themselves more peevish and angry as they talked.

'Some people get prosperity and happiness, others only poverty! Why should our first parents' disobedience and curiosity be visited upon us? We would not have behaved ourselves as they did!'

'Yes, we would!' said cripple Hans, all at once. 'It is all here in the book.'

'What is in the book?' asked the parents.

And Hans read for them the old story of the woodcutter and his wife. They also scolded about Adam's and Eve's curiosity, which was the cause of their misfortune. The king of the country came past just then. 'Come home with me,' said he, 'then you shall have it as good as I; seven courses for dinner and a course for show. That is in a closed tureen, and you must not touch it; for if you do, it is all over with your grandeur.' 'What can there be in the tureen?' said the wife. 'That does not concern us,' said the man. 'Yes, I am not inquisitive,' said the wife, 'but I would only like to know why we dare not lift the lid; it is certainly something delicate!' 'If only it is not something mechanical,' said the man, 'such as a pistol, which goes off and wakens the whole house.' 'O my!' said the wife, and did not touch the tureen. But during the night she dreamt that the lid lifted itself, and from the tureen came a smell of the loveliest punch, such as one gets at weddings and funerals. There lay a big silver shilling with the inscription, 'Drink of this punch, and you will become the two richest people in the world, and everybody else will become beggars!' – and the wife wakened at once and told her husband her dream. 'You think too much about the thing!' said he. 'We could lift it gently,' said the wife. 'Gently,' said the man, and the wife then lifted the lid very gently. Then two little active mice sprang out, and ran at once into a mouse-hole. 'Good-night,' said the king. Now you can go home and lie in your own bed. Don't scold Adam and Eve any more, you yourselves have been as inquisitive and ungrateful!'

'From where has that story come in the book?' said Ole. 'It looks as if it concerned us. It is something to think about!'

Next day they went to work again; they were roasted by the sun, and soaked to the skin with rain; in them were fretful thoughts, and they ruminated on them.

It was still quite light at home after they had eaten their milk porridge.

'Read the story of the woodcutter to us again,' said Ole.

'There are so many nice ones in the book,' said Hans, 'so many, you don't know.'

'Yes, but I don't care about them,' said Ole, 'I want to hear the one I know.'

And he and his wife listened to it again.

More than one evening they returned to the story.

'It cannot quite make everything clear to me,' said Ole. 'It is with people as with sweet milk, which sours; some become fine cheese, and others the thin, watery whey; some people have luck in everything, sit at the high-table every day, and know neither sorrow nor want.'

Cripple Hans heard that. He was weak in the legs, but clever in the head. He read to them from his story-book, read about 'The man without sorrow or want'. Where was *he* to be found, for found he must be!

The king lay sick and could not be cured, except by being dressed in the shirt which had been worn on the body of a man who could truthfully say that he had never known sorrow or want.

Messages were sent to all the countries in the world, to all castles and estates, to all prosperous and happy men, but when it was properly investigated, every one of them had experienced sorrow and want.

'That I have not!' said the swineherd who sat in the ditch and laughed and sang, 'I am the happiest man!'

'Then give us your shirt,' said the king's messengers. 'You shall be paid for it with the half of the kingdom.'

But he had no shirt, and yet he called himself the happiest man.

'That was a fine fellow,' shouted Ole, and he and his wife laughed as they had not laughed for a year and a day. Then the schoolmaster came past.

'How you are enjoying yourselves!' said he, 'that is something new in this house. Have you won a prize in the lottery?'

'No, we are not of that kind,' said Ole. 'It is Hans who has been reading his story-book to us, about "The man without sorrow or want", and the fellow had no shirt. One's eyes get moist when one hears such things, and that from a printed book. Everyone has his load to draw, one is not alone in that. That is always a comfort.'

'Where did you get that book?' asked the schoolmaster.

'Our Hans got it more than a year ago at Christmas-time. The master and mistress gave it to him. They know that he likes reading so much, and he is a cripple. We would rather have seen him get two linen shirts at the time. But the book is wonderful, it can almost answer one's thoughts.'

The schoolmaster took the book and opened it.

'Let us have the same story again!' said Ole, 'I have not quite taken it in yet. Then he must also read the other about the woodcutter!'

These two stories were enough for Ole. They were like two sunbeams coming into the poor room, into the stunted thought which made him so cross and ill-natured. Hans had read the whole book, read it many times. The stories carried him out into the world, there, where he could not go, because his legs would not carry him.

The schoolmaster sat by his bed: they talked together, and it was a pleasure for both of them. From that day the schoolmaster came oftener to Hans, when the parents were at work. It was a treat for the boy, every time he came. How he listened to what the old man told him, about the size of the world and its many countries, and that the sun was almost half a million times bigger than the earth, and so far away that a cannonball in its course would take a whole twenty-five years to come from the sun to the earth, whilst the beams of light could come in eight minutes.

Every industrious schoolboy knew all that, but for Hans it was all new, and still more wonderful than what was in the story-book.

The schoolmaster dined with the squire's family two or three times a year, and he told how much importance the story-book had in the poor house, where two stories in it alone had been the means of spiritual awakening and blessing. The weakly, clever little boy had with his reading brought reflection and joy into the house.

When the schoolmaster went away, the lady pressed two or three silver dollars into his hand for the little Hans.

'Father and mother must have them!' said Hans, when the school-master brought the money.

And Ole and Kirsten said, 'Cripple Hans after all is a profit and a blessing.'

Two or three days after, when the parents were at work at the big house, the squire's carriage stopped outside. It was the kind-hearted lady who came, glad that her Christmas present had been such a comfort and pleasure for the boy and his parents. She brought with her fine bread, fruit, and a bottle of fruit syrup, but what was still more delightful she brought him, in a gilt cage, a little blackbird, which could whistle quite charmingly. The cage with the bird was set up on the old clothes-chest, a little bit away from the boy's bed; he could see the bird and hear it; even the people out in the road could hear its song.

Ole and Kirsten came home after the lady had driven away; they noticed how glad Hans was, but thought there would only be trouble with the present he had got.

'Rich people don't have much foresight!' said they. 'Shall we now have that to look after also? Cripple Hans cannot do it. The end will be that the cat will take it!'

Eight days passed, and still another eight days: the cat had in that time been often in the room without frightening the bird, to say nothing of hurting it. Then a great event happened. It was afternoon. The parents and the other children were at work, Hans was quite alone; he had the story-book in his hand, and read about the fisher-woman who got everything she wished for; she wished to be a king, and that she became; she wished to be an emperor, and that she became; but when she wished to become the good God, then she sat once more in the muddy ditch she had come from.

The story had nothing to do with the bird or the cat, but it was just the story he was reading when the incident happened: he always remembered that afterwards.

The cage stood on the chest, the cat stood on the floor and stared at the bird with his greeny-gold eyes. There was something in the cat's face which seemed to say, 'How lovely you are! How I should like to eat you!'

Hans could understand that; he read it in the cat's face.

'Be off, cat!' he shouted, 'will you go out of the room?' It seemed as if it were just about to spring. Hans could not get at him, and he had nothing else to throw at him but his dearest treasure, the story-book. He threw that, but the binding was loose, and it flew to one side, and the book itself with all its leaves flew to the other. The cat went with slow steps a little back into the room, and looked at Hans as much as to say, 'Don't mix yourself up in this affair, little Hans! I can walk, and I can spring, and you can do neither.'

Hans kept his eye on the cat and was greatly distressed; the bird was also anxious. There was no one there to call; it seemed as if the cat knew it: it prepared itself again to spring. Hans shook the bed-cover at him; his hands he *could* use; but the cat paid no attention to the bed-cover; and when it was also thrown at him without avail, he sprang upon the chair and into the window-sill, where he was nearer to the bird. Hans could feel his own warm blood in himself, but he did not think of that, he thought only about the cat and the bird; the boy could not help himself out of bed, could not stand on his legs, still less walk. It seemed as if his heart turned inside him when he saw the cat spring from the window, right on to the chest and push the cage so that it was upset. The bird fluttered wildly about inside.

Hans gave a scream; something gave a tug inside him, and without thinking about it, he jumped out of bed, flew across to the chest, tore the cat down, and got hold of the cage, where the bird was in a great fright. He held the cage in his hand and ran with it out of the door and out on to the road.

Then the tears streamed out of his eyes; he shouted with joy, 'I can walk! I can walk!'

He had recovered his activity again; such things can happen, and it had happened to him.

The schoolmaster lived close by; Hans ran in to him with his bare feet, with only his shirt and jacket on, and with the bird in the cage.

'I can walk!' he shouted. 'My God!' and he sobbed and wept with joy.

And there was joy in the house of Ole and Kirsten. 'A more joyful day we could not see,' said both of them. Hans was called up to the big house; he had not gone that way for many years; it seemed as if the trees and the nut bushes, which he knew so well, nodded to him and said, 'Good-day, Hans, welcome here!' The sun shone on his face as well as in his heart. The master and mistress let him sit with them, and looked as glad as if he had belonged to their own family.

Gladdest of all was the lady, who had given him the story book, given him the singing-bird, which was now as a matter of fact dead, dead of fright, but it had been the means of restoring him to health, and the book had brought the awakening of the parents: he had the book still, and he would keep it and read it if he were ever so old. Now he could be a benefit to those at home. He would learn a trade, by preference a bookbinder, 'because,' said he, 'I can get all the new books to read!'

In the afternoon the lady called both parents up to her. She and her husband had talked together about Hans; he was a wise and clever boy: had pleasure in reading, and ability.

That evening the parents came home joyfully from the farm, Kirsten in particular, but the week after she wept, for then little Hans went away: he was dressed in good clothes; he was a good boy; but now he must go away across the salt water, far away to school, and many years would pass before they would see him again.

He did not get the story-book with him, the parents kept that for remembrance. And the father often read in it, but nothing except the two stories, for he knew them.

And they got letters from Hans, each one gladder than the last. He was with fine people, in good circumstances, and it was most delightful to go to school; there was so much to learn and to know; he only wanted to remain there a hundred years and then be a schoolmaster.

'If we should live to see it!' said the parents, and pressed each other's hands, as if at communion.

'To think of what has happened to Hans!' said Ole. 'Our Father thinks also of the poor man's child! And that it should happen just with the cripple! Is it not as if Hans were to read it for us out of the story-book?'

Auntie Toothache

WHERE DID we get the story from?

Would you like to know that?

We got it from the barrel, the one with the old papers in it. Many good and rare books have gone to the chandler's and the greengrocer's, not as reading, but as necessary articles. They must have paper at the grocer's for starch and coffee-beans, paper for salt herrings, butter, and cheese. Written things are also useful. Often there goes into the barrel what should not go there.

I know a greengrocer's boy, the son of a chandler; he has risen from the cellar to the shop: a man of great reading, paper-bag reading, both the printed and the written kind. He has an interesting collection, and in it several important documents from the waste-paper basket of one and another, absent-minded and too much occupied and official: confidential letters from lady friends to each other; scandal-communications, which must go no farther, and not be spoken of to anyone. He is a living rescue-institution for no small part of literature, and has a large field to work in; he has the shops of his employer and his parents, and in these he has rescued many a book, or pages of a book, which might well deserve a second reading.

He has shown me his collection of printed and written things from the barrel, mostly from the chandler's. There were two or three leaves of a bigger copy book: its peculiarly beautiful and distinct writing drew my attention to it at once.

'The student has written that,' he said, 'the student who lived right opposite here, and died about a month ago. One can see he has suffered severely from toothache. It is very amusing to read! Here is only a little part of what was written; it was a whole book and a little more; my parents gave half a pound of green soap for it, to the student's landlady. Here is what I rescued.' I borrowed it, and read it, and now I communicate it. The title was:

AUNTIE TOOTHACHE

Auntie gave me sweet things when I was little. My teeth held out and were not destroyed; now I am older, and have become a student, she spoils me still with sweet things, and says that I am a poet. I have something of the poet in me, but not sufficient. Often when I am walking in the streets of the town, it seems to me as if I walk in a big library. The houses are bookcases, every floor a shelf with books. There stands an everyday story, there a good old comedy, scientific works in all departments, here filthy literature and there good reading. I can both exercise my fancy and philosophise over all the literature. There is something of the poet in me, but not sufficient. Many people have certainly as much in themselves as I, and yet wear neither badge nor neck-band with the name 'Poet'.

There is given to them and to me a gift of God, a blessing big enough for oneself, but far too small to be given out again to others. It comes like a sunbeam, and fills the soul and the thoughts. It comes as the scent of flowers, as a melody which one knows and remembers, but cannot tell from where.

The other evening I sat in my room, wanting to read, but had neither book nor paper; just then a leaf, fresh and green, fell from the lime tree. The wind bore it in at the window to me.

I looked at the many spreading veins; a little insect crawled over these, as if it would make a thorough study of the leaf. Then I had to think of the wisdom of men; we also crawl about upon a leaf, know only it, and then at once hold a discourse about the whole big tree, the root, the trunk, and the crown, the great tree – God, the world, and eternity, and know of the whole only a little leaf!

As I sat there, I had a visit of Auntie Milly. I showed her the leaf with the insect, told her my thoughts about it, and her eyes shone.

'You are a poet! said she, 'perhaps the greatest we have! If I should live to see it, then I shall willingly go to my grave! You have always amazed me with your powerful imagination, from the very day of Brewer Rasmussen's funeral.'

So said Auntie Milly, and kissed me.

Now who was Auntie Milly, and who was Brewer Rasmussen? Mother's aunt was called 'Auntie' by us children, we had no other name for her.

She gave us jam and sugar, although it was a great destruction for our teeth, but she was weak where the sweet children were concerned, she said. It was cruel to deny them the little bit of sweetstuff they thought so much of.

And because of that we thought so much of Auntie. She was an old maid, as far back as I can remember, always old! She stood still in the years.

In earlier years she suffered much from toothache, and always spoke about it, and so it was that her friend, Brewer Rasmussen, who was witty, called her 'Auntie Toothache!'

He lived on his money, and came often to see Auntie, and was older than she. He had no teeth, only some black stumps.

As a child he had eaten too much sugar, she told us children, and so one came to look like that. Auntie had certainly never in her childhood eaten sugar; she had the most lovely white teeth. She saved them too, 'and did not sleep with them at night!' said Brewer Rasmussen.

That was malicious, we children knew, but Auntie said he did not mean anything by it.

One morning, at breakfast, she told of a nasty dream she had had in the night: one of her teeth had fallen out.

'That means,' said she, 'that I will lose a true friend.'

'Was it a false tooth?' said Brewer Rasmussen, and laughed; 'then it may only mean that you will lose a false friend!'

'You are a rude old gentleman!' said Auntie, angry as I have never seen her, before or since.

Later on she said, it was only the teasing of her old friend. He was the most noble man on earth, and when he died he would be one of God's little angels in heaven. I thought much over the change, and whether she would be in a position to recognise him in the new shape. When Auntie and he were both young, he had courted her. She considered too long, sat still, remained sitting too long, and became an old maid, but always a faithful friend. And then Brewer Rasmussen died.

He was carried to the grave in the most expensive hearse, and had a great following of people with orders and uniforms.

Auntie stood in mourning at the window with all us children, with the exception of the little brother whom the stork had brought a week before. When the hearse and the company had gone past, and the street was empty, Auntie turned to go, but not I; I waited for the angel, Brewer Rasmussen; he had become a little, winged child of God, and must show himself.

'Auntie,' said I, 'don't you think he will come now, or that when the stork again brings us a little brother, he will bring us Brewer Rasmussen?'

Auntie was quite overpowered with my fantasy, and said, 'The child will become a great poet!' and she repeated it during the whole of my school-time, even after my confirmation, and now in my student years. She was, and is, to me the most sympathetic friend both in poetic ache and toothache. I have attacks of both.

'Write all your thoughts down,' said she, 'and put them in the table-drawer; Jean Paul did that; he became a great poet, whom I really don't think much of: he doesn't excite one! You must excite, and you will excite!'

The night after this conversation, I lay in longing and pain, in vehement desire to become the great poet Auntie saw and perceived in me: I lay in poetic ache, but there is a worse ache – toothache! It crushed and pulverised me; I became a writhing worm, with a herb bag and Spanish flies.

'I know what that is!' said Auntie.

There was a sorrowful smile about her mouth; her teeth shone so white.

But I must begin a new section in Auntie's history and mine.

2

I had removed to new lodgings, and had been there a month, and I was talking to Auntie about it. I stay with a very quiet family; they do not think about me, even if I ring three times. For the rest it is truly a rackety house, with noise of wind and weather and people. I stay right over the gate; every cart which drives out or in, makes the pictures shake on the walls. The gate bangs, and the house shakes as if there was an earthquake. If I lie in bed, the shock goes through all my limbs, but that is said to be good for the nerves. If it blows, and it is always blowing here in this country, then the window-catch swings back and forward and knocks against the wall. The neighbour's doorbell rings with every gust of wind.

The people in our house come home in detachments, late in the evening, and far on in the night; the lodger right above me, who in the daytime gives lessons on the bassoon, comes home latest, and does not go to bed until he has gone for a little midnight walk, with heavy steps and iron-nailed boots.

There are not double windows, but there is a broken pane, over which the landlady has pasted paper. The wind blows through the crack and makes a noise like the buzzing of a hornet. It is a lullaby.

When I do fall asleep at last, I am soon wakened by a cock. Cocks and hens from the cellar-man's hen-run announce that it will soon be morning. The little Norwegian ponies (they have no stable, but are tethered in the sand-hole under the stair) kick against the door in turning themselves. The day dawns; the porter, who with his family sleeps in the garret, rattles down the stair; the wooden shoes clatter, the door bangs, the house shakes; and when that is finished, the lodger upstairs begins to exercise his gymnastics, lifts in each hand a heavy iron ball, which he cannot hold: it falls and falls again; whilst at the same time the young people of the house, who are going to school, come tearing downstairs shrieking. I go to the window, open it to get fresh air, and it is refreshing when I can get it.

For the rest it is a rare house, and I live with a quiet family. That is the report I gave Auntie of my lodgings, but I gave it in a more lively way; verbal narration has a fresher effect than the written.

'You are a poet!' cried Auntie. 'Write your thoughts down and you will be as good as Dickens! Yes, you interest me much more! You paint, when you talk! You describe your house so that one can see it! One shudders! compose further! Put something living into it, people, delightful people, especially unhappy people!'

I really did write about the house, with all its sounds and lack of soundness, but with only myself in it, without any action; that came later.

3

It was in winter, late in the evening, after the theatre, frightful weather, a snowstorm, so that one could hardly force oneself forward.

Auntie was at the theatre, and I was there to take her home, but one had difficulty in walking alone, to say nothing of taking another. The cabs were all seized upon: Auntie lived a long way out in the town; my lodging was, on the contrary, close to the theatre; had that not been the case, we must have stood in the sentry-box until further notice. We stumbled forward in the deep snow, surrounded by the whirling snowflakes. I lifted her, I held her, I pushed her forward. We only fell twice, but we fell softly.

We approached my gate, where we shook ourselves; we also shook ourselves on the stair, and had still enough snow on us to fill the floor of the lobby. We got off our overcoats and goloshes, and everything which could be thrown off. The landlady lent Auntie dry stockings, and a dressing-gown; it was necessary, the landlady said, and added, which was true, that Auntie could not possibly go home that night, and invited her to use her sitting-room, where she would make a bed on the sofa in front of the door into my room, which was always locked. And so it happened.

The fire burned in my stove, the tea-things stood on the table, it was comfortable in the little room, although not so comfortable as at Auntie's, where in winter there are thick curtains on the doors, thick curtains on the windows, double carpets, with three layers of paper underneath; one sits there as if in a well-corked bottle with warm air. Yet, as I said, it was also comfortable in my room; the wind whistled outside.

Auntie talked and talked. Youth returned, Brewer Rasmussen returned, and old memories.

She could remember when I cut my first tooth and the family joy over it.

The first tooth! The tooth of innocence, shining like a little white drop of milk, the milk tooth. There came one, there came several, a whole row. Side by side, above and below, the most lovely children's teeth, and still only the advance troops, not the real ones which should be for the whole life. They came and also the wisdom teeth with them, the men at the wings, born with pain and great difficulty. They go again, every single one! they go before their time of service is over, even the last tooth goes, and it is not a festival day, it is a day of sadness.

Then one is old, even although the honour is young. Such thoughts and conversation are not pleasant, and yet we talked about all that, we came back to childhood's years, talked and talked; the clock struck twelve before Auntie retired to rest in the room close to mine.

'Good-night, my sweet child,' she called, 'now I sleep as if I lay in my own clothes-chest!'

And she went to rest, but rest there was none, neither in the house nor outside. The storm shook the windows, knocked with the long hanging window-catches, rang the neighbour's bell in the backyard. The lodger upstairs had come home. He went for a little evening walk up and down, threw his boots down, went to bed and to rest, but he snored so loud that one with good hearing could hear him through the roof.

I found no rest, the weather did not go to rest either, it was lively in an unmannerly degree. The wind whistled and blew in its own manner, my teeth also began to be lively, they whistled and sang in their own way. It turned into a great attack of toothache.

There was a draught from the window. The moon shone in on the floor. The light went and came as clouds came and went in the storm. There was restlessness in the light and shade; I looked at the movement, and I felt an icy-cold blast.

On the floor sat a figure, long and thin, as when a child draws on a slate with a pencil, something which shall represent a man: a single thin stroke is the body, two strokes are arms, the legs are also two strokes, the head is many-cornered.

Soon the figure became more distinct; it got a kind of cloak, very thin, very fine, but it showed that it was a woman.

I heard a buzzing. Was it she, or the wind buzzing like a hornet in the window crack. No, it was herself, Mrs Toothache! her terrible Satanic Majesty, God preserve and save us from her visit!

'It is good to be here,' she buzzed, 'here are good quarters, boggy ground, mossy ground. Mosquitoes have buzzed here with poison in their sting, now I have the sting. It must be sharpened on human teeth. They shine so white as he lies here in bed. They have defied sweet and sour, hot and cold, nutshells and plum stones! but I shall shake them, feed the root with draughts, give them cold in their feet.' That was frightful talk, and a terrible guest.

'So you are a poet!' said she; 'I shall make poems about you in all the metres of pain! I shall put iron and steel in your body, put strings in all your nerves.'

It seemed as if a glowing awl was pushed into the cheekbone. I writhed and turned myself.

'An excellent toothache!' said she, 'an organ to play on. A magnificent concert on the Jew's-harp, with kettledrums and trumpets, flutes, and the bassoon in the wisdom tooth. Great poet, great music!'

She played up, and she looked horrible, even if one saw no more of her than the hand, the shadowy grey, icy-cold hand with the long thin fingers; each of them was an instrument of torture. The thumb and the forefinger had a knife-blade and a screw, the middle finger ended in a pointed awl, the next one was a gimlet, and the little finger squirted mosquito venom.

'I shall teach you metres,' said she. 'Great poets shall have great toothaches; little poets, little toothaches!'

'Oh, let me be little,' I begged. 'Let me not be at all! and I am not a poet, I have only attacks of composing, attacks as of toothache; go away, go away!'

'Do you recognise, then, that I am mightier than poetry, philosophy, mathematics, and music?' said she. 'Mightier than all these painted and carved marble conceptions! I am older than all of them together. I was born close by the garden of Paradise, outside where the wind blew, and the damp toadstools grew. I got Eve to clothe herself in the cold weather, and Adam too. You can believe that there was strength in the first toothache.'

'I believe everything!' said I; 'go away, go away!'

'Yes, if you will give up being a poet, never set verse on paper, slate, or any kind of writing material; then I shall let you go, but I will come again if you make verses.'

'I swear!' said I. 'Let me only never see or think of you again.'

'See me you shall, but in a fuller, and to you a dearer shape than I am now! You shall see me as Auntie Milly; and I will say, "Versify, my sweet boy! You are a great poet – the greatest, perhaps, that we have!" but believe me, and begin to make poetry, then I will set your verse to music, and play it on the mouth-harp! You sweet child! Remember me, when you see Auntie Milly.'

Then she vanished.

I got a glowing awl-prick in the jawbone as a parting shot; but it soon subsided, I seemed to glide on the soft water, saw the white water-lilies with the broad green leaves bend themselves and sink down under me, wither and decay, and I sank with them, was dissolved in rest and peace.

'Die, melt like the snow!' it sang and sounded in the water, 'evaporate in the cloud, disappear like the cloud.' Down to me, through the water, shone great, illuminating names, inscriptions on waving banners, the patent of immortality written on the wings of ephemeral flies.

The sleep was deep, sleep without dreams. I neither heard the whistling wind, the banging gate, the neighbour's doorbell, nor the lodger's heavy gymnastics.

Blessedness! Happiness!

Then there came a gust of wind and the unlocked door into Auntie's room burst open. Auntie sprang up and came in to me.

'I slept like an angel of God,' she said, and she had not the heart to waken me.

I woke of myself, opened my eyes, had quite forgotten that Auntie was here in the house, but soon remembered it, and remembered my toothache apparition. Dream and reality were mixed up together.

'You have written nothing last night, after we said Good-night?' she asked; 'I would like if you had! You are my poet, and that you will remain!'

I thought that she smiled so cunningly. I knew not if it was the real Auntie Milly who loved me, or the terrible one I had made a promise to in the night.

'Have you composed, sweet child?'

'No, no!' I cried; 'you are really Auntie Milly?'

'Who else?' said she, and it was Auntie Milly; she kissed me, got into a cab, and drove home.

I wrote down what is written here. It is not in verse and shall never be printed . . .

Here the manuscript stopped.

My young friend, the future grocer's assistant, could not discover the rest; it had gone out into the world as paper for smoked herring, butter, and green soap. It had fulfilled its destiny.

The brewer is dead, Auntie is dead, the student is dead, he from whom the sparks of thought came into the barrel: that is the end of the story – the story of Auntie Toothache.

A Picture-Book Without Pictures

Introduction

IT IS A strange thing, that when I feel most fervently and most deeply, my hands and my tongue seem alike tied, so that I cannot rightly describe or accurately portray the thoughts that are rising within me; and yet I am a painter: my eye tells me as much as that, and all my friends who have seen my sketches and fancies say the same.

I am a poor lad, and live in one of the narrowest of lanes; but I do not want for light, as my room is high up in the house, with an extensive prospect over the neighbouring roofs. During the first few days I went to live in the town, I felt low-spirited and solitary enough. Instead of the forest and the green hills, I had here only the grey chimneys to look out upon. And I had not then a single friend; not one familiar face greeted me.

So one evening I stood at the window, in a desponding mood; and presently I opened the casement and looked out. Oh, how my heart leaped up with joy! Here was a well-known face at last – a round, friendly countenance, the face of a good friend I had known at home. In fact, it was the Moon that looked in upon me. He was quite unchanged, the dear old Moon, and had the same face exactly that he used to show when he peered down upon me through the willow trees on the moor. I kissed my hand to him over and over again, as he shone straight into my little room; and he, for his part, promised me that every evening, when he came abroad, he would look in upon me for a few moments. This promise he has faithfully kept. It is a pity that he can only stay such a short time when he comes. Whenever he appears, he tells me of one thing or another that he has seen on the previous night or on that same evening.

'Just paint the scenes I describe to you!' – this is what he said to me – 'and you will have a very pretty picture-book.'

I have followed his injunction for many evenings. I could make up a new 'Thousand and One Nights', in my own way, out of these pictures, but the number might be too great, after all. The pictures I have here given have not been selected, but follow each other, just as they were described to me. Some great gifted painter, or some poet or musician, may make something more of them if he likes; what I have given here are only hasty sketches, hurriedly put upon the paper, with some of my own thoughts interspersed; for the Moon did not come to me every evening – a cloud sometimes hid his face from me.

First Evening

'Last night! – I am quoting the Moon's own words – ' last night I was gliding through the cloudless Indian sky. My face was mirrored in the waters of the Ganges, and my beams strove to pierce through the thick intertwining boughs of the plane trees, arching beneath me like the tortoise's shell. Forth from the thicket tripped a Hindu maid, light as a gazelle, beautiful as Eve. There was something so airy and ethereal, and yet so full and firm in this daughter of Hindustan: I could read her thoughts through her delicate skin. The thorny creeping plants tore her sandals, but for all that she came rapidly forward. The deer which came from the river where it had quenched its thirst, sprang by with a startled bound, for in her hand the maiden bore a lighted lamp. I could see the blood in her delicate fingertips, as she spread them for a screen before the flame. She came down to the stream, and set the lamp upon the water, and let it float away. The flame flickered to and fro, and seemed ready to expire; but still the lamp burned on, and the girl's black sparkling eyes, half-veiled behind their long silken lashes, followed it with a gaze of earnest intensity. She well knew that if the lamp continued to burn so long as she could keep it in sight, her betrothed was still alive; but if the lamp was suddenly extinguished, he was dead. And the lamp burned and quivered, and her heart burned and trembled; she fell on her knees, and prayed. Near her in the grass lay a speckled snake, but she heeded it not – she thought only of Brahma and of her betrothed. "He lives!" she shouted joyfully, "he lives!" And from the mountains the echo came back upon her, "He lives!" '

Second Evening

'Yesterday,' said the Moon to me, 'I looked down upon a small courtyard surrounded on all sides by houses. In the courtyard sat a hen with eleven chickens; and a pretty little girl was running and jumping around them. The hen was frightened, and screamed, and spread out her wings over the little brood. Then the girl's father came out and scolded her; and I glided away and thought no more of the matter.

'But this evening, only a few minutes ago, I looked down into the same courtyard. Everything was quiet. But presently the little girl came forth again, crept quietly to the hen-house, pushed back the bolt, and slipped into the apartment of the hens and chickens. They cried out loudly, and came fluttering down from their perches, and ran about in dismay, and the little girl ran after them. I saw it quite plainly, for I looked through a hole in the hen-house wall. I was angry with the wilful child, and felt glad when her father came out and scolded her more violently than yesterday, holding her roughly by the arm: she held down her head, and her blue eyes were full of large tears. "What are you about here?" he asked. She wept and said, "I wanted to kiss the hen and beg her pardon for frightening her yesterday; but I was afraid to tell you."

'And the father kissed the innocent child's forehead, and I kissed her on the mouth and eyes.'

Third Evening

'In the narrow street round the corner yonder – it is so narrow that my beams can only glide for a minute along the walls of the house, but in that minute I see enough to learn what the world is made of – in that narrow street I saw a woman. Sixteen years ago that woman was a child, playing in the garden of the old parsonage in the country. The hedges of rose bushes were old, and the flowers were faded. They straggled wild over the paths, and the ragged branches grew up among the boughs of the apple trees; here and there were a few roses still in bloom – not so fair as the queen of flowers generally appears, but still they had colour and scent too. The clergyman's little daughter appeared to me a far lovelier rose, as she sat on her stool under the straggling hedge, hugging and caressing her doll with the battered pasteboard cheeks.

'Ten years afterwards I saw her again. I beheld her in a splendid ballroom: she was the beautiful bride of a rich merchant. I rejoiced at her happiness, and sought her on calm quiet evenings – ah, nobody thinks of my clear eye and my sure glance! Alas! my rose ran wild, like the rose bushes in the garden of the parsonage. There are tragedies in everyday life, and tonight I saw the last act of one.

'She was lying in bed in a house in that narrow street; she was sick unto death, and the cruel landlord came up, and tore away the thin coverlet, her only protection against the cold. "Get up!" said he; "your face is enough to frighten one. Get up and dress yourself. Give me money, or I'll turn you out into the street! Quick – get up!" She answered, "Alas! death is gnawing at my heart. Let me rest." But he forced her to get up and bathe her face, and put a wreath of roses in her hair; and he placed her in a chair at the window, with a candle burning beside her, and went away.

'I looked at her, and she was sitting motionless, with her hands in her lap. The wind caught the open window and shut it with a crash, so that a pane came clattering down in fragments; but still she never moved. The curtain fluttered like a flame about her; she was dead. There at the window sat the dead woman, preaching a sermon against *sin* – my poor faded rose out of the parsonage garden!'

Fourth Evening

'Last evening I saw a German play acted,' said the Moon. 'It was in a little town. A stable had been turned into a theatre; that is to say, the stalls had been left standing, and had been turned into private boxes, and all the timberwork had been covered with coloured paper. A little iron chandelier hung beneath the ceiling, and that it might be made to disappear into the ceiling, as it does in great theatres, when the *ting-ting* of the prompter's bell is heard, a great inverted tub had been placed just above it.

' *"Ting-ting!"* and the little iron chandelier suddenly rose at least half a yard and disappeared in the tub; and that was the sign that the play was going to begin. A young nobleman and his lady, who happened to be passing through the little town, were present at the performance, and consequently the house was crowded. But under the chandelier was a vacant space like a little crater: not a single soul sat there, for the tallow was dropping, drip, drip! I saw everything, for it was so warm in there that every loophole had been opened. The male and female servants stood outside, peeping through the chinks, although the policeman was inside, threatening them with a stick. Close by the orchestra could be seen the noble young couple in two old armchairs, which were usually occupied by his worship the mayor and his lady; but these latter were today obliged to content themselves with wooden forms, just as if they had been ordinary citizens; and the lady observed quietly to herself, "One sees, now, that there is rank above rank;" and this incident gave an air of extra festivity to the whole proceedings. The chandelier gave little leaps, the crowd got their knuckles rapped, and I, the Moon, was present at the performance from beginning to end.'

Fifth Evening

'Yesterday,' began the Moon, 'I looked down upon the turmoil of Paris. My eye penetrated into an apartment of the Louvre. An old grandmother, poorly clad – she belonged to the working class – was following one of the under-servants into the great empty throne-room, for this was the apartment she wanted to see – that she was resolved to see; it had cost her many a little sacrifice and many a coaxing word to penetrate thus far. She folded her thin hands, and looked round with an air of reverence, as if she had been in a church.

' "Here it was!" she said, "here!" And she approached the throne, from which hung the rich velvet fringed with gold lace. "There," she exclaimed, "there!" and she knelt and kissed the purple carpet. I think she was actually weeping.

' "But it was not *this very* velvet!" observed the footman, and a smile played about his mouth.

' "True, but it was this very place," replied the woman, "and it must have looked just like this."

' "It looked so, and yet it did not," observed the man: "the windows were beaten in, and the doors were off their hinges, and there was blood upon the floor."

' "But for all that you can say, my grandson died upon the throne of France." "Died!" mournfully repeated the old woman.

'I do not think another word was spoken, and they soon quitted the hall. The evening twilight faded, and my light shone doubly vivid upon the rich velvet that covered the throne of France.

'Now, who do you think this poor woman was? Listen, I will tell you a story.

'It happened in the Revolution of July, on the evening of the most brilliantly victorious day, when every house was a fortress, every window a breastwork. The people stormed the Tuileries. Even women and children were to be found among the combatants. They penetrated into the apartments and halls of the palace. A poor half-grown boy in a ragged blouse fought among the older insurgents. Mortally wounded with several bayonet thrusts, he sank down. This happened in the throne-room. They laid the bleeding youth upon the throne of France, wrapped the velvet round his wounds, and his blood streamed forth upon the imperial purple. There was a picture! the splendid hall, the fighting groups! A torn flag lay upon the ground, the tricolour was waving above the bayonets, and on the throne lay the poor lad with the pale glorified countenance, his eyes turned towards the sky, his limbs writhing in the death agony, his breast bare, and his poor tattered clothing half-hidden by the rich velvet embroidered with silver lilies. At the boy's cradle a prophecy had been spoken: "He will die on the throne of France!" The mother's heart had fondly imagined a second Napoleon.

'My beams have kissed the wreath of *immortelles* on his grave, and this night they kissed the forehead of the old grandame, while in a dream the picture floated before her which thou mayest draw – the poor boy on the throne of France.'

Sixth Evening

'I've been in Upsala,' said the Moon: 'I looked down upon the great plain covered with coarse grass, and upon the barren fields. I mirrored my face in the Fyris river, while the steamboat scared the fish into the rushes. Beneath me floated the clouds, throwing long shadows on the so-called graves of Odin, Thor, and Frey. In the scanty turf that covers the grave-mounds, names have been cut. There is no monument here, no memorial on which the traveller can have his name carved, no rocky wall on whose surface he can get it painted; so visitors have the turf cut away for that purpose. The naked earth peers through in the form of great letters and names; these form a network over the whole hill. Here is an immortality, which lasts till the fresh turf grows!

'Up on the hill stood a man, a poet. He emptied the mead horn with the broad silver rim, and murmured a name. He begged the winds not to betray him, but I heard the name. I knew it. A count's coronet sparkles above it, and therefore he did not speak it out. I smiled, for I knew that a poet's crown adorned his own name. The nobility of Eleanora d'Este is attached to the name of Tasso. And I also know where the Rose of Beauty blooms!'

Thus spake the Moon, and a cloud came between us. May no cloud separate the poet from the rose!

Seventh Evening

'Along the margin of the shore stretches a forest of firs and beeches, and fresh and fragrant is this wood; hundreds of nightingales visit it every spring. Close beside it is the sea, the ever-changing sea, and between the two is placed the broad high road. One carriage after another rolls over it; but I did not follow them, for my eye loves best to rest upon one point. A grave-mound stands there, and the sloe and blackberry grow luxuriantly among the stones. Here is true poetry in nature.

'And how do you think men appreciate this poetry? I will tell you what I heard there last evening and during the night.

'First, two rich landed proprietors came driving by. "Those are glorious trees!" said the first. "Certainly there are ten loads of firewood in each," observed the other: "it will be a hard winter, and last year we got fourteen dollars a load" – and they were gone. "The road here is wretched," observed another man who drove past. "That's the fault of those horrible trees," replied his neighbour; "there is no free current of air; the wind can only come from the sea" – and they were gone. The stage coach went rattling past. All the passengers were asleep at this beautiful spot. The postilion blew his horn, but he only thought, "I can play capitally. It sounds well here. I wonder if those in there like it?" – and the stage coach vanished. Then two young fellows came galloping up on horseback. There's youth and spirit in the blood here! thought I; and, indeed, they looked with a smile at the moss-grown hill and thick forest. "I should not dislike a walk here with the miller's Christine," said one – and they flew past.

'The flowers scented the air; every breath of air was hushed: it seemed as if the sea were a part of the sky that stretched above the deep valley. A carriage rolled by. Six people were sitting in it. Four of them were asleep; the fifth was thinking of his new summer coat, which would suit him admirably; the sixth turned to the coachman and asked him if there were anything remarkable connected with yonder heap of stones. "No," replied the coachman, "it's only a heap of stones; but the trees are remarkable." "How so?" "Why, I'll tell you how they are very remarkable. You see, in winter, when the snow lies very deep, and has hidden the whole road so that nothing is to be seen, those trees serve me for a landmark. I steer by them, so as not to drive into the sea; and you see that is why the trees are remarkable."

'Now came a painter. He spoke not a word, but his eyes sparkled. He began to whistle. At this the nightingales sang louder than ever. "Hold your tongues!" he cried, testily; and he made accurate notes of all the colours and transitions – blue, and lilac, and dark brown. "That will make a beautiful picture," he said. He took it in just as a mirror takes in a view; and as he worked he whistled a march of Rossini's. And last of all came a poor girl. She laid aside the burden she carried and sat down to rest by the grave-mound. Her pale handsome face was bent in a listening attitude towards the forest. Her eyes brightened, she gazed earnestly at the sea and the sky, her hands were folded, and I think she prayed, "Our Father." She herself could not understand the feeling that swept through her, but I know that this minute and the beautiful natural scene will live within her memory for years, far more vividly and more truly than the painter could portray it with his colours on paper. My rays followed her till the morning dawn kissed her brow.'

Eighth Evening

Heavy clouds obscured the sky, and the Moon did not make his appearance at all. I stood in my little room, more lonely than ever, and looked up at the sky where he ought to have shown himself. My thoughts flew far away, up to my great friend, who every evening told me such pretty tales, and showed me pictures. Yes, he has had an experience indeed. He glided over the waters of the Deluge, and smiled on Noah's ark just as he lately glanced down upon me, and brought comfort and promise of a new world that was to spring forth from the old. When the Children of Israel sat weeping by the waters of Babylon, he glanced mournfully between the willows where hung the silent harps. When Romeo climbed the balcony, and the promise of true love fluttered like a cherub toward heaven, the round Moon hung, half-hidden among the dark cypresses, in the lucid air. He saw the captive giant at St Helena, looking from the lonely rock across the wide ocean, while great thoughts swept through his soul. Ah! what tales the Moon can tell. Human life is like a story to him. Tonight I shall not see thee again, old friend. Tonight I can draw no picture of the memories of thy visit. And, as I looked dreamily towards the clouds, the sky became bright. There was a glancing light, and a beam from the Moon fell upon me. It vanished again, and dark clouds flew past; but still it was a greeting, a friendly good-night offered to me by the Moon.

Ninth Evening

The air was clear again. Several evenings had passed, and the Moon was in the first quarter. Again he gave me an outline for a sketch. Listen to what he told me.

'I have followed the polar bird and the swimming whale to the eastern coast of Greenland. Gaunt ice-covered rocks and dark clouds hung over a valley, where dwarf willows and bilberry bushes stood clothed in green. The blooming lychnis exhaled sweet odours. My light was faint, my face pale as the water-lily that, torn from its stem, has been drifting for weeks with the tide. The crown-shaped Northern Lights burned in the sky. Its ring was broad, and from its circumference the rays shot like whirling shafts of fire across the whole sky, changing from green to red. The inhabitants of that icy region were assembling for dance and festivity; but accustomed to this glorious spectacle, they scarcely deigned to glance at it. "Let us leave the souls of the dead to their ball-play with the heads of the walruses," they thought in their superstition, and they turned their whole attention to the song and dance. In the midst of the circle, and divested of his furry cloak, stood a Greenlander, with his small drum, and he played and sang a song about catching the seal, and the chorus around chimed in with "*Eia, Eia, Ah.*" And in their white furs they danced about in the circle, till you might fancy it was a polar bears' ball.

'And now a Court of Judgement was opened. Those Greenlanders who had quarrelled stepped forward, and the offended person chanted forth the faults of his adversary in an extempore song, turning them sharply into ridicule, to the sound of the drum and the measure of the dance. The defendant replied with satire as keen, while the audience laughed and gave their verdict.

The rocks heaved, the glaciers melted, and great masses of ice and snow came crashing down, shivering to fragments as they fell: it was a glorious Greenland summer night. A hundred paces away, under the open tent of hides, lay a sick man. Life still flowed through his warm blood, but still he was to die; he himself felt it, and all who stood round him knew it also; therefore his wife was already sewing round him the shroud of furs, that she might not afterwards be obliged to touch the dead body. And she asked, "Wilt thou be buried on the rock, in the firm snow? I will deck the spot with thy *kayak*, and thy arrows, and the *angekokk* shall dance over it. Or wouldst thou rather be buried in the sea?" "In the sea," he whispered, and nodded with a mournful smile. "Yes, it is a pleasant summer tent, the sea," observed the wife. "Thousands of seals sport there, the walrus shall lie at thy feet, and the hunt will be safe and merry!" And the yelling children tore the outspread hide from the window-hole, that the dead man might be carried to the ocean, the billowy ocean, that had given him food in life, and that now, in death, was to afford him a place of rest. For his monument, he had the floating, ever-changing icebergs, whereon the seal sleeps, while the storm bird flies round their summits.'

Tenth Evening

'I knew an old maid,' said the Moon. 'Every winter she wore a wrapper of yellow satin, and it always remained new, and was the only fashion she followed. In summer she always wore the same straw hat, and I verily believe the very same grey-blue dress.

'She never went out, except across the street to an old female friend; and in later years she did not even take this walk, for the old friend was dead. In her solitude my old maid was always busy at the window, which was adorned in summer with pretty flowers, and in winter with cress, grown upon felt. During the last months I saw her no more at the window, but she was still alive. I knew that, for I had not yet seen her begin the "long journey", of which she often spoke with her friend. "Yes, yes," she was in the habit of saying, "when I come to die, I shall take a longer journey than I have made my whole life long. Our family vault is six miles from here. I shall be carried there, and shall sleep there among my family and relatives." Last night a hearse stopped at the house. A coffin was carried out, and then I knew that she was dead. They placed straw round the coffin, and the hearse drove away. There slept the quiet old lady, who had not gone out of her house once for the last year. The hearse rolled out through the town gate as briskly as if it were going for a pleasant excursion. On the high road the pace was quicker yet. The coachman looked nervously round every now and then – I fancy he half expected to see her sitting on the coffin, in her yellow satin wrapper. And because he was startled, he foolishly lashed his horses, while he held the reins so tightly that the poor beasts were in a foam! they were young and fiery. A hare jumped across the road and startled them, and they fairly ran away. The sober old maid, who had for years and years moved quietly round and round in a dull circle, was now, in death, rattled over stock and stone on the public highway. The coffin in its covering of straw tumbled out of the hearse, and was left on the high road, while horses, coachman, and hearse flew off in wild career. The lark rose up carolling from the field, twittering her morning lay over the coffin, and presently perched upon it, picking with her beak at the straw covering, as though she would tear it up. The lark rose up again, singing gaily, and I withdrew behind the red morning clouds.'

Eleventh Evening

'It was a wedding festival,' said the Moon. 'Songs were sung, toasts were drunk, everything was rich and grand. The guests departed; it was past midnight. The mothers kissed the bride and bridegroom, and I saw these two alone by themselves, though the curtains were drawn almost quite close. The lamp lit up the cosy chamber. "I am so glad they are all gone now," he said, and kissed her hands and lips, while she smiled and wept, leaning on his breast as the lotus flower rests on the rushing waters, and they spoke soft and happy words. "Sleep sweetly," he said, and she drew the window curtains to one side. "How beautifully the moon shines," she said; "look how still and clear it is." Then she put out the lamp, and there was darkness in the room, but my rays beamed even as his eyes did. Womanliness, kiss thou the poet's harp, when he sings of life's mysteries.'

Twelfth Evening

'I will give you a picture of Pompeii,' said the Moon. 'I was in the suburb in the Street of Tombs, as they call it, where the fair monuments stand, in the spot where, ages ago, the merry youths, their temples bound with rosy wreaths, danced with the fair sisters of Laïs. Now, the stillness of death reigned around. German mercenaries, in the Neapolitan service, kept guard, played cards and dice; and a troop of strangers from beyond the mountains came into the town, accompanied by a sentry. They wanted to see the city that had risen from the grave illumined by my beams; and I showed them the wheel-ruts in the streets paved with broad lava slabs; I showed them the names on the doors, and the signs that hung there yet: they saw in the little courtyard the basins of the fountains, ornamented with shells; but no jet of water gushed upwards, no songs sounded forth from the richly-painted chambers, where the bronze dog kept the door.

'It was the City of the Dead; only Vesuvius thundered forth his everlasting hymn, each separate verse of which is called by men an eruption. We went to the temple of Venus, built of snow-white marble, with its high altar in front of the broad steps, and the weeping-willows sprouting freshly forth among the pillars. The air was transparent and blue, and black Vesuvius formed the background, with fire ever shooting forth from it, like the stem of the pine tree. Above it stretched the smoky cloud in the silence of the night, like the crown of the pine, but in a blood-red illumination. Among the company was a lady singer, a real and great singer. I have witnessed the homage paid to her in the greatest cities of Europe. When they came to the tragic theatre, they all sat down on the amphitheatre steps, and thus a small part of the house was occupied by an audience, as it had been many centuries ago. The stage still stood unchanged, and its walled side-scenes, and the two arches in the background, through which the beholders saw the same scene that had been exhibited in the old times – a scene painted by Nature herself, namely, the mountains between Sorrento and Amalfi. The singer gaily mounted the ancient stage, and sang. The place inspired her, and she reminded me of a wild Arab horse, that rushes headlong on with snorting nostrils and flying mane – her song was so light and yet so firm. Anon I thought of the mourning mother beneath the cross at Golgotha, so deep was the expression of pain. And, just as it had done thousands of years ago, the sound of applause and delight now filled the theatre. "Happy, gifted creature!" all the hearers exclaimed. Five minutes more, and the stage was empty, the company had vanished, and not a sound more was heard – all were gone. But the ruins stood unchanged, as they will stand when centuries shall have gone by, and when none shall know of the momentary applause and of the triumph of the fair songstress; when all will be forgotten and gone, and even for me this hour will be but a dream of the past.'

Thirteenth Evening

'I looked through the windows of an editor's house,' said the Moon. 'It was somewhere in Germany. I saw handsome furniture, many books, and a chaos of newspapers. Several young men were present: the editor himself stood at his desk, and two little books, both by young authors, were to be noticed. "This one has been sent to me," said he. "I have not read it yet, but it is nicely got up; what think *you* of the contents?" "Oh," said the person addressed – he was a poet himself – "it is good enough; a little drawn out; but, you see, the author is still young. The verses might be better, to be sure; the thoughts are sound, though there is certainly a good deal of commonplace among them. But what will you have? You can't be always getting something new. That he'll turn out anything great I don't believe, but you may safely praise him. He is well read, a remarkable Oriental scholar, and has a good judgement. It was he who wrote that nice review of my *Reflections on Domestic Life*. We must be lenient towards the young man."

' "But he is a complete ass!" objected another of the gentlemen. "Nothing is worse in poetry than mediocrity, and he certainly does not go beyond that."

' "Poor fellow!" observed a third, "and his aunt is so happy about him. It was she, Mr Editor, who got together so many subscribers for your last translation."

' "Ah, the good woman! Well, I have noticed the book briefly. Undoubted talent – a welcome offering – a flower in the garden of poetry – prettily brought out – and so on. But this other book – I suppose the author expects me to purchase it? I hear it is praised. He has genius, certainly: don't you think so?"

' "Yes, all the world declares as much," replied the poet, "but it has turned out rather wildly. The punctuation of the book, in particular, is very eccentric."

' "It will be good for him if we pull him to pieces, and anger him a little, otherwise he will get too good an opinion of himself."

' "But that would be unfair," objected the fourth. "Let us not carp at little faults, but rejoice over the real and abundant good that we find here: he surpasses all the rest."

' "Not so. If he be a true genius, he can bear the sharp voice of censure. There are people enough to praise him. Don't let us quite turn his head."

' "Decided talent," wrote the editor, "with the usual carelessness. That he can write incorrect verses may be seen in page 25, where there are two false quantities. We recommend him to study the ancients, &c."

'I went away,' continued the Moon, 'and looked through the windows in the aunt's house. There sat the be-praised poet, the *tame* one; all the guests paid homage to him, and he was happy.

'I sought out the other poet, the *wild* one; him also I found in a great assembly at his patron's, where the *tame* poet's book was being discussed.

' "I shall read yours also," said Maecenas; "but to speak honestly – you know I never hide my opinion from you – I don't expect much from it, for you are much too wild, too fantastic. But it must be allowed that, as a man, you are highly respectable."

'A young girl sat in a corner; and she read in a book these words:

> "In the dust lies genius and glory
> But ev'ry-day talent will *pay*.

It's only the old, old story,
        But the piece is repeated each day." '

Fourteenth Evening

The Moon said, 'Beside the woodland path there are two small farm-houses. The doors are low, and some of the windows are placed quite high, and others close to the ground; and white-thorn and barberry bushes grow around them. The roof of each house is overgrown with moss and with yellow flowers and house-leek. Cabbage and potatoes are the only plants in the gardens, but out of the hedge there grows an elder tree, and under this tree sat a little girl, and she sat with her eyes fixed upon the old oak tree between the two huts.

'It was an old withered stem. It had been sawn off at the top, and a stork had built his nest upon it; and he stood in this nest clapping with his beak. A little boy came and stood by the girl's side: they were brother and sister.

' "What are you looking at?" he asked.

' "I'm watching the stork," she replied: "our neighbour told me that he would bring us a little brother or sister today; let us watch to see it come!"

' "The stork brings no such things," the boy declared, 'you may be sure of that. Our neighbour told me the same thing, but she laughed when she said it, and so I asked her if she could say 'On my honour', and she could not; and I know by that that the story about the storks is not true, and that they only tell it to us children for fun."

' "But where do the babies come from, then?" asked the girl.

' "Why, an angel from heaven brings them under his cloak, but no man can see him; and that's why we never know when he brings them."

'At that moment there was a rustling in the branches of the elder tree, and the children folded their hands and looked at one another: it was certainly the angel coming with the baby. They took each other's hand, and at that moment the door of one of the houses opened, and the neighbour appeared.

' "Come in, you two," she said. "See what the stork has brought. It is a little brother."

'And the children nodded, for they had felt quite sure already that the baby was come.'

Fifteenth Evening

'I was gliding over the Lüneborg Heath,' the Moon said. 'A lonely hut stood by the wayside, a few scanty bushes grew near it, and a nightingale who had lost his way sang sweetly. He died in the coldness of the night: it was his farewell song that I heard.

'The dawn came glimmering red. I saw a caravan of emigrant peasant families who were bound to Bremen or Hamburg, there to take ship for America, where fancied prosperity would bloom for them. The mothers carried their little children at their backs, the elder ones skipped by their sides, and a poor starved horse tugged at a cart that bore their scanty effects. The cold wind whistled, and therefore the little girl nestled closer to the mother, who, looking up at my decreasing disk, thought of the bitter want at home, and spoke of the heavy taxes they had not been able to raise. The whole caravan thought of the same thing; therefore the rising dawn seemed to them a message from the sun, of fortune that was to gleam brightly upon them. They heard the dying nightingale sing: it was no false prophet, but a harbinger of fortune. The wind whistled, therefore they did not understand that the nightingale sang, "Far away over the sea! Thou hast paid the long passage with all that was thine, and poor and helpless shalt thou enter Canaan. Thou must sell thyself, thy wife, and thy children. But your griefs shall not last long. Behind the broad fragrant leaves lurks the goddess of death, and her welcome kiss shall breathe fever into thy blood. Fare away, fare away, over the heaving billows." And the caravan listened well pleased to the song of the nightingale, which seemed to promise good fortune. Day broke through the light clouds; countrypeople went across the heath to church: the black-gowned women with their white head-dresses looked like ghosts that had stepped forth from the church pictures. All around lay a wide dead plain, covered with faded brown heath, and black charred spaces between the white sand-hills. The women carried hymn books, and walked into the church. Oh, pray, pray for those who are wandering to find graves beyond the foaming billows.'

Sixteenth Evening

'I know a Punchinello,' the Moon told me. 'The public applaud vociferously directly they see him. Every one of his movements is comic, and is sure to throw the house into convulsions of laughter; and yet there is no art in it all – it is complete nature. When he was yet a little boy, playing about with other boys, he was already Punch. Nature had intended him for it, and had provided him with a hump on his back, and another on his breast; but his inward man, his mind, on the contrary, was richly furnished. No one could surpass him in depth of feeling or in readiness of intellect. The theatre was his ideal world. If he had possessed a slender well-shaped figure, he might have been the first tragedian on any stage; the heroic, the great, filled his soul; and yet he had to become a Punchinello. His very sorrow and melancholy did but increase the comic dryness of his sharply-cut features, and increased the laughter of the audience, who showered plaudits on their favourite. The lovely Columbine was indeed kind and cordial to him; but she preferred to marry the Harlequin. It would have been too ridiculous if beauty and the beast had in reality paired together.

'When Punchinello was in very bad spirits, she was the only one who could force a smile or even a hearty burst of laughter from him: first she would be melancholy with him, then quieter, and at last quite cheerful and happy. "I know very well what is the matter with you," she said; "yes, you're in love!" And he could not help laughing. "I in love!" he cried, "that would have an absurd look. How the public would shout!" "Certainly, you are in love," she continued; and added with a comic pathos, "and I am the person you are in love with." You see, such a thing may be said when it is quite out of the question – and indeed, Punchinello burst out laughing, and gave a leap into the air, and his melancholy was forgotten.

'And yet she had only spoken the truth. He *did* love her, love her adoringly, as he loved what was great and lofty in art. At her wedding he was the merriest among the guests, but in the stillness of night he wept: if the public had seen his distorted face then, they would have applauded rapturously.

'And a few days ago, Columbine died. On the day of the funeral, Harlequin was not required to show himself on the boards, for he was a disconsolate widower. The director had to give a very merry piece, that the public might not too painfully miss the pretty Columbine and the agile Harlequin. Therefore Punchinello had to be more boisterous and extravagant than ever; and he danced and capered, with despair in his heart; and the audience yelled, and shouted, *"Bravo! bravissimo!"* Punchinello was called before the curtain. He was pronounced inimitable.

'But last night the hideous little fellow went out of the town, quite alone, to the deserted churchyard. The wreath of flowers on Columbine's grave was already faded, and he sat down there. It was a study for a painter. As he sat with his chin on his hands, his eyes turned up towards me, he looked like a grotesque monument – a Punch on a grave – peculiar and whimsical! If the people could have seen their favourite, they would have cried as usual, *"Bravo, Punchinello! bravo, bravissimo!"* '

Seventeenth Evening

Hear what the Moon told me. 'I have seen the cadet who had just been made an officer put on his handsome uniform for the first time; I have seen the young girl in her ball-dress, and the Prince's young wife happy in her gorgeous robes; but never have I seen a felicity equal to that of a little girl of four years old, whom I watched this evening. She had received a new blue dress and a new pink hat; the splendid attire had just been put on, and all were calling for a candle, for my rays, shining in through the windows of the room, were not bright enough for the occasion, and further illumination was required. There stood the little maid, stiff and upright as a doll, her arms stretched painfully straight out away from the dress, and her fingers apart; and, oh, what happiness beamed from her eyes and from her whole countenance! "Tomorrow you shall go out in your new clothes," said her mother; and the little one looked up at her hat and down at her frock, and smiled brightly. "Mother," she cried, "what will the little dogs think when they see me in these splendid new things?" '

Eighteenth Evening

'I have spoken to you of Pompeii,' said the Moon; 'that corpse of a city, exposed in the view of living towns: I know another sight still more strange, and this is not the corpse, but the spectre of a city. Whenever the jetty fountains splash into the marble basins, they seem to me to be telling the story of the floating city. Yes, the spouting water may tell of her, the waves of the sea may sing of her fame! On the surface of the ocean a mist often rests, and that is her widow's veil. The Bridegroom of the Sea is dead, his palace and his city are his mausoleum! Dost thou know this city? She has never heard the rolling of wheels or the hoof-tread of horses in her streets, through which the fish swim, while the black gondola glides spectrally over the green water. I will show you the place,' continued the Moon, 'the largest square in it, and you will fancy yourself transported into the city of a fairy tale. The grass grows rank among the broad flagstones, and in the morning twilight thousands of tame pigeons flutter around the solitary lofty tower. On three sides you find yourself surrounded by cloistered walks. In these the silent Turk sits smoking his long pipe; the handsome Greek leans against the pillar, and gazes at the upraised trophies and lofty masts, memorials of power that is gone. The flags hang down like mourning scarves. A girl rests there: she has put down her heavy pails filled with water, the yoke with which she has carried them rests on one of her shoulders, and she leans against the mast of victory. That is not a fairy palace you see before you yonder, but a church: the gilded domes and shining orbs flash back my beams; the glorious bronze horses up yonder have made journeys, like the bronze horse in the fairy tale: they have come hither, and gone hence, and have returned again. Do you notice the variegated splendour of the walls and windows? It looks as if Genius had followed the caprices of a child, in the adornment of these singular temples. Do you see the winged lion on the pillar? The gold glitters still, but his wings are tied – the lion is dead, for the King of the Sea is dead; the great halls stand desolate, and where gorgeous paintings hung of yore, the naked wall now peers through. The beggar sleeps under the arcade, whose pavement in old times was trodden only by the feet of the high nobility. From the deep wells, and perhaps from the prisons by the Bridge of Sighs, rise the accents of woe, as at the time when the tambourine was heard in the gay gondolas, and the golden ring was cast from the Bucentaur to Adria, the Queen of the Seas. Adria! shroud thyself in mists; let the veil of thy widowhood shroud thy form, and clothe in the weeds of woe the mausoleum of thy bridegroom – the marble, spectral Venice!'

Nineteenth Evening

'I looked down upon a great theatre,' said the Moon. 'The house was crowded, for a new actor was to make his first appearance that night. My rays glided over a little window in the wall, and I saw a painted face with the forehead pressed against the panes. It was the hero of the evening. The knightly beard curled crisply about the chin; but there were tears in the man's eyes, for he had been hissed off, and indeed with reason. The poor Incapable! But Incapables cannot be admitted into the empire of Art. He had deep feeling, and loved his art enthusiastically, but the art loved not him. The prompter's bell sounded; *"the hero enters with a determined air,"* so ran the stage direction in his part, and he had to appear before an audience who turned him into ridicule. When the piece was over, I saw a form wrapped in a mantle creeping down the steps: it was the vanquished knight of the evening. The sceneshifters whispered to one another, and I followed the poor fellow home to his room. To hang oneself is to die a mean death, and poison is not always at hand, I know; but he thought of both. I saw how he looked at his pale face in the glass, with eyes half closed, to see if he should look well as a corpse. A man may be very unhappy, and yet exceedingly affected. He thought of death, of suicide; I believe he pitied himself, for he wept bitterly; and when a man has had his cry out he doesn't kill himself.

'Since that time a year had rolled by. Again a play was to be acted, but in a little theatre, and by a poor strolling company. Again I saw the well-remembered face, with the painted cheeks and the crisp beard. He looked up at me and smiled; and yet he had been hissed off only a minute before – hissed off from a wretched theatre by a miserable audience. And tonight a shabby hearse rolled out of the town gate. It was a suicide – our painted, despised hero. The driver of the hearse was the only person present, for no one followed except my beams. In a corner of the churchyard the corpse of the suicide was shovelled into the earth, and nettles will soon be rankly growing over his grave, and the sexton will throw thorns and weeds from the other graves upon it.'

Twentieth Evening

'I come from Rome,' said the Moon. 'In the midst of the city, upon one of the seven hills, lie the ruins of the imperial palace. The wild fig tree grows in the clefts of the wall, and covers the nakedness thereof with its broad grey-green leaves; trampling among heaps of rubbish, the ass treads upon green laurels, and rejoices over the rank thistles. From this spot, whence the eagles of Rome once flew abroad, whence they "came, saw, and conquered," a door leads into a little mean house, built of clay between two broken marble pillars; the wild vine hangs like a mourning garland over the crooked window. An old woman and her little granddaughter live there: they rule now in the palace of the Caesars, and show to strangers the remains of its past glories. Of the splendid throne-room only a naked wall yet stands, and a black cypress throws its dark shadow on the spot where the throne once stood. The earth lies several feet deep on the broken pavement; and the little maiden, now the daughter of the imperial palace, often sits there on her stool when the evening bells ring. The keyhole of the door close by she calls her turret window; through this she can see half Rome, as far as the mighty cupola of St Peter's.

'On this evening, as usual, stillness reigned around; and in the full beam of my light came the little granddaughter. On her head she carried an earthen pitcher of antique shape filled with water. Her feet were bare, her short frock and her white sleeves were torn. I kissed her pretty round shoulders, her dark eyes, and black shining hair. She mounted the stairs; they were steep, having been made up of rough blocks of broken marble and the capital of a fallen pillar. The coloured lizards slipped away, startled, from before her feet, but she was not frightened at them. Already she lifted her hand to pull the doorbell – a hare's foot fastened to a string formed the bell-handle of the imperial palace. She paused for a moment – of what might she be thinking? Perhaps of the beautiful Christ-child, dressed in gold and silver, which was down below in the chapel, where the silver candlesticks gleamed so bright, and where her little friends sang the hymns in which she also could join? I know not. Presently she moved again – she stumbled; the earthen vessel fell from her head, and broke on the marble steps. She burst into tears. The beautiful daughter of the imperial palace wept over the worthless broken pitcher; with her bare feet she stood there weeping, and dared not pull the string, the bell-rope of the imperial palace!'

Twenty-first Evening

It was more than a fortnight since the Moon had shone. Now he stood once more, round and bright, above the clouds, moving slowly onward. Hear what the Moon told me.

'From a town in Fezzan I followed a caravan. On the margin of the sandy desert, in a salt plain, that shone like a frozen lake, and was only covered in spots with light drifting sand, a halt was made. The eldest of the company – the water-gourd hung at his girdle, and by his head lay a little bag of unleavened bread – drew a square in the sand with his staff, and wrote in it a few words out of the Koran, and then the whole caravan passed over the consecrated spot. A young merchant, a child of the East, as I could tell by his eye and his figure, rode pensively forward on his white snorting steed. Was he thinking, perchance, of his fair young wife? It was only two days ago that the camel, adorned with furs and with costly shawls, had carried her, the beauteous bride, round the walls of the city, while drums and cymbals had sounded, the women sang, and festive shots, of which the bridegroom fired the greatest number, resounded round the camel; and now he was journeying with the caravan across the desert.

'For many nights I followed the train. I saw them rest by the well-side among the stunted palms; they thrust the knife into the breast of the camel that had fallen, and roasted its flesh by the fire. My beams cooled the glowing sands, and showed them the black rocks, dead islands in the immense ocean of sand. No hostile tribes met them in their pathless route, no storms arose, no columns of sand whirled destruction over the journeying caravan. At home the beautiful wife prayed for her husband and her father. "Are they dead?" she asked of my golden crescent; "Are they dead?" she cried to my full disk. Now the desert lies behind them. This evening they sit beneath the lofty palm trees, where the crane flutters round them with its long wings, and the pelican watches them from the branches of the mimosa. The luxuriant herbage is trampled down, crushed by the feet of elephants. A troop of Negroes are returning from a market in the interior of the land; the women, with copper buttons in their black hair, and decked out in clothes dyed with indigo, drive the heavily-laden oxen, on whose backs slumber the naked black children. A Negro leads by a string a young lion which he has bought. They approach the caravan; the young merchant sits pensive and motionless, thinking of his beautiful wife, dreaming, in the land of the blacks, of his white fragrant lily beyond the desert. He raises his head, and –'

But at this moment a cloud passed before the Moon, and then another. I heard nothing more from him that evening.

Twenty-second Evening

'I saw a little girl weeping,' said the Moon: 'she was weeping over the depravity of the world. She had received a most beautiful doll as a present. Oh, that was a glorious doll, so fair and delicate! She did not seem created for the sorrows of this world. But the brothers of the little girl, those great naughty boys, had set the doll high up in the branches of a tree, and had run away.

'The little girl could not reach up to the doll, and could not help her down, and that is why she was crying. The doll must certainly have been crying too, for she stretched out her arms among the green branches, and looked quite mournful. Yes, these are the troubles of life of which the little girl had often heard tell. Alas, poor doll! it began to grow dark already; and night would soon come on! Was she to be left sitting there alone on the bough all night long? No, the little maid could not make up her mind to that. "I'll stay with you," she said, although she felt anything but happy in her mind. She could almost fancy she distinctly saw little gnomes, with their high-crowned hats, sitting in the bushes; and farther back in the long walk, tall spectres appeared to be dancing. They came nearer and nearer, and stretched out their hands towards the tree on which the doll sat; they laughed scornfully, and pointed at her with their fingers. Oh, how frightened the little maid was! "But if one has not done anything wrong," she thought, "nothing evil can harm one. I wonder if I have done anything wrong?" And she considered. "Oh, yes! I laughed at the poor duck with the red rag on her leg; she limped along so funnily, I could not help laughing; but it's a sin to laugh at animals." And she looked up at the doll. "Did you laugh at animals?" she asked; and it seemed as if the doll shook her head.'

Twenty-third Evening

'I looked down on Tyrol,' said the Moon, 'and my beams caused the dark pines to throw long shadows upon the rocks. I looked at the pictures of St Christopher carrying the Infant Jesus that are painted there upon the walls of the houses, colossal figures reaching from the ground to the roof. St Florian was represented pouring water on the burning house, and the Lord hung bleeding on the great cross by the wayside. To the present generation these are old pictures, but I saw when they were put up, and marked how one followed the other. On the brow of the mountain yonder is perched, like a swallow's nest, a lonely convent of nuns. Two of the sisters stood up in the tower tolling the bell; they were both young, and therefore their glances flew over the mountain out into the world. A travelling coach passed by below, the postilion wound his horn, and the poor nuns looked after the carriage for a moment with a mournful glance, and a tear gleamed in the eyes of the younger one. And the horn sounded faintly and more faint, and the convent bell drowned its expiring echoes.'

Twenty-fourth Evening

Hear what the Moon told me. 'Some years ago, here in Copenhagen, I looked through the window of a mean little room. The father and mother slept, but the little son was awake. I saw the flowered cotton curtains of the bed move, and the child peep forth. At first I thought he was looking at the great clock, which was gaily painted in red and green. At the top sat a cuckoo, below hung the heavy leaden weights, and the pendulum with the polished disk of metal went to and fro, and said, "Tick, tick." But no, he was not looking at the clock, but at his mother's spinning-wheel, that stood just underneath it. That was the boy's favourite piece of furniture, but he dared not touch it, for if he meddled with it he got a rap on the knuckles. For hours together, when his mother was spinning, he would sit quietly by her side, watching the whirring spindle and the revolving wheel, and as he sat he thought of many things. Oh, if he might only turn the wheel himself! Father and mother were asleep: he looked at them, and looked at the spinning-wheel, and presently a little naked foot peeped out of the bed, and then a second foot, and then two little white legs. There he stood. He looked round once more, to see if father and mother were still asleep, yes, they slept; and now he crept *softly, softly*, in his short little nightgown, to the spinning-wheel, and began to spin. The thread flew from the wheel, and the wheel whirled faster and faster. I kissed his fair hair and his blue eyes, it was such a pretty picture.

'At that moment the mother awoke. The curtain shook; she looked forth, and fancied she saw a gnome or some other kind of little spectre. "In Heaven's name!" she cried, and aroused her husband in a frightened way. He opened his eyes, rubbed them with his hands, and looked at the brisk little lad. "Why, that is Bertel," said he. And my eye quitted the poor room, for I have so much to see. At the same moment I looked at the halls of the Vatican, where the marble gods are enthroned. I shone upon the group of the Laocoon; the stone seemed to sigh. I pressed a silent kiss on the lips of the Muses, and they seemed to stir and move. But my rays lingered longest about the Nile group with the colossal god. Leaning against the Sphinx, he lies there thoughtful and meditative, as if he were thinking on the rolling centuries; and little love-gods sport with him and with the crocodiles. In the horn of plenty sits with folded arms a little tiny love-god contemplating the great solemn river-god, a true picture of the boy at the spinning-wheel – the features were exactly the same. Charming and lifelike stood the little marble form, and yet the wheel of the year has turned more than a thousand times since the time when it sprang forth from the stone. Just as often as the boy in the little room turned the spinning-wheel had the great wheel murmured, before the age could again call forth marble gods equal to those he afterwards formed.

'Years have passed since all this happened,' the Moon went on to say. 'Yesterday I looked upon a bay on the eastern coast of Denmark. Glorious woods are there, and high banks, an old knightly castle with red walls, swans floating in the ponds, and in the background appears, among orchards, a little town with a church. Many boats, the crews all furnished with torches, glided over the silent expanse – but these fires had not been kindled for catching fish, for everything had a festive look. Music sounded, a song was sung, and in one of the boats a man stood erect, to whom homage was paid by the rest, a tall sturdy man, wrapped in a cloak. He had blue eyes and long white hair. I knew him, and thought of the Vatican, and of the group of the Nile, and the old marble gods. I thought of the simple little room where little Bertel sat in his nightshirt by the spinning-wheel. The wheel of time has turned, and new gods have come forth from the stone. From the boats there arose a shout: "Hurrah! hurrah for Bertel Thorwaldsen!" '

Twenty-fifth Evening

'I will now give you a picture from Frankfort,' said the Moon. 'I especially noticed one building there. It was not the house in which Goethe was born, nor the old council house, through whose grated windows peered the horns of the oxen that were roasted and given to the people when the Emperors were crowned. No, it was a private house, plain in appearance, and painted green. It stood at the corner of the narrow Jews' Street. It was Rothschild's house.

'I looked through the open door. The staircase was brilliantly lighted: servants carrying wax candles in massive silver candlesticks stood there, and bowed low before an aged woman, who was being brought downstairs in a litter. The proprietor of the house stood bareheaded, and respectfully imprinted a kiss on the hand of the old woman. She was his mother. She nodded in a friendly manner to him and to the servants, and they carried her into the dark narrow street, into a little house that was her dwelling. Here her children had been born, from hence the fortune of the family had arisen. If she deserted the despised street and the little house, fortune would perhaps desert her children. That was her firm belief.'

The Moon told me no more; his visit this evening was far too short. But I thought of the old woman in the narrow despised street. It would have cost her but a word, and a brilliant house would have arisen for her on the banks of the Thames – a word, and a villa would have been prepared in the Bay of Naples.

'If I deserted the lowly house, where the fortunes of my sons first began to bloom, fortune would desert them!' It was a superstition, but a superstition of such a class, that he who knows the story and has seen this picture, need have only two words placed under the picture to make him understand it; and these two words are: 'A mother.'

Twenty-sixth Evening

'It was yesterday, in the morning twilight' – these are the words the

Moon told me – 'in the great city no chimney was yet smoking – and it was just at the chimneys that I was looking. Suddenly a little head emerged from one of them, and then half a body, the arms resting on the rim of the chimney-pot. "Hurrah!" cried a voice. It was the little chimney-sweeper, who had for the first time in his life crept through a chimney and stuck out his head at the top. "Hurrah!" Yes, certainly that was a very different thing from creeping about in the dark narrow chimneys! the air blew so fresh, and he could look over the whole city towards the green wood. The sun was just rising. It shone round and great, just in his face, that beamed with triumph, though it was very prettily blacked with soot.

' "The whole town can see me now," he exclaimed, "and the moon can see me now, and the sun too. Hurrah!" And he flourished his broom in triumph.'

Twenty-seventh Evening

'Last night I looked down upon a town in China,' said the Moon. 'My beams irradiated the naked walls that form the streets there. Now and then, certainly, a door is seen, but it is locked, for what does the Chinaman care about the outer world? Close wooden shutters covered the windows behind the walls of the houses; but through the windows of the temple a faint light glimmered. I looked in, and saw the quaint decorations within. From the floor to the ceiling pictures are painted in the most glaring colours and richly gilt – pictures representing the deeds of the gods here on earth. In each niche statues are placed, but they are almost entirely hidden by the coloured drapery and the banners that hang down. Before each idol (and they are all made of tin) stood a little altar with holy water, with flowers and burning wax lights on it. Above all the rest stood Fu, the chief deity, clad in a garment of yellow silk, for yellow is here the sacred colour. At the foot of the altar sat a living being, a young priest. He appeared to be praying, but in the midst of his prayer he seemed to fall into deep thought, and this must have been wrong, for his cheeks glowed and he held down his head. Poor Soui-hong! Was he, perhaps, dreaming of working in the little flower-garden behind the high street wall? And did that occupation seem more agreeable to him than watching the wax lights in the temple? Or did he wish to sit at the rich feast, wiping his mouth with silver paper between each course? Or was his sin so great that, if he dared utter it, the Celestial Empire would punish it with death? Had his thoughts ventured to fly with the ships of the barbarians, to their homes in far distant England? No, his thoughts did not fly so far, and yet they were sinful, sinful as thoughts born of young hearts, sinful here in the temple, in the presence of Fu and other holy gods.

'I know whither his thoughts had strayed. At the farther end of the city, on the flat roof paved with porcelain, on which stood the handsome vases covered with painted flowers, sat the beauteous Pe, of the little roguish eyes, of the full lips, and of the tiny feet. The tight shoe pained her, but her heart pained her still more. She lifted her graceful round arm, and her satin dress rustled. Before her stood a glass bowl containing four goldfish. She stirred the bowl carefully with a slender lacquered stick, very slowly, for she, too, was lost in thought. Was she thinking, perchance, how the fishes were richly clothed in gold, how they lived calmly and peacefully in their crystal world, how they were regularly fed, and yet how much happier they might be if they were free? Yes, that she could well understand, the beautiful Pe. Her thoughts wandered away from her home, wandered to the temple, but not for the sake of holy things. Poor Pe! Poor Soui-hong!

'Their earthly thoughts met, but my cold beam lay between the two, like the sword of the cherub.'

Twenty-eighth Evening

'The air was calm,' said the Moon; 'the water was as transparent as the pure ether through which I was gliding, and deep below the surface I could see the strange plants that stretched up their long arms towards me like the gigantic trees of the forest. The fishes swam to and fro above their tops. High in the air a flight of wild swans were winging their way, one of which sank lower and lower, with wearied pinions, his eyes following the airy caravan, that melted farther and farther into the distance. With outspread wings he sank slowly, as a soap-bubble sinks in the still air, till he touched the water. At length his head lay back between his wings, and silently he lay there, like a white lotus flower upon the quiet lake. And a gentle wind arose, and crisped the quiet surface, which gleamed like the clouds that poured along in great broad waves; and the swan raised his head, and the glowing water splashed like blue fire over his breast and back. The dawn illuminated the red clouds, the swan rose strengthened, and flew towards the rising sun, towards the bluish coast whither the caravan had gone; but he flew all alone, with a longing in his breast. Lonely he flew over the blue swelling billows.'

Twenty-ninth Evening

'I will give you another picture of Sweden,' said the Moon. 'Among dark pine-woods, near the melancholy banks of the Roxen, lies the old convent church of Wreta. My rays glided through the grating into the roomy vaults, where kings sleep tranquilly in great stone coffins. On the wall, above the grave of each, is placed the emblem of earthly grandeur, a kingly crown; but it is made only of wood, painted and gilt, and is hung on a wooden peg driven into the wall. The worms have gnawed the gilded wood, the spider has spun her web from the crown down to the coffin, like a mourning banner, frail and transient as the grief of mortals. How quietly they sleep! I can remember them quite plainly. I still see the bold smile on their lips, that so strongly and plainly expressed joy or grief. When the steamboat winds along like a magic snail over the lakes, a stranger often comes to the church, and visits the burial vault; he asks the names of the kings, and they have a dead and forgotten sound. He glances with a smile at the worm-eaten crowns, and if he happens to be a pious, thoughtful man, something of melancholy mingles with the smile. Slumber on, ye dead ones! The Moon thinks of you, the Moon at night sends down his rays into your silent kingdom, over which hangs the crown of pine-wood.'

Thirtieth Evening

'Close by the high road,' said the Moon, 'is an inn, and opposite to it is a great wagon-shed, whose straw roof was just being re-thatched. I looked down between the bare rafters and through the open loft into the comfortless space below. The turkey-cock slept on the beam, and the saddle rested in the empty crib. In the middle of the shed stood a travelling carriage; the proprietor was inside, fast asleep, while the horses were being watered. The coachman stretched himself, though I am very sure that he had been most comfortably asleep half the last stage. The door of the servants' room stood open, and the bed looked as if it had been turned over and over; the candle stood on the floor, and had burned deep down into the socket. The wind blew cold through the shed: it was nearer to the dawn than to midnight. In the stall, on the ground, slept a wandering family of musicians. The father and mother seemed to be dreaming of the burning liquor that remained in the bottle. The little pale daughter was dreaming too, for her eyes were wet with tears. The harp stood at their heads, and the dog lay stretched at their feet.'

Thirty-first Evening

'It was in a little provincial town,' the Moon said; 'it certainly happened last year, but that has nothing to do with the matter. I saw it quite plainly. Today I read about it in the papers, but there it was not half so clearly expressed. In the taproom of the little inn sat the bear-leader, eating his supper; the bear was tied up outside, behind the wood pile – poor Bruin, who did nobody any harm, though he looked grim enough. Up in the garret three little children were playing by the light of my beams; the eldest was perhaps six years old, the youngest certainly not more than two. Tramp! tramp! – somebody was coming upstairs: who might it be? The door was thrust open – it was Bruin, the great, shaggy Bruin! He had got tired of waiting down in the courtyard, and had found his way to the stairs. I saw it all,' said the Moon. 'The children were very much frightened at first at the great shaggy animal; each of them crept into a corner, but he found them all out, and smelt at them, but did them no harm. "This must be a great dog," they said, and began to stroke him. He lay down upon the ground, the youngest boy clambered on his back, and, bending down a little head of golden curls, played at hiding in the beast's shaggy skin. Presently the eldest boy took his drum, and beat upon it till it rattled again: the bear rose up on its hind legs and began to dance. It was a charming sight to behold. Each boy now took his gun, and the bear was obliged to have one too, and he held it up quite properly. Here was a capital playmate they had found! and they began marching – one, two; one, two.

'Suddenly someone came to the door, which opened, and the mother of the children appeared. You should have seen her in her dumb terror, with her face as white as chalk, her mouth half-open, and her eyes fixed in a horrified stare. But the youngest boy nodded to her in great glee, and called out in his infantile prattle, "We're playing at soldiers." And then the bear-leader came running up.'

Thirty-second Evening

The wind blew stormy and cold, the clouds flew hurriedly past; only for a moment now and then did the Moon become visible. He said, 'I look down through the silent sky upon the driving clouds, and see the great shadows chasing each other across the earth. I looked upon a prison. A closed carriage stood before it; a prisoner was to be carried away. My rays pierced through the grated window towards the wall: the prisoner was scratching a few lines upon it, as a parting token; but he did not write words, but a melody, the outpouring of his heart. The door was opened, and he was led forth, and fixed his eyes upon my round disk. Clouds passed between us, as if he were not to see my face, nor I his. He stepped into the carriage, the door was closed, the whip cracked, and the horses galloped off into the thick forest, whither my rays were not able to follow him; but as I glanced through the grated window, my rays glided over the notes, his last farewell engraved on the prison wall – where words fail, sounds can often speak. My rays could only light up isolated notes, so the greater part of what was written there will ever remain dark to me. Was it the death-hymn he wrote there? Were these the glad notes of joy? Did he drive away to meet his death, or hasten to the embraces of his beloved? The rays of the Moon do not read all that is written by mortals.'

Thirty-third Evening

'I love the children,' said the Moon, 'especially the quite little ones – they are so droll. Sometimes I peep into the room, between the curtain and the window-frame, when they are not thinking of me. It gives me pleasure to see them dressing and undressing. First, the little round naked shoulder comes creeping out of the frock, then the arm; or I see how the stocking is drawn off, and a plump little white leg makes its appearance, and a little white foot that is fit to be kissed, and I kiss it too.

'But about what I was going to tell you. This evening I looked through a window, before which no curtain was drawn, for nobody lives opposite. I saw a whole troop of little ones, all of one family, and among them was a little sister. She is only four years old, but can say her prayers as well as any of the rest. The mother sits by her bed every evening, and hears her say her prayers; and then she has a kiss, and the mother sits by the bed till the little one has gone to sleep, which generally happens as soon as ever she closes her eyes.

'This evening the two elder children were a little boisterous. One of them hopped about on one leg in his long white nightgown, and the other stood on a chair surrounded by the clothes of all the children, and declared it was a tableau, and the others were to guess what it was. The third and fourth laid the playthings carefully in the box, for that is a thing that has to be done; and the mother sat by the bed of the youngest, and announced to all the rest that they were to be quiet, for little sister was going to say her prayers.

'I looked in, over the lamp, into the little maiden's bed, where she lay under the neat white coverlet, her hands folded demurely and her little face quite grave and serious. She was saying the Lord's Prayer aloud. But her mother interrupted her in the middle of her prayer. "How is it," she asked, "that when you have prayed for daily bread, you always add something I cannot understand? You must tell me what that is." The little one lay silent, and looked at her mother in embarrassment. "What is it you say after *our daily bread*?" "Dear mother, don't be angry: I only said, *and plenty of butter on it*." '

THE END

THE CAMBRIDGE ANCIENT HISTORY

EDITORS

Volumes I–VI	*Volumes* VII–IX
J. B. BURY, M.A., F.B.A.	S. A. COOK, LITT.D.
S. A. COOK, LITT D.	F. E. ADCOCK, M.A.
F. E. ADCOCK, M.A.	M. P. CHARLESWORTH, M.A.

VOLUME IX

THE
CAMBRIDGE
ANCIENT HISTORY

VOLUME IX

THE ROMAN REPUBLIC
133—44 B.C.

EDITED BY
S. A. COOK, Litt.D.
F. E. ADCOCK, M.A.
M. P. CHARLESWORTH, M.A.

CAMBRIDGE
AT THE UNIVERSITY PRESS
1966

PUBLISHED BY
THE SYNDICS OF THE CAMBRIDGE UNIVERSITY PRESS

Bentley House, 200 Euston Road, London, N.W.1
American Branch: 32 East 57th Street, New York, N.Y. 10022
West African Office: P.M.B. 5181, Ibadan, Nigeria

First Edition 1932
Reprinted with slight corrections, 1951
Reprinted 1962
1966

Printed in Great Britain at the University Printing House, Cambridge
(Brooke Crutchley, University Printer)

PREFACE

THE narrative in this volume begins with the Gracchi and ends with Caesar. These are the first and last of a succession of men whose strength or weaknesses were not readily to be reconciled with the control of the State by a tradition-bound aristocracy of office. Great as had been the achievement of Senatorial government in solving the problems of foreign policy or in knowing when to allow them to solve themselves, its domestic policy had become narrow and inert, and the institutions of the Roman city-state required, at the least, adaptation to the needs of an empire. Within Italy, Rome had neither faced the problems raised by an inevitable shifting of economic conditions nor been willing to give to her allies the share in her success that their services merited.

The first of these problems was, in part at least, solved by the Gracchi, but in the course of the solution the convention of Senatorial government was challenged, so that the sovranty of the Roman People was revived as an overriding force which could be invoked, not only for much-needed reform, but in support of personal ambitions by those who found themselves in opposition to the governing nobility. The equestrian order became a political power which could become effective at moments at which its financial interests appeared to be threatened. Concessions to the claims of the Italian allies at Rome were postponed by a Senatorial reaction which reflected the selfishness of the whole citizen-body. Problems of defence and of prestige arose which overtaxed the self-limited resources of the State. These led to the creation of a formidable Fourth Estate in an army professional in recruiting and sentiment. The Senatorial government failed to provide this army with commanders who were always loyal to the existing order and left it to look to powerful generals for the final rewards of its service. An army which might not obey the Senate, an Italy which had come to resent its exclusion from the Roman franchise, and a group of politicians and soldiers who were denied a career by the influence of the ruling families endangered the domestic power of the government. Then followed the Social War, in which part of the Italians fought for a full entry into the Roman State while part strove to reverse the verdict which had made Rome the mistress of Italy. By fighting and by concessions the Senate averted disaster. An extension of the franchise made peninsular Italy Roman and extended the recruiting ground for the new army. Even so, the Senatorial government was grudging and maladroit, so that while its best general, Sulla, was engaged in a campaign abroad, the ambitious men of the Opposition enjoyed a brief interlude of power. The government had already compromised its claim to govern by the use of violence in the name of order, and had allowed Sulla to bring his legions within the city. Now Sulla returned at the head of his army of the East and restored Senatorial government by the wholesale destruction of its opponents and their supporters.

But Sulla was no mere reactionary. He recognized the duties of the government and strove to create a machinery which would enable the Senate to discharge them, secure from the pressure of army-commanders and unhampered by the full sovranty of the People and the powers of the Tribunate which the Gracchi and his own enemies had called into activity. But to achieve his ends he created a dictatorship which pointed straight to a Republican autocracy, and no sooner had Sulla abdicated than there sprang up dangers which refuted his calculations. The army had not been made the servant of the State; the Senatorial government was forced to look for military skill to men who were impatient of its control; in Italy itself there was a formidable revolt of gladiators and slaves. Within eight years of Sulla's death, two of his lieutenants, Crassus and Pompey, joined forces to impose upon the Senate the partial destruction of the Sullan constitutional reforms. The Tribunate regained its power to thwart or reverse the policies of the Senate. The failure to provide any means by which the extension of the franchise led to the representation of Italy as a whole left the decision of questions to what was called the Roman People, but was in the main the venal and disorderly populace of a single city.

Then followed a decade of intrigue at Rome during which Lucullus and Pompey dealt with the enemies of Rome in the East. The methods by which Sulla had crushed his enemies and had settled in Italy veterans who failed to cultivate the farms which had been seized for them, left ample discontent and the means of fomenting it. Bribery had become the road to office, which was no longer the preserve of a group of families; successful bribery led to the exploitation of provinces, unsuccessful bribery to debt and a readiness for revolution. The career of Pompey pointed the way to the ambitious. To allay these dangers Cicero strove to bring about a union of hearts between the Senate and the steady substantial citizens of Italy. But the attempt, beset as it was by civilian illusions, failed.

Pompey returned from a great command which broke with the traditions of the State to be thwarted by the Senate. The result was a coalition in which a new figure—Caesar—found a place. What is called the First Triumvirate aimed at the satisfaction of ambition together with the reform of administration in despite of the Senate. For a time the coalition dominated Roman politics, but the satisfying of Crassus' ambition ended him in the deserts of Mesopotamia, while the satisfying of Caesar's ambition procured him a strong and devoted army, though it won Rome a province. Thus was prepared the way for an armed contest between Caesar and a government which, with Pompey's help, wished to treat him worse than it had treated Pompey on his return from the East. The decision lay with the armies, and the decision fell in favour of Caesar, who established an autocracy, Republican in form, but inconsistent with the ancient traditions of the Republic. This autocracy perished with Caesar on the Ides of March, and his death left Rome still faced by her constitutional problem. Neither in the predominance of a tribune like Gaius Gracchus, nor in a restoration of Senatorial control like that carried through by Sulla, nor in the dictatorship of Caesar was any lasting solution to be found. For it cannot be said that either the success or the death of Caesar marked the end of the Republic or inaugurated a permanent monarchical form of government. Moments in the career of Pompey foreshadowed a compromise between the Senate and a protector who would give it security and a full share of power. But the decisive answer to the question how Rome was to rule the world in peace was given not by Pompey or by Caesar but by Augustus. At last there came the man who answered the riddle of the Sphinx rightly and survived. But the answer was conditioned by the events that followed Caesar's death, and these events are reserved for the following volume, which will have as its theme the first working out of the Principate.

The inheritance of the Republic passed to the Principate un-challenged in a world that longed for peace and security under a strong hand. In the ninety years that lie between the beginning and the end of this volume Rome had shown clearly enough that, despite political and military blunders, she stood without a rival in power. Even when a narrow and selfish policy roused the Italian allies of Rome to revolt, the Romans had known well how to fight and where to yield. The pre-occupation of Rome in this domestic crisis per-mitted the threat of a movement of the East against her, but the

threat was warded off, as it were with one hand, until the time
came when Mithridates, the leader of this movement, could be
defeated and crushed. Under negligent Senatorial government
the Mediterranean had become infested with pirates. A single
campaign delivered the seas, and Pompey passed on to make a
settlement of the East which established Roman power firmly and
allied with it the sentiment of the Hellenistic communities. At
the close of the second century Italy had to fear an invasion by
barbarians from the North; fifty years later the frontier of her
empire had reached the English Channel and the Rhine. Even
in domestic affairs the work of Gaius Gracchus, of Sulla and still
more that of Caesar showed that the administrative genius and
political resource of the Roman aristocracy had not perished. The
Civil War itself strengthened rather than weakened the military
establishment of the Republic and proved beyond doubt the
supremacy of legions in the field. The King of Parthia might
contemplate the standards of a Roman army defeated at Carrhae,
but the world was well aware that in Rome and Italy it must find
its masters. By the side of civil wars and defeats, misgovernment
and the corruption of politics must be set a series of achievements
of which any people might be justly proud, so that neither Rome
nor the world despaired of the Republic. When Augustus laid
the foundations of the Principate, he was building on a political
prestige and a military predominance which the vicissitudes of the
previous century had failed to destroy.

Far steadier was the advance of Roman art and letters. With
the union of Italy in a more than political sense there had already
arisen a truly national Roman art, which fused with itself Etruscan
Greek and Samnite forms. From the time of Sulla onwards the
city itself had begun to assume a dignity not unworthy of its
primacy. Latin poets not only wrote in the manner and spirit of
the Greeks, but developed the resources of their own language so
as to make possible the triumphs of the Augustan age. In a city
which was becoming ever more cosmopolitan, and receptive of
ideas from the Greek East, Roman culture came to have a meaning
of its own, and Cicero was beyond all doubt the greatest man of
letters of his day. Nor did he stand alone. The erudition of Varro
was no more than an extreme form of the scholarship possessed
by many members of the Roman aristocracy. The last century and
a half of the Republic witnessed a modernization of Roman law
which, although it owed something to Greek thought and to the
regulation of relations between citizens and foreigners, was the
achievement of native Roman jurisprudence. From the Gracchi

onwards there appears a succession of orators who added grace to the force and mother wit that belonged to the Roman character. It is true that these talents were too often the servants of malignity and partisanship. Beneath the formal urbanity of Cicero's correspondence may be seen not only the subtlety the vanity and the tact of Cicero himself but the hard pride and egotism of the nobles of his day. In an age of constant feuds, of venality, and of ruthlessness many of the finest spirits of Rome were the victims of baser men. But the administrative and military capacity of the Romans approved itself again and again. With all their faults, old and new, they were still the shrewdest and strongest among the peoples.

Outside the area of Roman activity there were signs of the future. The close of the second century had witnessed a transient intrusion of barbarians from the North into Mediterranean lands. The obscure movements which set peoples adrift were felt on the northern borders. In the region of the Black Sea Greek cities found themselves threatened more and more, and were saved by the help of the new power of Pontus. In Asia Minor this power came to overshadow its neighbours while new forces, Eastern in character, asserted themselves against the Western element in Hellenism. The Seleucid monarchy dwindled and vanished. Within the borders of Palestine the Jewish national State developed the setting of religious ideas in which Christianity was to arise. In Egypt the Ptolemaic dynasty preserved a faded troubled reign, rarely loved at home and in constant danger of annexation by Rome. Farther east there had arisen a new power. Iranian nomads from the steppes beyond the Caspian were welded together into a people by the skill and force of the dynasty of the Arsacids and won an empire at the expense of the failing Hellenistic kingdoms of the East. The rise of this power was timely. During the last three decades of the second century wide-spread dislocations of peoples from China to the Oxus brought a flood of nomads pressing hard against the eastern frontiers of the Hellenistic world. To the new Parthian State belongs the credit for breaking and thrusting back these peoples. Thus a warrior race from the North became the rulers of what had once been the heart of the Persian Empire, borrowing the machinery of government from the Seleucids and using rather than absorbing culture from the hellenism of their subjects and neighbours and the brief revival of Babylonian civilization. This aristocratic monarchy, with its one native accomplishment of war, came into contact with Rome when Lucullus and Pompey carried the arms of the

Republic to the Tigris and the Euphrates. Crassus made Rome an active enemy of Parthia; Caesar meditated at least a demonstration that the secret of victory was with the West. The stage was set for a long though not equal rivalry between the Empire and the Parthian Monarchy.

In the economy of the volume military history has in general been subordinated to political history so that many interesting problems of topography have been left almost or entirely undiscussed. Where the necessity for this, imposed by considerations of space, has led to any appearance of dogmatism in a field in which certainty is often unattainable the responsibility rests with the editors rather than with the contributors. A sketch of the literary authorities is given in order to enable readers to make a rough evaluation of the sources mentioned in the notes at the beginning of the chapters and in the Bibliography. In this sketch there are points, especially of detail, which are controversial, and the Appendix does not claim to do more than to serve its declared purpose. The chapters on Pontus and its neighbours and on Parthia follow the general practice of this work in including that part of their history which precedes their effective entry into the history of the ancient world as a whole. The religious movements in the Roman world during the close of the Republic and the beginning of the Principate will be reviewed in volume x. In the Bibliographies the ancient sources for the main political narrative have been given more by general reference than by detailed citation. The modern literature, indeed, on the main topics of the volume is so considerable that it has been necessary to proceed by rigorous selection. For special topics more elaborate and independent information is supplied.

In the present volume the political history of Rome from the Gracchi to the departure of Pompey to the East is narrated by Mr Hugh Last (chapters i–iv and vi–vii). The military history of this period is written by the same author, apart from the Social War, Sulla's campaigns in Italy and the war against Sertorius, which are described by Mr R. Gardner. Professor Rostovtzeff contributes the account of Pontus and her neighbours in chapter v, Professor Ormerod the narrative of the Mithridatic Wars before the advent of Pompey and of the operations against the pirates of the Levant (in chapters v and viii). In chapter viii Dr Cary has described the contemporary history of Ptolemaic Egypt and Pompey's settlement of the East. Dr Edwyn Bevan has continued his account of the Jews in chapter ix; in chapter x Mr G. H.

Stevenson treats of the extension, protection and government of
the Provinces. The narrative of political history is resumed in
chapters xi and xii, which are written by Dr Cary. Of the two
succeeding chapters that on Parthia is by Dr Tarn, that on the
Conquest of Gaul is by Mr C. Hignett. In chapters xv–xvii
Professor Adcock describes the events that preceded the Civil
War, the war itself and the Dictatorship of Caesar. The chapter
on Literature in the Age of Cicero is by Mr Sikes, that on
Ciceronian Society by Professor Wight Duff. Mrs Strong contributes chapter xx on the Art of the Roman Republic, Professor
de Zulueta chapter xxi on the Development of Law under the
Republic. For those parts of the Appendix on literary authorities
which are concerned with the first half of the volume we are
indebted to Mr Last, who also contributes Notes 1–3; Note 4 is
by Professor Ormerod, Notes 5 and 6 are by Professor Adcock.

The first duty of the Editors is to thank the contributors for
their co-operation and for the help which they have generously
given on matters allied to the subjects of their chapters. Professor
Rostovtzeff wishes to express his obligations to Professor Lambrino and Professor Oliverio, who permitted him to make use of
material then unpublished. Dr Bevan wishes to thank Dr C. J. G.
Montefiore and Professor W. O. E. Oesterley for valuable
criticism and suggestions. Dr Tarn desires to acknowledge his
indebtedness for assistance to M. Cumont, Professor Rostovtzeff,
Dr G. F. Hill, Mr Sidney Smith and Mr C. J. Gadd. Mrs Strong
wishes especially to thank Professor A. Boëthius. Professor de
Zulueta desires to express his gratitude to Professor Buckland.
Finally, Professor Adcock is obliged to Dr Tarn, Dr Cary and
Mr Last for constructive criticisms, which he greatly appreciates.

The volume is indebted to contributors for the bibliographies
to their chapters and for their share in the preparation of maps, to
Mr Last for Maps 4 and 5, to Mr Gardner for Maps 6 and 10,
to Professor Ormerod for Map 7, to Dr Cary for Map 11, to
Mr Hignett for Map 13 and to Dr Tarn for Map 14. Mr Charlesworth is responsible for Maps 2 and 9 and for Map 12 in consultation with Mr Stevenson, Professor Adcock for Map 8, in
consultation with Professor Rostovtzeff, and for Maps 1, 3, 15, 16,
17 and 18. For the geographical detail of Map 9 we are indebted
to Messrs Macmillan, for that of Maps 15 and 17 to Messrs
Wagner and Debes, Leipzig, for Map 18 to the Imprimerie
Nationale, Paris. We have to thank Mrs Strong for drawing up the
Sheet of Plans, and the Oxford University Press for Plan 1,
Dr R. Delbrueck of Bonn and Messrs Walter de Gruyter & Co.,

Berlin, for Plan 2, the Ufficio Antichità e Belle Arti of the Gover-
natorato of Rome for permission to use their plan of the temple
of the Largo Argentina (Plan 3), Messrs Julius Springer, Berlin,
for Plan 4, and Professor Lugli and Messrs Danesi, Rome, for
Plan 5. We owe much to Mr Seltman for his assistance with the
reproduction of the plans and for his ready co-operation in the
illustration of the volume. The fourth Volume of Plates, which he
is preparing, will illustrate this and the following volume and will
be published at the same time as Volume Ten. For the illustration
of the chapter on Roman Republican Art we are greatly indebted
to Mrs Strong, who in turn wishes to express her appreciation of
the courteous assistance of scholars who have supplied her with
valuable material for illustrations. Specific acknowledgments will
be made to them in due form in the Volume of Plates.

Dr Tarn has drawn up the table of Parthian Kings and prepared the Genealogical Tables of the Ptolemies and Seleucids,
which are taken with slight modifications from volume VII. Professor Rostovtzeff has supplied the material for the list of Kings
of Pontus: Mr Charlesworth is responsible for the lists of the
dynasties so far as they are not those published in volume VII, for
which we have also to thank Dr Tarn. The General Index and
Index of passages are the work of Mr B. Benham, whose care has
been of constant assistance to the Editors. Finally it should be
said that our task has been much the lighter for the skill and
resource of the Staff of the University Press.

The Director of the Museum at Naples has permitted us to
reproduce on the cover the head of Caesar from the statue in that
Collection, the work of art which probably presents, more nearly
than any other, the authentic features of the Dictator at the height
of his power.

S.A.C.
F.E.A.
M.P.C.

September, 1932

TABLE OF CONTENTS

CHAPTER I

TIBERIUS GRACCHUS

By Hugh Last, M.A.

Fellow of St John's College, Oxford, and University Lecturer in Roman History

CHAPTER II

GAIUS GRACCHUS

By Hugh Last

CHAPTER III

THE WARS OF THE AGE OF MARIUS

By Hugh Last

CONTENTS

CHAPTER IV

THE ENFRANCHISEMENT OF ITALY

By Hugh Last
and R. Gardner, M.A.[1]
Fellow of Emmanuel College, Cambridge, and University Lecturer in Classics

[1] Sections I–V and VIII–IX are by Mr Last, sections VI–VII by Mr Gardner.

CHAPTER V

PONTUS AND ITS NEIGHBOURS: THE FIRST MITHRIDATIC WAR

By M. ROSTOVTZEFF, Hon. Litt.D. (Cantab.), Hon. D.Litt. (Oxon.),
Hon. Litt.D. (Wisconsin),
Professor of Ancient History in Yale University,
and H. A. ORMEROD, M.A., F.S.A.,
Rathbone Professor of Ancient History in the University of Liverpool[1]

[1] Sections I–IV are by Professor Rostovtzeff, sections V–VIII by Professor Ormerod.

CONTENTS

CHAPTER VI

SULLA

By Hugh Last and R. Gardner[1]

[1] Sections I–III and V–XV are by Mr Last, section IV is by Mr Gardner.

CONTENTS

CHAPTER VII

THE BREAKDOWN OF THE SULLAN SYSTEM AND THE RISE OF POMPEY

By Hugh Last and R. Gardner[1]

CHAPTER VIII

ROME AND THE EAST

By H. A. Ormerod
and M. Cary, D.Litt.
Reader in Ancient History in the University of London[2]

[1] Sections I–III and V–IX are by Mr Last, section IV is by Mr Gardner.
[2] Sections I–VI are by Professor Ormerod, sections VII–X by Dr Cary.

CHAPTER IX

THE JEWS

BY E. R. BEVAN, Hon. Litt.D. (Oxon.); Hon. LL.D. (St Andrews)
Hon. Fellow of New College, Oxford, and Lecturer in Hellenistic History
and Literature at King's College, London

CONTENTS

CHAPTER X

THE PROVINCES AND THEIR GOVERNMENT

BY G. H. STEVENSON, M.A.

Fellow of University College, Oxford, and University Lecturer in Ancient History

CHAPTER XI

ROME IN THE ABSENCE OF POMPEY

By M. Cary

CHAPTER XII

THE FIRST TRIUMVIRATE

By M. Cary

CHAPTER XIII

THE CONQUEST OF GAUL

By C. HIGNETT, M.A.
Fellow of Hertford College, Oxford

CHAPTER XIV

PARTHIA

By W. W. Tarn, Litt.D., F.B.A.
sometime Scholar of Trinity College, Cambridge

CHAPTER XV

FROM THE CONFERENCE OF LUCA TO THE RUBICON

By F. E. Adcock, M.A., Hon. D.Litt. (Durham)
Fellow of King's College and Professor of Ancient History
in the University of Cambridge

CHAPTER XVI

THE CIVIL WAR

By F. E. ADCOCK

CHAPTER XVII

CAESAR'S DICTATORSHIP

By F. E. Adcock

CONTENTS

CHAPTER XVIII

LITERATURE IN THE AGE OF CICERO

By E. E. Sikes, M.A., President of St John's College, Cambridge

CHAPTER XIX

CICERONIAN SOCIETY

By J. Wight Duff, M.A., D.Litt., LL.D., Hon. D.Litt. (Durham), F.B.A.

Professor of Classics, Armstrong College (in the University of Durham),
Newcastle-upon-Tyne

CHAPTER XX

THE ART OF THE ROMAN REPUBLIC

By EUGÉNIE STRONG, C.B.E., M.A., Litt.D. (Trin. Coll., Dublin),
Hon. LL.D. (St Andrews), Hon. Litt.D. (Manchester), F.S.A.

CHAPTER XXI

THE DEVELOPMENT OF LAW UNDER THE REPUBLIC

By F. DE ZULUETA, D.C.L., F.B.A.

Fellow of All Souls College and Regius Professor of Civil Law
in the University of Oxford

CONTENTS

CHAPTER I

TIBERIUS GRACCHUS

I. THE PROBLEMS OF THE AGE

THE tribunate of Tiberius Gracchus opens a new epoch in the affairs of Rome. Hitherto her history had been one of wars—of wars whose outcome, though the Romans had taken arms more often in self-defence than for purposes of aggression, was a steady extension of Roman authority, first over the Italian peninsula and then beyond. Since the end of the third century there had, indeed, been a break in the process of annexation, but the interval had been so much disturbed by fighting in the Balkan peninsula and the East that there had been no opportunity, even if there was the inclination, to undertake that drastic re-shaping of the constitution which alone could fit the Roman State to shoulder the obligations of Empire. With the creation of provinces in Africa and Greece, annexation began anew; but thenceforward, though fresh territory was acquired from time to time, the acquisitions were won by fighting of a very minor kind, and that only when they were not due to the testamentary arrangements of monarchs whose benefactions Rome had somehow managed to attract. Towards the middle of the second century B.C. a new era in Roman history begins. The triumphs of the younger Africanus over Carthage and of L. Mummius over the Achaeans bring down the curtain on the age of warfare and expansion: the tribunate of Tiberius Gracchus inaugurates a period which finds its theme in the domestic history of the city.

Though it would be untrue to say that Rome had outgrown her strength, the events of the century which opens with the destruction of Carthage were conditioned by the fact that an empire had

Note. Some account of the sources in general for the history contained in this Volume will be found in the Appendix, pp. 882 *sqq.* The authorities for the internal history of Rome from 133 to 66 B.C. are enumerated in the Bibliography to Chapters I, II, III, IV, VI and VII. Particular sources requiring comment are discussed in the text as they become relevant.

References to Plutarch's *Lives of the Gracchi* are made by the numeration of chapters which runs continuously: those to the *Life of Gaius Gracchus* may be converted to the other system by deducting 21 from the chapter-number here given. Th. Stangl's *Ciceronis orationum scholiastae*, Vol. II, is quoted as 'Stangl, II'.

been won at a speed which left no time for its assimilation. New provinces had made new demands on a government and an administration inadequate to meet them. The constitution had not, indeed, collapsed; but it was already ill-fitted for its task, and that it continued to work at all was due only to the unfailing resourcefulness of Rome in political expedient. Nor were the effects of Empire felt by the constitution alone: the burdens of an imperial people, and the wealth which its leaders had amassed, produced economic consequences of a kind which called for drastic treatment. Rome in fact, when a lull in her military operations gave opportunity for a survey of the situation, found herself beset by problems unlikely to be solved in a day. Her constitution and her social structure were those of a city-state; but the city-state of Rome now found herself mistress of an empire which included the whole peninsula of Italy and provinces so remote as Spain, Africa and Macedonia. In the history of the *polis* this was something altogether new. To meet new needs the old forms demanded more than mere adjustment. Political innovation could not be escaped, and after long years of experiment the successful innovator was found at length in the person of Augustus. But in the second century B.C. the time was still far off when the constitutional question would be answered by a Principate, whose supreme achievement would be to make the empire and its government the first call on the energies of Rome. That happy ending was to be the outcome of another hundred years or more—a century which, from the violence wherewith the need for change forced itself on the attention of the world, is fitly called the century of revolution. For the present, the empire remained as it had been hitherto—an unparalleled excrescence on the fabric of a city-state. The main and most difficult problem—the problem of welding *polis* and empire into an organic whole—was shelved. The reasons for this delay were two. The problem itself had yet to become acute; and there were others which, though less grave, were at the time more urgent. One of these—that of the relations to be maintained between Rome and her allies in Italy—though Gaius Gracchus made an attempt to face it at least in part, was only settled by the Social War: the other—an economic crisis—it was the work of Tiberius Gracchus to tackle, and to tackle with some measure of success.

II. THE ECONOMIC CRISIS

Our authorities for the economic history of Italy during the earlier decades of the second century B.C. leave much to be desired. The bulk of their information is large: Cato's treatise *de agri cultura* is both contemporary and explicit on the subjects with which it deals, and epigraphic monuments yield facts of the first importance. Later writers too—even though so far removed in time as Appian and so prone as he to misunderstand their sources—give evidence which, so far as it can be tested, is sound. But all alike describe the reforms, or the difficulties which they were designed to meet, rather than the process by which these difficulties had been produced. The course of events which led up to the crisis of the Gracchan age can be recovered only by inference and surmise. Causes which contributed to the final result may be divined with confidence, but the relative importance of their respective contributions can never be precisely determined. The complexity of Italian economic developments during this period offers a dangerous temptation. Plausible dogmatism about details is easy, but it is forbidden by the nature of the evidence. All that is possible is to describe in a general way the position which Tiberius Gracchus was inspired to face, and to indulge in speculation about its origin—remembering how much is mere conjecture—only so far as speculation of such a kind is an essential background to any rational version of the programmes formulated by him and his successors.

Italy in the early days of the Republic had been a land of small farmers, engaged in producing food for themselves and their families, with perhaps a small surplus for sale in the local town if one were to be found conveniently near. By the middle of the second century B.C. a transformation had been wrought. Though the small farmer had by no means disappeared, in many parts of the country he had given place to men who made an income—not large, indeed, but handsome for its day—by working estates of some dimensions. Of the use to which these broad acres were put no brief account can be wholly true, but it is clear that to a great extent, if not predominantly, they were employed for grazing. Pasturage and the *pecuarii* whom pasturage implies are a recognized feature in the life of Italy after the Second Punic War: old Cato[1] seems to have preached that, at least in certain parts of the peninsula, pasturage, whether good, bad or indifferent, paid better than any of its rivals; and when Popillius Laenas[2] records that his business—apparently in giving effect to the *lex agraria* of 133 B.C.—was to secure 'ut aratoribus cederent paastores,' he shows that it was stock-farming above all which was

---

[1] Cicero, *de off.* ii, 25, 89; cf. Pliny, *N.H.* xviii, 29. In *de agri cult.* i, 7, Cato has in mind the small home-farm of about 100 *iugera* on *ager privatus.*
[2] Dessau 23.

practised by the great land-holders whose holdings Tiberius Gracchus raided to provide land for his small allotments.

But though the decline of the small farmer is beyond dispute, and though it is clear that his arable husbandry was not continued by the rancher who absorbed his land, the causes of this change are to seek. Two, which have often been alleged, may be briefly dismissed. First, the competition to which the corn grown in Italy was subjected by importations from abroad cannot explain the failure of cereal production throughout Italy as a whole. Though it may be admitted that the coastal cities, such as they were, might use supplies from overseas, there is no evidence for extensive importation to any other place than Rome itself. But, once in Rome, grain can only have competed with the local produce in that part of Italy on which Rome had depended for its food before importation began—a region which cannot have extended much more than twenty miles from the city; and to that region—a trifling fraction of the Italian peninsula—the effects of foreign competition were almost wholly confined. Secondly, among the causes of the transition from corn-growing to pasturage no leading place can be given to the devastation wrought in the Hannibalic War. The ravages of invasion, even at their worst, are superficial: where land is good, they do not cause it to be abandoned, nor do they produce a revolution in the use to which the land is put, if that use is already the most remunerative. In the Champagne there are vineyards which have endured ravages worse than those of Hannibal: yet they do not remain derelict, nor have they been converted into sheep-farms. A change such as that which took place on the Italian countryside could not have been so widespread or so permanent had it not been sanctioned by the economic facts of the situation in which it occurred. Small farms devoted to the production of corn gave way to the grazing-ranch because grazing was more profitable; and if the land paid better under pasturage than under arable cultivation, pasturage was bound to advance at the expense of cereal farming, whether the land had been laid waste by war or not.

The soil of Italy varies widely in character and value; but, if the high Apennine be left out of account, in a brief description such as this it is enough to notice two rough classes into which the remainder of the country may be divided. First, on either side of the central ridge is a broad tract of rolling upland, which at times rises into hills of considerable height and at times is cut deep by river-valleys. Secondly, between this region and the coast is a plain which differs greatly from place to place both in breadth and in natural fertility. On the east coast it is generally narrower than on the west; and on the west there are to be found both the wretched soil of the Tuscan *maremme* and one of the richest regions in Europe—Campania. The better parts of the coastal plain may be grouped with a few inland tracts, particularly the broader valley-floors, as land of high productivity. The bulk of the hill-country goes with the poorer stretches of the plain to form a class of much less certain value. Land of this second type varied in character within the widest limits. One plot might be of great fertility, yet with neighbours scarcely worth cultivation, if on them the soil happened to have been washed thin. But on the whole, the soil was poor, and it was on this part of Italy—not everywhere, indeed, but in Etruria and still more in the south—that pasturage tended to spread at the expense of arable farming, because pasturage paid best of all the uses to which such country could be put.

Ranching, however, in its most profitable form demanded large estates. Apart altogether from the greater efficiency which rural operations on a large scale can show against their less pretentious rivals, there was a peculiar circumstance in Italy working to make the ranches big. The climate of the peninsula and its physical formation combine to make it desirable, and in some places even necessary, that a grazier should control feeding-grounds at different levels. For the summer months pasture is needed on the hills, and for winter on the lower ground. If both kinds of grassland were to be found within the limits of a single ranch, its limits must obviously be wide; but, even in cases where this was not possible, the grazier who could command two separate regions for use in winter and summer respectively was bound to be a man in an extensive way of business. Thus on this land of dubious value the raising of beasts was the most profitable occupation; and it was a business which to be its best must be conducted on a considerable scale.

At this point there arises the question of finance. Ranching in the grand manner cannot be begun without the help of capital, and for that reason the conversion of their land to pasturage in its most advantageous form was beyond the means of the smaller peasants. But into the pockets of certain sections in the Roman population capital had flowed in an abundant stream during the fifty years which followed the Hannibalic War. Great and memorable distributions of booty did something to place large sums of liquid cash in the hands of potential investors: the demand for productive securities must have been severe when, in 187 B.C., the equivalent of a *tributum simplex* for twenty-five years was refunded:

and again it is difficult to avoid the conclusion that the final abolition of the *tributum* in 167 B.C. increased the investing power of the
population. More powerful still, however, was the effect of those
opportunities for making money which the permanent possession of
provinces gave to the imperial people. Officials did not come home
empty-handed, and the rising class of commercial adventurers had
already embarked on those widespread and remunerative operations
which by the end of the century were to become a powerful influence on the foreign policy of Rome.

The liquid wealth which these circumstances concentrated in
Roman hands produced its usual effect. In a world which had
yet to learn the value of a national debt and the financial system of
which that debt is the foundation, land was the one gilt-edged
security[1]. A sudden influx of wealth was followed by a sudden rush
to invest it in the soil, and in Roman territory of the second
century B.C. such investments were not difficult to find. The antiquated arrangement whereby Rome in this period was fighting
the wars of an empire with the army of a city-state made the lot of
the small-landholder hard to a degree. He was summoned for
service in the citizen militia; but, instead of the brief campaign for
which such a militia was designed, long wars now generally awaited
him in theatres often far removed from home. In his absence the
family holding fell into neglect. At best, the work was carried on
with success enough to keep starvation from the door: at worst, the
farm was seized either for debt or by the mere violence of some
powerful neighbour. And in what we may conjecture to have been
the majority of cases in which these humble soldiers found their
land intact when they returned, they found it in a condition the
reverse of encouraging. The labour needed to restore the family
fortunes to the condition in which they had been before the call to
arms, and the prospect that such labour might soon be thrown
away by the outbreak of another war, left these weary veterans
in no mind to resist an inducement to quit offered by some rich
man who coveted their land to include in his broad domain. Indeed, the reluctance of the troops to return to their former
homes had been admitted after the defeat of Hannibal; for its
own good reasons the government had provided allotments in
bulk and so had offered them a fresh start elsewhere. Thus
it was—by the difficulties which the demands of military service
put in the way of the humble farmers and by the amount of wealth
which they produced to await investment, rather than by the actual
devastation of the Italian countryside in the Second Punic War—

[1] See Cicero, *de off.* 1, 42, 151.

that the military occupations of Rome contributed to the rural revolution.

It must not be assumed that the attentions of the rich were confined to the poorer land alone: operations on a larger scale than before—a sure sign that the investor has arrived—began on the better land as well. But on land of the second sort the coming of capital had a less noticeable effect, because the best employment of such soil—whether under corn, vines or olives—was possible even in an age when the units of cultivation were small. Only on the bad land, where ranching paid best, was the most profitable line of business denied to the poor. But everywhere alike the efficiency of the large estate made the big man ready to encroach, and with him he brought labour in its cheapest form. Successful warfare had made slaves both plentiful and cheap, and in the second century slave labour was driving free workers off the land. Moreover, a farm under grass notoriously owes some of its attractions to the smaller number of hands it needs than the same farm under plough; and thus, where there was a change from cereal cultivation to grazing, a part of the rural population was bound to be displaced. But the tendency of the new masters to use servile labour made the displacement far more violent than it need otherwise have been. Both on the bad land and on the good, wherever their presence was felt, they introduced their living tools and turned the old free workers adrift to fend for themselves as best they might.

Since there was no longer a livelihood to be got on the countryside, there was a movement to the towns—a movement which, it must be confessed, is not necessarily an evil. The influx from rural England to the cities at the time of the Industrial Revolution was far from being a disaster; but in England the newcomers were to be employed on production of manufactured goods for export. In Italy, as here, the cities could already meet their own domestic needs, and an export trade was the only hope of employment for the fresh arrivals. But in Italy this was impossible. The country was large and communications were bad: transport by land, as always, was a costly business: and even Rome itself could boast no serious port nearer home than Puteoli. If goods were produced, they could not be got to the quay; and so from exports no help was to be expected. Commerce abroad offered better promise. Among the swarm of Italian traders which at this time was spreading round the coasts of the Mediterranean doubtless there were some at least drawn from the population till recently employed in agriculture. But commerce could not absorb more than a fraction of these who needed work: for the rest, the dispossessed peasants, when they reached the towns, began to form an idle proletariate—useless to themselves, useless to their neighbours and—not the least serious consideration—because they were paupers useless to the State for military service under the existing organization of the army.

Yet their uselessness was not all; they were also an active danger. There is no need to rehearse in detail the many evil results which followed the concentration of unemployed in Rome, but one aspect of the case calls for special mention because it has not always received the notice it deserves. The pernicious influence wielded by the *plebs urbana* in the Assemblies of the Ciceronian age is a commonplace of history. Though the country-voters, even from districts so remote as Cisalpine Gaul[1], came to Rome at election-times in numbers sufficient to make their votes important[2], on more ordinary occasions throughout the year the great majority of those present at a meeting of the Comitia or the Concilium Plebis was drawn from the inhabitants of Rome itself or its immediate surroundings. Even these were lax in their attendance unless the subject at stake touched their personal interests[3], but it was they who filled the Forum when it was worth their while to appear. Thus, at a time when the Populus Romanus was slowly spreading over the length and breadth of the Italian peninsula, there was a danger that its sovran powers would be wielded by that fraction of the whole which happened to live within easy reach of Rome. But against this danger safeguards were not unknown. Since the reform of the Comitia Centuriata in the third century (vol. VII, p. 801) the voting-groups in all Assemblies had been formed on the geographical basis of the tribes, so that the members of an urban tribe, however many of them were present, had no more influence in determining the decision of the issue than such few citizens as might at the moment be in Rome from, for instance, the tribe Velina, whose territory lay on the Adriatic coast. But if members of the tribe Velina were driven by stress of economic circumstances to migrate to Rome and merge themselves in the urban proletariate, the constitutional consequences were grave. The vote of a distant tribe might come to be decided, no longer by those of its regular residents who chanced to be at Rome, but by men whose connection with it had in fact been severed and whose political outlook was that associated with the *tribus*

---

[1] Cicero, *ad Att.* I, I, 2.   [2] Q. Cicero, *de pet. cons.* 8, 30.
[3] Cicero, *pro Sestio*, 51, 109.

urbanae. Thus, unless the censors used their power of transferring citizens from a rustic to an urban tribe much more freely
than they seem to have done in fact, the tribal organization of
the Assemblies must soon cease to prevent citizens in outlying
regions from being virtually disfranchised by those who lived
nearer Rome. It was doubtless considerations such as these
which in one section of opinion had prompted the anxiety,
familiar since the third century B.C. (vol. VII, p. 806), to see freedmen confined to the urban tribes (see further below, p. 96).
Freedmen naturally tended to settle in Rome; and if those who
came from the remoter parts of the peninsula were enrolled in
the tribes of their patrons, the result would be the same risk of
a tribal vote being unduly influenced by men who had no enduring ties with the locality of the tribe[1]. In the Gracchan age,
however, the problem was raised by citizens of free birth who
had drifted to the city. If large numbers of such could be
moved back to the countryside, one of the many beneficial
effects would have been to diminish an undeniable danger to an
element in the Roman constitution by which the Gracchi set
great store—the element which may in some sense be described
as democratic.

The urgent problem was one of unemployment, and the unemployed were not to be found in Rome alone: their presence in
the country towns is freely proved by the numbers who flocked to
Rome in support of the agrarian programme. It must not be supposed, however, that the removal of the free peasants from the soil
was complete. The census-lists show that in the twenty years
immediately before the tribunate of Tiberius Gracchus the net
loss of citizens eligible for recruitment in the army—whether by
pauperization or by other causes, such as emigration from Italy—
did not exceed seven per cent.; but seven per cent. of the Roman
citizen body concentrated in the cities as unemployed, and particularly in Rome, would have been more than enough to present
a problem sufficiently acute to explain all the energy of the
measures taken for its solution. And it was in the cities that the
problem arose.

The seat of the trouble for which Tiberius Gracchus essayed to
prescribe has sometimes been wrongly sought in the country instead of in the town. Plutarch[2], in his solitary quotation from a
pamphlet ascribed to Gaius Gracchus, preserves the story that the
need for economic reform was first borne in on the elder brother

---

[1] On this question see Livy IX, 46, 11 *sqq.* and Diodorus XX, 36, 4.
[2] *Gracchi*, 8, 4.

when, in 137 B.C., he was travelling through Etruria on his way
to Spain. The deserted landscape, in which such labourers as could
be seen were foreign slaves, started his thoughts on the course
which led to the legislation of his tribunate. But this does not
prove that Tiberius was an agrarian reformer in the ordinary
sense. If agrarian reform means an effort to convert land to a use
financially more profitable than the present, then the programme
of Tiberius cannot claim the name. He did, indeed, choose a *lex
agraria* as the means for the attainment of his end; but it was
a means and nothing more. The end itself—or the main end, if
Gracchus had several before him—was a reduction of the pauper
proletariate of the towns, as Plutarch suggests when, in the following sentence, he says that an even stronger incentive to Tiberius
than the sight of the Etruscan desolation was the steady appeal
of the poor—apparently in Rome—for grants of public land.

If the maximum profit from the soil was all that mattered, large
estates, whether used for ranching on the bad land or for other
purposes on the good, were justified beyond dispute. But farm
accounts were not the only consideration. The citizens might
reasonably claim a say in the use of at least such land as was the
property of the State, and they might rightly criticize an agricultural system which, however financially attractive, inflicted
grievous hardship on an essential section of the population. As
Greenidge observes, 'an economic success may be a social failure'[1];
and such was the situation which Tiberius Gracchus set himself
to face. Determined to meet the demand for land on which men
at present unemployed might for the future earn their livings, he
introduced a law to authorize the distribution of public land in
small allotments, even though this meant that the soil of Italy
would thenceforward yield a less bountiful return than under the
existing system. When Appian says that the programme of
Gracchus had moral, not economic, welfare as its aim[2], his
words contain more truth than some historians will admit. Nevertheless, whatever economic loss might be, the sacrifice was
justified. If the Gracchan scheme could be carried to success, a
livelihood would be found for the growing mass of unemployed,
the number of substantial citizens—on whom alone under the
prevailing system the army was supposed to draw—would be
increased, and Italy would lose some fraction of its slave population, which by now was becoming a pressing danger.

[1] *A History of Rome*, vol. i, p. 59.
[2] His proposals were directed οὐκ ἐς εὐπορίαν ἀλλ᾽ ἐς εὐανδρίαν:
Bell. Civ. i, 11, 43.

III. THE FIRST SERVILE WAR

Such in brief was the situation which called for treatment. The details, so far as they need attention, will for the most part be discussed in connection with the Gracchan proposals; but one of the problems presented by slavery demands separate attention. The invasion of the countryside by gangs of slaves had done something more than produce that unemployment among the free population which has been noticed already: to some extent at least it imperilled the whole safety of society by concentrating in rural Italy large bands of desperadoes who, if they were to combine against their masters, might form an army of the most menacing dimensions. In Italy itself ominous risings had occurred during the twenty years which followed the defeat of Hannibal (vol. VIII, pp. 351, 379), and Italy was not immune from repercussions of the latest and most violent upheaval. But Sicily was the seat of the unrest which, when Tiberius Gracchus became tribune, had become so grave as to call for the presence of a consular army; and, even if the trouble had been confined to that island, Sicily was near enough to Rome for it to have been impossible that Gracchus should fail to see the advantage to the public safety which a reduction of the slave population would bring.

Three centuries and more had passed already since Sicily for the first time served as the cockpit of the Mediterranean. As early as 480 B.C. the Greek victory over the Carthaginians at Himera had produced a glut of slaves[1], and the military character of Sicilian history thereafter had helped to maintain the supply. And not only were slaves freely to be found: Sicily was in the closest contact with Carthage, and from Carthage the Sicilian Greeks, whose example was followed in due course by such Romans as found Sicilian land a profitable field for investment, seem soon to have picked up the practice of using slave-gangs to supply the necessary labour on their estates. In the second century B.C. no more than about a fifth of its surface was under corn, though such was the fertility of the island that even this was enough to justify its being called, as later it was by Cicero, 'a granary of the Roman People.' Of the rest, by far the greater part was devoted to the usual pasturage; and, though it cannot be doubted that slaves were freely employed for arable cultivation as for all other forms of labour in the island, it may be surmised that the herdsmen on these wider lands, as always, were the most dangerous section of the servile population. They were the hardest

---

[1] Diodorus XI, 25, 2–3.

to keep under close control, and it was they who had the best opportunity to start an insurrection, whatever might be the sources from which it drew recruits when once begun.

There is no need to dwell on the brutality and degradation to which the victims of this system were subjected. Though there were favoured exceptions, it is difficult to conceive any lower depths of misery than those which were fathomed by the mass of these plantation-slaves. The hardest lot of all fell to those engaged in arable cultivation, but even the herdsmen, whose occupation inevitably demanded some degree of freedom, were left to shift for themselves and keep body and soul together as best they might by brigandage or any other means. That they made the country utterly unsafe for its free inhabitants and for the casual traveller was the least serious consequence of their presence: what mattered more was that nothing but a leader was needed for them to become a powerful army threatening the whole established social order.

From the middle of the second century B.C. Sicily had been shaken by sporadic outbreaks which finally, towards the autumn of 135 B.C., culminated in a rising far surpassing any that had gone before[1]. There now appeared a leader of ability beyond dispute—one Eunus, a native of Syrian Apamea, who was slave of a citizen of Enna named Antigenes. Eunus was a man devoid of military gifts, but it is clear that it was he who converted the spasmodic outbursts of discontent into a rebellion which called for the most vigorous action by armies of the Roman People. What he lacked in military skill he made good in vision and personality, whereby he was able to inspire his followers with a reverence which he did not scruple to increase by claims to inspiration and by a few simple devices of the medicine-man. Eunus was the prophet of better things who managed to transform a horde of slaves into a formidable fighting force.

The movement began near Enna on the estate of a Siceliote named Damophilus—a man renowned for his brutality even in

[1] Chronological certainty is impossible. For the most comprehensive recent study of the chronological problem see E. Ciaceri, 'Roma e le guerre servili in Sicilia' in his *Processi politici e relazioni internazionali*, especially pp. 70 *sqq.* In the opinion of the present writer attempts to show that the narratives of the First Servile War are corrupted by duplications of incidents in the second (see in particular A. Giacobbe, 'Sulle duplicazioni delle guerre servili in Sicilia' in *Rendiconti*, Serie VI, I, 1925, pp. 655 *sqq.*) have been adequately refuted by L. Pareti ('I supposti "sdoppiamenti" delle guerre servili in Sicilia' in *Riv. Fil.* N.S. V, 1927, pp. 44 *sqq.*).

a society whose heart was hard. A plot was hatched; Eunus announced the favour of the gods; and one night four hundred conspirators mustered outside the city. Then in the darkness Enna was stormed, and there followed a massacre of the free population. Later on the survivors were reviewed at leisure; and though a few chosen spirits known for their humanity towards the slaves were spared, of the rest all but those who could forge arms for their new masters were summarily put to death. The success of this initial move was wisely exploited by Eunus to strengthen his own influence. He himself became king and took the honoured name 'Antiochus'; his concubine was dignified with the title 'queen'; and his people were to be known collectively as 'Syrians'[1]. At the same time some of the ablest rebels, among whom a certain Achaeus was outstanding, were formed into a Council of State; and from this point onwards it is Achaeus who directs operations, while Eunus, withdrawn into regal seclusion, provides a focus for the common allegiance on which the unity of the movement depended. The first business of Achaeus was to build up his forces. Accordingly, all the *ergastula* within reach were opened without delay, and in three days the original four hundred had swelled to six thousand. But the force still grew apace, and about a month after the capture of Enna it received a notable accession from an unexpected quarter. Fifty miles south-west of Enna lay Agrigentum, the greatest city on the south coast of the island, and here by a stroke of luck a new base was acquired for the cause. Among the slaves of that region was a Cilician named Cleon, who combined the practice of highwaymanship with his more proper duties of horse-keeping. This individual was moved by the news from Enna to emulate the exploits of Eunus by seizing Agrigentum[2]. Yet such was the prestige of Eunus that, despite the success of his independent *coup*, Cleon made no attempt to establish a rival power: with a self-sacrifice which does credit to his intelligence he offered himself, his men and all the resources at his command to the leaders of the original revolt, who thus found another five thousand troops at their disposal. And still recruits came in, until at length, when first they fell foul of a Roman army, the insurgents numbered twenty thousand.

From the outset it had been the policy of Eunus to win Sicily

[1] At Enna he issued coins with the name and royal title: see E. S. G. Robinson, 'Antiochus, King of the Slaves,' in *Num. Chron.*, Fourth Series, xx, 1920, p. 175. See Volume of Plates iv, 2, *a*.

[2] That Agrigentum fell into the hands of Cleon is strongly suggested by Diodorus xxxiv–v, 43.

and hold it. For reasons which are not recorded, though they may be divined, he made no attempt to organize a return of the slaves to their homes in the East. Such a project can have had little to commend it, even if it were possible to prevail on the corsairs of the Mediterranean to provide the necessary transport. United the rebels had some hope of resisting Rome with success, but once they were dispersed to their native places they would fall easy victims to whatever punitive measures might be taken by the Roman government and its clients. Moreover, it is safe to assume that of the youngest and most effective members of the rebel force many had been born in slavery: for such men Sicily was home, and it is not to be supposed that they would have found a ready welcome in their ancestral cities. Thus the efforts of the leaders were directed to the strengthening and extension of their grip on Sicily. Tauromenium and Catana fell into their hands, and from this it may be inferred that the rich plain south of Etna lay under their control. The limits of their occupation are not accurately known, but it is of more interest to find that, wherever the slaves were established, their behaviour was of a piece with their general policy of building up a permanent power in the island. Looting was banned, property was spared, and the responsibility for such damage as was done lay rather with the free proletariate, which made use of the occasion to vent its own resentment against the rich, than with the slaves themselves[1].

Faced with a threat to sever from the Empire its oldest province, the Roman government was bound to take measures more drastic than those which in preceding years had barely sufficed to prevent sporadic risings from turning into open war. The dangers of the situation needed no emphasis: if they had, emphasis might have been supplied by the more or less contemporaneous outbreaks which occurred in other parts of the Mediterranean. There was trouble in Attica and Delos[2], as well as in many other places; and Italy itself was not immune[3]. A rising at Rome was of negligible proportions, but at Minturnae and Sinuessa the severity of the vengeance taken when order had been restored betrays the alarm felt by public opinion[4]. Evidence is lacking to support the view that these widespread signs of disaffection, to which the revolt of Aristonicus in Asia may be added[5] (see below, pp. 103 *sqq.*), reveal the presence of a single organization whose object was to secure a

---

[1] Diodorus xxxiv–v, 2, 48.   [2] Diodorus xxxiv–v, 2, 19.
[3] P. Popillius Laenas during his praetorship had already returned to Italy 917 fugitive slaves who had escaped to Sicily (Dessau 23).
[4] Orosius v, 9, 4.   [5] Diodorus xxxiv–v, 2, 26.

general revolution. Yet it cannot be denied that they had a grave significance. They served to show that conditions of slavery, at least in the mines and on large estates, were in many places so utterly bad that the victims were ready for recourse to violence to right their wrongs. A success for the insurgents in Sicily might have moved their fellow-sufferers elsewhere to feats of emulation whose consequences could not be lightly contemplated by up-holders of the existing order. Strong action was demanded, and it was not taken too soon.

If the revolt at Enna belongs to 135 B.C., it was probably at the end of the same year that L. Hypsaeus faced the rebels with an army of 8000 men. He was outnumbered by more than two to one, and his defeat had the inevitable effect of giving fresh strength to the enemy[1]. The details of what followed are obscure. C. Fulvius Flaccus, consul of 134, came out to take command but met with no success. He was followed by L. Calpurnius Piso, consul of 133, who seems to have improved the discipline of his troops and to have made some sort of headway: the discovery at Enna of sling-bullets bearing his name suggests that he penetrated to the walls of the enemy's citadel[2]. It was left, however, for P. Rupilius, consul of the succeeding year, to win the decisive victory: Numantia had fallen in 133, and it is possible that one result was to set more troops free for use in Sicily. The attack on Enna begun by Piso may for the moment have been broken off; at any rate the scene of Rupilius' opening operations is Tauromenium. Tauromenium fell after blockade had reduced its garrison to the last extremity of starvation, and thereafter Enna itself suffered the same fate. Cleon was killed in a *sortie* from the city; Achaeus had already disappeared; and Eunus alone of the leaders contrived to get away. Thus in 132 B.C. the back of the revolt was broken, and it only remained to run down fugitive bands which might still disturb the peace. Accordingly Rupilius seems to have organized a series of flying columns which combed the country so effectively that Sicily soon enjoyed a calm unknown for decades. Eunus himself duly fell into Roman hands; but strangely enough he was allowed to live in captivity until he died a natural death. Drastic as the Romans had been in their punishments so long as the rising

---

[1] Diodorus (xxxiv–v, 2, 18) certainly exaggerates when he says, if the text be right, that their army grew to be 200,000 strong; and the estimate of 70,000, given by Livy (*Epit.* 56), if it is meant to be the number of the whole body, is more plausible. But it is clear that the force now reached the most threatening dimensions.

[2] *C.I.L.* I², 847.

was a danger, once Enna had fallen their policy seems to have
been one of restoring the rebels to their rightful owners: for a
massacre of slaves meant confiscating the property of those on
whose behalf Rome had taken arms. So ended the First Servile
War, and the settlement was sealed by a re-organization of the
Sicilian province. Rupilius was sent a senatorial commission of
ten members[1] and with their aid he drew up a provincial charter
—the Lex Rupilia—of whose arrangements, in judicial matters
at least, we know something from the second of Cicero's speeches
for the second *actio* against Verres.

The episode belongs in the first place to the history of Sicily.
During the rising of the slaves the island is said to have suffered
even more severely than in the fighting with the Carthaginians[2],
and the permanent effects of the upheaval were profound. It is
difficult to escape the conclusion that the Servile Wars were the
cause of that partial return to the ownership of land on a small
scale, the results of which are visible in the following century[3].
But, on the other hand, its bearing on the general course of Roman
history is direct. The war was in full career when Tiberius Gracchus
entered on his tribunate, and it cannot have failed to lend a force,
which the most indifferent must have felt, to his plea for a restoration of small farmers to some part at least of the Italian countryside.

IV. THE *AGER PUBLICUS*

When the programmes of Roman politics demanded land for
their fulfilment, the land to which their authors naturally turned
was the *ager publicus populi Romani*—the accumulated product of
Rome's advance in the Italian peninsula. After a successful war
it had been the Roman habit to take from the vanquished enemy
a fraction of his land which varied with the vigour of his resistance
or the measure of his guilt. The revolt of Privernum in the fourth
century (vol. VII, p. 589 n. 1) had been punished by the loss of
two-thirds of the city's territory[4], but in the majority of cases Rome
seems to have been content with half of this amount. Of the area
thus acquired much had been converted already into private property. It was on *ager publicus* that Rome relied when a site had to
be found for a colonial foundation, or again when individuals were
to receive allotments such as those distributed on the so-called

---

1 Cicero, II *in Verr.* II, 13, 32 and 16, 39.
2 Florus II, 7 (III, 19), 2.
3 Cicero, II *in Verr.* III, 11, 27.
4 Livy VIII, 1, 3.

ager Gallicus, first by the famous law of C. Flaminius in 232[1] (vol. VII, pp. 806 *sq.*) and afterwards in 173[2] (vol. VIII, p. 332), or again in southern Italy to the veterans of the Second Punic War[3]. Some, too, had virtually been sold, like that made over to the lenders in payment of public debts (*ib.* p. 112)[4]. But such land is irrelevant to the Gracchan legislation. Save what was surrendered to creditors—which technically remained public, though in fact it could not be resumed, all this land passed from the *dominium* of the Roman People and became the private property of the recipients. The *ager publicus* of the Gracchan age was only what remained after these large deductions—an area which did not exceed two million acres, or one-seventh of the territory of Rome. Yet not even the whole of this was affected by the Gracchan scheme: that much of it was left untouched we know from the law of 111 B.C.[5]

Like the soil of Italy as a whole, that part of it which still was the property of the Roman People fell naturally into two sections —the good and the comparatively poor. The better land was a valuable asset: that part of it which lay in Campania and was known as the *ager Campanus* is even said by Cicero to have produced revenues that were an important item in the finances of Rome so late as 59 B.C. And because it was valuable, it was kept under proper control and let on definite leases by the censors[6]. If they did their duty—and we need not suppose that they regularly failed[7] —the richer parts of the *ager publicus* must have been immune from the abuses which arose elsewhere—a fact which will explain their apparent exemption from the attentions of the *lex agraria*. But with the poorer class of public land—the land on which arable cultivation was precarious and where pasturage was generally more profitable (see above, p. 5)—the case was different; and it was with this that the Gracchi were concerned. Its value was not high and its quality varied from place to place. If it was to be let effectively at the highest rent it would sustain, a survey of the imperial type was needed; and that such a survey was impossible was one of the many unhappy features of the time which were due to the lack of an adequate civil service. Nevertheless, State property could not lie idle, and in the helter-skelter of expansion a rough and ready means of using it was devised. Public an-

---

[1] Polybius II, 21, 7–8.   [2] Livy XLI, 16, 9; XLII, 4, 3–4.
[3] Livy XXXI, 4, 1; 49, 5.   [4] Livy XXXI, 13.
[5] Bruns, *Fontes*[7], 11.   [6] Appian, *Bell. Civ.* I, 7, 27.
[7] There had indeed been a certain laxity in Campania before 172 B.C.: see Livy XLII, 19, 1.

nouncement was made that country of this sort was vacant, and
the right to squat thereon was offered to anyone—perhaps even
though he were not a Roman citizen[1]—who was prepared to pay
the State a fixed fraction of the produce which land so occupied
might yield. The offer was eagerly accepted, but the State control
was slight: and, whether from the outset or in course of years,
estates in these regions grew to large dimensions.

Tenants of *ager publicus* held their *possessiones* for the consideration of a rent (*vectigal*). On land of the better sort this was
fixed by the censors for each individual holding, generally, we
may assume, in cash[2]. Not so, however, on the poorer ground.
Here, according to Appian's account[3], the terms offered to
prospective squatters had been that they should pay as rent a
varying amount determined from year to year by the use to which
their holdings were put. For plough-land the payment was a
tithe of the annual produce; for vineyards, orchards and garden
plots a fifth. Graziers alone paid dues which were set from the
first in cash, and these were fixed as a poll-tax on the stock—
at rates which differed with the nature of the beasts. Under
such a system the difficulty of agreeing the sums due was enough
to encourage laxity in collection. The rigour with which these
rents were exacted is a matter of some obscurity: that they had
been wholly forgone during the financial stringency of the early
second century is improbable, but when they were imposed again
in 118 B.C. Appian suggests that legislation was required[4]. Unless
these dues had been remitted by Tiberius Gracchus, which is not
impossible (see below, p. 25), it must be assumed that before
his time their collection had become slack; but even if rent had
still been regularly paid, the readiness of the Romans to acquiesce
in the conception of *ager privatus vectigalisque*—land private and
yet yielding rent to the State—is enough to show that its pay-

---

[1] It is difficult, if not impossible, to explain the sequel to the agrarian
legislation of Ti. Gracchus, unless a certain amount of the *ager publicus* was
occupied by individual members of the allied communities, whether such
possessio by non-Romans was strictly permitted by law or was due to a mere
custom which had been allowed to grow up.

[2] That the censorial *locatio agri* was, among other things, a lease of the
land to tenants and not, as Niebuhr held, merely a lease to *publicani* of the
right to collect the *vectigalia* therefrom, is strongly suggested by various pieces
of evidence, of which perhaps the most cogent is the application of the phrase
[agrum con]ductum habere' to *possessores* in Bruns, *Fontes*[7], 11, l. 32. For a
discussion of Niebuhr's account, see E. G. Hardy, *Six Roman Laws*,
pp. 86 *sqq.*

[3] *Bell. Civ.* 1, 7, 27.   [4] *Bell. Civ.* 1, 27, 122.

ment was not incompatible with the central fact about land in this position. That fact was the tenants' belief that, in practice if not in theory, it was their private property. If rent were expected, rent might still have to be paid; but, so long as this was done, they felt secure against eviction. The date of the various praetorian rulings on this point cannot be determined with precision, but it is in every way probable that already by this time there had been established the interdicts which guaranteed against ejectment by rival claimants[1] and even authorized the passing of tenancies by bequest[2].

Nevertheless, even if the State did not desire to get its land in hand—which in theory it might do by merely giving notice to quit—the legal position of the tenants was by no means always sound. Since the legislation of C. Licinius and his colleague L. Sextius in 367 B.C. (vol. VII, pp. 538 *sqq.*), occupiers of public land, in whatever class it fell, had been subject to restrictions in the amount which any individual might hold. The maximum originally fixed in the fourth century and the detailed history of later modifications, if such were made, are alike uncertain, but it may be said on the authority of Cato[3] that in 167 B.C. the figure was still supposed to be one of five hundred *iugera* (roughly three hundred acres), though the provisions of the law may no longer have been observed. There were easy methods of evasion. Plutarch[4] and Appian[5] both record that land-holders who had already reached the limit contrived to extend their holdings still further by employing relatives or dependents as bogus lessees; and by the tribunate of Tiberius Gracchus the administration of the law seems to have become so casual that even these formalities were in most cases omitted. Thus, when land was needed for distribution to the poor, means of obtaining it were at hand. If *possessores* were deprived of all that they held beyond the maximum allowed by law, the amount of land set free would be enough to provide small allotments on a considerable scale.

V. TIBERIUS GRACCHUS AND HIS CONTEMPORARIES

Tiberius Gracchus was not the first to recognize the abuse. According to Plutarch[6], the question of the public land had already been broached by the younger Laelius—we may assume

---

[1] Festus, p. 260 L; Cicero, *pro Tullio*, 19, 44.
[2] Cicero, *pro Cluentio*, 60, 165.
[3] Frag. 95e P.
[4] *Gracchi*, 8, 2.
[5] *Bell. Civ.* I, 8, 34.
[6] *Gracchi*, 8, 3.

in some year between his tribunate in 151 B.C. and his consulship in 140 B.C.; but the reception of his scheme had been so hot that, with the caution which not infrequently paralysed the beneficent plans of Scipio Aemilianus and his friends, he allowed his proposals to drop. Thereby, Plutarch holds, he won the title 'Sapiens.' It must be admitted that Cicero knows nothing of all this, and that in repeatedly connecting the *cognomen* of Laelius with his character and attainments, rather than with any political discretion, he seems to have the contemporary authority of Lucilius on his side[1]. But in its general drift the story is not improbable. By the middle of the second century the dangerous growth of unemployment had reached dimensions which could not escape the notice of observant men; and that they should have seen the danger and made none but the feeblest efforts to meet it is characteristic of the honourable but easy-going *coterie* which takes its name from the younger Africanus. Effective action was left to another of the political groups, though to one not unconnected with that of Scipio.

The Gracchi were a family which had risen to prominence so late as the Second Punic War, and its most famous member hitherto was Tiberius, the father of the two reformers. Though he did not always approve the conduct of his father-in-law, this man had married the daughter of the elder Africanus and had befriended Lucius Scipio, under whom he had served in Greece, at the time of the Catonian attack (vol. VIII, p. 371). With culture which enabled him to deliver a speech in Greek he combined a simple severity of life which made his censorship an occasion to be remembered among the more advanced sections of society; and to these domestic virtues he added military prowess of no mean order. The triumphs which rewarded his achievements in Spain and Sardinia had been fairly won, but he had a still stronger claim to fame in the character of his provincial government. During his service abroad, and particularly in Spain, he had done much to raise the prestige of Roman arms, and he had wrought even better in winning for his country some sort of reputation for honesty and straight dealing. Such was the man who by a somewhat early death left the education of his family to his widow. There had been twelve children born, but of these only three—Tiberius, Gaius and Sempronia, the wife of Scipio Aemilianus—survived their youth. Under the guidance of their mother they received a training of the kind which might be expected from a lady whose father had been one of the foremost philhellenes in Rome and whose own

---

[1] Cicero, *de fin.* II, 8, 24.

hand was sought by a reigning Ptolemy. She was not content with the elementary teaching which for Cato's son had been enough: the young Gracchi were to sit at the feet of men who could expound the culture and the political experience of Greece. If it may be assumed that from their Hellenic teachers the two brothers derived the undoubtedly Hellenic ideas which appeared in their public life at Rome, those teachers can claim a place in Roman history. Blossius of Cumae, who came of a stock which had possibly provided the leaders of the Capuan rebellion in 210 B.C.[1], had studied under Antipater in the Stoic school at Tarsus—perhaps with Panaetius himself: another, Diophanes, was a Mytilenaean and one of the most famous rhetoricians of his day. The early training of the Gracchi was not unworthy of their ancestry and their connections.

The active career of Tiberius Gracchus opens with two events —his co-optation to a place in the college of augurs and his marriage to Claudia, whose father—Appius Claudius Pulcher, the Princeps Senatus—was not on the best of terms with Scipio Aemilianus. In spite of this, however, Scipio took the young man to Africa as a *contubernalis*, and there, at the siege of Carthage, he was introduced to war. Warfare awaited him again when, as quaestor in 137, he served under C. Hostilius Mancinus in Spain. The diplomatic difficulties which arose when, by the use of his father's reputation, he saved the Roman army when it could not save itself, belong to another story (vol. VIII, p. 320 *sq.*); but the Spanish episode in his life deserves notice here for a double reason. It was on his journey towards Spain that Tiberius is said to have observed the conditions in Etruria which turned his thoughts in the direction of agrarian laws, and it was his salvation of the army at Numantia which, at least among the dependents of the troops, did not a little to win him that wide affection which he afterwards enjoyed. The months which followed his return to Rome must have been largely occupied by the discussions which ended with the consignment of Mancinus to the mercy of his enemies in Spain; but by the middle of 134 Tiberius was ready to set his hand to the task of social reform. He was elected tribune in the summer, and on 10 December the memorable year of office began.

In the task which his enthusiasm had chosen to attack Tiberius' youth was not without the support of age. Blossius and Diophanes supplied advice which, if not always judicious, might at least have claimed to be detached, and to their exhortations were added others from sources more responsible. Though

---

[1] Livy XXVII, 3, 4–5.

the conservatives were inevitably hostile and the Scipionic section was from the first lukewarm, Tiberius had friends of his own among the oligarchs. His father-in-law was one; but a quarrel with the *patres* about a triumph less than ten years before must have done something to detract from the proper influence of the Princeps Senatus. More serious was P. Licinius Crassus Mucianus, who had become by adoption the leading member of a family already famous for its wealth and who was soon to be Pontifex Maximus. Crassus seems consistently to have lent the scheme the weight of his great prestige, and even after the murder of Tiberius his appointment to the vacant place on the agrarian commission was regarded as a concession to the Gracchan party. His brother, who also lived to hold the office of chief pontiff— P. Mucius Scaevola, one of the two leading jurists of his day— was likewise well-disposed; but though, when they were clamouring for Tiberius' blood, he refused as consul to countenance the violence of the diehards whom afterwards he upheld, Cicero[1] suggests that his sympathy for the Gracchan cause had never found the most outspoken expression. If Plutarch's tale of Laelius is not wholly false, the evil to be attacked was one whose existence the Scipionic party could not well deny; and, when men like Appius Claudius, Crassus and Scaevola were on the reformer's side, the proposals he produced could not lightly be brushed aside as the fantastic dreamings of too generous youth.

VI. THE *LEX AGRARIA*

The *lex agraria* was a simple measure, designed to provide allotments for the poor. To find land for distribution it proposed that the State should deprive its tenants of all *ager publicus* held in excess of a maximum fixed by law. It has been said already (p. 19) that such a maximum was set by the Licinian-Sextian legislation in the fourth century, and that it seems still to have remained in theory down to Cato's time. But though the provision was to be revived and enforced, it was to be revived with a qualification of which there is no hint before. The practice whereby *possessores* exceeded the legal limits in the extent of their holdings by using relatives or dependents as bogus lessees (p. 19) was not in all instances an equal abuse. The father of a family whose surplus land was held by sons of age was clearly in a stronger position before public opinion than the bachelor who employed freedmen to hold an estate from which his profits might be increased; and it

[1] *pro Plancio*, 36, 88; *Acad.* ii, 5, 13.

was to the credit of Tiberius that between such cases he sought to distinguish. Though in theory the old limit of five hundred *iugera* was to be restored, tenants who had sons were to be allowed an additional two hundred and fifty for each[1]—possibly with the provision that no holding should thereby be made to exceed one thousand in all[2]. Of this concession the majority could doubtless take advantage. And not only so. As a set-off against the reduction of their estates, such land as the old *possessores* retained was to be held for the future not in precarious occupation, which might at any moment be terminated by the State, but in perpetuity without the payment of *vectigal*[3].

Whatever the legal implications of this provision, its effect was undoubtedly to convert these holdings from *ager publicus* into what was, for all practical purposes, private property. That the terms offered by Tiberius were better still, and that he proposed to compensate tenants for improvements made on the land to be surrendered, cannot be alleged with confidence. The vague expression of Plutarch[4] is perhaps no more than a garbled version of the arrangement for perpetuity of tenure more accurately recorded by Appian, though it may be conjectured that, had he proposed the purchase of such improvements by the State, Tiberius might have been following a precedent conceivably set when some Campanian land was resumed about 166 B.C.[5] But even without such monetary compensation, the concession made to tenants with sons, and the alienation by the Roman People of such land as these tenants were to retain, are provisions of generosity enough to show that the *lex agraria* was no narrow measure conceived in a spirit of petty hostility against the class on which fortune had smiled in the past.

The land thus rendered vacant was to be distributed to the poor in allotments of uncertain size: Mommsen once inferred from the law of 111 B.C. (Bruns, *Fontes*[7], 11, l. 13) that none was to exceed thirty *iugera*, but the story of similar grants in the past suggests that the majority of the plots were less extensive than this. In any case, since the law was framed at a time when neither the number of potential recipients nor the amount of land available was known, it is difficult to believe that the measure itself fixed any standard area for the small holdings. That matter was probably left to the discretion of the executive; but in a more vital issue rigorous provision was made. If the scheme was not to be a farce,

[1] Appian, *Bell. Civ.* 1, 9, 37; 11, 46.   [2] Livy, *Epit.* 58; *de viris ill.* 64, 3.
[3] Appian, *Bell. Civ.* 1, 11, 46.   [4] *Gracchi*, 9, 2.
[5] Cicero, *de lege agr.* 11, 30, 82; Licinianus, p. 9 F.

means must be found to ensure that its benefits should reach their proper destination and not fall into the hands of any enterprising opportunist who might ask for land in order to raise ready cash by immediately assigning his tenancy. For this purpose Tiberius enacted that the holdings awarded under the Lex Sempronia, though capable of passing by inheritance, should not be alienable by transfer for a consideration; and, possibly in order to keep alive the State's *dominium* without which this provision could not be effectively enforced, he seems to have insisted that the tenants should pay a rent[1]. To answer the familiar question whether Tiberius intended his veto on alienation to be permanent is more than the evidence allows. But nothing known of him lends colour to the assertion that he committed himself to an economic absurdity, nor was the purpose which the clause was clearly meant to serve more than temporary[2]. It is impossible to prove, and not easy to believe, that, had Tiberius been alive in 121 B.C. when the enactment was repealed after its work was done, he would have offered opposition.

VII. THE INTERVENTION OF M. OCTAVIUS

Such was the Lex Sempronia agraria—a drastic measure to deal with a serious social evil, and yet at the same time one which inflicted no unnecessary hardship. Once the method of land-allotment had been chosen as the means whereby employment was to be found, it is difficult to see how it could have been more fairly executed. Inevitably, when abuses have taken root, they cannot be eradicated without a wrench; but the force used by Tiberius was, initially at least, applied with gentleness, and the concessions he made to vested interests would justify from a less partial historian Plutarch's judgment that 'to meet illegalities and greed on such a scale there had never been drafted a milder law or a less violent[3].' But, in spite of this, resistance was strong: the great *possessores* bulked large in the Senate, and the Senate had recourse to its usual device. When the bill came before the Concilium Plebis a tribune was found to exercise his veto—one M. Octavius,

---

[1] The only evidence for this is Plutarch's statement (*Gracchi*, 30, 2) made in recording that the exaction was abolished by Livius Drusus in 122 B.C. Though Drusus is said to have won some popularity by its remission, the amount of this rent cannot have been large.

[2] It is to be noticed that Caesar in 59 B.C. fixed twenty years as the period during which his allottees were to be prevented from selling their holdings (Appian, *Bell. Civ.* III, 2, 5 and 7, 24).   [3] *Gracchi*, 9, 2.

a youth whose character would bear inspection and who is said by
Plutarch[1] to have been a personal friend of Gracchus. The results
of this opposition were grave. First, it seems that Tiberius, in
resentment at finding petty partisanship endeavouring to wreck
a measure conceived in the broad-minded spirit of a statesman,
amended his bill to give it a tone more in harmony with the
sectional spite of his opponents. Plutarch, who alone records that
the bill was passed in something other than its original form[2],
does not explain the alterations; but it is clear that, unless Plutarch
is completely wrong, the concessions made to existing *possessores*
were reduced. The nature of the change can only be conjectured.
It appears from the subsequent course of agrarian history that the
land such people were allowed to retain did not become their
private property until 111 B.C.; but, though these holdings of
500 *iugera* were left by Tiberius in the category of *ager publicus*
where he found them, such evidence as we have suggests that he
did not in these cases revive the claim to a *vectigal*. A rent was
demanded from occupiers of this class in 118 B.C., and unless
some unrecorded remission had been given since 133[3] a rent cannot have been exacted by Tiberius. Thus it seems that the first
result of factious opposition was to cause the withdrawal of the
proposal that so much of their holdings as the old *possessores* were
to keep should be converted into something which might be
regarded as *ager privatus*: they remained tenants of the State
whose tenancies might be still further curtailed in the future—as
Gaius Gracchus perhaps proposed to do—though their position
was still peculiar, because even now Tiberius did not insist on the
payment of a rent. And besides this, it is almost certain that any
offer of compensation for improvements on surrendered land
which Tiberius may originally have made was forthwith
dropped.

More serious, however, than these results of opposition on the
vested interests in land were the consequences for the constitution.
Tiberius did not, indeed, act with haste. To the first threat of veto
from Octavius he merely replied with a general suspension of
public business[4]; and even later he was still prepared to acquiesce
in the suggestion made by two ex-consuls that he should submit

---

[1] But see Dio, frag. 83, 4.

[2] *Gracchi*, 10, 2. For the view that this story is mere invention see
P. Fraccaro, *Studi sull' età dei Gracchi*, 1 (Città di Castello, 1914), pp. 96 *sqq.*

[3] It is hard to interpret Plutarch, *Gracchi*, 30, 2, as meaning that Livius
Drusus abolished *vectigal* on the old *possessiones*, as well as on the new
allotments.   [4] Plutarch, *Gracchi*, 10, 4.

the bill to the consideration of the Senate, which had hitherto been ignored. It was only when this last attempt at an agreement had met with its inevitable fate at the hands of the oligarchs that Gracchus mooted his drastic proposal to divest Octavius of his tribunate (a proposal against which no threat of veto is recorded). But, when milder means had failed and one course alone was left if Gracchus was not to be paralysed throughout his remaining months of office, that course he took with resolution. Reluctantly and with many appeals that his colleague should relent, but still without sign of flinching, he passed a *plebiscitum* whereby Octavius was deposed. Soon afterwards a successor was elected. The weapon of the obstructionists was broken in their hands and the way of the reformer lay clear.

On this action of Tiberius the most divergent judgments have been passed: indeed, the complexity of the Roman governmental system, and the difference between the practice and the imperfectly formulated theory, make it possible to argue with plausibility for almost any view. In the present place it will be enough to mention some of the leading considerations. Though the peculiar origin of the tribunate cannot be denied, the office had undergone an extraordinary change since its institution. With the successful issue of the plebeian struggles against the *patres* and with the subsequent legislation on *provocatio* the tribunes had lost their primary *raison d'être*; but when their services were no longer needed for the protection of the Plebs, other functions were found to justify their existence for the future. After the Struggle of the Orders, when plebeians began to make their way into the Senate, they brought to the new *nobilitas* a most powerful ally: the tribunate was refashioned and made into an invaluable check on popular assemblies whose powers, though not supreme, were dangerously great. Thus the tribunes became the 'mancipia nobilium[1].' Without the *rogatio* of a presiding officer, no assembly could act; but if magistrate and people were agreed on a measure, however pernicious to the State, the Senate, for all its prestige, in the last resort was powerless even to impose delay. Except for the extremely inconvenient methods of proclaiming a general suspension of business or faking unfavourable auspices, no check could be exerted but the veto of a tribune, and this was now the most important purpose for which tribunes had come to be employed. The negative and obstructive powers of the office made it singularly well suited to supply the conservative element in the State with an instrument of obvious value, and as a result of the

[1] Livy x, 37, 11.

services which they could render in this capacity the tribunes had entered more and more deeply into the constitution of Rome. To claim that the tribunes were not magistrates but merely officers of the Plebs was, in the Gracchan age as always, theoretically just; but at this time it would involve a somewhat academic appeal to the past, and it was a claim which, if its implications were pushed to their full extent, might have entitled its enemies to deprive the tribunate of several functions, acquired in course of years, which its supporters would have been reluctant to surrender. If Tiberius had claimed that tribunes were to be treated otherwise than as magistrates—and there is no evidence that such a claim was made —his interpretation of the facts could not be called less than pedantic. A less captious line of argument might have urged that the new conditions of the second century demanded that the tribunes should resume the functions they had discharged in the fifth and fourth. In ancient days they had championed the Plebs against patrician oppression, and now they might break with the recent past to render a like service to the masses who were suffering at the hands of the new nobility. But this again is an argument of which the authorities preserve no trace.

The passage in which Plutarch[1] implies that Tiberius attacked the whole principle of collegiality by asserting that, if colleagues disagreed, one or other might properly be deposed, cannot bear the stress which it has sometimes been required to support. The suggestion stands alone: it is unconnected with the arguments elsewhere ascribed to Tiberius: and it should probably be regarded as the thoughtless embellishment of an historian who did not appreciate the significance of his words. If this sentence may be disregarded, the attitude of Tiberius becomes more precise and more definitely democratic. He contended that, since he and Octavius were in diametric opposition, the voters might rightly depose whichever of them was thwarting the popular will. The contention carried with it a constitutional innovation of the gravest moment. The words in which Polybius[2] says that 'tribunes are supposed always to do what the People approves and above all to aim at the achievement of its desires' are capable of conveying more than was recognized in Roman practice: they certainly fail lamentably to fit the tribunate of the second century; and, unless they are prompted by Gracchan history, they must be taken as no more than a vague reference to the duties which the origin of the office might be interpreted to imply. Its business at the outset was admittedly to uphold the general

[1] *Gracchi*, 11, 4.   [2] vi, 16, 5.

interests of the masses; but from the fifth century onwards to the tribunate of Tiberius there is no hint that the tribunes were a mere executive appointed to carry out the wishes of the Plebs and in major issues were without a discretion of their own. In the Roman constitution the People were not completely sovran, nor were the magistrates, to whom the tribunes had become more and more closely assimilated, the mere agents of the assemblies. Sovranty rested with the People and magistrates in conjunction. Only by magistrates and People acting together could legislation be secured, and in this matter, as in others, magisterial and popular authority had always been treated as strictly co-ordinate. If the story of L. Brutus and Tarquinius Collatinus is an invention later than the Gracchi, no precedent could be quoted for the deposition by the People of a magistrate actually in office or of a tribune; and, even if such a step had been taken in the past, it would have been irrelevant unless the complaint had been the failure of the victim to carry out the wishes of his electors. In both respects it was left for Gracchus to make the new departure, and the change which he proposed was innovation indeed. The tribunes at least—and in the Gracchan age the curule magistracies could scarcely be un-affected by doctrines applied to the tribunate—were to be a mere executive. The tribunate was to be to the Concilium Plebis what the Cabinet is to the House of Commons, and the People was to wield a sovranty as complete as that of a Greek assembly, without even limitations like those imposed at Athens by the *graphe paranomon*. Tiberius Gracchus and his brother were perhaps the first true democrats in Rome—and, it may be added, the last.

To say that Tiberius brought to Rome something of the political experience of Greece is not to pass condemnation: Greek democracies had merits of their own, even though the unrestricted supremacy of the citizens assembled was not well suited to a State whose members were spread over so wide an area as the *ager Romanus*. Yet even the Athenians had checks of a kind, not strong enough indeed or wide enough in application: but at least legislation of a revolutionary kind was impossible so long as the constitution was not suspended or ignored. The sinister and alarming feature of Octavius' deposition was, not that it implied a degree of popular sovranty unknown at Rome before, but that, for all that Gracchus proposed, the sovran People was to be left to exercise its powers unchecked. If the tribunician veto could be evaded once, it could be evaded whenever it was applied to the pro-gramme of a demagogue; and in that case there was nothing to stand between the State and legislation however disastrous save ex-

pedients of a kind on which no reliance could be placed. A general
suspension of business could not last for ever, and the age was one
which would soon discover how to deal with attempts at obstruction by the announcement of ill omens. Tiberius Gracchus must
not be condemned outright. His cause was good and the opposition was of a kind which deserved not the slightest consideration.
But in the excitement of the fray and in the knowledge that he
had the welfare of Rome at heart, he was led to take a step
fraught with peril for the future. The unbridled supremacy of a
citizen assembly is always dangerous, but it is doubly so when the
citizen body is scattered so far afield that only a fraction of the
whole—and that fraction not representative—is normally present
to vote. Such power, though probably he did not appreciate the
implications of his act, Tiberius was giving to the urban mob; and
the gift was rash.

VIII. THE AGRARIAN COMMISSION

Once the resistance of Octavius had been broken, the land bill
in its amended form was passed. To carry out its provisions
a board of three commissioners was set up, and, apparently by a
subsequent enactment[1], it was equipped with power to give
judgments of legal validity in cases where the State's claim to the
ownership of land was in dispute. The commissioners, in fact, were
to have *imperium*—a circumstance which explains their mention
among the magistrates in the Lex Acilia of 122 B.C. Another
feature of their appointment has given rise to much controversy.
According to Appian[2] the commissioners were to 'change every
year'—a phrase which is generally regarded as a slight misrepresentation of an arrangement whereby the office was made annual,
though the existing commissioners were always eligible for re-
election[3]. It has been argued, however, that the meaning is wholly
different, and that the reference is to an annual rotation of the
presidency of the commission—a system whereby, if the president
alone was indispensable to the progress of the work, any individual
member might be free for other public duties, if he so desired, for
two years out of every three[4]. The election seems to have lain with

---

[1] Livy, *Epit.* 58.   [2] *Bell. Civ.* 1, 9, 37.

[3] Strictly interpreted the words ἐναλλασσομένους κατ᾽ ἔτος cannot mean
that the original members should merely have to undergo the annual
formality of re-election: they imply an annual change of *personnel*, which is
not in accordance with the facts.

[4] See J. Carcopino, *Autour des Gracques*, pp. 125 *sqq.* If this interpretation is on the right lines, in the judgment of the present writer its author

the Concilium Plebis; and when this met under the presidency of
Tiberius, its choice fell on Tiberius himself, his brother Gaius who
at the time was away in Spain, and his father-in-law Appius Claudius
Pulcher. This family gathering was in one respect peculiar. Unless
special exemption had been granted in the *lex agraria*, the election
of Tiberius violated the provisions of certain laws which forbade
the proposer of a bill to sit on any commission created thereby[1];
and that there was some such irregularity is suggested by the
attempt of Livius Drusus in 122 B.C. to make political capital by
a righteous refusal to take any part in the execution of his own
measures[2].

Nevertheless the commissioners went to work and laid the
foundations of an achievement whose dimensions must be considered later (see p. 43 *sq.*). But their course was not easy. By the
methods adopted in the passing of the bills the Senate had been
utterly antagonized, and before long its hostility found expression.
In accordance with a long-standing custom none but a consul
might draw on the public funds without express authority from the
Senate, and now the Senate saw in its hold on the purse-strings an
opportunity to obstruct the process of allotment. The commissioners themselves were refused all but the most ludicrously inadequate supplies to meet their own expenses, and for the more
important purpose of providing capital wherewith the new yeomen
might stock their farms nothing was forthcoming. But when the
tresviri were in a predicament already acute, fortune came to the
rescue[3]. There suddenly arrived in Rome a Pergamene named
Eudemus, who brought with him a will wherein Attalus III had
instituted the Roman People his heir. Here was a windfall
which Tiberius could not afford to neglect, and in using it he
raised a second constitutional issue. To the Senate's attempt to
obstruct by employing against him its financial control he replied

goes too far when he suggests that this rotation of the presidency was laid
down in the text of the law itself and was not rather a private arrangement
made among the members for their own convenience. Nor is it easy to believe that, when two commissioners out of three were present in Italy without other occupation, the available commissioner who was not president at the
moment would refrain from all activity in connection with the work of
distribution.

[1] For the Leges Licinia and Aebutia see Cicero, *de lege agr.* II, 8, 21;
de domo sua, 20, 51. For a different view of these dates see Mommsen,
Staatsrecht I³, p. 501, n. 2.   [2] Plutarch, *Gracchi*, 31, 1.

[3] See Carcopino, *op. cit.*, pp. 35 *sqq.* for an attempt to disprove this story
by showing that Ti. Gracchus died before Attalus III. A brief criticism
of the argument will be found in *J.R.S.* XVIII, 1928, p. 229.

with a direct attack on its ancient claim to manage provincial and foreign affairs. What part of the bequest he proposed to hypo-thecate is uncertain, but a bill was introduced before the Concilium Plebis ordering that some of the wealth thus left to Rome should be set aside to provide for the needs of the new allottees. And, more serious still, the bill was accompanied by an announcement that the affairs of the Attalid Kingdom were no business of the Senate but that measures for their settlement would be laid by Tiberius himself before the People. That the bill to find capital for the small-holders from the revenues of Pergamum was ever passed we do not know: if it was not, we must assume that as a bare threat it was effective enough to break down the existing financial deadlock. But, whether enacted or not, the mere proposal of the measure had a deep significance as another assertion of the People's supremacy. Not only in issues of a domestic kind, like that at stake when Octavius was deposed, but in imperial matters too the Concilium Plebis was to be sovran in fact. And just as the check of tri-bunician veto had been removed from the activities of the People in purely Roman matters, so now the trammels of senatorial consent were to be destroyed where external affairs were concerned. In questions of provincial policy, where Rome hitherto had been blessed with a control on the waywardness of the masses more effective by far than that exercised in fifth-century Athens by the *boule*, the assemblies were to work their will for the future without let or hindrance. As before, the intentions of Tiberius were above reproach; but here again his enthusiasm led him to provide a precedent fraught with danger for time to come.

IX. THE DEMAND OF TIBERIUS FOR A SECOND TRIBUNATE

By now it was the summer of 133 B.C.; and when the election of tribunes for the following year was at hand, it seems that Tiberius, not without justice, regarded the position of the agrarian com-missioners as still precarious. Accordingly he began to moot a proposal for his own continuance in office, and to this end Plutarch asserts that he developed a new programme of legislation[1]. The period during which citizens were liable for military service was to be shortened, *provocatio* was to be granted against the decisions of judicial commissions appointed by the Senate, and the jurors in the *quaestio repetundarum* were to be half senators and half 'equites,' instead of being wholly drawn from the Senate as at present. Such

[1] *Gracchi*, 16, 1.

is perhaps the most plausible interpretation of the suggestions which Plutarch preserves; but his words are not explicit and other authorities do nothing to help their explanation. Indeed, Dio[1] alone among the rest of our extant sources lends confirmation to Plutarch's tale by so much as mentioning such further projects.

The programme is one which cannot with confidence be rejected: the need for some change in the regulations for military service was already acute (see below, pp. 133 *sqq.*), the enforcement of a claim to the universal right of *provocatio* is no matter for surprise, and the introduction of a new element into the juries of the *iudicia publica* may as well have commended itself to Tiberius as it did to his brother ten years later. On the other hand they cannot be accepted outright. The silence of Appian tells against them, and proposals which admittedly Tiberius never managed to enact are of all the features in his career the one most exposed to corruption. And when it is recalled that all three measures were later passed by Gaius, the possibility cannot be ignored that their ascription to Tiberius is an illicit retrojection, prompted partly by a desire of his detractors to load him with some of the unpopularity incurred by the still more objectionable Gaius, and partly by a widespread but erroneous assumption that the aims of the two brothers were to a large extent the same. But though the details are suspect, it is not improbable that Tiberius did in fact do something to provide a programme which would justify his re-election; and there can be no doubt at all that the new appeal to the electors was the occasion of his death. When they had failed in their various attempts to scotch the scheme of allotments, the oligarchs retired in sullen hostility to console themselves with the thought that this visitation would afflict them only for a year: in December 133 B.C. Tiberius would become a private citizen again, and then it might be possible with more success to burke a reform whose author would no longer be able to defend it with the authority of a tribune. To these calculations the re-election of Tiberius would be fatal. A second year might be followed by a third; and by that time, even if no new devilry had been started, the damage wrought to vested interests by the activities of the commission might well be irreparable. At all costs the re-election must be stopped; and so

---

[1] Frag. 83, 7. The speech of Scipio Aemilianus *contra legem iudiciariam Tib. Gracchi* (Malcovati, *Orat. Rom. Frag.* I, p. 240 *sq.*) must have been part of Scipio's attack on the agrarian commission in 129 B.C. (see below, pp. 42 *sqq.*), unless Macrobius (*Sat.* III, 14, 6) is completely mistaken in his attribution. It cannot belong to the tribunate of Tiberius: Scipio at the time of Tiberius' death had been in Spain since 134.

strongly were the oligarchs convinced of this necessity that to achieve it they had recourse to the basest methods of the mob.

Had the office of Tiberius been a curule magistracy, no claim to re-election could have stood. In 180 B.C. the Lex Villia had imposed a drastic check on the progress from one curule office to another, and about the middle of the second century it had been enacted that no man might hold the consulship more than once (vol. VIII, p. 367). It is true that this rule had been relaxed in favour of Scipio Aemilianus in 135, but in the absence of such dispensation, the legal position as regards curule magistrates admitted no dispute. Tiberius, however, was a tribune, and in the days when the tribunes led the opposition to the patrician government, it had been a familiar practice, after a tribunician college had formulated some precise demand, to keep those tribunes, or their leaders, in office until the demand was granted. It is true that, since the most famous use of this device in the ten years before the legislation of C. Licinius and L. Sextius (vol. VII, p. 524 *sq.*), the need for it had gradually grown less until it had become a half-forgotten expedient of an age which was now remote: but, in spite of protests, the right remained, and there were even precedents for the re-election of a single tribune. It may be said with confidence that in the case of tribunes *refectio* had never been forbidden by law: not even the authorities most hostile to the Gracchi can quote any statutory bar. The Gracchan party were making a concession to their opponents when Carbo in 131 (see p. 38 *sq.*) proposed to legalize a re-election which no legislation forbade. But, as Great Britain was reminded in 1909, sudden insistence on a dormant legal right often involves dangers worse than its surrender; and the same is true of Tiberius' claim to a second tribunate. Though his position was sound in law, it compelled him to appeal from the present to a past whose precedents were to a large extent irrelevant.

Here again it is to be remembered that the tribunate owed much of its enormous power to its gradual assimilation to the curule magistracies; and, though it was strictly immune from conditions by which these magistracies were governed, an argument which depended on this theoretical immunity was one which, besides being pedantic, might soon recoil on its author. If the tribunes were for all practical purposes to be treated as magistrates, it was far from reasonable for them to claim exemption from what was perhaps the most important of all the rules by which magistrates were governed—the rule which alone stood between the Republic and a principate. By offering himself as a candidate at the elections in 133 B.C. Tiberius raised an issue of the first magnitude. It was an issue destined to force itself on public notice more insistently as the revolutionary age took its course, and destined finally to be settled by Augustus in the sense which Tiberius Gracchus had proposed. But, for all this, it is idle to suggest that the troubles of the next hundred years would have been avoided if Gracchus had been allowed his way. A principate provided the lasting solution of Rome's constitutional difficulties, and it was at some sort of personal pre-eminence that Tiberius seemed to aim. But between the position of Augustus, secure in the possession of *imperium*, and that of a tribune annually re-elected by the Concilium Plebis there was all the difference in the world. One could afford to snap his fingers at the clamour of the urban mob: the other depended on it almost entirely for his political survival. Gracchus was steering Rome straight for ochlocracy; and, though such an issue was probably far from his own intention, there was truth in the oligarchic allegation that, in the fashion familiar among the Greeks, this champion of the people was threatening to establish a tyranny. The tyrant, it is true, would be controlled by his supporters; but he would be none the less a tyrant for the fact that he was bound to fall if ever he forfeited the friendship of the *plebs urbana*.

X. THE DEATH OF TIBERIUS GRACCHUS

Much can be said in extenuation of the oligarchic resistance, but there can be no justification for the methods it employed. If ever the folly of political violence was proved by its results, that proof was given by the consequences which flowed from the murder of Tiberius Gracchus. When there at length arrived the day on which the election was to be made, the Senate met in the Temple of Fides, and at its meeting the presiding consul— P. Mucius Scaevola—was directly asked by P. Scipio Nasica, the Pontifex Maximus, to save the State and destroy the tyrant. To this demand Scaevola made the right reply—that he would do nothing illegal, but that if illegality were committed by the People he would refuse to regard the act as valid. By the contentions of Tiberius, Scaevola was not convinced. The claim to the right of re-election in his opinion was unsound, and if the Concilium Plebis went through the form of appointing Tiberius to another year of office the ceremony would be of no effect: but, in spite of this, it was inexpedient to stop the ceremony by force. To Nasica and his friends this was temporizing with revolution. Since the

consul was betraying the State, they would uphold the banner of
the constitution. And so the diehards set forth to inaugurate the
rule of force. Tiberius was clubbed with the leg of a chair, three
hundred of his supporters were done to death without so much as
a pretence of trial, and the champions of the constitution could
boast that they had shed the first blood drawn in civil war since
the expulsion of the second Tarquin.

Tiberius Gracchus was a young man whose enthusiasm had
carried him away. His intentions were of the best, though anxiety
for the cause of social reform had led him to constitutional innovations which were ill-considered and impracticable. But even if
it be admitted that his programme could not be enacted as it stood
without injury to the State, the manner of his death stood as an
indelible condemnation of the system which his opponents were
claiming to uphold. The appeal of Tiberius was made by argument: the reply was made by force. If the rational demand for
reform could be refuted by reasoned defence of the existing
system, the use of violence by his enemies admits of no extenuation.
If the suggestions of Tiberius, however dangerous their conclusions, could not logically be shown to contradict the fundamental principles implicit in the constitution, then the constitution
was in need of change. In any case the fate of Tiberius Gracchus
left his enemies convicted: if they were not unjust stewards
of a system which was good, they were the worthy champions
of a system which was bad. Such was the predicament in
which the oligarchy found itself involved by the uncurbed folly of
its extremists. Yet the Senate as a whole was not guilty in the first
degree. Though Cicero can quote the consul Scaevola as one who
approved the deed, Scaevola was on the side of law during the
crisis itself; and though Scipio Aemilianus is said to have prayed
that the fate of Tiberius might be shared by all who did the like
again[1], it is difficult to suppose that he and his friends would have
supported violence on the day of the elections. Yet if among the
senators there was wisdom, folly was so widespread that wisdom
could not prevail; and the oligarchy betrayed its latent weakness
by recourse to bloodshed in a difficulty so slight that the sanctions
of any stable constitution should have mastered it with ease.

[1] Plutarch, *Gracchi*, 21, 4.

XI. THE RESTORATION OF SENATORIAL AUTHORITY

When the struggle at length was over and the oligarchs had emerged, battered but supreme, they set their hand forthwith to the task of repairing the damage. To have invalidated the *lex agraria* outright, on the ground that the deposition of Octavius, by which alone its passage had been secured, was illegal, would have been to raise an issue so complicated that the advantages of such a course were at best a speculation. Certainty of success there was none, and the Senate of the Gracchan age was experienced enough to refrain from staking its interests on a very dubious contention. There was a better way than this—to accept the land-commission for the moment and to wait for such opportunities as might occur of hampering its activity. But the commission was not the most sinister feature in the situation. Much as the senators disliked the economic programme of Tiberius, there can be no doubt that opposition owed its strength to the challenge which had been thrown down to the existing constitutional arrangements. To promulgate a bill which, so far from approving, the Fathers had not even discussed, to devise a short way of dealing with the veto of a conservative tribune, to submit financial questions from the provinces to the People direct, and to threaten the establishment of a system dominated by a popular tribune elected year after year—these were the crimes for which the Senate was most concerned to brand the memory of Tiberius. Imitators of these must at all costs be deterred: so a court was created with instructions to punish everyone proved guilty of aiding Gracchus in his pernicious undertakings.

This congenial task was entrusted to the consuls of 132 B.C.—men suited for their work by the union of a certain moderation with unshaken loyalty to the oligarchs. P. Popillius Laenas, though he came of a family with an ugly reputation for violence and brutality, did not shrink from boasting that he was the first to carry out the provisions of the Gracchan land-law[1]. His colleague, P. Rupilius, who left an honourable monument of his services in the charter of the Sicilian province, was a political friend of Scipio Aemilianus; and this connection, which was perhaps responsible for the presence of Laelius on the *consilium* of the consuls, is enough to suggest that, even though the egregious Nasica was a member too, the court would conduct itself with some sort of honesty and reason. Nevertheless, its orders from the

---

[1] Dessau 23.

Senate were of the severest kind, and though the instructions 'ut
in eos, qui cum Graccho consenserant, more maiorum animad-
verterent[1]' were not strictly interpreted to mean that the guilty
were to be done to death by crucifixion (or scourging), by various
methods, all of sufficient brutality, the active following of Tiberius
was destroyed. His most distinguished friends, who naturally
were not involved in the more violent incidents of the affair,
were left untouched: no attack was made on Crassus or Appius
Claudius, and Scaevola had atoned for earlier aberrations by the
prudence of his consulship. But on the rest the court fell with
a heavy hand: adherents of the cause were freely condemned,
and those who contrived to evade arrest were banished without
trial. Blossius alone of those who appeared before the court is
recorded to have emerged alive, and even he thought fit to betake
himself to Asia, where he died by his own hand on the suppression of Aristonicus two or three years later.

Thus the challenge to senatorial supremacy received an un-
equivocal reply, and admirers of democracy for the future were
under no delusion about the penalty of failure in an attempt to
impose it on Rome. Meanwhile one slight adjustment was needed
to set the Senate's own house in order. Its enemies were not slow
to suggest that the champions of the existing order had a curious
friend in one who had led the lynching of an elected officer of the
Plebs, protected by all the sanctity of the tribunate. In a crisis
Scipio Nasica was a tower of strength to the craven-hearted constitutionalists; but now that the Senate had regained control his
recent achievements made him a somewhat embarrassing ally. So
weak was his position that he was even threatened with prosecution; and to the oligarchs, therefore, the rising of Aristonicus
in Asia provided an opportunity not unwelcome. Clearly a committee of the Senate was needed to investigate the affairs of the
province, and none could deny that on such a board Nasica might
appropriately receive a place. So to Asia he was consigned, and in
Asia he died.

Meanwhile the land-board was at work. The Senate did not
interfere; and when the time came to elect a new commissioner in
place of Tiberius, it prudently refrained from taking part in a
scheme of which it disapproved. Accordingly it acquiesced in the
appointment of the new Pontifex Maximus, P. Licinius Crassus
Mucianus, the father-in-law of C. Gracchus. Thus the commission
remained in the family. But its members were not without distractions. In 131 B.C. Crassus was consul, and his attention seems

[1] Val. Max. IV. 7, 1.

chiefly to have been occupied by the disturbances in Asia, where he died in the following year. Soon afterwards another place became vacant by the death of Appius Claudius Pulcher, and C. Gracchus had to look for two fresh colleagues, whom he found in M. Fulvius Flaccus and in a rising member of an hitherto undistinguished house—C. Papirius Carbo, a person of little principle but great oratorical power. Flaccus, probably the successor of Crassus, was an old supporter of the Gracchan cause, and Carbo, who took the place of Appius Claudius, had declared his faith as tribune in the consulship of Crassus Mucianus—131 B.C.

The year 131 B.C. had been one of some excitement. For the first time in history the censorship had been held by two plebeians together, and one of them—the famous Q. Metellus Macedonicus—contrived to make his tenure of the office memorable. Not only did he combine the most utilitarian view of the female sex with a policy of enforcing marriage for patriotic purposes—his speech 'de prole augenda' was once inflicted at length upon the Senate by the Emperor Augustus[1]—but by his attempt to remove from the Senate a tribune named C. Atinius Labeo Macerio he provoked one of the latest manifestations of the tribunician practice in its primitive form. Atinius, who may conceivably have given Plebiscitum Atinium its name, so far resented his removal from the Roll of the House as to waylay the censor and drag him by force towards the Tarpeian Rock. But happily before they reached the edge, Metellus was rescued by some rival tribunes, and it seems that a subsequent attempt to deprive him of his property by consecration met with no better success. The tribunate of Carbo, however, had revived a graver issue. His *lex tabellaria*, though a measure of prime importance, can scarcely have been controversial. The use of the ballot, introduced for elections in 139 B.C., had been extended two years later to voting on judicial issues (with the exception of cases of *perduellio*), and this extension had been supported by Scipio Aemilianus. Now the ballot was to be used in legislation, to the great advantage of the *plebs urbana*. Voters who, in whatever way, were dependent on the rich might hope for the future to exercise their rights without fear of victimization. But the most serious proposal made by Carbo was another—to declare legal the annual re-election of a tribune for a period limited only by the tribune's ability to retain the electorate's support. Not only was this an imprudent and unnecessary suggestion that law had been on the Senate's side in 133: it was also a barefaced attempt to force on the Senate one of the

---

[1] Suet. *Aug.* 89, 2.

most objectionable principles in the programme of Tiberius
Gracchus. His threat to establish a principate had been defeated;
but now Carbo was proposing to smooth the way for some
successor. To meet this menace, besides their own formidable
influence, the oligarchs were able to count on the support of
moderate opinion. The Scipionic circle was stirred: first Laelius
raised his timid voice in opposition, and the measure was finally
rejected when Scipio himself assailed it with all the power of his
oratory and all the weight of his prestige. For the moment, the
radical advance was stayed.

CHAPTER II

GAIUS GRACCHUS

I. THE PROTEST OF THE ALLIES

THE agrarian commissioners now held the centre of the stage. Gaius Gracchus, Carbo and Fulvius Flaccus—a triumvirate which was in office continuously from 130 to 122—set to work with such energy that, before long, they had raised a problem greater than they knew. From the outset the *lex agraria* had threatened vested interests in public land, and the interested parties made their inevitable complaint. Those of them who were Roman *cives* had resisted the bill in 133; and, when it was passed, their opposition could fairly be said to have been overruled. Resentful they undoubtedly remained; but their case had been heard, and after its rejection they were without any legal ground for grievance. Now, however, the Latins and Italians took a hand, and with such effect that the work of the commission was soon in the gravest peril. The nature of their complaint is still to some extent obscure, but the evidence is enough to show the outline of their case. Much has been made of the fact that the territory of communities belonging to the Latin Name had sometimes been extended by block-grants of *ager publicus*, to be occupied corporately by the community concerned as tenant of the Roman People[1]: this, it is said, was the land whereto the Latins feared the application of the Lex Sempronia. But, as these blocks had been granted to the Latin cities for use at their own discretion, it is hard to believe that they were exposed to the provisions of the Gracchan law: it is not in this direction that the grounds for apprehension must be sought. On the other hand, when Italian communities became allies of Rome, they had generally surrendered part of their land to be made *ager publicus populi Romani* and had been allowed to retain the rest. Here at least there was room for doubt about the precise limits of the public land over which the triumviral jurisdiction ran, and disputes in such circumstances as to what was *ager publicus populi Romani* and what was not do something to explain the bad feeling which arose. Besides this, however, there was another source of trouble. Though the evidence is not explicit, it is scarcely possible to doubt that, when *ager publicus* of the poorer

[1] Bruns, *Fontes*[7], 11, l. 31.

sort had been offered for occupation by squatters, advantage was
taken of the opportunity by people who were not citizens of Rome.
If on occasion more land was available than could be furnished
with Roman *possessores*, it was clearly in the interests of the State,
rather than allow part to remain unproductive, to seek tenants for
it where tenants could be found. Latins, who of course enjoyed
the *ius commercii* with Rome, and probably Italian allies too, were
tolerated, if not welcomed, as settlers on the vacant land, and thus
the Roman *ager publicus*, no longer a purely domestic concern,
acquired an interest for other peoples in the peninsula and became,
at least potentially, a matter of international importance.

There were thus two ways in which the operations of the commission might give trouble to the Latin and Italian allies. First,
where land left in the ownership of an Italian community marched
with *ager publicus populi Romani*, the local inhabitants might be
called upon to produce evidence establishing their title to that
which they claimed to be theirs: and, secondly, there were the
Latins and Italians who had settled on land which admittedly belonged to Rome. So far as our evidence goes, it does not suggest
that the commissioners proposed to treat Latin and Italian *possessores* less favourably than *possessores* who were Roman citizens;
but, if all alike were to suffer no more than a reduction of their
holdings to the maximum allowed by the Lex Sempronia, it by no
means followed that the resentment of the non-Roman section
would be removed by the reflection that they were in no worse
plight than their Roman neighbours. It is true that the hardships
brought upon the allies by the agrarian legislation were not by
themselves enough to provoke any dangerous degree of discontent: the trouble was that they came at a time when the allies were
already for other reasons in a sullen and suspicious frame of mind.
For something like a hundred years their treatment at the hands
of Rome had slowly grown more scurvy: their services had been
drawn on ever more freely to fight the wars which won Rome
her empire beyond the frontiers of Italy, but their reward, so far
from being admission to some kind of partnership with the imperial power, had been nothing more than a series of exasperating
pin-pricks which served to emphasize the inferiority of their position (see further below, pp. 46 *sqq.*). The undeniable lack of gratitude on the part of Rome, and her cynical determination to exploit
the allies for her own purposes, had their inevitable result. There
was resentment which only needed an opportunity for expression,
and this opportunity came with the activities of the agrarian commission. Latin and Italian squatters were to be told—or so at

least they feared—to give up part of the land on which they lived
in order that it might be bestowed on members of the Roman
proletariate—on people who were not even eligible for military
service. Thus the agrarian programme touched off the inflammable
material long present in the allied communities, and an active
agitation began.

II. THE INTERVENTION OF SCIPIO AEMILIANUS

When the agitators arrived in Rome they found powerful influences on their side. For what it was worth, they could count
with assurance on the support of the senatorial diehards—men
who would lend their aid to any movement which promised to
strike a blow at the detestable work of Tiberius Gracchus. But
these senators were no true friends: they might help the Italians
now, when it suited their own interests, but it was they who
had caused and countenanced most of the abuses out of which
Italian discontent had grown. There were more honest helpers
than these. The foremost figure at Rome—Scipio Aemilianus—
owed his prominence above all things to his achievements in war,
and in the field he had learnt to appreciate the truth that without
the help of the Italians the victories of Rome could never have
been won. When it came to weighing the claims of the allies
against those of the Roman unemployed, Scipio was not the man
to be blinded by the glamour of the title 'civis Romanus'. In him
the Italians had a friend whose friendship rested on a knowledge of
their services to Rome, and to him they turned.

Early in the year 129 he took action. The intervention of Scipio
was an event of the first importance, but unfortunately it is one
on which the evidence is lamentably weak. Appian is our only
authority, and his account is vague to a degree. It is usually said
that, after enlarging on the unpopularity of the land-law among
the allies and their distrust of the commissioners, he secured the
passage of a measure whereby the commissioners were deprived
of their judicial powers. These powers were then transferred to one
of the consuls—C. Sempronius Tuditanus, who promptly went
off to Illyricum and left the *tresviri* in a state of paralysis, from
which they were only restored by the *lex agraria* of Gaius Gracchus
in 123. The truth of this account, however, is by no means beyond
dispute. It cannot be denied that, when powers of judicial decision had been given to the commissioners by a plebiscite,
nothing less than another law would have sufficed to take these
powers away: yet Appian is silent about an amending act being

passed by an Assembly and seems to confine the whole incident to a scene in the Senate. Again, if authority to settle cases where the status of land was in dispute had simply been transferred to magistrates who were out of sympathy with the whole programme of agrarian reform, the operations of the commissioners must rapidly have been brought to a standstill: yet Dio[1] records that, after the death of Scipio, they were as active as ever. Finally there is the evidence of the census-lists. As they stand in the *Epitomes* of Livy, these give totals of 317,933 in 136/5, of 318,823 in 131/0, of 394,736 in 125/4 and of 394,336 in 115/4. Whatever the explanation of the similarity between the last two returns, there is no valid reason for denying that a large increase occurred after the census of 131/0; nor can there be much doubt that the cause is to be found in the work of the agrarian commission.

Precisely how this result was produced depends on the view which is taken of the lists whose totals are thus recorded. If, with Herzog, we believe that the numbers are those of Roman citizens qualified by property for military service—numbers, that is, which do not include those of the *proletarii*—the increase will be due to a mass of *proletarii* having acquired property enough in the course of the land-allotments to raise them into the ranks of *assidui* and so to make them eligible for reckoning in the census-lists. This, however, involves the assumption that plots of *ager publicus*, held apparently in mere *possessio*, were regarded as private property for the purpose of assessment. If, on the other hand, with Mommsen in his later phase, we believe that the numbers recorded are those of Roman citizens, whether *proletarii* or not, who by age could be reckoned as *iuniores*, or if with Beloch we hold that the whole body of adult male citizens is included, we must assume that poorer members of the population, about whose enrolment the censors had not troubled in the past, now began to insist on their registration, presumably because the *lex agraria*, by the grants which it promised to Roman citizens, had made effective citizenship a privilege on which those who were entitled to it found it worth while to insist. Now if the rise which occurs between the numbering of the people in 131/0 and that in 125/4 were due to transformation of *proletarii* into *assidui*, it would be difficult to believe that the work which this involved could have been carried out by the *tresviri* between the end of the census of 130 and the intervention of Scipio in 129. If, on the other hand, it was the attraction of possible allotments which induced poorer members of the population, hitherto unregistered, to enrol, their enrolment will only be

[1] Frag. 84, 2.

intelligible if it happened at a time when allotments were still to be had; and their enrolment is to be placed, at earliest, in 125. In either case it seems that the census-lists confirm Dio in his assertion that Scipio did not bring the work of the commission to an end.

There is much to be said for an alternative account[1]. Appian's narrative of the incident seems to make the Senate-House its scene: the trouble was provoked by the agitation of Latins and Italians: and the relations between Rome and these peoples were international affairs, which had long been claimed by the Senate as one of its own particular preserves. It is possible, therefore, that the Senate merely warned the Gracchan commissioners off public land occupied by non-Romans, alleging that this might raise international issues with which it was its own affair to deal, and nominated its own representative—Tuditanus—to take any action which might be necessary in connection with land of this particular kind. Tuditanus, of course, did nothing, and the Latin and Italian *possessores* were left undisturbed; but the Gracchan commissioners were free, as before, to continue their work on *ager publicus* where the tenants were Roman citizens. If so, their operations need not be cramped within a narrow period of years; they may have continued even after the census of 125/4; and thus it becomes possible to divine why Gaius Gracchus, when his turn came to take up the task of finding a livelihood for the unemployed, seems to have looked to Africa for his agrarian allotments and to have done no more in Italy itself than to design colonies on sites whose value was less agricultural than commercial. By 123 the available *ager publicus*, except that fraction which was occupied by Latins and Italians, may well have been treated by the commissioners with such thoroughness that room could no longer be found for more than a negligible number of new farmers.

Whatever the truth about Scipio's *coup* may be, it did not commend itself to the mob of Rome. Already in 131, when he opposed Carbo's measure to declare legal the re-election of tribunes, he had fallen foul of the Gracchan voters and there had been some undignified exchanges of repartee. Now the scenes broke out again: men so prominent as Fulvius Flaccus took a hand, and Scipio found himself held up to almost daily execration. After one of these wrangles in the Forum, Scipio returned home, escorted by a great following of his admirers, to prepare a reply for the morrow. Next morning he was found dead. The cause of the fatality will never be known. Foul play was freely suggested, and as time went on allegations were made against the widow, against all three mem-

---

[1] For this suggestion see E. G. Hardy, *Six Roman Laws*, p. 39.

bers of the agrarian commission, and even against Cornelia, mother of the Gracchi. But the official view, which is to be found in the scanty remains of the *laudatio* pronounced by the faithful Laelius[1], held that death was due to natural causes. This account is undoubtedly supported by the failure of Scipio's friends—of whom there were many—to bring the charge of murder home to any individual; but, if it is true, it must be admitted that Nature rid the reformers of a powerful opponent by a peculiarly well-timed intervention[2].

III. THE PRELUDE TO THE TRIBUNATES
OF GAIUS GRACCHUS

With the death of Scipio the fog which enshrouds the history of the Gracchan age grows thicker, and all we can discern is a continued agitation in the Latin and Italian cities. Proposals to enfranchise the allies were heard; Latins and Italians thronged to Rome; and the curtain had risen on the drama which ended with the Social War. According to Appian's account[3], the Roman citizenship was offered as a mere bribe to secure allied acquiescence in the fullest application of the *lex agraria*; but such a version is certainly too narrow. The activities of the land commission were not the only grievance of the allies. They were merely the occasion on which long-standing discontent found audible expression, and it is for this reason that the agitation continued even after Scipio had relieved Italian anxieties on the matter of the land. The course of the negotiations, if negotiations there were, is wholly obscure. All we know is that, when the census of 125/4 was near at hand, such a mass of strangers had been attracted to Rome by the news that some relief of their burdens was in sight that recourse was had to a familiar means of preventing fraudulent enrolment of men who were not entitled to the Roman *civitas*. A tribune who probably held office for the year 126/5[4]—M. Junius Pennus—passed a law of great severity, forbidding aliens access to the city: it was a measure which deserved the censure passed on it by Lucilius[5]. A phrase from a speech delivered by Gaius Gracchus in opposition

---

[1] Stangl, II, p. 118. See J. Carcopino, *Autour des Gracques*, pp. 114 *sqq.*
[2] See Carcopino, *op. cit.*, pp. 83 *sqq.*　　　[3] *Bell. Civ.* I, 21, 87.
[4] See Carcopino, *op. cit.*, pp. 194 *sqq.* Carcopino's connection of the Lex Junia Penni with the proposal for enfranchisement made by M. Fulvius Flaccus in 125 B.C. is plausible, though it is impossible to prove that the first was a direct reply to the second.
[5] See C. Cichorius, *Untersuchungen zu Lucilius*, pp. 212 *sq.*

to Pennus[1] reveals that the measure was represented by its author
as one designed to help the allied States. Certainly there had been
several occasions in the recent past when these communities had
complained that they were being depopulated by the flow of their
citizens to Rome, where the *civitas* could be gained by simple misrepresentation to the censors (vol. VIII, p. 355). But, if consideration for the allies prompted this effort to conserve their strength,
the goodwill of Pennus contrived at the same time to prejudice
the prospects of the agitation in Rome: for, though the Italians
had no votes at all and the Latins none that counted on any serious
occasion, there can be no doubt that the presence of large numbers in the city, clamouring incessantly for satisfaction and redress,
lent weight to the arguments of the orators who took up their
cause. One such was M. Fulvius Flaccus, land-commissioner
since 131 and consul in 125: another was Gaius Gracchus, lately
back from his quaestorship in Sardinia. The consulship of Flaccus
was made famous by a measure, premature indeed, but nevertheless one that showed some appreciation of the dangers with which
Rome was faced. It was proposed, on terms which in detail still
remain obscure, to enfranchise those of the allies who were willing
to become citizens of Rome and to confer on those who preferred
to remain outside the Roman State the right of appealing to the
Populus against acts of tyranny by Roman magistrates.

The alternative deserves some notice. To say that what the
Italians wanted was citizenship of Rome is untrue, if it implies
that they wanted the Roman citizenship as an end in itself. They
did not, and Flaccus recognized as much by offering the *ius pro-
vocationis* to those who were unwilling to accept the full *civitas*.
They had, indeed, a strong claim to what Appian[2] would call a
'partnership in the hegemony' (κοινωνία τῆς ἡγεμονίας); for the
hegemony which Rome showed every sign of keeping to herself
was the hegemony of an empire which could not have been won
without allied aid. But there was more at stake than a mere question of prestige. In general the allies needed relief from the exploitation to which they were being subjected by Rome: in
particular they sought protection from the minor outrages of
Roman magistrates—outrages which were not the less exasperating because they directly affected only a few individuals here and
there. To accept the Roman franchise was a means by which the
allies might attain both ends at once: but, though for several
reasons the best, it was not the only way. Another was to cut the
painter and set up a confederacy independent of Rome, as was

---

[1] Malcovati, *Orat. Rom. Frag.* II, p. 131.   [2] *Bell. Civ.* I, 34, 152.

actually done for a moment during the Social War (p. 185 *sq.*). Each method had its advantages, but the bill of Fulvius Flaccus is enough to show that the first did not find universal favour. The reason is simple. Rome had yet to teach the world one of her most precious lessons—that men could combine the citizenship of Rome with that of their native States, and yet not jeopardize the survival of the smaller groups. In the second century B.C., though in practice Rome was coming near the great discovery, the peoples of Italy in general had still to shake off the old idea that no man could be a citizen of two States at once. They believed, in fact, that, if the whole citizen body of Naples entered the *civitas* of Rome, Naples as a political unit would forthwith cease to be; and consequently local patriotism looked askance at the prospect of enrolment in the Roman body politic. For that reason Fulvius Flaccus offered an alternative.

But, in spite of all his statesmanship, the measure failed to pass. Though his election to the consulship by itself is enough to show that progressive elements were now powerful in Rome, and though Gaius Gracchus supported him with all the strength of his family prestige, Flaccus found the Roman voters singularly lacking in enthusiasm for a proposal which invited them to share their privileges with their neighbours. Such was the apathy of the masses, if not their open opposition, that the Senate took courage to intervene, though extensions of the franchise had long been recognized as business for the assemblies alone. After much persuasion, Flaccus was induced to enter the Curia, and there he found himself the object, not so much of reasonable advice, as of passionate appeals to desist. The result was surprising: for whatever reason, whether statesmanship counselled retreat or for some less worthy cause, the faithful henchman of the Gracchi threw in his hand and accepted a military command in Gaul. Thus, for the moment, reform was blocked.

But events moved fast, and the diehards were vouchsafed none but the most fleeting enjoyment of success. Before the year was out, not Rome alone but the whole of Italy was faced with a menace of intestine war graver than had been known for two hundred years. The broad and fertile valley of the Liris, the valley which formed one of the two main arteries of communication between Latium and Campania, was the centre of a group of Latin colonies, and of these colonies none was more famous than Fregellae. Fregellae was a large and prosperous town, with an unbroken record of fidelity to Rome: indeed, in the crisis of 209 B.C., Fregellae had been the leader of those colonies which remained loyal[1]. But now, when the failure of Flaccus became known, Fregellae rose in what was regarded as revolt, and the complacent opponents of generosity to the allies suddenly discovered that Rome's Italian hegemony was in danger of collapse.

The peril was plain. If one Latin city—and one of unrivalled loyalty—was impelled by its grievances to take up arms, there was every danger that the rest of the Latin Name would follow: and if the Latins rebelled, ingenuity would be taxed to find a reason why the Italians should refrain. Rome, in fact, was threatened with a Social War—and in 125 B.C. the threat was graver than it could be in 91. By her treatment of Fregellae Rome gained a respite of more than thirty years, and these years she used to advantage. In the Gracchan age it could not be claimed that Roman troops, man for man, were better than those of the allies: but the Marian reform in legionary recruitment, though it still left Rome without anything that can properly be called a standing army, did in fact give her legions composed of soldiers who were something like professionals. In the Social War, when finally it broke out, Rome could put troops in the field with a training probably higher than that still to be found among the bulk of the Italian levies, and this superior efficiency can scarcely have been without bearing in the issue. But when Fregellae threatened trouble, Rome's military position made it imperative to prevent the rot from spreading: and this was done. Fortune, indeed, was kind. If a large part of the Roman army had been entangled in a protracted siege, the opportunity might have been too tempting for other disaffected peoples to resist: indeed, there is just a hint that, even as things were, Asculum took up arms[2]. But timely treachery delivered Fregellae into the hands of Rome, and Rome stood free to face such others as might challenge her control. That by itself was a sobering fact: but, still further to discourage impetuous emulation, the results of failure were displayed. Taking its courage in both hands—for the effects of such a policy can hardly have been clear—the government imposed an ostentatious penalty. Though its inhabitants were spared, Fregellae was destroyed, and next year the colony of Fabrateria was founded to efface its memory and to take its place.

Severity had paid: no other allied city moved: and for the moment Rome could survey her confederacy intact. But the protest was not in vain; for the end of Fregellae marked the beginning of a new phase in Roman history. Hitherto the con-

---

[1] The doubts which have been cast on this incident (see B. Niese, *Grundriss etc.*[5] p. 129, n. 2) are gratuitous.   [2] *de viris ill.* 65, 2.

servative aristocracy and the selfish rabble of the city might scoff
at suggestions of a need for juster treatment of the allies: now
their eyes were open, and, though anger might find vent in prosecutions against men alleged to have aided and abetted the rebels,
none but the blind could fail to see that there was an urgent problem to be faced and one which brooked no trifling. Beyond all
doubt the grievances of the allies had become the foremost question of the day. Such were the circumstances in which, towards
the middle of 124, Gaius Gracchus was first elected tribune.

IV. THE CHRONOLOGY OF THE LEGISLATION

Gaius entered office on 10 December 124, and forthwith there
began two years of political activity which in significance for the
future—as well as in the difficulty of the problems they present—
are unique in the story of the Roman Republic. The difficulties
are due, above all, to the lack of any first-class authority. Of those
which have survived, Appian is perhaps the most valuable, though
his account of Gaius Gracchus lacks the outstanding merits of his
chapters on Tiberius. But, even so, Appian is a slender reed to
lean on: the first book of the *Civil Wars* is, at most, the briefest
sketch of the period with which it deals, designed to serve as an
introduction to what follows, and nothing more. Velleius frankly
makes no attempt at an ordered account of these two years. It is
Plutarch who gives the fullest version, and on Plutarch it is often
necessary to rely. Among his sources may be discerned one which
Appian ignored, and this source is by no means of the best.
A statement cannot, indeed, be rejected merely because it rests on
the authority of Plutarch alone; but doubts about its value must
exist, and the result is to make any reconstruction of the tribunates of Gaius largely hypothetical. Too often the basis must
be an assumption that what Plutarch says is true. It remains to
mention our most grievous loss, the loss of Livy's sixtieth book—
of which nothing of value but the *Epitome* survives. The brief
accounts of Appian, Velleius and the Epitomator naturally concentrate on the small achievements of these years: the full text of Livy
would have revealed the greater aspirations. It is our inability,
with any kind of confidence, to set the measures actually passed in
the context of the whole programme of which they formed a part
that too often makes the history of Gaius Gracchus a matter of
mere speculation.

Any account of Gaius' tribunates must begin with some consideration of the order in which his measures were produced: for,

in such a case as this, chronology gives some of the most useful clues to the nature of the programme as a whole. Here, unfortunately, the contemporary evidence of his speeches, fragments of which are freely preserved, fails to do more than reveal that several measures were proposed together: this much may be inferred from the existence of an oration 'de legibus promulgatis'. At the outset the general situation must be recalled. The events of the last twelve months, and above all the rebellion at Fregellae, had made the question of Rome's relations with her allies in Italy a matter of such burning urgency that beyond all dispute it was the paramount problem of the day. Even if the authorities were less lucid than they are, it would still be possible to say with some assurance that no statesman in office in 123 B.C. can have failed to make it, if not his only aim, at least one of the chief objects of his endeavour to satisfy the just claims of the Latins and Italians. And in the case of Gaius Gracchus this conjecture is confirmed. Plutarch, at least, is clear, not only that the culmination of his activity as tribune came in a struggle over a bill designed to meet the allied demands, but—what is more—that it was in the interests of this reform that Gaius risked, and lost, all his hard-won influence[1]. This was, of course, only one of many tasks to which he set his hand, but there is sufficient evidence to show that it was among the nearest to his heart. Though it would be an exaggeration to say that a solution of the Italian problem was an end to which all the other measures of Gaius Gracchus were, in one way or another, the means, there can be no doubt that his proposals about the allies were the dominating feature of his designs.

Such is the first consideration; and with these proposals, too, the second is concerned. Sometime in the winter of 123–2, soon after the beginning of Gaius' second year of office, the leadership of the opposition was assumed by another tribune, M. Livius Drusus. Drusus set himself to destroy the Gracchan majority in the Concilium Plebis, and to this end he countered several of the most serious proposals made by Gaius with others which were framed to appeal more strongly to the vulgar taste. Now, when Plutarch includes among these counter-measures one which secured to the Latins immunity from flogging even on active service, he gives an invaluable clue to the history of the Gracchan programme. Drusus was not unfolding any original policy of his own: he was merely hanging on the heels of his rival and trying to cap each move that Gaius made with another which, though tending in the

---

[1] *Gracchi*, 33.

same direction, might win a larger meed of popular support. Thus Plutarch is wholly plausible when he says that Gracchus had already broached the question of the Latins before Drusus produced his alternative plan for its solution.

But there is more than this. The literary evidence for the Italian policy of Gracchus falls naturally into two classes. On the one hand Velleius[1] is definite that he offered the citizenship to all Italians, and with this testimony goes a passage in Plutarch[2]. On the other hand Appian[3], possibly supported by Plutarch elsewhere[4], suggests a bill which affected the Latins alone, and it is this suggestion which the action of Livius Drusus confirms. There is no reason to deny that Italians and Latins had come to Rome in numbers to air their grievances; but they were not the people whose favour Drusus tried to win. The objects of his blandishment were the citizens of Rome, whose votes it was his business to detach from Gaius Gracchus; and it was for Roman citizens alone that Drusus' bait was laid. About the nature of the bait itself there is no dispute: it was his proposal to protect Latins from scourging by Roman officers. Nor need there be any less certainty about the form of its appeal. One of the features which appears most regularly in Roman history of the second century B.C. is the reluctance of Roman citizens to share their privileges with others: only two years before it had been seen in the consulship of Flaccus. If that be remembered, the reasoning of Drusus is clear. Beyond all doubt his contention was simply this—that his own proposal was enough to deal with the issue at stake, and that there was no need for the Roman voters to go to such lengths of distasteful generosity as those to which Gaius Gracchus was inviting them. Gracchus, as has been seen, had already adumbrated a change in the status of the Latins: apparently he had advocated their enfranchisement outright. Drusus replied that such a concession was uncalled for: the Latins would be satisfied with a final guarantee against corporal punishment.

So much is familiar; but the argument may be carried further[5]. The action of Drusus implies, indeed, that Gracchus had already raised the question of the Latins; but it implies with almost equal force that Gracchus had not yet raised the question of the Italians in general. As a counterblast to an offer of the Roman *civitas* to the

[1] II, 6, 2. [2] *Gracchi*, 26, 1.
[3] *Bell. Civ.* I, 23, 99.
[4] *Gracchi*, 29, 2. It is impossible to say whether Plutarch is here referring exclusively to the recruitment of the Gracchan colonists or not.
[5] On this see W. Warde Fowler in *Eng. Hist. Rev.* xx, 1905, p. 424.

Latin Name, the suggestion ascribed to Drusus is intelligible: but it would become meaningless, or nearly so, if Gracchus at this stage had formulated his plan for dealing with the Italians as well. To meet a scheme which included in its scope the whole non-Roman population of Italy, so far as it was free, with a paltry proposal which envisaged a concession to the Latins and did nothing for the Italians at all would have been absurd. Our evidence is admittedly inadequate; but, so far as it goes, it points straight to the conclusion that, when Drusus intervened, Gaius had still to reveal his intentions about the Italians at large. Thus confirmation is forthcoming for the suggestion of our authorities that in the history of Gaius' policy for dealing with the allies of Rome two phases are to be distinguished. In the first, which falls before the campaign of Drusus, his attention was confined to the Latins alone: in the second, which cannot be placed long before the elections in the summer of 122, his net was cast wider, to cover Latins and Italians alike.

The troubles of the allies are not the only subject on which the Gracchan policy shows a visible development: two distinct measures can be detected again in the evidence for his dealings with the *quaestio repetundarum*. According to the Epitomator of Livy, Gaius Gracchus intended to leave the juries as he found them: they were still to be composed of senators, and the only change he would have introduced was an increase in the numbers of the Senate from three hundred to nine, by the addition of six hundred recruits from the richest class outside the senatorial order. Plutarch's story is the same in all respects save one—that it reduces the new senators from six hundred to three. But against Plutarch and the Epitomator there stands a solid mass of evidence for the view that what Gaius did, so far from being merely to enlarge the Senate, was to deprive senators of their right to sit on juries altogether; and this view is confirmed by the contemporary testimony of the *repetundae* law still in part preserved. There can be no serious doubt that this was the final outcome of Gaius' attempt to improve the administration of criminal justice, but the significance of the variant account given by the Livian *Epitome* and Plutarch is less clear. One fact, however, is beyond dispute: the emphatic repetitions of the Epitomator make it plain that he was surprised at the statements of the text before him. Surprise provokes attention, and in such a case it is impossible to suppose that the abbreviator failed to understand his original. Thus, whether Livy be right or wrong, there is a strong presumption that his authority is behind this story of

additions to the Senate, and it is also to be observed that
Plutarch shows a version which in essentials is the same. Yet, even
so, there remains the possibility that Livy was mistaken. A possibility it is; but Livy on the second century is not Livy on the
fifth, and it is wholly improbable either that he himself confused
Gaius Gracchus with the younger Livius Drusus or that he blindly
followed a source which fell into so gross an error.

On its merits alone, the tale should be accepted, even though it
may record no more than a tentative suggestion which Gaius threw
out; but there are also other considerations on its side. When Appian
asserts that it was the prevalence of corruption which turned the
attention of Gaius to the *iudicia*, his assertion gains credence from
the fact that bribery in court was a subject on which Gracchus
passed a law. His proposals, in fact, were not aimed at party ends
alone: the juries were not above reproach, and he tackled their
constitution because they stood in need of serious reform. Now
such an undertaking, of undoubted value and limited extent, belongs to a type with which Gaius seems to have opened his legislative career: its appropriate place is in 123 B.C. But 123 was a
year during a large part of which, if Plutarch is to be believed[1],
Gracchus showed himself so moderate that even the Senate did not
openly oppose him: indeed we gather that the earliest sign of open
hostility was seen in the advent of Livius Drusus. It cannot, however, be supposed that the comparatively good relations between
Gracchus and the Senate survived a proposal to expel senators
from the juries neck and crop; and consequently it may be
inferred that, if, as is probable, some plan to improve the administration of justice was promulgated before Drusus arose, it must
have been mild in character, like that which Livy and Plutarch
record.

By itself, perhaps, such an argument in favour of an earlier
scheme, which finally gave place to one of a more drastic kind,
might justly be set aside as the merest speculation; but it finds
powerful support from another direction. Among the measures
of Gaius Gracchus whose existence allows no dispute was one
which made the bribery of jurors a criminal offence, and this law,
as Cicero explicitly records[2], was remarkable for a great peculiarity
—that it did not apply to courts constituted under the famous
Gracchan *lex iudiciaria*. The origin of this anomaly has been
variously explained. Some have found it possible to believe that
Gracchus was concerned for the rectitude of special courts which
the Senate, with or without the concurrence of the People, might

---

[1] *Gracchi*, 27, 1.   [2] *pro Cluentio*, 56, 154.

form from time to time, and that he purposely refrained from including the permanent *iudicium* for the trial of charges of extortion within the scope of his law. But that the jurors serving in what was now the most stable element in the whole administration of criminal justice should have been deliberately exempted from penalties for corruption is a supposition which only the strongest evidence would commend; and, when we recall that it was the corruption of this very court which is said to have moved Gracchus to action, it seems far more probable that the true explanation lies elsewhere. Until Gaius Gracchus decided to draw jurors from another source, jury-service in these cases had been confined to members of the Senate, and it is by far the most plausible assumption that he drafted a law against bribery in a form affecting none but senatorial jurors at a time when he had not yet envisaged the idea of recruiting juries from another source. The law against bribery and the proposal to augment the numbers of the Senate belong to one phase in his career, when he was still content with the existing constitution of juries: the final *lex iudiciaria* marks a later stage, when his tolerance of senators had passed.

So much is enough to provide a chronological framework for the legislation of Gaius Gracchus. Two of the most serious problems which he essayed to solve were those of the relations between Rome and her allies and of the judicial system in one of its main departments, and in both connections his proposals are two. Each pair consists of one measure which is mild and of another more drastic, and in each case the more modest scheme comes first. In the light of these considerations it is easy to see that Gaius' tribunician career is itself to be divided into periods, in the first of which his attitude was far less radical than in the second. Where the division should be placed the evidence is too vague to show with any great precision; but in the surviving records it is the intervention of Livius Drusus which marks its coming, and this is probably to be put either at the very end of 123 or in the first weeks of 122 B.C. In a case where stricter accuracy is impossible, 123 may be regarded as the year of Gracchus' moderation and 122 as that of his more violent reforms. To 123 belong his schemes to enfranchise the Latins and to strengthen the juries by adding new members to the Senate, to 122 his more sweeping plan to deal with Latins and Italians together and his famous law which took the juries out of senatorial hands and gave them over to another order in the State.

To a proper understanding of Gaius Gracchus' tribunician career the main essential is an appreciation of the development which his outlook underwent after he had taken office. He began as a statesman, anxious to effect necessary reforms with the smallest amount of friction. For a time he succeeded: but at length his opponents declared open war through the mouth of Livius Drusus, and from that moment Gracchus was driven to the less pleasing methods of the party politician. Such is the tale in outline: the details must now be added.

V. THE INITIAL MEASURES: THE *LEX FRUMENTARIA*

The most urgent necessities of the moment found a response in the personal interests of Gaius Gracchus: the outstanding need was for a settlement of the Italian problem, and Gaius' sympathy with the allies was already so notorious in 124 that he was included among those who were haled before a court to answer the charge of aiding Fregellae in her revolt. But, though we may believe that from the start his supreme ambition was to remove the causes of that ill-will which was jeopardizing the relations of Rome with her confederacy, this was not the subject of his earliest bills. Such information on the order of events as has survived is unanimous in assigning to the first months of office a varied assortment of measures, intended perhaps in different degrees to prepare the way for greater undertakings to come. At the outset there are two proposals, marked off from the rest and connected with one another by their undoubted reference to single incidents in the recent past. In the agitating tribunate of Tiberius nothing had raised wider issues or more furious disputes than the deposition of Octavius by popular vote. The principle that the People might remove a tribune who thwarted the People's will was a principle by which Gaius, steeped like his brother in the political doctrines of Greece, seems to have set great store. Somehow, if the Gracchan ideal of the tribunate as the mouthpiece and executive of the People was to be attained, the principle must be set up: the question was—how? Boldly to proclaim it would be to invite the criticism that a new and alien element was being grafted on the Roman constitution: a better way was to assume its presence from the start—a pedantic assumption, it is true, though one for which plausible arguments could be produced. Accordingly, Gaius gave notice of a measure to debar from further office any magistrate or tribune of the *plebs* whom the People had deposed. Unquestionably it was inspired by the case of Octavius, but there is no reason to suppose that personal animosity was the motive. Gaius was aiming far higher than at any individual: he was threatening the oligarchs' ancient practice of using the tribunate to block reform. It was a bold gambit for a young man new to power, perhaps too bold. Cornelia disapproved, and the bill was withdrawn: but a proposal at once so subtle and so drastic served at least to show that an able man had arisen whose views of reform stretched far[1].

The second measure was less extreme and for that reason met a better fate. On occasions when the Senate had successfully overcome a movement of some danger to its own interests or to the safety of the State it had been in the habit of establishing a special court to try the alleged offenders. A magistrate was appointed to take charge of the proceedings; he chose his *consilium*; and thus was formed a tribunal which might pass, if not execute, any sentence known to the law. Such had been the body which wreaked almost indiscriminate vengeance on the supporters of Tiberius (see above, p. 36 *sq.*) and such was the body which dealt with the friends of Fregellae—among them, possibly, with Gaius Gracchus himself. In the last resort the action of courts like these derived its validity from the power of *coercitio* latent in the *imperium* of the presiding magistrate; and that power was one which, in its inappellable form, it was the express purpose of the *leges de provocatione* to confine to cases of less than capital degree. If a court established by the Senate denied the right of appeal from its judgments in cases even of the gravest kind, the claim could not be sustained: the limitations which beset a magistrate's *imperium* when he was acting on his own initiative remained in law unchanged when he acted at the Senate's instigation. That was the fact which Gracchus now proposed to set beyond dispute. The extent and details of his measure are obscure. That judicial bodies erected by the Senate were the main object of his concern, whether he also reasserted the right of *provocatio* in general terms or not, is suggested by the words of Cicero[2] and proved by the immediate sequel. Just as M. Octavius had been recognized as the target of the proposal to disqualify from further office those who had once been deposed, so now Popillius Laenas saw the first intended victim in himself. As consul in 132, Popillius had sat on the bench before which the associates of Tiberius Gracchus were arraigned, and now he was chosen as the scapegoat whose sacrifice was to

---

[1] The authenticity of the quotations purporting to come from the letters of Cornelia is so dubious that the fragments cannot safely be used as evidence for such minor problems as they affect. A convenient bibliography of the subject is to be found in *Hermes* LVI, 1921, p. 273 n. (E. von Stern), to which should now be added H. Malcovati in *Athenaeum*, 1920, p. 92 and J. H. Thiel in *Mnem.* LVII, 1929, p. 347.   [2] *pro Rab. perd. reo*, 4, 12.

atone for outrage done to the rights of Roman citizens. Gaius himself was foremost in the prosecution, and Popillius was driven into exile, accompanied, perhaps, though this is doubtful, by the worthy Rupilius whose misfortune it had been to find Popillius his colleague in the consulship. The reformers had scored a point, and Gracchus had established his contention that none but the People could alienate the People's right to the final word when the *caput* of a Roman citizen was at stake[1].

Such were the measures which political prudence demanded as a reply to the Senate's behaviour in the past. If one was withdrawn, the other was passed: and even the former had served a useful purpose by proclaiming the doctrine that a magistrate might be deposed—a doctrine which was not rejected, because no vote was taken on the bill. Next come the schemes which looked rather to the future—schemes for progress and reform, which are the true contribution of Gaius Gracchus to the history of Rome. Among the first of these we have the authority of Appian for placing the famous *lex frumentaria*—a law which, because it has usually been misunderstood, has done more damage to its author's reputation than all his other measures combined. He has been accused of bribing the voters, of corrupting the poor by the promise of partial maintenance at the public expense, and even of stultifying himself by spoiling the markets in which his smallholders would have to sell their corn and by offering with one hand new temptations to a life of idleness in the city while in the other he held out land-allotments and colonies to attract the unemployed to a life of industry elsewhere. But such charges are wide of the mark. Since the great famine which began in 329 B.C. the cities of the Hellenistic world had recognized more and more widely that it was the business of a government to see that the food-supply of the community was both adequate and cheap: indeed, some of the smaller states had gone so far as to make arrangements whereby the food of the poorer citizens, in one way or another, was supplied free[2]. To lengths so extreme as this Gaius Gracchus was not prepared to go; but the view that the feeding of the people is a matter for the State he adopted without reserve. And there was need. Except in the stress of the Second Punic War, Rome

---

[1] The procedure against Popillius also suggests that Gracchus carried the constitutional development a stage farther by entrusting the sanctions of this law to the Concilium Plebis instead of to the Comitia Centuriata. See A. H. J. Greenidge, *Legal Procedure of Cicero's Time*, pp. 324 *sqq.*

[2] The evidence for this may be found conveniently collected by W. W. Tarn in his *Hellenistic Civilisation*, ed. 2, p. 99, with notes.

had not lately known a famine; but there is evidence enough to show that the volume of supply had fluctuated so violently as to involve seasonal variations in price of serious dimensions: and at this time the situation was especially acute because Sicily was still suffering from the effects of the Servile War and the African harvest had been gravely damaged by an unprecedented swarm of locusts (see below, p. 73). Strictly contemporary evidence for these fluctuations is lacking, but there are illustrations of the uncertainty of the market in other periods which are not wholly irrelevant to the Gracchan age. Cicero, for instance, records that in Sicily the year 76 B.C. was one of low prices whereas in 75 prices were extremely high[1], and that in 74 wheat, which had been fetching the extraordinary figure of five *denarii* a *modius* before the harvest, became dirt-cheap as soon as the new crop was available[2]. Sudden variation of price was the source of the most serious trouble, and to ensure that throughout the year corn should be on the market in sufficient quantities and at a stable figure was the most laudable of aims. It was this that Gracchus set out to achieve. Though it is not expressly stated by our authorities, there cannot be the slightest doubt that the great granaries which he built beneath the Aventine were an essential part of the scheme. The corn itself might come in part from the provincial *decumae*, but the rest must be bought either under the provincial arrangements for *frumenti emptio* or in the open market; and it was clearly the function of these barns to store corn long enough to allow such purchases as were inevitable to be made when prices were at bottom or near it. The wasteful method of buying for immediate consumption without regard to the state of the market was at an end, and it remained to fix the charge at which the stuff should be sold to the consumer.

The question of the charge is vital: on its relation to the economic cost of the corn thus put upon the market any true judgment of the scheme must depend. The price at which Gaius Gracchus offered his corn for sale was $6\frac{1}{3}$ *asses* a *modius*, a figure which by itself is of interest because it is singularly unlike the round sum of a purely nominal charge. Unfortunately our evidence for the normal cost of corn in the Gracchan age is almost wholly to seek, but it is worth while to notice a relevant passage of Polybius[3]. When he passed through the valley of the Po, probably not more than fifteen years before the tribunates of Gaius Gracchus, Polybius was astounded at the fertility of the country, where a Sicilian *medimnus* of wheat could be bought for four obols, or a

---

[1] II *in Verr.* III, 93, 216.   [2] *Ib.* 92, 214–5.   [3] II, 15, 1.

Roman *modius* for 1⅓ *asses*: and barley fetched only half this price. Thus the charge on which Gracchus decided for the sale of wheat in Rome was between four and five times as high as its cost in the open markets of Cisalpine Gaul when Polybius was there. Though the soil of the Lombard Plain was exceptional and though Polybius admittedly saw it in a bumper year, the figures he gives may perhaps be taken to suggest that the Gracchan charge in Rome was not wholly ludicrous. Doubtless it was far below the prices which had generally prevailed when the market was uncontrolled, but it was perhaps not lower than the price at which, with the help of judicious buying on a large scale when grain was most freely to be had, the State might hope to sell without serious loss to itself. Such a suggestion is confirmed by Cicero's remark[1] that the speeches of Gracchus read like those of a champion of the Treasury, though it is to be observed that Gaius seems to have made some effort to raise new revenue by extending the system of *portoria*[2]; and even so the needs of the corn-supply were found to be a drain on the exchequer (see below, p. 95).

Whatever the relation in which this price may have stood to the prices prevailing before, the project was not one which can justly be called a dole. The work of Gaius was open to none of the damning criticisms which may be brought against the demagogic abuses grafted on to it, possibly by Saturninus (p. 165 *sq.* below) and certainly by Clodius (p. 524 below). Gracchus did not give away something for nothing, and it is plain that the penniless could no more pay 6⅓ *asses* for a *modius* of wheat than they could pay whatever wheat had cost in the days before control. The *lex frumentaria* did little, if anything, to keep in Rome those whom it was the object of other laws to settle in colonies or on the land. Nor did it affect the livelihood of the small-holders set up by his brother and himself. It has been seen already (p. 4) that it was not on such as these that the city of Rome depended for its food. Difficulties of transport by land compelled men scattered up and down the peninsula to sell in the nearest town so much of their crops as they did not need themselves. Generally the surplus could not be sent to Rome, and it is a gratuitous assumption that the road-building which Gracchus undertook[3] was meant to ease the carriage of corn from the country districts to Rome. There is no reason to suppose that this was more than one of many means to the temporary relief of unemployment, or to deny that its permanent value was to be

[1] *Tusc. Disp.* III, 20, 48.
[2] Vell. Pat. II, 6, 3; Gellius, *N.A.* XI, 10, 3.
[3] Plutarch, *Gracchi*, 27, 2; Appian, *Bell. Civ.* I, 23, 98.

found in the improvement of local communications rather than those of the rest of Italy with Rome[1].

About the arrangements in their details our evidence is almost wholly silent. We do not know what limit, if any, was set to the amount of corn which any individual might buy at the Gracchan price, nor is it certain that it was sold to any citizen who applied and not merely to the poor. The fact that the institution was not a dole makes it probable that all citizens were served alike, and the probability is strengthened by other considerations. If the privilege had been confined to a section of the people, it is unlikely that the machinery for drawing up the lists of authorized recipients would still have needed, eighty years later, the elementary attention which it received from Julius Caesar[2]. Again, if such had been the case, there would be little point in a tale which Cicero tells[3]: L. Piso—annalist, author of Lex Calpurnia repetundarum, consul in 133 B.C. and staunch opponent of Gaius Gracchus—attained some notoriety by presenting himself when corn was being sold and demanding his rightful share.

Livy and Appian, our only authorities for the order of the Gracchan laws, agree that the *lex frumentaria* belongs to the first year of office. All the rest are put into the second by Appian, and by Livy—with the exception of the colonial schemes—into the first. To reconcile these divergent views, though with evidence so scanty conjecture can be plausible at best, no attempt is more attractive than that which assumes that Appian has mistaken the election of Gracchus to a second tribunate for his entry on a second year of office: he has confused some month about July in 123 with the following December[4]. If that assumption be right, much at any rate of what Appian assigns to the second year belongs to the latter half of the first; and it has often been observed with justice that no time is more appropriate to the intensest political activity of Gaius Gracchus than the period immediately after his re-election, when his position was assured for eighteen months to come. Thus, though it would be rash to assert that none of the measures next to be discussed was passed before the tribunician elections of 123, since they can be treated best together, their most fitting place for notice is after the election itself.

---

[1] For a suggestion that Tiberius Gracchus had laid the foundations of an Italian postal service see A. M. Ramsay, in *J.R.S.* x, 1920, p. 84 *sq.*

[2] See Bruns, *Fontes*[7], 18, ll. 1 *sqq.*

[3] *Tusc. Disp.* III, 20, 48.

[4] See Ed. Meyer, *Kleine Schriften*, I[2], p. 394, n. 3.

VI. THE RE-ELECTION OF GAIUS GRACCHUS

The circumstances in which Gracchus became tribune for a second time are something of a puzzle. It was in seeking to secure a second term that Tiberius, ten years before, had provoked the final crisis in his career: he had been lynched in making an attempt which his brother Gaius now repeated with safety and success. In 131 B.C. Carbo had essayed to declare legal the continued tenure of the tribunate; but the influence of Scipio Aemilianus had been lent to his more extreme opponents and Carbo had failed[1]. Then, in 123, Gaius Gracchus was made tribune for the following year, and nothing is heard of resistance or complaint. It is natural to assume that since 131, though his fame has perished from the records, some more fortunate successor had carried the project of Carbo into law; and this, indeed, is what Appian would have us understand. But that his story is more than mere assumption it is difficult to say. He purports to give some details of the measures whereby re-election was authorized, but, as they stand, his words are almost meaningless. They allege that by this supposed enactment the People might choose one of the existing board to hold office again in the following year if at the elections there were fewer candidates than places to be filled—a story which is most unsatisfactory. However suave his manner may have been, there must have been some people in Rome prepared to take the simple steps required to have done with Gracchus; and if this version were correct, to end his tribunician career forthwith it would have been enough for them to see that ten plebeians, it mattered not who, stood for the tribunates of 122. With the various proposals that have been made to emend the words of Appian this is no place to deal; for there is some reason to believe that no such law was passed. Sallust, in a passage which bears closely on the present issue, records that in 110 public business in Rome suffered long and serious delays from the wranglings which were started when two of the tribunes, P. Lucullus and L. Annius, tried to secure office for a second year[2]. It is not easy to believe that disputes so protracted as these could have occurred if the subject was one on which legislation had been passed less than twenty years before. Appian may be obscure; but the law itself, had it existed, must have been capable of interpretation in less than the months that were spent in argument. Though confidence on such a point is impossible, it is by no means unlikely that no measure on this subject had been passed so recently as the Gracchan age.

---

[1] See above, p. 38 *sq.*　　　　　　　　[2] *Bell. Jug.* 37, 2.

It was custom, not law, which stood in the way of a tribune seeking to remain in office (see above, p. 33 *sq.*); and when convention is the obstacle prestige is the strength of an attack. Gaius Gracchus, a man whose personal influence was far greater than his brother's, may well have succeeded where his brother failed; and it is possible, though by no means certain, that Appian's story of a law which authorized this re-election is a mere inference made by some historian who failed to understand that custom was the barrier and that Gaius had authority enough to break it down. Whatever the truth may be, the renewal was secured, and when the elections were over Gracchus could count on something like eighteen months of office in which to carry the more serious of his reforms. Circumstances now seemed favourable. Fulvius Flaccus was on the new board of tribunes, and even in the consulship there was an ally. Of the consuls of 123 one at least, Q. Metellus Balearicus, son of the censor of 131, was no friend of progress, nor is it known that his colleague, T. Flamininus, did anything to help the Gracchan cause. But at the elections for 122, when some suggested that Gaius had ideas of the consulship for himself, he suddenly began to canvass for Gaius Fannius, a Whig of the Scipionic type; and Fannius was duly elected. In the end he proved a broken reed; but at the start he doubtless seemed a staff to lean on.

VII. THE MINOR REFORMS

The measures which compose the main body of the Gracchan programme fall naturally into three rough groups. There are those which continued the work of Tiberius in providing for the surplus population, those which dealt with the administration of justice, and finally the proposals made to solve the central problem of the day—the problem of Rome's relations to the rest of Italy. But, besides these, there are a few enactments which stand in isolation: though they lack neither interest nor value, they show no obvious connection with one another or with the rest, and they may conveniently be dismissed at once. One was an army-law, which forbade the enlistment of youths below a certain age[1] and laid upon the State the burden of supplying the clothing of the troops.

---

[1] The age seems to have been seventeen (Plutarch, *Gracchi*, 26, 1). The statement of Diodorus (xxxiv–v, 25, 1) that Gaius Gracchus relaxed the discipline of the army is too vague by itself to be of value, and certainly it does not authorize the conclusion that the *lex militaris* gave citizens on active service the right of *provocatio* against capital sentences passed by their commanders. This protection had been granted already, probably by one

However desirable, the reform by itself was small; but it deserves notice as the herald of a more drastic change to come. By the centuriate system legionary service was normally confined to citizens of substance, able to equip themselves when they were called to arms, and no use was made of the humblest class which could best be spared from civil life. Nevertheless, in course of time the minimum assessment required to make men eligible for the army had gradually been lowered until now there were legion-aries so poor that they could neither find their own equipment nor afford the stoppage from their meagre pay made when it was provided by the State. The day was at hand when Marius would enrol the *proletarii* without disguise.

Next may come a pair of bills concerned with provincial ad-ministration. By a long-standing custom, after consuls had been elected by the People, the Senate chose provinces which they should govern when the time came for them to take command abroad. This practice was one which accorded ill with the doctrines of democracy. That the Senate had regularly abused its power of patronage cannot be alleged: the empire itself was sufficient re-futation of such a charge. But the privilege was still objectionable, especially in times when party-feeling ran high; for by this arrangement the Senate was enabled to adjust a consul's rewards to his service towards itself. Loyal oligarchs received the plums of empire, whereas a radical might find himself condemned to a thank-less term of exile in Sardinia or the like. But, though temptation was there, we cannot point to a specific case in which the Senate's action was such as to call for immediate reform: more probably it was because he regarded the prevailing custom as 'pessimi exempli nec sui saeculi' that Gracchus intervened. By the Lex Sempronia de provinciis consularibus, while the Senate was left with its right to assign the provinces—a provision quite in harmony with the moderate tone which Gracchus adopted at this stage of his career, it was ordained that the Senate should come to its decision before the consuls were elected, and not after. The change involved was great. Hitherto the Senate had assigned provinces to consuls already elected: now the People were to elect consuls to provinces already assigned. Yet, however necessary it may have been to satisfy the purism of the democratic doctrinaires, the change was

of the Leges Porciae. In any case the proposal of Livius Drusus, if it extended *provocatio* to Latins even when serving, as Plutarch asserts, implies that Roman citizens had the same privilege, and this is also to be deduced from Bruns, *Fontes*[7], 10, l. 78. It is inconceivable that Latins should have been put in a better position than *cives*.

not one to move the applause which belongs to true reform. The incompetence and venality of the many were preferred to the possible dishonesty of the few: in the light of events during the next eighty years it is difficult to say which was the graver peril. One fact alone need be added. There is a passage of Cicero[1] which seems to show that a clause was included in this law to render the Senate's allocations immune from tribunician veto—a notable recognition by the most famous tribune in Roman history of the misuse to which his office might be put. The misuse itself is familiar enough: but here it is revealed that Gaius did not trust the threat of legal deposition to keep tribunes faithful to the cause they were conceived to represent[2].

The second enactment on imperial administration concerned the affairs of a specific region—the troublesome province of Asia. In spite of the Lex Aquilia (see below, p. 106), the bequest of Attalus III still supplied enough to occupy the attentions of Roman statesmen in such time as they could spare from the calls of domestic legislation. The fate of those outlying districts which were not worth the trouble of annexation was still a subject of almost continual intrigue; but even the province itself had yet to be reorganized as a unity for the purpose of taxation. The significance of the arrangements made by the Lex Sempronia de provincia Asia, so far as it deserves a place in the history of provincial government, will be discussed elsewhere (see below, pp. 467 sqq.); but this measure has so close a bearing on the political position in Rome itself that it cannot be left unnoticed in the present place.

The system whereby the direct taxes were assessed as a fixed fraction of the annual produce was one well suited to the economy of the ancient world: when the main source of revenue was the soil, nothing could be more equitable than that the State should share with the tax-payer in the ups-and-downs of seasonal vicissitudes. But the system had its defects, of which the most serious was its complication. The labour involved in settling the amount due from individual land-owners called for a staff of some dimensions, and such a staff it was beyond the power of the government to provide. The Romans were still amateurs in empire: the days

---

[1] de prov. cons. 7, 17; cf. Bruns, Fontes⁷, 10, l. 70 sq.

[2] The tale, preserved in the second of the two Suasoriae ascribed to Sallust (ad Caes. II, 8, 1–2), that Gaius attempted some reform in the Comitia Centuriata may be ignored. The author, a rhetorician probably of the second century A.D. (see C.Q. XVII, 1923, pp. 94 sqq.), has no clear idea of what he is trying to describe (ib. p. 98), and even he does not assert that this proposal ever became law.

of bureaucracy were still remote, and such a civil service as they could boast was as yet the merest embryo. When Gaius Gracchus decided that Asia should pay Rome an annual tithe, he solved the problem of collection by a device which had long been familiar: the State was to shuffle off its duties on to other shoulders, and private contractors were to be invoked to supply the necessary labour. Contractors had been freely employed in the past. It was they who worked the mines and other such productive properties of the State; it was they who collected the customs-dues and so made good the lack of a public customs-service; and it was they who undertook both the building and the maintenance of what we should call public works. Even in the tax-collection in Sicily they had a part to play; but the smallness of the tax-areas into which Sicily was split meant that there the local financiers could compete with any rivals from Rome. Now, however, the direct taxes of Asia as a whole were to be put up for auction at Rome: the State would take the highest bid in lieu of the revenue and the bidder would then be authorized to recoup himself by collecting the taxes throughout the province. These contractors might at least be expected to employ an adequate staff: efficiency thereby would be increased: and the State might hope to benefit by an augmentation of the revenue which appears to have been one of the aims which Gracchus had in mind.

But such operations required capital: they could only be undertaken by companies of wealthy men: and these men, though generally not members of the Senate, were people in ability and education scarcely inferior to the senators themselves. Already the influence of these financiers had been felt in the political world: new provinces meant new opportunities for the investment of their capital, and the policy of the Senate in the East, and particularly in Macedonia, had not been all that they desired. But, though their need for fresh regions to exploit had conflicted with the Senate's dislike of fresh provinces to govern, there is no evidence to show that senators and financiers were open enemies in 123 B.C. So far as can be seen, it was the Gracchan *lex iudiciaria* which first set the orders in bitter opposition, and until that measure was mooted, if not passed, they were divided perhaps on questions of imperial policy but by no means the deadly foes which, in spite of Cicero's endeavours, they remained thereafter till the fall of the Republic. Unfortunately we are in the dark about the precise date at which the Asiatic system was set up. It may have belonged to the second period of Gracchus' career, when he was reckless of offence to the Senate and anxious to strengthen the ties which bound him to his latest friends. But if, as is equally possible, it was passed in 123, it need not have been a blow in the Senate's face. Admittedly their rights in Asia soon became the most profitable privilege of the monied men in Rome, but it was a privilege which, before the judiciary reform drove a wedge between the orders, the Senate need not necessarily have grudged. It had no great quarrel with the financiers; they were useful servants of the Senate; and it is hard to see any possible arrangement which would have diverted the pickings from the Asiatic tithe into senatorial pockets. Moreover, neither the Senate nor Gracchus himself had any evidence to show the extent of the abuses to which the system would give rise. The method of assessment was, in theory, fair: the mode of collection was indicated by existing practice, and no obvious alternative was available. And so it remains possible that in the *lex de provincia Asia* is to be seen a well-intentioned effort to set up a fiscal machine which would ensure to Rome her due without involving the formation of a provincial civil service. Undoubtedly the best agents of the government would have been a force of officials paid and controlled by the State: but for this the time was not ripe, and it is idle to blame Gracchus for failing to anticipate the bureaucracy of the Principate.

VIII. LAND ALLOTMENTS AND COLONIES

Next come the measures devised to deal with the central subjects of the programme, and of these we may begin with the pair which have their origin in the work of Tiberius. The *lex frumentaria*, which bulks large in the social legislation of Gaius, has been discussed already, but this legislation included at least two other bills—both of them devised, in the spirit of 133 B.C., to find work for the workless. One was a *lex agraria*, of which our knowledge is lamentably vague. From the extant law of 111 B.C., where it is mentioned as the complete expression of the Gracchan policy, we may infer that, far from merely adding supplementary provisions to the Lex Sempronia of Tiberius, it covered the whole subject and superseded the earlier enactment. But the need for this new proposal is not easy to divine. It is impossible to accept the view that a continuation of the land allotments was the main aim of Gaius Gracchus and that his proposals for the enfranchisement of the allies were no more than a means of reconciling the Italians to the resumption of land now in their occupation. After the revolt of Fregellae no sane statesman could fail to see that the

Italian problem was a pressing issue in its own right, which could not be treated as subordinate to the economic difficulties of Rome. Nevertheless, if the allied communities accepted the Roman *civitas*, they would fall under Roman law, and all the *ager publicus* they held would be exposed to the effects of the agrarian legislation. Against this contingency the preservation of the commissioners' powers was doubtless to be desired; but the contingency was somewhat remote, and there were perhaps other more immediate reasons for action. Conjecture must depend to some extent on our view of what happened in 129 B.C. (see pp. 42 *sqq.*). If Scipio had induced the People to deprive the *tresviri* of their judicial powers and had thereby brought their operations to a standstill, it would be tempting to believe that Gaius merely carried again his brother's measure in its original form. If, on the other hand, Scipio had only prevailed on the Senate to warn the commissioners off such *ager publicus* as was in allied possession, Gaius may have re-enacted the law in a form which made it clear that no public land was exempt from the authority of the duly appointed agents of the People: and this may well be the truth[1]. It is clear, however, that the *lex agraria* was not the measure on which Gaius Gracchus chiefly relied to carry on his brother's fight against unemployment: indeed we may well believe that in 123 B.C. he found that the original scheme had been brought so near to completion that, of such land as it had set free after the limitations of 129 B.C., none but a trifling amount still remained for distribution. But, if the expedient of land allotment to individuals was exhausted, Gaius had an alternative device; and there is a possibility that this device was recognized in the *lex agraria* itself. Cicero[2] records that under a Gracchan law some *tresviri*, whether the land-commissioners or others, received power to

---

[1] The statement of Siculus Flaccus (*Corpus Agrimensorum*, ed. Thulin, I[1], p. 100) that Gaius Gracchus 'legem tulit ne quis in Italia amplius quam *ducenta* iugera possideret' might be thought to suggest that he tried to find more land for allotment by cutting down the normal maximum which *possessores* of long standing were allowed to retain from five hundred *iugera* to two. It would not be surprising if the first impulse of Gaius was to press his brother's principles still farther and squeeze even more acres for the poor out of the holdings which the rich had been allowed to keep. But, even if the words of Flaccus do not in fact refer rather to allotments made in the Gracchan colonies (cf. Bruns, *Fontes*[7], 11, l. 60), the silence of the other authorities makes it impossible to believe that the *lex agraria* of Gaius Gracchus, in its final form, contained any provision for a new reduction in the maximum amount of *ager publicus* which sitting *possessores* might retain.

[2] *de lege agr.* II, 12, 31. See J. Carcopino, *Autour des Gracques*, p. 254.

found colonies—a grant which naturally connects itself with the succeeding bill.

Whatever may have been the purpose of his *lex agraria*, it is plain that, in his attempt to carry on the work of Tiberius in providing for the unemployed, the means on which Gaius relied was the establishment of colonies. The foundation of colonies to relieve the pressure of surplus population was a practice sanctioned by custom as old as the fifth century, and, though military considerations had often been involved, the practice had never lost its economic purpose. Now it was to be revived, but with several innovations. Colonies in the past had been predominantly agrarian, founded in the richer corners of Italy where settlers could make a living from the land. With Gaius Gracchus colonies began to take a commercial tone, possibly in order to provide for a section of the unemployed which had so long been out of touch with farming as to be unsuitable for settlement in purely agricultural regions. Though some of the foundations attributed to him were certainly of the older kind, it is impossible to believe that the sites of others were not chosen with an eye to the opportunities they offered for trade. Neptunia, the only Italian colony which Gaius is recorded to have organized, and Scolacium, for which he may have been responsible as well, were both on that southern coast of the peninsula round which ran one of the great trade-routes. Here lay the way between eastern and western basins of the Mediterranean, and here were the sites of Greek cities whose decay was due more to political causes than to any change in the direction of commerce. Scolacium was under the toe of Italy at one of the many points which had been made attractive in earlier days by its convenience for a portage across to the Tyrrhenian Sea: Neptunia stood hard by the city of Tarentum itself, a city whose departed glory it was the mission of the settlers to revive.

In the selection of such sites there was something new, and there was novelty again in the choice of settlers. Undoubtedly the bulk of the recruits came from that pauperized section of the people whose betterment had been the object of the agrarian legislation: but, though many of the colonists must have been destined to work the land in the old familiar way, there seems also to have been some idea of mercantile development, and the hint to this effect which may be found in the choice of sites is confirmed by an unusual feature in the population. Even to dabble in commerce a community must have capital at its call, and it was perhaps to meet this need that Gracchus leavened his settlements with a sprinkling of substantial citizens—to such an extent, indeed, that

Plutarch[1] can allege the colonists as a whole to have been drawn from the most prosperous stratum of society. This is an exaggeration: but that there is some plausibility in the suggestion may perhaps be inferred from the fact that in his later colonial enterprise at Carthage Gracchus seems to have enlisted at least a certain number of recruits with money enough to finance holdings of two hundred *iugera*[2].

Thus in general the scheme was one devised to carry on the work which Tiberius had begun. Its object was still to settle the urban unemployed in places where they might earn their own living for the future, but it differed from the *lex agraria* in one respect. Whereas the recipients of land allotments were all intended to employ themselves in agricultural work, the colonists, at least to some extent, were to develop sites of commercial value. But, however promising the plan, its immediate results were small. Velleius asserts that the colonies at Scolacium and Tarentum were actually founded in 123, but the other sites at which the *Liber Coloniarum* places settlements of Gracchan origin find no mention in other records of Gaius' career. It is possible that they were colonized, under the Lex Sempronia indeed, but after its author's death or at the instigation of Livius Drusus. Junonia, the one remaining foundation in which we know that Gracchus was involved, comes later in the story and must be separately discussed.

IX. THE *QUAESTIO REPETUNDARUM* AND THE ALLIES: THE FIRST PHASE

With the *lex frumentaria* passed and the social programme launched by the promulgation of the *lex agraria* and the *lex de coloniis deducendis*, Gracchus turned his attention to the problems of judicial administration. The great experiment of the Lex Calpurnia, whereby a standing court had been established to try charges of extortion brought against Roman officials, suffered from at least one obvious defect: only senators could be arraigned, and it was senators who gave the verdict. This feature by itself was enough to bring the system under suspicion in the minds of other interested parties; but there were also some specific reasons for thinking that convictions were not so easy to obtain as strict justice would demand. According to Appian[3], Gaius Gracchus was able to throw at least three cases in the Senate's teeth: in one of them a man had been acquitted merely because the court resented the personal influence of the prosecutor, Scipio Aemilianus, and on another

---

[1] *Gracchi*, 30, 2.   [2] Bruns, *Fontes*[7], 11, l. 60.   [3] *Bell. Civ.* i, 22, 92.

occasion—not more than two years before Gracchus became tribune—M'. Aquilius had managed to escape, to the general surprise and indignation (see below, p. 106). There is evidence enough to show that all was not well. The quality of juries was such that an improvement was easily within the compass of human ingenuity; and still easier to draft was a much-needed law to make judicial corruption a criminal offence. The former and more difficult of these problems Gracchus sought to solve by a proposal of much moderation: service on juries should still be confined to members of the Senate, but the Senate was to be enlarged by the addition of perhaps six hundred new members drawn from the wealthiest men in Rome. If anything was to be done at all, it is difficult to suggest a method less offensive to senatorial susceptibilities than this. At the same time a measure for the punishment of bribery was passed—a measure which could scarcely be opposed by any but an avowed upholder of corruption, and one whose main interest lies in an almost accidental feature: the only jurors for whose morals it was concerned were senators, presumably because no other jurors were known or contemplated (see above, p. 53 *sq.*). The *lex ne quis iudicio circumveniatur* was enacted forthwith, but the plan to enlarge the Senate remained a mere proposal: its final fate belongs to a later stage (see below, pp. 75 *sqq.*).

In the programme of Gaius Gracchus during the first phase of his tribunician career there now remains nothing but the most important feature—the policy designed at least to make a start in dealing with the urgent problem of the allies. Its importance was due partly to the gravity of the situation and partly to the political advantage which his opponents were able to gain from Gracchus' difficulty in winning popular support for a measure which was bound to take the nature of a liberal concession by Rome. The grievances which it was his aim to remove were felt by the whole non-Roman population of Italy, and the chosen means for their removal was the admission of the allies to some or all of the privileges belonging to Roman citizens. But, warned by the misfortunes of Fulvius Flaccus in 125, Gaius was more prudent than suddenly to introduce so sweeping a proposal as one for the enfranchisement of all Italians alike: he approached the problem by stages, and his first step was to broach suggestions to meet the demands of a well-defined section of the aggrieved—the Latin Name. This is the point at which it is most reasonable to place the limited proposal affecting the Latins alone, the existence of which is alleged by Plutarch and confirmed both by the phraseology of Appian and by the counter-proposal of Livius Drusus (see above, pp. 50 *sqq*.). About its nature there is little doubt—the Latins were to receive the citizenship of Rome. Since Fulvius Flaccus was at Gaius' right hand, it is possible, indeed, that the grant depended on the consent of the recipients; but it is not to be imagined that a firm offer would find many to refuse.

X. THE INTERVENTION OF M. LIVIUS DRUSUS

The career of Gaius Gracchus now approached its crisis. Hitherto the oligarchs had been sullenly acquiescent: now they came out in open hostility. It can scarcely be supposed that their earlier passivity had proclaimed the sincerity of their admiration: the cause is rather to be found in the impossibility of any other attitude. By his social legislation, by the *lex militaris* and by the measure about *provocatio* Gracchus had undoubtedly won the support of the Concilium Plebis, nor was there anything in his work on the administration of the provinces and the courts which would damp the enthusiasm of the masses. But the demand for a concession to the Latins was another matter: it made a call on the generosity of the voters, and thereby it gave a handle to the opposition. By an appeal to their selfishness and jealousy the fickle friends of Gracchus might be seduced from their allegiance, and this was the alluring task which M. Livius Drusus, a tribune of the optimate persuasion, was commissioned to perform.

The family which, by a lucky adoption, was to achieve enduring fame through the famous consort of Augustus had risen to nobility since the end of the Second Punic War; but its rise, though late, was abundantly justified by the ability of its members. C. Drusus, who held a high place among the jurists of the second century, was brother of the tribune, and of the tribune himself not even the most fanatical admirer of the Gracchi could deny that he showed both skill and dignity in the execution of his somewhat shabby job. At first he seems to have met the outstanding features of the Gracchan programme with a simple veto—a veto which may well have given their quietus to the bills for the enlargement of the Senate and the enfranchisement of the Latin Name. But soon he had recourse to subtler ways. His aim was simple—to destroy the majority on which Gaius relied in the Concilium Plebis: his method was effective—to give Gaius the lead and trump his winners one by one. When Gracchus promulgated a proposal, Drusus retorted with a variant; and though he confined himself strictly to the subject which Gracchus had broached, his retort was nicely calculated in every case to make the stronger popular appeal. Under the Lex Sempronia de coloniis deducendis, however large the programme which the law envisaged, Gracchus had not started more than two foundations—and neither of them was recruited exclusively from the poorest class of all: Drusus, leaving nothing to chance, proposed twelve forthwith, possibly the full number of the original Gracchan scheme[1], and these each with three thousand settlers drawn wholly from the lowest of the low. Gracchus, following his brother's practice, had exacted a rent from the recipients of allotments under the *lex agraria*: Drusus announced that the land should be held rent-free. And finally, when Gracchus mooted the enfranchisement of the Latin Name, Drusus appealed to the basest instincts of the mob by a suggestion that so generous a concession might be evaded if the Latins were offered some guarantee against the tyranny of Roman magistrates, perhaps even in time of war. The credit for all this was given to the Senate, and it was all accompanied by a parade of rectitude typical of that moral snobbery which is among the least pleasing features in the characters of both Drusus and his son. Even if the legal prohibition was first enacted after the Gracchan age[2], Gaius seems to have fallen foul of the purists in constitutional practice by himself carrying out the provisions of his own laws: so it was not for nothing that, when commissioners were appointed to execute the terms of the Leges Liviae, it was found that Drusus himself was not among them.

The fate of Drusus' proposals is obscure. That commissions were nominated to carry them into effect is evidence to show that they were passed, and indeed there is a famous incident in the Jugurthine War which can scarcely be explained, if the vulgate text of Sallust be right[3], unless the Latins by then enjoyed the protection which Drusus had proposed[4]. If that be so, it is plausible to assume that the other measures were enacted too, so that from this time onwards the Gracchan allottees were relieved of the burden of rent. But, whatever may have befallen the proposal about colonies, it is as certain as anything in this period can be that the twelve colonies it authorized were never founded[5]. Nothing is heard of them again, and it was his failure, once the measure had served its immediate political purpose, to

---

[1] See J. S. Reid in *J.R.S.* 1, p. 83.   [2] See above p. 30 n. 1.

[3] Sallust, *Bell. Jug.* 69, 4: see below p. 124 n. 2.

[4] For another view, however, see J. S. Reid in *J.R.S.* 1, pp. 77–83.

[5] An inscription of the third century A.D. (*C.I.L.* x, 1117), if it is correctly read, does indeed suggest that 'Livia' appeared in the title of Abellinum—one of the seven places said in the *Liber Coloniarum* to have been

carry his colonial schemes to completion which was the strongest evidence in the case of those who regarded Drusus as a mere demagogue who did not scruple to bribe the masses to his side. But, though doubts exist about the reception of his measures in detail, their effect is plain. Thanks to the skill with which they had been framed and to the opportunity which Gracchus had given his opponents when he asked the People for a liberal policy towards the Latins, the foundation of Gracchus' position—his majority in the Concilium Plebis—was undermined. If his career was to escape an abrupt and premature end, the damage must be repaired forthwith, and repairs could only be made by the help of measures conceived in the spirit of Drusus himself. By the operations of his opponents Gracchus was driven to the methods which hitherto he had scorned. In the past he had been a reformer—he might even have been called a statesman—who made no appeal to the baser instincts of the mob: now he must stoop to use the weapons which the Senate had taken up, and he became a party politician.

XI. JUNONIA

Such were the circumstances in which Gracchus embarked on the second and less creditable phase of his career. When Livius Drusus, presumably after his election though possibly before his year of office had actually begun, unfolded his artful scheme, Gracchus showed undoubted wisdom in meeting the threat forthwith. He enlisted the aid of a colleague in the tribunate for 123/2[1] —a certain Rubrius—to propose a law which should show that, whatever criticisms Drusus might have made of the modest colonies at Scolacium and Tarentum, it was by no means true to say that they marked the beginning and the end of Gracchus' intentions. In 125 the province of Africa had been devastated by a plague of locusts, and this visitation had been followed by an outbreak of disease which is said to have carried off more than two hundred thousand of the inhabitants in the region round Utica and Carthage alone[2]. Thus one of the richest tracts in the Roman world was derelict, and under these circumstances it was intelligible that the Lex Rubria should authorize the foundation of a colony hard by the site of Carthage on the edge of the great

---

colonized under a 'Lex Sempronia' or 'Gracchana': but it would be rash to claim this as evidence that the elder Livius Drusus was in any way responsible for its colonization. For Abellinum see *Lib. Col.* in *Gromatici veteres*, ed. Lachmann, i, pp. 229, 16 *sqq.*

[1] See Note 1 on p. 891 *sq.*   [2] Orosius v, 11, 2 *sqq.*

plain which lies round the lowest reaches of the Medjerda (Bag-radas). The number of settlers was fixed at something less than six thousand and the work of organization was entrusted to *tresviri*, whether these were a special board created by the law or merely the Gracchan commission now equipped with powers to undertake the planting of colonies (see above, p. 67 *sq.*).

Rubrius did not carry his proposal without serious opposition; for, though in this very year or the next Q. Metellus, consul in 123, was founding Palma and Pollentia in Majorca[1], the strongest exception was taken to the extension of Gracchus' colonial acti-vities beyond the boundaries of Italy. People pointed to the warnings of the past and shook their heads over the lessons of *metropoleis* whose daughters had grown greater than themselves[2]. Massilia had outdone Phocaea, Syracuse Corinth, Cyzicus and Byzantium had both surpassed Miletus and, most ominous of all, Carthage had attained a power and prosperity which Tyre had never known. So much it was possible to say outright: appeals to the inevitable prejudice of the unemployed against emigration as a remedy for their troubles had to be made with more discretion. Nevertheless, the bill became law: indeed, among its provisions were some of such attractiveness that its rejection was unlikely when it was offered, not as an alternative, but as a supplement to the schemes of Drusus. Land in Africa was abundant, and some, though almost certainly not all, of the allotments were to be plots of two hundred *iugera*—an area which, though by no means without parallel in Roman history or even the largest known, was something very different from the miserable doles, less than one-sixth of the size now proposed, with which settlers in Italy under the agrarian law of Tiberius had been perforce content. Nor, perhaps, did the generosity of the scheme end here if, by an in-novation which finally developed into the so-called *ius Italicum*, in spite of the fact that the land was in a province of the Roman People, it was removed from the legal category of *solum provinciale* and made capable of ownership *optimo iure Quiritium*[3]. The voters might, indeed, make the best of both worlds by accepting the baits of Gracchus and of Drusus alike: but what Gracchus had to offer them was something of value, and it is easy to understand how, in spite of the rising opposition, the bill of Rubrius became law.

[1] Strabo III, 167.   [2] Vell. Pat. II, 14, 3.
[3] This is the view taken by Mommsen (*Ges. Schr.* I, p. 123): for a dif-ferent interpretation of the evidence see A. A. F. Rudorff in *Zeitschr. für gesch. Rechtswissenschaft*, x, 1842, pp. 118 *sqq.*

XII. THE JUDICIARY LAW: THE SECOND PHASE

Whatever its value as a means to restore the failing fortunes of the Gracchan cause, the Lex Rubria did not stand alone as a political expedient. It was accompanied, or soon succeeded[1], by another proposal which undoubtedly belongs to the partisan period of Gracchus' career, even though it may not have purposely been designed to act as a political bribe. The final *lex iudiciaria*, judged by its effects on later history, is certainly the most important of the Gracchan laws, as it is also the most difficult to assign to its proper place in the chronological sequence of the legislation. Whether it was passed before or after the expedition which Gracchus undertook to found his colony at Carthage there is not enough evidence to show: all that can be said with confidence is that it falls in the period after Drusus had delivered his attack. Nor are the details of the measure any easier to ascertain[2]. Attention is due first of all to the nature of the court which it was intended to affect. The Lex Calpurnia of 149 B.C. had established a permanent procedure for dealing with charges of extortion brought against officials serving in the provinces, but there is no definite proof that this system had been extended to other offences by 122 B.C. Even if such proof were forthcoming, the peculiar position of the *quaestio repetundarum*—which was no mere domestic tribunal but an element in the administrative machinery of the Empire—would make the action of Gracchus intelligible if, as the present writer is inclined to think, his famous judiciary reform was concerned with this court alone. Such a limitation of his outlook will be the less surprising when it is remembered that the scandals quoted as the original cause of Gracchus' concern with the courts are all scandals connected with charges of misgovernment in the provinces. From this small but important corner of the judicial field Gracchus sought to eradicate the worst abuses by an enactment still in part preserved. The Lex Acilia de rebus repetundis[3], which took its name from one of his lieutenants though Gracchus himself was its real author, not only enlarged the juries but boldly changed their constitution by excluding members of the Senate and putting in their places men of substance drawn from the wealthiest class outside the governing oligarchy. Such was the gravest provision of what is perhaps the most famous feature in the legislative achievement of Gracchus.

---

[1] See Plutarch, *Gracchi*, 33, 1.
[2] A summary of the reasons for the conclusions here adopted will be found in Note 2, on pp. 892 *sqq*.   [3] Bruns, *Fontes*[7], 10.

If the theory here adopted be sound, an immediate answer can be given to one of the most controversial questions which have been debated since modern study of the Gracchi began—the question whether Gracchus changed the constitution of the civil courts, whether senators were debarred from service as the *unus iudex*, as *recuperatores, decemviri* and *centumviri*. Gracchus made no change in the recruitment of these bodies. It must, indeed, be admitted that, just as the civil law had influenced the criminal when the Lex Calpurnia was passed in 149 B.C., so the Gracchan innovations in the criminal *iudicium publicum* reacted to some extent on the civil tribunals. After 122 B.C. *iudices* below senatorial rank are found, and it is probable that their choice was to some extent suggested by the prevailing arrangements on the criminal side: but there is nothing to show that senators were disqualified for service in civil suits, and it is most improbable that the civil courts were ever subjected to sweeping changes in recruitment such as those which befell the *iudicia publica*. The earlier proposal of Gaius Gracchus—the proposal for an enlargement of the Senate—would indeed have affected the judicial system on both sides: but the incidents said to have moved him to action in this matter were incidents in the *iudicium repetundarum*, and it was with this court alone that his final enactment—the Lex Acilia—was concerned.

Some estimate of this memorable law and its justification must now be attempted. As a contribution to the history of the Roman judicial system its first claim to notice lies in the debt which it incurred to Greece. Many of its minor provisions, and above all the large juries which it invoked[1], are Hellenic institutions unknown in the Rome of earlier days, and their adoption by Gaius Gracchus is one among the many signs by which his obligations to Hellas are revealed. More memorable still was the effect on the political life of Rome. The law stands out among the works of Gaius as one which shows utter disregard for the feelings of the Senate: in the manner of faction undisguised it removes a privilege from one section in the State and bestows it on another. Yet it is easy to do Gracchus an injustice. This feature of the measure was not his own ideal: at first he would have been content to prohibit bribery and to strengthen the Senate. It was a *pis aller*, accepted when Gracchus had been forced to adopt the methods of the party politician; and, though these methods cannot be held up to admiration, it must be remembered that it was the Senate and Livius Drusus who had imposed their use. When factious opposi-

---

[1] See H. F. Hitzig, *Die Herkunft des Schwurgerichts im römischen Straf-prozess*, pp. 47 *sqq.*

tion was let loose, unless reform was to be finally abandoned, a
measure must be drafted which, without being necessarily a
political bribe, would attract sufficient doubtful votes to secure a
passage through the Concilium Plebis. Such was the Lex Acilia.
The Senate was implacably opposed to reform—indeed, by its
behaviour in the recent past it had forfeited every claim to consideration—and Gracchus turned to the wealthy men of business who,
by their own votes and those of their dependents, might well
enable him to win the day. But to say so much as this is by no
means to admit that Gracchus played ducks and drakes with the
interests of the State for the mere gratification of getting his own
way: these wealthy men to whom he looked were neither fools nor
scoundrels, but Roman citizens who seem to have responded well
to the call which Gracchus made. It may be admitted that the
condemnation of P. Rutilius Rufus in 92 B.C. was a scandal (see
below, p. 175 *sq.*), but it must be remembered that Cicero[1],
speaking at a time when the juries were still composed of senators
even if their monopoly was doomed, felt himself justified in boasting
that in the period of almost half a century between the tribunates
of Gaius Gracchus and the dictatorship of Sulla the *equester ordo* had
filled the juries without the slightest suspicion of bribery—an enthusiastic testimonial, perhaps, but one which would have been absurdly
maladroit if the equestrian régime had been a welter of corruption.

There is no need to deny that the Lex Acilia had regrettable
results; but these results were not due to any marked unsuitability
for their task in the men to whom power was given. The evil
effects flowed from another source, and one which it was easy to
overlook. By changing the jurors in the *iudicium publicum* Gracchus
made control of the criminal courts a prize of party politics—and
it was a prize which grew the more valuable as the number of the
courts increased. And not only so; as Pliny records[2], it was the
rivalry thus started which fused the wealthy business men into a
definite *ordo*, conscious of its individuality and regularly at loggerheads with the Senate. This was a disaster of the first magnitude:
it meant the formation of parties of the most pernicious type.
Parties in themselves are no necessary evil: if each stands for an
ideal of government, no harm is done, however much their ideals
may be opposed. But in the last century of the Republic Senate
and *equites* had little use for ideals: they struggled not for principles so much as for the advancement of their own interests and
the detriment of their rivals. There were honourable men, of
course, who tried to raise politics to a higher plane: but the tragic

[1] 1 *in Verr.* 13, 38. [2] *N.H.* XXXIII, 34.

failure of Cicero's dogged efforts to form a Concordia Ordinum is a measure of the depth to which public life could sink. And it was Gaius Gracchus who by his well-meant change in the recruitment of juries set men irrevocably on the downward path.

XIII. GRACCHUS AND THE ALLIES: THE SECOND PHASE

There remains one other measure in the final phase of Gracchus' career—his last attempt to solve the most urgent problem of the day. It has been said already (p. 51 *sq.* above) that in his attempts to meet the demands of the Roman allies Gracchus had produced no more than a proposal affecting the Latins alone when Livius Drusus delivered his fatal stroke. If that be so, the bill which extended his attentions to the Italians in general must belong to the second period of his activity, and this is a conclusion confirmed by independent evidence of two kinds. First, C. Fannius—the man whom Gracchus had supported for the consulship of 122 and who afterwards went over to the other side—left an oration 'de sociis *et* nomine Latino contra Gracchum[1]' which it is highly probable that he delivered during his year of office: thus it appears that the wider proposal was under consideration in 122. Secondly, Plutarch strongly suggests[2] that agitations in which the Italians were concerned, and which were therefore probably connected with a bill for the settlement of their grievances, were the main feature of Roman public life at a period just before the tribunician elections in the summer of 122; and to this suggestion may be added the numerous hints that, when Gaius finally lost the favour of the masses, a loss first indicated by his failure to secure election again as tribune for the year 121, the defection was due to the unpopularity of his liberal attitude to the allies. So far as it goes, the evidence points to a simple version. At the outset Gracchus had intended to approach his greatest task, the re-organization of the Italian confederacy, by stages; but his original intentions were changed perforce when, in taking the first step of all with a proposal for the enfranchisement of the Latin Name, he was tripped up by Livius Drusus. The immediate result was to make his whole position insecure. He could not count on an indefinite prolongation of his tribunates, and the prospect of office continued long enough to allow the passage of a gradual and protracted programme was remote: either the problem of the Italians must be dropped

---

[1] Cicero, *Brutus,* 26, 99.   [2] *Gracchi,* 33.

or everything must be staked on a single throw. In these circumstances Gracchus chose the bolder course and introduced a comprehensive bill, which on the strength of the words of Cicero
quoted above is often called a 'lex de sociis et nomine Latino.'

The details of this measure are wrapped in obscurity, and many
of them provide material for nothing but the most tentative conjecture. There can, indeed, be little doubt that, so far as the Latins
were concerned, the project of the previous year was revived: the
Roman *civitas* was to be offered to the whole Latin Name. But the
most important clauses of this new bill were those in which it went
beyond the earlier scheme, and it is with them that speculation
begins. The words of Velleius[1] would suggest that Gracchus would
have treated Latins and Italians alike—that he would have admitted
the whole free non-Roman population of Italy to the citizenship of
Rome, as Fulvius Flaccus had sought to do two years before: and
Velleius may possibly be right. On the other hand, Appian[2] preserves a hint that the distinction between Latins and Italians was
to be maintained: if the Latins were to become Roman citizens,
the Italians, though their position was somehow to be improved,
would still be denied the privilege of full enfranchisement. This
version finds some support in a piece of evidence which deserves
notice because it is contemporary: in a speech of which a few
phrases are quoted by Julius Victor[3], Fannius, the renegade consul
of 122, appeals to the selfishness of the voters by asking them what
room will be left for them at games and festivals when they have
given citizenship *to the Latins*. If this is the famous speech ' de
sociis et nomine Latino', the mention of Latins as the sole candidates for admission to the Roman franchise carries the clear
implication that the Italians were to be content with some smaller
boon. Such are the considerations which influence those who
believe that the idea of Gaius Gracchus was to move each section
of the allies one step up on the political ladder: the Latins were
to become Roman citizens and the Italians were in future to
enjoy the *ius Latii*. Between these possibilities the evidence does
not allow a decision, though the latter is perhaps slightly the more
probable; nor would it be of much value to discover the details of
a measure which was never passed, when its general intention is
beyond dispute.

Whatever its terms may have been, the bill provoked an immediate crisis. Fannius, the one time friend, now became the open

---

[1] ii, 6, 2.　　　　[2] *Bell. Civ.* i, 23, 99.
[3] Malcovati, *Orat. Rom. Frag.* i, p. 247.

enemy of Gracchus, and to defeat the scheme he had recourse to methods of a kind to which Livius Drusus had never stooped. Not only did he seek the favour of the voters by unblushing attempts to work upon their greed and jealousy, but, when allies began to make for Rome in hopes of doing their humble best to bring home to the sovran People the gravity of the situation which Gracchus was trying to relieve, he lent himself to a repetition of the device whereby Fulvius Flaccus had been deprived of his most active helpers. The Latin vote was negligible, but Latins and Italians alike could do much to whip up Roman citizens and to impress on them the urgency of reform. So the consuls were instructed by the Senate to see that, when the bill came before the People, no alien without a vote in the Concilium Plebis should be allowed within five miles of Rome; and Fannius, despite threats and protests from the Gracchan side, carried out his instructions with gusto. The Senate had now dropped all pretence of indifference and was out for a decisive victory. It had the advantage of position, because it was Gracchus who was trying to commend a measure which, however necessary and inevitable, could never have aroused enthusiasm among the voters of Rome; and this advantage was increased by the actitivies of Fannius. The greatest of all the reforms to which Gracchus set his hand came, for the time being, to naught. Whether the bill was vetoed by Livius Drusus, whether it was actually rejected or even brought to the vote, we cannot say: but somehow it was scotched, and thereby Gracchus was condemned to failure in the supreme task of his legislative career.

Vague as is our knowledge of everything that concerns the second phase of Gracchus' tribunician activities—the phase which produced the Lex Rubria, the Lex Acilia and the bill about the allies and the Latin Name—it is nowhere less adequate than in the matter of the order in which these measures were proposed. Nothing can be said with confidence except that during the spring of 122 Gracchus was away from Rome for seventy days on a visit to Africa, making preparations for the colony of Junonia; and even for this visit the limits of date are wide[1]. If it is true that

---

[1] About the nature of the work performed by Gracchus during his visit to Africa no information is to be had from the surviving traces of centuriation: on this see Ch. Saumagne in *Bull. du Comité*, 1924, pp. 131 *sqq.* The layout of Junonia appears to have been based on the centuriation of the province as a whole, which had probably been marked out in the years immediately after 146 B.C.: see S. Gsell, *Histoire ancienne de l'Afrique du Nord*, VII, pp. 13 *sqq.* and, for another view, J. Carcopino in *Rev. hist.* 162, 1929, p. 92.

Rubrius was a tribune of 122, his *plebiscitum* cannot have been passed before the end of 123, and the consequent expedition of Gracchus cannot have begun before that date. Afterwards, we find Gracchus back in time for both tribunician and consular elections in the summer of 122. Thus his absence may be placed in the first six months of that year; but whether it came before or after the promulgation of the Lex Acilia and the bill concerning Rome's relations with her allies, it is impossible to say.

With the expedition to Africa, the curtain rose upon the final act. It may be surmised that, in pressing on with his colonial plan even at the cost of a most inconvenient absence from Rome, the policy of Gracchus was to rely for his political security on the prestige of a beneficent scheme successfully achieved. It was, therefore, one of the first objects of his opponents to see that Junonia ended in fiasco. Almost as soon as work on the site began, a stream of the most sinister reports burst upon the credulous ears of the Roman populace. Winds of supernatural force had torn a standard from its bearer's grasp and had blown victims from the altars to such a distance that they were found outside the *pomerium* of the city: wolves had torn up the boundary stones and carried them off like mutton-bones in their mouths. Clearly life in such surroundings would be hard, even if it were not obvious that these portents revealed the displeasure of the gods. But, idiotic as the stories were, it was idle for Gracchus and Fulvius to deny their truth or challenge their interpretation: sedulous repetition lent plausibility to tales however wild, until in the end the belief was widely spread that Junonia was an offence to heaven. Yet this was not the only line of attack. According to Appian[1], when Gracchus recruited six thousand settlers, he was charged with having set aside the Lex Rubria itself by exceeding the highest number it allowed. Nor was this his only slip: in the following words Appian records that these unhappy colonists were collected 'from all parts of Italy'—a phrase which strongly suggests that Gracchus had been trying to carry out a clandestine enfranchisement of his Italian friends on a small scale. Such were the means whereby his opponents contrived to neutralize whatever strength he gained from his honest efforts to make the colony of Junonia a success.

---

[1] *Bell. Civ.* I, 24, 104.

XIV. THE *S.C. DE RE PUBLICA DEFENDENDA* AND THE DEATH OF GAIUS GRACCHUS

Their efforts were not without reward. By the time of the tribunician elections in 122, the tide had definitely turned, and the fortunes of the Gracchan cause were on the ebb. When the day arrived to choose tribunes for the following year, Gracchus was again a candidate; but he was a runner greatly changed from the form of a year before. Then he could claim support from citizens of every class outside the incorrigible reactionaries: now his hopes rested almost wholly on the poorest of the poor. Doubtless he could count on the friendship of the rich families from whom his new *iudices* were drawn, but their votes and those of their retainers were too few to carry the day unless the urban proletariate could be mobilized as well. And this was difficult; for the promise of Junonia had done little to restore the enthusiasm which had been damped, if not destroyed, by the machinations of Livius Drusus. So, from the time of his return from Carthage, Gracchus set himself to cultivate afresh the fickle affections of the rabble. He moved house from the Palatine to one of the humbler quarters—apparently to the Velabrum or its neighbourhood—and, when the view of a gladiatorial show was threatened with some obstruction by a stand erected for those who could afford to pay, he first protested and finally had the edifice pulled down on the night before the performance began. But neither theatrical appeals nor reasoned argument could restore the loyalty of the mob. Whatever the circumstances—and our only authority suggests that the poll was not honestly declared—when the result was announced Gracchus was not among the tribunes of 122/1, and consequently on 10 December his tribunician career would at length be closed.

That the rejection of Gaius was in accord with the prevailing sentiment is shewn by the elections for the consulship of 121 B.C., when the chosen pair included a man of the most ominous repute. His colleague, indeed, Q. Fabius Maximus Allobrogicus, nephew of Scipio Aemilianus, had sown his wild oats early and was now in the course of an honourable public career: but L. Opimius, who was remembered long after the struggles of the Gracchan age had been forgotten by the celebrated vintage of 121 to which he gave his name, was an unscrupulous ruffian whose one claim to notice was the violence of his behaviour towards the rebels of Fregellae in 125 B.C. He became consul at a moment when the *lex de sociis et nomine Latino* had brought the problem of the Roman allies into the forefront of the political stage; and whether that measure had already been rejected or, as is more probable, had still to be submitted to the verdict of the vote, his election showed beyond all doubt that the old policy of niggardly exclusiveness was to be maintained.

The affairs with which Gracchus occupied himself in these final months of office, when his failure at the elections had proclaimed that the public confidence was withdrawn, are left to our imagination. There is little doubt that the question of the juries had been settled already by the Lex Acilia, though that measure had apparently been passed at a time so near the end of Gracchus' days of power that no opportunity was left to enact a consequential amendment of the law on judicial corruption (see above, p. 70): but it is not impossible that wranglings over the *lex de sociis et nomine Latino* still dragged on their weary course after the elections were over and that the scheme was not finally killed until after the fate of Gracchus himself had been sealed. On this period our authorities are dumb, and their silence is unbroken till the death of Gracchus is at hand. We are now in the year 121: Opimius is consul and Gracchus himself, no longer tribune, is a mere member of the agrarian commission. One of his successors in the tribunate, a certain Minucius Rufus, was engaged in an attempt to repeal the Lex Rubria[1], and while this undertaking was in train Gracchus foolishly yielded to his more reckless henchmen and formed a body-guard of his most loyal supporters. There followed a fracas in which one of the consul's criers, a man named Antullius, was killed, and the corpse of this unhappy victim immediately became an article of propaganda. In the course of a skilful parade this object was carried past the door of the Senate House itself, where the practised Fathers duly responded to the sight with an outburst of fitting indignation. Though the deed had been done in a drunken brawl, it was greeted with all the sentiments which calculated violence evokes: the guilty hand was Gracchan, and that fact by itself was enough to make pointless any reference to the precedent of Scipio Nasica and his friends. But, in spite of their emotions, the horrified senators did not fail to turn the incident to the advantage of their party: indeed, they made it the occasion of a step which led to grave results and to a controversy which lasted almost as long as the Republic itself. Opimius was finally encouraged to take measures for the safety of the State, and thus for the first time in Roman history was passed the resolution commonly known as the *senatus consultum ultimum*[2].

[1] *de viris ill.* 65, 5.
[2] The origin of this expression is Caesar, *B.C.* 1, 5, 3.

The difficulties to which this measure gave rise from the time of Gaius Gracchus down to the outbreak of the Civil War in 50 B.C. make discussion of its nature inevitable. The long-standing practice whereby in times of crisis a dictator had been appointed to act as a temporary autocrat found less and less favour with the Senate as the pretensions of that body increased, and at the end of the third century the dictatorship fell upon a period of dis-use which was only ended when Sulla revived the office in a new and modified form. In the second century the Senate preferred to meet special dangers by giving special instruction to the ordinary magistrates, and this had several times been done: but the situa-tion shortly before the death of Gaius Gracchus was in some ways peculiar, and its peculiarity led to a modification in the action of the Senate. There was now no individual or body of men actually in arms against society. It is true that Antullius had been killed, but this was no more than a case of murder; and, even by forming a bodyguard of his own, Gracchus himself had committed no illegality. Yet, though the threat was vague, there was undoubted danger of an explosion, and the Senate sought to meet the menace in advance by giving the consuls backing which would suffice for any possible contingency. So a decree was passed in which the magistrates were urged to 'defend the State and to see that it took no harm.' Such, at least in later days, was the injunction of the *s.c. de re publica defendenda*. Both in its matter and in its form this resolu-tion deserves the closest notice. Defence of the public weal was no special or exceptional function for the magistrates to undertake: it was only the most important of their normal duties. Conse-quently, the substance of this decree was no more than an exhortation to the executive to attend to the business which it was appointed to perform. Moreover, in its wording the formula made no pre-tence of setting law aside, or even of encouraging the magistrates to disregard the legal limitations of their power: it was simply the expression of a hope to which any citizen might give vent at any time—of a hope that the magistrates would do their job. The nature of the occasion which prompted this public encouragement is obvious: it was not any special unfitness of the magistrates for the duties which their office imposed, but the special gravity of a crisis with which they seemed likely soon to be confronted. Such were the circumstances; and, when they are considered in con-junction with the decree itself, it becomes clear that the *ultimum consultum* of the Senate was in essence only an attempt to strengthen the resolution of the magistrates in face of a danger which might call for action of peculiar vigour and determination. It implied a promise of senatorial support; but neither in theory nor in fact did it add to the legal powers which they already held. It conferred on them no new authority nor did it even purport to remove any of the restrictions which were imposed by statute on the use of their *imperium*.

The effects of this encouragement on the willing Opimius were immediate. His first step was to make good the lack of an effective police force in the city by calling the senators and *equites* to arms, and in fairness to the other side it must be added that, according to Plutarch, the *equites* were asked each to provide a couple of armed slaves. In face of this formidable threat the counsels of the Gracchans were divided: Fulvius Flaccus was in favour of meeting force with force, but Gracchus himself seems at first to have inclined towards unresisting submission. It was not long, however, before circumstances forced a decision. When Opimius summoned both leaders to appear in the Senate House, the fatal consequences of compliance were so obvious that Gracchus gave way to the more spirited advice of his lieutenant. Flaccus and his supporters, with Gracchus diffidently following in their wake, seized the Aventine, and from that moment a violent settlement of the issue was inevitable. It is true that, even at the eleventh hour, some attempt at negotiation was made: but, in spite of a courageous offer by Gracchus himself, neither Flaccus nor the rank and file would agree that the leaders should put themselves in the power of the Senate, and the consul, on his side, resolutely refused to deal with any but the principals of the opposition. So the offers made through Flaccus' young son led to no result, and at length Opimius had the satisfaction of finding the stage prepared for his final triumph. Amid scenes not unworthy of a field of battle the stalwarts of the constitution stormed the stronghold of the Aventine. Its garrison was put to flight, and the leaders, soon run down, were killed, together with many of their supporters. Flaccus and his son were slaughtered by the enemy, and the enemy was responsible for the death of Gracchus too, whether the hand which took his life was hostile or that of a faithful slave ordered to save his master from the consequences of capture.

Such was the melancholy end of Gaius Gracchus, and such was the result of the Senate's anxiety for the public defence. If its justification is a matter of dispute, the grounds on which it must be upheld or attacked are plain. Though the expediency of the Senate's decree was questioned by Caesar in the trial of C. Rabirius (see below, p. 489 *sq.*), no one was ever found to deny that the Senate was entirely within its legal rights in formally recording its earnest hope that the magistrates would not fail to protect the commonwealth from a threatening danger. The vital question concerns the effect which this declaration had on the position of the magistrates concerned, and the answer may be brief. In law the effect was nil: the resolution did not even purport to alter or suspend the constitution. Even after its adoption by the Fathers, to put a citizen to death without trial and appeal to the People was as much an infringement of the *leges de provocatione* as before.

But in practice the effect was great. Rome, like every other State, claimed the right to preserve itself from destruction and, if necessary, to use all the means at its disposal to secure this end. When a situation has passed beyond control by the normal legal methods, it is essential, in order both to warn the law-breakers of what they must expect and to provide the champions of order with a reply to charges of illegality which may afterwards be brought, that some responsible person or body of persons should publicly declare that at any moment the necessity for non-legal measures may arise and that, when it does, these measures will forthwith be taken. In practice this was the effect of the 'last decree.' By exhorting the magistrates to make the safety of the State their supreme care the Senate implied its consciousness of a peculiar danger, and the consuls were urged at all costs to take adequate precautions to meet it, even if these precautions involved some infringement of the prevailing rules of law. Such was the encouragement which Cicero held out to holders of the *summum imperium* in his famous precept that, to them at least, the 'salus populi' should be the 'suprema lex[1].'

The value of the decree was to be found in the evidence it supplied that, in the considered opinion of the Senate, the State had been faced with a menace of the kind which might call for a temporary neglect of the procedure normally imposed by law. In any subsequent prosecution of the magistrates for illegal action their proper defence—that they acted in circumstances under which the overriding obligation to maintain the security of the State made it impossible to observe the formalities of arrest and trial—found the strongest support in the Senate's declaration that such circumstances were clearly to be foreseen. Thus to say that the behaviour of Opimius was contrary to the provisions of the law is irrelevant to the question of his justification. The only issues which could reasonably be raised were, first, whether the crisis was in fact of the gravity which the Senate feared and the consul claimed; secondly,

[1] *de legibus,* III, 3, 8.

if it was of such a nature, whether the consul used no more than the minimum degree of non-legal action required to bring the situation back under control by ordinary means; and, thirdly, whether the consul's action was, in fact, directed to preserve the safety of the State. If all these questions could be answered with an affirmative, no honest jury of loyal citizens could deny that his behaviour was justified, whatever laws he had for the time being ignored[1].

So much for the position of the executive: it may be well to add a word about the rights of the people whose behaviour had caused the commotion. On certain occasions in later Republican history the Senate, at the time of passing its 'ultimate decree,' put the identity of those from whom danger was foreseen beyond all doubt by declaring them individually *hostes*. This elaboration in the procedure deserves notice both because it calls attention to the attitude of the law towards such obstinate disturbers of the public peace and also because its effect has often been misunderstood. Every Roman *civis* was entitled, if suspected of crime, to be formally charged and duly tried in accordance with the prevailing rules for the administration of criminal justice, and one of these rules was that no capital sentence should be executed without the consent of the Roman People. A *hostis*, on the other hand, was an active enemy of the State who might be killed at sight by any citizen with complete impunity, so far at least as the law of Rome was concerned. Now the Senate, for all its pretensions, never made the monstrous claim that it could turn a *civis* into a *hostis*, that it could deprive a Roman citizen, merely because he was suspected of crime—however strong the suspicion, of the right to legal trial which was inherent in his citizenship. What the Senate could do was to point its finger at a man and observe that by his own behaviour he had made himself a *hostis*. A malefactor whose arrest the magistrates desired to effect, if he resisted apprehension by forming a bodyguard of such dimensions as to be in effect an army, was setting the State at defiance in precisely the same way as another State might do at a time of international crisis. Towards both the proper attitude was a declaration of war, but between the two cases there was one slight difference. Whereas Rome might declare war on another power in spite of all that power's efforts to prevent it, she could not declare war on a section

---

[1] A most lucid treatment of these and cognate questions is to be found in the *Report of the Committee appointed to inquire into the Circumstances connected with the Disturbances at Featherstone on the 7th of September 1893*, pp. 9 *sqq.* (C.—7234. Stationery Office; 1893). The chairman of the committee was Lord Bowen.

of her own citizens until they had in fact, though not necessarily
in word, declared war on her. Thus, when citizens were proclaimed
hostes, the proclamation was purely declaratory: it merely recognized the effects of their own action. In fact, the only person
who could turn a citizen into a *hostis* was that citizen himself. And
so, when in later practice the Senate backed up its 'ultimate
decree' by an announcement that certain persons were enemies,
the one result of this addition was to enunciate an already existing
fact in order to indicate more definitely where the magistrates
should look for the danger against which the *s.c. de re publica
defendenda* gave them special encouragement to provide.

Though there is no evidence to show that on this occasion such
a declaration was made, by seizing the Aventine in force and by
openly flouting the orders of a consul the Gracchans had put themselves in a posture of hostility to the State. They had appealed to
the judgment of force, and there can be no shadow of doubt that
the government was justified in using force to secure the verdict
for itself. So much can be said in favour of the court which in 120
acquitted Opimius of all criminality in the methods he had employed to suppress the incipient revolt on the Aventine (see below,
p. 93). But the court went further than to approve the use of
violent and non-legal methods to deal with an insurrection which
could be controlled by no other means. Of the three thousand
victims for whose death the operations of Opimius were responsible by no means all had been killed in the assault on the
Aventine or in the subsequent pursuit. Some, at least, and according to Appian a very considerable number, had been arrested
and put to death by the consul without any semblance of trial after
the back of the revolt had been broken—at a time when a state of
acute emergency could no longer be said to exist. The case of
these unfortunates was wholly different from that of the men who
had fallen in the heat of battle during the storming of the Gracchan
position and its immediate sequel: they had been executed out
of hand by the consul, in defiance of the law, at a time when there
was no valid reason whatever for denying them the trial and the
exercise of *provocatio* against a capital sentence to which every
citizen was entitled. For such action Opimius might justly have
been condemned: but in fact he was acquitted, and thereby the
Senate gained a most valuable victory. In his *lex ne quis iniussu
populi R. capite damnetur* Gaius Gracchus had deprived it of a
powerful weapon by preventing the creation of special senatorial
courts with inappellable jurisdiction to take vengeance on particular bodies of people who had incurred its displeasure. This

disability the Senate now repaired by using the unsupported *imperium* of a consul to authorize executions of the kind which hitherto had only been carried out after sentence by one of those courts at which the law of Gracchus had been aimed. The device was indefensible. Once order had been restored, there was no justification whatever for execution in defiance of the laws on *provocatio*. But in spite of this, after a trial in which the arguments of the prosecution seem to have been developed with great elaboration, Opimius secured his acquittal, and thereby the Senate won a notable success. If the action of Opimius became a precedent, one of the most salutary of the Gracchan laws would have been circumvented, and for the senatorial courts which it had been designed to check would be substituted a still less desirable form of jurisdiction—the consular *imperium* freed from every limitation.

XV. THE ACHIEVEMENT OF THE GRACCHI

The significance of the Gracchi in Roman history has been described in the most divergent terms. Champions of Socialism in its extremest forms have found in them the heralds of doctrines which even now are thought advanced, and by others they have been dismissed as demagogues of the most commonplace type, not even distinguished from the rest of their kind by any serious contribution to the political ideas of the age in which they lived. Both estimates are wide of the mark. The Gracchi were children of their time, and it was with the special problems of Rome in the latter half of the second century B.C. that they were concerned. The business of Tiberius was to relieve the widespread unemployment of the urban population, and the plan he adopted to achieve this end was a scheme for the partial redistribution of the public land— a scheme so sane in its conception and so successful in its results that it is futile to charge its author either with reckless vote-catching or with the Utopian aspirations of unpractical ignorance. This work it was one of the tasks of Gaius to continue, though in his continuation a slight change of method appears. Probably because most of the scattered land, only suitable for distribution among individual settlers, had already been assigned, Gaius had recourse to the foundation of colonies, some at least of which were intended to provide opportunities for commercial employment. But the *lex agraria* of Tiberius Gracchus had provoked open expression of a grievance which for long had riddled the peoples of Italy with discontent: the time had come when a re-organization of the Roman confederacy could no longer with safety be delayed. This was the final goal towards which Gaius set his course, and on its attainment he staked not only his political future but his life. If he failed, his failure was inevitable: all the appeals and arguments of one young man could never break down the incorrigible selfishness of the Roman 'democracy,' from which nothing less than the menace of the Social War was enough to wring concessions.

For the rest, his achievements consist of minor changes in the administrative system; and they were changes which were salutary in themselves and free from the taint of political corruption. Even in the final phase of his career, when Gaius had undoubtedly ceased to respect the feelings of his oligarchical opponents, it is impossible to find a measure which can be said with assurance to have been framed as nothing but a bribe to some section of the people. It is not to be denied that by several of his proposals he must have gained friends for himself, as the author of any true reform is bound to do: but even the transference of the *quaestio repetund-arum* to the wealthiest class outside the senatorial ring was an act which not only may well have seemed expedient at the time but also was by no means condemned by its effect. Of Gaius Gracchus it may be said that, however much some of his reforms may have served to strengthen his own position, he never helped himself by a measure which did not help the State as well. And the figures in Roman history to whom a higher tribute can honestly be paid are few indeed.

But the programmes of the Gracchi were of far less importance than the issues which they raised unwittingly. Tiberius had called attention to the problem of the unemployed: Gaius had put the gravity of the Italian question beyond dispute. But more serious even than these was the challenge which they flung down to the whole practice of the constitution and the prevailing domination of the Senate. That they were prepared to approach the Concilium Plebis with proposals for legislation which had not received sena-torial approval was a trifling breach of custom, and not without parallel. If the Senate could not stop the promulgation of a bill, it had every reason to believe that a tribune would easily be found to use his veto against it. The first danger came with the deposition of Octavius. If tribunes distasteful to the People's passing mood were to be deprived of office, the way to demagogic control was barred by nothing but the Senate's claim to probouleutic powers —a claim which had no statutory sanction and which had been regularly flouted in the Gracchan age—and the flimsy obstacle of *obnuntiatio*. Barriers such as these were useless. If the right to unseat an obstructive tribune were admitted, the senatorial position was lost. Tiberius Gracchus, in his dealings with Octavius, took a long step towards constitutional revolution. Still more drastic was the doctrine—adumbrated by Tiberius and made effective by Gaius—that a tribune should be capable of immediate re-election, and for an indefinite number of years. The supremacy of the first citizen, unhampered by the veto, was to be limited by nothing but the endurance of popular support; and, as can be seen from Tiberius' handling of the Asiatic bequest, no branch of government was to be immune from direct interference by the People and their chosen leader.

Such were the gravest implications of these famous tribunates. It was not the professed objects of the Gracchan programmes which mattered most, nor was it the violence which marked their authors' ends. The true cause for justifiable alarm lay in the tendency towards democracy of the most reckless type. The insignificant and unworthy fraction of the Roman People which formed the Concilium Plebis on all but exceptional occasions was to be freed of every trammel in the exercise of its legislative powers. From day to day, as bills were introduced, nothing was to prevent the enactment of those proposals which appealed most strongly to the taste of the urban mob. That way disaster clearly lay. Not even the most zealous democrat could seriously maintain that the *plebs urbana* was well equipped for the task of governing an empire, nor was it probable that the proletariate of Rome would for ever refrain from a selfish use of its authority to the detriment of the interests of the Populus Romanus as a whole.

Yet it is easy to misjudge the Gracchi. The issue, raised most acutely by the problem of Appian's value as an authority for the career of the elder brother and associated in recent times particularly with the names of Schwartz[1] and von Pöhlmann[2], between those who would call them revolutionaries and those who regard them as mere reformers cannot be decided outright. A distinction must be drawn between the content of the programmes and the implications of the methods adopted to secure their passage into law. The legislative proposals contained nothing to which constitutional objection could be raised, and on this score their authors could claim to be reformers of the most legitimate type. But on the other hand it cannot be denied that some of the expedients employed in carrying the reforms could not be reconciled

[1] *Gött. Gel. Anz.* 1896, pp. 792 *sqq.*
[2] In *Sitzungsberichte der philos.-philol. u. hist. Klasse d. Kgl. Bayer. Ak. d. Wissenschaften,* 1907, pp. 443 *sqq.*

with the existing constitution. They implied the destruction of that equilibrium between the magistrates, the Senate and the People to which Polybius rightly ascribed much of Rome's past success, and the development in its place of an unfettered democracy wherein effective sovranty would lie with that section of the citizen body which chanced to live at Rome. But, though their behaviour reveals a familiarity with the practices of Greece which is intelligible in pupils of Blossius and Diophanes, there is no reason to believe that either of the brothers set out from the beginning to create a democracy of the Hellenic type. So far as can be seen, if no attempt, like that of M. Octavius, had been made to block the *lex agraria* by veto, Tiberius would have left the constitution unimpaired. He was honestly convinced of the value of his agrarian scheme; and, if so excellent a measure had been accepted without protest, the weapon of obstruction would have been left intact for use against less worthy proposals. But when resistance came, Tiberius, convinced of the justice of his cause and declining to see his programme burked, secured its passage by recourse to means which boded ill. The dormant sovranty of the People was stirred to a new and sinister activity. There was, indeed, no cause for alarm so long as the popular hero, whose plans it would be the business of the assembly to enact, was a man with the honesty and patriotism of a Gracchus. But the peril of a democracy swayed by its first citizen is the shortness of the step from Pericles to Cleophon; and the error of the Gracchi was their failure to reflect that not all tribunes could boast a rectitude and public spirit such as theirs. Undoubtedly the system which they adumbrated was one which differed widely from the existing practice, and to that extent the Gracchi may justly be branded as revolutionary. But constitutional change found no place in their programmes as originally conceived. The measures wherein it was latent were hurriedly framed at a later stage to counter the irrational opposition of the conservatives, and the worst that can be said of the ill-considered replies is that their authors, in the enthusiasm of youth for a noble cause, did not pause adequately to consider the dangers which the State might run in days when there were tribunes less honest than themselves.

Whatever judgment may be passed on the characters and motives of the Gracchi, the wider significance of their careers, as a milestone in the course of Roman history, is clear. An elaborate attempt to remove some crying abuses of the day had been thwarted by the forces of conservatism. The mainspring of the opposition was the Senate, and to the Senate a challenge had been flung down.

The Assemblies had been used by both sides, and they were to remain pawns in the struggle henceforward. Issue had been joined about the future of the Roman constitution, and the revolutionary age had begun. When it ended with the principate of Augustus the tribunate and the Assemblies alike had sunk into insignificance, and the Senate itself only survived because its independence was henceforward to be curbed by monarchical control.

XVI. THE SENATE AND THE SETTLEMENT

The ten years which followed the death of Gaius Gracchus were a period of transition. First, by a judicious exploitation of its success, the Senate was returning to its old position of supremacy in the constitution; and secondly, though Roman history had not yet entered on the military phase which occupied the last decade of the century, domestic issues were receding into the background and there appears the man who, after the struggles with Jugurtha and with the Germanic invaders, was to become the first in that line of military *principes* which led in direct succession to Augustus.

At the outset there were some personal questions to be answered. The Gracchans, though the death of Gaius had been compassed with far more respect for the appearance of legality than that of his brother twelve years before, were by no means reconciled to the new weapon adopted by the Senate—the *s.c. de re publica defendenda*—and they determined to put to the test of a public trial the far-reaching claims which the action of the consul had implied. Accordingly Opimius was accused, and before long the People found themselves listening to what must have been one of the most acute and entertaining debates on the nature of law which ever flattered a Roman court[1]. The result is as surprising to us as it must have been gratifying to the Senate: Opimius was acquitted, and thereby the oligarchy won a signal victory, the significance of which has been discussed above (p. 89). Nor was this all. In the same year, 120 B.C., another tribune—L. Calpurnius Bestia, later one of the villains of the Jugurthine War —induced the People to go back not only on Gaius Gracchus but on itself by recalling P. Popillius Laenas, who had been the first victim of the Gracchan law against criminal courts established by the Senate (see above, p. 56 *sq.*).

Yet the conservative triumph was not complete: the most controversial of all the Gracchan laws—the Lex Acilia—still remained

---

[1] Cicero, *de orat.* ii, 30, 132; *part. orat.* 30, 104 *sqq.*

intact. Nor was there any lack of active opposition. It was a mere
symptom that Q. Scaevola, the son-in-law of Laelius and known
to posterity as the Augur, was prosecuted, probably in 119 B.C.,
on a charge of extortion in Asia, which he had lately governed:
but more importance belongs to the attack on C. Carbo. Carbo,
the ally of Gaius Gracchus and still a member of the agrarian
commission, had deserted the friends of his youth in a way which
could not command admiration. By whatever means he was
elected, he secured the consulship for 120 B.C. and marked his
tenure of the office by a defence of Opimius so whole-hearted that
he did not hesitate to assert that Gaius Gracchus had been justly
killed[1]. In the following year Carbo was accused, on a charge
which cannot now be ascertained, by a young man just embarking
on an oratorical career of a distinction unsurpassed until the age
of Hortensius and Cicero. This was L. Crassus, who in these early
days of his political life was far from being the staunch champion
of the Senate which he became in his later years[2], and his attack
was crowned with a success so great as to cause its author some
remorse when Carbo, without waiting for the verdict, ended his
life by eating Spanish flies.

The death of Carbo called for little lamentation in any quarter,
and such satisfaction as it gave the Gracchan party was at best the
pleasure of a small revenge on one who had deserted a sinking
ship. But though men could not appreciate its significance at the
time, the history of the year contained a promise of higher hope
for the fortunes of the cause which the Gracchi had at heart. It saw
the first political activity of one who, for all his faults, was to do
much towards raising the efficiency of the Roman government.
Gaius Marius, whose home was an obscure village in the territory
of Arpinum, had served with distinction under Scipio Aemilianus
in Spain; but nothing is known of his public career at Rome until
in 119 B.C. he held the tribunate. After the death of Scipio, Marius
found his most influential support in the great family of the
Metelli, who at this period dominated the political stage in
Rome. One of them—L. Metellus, afterwards Delmaticus—
was consul in this same year: and this fact gave the tribune an
opportunity to show the stuff of which he was made. He had
introduced a bill designed to carry on the good work begun by
the ballot-laws and still further to reduce the opportunities for
exercising pressure on the voters. The scope of the measure is

[1] Cicero, *de orat.* ii, 25, 106.
[2] This is shown by his attitude on the question of Narbo (see below,
p. 112 *sq.*).

obscure, but it was so much resented by the nobility that L. Cotta, the colleague of Metellus in the consulship, induced the Senate to summon Marius and demand an explanation of his conduct in promulgating a bill for which the previous approval of the Fathers seems not to have been asked. Marius came: there was an angry debate: and, when Metellus supported Cotta, Marius is said to have ordered Metellus' arrest. Thereupon the opposition collapsed; the bill was passed; and the People knew that it had at least one champion who was not afraid to face the Senate. Yet Marius was not an unmitigated demagogue: on another occasion during his tribunate he showed his ability to defy the clamour of the mob. The *lex frumentaria* of Gaius Gracchus was repealed at the instance of a certain M. Octavius[1]—not to be confused with the tribune of 133 B.C.—who proposed in its place an alternative less burdensome to the public finances[2]. When this happened we cannot say, and it is a mere possibility that 119 B.C. is the date. But, however that may be, the question of corn-distributions became an issue while Marius was tribune, and he did not hesitate to resist, with success, a measure which appears to have passed the limits of expediency in its popular appeal[3].

After failing to secure election as aedile, Marius scraped home last of the successful candidates for the praetorships of 115 B.C., and this office he managed to retain in spite of a prosecution for bribery. But his praetorship was not distinguished, and the year owes its interest rather to the consuls and the censors. One of the former was M. Aemilius Scaurus, made Princeps Senatus before his consulship was over—a man whose career demands notice for its similarity to that of Marius and also for its difference therefrom. Though Scaurus may have been descended from a family of some repute, he and Marius were alike in rising from humble beginnings to the highest offices of State. Both retained much of the brusque ruggedness which marked the class from which they had emerged, and neither was free from that greed for gain which the opportunities of office aroused in almost every Roman, and most of all in those to whom wealth was strange. But between these two there was one difference of the greatest moment. Scaurus, like Cicero, owed his highest advancement to the favour of the Senate. Though his policy was on some occasions his own, he married a daughter of Metellus Delmaticus—a lady who was subsequently wife of the dictator Sulla—and became in time the foremost spokesman of the senatorial cause—'cuius nutu prope terrarum

---

[1] Cicero, *Brutus*, 62, 222.   [2] Cicero, *de off.* II, 21, 72.
[3] Plutarch, *Marius*, 4, 4.

orbis regebatur[1]'—thereby acquiring a favourable repute in the
bulk of the historical tradition. Marius rose to power in the
Senate's despite, and the enormous influence which he won was
used against that body. Marius, therefore, had a hostile press;
and, were it not for Sallust, our knowledge of his achievement
would leave much to seek. Thanks to the monograph on the
Jugurthine War, the significance of his career is plain: the *novus
homo* who made his way on his merits, without help from the
nobility and despite their opposition, was the first of the *populares*
(see below, pp. 137 *sqq.*).

When Marius became consul another step had been taken
towards the Principate; but the consulship of Scaurus was a more
humdrum affair. Its most notable feature was the passing of a
Lex Aemilia dealing with the distribution of the freedmen through
the tribes. The problem was one which raised constitutional
issues of the first importance (see above, p. 8 *sq.*), but the detailed
considerations which determined the political opinion of the day
are not easy to ascertain. The votes of the freedmen were of use,
if to anyone, to their patrons; and, in other days, it would have
been in the interest of the senatorial class to give the freedman
vote the greatest influence which its numbers justified. Now, however, the position had been altered by the advent of the ballot: it
was no longer possible for a patron to count on the votes of his
freedmen as his own, and in less than thirty years the distribution
of the freedmen throughout the whole body of the thirty-five
tribes was to become a plank in the platform of the Senate's
enemies (see below, p. 203 *sq.*). The freedmen, to whom at first
the four urban tribes had been open, and who had later crept, on
strict conditions, into the rustic tribes as well, had been confined,
with the exception of those who were passing rich, to the single
urban *tribus Esquilina* during the censorship of Ti. Sempronius
Gracchus in 169 B.C. If that arrangement had hitherto been
observed, Scaurus must have proposed something of a more
liberal nature: but if, as is by no means unlikely, the obvious
unfairness of the system had led to its being tacitly ignored,
Scaurus may be assumed to have enacted rules which, while more
reasonable than to confine freedmen to one tribe out of thirty-five,
would serve nevertheless to protect the *tribus rusticae* from con-
tamination by a class which was clearly regarded with distrust.
In that case, the Senate was still looking to the country-tribes
for help against the city-following of any new Gracchus who might
arise. Scaurus also passed a law against the luxuries of the table,

---

[1] Cicero, *pro Fonteio*, 7, 24.

and in his campaign on behalf of public morals he had the assistance of the censors. Not only were thirty-two senators removed
from the Curia, but the stage was purged and its performances
reduced to a jejune simplicity scarcely to be commended by the
legitimate claim that its art was now wholly Italian.

Yet, in spite of these precautions, all was not well. In the
autumn of 114 b.c. Rome was stirred to its depths by rumours of
licence among the Vestal Virgins: suspicion fell upon three, but
when the Pontifex Maximus and his colleagues held an investigation only one was condemned. With the new year there followed an
assertion of popular authority significant enough even though the
occasion was not purely political. In indignation at the supposed
connivance of the *pontifices*, on the proposal of S. Peducaeus, a
tribune, the People established a court of its own to try the case
afresh, and in charge of it was put a man famous for his rigorous administration of justice. This terror to evil-doers—whose court was
called the 'scopulus reorum'—was L. Cassius Longinus, famous
for his inevitable question *Cui bono?*, and he brought to the investigation methods which must have satisfied the most raging thirst
for blood. Indeed it was agreed in later days that his conduct was
less than judicial. But the masses were in no mood for mercy, and
for the moment there was satisfaction at the punishment of the
two women formerly acquitted, together with some others: the
men involved were also attacked, but in their case no conviction is
recorded. And this was not all. Reference to authority, probably
of Etruscan origin, was found to indicate the propriety of making
human sacrifice. Accordingly, two Greeks and two Gauls were
slaughtered in the Forum Boarium[1], and Rome was dishonoured
by descent to a practice wholly foreign which, to the credit of the
Romans, was formally repudiated in 97 b.c. Such were the frenzied
efforts of a superstitious populace to placate the gods. Nevertheless
two years later, in 111 b.c., for three days the sky rained milk
and a large part of the city was destroyed in a disastrous conflagration[2].

XVII. THE STABILIZATION OF THE AGRARIAN
POSITION

In the period before the Jugurthine and Teutonic wars came
to occupy all the energies of Rome only one feature remains—
the series of measures whereby the status of the *ager publicus*, left
in great obscurity by the Gracchi, was reduced to order. The

[1] Plutarch, *Quaest. Rom.* 83.   [2] Obsequens 39 [99].

policy pursued in this matter has been the subject of much discussion. Some have seen in it an oligarchical attempt to undo the Gracchan achievement: others regard it as an honest effort to remove existing difficulties without disturbing the general situation. It has been observed above that the years following 121 B.C. were not marked by any overwhelming reaction: the Senate was again in the ascendant, but its enemies were by no means crushed. A ray of light on the agrarian history of the time may possibly be shed by a fragmentary inscription from La Malga[1] which contains in part three names, capable of restoration as those of C. Papirius Carbo, C. Sulpicius Galba and L. Calpurnius Bestia. According to the conjecture of Cichorius[2], a conjecture which is ingenious and attractive though admittedly beyond the reach of proof, this document preserves the composition of the agrarian commission after the deaths of Gaius Gracchus and M. Fulvius Flaccus, whom Galba and Bestia thus succeeded. If this interpretation were correct, it would be relevant to recall that Galba was son-in-law of a previous commissioner—P. Crassus Mucianus, who was himself the father of Gaius Gracchus' wife—so that one of the two vacant places would have been kept within the family as before. But, on the other hand, the attitude of Carbo had completely changed at latest by 120 B.C.: he was by then the Senate's man, Bestia had been foremost in securing the recall of Popillius Laenas, and, for the rest, both Galba and Bestia were among the senatorial victims of the Mamilian Commission in 109 B.C. Thus it appears that, if we know anything at all about the land-board after 121 B.C., our information suggests that it had a bias in favour of the conservative point of view, though the presence of Galba may betoken a desire to conciliate the other side.

The attack on the Gracchan legislation had begun even before the death of Gaius: Minucius Rufus had already sought to repeal the Lex Rubria (see above, p. 83), and in this he was ultimately successful. But the government did not abuse its return to power: for, though Junonia ceased to exist as a colony under that name, the settlers on the spot were allowed to retain their allotments, apparently on the same terms as the allottees in Italy[3], and it is also possible that Neptunia and Minervia were spared. For what follows Appian is our fundamental authority, and in the next ten

---

[1] Dessau 28.　　　　　　　　[2] *Römische Studien*, pp. 113 *sqq.*
[3] If the grants had originally been capable of ownership *optimo iure Quiritium*, they became *ager privatus vectigalisque*, either now or soon afterwards. Cf. E. Beaudouin in *Nouv. rev. hist. de droit français et étranger*, Année XVII, 1893, pp. 620 *sqq.*

years or so he records three laws dealing with the *ager publicus*[1]. First, perhaps still in 121 B.C., the Gracchan grants were made alienable. The clause of the Lex Sempronia now repealed has been discussed above (p. 24). It may well have been a temporary expedient, and it would be rash to assert that even its author would have resisted its withdrawal at this late date, when its purpose had probably been served. Still more dangerous is the assumption that the repeal was meant to open the way for a return of the *latifundia*. Appian's language is here so inaccurate that, as often, he is convicted of confusion, and his interpretation of the measure cannot be accepted as it stands. It is enough to reflect that, if, as we know to have been the case, the Gracchan plots still remained *ager publicus*, they would be debarred from incorporation in large estates unless the limit imposed by Tiberius Gracchus on the size of *possessiones* had been rescinded: no such *derogatio* of the Lex Sempronia is recorded, and the evidence of the extant *lex agraria* forbids its assumption. Under these circumstances the law of 121 B.C. is best regarded as the non-contentious cancellation of a clause, rightly enough inserted at the outset by Tiberius Gracchus, which, if retained, would have resulted in the absurdity of tying permanently to their allotments those small-holders who had failed to pay their way.

There follow the two measures whereby the existing situation was fixed and stabilized. First, probably in 119 B.C., the minds of those who still feared for the security of their tenure were set at rest by the abolition of the land-board: by now its work had been done (see above, p. 44), and there was no reason to protract the existence of a body whose mere presence was thought by some to be a threat. At the same time the concession, originally offered to the large *possessores* by Tiberius Gracchus but withdrawn before the passage of his bill, was restored. They were to be guaranteed the perpetual tenancy of such *ager publicus* as they had been allowed to retain, though in return for this assurance they were henceforward to pay the State that rent which had been due in the past until it was remitted by Tiberius[2]. The revenue thus gained was to be expended on some object of popular appeal, conceivably to make less unattractive than it would otherwise have been that modification of the *lex frumentaria* which was in the air at this time (see above, p. 95). After this there must be mentioned an enact-

---

[1] *Bell. Civ.* 1, 27.
[2] It is not easy to believe that the recipients of the Gracchan allotments, who had probably been exempted from the payment of rent by Livius Drusus (see above, p. 72), were now required to pay again.

ment, apparently passed in 112 B.C. when M. Livius Drusus was
one of the consuls, to confer some benefit on Latin and Italian
holders of public land; but nothing is known of its scope[1].

The settlement was completed by the measure preserved in
part on the back of the bronze sheet whose other side bears the
text of the Lex Acilia. This act[2], which may be dated with probability to 111 B.C., is a complicated attempt to have done with
disputes and to banish uncertainty, but its main intentions may be
briefly stated[3]. First, all *ager publicus* in Italy which had been dealt
with by the Gracchan commissioners, whether they had assigned
it in small lots either to isolated applicants or to prospective members of a colonial foundation, or had left it in the hands of long-
standing *possessores*, was, so long as the limits of the Lex Sempronia
were observed, to become the private property of its occupants.
The rent imposed by the previous law was in these cases consequently abolished. Secondly, *coloniae* and *municipia*, whether
Roman or Latin, were to be secured in their tenancy of all *ager
publicus* the use of which had been assigned to them corporately.
Finally, the system of squatting was to end: henceforward what
ager publicus remained was either to be let piecemeal on lease by
the censors or to be left open as common land (*ager compascuus*).

Such are the more important effects of the law so far as Italy is
concerned. The second half of the extant clauses deal with land in
Africa and at Corinth. Here the main object was to raise money
by the sale of public domain, possibly to make good in some degree the loss of revenue from Italy, but more probably to provide
funds for the war which had been declared on Jugurtha the
year before. In the present place these clauses call for notice
only because of the anxiety they display to safeguard all vested
interests, among others those of the colonists whom the Lex
Rubria had settled round Carthage. Both in its provincial arrangements and in those which bore on Italy the law displayed no
tendency to go back on the past: it accepts and simplifies the

---

[1] Bruns, *Fontes*[7], 11, l. 29.

[2] Bruns, *Fontes*[7], 11. About the authorship of this law it appears to the
present writer that Cicero (*Brutus*, 36, 136) and Appian (*Bell. Civ.* 1, 27, 122)
are in conflict, that Cicero should be preferred and, consequently, that the
man from whom it took its name was Sp. Thorius. But in a matter of much
uncertainty there is no need to insist on this point. For another view see Th.
Mommsen, *Ges. Schr.* 1, p. 70, and E. G. Hardy, *Six Roman Laws*, p. 47 *sq.*

[3] A completely different account of this measure would be required if the
suggestions of Ch. Saumagne (*Revue de Philologie*, Série III, vol. 1, 1927,
pp. 50 *sqq.*) could be accepted. Reasons for their rejection are given by
M. A. Levi in *Riv. Fil.* N.S. VII, 1929, pp. 231 *sqq.*

existing situation, and, though it did indeed pave the way for the growth of large estates in Africa, it rather helped than injured the classes whom it had been the design of the Gracchan programme to benefit. The moderation of the settlement may have been partly due to the circumstances of the moment: the beginning of a war is not the most appropriate time for controversial enactments on subjects unconnected with the main issue of the day. But the measure is in accord with the whole trend of agrarian legislation since the death of Gaius Gracchus. The work of the Gracchi was accepted: those who had profited were left with their gains intact: the situation of 121 B.C. was not undone but, so far as possible, made permanent: and the status of the public domains was subjected to a salutary simplification. So closed an epoch in the history of the *ager publicus*. As a source from which land could be found for distribution it was now near exhaustion. Little remained that was suitable except the precious Campanian domain; and so, if land was needed by the State hereafter, either confiscation or purchase in the open market would soon become inevitable. In another context too, the year 111 B.C. is a turning point. Hitherto land-allotments had been used to relieve unemployment due to ordinary economic causes: henceforward, thanks to the army reforms of Marius, the most pressing claim came from the ex-service man.

CHAPTER III

THE WARS OF THE AGE OF MARIUS

I. ASIA AND THE REVOLT OF ARISTONICUS

On his death in 133 B.C. Attalus III, the eccentric king of
Pergamum, was found to have left a will wherein the Roman
People had been instituted heir. The doubts cast on this story by
Sallust[1] were finally dispelled by the publication in 1890 of conclusive epigraphic evidence[2]; but the details of the bequest and
the reasons for which it was made still remain uncertain. It is a
plausible conjecture of Mommsen's that the action of Attalus, who
had no issue, is to be explained by nothing more subtle than the
traditional philo-Roman policy of his house and the reflection that
the greatness of Pergamum was due in reality to the generosity of
the settlement made by Manlius Vulso after the victory of Magnesia (vol. VIII, pp. 232 *sq.*). In any case his action did little more
than anticipate the consequences which before long must inevitably follow from Rome's habitual use of Pergamum as the
centre of the close control which she exercised over the affairs of
Asia. But, if the causes of the bequest are no great mystery, its
details remain to some extent obscure. When Florus[3] says that the
king left 'his property' to Rome, this is something less than the
whole truth. It appears from the inscription already mentioned
that the city of Pergamum itself, together with part of the surrounding country marked off by the testator as its special *territorium*, was to remain free; and it is not impossible that similar
exemption from the general purpose of the will was granted to
other Greek cities in the realm.

When news of the royal dispositions was brought to Italy, Rome
was in the midst of the exciting tribunate of Tiberius Gracchus,
and the way in which Gracchus sought to divert some part of the
bequest to the purposes of his agrarian scheme has been described
above (p. 30 *sq.*). It remains to consider the problem of foreign
policy with which Rome was now confronted. For fifty years or
more Asia had been included in the area whose affairs lay under
the general direction of Rome; but Roman influence had hitherto

---

[1] *Hist.* IV, 69, 8 M.   [2] *O.G.I.S.* 338 = *I.G.R.R.* IV, 289.
[3] I, 35 (II, 20) 2.

been exercised through her faithful henchmen on the throne of Pergamum. The development now in prospect was not one to be faced with confidence. For Rome suddenly to be saddled with the task of governing a large part of Asia Minor meant a change which, in the absence of a proper civil service or even of any adequate scheme of imperial administration, might give pause to minds less prejudiced against annexation than those which normally determined the action of the Senate. Nevertheless, the bequest of Attalus was accepted without hesitation, and its acceptance is a sign of that new spirit in foreign policy which marks the emergence of the commercial class as a power in the affairs of Rome.

The death of Attalus III seems to have befallen at a time when his kingdom, or at least its capital city, was shaken by social unrest. There was discontent among the less wealthy classes, which may well have been roused by the widespread repercussions of affairs in Sicily, and this is perhaps the explanation of a hurried measure taken by the citizens of Pergamum even before the will of the late king had been formally recognized by Rome. In the hope, it may be, of avoiding a servile war, the Pergamenes made generous grants of privilege to those sections of the population from which danger was particularly to be feared or whose loyalty was of especial value. Full citizenship was conferred on the *paroikoi* (vol. VIII, p. 598) and on several categories of mercenary troops, and at the same time certain slaves were raised to the status of *paroikoi*: but these concessions were categorically denied to all individuals who had left their homes already or might subsequently do so. The object of the enactment was apparently to stop the recruitment of some hostile force from a source whereon it might expect to draw. Meanwhile, in the latter part of 133 B.C., the Senate at Rome had passed a decree confirming all the acts of the kings of Pergamum up till the day before the death of Attalus III[1]; and at some time thereafter, probably not before the beginning of 132, a commission of five members, which included the egregious Scipio Nasica, was sent to Asia to make such arrangements as the situation required.

Whatever may have been the reasons for the appointment of this board, the presence of competent Roman representatives in the East was made the more urgent by a menacing development. The revolutionary elements suddenly found a leader during the early months of 132 B.C. in the person of a certain Aristonicus, who was thought to be the son of Eumenes II and an Ephesian concubine. This individual, whose achievements show him to have been

---

[1] *O.G.I.S.* 435 = *I.G.R.R.* IV, 301.

no fool, contrived to work up the widespread dissatisfaction with
the existing social order and the intelligible resentment felt in
certain quarters against the late king's bequest of his dominions to
Rome into an organized resistance to the new suzerain and all her
friends: thus the Roman government was given an immediate experience of the obligations incurred by accepting the inheritance
of the Attalids. Before long, isolated violence had developed into
warfare on an alarming scale. Like Mithridates Eupator in the
next century, Aristonicus seems at first to have conceived hopes
that the Greeks of Asia would join his cause; but though he got
possession of Leucae, and though Phocaea may have moved as
well, the fleet which he somehow contrived to raise was defeated
off Cyme by the Ephesians. Thus ended the first phase of the
affair. Aristonicus was now thrown back on the native populations
of the hinterland, whose interests naturally induced him to emphasize his programme of social reform and to allow nationalist
aspirations for independence to fall into the background.

This movement, which apparently began among the serfs of
the large estates and seems now to have drawn its main strength
from the semi-independent population of the Mysian uplands and
the regions to the south, took on a Utopian tone: Blossius of
Cumae (see above, p. 21) arrived from Italy, and the 'City of the
Sun'—the name of the Blessed Isle in the romance of Iambulus
(vol. VII, p. 265 sq.)—was the title chosen for the State which it
was proposed to found. At first Aristonicus met with some success.
even perhaps to the extent of winning Pergamum to his side[1]; and
there was a moment when other Greek cities, either perforce or
of their own free choice, lent him their support. Thyatira and
the neighbouring Apollonis were captured by the rebels[2], and in
due course revolt spread southwards towards Caria, where Halicarnassus was affected[3] and the loyalty of Samos and Myndus was
undermined. It was in the north, however, that the danger became
most grave; for there the attacks delivered on the coastal towns by
the Asiatic rebels were reinforced by a sympathetic movement of
the Thracian population beyond the Hellespont[4]. Thus the trouble
with which Rome was called upon to deal spread from Thrace down
to Caria, and its dimensions were such as to brook no trifling.

The commission sent out from Rome in 132 B.C. could do no
more than organize the inadequate materials for resistance available on the spot, which consisted of nothing but the armies of such

---

[1] *I.G.R.R.* IV, 292, ll. 13 *sqq.*   [2] Strabo XIV, 646.
[3] See A. Wilhelm in *Jahreshefte* XI, 1908, p. 69 *sq.*
[4] *O.G.I.S.* 339, ll. 16 *sqq.*—Sestos: cf. *I.G.R.R.* IV, 134—Cyzicus.

neighbouring kings as would direct their policy at Rome's behest. Such as they were, these monarchs loyally discharged their obligations. The faithful Mithridates V Euergetes of Pontus, who had shown his devotion to Rome during the Third Punic War, seems to have been responsible for the suppression of the movement in Pergamum itself[1], a service for which he was not to go unrewarded (see pp. 106, 221 sq.); Nicomedes II of Bithynia and Pylaemenes of Paphlagonia lent a hand; and Ariarathes V of Cappadocia, whose conduct in the past had not always been above reproach, actually fell in the course of the war [2]. But all this was not enough: it was obviously necessary that a Roman army should be sent to Asia. Accordingly troops were raised, and in 131 B.C. they reached the scene of operations under the consul Crassus Mucianus. The campaign of Crassus against Aristonicus is too ill-recorded to be followed in detail. At some time early in 130 B.C., he is found engaged in the siege of Leucae, the earliest headquarters of the enemy; but a sudden attack compelled him to retire thence towards the north, and during the retreat he was captured by a squadron of Thracian cavalry, in whose hands he somehow met his death. The command of the Roman forces passed without delay to M. Perperna, consul of 130 B.C., with whose advent Rome began to win the upper hand. Aristonicus was so seriously defeated in the first engagement that he withdrew behind the walls of Stratoniceia, by which is probably meant the city of that name in Caria (Eski-Hissar); and there, after a siege, he and his followers were forced to surrender. Aristonicus, together with much wealth from the treasure of the Attalids, was forthwith shipped to Rome, where sooner or later he perished in the Tullianum: but Perperna did not live to enjoy the triumph he deserved. Sometime in 129 B.C. he was carried off by sudden death while still at Pergamum, and thus the way was opened for M'. Aquilius, consul of 129, who had already shown signs of a determination to see that Perperna should leave his natural successor some excuse for a campaign. But the revolt was now so completely broken that, for military operations, Aquilius had to be content with a solemn progress to restore order in such outlying regions as the remoter parts of Mysia[3], and for the rest he was free to proceed with the work which gives him a more serious claim to notice—the organization of the Roman province of Asia.

---

[1] I.G.R.R. iv, 292, ll. 13 sqq.   [2] Justin xxxvii, 1, 2.
[3] See M. Holleaux in Rev. É.A. xix, 1919, p. 2, ll. 13 sqq. It was on this expedition that Aquilius, by poisoning the wells, descended to a practice which even the Romans did not fail to resent (Florus i, 35 (ii, 20), 7).

Aquilius and the ten senatorial commissioners sent out to assist him seem to have set about their task with the characteristic determination to keep for Rome what was worth having and to dispose of the rest. The rich and fertile lands in the west of the peninsula were formed into the province of Asia, but the higher and less valuable country to the east was available to be bestowed on those of the neighbouring powers whose services to Rome deserved some tangible reward. For these boons there was long and troublesome competition. Lycaonia, indeed, soon learnt its destination: it was handed to the heirs of the Cappadocian Ariarathes V, who had died while fighting Aristonicus (pp. 105, 235). But a graver problem was presented by Greater Phrygia, the rough but by no means valueless region which stretched from Lydia up to the borders of Galatia. For this there were two rival claimants, neither of whom could be lightly brushed aside: one was Mithridates Euergetes of Pontus, the other Nicomedes II of Bithynia. So difficult was the decision between this pair that Aquilius and his colleagues, so it was alleged, simply knocked down the prize to the highest bidder, who happened to be the Pontic king. This decision, however, was violently contested both by the Bithynian party and by various interested sections in the political world at Rome. The dispute was long. Though Aquilius celebrated a triumph on 11 November 126 B.C., he was subsequently accused of corruption; and so widespread was the belief in his guilt that the acquittal in which the trial ended supplied Gaius Gracchus with one of his many arguments for the necessity of reform in the *quaestio repetundarum*[1]. But this was by no means all. Gaius Gracchus himself resisted a bill proposed by one Aufeius, whose object was to confirm the grant of Phrygia to Mithridates[2]; but, though Gracchus changed the financial administration of the Roman province (see above, p. 64 *sq.*), Rome was still refusing to recognize the Pontic claims to Phrygia when Mithridates V died in 120 B.C. Thereafter, possibly in 116 B.C.[3], the question was answered in a way which had much to commend it to the Roman point of view. Phrygia was not given to either set of claimants: instead, the preliminary grant to Pontus was finally revoked, if this had not been done some time before[4], and the communities of the country seem to have been organized into some loose form of league, which was perhaps placed under the general supervision of the governor of Asia. Thus in the end Rome emerged

[1] Appian, *Bell. Civ.* I, 22, 92; see above, p. 70.
[2] See Malcovati, *Or. Rom. Frag.* II, p. 137 *sq.*
[3] Cf. *O.G.I.S.* 436=*I.G.R.R.* IV, 752.   [4] Cf. Appian, *Mith.* 57.

with a province of the greatest value and with control over the vast
area of Phrygia; but the vacillation and corruption which marked
her progress to this satisfactory end are a discreditable chapter in
the history of Republican diplomacy.

II. THE EASTERN EUROPEAN FRONTIER

From the Black Sea to the Pyrenees Rome was engaged during
the period from 129 B.C. to the end of the second century in a
series of campaigns which, though often individually negligible,
together did much to lay the foundations of the later frontier.
Their most valuable result was to forge links of connection between the hitherto isolated areas of Roman occupation in Spain,
Italy, the Balkan Peninsula and Asia. In the section of the line
between the Black Sea and the Alps, Rome already controlled
three *points d'appui*. On the east lay the Thracian Chersonese,
which had formed part of the Pergamene legacy and had afterwards been loosely attached to the province of Macedonia. Next
came Macedonia itself. And, finally, on the west was Illyricum—
a district wherein Roman interests were so pronounced that the
first steps towards its organization as a province seem to have been
taken so early as 167 B.C. It was left for the Principate to establish
Roman arms along the whole length of the Danube; but during
the years here under consideration rapid progress was made towards stretching a continuous line of Roman territory along the
north coast of the eastern Mediterranean.

Such campaigns as were conducted to the north of the Italian
peninsula itself were so brief and so circumscribed in area that they
call for no detailed notice. In 118 B.C. Q. Marcius Rex attacked
the Stoeni, an Alpine tribe whose home is probably to be placed
in the mountains north-west of the Lago di Garda; but thereafter
nothing more of outstanding note is recorded to have happened
until 94 B.C., when Lucius Crassus, the orator, combed out the
southern foothills of the Alps and so did much to secure the
peace of the northern Italian plain[1]. Farther east, however,
activity was more continuous. The successes of Servius Flaccus
on the Dalmatian coast and of M. Cosconius in the hinterland
(135 B.C.) had produced no lasting settlement of Illyricum, and
Roman armies were again in the field by 129 B.C. C. Sempronius
Tuditanus, consul of that year, had taken himself off to the eastern
coast of the Adriatic for reasons which were not wholly military
(see above, p. 42); but, whatever its urgency may have been, he

[1] Cicero, *de inv.* II, 37, 111; *in Pis.* 26, 62.

called attention to his arrival by delivering an attack on the in-habitants of the Carso—a people known to Rome as the Iapudes. The result for the consul was an undeniable defeat, which it required the skill of D. Junius Brutus, the hero of the Spanish wars (vol. VIII, p. 316), to retrieve: but with the help of Brutus he won some signal successes of which notable monuments survive[1], and Roman arms were carried through Dalmatia as far as Zara and beyond.

For ten years after this there was peace, but in 119 B.C. a fresh rising of the natives opened a long period of continuous fighting. It seems that early in this year[2] the governor of Macedonia, Sextus Pompeius, found himself in conflict with the Scordisci, a great Gallic tribe who, during the migrations of the third cen-tury B.C., had settled south of the lower Save and whose territory extended to the east even across the Morava. In the course of the fighting Pompeius was killed, and, though the situation was retrieved for the moment by his quaestor, a certain M. Annius, Rome had sustained a reverse which could not be overlooked. The duty of restoring Roman prestige belonged to L. Metellus, possibly with the help of L. Cotta[3], his colleague in the consulship of 119 B.C. During this year and the next he conducted some successful campaigns which in the end brought him back to Salonae, where he passed a winter[4]. Thence he returned to celebrate a triumph in 117 B.C. and to assume the name 'Delmaticus.' Then, in 115 B.C. M. Aemilius Scaurus pushed eastwards from Aquileia across the Julian Alps and established Roman influence among the Taurisci and other peoples round the head-waters of the Save. But Mace-donia was still the scene of the most pressing danger. The next event of which any adequate evidence is preserved was a severe defeat inflicted by the Scordisci on C. Cato, consul of 114 B.C.—a defeat so decisive that the enemy were able even to raid Greece as far as Delphi; and the situation was made the more serious by the presence in these regions of the roving Cimbrian horde (see below, p. 141). In 113 B.C. Macedonia, now almost regularly a consular province, fell to C. Metellus Caprarius, whose attention seems to have been engaged by the tribes of Thrace; and in 112 B.C. he was joined by one of his successors in the consulship, M. Livius Drusus, the tribune of 122 B.C. Both those commanders subse-

[1] Pliny, *N.H.* III, 129; Dessau 8885. Cf. also B. Tamaro in *N.S.A.*, Serie sesta, I, 1925, pp. 1 *sqq.*

[2] Ditt[3]. 700: for the date see M. N. Tod in *B.S.A.* XXIII, 1918–9, pp. 206 *sqq.* and *ib.* XXIV, 1919–21, pp. 54 *sqq.*, especially p. 56.

[3] Appian, *Ill.* 10.   [4] Appian, *Ill.* 11.

quently triumphed in Rome; but a lacuna in the Fasti leaves us in
doubt about the identity of the people over whom Metellus won
his victories. Drusus, however, is definitely recorded as conqueror
of the Scordisci, and it may be assumed that it was he who repaired
the damage done by the disaster to Cato. Indeed, the success of
his operations is indicated by the story that he even advanced to
the banks of the river Danube[1].

Even so, however, the resistance of the Scordisci went on, and
M. Minucius Rufus, one of the consuls of 110 B.C., opened a new
campaign, which duly produced its triumph in 106 B.C. and there-
with a famous monument in Rome—the Porticus Minucia, the
scene of the public distributions of corn during the early Empire[2].
But the final pacification of this frontier was left for another hand,
and for one which cannot be recognized with confidence. The
vague story of Appian[3] shows that, while peace was made with
the Maedi of the Strymon valley and with the Dardani who lived
along the banks of the Morava, the Scordisci in the end were so
hard hit that only a remnant survived to take refuge on the
Danube or beyond. Yet they are recorded still to have been
fighting Rome in 76 B.C., and it must be assumed that about the
end of the second century some temporary pacification was
achieved which did not involve their final expulsion.

If the L. Scipio to whom Appian ascribes the final settlement
is the same as the consul of 83 B.C., the absence of serious fighting
during the fifteen years or so after 100 B.C. would suggest that the
back of the resistance had been broken by one of his predecessors;
but the identity of this person is hard to fix. One figure alone
stands out. In the last years of the second century T. Didius was
praetorian governor of Macedonia, and his period of office was
marked by an extension of the provincial frontiers[4]. This fact,
together with his celebration of a triumph[5] and his rapid rise to
the consulship in 98 B.C. although he was a *novus homo*, is our only
clue of value to the date of the decisive Roman success and to the
name of at least one among its authors. For the rest there is nothing to mention beyond some minor operations on the Thracian
front, where Roman successes are recorded in 104 and 97 B.C.:
but their importance was probably small, for no trace of them is
to be found in the Acta Triumphorum, which are extant for the
latter year. It seems that from the time of T. Didius quiet prevailed on the eastern European frontier until in the eighties of
the last century B.C. a fresh disturbance and another inroad into

---

[1] Florus I, 39 (III, 4), 5.   [2] Cf. also Dessau 8887.   [3] *Ill.* 5.
[4] *S.E.G.* III, 378, ll. 28–9.   [5] Cicero, *in Pis.* 25, 61.

Greece provoked the campaigns of Cn. Dolabella after his consulship in 81 B.C. and so inaugurated a period of renewed activity which culminated in the achievements of C. Curio and M. Lucullus.

III. THE WESTERN EUROPEAN FRONTIER

Even before the middle of the second century B.C. the peoples of southern Gaul, either under the pressure of incipient movements in the far North-East or, more probably, confident in the strength of the loose political unity which had been formed round the tribe of the Arverni, had raided the territory of Massilia and compelled Rome to support her old friend and ally by military intervention. The campaigns of Q. Opimius, though they led to no immediate annexation by Rome, left Massilia with her territory enlarged and her security against the surrounding tribes guaranteed by an arrangement for the permanent deposit of hostages in her hands (vol. VIII, p. 330). Less than thirty years later the Gallic pressure was renewed—at a time when the circumstances of Roman politics had so far changed that the incident was gratefully seized by the government as an excuse for military operations on a scale so extensive that the permanent occupation of southern Gaul was their almost inevitable result. Not only were the commercial classes a rising power in politics, but the Senate itself seems to have welcomed an undertaking which would distract the attention of the voters from alarming proposals of domestic reform. Accordingly, when the Massiliotes asked Roman aid against the raids of the Salluvii, an army was sent north under the command of M. Fulvius Flaccus, the friend of the Gracchi and a consul of 125 B.C. In that year or the next he marched across the Western Alps and fought against the Salluvii of the coast, and the Ligures and Vocontii to the north of the Durance, with such success that on his return to Rome he was allowed the honour of a triumph in 123 B.C. But the victories of Flaccus were not decisive, and it was left to a successor, C. Sextius Calvinus—a consul of 124 B.C.—to pacify the immediate neighbourhood of the Massilian territory. Calvinus had to face the same peoples as Flaccus, and he did so with determination. Pressure on the enemy was maintained by a long series of engagements, until finally a considerable army mustered by the Salluvii was decisively beaten, and the 'city' of that tribe, which probably stood on the plateau of Antremont, a couple of miles to the north-east of Aix-en-Provence, was captured. For the moment the war was at an end. The territory of Massilia was again enlarged, but this time peace was to depend on a surer guarantee than the deposit of hostages with the Massiliotes. By founding the *castellum* of Aquae Sextiae[1], the object of which was undoubtedly to reinforce Massilia in the task of keeping open communications between Italy and Spain, Sextius took the first irrevocable step towards the creation of a province in southern France[2].

When Sextius celebrated his well-merited triumph in 122 B.C., his achievements had already begun to produce their inevitable result. The defeat of the outlying Gallic tribes and the establishment of Roman occupation beyond the western Alps caused widespread alarm in Gaul, and before long the Arverni themselves, who claimed a general hegemony of the country, took the field under their king Bituitus. With them the powerful people of the Allobroges was in alliance, while their rivals the Aedui took the side of Rome[3]. Cn. Domitius Ahenobarbus, consul of 122 B.C., was sent north with an army of considerable dimensions, which even included a number of elephants; but, before opening hostilities, he tried the method of negotiation. However, when the Allobroges were summoned to surrender the fugitive leaders of the Salluvii to whom they were giving shelter, their reply was to march southwards against the Romans, and thereupon, probably in 121 B.C., Domitius set out to meet them. A mission sent by Bituitus could not fool him into delaying while reinforcements from the Arverni joined the Gallic forces already in the field, and on the banks of the Rhône, somewhere between Avignon and Orange, the Allobroges were crushingly defeated: according to Orosius[4] the enemy lost three thousand prisoners and twenty thousand killed. But the main strength of the formidable Arverni had not yet been brought to bear; so Rome sent out fresh troops under Q. Fabius Maximus, consul of 121 B.C. The Arverni and their allies, led by Bituitus himself, crossed the Rhône at a point not far from Valence[5], and there, on the eastern bank, in the month

---

[1] Aquae Sextiae probably did not receive the status of *colonia* until after the eclipse of Massilia at the end of the Republic.   [2] Strabo IV, 180.

[3] The authorities are here so discordant that the course of operations cannot confidently be described. On the general sequence of events the Livian tradition, supported by Valerius Maximus (IX, 6, 3), is in conflict with the stray remarks of Strabo and Velleius and is not easy to reconcile with the Acta Triumphorum. Nevertheless, the story told by Livy appears to have been on the whole more plausible than its rivals, and attempts to construct an alternative have not met with marked success.   [4] V, 13, 2.

[5] It is possible, however, that the Isar of Strabo (IV, 185) and the Isara of Pliny (*N.H.* VII, 166) and Florus (I, 37 (III, 2), 4) are not the Isère but the Eygues, in which case the battle would have been fought in the neighbourhood of Orange.

of August 121[1] they were beaten in a final and decisive encounter. By this battle the fate of southern Gaul was sealed. Though Bituitus himself was still at large, the control of the country south of the Cevennes was at the disposal of Rome, and Rome at this time was in no mind to refuse her opportunities.

While Fabius returned home to celebrate a triumph, which was commemorated by his new surname 'Allobrogicus' and by the Fornix Fabianus now erected at the east end of the Roman Forum, Domitius stayed behind in Gaul to complete the work of settlement. Not only was Bituitus captured and sent a prisoner to Italy, but the Allobroges formally submitted to Rome, and their neighbours followed suit in succession until Domitius found at his disposal a territory stretching from Geneva to the Pyrenees. Geographically, though it was marked off to some extent by the mountain barrier of the Cevennes, and though its population was ethnically different, at least in part, from that of the rest of Gaul, this region was not a perfect unity, and its security was scarcely assured even when a number of the surrounding peoples, among whom the Aedui and Sequani were the most famous, formally became the Friends and Allies of the Roman People. But, whatever its military weakness, it supplied the corridor between Italy and Spain which was one of Rome's most urgent needs, and for that reason alone the creation of a province was inevitable. Domitius was back in Rome before the end of 120 B.C.; for, like his colleague Fabius, he triumphed in that year. Yet, short as the time available had been, the province was already formed. Massilia, left in control of the coastal region through which the Via Julia Augusta later ran, was responsible for the safety of such traffic as might pass that way. Farther west, between the Rhône and the Pyrenees, the Romans addressed themselves to the construction of a great trunk road which connected Tarascon[2] with the Col du Perthus and took the name 'Via Domitia' from its designer.

There remained one further step—to begin the development of the new resources thus brought within the reach of Roman enterprise. In 118 B.C., or shortly before that date, it was proposed to send a colony of Roman citizens to Transalpine Gaul—a proposal painfully reminiscent of Junonia. In spite of resistance from the Senate, which seems even to have gone so far as to contest the project after it had been passed[3], Narbo Martius was founded as rival and successor to the large Celtiberian city of Nero,

---

[1] Pliny, *N.H.* VII, 166.   [2] Polybius III, 39, 8; Strabo IV, 178.
[3] Cicero, *pro Cluentio*, 51, 140.

thanks in some degree to the energetic support of the young L. Crassus, whose career as an orator was now beginning[1]. Though the circumstances of the dispute are lost beyond recall, the affair is significant. It shows the Senate by no means master of the political situation, even after Gaius Gracchus had been dead three years, and it invites the conjecture that the commercial interests were taking an active part in the determination of policy. Doubtless, even after the Gracchan legislation, there remained a surplus proletariate in Rome, some members of which may have been anxious for an opportunity to earn a substantial livelihood in Gaul: but it is difficult to believe that they alone were strong enough to overcome the opposition of the Senate, nor, to judge from his policy in later life, is it likely that these were the people for whom Crassus spoke. The influence which forced this foundation on the Senate, like that revealed in the occupation of the Balearic Islands and perhaps also in the Jugurthine War (see below, pp. 152 *sq.* and 132 *sq.*), is more probably to be found in the commercial section of the upper classes—a section which was now beginning to search with zest for new fields of exploitation and investment and which ended by striking its roots deep in Gallia Narbonensis, a region which soon could be described as 'Italia verius quam provincia[2].'

IV. THE *BELLUM JUGURTHINUM* OF SALLUST

The scene now shifts to the southern shore of the Mediterranean. Peace was being restored by degrees on the European frontier. Operations, indeed, might still be necessary in Illyricum and Macedonia, and the incalculable menace of the German invasion was not far off; but for the next eight years the focus of interest in Roman history is moved to Africa. The Jugurthine War was an episode of far-reaching influence, and Sallust does not exaggerate when he asserts that its repercussions may be traced down to the end of the Republic. The more serious aspects of the affair must be reserved for notice after a sketch of the campaigns; but at the outset, if the evidence is to yield the conclusions which it contains, something must be said in general about the nature of the authorities.

Though they may add an occasional mite, the minor extant sources—Livy (whose version is only known through the

---

[1] For a monument of the part played by Crassus in this affair see *B.M.C. Rep.* I, pp. 184 *sqq.* and III, plate XXX, 10–14, as interpreted by H. Mattingly in *J.R.S.* XII, 1922, pp. 230 *sqq.* See Volume of Plates IV, 2, *d*, *e*, *f*.   [2] Pliny, *N.H.* III, 31; cf. Cicero, *pro Fonteio*, 5, 11.

Epitomes and the derivative works of Eutropius and Orosius), Plutarch, Appian and Dio—are so superficial and so fragmentary that, with the aid of their contributions alone, it would be impossible either to reconstruct the story of the war or even to appreciate its significance. It is on the monograph of Sallust that our knowledge depends, and a proper use of the material which it provides is only possible if the nature and origin of the work are rightly understood. There is no reason to doubt that Sallust's interest in African affairs was stimulated by his personal connection with the country: he went there with Caesar in 47 B.C. and subsequently became the first governor of Africa Nova. But for a mind like his the war against Jugurtha had peculiar attractions of its own. After the hackneyed professions whereby the historians of the Hellenistic age were wont to justify their calling, Sallust goes on to ask the reader's notice for his theme, not only because the struggle was long and grim, with many vicissitudes of fortune, but also because it was the first occasion on which a challenge was thrown down to the proud claims of the *nobilitas* (*Bell. Jug.* 5, 1). This latter feature is the real subject of the work. The Gracchi, indeed, had shown undeniable signs of resistance to the Senate, but from a man of Sallust's outlook their achievement could exact at most a passing tribute of respect. Sallust was a follower of Julius Caesar, and the political descent of the great dictator was traced, not from the Gracchi, but from the earlier *populares*, among whom the Gracchi cannot strictly be included: and of the outstanding *populares* by far the most famous was Gaius Marius (see pp. 137 *sqq.*). The aim of Sallust is to show how Marius started on the course which was to leave him in the end the foremost citizen of Rome and to reveal how for the first time, though by no means for the last, a *novus homo* rescued the State from a situation which the incompetence and corruption of the *nobilitas* had rendered desperate.

If such was his object, it is idle to suppose that Sallust felt himself compelled to give an exact and detailed description of the African campaigns. Indeed, had he regarded accuracy and completeness as essential to his purpose, he could scarcely have essayed to write the work at all. When he was in Africa, more than half a century had elapsed since the end of the period with which he deals, and at that late stage to co-ordinate such oral tradition as survived would have been wholly beyond the power of a man whose time was absorbed by the business of administration. The bare outline of events might be more or less familiar, and doubtless a few of the more outstanding incidents lingered in popular memory: but it is obvious that, even if Sallust had conceived the idea of writing on the Jugurthine affair before he left Africa for good, his chief debt is to the scanty information preserved in literature.

About these sources little need be said, but that little is of the first importance. The outstanding peculiarity of the *Bellum Jugurthinum* is its unevenness. The work may be roughly divided into three sections—the story down to the beginning of 109 B.C. (cc. 1–42), the campaigns of Metellus (cc. 43–86), and the command of Marius (cc. 87–114)—and it is remarkable that on events in Africa Sallust has far better information for the first and second of these periods than for the third. This weakness of Sallust on the third phase becomes the more striking when it is remembered that here he is dealing with the crowning achievements of his chosen hero, and that the only passages in this section which lay any claim to detailed accuracy are those which concern the doings of a man for whom Sallust had no affection—the future dictator Sulla. The first conclusion from this evidence is clear: Sallust is not following any single contemporary source written on a scale approaching that of his own monograph. If he took as his basis some earlier record of the war as a whole—whether this be the work of P. Sempronius Asellio or the treatment to be found in the *Historiae* of Posidonius—this history was a superficial production of which the weakness is revealed in the final section of the *Bellum Jugurthinum*. At most it supplied a sketchy outline of the affair, which it was the task of Sallust to fill in with the aid of other documents more adequate though less continuous. Of the more copious sources there are three in particular which it is reasonable to conjecture that Sallust may have used. For the preliminary negotiations and the fighting during the command of L. Calpurnius Bestia valuable information must have been preserved in the three books *De vita sua* by M. Aemilius Scaurus—books which Cicero[1] describes as 'sane utiles, quos nemo legit': but, if Cicero himself had read them, Sallust may well have done the same, though it is obvious that this was not the source of those aspersions on the honesty of Scaurus with which Sallust makes free. In the second section, where Metellus is the central figure, there are signs of indebtedness to the writings of P. Rutilius Rufus, who himself was serving in Africa at the time. And finally, in the concluding chapters, where the operations of Marius are described, the economy of detail in almost every episode wherein Sulla takes no part lends colour to the obvious conjecture that

[1] *Brutus*, 29, 112.

Sallust is here filling in his outline with incidents taken from the *Memoirs* of the dictator. Thus it appears that Sallust's method was to block out a flimsy framework, derived from some source which can no longer be identified, with details drawn from various other publications of which three may still be recognized with some degree of probability.

Successful though it be as a work of art, in its construction the *Bellum Jugurthinum* is a patchwork, and its patchwork nature raises the question of the degree of chronological accuracy which Sallust is likely to have attained in the conflation of his varied materials. Had it been his object merely to provide a permanent record of the course which the war pursued, we might regret his failure and be grateful for the ingenuity which has been expended in modern times on the problems, both of topography and of time, which his text presents. But, if it be true that the interests of Sallust lay in the political life of Rome during the Caesarian age rather than in the details of warfare in Africa half a century before, it becomes rash to assume that his narrative was designed to stand microscopic examination. In what follows the main outlines of the story told by Sallust will be accepted, but no stress will be laid on minor points of geography and chronology: for these are just the points to which Sallust himself devoted no special care.

V. THE OUTBREAK OF THE JUGURTHINE WAR

The story of the relations between Rome and the kingdom of Eastern Numidia has for the most part been told already (vol. VIII, pp. 471 *sqq.*). Selfish as Roman policy had often been, the common hostility towards Carthage by which both powers were moved had preserved an unbroken friendship between Rome and Masinissa from 204 B.C. until the death of the king at the age of ninety in 148. To the Numidians this friendship had by no means been without profit. Though the country was a Roman protectorate, its boundaries had been so generously extended as to make it one of the largest states in the contemporary world. After the capture of Syphax, Masinissa had been given western Numidia as an addition to his own dominions, and before his death his realm stretched from Mauretania in the west to the borders of Cyrene in the east. Such was the happy situation when, within the space of three years, two dangerous events occurred. In 148 B.C. the passing of Masinissa removed a staunch friend of Rome from the control of Numidian affairs, and two years later the destruction of Carthage finally banished the fears which, since the end of the third century, had driven Numidia consistently to seek the support of her Italian ally.

For the moment, however, peaceful relations were maintained. The heritage of Masinissa was divided by Scipio Aemilianus between the three legitimate sons of the dead king—Micipsa, Gulussa and Mastanabal; and when, soon afterwards, the deaths of Gulussa and Mastanabal left Micipsa the sole heir to the kingdom of his father, Micipsa showed himself faithful to his father's policy towards Rome. After Mastanabal had died, Micipsa, who seems still to have been childless himself, gave shelter at his court to a son of Mastanabal named Jugurtha, whom Masinissa had refused to recognize as a prince of the blood because his mother was a concubine. Before long, however, Micipsa himself became the father of two sons—Adherbal and Hiempsal, a pair whom it was natural for Jugurtha to regard with the jealousy of a rival, and already by 134 B.C. Jugurtha had shown himself a man of such force and popularity that Micipsa placed him in command of the Numidian contingent sent to the siege of Numantia, hoping, according to Sallust, that he would leave his bones in Spain. But so far was this from being his fate that Jugurtha won the high esteem of Scipio, besides an intimate familiarity with Roman methods of warfare and a claim on the goodwill of Rome; and when he returned to Africa, he brought from the commander a letter of generous testimony to his merits. Thereafter, at a date which it is impossible to fix, for this or for some other reason Micipsa adopted Jugurtha as his son, and on his death about 118 B.C.[1] left him joint heir to the kingdom with Adherbal and Hiempsal. The interest aroused in Rome by this event may perhaps be seen in the visit to Africa of M. Porcius Cato, consul of 118 B.C., who died before his work there, whatever it may have been, was finished[2].

Bickerings began forthwith. Probably in 117 B.C.[3], even before the division of the kingdom had been arranged, Hiempsal was murdered at Jugurtha's instigation, and Numidia was immediately rent by faction: the majority remained loyal to Adherbal, but a strong party of the bolder spirits gathered round Jugurtha. Having sent a mission to Rome to report his brother's death, Adherbal offered armed resistance to Jugurtha when his

[1] Livy, *Epit.* 62.
[2] Gellius, *N.A.* xiii, 20(19), 9–10. See, however, S. Gsell, *Histoire ancienne de l'Afrique du Nord* vii, p. 65 *sq.*
[3] Livy, *Epit.* 62.

own turn came to be attacked, but he was completely defeated at the opening of the campaign and followed his envoys to Italy as a fugitive. The time had now arrived when Jugurtha, for the moment undisputed master of Numidia, must consider the attitude of his suzerain; and accordingly he too dispatched an embassy to Rome, laden, it is said, with the bribes whose potency on the Roman nobility he had come to know at Numantia. Thus, in 116 B.C. or thereabouts, the Senate was called upon to mediate between the rival claimants to the Numidian throne. The merits of the case cannot have been easy to assess. Stories in flat contradiction were told by the contending sides, and the Senate had no means of testing their veracity, save perhaps by observing the flagrant bribery practised by the Jugurthine deputation. This open corruption led M. Aemilius Scaurus and a few others to uphold Adherbal's cause: but, so far as could be seen, both sides were alike in their devotion to Rome, and the Senate not unreasonably decided on a compromise. A commission of ten, led by the notorious L. Opimius, was sent to Africa with instructions to divide Numidia between the cousins; and in the end, after negotiations in which bribes are again alleged to have played their part, Jugurtha received the west and Adherbal the east, with Cirta as his capital.

Such was the settlement of 116 B.C. The chronology of the following events is lost beyond hope of recovery. Before long the restless Jugurtha sought to provoke a war with Adherbal by making a sudden raid on his territory, and, when this produced no more than a diplomatic protest, it was followed by a full-dress invasion. Adherbal was now forced to resist; but his army was routed in a night attack on its camp between Cirta and the sea, and Cirta itself would have fallen immediately had not Adherbal escaped to the city and organized the resident Italian traders for its defence. Meanwhile, as soon as news arrived that fighting had been renewed, the Senate had sent a deputation of three young men to demand a cessation of hostilities; but the mission, though it was courteously received by Jugurtha, was denied access to Adherbal and returned to Italy with nothing done. Next came a letter, smuggled through the enemy lines at Cirta, in which Adherbal implored the Senate to take immediate action for his relief, and by this appeal opinion in Rome was so far stirred that, in spite of the activity of Jugurtha's partisans, a new embassy, in which Scaurus himself had a place, was on its way to Africa within three days. Having delivered an unsuccessful assault on Cirta, Jugurtha tightened the siege and then obeyed the summons of the ambassadors to meet them in the Roman province: but much talk again produced no result, and the Romans returned to Italy while Jugurtha settled his account with Adherbal. After the lamentable weakness which the Senate had displayed, Adherbal was at the mercy of his enemy, and by opening the gates of Cirta at the instance of the Italians, who had been the backbone of the defence, at most he anticipated an inevitable fate. That Adherbal was done to death without delay is no matter for surprise; but it was a startling sign of Jugurtha's contempt for Rome that, besides the native garrison, he slaughtered all those Italians who had fought against him[1].

When the news of these events reached Rome during the latter part of the summer of 112 B.C., any danger that the friends of Jugurtha in high places would induce the Senate to condone their patron's behaviour was averted by the energetic action of one Gaius Memmius, who had already been elected tribune for the following year. Whether of its own free will or through fear of the popular indignation to which Memmius gave voice, the Senate made Italy and Numidia the provinces for the consuls of 111 B.C.; and, after P. Scipio Nasica and L. Calpurnius Bestia had been elected, Numidia fell by lot to the latter. Bestia, the tribune of 121 B.C. (see above, p. 93), was an able man whose gifts were ruined by his venality: Scipio, a person of outstanding honesty and attractive character, died before his consulship was done. The government was now filled with determination. When an embassy from Jugurtha approached, it was expelled from Italy: an expeditionary force was recruited, Bestia formed a staff which included Scaurus, and in 111 B.C. the army opened operations in Africa. But then there followed a surprising change. Bestia had penetrated no more than the fringe of Numidian territory when negotiations were suddenly begun; and, before the summer was over, Jugurtha had contrived to purchase recognition by the surrender of thirty elephants, large numbers of cattle and horses and a small sum of money.

The reason for Bestia's agreement to these easy terms Sallust is quick to supply by suggestions of the familiar bribes, and there is no good reason to doubt that Bestia at least had been influenced thereby: but the further allegation that Scaurus was likewise in-

---

[1] The doubts cast on Sallust's version (*Bell. Jug.* 26, 3) of this incident by Ihne (*History of Rome*, vol. v, p. 21, n. 1), and in particular Ihne's deductions from *Bell. Jug.* 47, 1 (*ib.* p. 43, n. 1), are to the present writer wholly unconvincing.

volved is by no means invulnerable to criticism[1]. Yet there was something to be said for the accommodation: a war of unknown difficulty had been avoided, and peace was restored by an agreement which tacitly acknowledged Numidian dependence on Rome. In Italy, however, public opinion was roused. Memmius was indefatigable in his protests, and the agitation gathered strength until L. Cassius Longinus, one of the praetors of the year, was commissioned to fetch Jugurtha to Rome in order that he might reveal the names of those he had corrupted. Under safe-conduct he duly came; but, when Memmius in the presence of the expectant People asked him the solemn question about his tools, another tribune, C. Baebius, ordered him to hold his peace. Thus for the moment the king had got the better of his enemies.

Yet Jugurtha, a potentate whose energy outran his wisdom, was not to leave Italy without damage to his cause. The slaughter of the Italians in Cirta had been foolish, and now another error of the same kind was to come. There was in Rome a certain Massiva, son of Gulussa and cousin of Jugurtha, whom Spurius Albinus, one of the consuls for 110 B.C., had induced to claim the Numidian kingdom for himself. So seriously did Jugurtha regard this rival that he instructed a member of his suite, Bomilcar by name, to procure his immediate assassination: but the murder was bungled, the murderer was caught, and when he incriminated Bomilcar the responsibility of the king could no longer be concealed. Even so, however, the government took no energetic measures. Bomilcar, for whose appearance in court Jugurtha had found bail, quietly went home to Africa, and soon afterwards his master followed. Five years later he was to visit once again the 'city up for sale and destined soon to perish, if it finds a buyer'—this time as a prisoner; for even at Rome there were some things beyond the power of gold.

Rome at length meant business, and meant it so seriously that she was committed to a bitter struggle in circumstances of which the difficulties were perhaps even yet not fully known. The military strength of Numidia lay, not in the coastal plain where most of its wealth was to be found, but in the broad and rugged plateau which rises to the south and stretches down to the desert beyond; and on these uplands, where the tangled hills offer obstacles made more serious by the heat of summer and the

[1] On this question see in particular G. Bloch, 'M. Aemilius Scaurus: étude sur l'histoire des partis au VIIe siècle de Rome' in *Mélanges d'histoire ancienne*, pp. 44 *sqq.*

torrential rains of spring, Rome was to learn the weakness of her slow-moving legions before the light and mobile native levies. Rome had to acquire a new technique of war: in the end experience taught the lesson, but its cost was high. When the campaign was resumed in 110 B.C., the achievement was small. Before anything worth mention had been accomplished, the consul Spurius Albinus returned to Rome for the elections, which were long delayed by tribunician struggles (see above, p. 61), leaving in command his brother Aulus—a man whose abilities as a general were not equal to his thirst for glory. Probably in the autumn of 110 B.C. this jack-in-office attempted to capture the town of Suthul, where some of the Numidian treasure is said to have been stored, and after a battle which Orosius (v, 15, 6) locates at Calama —surprisingly far to the west—the Roman camp was stormed at night and terms were dictated by the enemy. The army was spared on conditions which, though Sallust's account may be exaggerated, included its withdrawal from Numidia within ten days.

If the treaty made by Bestia in 111 B.C. had been unworthy, the capitulation of Albinus was an outrage and a disgrace: no section of opinion at Rome could accept this as the last word with Jugurtha. Accordingly, while the Senate enunciated the unimpeachable doctrine that no valid treaty could be made without its own consent and that of the Roman People, one of the tribunes, C. Mamilius Limetanus, renewed the precedent set up in the case of the peccant Vestals (see above, p. 97) and induced the Concilium Plebis to establish a court for the trial of all persons alleged to have prejudiced the interests of Rome in her relations with Jugurtha. When the members of the court came to be chosen, it was seen with some surprise that a seat on the bench had been given to Scaurus, whom Sallust at least regards as better qualified for the dock: but it must be admitted in making this particular choice the People, besides doing something to clear Scaurus of the aspersions cast by his political opponents, seems in no way to have impaired the honesty of the investigation. L. Opimius, Bestia, Sp. Albinus, C. Cato and C. Galba, the last of whom was one of the *pontifices*, were only the most prominent among the senatorial leaders on whom condemnation was pronounced; and the result of this exemplary visitation, however much its inception may have been due to popular hostility towards the Senate, was to make it clear beyond all possibility of doubt that those who offered their services against Jugurtha thereafter would compromise the interests of Rome, whether through incompetence or through love of gain, only at their own most grievous peril.

VI. THE CAMPAIGNS OF METELLUS

Meanwhile, provision was being made for the resumption of the war. Towards the end of 110 B.C., though the tribunes had prevented him from embarking reinforcements, Sp. Albinus had returned to Africa intent on retrieving the family reputation: but finding the army, now withdrawn to the Roman province in accordance with the conditions of his brother's treaty, in a state of utter demoralization, he remained inactive and awaited instructions from Rome. The consuls for 109 B.C. were M. Junius Silanus and Q. Caecilius Metellus, brother of Metellus Delmaticus and nephew of the great Metellus Macedonicus; and to the latter fell the Numidian command. As leader of the Roman forces against Jugurtha, Metellus enjoyed advantages which none of his predecessors could boast: not only was he a man of high ability, but his honesty was above suspicion and his influence with the Senate such as few but a Metellus could wield. At the outset his efforts to raise troops were backed by a suspension of obstructive laws[1], and the allies of Rome in Italy, besides friendly kings outside, were moved to swell the army with contingents of volunteers. Then, with C. Marius and P. Rutilius Rufus on his staff, Metellus set out for Africa, where his first business was to restore the morale of the troops which he took over from Albinus. The task of forming the army into an effective force was long, but it seems to have been completed soon enough for some use to be made of the summer of 109 B.C., even after more time had been spent in fruitless negotiations with an embassy from Jugurtha.

The short campaign of this year presents geographical problems whose difficulty is so much greater than their importance that it will be enough merely to indicate their nature. Starting from the Roman province, Metellus began a drive westwards into Numidia, and, after a digression to occupy the thriving commercial town of Vaga, he met Jugurtha in battle on a river which Sallust calls the Muthul. The identification of this Muthul, which is mentioned nowhere else in literature, is hard; but the serious possibilities are only two. If the Romans were moving along the normal route up the valley of the Bagradas, Sallust's description of the Muthul is best satisfied by the Oued Mellag, which flows into the Bagradas from the south-west just east of Bulla Regia[2]. If, on

---

[1] Cicero, *pro Corn.* ap. Ascon. p. 68 c.

[2] Ch. Saumagne in 'Le champ de bataille du Muthul' (*Revue tunisienne*, N.S. 1, 1930, pp. 3 *sqq.*) would place the battle on the east bank of the Oued Tessa—a stream to the east of the Oued Mellag: but, whichever of these rivers is the Muthul, the direction of Metellus' march is in effect the same.

the other hand, Metellus struck towards Hippo Regius, a town
which would have served as an admirable base for operations
against Cirta and its neighbourhood, the Muthul may be
recognized in the Oued Bou Namoussa and the battle may
be placed near the modern town of Combe[1]. On this Muthul,
wherever it may have been, the rival armies fought a long-
drawn encounter ending in a definite but wholly indecisive
Roman victory. Jugurtha himself was still at large; though one
army had been broken up, he was free to raise another; and,
worst of all, experience had shown that no amount of successes
like that on the Muthul would bring the war to an end, unless
by chance Jugurtha was captured or killed in action. For that
reason the most important outcome of the conflict may be seen
in the change which it wrought in the Roman strategy. Instead of seeking pitched battle again, Metellus essayed to deprive
the king of his *points d'appui* and to shake the allegiance of the
civilian population by capturing the inhabited centres, of which
some were destroyed and others occupied by garrisons. To this
end it was necessary to split the army into flying columns, which
soon, as a precaution against the sudden raids of the Numidians,
were formed into two groups under the charge of Metellus and
Marius. Operations of this kind, which probably extended into
the winter of 109–8 B.C., were conducted in the region east of the
Oued Mellag, and before Metellus led his troops back into the
province for the rainy season, though the Romans had occupied
Sicca, Jugurtha had the satisfaction of forestalling their attempt
to capture the more important city of Zama (Regia). Thereafter
Metellus withdrew the bulk of his forces behind the frontier,
leaving detachments in such of the places gained as were capable
of defence.

During the idle period when the armies were in winter quarters
Metellus did not relax his efforts to end the war. By lavish promises he tried to induce the infamous Bomilcar to betray his
master: but, though Jugurtha went so far in response to Bomilcar's
plea for an immediate peace as to surrender a large quantity of
money and material, he wisely refused to appear in person in the
Roman camp; and finally, when the weather made fighting possible

---

[1] This view, which for the present writer has some attractions, is propounded by M. A. Levi, 'La battaglia del Muthul,' in *Atene e Roma*, N.S.
VI, 1925, pp. 188–203. It is, however, summarily rejected by Gsell
(*op. cit.* VII, p. 191, n. 1), and in default of further investigation on the
spot final judgment on the theory is perhaps best suspended.

again, he renewed the war. By this time the command of Metellus had been prorogued for the year 108 B.C.

The initial operations of the new campaign were determined by an event which had occurred during the course of the winter. On the Feast of the Cereres there had been a sudden rising at Vaga, where every man of the garrison and of the resident Italian population was massacred by the native inhabitants with the exception of the commander, T. Turpilius Silanus[1]. The first business, consequently, was to avenge this crime. Vaga was recovered and Turpilius, though a Latin, was put to death[2]. Next, after Jugurtha had detected a plot formed against his life by Bomilcar and one Nabdalsa, both of whom perished for their pains, the two armies came into contact: Jugurtha was again defeated and fled to a place called Thala, the site of which cannot be located with confidence. Thither Metellus pursued, though the city lay fifty miles from the nearest river which could be used for a regular supply of water, and at his approach Jugurtha immediately decamped. But Thala was an important city, which contained one of the king's many stores of wealth, and its capture seemed worth while even though the greatest prize of all had flown. Accordingly Metellus undertook a siege, which after forty days—a number which in Sallust should not be taken literally—delivered the town into his hands.

Such is Sallust's meagre account of the campaign of 108 B.C., and the account is certainly incomplete. When Jugurtha escaped from Thala, at a time which was probably still in the spring, he broke off contact with Metellus and was engaged on business of his own which cannot have taken less than several months. First he went south to the Gaetulian country where he raised and trained another army, and after that, like Abd-el-Kader at the corresponding period of his history, he turned for aid to people of Mauretania. Bocchus, the king of that region, had married one of his daughters to Jugurtha, but in spite of this bond his intentions were not wholly friendly. Undoubtedly he yearned to extend his own realm eastwards at the expense of Numidia, and it can only have been the fear that, if Jugurtha's power collapsed, he might find in the Romans a neighbour still more dangerous that induced Bocchus to lend ear to proposals for a military alliance. At length,

---

[1] A brilliant interpretation of Sallust, *Bell. Jug.* 66, 2 is given by J. Carcopino in 'Salluste, le culte des *Cereres* et les Numides,' *Rev. hist.* 158, 1928, pp. 1 *sqq.*

[2] Sallust, *Bell. Jug.* 69, 4. On this see H. Stuart Jones in *Eng. Hist. Rev.* XXVIII, 1913, p. 142. It must be remembered, however, that the reading 'civis ex Latio' is so badly attested as to be little better than a conjecture.

however, an agreement was reached and the two monarchs advanced together towards Cirta, where they found Metellus[1]. But still the decisive engagement was postponed: for his own good reasons the Roman commander refused a battle and contented himself with an attempt to dissuade Bocchus from committing himself irrevocably to the Numidian cause.

VII. THE CAMPAIGNS OF MARIUS

Jugurtha, by now deprived of eastern and central Numidia, was an enemy whose final subjugation seemed only a matter of time; but energetic action was still required, and the explanation of Metellus' inactivity was purely personal. By prolonged pressure on his commander, Gaius Marius had at length secured leave to return to Rome in 108 B.C. and present himself as a candidate at the consular elections for the following year. Once he was in the field, his cause enjoyed an ominous popularity. The ground, indeed, had been prepared; for Marius, with a skill which would have done credit to the old nobility whose political craft he contemptuously disclaimed, had ranged public opinion on his side while he was still in Africa. Reports had been sedulously sent home to the effect that, through love of glory or ignorance of war, Metellus was needlessly protracting the campaign, and these announcements had their intended effect. The commercial class whose first desire was to see Numidia re-opened to Roman trade, the more substantial citizens whose liability to recruitment filled them with dislike for long-drawn wars, and men of insight from whatever quarter who appreciated the danger which now threatened Rome from the North, must all alike have listened with attention to the words of an experienced soldier who had boasted that with half the army of Metellus and a free hand he would have Jugurtha a prisoner within a few days. Accordingly Marius was elected, and shortly afterwards, as a result of popular interference

---

[1] The failure of Sallust to explain how the Romans came to be far to the west of the scene wherein their recent activities had been laid and how they gained possession of Cirta, the citadel of Numidia and one of the strongest positions in the world, is perhaps the gravest of his many omissions. It is the necessity for finding time wherein this extensive operation may be placed which leads the present writer to identify the winter mentioned by Sallust in *Bell. Jug.* 61, 2, with that of 109–8 B.C., so that the attack on Zama belongs to the late campaigning season of 109 B.C. and the following year is left free for the capture of Thala, with its preliminaries, and for a subsequent advance on Cirta.

with the arrangement of provincial commands already made[1]—an interference of great significance, which portends the action of the People for the benefit of Pompey and of Caesar—he was appointed to succeed Metellus in Africa.

In the coming conflict with Jugurtha the new commander did not propose to rely on skill alone. He soon revealed that, brief as the necessary campaign might be, its success after all would depend on reinforcements. Once his command had been assured, he set about the business of recruitment forthwith. All the sources drawn on by Metellus two years earlier—Latins, Italian allies and client states—were tapped again: but this time there was an innovation of the gravest moment. When Marius opened the ranks to citizens of whatever wealth, without regard to the classes of the centuriate organization, he was taking an unprecedented course which gave him an army not only larger than had been proposed but—so far as the Roman element was concerned—mainly composed of *capite censi* (see further below, pp. 133 *sqq.*). Munitions had been sent ahead under a *legatus*; and, when Marius followed, P. Rutilius in the name of Metellus handed over the command at Utica, while Metellus himself returned to Rome by another route to receive a well-merited triumph and the surname of Numidicus.

At the advent of the new commander, Jugurtha and Bocchus had separated, and Marius, after training his army in a series of attacks on ill-defended townships, was free to develop his plans along the lines of his own choosing. At first there were battles, and when these neither brought nor promised any decisive result Marius passed on to a policy singularly like that which Metellus had followed after the fight on the Muthul. If any difference is to be discerned between the methods ascribed to Metellus in *Bell. Jug.* 54, 5–6 and those of Marius as set forth in *Bell. Jug.* 88, 4, the difference at most is that, whereas Metellus directed his energies rather to terrifying the native population into passivity, Marius concentrated on the capture of all such places as might provide Jugurtha with a base. But both alike planted garrisons about the country; and, if those of Marius were more numerous than his predecessor's, their number is probably to be explained by the larger forces which Marius had at his disposal. It is to be noticed, however, that the narrative of Sallust in no way suggests that it was in order to make possible a more extensive system of occupation that the Roman army had been strengthened.

The incident in the campaign of 107 B.C. which Sallust has

---

[1] The details of this incident are lost through the uncertainty of Sallust's text in the relevant passage (*Bell. Jug.* 73, 7).

chosen to narrate is one which throws lamentably little light on the intentions of the general. He had been unable to take the field until the summer was advanced, and the skirmishes with Jugurtha had doubtless occupied some weeks. Thus, if his consulship was not to belie the hopes which it had raised, there was undoubted need for energetic action to impress public opinion at home and also, perhaps, to maintain the prestige of Roman arms among the Numidian population. He therefore decided to deliver an attack on Capsa—a town so far to the south that its only relevance to the war can have been its nearness to the Gaetulian allies of Jugurtha. Capsa was duly sacked, the spirits of the troops rose even higher than before, and the first consulship of Marius had one achievement to its credit.

When Capsa had been destroyed, Marius developed a general attack on the enemy strongholds throughout Numidia. This may well have continued during the winter of 107–6 B.C., even though Sallust's failure to mention winter-quarters is no cogent reason for denying a temporary suspension of hostilities. But it seems clear that by the spring of 106 B.C. the last hopes of resistance had been destroyed over all that region which lay between the frontier of the Roman province and a line running north and south somewhere to the west of Cirta. It now remained to deal with western Numidia—Jugurtha's original domain—and to end whatever danger may have existed that Bocchus and the Mauretanians would supply Jugurtha with the forces which his own territories could no longer provide. In the narrative of Sallust Marius next appears— we may assume with his *imperium* now prorogued—before a fortified position near the river Muluccha, which flowed about five hundred miles west of Cirta and divided the kingdom of Numidia from the realm of Bocchus. The attack on this stronghold and the happy accident by which the search for snails led a Ligurian to find a means of entry derive no special claim to mention from the fact that this incident alone in the whole campaign has been chosen by Sallust for record. Sallust's story deserves notice solely as a clue to the nature of the operations on which Marius was engaged in 106 B.C.—a long westward thrust designed at once to drive Jugurtha out of that part of his dominions which had not been denied him already and also to show the power of Rome on the frontiers of Mauretania.

The attempt, however, to awe Bocchus into neutrality was not a complete success. Jugurtha, whose cause was lost if he was to depend on his own resources alone, made offers to cede a third of Numidia in return for Mauretanian aid, and by this bribe Bocchus was finally persuaded. In face of this new danger Marius was strengthened by the arrival of reinforcements for his cavalry, and with them of a leader cast for an outstanding rôle. L. Cornelius Sulla, quaestor in 107 B.C., had been left in Italy to raise these mounted troops, and this contingent joined the army in Africa at some time during the western expedition[1]. After their demonstration the Romans were retiring eastwards to winter on the coast, where supplies could more easily be had, when news arrived of an event—possibly of two events—whose significance was grave. According to a story preserved by the Livian tradition[2], though to Sallust it is unknown, at about this time Cirta was temporarily lost: if this be true, the urgent necessity of recovering what was a nodal point on the Roman line of communications may have hastened the retreat of Marius and determined the direction of his march. In the narrative of Sallust the operations on the borders of Mauretania are directly followed by fighting in a region less than a hundred miles west of Cirta. Late one evening, while he was on his way, Marius was attacked by the army of the allied kings. After an even battle, he contrived to reach two neighbouring hills which gave his men protection for the night; and next morning, when the battle was renewed, a Roman victory was won. The march was then continued with every precaution against surprise, and on the third day, not far from Cirta itself, contact with the enemy was made again. The battle which followed was long and hard, but it ended with a result so decisive that the serious fighting of the war was over and Cirta—if it had ever been lost—was delivered to the Romans without resistance.

Four days later an embassy arrived from Bocchus. Marius himself seems to have concentrated on military business and in particular on preparations for an expedition to the south: the conduct of diplomatic affairs was left to A. Manlius and Sulla, of whom the latter had greatly distinguished himself in the recent fighting. The negotiations were protracted until Marius had returned from his southward drive; but in the end Bocchus sent a second mission with the request that it might be given access to the government in Rome, and, after a conference to which every senator within reach was summoned, permission for the journey was forthcoming. At Rome the deputation received a dexterous reply: Bocchus

---

[1] The suggestion of Sallust (*Bell. Jug.* 95, 1) that Sulla did not come up with Marius until the Muluccha had already been reached is probably due to Sallust's carelessness in fitting information from Sulla's *Memoirs* into the narrative of his basic authority: if so, it need not be taken seriously.

[2] Dio, frag. 89, 5: Orosius V, 15, 10.

might be granted pardon in the end, but first he would have to earn it. So back went the envoys to their king, whose relief at the hope of peace gave his policy a new determination. He asked for the presence of Sulla at his court, and thither Sulla made his way after a journey of many perils, among which was a march through the camp of Jugurtha himself. At first the king claimed peace in return for no more than promises of friendship; but, when Sulla insisted that deeds, not words, were what Rome demanded, with much reluctance he consented to a plot whereby Jugurtha should be betrayed. Jugurtha was duly made a prisoner, and thus, at some time in 105 B.C., by treachery and the help of an ally, Rome emerged triumphant from a struggle which had threatened, so long as she depended on her own strength alone, to lead to the establishment of a permanent military occupation of Numidia. The end of the war was timely. On 6 October in this same year the defeat of two Roman armies in Gaul opened the crisis of the Teutonic invasion (see below, p. 144). The European frontier needed above all a general of ability, and such a one Africa could now provide; for, though the final capture of Jugurtha was mainly due to the diplomacy of Sulla, public opinion gave all the credit to Marius, the commander. Before his return from Africa Marius was elected consul for 104 B.C., and his second year of office was opened on 1 January with a triumph, wherein the chief prize—Jugurtha—was shown once more to the gaze of the Roman mob. Thereafter he perished in the Tullianum.

Little need be said of the issue which still was debated at Rome when the Jugurthine War had long ceased to be contemporary history. The achievements of Metellus and Sulla were set against those of Marius, and praise or blame was distributed with the strictest loyalty to party. The nobility was right in its contention that Metellus had done more than half the work and that the final success was due as much to the diplomatic dexterity of Sulla as to the military operations of his commander. Yet, though it was absurd for them to say that Marius had converted utter failure into victory immediate and complete, the *populares* might with justice reply that the betrayal of Jugurtha by Bocchus was far from inevitable and was, indeed, the result of Marius' victories in the field. If Numidia had not been denied him, Jugurtha would not have been thrown back on Bocchus; and if Bocchus had not learnt in battle that Rome was no power to be wantonly antagonized, Jugurtha would never have been betrayed.

It is of more value, however, to consider the settlement which Rome adopted. Of a desire to annex she showed no sign: it is certain that the frontier of the Roman province was not seriously advanced, and it is highly doubtful whether the line was altered even by minor rectifications[1]. Rome was content with a considerable amount of booty and the assurance that among the powers of North Africa, over all of whom her suzerainty was now established, none would be found to claim the inheritance of Carthage. Though Marius may have settled a few Gaetulians on Numidian territory just beyond the Roman frontier[2], and though Leptis Magna had thrown off its allegiance to Jugurtha during the war, eastern Numidia suffered no encroachment by Rome; and this region duly received as its king one Gauda—a son of Mastanabal and half-brother of Jugurtha—who had been named as a secondary heir by Micipsa in his will. Gauda thus controlled at least that part of Numidia which had been awarded to Adherbal in 116 B.C. (see above, p. 118), and with it Cirta, the capital. Between this kingdom and the boundaries of Mauretania it is possible that an independent State was formed in western Numidia, to include some part at least of the district assigned to Jugurtha by L. Opimius and his colleagues[3]. But this creation, if it belongs to so early a date at all, was small, sandwiched between the powers of Gauda to the east and Bocchus to the west. Bocchus was the one party to the affair who emerged with profit. Not only did he become a Friend and Ally of the Roman People, but his kingdom was enlarged at the expense of Numidia. The line of his new frontier to the east cannot, indeed, be determined; but there is no doubt that Rome honoured an undertaking given by Sulla during the course of the negotiations that, if Bocchus proved his loyalty to Rome, he would be granted the whole of the region lately offered him by Jugurtha—a region which is described as a third of all Numidia. Thus, under the general superintendence of Rome, the native powers were left to control North Africa as before, and Rome herself, content with the existing province, withdrew from the country to the west with a memorable lesson on the dangers of meddling in dynastic struggles and the knowledge that Numidia, at least, was safe for the traders of Italy.

---

[1] For this possibility see T. Frank, in *Am. Journ. of Phil.* XLVII, 1926, pp. 56 *sqq.*, and on the other side S. Gsell, *op. cit.* VII, p. 9 *sq.*
[2] See S. Gsell, *loc. cit.*   [3] See S. Gsell, *op. cit.* VII, p. 263.

VIII. THE SIGNIFICANCE OF THE JUGURTHINE WAR

Trade in Numidia recalls the unhappy Italians slaughtered by Jugurtha when Cirta was surrendered by Adherbal (see above, p. 119), and the presence of these aliens in the Numidian capital raises the first of those problems which give the struggle an importance in Roman history far exceeding any which can be claimed for the military operations alone. That Rome, at a time when serious danger was threatening on her European frontier, should embark on a war in the most difficult country merely to settle the domestic differences of the Numidian royal house, that she should refuse an opportunity to withdraw, if not with glory, at least without disgrace, and that she should finally entangle herself so deep in this undertaking as to prejudice her ability to deal with the graver menace of the North—all these are matters which excite surprise and call for explanation. At the outset it must be remembered that nothing could stir Rome to more unreasoning fear than the prospect of a great power established in North Africa. After almost a century, the horrors of the Hannibalic War were still undimmed, and such was Rome's determination to avoid all further peril from the South that it may well have been in order to prevent Carthage falling into Masinissa's hands that the city was destroyed in 146 B.C. and its territory turned into a Roman province. With an outlook such as this, Rome might naturally act with energy when the kingdom of Numidia—an area of enormous extent and great potential wealth—fell into the hands of a king whose variable attitude towards Rome bordered, in its less gracious moments, on the contumacious. Yet, for all his indiscretions, Jugurtha did not want war: there is every reason to believe that he not only sought but needed the peace made with Bestia in 111 B.C., and nothing justifies the suspicion that, if its terms had been accepted by Rome, they would have been broken by the king. The policy of Jugurtha is plain. Having coveted the Numidian throne he won it; and then, when he desired nothing more than to be left in the enjoyment of his gains, he was prepared to pay a reasonable price for peace.

It was Rome who insisted on war to the end, and the reason for this insistence is to seek. Jugurtha, even before the murder of Massiva, had certainly behaved in a way which suspicious minds might interpret to imply a deep hostility: but he had done nothing which any rational judgment could interpret as evidence of a determination to challenge the Roman power or even to molest the province in Africa. Nevertheless Rome was set on his complete destruction. Whatever the reason for this may have been, it was not a lust for annexation: when the war had been brought to its victorious end, the meagre Roman territory in Africa remained almost exactly what it had been before. The course of events at the beginning of the affair makes it clear that Rome was not bent on war from the start: as usually happened, she suddenly discovered that a series of diplomatic exchanges had committed her to military operations which at the outset had not been envisaged at all. But, though so much may be freely admitted, it is less easy to divine the reason why, after a certain point had been reached, the government refused every opportunity to withdraw from the struggle until Jugurtha had been either killed or captured. The explanation suggested by the narrative of Sallust is that, when the prestige of Rome had been compromised by the incompetence of Bestia and the Albini, the masses took the bit between their teeth and insisted on the prosecution of the struggle until the supremacy of Rome had been vindicated beyond all dispute. In this there is doubtless truth, but it is perhaps permissible to suspect that Sallust, in his anxiety to uphold the wisdom of the Concilium Plebis and the tribunes, has given undue prominence to a factor which was not alone in guiding Roman policy. Numidia was a country still waiting for development. The agricultural policy of Masinissa[1] can scarcely have been carried to completion at so early a date as this, and there must have been many regions whose conversion from pas-turage to arable cultivation only awaited the capital which was needed for their equipment. Moreover, the country was rich in timber of the choicer kinds; and, though their development is barely recorded before Roman times, the mines and marble quarries of Numidia subsequently became an important element in the resources of the imperial age[2]. Such considerations as these are enough to show that there is no matter for surprise in Sallust's story of the Italian traders who fought for Adherbal at Cirta; and, if Numidia had already attracted the notice of Italian commerce, it is not impossible that the commercial interests of Rome did something to uphold the hands of those who were resolved to see the war through to an end of a kind which, besides restoring the shattered reputation of Roman arms, would have the very valuable advantage of making Numidia a land wherein Italians might move freely for the conduct of their business, whatever that business might be. Apart from the destruction of Carthage and Corinth

[1] Polybius xxxvi, 16, 7–8.
[2] For a general account of the economic possibilities of Numidia in the second century B.C. see S. Gsell, *op. cit.*, v, pp. 169–212.

and the foundation of Gracchan colonies, the affairs of the Balearic Islands (p. 152 *sq.*) and of Narbo Martius (p. 112 *sq.*) are perhaps enough to suggest the hand of the trader. If so, it is at least conceivable that commercialism played a part, not perhaps in originating, but at least in strengthening the policy pursued by Rome during the Jugurthine War[1].

Significant as may be the appearance of a commercial factor in the direction of Rome's affairs, its significance is overshadowed by that of another change which belongs to this period—a change which determined the nature of Roman history throughout the remaining years of the Republic. The innovation made by Marius in the recruitment of the legions probably did more than any other single factor to make possible that series of civil wars which only ended with the establishment of the Principate. Yet, grave as its results turned out to be, the work of Marius has often been exaggerated; and, if its author is to be fairly judged, it will be necessary to appreciate the seeming slightness of the reform from which such tremendous consequences flowed.

The Roman army which Marius found was still in theory what it had always been—a force of which the main strength was supplied by a citizen-militia enrolled in the legions. In its military organization, as in its system of civil administration, the State practised the strictest economy in the matter of a permanent establishment. When war was imminent, citizens were summoned to the colours and, though some concessions on this point were made in course of time (see above, p. 62 *sq.*), they were expected to supply their own equipment: when peace was restored, the army was disbanded, and it was assumed that the troops would return to their homes without any pension or gratuity beyond such share of the booty as had come their way. Thus Rome essayed to run her army without a War Office; but the simplicity of the system was purchased at a price. Apart from any doctrinaire theories which might suggest that the burden of military service most justly fell on those who had property for whose protection they could fight, the assumption that the troops should provide their own armament meant that service had to be confined to citizens of sufficient wealth to meet the inevitable expenses. The result was the system whereby liability to recruitment normally bore on none but those who were in one of the five *classes* of the centuriate organization, whereas the so-called *proletarii* or *capite censi*—citizens whose

---

[1] The writer must here acknowledge his debt to a lecture delivered in London on 23 June 1925 by G. De Sanctis, recently published as 'Sallustio e la guerra di Giugurta' in *Problemi di storia antica* (pp. 187 *sqq.*).

wealth was less than the minimum required for the lowest of the five *classes*—remained exempt. The most serious of its defects— the fact that it demanded military service, for periods which now were often long, from citizens of substance who could least well be spared from civil life, while the poor, who contributed little or nothing to the economic welfare of the State, were left at home— had been mitigated to some extent by successive reductions in the minimum census required for inclusion in the fifth of the *classes*. Indeed, Gaius Gracchus had been impelled by the poverty of at least some of the recruits to make arrangements for the supply of their equipment at the public cost. But, in spite of this, the system as a whole remained the same, in practice as well as in theory. Property was still a qualification; the levy was still com- pulsory; and, though the wealthiest families of all might contrive to get exemption for their members in one way or another, the legions still contained men of substance, even when some of their poorer brethren had been admitted as well.

It was over the more prosperous legionaries that difficulties arose. Their prosperity meant that they had some means of liveli- hood in civil life, and the existence of such ties with home made them anxious, not for campaigns of indefinite duration, but for demobilization at the earliest possible moment. Hence, though Roman patriotism did not fail when the dangers of the State were prolonged, there arose those agitations for discharge which are recorded from time to time during the second century[1], and which may even have lent strength to the claims of Marius during his canvass for the consulship in 108 B.C.[2] Such was the situation when Marius threw open the legions to volunteers and abandoned all inquiries about the census of the recruits[3]. In appearance the innovation was not great. On rare occasions already the govern- ment had adopted something like a voluntary system[4], and when Marius enlisted *proletarii* as such he only completed the process begun by the recent reductions in the minimum qualification for in- clusion in the *classes*. Nevertheless the result was enormous, and for this reason—that the system of recruitment was now in prac- tice voluntary and that the supply of volunteers was so large that there was no need to fall back on the latent power of compulsion. Thus the legions, which in the past had contained at least a leaven of citizens whose prosperity meant that they and their families had a means of livelihood at home to which they were naturally anxious

---

[1] See Livy xxxiv, 56, 9; xl, 35, 11.   [2] Sallust, *Bell. Jug.* 65, 4.
[3] Sallust, *Bell. Jug.* 86, 2.
[4] Livy xxviii, 45, 13; xxxi, 14, 1–2; Appian, *Iber.* 84.

to return, were now composed entirely of men who had enlisted because, to them, the army held out greater attractions than civil life. In the past the soldiers of substance had regarded military service as a tiresome interruption in their work at home, to be ended with the least possible delay: now the army was composed of men to whom military service was the occupation of their choice, to be protracted as long as possible. The great and vital change which Marius introduced was, not to admit the *proletarii* (for that had been done in all but name before), but to rid the legions of that element which demanded—with an insistence, because of its wealth, not lightly to be disregarded—demobilization at the earliest opportunity. Henceforward the legions were prepared to serve as long as an excuse for service could be found.

Such was the greatest of the Marian reforms: but it is important to remember its limitations. Though, as will be seen, its effect was to give the army a place of unprecedented power in the political life of Rome, the theory of the military system remained what it had been hitherto. Armies were still recruited for this war or that: there were as yet no permanent camps in which legions might be quartered when not on active service. Recruits still enlisted for service in some particular series of operations, and when these operations were over they might expect to be disbanded. Rome was still in theory without a standing army: if the armies were chronic, the reason for that was simply that during the remainder of Republican history wars were continuous. Nor was there any change in the period of service. According to the Roman practice, liability for legionary duty was confined at ordinary times to the *iuniores*—citizens between the ages of seventeen and forty-six; but if, owing to the warlike nature of the times, it happened that a man had served in the field for more than a certain number of years (which need not necessarily have been continuous) before reaching his forty-sixth birthday, he was allowed forthwith to regard himself as a *senior* and to enjoy the exemption from further fighting in the field which that status implied. The number of campaigns required to earn this exemption seems to have varied. The figure given in the text of Polybius[1] is corrupt, but there can be no doubt the *legitima stipendia* were normally more than the six which were accepted as enough in 140 B.C.[2], when the Roman army in Spain was in a state of such exceptional discontent and insubordination that it had to be humoured by special concessions: during the twenties of the second century ten years seem to have sufficed[3]. The precise number of campaigns which entitled to

---

[1] VI, 19, 2.   [2] Appian, *Iber.* 78.   [3] Plutarch, *Gracchi*, 23, 4.

discharge during the period between Marius and Augustus is unimportant and cannot be determined with certainty, though it is clear that some such limit was recognized. For instance, in 68 B.C. steps were taken to discharge those of Lucullus' troops who had, apparently, been recruited in 86. The point, however, which calls for all possible emphasis is that, whereas in the days before Marius it was the troops themselves who demanded the discharge to which they were entitled, after recruitment had become wholly voluntary the release of time-expired men is an issue only raised by the political enemies of the *imperator* concerned. Though it must be admitted that Lucullus was no great favourite with his troops, the true attitude of the legions in Asia whose discharge was ordered from Rome in 68 B.C. and among whom Publius Clodius had been engaged in fomenting discontent upon the spot is revealed by the fact that, having been once, if not twice, demobilized on the ground that their *legitima stipendia* had been served, they nevertheless took the first opportunity of enlisting again under Pompey[1]. So too the supposed grievances of such soldiers in Caesar's army as were entitled to discharge would never have been canvassed in 51 B.C. had not their exploitation suited the political convenience of his opponents[2].

Thus the effect of the change in the method of recruitment was to constitute the legions of men who made soldiering a profession and whose natural reluctance to lose their livelihood left them indifferent to the nature of the cause in which they fought. When the war for which they were recruited was ended, it was all to the good if their general found some other excuse for keeping his army together, and it mattered nothing to the troops if the excuse was no more than a selfish and treasonable struggle for the general's own political advancement. But it was not merely gratitude for continued employment or devotion bred of long companionship in arms that united the legionaries to their commander by a bond which the claims of patriotic duty could not sever. There was a very special reason which impelled the troops to stick to their leader even though he proposed to use them, no longer in the interests of the State, but in his own. When men make the army a profession, they cut themselves off from civil life; and, if it is their good fortune to survive till the age when they are too old for further active service, they may reasonably expect some provision to be made for their declining years. The long and continuous service rendered by the legionaries after the time of Marius demanded a system of pensions as its reward, and such a system did not yet

---

[1] Dio xxxvi, 16, 3.   [2] Cicero, *ad fam.* viii, 8, 7.

exist. To meet the need nothing more than an haphazard expedient was devised: when an army was to be demobilized, a *lex agraria* was passed to provide the veterans with allotments of land. But to secure the passage of such a bill, as was revealed most clearly by the experience of Pompey in 60 B.C., all the influence of the *imperator* himself—and more—was needed: if the veterans were not to be cast destitute upon the street, they must follow their commander to the bitter end. Such was the most potent cause of the tie which united generals to their armies during the last decades of the Republic; and the union was one of most disastrous consequences to Rome. Indeed, it made possible the civil wars. Before many years had passed it became one of the most urgent problems facing Roman statesmanship to break the tie between commanders and their men, and to leave the Senate and Roman People the sole claimants on the allegiance of the army. The solution was long in coming. Sulla sought it in vain, and it was left for the genius of Augustus, by instituting the *aerarium militare*, to make the State itself responsible for pensions in a way which rendered it unnecessary for the troops to pin their hopes on any individual.

Such were the far-reaching consequences of filling the legions by voluntary recruitment and so forming an army of professional soldiers. The remaining military reforms ascribed to Marius will appropriately receive such notice as they deserve in connection with the history of the Germanic invasions (p. 146 *sq.*). But there still remains one feature of the Jugurthine War which calls for particular attention—the career of Marius himself. In the concluding age of the Roman Republic Marius was regarded as their greatest hero by that section of the political world which passed under the name of *populares*, and it was undoubtedly to glorify the patron of the cause for which the *populares* stood that Sallust wrote the *Bellum Jugurthinum*.

The *populares* are often loosely described in modern times as democrats, but this is both unjustified and misleading: indeed, it is the presence of a genuinely democratic element in their programmes which makes it impossible to call the Gracchi *populares* in the ordinary sense of the term[1]. The great *populares* of Rome— Marius, Cicero in his earlier days, Caesar and, to some extent, Augustus himself—were as oligarchical as their Optimate opponents, and the name *populares* describes at most an incidental feature of their activities. They were violent opponents of the class

[1] On the *populares* and their ideals see M. Gelzer, 'Die römische Gesellschaft zur Zeit Ciceros' in *N.J. kl. Alt.*, xlv–vi, 1920, pp. 1–27.

which formed the vast majority in the Senate, and during their struggle with that most powerful institution they needed the help of every ally they could find. It was natural that they should turn for aid to the popular assemblies, whose value against senatorial obstruction had been demonstrated by the Gracchi: but the alliance was one of convenience alone, which was far from implying the slightest devotion to the principle of democracy on the part of the so-called *populares*. Their quarrel was with the Senate, and it started during the second century B.C. when the Senate began to mismanage imperial affairs and to set its own desires above the interests of other classes at Rome and above those of the State as a whole.

In general the *populares* stood for efficiency and public spirit in the direction of affairs; but in particular they were opposed to the Optimates on a narrower issue. Just as the patricians in the early days of the Republic had sought to deny the plebeians all access to the magistracies of the Roman People, so now the *nobilitas*—a body of patricians and plebeians which had been consolidated into something like a close corporation since the Plebs had won its way to power during the fourth century—claimed to do the same. Whether 'nobility' belonged to the descendants of all holders of curule office or only to those who could boast dictator, consul or *tribunus militum consulari potestate* among their ancestors[1], it was the doctrine of the Optimates that nobles alone should be regarded as eligible for the consulship: any man born outside this ring who essayed to rise on his merits to the highest magistracy was a *novus homo*, exposed to all the obstruction and petty resentment which are the inevitable lot of the social upstart. This was the issue over which the fight waxed hottest. According to their enemies' account, the *nobiles*, 'quibus omnia populi Romani beneficia dormientibus deferuntur[2],' were unworthy of the responsibilities reserved for them in virtue of their birth, and, what was more, they were violating the intentions of the Roman constitution: for, when the monarchy was abolished at the end of the sixth century, the People in their wisdom 'ita magistratus annuos creaverunt ut consilium senatus rei publicae praeponerent sempiternum, deligerentur autem in id consilium ab *universo* populo aditusque in illum summum ordinem *omnium* civium industriae ac virtuti pateret'[3].

Thus, though higher efficiency in government was the supreme aim of the *populares*, one of their most insistent and controversial demands was for a *carrière ouverte aux talents*. Candidates for office

---

[1] On this question see M. Gelzer, *Die Nobilität der römischen Republik*, pp. 21 *sqq.*   [2] Cicero, II *in Verr.* V, 70, 180.

[3] Cicero, *pro Sestio*, 65, 137; cf. Livy IV, 3, 13.

should be sought from the citizen-body as a whole, and magistracies should be conferred on the ablest men that could be found, irrespective of their antecedents. The relevance of the Jugurthine War to a dispute such as this is too obvious to need discussion. So long as the command lay with men appointed on the principles for which the Optimates contended there had been corruption, incompetence and, even after the appointment of Metellus, no rapid march to victory. But when the People overrode the wishes of the Senate and put Marius, the *novus homo*, in charge, not only was the war in Africa soon brought to a triumphant end, but there was revealed to the world a general who led Rome safely through the far graver perils of the Germanic invasion. Such a version might assume a somewhat generous interpretation of the services rendered by Marius in Africa: but to the ignorant vulgar there is no commendation like success, and it could not be denied that after the appointment of Marius the war had made steady progress to its proper outcome. If Marius had not fulfilled his earlier promise by his defeat of the Cimbri and Teutoni, the moral to be drawn from his performances in Africa might have been less cogent; but, as things were, the Jugurthine War seemed to give incontrovertible proof of the immense advantages to be gained by the judicious appointment of *novi homines* to the consulship.

IX. THE CIMBRI AND TEUTONI

When Marius came home from Africa, Rome lay under the shadow of a menace from the North. For eight years now, Germanic wanderers had been searching without success for a new home in Europe outside the Roman frontier, and their continued failure made it ever more certain that in the end they would be driven to stake their future on a bolder throw. When other regions had been tried in vain, they would turn to the Roman provinces, if not to Italy itself. The movement of these peoples is an event of oecumenical significance. Not only was it the occasion of Rome's first contact with the Germans, but, even though the later phases of the Celtic migration may be attributed in part to Germanic pressure, it was the first unmistakable warning of that great expansion which in the end was to shake the whole fabric of the Roman Empire, to deprive it of its western half, and to establish Germanic powers in Britain, France, Italy, Spain and even Africa. The history of northern Europe during the emergence and the settlement of the Celts has already been recounted (vol. VII, chap. II), and the later fortunes of these peoples are so largely determined by their relations with Rome that they are best described in connection with Roman policy in the provinces. The story of the Germans down to the middle of the second century A.D. will be surveyed as a whole in a later volume, at the time when the Empire is about to face that insistent Teutonic advance which was not the least potent among the causes of its disruption. In the present place no more need be said about the early history of these tribes than is essential for the understanding of the threat with which Marius was called upon to cope—a threat which, ominous as it indubitably is when interpreted in the light of subsequent developments, owed its meaning in the eyes of contemporaries, partly of course to the magnitude of the immediate danger and to the disasters which it involved, but in part as well to its effects on the course of politics in Rome.

During the first half of the last millennium B.C. the Celts of north-western Germany were subjected to increasing pressure from tribes which may reasonably be called Germanic, and thus was started a movement which before the end of the sixth century had carried Celtic peoples across France and even into Spain, which brought others to Italy early in the fourth, and which finally, in the fourth and third centuries, produced that drift towards the south-east which left a Celtic deposit in the regions south of the middle Danube and even in Asia Minor (vol. VIII, pp. 59 sqq.) The source of this thrust is to be seen in the lands which lie within a radius of about three hundred miles round a centre roughly marked by the site of Copenhagen. Here was the earliest known home of the Teutons, and from this breeding place there issued a succession of closely-related peoples, all seeking wider territories and all of a prowess in war which made their name a terror to those who barred their progress. Forerunners of these invaders had already crossed the Rhine; for there is no reason to doubt the presence of a strong admixture of German blood in the Belgic population now settled in north-eastern Gaul: but it was not till the end of the second century that Gaul was attacked by Germans of pure extraction. These were the Cimbri and Teutoni, whose Germanic origin may be accepted with confidence in spite of modern speculations which would claim Celtic affinities for the latter, if not for the Cimbri as well. From their homes in the peninsula of Jutland and in the districts round its base the Cimbri and their kinsmen[1] set out at some time about 120 B.C., having no

---

[1] Though the migrants were perhaps reinforced at later stages by new arrivals from the North, it is probable that Teutoni, as well as Cimbri, took part in the movement from the start. See Ed. Meyer, 'Tougener und Teutonen' in *Kleine Schriften* II, especially p. 501, and, for a different view, F. Stähelin, *Die Schweiz in römischer Zeit*, ed. 2, pp. 45 sqq.

clear idea of their destination, but trekking in search of broader lands and of adventure by the way. According to a tradition accepted in the Graeco-Roman world they were set moving by a great encroachment of the sea[1], but, though this need not be doubted, it is hard to accept it as the only cause. The Germans had already taken to settled agricultural life at least so far as to make their demand one for fertile lands, and even cities, in which to live, and it would not be rash to assume that the growth of population in Germany, accentuated perhaps by the advance of neighbours from the north and east, did something to impel the Cimbri and their brethren to seek a less congested territory and one where Nature was more benign. Though enough of the Cimbri stayed behind to keep their name alive in the region from which they started[2], the movement came near to being the migration of a whole people. Women and children followed with the waggons which served as homes; and it is not unlikely that, with the recruits who joined at later stages, at its greatest strength the host approached half a million souls. Any such estimate must remain conjecture; but there is no need to make drastic reductions of the recorded numbers in order to bring the fighting force of the invaders nearer to equality with the Roman armies by which it was finally defeated. The Germans laboured under a handicap which made them, man for man, no match for their opponents. Apart from their inferior discipline, they suffered from the lack of body-armour. With nothing but a shield for defence, the invaders were at the mercy of the well-protected legionaries, when once the legions were under intelligent command.

At the outset they made towards the south, probably along the natural route provided by the Elbe, past Magdeburg and Dresden roughly in the direction of Vienna. In Bohemia they found no haven; for the Boii sped their passage by force. Their next appearance is south of the Danube in the neighbourhood of Belgrade. Here they were repulsed again—this time by the Scordisci, and thence they turned westwards, moving perhaps up the valley of the Drave until they reached Carinthia. In Carinthia for the first time they were face to face with Rome. The friendship between Rome and the Taurisci established by the operations of Scaurus two years before (see above, p. 108) led the Roman government to concern itself with the protection of Tauriscan territory, and Cn. Carbo, consul of 113 B.C., was sent with a large army to resist the threatened invasion. The Cimbri were in no mood to court a new defeat: at the consul's order to retire they

[1] Strabo VII, 293; Festus, p. 15 L.
[2] *Res Gestae Div. Aug.* 26; Tacitus, *Germ.* 37, 1.

obeyed. But Carbo was out for glory. Fearing that his victims might escape, he hurriedly prepared for their destruction; and when treachery had provoked the battle for which ambition sought, the incompetence of their general involved the Romans in a defeat which would have been annihilation but for the timely intervention of a thunderstorm. Such was the battle fought near Noreia, midway between Klagenfurt and Ljubljana. When he had returned to Rome, Carbo was prosecuted by the young orator Antonius; and, like his brother Gaius (p. 94), he died an unlamented death by poison.

The ignominy of his end became him well: by conduct of the most culpable ineptitude he had thrown away an army, and—what was worse—had given the migrant horde its first taste of victory. After Noreia the Germans proved less amenable to orders for their own departure. Yet even now, though the road to Italy was open, they turned away to the north-west instead, and for the next three years they were moving round the northern foot-hills of the Alps towards the sources of the Danube. At length, in 111 or 110 B.C., they crossed the Rhine, perhaps at a point not far below Schaffhausen[1], and thence they seem to have followed the natural route up the valley of the Aar to the Jura, and so to Gaul. In this part of their wanderings they were joined by numerous recruits, some of whom at least were of Celtic stock: in particular the records make mention of the Tigurini—a section of the Helvetic people, and it is not impossible that at this stage there also arrived German reinforcements from the North. Thus it was a host more formidable even than before which, when it entered Gaul, came once more within the ken of Rome.

M. Junius Silanus, consul of 109 B.C., had been sent to Gaul to maintain the integrity of the province and to support the tribes in alliance with Rome[2]. To him the invaders presented their demand for land, and the demand was formally referred to the government at home. But it was not the moment to accommodate whole tribes of immigrants within the empire, and the German request was refused: Silanus, like Carbo, sought a battle: and somewhere in the valley of the Rhône, probably at a point beyond the frontier of the Roman province, his army was decisively defeated. The effects of this were grave. The invaders gained fresh confidence, and the prestige of Rome sank so low that the Celts themselves began to toy with thoughts of a *revanche*. While the Cimbri withdrew to the interior, their allies the Tigurini, possibly reinforced by other

---

[1] Vell. Pat. II, 8, 3, on which, however, see Stähelin, *op. cit.* p. 46 *sq.*

[2] For the operations which follow see above, Map 4.

Helvetic elements, hovered round the Roman frontier, and before long revolt broke out among the Volcae Tectosages, a people allied with Rome whose homes lay round Tolosa (Toulouse).

To meet these dangers the Senate had another army in the field by 107 B.C., under the command of the consul L. Cassius Longinus, who turned out to be as bad as his predecessors. He did, indeed, drive the Tigurini from the neighbourhood of Tolosa; but an ill-judged pursuit down the valley of the Garonne ended in a great disaster[1]. Longinus himself and L. Piso—the latter an ex-consul now serving as *legatus* and, as was afterwards remembered, an ancestor of Julius Caesar's third wife[2]—were killed, and such remnants of the troops as reached the camp alive only escaped destruction because the senior surviving officer, C. Popillius Laenas, bought their lives by surrendering half the baggage and even agreeing that they should pass beneath the yoke. The credit for this victory belonged to a young chief of the Tigurini named Divico, who lived to encounter Julius Caesar. Yet even now the tale of Rome's misfortunes was not told. Longinus was followed by a consul of 106 B.C., Q. Servilius Caepio—a man who, compared with his predecessors, might claim to be a general of experience: for, slender as his military gifts turned out to be, they had at least won him a triumph in the previous year for his achievements in Spain. At first the appointment seemed to justify itself: Caepio addressed himself to the easy task of dealing with the Volcae who, now that their Helvetian allies had withdrawn, were in no position to oppose the might of Rome. Tolosa was recovered without a struggle, and disloyalty was visited with a fitting punishment. The sacred places of the city contained an accumulated wealth of offerings whose origin became the theme of legend and whose value was set at figures of prodigious size: but even fifteen thousand talents of gold and silver, the estimate of Posidonius[3], would have been a most welcome windfall to an exchequer drained by wars in Africa as well as Gaul. Caepio, therefore, seized the treasure; but on its way to Massilia for transport to Rome the convoy was attacked, the escort overpowered, and the precious objects vanished, none could tell whither.

Afterwards men said that the robbery was a fake, arranged by Caepio to conceal his own embezzlement (see below, p. 159 *sq.*). At first, however, there were no suspicions, and the command of Caepio had been so far a success that he was continued in office as

---

[1] If the texts of Livy (*Epit.* 65) and Orosius (v, 15, 23) are to be accepted, the battle was fought to the south-east of Bordeaux.

[2] Caesar, *B.G.* i, 12, 7.   [3] In Strabo iv, 188.

proconsul for 105 B.C. But now he was not alone: a renewal of the Cimbric threat brought Cn. Mallius Maximus on the scene, with a second army and the authority of a consul. Mallius was a *novus homo*, but the experiment so triumphantly vindicated by Marius was less fortunate in its repetition. His arrival in Gaul meant that the control of the Roman forces was divided; and the jealousy of the two commanders made effective co-operation impossible. When the Germans marched southwards down the Rhône, Caepio remained on the western bank while Mallius was on the east, with an advance-guard to the north under M. Aurelius Scaurus. Scaurus sustained the first attack: he lost his whole force, and himself was captured. The military situation now grew clearer: since the enemy was marching along the eastern bank, Caepio must cross the river and join Mallius before the fight began. Mallius issued orders to this effect, and with much reluctance Caepio obeyed; but, even so, he refused a proper junction and kept his troops in a separate camp so far from his colleague as to be almost out of touch. There followed a period of negotiations, first between the Romans and their enemy, who now renewed the old demand for land, and then between the rival generals on the Roman side: but even the good offices of a deputation from the Senate failed to persuade Caepio and Mallius to sink their differences. Thus, when at length the battle broke, the invaders could destroy the two halves of the Roman force in detail. On 6 October 105 B.C. close by the town of Arausio (Orange) the barbarians fell first upon Caepio, and the two Roman armies were cut to pieces in succession. Retreat was impossible—for they had chosen to fight with their backs to the river; and their losses in fighting men, apart from non-combatants, were reported to be eighty thousand. Though both the generals survived—to present the Roman government with a thorny problem of military discipline (see below, pp. 158 *sqq.*)—the Gallic province and even Italy itself now lay open without defence.

The colleague of Mallius in the consulship of 105 B.C. was P. Rutilius Rufus, a figure whose high repute in history was more than a mere tribute of sympathy with the injustice of his fate (see below, p. 175 *sq.*). When news of the disaster arrived, Rutilius acted with energy. He had perhaps already sought the aid of gladiatorial trainers to improve the legionaries' skill in fighting at close quarters[1], and it is possible that he had also passed a measure whereby officers of tried efficiency might be more freely chosen as

[1] Val. Max. II, 3, 2.

tribuni militum, though the evidence for this admits no certainty[1]. Now in the crisis he required men of the normal military age to swear that they would not leave Italy, and orders were sent to the ports that none under thirty-five should be permitted to embark[2]. But the few weeks of power which remained left him time for none but the roughest preparations, and the situation he bequeathed to his successors was still acute. On New Year's Day 104 B.C. Marius, already elected in absence to his second consulship, celebrated his return to office by the triumph which marked the end of Rome's African distractions. Serious as had been the strain imposed by the Jugurthine War on the sources of recruitment, its most ominous result was the revelation of Rome's poverty in competent commanders. So rare had able generalship become, that Rome, it seemed, could not fight with success on two fronts at once: but now at length Marius was released and it was the turn of the northern campaign to engage the attention of the one proved artificer of victory.

Fortune gave Marius time to make his preparations. After the defeat of Caepio and Mallius the invaders had refused once more to follow up their success with an advance on Italy. Instead, the Cimbri made off to Spain while the Teutoni roved about in Gaul, and it was probably not before the end of 103 B.C. that the Cimbri returned from the West and joined their brethren for a concerted thrust across the Alps. The army under Marius was not of enormous size: at the battle of Vercellae in 101 B.C. he had thirty-two thousand men[3], and it is unlikely that many more than this had been at his disposal in Gaul. But, as always when Marius was in command, lack of numbers was made good by high efficiency. From the moment of his departure from Rome, with the help of an active staff, which included men like Sulla and Quintus Sertorius, the general made it his foremost care to raise his troops to the standards attained by the veterans from Africa. The material, indeed, was of varied value. Among the auxiliaries, useful as these had shown themselves in guerrilla warfare, were contingents strange to the discipline needed in a general engagement: but the legionaries themselves were of the proper stuff and responded in time to persistent training. All through the summer of 104 B.C. the troops were kept within the province, engaged in nothing

---

[1] On the 'Rufuli,' whose name is not to be connected with Rutilius, see Festus, pp. 316–7 L., and on the date and author of this reform E. Pais, *Dalle guerre puniche a Cesare Augusto,* I, pp. 84 *sqq.*, with the literature there cited.   [2] Licinianus, p. 14 F.

[3] Plutarch, *Marius,* 25, 4.

more than the assertion of Rome's authority. The last traces of rebellion were stamped out: Sulla repeated his African success by capturing a king of the Tectosages: and Marius turned his thoughts to still further technical improvements in the army.

It was either now or soon afterwards that he modified the *pilum*[1], and to this period of his career may belong that improvement in the legionary equipment of which he was probably the author. These innovations revealed him as a soldier of ideas; but the claim that he was responsible for a far more radical change must be rejected. Though it may be admitted that the light-armed *velites*, first found in 211 B.C.[2], are not recorded after the Jugurthine War and that Marius was the cause of their disappearance[3], there is no good evidence for the widespread belief that at a stroke he made the cohort the tactical unit for legionary troops. In earlier days the maniple had doubtless been the basic formation for Roman infantry, but the cohort—a group of three maniples—had evidently been growing in favour for many years before this time[4]. Again, though the cohort had long been a regular formation among the Italian allies of Rome, it is difficult to believe that all the references made to such bodies by Livy[5] are meant to concern allied contingents alone. It is, indeed, a bare possibility that passages of this kind, though describing Roman troops, are anachronisms; but the assumption is one which has little probability if the change from an organization by maniples to one by cohorts was the work of any single individual—an individual whose identity could scarcely have failed to be remembered. Still stronger testimony is supplied by Sallust. As early as 109 B.C., when Marius was still a subordinate, he clearly recognizes the cohort as a tactical unit in the legion[6]; and this he is hardly likely to have done had the cohort been put in the place of the maniple by a sudden change whose author was his chosen hero.

The indications of the evidence are plain. From some time in the third century the maniple had been proving too small a unit for tactical convenience, and it had grown more and more common

---

[1] Plutarch (*Marius*, 25, 1–2) ascribes this change to 101 B.C., but a slightly earlier date is more probable.   [2] Livy XXVI, 4, 4–5.

[3] On this see Festus, p. 274 L., and A. Schulten, 'Zur Heeresreform des Marius' in *Hermes*, LXIII, 1928, p. 240.

[4] The reference in Frontinus, *Strat.* 1, 6, 1, to the use of cohorts by Cn. Fulvius (cos. 298 B.C.) may well be anachronistic; but the appearance of cohorts in Spain in the last decade of the third century is securely attested by Polybius XI, 23, 1.   [5] See *e.g.* XXII, 5, 7.

[6] *Bell. Jug.* 51, 3; 56, 3–4: cf. 55, 4 and 100, 4. The last of these passages alone falls during the period of Marius' command.

to group the maniples in cohorts. This process was completed
during the later life of Marius, and in the subsequent wars of the
revolutionary age maniples no longer play an independent part.
When this stage was reached, a consequential change became inevitable. The abandonment of the maniple as a separable unit
made it pointless to retain the old distinctions of age and armament
between the maniples of *hastati, principes* and *triarii*. These were
accordingly dropped, very possibly by Marius himself. All legionaries were now armed alike, with the *pilum* as the one missile
weapon and the sword for fighting at close quarters. By this
assimilation the cohorts were still further consolidated. They were
now the standard units of manoeuvre, and with them was built up
a fighting line of a solidity unknown before, wherein, thanks to the
discipline of highly trained troops under the immediate control of
competent centurions, the increased size of the component parts
involved no serious loss of flexibility. Such was the final phase of
a development which ended by giving Rome an infantry whose
efficiency was never surpassed in the history of the ancient world.

When autumn came without the appearance of the foe, Marius
was elected, again in absence, to the consulship for the following
year. But still there was no enemy, and 103 B.C. had to be passed
in waiting. To occupy his men in something more profitable than
the monotonies of drill, Marius designed a canal which should do
for the Rhône what the Emperor Claudius did later for the Tiber.
To escape the silt which made access to the river difficult by its
natural estuary, an artificial channel was dug from a point on the
coast just south of the modern Fos to the main stream above the
bar, and thus an open waterway was left which avoided the old
obstacles to shipping. The *fossa Mariana* was a memorable achievement: in the hands of the Massiliotes, to whom it was made over
after the war, it produced a lucrative revenue in dues[1], and it laid
the foundations for the commercial development of Arelate (Arles).
Again, apart from its value to Massilia and to all traders whose
business was with Gaul, it was a forerunner of those public works
which the standing army of later Roman history was to leave as its
monuments throughout the Empire.

Towards the end of 103 B.C., when it was certain that the impending struggle must be delayed yet another year, Marius left
his troops under the command of M'. Aquilius, and went back to
Rome, where, with the help of the tribune Saturninus, he was
elected consul for the fourth time. While he was still in Italy, news
arrived that the Cimbri were returning from the west, a return

[1] See Strabo iv, 183.

which meant that the decisive clash would come with Marius still in control. Soon he was back in Gaul; but the greatest crisis of his military career was suddenly made less critical by a new decision of the enemy. For the moment the whole horde was united somewhere in northern France[1]; but after some conflicts with the Belgae, who contrived to hold their own[2], they left their superfluous belongings under a guard of 6000 men in the valley of the Meuse[3] and embarked on a manœuvre of amazing rashness and stupendous scale. Italy was to be attacked on three fronts at once. The Teutoni were to advance along the coast road from the west; the Cimbri were to descend on Lombardy from the Brenner; and to the Tigurini fell the still harder task of making their way to Pannonia and striking at Aquileia over the Julian Alps.

Vast as their numbers might be, by adopting such strategy as this the barbarians played straight into the hands of Rome. Marius and his lieutenants were allowed to operate on interior lines against three independent forces which, though united they might have been of overwhelming strength, individually were by no means invincible. The Roman army was holding a camp on the east bank of the Rhône, probably near the crossing below the confluence of the Durance[4], and here the Teutoni sought to provoke a battle. Marius refused, and when a direct assault on his position had failed to bring out his troops, the enemy decided to leave him where he was and start on the way to Italy. At the head of the column went the Ambrones, a people who had apparently shared in the fortunes of the migration from the beginning and were either part of the Teutoni or their kinsmen in close relation. Once the whole mass was strung out in the long line of march, Marius broke camp without delay, and by other routes reached Aquae Sextiae before any but the Ambrones had arrived. Thus the upper valley of the Arc was blocked, and the barbarians must either fight or retire. The Germans now made a new mistake. Without waiting for their main body to come up, the Ambrones crossed the river and attacked the Romans in the position of their own

---

[1] The locality depends on the reading adopted in the last sentence of Livy, *Epit.* 67.   [2] Caesar, *B.G.* II, 4, 2.

[3] This body was the nucleus of the tribe known to later times as the Atuatuci: Caesar, *B.G.* II, 29, 4–5.

[4] Orosius (v, 16, 9), our only explicit authority, places this camp north of Valence, at the point where the Isère joins the Rhône. But this site is in conflict both with the suggestion of Plutarch (*Marius*, 15, 1–2) and also with general considerations of probability, which point to a site much farther to the south. See M. Clerc, *La bataille d'Aix*, pp. 65 *sqq.*

choosing on the slopes to the south. Thirty thousand men advanced to the assault, but they were thrown back across the river and none but a remnant survived to join the main force in the final battle. The interval which followed was brief, but it gave Marius time to send a body of three thousand men to circumvent the enemy and conceal itself on the heights in his rear. Then on the next day or, at latest, two days after the first engagement, the Romans offered battle again[1]. The fight was long and stubborn; but superior equipment, sounder discipline, the advantage of position and the confusion caused among the enemy by the unexpected attack of the three thousand from behind finally gave Marius a victory decisive beyond hope. Not only was Italy freed from all fear of invasion from the west, but the enemy was annihilated and the turmoil in Gaul was at an end. Killed and captured are put by the lowest estimate at more than a hundred thousand.

Little remained to do in Gaul. The prestige of Rome was restored, and Marius, now designated to his fifth consulship, could turn to the problems of the future. These lay in Italy, where amateur generalship had lived down to its traditions. When the barbarians unfolded their design for a triple thrust across the Alps, Marius in Gaul had been compelled to leave the defence of Italy to his colleague in the consulship of 102 B.C.—Q. Lutatius Catulus. Catulus was a man more noted for his culture than for knowledge of the art of war. He had the opportunities which Napoleon knew how to use; but the brilliance which shone at Castiglione, Bassano, Arcola and Rivoli was not his to show. When the Cimbri were found to be moving southwards from the Brenner, Catulus, instead of waiting to destroy them as they debouched on to open ground, advanced up the Adige far into the hills. There he chose a position, probably in the neighbourhood of Trento, and essayed to block the way. But the choice was foolish: in the narrow valley there was no room for manœuvre, nor even for the legions to deploy. In place of a battle wherein discipline and training might have told, the Romans were threatened with a hand-to-hand struggle round a bridge—a struggle of the sort in which skill goes for nothing and attrition leaves victory with the larger numbers. From this miniature Thermopylae Catulus was ejected by the good-sense or cowardice of his troops. For whatever reason, the men refused duty in such circumstances: with difficulty the army

---

[1] On the site of this second battle, which has been made the subject of many theories, the present writer accepts the view of C. Jullian: see id. *Histoire de la Gaule*, III², p. 82, n. 3 and the literature there mentioned.

was disengaged: and from Trento it retired south of the Po, leaving the invaders in undisputed possession of all Transpadane Gaul which they might care to occupy.

The authorities are at variance on the date of these events, but it is clear that the barbarians had entered Italy by the early winter of 102 B.C., if not before. When news of their advance reached Rome, Marius, who had returned to the city at the end of his campaign in Gaul, postponed the holding of his triumph, ordered his army to Piedmont and himself set out for the North. For the campaign of 101 B.C. he and Catulus, whose *imperium* had been prorogued, between them could muster more than fifty thousand men, and with this force they crossed the Po to seek a decision on the northern bank. The preliminaries seem to have been long: it was not till after midsummer that the two armies found themselves face to face near Vercellae. There, at a place called Campi Raudii, the carnage of Aquae Sextiae was renewed. According to Florus[1], the Cimbri lost sixty-five thousand dead, though others put the number more than twice as high; and all who survived were captured. The victory was conclusive: the Tigurini, who now alone remained, did not wait to share their allies' fate, but left their station in the eastern Alps and returned peaceably to their homes in Switzerland. Next year a colony to watch the St Bernard routes was planted at Eporedia among the Salassi[2], whose gold-bearing territory had already attracted Roman notice. So Rome emerged, battered but supreme, from the earliest of her conflicts with the Germans.

When Marius and Catulus began to wrangle over the laurels of Vercellae, their dispute was on a minor issue. Though they triumphed together in 101 B.C., men had no doubt with which the credit lay. It was Marius who had saved the State and was hailed, after Romulus and Camillus, as the third founder of Rome. But his glory was not earned in the final battle. Whatever he may have contributed to the last campaign, his supreme service had been rendered the year before, when, with Rome fighting on two fronts at once, he had destroyed the enemy in Gaul single-handed and so enabled both Roman armies to be concentrated against the invaders across the Alps. Aquae Sextiae, like Salamis, was the crisis of the war: Vercellae was a sequel, like Plataea. Yet the Germanic movement of those years cannot be compared in significance with the Persian attack on Greece. The Gallic raid in the fourth century and the devastation wrought by Hannibal had left Italy with a dread of invasion which magnified every menace, and in this case

---

[1] I, 38 (III, 3), 14.   [2] Vell. Pat. I, 15, 5.

the dangers of the German threat were made the more alarming by disasters due to military incompetence. But, for all their numbers, the Germans were doomed as soon as Roman generalship became worthy of its past. Though they had worked their will among the Celts of Gaul, a people who had been driven off the Danube, who were helpless before the Belgic tribes in the northwest and who failed to gain a footing across the Pyrenees, were no match for the power which had destroyed Carthage and imposed its terms on Antiochus the Great. The migration was one which only energetic opposition could stop, and it came at a time when Rome's energies were in large part absorbed elsewhere; but the loss of five Roman armies, which alone gave its alarming aspect to the affair, was needless flattery of the foe. The episode of the Cimbri and Teutoni is entitled to remembrance, not for any peril to the Roman State, but for the heights of influence to which Marius, a mere soldier, was raised, for the lesson which Rome learnt about the value of control beyond the Alps if the Alps themselves were to be inviolate, and for Rome's first contact with Germans, a people who in later centuries were to bulk large in Roman history.

X. THE WARS IN THE ISLANDS AND THE SECOND RISING OF THE SICILIAN SLAVES

There remain for notice three episodes, of varied importance, which attracted attention to the islands of the western Mediterranean at different times during the last thirty years of the second century B.C. First comes Sardinia. In 126 B.C. the restless peace which had prevailed in that turbulent country since the triumph of the elder Tiberius Gracchus, forty-nine years before (vol. VIII, p. 331), was so far broken that the consul L. Aurelius Orestes sailed with an expedition only notable for the presence of the young Gaius Gracchus as the consul's quaestor. It was he who induced the people of the cities voluntarily to provide clothing for the army when the Senate had allowed their appeal against a compulsory requisition, and it was regard for the name of Gracchus which is said to have moved the Numidian Micipsa to offer supplies of corn. But, though the Senate is alleged to have prorogued the command of Orestes in order that his quaestor might have to stay in Sardinia too, Gaius was back in Rome, well satisfied with his own behaviour[1], before the end of 125 B.C.; and about the

---

[1] See Malcovati, *Orat. Rom. Frag.* II, pp. 132 *sqq.*

course of the campaign after his departure our ignorance is complete. At most we can say that it was long, and not without success; for Orestes finally triumphed, though not until December 122 B.C.

Even less is known of the operations conducted by M. Metellus —one of the sons of Metellus Macedonicus—who was sent to Sardinia after his consulship in 115 B.C. and celebrated a triumph on 15 July 111 B.C.—an occasion made famous by the fact that his brother Gaius triumphed on the same day for his services in Thrace. For the rest, nothing is recorded of the achievements of Marcus in Sardinia except the fact, revealed by a document of A.D. 69[1], that he was the author of administrative arrangements which involved the demarcation of some boundaries. There the affairs of the island may be left; for the campaign of the Epicurean T. Albucius is memorable for nothing but his insolent celebration of a triumph on his own authority in Sardinia itself[2].

Of greater significance than these trivial incidents was the occupation of the Balearic Islands. Roman intervention in this quarter was provoked by the activities of pirate fleets, which used the islands as a base, even if they were not wholly manned by the local population; and it must be assumed that the first object of the war was to free the sea routes which ran to Spain. But the islands themselves were by no means to be despised: apart from the military value of the native slingers, the soil was good and subsequently became famous for its production of corn and wine. The operations were entrusted to one of the consuls of 123 B.C.— Q. Metellus, the eldest brother of Marcus and Gaius—but their conduct seems to have called for no great skill. The fleet was protected from the sling-bullets of the enemy by special screens rigged up on deck, and after a landing had been made the occupation of the country was so speedy and complete that almost at once it became possible to found two colonies of Roman citizens in Majorca. These colonies, Palma and Pollentia, deserve notice, not only because their origin was due to a man who, so far as we can say, belonged to the senatorial oligarchy, but also because their object was something other than the relief of over-population in Italy. Three thousand of the settlers, certainly a considerable fraction of the whole, were drawn from the Roman (or Italian) population of Spain[3]. That fact is noteworthy. Roman policy may, indeed, have been determined by the military value of the island population; but it is also possible that some effect should be ascribed to those

---

[1] Dessau 5947, l. 7.   [2] Cicero, *de prov. cons.* 7, 15; *in. Pis.* 38, 92.
[3] Strabo III, 168.

commercial considerations which now begin to be discernible and which, in later times at least, carried peculiar weight with the Italian emigrants who made their homes in Spain. Whatever may have been the motive of the expedition, its importance was enough to earn the surname 'Balearicus' for its leader and to win him the honour of a triumph in 121 B.C.

The final episode in the military history of these years has Sicily for its scene[1]. In 104 B.C. there broke out the insurrection which passes as the Second Servile War; but, unlike its predecessor, this later affair holds a place in the story of Rome thanks rather to an accident of its circumstances than to any intrinsic interest of its own. Such warnings as a rising of this kind could give about the dangers latent in a society using slave-gangs to supply its labour had been given already by Eunus and Achaeus: the movement led by Salvius and Athenion is remembered because, when Rome had at length shaken herself free of entanglements in Africa, it provided a new and unexpected embarrassment during the crisis of the struggle with the Germanic invaders.

Though there may have been a tendency since the end of the First Slave War for small holdings in Sicily to extend at the expense of large (p. 16), the general conditions of the island had escaped all fundamental change, and in essence the later outbreak is not to be distinguished from the earlier. As on the former occasion, the explosion in Sicily was heralded by rumblings in Italy itself. There was an outbreak at Nuceria, another at Capua, and then a third in the neighbourhood of Capua again—this last a most extraordinary affair. Probably in 104 B.C., a Roman knight named T. Vettius, whose amatory propensities had plunged him into hopeless debt, bought five hundred suits of armour—on credit, equipped his own slaves for war, and soon, by forcibly enlisting the servile population of the district, found himself at the head of an army of 3500 men. Against this enterprising bankrupt the Senate was compelled to send a praetor, L. Lucullus—a man best remembered as the father of two more famous sons. Despite the demands of the northern front, a force of four thousand odd was somehow raised, and Lucullus, not without vicissitudes and recourse to treachery, finally captured the adventurer.

When this could happen within two hundred miles of Rome, far worse was possible in the remoter parts of Sicily. It was about now that the difficulties which Marius had encountered in securing contingents from the client kings led the Senate to issue

[1] The fragments of Diodorus xxxvi are our only serious authority for the history of the Second Sicilian Slave War. See above, Map 1.

a decree ordering the immediate release of all citizens of allied States held as slaves in the provinces of the empire. When, however, this enactment came to be applied to Sicily in 104 B.C., it caused so much excitement among the local slaves and such resentment among their owners that the governor, P. Licinius Nerva, desisted from the work of liberation after about eight hundred had been freed. The immediate result was a small outbreak at Halicyae, a township of western Sicily between Segesta and Selinus. By the familiar use of treachery this was soon put down, but it was followed at once by a more serious rising which had its centre on the south coast, in the territory of Heraclea Minoa. After the defeat of a Roman contingent the rebels soon mustered 6000 men, and organized themselves into a regular army. A certain Salvius, who took the title 'King,' was chosen as their leader, and before long, with a force of 2000 cavalry and 20,000 foot, he marched into the fertile regions of the east, where he essayed an attack on the city of Murgantia. An attempt by Nerva to raise the siege ended in a failure whose only result was to double the numbers of the enemy. The siege was resumed, and though Murgantia was preserved intact, it seems that, when the enemy withdrew, his strength was still further increased by the folly of Nerva in rescinding an offer of freedom whereby the citizens had sought to retain the loyalty of the slaves within the walls. When the promise was not fulfilled, they went off to join the rebels.

In the same year an independent movement was started in the far west of the island, where a Cilician named Athenion collected a large following and used it with intelligence. Instead of arming all his men, he enlisted none but the most fit and kept the rest at their ordinary occupations in order to provide supplies. Then, with his striking force, he attacked Lilybaeum. The siege did not prosper, and Athenion thought it prudent to withdraw; but though he lost a certain number of men during the retreat when some African troops, who had come to help their friends in Lilybaeum, fell upon his force, the rebels disengaged themselves without serious damage and remained a threat of the first magnitude to the established social order. By this time all Sicily was in a ferment. The slaves were soon reinforced by discontented elements from the free population, and the danger was made many times greater by a junction of the forces under Salvius, who now called himself King Tryphon, and Athenion. They met at Triocala north of Heraclea, and made it their headquarters: shortly afterwards Tryphon ensured unity of command by putting Athenion under temporary arrest.

So far the Roman resistance seems to have been maintained by the small forces normally in the island, together with such emergency levies as could be raised: henceforward it was to draw more and more freely on the resources of the empire as a whole. In 103 B.C. Nerva was succeeded by L. Lucullus, whose operations at Capua the year before have been mentioned already; and Lucullus was given an army of 17,000 men, which included recruits from Acarnania, Thessaly and even Bithynia. His advance provoked a council of war at Triocala, where it was decided on the advice of Athenion, now released from custody, not to invite a siege but to offer battle in the open country. The slaves outnumbered the Romans by more than two to one: but training told in the end. Athenion was wounded and only escaped capture by feigning death; the rebel losses amounted to something like half their whole force; and the survivors who finally found safety behind the walls of Triocala were so utterly demoralized that they seriously contemplated surrender forthwith. But Lucullus failed to follow up his advantage: it was not till more than a week later that he appeared before the city, and by that time the garrison had plucked up courage enough to beat off his assaults. Finally Lucullus withdrew, and on his return to Rome he found himself in trouble. It is hard to believe that he had accepted bribes, but there is no lack of reason for his fall if Diodorus tells the truth when he says that Lucullus, hearing that a successor was on his way to take over the command, disbanded his army in a fit of pique and even destroyed his camp. Whatever the state of affairs which awaited him, the new governor achieved nothing in 102 B.C., and in the following year, when he was back in Rome, he tried to divert attention from his own defects by displaying those of his predecessor[1]. After much dirty linen had been washed in public, a rough justice was finally done by the exile of both parties to the squabble.

The year 101 B.C. brought the long-sought turn of fortune. The victory of Aquae Sextiae had so far dispelled the German menace that M'. Aquilius, now colleague of Marius in the consulship, could be sent to take charge of Sicily in person. Aquilius was a soldier of experience in whom Marius had already shown his confidence by leaving him in command of the army in Gaul when he returned to Rome in the summer of 103 B.C.[2]; and in Sicily he displayed unbounded energy. First he tackled the urgent problem of the food supply. Since the withdrawal of Lucullus from Triocala,

---

[1] On this see F. Münzer in P.W. *s.v.* Servilius, col. 1763 *sq.* and *s.v.* Licinius, col. 375 *sq.*   [2] Plutarch, *Marius*, 14, 7.

the slaves had played such havoc with the economic life of the country that an island which normally was one of the granaries of the Roman world now stood in danger of starvation. Next he opened his campaign. The rebels were defeated in a battle, Athenion—whom the death of Tryphon had left in sole command —was killed, and the fugitives were pursued with relentless determination until they were either captured outright or starved into surrender. The prisoners were later sent to Rome, where they died gloriously at the hands of one another rather than fight with beasts to amuse the Roman mob.

Aquilius did not receive his *ovatio* until 99 B.C.: until then he seems to have stayed in Sicily, restoring peace on so firm a foundation that neither the rising of Spartacus in southern Italy nor the outrages of Verres affected the tranquillity of the island. It is true that his administration was subsequently arraigned, and the belief in his avarice seems to have been shared by Mithridates, who ended his career in 88 B.C. by pouring molten gold down his throat. Cicero, too, had no doubt of his guilt[1]; but thanks to the influence of Marius and to a most memorable piece of oratory by M. Antonius, who led for the defence[2], gratitude got the better of justice and the trial ended in acquittal. Aquilius had, indeed, deserved well of the State. Under his auspices the Roman cause had not looked back, and Rome had rapidly been rid of an affair which, serious as it was, might easily have spread beyond the boundaries of Sicily[3] and so have become an even graver embarrassment to a government whose task on the northern frontier, at the time when Aquilius took charge, was still so vast as to demand its undivided attention and a concentration of all the resources at its command.

Thus ended a period of Roman history wherein the prevailing theme was one of war. Territorially the gains of Rome were small. In Asia the fighting had only preserved what had already become Roman by bequest; in Sicily nothing more was done than to restore order in the oldest of the provinces; and in Africa there was no tangible result to show for six years' fighting. In the North, it is true, the frontier had been straightened out and Gallia Narbonensis was an acquisition of immeasurable worth: but even here

---

[1] *pro Flacco*, 39, 98.

[2] Cicero, II *in Verr.* v, 1, 3; *de orat.* II, 47, 195–6.

[3] Posidonius (*F.H.G.* frag. 35 = *F.G.H.* frag. 35) records trouble at this time in the mines of Attica; but his words, as reported by Athenaeus (VI, p. 272, E–F), do not suggest that it was directly provoked by the Sicilian affair.

the supreme effort had been spent on the unremunerative task of defence against invasion. Yet, though the positive rewards compared so ill with the energy expended, the warfare of the age left a legacy of deep significance in the history of Rome. This was the professional army—the army which not only made possible the more impressive military achievements of later years but itself became an active force in politics, and one whose contribution to the downfall of the Republic was decisive.

CHAPTER IV

THE ENFRANCHISEMENT OF ITALY

I. THE PEOPLE AND ITS GENERALS

IN the years which lie between the close of the Gracchan episode and the outbreak of the Social War the domestic history of Rome is a melancholy and unremunerative study. The period was one of depression, when flaws in the fabric of the State were made uncomfortably plain yet nothing worth the mention was done for their repair. Attention may be confined to four features of the age —the search for means to impose a sense of responsibility on commanders in the field; the revelation by Glaucia and Saturninus of the dangers which would arise when the constitutional methods of the Gracchi found followers without scruples or ideals; the entry into politics of Marius—the first Roman who made military prowess a claim to direct the civil government and the earliest precursor of the soldier-emperors of the third century A.D.; and, finally, the preliminaries to the upheaval which ended with the enfranchisement of the Italians. These are the significant aspects of the story: the ups and downs of fortune in the petty struggle between the Senate and its rivals are incidents for which the briefest notice will suffice.

The scandals of the wars in Africa and the North presented a problem unknown before. The dearth of competent commanders and the low standard of morality which now pervaded public life had produced a whole series of generals who must at all costs be taught a lesson *pour encourager les autres*. Men in high places must learn the simple truth that the privilege of office involved obligations to the State. A beginning had been made by the Mamilian commission (p. 121), which was at least a reminder that corruption could not be tolerated; but the energy of that court had failed to impress on those whom it most concerned the further fact that wilful gambling with the interests of Rome, whether through personal ambition or indolent neglect of the most obvious precautions, was culpable to a degree deserving punishment. Carbo, the victim of Noreia, had forestalled by death any formal pronouncement on his conduct; but his successors in misfortune— Silanus, Caepio and Mallius—awaited a condemnation which, however richly merited, was not easy to secure. The charge hitherto preferred against citizens who had acted to the detriment of the State was *perduellio*—an offence which in course of time had been given the widest interpretation: before the end of the third century this process had been employed against Cn. Fulvius Flaccus though whether for failure in war is not clear.[1] To the use of this weapon, however, there were grave objections. Not only did it involve a clumsy procedure before the Centuries, but the charge itself was one of doubtful relevance to the crime. *Perduellio* properly understood was either actual warfare against the State or at least action of a kind which suggested that the agent was a *hostis*[2]; and it was easy to argue that negligence or imprudence, however gross, fell short of being a premeditated attack on the Roman People. The unsuitability of such a prosecution was made peculiarly plain by the minor case to which it was applied. In 106 B.C. C. Popillius Laenas, the *legatus* of Cassius Longinus who by the acceptance of humiliating terms had rescued the remnants of his army from the Tigurini, was solemnly arraigned for *perduellio*. The attack was led by C. Caelius Caldus, now tribune, and elaborate plans were laid for its success: Caelius even went so far as to pass a *lex tabellaria* extending the ballot to the voting of the Centuries in such a case[3]. Even so, it is difficult to see how on such a charge any honest court could have convicted a man for saving such survivors as he was able. The exile into which Popillius was finally driven was probably the result of a later trial under the new treason-law of Saturninus[4].

The battle of Arausio raised graver problems. Caepio and Mallius had been guilty of a reckless refusal to co-operate, and the crime of Caepio was aggravated both by the unpopularity of his *lex iudiciaria* (p. 161 *sq.*) and by the strong suspicion of dishonesty in the matter of the bullion from Tolosa (p. 143). Public opinion soon found expression. First he was deprived of his proconsular *imperium* by popular vote[5], and then in 104 B.C. he lost his seat in the Senate when L. Cassius Longinus, a son of the *iudex* in the scandal of the Vestals (p. 97), passed a tribunician law expelling from the House all members who had been condemned by the People on a criminal charge or whose *imperium* had been abrogated[6]. The leader in the attack on Caepio had been another tribune,

---

[1] Livy XXVI, 2, 7 *sqq.*; cf. De Sanctis, *Storia dei Rom.* III, 2, p. 460 n.
[2] See *Dig.* 50, 16, 234 (Gaius) and 48, 4, 11 (Ulpian).
[3] Cicero, *de legibus*, III, 16, 36.   [4] *ad Herennium,* I, 15, 25.
[5] Livy, *Epit.* 67; Cicero, *de orat.* II, 47, 197 *sqq.*
[6] Asconius, p. 78 c.

C. Norbanus, and his success had only been won after a struggle
so severe that rioting broke out. Other tribunes, among whom
L. Cotta and T. Didius are mentioned, threatened to use their
veto, and in the street-fighting which followed the Princeps Senatus
had his head broken by a stone. But opposition only made Norbanus and his friends the more determined. Not content with such
achievements, they insisted that Caepio must be tried; but the
elaborate plans now laid for compassing his fate belong to the
following year. Before they are described, two other trials of
104 B.C. need notice. One of the tribunes now in office was Cn.
Domitius Ahenobarbus, whose father's exploits against the Allobroges (p. 111 sq.) doubtless gave the son a special interest in the
affairs of Gaul. For this reason, and for others of a more private
kind, Domitius now attacked Silanus, the victim of the Germans
in 109 B.C. The charge is unknown, though the ground of complaint
was that Silanus had marched without instructions beyond the
borders of the province[1]: but in this case, as in his prosecution of
M. Aemilius Scaurus for neglecting his duties as augur, Domitius
miserably failed and both his intended victims were triumphantly
acquitted.

On 10 December 104 B.C. new tribunes entered office—and
among them L. Appuleius Saturninus, for whom was reserved
the final settlement of accounts with Caepio. On the sequence of
events which follows and on many of the essential details the extant evidence is so vague that no account can claim more than
probability; but it is clear that Saturninus, adopting the method
of Mamilius, secured the establishment of a court to try the
remaining villains of the Gallic piece. Both Caepio and Mallius
were condemned, though the latter was defended by M. Antonius:
Mallius' fate is not recorded, but Caepio lost his property by confiscation[2] and finally died in exile at Smyrna.

It remains to consider a more permanent result which may
possibly be ascribed to this series of prosecutions. Though the
evidence fails to support Mommsen's conjecture that the measure
which ordered inquiry into the scandal of Tolosa was the famous
Lex Appuleia de maiestate[3], and though he was perhaps rash to deny
that this law established a new standing court[4], there is plausibility

---

[1] Asconius, p. 80 c.
[2] The statement of Livy, *Epit.* 67, on this point is probably misplaced:
see F. Vonder Mühll, *De L. Appuleio Saturnino tribuno plebis*, p. 73, n. 3.
[3] Th. Mommsen, *History of Rome*, vol. III, p. 441 n.; cf. L. Lange,
Römische Alterthümer, vol. III², pp. 70 and 82.
[4] If H. Stuart Jones is right in regarding the Lex Latina Bantiae reperta

in his assumption that the failure of Roman generalship abroad did something to provoke this memorable enactment. Its date is uncertain, though it more probably belongs to the first tribunate of its author (103 B.C.) than to the second (100 B.C.); but its object is plain—if not to create, at least roughly to define the offence of wanton injury to the *maiestas populi Romani* and also to establish penalties for the crime. Undoubtedly this weapon is most often found in the hands of politicians engaged in party struggles, and it is possible to believe that it was forged by Saturninus in part at least to break down resistance to his own supremacy at Rome[1]. But on the other hand, men who claimed office on the strength of their *nobilitas* and then used the consequent command to fling Roman armies recklessly away were a menace whose gravity the last ten years had abundantly revealed. *Perduellio* was a charge ill-suited to their case, and it is by no means unlikely that failure was henceforward to be discouraged by the prospect of a more appropriate, and for that reason more dangerous, prosecution for *minuta maiestas*.

II. THE SENATE AND ITS ENEMIES AT ROME

In the creation of the Mamilian commission and in the election of Marius to the consulship in 108 B.C. the People had shown signs of alarming self-assertion; but even the most ardent admirer of the assemblies could scarcely urge that they were fit to conduct the daily business which campaigns abroad impose upon a government at home. The Senate alone could shoulder such a task, and, despite the incompetence of its chosen leaders in the field, the Jugurthine War, like all wars of the Republic, did something to maintain senatorial prestige. Marius' appointment was a criticism which admitted no reply; but in general, so long as their work was such as no other body could perform, the Fathers were left in peace. The lull in political strife allowed confidence to return, and in 106 B.C. the Senate revealed both its courage and its folly by a piece of legislation which in war-time must appear amazing. As if to mark their defiance of the 'new men' and the class from which they came, the *nobiles* took advantage of the domestic peace to launch an attack on the most controversial of all the Gracchan laws. Thereby was let loose a storm of opposition which did not

(Bruns, *Fontes*[7], 9) as a fragment of the Lex Appuleia de maiestate (*J.R.S.* XVI, 1926, p. 171), it would be virtually certain that a new *iudicium publicum* was created by this measure.

[1] See F. W. Robinson, *Marius, Saturninus und Glaucia*, p. 65 *sq.*

abate till eight years had passed. Q. Servilius Caepio, one of the consuls, found time before his departure for Gaul to introduce a bill which changed the constitution of juries in certain criminal trials. Though our information is lamentably defective and does not explain what courts were now concerned, if it is right to see in the Lex Servilia Glauciae de rebus repetundis a repeal of Caepio's work (p. 163), it follows that, whatever other *iudicia publica* may have existed at this time, it was to the *quaestio repetundarum*, the subject of the Gracchan Lex Acilia, that Caepio confined his attention. There is doubt again about the nature of the change now introduced. According to the Livian tradition[1], senators and 'equites' were to sit side by side on juries, though in what proportions we are not told: but Tacitus[2] has a rival version, that 'the courts were given back to the Senate,' and this account is perhaps made the more probable by Cicero's suggestion that senators and 'equites Romani' were never found together on a jury before the Lex Plautia of 89 B.C.[3] But, whatever its provisions, the ancient authorities contain no hint that the bill of Caepio failed to pass. Its passage had even been sped by the oratory of Crassus[4]; but at this stage of his career he could no longer speak for the commercial class, and when Caepio went off to Gaul he left behind him a political situation in which the bitterness of the Gracchan age had been reborn.

The Senate did not long enjoy its triumph. Towards the end of 105 B.C. the return of Caepio in disgrace offered an easy victim to the opposition; but the demand for reprisals against him and the other authors of disaster was not the only sign seen in 104 B.C. that senatorial influence was on the wane. It was probably in this year that the offensive judiciary law was repealed. C. Servilius Glaucia, the associate of Saturninus, is recorded to have passed a *lex de rebus repetundis* which, among other minor modifications, is said to have introduced procedure by *comperendinatio*[5] and to have authorized the prosecution of those who received money wrongfully extorted, even if they had not themselves been accessory to the act[6]. Such is the meagre scope often assigned to this measure, which Mommsen proposed to place in 111 B.C.[7] This account, however,

---

[1] Preserved by Julius Obsequens 41 (101) and Cassiodorus, *Chron.* in *Mon. Germ. Hist.*, Auctt. antiquiss. XI, p. 132.   [2] *Ann.* XII, 60, 4.

[3] *Ap.* Ascon. p. 79 c. The present writer may be allowed, however, to say that he does not share the prevailing confidence with which conclusions are drawn from this passage.   [4] Cicero, *Brutus*, 43, 161–44, 164.

[5] Cicero, II *in Verr.* I, 9, 26.   [6] Cicero, *pro Rab. Post.* 4, 8 *sq.*

[7] *Ges. Schriften*, I, p. 22.

is by no means satisfactory. Though it may be believed that the law was enacted by Glaucia as tribune, the arguments whereby it is proposed to fix his tribunate in 111 B.C. rest on so many hypotheses as to be wholly inconclusive: moreover, such a chronology deprives the act of its undoubted significance. If it had merely introduced some changes in procedure, Cicero could scarcely have said that Glaucia 'equestrem ordinem beneficio legis devinxerat.[1]' The only evidence of value for the date of Glaucia's tribunate is to be found in an obscure passage of Appian[2] which, when interpreted in the only intelligible way, reveals that it fell in a year immediately before one of the tribunates of Saturninus— that is in 104 B.C. or 101 B.C.[3] In either case, the Lex Servilia Caepionis had already been passed, and the way is open to the conclusion that the service whereby Glaucia won the goodwill of the 'equites' was the restoration of the privileges which Caepio had removed. The precise date is unimportant. The words of Appian as they stand favour the second possibility; but their obscurity shows that he was not clear about the meaning of his authority, and the brief validity which the arrangements of Caepio seem to have enjoyed would rather suggest that the tribunate of Glaucia, and with it the *lex de rebus repetundis*, belongs to 104 B.C.

Thus the Senate paid for its folly of two years before. But this was not all: the opposition had now taken the offensive, and Cn. Domitius, a second tribune of 104 B.C., found time amid his occupations in the courts to challenge the oligarchs at another point. Hitherto the religious machinery of the State had been left to their unfettered management, but even this was now to be brought under some sort of popular control. A vacancy in the augural college caused by the death of Domitius' father[4] filled the son with ambition to secure the place for himself; but the appointment was made by the usual co-optation, and the claims of Domitius were passed over in favour of another. The immediate responsibility for this was laid at the door of M. Aemilius Scaurus, who accordingly found himself arraigned on a frivolous charge (p. 160). But Domitius was out for more than personal revenge. The Lex Domitia de sacerdotiis extended to the whole of the great priestly colleges a practice, hitherto only known in the choice of the Pontifex Maximus, which in effect amounted to election by the People. When an appointment was to be made, the names of candidates were submitted to a unique assembly composed of

---

[1] *Brutus*, 62, 224.   [2] *Bell. Civ.* 1, 28, 127.

[3] See G. Niccolini in *Historia*, IV, 1930, pp. 44–7, and the authorities there cited.   [4] Suet. *Nero*, 2, 1.

seventeen tribes chosen by lot out of the whole thirty-five. Deference to the traditions of the past still preserved the forms of co-optation. The popular vote in theory was not final; but when the People's choice was presented for admission to office by the ancient procedure, the College could do nought but acquiesce. Little as the State religion had by this time come to mean, there can be no doubt of the importance set upon the Lex Domitia: within a few years of its passage, when Metellus Delmaticus died, Domitius was made Pontifex Maximus in his stead, and the measure itself was one which Sulla found it worth while to repeal and Caesar, in 63 B.C., to re-enact (p. 487).

III. THE TRIBUNATES OF SATURNINUS

If the year 104 B.C. saw other incidents of note, only one at most is recorded. Possibly at this time L. Marcius Philippus, a tribune destined for a remarkable career, proposed an agrarian law. Its object is unknown, though—if this be its date—we may conjecture that its benefits were meant at least in part for such veterans from Africa as were not transferred to Gaul: and, as it was withdrawn before the voting, it would not deserve mention at all had it not been in connection with this bill that Philippus made his memorable assertion that there were not two thousand men of real wealth in the State[1]. In the following year, however, the political struggle grew more violent. Hitherto the resentment against the Senate unloosed by the judiciary law of 106 B.C. had found expression in the Lex Servilia Glauciae—if this belongs to 104 B.C., in a few prosecutions, and in an isolated attack on the prerogatives of the nobility in the priesthood. Now, the opposition developed something like a consistent legislative programme, and the means whereby it was to be pressed indubitably found their inspiration in the Gracchi. The threat to the Senate seemed grave; for behind the tribunes there was soon to stand an ally such as the Gracchi had never known. When Marius led back the legions from Vercellae, his instincts were against the Senate; and had he thrown his weight on the side of its enemies, for all that men could tell his power might have made them irresistible. But in the end the government emerged victorious, thanks less to its own virtues than to the vices of its opponents. The failure of the opposition must be ascribed in the first place to the lack of ideals among its leaders. Though they courted the class from which the Gracchan *iudices* were drawn, they proved so reckless in their methods and

[1] Cicero, *de off.* II, 21, 73.

so barren of salutary reforms that responsible opinion set against them, until finally their fate was sealed by the desertion of Marius himself.

L. Appuleius Saturninus came of praetorian stock. He had some small pretensions as an orator, and his character was not above reproach; but nothing marked him for his later notoriety until, in some year which cannot now be ascertained, he gained the quaestorship and received Ostia as his province, with the business of superintending the passage of the corn-supplies to Rome. During his period of control there came a shortage, and—though Diodorus[1] is scarcely fair in saddling Saturninus with the blame—when prices rose, the Senate removed him from his post and transferred his duties for the time being to M. Scaurus, the Princeps Senatus, whose presence at Ostia would ensure that, when prices became normal again, the credit would accrue to the nobility. The result of this treatment was to fill Saturninus with a bitter hatred of the government: he became a *popularis*[2]: and, when he entered the first of his tribunates on 10 December 104 B.C., the time to pay off old scores had arrived.

Saturninus was tribune for the second time in 100 B.C., and our authorities are so lamentably unsuccessful in their attempts to distinguish his two periods of office that any attempt to reconstruct the course of his legislation must be even more tentative than in the case of Gaius Gracchus. Like Gracchus, Saturninus seems to have begun with a *lex frumentaria*, though, if our only information is correct about the suggested price, this measure had little in common with its model[3]. According to the treatise *ad Herennium*[4], corn was to be sold at five-sixths of an *as*, which meant, if this was the charge for a *modius*, that the cost to purchasers was reduced to little more than one-eighth of that established by the law of 123 B.C.[5] The introduction of this bill provoked instant opposition.

---

[1] XXXVI, 12.   [2] Cicero, *de har. resp.* 20, 43.

[3] The reasons which lead the present writer to place this measure in the first tribunate are (i) its obvious connection with the incidents of Saturninus' quaestorship; (ii) the probability that Saturninus was consciously following the course of Gaius Gracchus; and, most important, (iii) the virtual impossibility of putting the quaestorship of Q. Caepio (see *B.M.C. Rep.* I, p. 170 and III, plate XXIX, 12), who was in office when the *lex frumentaria* was proposed, in 100 B.C. (see F. W. Robinson, *Marius, Saturninus und Glaucia*, p. 63 sq.).

[4] I, 12, 21.

[5] It is, however, by no means impossible that in *ad Herennium* (*loc. cit.*) we should read 'senis et trientibus' for 'semissibus et trientibus': in that case Saturninus would merely have re-introduced the Gracchan arrangement,

The old complaints about the burden on the Treasury were heard again; the Senate solemnly recorded its opinion that to proceed with the measure would be against the interests of the State; and rival tribunes, as usual, were found to interpose their veto. When Saturninus ignored the obstruction of his colleagues, an enterprising quaestor, Q. Servilius Caepio, broke up the Concilium Plebis by force; and it is by no means certain that the bill was ever passed. Whatever its immediate effect may have been, the intervention of Caepio was such as to provoke reprisals: he was subsequently prosecuted for *maiestas minuta*, and we may well believe that against him, among others, the Lex Appuleia de maiestate was aimed (p. 161).

Having made his bid for popular support, Saturninus completed the work of his first tribunate, so far as it is known to us, by courting the goodwill of Marius. Besides lending help to the campaign which won Marius his fourth consulship (p. 147), Saturninus took it upon himself to provide pensions for the veterans of the Jugurthine War. By a measure which is definitely assigned to 103 B.C.[1] and which is also more appropriate then than later, generous allotments in Africa, each of a hundred *iugera*, were offered to troops on their discharge. At first the bill was blocked by the inevitable veto; but the hostile tribune was soon stoned off the field and the proposal in the end became law. Such is the suggestion of our one authority, and confirmation may perhaps be found in the existence of certain townships in the hill country south of the River Bagradas which so late as the third century A.D. bore 'Mariana' among their titles[2].

For all its limitations, the legislative achievement of 103 B.C. is not to be ignored. Saturninus had laid the foundations of a personal ascendancy, which he and his friends might use for good or ill. After the corn-bill had been launched, even if it proved abortive, the masses must have hailed its author as a disciple of the Gracchi: the African land law revealed a champion of the ex-service man: and the establishment of a *quaestio maiestatis* put a new and formidable weapon into the hands of those who were strong enough to use it. Saturninus, indeed, appeared to be recalling the Gracchan age with such success that an obscure adventurer, one L. Equitius, thought it worth while to proclaim himself a son of Tiberius. The

which had been suspended at some time after its author's death (see above, p. 95).   [1] *de viris ill.* 73, 1.

[2] Dessau 1334, 9405 (Uchi Maius) and 6790 (Thibari). For a suggestion that the colonists of these places were not Italians, see S. Gsell, *Histoire ancienne de l'Afrique du Nord*, vol. VII, pp. 10 and 263 *sq.*

man was a native of Firmum, but on his status the authorities are divided: one says that he was a freedman, others a runaway slave. His reception was naturally cool. The Senate could scarcely be enthusiastic, and a Gracchus, had his parentage been proved, might well have ousted Saturninus himself from the first place in the popular affections. But, to the general relief, Sempronia, sister of the tribunes and widow of Scipio Aemilianus, when brought on to the Rostra resolutely refused to recognize the impostor. After the danger of a rival had thus been removed, Saturninus turned the fellow to account. In spite of the family repudiation, he still retained credit enough with the masses to make his adhesion an asset to the cause; and if his appearance is rightly placed in 103 B.C.[1], for three years he played his humble part until in 100 he was elected to the tribunate and killed on his first day of office.

The year 102 B.C. opened with quieter promise. Saturninus and Glaucia were both *privati*, and the centre of the stage was yielded to leaders of the other side. Men might have hoped that domestic strife would cease until the crisis in Gaul had passed; but a new struggle was suddenly provoked by the most staid and dignified of all Roman institutions. When censors were due to be appointed, the choice of the Centuries fell on two Metelli—Numidicus and his cousin Caprarius. Worthier men could scarcely be conceived, and the *lustrum* might have been closed without mishap had not Numidicus allowed principle to override discretion. Feeling ran high when he refused to recognize the false Gracchus as a citizen, but his determination to remove Glaucia and Saturninus from the Senate came near to causing a disaster. He was assailed by the mob, and from his refuge on the Capitol he was only rescued after something like a battle. Fortunately Caprarius kept his head: he set his face against the misguided vigour of his cousin and, by withholding his consent to their removal, preserved the demagogues their status. The significance of this is plain: by rescinding the Lex Servilia Caepionis and by the legislation of 103 B.C. they had acquired a following which the Senate was not strong enough to flout. Such was the situation for which the Optimates had to thank their own imprudence in meddling with the Gracchan constitution of the *quaestio repetundarum*.

If the menace could not be met by force, it must be left alone in the hope that its leaders would work their own destruction. This in the end they did, though not before the movement had attained still more dangerous proportions. For the present the demagogues held their hands, but after Vercellae they took the

---

[1] *de viris ill.* 73, 3.

field again, with Marius now their open ally. First, however, Saturninus made a false move, which came near to proving fatal. In 101 B.C. there arrived in Rome an embassy from Mithridates Eupator, bringing with it, according to report, a large sum of money wherewith to bribe the Senate; and Saturninus for reasons of his own saw fit to assail the ambassadors in public with the most offensive abuse. Thereupon the strangers, not without encouragement from high quarters in Rome, made formal complaint: Saturninus was arraigned on a capital charge: and his conviction seemed certain till he invoked the faithful mob. Then, at a word from their favourite, his followers flocked in such numbers to the court that fear secured an unexpected acquittal, and the intended victim emerged unharmed, with his popularity increased by his recent peril.

The movement now gathered strength. With Marius released from duties in the field, the year 100 B.C. was chosen for the final challenge to senatorial control. Marius himself was to be consul for the sixth time, Glaucia praetor, and Saturninus was to hold a second tribunate. With the help of a single murder—the victim was a rival of Saturninus—the elections were negotiated with success, and the concentration of the talents was achieved. But once they were in office, there came a change. The new masters were revealed as men of straw, without a policy, without ideals and not even at one among themselves. For all his faults, Marius was not a fool. Experience in war seems to have left him, like the younger Africanus, with small respect for the political wisdom of the masses, and willing as he might be, like a true *popularis*, to use the People for his own good purposes, he had sense enough to see that nothing but harm could come of handing over government to the arbitrament of a rabble, even if the rabble drew its strength from the veterans of his own armies.

The rupture came slowly: at first the coalition was held together by common interest in schemes to distribute land—schemes which Marius needed for his soldiers and which would also serve the ends of Glaucia and Saturninus by earning favour with the proletariate of Rome. From the scanty evidence of our authorities it appears that measures were introduced for the grant of allotments in Gaul[1] and the foundation of colonies in various parts of the Empire,

---

[1] Appian, *Bell. Civ.* I, 29, 130. Though there can be no certainty that he has rightly understood his source, the words of Appian, interpreted in the light of his own usage elsewhere, suggest that these allotments were to be made in Transalpine, and not Cisalpine, Gaul. Possibly sites were to be found in the territory of the Volcae Tectosages.

among which Sicily, Achaea and Macedonia are named[1]. The plans
for settlements in Gaul came to nothing; but of the colonial policy
there is more to be said. Though Cicero records that the colonies
were never founded, he makes it clear that preparations were at
least begun[2]. By the Lex Appuleia, Marius was empowered 'in
singulas colonias ternos cives Romanos facere[3],' and we know
that in a few cases at least he had exercised his rights. It is not
their use, however, which matters so much as their implication.
If the number given in this crucial passage is not corrupt, and
if it is legitimate to assume that the power to nominate three
members of each colony would have been of negligible value,
'cives Romanos facere' must mean more than this. In that case it
follows that the *cives Romani* in these cities were to be a privileged
class, that the communities as a whole were not to be *coloniae
civium Romanorum* and, consequently, that they were almost certainly designed to hold the Latin right. To this conjecture another
may be added. If the colonies were to receive the Latin status,
it is most unlikely that their members were all to be drawn from
the existing body of Roman citizens, and it may be surmised
that they were to be recruited in part at least from allied communities as well[4]. In such a measure there was enough material
for jealousy and to spare. Whatever benefits Saturninus may have
intended for the city proletariate, it seems that the needs of the
ex-service men were given such prominence as to raise violent
antagonism among the self-seeking idlers of the Forum; and, in
addition to the bad feeling within the Roman State, there was
rivalry between Romans and Italians. As in the time of Gaius
Gracchus, a suggestion of modest generosity to the allies who
had fought for Rome roused the worst passions of the citizens
themselves, and it is possible, too, that the Italians, on their side,
were made anxious by the threat of a new search for land to be
distributed in allotments. The agitation among the allies with
which the government thought fit to deal in 95 B.C. may well have
been due in some degree to the activities of Saturninus.

---

[1] *de viris ill.* 73, 5.

[2] Of the colonies actually recorded in this period there is nothing to prove
that Dertona and Eporedia (Vell. Pat. I, 15, 5) owed their origin to the
Lex Appuleia, and the date of the 'colonia Mariana' in Corsica (Pliny,
N.H. III, 80) is unknown.   [3] *pro Balbo*, 21, 48.

[4] This view is not to be supported by the passage of Appian (*Bell. Civ.*
I, 29, 132) which has often been used as evidence in its favour. The
Ἰταλιῶται there are not Italian allies but Roman citizens of the country
districts: see D. Kontchalovsky in *Rev. hist.* 153, 1926, pp. 173 *sqq.*

These, however, were not the only difficulties. Saturninus had incurred the bitter hostility of the Senate by inserting a *sanctio* in the bill, requiring every member of the House, under pain of exile and a fine, to swear an oath within five days of its enactment that he would abide by its provisions. When the day for voting arrived, recourse was had to the familiar methods of obstruction. Tribunes were found to intercede and unfavourable omens were announced; but with the aid of the faithful veterans, after a momentary success, the enemy were chased off the field and a farcical pretence of voting made the measure a law of the Roman People. It was now the business of Marius to ask the Fathers for their oaths. At the first meeting Metellus Numidicus declared his determination to refuse, and such was the support he secured that the sitting broke up with nothing done. But later, when four of the five days had gone, the House was convened again and Marius suggested a course which revealed his attitude towards his friends. He proposed to take the statutory oath subject to the validity of the law, and at the same time he encouraged the senators to reflect that, once the mob had gone back to its homes, there would be no difficulty in proving that a measure passed by violence and in face of hostile auspices must be set aside. With this reservation Marius then swore his oath, and his example was followed by the rest, with the solitary exception of Numidicus, who soon retired to exile.

Political incompetence had wasted so much time in securing this miserable achievement that no more could be done before the elections for the next year fell due. Saturninus managed to get himself returned as tribune for the third time, with the 'false Gracchus' as his colleague; but the consulships were more difficult to secure. Though M. Antonius had claims for one place which could not be overlooked, the other remained open. For this, in flat defiance of the Lex Villia annalis since he was praetor at the time, Glaucia became a candidate, and after he had secured the murder of his most serious rival his election seemed not improbable. By now, however, the experience of the Senate and the folly of its opponents had begun to tell. Responsible opinion had been alienated by the outrageous violence of the new régime, and its appeal to force had been cleverly countered when the Senate turned to its own uses the resentment felt by the city mob at the political activities of the veterans from the countryside. It happened that the victim of the assassination was C. Memmius, the man who by his denunciations of corruption as tribune-designate in 112 B.C. had given earliest voice to that demand for vigour in the Jugurthine campaign which had led in the end to the appointment of Marius. Memmius was no friend of the Senate. His criticisms as tribune had been continued by opposition to the Lex Servilia Caepionis in 106 B.C.; but, even if his sympathies lay with the financial class, he was a serious politician who had done service to the State and had never stooped to hooliganism of the kind which caused his death. His murder was the signal for drastic action. Before Glaucia could summon his gangs in strength, he found himself besieged on the Capitoline Hill with Saturninus and another ruffian named Saufeius, who was quaestor. The Senate then passed its formidable *s.c. de re publica defendenda*; Marius was instructed to restore order, which meant that he must arrest his quondam friends; and, after the water-supply had been cut, the whole party surrendered. Their lives were now in the gravest danger; for the mob was athirst for blood. In hopes of frustrating the threatened lynching Marius locked up his prisoners in the Senate House, but on 10 December, the day when new tribunes entered office, a band of stalwarts climbed the roof and, tearing off the tiles, pelted the crowd beneath to death. Among the assailants was a young man named C. Rabirius, who thirty-seven years afterwards was to be charged with *perduellio* for his part in this affair (see below, p. 489).

When once the leaders were dead, their following was impotent, and it seems that the offensive legislation was forthwith declared invalid. Thus, after violence had destroyed its authors, Rome at length emerged into a period of uneasy peace when it was time to reflect on the meaning of what had passed. Glaucia and Saturninus were little men. To the political experience of Rome they brought nothing of their own save perhaps the use of unbridled violence and an utter disregard of law—a contribution which, to the credit of their contemporaries, repelled the sympathies of almost every class. Nevertheless, though their littleness may serve as a reminder of the full stature of Gaius Gracchus, it is to a legacy from the Gracchi that the worst features of their domination must be ascribed. Materialism of aim and violence in its pursuit were the inevitable outcome of a system which allowed unfettered liberty of legislation to a body of voters such as the Concilium Plebis: and this was the system which, though they knew not what they did, it had been the most sinister achievement of the Gracchi to explore (see above, pp. 90 *sqq.*).

Yet, despite its dangers, the episode gave certain grounds for hope. Demagogy unleavened by ideals had been countered with success, and—what was more important—the military triumphs of Marius had failed to compensate for his total lack of political ability. Mistrusted by the Senate and despised by his former friends, the man who had been five times consul by the age of fifty-six stood helpless in utter isolation. In 98 B.C., after a feeble protest against the recall of Numidicus, he retired to Asia and temporary oblivion. This elimination of Marius was an encouraging surprise. The professional armies first formally recruited in 108 B.C. were a menace to free government of the utmost gravity—and a menace which was to cause the fall of the Republic; but the failure of Marius showed that there were limitations to the power of the troops. In the past Rome had been no stranger to soldiers who were statesmen as well; and, when such appeared again, they would find in the fidelity of long-service armies an asset of immeasurable value. What Marius' fate revealed was that even now no claim to supremacy at home could rest on military gifts alone, without the support of some political sagacity: it was left for the Thracian Maximinus, after more than three hundred years, to be the first mere soldier raised to supremacy by his men.

IV. THE SENATORIAL RECOVERY

With the departure of Marius, the tide ran fast in favour of the Senate. Metellus Numidicus returned in triumph, and soon the survivors of the vanquished party were called on for the usual settling of accounts. P. Furius, a political adventurer, who as tribune had dared to oppose Numidicus' recall, was put on trial, but before he could be condemned the mob had torn him limb from limb: C. Appuleius Decianus was found guilty on some charge because he had rashly lamented the manner of Saturninus' end: Sextus Titius, who as tribune in 99 B.C. had tried to revive the agrarian scheme[1], was condemned, partly at least because he kept a bust of Saturninus in his house: and to this period we should probably assign the celebrated prosecution of C. Norbanus, who as tribune in 104 B.C. had played a leading part in the attack on Q. Caepio for the scandal of the 'aurum Tolosae.' Their common sufferings at the hands of Saturninus and Glaucia had by now so far healed the breach between the Senate and its rivals in the courts that Norbanus was arraigned in the *quaestio maiestatis*. His character commanded small respect, and it is possible that he had compromised himself by association with Saturninus; but, whatever the precise reason for their hope, it is significant that the nobility conceived it possible that a court of Gracchan *iudices*

---

[1] Julius Obsequens, 46 (106); Val. Max. VIII, 1, *Damn*. 3. If the law of Titius was passed, it must have been immediately repealed.

might convict the enemy of their own detested foe. The prosecution was led by a young aristocrat of high promise, P. Sulpicius
Rufus; the defence by M. Antonius himself, under whom Norbanus had once served as quaestor. After an outstanding performance by Antonius, which Cicero describes at length[1], the
trial ended in acquittal; but that it should ever have been begun
is a sufficient sign of the extent to which all decent citizens had
been united by the experience of 100 B.C.

When old scores had thus been paid, Rome enjoyed a period of
unwonted peace. Abroad there were none but minor campaigns
in Spain (p. 319), and at home the Concordia Ordinum bid fair
to last. For a time the State came near to the felicity of those who
have no history. The consuls of 98 B.C.—T. Didius, a 'new man,'
and Q. Caecilius Metellus Nepos, a son of Balearicus—passed a
small but salutary piece of legislation. To improve the chances of
a doubtful measure by uniting it with another of more compelling
appeal is a familiar political manœuvre; and a no less obvious
recourse for the demagogue in fear of opposition is to rush a bill
through all its stages without leaving that interval before the final
vote which, in days when news travelled slow, was peculiarly valuable
to an assembly whose members were widely scattered. Though it
is scarcely more, there is a strong suspicion that both these tricks
had been played by Saturninus; and by the Lex Caecilia Didia
both were made illegal. 'Tacking'—the inclusion of unconnected
proposals in a single bill—was forbidden[2], and the customary
promulgatio followed by an interval of three *nundinae* was made
obligatory before a measure could be submitted to the vote.
Henceforward there was to be no doubt that the perfunctory procedure of demagogues in a hurry did not produce valid law. In
the following year, when L. Valerius Flaccus and M. Antonius
were censors, another small advance was made, this time in a different direction. The Senate passed a decree against human sacrifice—an alien custom which sixteen years earlier had come near to
winning the approval of the State (see above, p. 97) and which,
in spite of all attempts at its suppression, lingered long in Rome[3].

But, if Rome was exclusive in her religion, she was more
catholic in her culture. When the next censorship fell due in
92 B.C., the office was entrusted to L. Crassus, the orator, and
Cn. Domitius Ahenobarbus, the tribune of 104 B.C., who now was
Pontifex Maximus. The liberal tastes of Crassus did not find favour

---

[1] *de orat.* II, 48, 199–50, 203.
[2] That this prohibition was not altogether new is proved by Bruns,
Fontes[7], 10, l. 71.   [3] Pliny, *N.H.* XXVIII, 12.

with the grim austerity of his colleague, and the dissensions which ended in their abdication became the theme of many stories. But on one point they agreed. In spite of their suppression seventy years before[1], teachers of rhetoric had begun to show their heads again, and among them there now appeared men of a new type, who confined their instruction to Latin. In earlier days the prejudice had been against Greeks; now, however, though the case was probably affected by personal considerations[2], the Latin teachers were chosen for attack. Of the Greek rhetoricians it could at least be said that, whatever their faults, they taught something more than how to move a mob; for Greece had a literature worthy of the name, which Rome so far had not, and Crassus, who had trained his own gifts by laboriously translating the masterpieces of Greek oratory, may well have seen no good in schools for demagogues[3]. So the censors by edict condemned the Latin rhetoricians[4], and the Roman youth, when it learnt the art of public speaking, was encouraged to seek help in the legacy of Greece.

Amid such trivialities as these, two incidents of profounder significance stand out. A quarter of a century had passed since the fall of Gaius Gracchus had frustrated the hopes of those who, by open-handed generosity toward the Italian allies, would have anticipated the concessions wrung out of Rome by the Social War. During the years of anxiety which followed, the grievance was not pressed. So long as Rome was engaged with Jugurtha and the Germans, the allies held their hand; for it had never been their custom to turn the difficulties of Rome to their own advantage, and it may be suspected that, when troubles abroad gave immediate value to Italian help, the Roman magistrates refrained from the worst extremes of tactlessness. When at length the fighting was done, it was the aggressive jealousy of Rome, rather than the insistence of the Italians on redress, which led in ten years to the outbreak of intestine war. As early as 100 b.c., when Italians were to share with Roman citizens in the benefits of the colonial foundations, the signs of protest had been discerned, and resentment at liberality to the allies seems to have combined with dislike of Roman veterans from the country to lose Saturninus the support of the city mob. In 95 b.c. the allies suffered a severer blow. Five years earlier they might have reflected that the considered judgment of the Roman People was not necessarily to be

---

[1] Gellius, *N.A.* xv, 11, 1.
[2] See A. Gwynn, *Roman Education from Cicero to Quintilian*, pp. 60 *sqq.*
[3] Cicero, *de orat.* iii, 24, 93–95.   [4] Gellius, *ib.* 2; Suet. *de rhet.* 1.

heard in the selfish clamours of the Concilium Plebis; but now by
the action of the consuls, taken with the Senate's full assent, the
fear that the masses spoke the mind of Rome was confirmed beyond
dispute. During the recent troubles Latins and Italians had flocked
in large numbers to Rome, where for two reasons their presence
was unwelcome. By public demonstrations, like those of the
Gracchan age (p. 80), they could subject the Concilium Plebis
to a pressure which, puny as it might be, was resented as an alien
interference with the affairs of Rome; and by bold assumption of
the part, if not by false declarations to the censors, they might
even gain the effective benefits of that *civitas* which Rome was determined to withhold. The consuls Crassus and Scaevola accordingly
enacted what was to become the most famous of all the expulsions
of aliens from Rome. Though we may assume that exemption
was allowed to such as could justify their visit, the generality
of Latins and Italians to be found in the city were removed[1]. And
this was not all. The many who without legal right were passing
as Roman citizens[2], if on challenge they still maintained their
claims, were subjected to an examination of such severity that
false pretences can rarely have escaped detection[3]. Such was the
measure whereby the consuls of 95 B.C. not merely embittered the
minds of the Italians but, if Asconius is to be believed[4], precipi-
tated the Social War. The Lex Licinia Mucia, though it was the
work of honest and able men, was an astounding blunder[5]. It declared in solemn and authoritative form the adamant exclusiveness
of Rome, and it did so at a time when the patience of the allies
was near its end. The warnings of Gaius Gracchus were forgotten. By a blindness which it is difficult to conceive the loyalty
of Italy during the Jugurthine and Germanic Wars was mistaken
for acquiescence in the existing order: and two of her most distinguished public men came near to losing Rome her imperial
position. Henceforward the question of the allies was a burning
issue.

Three years later the Concordia Ordinum collapsed. As praetor
in 98 B.C. Scaevola had been given the command of Asia, and as
his *legatus* in that responsible position he had chosen P. Rutilius
Rufus, the consul of 105 B.C., a man whose character and ideals
were as noble as his own. Both Scaevola and Rutilius belonged
to that estimable class which, largely because of its familiarity

---

[1] Schol. Bob. *ap.* Stangl, II, p. 129.
[2] Cicero, *de off.* III, 11, 47; Asconius, p. 68 c.
[3] Cicero, *pro Balbo*, 21, 48.   [4] p. 68 c.   [5] Cicero *ap.* Ascon. p. 67 c.

with the culture of Greece, did much to develop the Civil Law during the last century of the Republic. On this score Rutilius, in particular, was long remembered. His is the first name to occur in the recorded history of the Edict, and his innovations are worthy both of his own reputation and of his master Panaetius (p. 850). The administration of this pair in the East gave the provincials an unusual experience of honest government—an experience so rare that the memory of Scaevola was afterwards kept green by festivals founded in his honour[1]. By chance it befell that with this happy time Rutilius was connected almost as closely as Scaevola himself; for after nine months the proconsul left the province[2] and Rutilius was in charge until the arrival of a successor. This accident subsequently cost him dear. Traders and tax-gatherers bided their time: five years passed before they struck. Scaevola, with the prestige of exalted birth and the authority of a Pontifex Maximus, promised to be no easy victim: Rutilius, a 'new man,' might prove a simpler prey. So in 92 B.C. Rutilius was accused of illegal exaction by one Apicius. Disdaining the help of the great orators of the day and allowing none to speak on his behalf save C. Cotta, his nephew, Rutilius defended himself in Socratic style: conscious of his honesty, he proudly refused an apology for his conduct and, instead, bewailed the misfortunes of the State. But evidence and speeches were a formality: the jurors were determined to teach the Senate that its members could not safely thwart the financiers' quest for wealth; and the influence of Marius, slight but malign, backed up the scheme to deal the Senate a blow. So Rutilius was condemned; and when his property proved too small to make restitution of what had never come into his hands, he retired to Smyrna and lived as an honoured guest among the grateful victims of his alleged rapacity.

Though an attempt to follow up this success by an attack on M. Scaurus, the Princeps Senatus, seems to have led to no definite result, the outcome of the trial of Rutilius was no ordinary scandal. By it men might know what provinces meant to a powerful section of society at Rome, whose growing influence on policy had more than once appeared. The knowledge was not encouraging. If Rome was to become worthy of her mission, there must be a change of heart which could not be wrought in a day. It was left for Augustus to create a government which recognized the duties of an imperial power. But there was another aspect of the affair which called for more immediate action. The verdict was not only

---

[1] *I.G.R.R.* IV, 188; Ps.-Asconius, *ap.* Stangl, II, p. 202.
[2] Cicero, *ad Att.* V, 17, 5.

a declaration of war on the Senate by the class from which Gaius
Gracchus had drawn his jurors: it was a condemnation of that class
itself. Corrupt the senatorial jurors of earlier days may have been;
but their successors appeared to be worse. Though scandals had
not been numerous, the case of Rutilius by itself was enough. The
experiment of the Lex Acilia had failed, and there was need for
reform forthwith, if provincial administration was not to become
a farce.

V. THE TRIBUNATE OF M. LIVIUS
DRUSUS THE YOUNGER

Rome was still stirred by the outcome of this trial when, on
10 December 92, M. Livius Drusus entered on his tribunate.
Drusus, the son of Gaius Gracchus' rival, came of a distinguished
stock whose lustre he increased by the adoption of a child destined
to be the father-in-law of Augustus. His aims were lofty, his
character above reproach, and though some might call him a moral
snob, he was on terms of intimacy with the most enlightened members of his generation. Special mention is made of his friendship
with P. Sulpicius Rufus and C. Cotta, and among his seniors he
won the goodwill of the orator Crassus and of Scaurus, the
Princeps Senatus. Like Tiberius Gracchus, Drusus did not fail
for lack of sound advice; yet, in spite of all the wisdom which the
Senate placed at his disposal, his policy owed its greatest debt to
the example of Gaius Gracchus. So much, at least, is plain; but
the lamentable defects of our authorities for his career leave some
of the most vital problems obscure and do not even allow a confident conclusion about the order in which he addressed his many
tasks. For a year to which Livy devoted more than a whole book
we are dependent on casual notices which together would not fill
more than a few pages, and even of these the earlier and more
trustworthy, like those of Cicero, are often deprived of value
because they assume familiarity with the facts.

For a man with the outlook of a Drusus the urgent issues of
the day were two. After the fate of Rutilius no decent citizen could
be satisfied with the way in which the *quaestio repetundarum* was
using its powers: after the history of the last forty years, with its
lesson driven home by the events which produced the Lex Licinia
Mucia of 95 B.C., no Roman of intelligence could fail to see, however little the prospect may have pleased, that the claims of the
Italians could no longer be ignored. To remove the grievances
of the allies by a drastic change in the relations between Rome

and the rest of Italy was now the supreme duty of Roman statesmanship, and there need be no doubt that Appian[1] is right in
his suggestion that this was the object which from the beginning
Drusus set out to reach. But, though the events of this crowded
tribunate must have followed one another in rapid succession,
Appian finds less support in the other authorities when he
arranges his account in a way which, to a superficial reading at
least, implies that a measure to extend the franchise was launched
early in the year. Probability, as well as the weight of evidence,
is on the side of Velleius[2] when he lets it be understood that proposals for the benefit of the Italians were only broached in public
after other projects had been long enough under discussion for
their fate, if not to be decided, at least to have been put beyond
all reasonable doubt. Cicero[3] is emphatic that Drusus began his
tribunician career as a champion of the Senate, and this clue, confirmed by other evidence, is authority enough for the conclusion
that the first memorable reform which he essayed was one affecting
that institution with which the Senate was now most acutely concerned—the *quaestio repetundarum*.

But to say so much is not to deny that this proposal was accompanied by others. If Drusus was to establish his political authority,
it was essential for him to secure the goodwill of the masses, whose
interest in the struggle for control of the courts was mild at the
most. There is every likelihood that at the outset he sought,
in the true Gracchan style, to attract a solid body of support by
schemes of a charitable kind. He was the author of a bill *de
coloniis deducendis*, the purpose of which almost certainly was to
complete the schemes of settlement once sponsored by his
father[4] (p. 72), and besides this there were a Lex Livia and a Lex
Saufeia, both apparently designed to authorize the distribution of
land in allotments to individuals[5]. Finally came the inevitable
appeal to the stomach in new arrangements for the public *frumentationes*[6]. Though their details are unrecorded, all these measures
seem to have been passed: of the colonial bill alone this is not positively asserted. Such sudden generosity seems to have produced its
natural result in a crisis at the Treasury: there was a lack of ready

---

[1] *Bell. Civ.* 1, 35, 155.   [2] 11, 14, 1.
[3] *de orat.* 1, 7, 24; cf. *pro Milone*, 7, 16.   [4] Appian, *Bell. Civ.* 1, 35, 156.
[5] Dessau 49. The commission appointed to apply the Lex Livia agraria
has perhaps left a record of its constitution (*C.I.L.* x, 44 and *add.* III,
p. 1003): if C. Cichorius (*Römische Studien*, pp. 116 *sqq.*) is right in his
interpretation of this text, it shows a distinguished board with the orator
Crassus as its outstanding member.   [6] Livy, *Epit.* 71.

money, which Drusus sought to meet by a dangerous device. He debased the silver coinage, probably by striking one *denarius* in every eight of silver-plated bronze[1]—a step which, with others, was to lead before long to disastrous confusion (p. 266). Nevertheless, the programme as a whole won a passing popularity for its author[2], and Drusus might hope to count on a majority in the Concilium Plebis when he came forward with a contentious project which had no bearing on the interests of the ordinary voter.

The measure whereby Drusus sought to mitigate the scandal of the *quaestio repetundarum* is described by our authorities in terms which are completely contradictory. According to Velleius[3], its aim was simply to substitute senators for the Gracchan *iudices*. Appian[4], on the other hand, qualifies this version with the suggestion that the Senate which would now supply the jurors was to be the existing body of three hundred, or thereabouts, enlarged by the addition of as many new members drawn from the wealthy business class: this account of the reform makes it in essentials the same as the first judiciary proposal ascribed to Gaius Gracchus (p. 70). Finally, there is the Livian tradition[5], which envisages mixed juries and differs from the story told by Appian in implying that, though senators were now to have a place, those jurors who represented the commercial interests were still to remain outside the Senate. A decision between these rival possibilities can be made with the help of evidence supplied by Cicero and Appian on a cognate matter. It has been seen already that judicial corruption was an offence governed by a law which Gaius Gracchus had passed in the days before he envisaged the drastic reconstitution of the *quaestio repetundarum* enacted by the Lex Acilia (p. 53 *sq.*). The measure seems to have applied to senators alone; and, when senators were ousted from the juries, the *Gracchani iudices* who succeeded them claimed immunity from its provisions. This monstrous anomaly Cicero[6] and Appian[7] agree in saying that

---

[1] Pliny, *N.H.* xxxiii, 46. It has been suggested by H. Mattingly (*Num. Chron.* Series v, vol. iv, 1924, p. 46) that this notice may refer to the tribune of 123/2 B.C.

[2] Pliny, *N.H.* xxv, 52.　　　　　[3] ii, 13, 2.

[4] *Bell. Civ.* i, 35, 158.　　　　　[5] Livy, *Epit.* 71.

[6] *pro Rab. Post.* 7, 16. The theory of Mommsen (*Staatsrecht*, iii, p. 532, n. 1) that this passage describes nothing more than the establishment of a court to investigate cases of corruption among *Gracchani iudices* in the past would seem to the present writer most improbable, even if Mommsen's insistence on the reading 'iudicatam' were justified. Livius Drusus was certainly in no position to indulge in measures of mere vindictiveness.

[7] *Bell. Civ.* i, 35, 158 and 161.

Drusus sought to end, and their words strongly imply that this end was to be attained by fresh legislation. Since the old Lex Sempronia was still in force and ready for application to any senators who might find themselves serving in the courts, it follows that the jurors at whom the new act was aimed were not members of the Senate; and therein is to be found confirmation of the Livian account that juries henceforward were to be mixed. Whether, besides admitting senators to a share in the constitution of the courts, Drusus also proposed to enrol three hundred new members in the Senate, as Appian suggests, the evidence does not permit us to decide: but the readiness with which the Senate annulled the work of Drusus is certainly in favour of this assumption[1].

The reception of these proposals was of the kind which compromise has always to expect. While the class from which Gaius Gracchus had drawn his jurors was implacably opposed to a scheme which would deprive it of its unchallenged control of the courts and put an end to its precious privilege of receiving bribes with impunity, the concession to the Senate of a mere share in the composition of the juries was too meagre to fill that body with any abiding enthusiasm. Voices began to be raised in opposition. There was a quarrel between Drusus and his brother-in-law, Q. Servilius Caepio; and one of the consuls, L. Marcius Philippus, led a doughty resistance both in the Senate and outside. In the Forum there were scenes in which a Saturninus would have felt at home. On one occasion, when Philippus had tried to break up an assembly, Drusus set one of his clients on to the consul, who was so roughly handled that his nose began to bleed, greatly to his political advantage. On another, the unhappy Caepio, whose conduct became almost as violent as that of Drusus, was threatened with death by the Tarpeian Rock. In the Senate, too, feeling ran high, and reached its climax in September[2]. The circumstances are obscure; but it was possibly because the Fathers had shown a less drastic resistance to Drusus than he desired that Philippus solemnly announced in public that it was impossible for him to carry on the government with such a body of advisers. At a sitting of the Senate on 13 September Drusus warmly protested against such language, and Crassus excelled himself on the theme of a consul's obligations. After some bitter repartee, Crassus moved the House to record its firm conviction that its good faith and sound advice had never failed the State. But though he had rapped the knuckles

[1] For this view see P. A. Seymour in *Eng. Hist. Rev.* XXIX, 1914, p. 422.
[2] Cicero, *de orat.* III, 1, 1–2, 6.

of Philippus, he had failed to stem the growing distrust of Drusus among the Fathers. This was his last appearance in public life. A week later the great orator was dead, and when it lost the aid of its most powerful supporter the tribunician programme soon came to a standstill.

The work of Drusus was now seriously complicated by his pledges to the Roman allies. It is clear that he had long been deeply committed to an attempt at the solution of what was undoubtedly the most pressing problem of the day: indeed it seems that from the beginning of his tribunate large numbers of Italians had quartered themselves in Rome to agitate in favour of the man whose programme, if he kept his word, would culminate in a measure enuring to their advantage. One of the most prominent leaders of the Marsi, Q. Pompaedius Silo, actually lived for some days as the guest of Drusus in his house; but, though there is a wealth of evidence such as this to show the direction of the tribune's sympathies, there is no good reason to believe that he was the conscious centre of a widespread conspiracy[1]. At first Drusus had concealed his designs for an extension of the franchise, but the presence of so many Italians in the city was enough to rouse suspicion. As early as the time of the Feriae Latinae, which normally were held in April (though in this year there may conceivably have been a later celebration), Drusus had betrayed a strange familiarity with allied plans by warning Philippus of a plot to murder him during the festival on the Alban Mount. Before long suspicion hardened into firm belief, until Drusus was soon confronted with all the hatred regularly reserved for the authors of a liberal policy towards the Italians. But difficult as his position had been made by the leakage of his schemes, the need for a measure of enfranchisement had become more urgent through his own activities. Not only had he raised hopes to a pitch at which disappointment would be most dangerous, but his agrarian and colonial laws, which clearly demanded land for their effective application, had started the old fears among Italians whose estates might be alleged to include *ager publicus populi Romani*. Some of these people, particularly from Umbria and Etruria, even came to Rome to join in the protests of Philippus against the *lex agraria*, and of the rest it could be said that, if they lent their support to Drusus' programme as a whole, they only did so for the sake of the promised concessions to which in the end it was to lead. But,

---

[1] The oath preserved in a fragment of Diodorus (XXXVII, 11) is a document of the most dubious value, probably produced during the series of vindictive trials which followed the outbreak of the Social War.

whatever bill for the benefit of the allies Drusus had in mind, it seems never to have reached the stage of promulgation. As his intentions grew clearer, public opinion set against the tribune with increasing strength until at length the Senate responded to the pressure of Philippus and struck.

Like the preliminary measures on land-allotments, colonies and the *frumentationes*, the proposals for reform in the judicial administration had apparently been passed into law[1] when the Senate boldly declared the whole legislation of Drusus invalid. The reasons for this step are as obscure as its justification. The judiciary reform had doubtless disappointed senatorial hopes; and, if it involved the admission of new members to the House, it may well have roused active resentment. But this was not the only ground for complaint. At the outset, when he had passed as the Senate's man, Drusus had squandered the public resources on political bribery to such an extent that he could boast 'nemini se ad largiendum praeter caelum et caenum reliquisse'[2]; and in the later stages, on top of this reckless generosity, there had come an overbearing insolence which foretold the establishment of a *tyrannis* as odious as anything feared of Gaius Gracchus. Whatever its motives, the Senate swept the whole work of Drusus aside by a simple declaration that his laws did not bind the Roman People.

For this drastic step ingenuity could find plausible pretexts. The suggestion that Drusus had violated the Lex Caecilia Didia of 98 B.C.[3] need not be doubted, but it must not be taken to mean that Drusus had so flagrantly disregarded a very recent piece of legislation as to merge all his proposals—frumentary, agrarian, colonial and judiciary—into a single bill. If he was guilty of 'tacking' at all[4], the probability is that he had run together the whole of his legislation on the judicature—both the admission of senators to criminal juries and the quite different provision whereby Gracchan *iudices* were exposed to charges of corruption[5]. But the *lex satura* was not the only abuse against which the law of 98 B.C. had been passed, and it is clear that other objections were alleged against Drusus' procedure. Auspices had apparently been ignored[6]; there had been earthquakes which, like the wolves of Carthage in the time of Gaius Gracchus (p. 81), might be taken as clear signs of the divine displeasure[7]; and in general there could be no denying that the whole business had been transacted to the

---

[1] Livy, *Epit.* 71.
[2] *de viris ill.* 66, 5.
[3] Cicero, *de domo sua*, 16, 41.
[4] *ib.* 19, 50.
[5] See E. G. Hardy in *C.R.* xxvii, 1913, p. 262.
[6] Asconius, p. 69 c.
[7] Julius Obsequens, 54 (114).

accompaniment of frequent violence. All this was more reason than enough for declaring the legislation invalid, once public opinion had been alienated from its author.

Drusus accepted the Senate's decision. In spite of all his vicarious generosity, the majority of the Concilium Plebis had turned against him, and it was useless either to fight in defence of measures already passed or to struggle on towards a *lex de civitate*. His tribunate had failed, and before long Drusus was struck down by the hand of some unknown assassin. The significance of the cause for which he stood may be measured by the gravity of the crisis for which his death was the signal. In him the Italians lost their last hope of reaching a peaceful settlement of their differences with Rome, and now the issue was committed to the final arbitrament of war.

For Drusus it can at least be claimed that he recognized the duties of Roman statesmanship and had his eyes open to the most urgent problem of the hour. But beyond this it is difficult to go. The end for which he set himself to work was undoubtedly most difficult to attain: greater men than he had been beaten before by the inflexible jealousy which the Roman masses showed towards their allies. Yet it is difficult to find much material for praise in the methods of his choosing. Bribery of the voters was of no avail; for they took the bribes and then, when it was empty, turned to rend the hand that bribed them. Nor was he any more successful in his dealings with the leaders of opinion at Rome. All the recorded evidence supports Cicero[1] in his view that the fate of Drusus was sealed by the failure of his proposals for a reform of the judicial administration; and the reasons for that failure are not far to seek. The experience of Gaius Gracchus had been enough to show that Rome of the revolutionary age was no place for nicely-balanced compromise: in the ' faex Romuli ' politicians must depend on one section or another, and hope that the party of their choice would for a few months command a majority. By his judiciary schemes Drusus earned the undying hatred of the rich men outside the oligarchy, and yet he did not go far enough to stimulate the enthusiasm of the Senate. His dealings with the great political interests of Rome foreshadow the experience of Cicero and his Concordia Ordinum. In his outlook, on the other hand, and in his methods with the voters he finds his parallel in Gaius Gracchus. Both Gracchus and he worked for a settlement of the Italian problem, and, though the precedent of Saturninus may have authorized a more open form of bribery than was known to

[1] *de off.* II, 21, 75.

the Gracchan age, Drusus sought to win a following among the masses by measures which seem to have been inspired directly by the example of his great predecessor. It may even be admitted that Drusus had all the high ideals and earnest determination to serve the public weal with which the Gracchi had been filled; yet, between Drusus and the Gracchi there was a difference of the greatest moment. Partly because in 91 B.C. there was no urgent social problem like that which had won permanent gratitude for the Gracchi when they attacked it with success, and partly because Drusus himself was a man of conscious superiority and unsympathetic character, he never attained a popularity which would serve as the foundation of even a temporary control of Roman public life. Drusus was a well-meaning man, but not a born leader, and, if comparison is needed with those who had gone before, it will be enough to accept the judgment of that unknown critic who called him 'a pale reflection of the Gracchi[1].'

The history of Rome now becomes a tale of war; but not even the perils of the Italian revolt prevented that settlement of political accounts which was the normal sequel to the fall of an outstanding politician. One of the new tribunes who entered office on 10 December 91 B.C.—Q. Varius Hybrida by name—set himself to exploit the indignation felt against those who had in any way contributed to the Italian rising as a means whereby the business class might win a revenge against the Senate. In defiance of tribunician veto a court of *Gracchani iudices* was set up to investigate the conduct of all who might be alleged to have encouraged the allies in their warlike plans. The result was a persecution severe enough to teach the Senate its folly in throwing Drusus overboard. C. Cotta was an early victim[2], and Varius even went on to attack the unfortunate M. Scaurus, the Princeps Senatus[3]. But as the military position became graver, men appreciated that the time was ill-suited for party strife at home, and at length the Senate found itself in a position to suspend the court for the duration of the war[4]. When at length its operations were resumed, its nature and purpose had been changed by the passage of the Lex Plautia iudiciaria (p. 196).

---

[1] *ad Herennium*, IV, 34, 46.   [2] Cicero, *Brutus*, 56, 205.
[3] Asconius, p. 22 C.   [4] Asconius, p. 74 C.

VI. THE FIRST PHASE OF THE SOCIAL WAR[1]

Ever since the passing of the Lex Licinia Mucia in 95 preparations for war must have been afoot among the Italians. The time had come for them to seize by force the privileges which they had failed to acquire by persuasion. In 91 the forthcoming struggle was foreshadowed by two events which preceded the death of Drusus. First, we are told that the Italians planned to murder the consuls Caesar and Philippus when they were celebrating the Feriae Latinae on the Alban Mount, and that Drusus warned Philippus of his danger. In view of this revelation the Senate no doubt decided to ascertain the intentions of the allies and dispatched emissaries to various parts of Italy. Secondly, a certain Domitius, probably one of these emissaries, encountered Q. Pompaedius Silo, leader of the Marsi and an intimate friend of Drusus, marching on Rome at the head of 10,000 armed men, and persuaded him to withdraw by an assurance of the goodwill of the government. But the murder of Drusus brought matters to a head. C. Servilius, a praetor with proconsular powers who was on reconnaissance in Picenum, was informed of the exchange of hostages between Asculum and another city. His effrontery at Asculum was a signal for the massacre of every Roman in the city. Thereupon the allies sent an embassy to Rome to complain of their continued exclusion from citizenship, but the Senate refused to meet them in any way unless they were prepared to make amends for the massacre. Realizing, therefore, that they were too deeply compromised, they had no choice but to draw the sword.

A binary league of two groups of cantons, Marsic and Samnite, formed the nucleus of the Italians who seceded from Rome, and it is probable that a coin bearing the name of Q. [Pompaedius] Silo and representing eight warriors swearing alliance may record the number of peoples who formed the league: Picentines, Marsi, Paeligni, Vestini, Marrucini, Frentani, Samnites and Hirpini[2]. Born within the tangle of mountain and glen between the upper Anio and the lower Aternus, the revolt spread over the highlands of central and southern Italy and was indeed well named the

[1] Ancient tradition ascribed to this war three names, *bellum Marsicum*, *bellum Italicum*, *bellum sociale*. The first two names were in general use till the end of the first century A.D.; *bellum sociale* did not appear till the second century. No doubt *bellum Marsicum* was the oldest name, but *bellum Italicum* was officially used as early as 78 B.C. (*C.I.L.* I², 588).

[2] Volume of Plates iv, 2, *b*. For a slightly different interpretation of the coin see A. v. Domaszewski, *Bellum Marsicum*, p. 15.

Marsic War from that mountain folk whose gallant service under
the Roman eagles had given rise to the proverb that no triumph
had been won without them, and whose leader Q. Pompaedius
Silo is traditionally associated with the creation of the confederacy.
In Lucania, Apulia and southern Campania ground was soon
gained by the rebels, but Etruria and Umbria held aloof for some
time. Calabria remained outside the war, and in Bruttium peace
was broken only at the end. The bond which existed between the
Roman government and the Italian upper classes may explain the
loyalty of certain isolated communities in the insurgent districts.
For example, Pinna refused to make common cause with the
Vestini; Minatus[1] Magius of Aeclanum, great-grandfather of the
historian Velleius Paterculus, raised a legion in the Hirpinian
country and rendered valuable aid to Sulla in 89; and in Apulia
the upper classes resisted Vidacilius. Nor did the Greek maritime
towns and the most favoured communities of allies hesitate to
adhere to Rome. In southern Campania Roman influence was
very strong, and the Greek cities of Neapolis, Heraclea and
Tarentum were so content with their status that later they refused
incorporation under the Lex Julia (see below, p. 195).

The headquarters of the league were established at Corfinium,
renamed Italia, a Paelignian town, set amid the grandeur of the
central Apennine, a strategic centre rather than a fortress. The
constitution of the league is not a matter of certainty, for the evidence of Diodorus (XXXVII, 2, 5) and Strabo (V, 241) is inconclusive. The former speaks of two consuls and twelve praetors, of
a senate of five hundred and, possibly, of an inner council; the
latter says that the Allies gathered at Corfinium and chose consuls
and praetors. Two fundamental questions arise in the consideration of this evidence. Was the constitution of the league modelled
upon that of Rome, and to what extent did the Italians produce
a representative system? These questions have been confidently
answered in various ways[2]. In the opinion of the present writer
there is much to be said for the view[3] that the Allies made use of
existing cantonal arrangements to form a binary league. Their
generals were apparently chieftains appointed by the cantons with

---

[1] On this name see F. Münzer, in *P.W.* *s.v.* Magius, col. 439.

[2] Mommsen, *History of Rome*, III, pp. 504–506, said that the arrangements of the Allies were a copy of those of Rome and scouted the idea
of a representative principle which, first suggested by Kiene, *Bundesgenossenkrieg*, p. 190, has recently found favour with Tenney Frank, *Roman
Imperialism*, pp. 301, 311; *Classical Journal*, XIV, p. 547.

[3] Domaszewski, *op. cit.* p. 15 *sq.*

a superior commander, Pompaedius Silo, for the Marsic and a superior commander, Papius Mutilus, for the Samnite group; and possibly there was a war council at Italia. If this is so we must discard the statement of Diodorus that the Italians devised a constitution inspired by Rome and we must regard it as improbable that they made use of the representative principle. The Italians, who had for long resented Roman exploitation, took up arms against tyranny. To establish an independent State and to acquire the Roman citizenship were only alternative means and were not ends in themselves.

Their armies consisted of Sabellian and Oscan dalesmen, excellent fighting material, stiffened by veterans who had seen service under the very generals who were to take the field against them. Since Rome had command of the sea, the Italians were dependent upon their own resources, but the stories of a Cretan bowman[1] and of Agamemnon a Cilician pirate[2] hint that they gladly pressed into service any foreign desperadoes who were temporarily out of employment. The idea of help from Mithridates was entertained by the Samnite element only as a counsel of despair.

There was no more significant expression of their defiance of Roman authority and of the setting-up of a rival state in Italy than the issue of coinage[3]. A personification of Italia, the sovereign deity of the insurgents, is most commonly seen on the obverse of the coins; on the reverse there were recorded or symbolized incidents of the struggle. The coins enliven the meagre records of the war by their vivid expression of the spirit of the confederacy. There could be no more graphic symbol of Roman reverses than the goring of a Roman wolf by an Italian bull.

Whether the outbreak of revolt was from the point of view of the confederates premature or timely, the Romans were certainly taken by surprise. The first act of the party which had triumphed upon the death of Drusus was to take vengeance upon those whom they believed to have been responsible for the revolt, and the sentences of the commission of high treason established by the Lex Varia thinned the ranks of the senators favourable to Drusus. This terrorism and the imminence of hostilities produced at least the semblance of political unity. The government began to array their forces in Italy and to draw reinforcements and supplies from the provinces. Their Italian power was formed by the Romanized district once inhabited by Sabines and Aequi, Latium, the *ager Campanus* and the Roman and Latin colonies. Of the loyalty of

[1] Diodorus XXXVII, 17.   [2] Id. XXXVII, 19; Orosius V, 18, 10.
[3] Volume of Plates iv, 2, *b, c.*

the Latin colonies, exemplified by Alba Fucens and Aesernia, and of the outstanding importance of the *ager Campanus* as a source of revenue and a base of operations we have ample evidence. All the best harbours were in the hands of Rome. From Cisalpine Gaul, where Sertorius himself, already a tried soldier, was quaestor, from Spain, Sicily and Numidia came troops and munitions of war; from the East some naval aid[1]. To the bitterness and horrors of the struggle Diodorus and Sisenna, in particular, bear frequent witness, and we hear from another source[2] that the Senate had no mercy upon a certain C. Vettienus who cut off the fingers of his left hand in order to avoid service.

The insurgent country was divided into two main theatres of war: the northern extended from Picenum to the mountains on the south and east sides of the Fucine Lake, the southern included Samnium and the rest of southern Italy[3]. In each of these theatres a Roman opposed an Italian commander-in-chief. P. Rutilius Lupus, who with L. Julius Caesar was consul in 90, took the field in the northern theatre against Q. Pompaedius Silo. Under him at the outset served five *legati*, Cn. Pompeius Strabo, father of Pompey the Great, Q. Servilius Caepio, son of the Caepio who had been defeated at Arausio, C. Perperna, Marius himself and Valerius Messalla. The southern campaign against C. Papius Mutilus was entrusted to L. Julius Caesar whose subordinate commanders were P. Lentulus, T. Didius, a veteran who had to his credit triumphs over Scordisci and Celtiberi, P. Licinius Crassus, who had triumphed for victories in Lusitania, Sulla fresh from his Cilician command, and M. Claudius Marcellus, who had served under Marius at Aquae Sextiae. With the exception of Catulus, who may have served in the second year of the war, these commanders well represented the cream of the military experience at the disposal of the State.

Much of the energies of the Italians was absorbed by the investment of fortresses in their territories which adhered to Rome. Although they conducted offensives against southern Campania and Apulia we can detect no sign of a concerted movement made by them against Latium and Rome. It may be that the Roman road-system served the Roman defensive better than the allied offensive. The Romans had to counter the enemy in many theatres simultaneously, and even if they had been in a position to con-

---

[1] *C.I.L.* I², 588. Memnon, 29.   [2] Val. Max. vi, 3, 3.

[3] Diodorus xxxvii, 2, 7. The phrase ἀπὸ τῶν Κερκώλων καλουμένων is a puzzle. But the reference may possibly be to the mountain barrier just south of Sulmo which divides the Marsic from the Samnite country.

centrate their forces, it is difficult to indicate any objective where success, at any rate in the first year, would have decided the course of the war. Recent investigations have indeed thrown light upon difficulties and done much to fix a sequence of events and elucidate strategy, but there is no reason to upset Mommsen's verdict that 'a clear and vivid picture of such a war cannot be prepared out of the remarkably fragmentary accounts which have come down to us[1].'

The northern campaign falls into two parts: an offensive against Asculum, and operations in the Apennines against the Marsic group. The Roman objectives were the isolation of Picenum, the relief of Alba Fucens and an attack upon Corfinium.

The legate Cn. Pompeius Strabo, a large land-owner in Picenum, was naturally marked out to command there and to avenge the massacre at Asculum. The possession of this strong fortress and road-centre would help the insurgents to spread revolt in Umbria and northern Etruria and to deny to Rome an important line of communication with Cisalpine Gaul. Moreover, Rome would not relax her efforts until the blood of her murdered citizens had been avenged. It is, therefore, not surprising that for the best part of two years there was hard fighting for the possession of this city. It appears that Strabo met with a rebuff upon his arrival before Asculum[2]. An army of Picentine and Marsic rebels commanded by C. Vidacilius of Asculum, T. Lafrenius and P. Vettius Scato forced him to retreat northwards. He was defeated in the mountains near Falerio and driven to Firmum. While Lafrenius remained to invest Firmum, Vidacilius and Vettius Scato withdrew to other theatres of war. How long Strabo remained pent up in Firmum we cannot say. But the situation was changed by the

---

[1] The authorities for this war are numerous but unsatisfactory. For a continuous narrative we rely solely upon Appian (*Bell. Civ.* 1, 38–53); sketches of the outlines are given by Velleius Paterculus, the *Epitomes* of Livy and Orosius. The contribution made by Cicero is large, but is less noteworthy than might be expected. Plutarch is scanty and disappointing. Much valuable information is to be found in Diodorus, Strabo, Frontinus and Pliny the Elder; occasional details are supplied by Dio, Florus and other late writers. Very few inscriptions have survived, but the coins minted by the Italians and the sling-bullets found at Asculum are interesting and valuable. The loss, therefore, of the history of L. Cornelius Sisenna (119–67 B.C.), which contained a narrative of the war, is to be deplored; the surviving fragments are occasionally illuminating and always tantalizing.

[2] Orosius v, 18, 10; Frontinus, *Strat.* III, 17, 8.

arrival of relief under a certain Sulpicius[1] who may well have come
with reinforcements from Cisalpine Gaul and who co-operated so
successfully with Strabo that Lafrenius was defeated and the siege
raised[2]. Asculum was at once invested by Strabo. No doubt this
success contributed to the election of Strabo as consul for 89.

There can be little doubt that at an early stage in the war the
insurgents laid siege to Pinna, a city of the Vestini, where the upshot of bitter party strife was that the city remained loyal to Rome.
A siege was endured and we are told that the gallantry of the
garrison rivalled that of the defenders of Alba Fucens[3]. In all
probability Pinna fell, and, if so, the authority[4] which makes the
Romans the besiegers may well refer to an incident of the Roman
counter-offensive in 89.

Operations against the tangle of mountain and valley around
the Fucine Lake, the stronghold of the Marsic group, were undertaken by the consul P. Rutilius Lupus and his legates. Although
the records of these campaigns are so imperfect that we cannot
fix the site of a single battle, it is natural to expect fighting on and
around the two lines by which the Marsic group could invade
Latium, namely the upper Liris and the Via Valeria which between Carsioli and Alba Fucens cuts through the Apennines by
the Monte Bove Pass (4040 feet). We know that the insurgents
at once laid siege to Alba Fucens, and, as the territory of Carsioli
was devastated in the war[5], the Marsi must have swept down
through the Monte Bove Pass upon that fortress. No doubt there
was a struggle also for the possession of Sora, the Latin fortress
which secured the upper Liris[6].

At the outset the Romans sustained reverse upon reverse.
First, Perperna was routed by Presenteius. He lost his command,
and the remnants of his army of 10,000 were transferred to Marius.
Worse was to follow. The consul was obstinate enough to scout
the advice of Marius that his levies should be trained and dis-

---

[1] The ingenious suggestion of Cichorius (*Römische Studien*, p. 138) that
this officer was Servius Sulpicius Galba who rendered distinguished service
under Strabo in 89 and who in all probability was the fourth member of
Strabo's *consilium* at Asculum (Dessau 8888) is here accepted.

[2] Livy, *Epit.* 73, mentions a victory over the Paeligni. Servius Sulpicius
should be read as the victor and not, as Domaszewski proposes (*op. cit.* p. 25),
Sextus Julius Caesar. The effect of the victory was to free Pompeius at
Firmum. It is possible that Paeligni is a mistake for Picentes and that Appian
(*Bell. Civ.* 1, 48, 210) gives a garbled reference to the same victory.

[3] *ad Herennium* II, 28, 45.   [4] Val. Max. V, 4, 7.

[5] Florus II, 6 (III, 18), 11.   [6] Servius, *ad Aen.* IX, 587.

ciplined before they were rushed into battle. Accordingly, on June 11th the valley of the Tolenus was the scene of a pitched battle between Lupus and Vettius Scato in which the consul was defeated with heavy loss and killed. Although Ovid's[1] statement that the battle was fought on the Tolenus renders valid any suitable site in the whole valley from Carsioli down to the confluence with the Himella between Reate and Interamna, it is tempting to suppose that Rutilius was endeavouring to force the crossing of the Tolenus between Carsioli and the western exit of the Monte Bove Pass and break through the Pass to the relief of Alba. Of Appian's account of the battle it is enough to say that Rutilius was lured by Vettius Scato into an ambush on the north bank of the river where he was mortally wounded and 8000 of his men were killed. But Marius, who was in position farther down the valley, observing from the bodies brought down by the stream that Rutilius and Scato were in action, crossed and captured Scato's weakly guarded camp with the result that on the following day the rebels were forced to retreat through shortage of supplies. Moreover, the statement of Orosius (v, 18, 13) that Marius' troops straightway slew 8000 of the enemy strongly suggests that he counter-attacked successfully. If so, he had indeed retrieved the situation. However, the exhibition in Rome of the bodies of the consul and of other fallen officers so depressed the public spirit that the Senate decreed that in future the fallen should be buried where they fell. Nevertheless, the chief command was withheld from Marius. A success gained by Q. Servilius Caepio, a violent opponent of Drusus, was an excuse for dividing the command between Marius and him. But Q. Pompaedius Silo with a force of Marsi and Vestini lured Caepio into an ambush where the Roman lost his army and his life[2]. Thereupon Marius assumed sole command. His outstanding achievement was a great victory gained over the Marsi and Marrucini, possibly in Marsic territory. The rebels, who were the aggressors, were driven in flight to some vineyards and sustained heavy losses when scaling the walls. Later, their

---

[1] *Fasti*, vi, 563–6. This passage enables us to fix the date. Appian, *Bell. Civ.* i, 43, 191, wrongly puts the scene of the battle in the Liris valley.

[2] Orosius v, 18, 14. Although Caepio may have fallen when attempting a surprise relief of Alba from the north it is easier to suppose that the defeat took place nearer Rome, especially as part of the tombstone of some members of the *gens Sergia* who fell *quom Q. Caepione est occisus* has come to light on the Via Laurentina outside the Porta S. Paolo (*C.I.L.* i², 708). Appian, therefore, may be mistaken in saying that it was after the defeat of Rutilius that the burial order was suspended.

rout was completed by Sulla[1], who intercepted the fugitives when endeavouring to escape and cut them to pieces with the loss of Herius Asinius, general of the Marrucini.

The net result of the operations against the Marsic group entitles us to doubt the truth of Plutarch's statement (*Marius*, 33) that Marius lost reputation in the war. Compared with his colleagues he had rendered notable services. The deplorable situation created by the defeats of Perperna, Lupus and Caepio had been repaired, the enemy's territory had probably been invaded[2], and heavy loss had certainly been inflicted on the Marsic rebels. But we are left to speculate upon the fate of Alba Fucens.

Meanwhile the armies serving in the southern theatre under the consul L. Julius Caesar were confronted by tasks bewildering in their variety. To maintain communications between Rome, Campania and the south, to check the spread of revolt and to defend fortresses threatened by the insurgents were among the most pressing. Our knowledge, however, of operations in the southern theatre is confined to the siege of Aesernia, the invasions of southern Campania and the spread of revolt in Apulia and Lucania.

It is not surprising that the insurgents immediately assailed the colony of Aesernia, which commanded the road down the Apennines from Corfinium to Beneventum, by which the northern rebels could communicate with central and southern Samnium, and from which, by a branch road through Venafrum, they could threaten Roman communications with Campania by the Via Latina.

L. Caesar's first attempt to defend Aesernia was disastrous. He was heavily defeated, presumably in the upper Volturnus valley, by the ubiquitous P. Vettius Scato, who then marched to Aesernia and began or continued the blockade. Determined but unsuccessful attempts at relief were made, perhaps by Caesar[3] himself and certainly by his legate Sulla[4]. The former was heavily defeated by Marius Egnatius, possibly in the Volturnus valley south of Venafrum; the latter gained some success but had to abandon the city to its fate. Fragments of Sisenna (16 P.) and

---

[1] Appian (*Bell. Civ.* 1, 46, 201–2) may be wrong in associating Sulla with this victory, but as Sulla's name occurs elsewhere only twice in our records of the campaigns of 90, namely in connection with the siege of Aesernia, he may have served on the northern flank of the southern command and have been able to co-operate with Marius.

[2] In the opinion of the present writer this is a fair assumption from Diodorus XXXVII, 15 (ὁ Μάριος ἤγαγε τὴν δύναμιν ἐπὶ τὸ Σαυνιτῶν πεδίον) after allowance is made for the geographical error in Σαυνιτῶν (he must mean the Marsic country).   [3] Appian, *Bell. Civ.* 1, 45, 200.

[4] Orosius v, 18, 16; Frontinus, *Strat.* 1, 5, 17.

Diodorus (xxxvii, 18) bear witness to the horrors of the siege: the garrison drove their slaves out of the city and when their food was exhausted ate the flesh of dogs and other animals. Thus reduced, the gallant commander M. Claudius Marcellus capitulated to the Samnites before the end of the year.

While the Romans were in distress in the upper Volturnus valley, an invasion of southern Campania was carried out by a Samnite army under C. Papius Mutilus, who saw that successes in that rich and populous territory would cut Roman land communications with the south and east and would menace the *ager Campanus*, mainstay of the Roman treasury and base of the southern armies. Moreover, the insurgents would derive great advantage from the capture of part of Campania and its coast, a rich prize. At the outset the invasion was successful. Treachery placed in his hands Nola on the Via Popilia 20 miles south-east of Capua. From Nola he captured Stabiae, Salernum and Surrentum, pressing prisoners and slaves into his army. Nuceria remained loyal to Rome, but other towns in the neighbourhood, including Pompeii and Herculaneum, fell before him. Master, therefore, of a large army and of the greater part of southern Campania he laid siege to Acerrae. But there he was confronted by L. Caesar, whose army after its misfortunes in the Volturnus valley had been reinforced at Teanum by 10,000 Gallic foot and by horse and foot from Numidia. At the outset Papius succeeded in undermining the loyalty of the Numidians, who deserted in such numbers that they had to be disbanded[1]. Hostilities then opened. Papius attacked Caesar's camp, but was surprised and routed with the loss of 6000 men. Upon this success Caesar was hailed *imperator*, and the wearing of civilian dress was resumed at Rome. Touch is then lost with the war in Campania. Caesar must have left for Rome, where he held the elections and carried through the Lex Julia.

One result of the Samnite drive into Campania was that a Roman army in Lucania under P. Licinius Crassus was cut off, and rebellion in south-eastern Italy spread as it pleased. The Lucanians had begun by seizing a Roman emissary, who owed to a woman his escape from the danger of such an end as that of Servilius at Asculum. Then Crassus was defeated by the Lucanian general M. Lamponius and driven to Grumentum, his camp being set on fire and his army barely escaping destruction[2]. It is even highly probable that he did not succeed in saving the town itself (see below, p. 200). In Apulia Rome sustained severe losses through the enterprise of Vidacilius, who had dashed down from

[1] Appian, *Bell. Civ.* i, 42, 189.   [2] Frontinus, *Strat.* ii, 4, 16.

Picenum and won over many cities, including Canusium and the strong fortress of Venusia, thereby cutting Roman communications with Brundisium. In these cities the upper classes who stood by Rome were put to death, but the lower classes and the slaves joined the insurgents. Thus the allies had conducted their campaigns in southern Italy with vigour and success.

VII. ROMAN CONCESSIONS: THE COLLAPSE OF THE CONFEDERACY

The hostilities thus far described produced a grave situation, although as the year advanced the Romans recovered somewhat from the disasters which had marked the beginning of the war. Matters were made no better by the news that Mithridates was menacing the province of Asia and that the governor of Transalpine Gaul was having trouble with the Salluvii. It was significant of the exhaustion of Rome's resources that freedmen had to be enrolled to guard the coast from the city to Capua. Thus a widespread and determined revolt in Etruria and Umbria, where loyalty had so far prevailed, would have rendered this situation intolerable; land-communications with Gaul and Spain would have been cut, a large area would have been added to the territory of the confederacy, and in Italy Rome would have been at bay. There can be little doubt that the northern confederates in the flush of success strained every nerve to engineer revolt in Etruria and Umbria. The prospect of revolt there and the situation elsewhere forced the hand of the government: citizenship was offered to those allied communities that remained loyal, an offer which was accepted by the Etruscans. Apparently there was some fighting in Etruria[1], but if we may judge from the silence of Appian no serious operations. The probability is that, although the offer of citizenship averted a general rising, military action had to be taken against certain communities which actually revolted.

This offer was made in the nick of time. When L. Julius Caesar returned from Campania to hold the elections for 89 he found that adversity had been preparing the way for concession, and the Lex Julia which the consul carried before retiring from office, is proof that the Italians had indeed cut their way into the state by the sword. The law offered full Roman citizenship to all Latins and to all communities in Italy which had not revolted[2]. It was to

---

[1] Livy, *Epit.* 74; Orosius v, 18, 17.

[2] Appian, *Bell. Civ.* I, 49, 212; Cicero, *pro Balbo*, 8, 21; Gellius, *N.A.* IV, 4, 3. It is sometimes assumed from Vell. Pat. II, 16, that communities

whole communities **not to** individuals that the offer was made, and a decree accepting citizenship had to be passed by each community before the law could take effect. We also know that under the Lex Julia it was possible for citizenship to be won as a reward for distinguished service in the field[1]. The Lex Julia was followed, probably very soon after the tribunes of 89 had come into office, by a supplementary statute, the Lex Plautia Papiria[2], which provided that any man who was on the register of an allied community and whose permanent home was in Italy, might acquire Roman citizenship by making application to a praetor in Rome within 60 days from the date of the passing of the law. This law enabled citizenship to be acquired by individual members of allied states which had not accepted incorporation under the Lex Julia. Moreover, it does not seem unreasonable to say that the law also applied to members of allied states still in revolt, because it was clearly in the interest of Rome, now that the principle of concession had been accepted by her, to attempt to divide and weaken the insurgents' forces by a short-term offer which would encourage desertions before the campaigning season re-opened.

In consequence of these concessions it was found necessary to frame a special statute to meet conditions prevailing in Cisalpine Gaul. Although the population immediately south of the Po had originally been largely or mainly Celtic and this racial distinction was marked by a line running from the Arnus on the west to the Aesis on the east, it is certain that the whole peninsula up to the Alps was regarded as Italy, many colonies both Roman and Latin having been founded in it and most of the other towns having become members of the Italian confederacy. It is true that the country north of the Po was thoroughly Celtic, but between conditions prevailing south of the Po and those in northern Etruria and Umbria there could have been little, if any, difference. The operation of the Lex Julia in north Italy meant the promotion of all the Latin colonies to the rank of Roman municipia. Moreover, all the other towns would have been elevated to that status had not a special statute been framed, the Lex Pompeia[3], which confirmed

---

which had revolted but laid down their arms could acquire citizenship by the Lex Julia. Although the words *qui arma...deposuerant maturius* could be interpreted in this sense, it could apply equally well to those individuals who were enfranchised under the Lex Plautia Papiria shortly afterwards.

[1] *C.I.L.* I², 709 and p. 714; Dessau 8888. A Lex Calpurnia (Sisenna, frag. 120 P.), presumably passed in 89, dealt also with this topic.

[2] Cicero, *pro Archia*, 4, 7; Schol. Bob. p. 175 Stangl.

[3] Asconius, p. 3 c.; Pliny, *N.H.* III, 138.

the grant of citizenship already made to the Latin colonies by the Lex Julia, conferred the *ius Latii* upon the Transpadane towns and 'attributed' native tribes to the urban communities[1].

The value of the franchise to the Italians was impaired, it is true, by the restriction of the new citizens to eight of the existing thirty-five tribes[2]. This narrow-minded cunning was to overreach itself and revealed the limitations of senatorial statesmanship; but the concessions, whether or not they all took effect before the opening of the campaign in 89, exercised a profound influence upon the course of the struggle. Though hard fighting still lay before them, the Romans could count themselves certain of ultimate victory: in resources, leadership and morale they could hardly fail to prove superior. On the other hand, the insurgents could not expect a repetition of their early successes; their numbers would diminish rather than increase, their unity would suffer from Roman concessions, their leaders would realize that they were championing a losing cause. But allied loyalty and Roman pride, simplest of human emotions, prolonged the struggle till Asculum had paid the penalty and the thinned ranks of the rebels saw no choice other than surrender or death.

Meanwhile at Rome, whether because the war made it difficult to man the courts or as a reaction against the vindictiveness with which the war began, the Lex Plautia iudiciaria[3] introduced a new principle in the choice of judges; each tribe elected 15 of its own members without regard to their class or quality, and from the list of 525 men thus elected, jurors for this year were to be drawn. By a stroke of irony the Lex Varia now recoiled upon its author, for Q. Varius himself was brought to trial under his own law and condemned.

In 89 Cn. Pompeius Strabo and L. Porcius Cato were consuls. Strabo continued his command in Picenum and Cato succeeded Marius on the Marsic front. Marius disappeared from the war.

---

[1] It is possible that the Lex Pompeia was no less than the *lex provinciae* of Gallia Cisalpina (so E. G. Hardy, *J.R.S.* VI, pp. 65 *sqq.*). See however, below, p. 301.

[2] Vell. Pat. II, 20. Certainty between this statement and the conflicting evidence of Appian, *Bell. Civ.* I, 49, 214, for a new group of ten tribes is impossible. The tantalizing fragment of Sisenna (17 P.) 'L. Calpurnius Piso ex senati consulto duas novas tribus...' may refer to a separate enfranchisement of those who had distinguished themselves on the side of Rome (see frags. 119, 120 P). It is however possible that Velleius intends to speak of eight new tribes and that these with the two mentioned by Sisenna make up Appian's ten; see T. Rice Holmes, *Roman Republic*, I, p. 356.

[3] Asconius, p. 79 c.

If we are not prepared to believe Plutarch's[1] statement that he re-signed his command owing to age and infirmity, we must suppose that his retention in the field was not acceptable to the party in power. Sulla, still as *legatus*, took over the troops left by L. Julius Caesar in Campania.

At the outset the Romans sustained a reverse on the Marsic front. In spite of insubordination among his men[2] Cato pene-trated as far as the Fucine Lake, but was defeated and killed. Strabo then extended his command over the Marsic front and thanks to his legates Murena, Metellus Pius and Sulpicius, over-came the failing opposition of the enemy.

In Picenum all turned on the siege of Asculum, where both sides concentrated every available man. The inscribed sling-bullets[3] found in such profusion on the site are interesting from a human no less than from a statistical standpoint; no doubt the messages scratched upon them—*feri Pomp[eium], em tibi malum malo, ventri*—added to their efficacy as missiles. The story of the latter part of the siege seems to transport us back to the heroic days of the Samnite wars, the issue of which was decided on a field not so very far from Asculum (vol. vii, p. 612). The bold thrust of the Samnites before Sentinum was repeated: a prodigious effort was made to cut through the Apennines, relieve Asculum and join hands with fellow rebels in Umbria and Etruria. It is not in-credible that in the battle which decided the destiny of Asculum and the northern rising 75,000 Romans fought against 60,000 Italians[4]. A force of Marsi seems to have survived the rout, only to be cut to pieces by Pompeius Strabo in some mountain pass. It was winter, for the fugitives took to the heights and perished in the snow.

Perhaps in the course of this battle the heroic Vidacilius broke through the Roman lines and forced his way into his native city. But later the situation within and without drove him to a dramatic suicide. The city must have fallen to Strabo on or before November 17th, and the massacre was at length avenged. All officers and leading men were scourged and beheaded; the rest of the popula-tion were allowed to leave the city, free but destitute; slaves and loot were sold under the hammer. We hear that the proceeds of the auction were not remitted by Strabo to the treasury[5], and that the financial strain at the time was so severe that sites around the

---

[1] *Marius*, 33.   [2] Dio xxx–xxxv, frag. 100; Sisenna, 52 P.
[3] For the fullest list see E. Lommatzsch in *C.I.L.* i², pp. 560 *sqq.* Illustrations are given by C. Zangemeister, *Glandes plumbeae latine inscriptae*, Eph. Epig. vi, 1885, pp. 5–47.
[4] Vell. Pat. ii, 21, 1.   [5] Orosius v, 18, 26.

Capitol in the occupation of the priestly colleges had to be sold. The enfranchisement by Strabo of thirty men of a squadron of Spanish cavalry for services rendered during the siege is a landmark in the history of western civilization. The inscription[1] which records this act is the principal addition made by the present century to the ancient evidence for the Marsic War, and the list which enumerates the members of the general's *consilium* seems to contain the names of such personalities as Lepidus, consul in 78, Catiline, and a Cn. Pompeius who cannot be other than Strabo's seventeen-year old son who became Pompey the Great.

On December 25th 89 Pompeius Strabo celebrated his triumph *de Asculaneis Picentibus*. Among the captives marched a young Picentine, P. Ventidius, who was himself destined to lead Parthians in triumph fifty-one years later. After his triumph Strabo returned to the field as proconsul in order to extinguish any flames which might burst out anew from the dying embers of the conspiracy in the north.

Of the remaining operations against the Marsic group it is impossible to give a detailed version. They were profoundly influenced by the siege of Asculum and by the Roman offensives in Campania, Samnium and Apulia. It is highly improbable that organized opposition outlasted Strabo's triumph, because the land of the Marsi and their neighbours must have been drained of fighting men by heavy losses and especially by efforts to relieve Asculum. We may suppose that by the end of 89 the Marsi had surrendered to Strabo's legates L. Murena and Q. Caecilius Metellus Pius, son of Metellus Numidicus, and that Sulpicius had subdued the Vestini and the Marrucini. Moreover, when the Paeligni turned upon their leader P. Vettius Scato, and would have handed him over to Strabo had not his slave slain him on the spot[2], it was time for Italia to be abandoned and for Pompaedius Silo, undismayed by the collapse of the northern rising, to fly to the mountains of Samnium. War against an Italian confederacy had ceased; the Samnite cantons with Lucanian help alone remained in the field.

We pass to Campania, where Sulla was in command and where his generalship soon loosened the grip which the Samnites had won in the previous year. Siege was laid to the coast towns.

[1] *C.I.L.* I², 709 and p. 714 (= Dessau 8888). Cichorius conjectures (*op. cit.* p. 133) that the name of the cavalry squadron *Turma Sallvitana* may come from that of its commander (perhaps Salvitto), not from a place in Spain. On Strabo's title *imperator* see A. Momigliano, in *Bull. Com. Arch.* LVIII, 1930, pp. 45 *sqq.*   [2] Macrobius, *Sat.* I, 11, 24.

Before Pompeii, where the Roman fleet operated by sea and a legion enrolled from the Hirpini by Minatus Magius of Aeclanum lent welcome aid on land, there was a notorious example of insubordination. Mutiny broke out in the fleet commanded by a *legatus* A. Postumius Albinus[1], who was done to death with sticks and stones. The disciplinary action taken by Sulla was marked by characteristic adroitness; he merely exhorted the mutineers to atone for their crime by gallantry in action. Nor was abstract justice expedient at the moment, for a strong Samnite army under Cluentius was straining every nerve to relieve Pompeii. But Sulla's generalship and luck prevailed. In the decisive battle Cluentius' troops, reinforced by Gallic deserters from the Roman armies, broke and fled towards Nola. Few only gained the city. With this victory came the turn of the tide. On April 29th Stabiae was captured by Sulla[2]. On June 11th T. Didius and Minatus Magius stormed Herculaneum[3]; and thus isolated, Pompeii must soon have fallen. Nola alone seems to have been held by the enemy when Sulla left for his campaign in Samnium.

This brilliant manœuvre dealt telling blows against the Samnites and must have aided the operations in Apulia and Lucania. Sulla first marched against the Hirpini and captured two of their cities, Aeclanum and Compsa. At Aeclanum he forestalled the arrival of help from Lucania by giving the inhabitants one hour's notice of battle; he then set fire to the wooden walls and captured the city. Bursting into central Samnium by an unexpected route he surprised the Samnite commander, Papius Mutilus, and drove him in rout to Aesernia. This success enabled him to strike at Bovianum Vetus, a principal city of the Samnites and a rebel headquarters, which fell after a short engagement. Leaving an army to blockade Nola, he went to Rome to stand for the consulship. In Apulia a competent legate, C. Cosconius, recovered practically all the ground which had been lost to Vidacilius in the previous year. He burned Salapia and crushed a Samnite army on the northern bank of the Aufidus near Cannae. Winning freedom of movement by these victories he ravaged the territories of Larinum, Ausculum and Venusia and secured the undulating moorlands which lie north of the Via Appia between Venusia and Tarentum. At the end of the year he was succeeded by Q. Caecilius Metellus

---

[1] Since he is called *consularis* (Orosius v, 18, 22) he must be the consul of 99, who in 110 had done so ill against Jugurtha (p. 121).

[2] Pliny, *N.H.* iii, 70.

[3] Didius fell in the assault, Ovid, *Fasti*, vi, 567–8. In any event, Herculaneum, like Pompeii, cannot have held out for long.

Pius, fresh from his successful campaign against the Marsi. In Lucania two legates, A. Gabinius and Carbo, were in the field. Gabinius captured several towns, but fell at the siege or the storming of a place which may well be Grumentum, probably lost in the previous year[1].

The disruption of the confederacy and the abandonment of Italia were the natural results of the operations in 89. Of the Italian manhood which had risen against Rome thousands had made a sacrifice which had won for many of their comrades the prize of Roman citizenship. Others who had surrendered too late to benefit by the franchise legislation, were in the position of *dediticii* awaiting Rome's pleasure. But the man who above all had been the soul of the insurrection, Q. Pompaedius Silo, undismayed by the capitulation of his own people, fled to the Samnites and inspired them to further resistance. The Samnite cantons, therefore, under their own leaders, with Pompaedius as commander-in-chief, continued the struggle and once more sought to force Rome to recognize that independence which they had lost two centuries before. The headquarters of their organization were established at Aesernia, the fortress that once had curbed their freedom. An army was raised of 30,000 infantry and 1000 cavalry. If, as we are told, 20,000 manumitted slaves were enrolled, then the Samnites in their despair must have encouraged a servile rising. The movement soon met with success, for the commander-in-chief recaptured Bovianum Vetus and entered the city in triumph. But their fortunes changed in the course of the year. Various conflicting summaries of the operations are given, and we can be certain of nothing more than the final result, the defeat and death of Pompaedius Silo in a decisive battle. The time was then ripe for the surrender of Venusia which capitulated to Metellus after having remained in possession of the insurgents for about two years; over 3000 prisoners gave themselves up. According to Diodorus (xxxvii, 2, 11) it was at that point that the rebels as an act of despair in vain sent ambassadors to Mithridates entreating him to invade Italy in their interest. But with the fall of Pompaedius Silo, the Samnites were no longer a danger. Nola indeed and Aesernia remained in the hands of the rebels, while the guerrilla chieftains Lamponius and his colleagues roamed at large in the solitudes of Lucania. When these last had been repulsed before Rhegium by Norbanus the governor of Sicily the curtain falls upon the last act of the Marsic War.

[1] The recovery of Grumentum by the Romans is deduced from Claudius Quadrigarius frag. 80 P.

VIII. THE *LEGES SULPICIAE*, AND THE FIRST CAPTURE OF ROME

By the end of the year 89 B.C. the military crisis was passed. In several parts of the peninsula embers from the conflagration still smouldered on; but the danger had been mastered, the plans for reconstruction had been sketched, and in 88 B.C. Rome could begin to face in detail the problems which were the legacy of the war. This task she approached under the leadership of consuls whose past gave little cause for hope that they would handle the issues of the day with the statesmanship which alone could lay sound foundations for the future. One was L. Cornelius Sulla, whose sole claim to the suffrage of the People lay in his distinguished services in the wars of Africa, Gaul, Asia and Italy; the other was Q. Pompeius Rufus—a man remarkable for nothing but the part he had played as tribune in securing the recall from exile of Metellus Numidicus. Consuls such as these were not the men to extort from a reluctant Senate a large-minded and liberal answer to the questions with which the newly united Italy was beset. To Sulla had fallen the Eastern command, and his one anxiety was to set out with the least possible delay: Pompeius Rufus, who was to remain in Italy, showed no sign of activity. And thus it happened that the initiative in legislation was left to a member of the tribunician college.

P. Sulpicius Rufus, who modelled his style of speaking on that of the great Crassus—now two years dead, is acknowledged by Cicero to have been an orator unrivalled by any of his contemporaries, save only by C. Aurelius Cotta. These two, alike in their forensic pre-eminence, were alike in their politics as well: they both belonged to that progressive section of the nobility whose wisdom was to be a sheet-anchor to Rome in the stormy years to come, and whose traditions were the earliest and most powerful influence on the mind of Cotta's second cousin—Julius Caesar. Both had supported the younger Livius Drusus in 91 B.C., and Sulpicius was on terms of intimate friendship with Pompeius Rufus, the consul. Of a man like Sulpicius it was not to be expected that he would turn into a revolutionary, and at the elections it seems that he commanded the oligarchical vote. Yet before the year was out he had undergone so startling a change that the senatorial tradition preserved by Diodorus, Plutarch and Appian regards him with an aversion usually reserved for open enemies. The injustice of this attitude is suggested by certain inconsistencies which it betrays; but it is the testimony of Cicero and of the author

of the treatise *ad Herennium* which reveals that, surprising as were
the lengths to which he went, Sulpicius was no mere irresponsible
demagogue. From these authorities it appears that in the early
days of his tribunate his conduct was beyond reproach; and, though
he later fell from grace, the change was not one to justify his condemnation out of hand, however well it merited the hatred of the
extreme conservatives.

The political history of the year 88 B.C. opened with a proposal
from some unknown quarter for the recall of all the exiles who had
been banished unheard either by the Varian Commission or by
the court established under the Lex Plautia of 89 B.C.[1]: against
this Sulpicius, for some reason which is difficult to discover in a
friend of Livius Drusus, interposed his veto[2]. But soon afterwards
there came a transformation; and though Sulpicius earned senatorial admiration by one other achievement in this year—when he
prevented C. Julius Caesar Strabo, who perhaps coveted the
command against Mithridates for himself[3], from standing for the
consulship before he had been praetor—the rest of his activities
were of a kind on which optimate eyes looked with the gravest
disapproval. The famous Leges Sulpiciae were four—two of them
of minor significance, one dangerously controversial, and the fourth
a bold and beneficent proposal which entitles its author to a place
of honour in the history of his time. It was a small matter that
senators in debt to the extent of 2000 *denarii* or more were to lose
their seats in the House; nor would the recall of the exiles—a simple
and salutary measure of reconciliation—call for notice, had not
Sulpicius himself been foremost in opposing it earlier in the year.
But it was otherwise with the demand that Sulla should be removed from his command in the Mithridatic War and that it should
be conferred on Marius in his stead.

It could, indeed, be urged that Marius was the most distinguished general then alive: it might even be maintained that
Rome had never produced a greater. Yet, on the other hand, Sulla
had by this time proved his worth beyond dispute; and, unless
there had been some unrecorded failure to observe the provisions
of the Lex Sempronia de provinciis consularibus, he held the
Asiatic command by a title which—in the absence of some constitutional *tour de force*—nothing but his death or the abrogation
of his *imperium* could destroy. Moreover, even if it be untrue that
Marius had returned to Rome after his victories in the Social
War because he could no longer stand the rigours of a campaign

---

[1] See p. 196.   [2] *ad Herennium* II, 28, 45.
[3] Diodorus XXXVII, 2, 12.

(p. 197), the fact remained that he was approaching seventy and had reached an age when his appointment to the East would be something of a speculation. The sudden support lent by Sulpicius to the ambitions of a veteran whose reluctance to admit the signs of advancing years combined with his jealousy of Sulla to fill him with desire for the Eastern command must be ascribed to political considerations. It may be conjectured that the tribune, seeing the need for strong backing in the Concilium Plebis if the obstructive tactics of the Senate were to be met, turned to that large body of voters whom the name of Marius could stir as nothing else. Marius was not only a man of the people, whom the masses could trust more readily than any Optimate; he was more even than a great soldier who retained the allegiance of his veterans. Besides all this, he was the first and most famous of the *populares* (pp. 137 *sqq.*), and for that reason to the votes of *plebs urbana* he could join the backing of the upper classes outside the Senate—classes whose support we know that Sulpicius was ultimately able to command. Thus the help of Marius could not be despised, and all of it was needed; for Sulpicius, in the greatest of his laws, proposed a change which could not fail of the most bitter opposition.

The claim of Sulpicius to an honourable place in history rests on his bill to distribute the freedmen and the new citizens over all the thirty-five tribes. The limitations of the Lex Aemilia of 115 (p. 96) were to be abolished; and, what was far more important, Rome was fairly to face the effects of the Social War. About the question of the freedmen there is little to be said. In numbers they were comparatively few, and, since the passing of the Lex Papiria tabellaria in 131 B.C. (p. 38), they could no longer be controlled by their patrons—the only people to whom the freedmen's votes can have been of serious value. Their inclusion in the measure of Sulpicius was perhaps no more than the expression of a belief that the time had gone when any particular section of the population could reasonably be confined to a few selected tribes. But it was not the freedmen who gave this bill its significance: the people whose treatment was of vital importance were the new citizens who had won the franchise in the war. Unlike the freedmen, they were numerous; and, because their numbers might have counted had they been incorporated evenly in all the tribes, Roman jealousy had tried to destroy their influence by confining them to a small minority (p. 196). It was an expedient typical of the Roman at his worst: with one hand the *civitas* was bestowed, with the other the *ius suffragii* was rendered nugatory. But sharp practice such as this is apt to recoil on its authors, and it was perhaps well for Rome that Sulpicius called attention to the trick before it had bred a grievance in the minds of its victims. His proposal, the proposal of a man who stood in the direct line of succession from Gaius Gracchus and the younger Livius Drusus, was that the enfranchisement of the allies should be accepted with all its implications. The vexatious restrictions of the year before— restrictions which in their constitutional aspect were an attempt, by grafting the Italians on to the existing citizen-body instead of merging them therein, to preserve such traces of the Roman city-state as could still be saved—were to be withdrawn. Man for man, the new citizens were to be equals of the old. And the citizenship of Rome, no longer Roman in anything but name, was to be the citizenship of Italy. In fact, if not in theory, Italy was not to be the *territorium* of Rome: Rome was to be the capital of Italy. The city-state, in brief, was at an end.

The justice of this measure needs no demonstration, but fairness to its author demands that the circumstances of its proposal be examined with care. The narrative of Appian, definitely oligarchical in its bias, encourages the inference, which has often been drawn, that Sulpicius urged a distribution of the new citizens throughout the tribal body merely in order to increase the power of voters who, from gratitude for this reform, would lend valuable support to its author when the issue between Marius and Sulla came to be decided. But Appian himself[1], and Plutarch too[2], give the impression that the constitutional proposal and the transference of the Mithridatic command were enacted, if not simultaneously, at least in such quick succession that there can have been no opportunity to carry out the complicated task of redistributing the new citizens before the vote was taken on the question of the Eastern appointment. The supersession of Sulla by Marius, if it was to happen at all, could only reasonably be carried out at once, before the opening of the campaign; and in that case the struggle would be over before the complicated task of re-organizing the tribes could even be begun. More probably the bill about the new citizens was regarded by Sulpicius as an end in itself; and it is because, if this view be right, he set himself to secure this beneficent reform for its own sake, that Sulpicius deserves the reputation of a serious statesman. In the excellence of his chief objective he can claim some extenuation of the dangerous concessions made to his ally Marius, without whose help there can have been little chance of carrying forthwith so controversial a bill.

The programme of Sulpicius was greeted with howls of in-

[1] *Bell. Civ.* I, 56, 249.   [2] *Marius*, 35, 4.

dignant protest. Honest dislike of fresh generosity to the Italians combined with the personal loyalties which centred round the figures of Marius and Sulla to produce a political crisis of the utmost gravity. It was a crisis only ended by an expedient which ushered in the last phase in the decline of the Republic. There was the inevitable recourse to violence. Sulpicius is alleged to have surrounded himself with 600 young *equites* and, besides these, to have maintained a body of 3000 men at arms. About the forces on the other side our authorities are discreetly vague, but it is unlikely that the consuls and their friends passed about the streets of Rome without the precautions which prudence advised. When the situation grew threatening, Sulla and Pompeius Rufus threw down a direct challenge to the tribunate. They announced an indefinite suspension of public business (*iustitium*), and thereby seem to have claimed for the consulship a *potestas* so great as to be capable even of blocking the legislative activities of the tribunes[1]. Sulpicius retorted that such action was illegal, and certainly no precedent could be quoted; for the action of Tiberius Gracchus as tribune was irrelevant (p. 25). But Rome in 88 B.C. was no place for constitutional niceties. Soon there came a clash in the Forum. Pompeius Rufus got away, though his son was killed, and Sulla is said to have sought safety in the house of his rival Marius—an incident which later he was at some pains to explain. Whether he actually owed his life to Marius or not, he was somehow induced to terminate the *iustitium* and forthwith set out for the more tranquil atmosphere of his camp at Nola.

No sooner had the consuls disappeared than the whole programme of Sulpicius was passed into law. For a moment the *populares* were supreme; but their triumph was brief. When messengers were sent to Nola with instructions to bring the army north to meet Marius, its new commander, they found that Sulla had been before them: the troops would not change their allegiance, and the envoys of Sulpicius were stoned to death. For the first time in history a Roman army had declared war on the government in Rome, and from that moment politics in the city became a mere phantom rout, condemned to fade away whenever a successful

---

[1] This account, which is derived from Plutarch (*Sulla* 8, 3), is perhaps slightly preferable to the version of Appian (*Bell. Civ.* 1, 55, 244), who may be thought to suggest that the consuls were conscious that they did not wield a *maior potestas* against the tribunate and endeavoured to make good the lack by proclaiming, as was certainly within their power, a series of *feriae imperativae*, during which no business could be conducted. See, on this question, M. A. Levi, *Silla*, pp. 163–7, with the authorities there cited.

general took the stage. Sulla was soon in motion. With six legions
at his back he started northwards, yielding his own qualms about
a seizure of the city to the encouragements of the soothsayers and
the enthusiasm of his men. Marius and the government at Rome
were defenceless against such a force. Deputations, indeed, they
were not slow to send; but even two praetors, who undertook one
such mission, barely escaped with their lives. Of troops, however,
they had none: almost without resistance Sulla and Pompeius
Rufus entered Rome. For a few hours there was street-fighting
on the Esquiline, hours few indeed, but enough to allow Marius
to incur a disgrace to which not even Catiline would stoop—
the disgrace of summoning the slaves to arms and promising freedom to those who came. Even so, there was no response; for the
issue was already decided, and before the day was done Marius
had fled and Sulla was undisputed master of the city. Thus for
the first time Rome was captured by a Roman army.

IX. THE FIRST CONSULSHIP OF SULLA

Yet this did not exhaust the novelties of the year: the citizens
had another new experience when government began to be
conducted by a military despot. It is true that Sulla remained
consul, and as consul he carried on his task. He even observed
the forms of constitutional procedure. But it was a new thing for
measures of a most drastic kind to be forced through the assemblies
without argument and without the possibility of resistance: and
the reason for all this was the army at Sulla's back. At the outset,
we may assume, though the narrative of Appian is here obscure,
the Senate was compelled, by an act of doubtful legality and one
against which Scaevola the Augur protested (though not on legal
grounds[1]), to declare Marius, his son, Sulpicius, still a tribune of
the Plebs, and several of their leading supporters to be enemies of
the Roman People, whose lives might be taken with impunity and
whose property was forfeit[2]. It was a strong measure and a
dangerous precedent. The victims had certainly been guilty of
inciting the slaves to rise, and they had indubitably flouted the
authority of the consuls; but even so they were not an obvious
menace to society, and to proclaim them outlaws straight away was
little less than to deprive Roman citizens of their right to trial
merely because crime was alleged against them. As a result,

---

[1] Val. Max. III, 8, 5.
[2] Vell. Pat. (II, 19, 1) is alone in suggesting that this decision was embodied in a law.

Sulpicius was murdered. Marius, however, made his way to Minturnae and thence escaped to Africa. Thereupon the Leges Sulpiciae were declared to have been carried *per vim*[1] and to be, accordingly, invalid. The argument, we may conjecture, was that, though the *iustitium* had ended before their enactment, its ending had been forced upon Sulla by the threats of the mob.

After these preliminaries Sulla was free to set about the legislation of 88 B.C., for which Appian[2] is virtually our only source of value. The measures which he ascribes to Sulla on this occasion have provoked many unnecessary doubts; but, if the circumstances of the time are properly appreciated, their acceptance becomes easy, if not inevitable. That a record of these laws should have been preserved by Appian alone is hardly surprising, the less so when it is remembered that our other outstanding authority—Plutarch in his *Life of Sulla*—does not even trouble to describe the legislative work of Sulla as dictator. In any case, the reforms of the years from 81 to 79 B.C. so far exceeded in importance whatever may have been achieved in 88 B.C. that it is scarcely strange if all but one of our meagre authorities regarded —and rightly regarded—the later legislation as Sulla's real monument, which alone was entitled to permanent record. Such a view, indeed, is just. After his return from the East Sulla undertook a drastic reform of the Roman constitution: in 88 B.C., before his departure, he neither accomplished nor essayed anything of the kind. In his first consulship, after the struggle with Marius and Sulpicius, time was short: it was his urgent duty to start for the Mithridatic War with the least possible delay. The most he could do before leaving Rome was to patch up the defences of his party position, and this he attempted by a few simple measures—crude, indeed, but effective, and of a kind which could be drafted in a few hours. Since they were designed to meet the dangers of the immediate future until the time of his own return to Italy, it would be a grave mistake to assume that all these laws, which were repealed by Cinna in 87 B.C.[3], were re-enacted by Sulla when he had leisure as dictator for a thorough re-casting of the constitution. If this be so, it is idle to criticize Appian's version of the laws of 88 B.C. on the ground that some of them, at least, were demonstrably not in force during the years immediately after 79 B.C.: the only sound objection which could be taken to Appian's account is one to which that account is not exposed—the objection that the measures are too complicated or too petty for Sulla to have had the

---

[1] Cicero, *Phil.* viii, 2, 7. [2] *Bell. Civ.* i, 59, 266–8.
[3] Appian, *Bell. Civ.* i, 73, 339.

time or inclination to pass them when he was urgently needed in the East.

The programme was brief. First, by a return to an arrangement of the kind which had prevailed in law until the passing of the Lex Hortensia in 287 B.C. (vol. VII, p. 553) and in normal practice to the time of Tiberius Gracchus, it was ordained that nothing should be brought before the People without the previous approval of the Senate. About the application of this law there can be no shadow of doubt: if it affected the tribunes at all, which is by no means certain, the remotest acquaintance with Sulla's attitude to the curule magistrates at the time of his dictatorship is enough to show that, as Appian implies, it affected consuls and praetors as well. After all, if Marius himself held office again, it would not be as tribune but as *consul VII*. Secondly, there was a law to the effect that all business[1] submitted to the People should be submitted to the People in their Centuries. The Comitia Centuriata, wherein wealth wielded its strongest influence, was to be the only active assembly of the Populus Romanus: the Comitia Populi Tributa was condemned to idleness, and the Concilium Plebis was apparently to do nothing but elect its tribunes.

Though Appian hints at other limitations to its power, the tribunate itself remained: Sulla had no need to risk the fearsome penalties of the *plebiscitum* passed by M. Duillius against those who left the Plebs without its champions (vol. VII, p. 481). But, if the view here maintained is right, the tribunes lost their initiative in legislation. Lacking, as they did, the *ius agendi cum populo*, they were debarred from submitting *rogationes* to the Comitia Centuriata, which was now to be the only legislative body. And so it may be said that by the first of Sulla's laws—the law which required that every project put before the People should receive preliminary approval from the Senate—not the tribunes, but the curule magistrates were to be brought under control. But to give the Senate a veto on legislation was futile unless that body was strong enough to defend its rights and to use them with effect. For this reason, and also because it was the Senate which, during Sulla's absence, would have to lead the resistance to Marius and his friends, it was essential that the Senate should be strong: and at this time it was weak. The censors now in office would at best recruit the House to its normal size of 300 or thereabouts; but this was not enough. Accordingly, the consuls took measures of their own—whether

---

[1] The word used by Appian is χειροτονίαι, and this has often been taken in its narrower sense of 'voting at elections.' More probably it means voting of whatever kind, as *e.g.* in *Bell. Civ.* I, 23, 99; 49, 214; 53, 231.

by passing a law or not we do not know—to authorize the addition
of 300 members more. Thereby the Senate would be raised to
twice its former size, and, by this infusion of new blood, its
strength could scarcely fail to be increased. The plan did credit to
the wisdom of its author, but it may be doubted whether it was
given effect. To select three hundred candidates for positions so
responsible as seats in the House was a task requiring time : it can
hardly have been more than begun when Sulla left Rome, and his
departure was the signal for a rapid recrudescence of the turmoil
in which the quiet work of ordinary administration was dropped
forthwith.   Probability is in favour of the view that the new
senators were never chosen, and this conclusion is confirmed by
the fact that Appian records another measure to the same effect
when Sulla had returned to Italy.

Such were the rough and ready methods whereby Sulla sought
to ensure the political supremacy of his friends during the period
of his own absence in the East. The scheme looked well enough on
paper—as good as any paper scheme could be. But what if some
second Sulla arose on the other side ? For all his care, the Senate
was as impotent when Marius marched an army to the gates of
Rome as it had been a few months before when Sulla himself had
seized the city. The legislation of 88 B.C. is evidence, perhaps, for
Sulla's political position, if evidence for that be needed; but it is
a trivial episode, and one which gives no clue to the greatness
which its author was to display when the dictatorship gave him
leisure to re-organize the State.

Though they were certainly the most important, it is unlikely
that these were the only laws passed by the consuls of 88. Festus[1]
preserves a fragmentary reference to a measure about debt—a
measure which perhaps limited the rate of interest to 12 per cent.
per annum—and the *Epitome* of Livy[2] records that colonies were
founded. The Epitomator is silent about their purpose; but it is
more likely that Sulla was looking forward to the time when the
soldiers now under arms would need settlement on the land than
that these places were intended for the newly-enfranchised Italians.
Speculation, however, is vain; and there is only one other point
which calls for notice. During the excitements of the year, the
citizens of Rome had raised one feeble protest against the new
military tyranny. At the elections for the magistracies of 87 B.C.
two candidates were rejected, of whom both had Sulla's special
favour and one was his own nephew. Of the consulships, one
indeed was safe in the hands of Cn. Octavius—a loyal Optimate

[1] p. 516 L.   [2] *Epit.* 77.

and possibly nephew of M. Octavius, the hero of 133 B.C.; but the other went to a man of very different complexion—L. Cornelius Cinna, who, though he had lately been serving as *legatus* to Metellus Pius, was known to have leanings towards the Marian side. Sulla took these rebuffs in sporting spirit, but he betrayed his fears of Cinna by forcing him to swear a mighty oath that he would preserve a friendly attitude towards Sulla and his cause. After this solemn farce[1], Sulla set out for his army and the East— the more readily, it was said, because his colleague Pompeius Rufus had suddenly been murdered. Rufus had been appointed to succeed Pompeius Strabo as commander of the forces in Picenum; but the change was resented by the men, and, with a licence which was soon to be familiar, they had killed their new general in order to keep the old. Such was the devotion of the armies to their leaders. It was a devotion which recked little of duty to the State; but it had its value for the favoured few. The legions of Sulla had already shown that in their keeping he was safe: so to them he went. Cinna was left to do his worst: almost before Sulla's back was turned he sped the consul's going with a threat of prosecution.

---

[1] For Cinna's view of the oath see Sallust, *Hist.* I, 26 M.—'nihil esse de re publica neque libertate populi Romani pactum.'

CHAPTER V

PONTUS AND ITS NEIGHBOURS: THE FIRST MITHRIDATIC WAR

I. THE COUNTRY. SOCIAL AND ECONOMIC CONDITIONS

ASIA Minor is divided by nature and has been divided by history into two parts. There is the western seaboard which, with its mild climate, its fair and rich river-valleys and excellent harbours, looking towards the open Aegean whence came the civilizing influences of Hellenism, may fittingly be called Anatolian Greece. In contrast with this, there is the eastern interior, which has for its home waters the landlocked Black Sea, once an Iranian, Scytho-Persian lake, and which looked to the East and lived the life of the neighbouring Oriental monarchies[1]. Of this part (which also included Armenia, Commagene, Galatia, Lycaonia and a part of Phrygia) Pontus or Pontic Cappadocia, the nucleus of the Mithridatic empire, and Great or Tauric Cappadocia form the western sector. These Cappadocian lands were once the centre of the eastward-looking Hittite empire; then, after that empire broke up, there came anarchy, until in due course they became part of the Phrygian empire and later a satrapy of Persia. Even after Alexander, these Eastern-Anatolian fragments of the Persian empire remained closely connected with the East, with the Seleucid empire and also with that of Parthia, and absorbed very little Greek life and civilization.

Cappadocian Pontus, including the mountains of the Paryadres and Paphlagonia, occupies a peculiar position among the lands of Eastern Asia Minor. Though closely connected with the rest and showing the same general geographical features, the northern part of Cappadocia, the mountainous land along the southern shore of the Black Sea and the regions north and west of the deep channel of the 'red' or 'salt' river Halys, is more diversified climatically, more varied but with less violent contrasts than the adjoining Cappadocian plateau, of which the northernmost section was also regarded as belonging to Pontus. The mountain ranges which branch off the Caucasus and run west parallel to the southern shore of the Black Sea are intersected by rivers which work their

[1] On these connections see R. Dussaud, *La Lydie et ses voisins aux Hautes Epoques*.

way painfully through the mountains towards the sea. Short and swift in the east they become longer and less torrential the more we advance towards the west. Three of them—the Thermodon, the famous river of the Amazons, the Iris and the Halys—form in their lower courses wide fertile deltas which are the only points in the Pontus where the mountains recede from the shore and where the coast affords safe harbourage from the storms and winds of the inhospitable sea (Pontus Axeinos).

Behind the coast the country is a sequence of river-valleys, wide or narrow, of broad lakes, of gentle hills, of high mountains with green slopes, often covered with groves of trees, including wild fruit-trees, and rising to bare rocks and peaks. The climate in these mountains and by the shore is much milder than that of the Cappadocian table-land, so hot in summer and so bitterly cold in winter, and the soil is much more fertile. Pontus had the reputation of being a rich land: cattle, sheep and horses, crops and fruits, especially grapes and olives and the famous Pontic nuts and cherries—a name said to be derived from Cerasus, a Greek city on the coast—and an amazing profusion of flowers and aromatic shrubs are enumerated as characteristic products.

Still more important was the fact that the eastern part of Pontus was very rich in metals: first and foremost iron, but also copper and silver. It was the mining district *par excellence* of the ancient Near East including Egypt; and the almost unanimous tradition of the ancient world ascribed the 'invention' of iron and steel to the clever smiths of the Chalybes. It was this wealth in metals which, above all, governed the historical destinies of Pontus. For hundreds of years caravans had carried its metals to Assyria, Babylonia, Syria, Phoenicia and Palestine, and even to the shores of the Sea of Marmara and of the Dardanelles and to the western coast of Asia Minor. It was, however, not long before the Greeks realized to the full the advantage of using the Black Sea for the export of metals into their home countries. It was the beginning of Greek colonization of its southern shores. Sinope and Trapezus, the first a clearing-house for commerce in metals, the second the harbour of the mining districts, were the earliest foundations in this region, and they kept this trade in their hands for centuries. Next was settled Amisus, the Athenian Piraeus of the Black Sea, a rival of Sinope for the trade with the Crimea and the South Russian Greek settlements, and, last of all, Heraclea and the towns which later combined to form the city of Amastris much farther to the west on the Bithynian coast, communities which set themselves to compete with Amisus and Sinope alike.

With the Greek cities came Hellenic life and culture. Were it not for the comparatively detailed descriptions of Strabo we should know little about them before the Roman period, for no one of these cities has been excavated, nor have they been often visited and studied by modern archaeologists. But we may fairly deduce that they resembled other Black Sea colonies, and we can be certain that their presence made the life of the coast Greek. Yet for a long time the hellenized coast remained the fringe of a land that was alien and designed by nature to remain so. From time immemorial the land of Pontus has turned its back to the sea. The mountains rarely slope gently down to the coast, and most of the rivers are either not navigable at all or for a short stretch only of their course. The hellenization of the coast had no significance for the economic development of Pontus as a whole; it was, indeed, dictated by considerations that had almost nothing to do with Pontus, except for the minerals produced in one remote corner of it. Thus the prosperity of these Greek cities is not the index of the prosperity of the hinterland and was not dependent upon it. As the inland valleys and mountains of Pontus meant little or nothing to these Greek cities, so these cities did little or nothing to influence the culture of Pontus.

Thus even after the Greek colonization of the coast, the political, social and economic structure of the interior remained almost exactly what it had been in the Hittite period. It was of the same Anatolian character as that which is plainly to be detected in Seleucid Asia Minor and Pergamum (see vol. VII, p. 176; vol. VIII, chap. XIX). But nowhere else in Asia Minor was it so well preserved in Hellenistic and early Roman times, and for no other region (except Commagene) have we so full and trustworthy a description of it as we have for Pontus and Cappadocia. For Pontus was the native land of Strabo, and his exceptionally detailed account of it affords evidence which is here in place, since this structure was the backbone of Pontic strength in the period of the Great Mithridates.

It was in Cappadocia proper that this order of things existed in its purest form. The land was ruled by kings and subdivided into ten districts or *strategiai* each with its own governor. Two governorships alone—Tyana and Cilicia—had urban centres. The capital of Cilicia—Mazaca or Eusebeia (in the Hellenistic period) —was the national metropolis, the fortified residence (like a military camp) of the king. No cities existed in the rest of Cappadocia[1]. Most of the people lived in villages, or in what Strabo

---

[1] Strabo XII, 537.

calls *komopoleis* or *polichnia*. Even more characteristic were the strongholds mostly built high up on hills and mountains. Some of them were held for the kings and gave security to the royal possessions and slaves and serfs, while others rendered the same services to the friends of the king or the leaders (*hegemones*), feudal barons of the country.

Another typical feature of Cappadocia were the temples. Four leading temples are described with great detail by Strabo; the temple of Ma at Comana, of the Cataonian Apollo, of Zeus Venasios, and of Artemis Perasia. Another temple of Zeus near the mount Ariadne is mentioned by Diodorus (xxxi, 34) as rich and important enough to be pillaged by Orophernes in 158 B.C. (vol. VIII, p. 522). Some of the temples, such as that of Apollo, had daughter foundations scattered over the countryside. All had the same character. The fullest description is given by Strabo where he speaks of the temple of Ma at Comana. 'In this Antitaurus,' he says (XII, 535), 'there are deep and narrow valleys, in which are situated Comana and the temple of Enyo, whom the people there call "Ma." It is a considerable city; its inhabitants, however, consist mostly of the divinely-inspired people and the temple-slaves who live in it. Its inhabitants are Cataonians, who, though subjects of the king, in most matters obey the priest. The priest is master of the temple, and also of the temple-slaves, who on my sojourn there were more than six thousand in number, men and women together. Also, considerable land belongs to the temple, and the revenue is enjoyed by the priest. He is second in rank in Cappadocia after the king; and in general the priests belonged to the same family as the kings.'

The social and economic structure of the Pontic region[1] was, apart from some modifications which will be mentioned later (p. 223), almost exactly the same as that of Cappadocia. The king's residences were scattered all over the country. The capital city of the Mithridatid dynasty was Amasia, whose citadel was held by a garrison under the command of a military governor (*phrourarchos*)[2]. No man was allowed to enter the citadel without a special permission of the *phrourarchos*[3], who often was an eunuch[4]. In the citadel were the palace of the kings and a large altar, dedicated no doubt to the divine protector of the dynasty—the Iranian Ahuramazda, slightly hellenized under the name of Zeus Stratios. Rockcut tombs beneath the citadel contained the mortal remains

---

[1] Strabo XII, 540 *sqq.*   [2] *O.G.I.S.* 365; *Studia Pontica*, III, no. 94.
[3] *Studia Pontica, ib.* no. 278.
[4] Ammianus Marcellinus, XVI, 7, 9; cf. Plutarch, *Demosthenes*, 25.

of the first four Mithridatidae. The rulers who preceded them had dwelt elsewhere, as in the strongholds of Gaziura and Cabeira[1].

Like Cappadocia, Pontus was subdivided into districts or provinces called eparchies as in Parthia, probably with *strategoi* as governors[2]. As in Cappadocia, fortified strongholds both of the kings and of the nobles were scattered all over the country. Strabo mentions the *Kainon Chorion*, Ikizari (or Kizari), Sagylion, Kamisa, Pimolisa and Kimiata. The owners of these castles, the feudal barons, were most of them of Iranian origin; one of them known from a Greek inscription is called Pharnabazus, while his vassal bears a Greek or hellenized name—Meriones[3]. No cities existed in Pontus except the Greek cities of the coast. Those which are mentioned in our sources as Greek cities, not as native quasi-cities, were created by the Mithridatid dynasty and will be dealt with later. The typical form of settlement was the village. The rich plain near Amasia had the name of Chiliokomon (thousand villages) and we are told that Murena overran in one raid four hundred villages (p. 353).

Temples of exactly the same character as those of Cappadocia play a great part in the life of the country. It is interesting to note that though these were dedicated to gods of various origin (the Cappadocian Ma, the Anatolian Men Pharnaku, the Iranian Anaitis with her two acolytes, and the hellenized Zeus Stratios), they all were organized in the Oriental fashion with a chief priest, with a large number of sacred slaves or serfs of both sexes, some of the women slaves being temple-prostitutes, and with vast stretches of land from which the income went into the treasury of the temple or the chief priest. Near the large *komopolis* of Ameria was situated the temple of Men, a god important enough to play the leading rôle alongside the Tyche of the king in his royal oath. The temple at the large village of Comana in Pontus was the counterpart of that in Cappadocia. Comana itself was the chief emporium for commerce with Armenia, and the temple, with its 6000 sacred serfs, and the town were noted for their luxury and

---

[1] Strabo XII, 547, 556.

[2] Cf. the inscription *Studia Pontica*, III, no. 66, l. 37, and Th. Reinach, *ib.* p. 85. The inscription mentions ὑπαρχίαι in Paphlagonia, and Reinach, contrary to his former opinion, was inclined in 1910 to correct the ἐπαρχίας of Strabo XII, 560 (on which the statement in the text is based) into ὑπαρχίας. The present writer sees no reason for such a correction. The Pontic ἐπαρχίαι were probably subdivided into ὑπαρχίαι. On Parthia, see M. I. Rostovtzeff and C. B. Welles, *A Parchment Contract of loan from Dura-Europus*, Yale Classical Studies, II, 1930, p. 49.

[3] *Studia Pontica, ib.* no. 95 a.

dissipated life, a paradise for soldiers and for merchants. No less famous was the temple of Anaitis near Zela. The excavation of one or more of the Pontic or Cappadocian temples, which has hitherto not been attempted, would throw a much needed light on the organization and culture of these great centres of Anatolian life. Of the variety of races which lived together, the various cults which met in the Pontus are eloquent and our sources speak of twenty-two languages spoken in the region, a fact which indeed is not surprising in view of the many languages which were in use during the Hittite period.

Such in short was the land which was organized into a solid state by the efforts of the dynasty of the Mithridatidae of which the greatest representative was Mithridates VI Eupator, who at last, in 89 B.C., ventured to challenge the power of Rome.

II. THE MITHRIDATID DYNASTY

It is beyond doubt that the dynasty of the Mithridatidae, which ruled in Pontus from at least 302 B.C. until the last offspring of it, Darius, son of Pharnaces II, was removed from the throne, belonged to the highest Persian nobility (their claim to be descendants of the Persian king has, of course, no foundation), to a family which was connected with Asia Minor for many generations. The identity of the earliest two representatives of the family, Mithridates and Ariobarzanes, is still a matter of controversy. It seems, however, more or less certain that the Mithridates whose end was reported by the historian Hieronymus[1] was one of the lesser city-dynasts of Asia Minor of the late Persian and early Hellenistic period. His city was Cius on the Propontis. Whatever his early history may have been, in the closing years of the fourth century, when he was more than eighty years of age, he supported Antigonus and planned to betray him. Whether he was at that time with Antigonus or in his own city of Cius while his son, also named Mithridates, was with Antigonus, or whether both of them were in Antigonus' camp we do not know. So much is certain, that the king became suspicious and decided to get rid of his former allies, both father and son. Warning was given of it to the younger Mithridates by his friend, the prince Demetrius, who

[1] Of the birth of the Pontic kingdom there existed in ancient historical literature a complete and reliable account, that of Hieronymus of Cardia. His statements, however, in the hands of later writers, became hopelessly confused, and as a result we are still trying to find the way of restoring the account of Hieronymus in its original version.

was almost of the same age, and Mithridates fled, perhaps together with his father, who was soon killed either on his flight in
Paphlagonia, or near his own city.

In the turmoil of the events after Ipsus Mithridates the younger,
who established his residence in Paphlagonian Kimiata, one of the
Pontic strongholds, gradually succeeded in building up for himself a kingdom which he successfully defended against Seleucus I.
Whether, however, he or his father is to be regarded as the founder
(*ktistes*) of the kingdom and dynasty is a matter of controversy.
Almost all modern scholars are inclined to give the credit to the
younger Mithridates, but this opinion must be revised in the light
of an inscription which, though several times published, has not
been taken into account by recent historians of the Pontic kingdom[1].

The problem is closely connected with the question of the
Pontic Era. It is known that Mithridates the Great used an era
which started with the year 297 b.c., the first year of the Bithynian Era[2]. This era was still in use in the Bosporan kingdom in
imperial times, and we have a synchronism which admits of no
doubt as regards its starting-point. The same era was apparently
used by Eupator's predecessor and father Mithridates Euergetes, as is shown by an inscription found at Ineboli (Abonuteichos) and dated by the king Euergetes and the year 161 of an
unknown era[3]. If this era be the Bithynian and Pontic Era, the
inscription belongs to the year 137/6 b.c. If we assume the
Seleucid Era, the adoption of which by the Mithridatidae is perhaps less difficult to explain than the adoption of the Bithynian
Era, then the date corresponds to 151 b.c., a date which fits equally
well, since Euergetes was no doubt ruling as early as 149.

The era of Euergetes may then be either the Bithynian or the
Seleucid. But, twenty years ago, the important inscription mentioned above was found in the ruins of Chersonesus in the Crimea
(see further below, p. 221). It contains the oaths taken by the city
of Chersonesus and a king Pharnaces of Pontus and is dated as in

[1] The inscription from Chersonesus, first published and discussed by R. Chr.
Loeper, *Bull. de la Comm. Arch.*, xlv, 1912, pp. 23 *sqq.*; cf. E. H. Minns,
Scythians and Greeks, p. 646, no. 172 (cf. p. 518 and p. 590, n. 1); *Ios. P.E.*
I², 402.
[2] Loeper, *Bull. de l'Inst. Arch. Russe de Constantinople*, viii, 1903,
pp. 159 *sqq.* (in Russian), is of the opinion that both the Bithynian and the
Pontic Era started with the same year, because the rulers of both realms
assumed the royal title in this year, a little later than the other Hellenistic kings.
[3] Loeper, *ib.* viii, 1902, pp. 153 *sqq.*; Th. Reinach, *Num. Chron.* v,
1905, pp. 113 *sqq.*

the year 157 of the era of Pharnaces. This era cannot be the same as that used by Eupator, for if it is the Bithynian, it gives the date 140 B.C., when Pharnaces I was long dead and buried, and Pharnaces II was not yet born; and if it is the Seleucid, it gives the date 155, which is also too late for Pharnaces I, since his brother and successor Mithridates Philopator Philadelphus was ruling in 156[1]. The era of Pharnaces must then have some other starting-point, which may be discovered. A treaty between Chersonesus and Pharnaces is most intelligible if it followed closely upon the war which raged from c. 183 to 179 B.C. between Pharnaces and a coalition of Anatolian states. In the peace which ended the war Chersonesus was included, and it seems logical to connect the treaty of the inscription with the peace-treaty, and to place it about the year 179. If that is so, then the era used by Pharnaces will begin in 336 B.C., which is precisely the year in which, according to Diodorus, the elder Mithridates began to rule in Cius. From this it follows that Pharnaces used an era which went back to the rule of the elder Mithridates and thus treated him as the founder of the dynasty[2]. Why Mithridates Euergetes changed to the Seleucid or the Bithynian Era and why Eupator used only the Bithynian we cannot tell. If then we place the ruler of Cius at the head of the dynasty as Mithridates I, it becomes possible to avoid the expedient of inserting a hypothetical Mithridates into the list of the kings in order to make Eupator what our sources declare him to have been, the sixth Mithridates and the eighth king of Pontus[3]. It also becomes possible to explain the number of royal graves at Amasia, the capital of the early kings. There are four of these and a fifth still unfinished. It was Pharnaces I who moved to Sinope and probably was buried there so that the unfinished fifth tomb may well be his; and if so the other four just suffice for the elder and younger Mithridates, Ariobarzanes and Mithridates the father of Pharnaces[4].

We may then assign to the younger Mithridates the credit, not of founding the dynasty, but of building up the power of Pontus. His endeavours, as those of his immediate successors, were directed towards the same goal as those of his neighbours of Bithynia,

---

[1] Polybius XXXIII, 12. This argument holds good unless we assume not only that Pharnaces and Mithridates Philopator ruled together, but that Polybius omitted the name of Pharnaces and that Philopator enjoyed only a very short reign after the brother's death.

[2] This was first suggested by Loeper.

[3] Appian, *Mithr.* 9 and 112; Plutarch, *Demosthenes*, 4.

[4] See the list of Pontic kings at the end of the volume.

Pergamum and Cappadocia. Amid the political chaos of the times they sought to extend their borders and, above all, to include within them as many Greek cities as possible. From time to time in the course of these endeavours the Pontic kings emerge for a moment into the light of history, and it is possible to detect some of the stages in the growth of the monarchy from its beginning to the accession of Mithridates VI.

It is not known when they succeeded in adding to their kingdom the city of Amisus and its rich territory inhabited by people who in Roman times were reputed excellent agriculturists[1]. In about 255 B.C.[2] Amisus was certainly dependent on Mithridates III, since the city supplied the king and his army with grain sent through Heraclea at the time of a Gallic invasion. Since, however, the Pontic kings never thought of making the city their capital, it seems that Amisus retained a good deal of its autonomy and probably was, at least in theory, an allied not a subject city. It is equally unknown when the Pontic kings, while leaving alone for the moment the territory of Sinope, first reached the coast to the west of that city. Since Amastris was given to Ariobarzanes, the son and co-ruler of Mithridates II, by Eumenes its dynast as early as 279[3], the cities to the east of Amastris were no doubt reduced to obedience still earlier (we know that Abonuteichos was Pontic in 137/6 or 151/0 B.C.). Thus from 279 onwards the river Parthenius marked the frontier of Pontus to the west. How far the first four Mithridatid kings extended their power to the east and south we do not know. Armenia Minor was probably a vassal state, and Pontus had control of the rich mining districts of the Chalybes, perhaps even before the conquest of Pharnaces I. It was under the first four kings that a close connection was established between their dynasty and the Seleucids, when Mithridates III married Laodice, sister of Seleucus II and daughter of Antiochus II, and gave his own daughter Laodice to Antiochus III.

A new epoch begins with the reign of Pharnaces I, the ambitious and talented son of Mithridates III. He appears on the horizon for the first time in 183 B.C., when he was trying, after the downfall of the great Seleucid monarchy, to enlarge his kingdom at the expense of his neighbours, the Pergamenes and the Bithynians. In the main the attempt was abortive. However, Pharnaces I succeeded in taking and keeping Sinope and its territory, thus making good the failure of his predecessor in 220 B.C., when the city received the efficient help of Rhodes (vol. VIII, p. 625). It

---

[1] F. and E. Cumont, *Studia Pontica*, II, p. 126.
[2] Memnon, 24.   [3] Memnon, 16.

was at Sinope that from 183 onwards was established the main residence of the kings, an event eloquent of the claim of Pontus to belong to the family of completely hellenized monarchies.

In the great war which began with the taking of Sinope Pharnaces aimed at creating a kind of empire such as was later achieved by his grandson Eupator. It is surprising to find mentioned in the treaty which ended the war[1], alongside the important monarchies and cities, the relatively insignificant town of Chersonesus and Gatalus, the Sarmatian, apparently its ally. We have seen, too, that this inclusion of Chersonese in the treaty was probably closely followed by a special treaty between Pharnaces and Chersonesus. These two facts and the interest which Rome took in Chersonesus can only be explained by assuming that Pharnaces sought to extend his empire into the Crimea and to seize Chersonesus as his starting-point. This attempt explains the general character of the treaty, which aims chiefly at denying to Pharnaces the right to encroach on the liberty and democracy of Chersonesus; it also helps us to understand the fact that both Heraclea (together with Mesembria and Cyzicus) and a Sarmatian king, no doubt allies of Chersonesus, took part in the war. Gatalus, the Sarmatian, was probably used as a check upon the Scythians, allies of Pharnaces[2], whereas Heraclea, Cyzicus and Mesembria were anxious to maintain freedom of trade in the Black Sea. The failure of Pharnaces was also attested by his retrocession of Tieum or Tius, the neighbour of Amastris, which he had succeeded in conquering during the war, a conquest which probably gave Heraclea additional cause to take an active part in the war. For a while, no doubt, the progress of Pontus was stopped, though it is very probable that, either in the same war or perhaps later, Pharnaces succeeded in extending his territory on the sea coast towards the east, where he annexed the colonies of Sinope, Cerasus and Cotyora, and transported their populations to a new city named after himself Pharnaceia. In the second half of his reign, however, the king was still feeling the results of his failure. An Athenian decree set up at Delos[3] shows that in 172/1 or 160/59 he was still suffering under a serious financial strain and found it difficult to meet his previous obligations towards Athens.

---

[1] Polybius xxv, 2.
[2] They are not mentioned in the treaty, but compare the story of Amage the Sarmatian in Polyaenus VIII, 56.
[3] *I.G.* XI, 4, 1056; *O.G.I.S.* 771; Durrbach, *Choix*, 73; A. Wilhelm, *Jahreshefte*, XXIV, 1929, pp. 174 *sqq.*; R. Laqueur, *Epigr. Unters. z. d. griech. Volksbeschlüssen*, pp. 55 *sqq.*

The reason was probably the heavy cost of the war and of the war-indemnities which the treaty forced him to pay. And yet he was not discouraged, and worked hard to counteract the progress of Rome, if that is the explanation of his marriage late in life with Nysa, the daughter or grand-daughter of Antiochus III, a marriage which is attested by the same decree.

The date of his death is unknown. The current view is that he died about 170/69, when Polybius gives a short characterization of him. But it is far from certain that similar general remarks of Polybius are obituary notices, and it is not impossible that he lived longer[1]. In his policy, perhaps during the second part of his reign, he was assisted by his brother, who became his successor and, presumably after his death, married their common sister Laodice. We have beautiful coins[2] of both Pharnaces and his brother and successor Mithridates Philopator Philadelphus and his sister-wife Laodice, while the coins of two kings named Mithridates, which, no doubt, are earlier than those of Pharnaces, may be assigned to Mithridates II and Mithridates III[3]. A Delian inscription[4], indeed, suggests that Philopator like Ariobarzanes before him ruled together with his brother, and the same inscription suggests further that Laodice, their sister, had a share in this joint rule. This fact makes it the more difficult to find out the exact date of the death of Pharnaces. The fact, however, that Philopator made a dedication in Rome probably soon after 168/7[5], and that he alone is mentioned as helping Attalus against Prusias in 156 B.C. makes it probable that Pharnaces died not very long after 172/1 B.C., one of the two possible dates of his marriage with Nysa[6].

Philopator, who ruled on behalf of Euergetes the young son of Pharnaces and Nysa, was probably dead before 149 B.C., for in this year Euergetes helped the Romans against Carthage. Later, in 133 B.C., Euergetes appears again assisting the Romans, this time against Aristonicus (p. 105). As has already been mentioned he appears in an inscription belonging to 137/6 B.C. or to 151/0 (p. 217)[7].

The most important event in the reign of Euergetes was his

---

[1] If we date the inscription of Delos quoted above in 160/59 instead of 172/1.   [2] See volume of Plates iv, 2, *m, n, o*.   [3] *Ib.* 2, *k, l.*
[4] Durrbach, *Choix*, no. 74; cf. the text of the treaty of 179 (where Pharnaces is associated with Mithridates), Polybius xxv, 2.
[5] Dessau 30, cf. 31; *O.G.I.S.* 375, cf. *ib.* 551.
[6] The other, later, date 160/59 seems therefore improbable.
[7] It is worth mentioning that before the discovery of the inscription and of the coins of Philopator some scholars were inclined to identify Philopator and Euergetes.

participation in the war against Aristonicus and what happened
after the end of this war. He and Nicomedes king of Bithynia
were rivals for the possession of Phrygia (p. 106), and an inscription found near Synnada[1] shows that he was successful in his
endeavours and ruled over Phrygia until the end of his life. This
suggests that he had both Paphlagonia and Galatia under his
control. He was equally successful in occupying Cappadocia
and placing on its throne a king who was practically his vassal
(Ariarathes Epiphanes, who married the daughter of Euergetes)
and in adding to his kingdom the part of Paphlagonia which was
still ruled by its own kings. The last of them, Pylaemenes, bequeathed his kingdom to Euergetes. Euergetes was married to a
queen whose name is not known to us, but who was probably a
princess of the Seleucid house[2].

Scanty as is the information which we possess on the first
Mithridatidae we can recognize the general lines of their policy.
Their chief aim was to consolidate and to increase their kingdom,
and to this end they used all the available means, no more disturbed about their moral or immoral character than all their
crowned and uncrowned contemporaries. One of these means was
the use of the resources which Greek civilization offered them.
This, along with the increased income which could be derived
from the Greek cities, made them strive first and foremost to incorporate their Greek neighbours in their kingdom. What they
needed from them was their help in organizing an efficient army
and navy, in improving the organization of their revenues and in
assisting them to acquire a good reputation in the eyes of the
Greek world, for which they cared very much indeed.

How far they intended to hellenize the non-Greek parts of
their kingdom it is very difficult to say. No doubt they had not the
slightest desire to force urban life upon Pontus as a whole. Only
one city designated by a dynastic name and at all comparable
with those which were created in scores by the Seleucids was
created by the predecessors of Eupator. It was Laodicea, known
to us only from coins and from the survival of the name (modern
Ladik)[3]. The synoecism of Cerasus and Cotyora and the creation
of Pharnaceia by Pharnaces I have nothing to do either with
urbanization or with hellenization.

---

[1] *O.G.I.S.* 436=*I.G.R.R.* iv, 752.
[2] Her identification with the Laodice of a silver tetradrachm is very
problematic.
[3] Volume of Plates, iv, 4, *j*. Compare the similar coins of Amastris and
Amisus, *ib.* iv, *k, l.*

So long as no one of these Greek cities has been excavated, we have no means of knowing how the Pontic kings treated the few cities which they incorporated in their realm. *A priori* it is probable that Amisus, Amastris and the other cities which were annexed before Pharnaces I enjoyed a larger amount of autonomy than Sinope, the capital of the later Mithridatidae, and the new creations Pharnaceia and Laodicea. On the other hand Pharnaceia as well as Amastris was allowed to mint copper earlier than the reign of Eupator[1].

Thus from the Greek point of view, Pontus after two centuries of the rule of the Mithridatid dynasty remained a country of villages and temples not of cities. This does not mean, however, that more or less hellenized urban centres did not develop there. The capital of Pontus before Pharnaces I and the home of Strabo, Amasia, had no doubt a large Greek population. The same is probably true of so important a market and caravan city as Comana. By intermarriage and social intercourse the Greeks must have done much to hellenize the native aristocracy. The best instance of it are the kings themselves, who were proud of their close family connection with the Seleucids and who, all of them, spoke and wrote Greek and showed a great appreciation of Greek literature and art. The same is true of the nobles with native names who were sent out as ambassadors, for example, to Rome. And yet the kingdom never became really hellenized. Until the end of its independent existence it remained as it used to be before the founding of the dynasty. Proud as they were of their Greek training, the Mithridatid kings, especially Pharnaces I and his successors, were still more proud of their Iranian connections. They claimed to be descendants of the Persian kings, and they remained devoted to their native gods, especially to those who, like themselves, were of Iranian origin.

If we look at the coins of the Mithridatid kings we notice one interesting phenomenon. The rare coins of the predecessors of Pharnaces I are almost exact reproductions of the coins of Alexander and of those of the early Seleucids, Greek through and through[2]. With Pharnaces, however, the reverse types of the coins become more individual and Iranian. Pharnaces I indulges in a certain mystic syncretism, which was in the air in this period (see

---

[1] In the inscription of Abonuteichos mentioned above the city retains her *phratries*. The *strategos* in whose honour the inscription was dedicated may be a general of Euergetes or the chief magistrate and governor of the city appointed by the king. The same was the practice of the Pergamene kings (vol. VIII, p. 601).   [2] Volume of Plates. iv, 2, *k, l*.

vol. VII, p. 5 *sq.*). His god, the mysterious youthful god of his coins[1], was a beautiful youth wearing a *bashlyk*, holding the attributes of Hermes and those of Tyche and feeding a little stag with a branch of ivy or vine. This young god is no doubt related to Zeus: over his head there appears the thunderbolt. At the same time he belongs to the gods of the astral religion as shown by the crescent and star which from this time on become the main symbol or coat of arms of the dynasty. The god has been explained recently[2] as the Graeco-Oriental Aion, the divine son of Zeus who symbolizes the *Saeculum frugiferum*, the same mystic being, perhaps, as the similar figure on Roman coins and the divine child of the Fourth Eclogue of Virgil. However this may be, the god of Pharnaces is more Iranian than Greek (in this like the god of the kings of Commagene—Apollo-Helios-Hermes-Mithras), though it was a Greek artist who fashioned the cult-statue figured on the coins. Zeus, his father, is no doubt Ahura-mazda rather than Zeus, and his essence is nearer to the essence of Mithras and *Hvareno* (the kingly glory) than to that of Hermes and Tyche. We find the same Greek travesties of Iranian political and religious ideas on the coins of Pharnaces' successors: Perseus, the mythical ancestor of the Persians, appears on the coins of Philopator, and his horse Pegasus on those of Eupator[3]. No doubt we must regard the Dionysus of Eupator as an Anatolian not as a Greek god, a symbol, like the Ephesian stag, of his Anatolian empire.

It is worthy of note that nothing in the coins reveals any influence of Iranian art; they were made by Greeks in the purest Greek style. The portraits of the kings before Eupator are wonderful in their brutal realism[4]. We see before us the astute and cruel rulers of Pontus in all their original ugliness. Eupator dropped this style and preferred to appear as a new Alexander the Great with his hair floating romantically around his head[5]. While the portraits of the coins are real productions of a great art, Greek in their very essence, most of the reverse types of the coins, equally Greek, are trivial and of no artistic importance.

It seems that the Hellenistic period interrupted an evolution which started in North Asia Minor in the fifth and fourth centuries B.C. This period produced interesting monuments in a peculiar style which we call Graeco-Persian. To this style belong

[1] Volume of Plates, iv, 2, *m*.
[2] A. Alföldi in *Hermes*, LXV, 1930, p. 378.
[3] Volume of Plates, iv, 2, *n*; 4, *c*.   [4] *Ib.* 2, *l, m, n*.
[5] Cf. F. Winter, *J.D.A.I.* IX, 1894, pp. 245 *sqq.*

many objects found in the Bosporan kingdom[1], the front of the rock-grave of Kalekapu in Paphlagonia[2], the beautiful Perso-Ionian silver vases, one said to have been found in Armenia (one part is now in the Louvre, the other in the Berlin Museum)[3], another found in a fifth-century grave at Duvanli in Bulgaria[4], and, finally, the interesting Graeco-Persian gems[5]. On the other hand the Hellenistic period has not yielded anything similar to it, any object of art which would be an attempt at a synthesis of the Greek and Iranian artistic creative power. The attempt to create a new version of Graeco-Persian art came later, simultaneously in India, Parthia, Mesopotamia and even Commagene, at a time when Pontus had played its part in world history to a close[6].

Thus the Iranian and the Greek elements in Pontus were never fused in Hellenistic times into one unit: they lived on quietly side by side. Each had its special part in the policy of the Pontic kings. The same phenomenon may be noticed in the life of the Parthian Empire in the Hellenistic period (p. 595).

The leading political idea of Eupator, the creation of a Pontic Graeco-native empire including large parts of Asia Minor, was not first devised by Eupator. No doubt Pharnaces I had the same ideals, which he transmitted to his brother, his son and his grandson. This Pontic empire was not a national State like the Parthian empire: it was an unification of all the Pontic Greeks around one dynasty which was supported by the strength and cohesion of their Oriental subjects. It was an empire with a Greek sea-front and an Oriental hinterland.

III. THE CONQUEST OF THE BLACK SEA COAST

An end was put to the brilliant achievements of Euergetes by a court tragedy. He was assassinated by his friends, and a last will and testament (probably forged) appointed his wife to rule in the name of her two sons Mithridates Eupator, who was at that time (121/0 B.C.) eleven years old, and Mithridates Chrestos. It is very probable that Mithridates' mother helped in the assassination of

[1] See, for examples, volume of Plates iii, 84, d. (cf. the sword sheath recently acquired by the Metropolitan Museum of New York, *Bull. Metrop. Museum*, 1931, pp. 44 *sqq.*), 90, 92, b, c, 104.

[2] Best reproduced by R. Leonhard, *Paphlagonia*, pp. 246 *sqq.*

[3] Volume of Plates i, 324, d.   [4] *Ib.* iii, 62, e.

[5] M. Maximowa, *J.D.A.I.* XLIII, 1928, *Arch. Anz.*, pp. 648 *sqq.*; A. S. F. Gow, *J.H.S.* XLVIII, 1928, pp. 133 *sqq.*, pls. IX, X; A. Procopé-Walter, *Syria*, x, 1929, pp. 85 *sqq.*

[6] To this period belongs also the creation of the cult-image of the Roman Mithraea—Mithra Tauroktonos.

her husband in order to become the ruler of the kingdom. The murder of Euergetes was welcome to Rome, for he had begun to be too strong and therefore dangerous to the Romans. After his death, under one pretext or another they reduced Pontus to the size which it had before the time of Aristonicus and the successes of Euergetes in Cappadocia and Paphlagonia (p. 106)[1].

There gathered a staff of historians at the court of Eupator who certainly used all devices of late Hellenistic historiography to make the story of their patron a thrilling and romantic one. How much truth there is in their stories of the various plots and conspiracies against the life of Mithridates in his early youth and of his solitary life in the mountains for seven years cannot be found out. But sometime before 115 B.C.[2] a new *coup d'État* ended the rule of Mithridates' mother, and that ambitious woman spent the rest of her life in prison. The two boys were left alone to rule over the kingdom, until Chrestos was removed by his older brother.

The spirited young king suffered the humiliation of receiving from his mother a kingdom considerably reduced in size. On the other hand, the great programme of Pharnaces I and the achievements of Euergetes were there to spur his activity. The political situation was not unfavourable for ambitious plans. There was, it is true, a governor in the recently created province of Asia. But the Senate, being at this time without imperialistic aims and fully occupied with the tribunate of C. Gracchus, the Jugurthine War and the growing danger of invasion from the North, left Asia Minor to disorder and confusion.

We know very little of the chronology of the early wars of Mithridates. His great conquest of the south-eastern and northern shores of the Black Sea cannot be dated with any approach

---

[1] An inscription of 155 B.C. recently found at Cyrene and published by G. Oliverio (*La Stele di Tolemeo Neoteros re di Cirene* in *Documenti Ant. dell' Africa italiana* Vol. I. fasc. 1, 1932), containing the will in the form of 'donatio mortis causa' of Ptolemy the Younger (later Euergetes II), then King of Cyrene and claimant to Cyprus, in favour of the Romans, shows, if compared with the later similar acts of Attalus III, Nicomedes III and Ptolemy Apion of Cyrene, that the testaments of client kings were for a while a device in the foreign policy of the ruling party in the Roman Senate, a kind of disguised imperialism. It is very probable that the Romans expected Euergetes of Pontus to behave in the same way. In this they were mistaken. Euergetes was recalcitrant, and paid for it with his life.

[2] The date is fixed by the inscription of Delos (*O.G.I.S.* 369; Durrbach, *Choix*, 113) in honour of the king and his brother. Cf. *O.G.I.S.* 368; Durrbach, *Choix*, 114. The inscription is dated by the name of the dedicant. It is probable that the dedications were made after Mithridates' official accession, and, if so, the seven years in the mountains must be considerably reduced.

to precision. All that is certain is that it preceded the first war with Rome and probably began before the king's earliest activity within Asia Minor. The extant notices of these wars are scanty indeed. Had we not an inscription in honour of the Pontic general Diophantus[1], we should not be able to reconstruct from the scattered remarks of Strabo any connected history of even one part of the Crimean wars of Mithridates.

The history of the Bosporan Kingdom in the third and second centuries has been described in the preceding volume (chap. xviii). The new factor in the situation of the Greeks in the Bosporus, in Chersonesus and its territory (the fertile lands on the western shore of the Crimea), and in Olbia, was the appearance in the steppes of South Russia of one tribe of Sarmatians after another. The Scythian Empire in South Russia and in the northern part of the Balkan peninsula, weakened by the Macedonians under Philip, Alexander and Lysimachus and later by the Thracians and the Celts, was gradually retreating to the coast leaving the steppes of South Russia to the Sarmatians and the Danube region, except the Dobrudja, to Sarmatians, Thracians and Celts.

The process was a very slow one. In the third century the Greeks did not feel any unusual pressure from the Scythians, though from time to time Bosporus had to do some fighting while Chersonesus was mainly occupied in defending its territory against the raids of the Taurians[2]. The situation of Olbia was worse, for that city had already begun to feel the evils of the growing anarchy in the steppes of South Russia[3]. The more heavily the Sarmatians pressed upon the Scythians, the more difficult became the plight of the Greek cities. And yet in the first half of the second century conditions were still tolerable. Bosporus enjoyed at this time a kind of renaissance (vol. viii, p. 581), while Chersonesus was successfully fighting for her liberty against Pharnaces I and perhaps the Scythians, upon whom alliances with the Sarmatians were an efficient check. We hear twice of such alliances: once at the time of the Pharnacian war, and again when the Sarmatian queen Amage (who in the name of her drunken husband herself ruled like many Hellenistic queens) made a daring raid upon the Scythian capital in defence of the Chersonesites.

Towards the second half of the second century the situation of these Greek cities changed for the worse. There arose in the Crimea a comparatively strong and united Scythian State. The little we know of it shows that its founder, the king Scilurus, was a

[1] *Ios. P.E.* I², 352; Ditt.³ 709.   [2] *Ios. P.E.* I², 343, cf. 344.
[3] *Ios. P.E.* I², 32; Ditt.³ 495

very able ruler. It appears that he secured himself by means of treaties and concessions and became an ally of the most vigorous Sarmatian tribe, the Roxolani. His hands were therefore free for activity on the coast. How he succeeded in occupying Olbia and reducing her to vassalage we do not know, but the Olbians were probably glad to have a protector against the various oppressors who threatened their very existence. With the help of the Olbians Scilurus organized his Crimean State. He and his sons reduced some tribes of the Taurians to obedience and built fortresses in their territory[1], thus becoming near neighbours of Chersonesus. In the centre of the Crimea Scilurus built a fortified capital Neapolis, in which many Greeks lived, as is shown by their inscriptions in honour of the kings[2]. His income he increased in the most efficient way by organizing through the great merchants of Olbia—we know of one Posideos who was in close relations with Rhodes—an important export of grain to western markets like that of Masinissa of Numidia at about the same time. And to protect this export trade he used the naval experience of the Olbians. An Olbian merchant-condottiere suppressed for him the piracy of the Satarchae, a tribe of the northern Crimea[3].

It is interesting to observe that exactly the same state of affairs that we find in the Crimea obtained on the western shore of the Black Sea. An inscription of the Greek city of Istros[4] and many coins show that the Scythians at the mouth of the Danube followed the same policy as that of Scilurus. They reduced the Greek cities to obedience, and in return for this obedience and a heavy tribute protected them—as efficiently as they could—against the ever-renewed attacks of the Thracians. The tone of the inscription of Istros mentioned above shows that the Greeks were more or less reconciled with the Scythians. The enemies whom the Greeks dreaded were the Thracians, and not without reason. The Scythians never destroyed a Greek city; the Thracians did so repeatedly. Istros fell a victim to them[5] and later Olbia, which, while still a prosperous city, was destroyed by the Getae (between 67 and 50 B.C.), at a time when there were no Scythians to protect her.

---

[1] The royal residence *Chaboi* or *Chabon*, and Palakion (Strabo VII, 312) are to be regarded as fortresses.

[2] *Ios. P.E.* I², 668–673.   [3] *Ios. P.E.* I², 672, cf. *S.E.G.* III, 606.

[4] This inscription has been recently discussed in a meeting of the French Academy by Prof. Lambrino, and a publication of it is in preparation. Cp. *S.E.G.* II, 446, and the later decree for Aristagoras, *Ditt.*³ 708. Much later is the decree of Dionysopolis for Acornion, *Ditt.*³ 762; M. Holleaux, *Rev. E.A.* XIX, 1917, pp. 252 *sqq.*   [5] Ditt.³ 708.

Master of Olbia, Scilurus no doubt wished to extend his empire to the east and south as well and to consolidate and increase his Graeco-Scythian state, a little Parthia in the Crimea, by using the resources of Panticapaeum and the other cities of the Bosporus and of Chersonesus and her dependent cities. By heavier demands for tribute Scilurus found a way of interfering with the internal affairs of the Greek cities and, in case of necessity, of invading their territory and attacking the cities themselves. Nor was this the end of the story. When Scilurus died, a very old man, his many sons followed the same policy. They recognized the authority of one among them, Palacus, and continued their pressure on the Greek cities.

The resources of the Greek cities were exhausted. The last Bosporan king was probably forced to adopt a Scythian prince (Saumacus) and to give him a Greek education, thus preparing for Bosporus a Scytho-Greek new dynasty. The Chersonesites were hard put to it to ward off the attacks of the Taurians and the Scythians. Bosporus and Chersonesus alike were faced by the choice either to submit like Olbia and the cities of the Dobrudja to the slightly hellenized Scythian kings and rely upon them for their safety against the attacks of the Sarmatians and Taurians, or to find help from outside. The Greek cities of the Black Sea shore with which both the Bosporus and Chersonese stood in uninterrupted relations for centuries, Amisus, Sinope and Heraclea, were no longer able to help, for Amisus and Sinope were now subjects of Pontus and Heraclea had enough to do to defend her own independence. Rome was far away and not interested in the Crimea. The only hope was in the kings of the opposite coast, the Bithynian or Pontic rulers, who were a little more hellenized than Scilurus and his sons.

Chersonesus and Bosporus decided to appeal to Mithridates for protection. Their choice was probably dictated by previous diplomatic relations with the Pontus and by the interest which Pontus always showed in Crimean affairs. However that may be, after exchanges of embassies[1] the king dispatched a citizen of Sinope, Diophantus son of Asclepiodorus, with an army across the sea to help Chersonesus against the Scythians. Diophantus, who cannot be the same as the author of the treatise *Pontica*, was probably a well-known general of the usual type, a successful condottiere. Two expeditions were needed to break the resistance

---

[1] *Ios. P.E.* I², 349, cf. 351. *Ib.* no. 349, which mentions the envoy of a Pontic king, may be dated in the reign of Philopator or Eupator. In 351, honours are granted to a Sinopian who may have been an ambassador.

of Palacus and his allies the Sarmatians, and probably others, before the sway of the Pontic kings was extended to Olbia and the Greek cities across the Bosporan straits.

A long decree of the city of Chersonesus in honour of Diophantus, which has been mentioned above, gives us a good account of his two expeditions to the Crimea. The first is dealt with briefly (the events of this expedition were narrated in a previous decree voted after the end of the first expedition), the second in some detail. Many facts mentioned in the decree appear also in the excerpts of Hypsicrates' history of Mithridates inserted by Strabo into his description of Scythia and the Crimea. Among these excerpts, however, there are some which mention facts of a later date and one which tells a story which may be connected with the expedition of Diophantus, but is not mentioned in the decree.

The history of the occupation of the Crimea by Diophantus may be summarized as follows. After his arrival at Chersonesus he set out at once to invade the enemy's country. Palacus, to his great surprise, was well informed about his movements and met him at once in the open field. A brilliant victory opened to the arms of Pontus the way into the Taurian region and the Bosporan kingdom. After having crushed the resistance of the Taurians, and having founded in their country a fortified city perhaps called Eupatorion to match Mithridates' Eupatoria in Pontus, Diophantus entered Bosporan territory. Whether he reached the city and received the submission of the last Paerisades, who had offered it to him long before, cannot be ascertained. Returning to Chersonesus, Diophantus with his army and the civic militia invaded the country of the Scythians, took the two royal residences of Chabaioi (Chaboi in Strabo) and Neapolis, and reduced the Scythians to submission. After the end of this first campaign, which may have been carried out in two successive years, Diophantus regarded his work as finished, and embarked for Sinope after duly receiving the grateful thanks of Chersonesus.

However, some time later, probably not in the next year, the Scythians felt strong enough to refuse obedience to the Pontic kings and to start the war again. Between the two expeditions of Diophantus, shortly before the second, may be set the incident related by Strabo (VII, 312) which is not mentioned in the inscription. The episode, however, is not dated and may have happened earlier or later. The Scythians laid siege to a fortress built by Mithridates (Eupatorion, probably not to be identified with the fortress, perhaps of the same name, built by Diophantus in the country of the Taurians) across a bay either from the city of

Chersonesus or from a fortified Chersonesian town *Teichos*. The siege ended in the repulse of the besiegers[1].

Diophantus started his second expedition in the late autumn, and advanced at once into the enemy's country with the militia of Chersonesus and his own army. Bad weather and probably snow prevented him from crossing the Taurian mountains, whereupon he turned towards the western sea coast in order to rescue from the Scythians the cities dependent on the Chersonesites—Cercinitis, which lay near the modern Eupatoria, a lesser fortified town or towns, whichever is meant by the name *Teiche*, and Kalos Limen, of which the site is unknown. He took Cercinitis and the *Teiche* and had laid siege to Kalos Limen; whereupon Palacus appeared in force with a strong army which consisted of his own troops and of an allied corps of the Roxolani. According to Strabo (VII, 306) the Roxolani, or perhaps the whole of the army of Palacus, numbered 50,000 men, the forces of Diophantus six thousand. The battle, as had been foretold by the great goddess of Chersonesus, ended in a Pontic victory, and meanwhile the Chersonesites succeeded in reducing Kalos Limen[2]. Diophantus in turn marched against the two Scythian capitals and probably occupied them. From here he went, unattended by his army, to Panticapaeum and settled affairs there. Suddenly the Scythian Saumacus, adopted son of Paerisades, rose in revolt, killed the king and forced Diophantus to flee to Chersonesus. Here he collected the citizen militia, mobilized the fleet and his own army and moved in the early spring against Theodosia and Panticapaeum. The cities were taken, Saumacus surrendered and was sent to Pontus. The acquisition of the Crimea was achieved. After his two splendid expeditions Diophantus disappears from history. The war, however, was not yet ended.

---

[1] The topography of this siege is hopelessly confused in Strabo and is hotly debated by modern scholars. In the opinion of the present writer the most probable theory is that of Berthier Delagarde, who identified the city mentioned by Strabo with the ruins on the little peninsula which was called Parthenion by the ancients, where to-day the Chersonesian lighthouse stands. A further suggestion by the same scholar, that these ruins are identical with the 'old Chersonesus' of Strabo, is supported by the quite recent discovery of large and well-preserved ruins under the level of the sea opposite the lighthouse. Strong walls surround this city; the agora is well recognizable. Against the inroads from outside, the promontory on which this city stood was defended by a double wall which ran from the sea to the bay, ruins of which were discovered some years ago. No detailed account of the discovery has been printed yet. A preliminary report may be found in an article by Prof. Grinevich in the newspaper *Moskva Vecher*, Oct. 22, 1930, no. 247.

[2] *Ios. P.E.* I², 353.

Neoptolemus, the admiral of Mithridates, is found engaged with the barbarians of the other side of the Bosporan straits, presumably Sarmatians and Maeotians. It is reasonable to suppose that this enterprise, which led to two bloody battles, one by sea and one by land, the latter on the ice of the frozen straits, had for its purpose to rescue from the barbarians the Greek cities of the Taman peninsula and to annex them to the kingdom of Pontus[1].

Another expedition was organized in order to add Olbia and her territory to the acquisitions of Pontus. So much at least may be deduced from an inscription[2] which shows that during the wars with the Romans Olbia was in the hands of Mithridates; and a name mentioned incidentally by Strabo (VII, 306)—the tower of Neoptolemus not far from Olbia—suggests that it was Neoptolemus who led the expedition which ended with the annexation of Olbia. Here again we find a fortified stronghold built by the general of Mithridates near a Greek city—a sign that the king did not wholly trust the loyalty of his new subjects. From here no doubt Mithridates extended his help also to the Greek cities of the Dobrudja and came into touch with the Thracian and Celtic tribes. It is very probable that after some fighting with the most warlike tribes of these regions—the Sarmatians and the Bastarnae—a kind of Pontic protectorate was finally established over some at least of the Greek cities of the western shore of the Black Sea[3].

As a result of this sequence of expeditions, not one of which was led by the king in person, all the Greek cities of the Crimea and of the northern shore of the Black Sea with their territories became a part of the Pontic kingdom. The capital of Mithridates in this new realm was Panticapaeum. Here was the residence of his viceroy, who was generally one of the sons of the king (first Machares, later Pharnaces), to whom the other Greek cities were subject. How much of their autonomy they retained it is hard to say. It is probable that both Chersonesus and the cities of the Bosporus still coined their own money (silver and copper), with Mithridatic types[4]. Chersonesus and Olbia certainly kept their popular assemblies, their councils and their magistrates. Whether the 'free' Greek cities had to pay any tribute or not is not known, but in any event, their political independence was gone.

---

[1] Strabo VII, 307; II, 73.   [2] Ios. P.E. I[2], 35.

[3] The date of these operations is unknown, and they may be much later than the conquest of the Crimea. The protectorate is suggested by Mithridatic types on the coinage of the Greek cities of the western shore of the Black Sea and by their behaviour during the wars of Mithridates with Rome. See Volume of Plates IV, 4, *f*, *g*, *h*, *i*.   [4] *Ib.* 4, *j-o*.

Outside the city territories conditions remained the same as they used to be. No doubt the Scythians retained their native kings, the Maeotians their chieftains and the Sarmatians their petty kings or princes. Some of them may have been appointed by Mithridates; at all events the Scythian kings complained in Rome about their being evicted from their kingdoms[1]. Some paid a tribute, chiefly in kind. The revenue of Mithridates from his new province—200 talents in silver and 180,000 medimni of grain— may be regarded as including not only the customs-duties and possibly other taxes of the Greek cities, the tithes of the landowners and the rents of the farmers and 'royal peasants' of the crown domains in the Bosporus but also payments by some of the vassal kings. But the chief advantage which Mithridates derived from his conquests was the unlimited possibility of drawing upon the resources in men of his new vassals, who had long been wont in case of need to send to their suzerains allied contingents which were practically mercenary corps. The army of Mithridates came to consist largely of such detachments of Scythians, Sarmatians, Maeotians, Thracians and Celts[2].

While year after year Mithridates' generals were conquering for him the northern shore of the Black Sea, other enterprises un- noticed or ignored by the Romans extended his rule over its southern shore. From the time of Pharnaces Lesser Armenia regarded the Pontic kings as her suzerains. When Mithridates claimed to convert this suzerainty into actual sovranty her ruler Antipater, son of Sisis, surrendered without fighting. Lesser Armenia became a kind of stronghold or fortress for keeping the King's treasures: 75 *gazophylakia* were built here by Mith- ridates and they rendered him good service later. How and when Mithridates joined to Lesser Armenia the coast of the eastern Paryadres with the city of Trapezus and the kingdom of Colchis which opened to him the way to Iberia, Atropatene and Great Armenia is not known. The value of these accessions, which apparently were easily won, was not to be despised, for Trapezus was the chief harbour for the export of minerals from that region, while Colchis supplied timber and hemp for the Pontic fleet. This latter region was organized as a satrapy and was ruled some- times by a member of the royal family.

[1] Memnon, 30; Appian, *Mithr.* 13.
[2] Some of the Thracians, however, never became allies of Mithridates and sided with the Romans; see the decree of Chaeronea, M. Holleaux, *Rev. E.G.* XXXII, 1919, pp. 320 *sqq.*

IV. MITHRIDATES EUPATOR AND ASIA MINOR:
THE FIRST PHASE

At the very end of the second century Mithridates made a journey incognito round Asia Minor ending with Bithynia, which must have shown him the complication and anarchy which prevailed. Pontus was surrounded by many states—Cappadocia, Galatia, Paphlagonia and Bithynia—which occupied towards Rome and her province of Asia the same position as Pontus. Nominally, like Pontus, all these states were independent allies of the Roman People, practically they were Roman vassals. This they all felt, some of them with bitter resentment. By that time the development of these states and their attitude towards Rome and each other were on the eve of assuming more than local importance. It was to be the destiny of the king to bring them into the tide of world history, and his own early activity in this direction found a counterpart in that of the ruler of Bithynia.

Bithynia was gradually built up by the steady efforts of her Graeco-Thracian dynasty. Nicomedes I, Ziaelas, Prusias I corresponded in the history of Bithynia to the first Mithridatids of the Pontus. With Prusias II started the period of Roman intervention to which Prusias submitted in the most abject way. His murderer and successor Nicomedes II Epiphanes, the contemporary of Eupator, played in Bithynia more or less the part of Mithridates Euergetes. His ambition, however, equalled that of Eupator. His kingdom was rich and prosperous, and hellenization made much more progress than in the Pontus. The Bithynian kings were great city-builders: Nicomedeia, Nicaea, Prusa, Apamea, Prusias (formerly Cius) bear witness to this activity. Some of the ancient Greek cities of the coast submitted to them, as Chalcedon and Tieum. But Heraclea Pontica, a stronger city than Amisus, remained free despite many efforts of the Bithynian kings to conquer her, and Cyzicus, in this unlike Sinope, proudly remained to the end of the Bithynian kingdom an independent neighbour.

The situation of Paphlagonia was different. The best part of it was since the foundation of the Pontic kingdom in the hands of the Mithridatid kings. The rest was split between local dynasts, some of them of foreign Galatian origin. For a time in the reign of Pharnaces I Paphlagonia was united in the hands of the king Morzius, whose successor was that Pylaemenes, who bequeathed his kingdom to Mithridates Euergetes (p. 222). After the death of Euergetes Paphlagonia continued as before in independence and anarchy under many local dynasts.

The neighbouring Galatians had never recovered from the tremendous blow which was given to their pride by Manlius Vulso, after Magnesia (vol. VIII, p. 228 *sq.*). They lived the same tribal life as before, divided into three peoples each subdivided into tetrarchies; they had the same feudal society with immensely rich chieftains surrounded by clients, and they retained their war-like temper which made them excellent mercenary soldiers for anyone who wanted to hire them.

The strongest neighbour of Pontus was no doubt Cappadocia. The ruling house named after Ariarathes was of the same Iranian origin as the Pontic dynasty, and was also closely connected with the Seleucids. It probably came to power later in the turmoil of the early third century. After the defeat of Antiochus the Great Ariarathes V Eusebes Philopator (163–130 B.C.) transferred his allegiance to the Romans, and remained faithful and useful to them until his death in the Roman war against Aristonicus (see above, p. 105). His rule had the reputation of being the happiest time for Cappadocia. A friend of Pergamum and of Athens and all that Athens represented, he was the first to start a hellenization of Cappadocia, which however never went very deep[1]. His death was followed by a period of protracted anarchy, for his wife Nysa murdered her own five sons in order to keep the rule in her hands. She could not prevent, however, the sixth Ariarathes from taking power into his own hands. For a while a tool in the hands of his father-in-law Mithridates Euergetes, he reigned till 111 B.C. when he was murdered by Gordius, later a creature of Eupator. After his murder his wife Laodice, the sister of Eupator, ruled in the name of her son Ariarathes VII Philometor[2].

Such were the neighbours of Mithridates. The situation was favourable for his ambition, and after he had made an arrangement with the most powerful of his neighbours, Nicomedes, and quelled

---

[1] Important for the history of Ariarathes V are two inscriptions—one of Priene giving evidence on the darkest period in the life of Ariarathes when he was expelled from his kingdom by Orophernes (*O.G.I.S.* 351), another of Athens giving an eloquent testimony to his relations to the city of Athens and to art (*O.G.I.S.* 352; *I.G.*[2] II, 1330; A. Wilhelm, *Jahreshefte*, XXIV, 1929, pp. 184 *sqq.*); cf. Ditt.[3] 666 (the statue of the philosopher Carneades dedicated by Attalus and Ariarathes) and the inscription of Tyana, *S.E.G.* I, 466 (a Greek gymnasium at Tyana in the time of Epiphanes).

[2] The coins of these dynasties, like those of Pontus, are our main source of information both for their history and their culture. See Volume of Plates IV, 6.

a conspiracy in his own family—his sister-wife during his absence betrayed him and tried to kill him after his return—he started at once on his endeavours to create an Anatolian empire in addition to his Pontic empire, endeavours which lasted more than twenty years and led to a sharp and protracted conflict with Rome.

Paphlagonia was the first victim of the ambition of the two allied kings, who divided its territory between them unhindered by a weak protest from Rome. During the very presence of a Roman senatorial commission in Asia Minor Galatia was next occupied by the two kings and became their vassal. At Rome bribes sufficed to neutralize the stormy protest of Appuleius Saturninus (p. 168). Next came the turn of Cappadocia. At this point the two kings parted. By a *coup-de-main* Nicomedes suddenly occupied the country, and persuaded Laodice the mother of Ariarathes VII to marry him, thus becoming the legitimate ruler of Cappadocia. This breach of faith was bitterly resented by Eupator, who thereupon entered the country with a strong army and reinstated Ariarathes VII on his throne at Mazaca.

The entente between Ariarathes and Mithridates, which is attested by the dedication of a bust of Ariarathes in the Delian shrine dedicated to Eupator in 101/0 B.C.[1], did not last for very long. Mithridates urged Ariarathes to recall Gordius the murderer of his father. Ariarathes refused, and created (perhaps not without the help of Marius who was at that time in Asia) a coalition against Mithridates. The two armies met in Cappadocia. Before battle was joined Mithridates treacherously murdered Ariarathes, and the Cappadocian army then broke in flight. A son of Mithridates was set upon the vacant throne. The fiction was that he was another son of Ariarathes V. This boy—Ariarathes Eusebes Philopator—ruled quietly with the assistance of Gordius for about five or six years, until the country revolted and called on the son of the last legitimate king of Cappadocia, who lived in the province of Asia. This young man, however, died very soon and Cappadocia became Pontic again[2].

Suddenly the newly won power of Mithridates in Asia Minor fell to pieces at a touch. Jealous of Mithridates and afraid for his own safety Nicomedes appealed to the Romans, and the Senate felt that it was time to interfere. Explicit orders were given to the kings to leave Paphlagonia and Cappadocia alone. These orders were obeyed, but with anger and resentment. Paphlagonia received 'freedom'; the Cappadocians declined this privilege and asked

---

[1] *O.G.I.S.* 353; Durrbach, *Choix*, 136 g.
[2] See his coin as Ariarathes VIII, Volume of Plates iv, 6, n.

for a king, whereupon one of their own ruling class, Ariobarzanes, was elected by the Cappadocian grandees (*c.* 95 B.C.).

Mithridates, however, had not abandoned his ambitions. He
tried a new device. Another neighbour of Cappadocia, Armenia,
which under the rule of Tigranes, later surnamed the Great,
began a period of short-lived revival, a neighbour entirely independent of Rome and closely connected with Parthia, was ready to
help him. Tigranes married Cleopatra, a daughter of Eupator, and
in 93 B.C. invaded Cappadocia, expelled Ariobarzanes and appointed Gordius, the *alter ego* of Mithridates, ruler of Cappadocia. Thereupon Rome intervened again. Sulla, at that time
propraetor of Cilicia, was given the task of restoring Ariobarzanes
and carried it out with characteristic skill (92 B.C.). On the
Euphrates an envoy of Parthia met him, and a conference was
held in the presence of the Cappadocian king. It was the first
time that spokesmen of the two great rivals of the future met
face to face. Mithridates was the chief loser in the game. His
Anatolian dreams were once more shattered, and it became clear
to him that they could not come true so long as the Senate dictated
its will in Asia Minor. Conflict with Rome must come.

In the struggle which followed, Mithridates disposed of resources partly inherited by him from his ancestors, partly created
by himself. In the organization of his kingdom he had made
little change. His Pontic empire remained on a larger scale what
the Pontus of his ancestors had been, a combination of a few Greek
cities and of large areas peopled by subjects and vassals. Over his
subjects and vassals Mithridates ruled with the help of citizens of
his Greek cities. Among these the leading rôle belonged to the
citizens of Amisus, unless their prevalence among those grandees
of the court who were honoured in the Mithridatic shrine at
Delos[1] is due merely to the dedicator's possible personal relations
with the city of Helianax, but yet it is striking to find so many
Amisenes among the dignitaries of Mithridates. If Mithridates
did something to impose hellenism, that is, city life upon his
native kingdom, we know nothing about it. The fact that so
many centres of quasi-urban life were minting copper[2] during
his reign may suggest a certain amount of urban autonomy granted
to them by the king, but there may be other explanations of the
same fact.

The kingdom of Mithridates was as typical a Hellenistic
kingdom as any other. We know very little of the various offices
and court titles which were typical of the Hellenistic monarchies

[1] Durrbach, *Choix*, 133–136.   [2] Volume of Plates iv, 4, *j-o*.

in general. It is possible that some Hellenistic monarchies kept in this respect nearer to Macedonia, some others nearer to Persia. If that be true, we may class Pontus with the second. The few court titles of the time of Mithridates which survive suggest a more Iranian organization of the court than even the Seleucid organization, closely akin to what we know of Parthia in this respect[1]. However, we know too little to be able to speak with certainty.

No details are known about the organization of the Mithridatic army and fleet. It seems to have been the same combination of mercenaries, of soldiers recruited in the homeland of the Mithridatic empire, and of allied detachments sent by the vassals, as was the army of the Seleucids. The royal fleet was probably furnished by the large commercial Greek cities under Pontic suzerainty. Of Mithridates' revenues no precise estimate can be made; but we know that royal garrisons guarded accumulated treasure in the numerous *gazophylakia* throughout his Empire, and the vast booty brought home by Pompey in 62 B.C. gives some idea how great these treasures were (p. 396).

V. MITHRIDATES' ADVANCE IN ASIA MINOR AND GREECE[2]

In spite of his rebuff at the hands of Sulla in the year 92, the political situation both in Italy and Asia Minor once more offered to Mithridates the opportunity to achieve his long-cherished ambitions. Rome had to face the rupture with her Italian allies (p. 185), and the death of Nicomedes of Bithynia (*c.* 94 B.C.), followed by dissensions between his sons, had removed from Mithridates' path his only serious rival among the kings of Asia Minor. The claims of the two sons of Nicomedes II had been decided by the Senate in favour of the elder, Nicomedes III Epiphanes Philopator, shortly before the outbreak of the Social War, whereupon the younger, Socrates, betook himself to Mithridates. While the Romans were fully occupied with the Social War, Pontic troops drove Nicomedes from Bithynia and established Socrates in his place. Simultaneously, in conjunction with Tigranes, Mithridates once more caused Ariobarzanes to be driven from Cappadocia and placed upon the throne his own son, as

---

[1] Cf. M. I. Rostovtzeff and C. B. Welles, *A parchment contract etc.*, Yale Classical Studies, II, 1930, pp. 35, 53 *n.*, 71.

[2] The chief ancient sources for sections V–VIII are Plutarch's *Sulla*, 11–26 (which draws on Sulla's own memoirs), Appian, *Mithridatica*, 1–63, Memnon, fragments of *History of Heraclea*, XV, and fragments of Licinianus.

Ariarathes IX. The dispossessed kings appealed to Rome, whose hands were already becoming more free to deal with the problems which had arisen in Asia Minor. A commission was appointed to settle affairs in the East and orders sent to C. Cassius[1], governor of Asia, to co-operate in restoring Nicomedes. Similar instructions were sent to Mithridates himself.

It was scarcely to be expected that Mithridates would take the active part which the Romans, by virtue of the nominal alliance, had enjoined. He did, however, carry out orders to the extent of putting Socrates to death. He had no doubt expected greater results from the Social War and was disconcerted by the signs that it would speedily be terminated. But the attitude which he now adopted shows that he had little faith in his own ability to resist Rome, or that his preparations for war were not yet completed. The two kings of Bithynia and Cappadocia were reinstated without opposition from Mithridates or Tigranes. But whatever the motive which induced this passive acquiescence, the Roman commissioners were entirely deceived. The original appointment of their leader, M'. Aquilius, had little to commend it. He had proved himself a brave and capable soldier and had rendered good service to Rome in the Sicilian slave-war, but at the end of the campaign had narrowly escaped a hostile verdict on a charge of peculation (p. 156). Disappointed of the hopes of booty to be derived from a Pontic campaign, the commissioners, in order to make sure of the money promised by the impecunious Nicomedes in return for his restoration, urged him to attack the dominions of Mithridates. A raid carried out by Nicomedes' army on the ports of the Paphlagonian coast controlled by Mithridates as far as the city of Amastris provided the funds for which the commissioners were pressing.

Even so Mithridates, whose forces had retired before the advance of the Bithynian marauders, shrank from an open conflict. An envoy, Pelopidas, was sent to ask that the aggressor should be restrained, or that the Romans should stand aside. Failing to get satisfaction, Mithridates dispatched Ariarathes to seize Cappadocia, but once more Pelopidas appeared before the commissioners requesting that the whole matter should be referred to the Senate, to whom Mithridates himself actually sent a message of protest. Pelopidas, however, was bluntly told that his master must evacuate Cappadocia and leave Nicomedes alone, and preparations were made for a general advance into Mithridates' dominions.

[1] Ditt.[3] 741. Appian, however (*Mithr.* 11), calls him Lucius.

The Romans, who had no more than a legion of their own troops available in Asia Minor, were compelled to rely on the levies of their Asiatic allies, troops of inferior quality and uncertain number[1]. While Aquilius remained in reserve in the north, Q. Oppius, the governor of Cilicia, made a flanking movement from the south into Cappadocia, and Cassius advanced by the route from Nicaea to Ancyra. Nicomedes himself with the Bithynian army was sent forward to meet the main Pontic force and penetrated as far as the Amnias, a tributary of the Halys, in Paphlagonia. Here he soon met with disaster at the hands of the king's generals Archelaus and Neoptolemus, who had been sent forward to contain him with light troops and cavalry from Armenia Minor[2]. The way was thus cleared for the advance of the main Pontic army into Bithynia. Aquilius sought to retreat to the Sangarius, but was brought to battle and defeated, escaping with difficulty to Pergamum.

The two engagements decided the issue of the campaign. Cassius, who had retired southwards to the stronghold of Leontoncephalae, and thence had endeavoured to join Oppius at Apamea, found it necessary to fall back on the coast. Helped with provisions by a certain Chaeremon of Nysa[3], he contrived at last to make his way to Rhodes. Oppius was less fortunate. He succeeded in reaching Laodicea on the Lycus with a force of mercenaries and some cavalry, and prepared to stand a siege. But the inhabitants did not long resist the assaults and solicitations of Mithridates and surrendered the Roman commander. Oppius himself is said to have suffered no harm. Aquilius, who had fled from Pergamum but had fallen ill at Mytilene on his way to Rhodes, was surrendered with other Romans by the inhabitants to Mithridates, who, after exhibiting his captive everywhere in the province of Asia bound on an ass or chained to a gigantic Bastarnian horseman, finally, by way of rebuking Roman greed, caused molten gold to be poured down his throat.

[1] Appian's numbers, 50,000 foot and 6000 horse for the Bithynian army, 40,000 for each of the three Roman armies, are impossible, but beyond correction.

[2] The forces with which Mithridates entered Paphlagonia are given by Memnon (31) as 150,000 men. Although the passage suggests that the 40,000 men and 10,000 horse which formed the advance guard are to be regarded as additional, it is possible that the figure 150,000 which Memnon preserves was the nominal strength of Mithridates' total forces. Appian's figures of 250,000 infantry and 40,000 cavalry (exclusive of the 10,000 cavalry from Armenia Minor, the phalanx and the scythed chariots) are impossible.   [3] Ditt.[3], 741.

After entering Bithynia, Mithridates had entrusted the pursuit of Aquilius to his generals, himself turning southwards to follow Cassius. From southern Phrygia forces were dispatched to reduce the southern part of Asia Minor and arrangements were made for the government of newly acquired territory by satraps[1]. After the capture of Laodicea Mithridates marched by way of Magnesia on the Maeander to Ephesus. From the first he had posed as a deliverer. Native troops who had surrendered were set free and provided with means to reach their homes. But while the majority of the cities of Asia, deprived as they were of any means of offering resistance, are said to have welcomed him, nevertheless some resistance was encountered[2], and it is indeed probable that this was greater than appears in the literary sources. Parts of Paphlagonia were still unsubdued even after Ionia had been overrun[3]. The town of Magnesia ad Sipylum survived an assault by Archelaus, who was himself wounded in the fighting[4]. But the strongest resistance was offered in the south-west. In Caria Tabae[5] and Stratoniceia stood by the Romans, the latter undergoing a siege of some duration before it was compelled to surrender[6]. In Lycia and Pamphylia, which are said by Appian[7] to have been subjugated, a successful resistance was maintained by some of the cities throughout the war. From Telmessus and other Lycian towns reinforcements were being sent to Rhodes at the time of the siege (p. 243). Patara withstood a siege, and the country as a whole was rewarded by Sulla for its loyalty at the end of the war[8]. At a later stage we find the cities of Pamphylia contributing ships to Lucullus' fleet, and an inscription records the fidelity and losses of the city of Termessus, which commands the pass between Pamphylia and the Milyas[9].

The behaviour of Ephesus is perhaps typical of the attitude of the cities of Asia. After the defeat of the Roman forces it had at

---

[1] On the satraps see Appian, *Mithr.* 21, 46. One of them, Leonippus, is mentioned in Ditt.[3] 741, and seems to have been appointed to Ephesus before Mithridates himself arrived on the coast. At a later date (Appian, *Mithr.*, 48) we find Philopoemen, the father-in-law of Mithridates, established as *episkopos* at Ephesus, and hear of 'tyrants' in other cities, e.g. at Colophon (Plutarch, *Lucullus*, 3), Tralles (Strabo xiv, 649), Adramyttium (id. xiii, 614).　　　[2] So Memnon, 31.

[3] Appian, *Mithr.* 21. The resistance was perhaps organized by a native chieftain, if there is any basis for the statement in Orosius vi, 2 (cf. Eutropius v, 5), pulsis ex ea (i.e. Paphlagonia) Pylaemene et Nicomede regibus.

[4] Pausanias i, 20, 5; Plutarch, *Mor.* 809 c; Livy, *Epit.* 81.

[5] *O.G.I.S.* 442.　　[6] Appian, *Mithr.* 21; *O.G.I.S.* 441.　　[7] *Mithr.* 23.

[8] Appian, *Mithr.* 61; cf. *O.G.I.S.* 551.　　[9] Bruns, *Fontes*[7], 14.

first remained loyal, offering sanctuary to refugees and serving as the port from which a number were enabled to make their escape to Rhodes. But on the approach of the Pontic army the Ephesians without resistance admitted the enemy within their gates, and once in the power of Mithridates proceeded to give such demonstrations as were possible of devotion to their new master. Once the possibility of Roman protection had vanished, similar demonstrations were made elsewhere, and Mithridates, greeted as the preserver of Asia, the new Dionysus[1], conferred liberal benefits on individual cities[2], cancelling debts and conferring five years immunity from taxation throughout the province (Justin, XXXVIII, 3, 7).

One thing more was needed to convince the province that the rule of Rome was at an end, and it was deliberate policy that urged Mithridates to issue the orders which were to incriminate the Greek cities for ever in the eyes of Rome. Secret instructions were sent to the satraps and to the city governments for a simultaneous massacre of Romans and Italians throughout the province. At Ephesus, Pergamum and other cities refugees were torn from the sanctuaries and butchered, it is said, to the number of 80,000. How far would the Greeks without the strongest compulsion have dared such an action? The case of Tralles, where the citizens hired a barbarian to do the work for them[3], is typical—a sorry attempt to carry out the orders of Mithridates without incriminating themselves too deeply with the Romans. The feelings of the unfortunate citizens must have been shared by many other states in Asia.

In the meantime, the small Roman fleet, which at the beginning of the war had been stationed at Byzantium, had dispersed or surrendered to Mithridates, whose fleet now appeared in overwhelming strength in the Aegean. We have no means of arriving at an exact estimate of its numbers, which are said to have reached the total of 300 decked ships and 100 biremes, exclusive of the substantial additions made by the squadrons of the Cilician pirates (see below, p. 352). The attitude of the islanders was much

---

[1] Diodorus, XXXVII, 2 *b*; Cicero, *pro Flacco*, 25, 60. For the thiasos of Eupatoristae and the Mithridates vase see *O.G.I.S.* 367 and 370 and Reinach, *op. cit.* p. 284 and Plate iii.

[2] Enlargement of the area of asylum at Ephesus (Strabo XIV, 641); repair of the damage caused by earthquake at Apamea (Strabo XII, 579); benefits conferred on Tralles (Cicero, *pro Flacco*, 25, 59); maintenance of *Mucia* at Smyrna (Cicero, II *in Verr.* II, 21, 51). In the maintenance of the festival founded in honour of Mucius Scaevola one can see a deliberate policy.

[3] Dio, frag. 101; Appian, *Mithr.* 23.

the same as that of the cities of the mainland. While the people of
Mytilene surrendered Aquilius and other officers, the inhabitants
of Cos refused to withdraw the protection of their sanctuary from
Roman fugitives[1]. On the other hand, they received Mithridates
without resistance and surrendered to him the son of Ptolemy
Alexander, King of Egypt, who had been sent to the island by his
grandmother Cleopatra, together with her treasures and 800
talents of the temple-money deposited in the island by the Jews
of Asia[2]. Indeed, with the disappearance of the Roman fleet no
serious resistance could be offered, nor, with the exception of the
Rhodians, did any of the islanders attempt it.

In the early days of the war Rhodes had provided a refuge for
all the Romans who had made good their escape from Asia.
Previously the republic had maintained good relations with
Mithridates[3], but, in spite of the danger to be expected from any
resistance to the king, held fast to its traditional friendship with
Rome, and trusted in the skill of its seamen and strength of its
fortifications to resist until the Romans were in a position once
more to offer protection. Since Mithridates is said to have found
it necessary to raise a fleet specially for the attack on Rhodes[4], it is
probable that his main armaments had already been dispatched
across the Aegean. When his preparations had been completed,
he put to sea in overwhelming strength (autumn, 88), drove back
the Rhodian navy, and effected a landing on the island. The
transports bringing his main forces had not yet arrived, and
Mithridates was able to make little progress in his assaults on the
city. Meanwhile the Rhodians, who had drawn off the bulk of
their fleet from the first engagement, vigorously disputed the
command of the sea, twice gaining successes over the king's fleet
and inflicting heavy losses on the transports, which had at last
sailed from the Carian coast but were scattered by bad weather.
The arrival, however, of the remainder gave Mithridates the
numerical superiority which he required for an attack on the town.
A formal blockade was out of the question, since the winter
season was close at hand, and Mithridates attempted to capture
the town by assault. After a night attack by land and sea had
proved a fiasco, Mithridates brought up against the walls on the
sea side an immense flying bridge, known as the *sambuca*, which
was carried on two warships lashed together and could be hoisted

---

[1] Tacitus, *Ann.* IV, 14.

[2] Josephus, *Ant. Jud.* XIV (VII, 2), 112 *sqq.* On the whole episode see
Reinach, *op. cit.* p. 183.

[3] Cicero, II *in Verr.* II, 65, 159.   [4] Appian, *Mithr.* 22.

by an arrangement of pulleys from the masthead so as to overtop the city wall (see vol. VIII, p. 66). As the *sambuca* was brought into position, a general assault with rams and scaling ladders was to be delivered from the sea. Fortunately, however, for the Rhodians and not, it was said, without the assistance of Isis, the site of whose temple had been chosen as the place of assault, the *sambuca* collapsed under its own weight, and with the failure of this last assault Mithridates retired from his undertaking before winter set in.

VI. THE WAR IN GREECE.

Before the attack on Rhodes the main fleets of Mithridates had already crossed the Aegean and carried the war into Greece[1]. The situation was not unfavourable for the intervention of a new Antiochus. The governor of Macedonia, C. Sentius, had for some time (since 91 B.C.) been occupied with Thracian incursions[2], which on one occasion had penetrated as far as Dodona. There is nothing improbable in the view[3] that the attacks of the barbarians, with whom he could easily maintain communication from his Bosporan dominions, had been instigated by Mithridates himself. His agents were active also in Greece, and soon after the conquest of Asia a deputation arrived from Athens, which was ripe at this time for a popular uprising against the aristocratic form of government favoured by Rome, with one of them, a certain Aristion[4], a Peripatetic philosopher of servile origin, at its head. Aristion was received with every mark of favour and in his despatches did his utmost to persuade the Athenians both of the greatness of Mithridates' power and of the political and financial advantages which would accrue to them, if they embraced the cause of the king. On his return to Athens, where he was received with an extravagant welcome, Aristion, with the wildest tales of Mithridates' successes and lavish promises of benefits to come, completely won over the Athenian people and had himself elected hoplite general, nominating his colleagues[5]. His opponents, the aristocratic party in Athens, were murdered and their property

---

[1] See Map 3.   [2] Livy, *Epit.* 74, 76.   [3] Cf. Dio, frag. 101.
[4] Posidonius (*ap.* Athenaeus V, 211 F) calls him Athenion, his father's name. By other writers he is called Aristion and this name occurs on coins struck in Athens at this time. Since Posidonius' account closes with the Delos fiasco it has been supposed that Athenion was suppressed as the result and Aristion established in his place by Archelaus. See the full discussion of the question in W. S. Ferguson, *Hellenistic Athens*, p. 447.
[5] Before July, 88 B.C.; see Ferguson, *op. cit.* p. 444, n. 1.

confiscated, many of those who sought to escape from Attica being brought back and put to death.

The military value of the Athenians themselves to Mithridates was of course negligible. Their attempt to seize the island of Delos under Apellicon, a creature of Aristion's, ended in complete disaster, but Mithridates had now in the Piraeus a port of entry into Greece and a base from which the whole country could be overrun. Accordingly the fleets of Mithridates set sail from Asia under Archelaus. On the voyage the Cyclades were occupied without difficulty and the Romans were once more expelled from Delos or put to death. On his arrival in Athens Archelaus provided Aristion with a bodyguard to hold the town for Mithridates while he himself secured southern Greece. To the north a Pontic squadron under Metrophanes[1] had occupied Euboea, and was attacking the fortress of Demetrias and the territory of the Magnetes.

It seemed as if the whole of Greece would fall into Mithridates' power before the relieving army under Sulla could leave Italy. Fortunately for the Romans, however, Sentius was able to detach a small force under his legate Q. Bruttius Sura, who drove back Metrophanes from the Thessalian coast and with the ships at his disposal regained the island of Sciathos, which had been used by the invaders as a storehouse for their plunder. Bruttius then advanced into Boeotia, all of which Archelaus had won for Mithridates with the exception of Thespiae, to which he laid siege. Three engagements are said to have been fought in the neighbourhood of Chaeronea, as the result of which the Pontic advance was definitely checked and Archelaus was compelled to fall back on his base in Attica[2].

At this point the advance-guard of Sulla's army arrived in Boeotia under his quaestor L. Lucullus, from whom Bruttius

---

[1] Appian, *Mithr.* 29. Plutarch (*Sulla*, 11) assigns the conquest of Euboea to Archelaus; no doubt Metrophanes was his subordinate. Compare the similar case of Dorylaus and Zenobius in the affair of Chios (below, p. 254).

[2] Plutarch, *Sulla*, 11. Appian, *Mithr.* 29, after describing the reconquest of Sciathos, states that Bruttius, receiving reinforcements to the number of 1000 from Macedon, advanced into Boeotia, where he fought a three days' battle with Archelaus. When, however, Archelaus was joined by the Lacedaemonians and Achaeans Bruttius withdrew to the Piraeus, from which he was forced to retire when Archelaus brought up his fleet. This is clearly absurd. Plutarch's statement is that after the engagements at Chaeronea Bruttius drove Archelaus back to the sea. We have little guidance as to the precise chronology of Bruttius' campaign, which seems to have taken place in the autumn and winter of 88–7 B.C.

received orders to rejoin Sentius in Macedonia, now threatened by the advance of a new Pontic army through Thrace. The value of Bruttius' work had been enormous. By his Boeotian campaign northern Greece had been saved from Archelaus, so that Sulla, who had landed with five legions and a small force of cavalry and of auxiliaries, was able to raise reinforcements and provisions in Aetolia and Thessaly, while the cities of Boeotia at once returned to their allegiance. Sulla concentrated his energies at once on the reduction of Athens and the Piraeus, into which after a successful engagement[1] he drove Archelaus and Aristion.

Nevertheless, apart altogether from his relations with the Roman government (see p. 265), which rendered the receipt of reinforcements and supplies from home impossible, Sulla's position was extremely hazardous. With the near presence of the enemy and in view of the exactions which Sulla was compelled to levy in order to supply his own troops, dangerous outbreaks might easily occur among the Greek states. While Archelaus held command of the sea, his garrison in the Piraeus could be supplied and reinforced as necessary, and Sulla's communications through Boeotia were threatened by Neoptolemus based on Euboea and the fortress of Chalcis. To meet this danger Sulla was compelled to detach a force under Munatius to Boeotia, while another division under L. Hortensius, which had sailed from Italy after the main body, was diverted northwards to Thessaly to operate against the Pontic army advancing by land. Funds were raised for the payment of the Roman troops by the seizure of the treasures belonging to the Greek shrines, Epidaurus, Olympia and Delphi being the principal sufferers[2], and later in the year, the Rhodians being unable to put to sea, Lucullus was sent out to raise a fleet.

Sulla's first task was the reduction of the fortresses in Attica, where the Piraeus was held by Archelaus himself, Aristion commanding in Athens[3]. Realizing the necessity for speed, Sulla detached part of his army to invest Athens, while he himself attempted to carry the Piraeus by assault. The strength of the fortifications was such that no impression could be made by this form of attack and Sulla withdrew to Eleusis and Megara to prepare for a formal investment. The problem facing him differed in the case of the two fortresses. Whereas Athens, no longer connected with the sea by the Long Walls, was in itself of less account strategically and could be reduced by blockade, the Piraeus, until

---

[1] Mentioned only by Pausanias I, 20, 5.
[2] Plutarch, *Sulla*, 12; Diodorus XXXVIII, 7.
[3] For coins struck by him at Athens see Volume of Plates iv, 4, *d, e*.

such time as Sulla could raise a fleet capable of offering battle to
the king's fleet, could be attacked only on the land side and might
be provisioned and reinforced by the enemy at will. Moreover, in
the event of Sulla being forced to retire northwards to meet the
army commanded by the king's son Ariarathes[1], Archelaus would
advance from the Piraeus against the rear of the Roman army.

With a part of the Roman army blockading Athens, the force
attacking the Piraeus was from the outset outnumbered by the
garrison[2]. Nevertheless Sulla, having prepared his engines of
assault, the material for which was derived largely from Thebes,
once more advanced against the Piraeus. The second assault, which
took place in the late summer of 87, was conducted with an even
greater vigour. As his engines collapsed or were destroyed by the
enemy, timber for repairs was ruthlessly cut in the groves of the
Academy and Lyceum, the remains of the Long Walls being used
for raising mounds against the fortifications. His agents within
the Piraeus, moreover, kept Sulla informed of the intentions of
the enemy, so that on two occasions sorties of the garrison were
beaten back with heavy loss. Archelaus, however, twice reinforced
by sea, still maintained his superiority in numbers, and continually
increased the strength of his fortifications where danger threatened,
or by small sallies destroyed the Roman works.

The pressure was maintained until the beginning of winter,
when Sulla withdrew part of his army to his base at Eleusis,
maintaining, however, the blockade of Athens. Although his
cavalry were raiding up to Eleusis itself, Archelaus was unable to
penetrate the cordon round the capital, where there was already
imminent danger of famine. Accordingly, although the attacks
on the Piraeus were renewed before the spring[3], the weakened
state of the garrison of Athens offered hope of a speedy reduction
of the town, which would enable Sulla to concentrate all his
energies on the Piraeus. The Piraeus, therefore, was temporarily

[1] He is called Arcathias by Appian, Ariarathes by Plutarch.

[2] This is stated definitely by Appian, *Mithr.* 31. Kromayer's view
(*Antike Schlachtfelder*, ii, p. 391) that at the beginning of the siege Archelaus'
forces must have been smaller than those of Sulla is not here accepted. His
retirement to the Piraeus was a part of the general strategic scheme.

[3] The sequence of events is given by Appian, *Mithr.* 34 *sq.* Archelaus'
attempt to provision Athens took place on the same day as the defeat of
Neoptolemus near Chalcis by Munatius (in which Reinach [*op. cit.* p. 160]
rightly sees an attempt on the part of the Chalcis garrison to create a diversion
which would diminish the pressure on Athens). This was shortly followed by
a night attack on the Piraeus, after which the assaults, discontinued during
the winter, were regularly renewed.

masked on the land side[1], while the assaults on Athens became more intense. A deputation from the commandant, whose conduct during the siege was making him more and more odious to the inhabitants, was rejected, and a final effort on the part of Archelaus to relieve the town was beaten back. Sulla now received information that Aristion had neglected to secure the approaches to the Heptachalcum, between the Sacred and the Piraeic Gates, where the defences were weakest, and at this point ordered the final assault to be delivered. The starving defenders, reduced, it is said, to feed on human flesh, could offer little resistance, and the town, which fell on March 1st, 86, was given over to massacre and pillage, although in memory of their past achievements the city of the Athenians was spared from utter destruction. The tyrant himself made his escape to the Acropolis, first burning the Odeum in order that the beams might not be used for siege-engines. After resisting for some weeks, he was forced by lack of water to surrender to C. Curio, who had been left behind by Sulla to carry on the siege, when he himself marched north.

Sulla was now free to return to his attacks on the Piraeus. Although Archelaus fought every inch, one by one the defences succumbed to the violence of the Roman assaults, now rendered more intense by the imminence of the danger from the north. At last the garrison was confined to the peninsula of Munychia, which, protected on the sea side by a fleet, was impregnable. But Sulla's work was done. The Piraeus, laid in ruins, could no longer serve the enemy as a base, and Archelaus withdrew the remainder of his forces to his ships, finally effecting a junction with the northern army in Thessaly.

The heroic defence of the Piraeus had been stultified by the dilatory advance of the army under Ariarathes, who seems to have taken the view that the purpose of his mission was to create a kingdom for himself in Thrace and wasted valuable time in endeavouring to organize the conquered territory. We hear of little resistance being offered in Thrace itself, but with the approach of winter the difficulties of feeding the army were great and, until Amphipolis fell, threatened to endanger its safety. In Macedonia some resistance was encountered from the Roman troops in the province and from the inhabitants[2], and a further delay was caused by the illness and death of the king's son at the Tisaean promontory in Magnesia shortly before the capitulation of Athens.

[1] If we may so interpret the final words of Appian, *Mithr.* 37.
[2] Memnon, 32; Licinianus, p. 27 F.

After joining the northern army, Archelaus took over the command of the united forces from Taxiles, the successor of Ariarathes, and advanced southwards by Thermopylae. In the meantime Sulla had marched northwards. His advance was criticized on the ground that the Boeotian plains would provide a favourable terrain for the enemy's cavalry; but Sulla rightly realized the difficulty of feeding his troops in Attica, and, moreover, was anxious for the safety of the division under Hortensius, whose retreat from Thessaly was cut off by the Pontic occupation of Phocis, where Taxiles was now attacking Elatea[1]. Hortensius, however, extricated himself by a skilful march, apparently by the Asopus gorge and along the north-eastern slopes of Parnassus by Tithorea, joining Sulla at Patronis on the southern edge of the plain of Elatea. Their united forces then occupied the hill of Philoboeotus, a detached eminence rising from the plain[2]. Their strength is given as 15,000 infantry and 1500 cavalry. Opposed to them was an army perhaps three times as numerous[3].

The march northwards to join Hortensius had brought Sulla on to ground on which he had no intention of giving battle. The hill of Philoboeotus was easily defensible in itself and the approaches were further strengthened by trenches thrown up on the Cephisus, the course of which is said to have been thereby diverted. But the open plain of southern Phocis would enable Archelaus to make full use of his superiority in numbers and especially of his cavalry. For two days therefore Sulla remained on Philoboeotus and refused battle. His position, however, was a dangerous one, since enemy raiding parties were plundering as far south as Lebadea, and it was essential for him to maintain his communications with the south by way of the valley of the

[1] Pausanias 1, 20, 6, places the attack on Elatea before the capture of Athens, but obviously means the surrender of the Acropolis under Aristion, which clearly took place about the time of the battle of Chaeronea (cf. x, 34, 2).

[2] Plutarch's description of Philoboeotus (*Sulla*, 16) makes Leake's identification of it with Parori, a spur of Parnassus above the pass from Phocis to Boeotia, impossible. Kromayer's topography, including his identification of Philoboeotus with Kravassará, is here followed throughout.

[3] Plutarch (*Sulla*, 15) makes the northern army number 100,000 foot, 10,000 cavalry and 90 chariots on its arrival in Greece. Appian (*Mithr.* 41, cf. 45), who says that it had been made up by reinforcements to its original figure, gives 120,000 in all, Sulla's troops being less than one-third. Livy, *Epit.* 82, reckons the Pontic dead at 100,000. Memnon (32) gives the Pontic total at Chaeronea as over 60,000, which agrees with Appian's estimate of the relative strength of the two armies.

Cephisus and by Chaeronea. After leaving Phocis the river flows through a narrow pass between the eastern spurs of Parnassus (the modern Parori) on the right bank and Mt Hedylium (modern Belesi) on the left. The northern end of the pass is commanded by the acropolis of Parapotamii, a rocky hill above the left bank of the river connected with Mt Hedylium by a low saddle. When therefore the enemy advanced towards the pass with the intention of occupying Parapotamii Sulla hurriedly forestalled them and seized the position. A second attempt on the part of Archelaus to cut Sulla's communications by seizing Chaeronea was similarly anticipated by Sulla, who sent a legion to garrison the town. Archelaus' move on Chaeronea was a strategical error of the first importance. Since the valley of the Cephisus was closed to him by Sulla's occupation of Parapotamii, it is clear that he reached northern Boeotia by an alternative, though difficult, route to the east of Hedylium[1], which brought him down to the low ground between that hill and Mt Acontium, where we find his main body encamped. Sulla at once marched southwards from Parapotamii and established himself at the southern entrance to the pass, under Mt Hedylium and opposite the main body of the enemy. Archelaus accordingly was faced with the alternative of fighting a general action on ground unsuited to his cavalry and chariots, or of retiring by the difficult route to the coast. He had, however, sent a strong force to occupy the high ground of Mt Thurium above Chaeronea which could threaten the town itself and the flank of the Romans. Sulla, therefore, leaving his lieutenant L. Murena with a legion and two cohorts encamped opposite Archelaus, himself took up a position by Chaeronea, and sent a detachment to take in reverse the position on Mt Thurium.

This manœuvre enabled Sulla to force the general action which he desired. The enemy, dislodged from Thurium, fled northwards to rejoin the main body, suffering heavy losses from Murena's troops on the way. When Archelaus sent out his chariots and cavalry to cover the retreat, Sulla swiftly advanced his right to reduce the interval between the two armies and close the gap between his own force and Murena's division. To meet any outflanking movement by the enemy's cavalry, strong detachments under Hortensius and Galba were posted in reserve.

The main battle opened with a charge of sixty of the enemy's chariots, which proved ineffective except in so far as it enabled the Pontic phalanx to come into action. Though formed, it is said, mainly of liberated slaves from the Asiatic cities, the phalanx put

[1] See Kromayer, *op. cit.* II, p. 366.

up a stout resistance, which enabled Archelaus to carry out the expected flanking movement with his cavalry against the Roman left. To meet this danger, Hortensius, as had been arranged, came down with his reserve of five cohorts, but by the skilful tactics of Archelaus found himself cut off from Murena and in imminent danger of being surrounded. Sulla at once gathered his cavalry and crossed hastily from the right wing to succour his left, but on seeing his approach Archelaus disengaged his cavalry and began to transfer them to the other wing against the now weakened Roman right. This was the critical moment of the battle. With either wing broken the Roman army would have been surrounded and destroyed. Ordering Hortensius with four cohorts to support Murena, now engaged in repelling an attack by a *corps d'élite* under Taxiles, Sulla himself with his cavalry, one cohort of Hortensius' force and two fresh cohorts hitherto in reserve[1], returned with all possible speed to his original position and was in time to throw his whole right forward and fling the enemy, who had not yet re-formed after Archelaus' manœuvre, back across the Cephisus towards Mt Acontium. At the same time the troops of Murena and Hortensius had repulsed Taxiles on the left and were ready to join in a general advance.

The defeat of the enemy now became a rout. As the Romans advanced, they were pressed against the rocks of Mt Acontium or crushed in the narrow space between Acontium and Hedylium. Archelaus in vain endeavoured to rally his troops in front of the camp and closed the gates against the flying multitude. When the gates at length were opened, the Romans burst in with the fugitives, and of the king's army some 10,000 alone made their escape with Archelaus to Chalcis. It was a hard-won battle which attests Sulla's skill and does not need his embellishment that the Roman losses amounted to fourteen men, two of whom returned before night. The Roman victory was made complete by the destruction of the Pontic foraging parties as they returned, ignorant of what had happened, to the camp.

Sulla sought by a forced march with his light troops to intercept Archelaus at the Euripus but failing to do so withdrew to Athens, where the Acropolis had surrendered about the same time as the battle of Chaeronea took place[2]. The Thebans were heavily punished for their past misconduct, being compelled to surrender half their land, which was made over to the gods whose

---

[1] So Plutarch, *Sulla*, 19; Appian, *Mithr.* 43. Probably a reserve to the right wing and commanded by Galba.

[2] Licinianus, p. 24 F.; Pausanias I, 20, 2.

treasuries Sulla had robbed at the beginning of the war[1]. In Athens the partisans of Aristion were put to death, but Aristion himself for the present was kept alive. No further penalties, however, were inflicted on the Athenians, who, with the partisans of Rome once more established in power, were allowed to retain their liberty[2].

For the time being the Greek mainland was cleared of the enemy, but Euboea and the fortress of Chalcis remained in the hands of Archelaus, whose command of the sea was unimpaired. From Chalcis his fleet carried out a series of raids on the Greek coast as far as the island of Zacynthos, and penetrating into the Adriatic had destroyed a number of the transports carrying the advance-guard of Flaccus, who had been appointed by the Roman government to take over the command from Sulla and was already on his way (summer, 86). Chaeronea, therefore, had brought no more than a temporary respite to Sulla. With the prospect of a fresh Pontic army arriving in central Greece by sea, there could as yet be no thought of carrying the war by land to Asia Minor. A march northwards against the army of Flaccus would enable the enemy to recover central Greece without a blow if Sulla's plans miscarried and if Mithridates could expedite the arrival of the new army. Sulla, accordingly, took up a position at Melitaea in Phthiotis on the western slopes of Mt Othrys, from which the main route from Thessaly to Lamia could be watched, and from which he could return quickly to Boeotia in the event of any movement by Archelaus. All the strategical advantages therefore were once more in the hands of Archelaus. Reinforced during the summer of 86 by Dorylaus with an army which is said to have numbered 80,000[3], Archelaus crossed from Chalcis and while detachments of his army ravaged Boeotia, took up a position in the plain of Orchomenus, where his cavalry and chariots could have free play. Once more the Boeotians went over to the enemy.

The new development brought Sulla back at once to Boeotia, where he took up his position opposite Archelaus. Outnumbered as he was and operating on ground which was entirely in favour

---

[1] Plutarch, *Sulla*, 19; Pausanias IX, 7, 4.

[2] Livy, *Epit.* 81; Strabo IX, 398. For the arrangements in Athens, made probably at the end of the war, see Ferguson, *op. cit.* p. 456.

[3] So Appian, *Mithr.* 49, and Plutarch, *Sulla*, 20; the text of Licinianus seems to give Dorylaus 65,000 infantry, 15,000 cavalry and 70 chariots. Orosius VI, 2, 6, and Eutropius V, 6, 3 give 70,000. We have no figures from Memnon but if his original total of 150,000 (see above, p. 240, n. 2) is correct, Dorylaus' force cannot have exceeded 20,000.

of the enemy, Sulla sought to protect his flanks by cutting trenches ten feet wide to circumscribe the action of the enemy cavalry and force them towards the marshes of Copais. While the Romans were thus engaged, Archelaus delivered a general attack. His cavalry, posted on the two wings, surprised the working parties and threw back the detachments which were covering them. The Roman left seemed about to give way, when Sulla, riding forward, leapt from his horse and by his personal example rallied his men. The arrival of two cohorts from the right enabled them to drive back the enemy and regain the line of their entrenchments, on which the enemy delivered a second and still more furious attack[1].

In the centre Archelaus had posted his chariots, supported as at Chaeronea by the phalanx, with a detachment of heavy-armed troops and renegade Italians in reserve. To meet the charge of the chariots Sulla had drawn up his centre in three ranks with wide intervals between the flanks of detachments. As the chariots charged they became involved in the stakes planted by the second rank, behind which the front rank of the Romans withdrew, and at the same time they were assaulted by the Roman cavalry and light-armed, issuing by the intervals in the Roman line. Terrified by the shouts and weapons of the enemy the chariot horses bolted back on to the phalanx and involved it also in their panic. When Archelaus endeavoured to stop the rout by withdrawing his cavalry from the wings, Sulla charged it with his horse and drove the whole army headlong to its camp. The enemy had left some 15,000 dead on the field and were thoroughly demoralized. On the following day therefore Sulla proceeded to enclose their camp with a ditch. An attempt of the enemy to interrupt the work was thrown back and in the resulting confusion the Roman troops carried the camp by storm. The invasion of Greece was at an end. The remnants of the Pontic army were driven into the marshes of

---

[1] The accounts in Plutarch, *Sulla*, 21, and Appian, *Mithr*. 49, refer mainly to the fighting on the wings (especially the left), which as at Chaeronea was the most critical. Frontinus (*Strat*. ii, 3, 17) cannot, as has been supposed, refer to Chaeronea. He gives us valuable information regarding Archelaus' formation, namely that his cavalry was disposed on either wing with the chariots and phalanx in the centre. From Plutarch we learn that it was the Roman working parties and the covering troops (i.e. those on the flanks, cf. Frontinus: Sulla fossas...utroque latere duxit; Plutarch: ἑκατέρωθεν) which were surprised at the first onset, Appian stating that this happened διὰ δέος τῶν ἵππων. The enemy's losses were chiefly in cavalry, i.e. were lost in the fighting on the wings. Since reinforcements were brought from the right, it would seem that it was the Roman left which gave way at the beginning of the battle.

Copais. Archelaus himself after hiding two days in the swamps at length reached the coast and escaped in a small boat to Chalcis, where he sought to rally any detachments of the king's troops that remained in Greece.

VII. REACTION AGAINST MITHRIDATES, PRELIMINARIES OF PEACE.

Although he was not yet in a position to carry the war into Asia Minor, the news of Sulla's victories produced, as was to be expected, a remarkable change of heart among the cities of Asia. The appointment of governors and tyrants (see above, p. 241, n. 1) was scarcely calculated to maintain the first enthusiasm of the Greek cities for Mithridates, and the exactions and levies which were necessitated by the sending of a second army to Greece after Chaeronea increased their discontent. The first serious outbreak arose among the Galatians, whose leading men had been treacherously seized and murdered by the king at a banquet, on the ground of a plot against his life. The survivors raised rebellion throughout Galatia, expelling the king's satrap and his garrisons[1].

We next hear of trouble in the island of Chios, against which Mithridates is said to have borne a grudge since the time when a Chian ship had fouled his own in the operations off Rhodes. The Roman party in Chios was strong, and after confiscating the property of those who had fled, Mithridates, who suspected the Chians of being in communication with Sulla, gave orders for a detachment of the fleet of Dorylaus to occupy the island on its way to Greece[2]. The town walls were occupied by night, the citizens disarmed and hostages furnished to the king's officer Zenobius. A fine of 2000 talents was next imposed, but, accused by Zenobius of giving short weight, the defenceless inhabitants were carried off to Mithridates who ordered them to be transported to Colchis[3]. On the voyage, however, they were rescued by the people of Heraclea[4]. The fate of Chios was a warning to the rest of the treatment which they also might expect. When Zenobius presented himself before Ephesus, the inhabitants

---

[1] Appian, *Mithr.* 46, 58; Plutarch, *Mor.* 259 A–D.

[2] This gives us some indication of date. Reinach, *op. cit.* p. 182, places the episode before Chaeronea. In Appian, *Mithr.* 46, the officer charged with this task was Zenobius, στρατιὰν ἄγων ὡς ἐς τὴν Ἑλλάδα. Memnon, 33, says it was Dorylaus. Obviously Zenobius was detached from Dorylaus' forces on their way to reinforce Archelaus after Chaeronea.

[3] Nicolaus Damasc., frag. 95; Posidonius, frag. 38.   [4] Memnon, 33.

refused to admit his troops, and after deliberation arrested the king's officer and put him to death. A decree records the revolt of the city, its claim to have preserved throughout its good will towards Rome and the nature of the measures now taken for defence against the 'King of Cappadocia'[1]. The example of Ephesus was followed by a number of cities, among which are mentioned Tralles, Smyrna and Colophon. Some were recovered and brutally punished[2], but to prevent the revolt spreading, Mithridates, while nominally granting freedom to the Greek cities, increased the number of his partisans by the cancellation of debts, the freeing of slaves and extensions of citizenship. Even so conspiracies, real or imaginary, against his life drove Mithridates to organize a reign of terror against those suspected of good will towards Rome. On the information of his spies some eighty citizens of Pergamum were executed, and a conservative estimate puts the number of his victims in the province at 1600[3].

After the battle of Orchomenus further punishment had been inflicted by Sulla on Boeotia, and three of the coastal towns destroyed to prevent them being used by the enemy still in Euboea. He then marched northwards to Thessaly, to await the arrival of the army of Flaccus, and took up his quarters for the winter. Being still without news of Lucullus, he further set himself to build the fleet that was necessary for his projected invasion of Asia. In the meantime Flaccus had crossed from Italy with two legions, the advance-guard of which was now arriving in Thessaly (p. 266 sq.). Flaccus, greedy and incompetent, was unpopular with his troops, many of whom began to go over to Sulla. Further desertions, however, were prevented by his *legatus* Fimbria, but in the circumstances it did not seem wisdom to try conclusions with Sulla, but rather to march direct to the Bosporus. Considerable hardships were endured in the course of a winter march through Thrace, and resistance was encountered from the Pontic garrisons which still remained. But on the capture of Philippi, the king's troops evacuated their remaining stronghold of Abdera and withdrew from Europe. On the march, Fimbria had granted the division under his command unlimited license to plunder, and when the inhabitants appealed to Flaccus, encouraged his men to disobey the orders for restitution. At Byzantium further divisions broke out between the general and his *legatus*. In view of their previous conduct Flaccus had ordered the troops to encamp outside the city. Fimbria seized the opportunity of Flaccus' absence to

---

[1] Ditt.[3] 742.   [2] Livy, *Epit.* 82.
[3] Appian, *Mithr.* 48. The figure of 20,000 in Orosius VI, 2, 8 is ludicrous.

incite the legions to enter the city and billet themselves on the inhabitants, many of whom were killed in the disturbance. Later, when his division had already crossed into Asia, Fimbria, who after a fresh quarrel with Flaccus was threatening to throw up his command, found himself superseded by the appointment of a certain Thermus. He accordingly left for Byzantium, ostensibly on his way to Rome, but raised the troops against Thermus, drove out Flaccus on his return, and pursuing him to Chalcedon and Nicomedeia had him put to death. In spite of its disapproval the Senate was compelled to confirm him in the command which he had thus assumed[1].

On the news of Orchomenus Mithridates had turned his thoughts towards peace and issued instructions to Archelaus to arrive at an accommodation with Sulla. He still had hopes of retaining his acquisitions in Asia, since Sulla was unable to move from Greece and, the army of Flaccus not yet having arrived in Asia, there were prospects of playing one commander off against the other. Archelaus contrived to open negotiations with Sulla through an agent, and a conference was arranged to take place at Aulis[2]. The conference was opened by Archelaus, who proposed that on the basis of the *status quo* Mithridates should conclude an alliance with Sulla and provide him with the shipping, funds and troops required to carry on the war with his enemies in Rome. The insult was met, as we should expect, by a counter-invitation to Archelaus to surrender the fleet which he still commanded and join the side of the Romans.

The principals then proceeded to business, and a preliminary agreement was drafted in the following terms: the fleet commanded by Archelaus to be surrendered to Sulla[3]; prisoners, deserters and escaped slaves to be restored; Mithridates to retire from all conquered territory, including Paphlagonia, and pay an indemnity of 2000 talents. In return Mithridates was once more to become the friend and ally of Rome. Although at the outset Archelaus had protested at the suggestion that he should betray his master, it is obvious that he was fearful about his reception by

[1] The account in Dio, frag. 104, has been followed. Memnon, 34, places the murder of Flaccus after both divisions had crossed into Bithynia.

[2] Licinianus, p. 26 F.; Plutarch, *Sulla*, 22, says near Delium.

[3] So Appian, *Mithr.* 55, and Licinianus, p. 26 F.; Plutarch, *Sulla*, 22, 70 ships; Memnon, 35 (who gives only the terms finally agreed at Dardanus), 80 ships. Livy, *Epit.* 82: Archelaus cum classe regia Sullae se tradidit. Reinach, *op. cit.* p. 197, regards the withdrawal of his garrisons by Archelaus and the surrender of the warships under his command as part of a secret agreement between Sulla and Archelaus.

Mithridates and anxious to secure Sulla's goodwill. The fleet under his immediate command was immobilized or was actually surrendered, and the garrisons were withdrawn from the points which he still held. While the terms of the draft agreement were being conveyed to Mithridates, Archelaus remained as a distinguished guest at Sulla's headquarters, receiving the utmost consideration when he fell ill at Larissa, and being gratified with the death of Aristion, still a prisoner in Sulla's hands, against whom he nourished a grievance for his incompetent handling of the defence of Athens. Now or later, Archelaus also received large estates in Euboea and the title of friend and ally of the Roman People. While awaiting the king's reply Sulla spent the summer of 85 in operations against the northern tribes who had been troubling Macedon[1].

VIII. THE INVASION OF ASIA MINOR

During the early months of the year 85 the position of Mithridates was growing rapidly worse. Fimbria was conducting a highly successful, if brutal, campaign against the king and the Greek cities alike. Heavy contributions were laid on all, the money being shared among his troops, while towns which offered the least resistance were ruthlessly plundered, amongst them Nicomedeia and, at a later stage, Cyzicus, into which he had been received as a friend, and Ilium, whose people had given offence by sending to Sulla for assistance[2]. Mithridates had endeavoured to oppose Fimbria's advance from Bithynia on the Rhyndacus, where a large army was collected under his son Mithridates, recalled for the purpose from Pontus and assisted by Taxiles and the ablest of the king's generals. In the face of a greatly superior army, the Roman troops forced the passage of the river, and attacking the camp of the enemy at dawn, surprised them in their tents and destroyed the greater part of the army[3]. The younger Mithridates himself escaped with a part of his cavalry to join the king at Pergamum. But Fimbria, following up

---

[1] Appian, *Mithr.* 55. Plutarch, *Sulla*, 23, puts these operations after the return of the ambassadors and during Archelaus' mission to Mithridates. On the strength of Licinianus, p. 27 F., Reinach (*op. cit.* p. 198) would place a campaign undertaken by Hortensius in the north immediately after the conference, and a second expedition undertaken by Sulla himself during Archelaus' mission to Mithridates. But the diplomatic situation was such that Sulla could hardly have absented himself at this stage.

[2] Livy, *Epit.* 83; Appian, *Mithr.* 53; Dio, frag. 104; Strabo XIII, 574.

[3] Memnon, 34; Frontinus, *Strat.* III, 17, 5.

his victory, drove the king in flight to Pitane on the coast. He then beset the town on the land side, and sent an urgent message to Lucullus, who had at last arrived with something of a fleet and was cruising off the coast, to complete the blockade by sea. The language of the despatch, as given by Plutarch, was scarcely palatable to one of Sulla's partisans, nor was Fimbria's character likely to inspire confidence that he would abide by any agreement made with a political opponent. Lucullus refused to co-operate, and the great prize was lost[1].

Lucullus, it will be remembered, had been sent out by Sulla in the winter of 87–6 to raise a fleet among the maritime states of the East still loyal to Rome. With six vessels he had made his way through the enemy fleets to Crete and Cyrene. When the little squadron set sail for Egypt, most of it was lost to Mithridates' friends the pirates, and it was with difficulty that Lucullus himself made his way to Alexandria. Here he received a royal welcome from the Egyptian king together with a polite refusal to take part in the quarrel between Rome and Mithridates. He was, however, escorted in safety to Cyprus, where he was able to gather a few war vessels from the Cypriotes themselves, Phoenicia and Pamphylia. A year had elapsed since he had left Sulla. After spending part of the winter in Cyprus, Lucullus slipped through the enemy vessels which were waiting for him, and, as Sulla had ordered, joined his small squadron to that of the Rhodians in the spring of 85. The united fleet then proceeded to raise revolts among the islands and on the coast of Asia Minor. Cos and Cnidos were recovered, and the king's partisans driven out of Colophon and Chios. After refusing Fimbria's appeal at Pitane, Lucullus, sailing on northwards, defeated a Pontic squadron off the promontory of Lectum in the Troad, and in conjunction with the Rhodians overcame the fleet commanded by Neoptolemus off Tenedos. Regaining communication with Sulla, who had now advanced to Cypsela, Lucullus entered the Hellespont and waited at Abydos to transport the Roman army to Asia Minor[2].

When the ambassadors from the king returned to Sulla, Mithridates professed himself ready to accept the terms offered, with the exception of the clauses ordering the surrender of a part of his fleet and the evacuation of Paphlagonia. At the same time he hinted that better terms could be obtained from Fimbria. Sulla refused to abate the least of his demands and sent Archelaus to reason with the king. With the successes of Fimbria in Asia and

---

[1] Appian, *Mithr.* 52; Plutarch, *Lucullus*, 3.
[2] Plutarch, *Lucullus*, 2–3.

of Lucullus at sea Mithridates' position was desperate. Rejoining Sulla at Philippi, Archelaus brought word that Mithridates now requested a conference. At Dardanus in the Troad Mithridates in person accepted the terms dictated by Sulla, and after being reconciled to Nicomedes and Ariobarzanes, withdrew by sea to Pontus (August, 85 B.C.).

It is clear that considerable dissatisfaction was expressed by the army at the easy terms which had been granted to Mithridates, but Sulla excused himself on the ground that Fimbria and the king might have made common cause against him, and proceeded at once to deal with his rival. Fimbria had withdrawn southwards, and after carrying out a plundering raid through Phrygia was lying at Thyatira. When Sulla called upon him to surrender and began to enclose his camp, many of the Fimbrian troops deserted, others openly fraternized with Sulla's men, even to the extent of lending a hand in the works of circumvallation. Fimbria, having attempted unsuccessfully both to procure the assassination of Sulla and to bring him to an interview, fled in despair to Pergamum[1], where he committed suicide. His two legions were added by Sulla to his own army, only a few of the more desperate making their way to Mithridates.

There remained the settlement of affairs in Asia Minor. The states which had stood by Rome were suitably rewarded, Rhodes in particular receiving back a portion of the Peraea, which she lost after the Third Macedonian War (vol. vɪɪɪ, p. 289). Having sent Curio to restore Nicomedes and Ariobarzanes to their kingdoms, Sulla reduced such towns as still resisted in Asia, ordering the restoration to their masters of slaves set free by Mithridates, and punishing any further resistance or disobedience with slaughter, plundering and destruction of fortifications. Everywhere the partisans of the king were singled out for punishment. With the approach of the winter (85–4), Sulla provided for the comfort of the troops and the further punishment of the provincials by billeting his men on the inhabitants, special orders being issued for the entertainment of the soldiers and for their pay. Each legionary was to receive from his host the sum of 16 drachmae a day, centurions 50 drachmae together with two suits of clothing. Finally an indemnity of 20,000 talents, the estimated cost of the war and of the five years' arrears of taxes, was imposed, for which purpose the province was divided into districts, each

---

[1] Appian, *Mithr.* 60; Plutarch, *Sulla*, 25, places his death in the camp at Thyatira.

responsible for a fixed proportion of the debt[1]. The system seems to have remained the basis for the later financial organization of Asia, but that the right of farming the taxes in the province was withdrawn from the Equites seems improbable[2], well as it would have accorded with Sulla's political feelings towards that class.

To raise the sums demanded was beyond the resources of the province. Recourse as usual was had to lenders, and within a few years financiers and tax-farmers brought the country to despair. Not even the justice and fairness of Lucullus could make the burden tolerable. Shortly before his return to Rome in 80 B.C. Mitylene, which had incurred the especial displeasure of the Romans, ventured on a revolt that was not repressed without hard fighting. The coasts at the same time were being plundered by the pirates let loose during the war, with whom Sulla had no opportunity to deal. Leaving Murena with the two Fimbrian legions to administer the province, Sulla sailed from Ephesus in the year 84, and after a few months spent in Greece, embarked his army for Italy. Besides the spoils and treasures which were reserved for his triumph he brought with him something of more permanent value—the treatises of Aristotle, which after long concealment were now to be published to the world by scholars such as Tyrannio and Andronicus of Rhodes[3].

The crisis at Orchomenus had shown Sulla to be a soldier's general, but he was more than that. In strategy he was at once cool and daring, in tactics he was the first great master in the art of handling the more flexible weapon which the legions had become; in diplomacy he showed his hand had not lost its cunning. The rapid re-organization of Asia was, at the least, a great administrative feat and the Peace of Dardanus, if it was not a final settlement, gave Rome as well as Mithridates breathing-space. Having sacrificed his friends and imperilled his own career to meet the needs of Rome abroad, he was now to return to take vengeance and to reconstruct the Roman State.

[1] The number XLIV in Cassiodorus, *Chron.*, is uncertain both on palaeo-graphical and other grounds. For the *regiones* see V. Chapot, *Province romaine proconsulaire d'Asie*, pp. 89 *sqq.*

[2] See T. Rice Holmes, *The Roman Republic*, I, p. 395, where the question is fully discussed.

[3] Plutarch, *Sulla*, 26, 1; Strabo XIII, 608 *sq.* See above, vol. VI, p. 333.

CHAPTER VI

SULLA

I. THE SO-CALLED *BELLUM OCTAVIANUM* AND THE SECOND CAPTURE OF ROME

EVENTS in Rome and Italy during Sulla's absence in Greece are a sordid story, and their study ill repays the trouble. The stage was held by a contemptible troop, none of them effective and most of them corrupt, among whom for the first twelve months or so there stalked the dominating figure of Marius. But even the influence of Marius was all for evil; for by this time he was in his dotage—an old man with an *idée fixe*, thinking of nothing but the pleasures of revenge. Cicero, though he gratefully admits that from 85 to 83 B.C. Rome was so far free from fighting that the practice of oratory could be resumed[1], justly describes the times when he says, 'inter profectionem reditumque L. Sullae sine iure fuit et sine ulla dignitate res publica'[2].

The first move came from Cinna. Whether he had yet proposed the recall of Marius or not[3], he announced his decision to revive the programme of Sulpicius for dealing with the freedmen and the newly-enfranchised citizens. Immediately violence broke out again. The new citizens, of whom there were many in the city, crowded to support their champion, and they were soon joined by many more who flocked in from the country to lend a hand. The old Romans, among whom opposition to the change was stronger now that the influence of Marius had been withdrawn, found a natural leader in the other consul, Octavius. The signal for the final struggle was given when the inevitable tribunician veto was pronounced. There was a fight in the Forum: for a moment the cause of the conservatives was in peril, but Octavius himself arrived in time, and soon Cinna, making the usual appeal to the slaves, was driven headlong from the city. So the first round went to Octavius. But, if Cinna's position for the moment was weak, his own was little stronger. Neither party had an army, and victory in the end would go to him who had the skill to get one. This was the fact which made futile the next move of Octavius.

---

[1] *Brutus*, 90, 308. [2] *ib.* 63, 227.
[3] Cf. Florus II, 9, (III, 21), 9; *de viris ill.* 69, 2.

Instead of raising troops, he toyed with the feeble weapons of the constitution. The Senate, this time apparently on its own authority alone, declared Cinna no longer a citizen but an enemy of the State. His consulship, therefore, was at an end, and in his place was appointed L. Cornelius Merula. The choice was peculiar. Since Merula was Flamen Dialis and might not, therefore, look upon a corpse, the part he played in Roman politics was not likely to be large; and his usefulness was still further curtailed by the taboo which forbade him to enter the presence of an army. There can be little doubt that this singular selection was a political trick: for reasons which we cannot fathom, it was decided that Octavius in fact, though not in name, should be consul without a colleague.

Meanwhile Cinna was more profitably employed. Appius Claudius Pulcher, praetor of 89 B.C. and father of the famous Clodius, had an army in Campania, whither Cinna now made his way. He had already been joined by Sertorius, a tried soldier even at this early stage, by Marius Gratidianus and by other leading opponents of the Senate; and this party, on its journey to the south, picked up a motley following from the towns and villages through which they passed. When they reached Campania, the issue was not long in doubt. Appius Claudius was in no state to resist the demands of a man who, with some justice, could claim to wield the authority of a consul: indeed, Appius seems only to have retained his command thus long by flouting a law which had deprived him of *imperium*[1]. The army declared for Cinna without delay, and the return to Rome began. The progress was triumphant: one success, as ever, bred more, and the new citizens joined the standards in such numbers that Cinna soon had a formidable army at his back. More than this, on the news of Sulla's departure for the East, Marius had returned to Italy, and when he landed in Etruria he was soon able to raise a force of his own by enlisting slaves and declaring his devotion to the programme of Sulpicius. Thus Rome was threatened from north and south.

Against this danger the government at length bestirred itself. While Octavius and Merula hurriedly prepared defences round the city, appeals for help were sent to Pompeius Strabo, who still controlled the army in Picenum, and to the peoples of the region across the Po who might accept his leadership in gratitude for the passing of the Lex Pompeia de Transpadanis (p. 195 *sq.*). How far they responded we do not know, but any inclination they may have had to move was effectively checked by an expedition

[1] Cicero, *de domo sua*, 31, 83.

which Cinna sent up the Via Flaminia to Ariminum and the North. Pompeius himself obeyed the call: he came to Rome, pitched his camp outside the Colline Gate, and waited on events. His position was sufficiently difficult. The troops with Marius, indeed, were comparatively few: 6000 is the number given. But the army with Cinna was so large that, as it drew near to Rome, he could split it into three separate columns, commanded by himself, Sertorius and the enterprising Cn. Carbo. Despite the protests of Sertorius, who recognized the danger of such a friend, Cinna made the inevitable compact with Marius, and arrangements were then concerted for a fourfold attack on Rome.

Such was the gloomy situation when at length Pompeius Strabo, evidently not a man to be dismayed by odds, declared for the government and prepared to fight. His chief weakness was his lack of troops, and this lack the Senate had for some time been trying to make good. The Marians, by their promise to revive the Lex Sulpicia for the benefit of the newly-enfranchised Italians, had secured the support of the masses who had received the Roman *civitas* in 90 and 89 B.C. But there remained a great body of people who, by refusing to lay down their arms forthwith, had lost their chance of gaining the citizenship outright; and to them the Senate turned[1]. They were offered the franchise, apparently with no condition save that they should fight for the government in the coming struggle; but the offer, coming from such a quarter, was so obvious a bribe that the recruits it brought were only sixteen cohorts. For the rest, Metellus Pius was recalled to Rome and came with a section of his army; but the remainder of his force was immediately destroyed by the Samnites, who were thus set free to join the hosts of Cinna.

The siege of Rome would be a gloomy theme, even if the evidence were enough to allow its study: as it is, the authorities are so brief that only the outlines of the story can be traced. The senatorial forces held the inner lines, and their opponents were in four isolated divisions; but the attackers lay so close to the city, and the forces of the government were so inadequate, that not even a Napoleon could have hoped to destroy the enemy in detail. The outstanding incidents were few. Marius struck the most deadly blow when he captured Ostia and so gained control of the food-supply; but his subsequent advance on Rome, apparently by the Via Campana, was abruptly stopped after he had seized Janiculum. Somewhere in the region of the Borgo, Octavius blocked his way; and in the battle which followed the losses of

---

[1] Licinianus, p. 20 *sq.* F.

Marius were the heavier. Janiculum, it was said, might even have been recovered; but the city garrison had already been weakened in a heavy battle with Sertorius, and Pompeius Strabo forbade Octavius to follow up his success. Such was the spirit of the defence, and it was not the spirit to snatch victory from greater numbers. The feeble caution of the commanders soon had its effects on the men: desertions grew frequent, and discontent was fostered by disease. A first attempt to assassinate Pompeius was frustrated, but before long he died[1]; and thus there perished the one man in the city who, for all his evil character, could lay some claim to competence in war.

With Pompeius gone, the defence collapsed. The troops despised Octavius, and Metellus Pius had too meticulous a care for constitutional law to accept the invitation of the army and take over the command from a consul. The result of his refusal was immediate: the bulk of the legions deserted to the enemy and there was nothing left for the government but to open negotiations, if such they could be called. Cinna, refusing to give any promise that he would refrain from massacre, contented himself with saying that he would be as merciful as circumstances allowed: he insisted that he would enter the city as consul. The luckless Merula was, therefore, deposed; and then for the second time Rome fell before a Roman army.

II. THE DOMINATION OF CINNA

The first public act of Cinna after his return was to rescind the decree of outlawry against Marius and his friends. As soon as this had been achieved, Marius made his last and most sinister return to Rome. There followed a scene never forgotten by those who saw it and survived. The old man, consumed by the lust for vengeance, let loose his army and his liberated slaves against all his enemies, real or supposed. Octavius, the consul, was butchered with some ceremony, M. Antonius, the orator, with less. Q. Catulus, colleague of Marius in the consulship of 102, and the inoffensive Merula were honoured with prosecution in legal form, but neither waited for the formality of trial. Catulus suffocated himself with charcoal fumes, and Merula, having laid aside his mitre, bled himself to

---

[1] Vell. Pat. (II, 21, 4) is probably right in his suggestion that Pompeius died of disease. This is the meaning of the phrase 'sidere adflatus' used by Obsequens (56 a), misunderstanding of the original of which has perhaps generated the story of Plutarch, Appian, Licinianus and Orosius that he was killed by lightning.

death in the Temple of Juppiter, to be succeeded as Flamen Dialis
by the young Julius Caesar, now fourteen years of age. Of the
victims no count was kept. The heads of the senators who fell
were displayed from the Rostra, but the rest were left where they
lay, to be devoured as carrion because their friends dared not give
them burial. Thus the forebodings of Sertorius came true. The
guilt for this appalling slaughter rests with Marius alone. Sertorius took no part, and even Cinna found it more than he could
stomach. When terror had reigned five days and nights, he
surrounded the slaves who were the chief agents of Marius and
ordered the troops to kill them out of hand. Then at length the
carnage ceased.

The new masters now tried to set their house in order. What
votes and resolutions could do was soon achieved. Marius and
Cinna were declared consuls for the year 86 B.C., with only the
most perfunctory pretence of election, if even that: Sulla was proclaimed an outlaw, and his legislation was repealed *en bloc*. But
still the fact remained that Sulla himself, though his property was
confiscated, his house destroyed and his family in the direst
jeopardy until they escaped to Greece, was at the head of a large
and devoted army which enabled him to snap his fingers at the
farce in Rome. Had there been the slightest chance that the
action of Marius and Cinna would prove effective, had it been
conceivable that they could deprive the forces in the East of their
only tried commander before a successor had been found, that
action would have been the most criminal treason to the safety of
the State: as things were, the fidelity of Sulla's troops rendered it
merely fatuous. But powerless as it was to help its authors' cause,
it was an act of grave significance, most ominous for the future.
By this senseless decree the greatest figure in the Roman world
was forced into hostility with the government at home.

On January 13, 86 B.C., Marius died, and the vacant consulship
was assigned to a certain L. Valerius C. f. L. n. Flaccus—not
to be confused with his cousin L. Valerius L. f. L. n. Flaccus,
who had been consul in 100, censor in 97 and was soon to
become Princeps Senatus. Among the tasks which now faced
the government one at least was urgent. War in Italy had produced its invariable economic effect. Land and buildings, the
best of all investments, had slumped, and owners dared not
realize to pay their creditors because to do so would make them
hopelessly insolvent. If the lenders could wait, a moratorium
was clearly indicated until such time as property had recovered
its normal value: if not, debts must be scaled down to a point

at which assets would meet liabilities and still leave the debtors something on which to live. The difficulties of the problem were increased by the financial panic which followed the loss of Asia to Mithridates (p. 241) and by the lamentable state of the coinage at home. The well-meant experiment of the younger Drusus in debasing the *denarius* (p. 179) had led to a confusion in the currency which a deeper familiarity with money would have foreseen. Plated coins were worth less than the issues of solid silver, but their relative values were wholly a matter of opinion. The value of the *denarius* itself, as a denomination, became so doubtful that, according to Cicero, no man had any means of telling what he was really worth.

To meet this financial emergency two measures were devised. The chaos in the currency was resolved by a conference of the praetors and tribunes, whose decision was somewhat prematurely issued as an edict by the praetor Marius Gratidianus, to the great benefit of his personal popularity. On the details of his enactment our information fails; but Pliny's statement (*N.H.* xxxiii, 132) that it involved some system of assay suggests that debased coins, on detection, were either withdrawn from circulation or, as is perhaps more probable, kept in use for the time being at something less than their nominal value. The more general question of debt, with which Sulla and Pompeius Rufus had made some attempt to deal in 88 B.C. (p. 209), was the subject of a consular law introduced by Flaccus. It was a drastic measure which, though Sallust represents it to have been welcomed by responsible opinion, is more truly described by Velleius as disgraceful: creditors lost three-quarters of their loans and were compelled to accept a *sestertius* in the *denarius*—five shillings in the pound—in full discharge. Possibly it was the best that could be done, if something must be done forthwith: in that case, creditors had only themselves to thank for the consequences of their own impatience. But a comparison with the arrangements to meet a very similar crisis made by Caesar in 49 B.C.—arrangements which gave lenders a choice between immediate payment in part and deferred payment in full (p. 655)—is enough to show how feeble an effort was that of Flaccus to grapple with a problem of undoubted difficulty.

After the settlement of the economic problem, Flaccus was assigned a still harder task. Though he was wholly without military distinction and even, so far as our information goes, without experience in war, the unfortunate consul was chosen by his friends to lead an enterprise of the utmost peril. He was to take an army to the East and with it to attack either Mithridates or Sulla, whichever seemed the more yielding victim. If a strong force under a competent general had been organized to attack the Asiatic possessions of the king, while Sulla was holding a large part of the royal troops in Greece, the plan would have had much to commend it; but it is evident that, as things were, any strategic merits which the scheme might seem to possess were mere accidents in a piece of political intrigue. Flaccus, a man so brutal that his troops were constantly on the verge of mutiny, was a mere pygmy in the presence of such military giants as his opponents, and his stature was not noticeably increased by the device of mounting him on the shoulders of a *legatus*—C. Flavius Fimbria. Fimbria, whose only claim to notice hitherto had been an attempt to murder the Pontifex Maximus—Scaevola—at Marius' funeral, did, indeed, win some indisputable successes over the generals of the king, but even he could not induce his troops to turn their arms against Sulla. And it was against Sulla that the expedition was really aimed: its object was to destroy the power which nothing but destruction could prevent from proving fatal, in its own good time, to the government of Cinna in Rome. The proposed attack on Mithridates was, at the outset, a mere piece of camouflage, probably designed to hide the true nature of the business from the eyes of an army whose allegiance could not be trusted when Sulla was the foe: and in the upshot it was only by chance that the force found itself in Asia at all.

When at length they had crossed the Adriatic and begun to move east towards Macedonia, the commanders determined to turn south and seek out Sulla—a threat which Sulla advanced to meet; but desertions soon warned Flaccus and Fimbria that it would be folly to risk an engagement, and it was for this reason, and this reason alone, that, though Sulla was almost immediately entangled with the second Pontic army of Dorylaus, they refused their opportunity and moved on towards Byzantium for want of any other occupation. Thus, though it did some service to the Roman cause (see above, pp. 255 *sqq.*), this futile expedition failed of its real purpose, as it was bound to do. Sulla was at large, passing from strength to strength, and Cinna's domination was doomed to disappear so soon as Sulla could return to Italy.

Meanwhile Cinna at home was faced with the problem of the new citizens—a problem to which he might address himself the more enthusiastically because its successful solution could not fail to increase his power of recruiting forces for the coming fight. Promises to the Italians had been freely made. Cinna had undertaken to meet the demands of those who were enfranchised already by reviving the measure of Sulpicius to distribute them over the whole tribal body; and the Senate, in its quest for help against the Marians, had offered citizenship to those excluded from the benefits of the laws of 90 and 89 B.C. In less than two years these promises were to be redeemed; but though L. Marcius Philippus and M. Perperna, censors in 86, were more active than their predecessors of three years before, the work of registering the new citizens seems for the moment to have made most disappointing progress. Circumstances combined to delay their work: some of the praetors had been careless in compiling the lists required by the Lex Plautia Papiria[1], and the continued warfare, both in Italy and elsewhere, doubtless made it difficult for many of the Italians to hand in their applications. Whatever the causes, the returns showed only 463,000 names; and unless this figure is to be emended, the rise since 115 B.C. was one of less than 70,000.

But, besides the work of enrolment, there remained the task of merging the new citizens in the body politic of Rome; for, despite the long-drawn agitation for their repeal, the niggling arrangements of the Social War were still in force and the newcomers found themselves herded into a small minority of the tribes. Justice was done at length, though perhaps not till 84. It was in that year, according to the *Epitome* of Livy, that the citizens from Italy gained the *ius suffragii*: presumably they were spread throughout the tribes and their votes were thus made effective. Into the motives for the final concession, which was made by *senatus consultum*, there is no need to inquire. It belongs to a time after the Peace of Dardanus had brought Sulla's return very near, and, like other contemporary measures, it may have been primarily designed to win recruits: but, whatever the considerations which prompted it, the resolution of the Senate put the last touch to the triumph of the liberal cause. Though war still lingered in the remoter parts, only time was needed for the recalcitrants to gain the benefits which their more submissive neighbours were already able to enjoy. The principle of the settlement was irrevocably fixed. All the free inhabitants of Italy were to be equal members of a single State. The unification was achieved.

Meanwhile politics had been running a more tranquil course. The departure of Flaccus and Fimbria in 86 marked the beginning of a respite from the worst forms of strife, and for three years Rome resumed something of its normal aspect. It is true that Cinna had chosen as his colleague in the consulship of 85 B.C. the bitter and headstrong Cn. Carbo, who has already appeared as

---

[1] Cicero, *pro Archia*, 5, 9

commander of an army during the Marian siege of Rome; but, in spite of the character of his associates, Cinna himself seems to have behaved with a degree of moderation which enabled him to retain in the city at least some of the more prominent men who did not belong to his own party. His behaviour was not, indeed, above reproach. The means by which he got Carbo and himself made consuls for 85 B.C., and the formality whereby their office was continued for the following year, were, to say the least, so high-handed that men could deny that an election had been held at all. But in their main occupation—the preparation for the fight with Sulla—Cinna and Carbo could proceed without provoking open resistance: after its experience of armies in action, Rome was in no mood to boggle at mere recruitment, however sinister a future it might portend. Legions were raised, a fleet was collected, supplies were organized and money was provided to finance the war, when suddenly, towards the end of 85 B.C., there came an ominous pronouncement from the East. In a formal communication to the Senate Sulla rehearsed his services since the time of the Jugurthine War, complained of the treatment to which he and his friends had been subjected since 88 B.C., put it beyond doubt that he would respect all concessions to the new citizens, by whomsoever made, and finally stated his intention in the plainest terms of taking vengeance on the leaders of the movement designed to work his ruin. To this forthright letter the Senate was allowed to reply: Cinna seems to have lost his nerve. The Fathers offered to arrange an accommodation between the opposing sides, and ordered Cinna to stop his warlike preparations until Sulla's answer arrived: but the senatorial offer contained a sting—by proposing to guarantee his safety it assumed that, before long, Sulla would be a private citizen.

III. THE RETURN OF SULLA

In this alarming situation Cinna and Carbo did not belie their reputations. Professing obedience to the Senate's commands, they secured the continuation of their consulships to the end of 84 B.C. and pressed on energetically with plans for self-defence. The scheme was one which did credit to its authors: Sulla was to be fought in Greece, and Italy would thus be spared a renewal of the civil war at home. The forces, accordingly, were concentrated on the eastern coast, and the vanguard had already crossed the Adriatic before winter closed the seas. But in the spring of 84 B.C., when the second contingent had set sail, a fracas broke out among the troops still quartered in Ancona, and Cinna was suddenly murdered. Carbo was now the only consul, and he showed no desire for a colleague. Fearing for his safety in the city, he refused to visit Rome for the formalities of choosing a man in Cinna's place, until finally the tribunician college threatened to proceed with the abrogation of his own *imperium* if he stayed away. Then at length he came; but, after the proceedings had twice been thwarted by the auspices, his opponents bowed to the will of heaven and Carbo was left sole consul for the rest of 84 B.C.

With his position for the time being assured, Carbo was free to develop his own strategic plan—a plan sadly different from that of Cinna. Italy took the unenviable place of Greece as the destined scene of operations. The troops sent to Epirus had already been recalled, and Carbo now looked for means of strengthening his hold on the Italian peoples. His proposal to take hostages for their loyalty was resisted by the Senate with success, but a wiser way of winning their good will found senatorial support. It is to this period that we should assign the action of the Senate whereby citizenship was conferred on all to whom it had been promised and the new citizens were distributed over all the tribes.

About now there arrived from Sulla his reply to the Senate's offer of mediation. It said that, so far as he himself was concerned, he could never be reconciled with his enemies, though he would not resent it if the State should decide to spare their lives. Then came the clause which revealed the fate of Rome. Ignoring the offer to guarantee his safety, Sulla promised that he would protect the Senate and all those who had been driven for refuge to his camp—a promise which he was in a position to fulfil because he could depend on the loyalty of his troops. Thereby Italy was informed that the army would not be disbanded and that only defeat in battle could stop Sulla from becoming military despot.

In the year 83 the direction of affairs changed hands, and the outlook grew black: for superstitious minds it was evidence enough of the wrath to come that on 6 July the Temple of Juppiter Optimus Maximus was destroyed by fire, statue and all. Carbo, though he remained in Italy, had secured a powerful position for himself, and one which might be useful in defeat, by taking command of Cisalpine Gaul. Resistance farther south was left to the new consuls—L. Scipio Asiaticus and C. Norbanus, the prosecutor of Caepio in the case of the 'aurum Tolosae' (p. 159 *sq.*). Both of them belonged to the Marian party; but, though Scipio seems to have been a man of moderation and Norbanus was not without experience of war, neither was of the calibre required in leaders who were to face so formidable a threat as that of Sulla's return. They made such preparations as they could: it was perhaps in order to provide a base for their armies in Campania that M. Junius Brutus, father of the tyrannicide and tribune in this year, proposed that Capua should be made a colony—if, indeed, the measure which Cicero[1] ascribes to Brutus really belongs to his tribunate. But the consuls were acting on the defensive: their task was to wait on the moves of the invader, and it is Sulla who now begins to dominate the scene.

When Sulla left Greece in the spring of 83 with an army estimated at 40,000 men, something significant for the future had already been achieved. Either at their leader's instigation or of their own free will, the troops had sworn an oath that they would stay with the colours after their arrival in Italy and maintain a discipline which should save the countryside from all unauthorized destruction. Thus Sulla seemed to confirm the expression given by his first message to the Senate: he was a Roman who cared for Italy, and the object of his coming was only to chastise his enemies. Then, with the assurance that his army would not scatter to its homes as soon as it found itself in Italy again, he crossed the Adriatic and landed at Brundisium.

It now became his most urgent business to declare his attitude towards the new citizens of Rome. The disreputable government of the Marians commanded no respect, and so futile a set of schemers was not likely to redeem its position by the concessions it had made to the demands for an equitable application of the principles wrung by force out of Rome during the Social War. Sulla was the only man who could give strength to his opponents: if he had revealed a determination to go back on the work done in his absence to satisfy the just claims of the Italians, those Italians would inevitably have rallied round Carbo and his friends. But Sulla was a statesman, and a shrewd judge of his own interests as well. So far from seeking to upset the settlement, he accepted it entire and took steps to let his acceptance be known to those whom it most closely concerned. Early in his northward advance, he had a conference with the consul Scipio between Cales and Teanum Sidicinum about some of the most momentous issues of the day—the position of the Senate, the constitution of the State and, above all, the *ius suffragii*[2]. If agreement on the last of these questions existed, the fact was probably not published

---

[1] *de lege agr.* II, 33, 89.   [2] Cicero, *Phil.* XII, 11, 27.

abroad: the Marians could still make capital out of the new
citizens' anxiety about Sulla's attitude to their position in the
Roman State. But at the beginning of 82 their doubts were ended
when Sulla made what is called a treaty with some section of
these people, binding himself, in return for services unspecified,
to maintain their rights intact[1]. This pledge deserves notice. It
is one which Sulla never sought to break, and though it is sometimes overlooked in its martial setting, it marks the end of a chapter. With it the problem of the allies ceased to be a living issue.

IV. SULLA'S CONQUEST OF ITALY:
THE THIRD CAPTURE OF ROME

After landing unchallenged at Brundisium, Sulla had marched
along the Via Appia towards Campania as through a friendly
country[2]. His army was small, but seasoned and trustworthy: five
legions, 6000 cavalry and some troops from the Peloponnese and
Macedonia. Powerful supporters soon joined him, such as Q.
Caecilius Metellus Pius from Liguria who resumed the proconsular command conferred on him in 87, M. Licinius Crassus
from Africa, and L. Philippus, who was sent to occupy Sardinia.
And M. Lucullus struck a hard blow for him at Fidentia on the
Via Aemilia in Cisalpine Gaul[3]. No less important was the action
of the youthful Pompey, who foiled the attempts of the government to secure Picenum. Setting up the standard of the Sullan
party at Auximum he raised three legions, brushed aside the
forces sent against him, and reported at Sulla's camp, where he
was hailed *imperator*.

Sulla reached Campania before he met with opposition. The
consul C. Norbanus who was prepared to contest the crossing of
the Volturnus at Casilinum arrested envoys sent by Sulla to discuss
peace terms. Somewhere, in all probability between Mount Tifata
and Casilinum[4], a battle was fought and Norbanus was routed; of
the survivors some fled to the new colony at Capua, others to
Neapolis. Leaving these cities to be invested Sulla marched up
the Via Latina to Teanum where he met a second consular army
under L. Scipio. To him also he first made proposals for peace, an

---

[1] Livy, *Epit.* 86.   [2] See above, Maps 4 and 6.
[3] See C. Lanzani in *Rend. Linc.* Ser. vi, vol. ii, 1926, p. 7 on Plutarch,
Sulla, 27.
[4] Appian, *Bell. Civ.* i, 84, 382, says that a battle was fought at Canusium.
This is a mistake for some name in Campania, possibly Casilinum. The site
is indicated by Velleius (ii, 25, 4) and Florus (ii, 9 [iii, 21], 19).

armistice was concluded and such progress was made towards an understanding that Scipio sent Q. Sertorius to Capua to sound Norbanus. But Sertorius, with an eye to strategy and a distrust of the invader, secured a line of retreat to the Via Appia by seizing Suessa Aurunca which had joined Sulla. When Sulla complained of this, Scipio declared the armistice at an end. But in the meantime the persuasive manner of the veterans from overseas had undermined the loyalty of Scipio's recruits, so that the consul's troops passed over in a body. Well might Carbo fear the fox rather than the lion in the heart of Sulla. Scipio himself was set free, but soon began to enrol a fresh army. During the winter Norbanus was kept blockaded in Capua and would have none of his opponent's renewed attempt to make terms. Sertorius left to raise another army in Etruria.

The campaign of 82 was begun on both sides with increased resources and profound animosity. Sulla had secured Apulia, Campania and Picenum and was hoping to extend his power by guaranteeing to the Italian communities that citizenship which had been won from his opponents (p. 270). His glove was off and he made no secret of his intention to seize Rome. The revolutionary government also acted with vigour. Two extremists held the consulship, Cn. Papirius Carbo for the third time and C. Marius the younger. Large forces were raised in Etruria and Cisalpine Gaul. Under the lax régime of Cinna the Samnites and Lucanians had been enjoying independence, and in dread of a Sullan victory launched their last attack against the lair of the Roman wolf. Heavy fighting took place in three theatres of war, in Cisalpine Gaul, in Etruria and Umbria, and in Latium. The progress made by the Sullan armies in Cisalpine Gaul aided the collapse of the Marian cause in Etruria and Umbria; and these successes helped Sulla to maintain the blockade of Praeneste against the fury which later spent itself at the Colline Gate.

Early in the year, after a bitter winter, Sulla set out to seize Rome. Marching from Campania up the Via Latina he encountered Marius in the upper valley of the Trerus between Signia and Praeneste and engaged him at Sacriportus[1], possibly near the junction of the Via Latina and the Via Labicana. The Marian troops after heavy losses broke; many surrendered on the spot; the survivors fled to the fortresses of Norba and Praeneste. So vigorously did Sulla follow up his victory that thousands of

---

[1] The meaning and location cannot be determined. The *Torre Piombinara* or *Pimpinara* near Segni railway station is supposed (without good reason) to mark the site. See *Pap. Brit. School at Rome*, i, p. 280 and v, p. 422.

fugitives were massacred before the walls of Praeneste, and Marius himself barely escaped into the city. Leaving Q. Lucretius Ofella to reduce Praeneste by blockade, Sulla secured all the approaches to Rome and entered the city unopposed. Meantime Marius had imitated the ferocity of his father. Realizing that Rome was lost, he ordered the *praetor urbanus* L. Junius Brutus Damasippus before evacuating the city to put to death the most notable men of the other party. Among the victims of this atrocity were L. Domitius, consul in 94, and Q. Mucius Scaevola, Pontifex Maximus. After making some temporary arrangements to secure the city, Sulla marched into Etruria to oppose Carbo.

In northern Italy the insurrection in Picenum supported Metellus and Pompey in an offensive against Carbo and his generals Carrinas and Censorinus, whose base was Ariminum. Metellus defeated Carrinas at the Aesis, the northern boundary of Picenum. Carbo came up and checked him temporarily, but on hearing of the defeat of Marius at Sacriportus fell back upon Ariminum. During his retreat he sustained severe loss at the hands of Metellus and Pompey; not only did five cohorts desert to the former, but the latter cut up his cavalry and captured Sena Gallica. Thus the old *ager Gallicus* fell to Metellus. Carbo then left for Etruria to oppose Sulla, and Norbanus from Capua took over the command in the Po valley.

In Etruria and Umbria the Marians fought stubbornly but with scant success. Sulla invaded Etruria in person and soon established communications with Pompey and Crassus who had penetrated into Umbria from Picenum. The left division of his army was victorious at Saturnia; the right division encountered Carbo in the valley of the Clanis and crushed the feeble resistance of his Spanish cavalry. There followed a long and desperate engagement near Clusium which though indecisive temporarily checked Sulla's advance. Near Spoletium Carrinas was heavily defeated by Pompey and Crassus and blockaded in the town. He himself escaped under cover of storm and darkness, but a relieving army sent by Carbo was ambushed on the march by Sulla with the loss of 2000 men.

Meanwhile a decision was quickly reached in the valley of the Po. M. Lucullus was besieged at Placentia but in a *sortie* crushed his opponents. When Norbanus threw his troops, fatigued by a day's march, against Metellus at Faventia he was utterly routed; only 1000 survivors from a large army returned to Etruria. Finally, a Lucanian legion deserted and its commander Albinovanus treacherously murdered all the Marian commanders, save

Norbanus, before joining Sulla. The loss of Ariminum completed the collapse of the Marian cause; Metellus was supreme between the Apennines and the Alps; Norbanus fled to Rhodes and committed suicide. In Etruria, however, the Marians still had large forces in the field under Carbo. But the news of the loss of Cisalpine Gaul and the failure of the attempts, presently to be described, to relieve Praeneste broke the nerve of Carbo who fled from his camp and embarked for Africa. Part of his abandoned troops were destroyed by Pompey, the remainder dispersed. Isolated towns, like Volaterrae, still resisted but the bulk of the Sullan forces in Etruria were set free for service nearer Rome.

We have seen that Q. Lucretius Ofella had been left by Sulla to reduce Praeneste. The strength and the strategic importance of this fortress explain the desperate struggles which are the story of the siege. Since Sulla contrived to defeat the repeated attempts of the Marians to raise the siege it is in the opinion of the present writer very probable that his impregnable blockading lines extended over the whole of the broad pass between the spur of the Apennines upon which Praeneste stood and the north-eastern extremity of the Alban Hills[1]. Appian[2] indeed says that trenches were dug and blockading walls erected at some distance from the city itself. As relief by way of the mountains behind the citadel was out of the question, it was sufficient for Sulla to block the approaches on the remaining sides. Four unsuccessful attempts at relief were made. First, Censorinus with eight legions was sent by Carbo, but he was defeated by Pompey in Umbria and his army melted away. A more determined venture was made from another quarter. Seventy thousand troops, mostly Samnites under Lamponius, Pontius of Telesia and Gutta of Capua advanced from the south-east but could not break through the position. Then Marius tried to co-operate by making a sally and erecting a large fort between the city and Ofella's lines. But he could not gain his end. Next, Carbo dispatched two more legions from Etruria under Damasippus. 'But not even those could pass the narrow place (τὰ στενὰ), guarded as it was by Sulla[3].' Upon Carbo's flight to Africa Carrinas, Censorinus and Damasippus joining forces with Lamponius, Pontius and Gutta made a last desperate attempt to break through. Repulsed, they flung themselves against Rome. Leaving Ofella to hold his lines, Sulla marched post haste to save the city and during the afternoon of 1 November 82 B.C. launched his wearied troops against the enemy outside the Colline Gate.

[1] *Journal of Philology*, xxxv, 1919, pp. 1–18.
[2] *Bell. Civ.* 1, 88, 402.   [3] *Ib.* 1, 92, 423.

For long the issue was in doubt. The left wing which Sulla commanded in person was driven back upon the city wall; the gates were closed; and fugitives bore to Ofella the news that Sulla had fallen and Rome was lost. But on the right wing Crassus prevailed and pursued the enemy as far as Antemnae, thus enabling Sulla to recover. The surrender of a division of the enemy, who immediately turned against their comrades, put an end to the struggle. Perhaps the most ghastly scene of all was reserved for the third day after the battle when a meeting of the Senate in the Temple of Bellona was disturbed by the massacre in the Villa Publica of the Samnite captives, three or four thousand in number, including Carrinas, Damasippus and Pontius.

The Battle of the Colline Gate sealed the fate of Praeneste also. When the tokens of Sulla's victory, the heads of Carrinas and other leaders, were thrown into the city, the garrison surrendered to Ofella. Marius, when endeavouring to escape through one of the drain passages beneath the city, was captured and killed himself; most of the survivors were herded together and executed; the city was given over to pillage. In the main the war was over. Resistance was still offered in Samnium and Etruria, but elsewhere Italy awaited the pleasure of her conqueror.

Fifty-one years had passed since the sword began to play a decisive part in Roman politics, and it was by the sword at the outset that the victor of the Colline Gate sought to make his victory doubly certain. Thrice in seven years Rome had been the scene of political murder: the violent end of Sulpicius had been avenged by the massacres of the elder Marius, and in his turn Marius the younger had not shrunk from the slaughter of his opponents in and around the Senate House. But in the proscriptions of Sulla Italy endured the consummation of her sufferings. The execution of the captured Marian leaders and the butchery of the Samnite prisoners were followed by continual murders in the city, clearly with the approval of Sulla. It seemed that submission was not enough. At length one of his own partisans questioned him in the Senate as to his intentions. His response was the issue of a series of proscription lists, by which he outlawed all who had in any public or private capacity aided the cause of his opponents. It goes without saying that, apart from those senators who had sympathized with Marius and Cinna, the equestrian order, which had persistently opposed the nobles, was visited with Sulla's special hatred. Rewards were offered to those who murdered or betrayed any of these outlaws, and those who befriended or concealed them were liable to the severest penalties. The property of the victims was forfeited, and their sons and grandsons were excluded forever from office and from the Senate.

From the slaves of the proscribed Sulla selected and manumitted more than ten thousand of the youngest and strongest. Known as *Cornelii*[1] these men were potentially a standing army for employment in the capital and as *instrumenta imperii* corresponded to the garrisons of veterans who served his interests in Italy.

Although it was said that 4700 names were recorded in the lists, we can have no accurate knowledge of the total number of the victims. The innocent perished with the guilty, as the worst elements in the population seized the opportunity of enrichment, of gratifying personal grudges, and of securing indemnity for past and license for contemplated crimes. However little Sulla may have been moved by personal rancour against the mass of his victims, the house of Marius was indeed visited with fearful vengeance. The ashes of the victor of Aquae Sextiae were disinterred and scattered in the Anio, the monuments of his triumphs over Africans and Germans were overthrown, his adopted nephew, M. Marius Gratidianus, a popular figure who had twice been praetor, was dissected piecemeal as an offering to the shade of Catulus. These atrocities were not confined to Rome; they must have been repeated in country towns wherever the opportunity of legalized murder or confiscation presented itself. Side by side with these proscriptions went the punishment of whole communities who resisted even after the Colline Gate. Fire and sword were at work in Etruria; Samnium was laid waste, Aesernia being left in ruins. This reign of terror was never forgotten by the Romans. Whenever it seemed possible that some commander with a victorious army at his back might seize the government, there arose the fear that the horrors which had followed the Colline Gate might be repeated. Few of the letters of Cicero written early in 49 B.C. fail to testify how deeply the terror of the *Sullanum regnum* had bitten into the imagination of his fellow-citizens.

V. POMPEY AND THE MARIAN REMNANTS

In Italy Sulla was now undisputed master, free to proceed at once with his work of political reform; but in various outlying regions armies in the Marian interest were still at large, any one of which might form the centre of dangerous insurrection. Sardinia, which had been held by Q. Antonius Balbus, was occupied in 82 B.C. by the wily L. Marcius Philippus, whose allegiance

---

[1] Appian, *Bell. Civ.* I, 100, 469. See also *C.I.L.* 1², 722.

to the Sullan cause was now above suspicion: Spain, whither
C. Annius Luscus had been sent to suppress Sertorius, was about to
become the scene of a protracted struggle which is described elsewhere (see pp. 318 *sqq.*): and, finally, Sicily and Africa had given
harbour to large numbers of fugitives from the vengeance which in
Italy was now inevitable. The recovery of these two provinces, the
western granaries of Rome, was a matter of special urgency, and
for this purpose Sulla selected the young Pompey, whose services
since Sulla's return had won complete forgiveness for his earlier
aberration in the camp of Cinna[1].

Late in 82 b.c. or early in the following year Pompey, with the
Senate's support[2], was given praetorian *imperium*[3] and instructions
to expel the enemy from Sicily. The island was in the hands of a
violent Marian—M. Perperna, son of the consul of 92 b.c.; and
to his army was added a fleet brought up from the Marian base in
Africa by Carbo, who had betaken himself thither after the defeat
of Clusium and the failure of his efforts to relieve Praeneste. But
Sicily proved an easy prize. Perperna himself rapidly disappeared,
to be heard of next in the train of M. Aemilius Lepidus after the
death of Sulla: M. Brutus, a praetor of 88 b.c. who was now acting
under the command of Carbo, was surrounded on an expedition
of reconnaissance by the ships of Pompey and forthwith fell upon
his sword: and Carbo himself, caught in the island of Cossura
(Pantellaria), was put to death after long formalities by the general
who now began to earn from his enemies names like 'adulescentulus
carnifex'[4]. Nevertheless, if the somewhat biassed testimony of
Cicero may be believed[5], in his dealings with the Sicilian cities
Pompey showed notable moderation, and by the autumn of 81 b.c.
order had been so far restored that he could cross to Africa for the
second and more arduous phase of the undertaking.

The history of affairs in Africa during the eastern campaigns of
Sulla is wrapt in obscurity. It appears[6] that Metellus Pius had
taken refuge there for a time, but that he was supplanted in the
control of the country by a certain C. Fabius Hadrianus, of the
Marian persuasion, whose behaviour to the Roman citizens in the
province was so oppressive that he was finally burnt alive at Utica

---

[1] For the interpretation of Plutarch, *Pompeius* 5–6, 2 and Dio, frag. 107, 1,
see E. Wiehn, *Die illegalen Heereskommanden etc.*, p. 67 *sq.*, and the works
there mentioned.   [2] Livy, *Epit.* 89.

[3] Licinianus, p. 31 F. On the rare *aureus* with the legend MAGNVS (obv.)
PRO COS (rev.) see *B.M.C. Rep.* II, p. 464, n. 1, and Volume of Plates iv,
2, *g*.   [4] Val. Max. VI, 2, 8.

[5] *de imp. Cn. Pompei*, 21, 61.   [6] Livy, *Epit.* 84.

in his own *praetorium*[1]. Fabius was followed by Cn. Domitius Ahenobarbus—a son-in-law of Cinna[2]—who collected a considerable force in the peninsula to the east of the Gulf of Carthage and drew a certain amount of support from the Numidian region[3]. He is said to have found an ally in one Iarbas, who had ejected Hiempsal, son of Gauda, from his kingdom to the west of the Roman province, and it is possible that the party was joined by another potentate, named Masinissa[4], whose principality lay beyond that of Iarbas in the direction of Mauretania. Thus the recovery of Africa promised to demand military operations on an extensive scale, and Pompey accordingly set sail with 120 warships and 800 transports carrying six legions. The army was landed in two divisions at Utica and Carthage, and immediately it was swelled by the desertion of 7000 men from the enemy. Against this formidable attack Domitius could still muster a force of 20,000. But he was outnumbered; and, when the inevitable battle came, he was crushingly defeated and killed. After the victory Pompey did not take long to establish the authority of his government throughout the province, and thence he passed westward to Numidia. At this point help appeared from Mauretania, whence Bogud, son of the king Bocchus, led an expedition which caused Iarbas to take refuge in Bulla Regia. Bulla soon fell to Pompey, who put Iarbas to death and restored Hiempsal to the Numidian throne. There followed a general settlement of Numidian affairs, at the end of which Pompey returned to Utica having won back Africa for Sulla after a campaign marked by that rapidity for which later he became famous. According to Plutarch the whole business was over in forty days.

At Utica Pompey received orders from home which ill requited his achievements. He was to disband all his legions but one and to wait till his successor in the command of the province should arrive, which meant that he was to be denied the honour of a triumph. The result of this was such burnings of heart among the troops that Pompey was in some danger of being forced into open revolt; but in the end he took the less enterprising course and so spared both Italy and Sulla what would have been a struggle of some severity. Nevertheless, in spite of the dictator's reluctance and though he himself had held no magistracy, his own insistence and the pressure of his supporters finally, after long intrigues, won

---

[1] Cicero, II *in Verr.* I, 27, 70: cf. Pseudo-Asconius *ap.* Stangl, II, p. 241.
[2] Orosius V, 24, 16.   [3] See above, Map 5.
[4] *de viris ill.* 77, 2, on which see S. Gsell, *Histoire ancienne de l'Afrique du Nord*, VII, p. 282.

the concession of a triumph, and with its celebration on 12 March in a year which was probably 79 B.C. (though 80 B.C. is possible) the African episode was at an end.

VI. THE SETTING OF THE SULLAN LEGISLATION

With the Battle of the Colline Gate and the final establishment of Sulla's supremacy, sanity returns to Rome and her history becomes once more a subject fit for study. The convulsions of the last ten years had brought a new Rome into being, and its birth created problems whose solution would call for courageous reform. Daring and ability were necessary qualities in the man who would re-organize the State, and besides these he must have the means to translate his programme into action. The melancholy example of the Gracchi gave warning that statesmanship was futile if it relied on votes alone: nothing but armed force could uphold the man who undertook a task of such magnitude as that which now confronted Rome. There could be no doubt that Sulla was the one man living whose authority enabled him to face the work with confidence. By the fourth of his five marriages—to Caecilia, daughter of Metellus Delmaticus and widow of M. Aemilius Scaurus—he was connected with the most powerful elements in the State: of his ability it will be time to speak when his achievement has been surveyed.

His character, however, deserves some passing notice. Good looking and with a merry wit, in the days of his humble youth Sulla had drunk deep of the more sensuous pleasures. At dinner he was the best of company, and the vivacity of his surroundings was never marred by any squeamishness in his choice of friends. To the end he lived hard. When the golden hair had lost its sheen and gouty patches blotched the pale complexion, in his leisure hours he still remained faithful to the companions of other days. Sulla was a voluptuary at heart, with a cynic's contempt for the importance of human affairs. Nevertheless, they mattered enough to bring him into public life; and in public life the *bon viveur* became an altogether different being. There he was all efficiency. Whatever may be thought of the ends for which he chose to work, there can be only one opinion about his handling of the means. With a ruthless determination which made his name a byword for brutality he went on his way, crushing the opposition of friend and foe alike. The Marians were assured that, if any of them had been omitted from the lists of the proscribed, the omission was an oversight soon to be repaired; and, if any of his own party thought to trespass on the dictator's obligations for service in the past, the fate of

Ofella served to remind them that his will was only to be thwarted at their peril (p. 285). Like a man whose supreme conviction is that death comes soon or late to all, he never allowed the lives of a few hundred of his opponents to stand in the way of his considered policy. Yet, for all the forbidding savagery of his methods, he inspired unyielding loyalty in vast numbers of supporters. Indeed, his epitaph, which he is said to have composed himself, adequately expressed his outlook when it proclaimed to posterity that men had never known a truer friend or a more remorseless enemy[1].

In ancient times, largely because Cicero disapproved of his ideals, Sulla's public policy was often misrepresented, and in modern days it has been frequently misunderstood. It is difficult to conceive an account farther from the truth than that which describes him as a narrow-minded soldier who, finding himself supreme, used his supremacy to impose on Rome a kind of government which happened to accord with his private predilections. Sulla was far more than a capricious despot: he was the child of his age, whose task was dictated to him by his predecessors and whose solution of it was moulded as much by circumstances as by his own volition. There were many problems which he essayed to tackle, but those of outstanding difficulty were two. Of these two one had its origin in the Social War, the other in the army reform of Marius.

The enfranchisement of Italy had produced a situation to which the Roman constitution could only be adjusted by thorough-going change. Even in the third and second centuries the constitutional development had so far lagged behind the expansion of the State that no stretch of the imagination could find in Rome that effective sovranty of the assembled citizens which the theory itself assumed. The citizen-body was spread over an area so wide that the voters able to be present in Rome could not claim to be more than a fraction of the whole. So the theory was tacitly abandoned, and down to the tribunate of Tiberius Gracchus such functions as the assemblies discharged had generally been controlled by the influence of a Senate whose prestige was overwhelming. But the Gracchi had wrought a change: their attempt to revive the latent independence of the Concilium Plebis, and their threat to the Senate's use of the tribunate as a weapon against demagogic legislation, raised afresh the question of the claim that the voters in Rome should be regarded as adequately representing the citizen-body as a whole[2]. Then followed the Social War, with results which

[1] Plutarch, *Sulla*, 38, 4.　　　[2] See pp. 8 *sq.* and 91.

changed the face of Italy. Henceforward, since the *civitas* was to cover the length and breadth of the peninsula south of the Rubicon-Macra line, this handful of voters who lived at Rome and were largely drawn from the lowest stratum of society proposed to manage the affairs of all Italy. The proposal was clearly preposterous: the fate of the country could not be entrusted to the contents of the 'sentina urbis.' Constitutional reform was needed to create a government which would do justice to the interests of all classes of the population—a government, therefore, which would be immune from the dictation of the urban mob. Such was the first and greatest task which Sulla was called upon to undertake.

The second, which arose from the military reforms of Marius, has already been reviewed (p. 136 *sq.*). The need for pensions in the form of land bound the legionaries to their commanders: it was the commanders who would have to initiate the necessary legislation, and even so its passage might call for the active support of the soldiers themselves. Thus it happened in the end that armies became devoted to their generals, and the ties which united them grew ever stronger until the general deprived the government at home of the first claim on the legionaries' loyalty. The result was a danger—with which none can have been more familiar than Sulla himself—that the State would remain permanently at the mercy of rival commanders. Struggles like those between Octavius and Cinna and between Cinna and himself would become chronic, unless some means could be devised of effectively subordinating the armies to a central control. If the Republic was to survive, Sulla must be the last Roman to capture Rome. To ensure this was his second task. It was a task in which he failed, and in which failure meant the collapse of his most ambitious schemes; but the fact that he addressed himself to its achievement is essential to an understanding of his place in history.

VII. SULLA'S DICTATORSHIP

When order was at length restored, Sulla's most urgent need was to secure a legal basis for his own position. It is possible that the Senate had already done something to validate his acts—the Peace of Dardanus is perhaps an instance—and had granted him indemnity for his less regular proceedings: we may conjecture, for example, that he was allowed to retain his *imperium* though he had entered the city. But all this looked towards the past: for the future Sulla must seek something more than the Senate was able to bestow. Of the two consuls, Carbo had been killed in Sicily and the younger Marius at Praeneste. Thus the auspices had 'returned to the Fathers,' and Sulla suggested that they should take the usual step of appointing an *interrex*. Their choice fell upon L. Valerius Flaccus, the Princeps Senatus, and public opinion seems to have expected that he would proceed to the nomination of suffect consuls. But Sulla, who for the moment had retired from Rome, thought otherwise, and took care to let his thoughts be known. What was needed was a dictator, appointed without limit of time, who would retain command until the ship of State had at length been brought to port. Inevitably the submissive *interrex* agreed. There was, indeed, no precedent for a dictatorship of indefinite duration, and there was none for the naming of a dictator by any but a consul: but Flaccus did all that could be done to give the new despot some semblance of legality. Though it had never been known for an *interrex* to propose a law, he went to the Comitia and introduced a bill to make Sulla ' dictator legibus scribundis et rei publicae constituendae '[1] and leave him to enjoy this office until his task was finished and it was his pleasure to resign. Cicero grudgingly admits that Flaccus was not a free agent on this occasion, but the Lex Valeria itself fills him with a fury of indignation, though whether sincere or feigned is far from clear.

The law does, indeed, deserve notice, not because of Cicero's objections but because it marks a slight development in the practice of the constitution and sets a precedent for Julius Caesar and the members of the 'Second Triumvirate.' Undoubtedly there were features in the episode which found no parallel in the past. The dictators of the early Republic had been chosen for the general purpose of carrying on affairs (*rei gerendae caussa*), and in those later cases during the fourth and third centuries, when they had been appointed to discharge some special duty, the duty was generally of a very minor kind: Sulla, on the other hand, had specific functions of a sweeping sort, which involved nothing less than the drafting of a new constitution[2]. This, however, was a point of small significance: the one important novelty in Sulla's case was the absence of any limit to the period for which he might retain his office. It was a novelty which, by itself, was enough to raise the fears of a nobility whose mastering desire was for the earliest possible restoration of oligarchical control: but their fears

---

[1] For this phraseology compare Appian, *Bell. Civ.* 1, 99, 462, and *Res Gestae Div. Aug.* 1. Appian's accuracy here has been doubted by D. McFayden in *Papers in Memory of J. M. Wulfing*, p. 65.

[2] The use of 'constituere' in the sense of 'to organize, provide with a constitution,' is to be seen in Cicero, *ad fam.* XIII, 11, 3; cf. Bruns, *Fontes*[7], 11, l. 22.

were not stirred by this alone. The part played by the People in
Sulla's elevation was no less sinister. He was invested with his
powers by a *lex rogata*, and the implication was dangerously plain.
He was dictator by popular consent; his office was tenable without
any fixed limit of time; and there was no compelling reason why
he should retire until the support of public opinion was withdrawn.
Sulla, in fact, was too near akin to the tyrants of Greece. His
election postponed the oligarchical restoration to a date which none
could foresee, and in that fact lies the explanation of the resentment
felt in the circles from which Cicero's prejudices were derived.

But there were further objections to the new dictatorship which
others than oligarchs could urge. In reality it was not the early
dictatorships so much as the Decemvirates of 451 and 450 which
foreshadowed the office now conferred on Sulla (vol. VII, p. 459).
In the time of the Decemvirs, as now, the need was for drastic
changes in constitutional law, and on both occasions the con-
stituent authority was given inappellable power of life and death.
Whatever view be taken of the settlement which followed the fall
of the Decemvirate, a measure to forbid the creation of officers
from whose sentences appeal did not lie was both appropriate and
desirable in 449 B.C.; and it was because Sulla, like the Decemviri,
was to exercise autocratic powers over Roman citizens—and this
for an unlimited time—that his position gave cause for reasonable
alarm. So much may be admitted: but this is not to say that the
Lex Valeria expressly authorized the proscriptions. Though it undoubtedly implied a general indemnity for such measures as Sulla
might find necessary in the future for the proper discharge of his
task, if not for such as he had already taken in the past[1], the vague
suggestion of Plutarch[2] that the law empowered him to put his
political opponents to death is discounted by the testimony of
Cicero[3] that the proscriptions were the subject of a Lex Cornelia.
Nor again is it likely, in spite of the definite assertion made by a
Scholiast[4], that Sulla was encouraged in the Lex Valeria to do by
edict what properly was done by law. Probability is in favour of the
conclusion, with which none of the credible authorities disagrees,
that the Lex Valeria was a simple measure: it created Sulla dictator,
defined his task, and for the rest left him to his own devices.

When Sulla's position was established, the year 82 must have
been near its end. His triumph over Mithridates was celebrated

---

[1] Whether the Lex Valeria did anything to supplement the indemnity
for the past already granted by the Senate is uncertain: the only evidence—
that of Cicero in *de lege agr.* III, 2, 5—is equivocal.   [2] *Sulla*, 33, 1.
[3] II *in Verr.* I, 47, 123.   [4] Schol. Gron. D. *ap.* Stangl, II, p. 314.

in January 81; and though both Livy and Appian mention this
event after their account of his main legislative programme, it is
clear that the bulk of his laws must have been passed in 81 and 80,
even if they had been blocked out, and in some cases promulgated,
in the last months of 82. The consuls for the year 81—M. Tullius
Decula and Cn. Dolabella—were two creatures of the dictator,
men of no importance or interest save for the circumstances of
their appointment. It happened that, when the time for the election approached, the renegade Marian, Q. Lucretius Ofella, now
fresh from his success against the younger Marius at Praeneste,
was induced to put himself forward as a candidate. He hoped that
his services to the cause would close Sulla's eyes to the fact that he
was ineligible, not having been praetor or even quaestor. But
Sulla would not consent. Ofella was ordered to withdraw; and
when he refused, the dictator had him murdered in the Forum.
Sulla was now the constitutionalist with a vengeance.

After this, though the proscriptions were far from finished[1],
Sulla set about his task of reform. The chronological schemes of
our authorities are so frail that it would be impossible to fix the
order in which the legislation was carried, even if the order were
historically important. Fortunately it is not, and the measures
may best be taken in their logical sequence. The objects which
Sulla set out to attain can be briefly stated. His first business was
to stop the system whereby supreme legislative power, theoretically vested in the Magistrates and People, had in fact been
wielded, so far as the popular element was concerned, by the
urban proletariate which was in no sense representative of the
body politic as a whole. This he attempted to do by subjecting the
assemblies to strict control by the Senate. Secondly, all other
organs in the government had to be protected against the danger
of dragooning by the most powerful section of the executive—the
governors of the provinces and other army commanders. Thus it
falls naturally to consider first the measures taken to fit the Senate
for the predominant position which it was henceforth to hold.
Thereafter will follow the arrangements whereby its predominance
over the assemblies was secured. And finally will come the plans
designed to subordinate the proconsuls to the government at
home. So much will complete a sketch of the new constitution,
and all that will remain is the minor work of detail in various departments which was not essential to the main scheme of
constitutional reform.

[1] They appear to have ended officially on 1 June, 81: Cicero, *pro Roscio
Amer.* 44, 128.

VIII. SULLA AND THE SENATE

In 81 B.C. the Senate was below its normal strength. Seven years before, its members had been noticeably few; but it is doubtful whether the recruitment then proposed by Sulla had ever been carried out, and it is certain that since 88 the House had sustained further heavy losses. After the last census in 86, besides deaths from natural causes, there had been the inevitable casualties of the Civil War, and on top of these had come the proscriptions. Sulla himself is said by Appian with some precision to have been responsible for the ends of a hundred and five senators. But now there was need of a Senate even stronger than it had been immediately before the outbreak of the Social War. If it was properly to fill the rôle for which Sulla meant to cast it, the House must contain all the ability which could be made available and must be so constituted as to reflect every shade of responsible opinion. The proposal for an addition of three hundred new members was accordingly revived; and it was carried into effect with a broad-minded liberality which not even the malice of Sallust can disguise[1]. With a wisdom for which he is not always given credit, the dictator broadened the basis of senatorial authority by including in the House a selection of that affluent and ambitious class which had been the head and inspiration of the opposition since Gracchan times.

But this was not all. By an ingenious innovation, on which the most diverse interpretations may be put, Sulla provided for future recruitment by an arrangement which enabled him to set the censorship aside. Ever since the Ovinian plebiscite (vol. VII, p. 818) curule magistracies had conferred on their holders a claim to enrolment in the Senate, and since the dictatorship of M. Fabius Buteo in 216 B.C. tribunes and quaestors had been allowed some hope of a place. Thus the principle of indirect popular election had long been known; but hitherto it had always been qualified by the presence of the censors. The discretion of the censors was large, and despite all precedents and instructions its exercise was hampered by nothing but the necessity of finding some plausible reason for departure from the normal practice. But now,

---

[1] Though Sallust (*Cat.* 37, 6) and Dionysius (v, 77, 5) make the usual allegation that the new senators were men of no distinction, drawn in some cases even from the rank and file of the legions, it is abundantly clear from the result that Livy (*Epit.* 89) and Appian (*Bell. Civ.* 1, 100, 468) are nearer the truth in saying that they came from the 'ordo equester.'

by a law of which a fragment is still preserved[1], Sulla raised the numbers of the quaestorian college to twenty and enacted that these twenty quaestors should automatically pass into the Senate and so provide that regular supply of recruits needed to make good the wastage caused by death. Thus for the maintenance of the Senate the censors were no longer necessary; and, since they had been prone to use their powers on the strictest interpretation of the principles which the Optimates upheld, their deprivation of this duty might be hailed as a democratic measure designed to free the principle of popular election from its only trammel.

But, if this was a move in the direction of what passes as democracy, the risk it involved was small. Though the authority of the Senate might be increased by the fact that its members all held their places thanks to the suffrage of the People, the People was very far from being invested with the powers hitherto wielded by the censors. Its freedom of choice was severely limited by the necessity of selecting from a body of men who had yet to enter serious public life: they were little better known to the electors than the average parliamentary candidate of modern times, and the choice of those who could contribute most effectively to the discussions of the Fathers was made almost impossible by the lack of evidence for their qualities. But there was another aspect of the matter. Censors could admit to the Senate men who had made a name after that time of life at which they would have been prepared to hold the quaestorship and to start on the *cursus honorum* at that steady pace which alone the *lex annalis* allowed. Such people, making a career by their merits, were of the type from which Sulla had much to fear, and to them the censors' aid might prove invaluable. This was one of the reasons why, when Sulla had taken the recruitment of the Senate out of the censors' hands, its restoration became a plank in the platform of the *populares*[2]. Nevertheless, his attack on the office may well have made a wide appeal[3], and it was perhaps only the lack of censors between 86 and 70 B.C. which opened the eyes of certain classes to their value.

The Sullan Senate calls for careful notice. On it the dictator built his hopes; but it was not that Senate which had so lamentably failed in the recent past. Hitherto the class from which Gaius Gracchus drew his jurors had been in bitter opposition: now it was strongly represented in the House. Hitherto, though the results of popular election guided the censors' choice, in its immediate constitution the Senate had been imposed on the People from

---

[1] Bruns, *Fontes*[7], 12.   [2] Cicero, *Div. in Caec.* 3, 8.

[3] Cicero, *loc. cit.*; Pseudo-Asconius *ad loc.* (Stangl, ii, p. 326.)

above: henceforward, since they alone were to be responsible for its recruitment, the People might be expected to accept its judgments with something less than the reluctance of the past. There is even a suggestion in Appian that the three hundred members enrolled by Sulla were chosen with the People's help; and, though it is not to be supposed that an assembly was allowed to make a free selection of three hundred from a longer list, it is by no means improbable that Sulla tried to invest his nominees with the authority of popular consent by submitting his candidates, either singly or together, to the approval of the People by vote. Whatever be the truth about this, it must at least be admitted that by increasing the numbers of the House and by destroying the arbitrary influence of the censors on its composition, Sulla brought the Senate into closer relation with the Populus as a whole: and, whether his attempt was successful or not, the scheme can claim the whole-hearted admiration of so staunch a *popularis* and so stern a critic of Sulla as Cicero himself[1].

The uses to which Sulla put the Senate thus reinforced must be reserved for later notice; but here it may be observed that he did not fail to provide that increased opportunity for the reward of public service which the increased numbers of the House required. The colleges of the pontiffs and augurs, which had remained unchanged since the Lex Ogulnia of 300 B.C. (vol. VII, p. 427), were both enlarged. Each for the future was to have fifteen members and, by a repeal of the Lex Domitia of 104 B.C. (p. 163), Sulla ordained that these members should be chosen by the ancient principle of co-optation unqualified. The first occupants of the new places thus created were drawn from the brilliant band of young hopefuls by whom the dictator soon found himself surrounded.

IX. THE *LEX ANNALIS*

With the Senate thus strengthened to face the tasks to come, Sulla's next business was to secure its position against demagogic attack. There must be no repetition of the Gracchan episode: somehow or other a means must be found to prevent reckless politicians from running amuck on the backs of a venal proletariate which masqueraded as the sovran People. There is something to be said for the view that the most valuable of Sulla's expedients to confirm the restraining influence of the Senate over the assemblies was the reform, discussed above, whereby the Senate was made a body recruited by popular election. But though this fact might

[1] *de legibus*, III, 12, 27.

well affect the attitude towards the Fathers taken by citizens of responsibility, it was idle to expect that so subtle a change would fill the worthless mob with a respect for senatorial influence strong enough to outweigh the attractions of promises made by the unscrupulous victims of personal ambition. Something more was needed to thwart the threat of irresponsible legislation.

In the early centuries of the Republic the making of a law had required the co-operation of the Senate, the People and a magistrate, but by the Lex Hortensia of 287 the Senate had in theory been eliminated. Nevertheless, the legislative independence of the People still remained trammelled by the necessity of securing a magistrate to introduce a bill before the assembly could give its vote, and herein Sulla found an opportunity which in a full democracy he would have been denied. Thanks to the necessity for magisterial initiative, if he could bring the magistracy under senatorial control, he might curb the licence of the legislature without changing the constitutional powers of the assemblies or altering their composition so as to deprive the less substantial citizens of the franchise. We are not told that Sulla in his dictatorship revived the measure of 88 which gave the Senate a general right of veto against bills before their submission to the People; and it is unlikely that he did so. During the survival of Sulla's constitution, and particularly in 75 B.C., there are signs of consular laws for which it is difficult to believe that the agreement of the Senate as a whole had been forthcoming. The method to which Sulla pinned his faith was different. If periods of civil war be excepted, consular legislation had not been dangerous in the past: indeed the consulship, save perhaps during the predominance of Marius, had given singularly little cause for alarm. In normal times, which Sulla seems to have assumed would in future be unbroken, the consuls had been so loyal to the Senate that the dictator was content to leave them almost as much liberty as before. So far as they were concerned, his only precaution was to deprive them of a certain obvious temptation to pander to the rabble. The rewards of popularity took the form of office, and if office were made a rare and ephemeral incident in a man's career, he would be the less inclined to cultivate the affections of those by whom office was bestowed. Accordingly Sulla had recourse to a revision of the *lex annalis*.

The Lex Villia of 180 B.C., about which our information is lamentably defective, seems to have done no more than form the quaestorship, praetorship and consulate into an ordered *cursus*, wherein each stage was a necessary preliminary to its successor, and demand a minimum interval of two years between one office and the next (vol. VIII, p. 376). The result of this arrangement, if ten years' military service was required in candidates for the quaestorship, was in effect to prevent men from holding the quaestorship before the age of twenty-seven, the praetorship before thirty and the consulate before thirty-three: and, in the cases of those who held the curule aedileship, these minimum ages would be increased by three years for all subsequent offices. Sulla kept the essence of these rules but changed the details. Henceforward no man could hold the consulship until he was at least forty-two, the praetorship until he was thirty-nine and the quaestorship until he was thirty[1]. Thus two ends were achieved. Men could not rise to office of influence until they had reached years which should bring discretion and, secondly, since quaestors now passed automatically into the Senate, men would be members of the House for eight years at least before they could attain the praetorship—the first office which gave its holder power to do serious harm. By that time they might be expected to have gained some acquaintance with the conduct of public affairs and to have assimilated something of that political sobriety which was the best characteristic of senatorial tradition.

But this was not enough: the lure of repeated consulships such as Marius had held must be destroyed. By a measure which Livy assigns to the programme of L. Genucius in 342 B.C. (vol. VII, p. 529) but which is more probably to be regarded as a sequel to the introduction, fifteen years later, of the system by which *imperium* was prorogued, magistrates had been prevented from holding any office for a second time until ten had elapsed since the end of their first period; and this enactment, which obviously affected the consulship most of all, was followed up somewhere in the middle of the second century by a categorical rule that no man might be consul twice (vol. VIII, p. 376). So far as we know, neither of these laws had been repealed, though exemptions from

---

[1] The comparatively copious evidence which shows that thirty was the normal minimum age required for the quaestorship during the Ciceronian period will be found collected by Mommsen in the *Staatsrecht*, I³, pp. 570 *sqq.* The passage which leads Mommsen to the conclusion that Sulla required quaestors to have passed their thirty-sixth birthday (Cicero, *de imp. Cn. Pompei*, 21, 62) is of very doubtful value, because it is uncertain whether the phrase 'ullus alius magistratus' includes the quaestorship or not: see *Dig.* 50, 4, 18, 2. For the evidence on the problems connected with the *leges annales* see K. Nipperdey, 'Die *leges annales* der röm. Republik' in *Abhandlungen der philol.-hist. Classe der Königl. Sächs. Gesellschaft der Wissenschaften*, V (1865).

both had been granted to Scipio Aemilianus in 135 and though both had been flouted by Marius and Carbo.

Sulla seems to have repealed the second. It had been a dead letter since 105; and, rich in political ability as Rome might be, her resources were not so great that she could afford to employ her outstanding citizens in the highest magistracy only once in a life-time. The law, a monument of the fears which had seized the Senate when its own grip on affairs began to fail, was not likely to command the sympathy of Sulla, and he threw it over-board. But if repeated consulships were to be permitted for the future, there was to be no encouragement for aspiring imitators of Marius. The interval of ten years between a man's first consul-ship and his second was to be rigorously required, and the *lex annalis* of Sulla seems explicitly to have repeated the provisions on this point originally included in the law of the fourth century. Such were the simple means whereby Sulla sought to guard against the danger of subversive legislation passed by the Comitia with the help of curule magistrates. No man was to acquire the *ius agendi cum populo* until he had been steeped in senatorial tradi-tion for at least eight years and had left his impetuous youth so far behind as to be verging on middle age. And, secondly, for all alike the temptation to curry favour with the masses was reduced by the knowledge that office, the only return which the People had to make, could come but rarely to a man who had once attained the consulship.

X. SULLA AND THE TRIBUNATE

The next problem was more difficult. During the last two centuries the tribunate had been so far transformed that its most frequent function was to serve as a weapon wherewith the oligarchs could block the passage of bills which they disliked (p. 26). Nevertheless, on the comparatively rare occasions when the tri-bunician powers had fallen into the hands of an able and enter-prising opponent, the Senate had received a mauling far more severe than the worst outrages perpetrated by any curule magis-trate, apart, at least, from those who had captured Rome by force. It was the tribunes who had revived the dormant sovranty of the People. To meet this very urgent menace Sulla adopted a simple expedient. Again avoiding an infringement of the Plebiscitum Duillianum (p. 208), he enacted that election to the tribunate should permanently disqualify a man from holding any other office; and we may assume on the strength of Appian's testimony that, if iteration of the tribunate itself was not forbidden, re-election was only allowed after the lapse of the ten years' interval required in all other cases. The object of these arrangements is plain, though it has not always been observed. By cutting off tribunes from all hope of curule office Sulla was in fact trying to kill the tribunate. If people believed that his regulations would endure, as he himself undoubtedly intended them to do, no man of ability and ambition would voluntarily commit political suicide by becoming tribune. The tribunate would either die for lack of candidates or else the office would fall into the hands of complete nonentities and thus become innocuous.

So much is enough to show that the restrictions imposed by Sulla upon the powers of such persons as might hold the tribunate in future are of less importance than has sometimes been assumed. Nevertheless, they achieved so great a notoriety that their removal by Pompey and Crassus in 70 B.C. was thought to mark the final collapse of the Sullan constitution; and for this reason they cannot be passed over in silence[1]. The right of the tribunes to rescue a member of the Plebs from the clutches of a magistrate (*ius auxilii ferendi*) remained intact[2], but, though the general power of veto (*ius intercessionis*) was not wholly abolished[3], prohibitions of its use in specific circumstances, of the type incorporated by Gaius Gracchus in the Lex Acilia[4] and in his own *lex de provinciis consularibus* (p. 64), were probably multiplied[5]. The tribunes also found their judicial functions at an end; but this was perhaps not so much the result of a desire on Sulla's part to curtail their powers as the inevitable consequence of his reform in the sphere of criminal procedure (pp. 304 *sqq.*).

The gravest doubts, however, are those which surround the most serious issue—that which concerns Sulla's attitude to the activities of tribunes in initiating legislation by the Concilium Plebis. There lay the danger of the tribunate to senatorial government, and it is a disaster that just at this point our evidence for Sulla's counter-measures fails. The Epitomator of Livy is explicit[6] —the tribunes lost all power of moving legislation (*ius rogandi*);

[1] Whatever meaning Appian may have intended to convey by his language in *Bell. Civ.* I, 100, 467 (καὶ οὐκ ἔχω σαφῶς εἰπεῖν εἰ Σύλλας αὐτήν, καθὰ νῦν ἐστίν, ἐς τὴν βουλὴν ἀπὸ τοῦ δήμου μετήνεγκεν,) the passage is of no historical value: Appian himself admits that he is in doubt, and there is not the slightest reason to believe either that Sulla gave the Senate the duty of electing tribunes or that he made none but senators eligible for the office.

[1] Cicero, *de legibus*, III, 9, 22.
[3] Sallust, *Hist.* II, 21 M; Caesar, *B.C.* I, 5, 1; 7, 3.
[4] Bruns, *Fontes*[7], 10, l. 70 *sq.*   [5] Cicero, II *in Verr.* I, 60, 155.
[6] *Epit.* 89.

and a certain support for this view may be found in a vague phrase of Cicero's[1]. No certain case of legislative activity by tribunes is known during the age when the arrangements of Sulla prevailed[2], and there is nothing to compel the rejection of the Epitomator's story. On the other hand, it is conceivable that the Lex Plautia de reditu Lepidanorum was passed slightly before 70 B.C., and in that case, since this was almost certainly a tribunician bill, it would follow that the *ius rogandi* remained. If so, it was undoubtedly safeguarded by the provision that senatorial approval must be gained beforehand for any proposal to be submitted to the Plebs[3]. In either case the Epitomator is in all essentials right: the freedom of the tribunes in proposing legislation was gone, and the danger of a new Gracchus or Saturninus was, for the time being, at an end.

XI. SULLA AND THE ARMY COMMANDERS

Such were the devices whereby Sulla sought to protect the Senate against attacks from the curule magistrates and the tribunes: as the sequel will show they were not without success (p. 329). But in another direction there lay a greater peril, and here the precautions of the dictator proved less adequate. To complete a general sketch of the central features in the Sullan constitution it remains to consider the arrangements designed to regulate relations between the central government and the commanders of military forces abroad. This was the most vital task of all, as no man knew better than Sulla himself. Thrice within the last decade Rome had fallen to armed attack, and it was obvious that, unless a repetition of this military interference were made impossible for the future, the days of senatorial supremacy would be few. For the moment the Senate could rely on the sure support of Sulla and his troops, but, once this support was withdrawn, the arrival of a recalcitrant proconsul with his army at the gates of Rome would be instantly fatal. The Senate would either be compelled to submit or else would have to plunge the State into

---

[1] *de legibus*, III, 9, 22—'...vehementer Sullam probo, qui tribunis plebis sua lege iniuriae faciendae potestatem ademerit, auxilii ferendi reliquerit.'

[2] On the dates of the Lex Plautia de reditu Lepidanorum and the Lex Antonia de Termessibus (Bruns, *Fontes*[7], 14), see Note 3 on p. 896.

[3] It appears from Sallust, *Hist.* III, 47 M., that the Senate had at an earlier date not been opposed to the principle embodied in the Lex Plautia. If it could be proved that the Lex Antonia de Termessibus was passed before the legislation of Pompey and Crassus in 70 B.C., the phrase 'd(e) s(enatus) s(ententia)' in the preamble would point to the same conclusion.

civil war by arming some rival marshal to oppose the first. Accordingly it was necessary at all costs to secure that no provincial governor should find himself tempted to march on Rome, and this end Sulla essayed to achieve by weakening the bonds which bound governors to the troops serving under their command.

The evidence for the reforms which Sulla introduced is unfortunately for the most part circumstantial, but it is enough for the construction of an account which may be accepted, at least in outline, without much hesitation. Down to the time of the Social War provincial commands had been held by consuls and praetors both during the years in which they occupied these magistracies and in innumerable cases for a further period thereafter, during which they retained their *imperium* by prorogation[1]. From the time of Sulla onwards till 52 B.C., if commands which are clearly extraordinary be left out of account, it is rare for a consul, and unknown for a praetor, to be employed elsewhere than in Rome or Italy during his tenure of the magistracy itself: on the other hand, it is regular for ex-consuls and ex-praetors alike to govern a province in the year after their term of office in the city. Thus it appears that in the early part of the first century B.C. the distinction between magistrates and pro-magistrates became more definite: the former normally exercised their *imperium* at home, the latter in the provinces. It is by no means to be denied that a tendency in this direction had long been growing more pronounced, but probability is in favour of the view that Sulla carried the process on another stage. Apart from the conclusions which may be drawn from the provincial commands known to have been held in the years following 80 B.C., evidence that by 70 B.C. consuls were expected to pass on to a governorship abroad is to be found in Pompey's assertion that he would refuse to leave Rome for a province at the expiration of his consulship[2]; and this system may be traced back even to 76 B.C. or thereabouts, if the words put by Cicero into the mouth of Lucilius Balbus are true of the dramatic date of the dialogue in which they occur[3]. The indications are strong in their suggestion that on this point the Sullan age saw custom hardening into rule.

On the other hand, there is no reason to suppose that Sulla set up any rigid prohibition whereby consuls and praetors were debarred from military duties during their year of office, and that

---

[1] The attempt of Marquardt (*Staatsverwaltung*, I², pp. 518 *sq.*) to restrict this arrangement, so far as praetors are concerned, to the period after 122 B.C. is not wholly justified. See G. De Sanctis, *Storia dei Romani*, IV, I, pp. 504 *sq.* on the Lex Baebia de praetoribus.

[2] Vell. Pat. II, 31, 1.   [3] *de nat. deor.* II, 4, 9.

these duties were reserved for such magistrates in the twelve months immediately thereafter: instances to the contrary are too plentiful to be regarded as breaches of a categorical enactment, for the existence of which, it must be remembered, explicit evidence is altogether lacking. There is no need to search the history of the Ciceronian age: the ten years following the Sullan legislation provide material enough to show that the Senate was left with a wide discretion to continue the *imperium* of pro-magistrates and to bestow military commands on whom it would. First for some exceptional appointments. On two occasions the consuls took charge of armies: in 78 B.C. M. Lepidus and Q. Catulus were commissioned to deal with the trouble in Etruria (p. 315), and in 74 B.C. the Senate sent L. Lucullus and M. Cotta to fight Mithridates. Again, M. Antonius (Creticus) appears to have been praetor when he was appointed to face the menace of the pirates in 74 B.C.[1], and after the consuls of 72 B.C. had failed to make headway in their attacks on Spartacus, it was a praetor—M. Crassus—who was chosen to succeed them. Finally, the young Pompey twice received armies to command—in 78 B.C., perhaps as a subordinate of Q. Catulus[2], and secondly in 77 B.C. when he was certainly independent—though he had never held a magistracy of any kind at all: but it should be noticed that the new commission in Spain was offered in the first place to the consuls of 77 B.C. and only went to Pompey because they refused the task[3]. In these cases, however, the circumstances were to some extent unusual. The rising of 78 B.C. and the revolt of the slaves under Spartacus were not normal incidents in the life of Italy, the dispatch of Pompey to Spain came at a time when one ex-consul—Metellus Pius—was already there, the pirate war which occupied the attentions of M. Antonius made a quite special call on the resources of the government, and the Asiatic expedition of the consuls of 74 B.C. cannot have been unconnected with the bequest of Bithynia to Rome.

These incidents show that the Senate could provide as it willed for emergencies of whatever sort; but, though the government of the comparatively peaceful provinces seems generally to have been in the hands of ex-praetors or ex-consuls according to the later practice, even here the commands were by no means all confined to a single year. The prolonged control of Cilicia by P. Servilius Isauricus may have been due to the same set of circumstances as led to the commission of M. Antonius; but the two years of

---

[1] Vell. Pat. II, 31, 3.   [2] Plutarch, *Pomp.* 16, 1–2.
[3] Cicero, *Phil.* XI, 8, 18; Val. Max. VIII, 15, 8.

C. Cosconius in Illyricum[1] and the three during which Sicily suffered under Verres are not explained by any peculiar peril in the
local situation. Thus it seems that Sulla in no way tied the Senate's
hands. It was perhaps his ideal that praetors and consuls, having
been occupied for a year at Rome, should pass at once to the provinces for another year and no more, but the exceptions to this
practice are so numerous that Sulla cannot be supposed to have
formulated it as a binding rule. Nevertheless, there is every probability that this was the direction in which he looked. The two
Spains, the two Gauls[2], Macedonia, Asia, Cilicia, Africa, Sardinia
and Corsica which went together, and Sicily made ten provinces
in all for which governors had to be found, and it is significant
that, by raising the praetorian college to eight (p. 299), Sulla
secured that the number of praetors and consuls passing out of
office at the end of each year should be the same as that of the
provinces which these men were eligible to govern. Thus there
would be one man available for every province every year, and
provincial governorships would tend to become annual.

This was the end which, though he did not insist on an unbroken
observance of the system—indeed, it would have been absurd to
demand a yearly change of general in an important war—Sulla
put it in the way of the Senate to attain. At the very least some
sort of order would be introduced into the method of making
these appointments: the State need no longer live from hand to
mouth, leaving a governor in office year by year until someone
could be found to take his place, but a due succession of qualified
candidates would always be available. At best, if the Senate made
the most of its opportunities, governors would leave their provinces after twelve months' control, and in that brief period they
could scarcely find time to turn the troops under their command
into a personal following, prepared to set loyalty to a leader before
duty to the State. In that case something would have been
done to diminish the menace of those great soldiers whom the
Senate feared but could not do without.

If Sulla had been content with this, conjectures about his attitude to the proconsuls might reasonably be dismissed as idle
speculation: but fortunately he went farther and gave expression
to his views in a way which leaves no room for doubt. Since the
crimen maiestatis minutae was invented in 103 B.C. (p. 160 *sq.*), the
content of the charge had been largely left to the imagination of
the prosecutor and the court: it was Sulla who first formulated the

---

[1] Eutropius VI, 4; Orosius V, 23, 23.
[2] On Cisalpine Gaul, see below, p. 301 *sq.*

offences which might legally be interpreted as treason. And he did more than this. The nature of treasonable action—action dangerous to society in its existing form—varies with the nature of the constitution: many of the crimes which under an autocracy are the most heinous form of treason cannot even be committed in a full democracy, and some which are possible in both cases differ greatly in gravity according to their constitutional setting. A constitution needs a sanction if its stability is in danger, and when the constitution is changed the sanction must be changed as well[1]. It was Sulla who made the *lex maiestatis* the sanction of the constitution of Rome, and from his time onwards a new constitution regularly brought with it a new treason-law: if we knew more about the measures on this subject passed by Julius Caesar[2] and Augustus[3], we should be less uncertain than we are about the nature of their constitutional ideals. Fortunately, though the text of the Sullan law is not preserved, Cicero records[4] the gist of some of its provisions, and therein is revealed one of the sources from which Sulla foresaw danger to his dispensation. For a governor to leave his province, to march his army beyond its frontiers, to start a war on his own initiative, to invade the territory of a [client] king without orders from the Senate and Roman People—these are the acts which, doubtless among many others, were made treason; and they are all of them acts which, if committed at all, would be committed by some ambitious proconsul whose subservience to the Senate was less complete than the Sullan constitution required[5].

Thus Sulla betrays his fears, and his betrayal is evidence enough that in the provincial governors he found a menace to his arrangements. And so it may be said in conclusion that the dictator, having dealt with the risk of revolutionary legislation at home, essayed to protect the Senate against its military captains, partly by encouraging the reduction of their commands to an annual tenure and partly by making the least sign of independence in such quarters a criminal offence. The Senate's need was great, for here lay the gravest danger; and the sequel will show that this was the side on which the defences raised by Sulla had their weakest spot.

[1] See Cromwell's 'Act declaring what offences shall be adjudged Treason' of 17 July 1649, in S. R. Gardiner, *Constitutional Documents of the Puritan Revolution* (ed. 3), pp. 388 *sqq.*   [2] Cicero, *Phil.* 1, 9, 23.

[3] *Dig.* 48, 4; cf. Tac. *Ann.* III, 24, 3.   [4] *In Pis.* 21, 50.

[5] To deprive governors of an obvious temptation, Sulla even seems to have made it an offence for them to stay in their provinces more than thirty days after the arrival of a successor (Cicero, *ad fam.* III, 6, 3).

Such is the outline of the Sullan constitution—an attempt to establish senatorial government on a sounder basis than before and to surround it with safeguards against its most formidable enemies. The Senate was to be recruited entirely by indirect election, without any possibility of interference from the censorship, and its personnel was strengthened at the start by a large addition of new members drawn from the prosperous commercial class. The curule magistrates were given time to assimilate the senatorial outlook before they rose to positions of serious responsibility, and obstacles were set in the way of men whose outstanding ability might seem to justify a peculiar speed in their ascent to the highest offices of State. In particular, the arrangement that ten years must elapse between a man's first tenure of the consulship and his second discouraged ambition altogether, more especially if a consulship did not normally carry with it the expectation of a provincial command of more than twelve months' duration. The tribunate was closed to men whose gifts entitled them to hope for a serious political career, and the effective power of such as were willing to hold the office at all was destroyed. Finally, the menace of the proconsuls was reduced by the suggestion that their commands should be confined to the space of a single year and by the insertion of clauses in the *lex maiestatis* designed to repress thoughts of disloyalty to the prevailing constitution.

XII. MINOR REFORMS IN DOMESTIC ADMINISTRATION

Besides strengthening the authority of the Senate by making it more representative of the best elements in the State, Sulla's enlargement of that body served to provide a greater number of men eligible for the highest posts in the administration. The scarcity of civil servants was a long-standing difficulty, and some of Sulla's own innovations had rendered the need more pressing. His reorganization of the criminal courts made serious calls on the praetorship, and his attack on the censorship, whether he contemplated this result or not, led to a suspension of the office which left several important functions to be transferred to other shoulders. For whatever reasons, there was an expansion of the magistracy. It has been seen above (p. 287) that the quaestors were increased to twenty, of whom, since eleven were normally employed on provincial service, rather less than half would be available for duties in the city; and, besides this, new members were added to the praetorship. Here, however, the extent of the additions is a matter of dispute. The praetorship as Sulla found it was still in all probability a college of six—the number which it had reached in 197 B.C. and retained, apart from the ephemeral changes caused by the Lex Baebia (vol. VIII, p. 366), throughout the second century. In the Ciceronian age, before the dictatorship of Caesar, there is evidence enough to show that the praetors were regularly eight[1], and this is the number needed, with the addition of two consuls, to provide each of the ten provinces with a new governor every year. If eight was the normal number after Sulla's time, he would appear to have increased the praetorships by two, and this version of the change is almost certainly correct[2].

The eight praetors, except in the most unusual circumstances now wholly confined to work in Rome, had their hands adequately occupied by the demands of judicial administration, but they still occasionally found time to help the consuls with the business which the absence of censors soon threw on to other magistrates: thus it was that Verres and one of his colleagues came to be concerned with repairs to the Temple of the Castores[3]. In the first instance, however, it was the consuls on whom these duties fell, and the consuls are to be seen engaged in operations which suggest that they took over general responsibility for the work involved in the former *censoriae locationes*[4]. The tasks of the censors had grown so numerous in course of time that it is idle to ask in detail how provision was made for their discharge. Some, indeed, such as the recruitment of the *equites equo publico*[5], may have been left to the automatic working of a system as simple as that which fed the Senate from the quaestorship. Others had already lost their usefulness: as direct taxes had not been levied since 167 B.C. and conscription for the army had been abandoned in practice since 108 B.C., there was no compelling need for a general census of the citizen body.

[1] Compare Cicero, *pro Mil.* 15, 39 with *in Pis.* 15, 35 for 57 B.C.; and see *ad. fam.* VIII, 8, 8 for 51 B.C.

[2] The statement of the jurist Pomponius (*Dig.* 1, 2, 2, 32)—our only explicit authority for Sulla's dealings with the praetorship—that he added four new praetors and so, presumably, raised the college to ten—is nowhere else confirmed, nor is it saved by the theory of A. W. Zumpt (*Röm. Criminalrecht* II, 1, pp. 333 *sq.*) that Sulla allowed the Senate discretion to fix the actual number of praetorships at any figure between eight and ten inclusive to meet such needs as might arise from the creation of a new province. For this theory there is no adequate evidence relevant to the Sullan age.

[3] Cicero, II *in Verr.* 1, 50, 130.

[4] *Ib.* III, 7, 18.   [5] See Mommsen, *Staatsrecht*, III, p. 485.

Nevertheless, it is not to be supposed that Sulla's intention was for the censorship to be abolished. When the office was revived in 70 B.C. (p. 336), no repeal of legislation seems to have been required; and there is another consideration which suggests that the dictator contemplated that censors would be regularly appointed, after his time as before. Without a periodic census the Comitia Centuriata must rapidly become unworkable. Had he envisaged a system wherein censors had no place, he must either have looked to the consuls themselves to review the Centuries, as they had done in the early fifth century B.C., or else have reconciled himself to the certainty that the Centuriate Assembly would rapidly degenerate into a mere survival like the Comitia Curiata. Neither alternative is probable. The burden of the census would be a very heavy one, even for consuls now free from military calls; and it is difficult to believe that Sulla, who had shown his approval of the Centuries in 88 B.C. (p. 208) and who submitted to them his law depriving recalcitrant Italians of the citizenship[1] (p. 302), would have gratuitously acquiesced in the destruction of that Assembly which beyond doubt was most nearly in accord with his own political ideal. Many as were the functions which had passed from this body to the Comitia Populi Tributa or the Concilium Plebis, it was still the Centuries which performed the task— a task which under Sulla's arrangements was perhaps even more important than before—of electing consuls. Though it is certain that he took the composition of the Senate out of the censors' hands, the needs of the Comitia Centuriata combine with the complete silence of the authorities to forbid the conjecture that Sulls intended the censorship itself to fall into abeyance.

Little as we know of Sulla's views on the constitutional functions of the Roman People, scarcely more can be said about his social legislation. It is clear that recent wars in Italy and the East had produced a financial crisis, which it was the first business of a statesman to relieve. The measures taken by Sulla to raise revenue in Asia were drastic enough (p. 259 *sq.*), but they were not all. According to Appian[2], he exacted a forced levy of large dimensions on the whole Roman world beyond the frontiers of Italy, not even exempting States which had been granted *immunitas*; and, besides this, money was raised by the sale of political privileges for cash[3]. At the same time he took an obvious and attractive step to reduce expenditure: the public sale of corn to the Roman populace was

---

[1] Cicero, *de domo sua*, 30, 79.

[2] *Bell. Civ.* I, 102, 475.   [3] Plutarch, *Comp. Lys. et Sullae*, 3, 2.

abolished[1]. But Sulla's interest did not stop at public economies: ill as it became a man of his peculiar tastes, he legislated at length against private extravagance. A limit was set to expenditure on food, the maximum cost of tombs and funerals was prescribed and, in the same optimistic vein, the dictator went on to deal with the public morals. To such futility even a man of Sulla's common-sense could stoop: but belief in the value of sumptuary legislation was a delusion which even the most enlightened minds of Rome rarely managed to escape.

XIII. SULLA AND ITALY

The final feature of Sulla's work at home is one which belongs rather to the changes which he wrought in the organization of Italy. He left a permanent monument to his achievements in an extension of the *pomerium*, the sacred boundary of the city which, according to the custom at this time observed, might be altered by none but those who had increased the Italian territory of Rome[2]. On the Adriatic side the northern frontier had probably been advanced from the Aesis to the Rubicon before the time of Sulla, but his change in the course of the *pomerium* is enough to show that he could somehow claim to have added to Roman soil. The enfranchisement of the Italians might have supplied the necessary title if Sulla could have claimed that work as his, but it is perhaps more probable that some rectification in the boundary inland or to the west was carried out in connection with his arrangements for the government of Cisalpine Gaul.

Since the early years of the second century, the *ager Gallicus* round Ariminum and the great stretch of country northwards to the Alps had normally been, like Italy itself, under the direct charge of the consuls and their subordinates. Such in general seems to have been the case so late as 82 B.C.[3]; but seven years later Cisalpine Gaul was clearly one of the ordinary provinces governed by ex-magistrates[4]. As Mommsen saw, this reform can scarcely have been due to anyone but Sulla. Cisalpine Gaul was the key to

[1] This emerges from a passage of Licinianus (p. 34 F.) which appears to record a resumption of the *frumentationes* after Sulla's death.

[2] Seneca, *de brev. vitae*, 13, 8.

[3] Compare Cicero, II *in Verr.* I, 13, 34 with Appian, *Bell. Civ.* I, 87, 394–5; cf. *ib.* 66, 303 (87 B.C.). The view of E. G. Hardy (*J.R.S.* VI, pp. 65–8) that Cisalpine Gaul was provincialized in 89 B.C. is difficult to accept.

[4] Sallust, *Hist.* II, 98 D.M. The evidence of Sallust for 75 B.C. is confirmed by that of Plutarch, *Lucullus*, 5, 1, for the following year.

Italy: its unruly neighbours in the Alps made the presence of a
garrison almost essential: and, if the consuls were to be purely
civil administrators so long as they held the magistracy, they were
well rid of the obligation to administer this military region in the
north. Accordingly, Cisalpine Gaul became the tenth province of
the Roman Empire, and such it remained until the time of Julius
Caesar.

In Italy itself Sulla's work was of a more contentious kind. The
claims of his veterans must be met—a task difficult to achieve
without hardship to some part of the population; but in addition
there were some old accounts to settle, and the dictator was not
the man to let his enemies go without their due. It was a small
matter, though one which caused much trouble in the future, that
the descendants of those who had perished in the proscriptions
lost not only their property but part of their citizen rights as well:
more serious were the general expropriations of which Appian
draws a lurid picture[1]. The promise to the Italians (p. 271 *sq.*) was
honoured wherever it had been followed by loyal adherence to
the Sullan cause, but to those whose resistance had continued no
mercy was shown. Samnium was wellnigh devastated[2], and all
over the peninsula those who backed the loser paid the price: such
was the severity of Sulla's revenge that one city—Volaterrae—
fought on till 80 B.C. and then was only reduced after a siege
directed by the dictator in person. Fines were levied, property
was confiscated and, in virtue of a most drastic law, whole
communities lost the citizenship.

This remarkable enactment seems to have been directed chiefly
against some of those who might otherwise have claimed the
civitas under the legislation passed during the Social War; but the
validity of this attempt to disfranchise citizens by law was open
to grave objections, and, as we know from Cicero's speech on
behalf of Aulus Caecina, it was finally admitted to be indefensible.
Nevertheless, the troubles of Sulla's victims could not be ended by
attacks, however successful, on the law which was their cause, and
this for the sufficient reason that property set free by the resultant
confiscations had been bestowed on Sulla's veterans, who were not
men of the sort to be ousted with ease. The problem of finding
pensions for the ex-soldiers who looked to Sulla for their livelihood
attained dimensions never known before. The legions to be demobilized were variously estimated at twenty-three[3] or even
more[4], which meant the provision of allotments for over a hun-

---

[1] *Bell. Civ.* I, 96, 445–8.   [2] Strabo, v, 249.
[3] Appian, *Bell. Civ.* I, 100, 470.   [4] Livy, *Epit.* 89.

dred thousand men[1]; and when this mass had once been established in the places vacated by the victims of confiscation, it was not likely to be uprooted by anything less than a defeat in civil war. On such land as he could set free by fair means or foul Sulla planted his veterans in colonies, of which at least fourteen are known. Not all of them were wholly new: in some cases the settlers lived side by side with the survivors of the old community, as in the familiar instance of Pompeii, where quarrels between the rival sections of the population supplied material for a charge against a *patronus coloniae*—Cicero's disreputable client P. Sulla, a nephew of the dictator[2].

Such were the means by which Sulla paid his debts to the men whose loyalty had been the foundation of his success. For the moment, at the cost of much hardship to the people of Italy, his troops were satisfied; but the evil results of the social upheaval caused by their appearance were widespread and enduring. If Sulla intended them to form garrisons which would uphold the new constitution, his hopes were soon belied. Unyielding as was their devotion to Sulla himself, their enthusiasm for his friends was mild: the Senate was not a body which could stir the emotions of such men as these, and before long they were to be found among its most formidable opponents. Of the copious evidence for their fall from grace it will be enough to recall the fact that at the time of the Catilinarian affair the leaders of the discontent could rely for backing, not only on the victims of the Sullan confiscations, but also on the majority of the veteran settlers who, in the course of less than twenty years, had drifted into bankruptcy and were now yearning to repair their shattered fortunes with the plunder of another civil war (p. 492). These nests of violence and sedition were the monument which kept green the memory of Sulla on the Italian countryside, and it is no matter for surprise that the name of their founder soon came to be held in detestation.

The claim that the dictator's work in Italy contained other more beneficent provisions cannot be admitted. Though the veteran-colonies were doubtless given charters in the form of *leges datae*, there is nothing to show that, either for these or for the Italian communities lately incorporated in the Roman State, Sulla provided anything in the nature of a standard constitution. It is not to be denied that, thanks to the enfranchisement of the allies, the attention of Roman statesmanship was called to the problems of municipal organization; but the suggestion that the Sullan legislation included a general *lex municipalis* is as ill-founded as the view

---

[1] Appian, *Bell. Civ.* i, 104, 489.　　　[2] Cicero, *pro Sulla*, 21, 60–62.

that Cinna was responsible for such a measure, or the conjecture that regulations of this kind were to be found in the laws whereby the *civitas* was extended to the Italians during the Social War.

XIV. SULLA AND THE ADMINISTRATION OF THE CRIMINAL LAW

There remains what was to be the most abiding of Sulla's achievements—his reforms of the clumsy and obsolescent method whereby criminal cases had hitherto been tried. Such changes in the law as Sulla introduced will be considered elsewhere (pp. 876 *sqq.*): here it is enough to notice his changes in procedure. The existing arrangements bore many signs of their origin in days when Rome was still a small community, whose citizens could make all public business their own. In trials of a criminal nature, where punishment rather than reparation was sought, the exercise of the magistrate's *imperium* was hedged about by safeguards which demanded the intervention of the People. Judicial cognizance of an alleged crime might in theory be taken by any magistrate. The consuls and their quaestors might be expected to deal with the most serious: the praetors, though their main occupation was with civil suits, were not debarred from criminal cases: even the aediles, for all their lack of *imperium*, were invoked to take charge of minor offences where the penalty was at most a fine: and finally there were the tribunes, who in the great age of the Republic had ousted even the consuls and had appropriated to themselves, with general approval, the duty of proceeding against all grave malefactors whose supposed offences had any kind of political significance.

Yet by the second century B.C. all these magistrates and officers had been reduced to little more than prosecutors: they were no longer competent judicial authorities, because, though their right of passing judgment was unimpaired, their power of immediate execution was rendered almost negligible by the series of laws on *provocatio*. No capital or corporal punishment, not even a fine greater than a traditional maximum, could be inflicted on a Roman citizen before his appeal had been heard by the People and rejected. This had an inevitable result: every magistrate to whom there came a case in which the appropriate penalty was of a kind against which an appeal could not be refused took the matter to the People at the outset. The practice thus created was in many ways objectionable. Even if it was admitted that the urban *plebs* was a worthy representative of the Populus Romanus, it could scarcely be maintained that a public assembly of indefinite dimensions was the best possible jury to deal with issues often of some complexity. Accordingly, expedients to escape the difficulty were from time to time devised. At first by the People acting on the suggestion of the Senate, then by the Senate alone, and finally —from 113 B.C., the date of the Rogatio Peducaea (p. 97)—by the People in defiance of the Senate's desire, some magistrate or magistrates received a commission to hold the necessary trials when a grave offence was known to have been perpetrated on a considerable scale. The magistrates concerned then generally collected a *consilium* of prominent men and thus was constituted a court whose sentences, even when the People had not assisted in its formation, seem by a most remarkable development to have been capable of execution without appeal. It was against the Senate's claim, on occasions when such a court had been established without the concurrence of the People, to abrogate the right of the Comitia to have the final word in cases where a *caput* was at stake that Gaius Gracchus had protested in his *lex ne quis iniussu populi capite damnetur* (p. 56 sq.).

But there was one connection in which the second century B.C. had seen a more promising experiment than these haphazard attempts to provide an effective court whenever one was needed. It was inevitable that from time to time the provincial populations should complain that they had been fleeced by a rapacious governor, and these complaints presented a problem of some difficulty. Since their authors were not Roman citizens, the suits would most naturally go to the *praetor inter cives et peregrinos*, who then, in accordance with the practice which was regular in cases of an international character, would appoint a body of *recuperatores*. Such was the procedure followed on the classic occasion in 171 B.C. when the provincials of Spain asked for redress from their oppressors (vol. VIII, p. 310)[1], and something like it was not unknown even after Sulla's time[2]. But under such circumstances the suit remained a matter of private law, and this was objectionable for two reasons. In the first place the issue was clearly one of public interest; and, secondly, since the praetorian jurisdiction was essentially civil, it was difficult to brand extortionate behaviour by holders of *imperium* as a criminal offence, to be expiated only by

[1] Livy, XLIII, 2.
[2] When the young Caesar acted as *patronus* for the Greeks in 77 B.C., they were seeking simple restitution from C. Antonius in an action before the *praetor inter cives et peregrinos*, who on this occasion was M. Lucullus (Asconius, p. 84 c.).

a penalty and not by mere restitution, unless some other form of cognizance were devised.

In this direction the first and greatest step was taken by Lucius Piso, the consul of 133 B.C., who during his tribunate in 149 B.C. introduced a plebiscite whereby the system adopted in 171 B.C. was established as the regular procedure in all charges of extortion, and the court, no longer dependent on the *imperium* of the praetor, was founded on the surer basis of the authority conferred by a legislative act. Thus, though the penal element was not yet introduced, extortion was brought within the scope of public law, and procedure was formulated for the constitution of a court whenever the need for it arose. The history which begins with the plebiscite of 149 B.C. has three aspects to be noticed here. First, there is the struggle for the right to sit on the juries. At the outset senators alone were eligible, but from the time of Gaius Gracchus till that of Sulla, save for the brief interval due to the Lex Servilia Caepionis of 106 B.C. (p. 161 *sq.*), the privilege was confined to rich men outside the senatorial class. Secondly, the penal element in the result of a verdict adverse to the defendant received ever greater emphasis. And, finally, fresh courts, inspired by the model of 149 B.C., were formed to cover other parts of the field of criminal law. Here the *iudicium populi* rapidly gave way to the *iudicium publicum*.

It may be doubted whether this extension had begun when Gaius Gracchus passed the Lex Acilia[1], and Plutarch's story of Marius' prosecution in 116 B.C.[2] scarcely proves that a *quaestio* for charges of electoral corruption had been established by that time. But it is clear that before 95 B.C. murder had been brought under the new system by the creation of a *quaestio de sicariis et veneficiis*[3]. Soon afterwards a *quaestio de vi publica* had perhaps been added, though the date of the Lex Plautia cannot be accurately fixed; and it is not unlikely that the crime of *peculatus* had received similar provision by 86 B.C.[4]

This, however, is as far as the development appears to have progressed when Sulla set out to complete the scheme. His task was large, involving, as it did, not merely the creation of new courts, but the definition of all offences now under the jurisdiction of a *quaestio* and not adequately defined already. But it was not his business to frame a comprehensive criminal code. His affair was with those major crimes which called for punishment of a kind only permissible, under the old dispensation, after the People had given

---

[1] See Note 2 on pp. 892 *sqq.*   [2] *Marius*, 5, 2–5.
[3] Dessau 45.   [4] Plutarch, *Pomp.* 4, 1–3.

its consent: minor charges might be left to the magistrates as before. The matters with which Sulla had to deal were grouped for convenience under a number of heads, and for each a law was passed specifying the crimes concerned and creating machinery for their trial. Of these Leges Corneliae there were seven, two of them concerning crimes primarily of private life—injuries involving personal violence, and forgery, one—the *lex de sicariis et veneficiis*—dealing with murder and certain relevant cases of judicial corruption[1], and four devoted to outrages on the public life of Rome: these were laws on extortion, on peculation—both apparently aimed only at those who were guilty of these practices in an official capacity, on bribery at elections, and on treason. To this it should be added that at some time either shortly before Sulla's legislation or a few years thereafter, public violence was made the business of a special *quaestio* set up by a Lex Plautia. Thus the *iudicia publica* came to cover all the graver crimes, and the age of the *iudicia populi* was at an end.

Of the eight praetors now annually in office, two were required for the business of the civil law. The remaining six were each assigned the presidency of one of the *iudicia publica*; and, as there were not praetors enough for all the courts, the *quaestio de sicariis et veneficiis* was usually put under the charge of an ex-aedile with the title of *iudex quaestionis*. But, though the president for the year was known, it was a merit of the system that the jurors were not. About the composition of the juries, now drawn entirely from the Senate, our information is lamentably vague. It is clear that, when a case was beginning, the jury was empanelled by the prosecution and the defence exercising their right to challenge a certain number of the persons included in a *decuria* of the Senate: when this *reiectio* was complete, the survivors heard the case and gave the verdict. But it is an open question whether the Senate, at the beginning of each year, was divided into *decuriae* which were maintained for twelve months and assigned in turn to the courts as their needs arose or, as is perhaps more probable, a *decuria* was formed by sortition for each trial as it came on for hearing[2]. All that can be said with confidence is that, if the *decuriae* were periodically formed without regard to the immediate demands of judicial business, Sulla did not make the mistake of distributing them forthwith among the courts. For the parties to have known from the

---

[1] Cicero, *pro Cluentio*, 54, 148.

[2] The remarks of Schol. Gronov. B (Stangl, ii, p. 335) are not well informed: if they could be trusted, the second alternative would become impossible.

outset which *decuria* would take the case would have been an invitation to corruption, and those who attribute to Sulla so imprudent an arrangement as this do him an injustice for which there is no adequate authority.

Whatever may have been the method whereby a jury was obtained, there are two features in the system which call for final notice. One is that, by an enactment probably repealed in 70 B.C., Sulla left the defendant free to decide whether the jurors should give their votes openly or by ballot[1]. The other, and by far the more important, affects the part played by the Populus in criminal jurisdiction. Though the details of the theory are obscure, the fact that the *quaestiones* were established by law to investigate the evidence on which the defendant was alleged to fall within a class of criminals against whom the People had, in the law itself, already formulated the penalty which it thought fitting goes far to justify the claim that the verdicts of the *iudicia publica* should have final validity. To this may be added, first, the analogy of the *unus iudex* in civil procedure, whose findings had never been subject to appeal, and, secondly, a late concession whereby the execution of a death sentence could be escaped by voluntary exile. The attempt of Antony in 44 B.C. to allow appeal in cases of treason and public violence was regarded as a most unhealthy innovation, and his enactment ran only for the briefest time: when it was rescinded, the proposal was never afterwards revived.

Such in brief was Sulla's attempt to provide Rome with an adequate machine for the administration of criminal justice. Of all his works this was the most enduring. It survived the confusion of the revolutionary age and only fell into disuse when the advent of the Principate created a new and superior authority whose activities by degrees encroached on the *iudicia publica*, as on all other branches of the judicature. The manning of the machine soon became a matter of dispute: the Sullan courts inherited a legacy of political controversy from the *quaestio repetundarum* which was their model, and the Senate only maintained its monopoly of the juries till 70 B.C. But, just because this was the only political issue involved, the machine itself remained intact. In its creation Sulla found a task to which his peculiar genius was admirably suited: it gave scope to those amazing powers of organization which were his greatest gift, and, because the recruitment of the juries was irrelevant to the system as such, unlike his other undertakings, its value was not impaired by his excessive faith in the vigour and stability of the Senate.

---

[1] Cicero, *pro Cluentio*, 27, 75.

XV. THE RETIREMENT AND DEATH OF SULLA

The history of affairs at Rome during the period of Sulla's supremacy contains little more than the tale of his legislation. It is true that in the early months of 79 B.C. the youthful Pompey took a long step in his progress to pre-eminence by inducing Sulla to allow him, in spite of his never having held a magistracy, the honour of a triumph for his exploits against the Marian rump, and that in the previous year Cicero had won a place in the front rank at the Roman bar by his successful defence of the younger Sextus Roscius. But the political life of Rome was stifled under the incubus of the dictatorship. To that extraordinary office Sulla had added the consulship in 80 B.C., taking as his colleague Metellus Pius—a most estimable citizen, whose significance is chiefly due to his inheritance of his father's inability to win a war. The consul of 80 B.C. in due course took command of Spain, and there his failure against Sertorius gave Pompey the same opportunity as Marius had been offered by the ineffectiveness of Numidicus in Africa. For the following year Sulla was on the point of being elected again; but now his work was done, and at his suggestion the consulships of 79 B.C. were given to Appius Claudius Pulcher (see above, p. 262) and P. Servilius Vatia, later famous as the elder Servilius Isauricus. Then at last, confident in the loyalty of his supporters both in Rome and Italy, when his consulship had expired Sulla laid down his dictatorial powers. In 78 B.C. he died at his Campanian seat, and his public funeral in Rome, though it was not granted without protest, was held amid scenes which bore witness to the multitude of those who had cause for gratitude to the dead.

Sulla's achievement demands no complicated judgment. For all their interest to a moralist like Plutarch, his private life and character are of slight concern to the historian. That he was a hard liver and a man ruthless in his ways with opposition are facts beyond dispute; but they have no bearing on the central issue—the question of his place in the constitutional development of Rome. Nor, again, is there any need to dwell on his capacity for organization. The arrangements which he made in Asia (p. 259 *sq.*) and his enduring development of the *iudicia publica* are enough to show that, when it was a matter of constructing machinery to perform the work of daily administration, Sulla was not inferior to Augustus himself. But it is on his conception of the constitution most suitable for Rome that his reputation depends. As has been said above, the problem was not of his own creation. First, the

enfranchisement of Italy made it essential to curb the powers of
the urban *plebs* which, masquerading as a typical selection of the
Populus Romanus, had lately been claiming with a new insistence
to exercise untrammelled the tremendous powers of a sovran *de-
mos*. And, secondly, the Marian system of military recruitment
had brought with it armies capable of such dangerous devotion to
their leaders that measures were urgently needed to strengthen
the control of the central government over its executive in the provinces. But the means which Sulla took to secure these ends were
of his own choosing, and it is by the adequacy of these means that
the value of his reform must be assessed. Sulla's attempt to increase the authority of the Senate, both by enlarging its numbers
and the field on which it drew and by providing that indirect
popular election, without the possibility of interference by the
censors, should be the only mode of access to a seat, was an attempt
on the most promising lines. Though the censorship was revived in 70 B.C. for a time, the constitution of the Sullan Senate
differs from that of Augustus only in the lack of some minor regulations necessitated by the advent of a Princeps. Again, the
lex annalis, likewise adopted by the Empire without essential
change, served within its limits to curb the independence of the
consuls. Save in 70 and 59 B.C., curule magistrates caused little
trouble after Sulla's time, and on both these occasions it was an
army which made them dangerous.

The tribunate, however, presented a more difficult problem. In
fairness to Sulla it must be admitted that the positive powers which
he allowed the tribunes to enjoy were peculiarly like those which
they retained under the Augustan arrangements; but there was
one essential difference—that Sulla left the Concilium Plebis alive,
whereas under Augustus it was dead. So long as the plebeian
assembly and the tribunate both survived, there was a danger:
legislation might strive to keep them apart, but, if the legislation
failed, the way for a new Gracchus was clear. It has been seen
that, in this situation, Sulla's hope was to kill the tribunate by
depriving it of serious candidates for the office; but the blow he
delivered was not mortal, and the tribunate recovered. In the end,
his attack did no more than supply his enemies with a battle-cry
in the demand for a restoration of the tribunes' pristine powers.
But the attack itself was justified, and the misfortune of Sulla lay
rather in his inability to destroy the office outright and—what was
still more necessary—to end the activities of the Concilium Plebis
for ever. He must not, indeed, be blamed for sparing the assemblies—the time was not ripe for their suppression: but it cannot

be denied that the Julio-Claudians found a better way when they silently removed the People from the Roman Constitution. One point, however, must be added. Though Sulla did not permanently stop the demagogic agitation of the tribunes, he left the office so completely fettered that its holders were powerless for evil until their bonds were loosed. The sequel will reveal one fact of great importance—that in their struggle for freedom the tribunes could win no tangible success by their own efforts alone, and that it was only the championing of their cause by other men—men who had armies at their backs—which finally enabled the tribunate to throw off the shackles imposed by Sulla.

And so at length we reach the rock on which the Sullan system foundered. The divorce of the magistracy from the pro-magistracy was a development—hastened, indeed, by Sulla but started long before his time—which had the most beneficent effects when it was completed in 52 B.C., and subsequently accepted by Augustus. The arrangements to make possible an annual tenure of provincial commands were salutary so far as they might render it more difficult for governors to establish a personal claim on the loyalty of their troops. But all this went for nothing when politicians were generals and the armies depended on their generals for pensions at discharge. Even if commands had never run for more than a single year—a system most dangerous to the effective conduct of war—sooner or later, with the army as it was, a general and his troops were bound to discover that each could serve the other. To cope with such a threat no oligarchy could be competent: at best it could start a civil war by arming one of its members to meet the menace, and even that might mean no more than changing one master for another. Until the time should come when the armies would be the armies of the State, assured that the State itself had a system to reward faithful service with adequate provision for old age, and convinced that intervention in political affairs would be visited by punishment inevitable and condign, there was one way alone to provide security against recurrent military tyrannies. A monarch must be found to command all the Roman forces, and he must be allowed to choose his own subordinates, looking as much for loyalty to himself as for competence in the performance of their duties. For such a rôle Sulla was not cast. The age was not ready for a principate. The peril from the proconsuls had yet to be appreciated in all its gravity, and Rome had to pass through the fire of the Civil Wars before she would reluctantly accept even the veiled monarchy of Augustus.

For his day Sulla did well. The Senate could not be deposed;

and so long as the Senate remained supreme it is hard to see what greater powers it could have been given or what stronger defences could have been erected against its enemies. The weakness of Sulla's work is to be ascribed partly to his failure to have done for good with the travesty of popular sovranty exercised by the urban mob, and still more to his own great refusal of the crown. Yet the fault was venial. Caesar might say that by surrendering the dictatorship Sulla showed ignorance of the political ABC, but it was largely from Caesar's own career that men grappling with the problem of the Roman government learnt the essence of their task. To blame Sulla for his ignorance is to blame him for having lived thirty years too soon.

But Sulla's work was not wasted. In administrative organization he served Rome well, and there is not one of his enactments under this head which, if it did not survive intact, failed to bear fruit of value. Even in the sphere of politics Sulla taught his successors a lesson which none was so foolish as to ignore. His ideal of senatorial supremacy might be impossible, but his methods of seeking it were instructive. Once and for all he showed that an elaborate programme of legislation, of the sort which the Gracchi had lamentably failed to carry through with the support of the Concilium Plebis, could be enacted in all its parts by one who relied upon the army. Of the two legs which carried the Augustan principate the Gracchi had rested on the *tribunicia potestas*. It was Sulla who showed the political value of the *imperium*: and of these two the *imperium* was incomparably the more valuable. If the Sullan system collapsed, as it shortly did, its collapse would be due to the action of the army, and the task of the next reformer would be to bring the army under control. Sulla had shown the means to be employed—the army itself. And so it emerged from Sulla's work that the business of Roman statesmanship was with military support to create a government able to command unbroken allegiance from the army. Though he did not supply the answer, Sulla set the problem in a form which minds less acute than those of Julius and Augustus could scarcely fail to grasp.

CHAPTER VII

THE BREAKDOWN OF THE SULLAN SYSTEM AND THE RISE OF POMPEY

I. THE POLITICAL SITUATION AFTER SULLA'S DEATH

THE state of Italy in 78 B.C. was dangerous. When Sulla died and men had no more cause to fear a return of the dictatorship, grievances which are the inevitable legacy of drastic change began to find violent expression. Within a few months the Senate was confronted with a crisis. Its statesmanship and its competence to wield the powers put into its hands were submitted to a searching test; and this ordeal was only the first of many. Though its performance can scarcely be called distinguished, the government repelled the first attack—an attack delivered by M. Aemilius Lepidus, one of the consuls of 78 B.C.; but the continuous pressure of which the affair of Lepidus was only the beginning rapidly revealed the weakness of the senatorial position, and before ten years were out the citadel of the Sullan constitution had fallen.

The most vocal, though by no means the most formidable, section of the opposition was one which clamoured for an immediate emancipation of the tribunate. The tribunate was an office of the highest value to any aspirant for power whose gifts or opportunities gave no promise of a military command; and, when the restoration of its full authority was demanded by ambitious politicians, their claims found warm support among the masses. The prestige acquired by the early champions of the Plebs still lingered round the office, and in more recent days it was to the tribunes that the masses had been indebted for some of the most valued privileges of Roman citizenship: land allotments and cheap corn had not been the result of consular legislation. Amply as Sulla's attack on the tribunate had been justified, it had the unfortunate consequence of giving the enemies of his constitution a plausible and effective war-cry. Such was the most obvious source of discontent. A second, which showed its effects throughout the length and breadth of Italy, was the arbitrary confiscation whereby Sulla had taken property from his enemies in order to bestow it on his troops. The victims of expropriation could not be expected to refuse a chance of repairing their shattered fortunes, and the military settlers themselves—men for whom the monotonies of agricultural life held few attractions—were ready to welcome an opportunity of return to the more profitable excitements of war.

All this unrest was made doubly dangerous by the presence of men able and anxious to exploit it. Little was to be feared from the young hopefuls whose interests did not go beyond the tribunate: but, besides these, the Senate had to face the consistent hostility of the business class, whose aim was to recover its hold on the administration of criminal justice, and the natural ambition of its generals, who would not long refrain from protest when the obstructive arrangements of Sulla threatened to debar them from office and commands to which they were entitled by past success. There was thus no lack of discontents, or of leadership to make their agitation effective. In the history of the decade following Sulla's death two outstanding phases may be distinguished. First, the admirers of the tribunate are found making ineffective demands for its liberation; and secondly, failure is suddenly turned into success when their efforts are joined by those of the commercial interests and the military politicians. The Senate is then forced back at every point. Before this, however, there stands a somewhat isolated episode, whose central figure is M. Aemilius Lepidus.

II. M. AEMILIUS LEPIDUS

M. Lepidus, father of the triumvir and probably son-in-law of Saturninus, was a man of contemptible character, small ability and unlimited ambition. His praetorship in Sicily had given the provincials a foretaste of their subsequent experiences at the hands of Verres[1], and his later activities in Italy during the days when he was still a follower of Sulla had not been without considerable profit to himself[2]. But, though he had lent a hand against Saturninus in 100 B.C., his devotion to the oligarchical interest was a passing phase. The fellow was a mere adventurer, and there is nothing to show that at any stage of his career his policy was determined by more honourable motives than a resolve to play for his own hand alone. As the work of Sulla progressed, it became ever clearer that nothing more was left to do in the interests of the Senate. If anywhere there was need for a champion, it was on the side of those who sought to destroy the Sullan constitution; and towards them Lepidus soon inclined. When in 79 B.C. he stood as a candidate for the consulship, he did so as an open enemy of the dictator; and though Sulla did not strike him down, he made

---

[1] Cicero, II *in Verr.* III, 91, 212.   [2] Sallust, *Hist.* I, 55, 18 M.

no concealment of his displeasure at the help which the man was receiving from the young Pompey[1].

Lepidus was returned at the head of the poll with Q. Lutatius Catulus, son of Marius' rival at Vercellae (see above, pp. 149 *sqq.*). Catulus was a thoroughbred oligarch, and before long the consuls found themselves at loggerheads. Their earliest recorded quarrel was over the ceremonies at the funeral of the dead dictator, but later in the year Lepidus opened a far graver issue by proposing to reverse some of Sulla's most controversial enactments. Sequestrated land was to be restored to those from whom it had been taken, the exiles were to be recalled, and a bill for the resumption of *frumentationes* was introduced, perhaps even passed[2]. The attitude of Lepidus to the tribunate is a matter of some doubt. Before his brief career was ended he certainly lent his name to the demand for a restoration of its powers[3], but at an earlier stage he is alleged by Licinianus[4], in a passage which is admittedly not altogether accurate, to have urged that the office be left under the disabilities imposed by Sulla. If the views of Lepidus on this question underwent a change, there need be no surprise. Since the struggle of the Orders had closed, the old unfettered tribunate had become an institution whose veto was at least as useful to the Senate as its initiative in legislation was to the classes outside the oligarchy: it could be argued with some plausibility that on balance the People were not losers by its limitation. Such may have been the belief of Lepidus: but, on the other hand, the demand for its release from Sulla's trammels was one which could attract a large body of support among the masses, and nothing forbids the conjecture that the political value of the cry led Lepidus to change his tactics.

In face of the dangers thus suddenly provoked, the Senate induced the two consuls to swear that they would refrain from a resort to arms. But, though Lepidus agreed to keep the peace at least until his consulship ran out, there were disturbances in Italy which called for military intervention; and, if armies took the field for the maintenance of order, there was every likelihood that they would end by intervention in political disputes. There had been an ominous rising at Faesulae, where some of the dispossessed had attacked the Sullan settlers and deprived them of their holdings after a struggle in which several were killed. The veterans were not the men meekly to submit to such treatment as this, and both consuls seem to have gone north with troops to prevent the spread

---

[1] Plutarch, *Pomp.* 15, 1–2.   [2] Licinianus, p. 34 F.
[3] Sallust, *Hist.* I, 77, 14 M.   [4] Pp. 33–4 F.

of violence[1]. The sequence of the events which follow is far from clear. Lepidus had secured Transalpine Gaul as his province for the year 77 B.C., and this doubtless served as an excuse for levying troops. But he made no attempt to leave Italy, though he did not return to Rome when his presence was needed for the consular elections. Instead, he sought to consolidate his position in northern Italy, where he had an active lieutenant in M. Junius Brutus, father of the tyrannicide. When at length he was summoned by the Senate to the city to hold the elections already overdue, he marched on Rome with an army and a whole series of demands which now included the restoration of the tribunate and a second consulship for himself[2].

The immediate result was to put the leaders of the oligarchy on their mettle. With the unusual support of L. Marcius Philippus, the enemy of the younger Livius Drusus, they induced the Fathers to pass the *senatus consultum de re publica defendenda*, and then to take the still graver step of invoking the aid of the young Pompey. Creditable as these measures were to the energy of the Senate, they did not bode well for the future. Though Pompey was probably no more than a *legatus*, nominally serving under Catulus, it was utterly against the intention of the Sullan constitution that a man who had never held a magistracy of any kind should be given high military employment. His appointment suggested a dearth of generals among the elder statesmen, and the passing of the 'last decree' was no testimony to the government's confidence in itself. Lepidus was a puny figure: yet more than was done against him would scarcely have been possible if another Hannibal had stood at the gates of Rome.

Whatever their implications, these measures were at least effective. Lepidus, defeated by Catulus outside the city[3], retired to Etruria, whence he shipped the remnants of his army to Sardinia. Brutus was driven into Mutina by Pompey and, when he had surrendered on terms after a considerable siege, was basely murdered by order of his unscrupulous conqueror. In Sardinia Lepidus soon died, whether by violence, disease or disgust at the misconduct of his wife our authorities are undecided, and what was worth saving of his army was taken by M. Perperna to swell the forces of Sertorius in Spain. So ended an episode which, tiresome as it was while it lasted, had no great significance. However weak the Senate may have been, Lepidus was not the man to over-

---

[1] Licinianus, p. 35 F. [2] Plutarch, *Pomp.* 16, 4.
[3] According to Florus II, 11 (III, 23), 6, Pompey was present at this battle; but the other authorities restrict his activities to the northern campaign.

throw it. He had no ideals beyond his own aggrandizement, and he was rightly judged by a sagacious young man whom the death of Sulla had brought back to Rome: though he was no friend of the oligarchs, Julius Caesar left Lepidus severely alone[1]. Nevertheless, the affair is not without a place in history. It revealed an alarming degree of discontent in Italy: it showed the Senate behaving with that anxious energy which is the mark of feeble governments: and, above all, it provided Pompey with another stepping-stone in his unprecedented advance to the position of first citizen of Rome.

III. THE APPOINTMENT OF POMPEY TO SPAIN

The final settlement with Lepidus and his friends had been delayed till 77 B.C., and business had been so far suspended by the confusion that the year opened without consuls. For a time there was an *interregnum* until the vacant places were filled by two most worthy nobles—D. Junius Brutus and Mam. Aemilius Lepidus Livianus, the latter perhaps brother of the younger Livius Drusus[2]. These nonentities claim notice for one thing alone: they gave their names to a year which is a turning-point in the constitutional development. The aristocratic government, under whose direction the foundations of the Roman empire had been laid, fell into rapid decay during the last thirty years of the second century B.C.; but the decline, which in the days of Marius and Saturninus had threatened soon to prove fatal, was abruptly arrested by Sulla. The Senate was restored to a position of supremacy which, to all outward appearance, was farther beyond the reach of challenge than any it had occupied before, and the resuscitated oligarchy was equipped with an armoury of weapons for use against its divers foes. Its future seemed assured, provided only that it showed the strength and spirit to stand up against attack.

The first real test came in 77 B.C., when the failures of Metellus Pius in Spain made it necessary to send him a colleague more worthy of Sertorius (p. 320 *sq.*). For this appointment Pompey became an insistent claimant. When Catulus ordered him to disband the army he had used at Mutina, he found various excuses for delay, until finally—after search had failed to disclose even one outstanding member of the Senate who was both competent and willing to face Sertorius—he was given the coveted post on the proposal of that old man of the sea, L. Philippus. To the Sullan constitution

---

[1] Suet. *Div. Iul.* 3.
[2] See F. Münzer, *Römische Adelsparteien und Adelsfamilien*, p. 312.

this was a fatal blow. Pompey had no semblance of the qualifications which Sulla had required in candidates for such a command. He was not a senior member of the Senate; indeed, he was not a member at all: and—more important still—he was no sound friend of the oligarchy. He used it so long as it served his purpose; but his early support of Lepidus, and now his attitude to the vacancy in Spain, are evidence enough to show that his obligations to the Senate would not be allowed to hinder his own advancement. Now, for the second time within a single year, the Senate thrust an army into the hands of this enterprising youth. And on this second occasion he was not even nominally under the command of another. He went to Spain as the equal colleague of Metellus: he came back the superior, not only of all other military men in Rome, but of the Senate itself. Yet, though the Spanish mission of Pompey sealed the fate of Sulla's constitutional work, it is easy to sympathize with the difficulties of the government. If the two Luculli be left out of account—and neither of them was as yet of proper standing, though Lucius had got some special dispensation from the *lex annalis*[1], no other candidate came near to Pompey in military reputation. Lack of an alternative and knowledge that his qualifications were high—indeed, everything except the Senate's duty in its own interests to uphold the Sullan system—combined to suggest his appointment. Nevertheless, the choice was fatal. For the next six years, the Senate might appear to hold its own; but the power it had planted in Spain soon passed out of its control, and Pompey's return to Italy was the signal for a revolution.

IV. SERTORIUS AND THE SERTORIAN WAR[2]

After the burning of Numantia (see vol. VIII, p. 322) had closed a chapter in the efforts of the Lusitanians and Celtiberians to regain their freedom Spain was undisturbed by war for about thirty years. But we cannot assume either that the Roman rule became more acceptable or that the brigandage which was suppressed

[1] Cicero, *Acad. pr.* II, I, I.

[2] For Spanish affairs from the fall of Numantia to the Sertorian War we rely upon Appian, *Iberica*, 99–100, supplemented by occasional items in the *Fasti triumphales* and the *Epitomes* of Livy. The principal authorities for the Sertorian War are Plutarch, *Sertorius*, *Pompey* (17–20) and Appian (*Bell. Civ.* I, 108–15), supported by the fragments (Books I and II) of the *Historiae* of Sallust, the *Epitomes* of Livy, writers who abridged him, and numerous references in such authors as Cicero, Strabo and Frontinus. Two strains of tradition can be traced, popular and aristocratic. The popular sympathies of Sallust are reflected in the favourable narrative of Plutarch, but in Appian and the writings based upon Livy we can detect the opposite bias.

during the governorship of Marius (114 B.C.) was an isolated example of disquiet. When a new generation had grown to manhood revolt was ablaze once more. After Arausio the victorious Cimbri invaded Spain, but were expelled by the Celtiberians. This notable deed of arms incited both Lusitanians and Celtiberians to insurrection and during the next ten years much blood was shed. The Lusitanians, though checked at the outset by L. Cornelius Dolabella who triumphed in 98, immediately rose again in concert with the Celtiberi and Vaccaei. Two governors of consular rank, T. Didius (consul in 98), conqueror of the Scordisci, and P. Licinius Crassus (consul in 97), re-established the ascendancy of Rome by the usual methods and triumphed in 93, the former over the Celtiberians, the latter over the Lusitanians. Of the vigour of Didius there can be no doubt—rebellious towns were razed to the ground and the inhabitants of Termantia, a powerful and refractory city, were removed from their hill-fortress to an unwalled settlement on lower ground—but his treacherous massacre of unarmed Celtiberians[1] reminds us of the brutality of Galba towards the Lusitanians. Permanent peace, however, was not secured, for the Celtiberians had to be chastised again by C. Valerius Flaccus after his consulship in 93. Thus from the fall of Numantia to the Sertorian War Spain passed through a half-century of uneasy peace marred by one violent revolt. No doubt while high tribute continued burdensome and governors oppressive Roman *negotiatores* did not lose their opportunity of exploiting the Iberians. The stage was being prepared for the tragedy of Sertorius.

Quintus Sertorius, the last and greatest name in the story of Spain under the Roman Republic, was born a Sabine at Nursia in 123. He had escaped the stricken field of Arausio to serve under Marius against the northern barbarians, and his experience as a military tribune under Didius in the Celtiberian war where he gained an appreciation of his enemies and a profound knowledge of guerrilla warfare, marked him out as an exceptionally brave and capable officer. Moreover, by the end of the Marsic War where he served first as quaestor in Cisalpine Gaul and later as a commander in Italy, the scarred veteran of thirty-five had become a popular figure, but met with a rebuff in his first political campaign. In 88 when a candidate for the tribunate he was rejected through the opposition of Sulla, to whom the election of a distinguished officer of municipal descent and a potential if not already an actual opponent was doubly unwelcome. Ranked, therefore, with the Marian party but gravely mistrusting Marius himself, he played

[1] Appian, *Iber.* 100.

a part in, and was a restraining influence after, the seizure of Rome. We hear nothing further of him till 83, when after trying to stiffen the resistance offered to Sulla (p. 273) he was sent at the end of the year to govern Nearer Spain[1]. Thus the Marian leaders in Italy sent away their best general and may have been glad to see the last of a pungent critic. No doubt a man of his stamp who, as Sallust says[2], 'sought during the Civil War to be esteemed for justice and goodness,' was overshadowed by larger but inferior growths.

During the winter he crossed the Pyrenees by the Col de la Perche, having bribed the natives to let his army through. Once in Spain, he overcame the governors and spent the rest of the year 82 in raising a force of Celtiberians and Roman residents and building ships to hold the peninsula against Sulla. Aware of the danger, Sulla proscribed him at once and early in 81 sent out C. Annius Luscus with two legions to recover Spain. Outnumbered and handicapped by the treachery of a subordinate, Sertorius fled to Mauretania and during an interlude experienced those hardships and romantic adventures which are so graphically described by Plutarch[3]. But after cheating him of his desire to seek oblivion in the Isles of the Blessed, fortune smiled once more upon the exile. Entreated by the Lusitanians to lead them in yet another revolt from Rome, he landed in 80 at Baelo, west of Tarifa, where a force of 4700 awaited him, and soon defeated L. Fufidius, the governor of Further Spain, on the Baetis. By the end of the year he had raised his forces to 8000 and was ready to take the field against the best generals Sulla could send. Lusitanian and, later, Celtiberian hill-men, captivated by his personality and by his adroit appeal to their superstitions, were welded into an army officered by his Roman followers which learned to excel not only in the improvisations of guerrilla warfare, but also in more conventional battle-pieces. An organizer and a commander of genius, he remained for eight years (79–72) undefeated in any general engagement.

Serious hostilities began in 79 when Q. Caecilius Metellus Pius, the governor of Further Spain, planned to crush Sertorius between his own army and that of M. Domitius Calvinus from the Nearer province. But the combined manœuvre failed. While Sertorius kept Metellus occupied, L. Hirtuleius, his best lieutenant, defeated and killed Calvinus near Consabura (now Consuegra) between the upper valleys of the Tagus and the Guadiana; and Sertorius similarly dealt with Thorius, a legate of Metellus. Hirtuleius then marched against the defenceless northern province, while Sertorius

---

[1] From Appian, *Bell. Civ.* 1, 86, 392 it is clear that he had been praetor, possibly in 87.   [2] Sallust, *Hist.* 1, 90, M.   [3] *Sert.* 8–9.

harassed the southern and pinned Metellus down to cautious strategy. Exploration[1] has thrown light upon the advances carried out in 79 and 78 by Metellus from his headquarters on the Guadiana: to the north he penetrated as far as the Sierra de Guadarrama; on the west he advanced towards the mouth of the Tagus; and to the south-west he was worsted by the cunning of Sertorius at the siege of Lacobriga (now Lagos). But in 77 he seems to have withdrawn to the line of the Baetis, and in that summer Sertorius was free to march across central Spain and extend his power among the Celtiberi. Hirtuleius had already been operating there and had defeated L. Manlius, governor of Gallia Narbonensis, who attempted to interfere. From the story of the march of Sertorius from Lusitania to the Ebro we can appreciate his versatility as a commander; to oust the cave-dwellers of Caraca he pressed into service the north-east wind and a storm of dust, but against the fortress of Contrebia he employed more orthodox methods for forty-four days, and finally spared the garrison. By the end of the year, he was master of Spain from the Sierra Morena to the Pyrenees and his influence extended to Gallia Narbonensis and Aquitania.

He had created a Romano-Iberian power which under favourable conditions might enable him to interfere in Italian affairs. On the east coast, between the Roman stronghold of Nova Carthago and the Ebro, Saguntum and Lauro alone resisted him; Dianium was his naval arsenal and harboured his allies the Cilician pirates. From his Roman followers he appointed a senate of 300 to act as a Council of State, and at Osca, his capital, he opened a school where Celtiberian chieftains sent their sons and unwittingly provided him with hostages. Moreover, towards the end of 77, he was reinforced from Sardinia by the remains of the army of Lepidus, some 20,000 infantry and 1500 horse, commanded by Perperna (p. 316). Small wonder, therefore, that in the summer of 77 the Senate, fearful lest a second Hannibal might invade Italy, had been driven to the distasteful step of commissioning Pompey to set their Spanish house in order, as it was said, '*non pro consule sed pro consulibus*[2].' On the march out the new commander met trouble in Gallia Narbonensis, but outflanked the Salluvii by building a new road through the Cottian Alps (by Mont Genèvre) and reached Spain for the campaign of 76.

The second phase of the war then opened, a struggle for the

---

[1] For example a Roman camp near Caceres is to be regarded as a construction of Metellus. For this and other evidence see A. Schulten, *Sertorius*, pp. 66–73.   [2] Cicero, *Phil.* xi, 8, 18.

coast plain of Valentia, an arena where aggressors from the north were naturally challenged by defenders of the peninsula, and a region of vital importance for supplies. In his first campaign Pompey maintained this contest single-handed and unsuccessfully. He sought to win a base for operations against the Celtiberian highlands by attacking the plain of Valentia from two sides; he himself was to descend from the north, a quaestor, C. Memmius, was to land at Nova Carthago and march up from the south. Sertorius, who clearly expected that the east coast would be the decisive theatre, left Hirtuleius to watch Metellus in the southern province and posted Perperna, with Herennius in reserve, to prevent Pompey from crossing the Ebro. He himself remained in the upper Ebro valley so as to be able to intervene either against Pompey or against Metellus. At the outset Pompey forced the crossing of the Ebro and marched down to Saguntum; Perperna fell back upon Valentia. Sertorius thereupon descended from the upper Ebro and began to besiege Lauro, the capture of which would secure Perperna and Herennius at Valentia. Pompey's efforts to raise the siege were disastrous. Outstripped, first, in a movement to seize a commanding elevation west of the city he was then severely defeated in an attempt to crush Sertorius between his own army and the city. Later, his foraging parties were enticed to destruction and a legion sent to the rescue was annihilated. 'The pupil of Sulla' had indeed been taught a severe lesson[1]. Outmanoeuvred Pompey abandoned Lauro to Sertorius and marched back towards the Ebro.

Farther south, however, the calculations of Sertorius were rudely shaken, for Hirtuleius was routed at Italica by Metellus when endeavouring to prevent him from joining Pompey. Apparently his strategy was blameless, but his tactics in exposing his men to the burning heat of an August morning while the enemy were sheltered within their camp contributed to his defeat. After his victory Metellus refrained from intervention on the east coast, possibly because of the advanced season, and marched up to the eastern Pyrenees where he wintered. But Pompey, anxious to retrieve his failure, began to reduce the Celtiberi around the upper Ebro. The year's balance of success clearly lay with the rebels, for the repulse of Pompey outweighed the disaster to Hirtuleius. Moreover, it is possible that we should assign to the winter of 76–5 B.C. the conclusion of an agreement between Sertorius and Mithridates[2]. In return for 3000 talents and 40 ships Sertorius undertook to send him an officer and men and to recognize his

---

[1] Plutarch, *Sert.* 18.　　　　[2] See p. 358.

conquests in Bithynia and Cappadocia, but he was too loyal a
Roman to allow a claim to the province of Asia[1]. Closely allied
with the King that menaced Rome in the east and with the corsairs
that harassed her communications with every province Sertorius
was indeed at the height of his power.

The operations of 75 formed a climax. While Pompey again
attempted to win the plain of Valentia Metellus marched down
from the Pyrenees and inflicted upon Hirtuleius at Segovia a defeat which decisively influenced the course of the war. In tactics
the battle was on the pattern of Ilipa (vol. VIII, p. 89)[2]. Its results,
the loss of his second-in-command and the union of Pompey and
Metellus, were blows which presaged ultimate defeat for Sertorius. Meantime there had been severe fighting on the east coast.
Outside Valentia Pompey was attacked by Perperna and Herennius, but routed them with heavy loss and took the city. Herennius
was amongst the dead, but Perperna fell back upon Sertorius in
the lower Sucro valley. Elated by this success and anxious to
follow up his victory, possibly before Metellus should intervene,
Pompey flung his smaller army against the combined forces of
Sertorius and Perperna. Although the brilliant generalship of
Sertorius more than compensated for the failure of Perperna
neither side could claim a distinct advantage, but on the following
day Metellus joined Pompey and saved the situation. 'If that old
woman had not come up,' lamented Sertorius, 'I would have
thrashed the youngster and sent him back to Rome[3].' His army,
however, was shaken in morale by the news of Segovia and was
temporarily disbanded. The sacred fawn which was said to attend
upon Sertorius as the visible evidence of divine favour was not to
be found, but with its reappearance hope returned, and an army
again took the field. This time, however, Sertorius failed to make
good a defeat of Perperna by Metellus; but he threw himself into
Saguntum[4] and continued to defy his opponents. The Roman
generals, therefore, baffled by the skilful moves of Sertorius and
in constant anxiety about their supplies, abandoned their venture
in the plain of Valentia. Metellus, for whatever reason, withdrew
to Gaul, but Pompey spent the autumn in attacking Celtiberian
towns, like Clunia, between the upper Ebro and the Douro, always
with the hope of forcing Sertorius to a pitched battle. Leaving

---

[1] Plutarch (*Sert.* 23) is to be preferred to Appian (*Mithr.* 68), who
includes the province of Asia.

[2] Frontinus, *Strat.* II, 3, 5.   [3] Plutarch, *Sert.* 19.

[4] Sallust, *Hist.* II, 64 M., supports this interpretation of the vague account
in Plutarch, *Sert.* 21.

a *legatus* to winter among the Celtiberi[1] he retired towards the western Pyrenees and composed the despatch which was read to the Senate early in 74 B.C.[2] No exception could be taken to his demands for reinforcements, supplies and money, since the successes of Sertorius, the activity of the pirates and the failure of the Gallic harvest were sufficient explanation; and nerves already strained by agitation at home and grave trouble elsewhere abroad would not be eased by the studied pessimism of Pompey's concluding words: 'I warn you that unless you come to the rescue I shall be unable to prevent your armies here from marching back to Italy and bringing with them the whole Spanish war.' This outburst, supported from personal motives by the consul L. Lucullus who feared that the return of Pompey to Italy might menace his own Asiatic command, had the desired effect. Two legions and money were sent to Spain.

The arrival of this help coincided with a complete change in the conduct and fortunes of the war. The Roman generals, now convinced of the futility of struggling for the plain of Valentia against the combination of Sertorius and the pirates, changed their battle-ground and their strategy; they delivered a combined attack against the Celtiberian highlands and applied themselves to siege warfare. Operating in the mountains south-west of the middle Ebro Metellus captured such strongholds as Bilbilis and Sego-briga, while Pompey was busy around the head-waters of the Douro. But Sertorius still showed his quality; at Pallantia he forced Pompey to abandon the siege, and at the end of the year before Calagurris, the key to the upper Ebro, he worsted the combined armies of Pompey and Metellus with the loss of 3000.

But the situation had now completely changed, a crisis had been passed and the defeat of Sertorius was only a matter of time; in the south-east the Celtiberi had fallen away and their last strongholds to the north-west were beginning to totter. In 73 while Metellus remained in his province Pompey continued alone against enfeebled opposition, and by the end of the year few towns held out. This collapse is easily comprehensible. The Romans had been reinforced, they had profited by defeat and they were pressing home the superiority of a giant. Among the Iberians the will and the power to resist were failing; a century's struggle for freedom had taken toll of physical and spiritual stamina from tribes whose elation after victory had been equalled by depression after defeat.

---

[1] Schulten (*op. cit.* p. 121) ascribes two of the camps preserved near Renieblas east of Numantia to Pompey and his legate Titurius.
[2] Sallust, *Hist.* II, 98 M.

Moreover, their leader himself was driven by disappointment and mistrust to loss of self-control and to stern and even tyrannical measures. Perperna, his evil genius, took advantage of the collapse of his forces and of his growing unpopularity to plot against his life. In 72 the great outlaw, like Viriathus before him, was basely murdered. Perperna then fell an easy prey to Pompey, who crowned his victory by a great refusal to open the correspondence found in the enemy's camp. No doubt many a Roman noble who had intrigued with Sertorius breathed more freely. A few towns remained to be overcome, and the siege of Calagurris where the garrison devoured the bodies of women and children sets a seal of horror upon the tale of the war. The year 71 saw Pompey and Metellus back in Italy. The trophy of victory which the younger commander proudly erected upon the summit of the Col de la Perche commemorated his capture of eight hundred and seventy-six towns, but in accordance with a wholesome practice and a regard for truth made no mention of his invincible antagonist.

An examination of the career of Sertorius compels assent to the striking but guarded tribute paid to his memory by Mommsen[1]. 'So ended one of the greatest men, if not the very greatest man that Rome had hitherto produced—a man who under more fortunate circumstances would perhaps have become the regenerator of his country.' Although it is futile to speculate upon his political future had his career ended in triumph not in tragedy, the great capacity which he displayed as an outlaw would surely have been reproduced on the stage of public service. In any case he is worthy to take a place not far beneath two of the giant figures of Roman republican history, Hannibal as a commander and Julius Caesar as a personality. His achievements in war proclaim him a military genius; rare gifts of leadership and strategy were supplemented by that knowledge of Roman discipline and tactics which he acquired in the school of Marius and developed in his Celtiberian and Italian campaigns. While comparable with Marius in the training of soldiers and Pompey in organization, he possessed, like Caesar, the power of rapid and disconcerting movement, the initiative and resource that frequently bewildered his opponents by some daring stratagem and snatched victory from the jaws of defeat. In the Iberian hillmen he found excellent material for training, particularly as skirmishing troops, and in the Iberian peninsula a terrain admirably adapted to guerrilla warfare. Commanded by himself, these men were irresistible in open fighting, and even in

---

[1] *History of Rome*, IV, p. 302 *sq.*, followed by Schulten. For a less favourable view see H. Berve, *Sertorius*, in *Hermes*, LXIV, 1929, p. 199.

close encounters proved themselves worthy antagonists of trained Roman legionaries. But the issue of the pitched battles in 76 and 75 showed that ultimately the strength of Sertorius would be measured by that of his subordinate commanders. On the Sucro, for example, all his superb ability to rally beaten troops was required to compensate for the failures of Perperna. It is true that some of the spirit of Sertorius descended upon Hirtuleius, but the results of Italica and Segovia showed that even he was no match for the experienced Metellus. That his levies remained an effective force for so long is a tribute to his personal magnetism, no less than to the inspiration of success. While many of his measures proclaim his enlightenment and humanity, he could act ruthlessly when it was necessary to maintain discipline and morale.

His biographer has portrayed a personality who commands admiration and respect. In hardihood, integrity and frugality he is true to the type of the yeomen heroes who won Italy for Rome; and his descent from them seems to speak in those touches of grave humour wherewith he soliloquizes over a discomfited antagonist or laments a lost opportunity. He stands out among celebrated contemporaries as one richly endowed with military genius and promise as a statesman, and he was in advance of his age in his realization of the duties of Rome to her provincial subjects. It is one of the tragedies of history that through the curse of civil war his talents were devoted to defeating the armies, rather than promoting the good government, of his native land. He was bound to fail in his venture, and his shameful end places him among pathetic figures like the Gracchi, Scipio Aemilianus, the younger Drusus. Hunted as a rebel, with a price on his head, he was loyal to any Rome except the Rome of Sulla.

V. THE DEMANDS FOR A RESTORATION OF THE *TRIBUNICIA POTESTAS*

In the absence of the armies and their commanders, politics at Rome pursued a comparatively tranquil course. Gaius Caesar was able to make a quiet start in public life with two laudable undertakings in the courts: in 77 B.C. he prosecuted Gnaeus Dolabella for extortion in Macedonia, and also acted for the plaintiff Greeks in a civil suit for recovery against one of Sulla's agents, C. Antonius Hybrida, son of the orator and the future colleague of Cicero[1]. Next year Cicero, too, was back at work in Rome. But the

---

[1] For the date of this incident see Sallust, *Hist.* ed. B. Maurenbrecher, Prolegomena, p. 77.

absorbing interest of this period was the plight of the tribunes. In 76 B.C. an agitation was started by one Sicinius, himself a holder of the office: and though the unbending opposition of the consul, C. Curio, frustrated his immediate efforts, to him may belong the credit of having moved one of the consuls of 75 B.C. to take a more favourable view.

C. Aurelius Cotta, whose colleague L. Octavius was a man of utter insignificance, came of a family among the most interesting in Rome. Gaius was the eldest of three brothers, all nephews of the estimable P. Rutilius, and was himself a courageous reformer: of Marcus, his successor in the consulship, less is known: but Lucius, the youngest, is the friend whom Cicero held in high esteem. More significant still, Aurelia, the mother of Julius Caesar, was a relative—probably a first cousin: and we know that to his mother Julius owed not a little of his political outlook. These Cottae were a family outstanding among the Whig nobility[1]: Gaius had been intimate with the younger Livius Drusus and had even retired from Rome to escape the attentions of the Varian Commission. True, his restoration had been due to Sulla; but in the whole oligarchy it would have been hard to find a leader more sympathetic to any real grievance. The tribunes still carried on their agitation—this year through the mouth of Q. Opimius; but all this would have meant nothing without the goodwill of Cotta. Despite senatorial reluctance he somehow contrived to pass a bill which relieved the tribunes of their disability to hold other office. This was an ominous concession: it was the complete abandonment of Sulla's plan to destroy the tribunate by closing it to men of spirit and ambition, and it meant that henceforward, as before the time of Sulla, tribunes would be a power in public life. Yet this surrender does not seem to have been wrung from the Senate by force: there is no evidence of constraint, and the reform must rather be ascribed to the liberal outlook of Cotta and to his ability to prevent any successful resistance by the extremists on his own side.

The Senate was not long in repenting. Next year it vented its indignation on the luckless Opimius; and Cotta himself, unless our evidence is deceptive, soon came to regret his action. Another of his measures—an enactment of unknown content *de iudiciis privatis*—was repealed in the following year; but, when Cicero records[2] that the consul of 75 B.C. himself made a proposal in the Senate for the abrogation of his laws, it is only possible to justify the plural by the assumption that Cotta had changed his mind on

[1] See Sallust, *Hist.* III, 48, 8 M.   [2] See Asconius, p. 66 C.

the expediency of his *lex de iure tribunorum*. Whatever be the truth about this, the act remained in force and produced its natural result: now that young politicians might hold the office without detriment to their careers, they demanded more insistently than ever that all its old powers should be restored. In 74 B.C. the agitation was continued by another tribune, L. Quinctius, and in the year after by the historian C. Licinius Macer: but Quinctius was somehow reduced to silence by L. Lucullus[1], and the only point of interest in the activities of Macer, if the speech put into his mouth by Sallust[2] in any way expresses his real views, is his frank recognition that contemporary politics were a farce and that the issues of the day would be decided by Pompey on his return from Spain.

For five years now the tribunes and their friends had struggled with adversity, but the fruits of persistence scarcely gave cause for pride. The only progress made towards the emancipation of the office was due more to the charity of C. Cotta than to any efforts of their own. It is true that the needs of the masses had not been completely ignored. The scarcity and high price of corn had come near to provoking a riot in 75 B.C.[3], and two years later a consular law was introduced which did something to relieve the shortage. The Lex Terentia Cassia, which took its name from M. Lucullus and C. Cassius Longinus, sought to accelerate the flow of Sicilian corn to Rome and at the same time authorized the distribution of five *modii* a month—a prison ration[4]—to a body of recipients who probably did not exceed 40,000[5], apparently at the old Gracchan price of $6\frac{1}{3}$ *asses* a *modius*[6]. Likewise it presumably gave some general satisfaction when Cn. Lentulus Clodianus, a consul of 72 B.C., introduced a bill to cancel Sulla's remission of payment to those who had bought property set free by the confiscations[7]. The measure, in the end, did not become law, but effect seems to have been given to its intentions by several decrees of the Senate passed soon afterwards[8].

Even this step, however, was taken less to satisfy the popular resentment against Sulla's creatures than through the compelling necessity of a financial crisis. Already in 75 B.C. the drain of wars

---

[1] Plutarch, *Lucullus*, 5, 4. [2] Sallust, *Hist.* III, 48, 21–3 M.

[3] *Ib.* II, 45 M. [4] *Ib.* III, 48, 19 M.

[5] Cicero, II *in Verr.* III, 30, 72: see M. Rostowzew in *P.W. s.v.* Frumentum, col. 174.

[6] Asconius, p. 8 C., where it is to be observed that *SPM* agree in reading 'senis'; cf. Cicero, *pro Sestio*, 25, 55.

[7] Sallust, *Hist.* IV, 1 M; and, for the date, *ib.* Prolegomena, p. 79.

[8] Cicero, II *in Verr.* III, 35, 81.

in Asia, Macedonia and Spain—to which by now the campaigns against Spartacus must be added—had threatened the Treasury with bankruptcy[1], and the clamant demands of the generals, especially Pompey, were only met with difficulty (p. 324). The plain fact was that in the years from 78 to 71 B.C., when its enemies still lacked the backing of a successful general, the Sullan constitution on the whole stood firm: a foolish concession to the tribunate had been made through the influence of C. Cotta, and the fate of the Senate had already been sealed by the appointment of Pompey to his Spanish command. But the failure of the tribunes to recover their pristine powers is not to be denied, and the solid resistance which the government could oppose to their attack serves to emphasize the folly of the weakness which had allowed Pompey to build up a military power in Spain.

VI. THE WAR OF THE GLADIATORS

In 73 B.C. attention was diverted from the struggles of the Forum to an outbreak of domestic war in Italy[2]. Servile discontent had long been a familiar menace, but on this occasion the lead was taken by a type which, though peculiarly dangerous, had not been in the forefront of earlier revolts. Seventy-four gladiators in an establishment at Capua suddenly broke loose and, seizing such weapons as they could find, retired to the summit of Vesuvius. Thence they defied authority and rallied recruits at an alarming speed. Whereas the Servile Wars in Sicily had been waged by slaves of Asiatic origin, the Italian rising was mainly the work of Europeans. Gauls and Thracians formed the backbone of the rebel forces, with an admixture of captives from the Teutonic invasions. Leadership was supplied by the Thracian Spartacus, who in earlier days had seen service with the Roman armies, and by two Gauls, Crixus and Oenomaus. The efforts of the government to circumscribe the trouble met with no success. Operations began with an attempt by C. Claudius Glaber, a praetor of 73 B.C., to surround the rebels on Vesuvius, and ended, after an unbroken series of defeats, by leaving them masters of all southern Italy. Recruits now flowed in more rapidly than ever, and in the course of the winter so large a force collected that, when the new campaign began, Spartacus and Crixus were each at the head of an independent army. But, unlike the leaders of the Sicilian revolts, they lacked a consistent plan. The far-seeing Spartacus had no

---

[1] Sallust, *Hist.* II, 47, 6- 7 M

[2] On the outbreak of the Third Mithridatic War in 74 B.C. see below, p. 358 *sq.*

illusions about the danger of their plight. Italy would not fall permanently under the control of a band of slaves; and, if not, it was his business to lead his men out of the peninsula while time remained. Once across the Alps they might perhaps scatter to their homes with some hope of safety. Crixus, however, unable to tear himself away from the plunder of the south, condemned his following to an aimless policy of brigandage foredoomed to failure.

In 72 B.C. the Senate took energetic action. The two consuls— L. Gellius Publicola and Cn. Lentulus Clodianus—were each given armies to concentrate on the menace of the slaves. But though Gellius, or one of his lieutenants, ran down the wilful Crixus near Monte Gargano and destroyed him with all his force, the two together could make no impression on the more cautious Spartacus. In accordance with his considered scheme to break out of Italy across the Alps, Spartacus was moving northwards, with Gellius on his heels and Lentulus seeking to intercept him from the front[1]. Somewhere in Picenum two battles were fought in quick succession: first Lentulus and then his colleague were defeated so decisively that the Senate saw fit to supersede them both. Meanwhile Spartacus pressed on to the north, and at Mutina he opened the way to the mountains by routing an army under C. Cassius, proconsul of Cisalpine Gaul. But then came a fatal change of mind. It was doubtless easier for the army as a whole to escape from Italy than for the various contingents to make their ways home from the frontier through territory largely under Roman occupation. Whatever the reason, the day of parting never dawned: instead, the host turned again towards Italy, and it was probably at this time, if at all, that Spartacus toyed with the idea of an attack on Rome itself[2]. So rash a project deserved no consideration, but much might be said in favour of an attempt to seize Sicily for the rebel cause—for among the slaves of Sicily the rebels could count on whole-hearted support. This was the object with which Spartacus retraced his steps, making back to his old haunts among the Bruttii.

In place of the discredited consuls the Senate chose as its new commander in the field M. Licinius Crassus, now praetor. Crassus was a man by no means susceptible to the glory of facing fearful odds: to the remnants of the four legions of the consuls,

[1] The problems of the later phases of the war against Spartacus are discussed by T. Rice Holmes in *The Roman Republic*, I, pp. 386–90.
[2] This incident is dated thus by Florus—II, 8 (III, 20), 11, and more credibly than by Appian (*Bell. Civ.* I, 117, 545), who puts it immediately after the victories over the two consuls.

which losses had perhaps reduced to the equivalent of two[1], he added six more, and with this imposing host he set out to prevent Spartacus from reaching the Straits. Before long one of his subordinates sustained a slight reverse, which Crassus used as an excuse for decimating an unsteady cohort—with the most beneficent results to the morale of the remainder. Then followed various engagements, the result of which was to drive Spartacus to Rhegium, whence his attempts to cross to Sicily were frustrated, to some extent through the exertions of Verres. At this juncture Crassus set his hand to a scheme which, if it does little credit to his intelligence, at least reveals the dimensions of his army. He began to build a wall, thirty-seven miles long, right across the toe of Italy, hoping thereby to confine the rebels to a region wherein starvation would reduce them to surrender. But, though the mountains of the neighbourhood gave generous aid to the defence, not even the army of Crassus could hope to hold all vulnerable parts of the line in strength enough to resist the onslaught of the rebels if Spartacus concentrated his whole force on a single sector. When the rebels tried to break out, they did so without much difficulty.

Open warfare was now resumed, and its resumption, or the prospect of it, seems to have prompted a move at Rome which spurred Crassus to more feverish efforts. As the result of an agitation, in which it may be safely conjectured that the masses played a more active part than the Senate[2], Pompey, who had just returned from Spain, was commissioned to take his army south and co-operate with Crassus. It had been the intention of Spartacus, after the failure of his Sicilian plan, to escape from Italy by way of Brundisium, but retreat in that direction was suddenly blocked by the arrival of M. Lucullus with his victorious army from the Black Sea (see below, p. 357 *sq.*). Thus the only way left open to the rebels was the northern route which they had followed the year before, and this the forces of the government made it their business to close. The position of Spartacus was dangerous; and its dangers were increased by new dissensions among his friends. Two Gauls, Castus and Cannicus, formed a following of their own; and, when they took to independent action in the style of Crixus, Spartacus and the main body found themselves occupied more in saving the discontents from the results of their folly than in their proper business of defeating Crassus. At length, after various en-

---

[1] This is conceivably the meaning of the source behind Appian, *Bell. Civ.* 1, 118, 549.

[2] This is the plausible suggestion of Appian (*Bell. Civ.* 1, 119, 554).

gagements, Castus and Cannicus were destroyed in a battle fought among the mountains between Paestum and Venusia, whereby the back of the revolt was broken. Spartacus retreated southwards for a time, but a slight success is said to have encouraged his men to insist on another general engagement. Then at length, before Pompey had time to arrive, the last army of the rebels was routed and the war was over. Nothing remained but to round up the fugitives—an easy task in which Pompey thrust his unwelcome help on the reluctant Crassus. The work was quickly done: six months after his appointment Crassus had the satisfaction of staging the final scene, wherein six thousand prisoners were revealed crucified along the Appian Way from Capua to Rome.

Like Eunus and Salvius, Spartacus is a tragic figure, but the significance of his career is small. So far as his own achievements went, he did nothing more than repeat in Italy the warning which twice already had been given across the Straits. True, the devastation of the South was severe, and enough of the lesson was re-membered to prevent the recurrence of gladiatorial outbreaks on anything like this scale again. But the most notable legacy of the affair was its results on Pompey and Crassus. Crassus was left with a belief, by no means without foundation, in his own gifts as a military commander and with a deep-seated dislike of Pompey which, though Crassus was not a man of bitter disposition, always stood in the way of their effective co-operation. Pompey, indeed, had played the cad to gratify his invincible conceit; for, though his Spanish campaigns had earned him undisputed laurels whose glory far outshone the most that could be won in a servile war, he resolutely set himself to scrape a further meed of praise by pre-tending that the credit for the end of the Italian rising belonged as much to him as to his colleague. Crassus did not openly protest; but the bad feeling thus implanted lasted till his death and was a ponderable factor in Roman politics.

VII. THE FIRST CONSULSHIP OF POMPEY AND CRASSUS

The two marshals now advanced on Rome, where the Senate was even more defenceless than in 77 B.C. L. Lucullus, the most experienced of the generals on whom it could depend, was irre-vocably detained by the command in Asia which had cost him such efforts to obtain (p. 359). M. Antonius was already dead, and would have been useless had he been alive. Metellus Pius, who had not yet arrived from Spain, was no match for a Pompey in the field, nor was he the sort of man to fight his way through the

rough-and-tumble of a crisis: it was typical of his unfailing respect
for the law that, when at length he did return, he broke up his
army as soon as it had crossed the Alps. Besides these a few
others could be named, but there was only one man in Italy who
might have struck a blow for the Senate—M. Lucullus, lately
back from his campaign in the Dobrudja. The odds, however,
against him were long: he made no move on his own account, nor
was he invited, and so without resistance the Senate went meekly
to the sacrifice.

Crassus, praetor in 72 B.C., was due in the normal course to
hold a consulship in 70, and nothing debarred him from becoming
a candidate; but with his rival the case was different. There was
no sort of doubt that, if Crassus was to be consul the following
year, Pompey would insist on being his colleague. But, under the
Sullan *lex annalis*, there were two fatal obstacles to his consideration: he was still six years below the minimum age required for
the office, and he had never held the necessary preliminaries—the
quaestorship and praetorship. Nevertheless, with suave assurances that it was all due to the delay in the return of Metellus Pius
and that, as soon as they had celebrated their triumphs together,
the armies would be disbanded, Pompey sat with his legions at
the gates of Rome. And not only so: by announcing that he would
support the removal of all trammels from the *tribunicia potestas* he
won the frenzied enthusiasm of the masses. Such were the circumstances in which the Senate began to discover that the
obstacles in the way of his election were not insuperable.

The triumph itself had still to be voted; but this was duly done,
and before long the Senate had dispensed him from the laws by
which at present he was disqualified for the consulship. Herein
the latent power of the legions was decisive. The negotiations
between Pompey and the Senate were conducted, indeed, with every
appearance of politeness; but the Senate was not a free agent, and
there is no doubt that, had it attempted to refuse the dangerous and
illegal demands of the man whose professed object was to expose
it once more to the attacks of a tribunate freed from all restraint,
the legions would have entered Rome. There is, of course, no need
to deny that the tribunate had its value for the Senate, as for the
Senate's enemies (pp. 26 *sq.*, 315); but it was not for the sake of any
advantage it would bring the oligarchs that the rabble clamoured
for this measure and Pompey gave it his benediction. By yielding
to his claims to a consulship, the Senate put itself in the hands of
one who did not conceal his hostility, and an enemy was left free
to work his will on a constitutional system which, skilfully as it

had been constructed by Sulla, could never remain intact without constant and energetic defence. Nevertheless, the Senate can scarcely be blamed for its action. Now, it was at the mercy of the Spanish army: the irreparable damage had been done six years before, when Pompey was given his command.

When his own troubles had been overcome, Pompey had still to face the question of a colleague, but this was made easy by the presence of Crassus. There was, indeed, every reason to indulge his legitimate aspirations; for Crassus commanded the respect of that powerful financial class to which, much as it engaged his sympathy, Pompey himself did not belong. So the appreciative plutocrat, after the honour of personal support from Pompey in his canvass, found himself elected to the consulship for what was to be the most memorable year in Roman history since the death of Sulla.

Before any consideration of its legislative achievement, something must be said about the general political situation when Pompey and Crassus took office on 1 January 70 B.C. The Sullan constitution had already failed. In its more controversial aspects that system had been designed to attain two ends—to give the Senate effective control over the military commanders and to free public life from the disturbing activities of the tribunes. The former of these was the more essential, as well as the more difficult, to secure; but all the plans drawn by Sulla towards this end had already been torn to shreds. The appointment of Pompey to Spain in 77 B.C. and his election to the consulship in 71 were incidents precisely of the kind which Sulla had sought to make impossible: when they occurred, the failure of Sulla's safeguards was revealed, and on this side at least no legislation was needed to overthrow the Sullan constitution, because that edifice already lay in ruins. With the tribunate the case was little different. Sulla's attempt to destroy the office had been frustrated by the Lex Aurelia of 75 B.C. By the passage of that measure able men were again invited to become tribunes, as they had done before Sulla's time; and once such men were allowed back in the office, it was only an inevitable consequence of their return that its powers should be restored to all their old dimensions.

On another matter, however, something was left to the free initiative of the consuls. The degradation of the Gracchan *iudices* had justified Sulla's recruitment of the juries from the Senate; but by now the senatorial jurors had shown themselves to be as corrupt as their predecessors, and the administration of criminal justice was calling again for reform. For several years scandals had been piling up. The acquittal of Cn. Dolabella in 77 B.C. did nothing to increase public confidence in the courts, and in 74 there had followed the outrageous case of the elder Oppianicus. Whether that individual was guilty of an attempt to poison his step-son Cluentius or not, nobody seriously denied that the trial had been disfigured by unblushing bribery—bribery so blatant that it immediately became the theme of political controversy[1]. Under the assiduous care of the tribune Quinctius[2] the affair was turned into productive capital by the enemies of the Senate, and thenceforward the composition of the juries was once more a foremost issue of the day. Three years later definite proposals were in the air: M. Lollius Palicanus, tribune of 71, is said to have urged that jurors should be drawn from three orders—senators, *equites Romani* and *tribuni aerarii*[3]. And, more important still, at the same time came an assurance that action would follow words. Pompey, a true *popularis* in his demand for efficiency, knew that the government of the provinces was corrupt and that it could not be purged until honest courts sat again in Rome. In a speech delivered soon after his election to the consulship he dwelt on this abuse and, when he announced his intention to tackle it himself, the loud applause showed that he had widespread support[4].

The significance of this must not be overlooked. There is no reason to believe that men like Pompey and Crassus were deeply stirred by the troubles of the tribunate: the restoration of its powers was a bone flung to certain sections of the rabble whose goodwill might be of use. But the constitution of the criminal courts was a very different matter. Pompey undoubtedly had ideals of administration which for his day were high, and a man with the connections of a Crassus could not fail to stand for a return to the Gracchan *iudices*. Thus both consuls had an interest in this question of the courts, and it may not be far from the truth to say that this was the issue for which they chiefly cared. Q. Catulus at least—a responsible person, soon to be Princeps Senatus—went so far as to assert that, if only honesty were established in the courts, the grievance about the tribunate would die down[5]; and Cicero himself regarded the flagrant corruption of the juries as the foundation of the whole case against the senatorial government[6].

When the new year began, the consuls set to work forthwith, each in his own fashion. While Crassus regaled the populace with

---

[1] The extent of the abuse at this time can be gathered from Cicero, I *in Verr.* 13, 38–9.   [2] Cicero, *pro Cluentio*, 28, 77 and 29, 79.
[3] Schol. Gronov. B, *ap.* Stangl ii, p. 328.   [4] Cicero, I *in Verr.* 15, 45.
[5] Cicero, I *in Verr.* 15, 44.   [6] *Div. in Caec.* 3, 8–9.

Gargantuan entertainment, Pompey carried a law to satisfy the tribunician agitators. The tribunes had now recovered everything of which they had been deprived by Sulla; the last had been heard of a tiresome grievance; and the way was open for fresh experiments in ochlocracy. But the reform of the judicature was a more difficult, as well as a more important, task. A preliminary measure was the revival of the censorship, to which M. Lucullus and Cn. Lentulus Clodianus, consuls of 73 and 72, were appointed. According to Cicero[1], hopes were entertained that censors would be able in some degree to raise the standard of honesty in the administration of justice; and it was at least beyond dispute that, so long as any jurors were drawn from the Senate, the censors could see that no man remained eligible who was notoriously unworthy of his place. Doubtless the courts were none the worse for the loss of the sixty-four senators ejected on this occasion. But by now public opinion seems to have been roused to a pitch of resentment not likely to be content with a remedy which depended on an office so arbitrary in its working as the censorship; and, moreover, the censors could do next to nothing to gratify the yearnings of the business interests for a place in the courts.

The enemies of the Senate were determined: their cause was good, and the opportunity bid fair. To popular indignation at the scandals of the past was added widespread alarm at the state of provincial administration. It was in January of 70 B.C. that C. Verres returned to Rome from Sicily after a three years' governorship in which rapacity had cast all concealment aside. Scarcely had he arrived when there appeared embassies from every State in the island save Syracuse and Messana, all clamouring for his indictment on a charge of extortion. But, though the loudness of these demands could leave little doubt that the grievances were not wholly imaginary, Verres had powerful friends. The orator Hortensius, destined for a consulship next year, was his most doughty champion, and behind Hortensius stood other leading members of the aristocracy. There was P. Cornelius Scipio, later adopted by Metellus Pius and subsequently father-in-law of Pompey himself: there were no less than three Metelli, all brothers and probably the sons of Metellus Caprarius. These brethren were valuable allies. One of them, Quintus—later surnamed Creticus, was to be colleague of Hortensius as consul in 69 B.C.: another, Marcus, as praetor in the same year obtained the presidency of the *iudicium publicum* for the crime on which Verres was arraigned: and the third brother, Lucius, was his successor as proconsul of Sicily.

[1] *Div. in Caec.* 3, 8.

Against this formidable array the Sicilian cause was led—not, indeed, until at the cost of some delay he had brushed aside a dishonest rival acting in collusion with the defence—by Cicero, who was now the outstanding figure of the younger generation at the Roman Bar and who had won the goodwill of the provincials by the honesty of his conduct as quaestor at Lilybaeum in 75 B.C. Under the wily guidance of Hortensius the defence had recourse to subterfuges of impressive ingenuity, aimed above all at securing a postponement of the trial till the following year, when some of Verres' firmest friends would be in office; but all their tricks were confounded by Cicero's resource, and in August the case came on. In face of the overwhelming evidence Hortensius virtually abandoned his brief; Verres retired to exile; and the Sicilians had won. For Cicero the result was triumphant. In the courts henceforward he was admittedly supreme, a pleader to whom Hortensius himself must yield place[1]; and in the world of politics he became a power. Without delay he followed up his success. By publishing, in the form of five set speeches, the whole material collected by the prosecution he damningly impeached not only the character of his victim but the outrageous abuses in the provinces made possible by the lack of central control over the agents of the government abroad. The career of Verres was another reason why the *quaestio repetundarum* should be placed above reproach.

Adequate reform through the censorship alone was an idle dream: Cato himself could not have removed from the Senate men like Hortensius and the other friends of Verres. For the revival of the office by Pompey and Crassus some other reason may well be sought; and, though the connection of the censors with the juries will soon appear, a secondary reason is not difficult to suggest. In the Imperial age, when the equestrian order began to produce able administrators whose service was desired in posts customarily reserved for senators, the Emperors made use with increasing frequency of the *ius adlectionis*, whereby men of mature years could be enrolled in the Senate with the status appropriate to their age. This right was a feature of the *censoria potestas*, and the purpose it served was one near to the hearts of men who, like Pompey, contended for the opening of the public career to merit in whatever ranks of society it was found. Had censors been regularly appointed, it is scarcely probable that Pompey would have remained outside the Senate until he entered it as consul— a consul so completely unfamiliar with the House that he was constrained to persuade his friend M. Varro to write a handbook

[1] Cicero, *Brutus*, 93, 319–94, 323.

of procedure for his guidance[1]. The censorship, in fact, had two kinds of use in this connection: besides purging the Senate of undesirables, it could admit the forceful genius whose progress Sulla had essayed to baulk. It opened a way round the odious *lex annalis*, and it may be surmised that this was a consideration which weighed with Pompey when he consented to its renewal.

Positive proposals for a re-constitution of the courts were left to a praetor, L. Aurelius Cotta—a younger brother of the consul of 75 B.C. The drafting of a bill seems to have taken time; for, when the prosecution of Verres began on 5 August, the Sullan arrangements were still in force. Whatever the stages by which the final scheme was reached, details of the negotiations are lost beyond recall. All we know is the outline of the measure which in the end became law, and even here there are exasperating gaps in our information[2]. Henceforward the juries in the *iudicia publica* were to be composed in equal parts of senators, *equites Romani* and *tribuni aerarii*. So much at least is clear: but about the definition of the two latter classes no certainty can be attained. It may be said at once that, for reasons suggested elsewhere (p. 895), there is no necessity to assume that the 'equites Romani' of the Lex Aurelia were defined by the formula wherein the positive qualifications of the Gracchan *iudices* had been set forth. Admittedly it is conceivable that the relevant form of words was taken without change from the Lex Acilia; but there is nothing to prove that this was so. Indeed, probability is somewhat against the suggestion; for Gracchan *iudices* had disgraced themselves in the case of Rutilius no less signally than senators had done in more recent years, and it is not easy to see how any great improvement could be expected from a scheme which divided the majority of the places on every jury among two classes both of which had already proved unfit.

The appearance of the *tribuni aerarii* in connection with the courts as constituted by the Lex Aurelia[3] may be thought to imply that in the law they were named as such; for it is hard to believe that so obscure a title would have come into the tale at all if, as is often supposed, its only relevance lay in the fact that the monetary qualification alleged to have been required of candidates

[1] Gellius, *N.A.* XIV, 7, 2.

[2] In *Rendiconti*, Serie V, vol. XXXII, 1923, p. 84, it was announced that on 20 May 1923 V. Scialoja communicated to the Lincei two bronze fragments bearing parts of a *lex iudiciaria* either to be identified with the Lex Aurelia or to be closely related thereto: but the texts, published in *Studi Bonfante*, vol. I (Milan, 1930), pp. 3 *sqq.*, throw no light on the provisions of the Lex Aurelia.

[3] The most important evidence is that of Asconius, p. 17 C.

for a place on the third panel happened to be the same as that of these unfamiliar officials. The original functions of these tribunes is largely a matter of conjecture; but whether they were the heads of the tribes, as Mommsen supposed[1], or not, the explicit evidence of Varro[2] records that it was they who at one time acted as pay-masters of the troops—a duty which may reasonably be supposed to have been reserved for men of substance and good repute. By the last century of the Republic the office seems to have become a sinecure. Its financial duties had been usurped by the quaestor-ship, and any general supervision of tribal business which it may once have exercised had apparently passed to the *curatores tribuum*[3]. Nevertheless, it is probable that *tribuni aerarii* continued to be appointed: during the Ciceronian age they appear more than once as an *ordo* in the State, in contexts without special reference to their judicial privileges under the Lex Aurelia[4]. The property qualifica-tion required in holders of the office is unknown, though there is some suggestion that it was HS 300,000[5], and by a still more unfortunate failure of our authorities we are without any effective evidence for their numbers or for the length of their continuance in office.

If the *tribuni aerarii* were mentioned by that name in the Lex Aurelia, probability would strongly favour the view that the *equites Romani* were likewise defined as such. The law did not content itself with requiring a minimum amount of property, but insisted that jurors should have held certain positions in public life: one class must have occupied the office of *tribunus aerarius*, the other must have been *equites* in some fuller sense than that of merely owning as much property as was demanded of candidates for the *equus publicus*. This conclusion—that the second and third panels of the Lex Aurelia were more than mere property-classes—is supported, though not finally proved, by a passage in which Asconius[6] describes a modification of the Lex Aurelia proposed by Pompey in 55 B.C.: as before, jurors were to be chosen from the three *ordines* of senators, *equites* and *tribuni aerarii*, but hence-forward in each case a higher census was to be required. Thus it is possible to conclude that the third panel was recruited from those who not only had more than a stated minimum of property but also held the office of *tribunus aerarius*, the second from those who, besides attaining a somewhat higher assessment, were *equites*

---

[1] *Staatsrecht*, III, p. 189.   [2] *L.L.* 5, 181; cf. Festus, p. 2 L.
[3] See Mommsen, *op. cit.* III, pp. 190 *sq.*
[4] Cicero, *pro Rab. perd. reo*, 9, 27; *in Cat.* IV, 7, 15; *pro Plancio*, 8, 21.
[5] Schol. Bob. *ap.* Stangl, II, p. 91; Suet. *Aug.* 32, 3.   [6] P. 17 C.

Romani in some fuller sense—presumably because they held the *equus publicus*. It only remains to add that, since the Roman knights apparently surrendered the public horse before they reached the age of forty[1], considerations of age and numbers virtually demand the supposition that for purposes of jury-service 'knights' meant holders of the public horse past as well as present. If that be true, it may be conjectured that the term *tribuni aerarii* included those who had held this office besides those who retained it at the moment[2].

If what is said below about the Lex Acilia is not mistaken (pp. 892 *sqq.*) and if such an account of the Lex Aurelia is not completely wrong, the aim of Cotta becomes clear. The attempt of Gaius Gracchus to recruit his juries from the whole population outside the Senate which owned more than a certain fixed amount of wealth had ended in the scandal of Rutilius. Senatorial juries, in the days when Sulla had freed the Senate from censorial control, had proved no better. But now, while the business men were granted their demand for re-admission to the *iudicia*, opportunity was taken to arrange that the panels should be formed from classes which were regularly under the supervision of the censors. It was the duty of these officers to exclude all persons of bad character from the Senate: it was they who bestowed the *equus publicus*, for which evil living was a bar: and it may be assumed that men like the *tribuni aerarii*, whose business was to handle money, were not wholly exempt from investigations of their integrity. There is, in fact, a possibility after all that the revival of the censorship and the passing of the Lex Aurelia Cottae fell in the same year by something more than a coincidence.

One more point, and the judiciary reform may be left. The recruitment of the juries from three separate panels has led many historians to describe the Lex Aurelia as a compromise. A compromise it was, in a certain sense. If the issue lay between the claims of senators and those of wealthy men outside the House, both parties to the quarrel still found themselves represented in the courts. But it would have been strange if a measure passed under the aegis of Pompey and Crassus had shown strict impartiality, and, as might be expected, the Lex Aurelia marks a

---

[1] Plutarch, *Pomp.* 22, 5–6. Cf. Suet. *Aug.* 38, 3 and Mommsen, *Staatsrecht*, III, p. 261, n. 3.

[2] The evidence for this difficult question is set out and discussed by J. L. Strachan-Davidson in *Problems of the Roman Criminal Law*, II, pp. 84–95, and by T. Rice Holmes in *The Roman Republic*, I, pp. 391–5: their conclusions, however, are not the same as those of the present writer.

definite victory for the business interests. For the practical purposes of daily life *tribuni aerarii* were indistinguishable from
equites: the Scholiast of Bobbio[1] calls them 'men of the same order'
and Cicero[2] addresses the non-senatorial members of a jury collectively as 'equites Romani.' Thus, so far as its political aspect
was concerned, the Lex Aurelia left the Senate with only half as
many places on the juries as its rivals, and no doubt was possible
about the side which emerged victorious. Nevertheless, the measure
was not unworthy of its author. Commercial interests had their
representatives in the courts: the Senate, though its monopoly
was gone, still could not raise a real grievance: and juries henceforward were to consist of men who all at different times had won
the chary approval of the censors.

With the reform of the criminal courts the legislation of 70 B.C.
was complete. What fired the imagination of the masses was the
tribunes' recovery of their old prerogatives; but neither this, nor
the revival of the censorship, nor Cotta's honest effort to grapple
once more with the recurrent problem of the courts could claim
significance comparable with that of the consuls themselves. Their
election, due as it was to the compelling presence of their troops,
had proclaimed the failure of Sulla's scheme to banish the army
from politics. Once again the devotion of the legions had become
the key to office, and Rome had now resumed her inevitable
journey on the road to civil war.

VIII. TRIBUNICIAN LEGISLATION AGAIN: THE REFORMS OF 67 B.C.

Ominous as their consulships might be, the government of
Pompey and Crassus had been the mildest yoke. At the time of
the elections, though it would have been easy for them to insist
on the appointment of their own nominees, they refrained from
the obvious attempt to establish an enduring hold on affairs and
were content to acquiesce, apparently without resistance, in the
choice of successors who stood for the Sullan ideal—Q. Hortensius,
the orator, and Q. Metellus (afterwards surnamed Creticus). The
same thing happened again with the consulships of 68 B.C., which
went to L. Metellus, the governor of Sicily after Verres, and
Q. Marcius Rex—both of whom were apparently of the optimate
persuasion. For the moment the Senate seemed to have regained
control. Pompey and Crassus, their armies at length disbanded,
were in retirement, and during the years 69 and 68 B.C. public life

---

[1] Stangl, ii, p. 94.   [2] *pro Flacco*, 2, 4; *pro Rab. Post.* 6, 14.

in Rome pursued a placid course. Such was the tranquillity that men had time to notice an incident of the most trivial kind. Sometime in 69 or 68 B.C., shortly before he left Rome to serve his quaestorship in Further Spain, the young Julius Caesar lost two of his female relatives. One was his wife Cornelia, the daughter of Cinna, whom he had refused to divorce at Sulla's behest; the other, his aunt Julia, widow of C. Marius. At the obsequies it was observed with interest that the family connection with Marius was stressed: Caesar's adherence to the *populares* was to be put beyond all doubt. Moreover, in the *laudatio* of his aunt, he took care to recall that her lineage—and his own—claimed origins which on one side were royal, on the other divine. In later days this passage was remembered[1]. When he piled one dictatorship on another, and finally became dictator for life, men might be pardoned for wondering whether even at this early stage the young Julius had conceived monarchy to be Rome's only hope and had begun to consider himself as a candidate for the throne.

Though the consulships of 67 B.C. again were won by two sound conservatives—C. Calpurnius Piso and M'. Acilius Glabrio —there were signs that the Senate's grip was weakening. The consuls had only been elected after flagrant bribery, and, worse still, for the first time since the dictatorship of Sulla the tribunician college contained two *populares* of unbounded energy and determination. C. Cornelius and A. Gabinius were an ill-assorted pair. Of Cornelius, who had been a quaestor of Pompey, nothing but good is known, but the character of his colleague, though personal spite explains much of Cicero's later indignation, must have done something to invite the venomous attacks which only ended with his exile. Yet, different as their private lives may have been, in public these two carried a series of reforms which have often missed their proper meed of praise. The merits of their achievement must not be ignored merely because, unlike the younger Gracchus, they were content with a modest programme which might reasonably be enacted within the limits of a single year.

Whether by conscious arrangement or not, the work was so divided that, while Gabinius had charge of measures affecting provincial interests, Cornelius took over those which more directly concerned the government at home. The exact sequence of events is variously recorded, but in this case chronological precision is fortunately of small importance for their interpretation.

The two main proposals of Cornelius are both aimed at abuses which chance to be connected with the name of the consul Piso.

[1] Suet. *Div. Iul.* 6, 1.

First and foremost came a measure described by Mommsen, perhaps with some exaggeration, as 'a regulation which may well be compared with the law of the Twelve Tables, and which became almost as significant for the fixing of the later urban law as that collection for the fixing of the earlier[1]'—the Lex Cornelia 'ut praetores ex edictis suis perpetuis ius dicant.' In the Roman world so large an area of the legal field was covered, not by statutes, but by the common law and equity embodied in the edicts of the *praetor urbanus* and of provincial governors (pp. 863 *sqq.*) that, in the absence of an assurance that judicial officers would rigidly adhere to the principles which their edicts set out, there was the gravest danger of litigants finding their acts judged, not by the provisions contained in the edict at the time when those acts were committed, but by some different rules enunciated later. The objections to such a practice are plain: whenever it occurred, it involved one of the most dangerous abuses—retrospective legislation. Though corruption cannot be detected in the case wherein Piso himself appears[2], and though it is perhaps less certain than Mommsen would imply that the administration of the urban praetors gave ground for criticism, there is evidence enough to show that, in the provinces at least, dishonest magistrates had been ignoring their edicts to gratify such parties in the courts as would make it worth their while[3]. This scandal Cornelius set himself to stop, and, by a reform which may well be among the beneficent consequences of Cicero's attack on Verres, he ordained that for the future it should be an offence for magistrates to administer justice otherwise than in accordance with the rules they had published on entering office. Henceforward, as Mommsen observes, 'the edict was no longer subordinate to the judge, but the judge was by law subject to the edict.' The importance of the measure depends on the extent of the abuse; but if such malpractices were of more than the rarest occurrence, the Lex Cornelia may justly be claimed as one of the foundations of the rule of law throughout the empire.

The other proposal of Cornelius was directed against bribery at elections—a problem raised afresh by the methods employed to win office for the consuls of the year. His bill was one of great

---

[1] *History of Rome*, v, p. 434 *sq.*   [2] Val. Max. VII, 7, 5.

[3] Cf. Cicero, II *in Verr.* I, 46, 119. Cicero himself was once exposed to the temptation against which Cornelius sought to guard (*ad Att.* v, 21, 11; VI, 1, 5). The precise relation hitherto conceived to exist between the urban praetor and his edict is a matter of dispute. The evidence is acutely discussed by H. Lévy-Bruhl in *La* denegatio actionis *sous la procédure formulaire*—a book of which it must be admitted that the doctrine has so far failed to win general acceptance among civilians.

severity, designed not only to increase the penalties incurred by the principals who supplied the money but also to extend the threat of prosecution to the *divisores* who distributed it among the voters. Its severity, indeed, was so great as to provide the Senate with grounds for opposition. Alleging that such an enactment would defeat itself by deterring both prosecutors and juries from applying so rigorous a law, the Fathers instructed Piso himself to prepare a less Draconian draft. This in the end Cornelius accepted, and the disreputable consul was able to leave as the monument of his office a Lex Calpurnia de ambitu—a law which, besides mulcting offenders in a fine, excluded them from public life for ever.

Cornelius could claim the credit for yet a third piece of salutary reform. In the course of their negotiations with the Senate, Gabinius and he were somehow led to challenge the right of that body to grant to individuals dispensation from the laws[1]. In earlier days such *privilegia* had been formulated by the Senate and then submitted to the People for approval; but in the heyday of senatorial supremacy this reference to an assembly had gradually fallen into disuse. Cornelius now came forward with the doctrine, unimpeachable in its logic, that, if the People made the law, the People alone could grant exemptions from its effect. Thus far his point is plain. But the Senate might also use its authority to tempt praetors to set aside their edicts; and, if Cornelius was trying to prevent the passing of *consulta* such as that which confronted Cicero in 50 B.C.[2], this measure must also be regarded as a reinforcement of the Lex Cornelia on the praetorian courts. Again there was opposition, and it was on this occasion that Cornelius came into conflict with his colleague P. Servilius Globulus—a conflict which later led to his prosecution on a charge of *maiestas minuta* (p. 475): but again, by consenting to compromise, he showed the sincerity of his desire for reform. His case was good, and had his aim been only to make trouble he might have raised a telling cry by obstinate refusal to yield. But Cornelius was no mere demagogue: realizing that even the smallest improvement is better than none, he agreed to a proposal that *privilegia* should be given by the Senate as hitherto, only with the provision that two hundred members must be present at the vote. By this safeguard, at least the worst kind of hole-and-corner jobs would be prevented.

---

[1] The circumstances in which this question was raised are differently reported by Asconius (p. 58 c.) and Dio (xxxvi, 39, 1–2). In the opinion of the present writer, the former is to be preferred: for another view see W. McDonald, *The Tribunate of Cornelius* in *C.Q.* xxiii, 1929, p. 201.

[2] *ad Att.* v, 21, 12.

Meanwhile Gabinius had been attacking on another front. Provincial communities and foreign States from time to time had business to lay before the Senate, and these legitimate needs had been turned to lucrative account by various influential sections at Rome. Embassies arriving in the capital were met with a strange indifference. A favourable answer to their requests, even admission to the House, seemed impossible to obtain until it was borne in on the unhappy strangers that for sympathy with their case they must pay. Accordingly, large sums were borrowed from the moneylenders for bestowal on the magistrates and such other leading men as it might be necessary to buy. To end this monstrous exploitation Gabinius introduced a bill in terms originally formulated, at least in outline, by Cornelius[1]: henceforward, to lend money to provincials in Rome was forbidden, and any loans so made in contravention of the statute were to be irrecoverable at law[2]. In vain the Fathers protested that a *consultum* of 94 B.C. was sufficient safeguard: Gabinius persisted and his measure was accepted by the People. But by itself this was not enough. Bribery had been the normal means of access to the Senate, and it was idle to deprive ambassadors of the key to the Curia if the doors were to remain locked. So a second law was passed, probably in this same year[3], to confirm an arrangement already recognized[4], whereby during the month of February (and, in alternate years, during the intercalary month as well) the Senate was compelled to make the business of receiving embassies the first call on its time. Together these two measures constituted a reform which alone might mark its author as a worthy partner of Cornelius.

IX. THE COMMANDS OF POMPEY

But Gabinius has a higher claim to fame. Even at the beginning of 67 B.C. all other issues in public life had been overshadowed by the problem of the pirates. The spread of these pests and earlier attempts at their eradication are described elsewhere (pp. 350 *sqq.*, 354 *sqq.*): by now the whole Mediterranean was in their hands, and the uncertainty of the corn-supply at Rome was reflected in a rise of price. When their pockets were touched, the voters showed a righteous determination that the freedom of the seas

---

[1] Asconius, p. 57 c.   [2] Cicero, *ad Att.* vi, 2, 7.
[3] The only direct evidence for this law is a letter of Cicero's written in 54 B.C. (*ad Q.F.* ii, 13, 3). But its effect may perhaps be detected in February 61 B.C. (Cicero, *ad Att.* i, 14, 5), and its logical connection with the law about loans to provincials in Rome suggests that it was passed in the same year, 67 B.C.   [4] Cicero, ii *in Verr.* i, 35, 90.

should be restored: indeed, it is by no means improbable that their anxiety for energetic action afloat was the reason why Cornelius and Gabinius had been elected to the tribunate. Once in office, Gabinius tackled his task forthwith. A bill was introduced for the appointment of an admiral with powers the like of which had not been known before. His command was to be of three years' duration, extending over the whole Mediterranean and giving him equal authority with the provincial governors in all coastal regions up to fifty miles from the sea. Moreover, he was to have a grant of 6000 talents—which the Treasury could ill afford—a fleet of 200 sail, as many men as he demanded, and a staff of fifteen *legati*, all with praetorian *imperium*. For whom these powers were intended the bill did not disclose: but, with Pompey unemployed, it was enough for Gabinius, *popularis* though he was, to stipulate that their holder should be chosen from the ex-consuls.

Immediately the Senate rose in arms. Catulus, the Father of the House, and the orator Hortensius were in the forefront of the opposition; and in the Forum two tribunes were found to organize resistance. One of them, L. Roscius Otho, essayed to win the favour of a certain influential section by restoring to the *equites* a privilege which they had been granted at some uncertain date but which had subsequently been withdrawn, in all likelihood by Sulla—the privilege of occupying fourteen rows of seats in the theatre immediately in front of the orchestra. The other—L. Trebellius—used his veto and announced that the new command should only be set up over his dead body. There is no need to suppose that personal considerations were the only motive or that Gabinius was the mere mouthpiece of Pompey. The danger to the food-supply—even to Rome's communications with the empire—was acute, and all men who were so far *populares* as to desire efficiency in the government must have seen the need for drastic action. Nor is there any sign that in such quarters the action proposed was thought more vigorous than the emergency required. Protests came from the nobility alone, where the majority still clung to the Sullan ideal and realized with painful apprehension that the powers to be conferred on the new commander were such as to place the Senate itself beneath his heel.

The scenes which the bill provoked need not detain us. From an early stage the name of Pompey was freely canvassed. At one time the life of Gabinius was in danger: at another he gained Catulus a hearing. Finally he threatened Trebellius with the fate which Tiberius Gracchus had brought on M. Octavius in 133 B.C. (p. 25 *sq.*), and it was only when seventeen tribes out of the eighteen required had voted for his deposition that Trebellius withdrew his veto. Thereafter the bill was passed, and in its passage the forces allowed to the commander were increased. The fleet might be raised to 500 ships, 120,000 infantry and 5000 cavalry were named, and the staff was to consist of twenty-four (or twenty-five) *legati* with praetorian *imperium* and two quaestors. Once the bill was law, the tremendous powers it created were conferred on Pompey without delay: in the words of Velleius[1], 'paene totius terrarum orbis imperium uni uiro deferebatur.'

In this appointment, as in that of Marius, the *populares* were justified by the event. Though he used only a fraction of the means at his disposal, when the campaign began in 66 he cleared the whole Mediterranean by operations which lasted less than three months. But the Lex Gabinia de piratis persequendis had a significance deeper than any which could be claimed for a mere victory over the Optimates. It was a milestone on the road to monarchy. An *imperium* like that of Pompey—an *imperium infinitum aequum*—had been conferred on M. Antonius in 74 B.C.[2], but in the manner of its grant and in details of vital meaning it formed no precedent for the Lex Gabinia. In 108 B.C. the People had given the African command to Marius without reference to the Senate (p. 125 *sq.*): now they had created a power which nothing but the self-denial of the general could prevent from dominating the whole government of Rome. When he returned to Italy in 62 B.C., Pompey did, in fact, make the great refusal; but he was soon compelled to recognize his folly, and Caesar, as his term in Gaul drew near its close, knew better than to ignore the warning. Thus the ideal of Sulla was finally destroyed: the People had raised up a rival destined to depose the Senate from its supremacy for ever.

But the Lex Gabinia was more than a mere death-blow to the oligarchy: it made a positive contribution to the practice of the Augustan principate. The twenty-four *legati pro praetore* with whom Pompey was supplied suggested a development of which the full possibilities had yet to be explored. Their numbers were so great and their competence so large that, had he been so inclined, the commander-in-chief himself need never have left the capital. Each of them was equipped with authority enough to carry on active operations; and, if operations were to be conducted on several fronts at once, the general headquarters from which Pompey exercised his co-ordinating control were bound to be more or less remote from the actual scene of fighting. The old theory that supreme *imperium* should be applied by its holder in

[1] II, 31, 3.   [2] Pseudo-Asconius *ap.* Stangl, II, p. 259; see below, p. 355.

person on the field of battle had been abandoned. Once this tradition had been finally set aside, the way for advance lay clear. On this occasion Pompey did, in fact, go afloat and directed the movements of his forces, so far as possible, himself. But when in 55 B.C. the Lex Trebonia made him governor of the Spains, he drew out the potentialities already latent in the Lex Gabinia. Not for a few months, as had occasionally been done before, but for years in succession he left the conduct of his provinces to *legati*, while he himself remained at Rome. The Augustan system was now at hand. If a proconsul who stayed in Italy could govern Spain, what was to prevent him governing half the Roman empire? Save for a difference in the number of *legati* employed, the relation of Pompey to Spain after 55 B.C. was in all essentials the same as that of Augustus to the so-called 'private provinces.'

Great as were the powers already wielded by Pompey, they were soon to be increased. Among the tribunes who entered office on 10 December 67 B.C. was C. Manilius, a man of dubious past, whose gambit was a measure to deal with a long-standing problem —the franchise of the freedmen (pp. 9, 96, 203). On the last day of 67 B.C. a bill was passed allowing them to vote in the same tribes as their patrons; but on the morrow it was declared invalid by the Senate. Manilius now set himself a greater task—and one which has made him famous. For long there had been growing discontent at Rome with the conduct of L. Lucullus in the East (pp. 368 *sqq.*). As a general he lacked Napoleon's touch. He failed to maintain his troops' morale, and he had won so many battles without ever winning the war that men began to despair of a victorious peace. More serious still, as an administrator his ideals were too high: his magnificent scheme of reconstruction in Asia, which in four years had set a prostrate province on its feet, gave mortal offence to the financial interests. Accordingly there was an agitation for his recall. Already in 69 B.C. the province seems to have been withdrawn from his control: in 68 Q. Marcius Rex had been ordered to supersede him in Cilicia, apparently with instructions to take action against the pirates: and in the following year, on the authority of a plebiscite proposed by Gabinius[1], M'. Acilius Glabrio was sent out to take over Bithynia and Pontus. For a time the utter incompetence of Marcius Rex and Glabrio compelled Lucullus to retain command; but in 66 B.C., when Pompey was in Asia with the campaign against the pirates at an end, there came an opportunity which it would have been folly to forgo. With the whole-hearted support of the *populares*, Manilius

[1] Sallust, *Hist.* v, 13 M.

brought in a bill to transfer the command against Mithridates to Pompey. Cicero, now praetor, and Caesar, lately back from Spain, spoke in its favour; Catulus and Hortensius voiced the inevitable opposition of the Optimates; but not even the Senate could deny the freeing of the seas, and the bill was passed without a struggle. So there was vested in Pompey, not only control of the Mediterranean and its coasts, but the provinces of Asia Minor and the conduct of a war wherein victory would lead the victor—who should say whither?

This unparalleled concentration of public resources in the hands of a single individual marks the end of one epoch in Roman history and the beginning of the next. With its effects on the future this is no place to deal; but the time is a fitting one for retrospect. The struggle begun by Tiberius Gracchus was finished, and the overthrow of the Senate was complete. Yet the outcome would have surprised those who first flung down the challenge. The modest protest of the Gracchi against the Senate's exploitation of its powers had ended in something more than a mere purging of the oligarchy. Senatorial refusal to govern in the interests of the People as a whole had shown the need for more drastic methods than the tribunate could apply, and the military commanders had been invoked. The appointment of Marius in 108 B.C. set the final precedent. For a time its implications were averted by the energy of Sulla; but the weapons which he forged were useless in the palsied hands of a nobility already moribund, and within twelve years of his death the revolution was complete. The People had raised up a master for the Senate—and themselves: if Pompey chose to use his power to make himself master of the Roman world, none could gainsay him. That he held back did not affect the significance of his command. Its example remained. If one man failed to seize the crown, another would soon be found to make the same opportunity and grasp it. From fair beginnings the career of Pompey faded into futility, but the time could not be long before a Caesar would arise to push the precedent, once it had been set, to its inevitable conclusion. Henceforward, the fate of the Roman constitution was fixed: veiled or undisguised, autocracy must come. For a while its coming was postponed by the reluctance of Pompey, and for a few brief years the phantoms of the Ciceronian age flitted through the tottering edifice of the Republic. But when Caesar, after the defeat of Vercingetorix, found himself standing where Pompey stood in 62, the whole structure was overthrown forthwith and the site lay waiting for the builders of the Principate.

CHAPTER VIII

ROME AND THE EAST

I. THE PIRATES OF CILICIA

IN his hurried settlement of the East after the defeat of Mithridates there were many problems which Sulla had to leave to his successors. One of the most pressing was that which concerned the pirates of the southern coasts of Asia Minor, whose fleets had given Mithridates valuable help in the late war and whose activities, in spite of the Roman victory, continued unabated. The growth of their extraordinary power was largely the result of Roman negligence during the preceding century. The decline of Rhodes, the weakness of Egypt, and above all the restrictions placed by Rome on the activities of the kings of Syria had all combined to give the natives of Cilicia a freedom from restraint which enabled them to develop their predatory instincts to the utmost. The terms imposed on Antiochus after the battle of Magnesia had limited his navy to ten ships of war and prevented him from sending any armed vessel to the west of Cape Sarpedonium (vol. VIII, p. 229), with the result that, since in Cilicia Tracheia lateral communication is almost impossible for a large force, the whole district became independent of Syria, and of little interest to its kings, except in so far as it provided from time to time a convenient base for pretenders to the Syrian throne. It is indeed to one of these pretenders, Diodotus Tryphon, that Strabo[1] ascribes the origin of piracy on the Cilician coast. Diodotus had established himself in the stronghold of Coracesium, which he used as a base for his privateers. His followers made Coracesium henceforward the headquarters of Cilician malpractices. During the last quarter of the second century B.C. these activities became widely extended over the eastern Mediterranean, the 'golden sea'

Note. The chief sources for the narrative in this chapter are Livy, *Epit.* 90–102, Plutarch's *Lucullus* and *Pompey* (24–45), Appian, *Mithridatica*, 64–119, Memnon, fragments of *History of Heraclea*, XV–XVI, Dio XXXVI–XXXVII, 23, Justin XXXVIII–XL, and passages from Cicero, Strabo and Josephus, for which see the Bibliography.

[1] XIV, 668.

from Cyrene to Crete and the Peloponnese yielding a rich harvest to the freebooters[1].

For some years the Roman government confined itself to diplomatic representations to the States held to be responsible, and it was not until the close of the century that any direct action was undertaken against the pirates themselves. One of the reasons of this apathy had undoubtedly been the part which the pirates played as wholesale purveyors of slaves to the ancient world. The port of Delos could dispose of slaves in tens of thousands (vol. VIII, p. 644) and was openly frequented by their boats; Side on the Pamphylian coast provided them with a market almost as valuable. The pirates, therefore, fulfilled an important function in the economic life of the day and as kidnappers and slave merchants were equalled only by the Roman tax-farmers. At last, however, the complaints of the provincials and allied States had their effect. When, in reply to a demand for a contingent in the Cimbrian war, Nicomedes of Bithynia pleaded that the majority of his subjects had been carried off by tax-farmers and were now in slavery[2], the Senate decreed that all enslaved allies of free birth should be set free in the provinces, and ordered governors to see that the decree was carried out. Against the other chief purveyors of human goods an expedition was fitted out in 102 B.C. and M. Antonius was dispatched to the Cilician coasts. The offensive against the pirates was supplemented by a measure passed about the year 100 B.C., which definitely excluded them from the ports of the empire and of allied states[3].

The extent of Antonius' success, for which the customary triumph was decreed, is difficult to estimate. It is true that little is heard of the pirates for some years, and that the campaign was followed by the creation of the province of Cilicia. There is however nothing to show that this included anything more than the Pamphylian lowlands. Cilicia Pedias was not brought under Roman control until a later date; even if nominally reduced by Antonius, Cilicia Tracheia and eastern Lycia soon obtained their independence; parts of Pamphylia itself, which had supported Lucullus in the First Mithridatic War (p. 241), again fell into the hands of the pirates. In territory, therefore, the province was of small extent, the intention of the government being rather to

---

[1] Florus I, 41 (III, 6), 1–3; cf. Dio XXVII, frag. 93, for a Cilician pirate occupying Macella in Sicily c. 102 B.C.

[2] Diodorus XXXVI, 3.

[3] S.E.G. III, 378. On the date of this inscription, see the works cited in the Bibliography.

provide a base of operations against the pirates and a post of observation for southern Asia Minor in general.

The small success which attended the first of these objects may be estimated from the subsequent history of the pirates. Since the days of his famous tour in Asia Minor (p. 234) Mithridates had been fully aware of the value of the addition of their vessels to his own. At the outbreak of the first war his fleets were increased by the irregular squadrons of the pirates, whose activities it is not easy to distinguish from those of the Pontic navy. During the course of the war, when it became clear that the king would be unable to hold his conquests, greater license was granted to the Cilicians, whose organization was already reaching the perfection attained by the time of the Third Mithridatic War[1]. With the withdrawal of Mithridates' forces the depredations of the pirates continued unabated. Even after the conclusion of peace, the coasts of Asia Minor and the islands were still being scourged by these bands, who are reported to have sacked the temple of Samothrace while Sulla himself was in the island. Moreover, by this time their cruises were extended over the whole of the Mediterranean, if it is true that the pirates who co-operated with Sertorius in 81 B.C. were Cilicians[2].

Sulla had himself held the Cilician command and was fully aware of the difficulties which beset any attempt to achieve a final solution of the pirate problem. No reduction of the strongholds of the coast could be permanent without a complete subjugation of the whole of the Taurus, into the recesses of which the pirates of the coast could retire when attacked, and from which they could be reinforced at need by the brigand tribes of the hills. As the result of the First Mithridatic War the whole of southern Asia Minor was disturbed. The inhabitants of Cilicia Tracheia were supported by the inland tribes of the Isaurians; the Pisidian highlanders were noted for their predatory habits; important towns in Pamphylia, such as Attaleia and Side, were openly leagued with the pirates; in Lycia, a robber chieftain, Zenicetes, had made himself master of the Solyma mountains and the eastern coast. Accordingly, before the death of Sulla, a scheme of operations was drafted, which, though twice interrupted by fresh outbreaks of war with Mithridates, aimed at the penetration of the whole of this district from west to east and the subjugation of the tribes on both sides of the Taurus. A beginning was made by Sulla's successor, L. Murena, who occupied a part of the hinterland of Lycia, the Cibyratis, as the preliminary to a move on Zenicetes. Murena also

---

[1] Appian, *Mithr.* 63.   [2] Plutarch, *Sertorius*, 7.

collected a fleet for use against the pirates of the coast, but any further operations in this district were for the time prevented by a renewal of the war with Mithridates.

II. THE SECOND MITHRIDATIC WAR

Since the conclusion of peace Mithridates had been engaged in the re-organization of his kingdom and the suppression of revolts in Colchis and the Cimmerian Bosporus. Disaffection in Colchis had been appeased by the re-appointment of the king's son, Mithridates (Philopator Philadelphus[1]), as regent, although the young man was shortly recalled and put to death. Against the Bosporans Mithridates was preparing an expedition on a large scale, which was regarded with disfavour by Murena in view of the fact that the king had not yet restored the whole of the kingdom of Cappadocia to Ariobarzanes. Murena's expectation, real or pretended, that Mithridates was once more preparing for war with Rome was increased by the arrival of Archelaus, the king's general in the late war, who professed to confirm his suspicions. On this pretext he marched through Cappadocia and attacked Comana. The king at once appealed to the treaty, but since it had not been reduced to writing, its existence was denied by Murena, now wintering in Cappadocia (83–82 B.C.). While the ambassadors sent by the king to appeal to the Senate were on their way, Murena began another raid across the Halys, overrunning 400 villages in the king's territory and returning with his booty to Phrygia and Galatia. Here he was met by Calidius, who in answer to Mithridates' representations had been sent out by the Senate with orders that the king was to be left in peace; but what was believed to be a secret understanding between the two men induced Murena again to attack. This time he advanced directly on Sinope[2]. In self-defence Mithridates concentrated his forces against the invader. His general, Gordius, by a threat to Roman territory compelled Murena to fall back. Mithridates himself, coming up with the main body, joined Gordius[3] and inflicted a decisive defeat on the Roman army, which was compelled to retreat hurriedly into Phrygia.

The king had driven all Murena's garrisons from Cappadocia and appeared to be about to follow up his victory, when a peremptory message arrived from Sulla ordering Murena to refrain from further hostilities and enjoining Mithridates to be reconciled

---

[1] *O.G.I.S.* 375.　　　　　　　　[2] Memnon 36.
[3] Probably on the Halys; see Th. Reinach, *Mithridate Eupator*, p. 303.

with Ariobarzanes. Sulla's orders were carried out by both parties, Mithridates securing an additional slice of Cappadocia at the expense of Ariobarzanes and Murena receiving the ill-earned salutation of *imperator*[1] and later a triumph[2].

III. SERVILIUS VATIA AND ANTONIUS

The work of reducing southern Asia Minor, which had been thus interrupted by the Second Mithridatic War and was not resumed during the Cilician governorship of Dolabella (80–79 B.C.), was once more taken up by the Roman government in 78 B.C. and entrusted to the consul of the preceding year, P. Servilius Vatia. In continuation of Murena's work in the Cibyratis Servilius' first task was the suppression of Zenicetes in eastern Lycia. The territory of Zenicetes, an immigrant Cilician or more probably a native chieftain who styled himself king[3], comprised the whole of the eastern coast of Lycia with the towns of Phaselis, Corycus and Olympus, together with most of the Solyma mountains, the massive spur of the Taurus which overhangs the western shore of the Pamphylian Gulf and terminates in the Chelidonian promontory. The inhabitants of this district were, with the exception of the Greeks of Phaselis, far behind the rest of the inhabitants of Lycia in civilization and differed perhaps from them in race. From the Solyma mountains Zenicetes could overrun the Pamphylian plain, much of which he had occupied.

The first months of Servilius' command were devoted to preparations for the campaign, in particular to the raising of a fleet. In 77 B.C. he was able to open an attack on the Lycian coast. The enemy were defeated, probably off the Chelidonian islands[4], and the three coastal cities were captured. Servilius then reduced the hill country and stormed the mountain stronghold of Zenicetes, who perished with his household in the flames which he himself had kindled. The disloyal districts of Pamphylia were recovered, and the people of Attaleia were punished by confiscation of territory[5].

It is generally held that Servilius' operations in Lycia and

---

[1] Ditt.[3] 745; Cicero, *pro Murena*, 5, 12.

[2] Cicero, *de imp. Cn. Pompei*, 3, 8.

[3] Carapanos, *Dodone*, p. 107, XXVI, n. 8, 1. (See E. Ziebarth, *Beiträge zur Geschichte d. Seeraubs*, p. 111, no. 94.)

[4] *O.G.I.S.* 552, a Lycian contingent under Aechmon of Xanthus supporting the Romans (see Dittenberger's notes *ad loc.*).

[5] Cicero, *de lege agr.* 1, 2, 5.

Pamphylia were followed by an attack on the pirate strongholds of Cilicia Tracheia. There is, however, not a single point in Cilicia Tracheia which Servilius can be said to have captured or even attacked. The general plan of operations did, in fact, postulate that the northern face of the Taurus must first be cleared before any attempt was made to enter Cilicia Tracheia itself. The Lycian and Pamphylian part of his campaign had been completed by the year 76. In the following year Servilius was free to clear the northern face of the central Taurus range.

In this district Servilius is known to have reduced the people of the Isauri with their two fortresses Isaura Vetus and Isaura Nova. Cicero[1] mentions also territory taken from the Orondeis together with the otherwise unknown ager Aperensis and Gedusanus. The latter is perhaps a corruption of Sedasanus[2], Sedasa being a town of the Homonadeis, a tribe finally reduced by the Romans in 10–7 B.C. The combined territory of the two peoples extended from Lake Caralis on the west to the confines of the Isaurians, the reduction of whom, covering as they did the principal approaches from the north, cleared the way for an advance by land into Cilicia Tracheia.

The campaign against the Isaurians had been concluded in the year 75. The following year saw the creation of a special command which was intended to sweep the pirates from the seas, while their homes in the Taurus could be threatened from the north. But the Roman plan miscarried: on the land side operations were delayed by the death of L. Octavius, the consul of 75 B.C. (who had been appointed to succeed Servilius in Cilicia in 74 but died soon after taking up his command), and then brought to a standstill by the outbreak of the Third Mithridatic War.

At sea in this year, 74 B.C., a special command had been conferred on the praetor, M. Antonius, which anticipated that entrusted to Pompey in 67 B.C., and gave to Antonius control over the Roman fleets and the coasts of the Mediterranean for three years (see above, p. 347). On the principle of setting a thief to catch a thief the appointment promised success. The extortions carried out by Antonius and his subordinates are said to have proved even more grievous to the provincials than the depredations of the pirates[3]. But Antonius himself was utterly incompetent. No organized plan to clear the Mediterranean, such as

---

[1] de lege agr. ii, 19, 50.

[2] J.R.S. xii, 1922, p. 47.

[3] Sallust, Hist. iii, 2, M. An inscription from Gytheum (Ditt.[3] 748) refers eloquently to the necessities of the town 'when Antonius was present.'

later characterized the work of Pompey, can be traced. It is true
that we hear of operations on the Spanish coast[1], which may have
been intended to clear the western seas, but Antonius' principal
achievement, the attack on Crete, even if justified, was of quite
secondary importance to the reduction of the Cilician coast. The
Cretans, whose record in the matter of piracy was not above reproach (vol. VIII, pp. 145, 291, 627), were accused of supporting
Mithridates and supplying him with mercenaries, of supporting
the pirates and providing them with a refuge when pursued by
Antonius. A war was forced on them which ended in disaster for
the Romans and a humiliating peace concluded before the death
of Antonius (71 B.C.). The peace was naturally disregarded by the
government, which found itself, as the result of Antonius' command, faced with a new Cretan war (below, p. 375), while the
pirates, as the result of Roman incompetence, showed themselves
possessed of a new confidence and daring which amazed the
ancient world.

IV. THE THIRD MITHRIDATIC WAR: THE CONQUEST OF PONTUS

After the cessation of Murena's raids in 81 B.C., Mithridates
had resumed the task of recovering his Bosporan possessions
(p. 353), where his son Machares was now appointed viceroy. To
open communication by land with the newly recovered territory
a further expedition was launched against the tribes of the Achaei
beyond Colchis. The expedition, however, failed with heavy losses,
two-thirds of the force being lost either in battle or from the
climate. Mithridates then returned to his kingdom, where, as the
result of representations made by Ariobarzanes to Rome, he received orders from Sulla to surrender those parts of Cappadocia
which he still held. Once again the king obeyed and sent an embassy to Rome to secure formal ratification of the Peace of Dardanus. Before its arrival Sulla had died (78 B.C.), and since nothing
could be obtained from the Senate, Mithridates incited his son-
in-law, Tigranes, to occupy Cappadocia, from which some 300,000
of the inhabitants are said to have been carried off to swell the
population of Tigranocerta, the new capital of Armenia.

The sultan of the now united Armenia was the descendant of
the Artaxiad rulers of north-eastern Armenia or Armenia proper
(vol. VIII, p. 514). A part of his youth had been spent as a hostage

---

[1] Sallust, *Hist.* III, 5–6, M.

among the Parthians, his restoration being secured only by the surrender of seventy Armenian valleys to the Parthian king. After his accession in 95 B.C., Tigranes, backed by Mithridates of Pontus, utilized to the full the opportunity offered by the weakness of the Parthian kingdom which followed the death of Mithridates II. By the conquest of Sophene the whole of Armenia was united under his rule, while his frontiers were extended by the annexation of the northern provinces of the Parthian empire (see further below, p. 603). By 83 B.C. he had annexed the remnant of the Seleucid kingdom in Syria and Cilicia, from which, as later from Cappadocia, numbers of the inhabitants were transported to Tigranocerta. In the matter of territory Tigranes was now the most powerful monarch of the East, to the formal suzerainty of which he laid claim by the assumption of the title 'King of Kings.'

Besides the friendship of Tigranes, Mithridates could rely in the coming struggle with Rome on the co-operation of the Cilicians, whose naval power, at any rate, was untouched by the victories of Servilius Isauricus. The benevolent neutrality of the kings of Egypt and Cyprus had been secured by dynastic alliances[1]. In Europe his Bosporan agents could foment disturbances among the tribes of the Danube and the Haemus, and create a serious menace to the Roman province of Macedonia. During the years preceding the outbreak of the Third Mithridatic War the governors of Macedonia had been constantly engaged in repelling incursions into the province and in retaliatory expeditions into barbarian territory, but, so long as the power of Mithridates remained intact, they could achieve few permanent results. Although Appius Claudius is credited with victories over the Thracians and Sarmatians in 78 B.C., and his successor C. Scribonius Curio is stated to have penetrated to the Danube and ended the war in 75 B.C., it was not until the power of Mithridates had been broken by L. Lucullus, that his brother Marcus, the governor of Macedonia, was able to gain any permanent success[2]. Deprived of support from Mithridates, the Bessi and Dardani were defeated in a number of engagements; the whole of the country between the Haemus and the

---

[1] Appian, *Mithr.* III, states that the two daughters of Mithridates had been betrothed to the kings of Egypt and Cyprus, who are presumably the two illegitimate sons of Ptolemy Lathyrus. See below, p. 388, and E. R. Bevan, *History of Egypt*, p. 344 *sq.*

[2] Eutropius VI, 2; VI, 7; Florus I, 39 (III, 4), 6; Orosius V, 23; VI, 3; Livy, *Epit.* 91, 92, 95, 97. There is no confirmation of Florus' statement that M. Lucullus reached the Tanais and Lake Maeotis.

Danube was systematically laid waste and the fighting men mutilated. Even the Greek cities on the coast of the Black Sea, Apollonia, Callatis, Tomi and Istros, were captured and plundered. The results of the the campaign deprived Mithridates of one of the most valuable of his recruiting grounds and would have rendered abortive the design, with which he is credited after the fall of his Asiatic kingdom, of invading Europe from the Crimea (p. 391).

In the far west Mithridates sought another ally. Through the agency of two of the refugees from the Fimbrian army, Magius and Fannius, he opened negotiations with Sertorius in Spain, offering ships and money in return for the recognition of his own claims to Asia Minor. To the surprise of the king the demand was refused on the ground that it was impossible for Sertorius to consent to the surrender of any Roman territory. Sertorius, however, professed himself willing to admit the claims of Mithridates to Bithynia and Cappadocia, and undertook to supply officers to instruct the Pontic armies in Roman methods of warfare, a certain M. Marius accompanying the ambassadors on their return to Pontus (see above, p. 322 sq.).

The war, which both sides had foreseen and in view of which the Roman government had retained a force of four legions in Asia Minor[1], was kindled once again by the Bithynian succession. Late in the year 75 or early in 74 B.C. the worthless Nicomedes III had died, leaving, as the Romans claimed, no legitimate heir to the throne. Bithynia was declared a province, temporary arrangements for its annexation being entrusted to the governor of Asia[2]. That Bithynia and the control of the entrance to the Black Sea should pass entirely into Roman hands was intolerable to Mithridates, who declared himself the protector of an alleged son of Nicomedes and Nysa, and marched through Paphlagonia to invade Bithynia. At the same time a force was sent into Cappadocia under Diophantus, to garrison the towns and cover Pontus against attack from Cilicia. Now or later, Eumachus was dispatched into Phrygia, who, after creating trouble among the Pisidians and Cilicians in the south, was finally driven out by the Galatian Deiotarus[3].

The Romans were caught at a disadvantage. Octavius, the governor of Cilicia, had died in his province in 74 B.C. M. Juncus,

---

[1] Sallust, *Hist.* II, 47 M. [2] Vell. Pat. II, 42.
[3] Appian, *Mithr.* 75. His expulsion took place before the winter 74–73. There is a similar doubt about the date of the penetration of Marius into Asia (Plutarch, *Sert.* 24; Suet. *Div. Iul.* 4).

the governor of Asia, if we may judge from the fact that the young Julius Caesar did not hesitate to act against him or instead of him, was incompetent or had already been recalled[1]. Fresh commanders had therefore to be sent out from Rome, and after much debate and intrigue the consuls of 74 B.C. were appointed, M. Aurelius Cotta to the new province of Bithynia, L. Lucullus to the command of the forces in Asia and Cilicia.

The story of Lucullus' intrigue with Praecia, mistress of the political wire-puller Cethegus, to secure the command, whatever light it may throw on contemporary politics in Rome, does not alter the fact that Lucullus, in the absence of Pompey, was the only suitable officer available for the post. As quaestor to Sulla and later to Murena he had gained an intimate knowledge of affairs in Asia Minor, winning good opinions among the provincials for his justice and moderation. Both in Sulla's campaigns and later at the siege of Mitylene (p. 260), he had shown himself to be a capable officer, who had little to learn from the military textbooks he is said to have studied on his journey eastward.

The plan agreed between the two commanders was that Cotta should hold Mithridates in check in Bithynia, and with the help of a fleet gathered from the allies close the Bosporus against the Pontic navy. Lucullus, who brought with him one fresh legion, was to unite the veteran legions of Servilius in Cilicia with the Fimbrian legions in Asia[2], and advance through Phrygia against Mithridates' flank. His advance was delayed by the lack of discipline among the Fimbrian troops and the general state of affairs in the province of Asia. Lucullus had only reached the Sangarius when he heard that his colleague, who had been forced to retire on Chalcedon, had rashly offered battle to Mithridates' main forces and suffered a complete defeat. Although the fortress itself held out, the Pontic fleet had forced its way into the harbour, destroying four of the Roman vessels and capturing sixty.

The most serious part of the disaster was the loss of the fleet. For the rest the dangerous position in which the rapid advance of Mithridates had placed his army was aggravated by his determination to complete the conquest of the Propontis and enter the province of Asia from the north. A force was detached under the Sertorian Marius to observe Lucullus, now advancing from the Sangarius, which established contact with him at Otryae, near

---

[1] Vell. Pat. *loc. cit.*; Suet. *loc. cit.*

[2] Lucullus is credited with 30,000 infantry and 2500 cavalry (Plutarch, *Lucullus*, 8; Appian, *Mithr.* 72, puts the cavalry at 1600).

Lake Ascania[1]. When Marius was about to offer battle, the engagement was broken off by the appearance of a thunderbolt, and he was compelled by lack of provisions to retire. In the meantime, the king was hurrying towards Cyzicus, whose citizens had suffered heavy losses in the fighting at Chalcedon, and whose capture in the eyes of Mithridates would open the gate into Asia[2]. Evading the Roman army, Mithridates arrived first before the town and occupied the high ground, known as the Adrasteian hill, which fronts the city across the narrow strait separating it from the mainland[3].

The city of Cyzicus lay on the island of Arctonnesus, which has roughly the shape of a triangle with the apex turned towards the mainland[4]. At the present time the island is joined to the mainland by an isthmus some three-quarters of a mile wide, but at the time of the siege it was separated by a narrow strait spanned only by a single causeway[5]. The city itself lay at the apex of the triangle on low land facing the Asiatic shore. Mithridates, transferring the bulk of his forces to the island, brought up his fleet to blockade the strait and established his troops in ten camps round the town. Lucullus, arriving on his heels, occupied the so-called Thracian village behind Adrasteia, from which the supplies of the enemy could be threatened. The position of the king's army was serious enough for an investing force; it rapidly became precarious when, with the help of treachery on the part of the renegade Magius, Lucullus was able to seize the heights of Adrasteia and sever the king's communications with the mainland.

Only the early capitulation of Cyzicus could save the Pontic army from disaster, and all the energies of the king were directed to the storming of the town before the approach of winter interrupted the supplies which were reaching him by sea. For a time the citizens were ignorant of Lucullus' position, and it was not until he could send a vessel through the blockading squadron that certain information reached the town. Realizing that the success of Lucullus' plans depended on their own successful resistance, and heartened by a sudden storm which overthrew many of the enemy's siege engines, the Cyzicenes were encouraged to hold out to the last. In its cramped position on the island the investing

---

[1] Strabo XII, 566 (Otroea); see Sir W. M. Ramsay, *Historical Geography of Asia Minor*, p. 189.
[2] Cicero, *pro Murena*, 15, 33.
[3] Strabo XII, 575. See F. W. Hasluck, *Cyzicus*, p. 48.
[4] Hasluck, *op. cit.* pp. 1–4.
[5] Frontinus, *Strat.* IV, 13, 6. In Strabo's time (XII, 575) there were two.

force was already suffering from disease. By the winter the commissariat had broken down, and the troops were reduced to feeding on herbs or even human flesh. After a last desperate attempt to capture the town, Mithridates reluctantly consented to abandon the siege. First the cavalry with the baggage animals and the sick were sent away secretly into Bithynia. Though the pursuit was hampered by a snowstorm, Lucullus overtook and annihilated the retreating force on the Rhyndacus. Some 30,000 infantry seeking to withdraw to Lampsacus were caught at the crossings of the swollen Aesepus and Granicus; a mere remnant reached their destination, where they were embarked by the Pontic fleet. It was only his command of the sea that enabled Mithridates to save himself and the remainder of his army. Even so, many lives were lost at the embarkation in a panic caused or aggravated by an attack of the Cyzicenes on the camp, where the sick and wounded were ruthlessly butchered.

Though his fleet had suffered losses in a storm off Parium, Mithridates still hoped by its means to maintain himself in the Propontis. Marius was sent with 50 ships and 10,000 picked troops to create a diversion in the Aegean, and the king himself sailed to Perinthus, in the hope of opening communication with his European allies. Failing to take the town he retired to Nicomedeia. Lucullus elected to deal himself with Marius. It would appear that he had already made arrangements with the cities of Asia for the provision of a fleet and was able to decline the subsidy offered by the Senate for that purpose. A portion of the new fleet was placed at the disposal of his lieutenants, C. Valerius Triarius and Barba, who received orders to reduce the Propontis and the points in western Bithynia held by Mithridates. They are credited with the reduction of Apamea (Myrleia) and Cius on the coast, inland, of Prusa and of Nicaea, whose garrison withdrew to join Mithridates in Nicomedeia. Lucullus himself, passing through the Hellespont, annihilated the forces under Marius in two engagements off Tenedos and Lemnos.

The position of Mithridates at Nicomedeia was no longer tenable. Little remained to him in the Propontis; Cotta, moving out from Chalcedon, joined forces with Triarius and prepared to blockade the town by land. After his victories in the Aegean Lucullus sent forward Voconius with a part of his fleet to close the entrance to the gulf, preparing himself to follow with the rest. But Voconius, engrossed in the mysteries of Samothrace, allowed the king to escape into the Black Sea. Although what remained to him of his fleet suffered further losses in a storm, Mithridates himself, who had been rescued when in danger of shipwreck by his pirate friends, eventually reached Amisus in safety. So ended the first phase of the campaign (73 B.C.). The whole of his initial conquests had been lost and with them a large part of his army; the fleet was destroyed or scattered, even a squadron which at the beginning of the campaign had been sent to Crete and Spain being later caught and destroyed on its return by Triarius off Tenedos[1].

Arrived at Amisus, Mithridates sent urgent demands for help to Tigranes, to Machares in the Bosporus, and even to the kings of Scythia and Parthia. At no other time perhaps does Mithridates approach nearer to greatness. His allies were lukewarm, his friends and dependents thought only of making favourable terms for themselves with the Romans. Diocles, his envoy to the Scythians, deserted to Lucullus with the gold entrusted to him; Metrodorus of Scepsis frankly advised Tigranes to refrain from embroiling himself with the Romans; the court itself was full of traitors, if we may judge from the account which Strabo gives of his own relatives of the house of Dorylaus, the king's friend and foster-brother[2]. Nevertheless Mithridates resolutely set himself to the defence of his kingdom. On his journey to Amisus he had been fortunate enough to secure the town of Heraclea, into which he had thrown a strong garrison. That fortress and the towns of the Paphlagonian coast, together with Sinope, would inevitably detain a part of the Roman forces on their advance into Pontus. In the country itself he relied on a network of strongly garrisoned fortresses covering the principal roads in the western part of the kingdom[3]. Of these the most powerful, Amasia, Amisus on the coast, Themiscyra and Eupatoria, formed roughly a square, behind which Mithridates set himself to assemble a new army at Cabeira. His cavalry was still formidable[4] and was to be used to restrict further the Roman freedom of movement.

Lucullus, Cotta and Triarius had united their forces at Nicomedeia and prepared for an immediate invasion of Pontus. As Mithridates had foreseen, the Romans were compelled to detach a portion of their forces to reduce the Paphlagonian coast, this duty being entrusted to Cotta, who was to receive the naval sup-

---

[1] Memnon 48. A Milesian bireme, 'Parthenos,' serving with Triarius, O.G.I.S. 447.   [2] Strabo x, 478; xii, 558.

[3] Strabo xii, 557, ascribes the betrayal of no less than fifteen forts to his maternal grandfather.

[4] (Appian Mithr. 78) and Plutarch (Lucullus) 14, set it at 4000, against the 8000 of Memnon 43.

port of Triarius when he had dealt with the remainder of the king's
fleet in the Aegean (p. 362). Heraclea surprised the Romans by
its prolonged resistance of two years, its capture being followed
by the surrender of Tius and Amastris. It was not until the king
himself had been overthrown that Lucullus could effect the reduction of Sinope (probably in 70 B.C.).

Realizing the necessity of an immediate attack on Mithridates,
Lucullus had begun his advance into Pontus before the summer of
73 B.C. had come to an end. In his choice of route the existence of
the Pontic garrisons on the coast may well have decided him to
avoid the trunk road by the Amnias valley, which would have
brought him most directly into Pontus, and to adopt a more
southerly line through Galatia, where the difficulties of supplying
his troops on the march were met only by the friendly offices of
Galatian porters supplied by Deiotarus. When he had crossed the
Halys, Lucullus, leaving Amasia and Eupatoria on his right,
marched between the Halys and the Iris on Amisus, the 'maritime
capital[1]' of Pontus, through which Mithridates could receive
reinforcements from his son Machares in Bosporus. Having
plundered the country up to Themiscyra, he sat down to besiege
Amisus, which, however, Mithridates was able to provision
through the winter from Cabeira.

In the following spring (72 B.C.), leaving Murena with two
legions to continue the siege, Lucullus marched with three legions
against the main forces of Mithridates at Cabeira. The route which
he must follow would take him by way of Themiscyra and Eupatoria, a fortress not yet fully completed, which, lying at the junction
of the Iris and the Lycus, closed the approach to Cabeira by the
Lycus valley. So contradictory are our authorities that it is impossible to say with certainty at what stage of the campaign the
fortress was captured. Memnon[2] states quite definitely that
Lucullus assaulted and captured Eupatoria after the operations at
Cabeira were finished, but since he makes the same statement regarding Lucullus' attack on Amisus, which was certainly invested
by the summer of 73 B.C., it is probable that Eupatoria, whose very
existence barred any advance by the Romans up the Lycus valley,
was captured, or, as Appian hints[3], betrayed, before help could
come from the main Pontic army. The movement against Cabeira

---

[1] J. A. R. Munro, *J.H.S.* xxi, 1901, p. 52, whose account of the campaign
has been followed in general. On the topographical and chronological difficulties presented by these campaigns see below, Note 4, p. 897 *sq.*.

[2] Memnon 45.

[3] *Mithr.* 115.

was in any case a bold one on the part of Lucullus; with Eupatoria still standing, it would have been foolhardy, if not impossible.

On his arrival in the Lycus valley, Lucullus found his movements seriously hampered by the enemy cavalry, which dominated the low ground and heavily defeated the Roman horse. Mithridates had himself moved out from Cabeira down the valley with a view to cutting the communications of the Romans and forcing them into the hills, when Lucullus, guided by Greek prisoners from the locality by a route along the edge of the hills, appeared above Cabeira and occupied a strong point threatening the town. His new position was secure from direct attack, but he was cut off from his communications with the force at Amisus and dependent for supplies on a route southwards into Cappadocia, which crossed the Lycus valley dominated by Mithridates' cavalry. The rest of the campaign turned on the king's ability to intercept the Roman convoys. We have accounts of three engagements, the first of which, a mere skirmish, Mithridates claimed as a victory. In the second ten cohorts under Sornatius, escorting the supply train from the south, were violently attacked by Mithridates' troops but succeeded in beating them off. In the third a Pontic force comprising half the cavalry and 4000 infantry, which had been sent out to intercept a convoy protected by a force of legionaries under M. Fabius Hadrianus, unwisely attacked the Romans in a defile where the cavalry could not operate, and suffered a complete defeat. Exaggerated accounts of the reverse, which Mithridates had attempted to minimize, filled the Pontic camp. The king, who with the loss of half his cavalry had lost his superiority over Lucullus, appears to have expected an attack in force by the Romans and was making preparations to retire, when his intentions became known and a general panic arose in the camp. In the confusion Mithridates nearly lost his life, but was able to escape to Comana; his army was dispersed or cut up by the Romans. Lucullus at once urged the pursuit of the king, who was in imminent danger of capture by the Roman cavalry. He was saved only by the scattering of the treasure from the pack of one of his baggage mules. Though the Romans followed as far as Talaura, the treasure hunt had given him too long a start. Sending orders that the ladies of his harem at Pharnaceia should be put to death, Mithridates abandoned his kingdom and took refuge with Tigranes.

After the victory at Cabeira Lucullus received the surrender of the town, where he spent the winter of 72–71 B.C. There followed the reduction of Armenia Minor, of the tribes on the coast as far as Pharnaceia, and of Amisus, which had resisted through a second winter. With the fall of Sinope and Amasia, which was delayed perhaps by Lucullus' absence in the province of Asia, the conquest of Pontus was complete (70 B.C.). Before the capitulation of Sinope, Lucullus had already made a convention with Machares in the Bosporus, thus securing the cessation of the supplies which were reaching the town by sea.

Before the capture of Amisus (71 B.C.), Lucullus had sent his brother-in-law, Appius Claudius, to Tigranes to demand the surrender of Mithridates. The months which remained before his return were largely spent by Lucullus in regulating the affairs of Asia. The cities of the province were crushed beneath the huge indemnity imposed by Sulla (p. 259) and the exactions of the moneylenders and tax-farmers. Lucullus made arrangements for the indemnity to be met by a tax of 25 per cent. on crops, house-property and slaves. The measure appears drastic but provided an organized method of meeting the payments due, and was beneficial in its results. The extortions of the moneylenders were curtailed by fixing the rate of interest at 12 per cent., arrears of interest which exceeded the principal being disallowed; on the other hand, the rights of creditors were secured by guaranteeing to them annual payment of sums not exceeding one-fourth of a debtor's income. The advantages to the province were enormous, but it is not surprising that the financial classes in Rome came to regard Lucullus as their bitterest enemy and used every means to attack his position[1].

V. LUCULLUS' INVASION OF ARMENIA

Though allowing him the royal state to which he was accustomed, Tigranes had refused for twenty months to see his father-in-law, keeping him almost a prisoner in one of his castles. Appius Claudius, whom Lucullus had sent to demand his surrender, found Tigranes still absent in Syria and utilized the interval before his return in intriguing with his subjects. Appius may have lacked the gift of persuasion which had extracted Jugurtha from the court of Bocchus, but it is probable that Lucullus had no expectation that Tigranes would agree to his demands, and sought only a pretext for invading Armenia and curtailing the power of its sultan. Soon after Appius' return the last strongholds in Pontus were reduced. In the following year (69 B.C.), leaving Sornatius with 6000 men to hold the country, Lucullus marched with the rest of his forces to the invasion of Armenia. It was a daring move, but

---

[1] Plutarch, *Lucullus*, 23; Appian, *Mithr.* 83. See V. Chapot, *Province Romaine...d'Asie*, p. 41.

one that would have been justified, if Lucullus had contented himself with the demonstration of Roman power at Tigranocerta[1].

Drawing his supplies from Ariobarzanes, Lucullus marched across Cappadocia to the great crossing of the Euphrates near Melitene. The river was in flood but subsided sufficiently to allow Lucullus to cross without delay, in boats prepared during the previous winter by the king of Cappadocia[2]. He was well received and supplied by the people of Sophene, whose belongings he protected against the soldiery, and continued his march south-east, on the road later followed by Corbulo[3], for Amida (Diarbekr) on the Upper Tigris. The very audacity of the movement took Tigranes by surprise. Since the withdrawal of Appius Claudius the king had granted Mithridates a force of 10,000 men for the recovery of Pontus and was himself contemplating an invasion of southern Asia Minor. The news of Lucullus' advance was treated with incredulity. At last the king sent out a force under a favourite, Mithrobarzanes, who had dared to tell him the truth, with orders to bring Lucullus alive. The force was destroyed and its leader slain, and in the confusion which prevailed at the Armenian court Lucullus struck hard at the capital.

The statements of the ancient authorities regarding the site of Tigranocerta are so contradictory, that without fresh epigraphic evidence it is improbable that the views of any modern explorer will find universal acceptance[4]. Tacitus[5] places it 37 Roman miles

---

[1] The invading force is given by Plutarch (*Lucullus*, 24) as 12,000 infantry and rather less than 3000 cavalry, by Appian (*Mithr.* 84) as two legions and 500 cavalry. At Tigranocerta Lucullus commanded 10,000 legionaries, apart from the 6000 men besieging the city (Plutarch, *op. cit.* 27). We may conclude that he marched with three legions and a strong force of cavalry. The numbers of the Armenians are variously given, the highest total being Appian's 250,000 infantry and 50,000 cavalry. Plutarch's figures, which profess to be based on Lucullus' dispatches (*op. cit.* 26), are not less fantastic. The more moderate figure of 80,000 given by Memnon (57) for the Armenian force at Tigranocerta perhaps represents the nominal strength of the standing army. According to Phlegon (frag. 12) the united strength of Mithridates and Tigranes was 40,000 infantry and 30,000 cavalry. He is wrong in supposing that Mithridates was present at the battle, but we learn from Memnon (55) that he had received a force of 10,000 from Tigranes, which makes the figures given by the two writers equal.

[2] Sallust, *Hist.* IV, 59 M.

[3] Tacitus, *Ann.* XV, 26. By way of Kharput (*C.I.L.* III, *Suppl.* 6741/2), and Arghana Maden.

[4] For an admirable summary of the ancient evidence and results of modern exploration see Rice Holmes, *Roman Republic*, I, pp. 409–425.

[5] *Ann.* XV, 5.

from Nisibis (the site of which is well known), and Strabo[1] states
that Tigranocerta and Nisibis lay in Mygdonia at the foot of the
Masian mountains, a range which runs parallel with the Anti-
Taurus and is separated from it by the upper waters of the Tigris.
But our narratives of the campaign imply that the city lay on the
left bank of the Tigris, which Lucullus had first to cross, and that
Tigranes, flying northwards on his approach, withdrew into the
Anti-Taurus. If the testimony of Strabo and Tacitus may be
disregarded, the accounts of Lucullus' campaign would point
to Meiafarkin (Martyropolis), first identified as Tigranocerta
by von Moltke, which lies some 40 miles to the north-east of
Diarbekr.

On the approach of the Romans, Tigranes abandoned his
treasures and harem in Tigranocerta, entrusting the defence of
the city to Mancaeus, and retired within the shelter of the Armenian mountains to assemble his army. To intercept the levies
Lucullus sent forward two detachments, one of which captured
Tigranes' baggage train, the other destroyed a band of Arabs on
their way to join the king. He himself laid siege to Tigranocerta.
The town was of enormous strength and the investing army so
insufficient, that a force sent by Tigranes, alarmed for the safety of
his concubines, was able to penetrate the Roman lines and bring
away both them and a part of the royal treasure. Although the
Romans could make little headway, the defenders protecting
themselves with arrows and destroying the siege works with
naphtha, the siege was maintained as the surest means of bringing
the king to battle. When his mobilization was complete, Tigranes,
in spite of urgent messages from Mithridates and the advice of
Taxiles, advanced from the hills to destroy the Roman force 'too
large for an embassy, too small for an army.'

On the morning of October 6, Lucullus, leaving Murena with
6000 men before the town, moved out to meet Tigranes. The
armies were separated by a river and to reach the ford by which
he could cross, Lucullus was compelled to march along the bank
of the stream, which here makes a bend to the west. The Armenians interpreted the manœuvre as a retreat and were surprised
when the head of the column wheeled to cross the stream. Their
heavy cavalry, armed only with the lance but with men and horses
protected by armour, were stationed on the right of the line, below
a small hill which had been left unguarded. Lucullus at once
sighted the omission. Under cover of a flank attack by his Thracian
and Galatian horse, he himself with two cohorts made his way

[1] XI, 522; XVI, 747.

round to the rear of the enemy and occupied the hill. He then gave orders that without waiting to discharge their javelins the troops should close at once on the enemy's rear and strike at the riders' legs, which were not protected by armour. The battle was won. Thrown into confusion by the attacks on their flank and rear, the cavalry stampeded, involving the closely packed infantry in their flight, even before the greater part of it could come into action. A terrible slaughter followed all along the line, the Roman troops, who had received stringent orders against stopping for plunder, pursuing and slaughtering the demoralized enemy over some fifteen miles (69 B.C.)[1]. The battle was followed by the capture of Tigranocerta, where the Greek mercenaries of the garrison had mutinied against Mancaeus.

A large part of the southern dominions of Tigranes now came over to the Romans, Arab tribes, the people of Sophene and of Gordyene, whose king had previously been tampered with by Appius Claudius and had paid the penalty to Tigranes. Overtures were also received from the kings of Commagene and of Parthia. On the advice of Mithridates, Tigranes also had been seeking help from Parthia, offering to restore the territory previously captured, together with the valleys which had been the price of his own redemption (p. 357). Lucullus is said to have heard of these negotiations and to have contemplated an attack on Parthia, even sending orders to Sornatius to bring up the forces in Pontus. The troops, however, refused to march, and the news becoming known in Lucullus' camp increased the difficulties already becoming felt between Lucullus and his men.

That Lucullus intended to denude Pontus of its garrison seems incredible, but the fact remains that his relations both with his troops and with Rome were becoming more and more strained. His enemies of the equestrian party, mindful of his conduct in Asia, were accusing him of needlessly prolonging the war for his own purposes, and about this time the government was forced to withdraw from him the province of Asia; not long afterwards Q. Marcius Rex, the consul of 68 B.C., was designated to succeed him in the following year in Cilicia. His troops were becoming weary of the long campaigns and of his rigorous discipline, while the protection granted to Greek inhabitants of captured cities and their property was a further cause of murmuring among the Fimbrians.

---

[1] For a plan of the battle, if placed at Meiafarkin, see Eckhardt, *Klio*, x, 1910, p. 102. A plan as postulated by Sachau's identification of Tigranocerta with Tell Ermenek (south of the Masian mountains) is given *ib.* p. 109.

Nevertheless, Lucullus prepared in the following year for a final settlement with Tigranes.

Tigranes, who had fled precipitately from the field of Tigranocerta, was joined by Mithridates, all thoughts of the recovery of Pontus being for the time abandoned. The concessions which Tigranes was prepared to make to Parthia may be ascribed to the influence of Mithridates, who was now entrusted with the preparations for the further defence of Armenia. Stores were accumulated for the provisioning of the troops, fresh levies were called up and, so far as time permitted, were armed and organized on the Roman model; in particular, a large force of cavalry was assembled to harass and delay the enemy in his advance. Owing to the lateness of the Armenian season, it was not until the summer of 68 was well advanced that Lucullus began his march northwards.

Apart from a fairly certain inference, to be drawn from Plutarch's narrative, that Lucullus advanced by a route to the west of Lake Van and that he retired by a different road to the east of the lake, there are few indications of the exact line which he followed. To the west of the lake two alternative routes would bring him into the plain of Musch, where his foraging parties were subjected to violent attacks by the Armenian horse, though his attempts to bring on the pitched battle which he desired were unsuccessful. To achieve this object Lucullus decided to march on Artaxata, the capital of Armenia proper, and force the king to fight, as he had done by his threat to Tigranocerta. As the Romans were ascending the valley of the Arsanias (the eastern Euphrates), Tigranes and Mithridates appeared on the opposite bank with the obvious intention of fighting. Lucullus crossed the river with his army in two divisions, drove off the enemy's light horse, and uniting his forces defeated the heavy cavalry under Tigranes and put the whole army to flight. The march on Artaxata was continued, but the rigours of the Armenian tableland, with its early frosts and snow, and lack of provisions, proved too formidable. The men were spent, and, when Lucullus rejected their plea to retire, refused to move. The advance was abandoned, and retiring by a road to the east of Lake Van, the army arrived at Nisibis. Late in the year Lucullus attacked and captured the town, which was held by the brother of Tigranes and Callimachus the defender of Amisus, and there prepared to winter (68–67 B.C.).

In spite of the second defeat on the Arsanias, the Armenian forces were still numerous, while the discipline of the Roman army was rapidly breaking down as the result of reports of the hostility to Lucullus in Rome and the intrigues of Publius Clodius, the 'soldier's friend,' in the camp. Rumours were current that Lucullus had been superseded and that the Fimbrian troops had been released from service by special decree. No sooner had Lucullus retired from the highlands than the kings delivered their counterstroke. While Tigranes struck at isolated Roman detachments in the south, Mithridates with 4000 of his own troops and 4000 Armenians broke out from northern Armenia and advanced by the Lycus valley into the heart of his kingdom. The Roman forces in Pontus, under Fabius Hadrianus, were taken by surprise; the Thracian mercenaries of Mithridates, now in the Roman service, deserted to their former master, and the natives, after a brief experience of Roman rule, welcomed his return with joy. After two unsuccessful engagements, the second of which only the fortunate wounding of the king enabled him to break off, Hadrianus threw himself into Cabeira, where he was blockaded.

When Mithridates first advanced into Pontus, Lucullus had been prevented from returning, partly by the necessity of relieving the troops attacked by Tigranes, partly by lack of provisions for the march and the mutinous state of his troops, who were loth to leave their present quarters for a winter campaign. But on the news of Hadrianus' reverse the troops agreed to follow him. In the meantime, Hadrianus had been relieved by Triarius, who was marching from Asia to join Lucullus and had turned northwards to succour his colleague. In face of their united forces Mithridates withdrew across the Iris to Comana, but, as the Romans approached the river, he turned to attack them on the march. He himself recrossed the river and engaged Triarius, issuing orders to a part of his forces to cross by a second bridge and intervene when the enemy was fully engaged. The scheme failed owing to the collapse of the bridge, and Mithridates was forced to retreat. Both armies then retired behind fortifications for the rest of the winter, Triarius to Gaziura, covering the road to Amasia and Amisus[1].

It was essential for Mithridates to force an engagement before Lucullus could arrive. Early in the year 67 he moved out from his winter quarters and endeavoured to provoke the Romans to battle. Triarius, who was aware of his intention, at first refused to be drawn out, but when Mithridates attacked the fort of Dadasa, which contained the baggage of the Roman troops and much of the booty of the campaign, Triarius was forced by the clamours of the soldiery to move out and protect it. In the Scotian hills, some three miles from Zela, he was attacked by the Pontic army and defeated, with a loss of 7000 men, 24 tribunes and 150 centurions.

Lucullus arrived soon after the disaster and endeavoured to

[1] *J.H.S.* xxi, 1901, p. 58 *sq.*

repair the position by bringing Mithridates to battle. The king, however, avoided the error into which Triarius had fallen. Tigranes was advancing and already his advance-guard was in touch with the Romans. Mithridates retired to Talaura[1], a powerful fortress where he could await the arrival of Tigranes, against whom Lucullus now resolved to turn. But the Fimbrians broke out into open mutiny and in answer to the personal appeals made to them by the general flung their empty purses on the ground and bade him fight the enemy alone, since he alone knew how to get rich thereby. Lucullus appealed for assistance to Marcius Rex, the proconsul of Cilicia, but was refused on the ground that his troops were unwilling to march. M'. Acilius Glabrio, who under a Lex Gabinia of 67 B.C. had been appointed to the command of Bithynia and Pontus and was hurrying to an easy triumph, now refused to move beyond Bithynia. While Mithridates recovered the greater part of his kingdom and Tigranes plundered Cappadocia, Lucullus was compelled to remain inactive. By the end of the summer the greater part of the Fimbrians had deserted.

In the operations at Cyzicus and Tigranocerta Lucullus won for himself a high place among the great tacticians; his strategical schemes were boldly conceived and methodically executed. If at times he seems to err on the side of rashness, it is to be remembered that he had greater opportunities of calculating the strength of an adversary than his modern critics. The reason for his failure lay in his leadership. In his enforcement of discipline and his demands upon his men Lucullus followed his master Sulla, but, unlike Sulla, failed to relax when a crisis had been passed. It is true that a genuine love of the Greeks and wider considerations of policy frequently induced Lucullus to deny to his troops the pleasures of a sack, which Sulla would gladly have permitted; but Lucullus, while careful for the most part of the lives of his men, lacked the chief requisite in a commander of caring first for their well-being. In his Armenian campaign he demanded more than the legionary could endure, and with the re-emergence of Mithridates it seemed to the dispirited troops that there was no end to the demands that would be made upon them. While there is no doubt that Lucullus was the real conqueror of Mithridates, it is not to be denied that the Roman government, whatever its motives, was right in superseding him.

---

[1] Dio XXXVI, 14. The site is unknown. Mr Munro's suggestion (*loc. cit.*) that it is identical with the later Sebasteia (Sivas) is only tenable if Mithridates was trying to oppose Lucullus' march from Melitene. According to Appian (*Mithr.* 90) Mithridates withdrew on Lucullus' approach into Armenia Minor.

VI. THE CLIMAX OF PIRACY: THE ACHIEVEMENT OF POMPEY

The organization of the pirate forces, which had been growing during the First Mithridatic War when their fleets were serving with those of Mithridates (p. 242), had rapidly reached a remarkable perfection. The lighter type of vessel, the *myoparo* and *hemiolia*, was giving place to the bireme and trireme. The whole fleet, which was said to number 1000, was organized in squadrons commanded by admirals (*strategoi*), their vessels being lavishly adorned with gold, silver and purple. This attention to appearance reveals a new spirit in the piratical marine and distinguishes the Cilician warships from the dirty craft which normally practised piracy in the Mediterranean. In other respects they differed from the ordinary skulking pirate and even the peaceful sailor of antiquity. The excellence of their seamanship was such that their vessels could keep the seas even in winter and by speed and skilful handling could outstrip any pursuer. Their bases on the Cilician coast were well equipped with munitions and stores, their arsenals manned with captives chained to their tasks, while the numbers of the pirates themselves were constantly increased by men broken by the wars and misgovernment of the time, who joined them as the one escape from ruin.

By this time the pirates swarmed over the whole Mediterranean. We have already seen them assisting Sertorius in 81 B.C.; negotiations were being carried on with Spartacus in 72 B.C.; during Verres' praetorship in Sicily (73–71 B.C.) a pirate squadron destroyed the guardships off the coast and entered the harbour of Syracuse under the eyes of the governor. In the Third Mithridatic War the pirate vessels were again at the disposal of the king, who on one occasion, when in danger of shipwreck, had no hesitation in transferring himself to the vessel of an arch-pirate. Not all of the bands who infested the Mediterranean at this time can have been Cilicians; piracy had raised its head everywhere. But a common spirit animated all the groups, the closest connection being maintained all over the Mediterranean, so that when the safety of those in one area was threatened they could count on reinforcements and money reaching them from another.

The condition of the inhabitants of the Mediterranean coasts during these years was lamentable. Secure in the impotence of Rome and the support of his fellows, the pirate stayed openly on shore, carrying his raids inland and attacking towns, which he took by storm or siege. Four hundred cities are said to have been captured, islands such as Delos and Aegina were overrun, and the coasts were becoming deserted. Even if due allowance is made for rhetorical exaggeration of their depredations, there is nevertheless a long list of towns and temples which were sacked; in the list of well-known Romans who were captured at sea or on land occur the names of Julius Caesar, Clodius, and Antonia, the daughter of the commander in the campaign of 102 B.C. She was carried off from the neighbourhood of Misenum on the Italian coast, to which the pirates were now paying particular attention, partly owing to the richer booty to be obtained, partly from motives of policy, since by attacking Italy itself it was the more easy to terrorize the provincials. In Italy the neighbourhood of Brundisium and the coasts of Campania and Etruria were the most dangerous. Two Roman praetors were carried off with their insignia, the Appian Way was no longer safe, a consular fleet was destroyed in the roads at Ostia, ships dared not put out from Brundisium except in winter, the corn-supply of the capital was threatened and Rome was faced with the prospect of a famine.

It is not surprising that the business classes and the people united to demand that drastic action should be taken. After a short struggle against senatorial opposition Pompey was appointed with the widest powers (see above, p. 345 *sq.*). He is said to have raised 20 legions, 270 ships and 6000 talents[1]. One of his first measures was to secure the food-supply of the capital, where his appointment had at once been followed by a fall of prices.

Pompey had realized that the pirates could only be dealt with by means of simultaneous action over the whole Mediterranean. For this purpose the Mediterranean and Black Seas were divided into thirteen commands, each district being placed under the control of one of his *legati*, who was made responsible for the rounding up of pirate forces and the reduction of enemy strongholds within his district[2]. Special arrangements were made for co-operation between the group-commanders so as to isolate the scattered bands of pirates and frustrate their known tactics of reinforcing threatened units. One of the most important of the local commands was that held by Terentius Varro, who received the naval crown after this campaign. His sphere of operations extended from Sicily to the Cyclades, and from the straits of Otranto to the

---

[1] The most satisfactory discussion of these figures is by P. Groebe, *Klio*, x, 1910, pp. 375 *sqq.*

[2] For the details of the distribution of Pompey's forces, see *Annals of Archaeology*, x, 1923, pp. 42 *sqq.*

African coast. While his patrols closed the straits of Otranto to prevent the pirates of the Illyrian and Dalmatian coasts from issuing from the Adriatic, he also maintained contact in the south with the *legatus* in charge of the African coast, forming an effective barrier between the eastern and western halves of the Mediterranean and facilitating Pompey's scheme of clearing the west first. In the east the most interesting command is that of Q. Metellus Nepos. His district is described as Lycia, Pamphylia, Cyprus and Phoenicia. There was no question of any attack on the Cilician strongholds of the pirates until the rest of the Mediterranean had been cleared and Pompey himself was ready to deliver a direct attack on the Cilician coast. Metellus' business was to engage the pirates as they issued from the Cilician ports or sought to retire thither. Any that escaped him and endeavoured to fly westwards would fall in with Varro's patrols. The remaining commands were disposed in such a way as to cover the whole of the Mediterranean coast-line.

The campaign opened in the early spring of 67 B.C. with simultaneous attacks on the pirates in the various commands. Pompey himself with a mobile squadron of sixty ships swept the western seas, driving the scattered pirates on to the stationary forces already assembled. This part of his task was completed in forty days, and he was able to return to Rome to secure the good behaviour of his political opponents, before leaving for the East.

By the time he reached the East the cause of the pirates outside Cilicia had become desperate. After the victories of Lucullus at sea (p. 362) they had been deprived of the help of Mithridates. Now the overwhelming forces arrayed against them and the moderation which was shown towards captives induced numbers to surrender and reveal the hiding-places of the rest. There remained, however, the reduction of the fortresses of Cilicia, to which the most desperate had fled and were preparing for a final resistance. A powerful force equipped with siege-engines and prepared for all kinds of mountain warfare was made ready, the pirate fleet was defeated off Coracesium, and Pompey laid siege to the fortress. It was one of the most powerful in Cilicia, an eyrie on a precipitous rock above the sea and connected with the land only by a narrow isthmus. But resistance was hopeless; the defenders of Coracesium capitulated and were followed by the rest of the pirates throughout Cilicia.

The whole campaign had been completed in the short space of three months. It was a masterpiece of strategy, but Pompey's greatness is shown even more in the settlement adopted after his victory. Realizing that one of the chief causes of piracy was to be found in the misery of the times, he made due provision for the future of the survivors. Ruined men, who had joined the pirates in despair, were given a new start in life and transferred to inland districts where they were unlikely to relapse into their old habits. Many of them were settled in cities which had been depopulated, in Dyme in Achaea and the towns of Cilicia Pedias recently depopulated by Tigranes. It was long ago suggested that the old man of Corycus whom Virgil knew in Calabria was a reformed pirate who supported his old age by bee-keeping[1].

We are told that Pompey's moderation provoked some amount of criticism among his political opponents. More justifiable was the censure he incurred by another of his actions at this time. After the overthrow of Antonius (above, p. 356) wiser counsels had prevailed in Crete, and an embassy was sent to Rome to arrange the best terms possible. By personal appeals to individual senators the ambassadors contrived that a motion should be introduced into the Senate to the effect that the Cretans should again be received as friends and allies of the Roman people. The motion however was blocked by a tribune, and on the receipt of further complaints about Cretan behaviour an ultimatum was sent to the island. The Cretans were ordered to surrender their leaders with 300 hostages, to hand over their ships and pay an indemnity of 4000 talents of silver. The terms were rejected, and Q. Caecilius Metellus, the consul of 69, was sent with three legions to reduce the island.

Metellus set about his task with unnecessary brutality, with the result that the Cretans, hearing of Pompey's moderation, preferred to make their surrender to him. Pompey unwisely sent Octavius, an officer of his own, to the island. Finding himself ignored and the communities which had surrendered to him attacked by Metellus, Octavius sent to Greece for troops and, after the death of the colleague who brought them, endeavoured to meet Metellus by force. A minor civil war had broken out in Crete, Octavius joining one of the Cretan leaders and with him standing a siege in Hierapytna. But on the approach of Metellus himself Octavius withdrew and left him to complete the conquest of the island unhindered[2].

---

[1] Servius on *Georgics*, IV, 125.

[2] Gortyn appears to have joined Metellus against her rival Cnossus, becoming in consequence the capital of Roman Crete. The Gortynians struck coins at this time in honour of Metellus with a head of Roma and an elephant's head, the device of the Caecilii, as symbols. See J. Friedländer in *Zeit. f. Num.* x, 1883, pp. 119 *sqq.*, and Vol. of Plates, iv, 12, *a*.

VII. POMPEY'S CAMPAIGNS IN 66 B.C.

The resounding achievement of Pompey marked him out as the man destined to complete the work of Lucullus, to succeed where Lucullus had failed or had seemed to fail. Neither Q. Marcius Rex in Cilicia nor M'. Acilius Glabrio in Bithynia had proved other than incompetent, and the Romans realized that in unity of command lay the key to victory. By the Lex Manilia early in 66 B.C. Pompey was re-appointed High Admiral of the Roman fleet, was nominated governor of Cilicia and Bithynia, and was charged with the conduct of operations against the kings of Pontus and Armenia (see above, p. 348 *sq.*).

On receipt of this commission Pompey moved forward from his winter-quarters in Cilicia to the upper Halys. Here he had a preliminary trial of strength with Lucullus, who vented his chagrin at being superseded by ignoring Pompey's arrival and issuing orders for the pacification of the provinces conquered by him (and since lost)[1]. At the instance of their friends the rival commanders agreed to a conference in eastern Galatia, which began with an exchange of formal compliments and ended in volleys of vituperation. In subsequent proclamations Pompey derided Lucullus as a tragedy general, whose victories were mere stage effects; Lucullus likened Pompey to a carrion bird, come to feast on others' kill. This war of manifestos, however, was more degrading than dangerous, for Pompey, with law and force alike on his side, soon reduced Lucullus to impotence. He gave orders that Lucullus' edicts should be treated as dead letters, and detached from him the remnant of his soldiery, save a posse of 1600 men (presumably invalids) to escort him home.

Before he delivered his attack upon Mithridates, Pompey sent an envoy to suggest a friendly accommodation. After some delay the king asked for the Roman terms, but on being informed that he must lay down his arms, hand over his deserters, and place himself at Pompey's discretion, he broke off negotiations. No doubt Mithridates did not require the reminder which he received from his corps of Italian refugees, that these would use force to prevent their extradition. But Pompey could hardly have had a serious expectation that Mithridates would surrender without a further trial of arms. The real issue of the diplomatic campaign depended

---

[1] The law of Sulla, which allowed outgoing governors thirty days' grace after the arrival of their successors (p. 297, n. 5), left room for such conflicts of competence. A similar clash occurred in Cilicia in 51 B.C. between Appius Claudius and his successor Cicero.

on the result of two rival embassies which Pompey on the one
hand, and Mithridates and Tigranes on the other, sent to the
Parthian king Phraates (p. 603). Although the price which Pompey
offered for his assistance—the restoration of western Mesopotamia
—was no higher than that which Lucullus had promised in 69 B.C.,
and which Tigranes was still prepared to pay, the Parthian king
now overcame his long hesitations and took open sides with Rome.
In coming to this decision Phraates no doubt paid homage to
Pompey's formidable reputation, but his policy was chiefly influenced by a son and namesake of the Armenian king, who had
fled to the Parthian court because his father was unconscionably
slow in dying and dangerously quick in sending undutiful sons
before him.

The effect of the alliance between Pompey and Phraates was
that while the Parthian king held Tigranes, Mithridates was left
to face the Romans single-handed. Since his return to Pontus the
king had recruited an army of 30,000 foot and 2000 horse, but in
this force only the mounted men and the shrunken remnant of the
Italian refugees were fit for hard fighting. Despite the impotence
to which Lucullus had been reduced in 67 B.C., Mithridates had
not ventured to pit his recruits against him in open battle, but had
contented himself with forays into Bithynia and Cappadocia; in
66 B.C. he found himself outnumbered and outmatched by the
reconstituted Roman forces. In addition to the field-armies used
by him against the pirates, and the troops stationed in Bithynia
and Cilicia, Pompey had appropriated the remainder of Lucullus'
soldiers, and by the magic of his name he had induced most of the
veterans discharged from Lucullus' service to re-enlist. His total
numbers, exclusive of such allied contingents as he requisitioned
from the king of Cappadocia and the Galatian chieftains, may be
estimated at no less than 50,000 men[1].

In the summer of 66 B.C. Pompey ordered his fleet to patrol the
coasts of Asia Minor, and with his army advanced from Galatia
into Pontus. Employing the same strategy that he had used against
Lucullus in 73 and 72 B.C., Mithridates fell back towards the valley
of the Lycus, along which ran his main line of lateral communications, and sought to wear out his enemy in a campaign of raids
and forays. Pompey, who had apparently not made any extensive
drafts upon the mounted forces of his Cappadocian and Galatian
allies, had not enough cavalry to meet Mithridates on equal terms
in guerrilla warfare. He therefore attempted to break off by a

[1] On the strength of Pompey's army, see J. Kromayer in *N.J. Kl. Alt.*
XXXIII, 1914, p. 160.

side movement up the Lycus valley towards Armenia Minor, so as to cut off Mithridates from Tigranes, and to threaten his numerous treasure-castles in that region (p. 233). But Mithridates headed Pompey off, and barred his passage by occupying the rock-fortress of Dasteira (probably on the site of the later city of Nico-polis[1]). Resuming the guerrilla war round this position, the Pontic king again held the Romans at a disadvantage, until his horsemen, repeating the mistake which they had made in 72 against Lucullus, became over-eager, and were destroyed in an ambuscade. Having disposed of the Pontic horse, Pompey was free to replenish his supplies. At the same time the arrival of the reserve army, which he had called up from Cilicia, enabled him to draw a fortified ring round Dasteira. After a blockade of forty-five days Mithridates deceived the Roman night-watches with false flares and extricated all his army except the wounded. The king now endeavoured to slip away to Armenia; but his success in stealing away from Das-teira had been too complete. By saving his baggage-train he re-tarded his rate of march, so that Pompey, creeping round by hill tracks, was able to occupy unobserved a chain of bluffs com-manding a gorge of the Lycus and cutting across the enemy line of retreat. In the ensuing night (the third after the flight from Dasteira) he threw the Pontic camp into confusion by a sudden discharge of missiles from the overlooking heights, and broke in upon it before the combatants could disentangle themselves from the stampeding baggage-train. Once again, as at Cabeira, Mith-ridates cut his way out. But the 'battle of Nicopolis' (to use the accepted but not quite accurate name) proved an irreparable disaster.

Once more an exile from his kingdom, Mithridates passed into Greater Armenia and invoked the aid of his son-in-law Tigranes. But the Armenian king gave his guest an even chillier welcome than in 72 B.C. While Mithridates was engaged with Pompey, Tigranes had been driven back upon his capital Artaxata by the Parthian king, and had been held there under blockade; but when Phraates prematurely drew off part of the investing force, the Armenian king sallied out and scattered the remnant of the be-sieging army, which Phraates had left in charge of Tigranes' rebel son. The younger Tigranes' first thought now was to obtain as-sistance from Mithridates, but when he heard that Mithridates was himself in quest of aid, he turned off to find Pompey. Mean-time, however, the news of his intended overtures to the Pontic

---

[1] On this identification, see Th. Reinach, *Mithridate Eupator*, p. 385 n.; J. G. C. Anderson, *J.R.S.* XII, 1922, pp. 99 *sqq.*

king had reached his father's ears, and brought seeming confirmation of the Armenian monarch's suspicions in regard to his neighbour. Accordingly Tigranes answered Mithridates' request for help by setting a price upon his head. The Pontic exile made a hurried flight from Armenia to Colchis, and secured himself for the ensuing winter at the harbour of Dioscurias.

Meanwhile Pompey, having lost touch with Mithridates, ordered a blockade of the Black Sea ports, but did not press the pursuit. His army no doubt needed rest, for he left a sufficient number of wounded and sick men at Dasteira to form the nucleus of a new settlement, the future city of Nicopolis. But at the invitation of the younger Tigranes he crossed the Euphrates and advanced down the Araxes valley towards Artaxata. Not far from this town he met the Armenian king, who completely lost his nerve at Pompey's approach and made an abject surrender. Thus Pompey ended the Armenian wars without a further battle.

The campaign of 66 B.C. closed with a brief passage of arms in the valley of the river Cyrus, where Pompey pitched his winter camps under the shelter of Mt Caucasus. His occupation of the Armenian borderland alarmed the neighbouring Albanians, a nomad folk whose grazing grounds lay between the Cyrus, Mt Caucasus and the Black Sea. On the day of the Saturnalia (December 17) their chieftain Oroezes, taking advantage of the division of Pompey's force into three separate cantonments, attempted a triple surprise on the Roman leaguers. But Pompey and his lieutenants were on their guard, and beat off their ill-armed opponents with heavy slaughter.

VIII. POMPEY'S LATER CAMPAIGNS

In the spring of 65 B.C. Pompey resumed his tardy pursuit of Mithridates. Anticipating resistance by the Iberians—a well-organized agricultural folk, with an Iranian governing class, who dwelt in modern Georgia—he crossed the frontier passes and overawed their king Artoces into granting him passage across the Cyrus. Mistrusting a sudden flight by Artoces into the recesses of his realm, Pompey pursued him and made short work of his troops in a battle in which the Roman legionaries rushed the Oriental archers, like the Athenians at Marathon. After receiving the submission of Artoces, the Roman general proceeded unhindered along the Phasis to the Black Sea coast, where he rejoined a detachment of his fleet. From the Phasis estuary he threaded his way for a short distance along the coast, but found his further progress barred by the insurmountable cliffs of the Caucasus outspurs. For a second time Pompey left Mithridates to the care of his navy, and devoted the rest of 65 B.C. to the systematic conquest of the Albanians in the Caspian borderland. This seemingly superfluous campaign may be explained by a desire on Pompey's part to develop a trans-Caspian trade-route to the farther East[1]—a scheme which had occupied Seleucus I and was to engage the attention of Nero. But probably his main object was to gain the glory of a triumph over peoples whose very names were new to the Romans. Returning to the Cyrus valley by a detour through Armenia, he crossed the river without opposition, and similarly effected the passages of the Cambyses and the Abas. Beyond this last stream he enticed the Albanian forces into a miniature battle of Cannae, encircling them with his horsemen from right and left. After receiving the submission of King Oroezes Pompey marched without further hindrance towards the Caspian. But at three days' distance from that lake he turned back, and recrossing Armenia for the last time he ended the year's campaigns with the capture of Mithridates' remaining treasure-castles in Armenia Minor. His retreat from Albania was no doubt dictated by regard for his army, which had suffered from drought and dysentery on the summer marches, and found its way to the Caspian impeded by an adder-infested country[2]. With the fate of Lucullus before his eyes Pompey could not venture to overdrive his men.

After the capitulation of King Tigranes the relations between Pompey and the Parthians underwent a sudden change. An attempt which Phraates made in 65 B.C. to recover from Tigranes the borderland of Gordyene (on the upper Tigris) was promptly foiled by Pompey, who detailed his lieutenants Afranius and Gabinius to occupy the debatable territory. The Parthian king hereupon withdrew his troops and asked Pompey for a new treaty. But the Roman general, who seemingly saw in Phraates a half-hearted ally and enemy, and perhaps was toying, like Lucullus before him, with the idea of Roman conquests in Babylonia, refused his request, and addressed him in disdainful and even provocative terms. Yet in 64 B.C., when Phraates renewed his attack upon Tigranes, Pompey contented himself with sending

---

[1] According to Pliny (*N.H.* vi, 52), Pompey made inquiries as to the length of the Caspian route to India.

[2] Here Plutarch (*Pompey*, 36) is clearly right against Dio (xxxvii, 5, 1), who asserts that Pompey actually reached the Caspian.

three commissioners to patch up a peace. Having restored Gordyene to Tigranes, Afranius and Gabinius were sent on to Syria. While Afranius cleared the passes through Mt Amanus of brigands, Gabinius took possession of Damascus, where he was presently reinforced by M. Scaurus[1].

After a winter spent in Armenia Minor, Pompey proceeded in the spring of 64 B.C. to Amisus on the Pontic coast, where he gave audiences to client-kings and made a provisional settlement of Asia Minor. While engaged in this task he recovered touch with Mithridates. In the previous year the fugitive king had skirted the Black Sea coast from Dioscurias to the Caucasus, and with an improvised fleet had slipped past the Roman naval patrols to the Taman peninsula. From this position he opened war upon his son Machares, who had made his peace with Lucullus in 70 B.C. and had been acknowledged by him as ruler of Mithridates' Russian dominions. By the prestige of his name Mithridates at once recovered the allegiance of the native chieftains on the east side of the Sea of Azov, and fomented revolt against his son in the Crimea. With another ready-made fleet he crossed the straits of Kertch and cornered Machares in Panticapaeum, where the rebel, unable to gain his father's ear by repeated embassies, was driven to suicide[2]. Having thus recovered his Russian provinces, Mithridates applied to be restored to Pontus as a vassal of Rome. But Pompey, who had no mind to sign another treaty of Dardanus, required Mithridates' personal submission, and the king, more stiff-kneed than Tigranes, rejected these terms.

Still trusting to the slow pressure of his naval blockade upon Mithridates, Pompey followed his advance detachments to Syria. Since the expulsion of Tigranes by Lucullus this land had relapsed into its previous state of anarchy. The Seleucid prince Antiochus XIII Asiaticus, whom Lucullus had acknowledged as rightful ruler of Syria, had been kidnapped by Sampsiceramus, a sheikh of Emesa, and Philip II, a grandson of Antiochus VIII Grypus, had replaced him at Antioch. But the authority of this King of Brentford hardly extended beyond the city gates. The countryside from desert to coast was overrun with robber-bands, and such of the towns as had not succumbed to petty dynasts like Sampsiceramus were left to fend for themselves. In Palestine the

---

[1] The chronology of the Roman occupation of Syria, as given in Josephus' *Jewish Antiquities*, is sadly confused. His account in xiv [3, 1], 34–6, is here followed as against that of xiv [2, 3], 29–33.

[2] So Appian, *Mithr.* 102. Dio (xxxvi, 50, 3) states that Machares was killed by his own supporters at the instigation of Mithridates.

aggressions of the Maccabaean dynasty had been suspended by a family feud between the two sons of Alexander Jannaeus, Hyrcanus and Aristobulus II (p. 401 *sq.*). But this dispute was serving the no less dangerous ambitions of the Nabataean ruler Aretas III, who had taken the field in aid of Hyrcanus and invested Aristobulus in Jerusalem (65 B.C.). It is true that in this same year, or early in 64 B.C., the Jewish dispute was temporarily settled by Gabinius and Scaurus, to whom both the pretenders had offered substantial bribes for recognition. Pompey's lieutenants, believing that Aristobulus would pay his footing more promptly and with better grace, decided in the younger brother's favour, and Aretas raised the siege of Jerusalem when Scaurus advanced against him from Damascus.

The rest of 64 and part of 63 B.C. were spent by Pompey in restoring order in Syria. This he accomplished by sending out detachments in all directions to round up the robber-bands, to demolish the pirate forts on the coast, and to bring the dynasts to submission. In the autumn of 64 he received deputations from Hyrcanus, appealing against Gabinius and Scaurus, and from Aristobulus, in defence of their award, but he put off the suitors until the ensuing year.

In the spring of 63 B.C. Pompey moved from Antioch to Damascus, where he received Hyrcanus and Aristobulus in person. Uninfluenced by a gift of a golden vine, valued at 500 talents, from Aristobulus, he decided against the younger pretender. Herein he plainly acted in Rome's best interests, for Aristobulus was a true scion of the Maccabaean conquerors, whereas Hyrcanus had no political ambitions beyond the royal title. But for the moment Pompey made no announcement of his award, and took no overt action against Aristobulus. For the time being, he was preoccupied with preparations for an expedition to Petra, the capital of King Aretas. In this project the desire to acquire an important centre of the perfume and spice trade may have counted for something, but its principal object no doubt was to win for Pompey the distinction of extending Roman authority to the Red Sea. But Pompey had not proceeded far on the way to Petra before he began to suspect that Aristobulus had divined his intentions and was meditating resistance. His suspicions were confirmed when Aristobulus, having obeyed an order to surrender his other fortified positions in Palestine, returned to Jerusalem and prepared for war. On arriving at Jericho he summoned Aristobulus and overawed him into a promise that he would receive a Roman force into Jerusalem and pay an indemnity. But Aristobulus was not able to redeem this undertaking, for his officers refused to admit Pompey's lieutenant Gabinius into the city. Hereupon Pompey put Aristobulus under arrest and diverted his march towards Jerusalem. He took possession of the lower town and the palace quarters without resistance, but was compelled to lay siege to the Temple precincts. He collected materials for filling the deep ravine under the Temple plateau, and brought up artillery from Tyre. But it was not until the third month of the siege that he overcame the natural strength of the position and the stubbornness of its defenders. The first Roman over the fortress walls was Faustus Sulla, son of the dictator.

The capture of Jerusalem was the last of Pompey's military achievements in the East. Whether his ambition was now satisfied, or whether, as seems more likely, he had taken to heart recent murmurings among his troops, who complained that Pompey was forgetting Mithridates over these distant adventures, he did not resume the interrupted campaign against Petra. In 62 B.C. he sent a force under Scaurus against Aretas; but this commander achieved no more than to harry his territory, and at the suggestion of Hyrcanus' minister Antipater (father of King Herod) he withdrew the Roman troops on payment of a blackmail[1].

IX. EGYPT

While Pompey was sweeping up the débris of the Seleucid monarchy, he came within striking distance of Egypt. Here the Ptolemaic dynasty had since the death of Ptolemy VI Philometor, its last worthy representative (vol. viii, pp. 284, 525), become increasingly impotent to maintain order within its own house, and had ceased to be a power in Mediterranean politics. Its record of domestic strife and of palace revolutions is highly melodramatic, but historically unimportant.

After the death of Philometor in 145 B.C., the claims of his young son were set aside by a party in Alexandria, which had previously favoured the deceased king's brother, Ptolemy Euergetes II, nicknamed Physcon, and could now point to the dangers attendant upon a long minority reign by the lawful heir to the crown. Physcon, who had never acquiesced in his relegation to Cyrene, at once acted at a signal from his supporters and occupied the Egyptian capital, apparently without opposition. He also came to

---

[1] Four years later Scaurus, as curule aedile, did not scruple to issue coins on which Aretas was shown as a suppliant kneeling beside a camel. See Vol. of Plates, iv, 12, b.

terms with Cleopatra II, the sister and widow of Philometor, who consented to a second brother-marriage in order to recover a share of the throne, and made no overt protest when her new husband put her child by Philometor out of the way. But when Physcon repudiated Cleopatra II in favour of her daughter by Philometor, Cleopatra III, the divorced wife appealed to the Alexandrians, who once before had made and unmade Physcon (vol. VIII, p. 284), and now for a second time turned against the ruler of their own choice. As the nickname Physcon ('Puffing Billy') declares, the city mob took offence at the physical appearance of their king, who had carried the hereditary corpulence of his family to monstrous proportions; and they no doubt were genuinely incensed at his treatment of Cleopatra II, for a chivalrous regard for distressed queens was their redeeming virtue[1]. With the help of his mercenary troops Physcon repeatedly beat down the Alexandrian rioters, but in 131 or 130 B.C. he was at last driven out to Cyprus, and Cleopatra assumed sole rule at Alexandria. By way of reproving her unwifely conduct, the exiled king murdered their only child and sent her the body, with limbs torn asunder according to the rules laid down for villains in Greek mythology, as a present for her birthday. In 129 B.C. he won his way back to Egypt, and outwardly at least he arrived at a fresh understanding with the queen. Meanwhile, however, the dynastic conflict had extended to the country, where the troops and the natives took sides for king or queen and waged a confused and protracted civil war.

The eventual restoration of order in Egypt was marked by an Act of Grace issued in 118 B.C. in the name of the king, of 'Queen Cleopatra the Sister,' and of 'Queen Cleopatra the Wife[2].' In this notable ordinance the rulers confirmed all existing titles of possession in land, remitted all debts to the crown, and proclaimed an amnesty for recent political offences. For the future, they sternly admonished their officials to desist from the manifold extortions and oppressions which they had practised with impunity under cover of the civil war. This indulgence followed upon a series of similar proclamations at the close of previous periods of domestic strife[3]. It was also in keeping with the general policy of the Ptolemies in the second century, which acknowledged the need

---

[1] The status of the two Cleopatras, aunt and niece, evidently caused perplexity to the Ptolemaic officials in the country. In the papyri of the period either Cleopatra, or both, are cited as queens without any apparent system.

[2] *P. Tebtunis*, I, 5.

[3] *E.g.* in 164–163 B.C. (Wilcken, *Urkunden der Ptolemäerzeit*, vol. I, nos. 110–111); and in 145 (*P. Turin*, I, pp. 9, 21).

of making concessions to native unrest. Not only did these later rulers copy the example of the third-century kings in treating the indigenous priesthood with respect and in setting up new temples to the Egyptian gods, but they began to throw open the higher administrative offices to the native population. In the rebellions of the reigns of Physcon and of Lathyrus (p. 388) native officers were entrusted with military commands; and under Ptolemy Auletes an Egyptian was promoted to the post of Epistrategus or Governor-General of Upper Egypt, an office which had been created by the fifth Ptolemy for the very purpose of quelling disorder in that province[1].

The continuous domestic conflicts of the second century left an enduring mark upon the economic condition of Egypt. The area of cultivation fell back from the limits to which the early Ptolemies had expanded it; and the native peasantry, unable to overthrow their Greek masters by active rebellion, had recourse to the weapon of passive resistance, and made concerted refusals to take up leases on the Crown Lands. It is true that partial compensation for these losses was found in a new development of commerce with the lands of the Red Sea and the Indian Ocean. The stimulus which the eastern trade received was in some measure due to the active interest of Ptolemy Physcon and Cleopatra III. About 120 B.C. Physcon engaged a Greek venturer, Eudoxus of Cyzicus, to explore the open-sea route from Aden to India under the guidance of a castaway Hindu who had offered to reveal to him the secret of the monsoons; and after this king's death Cleopatra III equipped a second expedition for the same captain, who returned successfully from both cruises with a cargo of spices and precious stones. Owing to a dispute about the sharing-out of the proceeds, Eudoxus did not stay on in the Ptolemaic service, and it was probably not until the time of Augustus that Greek navigators definitely discovered the law of the monsoons and made the Indian Ocean familiar to Greek enterprise[2]. But the Ptolemies continued to take the eastern trade under their special protection, and the Epistrategus of Upper Egypt was charged with the patrol of the Red Sea and the waters beyond Aden[3]. Yet the increment in commerce

---

[1] Various minor alterations in the routine of finance and jurisdiction are recorded in the papyri of the second century B.C. It will suffice here to note the creation of an *Idiologos* or Keeper of the King's Privy Purse (in or before 162 B.C.), in whom some scholars (with doubtful reason) see the prototype of the *Procurator Rei Privatae* of the Roman Emperors.

[2] Strabo II, 98–99. On Indian Ocean exploration under the later Ptolemies, see E. H. Warmington, in Cary and Warmington, *The Ancient Explorers*, pp. 70–72.   [3] *O.G.I.S.* 132, 186.

under the later kings did not make up for the shrinkage in agricultural production. It is significant that while Philometor and his successors continued to strike good silver (in a Cyprian mint) for purposes of commerce, they restricted the issue of coins for internal use to copper pieces. A heavy drop in the weight of the copper drachma under Philometor should probably be interpreted as a species of State bankruptcy, of which the Ptolemies set the example to the Caesars[1].

In 116 B.C. Ptolemy Physcon died in peace. By his testament he left his widow Cleopatra III to rule Egypt in association with either of her two sons by him[2]; but he constituted Cyrenaica into an appanage for an illegitimate offspring named Ptolemy Apion. By this disposition Cyrenaica, which Physcon had temporarily reunited to Egypt in 145 B.C., was definitely separated from it. At Alexandria Cleopatra had selected her younger child to succeed his father, presumably because she deemed him more pliable to her will. But the city mob again took matters into their own hands and compelled the queen-dowager to transmit the crown to the elder son. Thus Ptolemy VIII, officially styled Soter II, but popularly nicknamed Lathyrus ('Chick-Pea'), became king at Alexandria, while the junior brother was appointed governor of Cyprus. At first, it is true, Cleopatra had little cause to regret the disarrangement of her plans, for Lathyrus deferred to his mother to the extent of dismissing his wife and sister Cleopatra IV, and marrying in her stead a younger sister, Cleopatra V (Selene). Eventually Lathyrus showed signs of assuming the part of Nero in opposition to his mother's Agrippina, but Cleopatra III forestalled him by framing against him an accusation of attempted murder, which the Alexandrians accepted in good faith. In 108–107 B.C. a riot in the capital compelled Lathyrus to take flight, and his brother returned from Cyprus to reign in his stead as Ptolemy IX Alexander I. But the fugitive king contrived to raise a force in Syria and to assume possession of Cyprus, so as to reverse the parts between the two brothers.

These conflicts within the Ptolemaic dynasty influenced the parallel movement of domestic discord among the Seleucids. The divorced queen Cleopatra IV sought compensation for the lost crown of Egypt by marrying a Seleucid pretender, Antiochus IX Cyzicenus. Had Cyzicenus succeeded in establishing himself firmly at Antioch, no doubt she would have prompted him to

---

[1] Th. Reinach, Rev. E.G. XLI, 1928, pp. 170 sqq.
[2] Since nothing is heard of Cleopatra II at this juncture, it may be assumed that she had died shortly before Physcon.

avenge her dethronement by resuming the secular warfare between Seleucids and Ptolemies. But in 112 B.C. Cyzicenus lost
his capital to a rival dynast, Antiochus VIII Grypus (vol. VIII,
p. 531), and Cleopatra was hacked to pieces at the altar of Apollo
at Daphne, to which she had fled for sanctuary. This sacrilege
casts a fierce light upon the curse that was working itself out
among the Ptolemies in mutual murder, for the ex-queen's executioner was her own sister Cleopatra Tryphaena, the wife of the
victorious Grypus. Nemesis claimed her next victim in the
following year, when Tryphaena fell into the hands of Cyzicenus
and was immolated to her murdered kinswoman.

Not long after these events Ptolemy Lathyrus, having followed
his first wife into exile, renewed her attempt to recover Egypt by
way of Syria. With an army recruited in Cyprus he landed at
Ptolemaïs on the Palestinian coast, and as protector of the Greek
cities of the seaboard and ally of Cyzicenus, he made war upon
the Hasmonaean Priest-King Jannaeus Alexander. At Asophon
near the Jordan he won a battle in which thirty thousand of Jannaeus' troops are said to have been killed, and for one moment it
appeared as if Coele-Syria might become once more a Ptolemaic
dependency. But his plans were crossed by his mother, the queen-
regent Cleopatra III, who made alliances with Jannaeus and Antiochus Grypus, and led an expedition into Palestine. Lathyrus, it
is true, slipped past Cleopatra's army and made for Pelusium, but
he was headed off by his mother's naval forces and presently retired
to Cyprus, abandoning all his gains. At the same time Cleopatra
withdrew to Egypt, and Coele-Syria once for all passed out of
Ptolemaic hands (see below, p. 399).

After the death of Cleopatra III, which befell about 101 B.C.,
Ptolemy Alexander I became ruler as well as king of Egypt, only
to discover that the Alexandrians had tolerated him merely to
please his mother. He fell under suspicion of having removed his
mother by foul play, and his unpopularity was increased by his
ungainly figure, which swelled out to the same proportions as that
of his father Physcon. In 89 B.C. a military émeute compelled him
to flee the country, and although he presently recaptured Alexandria with a mercenary force from Syria, he was promptly driven
out again by the city mob, which he goaded to fresh rebellion by
despoiling the tomb of Alexander the Great in order to pay off his
foreign soldiers. A second attempt on his part to fight his way
back with troops levied in Lycia was headed off by the Egyptian
fleet, and the exiled king lost his life in a naval battle (88 B.C.).

The death of Ptolemy Alexander I made room for his brother

Lathyrus, who now returned from Cyprus and was accepted by the Alexandrians without demur. But the second half of his reign in Egypt was troubled with a renewal of unrest in the Thebais. Despite recent concessions to the native Egyptians, each fresh disorder in Alexandria, by bringing heavier taxes in its train, or conferring greater licence of oppression upon the officials, was an incitement to further rebellion. At Thebes, moreover, the memories of the national uprising against the alien Hyksos (vol. i, p. 314 *sq.*) had been kept alive by the powerful priesthood of Amen, among whom leaders for a new revolt against foreign domination readily offered themselves. In 88 B.C. the Ptolemaic troops became involved in a three years' war in Upper Egypt which ended in the destruction of Thebes.

In 80 B.C. Lathyrus died without legitimate male issue. With the concurrence of the Alexandrians his daughter Berenice, who had previously been married to her uncle Ptolemy Alexander I, took the government into her hands. But she had reckoned without a son of Ptolemy Alexander by a former wife. This prince, who had been relegated by his grandmother, Cleopatra III, to the island of Cos, beyond the reach of Alexandrian factions, had fallen captive to Mithridates of Pontus in 88 B.C. (p. 243), but had subsequently escaped to the camp of Sulla and had been taken by him to Rome. Shortly after the death of Lathyrus he presented himself at Alexandria with a warrant from Sulla which the Alexandrians did not dare to dispute. The *protégé* of the Roman dictator was accordingly proclaimed as Ptolemy X Alexander II, and by taking Berenice to be his queen he apparently satisfied her claims to power. But on the morrow of the marriage a new struggle for ascendancy within the Ptolemaic house began; the king procured the murder of his refractory consort, and on the nineteenth day of his reign was himself lynched by the city mob, incensed at the death of their favourite princess.

In the absence of any legitimate claimants to the throne, the Alexandrians now raised up two illegitimate sons of Lathyrus, one of whom was made king of Egypt, while the younger brother was sent to Cyprus, where he established a virtually independent rule (see p. 527). The new Egyptian monarch, not content with the official titulature of Ptolemy Theos Philopator Philadelphos, added to this list the name of Neos Dionysos; but he was popularly known as Auletes (the 'Piper'), a nickname which summed up his accomplishments. But however acceptable Auletes might be to the Alexandrians, he had assumed power without the consent of Sulla, and as the supplanter of the dictator's nominee. He therefore created an 'Egyptian Question' in Roman politics, and reigned under the shadow of Roman intervention.

In 168 B.C. the Roman Republic had interfered drastically in defence of the Ptolemies against Antiochus IV of Syria. But once the danger of a Seleucid conquest of Egypt had been averted, its interest in the affairs of that country had become very desultory, and in the disputes between Ptolemy Philometor and his brother Physcon it had been but a half-hearted arbiter (vol. VIII, p. 283 *sq.*). To the advocates of imperial expansion at Rome Egypt indeed offered a tempting prize. Despite the misgovernment of the later Ptolemies, it still possessed a large funded treasure and might at short notice be converted into one of Rome's chief granaries. Amid the family feuds of the ruling dynasty specious pretexts for Roman interference would not be far to seek, and to the military resources of the Republic the natural defences of Egypt could offer no protracted obstacle. It may be not wholly without political significance that in the later half of the second century the Romans showed various signs of interest in the Ptolemaic kingdom. Roman merchants settled at Alexandria[1]; Roman senators made tours of inspection up the River Nile[2]; in 140 or (more probably) 135 B.C. Scipio Aemilianus in person paid a visit to Physcon and brought away a vivid impression of the ample natural resources of the country[3]. On the other hand, it was the set policy of the governing aristocracy of the later Republic not to burden itself with additional duties of overseas administration, and it had no less reason than the Roman emperors in later times to fear that a province of Egypt might serve as a base for an ambitious proconsul bent on personal aggrandizement. The Senate therefore allowed Ptolemy Physcon and his sons to fight out their dynastic wars without interference. The same insouciance was displayed by the Roman government in 96 B.C., when Ptolemy Apion died and bequeathed his principality of Cyrene to the Republic. Though it was not loth to receive into its hands the lucrative trade in silphium from that district, and accordingly sent a commissioner to take charge of the late king's domains, it left the government of Cyrenaica in the hands of the Greek cities, upon which it conferred

---

[1] *O.G.I.S.* 135.

[2] *P. Tebtunis*, I, 33 (112 B.C.). An exhortation by a *dioiketes* to a subordinate to receive a Roman Senator deferentially (and to feed the sacred crocodiles for his amusement).

[3] Diodorus XXXIII, 28 a; Posidonius, *ap.* Athen. XII, 549 D; Plutarch, *Moralia*, 200 E. For the date of Aemilianus' visit, see Bouché-Leclercq, *Histoire des Lagides*, II, p. 68 n. 1.

freedom. In the winter of 87–86 B.C. Sulla's lieutenant Lucullus, finding Cyrene at feud with its neighbours and a prey to petty tyrants, settled its affairs for the time being. But it was not until 74 B.C. that the Senate, intent on closing the Mediterranean coastlands to the pirates (p. 442), definitely converted Cyrenaica into a Roman province.

The visit of Lucullus to Cyrene was an incident on a voyage to Alexandria, where Sulla had instructed him to borrow the Ptolemaic fleet for use against Mithridates. Though he was received with every mark of deference by Ptolemy Lathyrus, he was unable to move the king from his attitude of anxious neutrality. The rebuff which Sulla thus received from Lathyrus was no doubt the reason which determined him in 80 B.C. to impose a nominee of his own upon Egypt. If it be true that he dictated to his client, Ptolemy X Alexander II, the testament produced at Rome after the king's death, in which he followed Ptolemy Apion's example in bequeathing his realm to Rome, we may conclude that Sulla intended to gather in Egypt for the Republic by the same policy of 'lapse' which Lord Dalhousie applied to the native kingdoms of India. Yet neither he nor the restored senatorial government after him took any steps to avenge the death of Ptolemy Alexander, or to give force to his supposed testament; and when Crassus, for reasons of his own, proposed the annexation of Egypt to the People, the Senate's spokesmen carried the day against him (p. 480). Therefore when Pompey entered Palestine, the Egyptian Question remained unsettled, and Ptolemy Auletes was still in possession of the throne. He realized the wisdom of currying favour with Pompey and in 63 B.C. sent 8000 cavalry to his assistance, but since this implied renunciation of the Ptolemies' own claim to Palestine, he increased his unpopularity in Egypt. In 62 Pompey could easily have found a pretext for supporting Ptolemy with military force and anticipating the exploits of his lieutenant Gabinius in 55 B.C. (p. 604). But for the time being he did nothing to repay the service rendered. At the end of 63 he went into winter-quarters at Amisus, and he spent the next year in Asia Minor, putting the finishing touches to his political settlement.

X. POMPEY'S SETTLEMENT OF THE EAST

While Pompey was on his march towards Petra, he had received news of the death of Mithridates. In leaving this enemy to be reduced by the Roman blockade Pompey took the same risks as Scipio Africanus in 208 B.C., when he lost touch with Hasdrubal

Barca (vol. VIII, p. 87); but the gamble was equally justified by events. Not that Mithridates was in danger of starvation in the Russian cornlands. He used his respite to raise a new fleet and an army of 36,000 men equipped in Roman fashion. With this force, and with auxiliaries recruited among the Balkan peoples, he planned a march up the Danube and across the Carnic Alps into Italy—a concept worthy of Hannibal or Attila. But this extreme effort, which the king pursued with unflinching determination, overstrained the loyalty of his subjects, who saw their very plough-cattle commandeered, and of his soldiers, none of whom, and least of all the Roman renegades, were willing to face an invasion of Italy. Early in 63 a revolt broke out at Phanagoreia (on the east side of the Kertch straits) and spread to the Crimea. Mithridates suppressed the insurrection with indiscriminating severity, yet he pardoned a favourite but discontented son named Pharnaces. In giving this grace he incited the culprit, who distrusted his father's mercy, to seek assurance in a second plot. At the head of the mutinous soldiery Pharnaces entered Panticapaeum and drove his father into the citadel. From this last refuge Mithridates attempted negotiations, but finding Pharnaces more merciless than himself, he massacred his remaining children and his harem, and attempted his own life with poison. Finding the poison ineffectual—for by a lifelong diet of prophylactics he had rendered himself immune beyond his own wish—he obtained death from one of his Celtic bodyguards.

The Roman Republic never encountered a stouter adversary in the East than Mithridates. His physical power and mental energy, which remained unabated to the end of his sixty-eight years of life, recalled those of the giants of Alexander's age. By his administrative talents he made the Oriental monarchy into a worthy successor of the dying Hellenistic kingdoms. He fostered the growth of commerce and of city life in Pontus, and out of its rising revenues he built up an army which he trained in Greek fashion, and re-drilled, like Vercingetorix, on a Roman pattern. In preparation for his conquests, he practised the various devices of diplomacy. He made a bid for the sympathy of the Hellenic populations by patronizing Greek artists and literary men; he held off the Romans by humouring them until he was ready to strike. Above all, his courage and resilience in adversity were never equalled among Rome's eastern antagonists. In his last hopeless struggle against Pompey, Mithridates displayed a stubborn pluck like that of a wounded boar returning again and again to the charge.

But success against the Roman Republic required either a

military genius or a prophet and leader of a holy war. For the rôle
of a crusader Mithridates was wholly unfitted, for as a personality
he struck cold: though he knew how to buy servants, he could not
win friends. As a father and husband he out-Heroded Herod; in
his political dealings he stooped to assassination, whether by his
own poniard or by the mass-attack of head-hunters. Moreover,
in breed and culture he was a hybrid whom neither East nor West
could claim as its own[1]. The Greeks who allied themselves with
him were bound by nothing but the precarious tie of a common
dislike of Rome; the Iranian nobility of his realm saw in him a
despot rather than a compatriot. Furthermore, if Mithridates was
a great war-minister, he was not a great general. A capable leader
of guerrillas, he won skirmishes but lost battles, and while in his
earlier wars he was well served by his Greek subordinates, Diophantus and Archelaus, in his last struggle against Rome he disposed only of his own mediocre talents. In a trial of strength
against the new professional army of Rome, led by three of the
Republic's ablest generals, he protracted the conflict to the uttermost, yet he achieved no more than to delay a defeat that was
certain.

Under the terms of the Lex Manilia Pompey carried out a
general settlement of the Near East, without the assistance of the
usual decemviral commission from the Senate. To safeguard
Roman authority, and to secure peace by land and sea, he enlarged
two of the existing provinces and created two new ones. Bithynia
was extended to the river Halys or, more probably, to the Iris[2].
Cilicia was enlarged by the permanent and effective occupation of
the coastland as far as Lycia, and of the inland districts of Lycaonia,
Pisidia and southern Phrygia[3]. The island of Crete was annexed
by right of conquest over the pirates; Syria was incorporated
partly for strategic reasons of frontier defence, partly to give its

---

[1] It is significant that Mithridates regarded the Anatolian, Iranian and
Hellenic cults in his realm with indifferent favour. He was in no sense a
precursor of Mohammed.

[2] See Map 11, facing p. 396. The statement that the eastern boundary
of Bithynia was fixed at the Halys rests on a doubtful interpretation of Strabo
XII, 544. (B. Niese, *Rh. Mus.* 1883, pp. 577 *sqq.*) From Strabo XII, 547,
where it is said that the seaboard east of the Halys was shared between the
Galatian Deiotarus and the city of Amisus (which presumably was included
in the Roman province), it may be inferred that the frontier-line was formed
by the river Iris.

[3] These inland regions had been nominally under Roman rule since 102
or at all events since 84 B.C., but they were not effectively annexed until after
the pirate wars.

people that protection against inland raiders and corsairs on the coast, which the last Seleucid kings had failed to supply[1]. By these acquisitions the whole seaboard of Nearer Asia, with the exception of Lycia, of the territories of Cyzicus and of Pontic Heraclea, and of eastern Pontus, was brought under direct Roman rule.

But where military considerations did not impose a policy of annexation, Pompey adhered to the established Roman principle of leaving the administration of the eastern lands to the dependent kings or city-states. In the Black Sea region he confirmed Pharnaces in the possession of his father's Russian dominions; he conferred the eastern half of the Pontic coastland, from the Halys or the Iris to Trapezus, together with the title of king, upon the Galatian chieftain Deiotarus; he left the seaboard of Colchis in the hands of a dynast named Aristarchus. The kings of Iberia and Albania were, nominally at least, enrolled as Roman vassals. In the interior of Asia Minor Pompey recognized several petty dynasts: Attalus and Pylaemenes in the mountainous inland of Paphlagonia, Tarcondimotus in the recesses of Mt Amanus. To Brogitarus, chief of the Trocmi in eastern Galatia, he gave a slice of inland Pontus with the town of Mithridatium. Whether he bestowed upon Deiotarus other territories than the eastern coastland of Pontus is not certain. But since this chieftain is found not long after in possession of Armenia Minor and of central Galatia (the land of the Tectosages) in addition to his native dominion of western Galatia, it seems not unlikely that he received these other territories from Pompey[2].

On the Euphrates border Ariobarzanes of Cappadocia and Antiochus of Commagene were confirmed in their several kingdoms and received the adjacent strips of Mesopotamia as bridgeheads. Lastly, Pompey did not follow the secularizing policy of the earlier Seleucids in regard to the great temple-domains of Asia Minor (vol. VII, p. 183), but left them under ecclesiastical administration. At the sanctuary of Ma at the Pontic Comana he appointed Archelaus, son of Sulla's former antagonist, as High

[1] On the importance of occupying the coast of Syria as a safeguard against piracy, see J. Dobiáš, *Archiv Orientalni*, III, 1931, pp. 244 *sqq*.

[2] Cicero's statement (*Phil.* II, 37, 94) that Deiotarus received Armenia Minor from the *Senate* does not exclude the possibility that the Senate herein acted in concurrence with Pompey: indeed it is not easy to find an occasion on which that body could have made a grant to Deiotarus without Pompey's consent. The statement of Strabo (XII, 547) that Deiotarus' new possessions in eastern Pontus extended *as far as* Armenia Minor should perhaps not be pressed.

Priest. Beyond the Euphrates he apportioned the debatable territory of Mesopotamia in disregard of his previous treaty with the
king of Parthia. Instead of recovering the whole of this country
from Tigranes, Phraates was put off with the district of Adiabene
(round Nineveh), while Tigranes was allowed to keep Gordyene
(round Nisibis); and Osrhoëne (in the loop of the middle Euphrates) was assigned to an Arab sheikh named Abgarus, who,
officially styled Abgar II, was commissioned to hold open the
gate for an eventual Roman advance into Mesopotamia (see
further below, p. 603 *sq.* and Map 14, facing p. 612).

On the outskirts of the Syrian province Pompey reinstated
Sampsiceramus of Emesa, Ptolemy of Chalcis, and several other
petty dynasts, and he restored Damascus to the Nabataean kingdom. He recognized Hyrcanus as High Priest and ruler of Judaea,
but withheld from him the title of king. Furthermore, he detached
from Judaea the entire seaboard from Gaza to Mt Carmel, the
district of Samaria, and a cluster of ten towns (henceforth called
the Decapolis) extending along the Jordan from Pella and Scytho-
polis to the Dead Sea, so that the Hasmonaean dynasty lost all its
acquisitions save Idumaea, Peraea and Galilee (p. 403).

In the new or enlarged provinces Pompey regulated the details
of administration by special charters. In Bithynia the 'Lex
Pompeia' was still in force in the days of the younger Pliny[1]. The
most distinctive feature in Pompey's administrative arrangements
was the stimulus which he gave to city life in the Near East.
Thirty-nine towns of Asia Minor and Syria were reckoned as his
foundations; in Pontus alone eleven cities were established by
him[2]. In some instances Pompey merely reconstituted older cities
which had become depopulated under the stress of pirate raids, of
prolonged warfare, or of Tigranes' transplantations: thus Pom-
peiopolis in Cilicia was a substitute for Soli[3]. Elsewhere he formed
new urban centres by drawing together the inhabitants of the adjacent villages. At Nicopolis he created a mixed community of
natives and of invalid soldiers from his army; but this is the only
known instance in which he settled Italian colonists on Asian soil.

In the cities founded or re-organized by him Pompey followed
the usual practice of prescribing a property qualification for ad-

---

[1] *ad Traian. imp.* 79, 80, 112, 114, 115.

[2] These included Diospolis (on the site of Cabeira), Megalopolis (subsequently renamed Sebasteia), and Magnopolis (the successor of Mithridates'
colony of Eupatoria).

[3] The bronze coins of the new city bear the head of Pompey and the
figure of Athena, the chief deity of Soli. See Vol. of Plates, iv, 12, *c*.

mission to political offices; but in other respects he gave them a full measure of autonomy. He likewise maintained the liberties of the older cities (including Antioch, Seleuceia on the Orontes, and the Phoenician towns), and confirmed the grants of self-government which Lucullus had made to Sinope and Amisus in Pontus. In the dominion of Pharnaces Phanagoreia was declared a free town, and similar privileges were no doubt assured to other cities outside the direct sphere of Roman rule. A sporadic coinage in bronze and silver suggests that Pompey generally conceded the right to issue money, although not many of the towns actually exercised it.

But if the cities of Asia Minor for the most part became 'liberae,' only a few highly favoured towns like Rhodes and Cyzicus remained 'immunes.' In general, the cities were required to pay the tithe on the produce of their lands to which they had been liable under their former rulers. Similarly all the kings, dynasts and high priests of the dependencies this side of the Euphrates were called upon to make a yearly contribution; the peasants of the crown lands of Bithynia and Pontus transferred their former tithes to the Roman exchequer[1]. The collection of the provincial revenues was left, according to the usual practice of the Roman Republic, in the hands of publicani who underwrote the risks of an uncertain yield under the quota system. But the collection of dues from the individual tax-payers on the municipal territories was left to the municipal authorities, who made collective bargains with the Roman tax-farmers[2].

At his triumph in September 61 B.C. Pompey exhibited placards declaring that he had conquered 1538 cities or strongholds and a population of 12,178,000 souls, and that he had carried Roman arms to the Sea of Azov and the Red Sea. These claims were partly untrue and for the rest gave a false impression. It is true that Pompey had exhibited great powers of strategic planning in the pirate war, and considerable tactical ability in the campaigns of 66 and 65 B.C.; and he had won the obedience of his troops without giving them the usual licence to plunder. Yet the taunt which Lucullus had hurled at him, that he had merely come to reap

---

[1] Little is known of Pompey's arrangements in regard to the extensive crown lands and royal domains of Bithynia and Pontus. Probably a considerable part of these territories was made over to the municipia, new or old. It is uncertain whether he took any steps to emancipate the serf populations on the royal domains and the temple domains. The important mines of Pontus were no doubt leased to *entrepreneurs*.

[2] On Pompey's arrangements for tax-collection, see T. Frank, *Roman Imperialism*, p. 323 *sq.*

what others had sown, was not without foundation. Lucullus, fighting against heavy odds, had broken the backbone of Mithridates' and Tigranes' armies; Pompey, with superior forces, delivered the finishing stroke at an enemy already crippled, and his only victories in the field over unbeaten antagonists were gained at the expense of half-civilized peoples like the Albanians and Iberians.

Yet Pompey's term of command in the East is a landmark in the history of Rome and of Nearer Asia. To the Roman Republic Pompey brought the largest increment of wealth that accrued from any of its foreign wars. After distributing a bounty of 384 million sesterces (£3,360,000) among his soldiers, he still had 480 million sesterces (£4,200,000) left to pay into the treasury, and he augmented the annual tributary revenue of Rome from 200 million to 340 million sesterces. In return for the taxes and indemnities levied by Pompey, the peoples of the Near East obtained peace such as they had not enjoyed since the fall of the Persian Empire. The seas were all but cleared of corsairs, Syria was delivered from anarchy, and apart from some lesser disorders due to the growing ambitions of King Deiotarus, Asia Minor long remained immune from war. In his settlement with Parthia, it is true, Pompey sowed the seeds of future trouble, but with Syria and the Euphrates crossings in the hands of Rome and her allies, a Parthian attack could henceforth be met, and usually was met, by a Roman invasion of Parthian territory. Lastly, in fostering city life in Asia Minor and Syria Pompey gave a new impulse to the diffusion of Hellenic civilization, and prepared for the economic renaissance of the Near East under the early Roman emperors. Though Pompey's conquests have little of the glamour of Caesar's Gallic Wars, they will bear comparison with these in their ultimate effects upon the course of ancient history.

CHAPTER IX

THE JEWS

I. JEWISH HISTORY TO THE RISE OF HEROD

THE events which have been recounted in the previous chapter brought the Jews to the notice of the Romans for the first time since the Senate meditated using them to hamper the recovery of Seleucid Syria (vol. VIII, p. 519). It is convenient at this point to describe their history in this period, and, at the same time, the development of their religion and ideas, which were destined to have an influence, through Christianity, far beyond the narrow limits of Palestine.

During the reign of the two sons of the High Priest John Hyrcanus the Jewish State in Palestine, now completely independent under its new Hasmonaean dynasty, reached its highest point of extension and power. Once more, nearly five centuries after Babylon had extinguished the old Davidic kingdom, a Jewish king reigned in Jerusalem with no Gentile overlord. Such a kingdom proved, however, to be only a transitory phenomenon belonging to the chaotic interim in the Nearer East between the break-up of the Seleucid empire and the day when Rome entered on the inheritance. A multitude of local dynasties shot up for their brief period of power over Syria and Asia Minor, and amongst these was the Hasmonaean dynasty in Palestine. In a former chapter it was shown how already in the days of John Hyrcanus three processes had begun which mark the early history of the house of Hashmon: one was the advance of the Hasmonaean High Priest to kingship, another was the growing enmity between the Hasmonaean house and the religious section of the people by whose help it had risen to power, and a third was the territorial expansion of the Jewish State. These culminated in the reign of Jannaeus Alexander (vol. VIII, pp. 531 *sqq.*).

The immediate successor of Hyrcanus was his son, who bore the Hebrew name of Judah and the Greek name of Aristobulus (104–103 B.C.). Josephus says that he assumed the style of king

Note. The chief sources for the narrative in this chapter are Josephus, *Antiquities*, XIII [11], 301 to the end of XIV; *Wars*, I [3, 1], 70—[18, 3], 357. See further, the Bibliography. See Map 2, facing p. 103.

and its Hellenistic emblem, the diadem; but his coins still bear, in Hebrew, only the legend 'Jehūdah, High Priest,' and, according to Strabo (XVI, 762), it was Jannaeus who first assumed the kingship. It may be that Aristobulus presented himself as king in his dealings with his hellenized neighbours or with Greeks resorting to Jerusalem, but did not yet bear the name of king for his Jewish subjects. With the Greeks Aristobulus was popular: Josephus uses a phrase 'styled philhellene' (χρηματίσας φιλελλην) which need not necessarily mean that *Philhellene* was an actual surname attached to him. The Alexandrian historian Timagenes (last century B.C.) called him 'fair-minded' (ἐπιεικής). In his domestic relations, however, he reproduced the worst type of Oriental despot: three of his brothers he kept in prison, one brother he killed, and his mother he starved to death. At least that is the account given by Josephus: it may be coloured, as has been suspected[1], by Pharisaic hatred. The brief reign of Aristobulus was chiefly memorable for an expansion of the Jewish State to the north—the conquest of Galilee, inhabited in part by a tribe of warlike hill-men, Ituraeans. According to the precedent set by Hyrcanus in Idumaea, the conquered heathen were compelled to accept circumcision and become Jews. The Galileans of the time of Jesus Christ must have had largely heathen ancestors.

Aristobulus was succeeded by his brother Jannaeus or Jannai whose Greek name was Alexander (103–76 B.C.). In him beyond all doubt the kingship was added to the High-Priesthood[2]. It was a departure from the traditional idea that a man of the tribe of Levi, not of the house of David, should be king in Jerusalem. If some of the religious disapproved of the combination, others were able to point to such foreshadowings of it in the sacred books as the figure of Melchizedek, both King of Salem and Priest of the Most High God. It is commonly believed to-day by scholars that Psalm CX, in which the psalmist tells some warrior ruler 'Thou art a priest for ever after the order of Melchizedek,' is an acrostic originally addressed to Simon: if so, a thought had already at that time become current which might embolden Simon's grandson to call himself formally King. In a document embodied in the *Testaments of the Twelve Patriarchs* Levi is represented as receiving a promise from heaven that of his seed one should arise 'called by a new name,' who would both be a king in Judah and 'establish a

---

[1] By Schürer, *Gesch. des jüdischen Volkes*, I, ed. 4, p. 276.

[2] Jannai at last puts the title of king on his coins—not only in their Greek legend Βασιλέως Ἀλεξάνδρου but in their Hebrew legend 'Jehônathan the King.' See Volume of Plates iv, 2, *h*.

new priesthood[1].' This shows at least that some religious Jews, when it was written, regarded the Levite priest-kingship as of Divine appointment. 'Draw ye near to Levi in humbleness of heart, that ye may receive a blessing from his mouth. For he shall bless Israel and Judah, because him hath the Lord chosen to be king over all the nation[2].'

The new Priest-King proved to be a savage ruffian. His reign was filled with fighting. His arms extended the borders of the Jewish kingdom till it practically coincided with the kingdom of David. The first of his enterprises, an attack on Ptolemaïs, brought about complications, for Ptolemaïs called in Ptolemy Lathyrus, at that moment ruling Cyprus in enmity with his mother Cleopatra III, who was ruling Egypt (p. 387). At Asophon in the Jordan valley Jannaeus sustained a severe defeat. Then Cleopatra plunged into the confusion with an army from Egypt, in which the Jew Ananias, a son of the Onias who had fled to Egypt and built the temple at Leontopolis (see vol. VIII, p. 517), held a high command. She drove Ptolemy's forces out of the field, and, according to Josephus (*Ant.* XIII [13, 2], 354), would have annexed Palestine once more to the Ptolemaic realm, had not Ananias warned her that this would displease the Egyptian Jews, with whom she could not afford to quarrel. She therefore evacuated the country, leaving Jannaeus to prosecute his plans (about 102 B.C.).

His first conquest was beyond Jordan: it included the Greek city of Gadara, illustrious for its literary men, and Amathus. Then he subjugated the hellenized Philistine coast; Gaza, which had sustained glorious sieges by Alexander the Great and by Antiochus the Great, had to capitulate after a year's siege to the Jewish Alexander, and was given to the flames (96 B.C.). The next years were marked by troubles and vicissitudes which might have quelled any one of less fiery spirit. The Nabataeans with their capital at Petra, enriched by the traffic across Arabia between the Mediterranean and the Persian Gulf, had in this interval between Seleucid and Roman rule established, like the Jews, a strong independent State, probably Arab in race and speech, though using Aramaic as the official and literary language. They were the most

---

[1] *The Testament of Levi*, VIII, 14. R. H. Charles (*Apocrypha and Pseudepigrapha of the New Testament*, II, p. 309) affirms that the 'new name' refers to an innovation in the style of the Hasmonaean High Priest, by which he was called officially 'Priest of the Most High God'—the title given to Melchizedek in Genesis. This is possible, but the documentary evidence is not such as to make it more than an ingenious conjecture.

[2] *Testament of Reuben* vi, 10.

dangerous rivals whom the Jews had. An expedition in which
Jannaeus was trying to extend his conquests beyond Gadara into
the hills of Gaulanitis brought him into collision with the Nabataean king, Obodas I (Obādath?), and Jannaeus came back to
Jerusalem, a fugitive, with only the relics of an army (about 90
B.C.). Meantime, hatred of the Hasmonaean High Priest amongst
the Pharisees and a large section of the Jewish people influenced
by them had become aggravated. According to a story told by
Josephus (*Ant.* xiii [13, 5], 372), Jannaeus had once been pelted,
while he officiated at the altar at the Feast of Tabernacles, with the
citrons which the people carried by a custom of the feast. When he
arrived at Jerusalem after the disaster in Gaulanitis, the people
rose in rebellion. After some two years' fighting, in which Jannaeus
used Gentile mercenaries, he was in extremities, ready to retire
into private life under certain conditions. But the insurgent Jews
would now be satisfied with nothing less than his death, and they
called in Demetrius III Eukairos, one of the Seleucid princes
fighting over the remains of the Seleucid kingdom, with his base
at Damascus (*c.* 88 B.C.). The forces of Demetrius and the Jewish
forces combined inflicted upon Jannaeus a defeat which might
have been decisive, had not a large number of Jews feared the
consequences of an alliance with the great-great-great nephew of
Antiochus Epiphanes and changed sides. From now the fortunes
of Jannaeus mended. In the end he completely beat down the
Jewish rebels under his feet, and celebrated his victory, Josephus
says, by having 800 of them crucified in rows where he could
watch their dying agonies from the terrace of his palace in Jerusalem while he caroused with the women of his harem. The civil
war had lasted some six years.

Meantime the power of the Nabataean Aretas III (Harethath)
had been expanding, and about 85 B.C. reached Damascus.
Aretas invaded Palestine and defeated Jannaeus at Adida in
Judaea. But he did not intend to annex Palestine to his kingdom,
and used his advantage only to extort various concessions before
he retired. And the Nabataean power did not prevent Jannaeus in
the last years of his life from making fresh conquests in Trans-
jordania. A number of Greek towns, Pella, Dium, Gerasa,
Gaulana, Seleuceia, Gamala, were taken by the Jews. Jannaeus
was besieging a fortress called Ragaba in Gerasene territory when
he succumbed to an illness brought on by drunkenness; although
he had suffered from it for the last three years, it had not deterred
him from actively prosecuting war (76 B.C.).

Over the Greek culture which had been rooted in Coele-Syria

through the Greek and hellenized cities the conquests of a barbarian like Jannaeus passed as a devastating storm. Once populous districts went back to wilderness: brigandage flourished. Amongst the cities of the coast Ascalon alone still stood unsubdued. But only thirteen years separated the death of Jannaeus from the coming of Pompey. The first nine years of those thirteen (76–67 B.C.) were a pause after the Hasmonaean kingdom had attained its culmination before the ruin began. They were years in which the head of the State was a woman, Queen Salome Alexandra, the widow of Jannaeus. This was an odd phenomenon in Israel, the only precedent in its ancient history being the sinister one of Athaliah. Perhaps it was another feature in the Jewish State showing assimilation to the Hellenistic dynasties, in which women played so powerful a part, especially in the neighbouring Egypt with its series of Arsinoes, Berenices, and Cleopatras.

The reign of Salome was marked by a complete reversal of policy. The queen threw herself upon the side of the Pharisees: they became the power behind the throne. According to the account given by Josephus in the *Wars* (1 [5, 2], 111), this was due to the superstitious dread which the queen felt for the party of zealous religion; according to the account in the *Antiquities* (XIII [15, 5], 400 *sqq.*) it was due to the statecraft of Jannaeus, who on his death-bed advised Salome to ally herself with the Pharisees. In any case, the Pharisees afterwards remembered those years as a period of almost millennial bliss. In a book of the Talmud it is stated that under the rule of Salome 'the grains of wheat were as large as kidneys, the grains of barley like olive-kernels, and the beans like gold denarii': it rained at night only, but then in sufficient quantity. As a matter of fact, the queen must have had to face grave troubles, both external and internal. Externally, the conquests of Tigranes, pushed ever farther towards Palestine, seemed, till near the end of Salome's reign, about to engulf the Jewish kingdom (p. 357). Internally, the struggle between the parties went on. By the fact that the head of the State was a woman, the kingship and the High-Priesthood were inevitably separated. The elder of the queen's two sons, Hyrcanus, a man, we are given to understand, of feeble mind, held the office of High Priest, and, like his mother, was directed by the Pharisees. The younger son, Aristobulus, inherited his father's fierce spirit, and continued to lead the priestly aristocracy who made the strength of the Sadducaean party. The dominant Pharisees remembered the atrocities inflicted upon them by Jannaeus and sought now to take their revenge upon the Sadducees, who had been his supporters and counsellors. Salome found that this policy brought her vehement protests from her younger son. Evidently, if Salome kept things together during her lifetime, the State was seething with unrest.

When Salome died in 67 B.C., the fatal rupture inevitably came. Open war broke out between the two brothers. Aristobulus soon had the better of it, and Hyrcanus agreed to his younger brother becoming both High Priest and King. But already a man had come upon the scene whose figure was to dominate during the next twenty-four years, and whose house was to hold the chief place in Palestine for the hundred years following. This was an Idumaean, Antipater, belonging to one of those Edomite families who had been forcibly Judaized by John Hyrcanus some half a century before. Antipater's father had been *strategos* of Idumaea for Jannaeus. Now, ambitious, supple and scheming, Antipater set about his long task of working his way to the supreme place. His plan was to use Hyrcanus, stand behind that feeble personage, and move him as a piece in the contest with Aristobulus. He had extended his connections as far as the Nabataean court; his wife Cypros belonged to an important family in that country[1]; now he induced Aretas III to intervene on behalf of Hyrcanus. The Nabataean forces beat those of Aristobulus; a great part of the people went over to the side of Hyrcanus, and Aristobulus was soon besieged with his adherents, largely priests, on the Temple hill.

Then the approach of a greater power made a wholly new situation. In 65 the Roman commander Scaurus, Pompey's lieutenant, coming south after the submission of Tigranes, reached Damascus (p. 381). The Nabataeans, at a word from the Romans, raised the siege of Jerusalem and went home. For each of the two Jewish factions everything now hung upon getting the support of Rome. In 63 Pompey himself was in Damascus, and he received appeals not only from the two warring brothers, but from representatives of the Jewish people who begged him to abolish the Hasmonaean kingship and make the head of the State a High Priest like those of old. Pompey moved on Jerusalem, and

---

[1] A. Schlatter (*Gesch. Israels*, ed. 3, p. 428, n. 205) affirms that the family was a *Jewish* one settled in Arabia. He refers to Josephus, *Wars*, 1 [8, 9], 181; but all that Josephus says in that passage is that Cypros was τῶν ἐπισήμων ἐξ ᾽Αραβίας. Nevertheless probability is in favour of Schlatter's hypothesis; it is unlikely that Antipater would have married a pagan. In *Antiquities*, XIV [7, 3], 121 Josephus seems to make the family Idumaean (παρ᾽ ὧν), if the text is sound.

Aristobulus, after a vain attempt at resistance, himself surrendered. But his party, led by the priestly aristocracy, still held the strong Temple hill against the Romans, and it took Pompey three months to storm it. It was then he insisted, like Antiochus Epiphanes, on entering the Holy of Holies—an outrage to Jewish feeling—though, unlike Antiochus, Pompey left the Temple treasure untouched. See above, p. 382 *sq.*

This was the end of the Hasmonaean kingdom. King Aristobulus was carried off to Rome, to walk in Pompey's triumph. Thousands of other Jews were sent to slavery in the West. In Palestine the kingdom was broken up, and the Greek cities liberated from subjection to the Jewish ruler. All the seaboard was lost to the Jews. But some of the acquisitions of the Hasmonaeans remained. Idumaea, where the population had been compelled to embrace Judaism, continued to be in political connection with Judaea; so too Galilee and Peraea, a stretch of country beyond Jordan, between Pella and the Dead Sea, where the population was now predominantly Jewish. The Samaritan country, as a whole, was detached, but the frontier of Judaea seems to have remained some way beyond the old frontier of a hundred years before. Hyrcanus was left by Pompey the nominal ruler of this reduced realm, with the title of *ethnarches*, no longer of King, and, of course, the office of High Priest. Like all the native powers, the Jewish *ethnarches* was to be under the control of the Roman proconsul of Syria. Partisans of Aristobulus were still at large under the leadership of his son, Alexander, and Aristobulus himself succeeded for a moment in returning to Palestine. The Romans had in the eight years following 63 to quell three attempts of these bands to recover the country. In 57 the proconsul Gabinius divided the Jewish country into five districts, each with a *synhedrion* of its own, districts whose capitals were Jerusalem, Gazara, Amathus, Jericho and Sepphoris. The measure was presumably meant to weaken the central power in Jerusalem. Although Jerusalem soon recovered the predominance, there are signs that these provincial councils retained a certain autonomy in later times[1].

The real director of the Jewish State in these days was the Idumaean Antipater, and the leading principle of Antipater's policy was to secure the favour of the ruler of the Roman world. Since, in the years which followed 63, rival war-lords were contending for the supreme power, and the ruler of to-day might be the vanquished of to-morrow, it required all Antipater's address to steer his course. In 54 Crassus was proconsul of Syria and used

[1] A. Schlatter, *op. cit.* p. 428 *sq.*

his opportunity to rob the Temple of its treasure; we are told that he carried off two thousand talents in money and precious objects worth eight thousand more. When the civil war between Caesar and Pompey broke out, Antipater was of course on Pompey's side till Pompey's defeat, and then a no less zealous adherent of Caesar. Before Pharsalus, Caesar had liberated the former King Aristobulus and sent him to wrest Judaea from Hyrcanus; but by Antipater's good luck he was assassinated by the Pompeians on his way. In 47 Antipater himself commanded the Jewish contingent which formed part of Caesar's army in Egypt. By Caesar's grace the Jewish State now recovered some of what it had lost in 63; the return of Joppa to the Jews, by which Jerusalem's connection with the sea was restored, was of special importance. To the Jews of the Diaspora, also, the dictator showed marked favour: at his assassination the Roman Jews were prominent in the mobs which demonstrated grief around his tomb. The civil war after Caesar's death constituted a new problem for Antipater, and the late friend of Caesar naturally sided with Caesar's murderers, who were at first masters of Syria. One of the murderers, Cassius, was proconsul of Syria in 43, and Antipater made himself exceedingly serviceable in finding the money which Cassius required. He did not live to see Philippi, but was killed by poison that same year— the act of a personal rival in Jerusalem.

The power which Antipater had built up did not end with his premature death; he left four sons, of whom the two eldest, Phasael and Herod, had already taken a prominent part in affairs. Phasael had held command in Judaea under his father and Herod in Galilee. As governor of Galilee, Herod had come into collision with Jewish bands under a leader called Hezekiah. These bands might be regarded, either as warriors fighting for the nation and for God, like the bands of Judas Maccabaeus, or as brigands, such as the Zealots a hundred years later were in the eyes of Josephus. It was as brigands that young Herod regarded them, as indeed any ordered government was bound to do, and he suppressed them with a firm hand, killing Hezekiah. To the people of Judaea, who largely regarded Hezekiah and his bands in the other light, Herod's action appeared a crime, and he was summoned to Jerusalem to stand his trial before the Sanhedrin. He presented himself with an armed following and escaped condemnation. But the incident planted in him a profound hatred of the priestly aristocracy. Caesar at that moment was still ruler of the Roman world, and his cousin, Sextus Caesar, was governor of Syria. From him Herod obtained a military command which put considerable

forces at his disposal. He now marched on Jerusalem with the
purpose apparently of slaking his desire for vengeance in blood,
but old Antipater induced him to hold his hand.

The sons of Antipater had hardly, with the help of Cassius,
avenged their father's death on the murderer, when the anti-
Caesarian cause went down at Philippi, and, in carrying on their
father's policy, they had to make a rapid transition to the victorious
side. In 41 Antony moved on Palestine through Asia Minor. The
Jewish people, who wanted to be delivered altogether from the
house of Antipater, saw their chance; they sent three several
embassies to Antony on his way, to Bithynia, to Antioch and to
Tyre, entreating him to suppress the family which had compromised itself so deeply by giving comfort to Cassius. Even so,
Herod succeeded in winning Antony's favour: there was probably
a congeniality of temperament between the pleasure-loving Roman
soldier and the handsome full-blooded manful young Edomite.
When Antony departed from the East at the end of 41, Phasael
and Herod were left in power in Palestine with the title of
tetrarchs.

The year 40 saw a surprising diversion. The progress of events
in the Roman world was interrupted by an invasion of the one
Eastern power which could be counted as Rome's rival. A
Parthian army overran Syria, and with the Parthians came a
surviving son of the Hasmonaean Aristobulus II, Mattathiah
Antigonus, to win back his ancestral kingdom from the Edomite
usurper. To the Jews the Parthians were heaven-sent deliverers,
and Jerusalem threw open its gates. Phasael was killed; Herod
fled to Masada, his fortress on the Dead Sea. Old Hyrcanus, who
had been quietly going on all these years as High Priest, had his
ears cut off, to disqualify him for the office, and was deported by
the Parthians to Babylonia. His nephew established himself as
King and High Priest in Jerusalem: the coins he issued show on
one side the legend in Hebrew, 'Mattathiah the High Priest, the
Commonwealth of the Jews,' and on the other side, in Greek, 'Of
King Antigonus[1].''

In one way it was a piece of good fortune for Herod that the
cause of his Hasmonaean rival had been identified with that of the
Parthians: it secured to Herod the sure support of Rome. From
Masada he succeeded somehow in making his way to Rome and
there, in 40 B.C., he was declared by the Senate to be 'King of the
Jews,' and, as such, he returned to Palestine to co-operate with the
Roman forces whose task it was to clear out the Parthians. But

[1] Volume of Plates iv, 2, i.

even when the Parthians had been expelled, Jerusalem under Antigonus still held out desperately against the Edomite. It was not till 37 B.C. that it capitulated, first the lower city and finally the Temple Hill, to Antony's lieutenant in Syria, C. Sosius[1], and to King Herod. Antigonus was beheaded, the first vanquished king to undergo this form of death at the hands of Rome. For the next thirty-three years Palestine was to lie, without possibility of resistance, under the strong rule of the new king, an Edomite by race, a circumcised Jew by professed religion, and mainly a pagan by practice. Before the fall of Jerusalem Herod had sought to affiliate himself to the dispossessed royal family by marrying Mariamne, the daughter of Alexander the son of Aristobulus II and the grand-daughter, through her mother, of Hyrcanus II.

II. JEWISH PARTIES AND THE LAW

The sixty-six years which elapsed between the death of John Hyrcanus and the establishment of Herod as king in Jerusalem had been important years in the development of Judaism. We have already seen how under John Hyrcanus the party zealous for legal purity, which had been known as the party of the Chasīdim, came to be called 'Pharisees,' and how the Hasmonaean High Priest broke his traditional connection with that party and went over to the Sadducees (vol. VIII, p. 532). These two parties still divided the allegiance of the Jewish people when Herod came to the throne. We have no adequate documents to show us what Pharisaism was in the earlier generations, after the name had first come into use. Indeed for Pharisaism as a whole our documents leave important questions unsettled.

The state of the case is this. We have no single document which professedly emanates from the Pharisaic party, though there are certain documents, like the Psalms of Solomon in the last century B.C. and IV Esdras in the first century A.D., which are conjecturally taken from internal evidence by modern scholars to represent Pharisaism. Evidence of this kind is uncertain. There can be little doubt that modern scholars are right when they see in such works strong affinities to what other sources tell us of Pharisaic religion. But it must be remembered, in the first place, that any party like that of the Pharisees would exert an influence outside

---

[1] A bronze coin has been found with the legend 'C. Sosius Imperator' and the figure of a trophy between a male and female Jewish captive. See Volume of Plates iv, 2, *j*.

its own limits, and there must have been various shades of religion amongst the Jews, which showed greater or less affinity to Pharisaism without conforming altogether to the Pharisaic pattern; and, in the second place, that, even if we could be quite sure that the authors of works like the Psalms of Solomon and IV Esdras were Pharisees in the strict sense, the character of such writings, poetical and apocalyptic, might well allow only certain elements in their religion to appear. Secondly, we have the account of Pharisees and Sadducees given by Josephus; but in regard to that we have to remember that the Pharisaism and Sadduceism of the first century A.D., which Josephus knew by direct acquaintance, may well have differed considerably from the Pharisaism and Sadduceism of 100 B.C., and, further, that in his very summary account, Josephus was concerned to present Pharisaism and Sadduceism in a way congenial to his Greek readers, and therefore to some extent travestied them by assimilating them to Greek philosophic schools. Thirdly, we have the representation of Pharisaism in the New Testament. This is based on lost Aramaic documents contemporary with the Pharisaism it depicts, and is, so far, valuable evidence; yet here it has to be remembered that the unfavourable sides of Pharisaism are given special prominence, and some of the statements in our Greek Gospels are hard to reconcile with what we know otherwise of Palestinian Judaism—for instance, the statement of St Mark that 'the Pharisees, and all the Jews, except they wash their hands diligently, eat not, holding the tradition of the elders.'

Fourthly and lastly, we have in the Rabbinical literature a number of scattered allusions to Pharisees and controversies with Sadducees, and a mass of material which professes to record sayings and doings of prominent Rabbis from the second century B.C. onwards. If these latter are not expressly called Pharisees in the Rabbinical books, it is quite clear that their attitude to the Law corresponds with that ascribed by Josephus and the New Testament to the Pharisees, and some of the Rabbis cited (Shemaya, Abtalyon, Gamaliel) are called Pharisees by Josephus or the New Testament. If, therefore, we could be sure that all the doings and sayings ascribed by the Mishnah, or later parts of the Rabbinical literature, to Rabbis in the first century of the Christian era, and earlier, were authentic, we should have in this literature a wholly trustworthy source of information regarding the Pharisaism of the century before and the century after the Christian era. But here it has to be remembered that the literature in question embodies traditions which did not begin to be put in writing till about A.D. 200. Many of the sayings and doings recorded are no doubt authentic, but it is plain that confusions, inventions, embroideries have also come plentifully into the oral tradition; it is absurd to take, for instance, what the Rabbinical books tell us about the sayings and doings of Simon ben Shetach in the days of Alexander Jannaeus as if it were a written contemporary account. It is quite possible that the Rabbinical tradition eliminated altogether features which belonged to the Pharisaism of New Testament times; the charges, for instance, which Jesus brings against the Pharisees in Mark vii, in regard to Corban and duty to parents, do not apply to the Judaism of the Rabbinical books, which in this matter took a view agreeing rather with that of Jesus. In short, we are very ill furnished for tracing the history and drawing the picture of early Pharisaism.

According to a statement of Josephus (*Ant.* XIII [5, 9], 171), the existence of Pharisees as a sect began in the days of Jonathan the High Priest (161–143 B.C.), at least, he says somewhat vaguely that the three sects of Pharisees, Sadducees and Essenes were in existence 'about this time.' The first events with which the Pharisees are connected are those of their quarrel with John Hyrcanus (135–104). The story of the quarrel appears both in Josephus and in the Talmud, though in the latter Alexander Jannaeus takes the place of Hyrcanus. It may well have been a real event transfigured in popular legend. As Josephus tells the story, Hyrcanus, who has up to this time been a disciple of the Pharisees, asks them in an assembly to indicate any illegality they might detect in his conduct, and one Pharisee replies that he ought to lay down the High-Priesthood, because his mother had been carried into slavery during the tribulation under Antiochus Epiphanes. Hyrcanus declares that the allegation is false and demands the judgment of the Pharisees as a body, what penalty the calumniator ought to suffer. They reply 'Scourging and imprisonment.' This infuriates Hyrcanus, because he had counted on their pronouncing a sentence of death, and he thenceforth ranges himself with the Sadducees. Whatever historical truth is behind the story, the ambitions of the Hasmonaean house once in power could hardly have failed to make it change over.

We can trace in outline the varying relations of the Pharisaic party to the powers that be, from its origin to the destruction of Jerusalem. What is obscure is the inner character of Pharisaism throughout this period. Its name, *Perūshīm* in Hebrew, *P'rīshayyā* in Aramaic, means 'Separated,' and it is generally believed that it was intended to indicate the separation of the Pharisees from the

multitude careless of contracting religious impurity[1]. Josephus
and the Gospels agree further that a leading characteristic of the
Pharisees was that they supplemented the written Law by a mass
of oral tradition handed down by Rabbi to Rabbi from 'the
elders.' The emergence of Pharisaism as a sect thus corresponds
with the rise to predominant importance amongst the Jewish
people of the class of expert teachers of the Law.

In the old Israel before the Exile the declaration of what
accorded with religious law had been a function of the priests.
When, after Nehemiah, the Pentateuch was circulated as a law-
book amongst the people generally, any one who had the leisure
could devote himself to the study of it and make himself an expert
in its prescriptions. An expert, again, could set up a school and pass
on his doctrine to disciples. During the last two centuries before
the Christian era, if not earlier, a definite class of legal experts had
come to be developed with an authority quite distinct from that of
the priests. There were priests amongst them, but a large number
were not of the priestly tribe. Apart from the schools in which
they instructed disciples, the experts communicated their teaching
to the people at large mainly in the synagogues. Their teaching
was of two kinds. One kind was concerned with the determination
of what the law required in all details of conduct; in the later
Rabbinical books it is distinguished as Halakhah, 'Walking,'
and was no doubt the kind which made the chief part of instruction in their schools; the other kind was concerned with the Old
Testament stories, filling up the gaps by imaginative additions
and inferences, or doctrine about the unseen world; the Rabbinical
books call it Haggadah, 'Showing forth'; this kind no doubt
made the chief part of the instruction given in their synagogue
discourses. One necessary part of the synagogue service in those
days was actual translation, since the Hebrew in which the Old
Testament was written was now not understood except by the
learned, though the language of Palestine at that time, Aramaic,
was a sister-language, and in Josephus and the New Testament is
called 'Hebrew,' in distinction from Greek. The oral translation of
the Old Testament from Hebrew into Aramaic in the synagogues
gave an occasion for incorporating comments derived from the
tradition of the scribes. Such Aramaic renderings with elaborations
constitute the Targums, 'Interpretations,' which have come down

[1] The view revived by R. Leszynsky, *Die Sadduzäer*, which connects the
name with *pārash* in the sense 'to explain,' so that it would mean 'ex-
positors,' has not been seriously regarded by Semitic scholars: the form of the
word is unquestionably passive.

to us in a form belonging to later centuries; the word is from the same Semitic root as the familiar 'dragoman,' interpreter (see vol. II, p. 335).

The Synagogue was the special sphere of the scriptural expert, as the Temple was the special sphere of the priests. It was not a merely accidental coincidence that the same period which saw the emergence of the class of experts saw the development of the Synagogue as a new centre of Jewish religion. This was an inevitable development when a great mass of the Jewish people were living too far from Jerusalem for resort to the Temple. But, when once developed, the local synagogue supplied religious needs which the Temple did not. Spectacular acts of religious worship— sacrifice and trumpet-blowing and the choral singing of a great multitude—for these the Temple was still the place; but for instruction in religious doctrine, for becoming acquainted with the scriptural narratives, for the prayer and praise and meditation of local groups, even for the rudimentary instruction of children, Jews now looked to the Synagogue. It is true that the forms of Synagogue-worship in some respects copied the forms of Temple-worship. In Jerusalem itself, synagogues sprang up in proximity to the Temple. It was the scriptural expert, not the priest, who now ruled the mind of the people, and it was the Synagogue which for the great mass furnished the regular means for communal worship. Thus when the Temple was destroyed and the priests as a class disappeared, Judaism could still go on, not essentially weakened, as a religion based upon the expert and the Synagogue.

It is curious that we do not know what term in Hebrew or Aramaic the Palestinian Jews used in the last century before the Christian era and in the first century succeeding it to describe the scriptural expert. In the New Testament they are sometimes called *nomikoi*, 'lawyers,' most commonly *grammateis*, 'scribes,' but the corresponding Hebrew word *sōpherim* was used, when the Rabbinical tradition came to be put in writing, to describe, not contemporary teachers, but wise men of the period between Ezra and the High Priest Simon 'the Righteous[1].' Contemporary experts in the Rabbinical books are commonly called *chakāmim*,

----

[1] It is uncertain whether Simon I is intended, High Priest round about 300 B.C., to whom Josephus attaches the surname 'the Righteous' (*Ant.* XII [2, 5], 43), or Simon II, High Priest round about 200 B.C., praised by Ben-Sira (Ecclesiasticus L). Schürer took the former view, Bousset the latter. G. F. Moore holds that Simon I never existed, and that Josephus simply misplaced the High Priest of 200.

'wise men.' It is quite possible, however, that this usage does not
go back to the time before the fall of Jerusalem: the 'scribes'
with whom Jesus had to deal may in their own day have been
called *sōpherim*. The term 'Rabbi,' commonly used to-day, is
properly a vocative, 'My Master': as early as New Testament
times it was regularly used in addressing a teacher of the Law, but
it was not yet used as a term of description in speaking about him.

Of necessity from the first day when there had been a written
Law at all there had been also a mass of traditional unwritten law
regulating details of the cultus and the conduct of men in the
various affairs of life. Much of this unwritten law might appear as
but the application to particular cases of the general injunctions
contained in the written Law, and thus possess sanctity and divine
authority. Since, however, there were considerable varieties of
practice and on many points doubt and disagreement, the 'scribes'
had here a vast field of activity open to them, discussing and
determining in their schools, or 'houses of study,' what the right
legal course in all imaginable circumstances was. A difference
could not fail to be recognized between the written Law and the
'tradition of the elders,' as the unwritten law came to be called,
and it was felt that the authority of a Divine commandment could
attach to the unwritten tradition only in so far as that too could be
traced to an inspired source.

In Rabbinical literature the idea is found that a certain part of
the unwritten tradition had been communicated orally by Moses
at Sinai and handed down through subsequent generations side
by side with the written Law; other ordinances were ascribed to
the *sōpherim*, that is, as has just been explained, the teachers
between Ezra and Simon the Righteous. It may, however, be
questioned[1] whether these ideas came up before the latter part of
the first century A.D., and the main way in which authority could
be secured for the tradition was to represent each detail of it as a
logical inference from something in the written Law. To this end
a fantastic ingenuity was developed in the schools of the scribes,
and one Rabbinical book (*Chagigah* i, 8) frankly compares some of
the rules deduced in this way to 'mountains hanging by a hair.'
On this assumption the scribes did not add anything to the written
Law; they only drew out what was implied in it. But the decision
of a teacher in effect amplified the Law, as the decision of a judge
does the Common Law of England, and became in its turn a *datum*
for further inferences. Naturally there was considerable disagree-

[1] W. Bousset, *Die Religion des Judentums im späthellenistischen Zeitalter*,
3rd ed. (ed. Gressmann), p. 156 *sq.*

ment between the decisions of different teachers, but those given by a teacher of especial personal authority tended to become general, so that in time a great body of traditional Law, consistent in its main outline, came into existence, handed on in the name of eminent teachers in the past. Just as the scribe in theory added nothing to the written Law, so in theory he added nothing of his own to the oral tradition: he only held fast in his memory what he had learnt at the feet of his teacher, and handed it on, applying its principles to all the new problems of practice which might arise.

The current oral tradition committed to writing, as has been said, about A.D. 200 constituted what is called the Mishnah, 'Repetition.' The Talmud consists of the Mishnah embedded in a mass of later commentary on the Mishnah. The Mishnah is composed of legal and religious teaching attributed by name to a large number of eminent teachers in the past, and a good part of its substance must really go back to the Christian era or the last two centuries B.C. From this, then, and from the rest of Rabbinical literature which claims to embody tradition regarding the great teachers of the past, we can form some notion of what the 'tradition of the elders' was in New Testament times. But, as was pointed out in connection with Pharisaism, the tradition as written down may have been in many ways different from the oral tradition of two hundred years earlier. The work of adjustment, of elimination, of schematization, which has gone on in the interval may to some extent falsify the picture. That the curious fantastic casuistry which Christendom has found so unpleasing in the Rabbinic books marked the teaching of the scribes as early as the time of Jesus is proved by the Gospel documents, but it may not, on the one hand, have reached the proportions it had when the teaching was written down, and it may, on the other, have contained at the earlier period elements, like the doctrine of Corban overriding duty to parents, which the better thought of Judaism weeded out.

But if it was the characteristic of the Pharisees in New Testament times that they regarded the oral tradition of the schools as having an authority parallel to, and in practice sometimes even overriding, that of the written Law, Pharisaism in that sense cannot have existed till the body of oral tradition was already there as something formulated. The scribes must have been doing their work for several generations at least before there could be any tradition for Pharisees to exalt. And how far back can we suppose the existence of a tradition like that embodied in the Mishnah? It is to be noted that, in attaching the tradition to eminent names in the past, the Mishnah has hardly anything to say of any teacher older than Hillel, who lived perhaps till about A.D. 20. The oldest authority of all of whom it speaks is 'Simon the Righteous,' but of all teachers before Hillel it has little to relate except a few religious apophthegms and a few legendary anecdotes. And if the tradition, as we know it, was only in the early phase of its formation in the days of Herod, how are we to think of the Pharisees in the days of John Hyrcanus?

If zeal for the Law marked the Chasīdim in the time of the Maccabaean revolt, and zeal for the Law (extended now to include the tradition) marked the Pharisees in the first century A.D., it is certain that zeal for the Law of some kind must have marked the Pharisees of the intervening period. Zeal for the Law indeed might be of different kinds. In a book like that of Ben-Sira (Ecclesiasticus), belonging to the time just before the Maccabaean revolt, we have an earnest zeal for the Law, as we have in Psalm cxix. But it may be questioned whether Ben-Sira thought of the Law as a complicated system of ritual practices and prohibitions in the manner of a Rabbi; what he insists upon is a number of broad moral principles of conduct; honesty, modesty, benevolence, patriarchal severity, self-control, and, of course, a sober fear of God. In this book at any rate, his interests are not those of the Mishnah. And if, at the time of the Maccabaean revolt, the system of casuistry embodying the 'tradition of the elders' had hardly begun to be developed, the zeal for the Law which marked the Chasīdim must have been something very different from the careful observance of a number of detailed prescriptions, even if it included the passionate observation of certain prohibitions, such as that which forbad the eating of swine's flesh. And if when the name of 'Pharisee' first came into use, it was applied to the same sort of people who had before been called Chasīdim, the zeal for the Law which marked those Pharisees of the second century B.C. can hardly have been predominantly a regard for the 'tradition of the elders.'

That the Pharisees formed a more or less organized body with a definite roll of members seems proved by the fact that Josephus gives their numbers as 6000. From Rabbinical literature it would seem that, while the people generally called them 'Pharisees,' the name given within the sect itself to members was *Chabērim*, 'Associates.' In this way the Pharisees would be one example of a tendency characterizing the Judaism of the last century B.C.—the tendency to form voluntary religious communities within the Jewish people. When the disciples of John the Baptist, and, later on, the disciples of Jesus, came to form particular communities within Palestinian Judaism, that will not have seemed something altogether novel to other Jews. The original Nazarene community in Judaea must have appeared only to be another sect of Jews, whose peculiar belief was that Jesus was the Messiah, just as the people of the 'New Covenant,' of whom we shall presently speak, were a sect whose peculiar belief was that the 'Star' had been commissioned by God to lay down the Law anew.

A theory has been put forward[1] that the Pharisees were originally a section of the priests who, stricken at heart for the shameful apostasy of a large part of the priesthood in the days of Jason and Menelaus (vol. viii, p. 502 sq.), reinforced by fresh prescripts the rules of purity incumbent upon priests during their period of service according to the Law. The next step, it is supposed, was that the Pharisees began to observe these rules in their ordinary life at home, and the further development was that earnest men, not priests, regarding a life so lived as one of peculiar holiness, adopted them, so that Pharisaism spread generally amongst the people outside the priestly order. Such a theory is highly speculative, though with our *data* so scanty, it is impossible to have any theory about the beginnings of Pharisaism which is not speculative. In any case, at the time of the Christian era the written Law was supplemented in the schools of the 'scribes' by a mass of oral tradition which claimed to be deduced from the written Law on the authority of teachers in the past, and the Pharisees were a section of the people who attempted to carry out such rules in practice. As doing this, they regarded themselves, and were generally regarded by the people, as the only true observers of the Law. Being drawn themselves from the people, not, like the priests, from a particular privileged class, they exerted upon the people at large an influence much greater than the priests did; they came to rule the general conscience in a peculiar way.

Thus the class of 'scribes' and the sect of Pharisees were not identical, though the persons who composed the two were to some extent the same. Probably the large majority of scribes were also Pharisees, but there must have been large numbers of Pharisees who were not scribes, and there were some scribes who were not Pharisees. The latter must have given interpretations of the written Law different from those in the 'tradition of the elders' which the Pharisees took as authoritative.

There were Sadducee scribes. If there are difficulties about Pharisaism, controversial questions are also connected with the Sadducees. We have seen that they were a section of the people

[1] It is the view of Schlatter, *op. cit.* p. 138.

recruited from, or taking its tone from, the priestly aristocracy. The view which connects the name Sadducee with Zadok, the High Priest of David's time (first put forward by Geiger in the last century), is the favourite one to-day[1]. But it would be a mistake to suppose that there were no men of earnest religion amongst the Sadducees; only since Sadduceism came to an end, when the priesthood lost its functions after the destruction of the Temple, whereas a large part of Pharisaism was carried on in Rabbinic Judaism, we are even worse off for means of knowing the inner character of Sadduceism at its best than we are for means of knowing about Pharisaism. We are told by Josephus that one salient characteristic of the Sadducees was that they rejected the authority of the 'tradition of the elders' which the Pharisees so reverenced, and declared that the written Law alone was authoritative. In that way they seem to stand on ground like that of Jesus in Mark vii. But no doubt this restriction in regard to the written Law might represent either an earnest emphasis upon the great moral principles embodied in the Law, or a cutting down of religious obligation to the minimum, as we might imagine a worldly churchman opposed to Methodist 'enthusiasm' in the days of Wesley saying that the plain rules of the Prayer Book were enough for *him*. And even if the Sadducees denied the authority of the oral teaching followed by the Pharisees, that does not mean that the Sadducees did not also in practice follow traditional rules. Where the Mishnah professes to state the controversies carried on in former times the Sadducees do not appear as having no traditional rules of ritual purity, but as having different rules from the Rabbinical ones. Josephus tells us that in the infliction of legal penalties the Sadducees were severer than the Pharisees. It seems probable that the body of rules which the Sadducees and their scribes upheld as authoritative were fewer and simpler than those in the Pharisaic tradition. A common view to-day is that the type of religion which we find in Ben-Sira represents what Sadduceism was at its best. If so, such Sadducees stood for conservatism, maintaining a kind of religion which had seemed adequate before the tribulation under Antiochus, but which, after the fiery trial and the death of martyrs, no longer met the exigence of ardent spirits[2]. Yet how impressively the priesthood could hold under

---

[1] It is however rejected by Eduard Meyer (*Ursprung und Anfänge des Christentums*, II, p. 291), who returns to the Rabbinic view that the Sadducees were called after a second-century Sadduk.

[2] In the Rabbinical books a sect of Boëthosaeans is closely associated with the Sadducees, possibly as a division of the Sadducees, whose name is said to

trial to the obligations it did recognize was seen when Pompey stormed the Temple and the priests allowed themselves to be cut down without deflecting the course of the ritual duties upon which they were engaged.

The tradition for which Pharisaism stood consisted, as has been pointed out, of Halakhah and Haggadah, rules of conduct and doctrines about the facts of the past or about the unseen world. Any valuation of Pharisaism must result from the value we assign to each of these two elements. In regard to rules of conduct Pharisaism has incurred the censure of Christendom on two main grounds, that it gave ridiculous importance to a mass of petty rules, by which the great principles of good conduct are stifled— whether it is lawful to eat an egg laid by a hen on the Sabbath, and so on—and that it provided casuistical means of evading duties laid down in the written Law, such as an oath (Corban) which could exempt a man from duty to his parents. In regard to the first charge, it has to be considered that the Pharisaic concern for details of conduct which seem to most men to-day indifferent follows logically from the belief that the Law had been dictated in its every syllable by God for Israel to obey. If the Sabbath Law really was a command of God's, problems such as the egg laid on the Sabbath were presented in actual life and had to be settled one way or the other. Jesus blamed the Pharisees for not attaching more importance to 'judgment and mercy and faith,' but he never blamed them for carefully tithing mint, anise, and cummin— 'these things ought ye to have done.' With regard to the second charge, there can be little doubt that the casuistry embodied in the 'tradition of the elders' was used sometimes to help men to evade obligations which were irksome: that is a danger besetting any system of casuistry. But it has to be remembered that if the oral tradition tended to weaken the injunctions of the written Law where they were just, but onerous, it also served to make the injunctions of the written Law elastic where they were over-rigid or cruel. The law, for instance, which laid it down that a betrothed woman taken in adultery should be stoned (Deuteronomy xxii. 23) was mitigated by the oral tradition's framing such rules of evidence for condemnation as to make condemnation practically impossible. The law, again, which cancelled all debts every seventh year bore in practice hardly upon the poor who wanted to borrow: the device of the *prosbol* (Greek, *prosbolē*, 'addition') by

be taken from that of their founder, a Boëthus placed in the second century B.C. Like the Sadducees they are said to have denied the resurrection and a future life.

which it was circumvented, a device ascribed to the inventiveness of Hillel, was really a boon to the poor. The work of adapting the written Law to the various circumstances of life and to more mature moral feeling was one that had to be done, and the oral tradition served to some extent a necessary and beneficent purpose.

When we turn to the Haggadic element in Pharisaism, we find that here the ground upon which it stood as against Sadduceism was approved by Christianity, indeed was built upon by Christianity in its own system of belief. In the books of the Old Testament earlier than Daniel there is little, if any, trace of a belief in the possibility of a happy existence beyond death; even more than amongst the Greeks interest is limited by the horizon of the visible world: Yahweh is indeed conceived to dwell in a heavenly palace with a host of attendant angels, but the angelic orders are vaguely and generally imagined; the supernatural beings, who occasionally in the old narratives intervene in the affairs of men, as Yahweh's agents, have no individual names or characteristics. If for the human individual there is any kind of existence beyond the grave, it is a poor and shadowy one. The book of Ben-Sira at the beginning of the second century B.C. still has such an outlook, and if that was the general outlook of pious Jews before the Maccabaean revolt, the Sadducees in this respect were simply old-fashioned. In the last two centuries before the Christian era a new set of conceptions became widespread amongst the Jewish people. For us their emergence is represented by the production of a new type of religious literature—the Apocalyptic.

III. THE APOCALYPSES AND ESCHATOLOGY

One of the earliest documents of Apocalyptic literature is the book of Daniel, which is discussed in the previous volume (vol. VIII, pp. 510 *sqq.*). The Hebrew or Aramaic originals of all the other documents have perished: we know them only through translations into Greek, or translations from the Greek into Latin, Syriac, Ethiopic, which circulated amongst Christians when the Synagogue had thrown all this literature aside. All these books professed to record revelations given to some person known through Scripture as a figure in the legendary past—Enoch, Methuselah, Noah, Abraham—or one of the great prophets, Elijah or Isaiah, or to the ancient scribe, Ezra. This literature offered to the Jews of the time two things which the older sacred books did not give them. One was descriptions of the unseen world, the palace of God in heaven, the places in which the souls of the righteous abode after death, the places of punishment for the souls of the wicked. Angels were now classified, good and bad, and a large number received individual names, Michael, Gabriel, Raphael. There was thus, for those Jews nourished on Apocalyptic literature, not a mere blank darkness beyond death, as apparently there was for Ben-Sira, or a shadowy world in which there was no distinction between righteous and wicked, but a world imaginatively mapped out in which each man reaped the recompense of his deeds here. The other thing which the Apocalypses gave was a much clearer idea of the world-process as a whole. Whereas the older prophets had been content with the picture of a national restoration in the Holy Land, the Apocalyptists saw the history of mankind as a succession of ages, leading up to great cosmic consummation. The men who wrote them felt intensely the evils of the present age—the people of Yahweh subject to Gentiles, or subject to profane and wicked rulers like Jannaeus and Herod, or in its inner life full of uncleanness and iniquity. The blackness of the present contrasted with the blaze of glory which would follow when the scheme of time was fulfilled, and God appeared to judge evil and set up a kingdom of righteousness. And the Apocalyptist was usually consoled by receiving assurance that the Great Day was at hand.

Between one writing and another there were great differences of detail: the schemes of ages differed; sometimes God in His own person appears to overthrow evil and establish His kingdom; sometimes the figure of an ideal future king is introduced, who will be God's agent. In regard to this Messiah again very different conceptions are found. In the book called the *Psalms of Solomon*[1], written about the middle of the last century B.C., the future king, 'the Son of David,' is a merely human king, though ideally righteous and powerful, who will reign in Jerusalem; in the 'Parables' of *Enoch* (XXXVII–LXXI), assigned to the earlier half of the last century B.C.[2], there already exists in heaven a Being called a 'Son of Man,' who even now is mysteriously manifested to righteous souls and who will be God's great agent in the final consummation. Or again, in regard to the life after death, some documents (*Enoch* XCI–CIV) seem to regard the spiritual existence

---

[1] The ascription of the Psalms to Solomon comes only from the copyist who put the headings to them. The Psalms do not themselves claim to be by Solomon, and they are not thus, properly speaking, pseudonymous.

[2] By Charles, *op. cit.* II, p. 171. M.-J. Lagrange (*Le Messianisme chez les Juifs*) pp. 89 *sqq.*) regards them as much later and influenced by Christianity.

of the disembodied person as sufficient, each man in this state reaping happiness or misery, according as he has sown on earth; other documents, from Daniel onwards, affirm a future resurrection of the body, before the transformation of the earth into its final state of glory.

There must have been an eager demand for such literature among the Jews after the Maccabaean struggle. How far the Pharisees coincided with the people who produced and propagated the Apocalypses which we have must remain obscure. The Rabbis of later centuries, who largely carried on the Pharisaic tradition, did not like Apocalypses, and it is only because Christians were interested in the Apocalypses written by Jews of earlier generations that those which we have were preserved. At the same time some of the beliefs which distinguished the Apocalyptic literature from the older Hebrew religion were still held fast by the later Rabbis. It seems likely, then, that the people who produced the Apocalypses were either themselves a section of the Pharisees, or that a section of the Pharisees was in close sympathy with them. It was a characteristic of the Sadducees that they would have none of these visionary explorations of a world beyond the horizon of this; doctrines of angels and spirits and a resurrection they definitely declared to be vain. And if those who gave their tone to the sect of the Sadducees had mostly the good things of this life in abundance, it is understandable that they should be little in sympathy with the other-worldly enthusiasm of those to whom the present life was hard and evil.

It was, as has been indicated, probably the experience of martyrdom in the great tribulation under Antiochus Epiphanes which had created the receptivity for belief in a life beyond death and a world to come amongst the 'Godly,' and among the Pharisees their successors: the old doctrine of faithfulness reaping a sure reward from God could no longer be squared with the visible facts of this world. But when once the need was there, its satisfaction probably did not come from wholly new conceptions arising in the Jewish soul: almost certainly the beliefs new amongst the Jews were shaped by suggestion from Persia. Centuries before there is any trace amongst the Jews of a belief in the blissful existence of the righteous and a miserable existence of the wicked beyond death and in a future resurrection, such beliefs had been rife amongst the Persian Zoroastrians (see vol. IV, p. 208). As early at any rate as the fourth century B.C.—as is proved by a quotation from Theopompus[1]—Zoroastrianism had mapped out the course

[1] *F.G.H.* no. 115, frag. 65.

of time into a sequence of ages, numerically determined, leading up to a kingdom of God in a world transformed. It is, of course, a very obscure question how far the Persian kings who ruled over the Jews before Alexander were of this faith, and a still more obscure question what the Zoroastrianism which existed under the house of Arsaces was like; but it is certain that Zoroastrianism was there in some form, and that its special ideas influenced the minds of non-Persian peoples. In the centuries round the Christian era, below the layer of Greek culture seen in the upper class throughout the cities of Nearer Asia and Egypt, a strange ferment and mingling of ideas belonging to different popular traditions was going on—Babylonian, Anatolian, Aramaean, primitive Iranian, Magian, Zoroastrian—a process which we have no data for tracing, though types of religion emerging here and there, for which we have fragmentary documents, imply such a process behind them. Central countries like North Syria or Babylonia, with their mixed populations, especially would be regions in which these different traditions would meet and coalesce. In Babylonia there was a large Jewish population, which could hardly fail to assimilate anything congenial in the environment. Here, then, it is likely that Zoroastrian ideas, certainly more congenial to the religion of Israel than those of any other Gentile religion, would infiltrate into Judaism. It is possible, too, that those are right who see in the Jewish Apocalyptic literature some elements derived, not from Zoroastrianism in its purer form, but from the old Babylonian mythology.

In one respect it may be regarded as certain that ideas which became current in the Judaism of the last two centuries B.C. were derived from Zoroastrianism—the development of the belief in evil spirits. In the Old Testament, except for one late passage (1 Chron. xxi. 1), the idea that personal spiritual forces, opposed to God, are at work in the world is wholly absent. A being called Satan (the 'Adversary') is indeed mentioned in Job and in Zechariah, but this being is an adversary of men, not of God; he is regarded as an agent of God, whose business it is to spy out human sins and defects and as public prosecutor bring them before God. But in Zoroastrianism the idea of an Evil Power opposing the Good Power, with a host of evil spirits subordinate to him, had long been prevalent. Jewish monotheism could never allow to any Evil Power the relative independence which Zoroastrian dualism conceded to Ahriman, but Judaism went a long way during these centuries in making Satan an Evil Power, who, by God's permission, opposed good in the world during the present age, and in

seeing human disease and sin as something caused by an army of
evil spirits under the one great Prince of darkness. By the time of
the Christian era the view was general amongst the Jewish people,
as the Gospels show. The most usual name given to the chief of
the evil spirits was Satan, translated in Greek by the word *Diabolos*,
'Slanderer,' but other names were current as well—Beelzebul,
Beliar, Sammael, Mastema, the last name (derived from the misunderstanding of Hosea ix. 7 *sq.*) being the one used in the *Book of
Jubilees*. If there were any doubt that the belief in personal forces
of evil at work in the world came to be a part of the Jews' outlook
in consequence of their contact with Persians, such doubt should
be dissipated by the fact that the name of the evil spirit in Tobit,
Asmodeus, is actually the Aeshma Daeva of the Avesta.

The ardent beliefs in a survival of the human person beyond
death, in another world of rewards and penalties, in a direction of
the whole time-process to a future kingdom of God co-extensive
with mankind, thus emerge in Jewish Apocalyptic literature,
clad in a vesture of imaginations largely fanciful and childish.
Whether the beliefs themselves were vain imaginations, and this
whole new development in Judaism merely another chapter of
human delusion, or whether one can distinguish within the imaginative vesture an advance in the apprehension of spiritual
truth, is a question upon which the historian, as such, is not competent to speak, any more than he can pronounce on the question
how far, supposing an advance in the apprehension of spiritual
truth took place, that was due to the operation of a personal
Reality greater than man upon, or within, the human mind. For
any religious valuation of Jewish Apocalypses those questions
have, of course, to be answered: but while the historian has to take
note of the development as a fact, its religious valuation lies outside his province. It does, however, lie within his province to
indicate that, whatever the value of this new development in
Judaism may be, it did actually make the ground upon which
later on Christianity arose. These beliefs in the other world, in the
direction of the time-process through a sequence of ages to a
kingdom of God, Christianity took over from Pharisaic Judaism
and built its own system upon them. If in regard to Halakhah
Christianity agreed with the Sadducees against the Pharisees,
rejecting the 'tradition of the elders,' in regard to Haggadah
it was altogether on the side of the Pharisees against the
Sadducees.

In days when the unseen world of spirits had come to interest
the Jews in a new way, and when imagination was exercised in

picturing its denizens, it was inevitable that some should seek to use for magical practices the knowledge which they believed they had of that world, procuring results desired in this world by the power of spirits, curing disease by incantations, exorcising the evil demons by which men were possessed. No doubt magical practices were looked on largely with suspicion or disapproval by the chief teachers of religion, but Jewish magic must have been fairly widely diffused in these days, and was resorted to by pagans for their purposes. Even the Roman proconsul of Cyprus, Sergius Paulus, is shown in Acts xiii. 7 keeping by his side a Jewish magician. The magical papyri found in Egypt show a strange mingling of Jewish and pagan elements. But apart from magical practices, occult speculations as to the constitution of the unseen world and the beginnings of the visible world were probably already in the last century B.C. pursued by some of the orthodox Pharisaic teachers. We know that this was the case in the middle of the first century A.D., when the chief teacher of the day, Johanan ben Zakkai, showed marked interest in them. Rabbinical literature distinguished two branches of occult lore—'In-the-beginning Matter,' that is speculation based on Genesis i about the beginning of the visible world, and 'Chariot Matter,' speculation regarding the nature of God and the heavenly spirits based on Ezekiel's vision of the chariot of Yahweh. This occult tradition of Palestinian Judaism in the centuries about the Christian era may have been one of the streams which ran later into the turbid sea of the medieval Kabbalah, but we cannot say how much the two had in common.

With regard to the character of Jewish piety generally at this period, an important question is how far there existed amongst the poor and humble a simple religion of Old Testament type beside the more elaborate legalistic religion of the Pharisees. That is connected with the difficult question what kind of person is meant by the phrase *Am ha-ares*, 'People of the Land.' Phrases of extreme contempt and reprobation regarding the *Am ha-ares* have been collected from the Rabbinical books and are sometimes understood to be directed against all simple ordinary Jews who did not know, or did not follow, the complicated mass of rules excogitated by the Pharisaic Rabbis: 'This multitude which knoweth not the law are accursed' (John vii. 49). On this view the term *Am ha-ares* would have been applied to people of sincere simple piety, the 'poor in spirit' whom Jesus pronounced blessed, and the attitude of the Rabbis to them would show Pharisaic pride. It has been pointed out that the *Am ha-ares* are spoken of as having their

own religious gatherings[1]. On the other side it has been contended
that the Rabbis fully recognized the piety of poor men unable to
follow the Pharisaic way, if they observed some few rules of
religion, and that the people denounced as *Am ha-areṣ* were Jews
definitely irreligious and wantonly neglectful of their primary
religious duties. In any case, the language used in some passages
of the Talmud about the *Am ha-areṣ* does not show a pleasant
spirit: it has, however, to be remembered that from other parts
of the same literature sayings may be collected which praise the
humble.

IV. THE NEW COVENANT OF DAMASCUS: THE ESSENES

Beside the main stream of Jewish life in the last two centuries
B.C. there were probably a number of peculiar developments in
groups which passed away and left no record. One such group re-
emerged into the light through an old Hebrew manuscript discovered by the late Dr S. Schechter in 1910 in the Genizah
Collection at Cairo and presented by him to the University
Library in Cambridge[2]. According to the book, a band of Jews,
profoundly concerned at the wickedness prevailing at Jerusalem,
the violation of the Law and the pollution incurred by following
the idolatry of the nations, migrated to Damascus, where under
the direction of some one described as the Lawgiver or the Star
they entered into what they called a 'New Covenant.' They seem
after this to have formed an organized society which carried on a
propaganda in Palestine and established local 'camps.' Within
the society the special position of Priests and Levites was carefully
recognized, though all members of the society were regarded, by
the application of a text in Ezekiel, as spiritually 'sons of Zadok.'
The society had a strongly puritan character, and their body of
regulations, professing to apply the written Law, went in practice
far beyond it. Not only was all fornication sternly condemned, but
polygamy also: divorce was forbidden, and the marriage of uncle
and niece, allowed by Rabbinic Law, was branded as incestuous.
The impurity from which the society sought to be free was not

[1] Moritz Friedländer, *Die religiösen Bewegungen innerhalb des Judentums
im Zeitalter Jesu*, pp. 80–82.

[2] On the vexed question of the character of this sect and the date of the
original writing see the works cited in the Bibliography. Schechter and
Charles described the sect as 'Zadokite' and placed the work at the end of the
first century B.C.; the majority of German scholars have assigned it to the
Maccabaean period; A. Büchler puts it in the eighth century A.D.

moral only, but ritual as well. The Sabbath Law was elaborated to a greater strictness, and even the exception which the Gospels tell us that the Pharisees allowed, pulling an ox or an ass out of a pit on the Sabbath day, was banned. At the same time great stress was laid on kindliness in the relation of man and man, and the bearing of a grudge was particularly condemned. The expectation of the Messiah was cherished in the community; it looked forward to a glorious future succeeding the present days of wickedness. Unlike the Samaritans, the people of the New Covenant evidently attached a high value to the other books of the Old Testament beside the Pentateuch; unlike the Essenes, they maintained animal sacrifice; unlike the Sadducees, they had an outlook beyond the present world. Such was the community of whose very existence we should have had no knowledge but for the chance discovery of this old book.

Another community off the main stream, of which we have some brief notices, is that of the Essenes. They are interesting as a curiosity in the Judaism of that time: the community faded away in the early centuries of the Christian era, and left no discoverable trace upon primitive Christianity or upon Rabbinic Judaism: neither the New Testament nor Rabbinic literature ever mentions them, and modern fancies which would connect John the Baptist or Jesus with the Essenes are generally regarded by scholars as irreconcilable with what little solid information we have about the community. The derivation and meaning of their name is quite uncertain. It is clear that their community was a closely organized one, living under a strict ascetic discipline, in many features resembling the later monastic orders of Christendom. Its numbers seem to have been small—according to Philo, only some four thousand. It was distributed in various country towns and villages of Palestine, but its main settlement was in the wilderness bordering the Dead Sea, near Engedi and Masada. Members of the order were distinguished by a white robe.

In some ways the Essenes seem like Pharisees of an intenser sort—the immense veneration in which they held Moses and the written Law, the rigid Sabbatarianism in which they offer so striking a contrast to Jesus, their separation from the impure world. In other points the Essenes departed from ordinary Judaism, most signally in repudiating all animal sacrifice. They were punctual indeed in sending offerings, other than sacrifices, to the Temple, but excluded themselves from the court in which sacrifice was offered. How they reconciled this view with their reverence for the written Law we are not told: presumably they explained the commandments relating to sacrifice as allegorical. Whether in their own food they were vegetarians is not clear, but they regarded all intercourse between the sexes, even in regular marriage, as a defilement, and they were careful never to void excrements in sight of the sun; they performed ceremonies of cleansing after each evacuation. They held it a profanation of the Sabbath to evacuate at all on that day. The direction in which they spat was religiously important to them. Nothing could be more unlike Jesus than this painful concern for an external imaginary cleanness. In one point the Essenes seem to have agreed, as against Judaism, with the Sermon on the Mount—in their condemnation of oaths: the condemnation must be understood of oaths used in common conversation, for new members admitted to the order had to bind themselves with terrific oaths. The Essenes lived a communal life, without private property; even a man's white robe did not belong to him, but to the order. Slavery they held to be wrong. Their occupations, other than the specific practice of religion, were agriculture, the tending of flocks and herds, the care of bees, the various kinds of handicraft needed to supply the community with tools and clothing and food. The communal meal was an important part of the fixed scheme of each day; it was a religious ceremony; each man put on a vestment in place of his working dress; food was prepared by the priests in the order, and the meal was eaten in impressive silence. The order had four grades; a novice was not admitted till after a year's probation, but it took three years for him to become a full member. The principle of the order was democratic in so far as the authorities were elected by a communal vote.

The Essenes were credited with occult powers and were consequently in demand both as healers and as predictors of the future. They must have cultivated a secret lore concerning the unseen world and its denizens, having a knowledge of the names of angels, which gave them magical power. With their view of the body and its functions as unclean, they seem to have approximated to Greek Orphics and Pythagoreans, looking forward to a state of discarnate bliss after death, not, like the Jews generally, to a bodily resurrection. But there is no trace of their believing in reincarnation, as the Orphics and Pythagoreans did. In this occult side of their religion the Essenes may quite probably have taken in elements from outside the Hebrew sphere, elements from that medley of traditions which was diffused through the East beneath the predominant Hellenistic layer, and which reappear in the various forms of Gnosticism. But some Essenes at any rate

could be ardent Jewish nationalists and take the sword against the
heathen. In the Great War against Rome, the Essenes were
marked out by their heroic endurance of torture.

In the account of the Jewish sects which Josephus gives he
makes a special point of their respective beliefs about Divine
predestination and human free-will. The Sadducees, he says,
excluded Divine determination altogether from human action: it
rested with a man alone whether he chose good or evil: the
Essenes made everything depend upon the will of God: the
Pharisees asserted that everything happened by Divine decree,
but at the same time allowed the reality of human choice in matters
of conduct. To some extent Josephus may have been led by his
desire to represent the Jewish sects to his Greek and Roman
readers in the guise of philosophical schools, when he gave
prominence to their divergence on the standing theoretical
puzzle, the relation of the human will to Fate; yet the Rabbinical
books prove that such questions did really exercise the Jewish
schools, and the view which Josephus ascribes to the Pharisees
corresponds with the dictum of the great teacher of the early
second century A.D., Akiba, 'Everything is envisaged by God,
and at the same time freedom is given.' It has also to be considered
that the question was not a merely theoretical one, but that a
different cast of piety resulted from the attitude taken up in
regard to it. The ascetic puritanism of the Essenes went, like
Calvinistic puritanism, with a belief in the absolute sovereignty
of the Divine decrees, and the commonsense formalism of the
Sadducees with the exclusion of any mysterious cause from human
actions, whereas the Pharisees, in asserting two apparently contradictory things both together, the reality of Divine determination and the reality of human choice, followed the line to which the
great body of Christian devotion has felt itself driven.

If communities like that of the 'New Covenant' and the
Essenes did not directly influence the later developments of
religion in Judaism and Christianity, they show tendencies and
ideas at work which are found afterwards in other embodiments.
The condemnation of divorce in the community of the 'New
Covenant' and the condemnation of oaths amongst the Essenes
reappear in Christianity. The lustrations which were important
in Essene religion may have had some affinity with the baptism
practised by John the Baptist and the later Christian baptism.
The Essene communal meal may to some extent have resembled
the communal meals of the early Church. But perhaps the most
signal way in which these communities show a similarity of

tendency to the Church is the very fact that they were organized
communities arising out of the general body of Judaism and
distinct from it. It has been pointed out (p. 413), as an important
phenomenon, that in the last century B.C. the community-forming
tendency within the Jewish sphere was already there.

V. THE SAMARITANS

The country between Judaea and Galilee was inhabited by the
Samaritans, descendants of the northern Ten Tribes of ancient
Israel, who had remained in the land after the Assyrian conquest,
but whose blood had undergone some alien admixture through
colonies of people from beyond the Euphrates imported by the
Assyrian kings. From Kutha, one of the Babylonian towns
whence the colonists were drawn, the name of Kuthaeans was
opprobriously fastened upon the Samaritans by their Jewish
kinsmen. They called themselves Israelites, as indeed by their
predominant strain they were: the name of 'Samaritans' given
them by the Greeks was taken from that of the country they inhabited, and the name of the country again from that of Samaria,
its chief city. Samaria *the city*, however, had been from the days of
the Diadochi to its destruction by the Jews *c.* 108 B.C., a Greek,
not an Israelite, city: Samaritans did not compose its citizen-
body, though some of them may have lived in the city, as native
Egyptians lived in Alexandria[1]; but the towns and villages of
Samaria *the country* had Samaritans for their main population. In
the seventh century B.C. the mixed Israelite and Babylonian people
had had an analogously mixed religion—a religion which must
have been like that of the Jewish military settlement at Elephan-
tine in the fifth century (vol. VI, pp. 178 *sqq.*). But ever since the
Pentateuch had been established in the country as the supreme
law-book—probably in the latter part of the fourth century B.C. by
a priest from Jerusalem—the reproach of polytheism could be
brought against the Samaritans with no more justice than it could
be brought against the Jews. They were certainly as strict as
Jewish Sadducees were in following the commandments regarding
the worship of the One God, regarding the Sabbath and festivals
and all other ritual practices laid down in the written Mosaic Law.

[1] A somewhat doubtful inference by analogy may be made from the
Samaria which was refounded as a Greek pagan city by Herod and called
Sebaste. If that is the city meant in Acts viii. 5 (the text is uncertain), part of
its population was Samaritan. The Gospel at that time was not yet preached to
pagans.

In two main respects only do they seem to have differed from the Jews: they repudiated the prophetic books and recognized only the Five Books of Moses as of Divine authority, and they maintained that the place chosen by the Lord for the one sanctuary had not been Jerusalem but Mount Gerizim. It was on Mount Gerizim that they had their Temple, served by priests who claimed Aaronic descent, till it was destroyed by John Hyrcanus in 128 B.C. It seems never to have been rebuilt: the site was desolate when Jesus passed that way, though it remained sacred to the Samaritans and their Passover lambs were killed there[1].

Although the Pentateuch by itself would hardly furnish ground for visions of a Messiah such as were rife amongst the Jews, it seems clear that the Messianic hope had spread to the Samaritans at the time of the Christian era. The medieval Samaritan literature speaks of a Messiah entitled 'Ta'eb,' 'Restorer (?),' but direct proof from Samaritan books of the hope at an earlier date does not appear to be forthcoming. An indirect proof however may be found in the statements of the New Testament, Josephus and Justin Martyr.

It is strange, when the religious differences between Jews and Samaritans were so small, that the Jews should have looked on their kinsmen with such steady abhorrence and contempt. No doubt the preference of Gerizim to Jerusalem touched them on the quick. One may note that the Samaritans, too, were represented by a Diaspora outside Palestine; the papyri show Samaritan settlements in Egypt, though the numbers of Samaritans must have been very small compared with those of the Jews.

VI. THE JEWS OF THE DISPERSION

Outside Palestine there was now a Jewish Dispersion (*Diaspora*) of large proportions in the countries of the Gentiles. This Dispersion was divided into two main masses, according as it spoke Aramaic, like the Jews of Palestine, or spoke Greek. The Jews of countries east of Palestine were probably mainly Aramaic-speaking, although Babylonia and Western Iran were at this time dotted over with Greek cities. The history however of Eastern

[1] Even to-day the Samaritans, who have gone on, through all the changes of twenty centuries, living in their old country, though now reduced to a poor little handful of some 200 at Nablus, offer their Passover sacrifice of seven lambs 'on an insignificant plot about ten minutes below the summit of the mountain in lieu of the holier sites' (J. Montgomery, *Samaritans*, pp. 35 *sqq.*).

Judaism in these centuries is for us almost a complete blank. In the third century A.D. the Rabbinical schools of Babylonia rose to an importance equivalent to that of the Palestinian schools, but although there must have been a large proportion of the Jewish people in Babylonia from the Captivity onwards we know hardly anything about them. That there were even now active schools of legal and religious study in Babylonia is indicated by the fact of Hillel's coming from that country in the last century B.C. already competent to debate questions regarding the sacred Law.

About the Jewish Dispersion in Greek-speaking countries, that is to say, in Rome and in all the eastern part of the Roman Empire, we know a great deal more. If the calculations upon which Harnack and Jean Juster base their estimate of its numbers are trustworthy, it must at the Christian era have formed a percentage in the total population of these countries about twice as great as the percentage of Jews in the United States to-day—about 7 per cent. as against $3\frac{1}{2}$ per cent. In Egypt out of a total population of about 8 millions about one million were Jews. Whereas the Jews of Palestine were mainly engaged in agriculture and stock-farming, the Jews of Greek-speaking lands were city-dwellers. Thus their language became Greek even in countries which had a non-Greek native population. In Egypt, for instance, though there are traces under the Ptolemies of little groups still speaking Aramaic, it is unlikely that many Jews could speak Egyptian. Greek became the language of the great bulk of Egyptian Jews to such an extent that they ceased to understand Hebrew. As early as the third century B.C. it became necessary to translate the Scriptures into Greek for the Egyptian Jews.

The story of the translation of the Old Testament into Greek by seventy (or seventy-two) scribes imported from Palestine by Ptolemy II, in order to furnish his Library, is universally recognized as fiction, but it has given its name to the Septuagint. Actually the Septuagint translation of the Old Testament was made only bit by bit in Egypt over a series of generations, but the translation of the Pentateuch seems to be already known to the Jewish writer Demetrius in the latter part of the third century. Ben-Sira's grandson, who translated his book into Greek (our Ecclesiasticus) in the latter part of the second century, speaks as if the Greek translation of the other Old Testament books were practically complete. When the papyri extended our knowledge of the current spoken Greek of the time, there was a tendency to explain all the differences between the Greek of the Septuagint and classical Greek as adaptations to the living language of the day. It is now generally recognized that this went much too far: some unclassical words and phrases in the Septuagint were no doubt current Greek, but the translation as a whole reproduces the idiom of the original so closely that the result would to an ordinary educated Greek be, if not quite unintelligible, at any rate uncouth, and often ridiculous. Probably hardly any one except Jews and proselytes ever looked at the Septuagint. For those who believed that it was inspired its obscurity and uncouthness would not be an offence: even Greeks held that oracles were often obscure and uncouth. And at the time of Philo (*c.* 20 B.C.–*c.* A.D. 40) the common belief amongst Egyptian Jews was that the Septuagint translation of the Law was as directly inspired, every syllable, as the Hebrew original had been. It was therefore unnecessary to enquire what Hebrew terms it represented: Philo himself seems never to have found out that the Greek *Kyrios* ('the Lord') stood for the ineffable Name YHVH. A hundred years later, Jews had repudiated this belief in the divine authority of the Septuagint, and it had passed to the Christians.

The communities of the Jews in the Greek and Italian cities held a peculiar position. They had little ambition to take part in the politics and social festivities of their Gentile neighbours: the two things by which they set store were freedom to practise their religion and the power to regulate the lives of their members by Jewish laws. And these two things the Hellenistic kings, as the Roman Emperors after them, seem as a rule to have been concerned to secure to them. It was usually made penal for any one to hinder the Jews in the exercise of their religion; they were allowed to levy the half-shekel tax on their members and send the sum raised to Jerusalem for the expenses of the Temple worship, and they had their own judicial courts, which could not only settle civil disputes, but inflict certain penalties such as fines and scourging. Our fragmentary notices seem to show the existence of local Jewish senates (*gerousiai*) under the presidency of a body of *archontes*, which could pass honorific decrees to be inscribed on tablets set up either in some public place (at the Cyrenian Berenice in the amphitheatre) or in the precincts of the synagogue. At Alexandria the Jewish community up to the time of Augustus had apparently a supreme head called *ethnarches*. Kings and Emperors generally regarded the Jews with favour as an element useful to their government: it was the Greek citizen-bodies who were apt to be hostile: they were compelled to concede the Jews, however much they hated them, a privileged position. It used to be believed, on the authority of Josephus, that the Jews had been actually made by the kings members of the citizen-body at Alexandria and Antioch, but later evidence, especially the letter of the Emperor Claudius published in 1924, seems to have proved that it is not true. It is possible that what the Jews were given in these two cities was 'isopolity,' that is, a kind of potential citizenship, which a Jew might take up on certain conditions[1].

Living as they did in a Greek environment, learning to speak and write Greek by a study of Greek authors used in schools, it was inevitable that the Hellenistic Jews should be influenced by Greek ideas to a greater extent than the Jews of Palestine. The close contact would not in all cases mean assimilation; it might in some mean an intensification of differences: St Paul, for instance, tells us that though his home was in Tarsus he had been brought up as a Hebrew of the Hebrews. But in a large number of cases Greek ideas penetrated, and the necessity of adjusting the two traditions, the religious Jewish one and the intellectual Greek one, caused trouble. For us the great figure representing the attempt at fusion is that of Philo of Alexandria, the main part of whose voluminous works has come down to us. Philo writes a highly literary Greek, with Plato always in view, but charged with poetical words and metaphorical phrases which show the influence of the later rhetorical schools. While fundamentally Philo's religion is the old Hebrew attitude of adoring abasement before a personal God, he has combined with this an idea of ecstatic contemplation, which derives from Plato, and a scheme of ascetic self-discipline directed to freeing the soul from bodily passions, which derives from the later Greek philosophic schools. Philo claims to draw all this idea of mystical devotion and all this scheme of life from the Old Testament—or rather from the Pentateuch, for his references to other books of the Old Testament are few—and he does it by construing both the narrative and

---

[1] G. De Sanctis, *Riv. di filologia* LII, 1924, p. 473. W. W. Tarn, *Hellenistic Civilization*, ed. 2, p. 193. But perhaps the question has not yet been cleared up. Josephus says that the Jews at Alexandria had a status equivalent to that of 'Macedonians' and were still, when he wrote, called 'Macedonians' (*contra Apion.* II, 37). He can hardly have made a specific statement which his readers in Alexandria would know instantly was not true. And the statement is confirmed by a papyrus in which two men who are apparently Jews call themselves Macedonians (*B.G.U.* no. 1151). U. Wilcken, *Grundzüge und Chrestomathie der Papyruskunde* I. p. 63, and W. Schubart, *Archiv für Papyrusforschung* V. pp. 111 *sqq.* have made it probable that the people called 'Macedonians' at Alexandria were distinct from the citizen-body. Possibly the 'Macedonians' had special connection under the Ptolemies with the army, and Jews, who served in the army, may have been put into this class.

the laws as allegories, according to a method which seems to us to-day fantastic and arbitrary in the extreme. The way of allegory indeed was the main way by which everything in Judaism which repelled the Greeks—circumcision, the distinction of clean and unclean foods, the Sabbath—could be made to appear reasonable. The method was not itself a new idea of Philo's; it had already been used freely by Greek philosophers to explain what was offensive in Greek mythology; but Philo applied it in a somewhat different way. Greek philosophers had explained Greek mythology mainly as an allegory of physical processes; Philo explained the Pentateuch as an allegory of virtues and vices and processes of the soul.

While, however, for us Philo stands almost solitary as a representative of this Alexandrian type of Judaism, it is plain from references in his works that he had had predecessors whose teachings have perished. He stood in a line of tradition. It is also plain that a certain section of Hellenistic Jews went farther than he did in volatilizing the taboos and other ritual prescriptions of the Law. There were Liberal Jews who declared that laws of circumcision and keeping of the Sabbath were not literally binding: all that God required was that men should have the virtues which these external things typified. Since Christians later on often took this line in regard to the external ordinances of Judaism, it is important to note that it had already been taken by a section of the Hellenistic Jews before the rise of Christianity. They can hardly have been a large section, or we should have heard of them in connection with Christian propaganda. Philo strongly disapproved of them; he contended that, although the external ordinances had their value as allegories, it was obligatory to observe them literally as well. It is significant that in the infant Church at Jerusalem the person who first infuriated the authorities by depreciating the Temple was the Hellenistic Jew Stephen.

If in Palestine we have noted the existence of peculiar communities beside the main stream of religious life, it is likely that among the Jews of the Dispersion also peculiar communities existed of which all memory has perished. A single writing of Philo has preserved knowledge of one community in Egypt—the *Therapeutai*. The people so described were apparently exceedingly like the Essenes—a kind of monastic order, including men and women, living a communal life of worship and contemplation, under a strict ascetic regimen, on the shores of Lake Mareotis. Though like the Essenes in many respects, the *Therapeutai* seem to have been in their ideas nearer the main stream of Judaism: Philo regards them as altogether orthodox Jews. It is never indicated that they condemned marriage or literal animal sacrifice: the order included married persons, as indeed, Josephus tells us, one section of the Essenes did. The description which Philo gives of them seemed to Christians later on so like that of the Christian monastic settlements in Egypt that Eusebius actually supposed, no doubt erroneously, that Philo had come across a community of early Christian monks. As to the name *Therapeutai*, Philo himself was not clear whether it ought to be understood as meaning 'Healers' or 'Worshippers.'

It was naturally the Hellenistic Jews who mainly carried on religious propaganda amongst Gentiles. An allusion in the Gospels indicates that zeal for making proselytes was also found amongst the Pharisees of Palestine, but it was the Hellenistic Jews, living as they did amongst Gentiles, who were most concerned with the Gentile world. A great part of the Hellenistic Jewish literature which survives was definitely intended to make an impression upon Greeks. To some extent the object was no doubt actually to draw Gentiles as proselytes to the Jewish community, but a more general object was to give Greeks a favourable view of Judaism, even if they did not attach themselves to it.

This was partly a measure of self-defence, for in the second century B.C. an Antisemitic temper was already arising in the populations of the Greek cities. The Greek notices of Jews belonging to the first generation after Alexander, taken from the Peripatetics, Clearchus and Theophrastus, or from Hecataeus of Abdera, are by no means unfriendly—one might call them in some points admiring—but by the second century the Jews were becoming unpopular. This was an inevitable consequence of their refusal to take part in the idolatrous public festivities of Greek cities, their social exclusiveness and their assurance that they had a superior religion. We do not hear of pogroms at Alexandria till A.D. 38 [1], but literary attacks on Judaism by Greek writers were already holding the Jews up to contempt more than a hundred years earlier. Mnaseas of Patrae or Patara, a contemporary probably of Antiochus Epiphanes, seems to have set in circulation the story that the Jews kept the image of an ass's head in the Holy of Holies.

---

[1] Apart from an isolated reference in Jordanes, *Getica*, 81 which refers to the times of Ptolemy Alexander I, *c.* 87 B.C. This Ptolemy may, however, have been put wrongly for Ptolemy VIII Soter II. See H. I. Bell, *Juden und Griechen im römischen Alexandreia*, p. 9.

On the other side, an apologetic literature in Greek naturally arose amongst Hellenistic Jews. Demetrius, Eupolemus, Artapanus, Aristeas and Cleodemus Malchus wrote accounts of Abraham and the origins of Israel, to counteract the accounts given by Greek Antisemites: it was Moses who invented writing; it was Abraham who had taught the Egyptians astrology; it was Joseph who had created scientific agriculture. Aristobulus (about the middle of the second century B.C.) gave a philosophical justification of Judaism. It was he, so far as we know, who first put forward the assertion (afterwards repeated by the Christian Fathers) that the Greek philosophers, Pythagoras, Socrates and Plato, had drawn their wisdom from the writings of Moses. Certain Jews (like certain Christians after them) resorted to forgery as a means of religious propaganda: verses condemning polytheism or idolatry, or inculcating the ethical principles of the Law, were set in circulation, as taken from old Greek poets, Phocylides or Aeschylus or Sophocles or Menander; a fabricated *Life of Abraham* was fathered upon Hecataeus of Abdera; but chiefly sham Sibylline Oracles were composed, imitating the pagan ones in circulation which professed to have been given forth by inspired Sibyls long before. It would not be fair to charge the Jewish community as a whole, any more than the Church as a whole, with approving of forgery as a means of propaganda. The individuals who composed the fabrications in question must have known that they were fraudulent, but unquestionably the religious Jews and Christians who afterwards brought forward these forgeries in evidence did so in good faith, never doubting but that they were genuine. And it may well be that the actual fabricators sincerely believed that they were doing God service: it was so much worse an evil for their pagan neighbour to believe in many gods than to believe that a verse recently fabricated was an old one, that it might well seem a good action if you could cure the worse delusion by inducing the slighter one.

Whether it was owing to Jewish efforts, or to the attraction of the religion in itself, numbers of Greeks were actually drawn to the Synagogue. With all the externals which seemed to a Greek repellent, the religion of the Jews had a quality which they found nowhere else, and with all the depravity of individual Jews, there were moral standards recognized in the community higher than those of pagan society. Such things as homosexual vice and the exposure of infants, lightly thought of amongst the Greeks, Judaism uncompromisingly condemned. We cannot know how far the increase of the Jewish community in Hellenistic times was due to the accession of Gentile proselytes. It is certain that Gentiles joined it in some numbers: the suspicion and dislike of proselytes which some later Rabbinic utterances show was probably a later development: Philo has words of very warm welcome for proselytes, and declares that they are to be put on a footing of complete equality with born Jews. Circumcision was the great deterrent for Greek men; and beside those who took on them the whole yoke of the Law, there were many Gentiles in a looser connection with the Synagogue, who took part in its worship and observed some of the Jewish ordinances, such as the Sabbath. To such half-proselytes a term which means 'those who fear God' was applied; but it is doubtful whether (as is commonly stated) it was used to distinguish half-proselytes from full proselytes, or whether it included both classes.

Of the literature produced in Greek by Hellenistic Jews (mainly in Egypt) some no doubt was intended rather for the edification of the faithful than for the Gentile public. This would probably have been true of the work which stands highest amongst the remains of that literature, both from a religious and from a literary point of view, the *Wisdom of Solomon*. The writer bases his style on that of the poetical books of the Old Testament, but he has enriched it with colours borrowed from the Greek poetical and philosophical vocabulary, by no means infelicitously. The book contains an impassioned assertion of the survival of the personality beyond death, apparently in deliberate opposition to the book of *Ecclesiastes* (possibly itself, though written in Hebrew, the work of an Egyptian Jew); but in *Wisdom* the survival is conceived rather, in Platonic fashion, as the survival of the soul alone; there is nothing said of a resurrection of the body. It is likely, too, that the historical work of Jason of Cyrene, narrating, in a somewhat tawdry Greek rhetorical style, the story of the Maccabaean revolt of which our II Maccabees is an epitome, was written rather for the Jewish than for the Gentile public, and the same may be said of the poetical literature which treated Hebrew themes in the metres and forms of Greek poetry, the epics of Philo (not the well-known Philo) and the Samaritan Theodotus, the drama of Ezekiel on the exodus. From the fragments preserved they seem to have been insipid conventional imitations. But, of course, the motives of edifying the faithful and of impressing the Greek world were not mutually exclusive: both might act together in the same work. In the case of Philo of Alexandria himself it is impossible to say how far his object was to lead Greek philosophers to become Jews, and how far to lead Jews to become philosophers.

While then the clash between the Jewish religion and Hellenism at Jerusalem under Antiochus Epiphanes resulted in a violent repudiation of Hellenism as altogether evil, Hellenism here being taken to include pagan religion, we see in Hellenistic Judaism a real attempt to combine Jewish religion with the literary and philosophic tradition of Hellenism, while still excluding, as staunchly as ever, the polytheism, the idolatry, the immorality, of the Greek world. When after the fall of Jerusalem Judaism all the world over became Hebrew and Rabbinic, Hellenistic Judaism, as such, withered away. The Synagogue cast its works upon the scrap-heap, and there would be no human memory of them now, had not the Christian Church, which succeeded to the great task of combining Hebrew religion with Greek culture, picked some of them up for its own guidance and preserved them for the Christians and Jews of to-day.

CHAPTER X

THE PROVINCES AND THEIR GOVERNMENT

I. THE GROWTH AND EXTENT OF THE EMPIRE

POMPEY'S settlement of the East marks a stage in Roman foreign and provincial policy. It is, therefore, appropriate to review the growth of the Roman provincial system and its organization at the moment which preceded the final crisis of the Republic of which Crassus' campaign against Parthia and Caesar's conquest of Gaul form a part.

When we speak of a Roman province we are accustomed to think of a well-defined geographical area which Rome had annexed and for the administration of which she had made herself responsible. It is however important to recognize that it was only in the last century of the Republic that the term 'provincia' came to be used almost exclusively in this sense. In the earlier days of Roman History it was applied freely to any piece of work which was allotted to a magistrate or pro-magistrate. Thus during the Hannibalic War the 'province' of a praetor might be the command of troops in Apulia or Etruria or the conduct of the war by sea, or it might be the government of one of the provinces proper, Sicily and Sardinia. The praetors whose duties were performed in Rome were said to have the *provincia urbana* and the *provincia peregrina*. For long Italy itself was described as a province which might be allotted to a consul, whose colleague was entrusted with a foreign command. Thus in 171 B.C. the consuls were instructed to draw lots for the provinces of Italy and Macedonia, though it was many years before the latter was actually annexed. In 112 B.C. the provinces fixed for the consuls of the next year were Italy and Numidia, *i.e.* the conduct of the war against Jugurtha, and in 88 B.C. the consul Sulla took as his province the war against Mithridates, leaving to his colleague Q. Pompeius the protection of his interests in Italy. As late as 59 B.C. we find the term 'provincia' used in its earlier sense: the Senate allotted to Caesar the 'provinciae minimi negotii,' the care of the woods and roads of Italy[1]. By this time, however, the provinces permanently annexed by Rome were so numerous that it was usually possible to give

---

[1] Suet. *Div. Iul.* 19; see p. 513

the status of a regular provincial governor to the general entrusted with the conduct of a war. Operations were conducted against the Teutoni and Cimbri by governors of Gallia Transalpina, and governors of Macedonia held in check the wild tribes of the Balkans. In 74 B.C. Lucullus and Cotta undertook the war against Mithridates as governors of Cilicia and Bithynia, and Pompey was governor of Nearer Spain during the campaign against Sertorius.

The government of the Republic recognized gradually and unwillingly that it was desirable to undertake permanently the duty of administering and protecting certain definite extra-Italian areas, and historians agree that annexation was postponed as long as possible. Twenty years passed after the defeat of Perseus before Macedonia became a province, and the long war against Jugurtha led to no important extension of the province of Africa. It was left to Augustus to annex Egypt, though this could easily have been done at any time during the fifty years which preceded the fall of Cleopatra.

This unwillingness to extend the Empire is to be attributed to a feeling on the part of those who were responsible for Roman foreign policy that the acquisition of provinces was imposing on Republican institutions a strain that they were scarcely able to bear. At the time when her power and prestige were increasing, Rome retained a machinery of government and administration which differed little from that of a Greek city-state of the Periclean age. Her executive consisted of annually elected magistrates: she possessed no body of permanent officials: her army was a citizen militia, normally commanded by generals who owed their position not to military experience but to election to a magistracy. She had indeed in the Senate a body to which no real parallel can be found in Greece, consisting as it did of all who had occupied responsible positions. But the authority exercised by the Senate rested on a precarious basis and was founded on custom rather than law. Even in its great days this authority was liable to be challenged, and after the Gracchan period it was easy to short-circuit the Senate by appealing to the popular assemblies. The powers which the Lex Hortensia of 287 B.C. had conferred on the assembly of the Plebs involved a danger which became greater as time passed. While the assembly became less and less representative of the citizen body, the problems with which it might be called upon to deal became more important as the influence of Rome extended through the Mediterranean world. Polybius asserts that representatives of foreign states considered the Roman

constitution to be aristocratic, because in his day their affairs
were dealt with exclusively by the Senate. A century later he
would have expressed himself differently. The Senate had indeed
its defects: it tended to be unenterprising and unduly distrustful
of men of ability. But it was far better qualified to deal with
questions of foreign policy than a popular assembly dominated by
tribunes who were in most cases merely the agents of ambitious
individuals. There is much truth in the saying which Thucydides
puts into the mouth of Cleon that 'a democracy cannot administer
an empire[1],' and in the statement of Sallust that 'to restore power
to the Plebs was to prepare the way for monarchy[2].'

It is therefore not surprising that both before and after the
Gracchan period the Senate was opposed to annexation, if it could
possibly be avoided. The possession of provinces raised administrative, military, and financial problems which could only be
solved by a complete transformation of the system of government
and by the creation of a professional army and a class of permanent officials. It was not a mere selfish desire to retain its
power which led the Senate to view with concern the growing
tendency to bring before the popular assemblies matters concerning provincial administration, but a justifiable feeling that
these matters could best be settled by a body whose members
had personal experience of the points at issue. Senators felt that, if
questions of foreign policy were going to be settled by an ignorant
proletariate, it was wise to incur as little responsibility as possible.

There is also no reason to think that a policy of annexation
normally formed part of the programme even of the 'popular'
party[3]. As was noted above, no large annexations in North Africa
followed the successful close of the Jugurthan War, though at that
period the popular leader Marius was all-powerful. It must not
be forgotten that the burden of military service was still borne
mainly by Italians, and that the acquisition of new provinces
would inevitably lead to an increase of this burden. The annexation of Spain and Macedonia involved Rome in long and costly
wars, the memory of which might well discourage the assumption
of further responsibilities. No doubt more was to be said for
imperialism on financial grounds. After the annexation of Macedonia direct taxation came to an end in Italy. But even civilized
and normally peaceful provinces such as Sicily brought in less to
the Roman treasury than might have been expected. The system
of tax collecting was wasteful, and though all governors were not

[1] III, 37.   [2] Bell. Iug. 31.
[3] See Tenney Frank, Roman Imperialism, pp. 266 sqq.

as unscrupulous as Verres, an undue proportion of the revenues of
a province found its way into the pockets of the official representatives of Rome. It is not certain that even the equestrian order
and the publicani were consistently favourable to annexation.
Their activities were by no means confined to Roman territory,
and their profits might even be diminished by the transformation
of a client kingdom into a province. On the whole it seems wrong
to treat Pompey and Caesar as agents of the 'capitalist' class, and
it is safer to attribute mainly to military considerations the extensions which they made to the Roman Empire in the east and
the north. It was certainly a sound military instinct which led
them to the Euphrates and the Rhine.

The Roman Empire was destined to include all the countries
facing on to the Mediterranean Sea, and to give political unity to
an area which seems intended by nature to be one both politically
and economically. In order to secure protection against barbarian
invasion, it ultimately proved necessary to include the hinterland
in the Empire by advancing the frontier to the Rhine and Danube
in the north and to the Euphrates in the east. To the south Rome
was to occupy the northern fringe of Africa, and to the west her
Empire was bounded by the Atlantic. In the period with which
we are concerned the annexation of this area had only just begun.
The provinces of the Republic were acquired piecemeal as circumstances made annexation inevitable, and although even in the
second century B.C. Rome was regarded as the greatest Mediterranean power, it was not till the Principate that all Mediterranean
lands were brought directly under her rule.

In the year 146 B.C. Rome possessed six provinces—Sicily,
Sardinia, the two Spains, Africa, and Macedonia. Of these the
first five had fallen to her as a result of the wars with Carthage,
while the last was unwillingly annexed in 148 B.C. after the collapse of an interesting experiment in self-government (vol. VIII,
pp. 273 *sqq.*). Part of the eastern coast of the Adriatic, the later
province of Illyricum, had come under her control in 167 B.C.,
and its inhabitants paid taxes, but there is no evidence that a
governor was sent regularly to the district before the time of
Caesar: the tribes and cities were probably left to manage their
own affairs without Roman interference. If trouble arose, the
district could temporarily be allotted to a consul as his 'province'
for the purpose of conducting a war. This happened in 129 B.C.,
when the consul Tuditanus gained a triumph for victories over
the Iapudes (p. 107 *sq.*).

The Romans would never have annexed Spain if it had not been absolutely necessary to keep it out of the hands of Carthage. Only at the very end of the period of Carthaginian domination did Hamilcar attempt to subdue the inner part of the peninsula, and when Rome took the place of Carthage her authority was probably scarcely recognized beyond the valleys of the Ebro and the southern rivers. Her long wars with the Spanish tribes have been described elsewhere (vol. VIII, chap. x, and above, pp. 318 *sqq.*). Here it is enough to say that not until the reign of Augustus was her power firmly established from the Pyrenees to the Straits of Gibraltar. The career of Sertorius shows on what slender foundations Roman authority rested as late as the Sullan period. Though such mines as Rome controlled were worked in the interests of the treasury, it is possible that the revenues of the Spanish provinces barely covered the cost of occupation.

The annexation of Sicily, Sardinia, and Corsica which followed the first Punic War, though due in the first instance to military considerations, brought considerable financial and economic advantages to Rome. These islands provided the Roman market with corn, and, except on one or two occasions, notably at the time of the slave rebellions in Sicily, did not call for the presence of large armies. 'Sicily,' says Cicero, 'has displayed such goodwill to the Roman people that the States of that island which have come into our alliance have never revolted afterwards, but many of them, and these the most illustrious, have remained firm in our friendship for ever[1].'

Republican Rome had no desire to found a great empire in north Africa. After the destruction of Carthage she was content to annex the territory immediately adjoining the city. The area of the province of Africa was only about 5000 square miles, a large proportion of which was allotted to the seven free cities which paid no taxes to Rome (vol. VIII, p. 484). The military defence of Roman interests in north Africa was normally left to her ally, the king of Numidia.

The annexation of the kingdom of Macedonia was postponed as long as possible, and the defence of this district against the Thracian tribes imposed a severe strain on the Roman military system. Though the province was usually governed by a praetor, in the period following 120 B.C. it was necessary to send to it a succession of armies under the command of consuls, and in the decade beginning in 80 B.C. victories were gained by Cn. Cornelius Dolabella, C. Scribonius Curio, and M. Lucullus, who were all ex-consuls. During the later Republic the authority of the

[1] II *in Verr.* II, 1, 2.

governor of Macedonia extended into Greece, which was not organized as the province of Achaea till 27 B.C.

The years which elapsed between the fall of Carthage and Pompey's eastern settlement saw a considerable extension of the provincial system. In 120 B.C. Rome took the important step of annexing the lower part of the Rhone valley and the coast from the Pyrenees to Nice as the province of Gallia Transalpina. As far back as 154 B.C. she had been called upon to assist her old ally Massilia against raiders from the north (vol. VII, p. 330), and the foundation of the new province may probably be attributed not merely to a desire to control the route from Italy to Spain, but to an appreciation of the fact that control of the Rhone valley was essential for the defence of the Mediterranean coast against invasion from the north. Rome's action was justified when the Teutoni and Cimbri made their appearance, a few years after the foundation of the province (pp. 139 *sqq.*).

Until 133 B.C. Rome refrained from annexations in Asia Minor, and adhered to her traditional policy of forming ties of friendship and alliance with the kings of Pergamum, Bithynia, Cappadocia, Pontus, and Galatia. But when Attalus king of Pergamum made her his heir, she accepted the inheritance and created the province of Asia (pp. 102 *sqq.*). The example of Attalus was followed by Nicomedes of Bithynia in 74 B.C., and some ten years later the *lex provinciae* of Bithynia was drawn up by Pompey. A governor of Cilicia is mentioned as early as 102 B.C., but the exact character of Rome's control of southern Asia Minor before Pompey's eastern settlement is uncertain. All that need be said here is that at the end of the Mithridatic Wars the coastline of Asia Minor and a considerable part of the hinterland had been annexed, while most of the plateau was left in the hands of the client kings of Galatia and Cappadocia. When Pompey made Syria a province he was continuing in the East the policy of annexing the Mediterranean coast (p. 392 *sq.*).

Only two more provinces remain to be mentioned. The district of Cyrene, which had been left to Rome by the will of Ptolemy Apion in 96 B.C., was finally given a provincial organization in 74 B.C., and the island of Crete which was annexed seven years later was probably put under the same governor. (The island of Cyprus, annexed in 58 B.C., was in the first instance added to the province of Cilicia.) Finally, one of the results of the Social War was the organization of north Italy as the province of Cisalpine Gaul, so that from the time of Sulla at latest this district was put under a regular governor.

In this way the number of the provinces, which had been six in 146 B.C., rose to ten in the time of Sulla and to fourteen after Pompey's eastern settlement. This increase complicated the problem of the appointment of governors, and, as will be shown below, led to a dissociation of provincial governorships from the annual magistracy which was to have far-reaching results.

It must be noted in conclusion that a large part of what was ultimately to be included in the Roman Empire was at the end of the Republic still ruled by 'client kings' who were described as 'friends and allies' of Rome, were definitely recognized by the Senate, and could even refer to their kingdoms as the gift of Rome. These kings paid no taxes, but were expected to render assistance in war and to subordinate their foreign policy to Roman interests. The most important of these were the kings of Numidia and Mauretania in north Africa, and the kings of Galatia and Cappadocia in Asia Minor. Even in the second century the kings of Egypt frankly recognized the primacy of Rome, and in 59 B.C. Ptolemy Auletes paid large sums to obtain Roman support (p. 518). Before the end of the Republic the authority of Rome was recognized in some form in most of the lands which were, under the Principate, to be included in her provincial system.

II. THE PROBLEM OF IMPERIAL DEFENCE

We have seen that one reason for the unwillingness of Rome to annex provinces was that to do so was likely to raise difficult military problems. The system of army organization which had barely proved adequate to the task of defending Italy against Hannibal was not well suited for the protection of overseas areas, and it is thus not surprising that the Senate preferred to trust as long as possible to alliances with foreign kings who, it was hoped, would employ their armies in the interests of Rome. Modern experience shows that, however capable a citizen army may be of defending its home at a crisis, the duty of garrisoning distant lands, at least in peace time, can best be performed by professional soldiers. This truth was fully realized by Augustus, and it was by long-service troops that the frontiers of the Empire were defended against barbarian invasion during the centuries which followed his reorganization of the army.

The close of the Hannibalic War left Rome in possession of a highly trained army, a group of experienced officers, and at any rate one first-class general, Scipio Africanus. But when the crisis was over it began to be felt that the permanent retention of this instrument was unnecessary, and inconsistent with the spirit of Republican institutions. Serious as were many of the wars which were waged during the following century and a half, the very existence of the Roman State was never again in danger. The result was a reaction against the professionalism which the necessities of the Hannibalic War had produced. We find what has been called 'a continuously wavering compromise between constitutionalism and practical necessity[1].' Under the later Republic the professional soldier and the professional general existed *de facto*, but their existence tended to be ignored and the army was not reorganized on a professional basis. The old idea lingered that it was essentially a citizen militia, and that its normal commanders were annually elected magistrates. Members of the leading families competed with each other for military commands calling for a knowledge and experience which they did not possess. The result was over and over again a loss of life and prestige which could easily have been avoided had it been recognized that highly trained armies were necessary and that amateurs were incapable of commanding troops in war time. In the long run it was generally necessary to call in a Scipio Aemilianus, a Marius, a Sulla, or a Pompey, whose task was made harder by the incompetence and inexperience of his predecessors.

The well-known account given by Polybius of the Roman army of the second century is very incomplete[2]. The four legions which he describes as being raised annually in Rome formed only a small part of the forces which existed at any given date, and should be regarded as primarily training units, employed on military duties in Italy itself, but seldom or never sent abroad. Men who had been trained in one of these *urbanae legiones* could be transferred to the forces in the field. Every Roman citizen was liable to sixteen years of service in the army. At an earlier date these campaigns had seldom been served continuously, but after the Hannibalic War practically continuous service became the rule rather than the exception. When a war was in prospect the general appointed to the command was authorized to raise whatever force seemed to the Senate to be adequate, and he would naturally wish to secure for his legions as many soldiers as possible who had already seen military service.

The situation in this period is admirably illustrated by a speech which Livy[3] puts into the mouth of a soldier named Sp.

---

[1] Kromayer and Veith, *Heerwesen und Kriegführung der Griechen und Römer*, p. 297.

[2] VI, 19–42.   [3] XLII, 34.

Ligustinus who in 171 B.C. volunteered for service in Macedonia. 'I became a soldier in the consulship of P. Sulpicius and C. Aurelius (200 B.C.) in the army which was sent to Macedonia, where I fought for two years as a private against King Philip: in the third year as a reward for bravery T. Quinctius Flamininus made me a junior centurion. When after the defeat of Philip and the Macedonians we were brought back to Italy and discharged, I at once went off to Spain as a volunteer with M. Porcius the consul (195 B.C.)....This general thought me worthy of promotion to a higher rank among the centurions. My third experience of soldiering was as a volunteer in the army which was sent against the Aetolians and King Antiochus: I received promotion from M'. Acilius (191 B.C.). When King Antiochus had been expelled and the Aetolians subdued, we were brought back to Italy. Then I served in two legions which were raised for a year. After that I served twice in Spain under Q. Fulvius Flaccus (181 B.C.) and Ti. Sempronius Gracchus, the former of whom as a reward for my courage let me take part in his triumph, while Gracchus actually asked me to go to his province. I have received thirty-two times rewards for bravery from my generals, four times within a few years I have been the first centurion of a legion, and I have received six 'civic crowns,' I have served twenty-two annual campaigns, and am more than forty years old.'

This Ligustinus was obviously to all intents and purposes as much of a professional soldier as any legionary of the Principate, but the conditions of his life were entirely different. He was not, like the latter, attached to a definite legion stationed for long periods (sometimes for centuries) in one frontier province. His life was more varied and adventurous, but his prospects were less certain. When no important war was in progress he might well find himself unemployed, and when his fighting days were over he could not look forward to a pension. On the other hand, he had probably greater opportunities of enriching himself during his period of service. Many soldiers, says Livy (XLII, 32, 6), volunteered in 171 B.C. because they knew of the wealth acquired by men who had served against Philip and Antiochus.

The conditions of military service were altered but not completely transformed by the changes which are attributed to Marius (see pp. 134 *sqq.*). Service was more continuous in the first century B.C. than in the second, indeed it is probable that the legionaries usually served for twenty years on end[1]. But the size

---

[1] H. M. D. Parker, *The Roman Legions*, pp. 24 *sqq.* See above, p. 136.

of the army was not fixed. The number of the legions varied according to need, and soldiers must often have been transferred from one legion to another. At the end of a campaign, *e.g.* those of Sulla and Pompey against Mithridates, many units were dissolved and great masses of troops disbanded. At a crisis a general was expected to improvise an army. The troops with which Caesar conquered Gaul were largely his own creation. When Pompey and Crassus were given commands in 55 B.C. they were explicitly allowed to raise as many citizens and allies as they wished[1]. After the appointment of a provincial governor the Senate decided what troops he should be allowed, and the size of a provincial garrison was determined entirely by the military situation. If a province seemed to be peaceful, it might be almost denuded of troops.

The situation in which Cicero found himself when appointed proconsular governor of Cilicia in 51 B.C. illustrates admirably the defects of the military system. Only two years before, the Parthians had inflicted on Roman troops the decisive defeat of Carrhae, and retaliation on the Roman provinces for the offensive of Crassus was only to be expected (p. 612). Yet Cicero and his neighbour Bibulus in Syria seem to have been left with forces quite incapable of dealing with a serious invasion. His two legions were below strength, disorganized, and undisciplined. 'The situation is such,' he writes to the Senate, 'that unless you send with all speed to these provinces as large an army as you generally send to a great war, there is the greatest danger of the loss of all the provinces on which the revenues of Rome depend. You must not base any hopes on recruiting in the provinces. Few recruits are available, and those who are available take flight when threatened with military service. Bibulus showed what he thought of this kind of soldier when he refused to hold the levy which you permitted him to hold in Asia. Our rule is so harsh and oppressive that the auxiliary forces of our allies are either too weak to help us much or so much estranged from us that we can neither expect any help from them nor repose any confidence in them.... Though I am so short of soldiers I shall not lose heart, and hope that I shall find a way out of my difficulties: but I don't know what will happen[2].' Cicero's letters make it clear that in Asia Minor, even after the annexation of several provinces, Rome still evaded the responsibility of defending them against invasion, and trusted unduly to the forces of client kings, most of whom were unable or

---

[1] Dio xxxix, 33.   [2] *ad fam.* xv, 1, 5.

unwilling to fight her battles for her. He himself was fortunate in having in Deiotarus of Galatia an ally whose troops were of real value.

Though Republican Rome was not lacking in energy at a crisis, and was prepared to take almost any steps to secure the defeat of a dangerous opponent, she may fairly be accused of neglecting her duties in the matter of imperial defence. She still regarded the soldier primarily as a fighting man to be used in an emergency, and in spite of the gradual professionalization of the army seldom regarded it as a garrison force. If immediately after the annexation of the south of Gaul a strong permanent garrison had been established there under the command of a competent general, it is probable that the menace of the Teutoni and Cimbri would have been far less threatening. As it was, a succession of hurriedly raised armies were defeated, and the northern invaders were able to stream over into Spain and into Italy itself. The situation was only saved by the conferment on Rome's best general of a series of consulships which finds no parallel in Roman history. The establishment by Augustus of a well-defended frontier on the Rhine prevented the recurrence of such a calamity till the middle of the third century A.D.

In Macedonia things were equally unsatisfactory. Cicero describes it as a province 'adjoined by so many barbarian tribes that its governors have always held that the boundaries extend as far as their swords and javelins can reach[1].' Few praetorian governors, he says, and no consulars have returned from it unscathed without being awarded a triumph. Not many details of the Macedonian Wars have reached us, but it is clear that their management reflects no credit on Rome. It is incredible that the power which had defeated Carthage and the kings of Macedonia could not have crushed the Balkan tribes if it had taken the matter in hand with vigour. As it was, Rome disarmed the native population of Macedonia and yet took no adequate steps to protect it against its warlike neighbours. Subsequent history shows that the only satisfactory solution was an extension of the frontier to the north. From the time of Augustus, Macedonia developed peacefully as an 'unarmed' province, ruled by the Senate and protected by the garrison which the Emperors maintained on the Danube in the province of Moesia. The task allotted by the Republic to the governor of Macedonia would have been a difficult one even if the military system had been more satisfactory, for he was re-

[1] in Pis. 16, 38.

sponsible for the defence of an enormous area stretching from the
Adriatic to the Black Sea. The tribes which gave most trouble
lived in modern Serbia in the valley of the Morava: the Scordisci,
who killed a Roman praetor in 119 B.C., appear as enemies of
Rome till after the time of Sulla[1]. More than once armies had to
penetrate as far as the Danube, and we read of fighting in the
valley of the Maritza in what is now Bulgaria. The proconsul
M. Lucullus in 72 B.C. even reached the shores of the Black Sea,
where he captured some half-Greek towns. In spite of all the
triumphs celebrated by Roman generals, the heart of the province
was never safe. When Cicero's enemy, L. Calpurnius Piso, was
governor in 57–55 B.C. three Thracian tribes reached Salonica
itself. Here as elsewhere the cause of the trouble was threefold
—the inadequacy of the garrison, the absence of a satisfactory
frontier, and the shortness of the period during which the governor
held office. The long command of C. Sentius Saturninus (92–88
B.C.) may be attributed to the conditions arising from the Social
War in Italy: few of the other governors whose names we know
remained more than two years in the province.

The military policy of Rome in Asia Minor is equally discreditable to the government of the Republic. The province of
Asia was annexed in 133 B.C., and during the following years the
trouble with Aristonicus necessitated the sending of consular
armies. But after his defeat by Perperna (consul of 130 B.C.) and
the organization of the province by Aquilius, the consul of the
following year, no steps seem to have been taken to defend it
against possible enemies. It was still hoped that what was necessary would be done by the client kings of Asia Minor, and, when
the intrigues of Mithridates in Bithynia and Cappadocia began,
Rome was as a rule content with diplomatic action. Sulla acted
vigorously in Cappadocia in 92 B.C., but after his recall nothing
was done to assert Roman authority. The result was the débâcle
of 88 B.C., when Mithridates overran Asia and massacred 80,000
Italians. At this period the province seems to have contained
practically no Italian troops, and the Roman representatives could
do nothing with the Asiatic levies which they hurriedly raised.
Rome's neglect to defend the life and property of her subjects
in Asia seems little less than criminal: Mithridates had been
giving trouble for many years, and his ability, his resources, and
his ambition were well known. The exercise of a little foresight
might have rendered the province of Asia safe from attack.

---

[1] On the wars in this region prior to Sulla, see above, pp. 107 *sqq.*

The long and costly wars waged by Sulla, Lucullus, and Pompey need never have been fought had Rome on the annexation of her eastern provinces taken the steps which were afterwards taken by Augustus to defend her frontiers against barbarian assaults. The account which has been given above of the forces in Cilicia at the time of Cicero's governorship shows that even after the defeat of Mithridates this lesson had not been learned.

Further illustrations of the same point may be obtained from the study of the campaigns against Sertorius in Spain during the years 80–72 B.C. (pp. 320 *sqq.*). When he landed in the south of Spain and hastily collected a force of some 8000 men, only a small proportion of whom were armed with Roman weapons, he defeated without difficulty Fufidius, governor of Further Spain. Equal success attended the efforts of his colleague Hirtuleius against Calidius, governor of the other province, whose forces were so inadequate that he had to appeal for assistance to Manlius, governor of Gaul, who sent him three legions: these were however defeated and driven across the Pyrenees, where they were cut to pieces by the Aquitanians. It is clear that at this period the forces at the disposal of the governors of both Spanish provinces were far too weak. The result was that though the government realized the seriousness of the situation and sent out first Q. Caecilius Metellus and then Pompey, Sertorius and his colleagues were given time to organize resistance and to obtain control of the greater part of the peninsula. Metellus brought with him two legions, and Pompey a force of 30,000 infantry and 1000 cavalry; but these troops had been hurriedly raised, and, although they no doubt contained good material, it took some time before they could be transformed into efficient military instruments. Rome's two most competent generals required several years to deal with the rising, and the collapse of Sertorius was due less to the military superiority of his opponents than to the disloyalty of his own supporters. If the Spanish provinces had been sufficiently garrisoned in 80 B.C., he would not have been given time to collect and train the force by which Pompey and Metellus were so long baffled.

The career of Sertorius, whose army was largely composed of Spaniards, illustrates another weakness of the army system of the later Republic, its failure to make adequate use of the excellent material provided by the provinces. When the army was re-organized under the Principate, the burden of military service was borne to an increasing extent by provincials, so that by A.D. 21 the leaders of a Gallic revolt were able to declare that the only good troops in the Roman army were non-Italian[1]. With the extension of the citizenship to the provinces the legions came to be more and more recruited outside of Italy, and from the time of Augustus an attractive military career was offered to provincials who were enrolled in the *auxilia*. Eventually the task of defending the provinces was largely in the hands of men who regarded them as their home. The situation was very different under the Republic. Rome pursued different policies in Italy and in the provinces. Before the Social War her Italian allies were not taxed, but were expected to render military service, the burden of which became heavier as provinces were annexed and wars waged outside of Italy. On the other hand, provincials, who paid taxes to Rome, were practically disarmed. They did not serve in the army, although, as will be seen below, they might be called upon to provide ships, manned by themselves. Such provincials as served in the army of the Republic were specialist troops, archers, slingers, and especially cavalry. The Italian cavalry, which had never been good, practically disappeared by the end of the Republic. In the Social War we find Spanish cavalry, in Caesar's army Gallic and Spanish horsemen, and in the Jugurthine War Thracians and Numidians. These men, who were not always inhabitants of Roman provinces, served for pay, and were probably well satisfied with their conditions. The mass of the provincials, however, rendered no military service to Rome. The few who possessed the citizenship were eligible for the legions, but we have seen what was Cicero's opinion of this material in Cilicia. It was only at a great crisis that the rule was relaxed according to which every legionary was a Roman citizen. The discontent with Roman rule, about which Cicero is so frank, was such that it was considered unsafe to recruit and train provincials. The success of Sertorius must have opened the eyes of the government to the excellence of the material which it had neglected, but till the fall of the Republic the old system continued. During the civil wars heavy financial burdens were imposed on the provinces, but the legions were still composed mainly of Roman citizens, most of whom were of Italian birth. Nothing is more significant of the defects of the provincial government of this period than the fact that it was not considered safe to arm the provincials in defence of their own homes. When trouble arose, the garrison, if it existed, was generally inadequate, and it was necessary to rush troops from Italy which could not arrive till irreparable damage had been done,

---

[1] Tacitus, *Ann.* III, 40.

and which had to undertake long and costly operations in order to restore Roman authority.

If the measures taken by the Roman government of this period to provide the armies capable of defending the provinces were totally inadequate, even more serious criticism can be brought against its naval policy. In spite of the experience gained in the Punic Wars and in the Illyrian Wars of the second century B.C., Rome did not under the Republic possess a permanent fleet. Her fleets were improvised to meet an emergency to an even greater extent than her armies. After the fall of Carthage so little attention was paid to the navy that Sulla had scarcely any ships at his disposal when he had to face Mithridates and his fleet assessed at 400 sail. It took Lucullus two years to collect from the cities of the eastern Mediterranean the fleet which at last in 85 B.C. defeated the Pontic navy. The situation was much the same in the war which broke out in 74 B.C. Most of the enemy fleet had been destroyed by storm before it was possible for the Roman ships to enter the Black Sea and support the land operations. Rome's dealings with the pirates show the same incompetence until the matter was taken in hand by Pompey. An inscription which is probably to be dated about 100 B.C.[1] shows that at that time the weak kings of Cyprus, Egypt, Cyrene, and Syria were expected to do something to check their depredations. Two years before, a special force had been sent against them under M. Antonius, and in 74 B.C. an *imperium infinitum* was conferred on his son with the same object, but neither seems to have accomplished much. Until Pompey's operations in 67 B.C. it was not realized that a 'fleet in being' was necessary to secure the adequate policing of the Mediterranean.

The defects of the system are well illustrated by Cicero's racy account of the state of things in Sicily under the rule of Verres[2]. The cities of the island, even some of those which were free from tribute, were obliged to provide ships and a certain number of sailors as required by the governor. Verres insisted that the sums which were paid to the captains for expenses should be handed over to him, and in addition accepted bribes in return for exempting cities and individuals from naval service. The wretched squadron which was raised to oppose the pirates was put under an incompetent Syracusan with whose wife Verres had an intrigue, and, as might be expected, it was utterly defeated. Each province

---

[1] *S.E.G.* iii, 378, B ll. 8–13; see H. Stuart Jones, *J.R.S.* xvi, 1926, pp. 155 *sqq.* See above, p. 351.

[2] ii *in Verr.* v, 17, 42 *sqq.*

was evidently made responsible for its own naval defence. The squadrons were a heterogeneous collection of ships, and no arrangement seems to have been made to secure training or experienced leadership. Cicero's speech on behalf of Flaccus who governed Asia in 62 B.C. suggests that even after Pompey's operations the situation was not much better. It was made a complaint against this governor that he exacted from the cities of his province a sum of money for the provision of a fleet, as he was entitled to do, and it was suggested that this action was a slight to Pompey. Cicero has to make the obvious reflection that if the pirates were not troublesome, the reason was that a fleet existed to deal with them. Apparently it was left to the discretion of each governor to decide on his policy in this important matter. Q. Cicero, who followed Flaccus in Asia, considered that there was no need of a fleet. 'He thought that if at any time news were heard of pirates he could get together a fleet as quickly as he liked[1].' This passage shows how far the Roman authorities were even now from realizing the magnitude of the task of policing the Mediterranean, and there is ample evidence for a partial revival of piracy during the forty years which followed Pompey's great achievement. It was only under the Principate that trading voyages could be made in real security.

This recital shows that the later Republic dealt very inadequately with the military and naval problems raised by the annexation of provinces. At this period Roman generals and Roman soldiers were individually as efficient as under the Principate. It was the system that was at fault. Legions hurriedly raised and devoid of *esprit de corps* could not possibly be efficient, at any rate at the beginning of a war. Rome had still to establish a scientific frontier and provide it with protecting troops even at a time when danger seemed not to be imminent.

III. THE PROVINCIAL GOVERNOR

In the early days of Roman provincial administration, as has been seen, the government of Sicily or Sardinia was regarded as merely one of a variety of tasks which might be allotted to a magistrate during his year of office. In Rome, as in the city-states of Greece, there were few or no permanent officials, and all administrative duties were entrusted as far as possible to popularly elected magistrates. In fifth-century Athens it had been possible to re-elect the same man to a magistracy for an indefinite number

---

[1] *pro Flacco*, 14, 33. Pompey and Sulla were more provident (*ib.* 13, 30 and 14, 32).

of years, with the result that under Pericles the government was 'nominally a democracy, but really the rule of the leading man.' But in Rome such re-election was rare, and generally forbidden by law. Even in the crisis of the Hannibalic War the consulship was very seldom held in successive years, and the sequence of consulships held by Marius in 104–100 B.C., and by Cinna in 87–84 B.C., was quite unconstitutional. The conditions were thus very unfavourable to the creation of a class of experienced provincial governors: with the best will in the world not much could be done in a single year.

In practice, however, the provincial governors of the later Republic frequently retained their posts for several years. When Sicily, Sardinia, and Spain had been annexed, the number of the praetors was increased from two to six, but this policy was not followed when Macedonia, Africa, Asia, and Gaul were added to the Empire. Not until Sulla's dictatorship was the number raised to eight. The result was that after 148 B.C. it was impossible to provide the necessary number of governors from the magistrates of the year, and it was often necessary to retain a man in his province after his magistracy had expired. Among the early governors of Macedonia, to take one example, several seem to have remained two or even three years, and C. Sentius probably did so from 92 to 88 B.C. In the Ciceronian age three years seems to have been a very usual term: this was the length of the governorship of Verres in Sicily (74–71), of Servilius Isauricus (78–75) and Lentulus Spinther (56–53) in Cilicia, of Q. Cicero in Asia (61–58) and of Gabinius in Syria (57–54). If a serious war was on foot, the term of office might be even longer: thus Lucullus, who went to Asia Minor as consul in 74 B.C., remained till he was superseded by Pompey in 66.

Quite early in Roman history it had proved impossible to carry on the work of government efficiently without making use of ex-magistrates. The *prorogatio imperii*, first found in the Samnite Wars (vol. VII, p. 530), which made it possible to retain the services of a magistrate without violating the rule against re-election, proved invaluable during the struggle with Hannibal: in any year important duties were allotted to ex-magistrates as well as to men who were actually in office. The pro-magistracy possessed the practical advantage that it was not necessarily limited to a year, and thus the duration of an office of this character could be determined by the qualifications of its holder. Flamininus, who went to Macedonia as consul in 198 B.C., did his work so well that he retained his command till 194.

Thus long before the time of Sulla, to whom is often attributed the policy of sending only pro-magistrates to govern the provinces, it had been necessary to employ them for this purpose. In the 'Pirate Law' of about 100 B.C. (see p. 451) there are references to the 'consul or proconsul who may be sent to the province of Asia' and to the 'praetor or propraetor or proconsul' who will govern the province of Macedonia. The Lex Antonia de Termessibus (p. 896) speaks of the 'magistrate or pro-magistrate or legatus' who might be in command of Roman troops. Both before and after Sulla the representative of Rome in a province was often a pro-magistrate. The main difference probably is that, whereas in the pre-Sullan period a provincial governor normally began his period of office as consul or praetor, after Sulla it became usual for magistrates to spend their year of office in Italy and to proceed to their province after its expiration. But exceptions to this rule can be found. Marius governed Spain and Sentius Macedonia after their praetorships, and on the other hand Lucullus went to Asia Minor before his consulship had expired.

In spite of the growing importance of the pro-magistracy, it is worth noting how long the idea survived that the most important piece of work which had to be done in any year must be allotted to one of the consuls in office. During the twenty years beginning in 153 B.C. consuls were very frequently sent to Spain, usually as governors of the Nearer province. Scipio Aemilianus was elected consul in 147 B.C. in order to deal with Carthage, and again in 134 B.C. in order to finish the Numantine War. Between 120 and 110 B.C. we find a succession of consuls acting as governors of Macedonia, and in the following decade as governors of Gaul during the Cimbric War. It was as consul that Sulla went against Mithridates in 88 and Lucullus in 74.

This close connection between the magistracy and provincial administration was an unfortunate one, and led to many disasters. The consuls and praetors were elected often on purely political grounds by a popular assembly which was very unrepresentative and very corrupt. They were entitled to a province the administration of which might well call for qualities which they did not possess. The Senate, though it had some control of the provincial arrangements, was limited to magistrates in its choice of governors. The result was that important military commands, as those against the Teutoni and Cimbri, were entrusted to men who, even if the organization of the army had been more efficient, were quite incapable of undertaking them. At a crisis all the ordinary rules had to be suspended. As far back as 210 B.C., Scipio Afri-

canus was sent to Spain though only twenty-five and of aedilician
rank. In 134 B.C. Scipio Aemilianus was irregularly re-elected to
the consulship as the only man who could deal with Numantia.
Later examples are the re-election of Marius to the consulship
for five years on end, and the extraordinary commands of Pompey
against Sertorius, Mithridates, and the pirates.

This is perhaps the most significant feature of Pompey's
career. None of the other great soldiers of the revolutionary
period treated the annual magistracy with such disrespect.
Marius, Sulla, Cinna and even Caesar took the consulship
seriously and sought to be elected to the office. But Pompey's
most important commands were granted to him when he was
technically a private citizen. To him the only power worth having
was a *proconsulare imperium,* if possible of unlimited duration, the
holder of which was not hampered by a colleague. It is true that
he was consul three times, but in 52 B.C. he held the office without
a colleague. In that year he passed a law which had far-reaching
results. In future an interval of five years was to elapse between
a magistracy and a provincial command, so that the pro-magistracy
was henceforth not merely an extension of the consulship or praetorship but a separate office. When Cicero went to Cilicia in the
following year he was a private citizen of consular standing invested with proconsular *imperium.* Caesar, on whose position in
Gaul this law had an unfavourable effect, complains that 'a new
kind of command has been created: no longer, as always before,
are men sent to the provinces after the consulship or praetorship,
but after they have been chosen and approved by a clique' (*B.C.*
I, 85). The ultimate result of Pompey's law was that a magistracy
did not necessarily lead to a provincial command. Whatever may
have been Pompey's immediate motives, his action was characteristic of a man who felt that provincial government called for experts
and who was impatient of the working of popular institutions.

It has been noted above that the appointment to provincial
governorships was to some extent in the hands of the Senate.
But even before its power had been weakened by the Gracchan
legislation, this body was very far from omnipotent. Not only was
its choice limited to those who had been elected to a magistracy,
but the allocation of provinces among the qualified candidates was
largely determined by lot. The Senate might decide which provinces were to be consular and which praetorian, but it was
usually left to the lot to decide which was to fall to each individual.
Incredible as it may seem, the lot determined whether Flamininus
or his colleague was to command in the war against Philip. The

magistrates were sometimes allowed to make an amicable arrangement among themselves about the distribution of provinces, but only
occasionally a province was allotted *extra sortem* to an individual.
(See vol. VIII, p. 360.) The control exercised by the Senate in the
second century B.C. concerned rather the length of the tenure of
a provincial command than the appointment to it in the first
place. Polybius notes that the Senate controlled the magistrates by
its power of deciding whether or not a successor should be sent
out; normally a governor retained his post till he was superseded.

By the law of C. Gracchus, which under ordinary circumstances
regulated the appointment to provinces until Pompey's introduction of a new system in 52 B.C., the power of the Senate in
this matter was considerably weakened (p. 63 *sq*.). Gracchus was
not indeed prepared to transfer this delicate task to the popular
assemblies, but he took steps to secure that the Senate should not
exercise its power against its political opponents. After the passing
of the Lex Sempronia de provinciis it was forced to decide before
the election of consuls what their provinces were to be: it could
not give undesirable posts to men of whom it disapproved. But
the law did not deprive it of all influence. By making a province
consular it could give notice to the governor that he would be
superseded at a pretty definite date. Thus when Cicero delivered
his speech on the Consular Provinces in the spring of 56 B.C. he
urged that Syria and Macedonia, then governed by his enemies
Gabinius and Piso, should be given to the consuls of 55, who
under the existing system would go to them early in 54.

Though this particular law of C. Gracchus showed moderation,
the effect of his legislation as a whole was to diminish the Senate's
influence on provincial appointments. The popular assemblies,
now conscious of their omnipotence, frequently in the post-
Gracchan period interfered with the Senate's arrangements.
Marius was in 107 B.C. given the African command by special
decree of the people, and in 88 a *plebiscitum* was passed giving
him the command against Mithridates, although he was at the
time a private citizen. Later examples of similar procedure are
the Lex Gabinia (67), the Lex Manilia (66), the Lex Vatinia (59),
the Lex Clodia (58) which appointed Gabinius and Piso to Syria
and Macedonia, and the Lex Trebonia (55). Of the author of the
Lex Clodia Cicero says 'provincias consulares sine sorte nomin-
atim dedisti[1]': such appointments may have been legal, but they
were inconsistent with constitutional usage.

---

[1] *de domo sua*, 9, 24.

Sulla has been credited with the wish to introduce a rigid system according to which each consul and praetor performed the duties of his magistracy in Italy and then went to a province for a single year; he did indeed raise the number of the praetors to eight, so that each year there were ten men (two ex-consuls and eight ex-praetors) available for the ten provinces more or less which then composed the Empire. This limitation of the term of provincial commands was a reactionary step which in practice proved unworkable. Between 80 and 70 B.C. we find only four governors of Macedonia, and, as was noted above, in the following period provincial commands lasting several years seem to be normal. Sulla's supposed calculations were upset by the annexation of Bithynia, Crete, Cyrene, and Syria. It is indeed more than possible that the policy described should not really be attributed to him. He did not repeal the Lex Sempronia, which continued to regulate the normal procedure. Though after his time it was rarely that a magistrate went to his province during his year of office, cases occurred in 74 and 67 B.C., and a passage of Cicero suggests that it was proposed to send the consuls of 51 against the Parthians[1].

The method of appointing provincial governors which has been described was not entirely without merits. If a man was doing good work, it was not difficult to prolong his governorship for several years. At a crisis it was always possible to suspend the ordinary procedure and appoint the essential man to a post. 'I need not remind you,' says Cicero in his speech in support of the Lex Manilia, 'that our ancestors were in peace time always guided by precedent and in war time by convenience; that they always adopted a new policy to meet a new situation; that two great wars in Africa and in Spain were brought to an end by one general and that two powerful cities, Carthage and Numantia, which threatened the existence of the Roman Empire, were both destroyed by Scipio. I need not mention that you and your fathers placed all your hopes for the Empire on C. Marius and entrusted him with the war against Jugurtha, against the Cimbri and against the Teutoni[2].' But on the whole the system was a faulty one and called for the revision which it underwent in the Principate. The connection between the ordinary magistracy and provincial appointments was too close. It was not fully enough recognized that to govern a province called for special qualifications, and the popular assemblies had too much influence on the appointment of

---

[1] *ad fam.* VIII, 10, 2.   [2] *de imp. Cn. Pompei*, 20, 60.

governors. If the Senate was unduly suspicious of the brilliant man, his influence on the people was apt to be excessive. The problem was solved under the Principate, when the most important provinces were ruled by men who were personally selected by the Emperor, who were responsible to him and who were assisted by a body of knights and freedmen, comparable to the Civil Service which a new Viceroy finds in India. Such conditions made it possible for a class of professional governors to be created.

In a letter which Cicero addressed to his brother Quintus, then proconsul of Asia, he contrasts the position of a provincial governor with that of a magistrate in Rome[1]. The latter is hampered on all sides by his colleagues, by the Senate, and by the popular assemblies; on the other hand, the provincial governor is almost omnipotent: the happiness of thousands depends on the nod of a single man. 'There is no appeal, no means of complaint, no Senate, no public meetings.' Cicero emphasizes the duty of the governor under those conditions to maintain a high moral standard. It is almost amusing to note the stress which he lays on the obvious virtues of *integritas* and *continentia*, and how he congratulates his brother on the exercise of common honesty. During three years, he says, he has not made use of his power to secure for himself pictures, clothing, precious vessels, or slaves. Unfortunately the system of appointment was such that Rome was often represented in the provinces by men whose standard of conduct was not so high.

While under the Principate a governor could be sure of finding in his province a considerable number of Roman officials, the situation was very different under the Republic. His very considerable staff came with him and went with him. The Senate allotted to him a number of *legati*, men of senatorial rank, the number of whom varied with the importance of the province: to them he could allot military duties and civil jurisdiction. Cicero describes them as *comites et adiutores negotiorum publicorum*. Next there was the quaestor, who was nominally responsible for the administration of the funds entrusted to the governor, of which he had to render an account at the end of his year of office. But he was young and inexperienced, was chosen by lot, and can rarely have been in a position to thwart his superior officer, to whom he was supposed to stand in a filial relation: occasionally he was considered qualified to act as his representative under the

[1] *ad Q.F.* i, 1, 7, 22.

title of *quaestor pro praetore*. In addition to his legati and his quaestor, a governor was accompanied by a large number of men of all ranks who were commonly described as his *comites* and his *cohors praetoria*. Of these the most important were the praefecti, often relations of himself or his friends, and among the others were secretaries, attendants, doctors, soothsayers, and public criers. Cicero's letters to his brother make it clear that it was not always easy to keep them in order. When Caesar was preparing to march against Ariovistus, he was embarrassed by the panic which broke out among the 'tribunes of the soldiers, the prefects, and the others who had followed him from the city out of friendship and had no great experience of soldiering' (*B.G.* I, 39). The sum granted by the Senate to the governor at the time of the *ornatio provinciae* was supposed to be adequate for the support of his staff. Provision was made for the purchase of grain in the province at a fixed price: when this differed from the market price, devices were employed, as readers of the *Verrines* will remember, to make a settlement with the growers which generally gave less satisfaction to them than to the governor.

It would however be a great mistake to suppose that a provincial governor of the later Republic had quite a free hand and was *de iure* as well as *de facto* omnipotent. The length of his tenure of office was uncertain, and, if he were notoriously incompetent, his opponents in Rome would use their influence to have his province allotted as soon as possible to one of his successors in the magistracy. A law of Sulla required him to leave his province within thirty days of the arrival of his successor and return to the city, where he might well find himself in trouble. The Lex Calpurnia of 149 B.C. was only the first of a series of laws under which an ex-governor might be prosecuted on a charge of extortion, and though, as is shown in other chapters, the constitution of the courts before which the charge was tried was usually unsatisfactory, a really bad governor ran a fair chance of being condemned. The letters of Cicero from Cilicia are full of references to the Lex Julia of 59 B.C., which imposed many restrictions on the activities of himself and his subordinates. This law of Caesar's, which enumerated in 101 clauses offences which a governor could commit, remained in force even under the Principate. In this connection mention may be made of the law of Sulla against *maiestas*, which rendered liable to prosecution a governor who led an army out of his province, waged war without permission, or entered a client kingdom without having been specially authorized to do so (p. 297).

The hands of a governor were tied not merely by laws which were of general application, but by the *Lex Provinciae* of his own province. These charters, which were drawn up by a senatorial commission soon after annexation, provided the basis of the provincial organization. They stated the privileges enjoyed by certain cities and regulated local government in some detail. The Lex Pompeia of Bithynia, which was still in force when Pliny governed the province under Trajan, dealt with the age-limits for magistracies, the qualifications for membership of local senates, and the conditions under which local citizenship could be acquired. Similar matters were determined by the Lex Rupilia of Sicily, which laid down in detail the procedure to be adopted in lawsuits between citizens of the same city or of different cities, between Romans and natives, and between private individuals and public bodies. These provincial laws grouped the cities into *conventus*, in the leading city of which justice was administered by the governor. Though no doubt the charters of the various provinces contained some common features, they must have differed considerably. Conditions were very different, for example, in Sicily and Spain, and the Roman government could not have imposed a rigid uniformity, even if it had wished to do so.

Points which were not determined by the *Lex Provinciae* were settled by the edict which each governor issued on entering into office. Just as in Rome itself the legal system grew out of a succession of edicts issued by the city-praetors, so in the provinces the governor was not bound to take over as it stood the edict of his predecessor, but was entitled to introduce such modifications as he considered desirable. These modifications might or might not commend themselves to his successor, and thus there was gradually evolved a system of law based on experiment. In Cilicia, for example, where the provincial law seems to have been vague on the subject, Cicero conferred on the Greek cities by his edict an amount of autonomy to which they were not accustomed[1]. In drafting his edict he had been guided by the example of a successful governor of Asia, Q. Mucius Scaevola. The first part of it concerned the finances of the cities, the maximum rate of interest, and their relations with the *publicani*. In the second section he was concerned with private law, and specially mentions rules about inheritance, sales and bankruptcy. The third part of his edict was 'unwritten' and he states that he intended to be guided by the edicts of the city-praetor: it is interesting to see how the

---

[1] *ad Att.* VI, I, 15.

principles of Roman law were gradually being extended to the provinces. Perhaps the most delicate subject with which the edict was concerned was the rate of interest, as this affected the publicani, whose relations with the governor will be discussed below[1].

The duties of a provincial governor were both military and judicial. Even in peaceful provinces there were enough troops to suppress disorder. 'Asia ought to realize,' writes Cicero to his brother, 'that our government has saved it from the horrors of foreign war and domestic discord, and that it ought not to complain of sacrificing part of its wealth to support a rule which has brought it permanent peace[2].' As was shown in the previous section, the boast that Rome protected her provinces from foreign invasion seems hardly justified; but even under the Republic she was fairly successful in policing them, and this is all that was required from most provincial governors.

The amount of judicial work expected of a governor probably varied considerably in the different provinces, for the extent to which cities enjoyed autonomy was determined by the *Lex Provinciae* and the governor's edict. But there is no doubt that all important cases, both civil and criminal, were decided by him with the assistance of a *consilium* consisting of Roman citizens resident in the province. It is probable that litigants often were glad to have their disputes settled by a judge who had some experience of Roman legal procedure. In the infliction of punishment the governor's power seems to have been practically unlimited, and we find no parallel under the Republic to the 'appeal to Caesar' with which we are familiar in the cases of St Paul and the Bithynian Christians. It was indeed possible for the Senate to instruct the consuls to summon the accused to Rome, but this procedure was rare and seems to have been confined to political cases. Verres frequently scourged, condemned to the mines, and even executed Roman citizens, and though Cicero in a famous passage speaks of the awful effects of this conduct on Roman prestige abroad, he does not actually assert that it was illegal[3].

IV. ADMINISTRATION AND TAXATION

In dealing with Roman provincial administration it becomes difficult to generalize, for, as has been so often remarked, the Romans, like the British, had an instinctive dislike of abstract principles, and preferred to apply common sense to the solution

[1] See pp. 469 *sqq.*　　　　[2] *ad Q.F.* i, i, 11, 34.
[3] ii *in Verr.* v, 61, 158 *sqq.*

of each problem as it arose. Even under the Principate, when power was centralized in the hands of a single individual, and the work of administration was mainly entrusted to carefully selected officials, no attempt was made to introduce rigid uniformity. It was fully realized that the problem of government varied according to the political, social, and economic conditions of each province. Methods which might be applicable to the province of Asia, which was permeated by Greek civilization, would be inapplicable to Egypt, a land of absolutist traditions, or to Gaul or Britain, where tribal life still persisted, and where Greek and Latin alike were foreign languages. The secret of Rome's success as a governing power is to be found in her realization of this fact. If peace were maintained and taxes regularly paid, she cared little how her subjects were organized, what language they spoke, or what gods they worshipped. In time this patience had its reward, and a fairly homogeneous civilization penetrated even to the outposts of the Empire. Provincials came to realize the advantages which would be derived from the adoption of the Roman language and of Roman ways of life. Italy lost its privileged position, and the Empire was governed and administered largely by men of provincial birth.

In the period with which the present volume is concerned this ideal state of things was still far in the future. The process by which Rome was transformed from a city-state into the capital of an Empire had only just begun. It is indeed true that before the Social War her citizenship had been so widely extended that she had almost ceased to be a city-state in the Greek sense. But this extension of the citizenship even to Italians was viewed with some nervousness in conservative circles, where it must have been felt that it was bound to lead to a revolution in the system of government. Although after the revolt of the allies the franchise was conferred on the whole peninsula south of the Po, during the following period any further extension was strenuously opposed, and it was only in Caesar's dictatorship that the process began which was eventually to lead to the Romanization of the provinces and was to culminate in the edict of Caracalla, conferring citizenship on the whole Roman world.

While, as Aristotle points out, it was essential that the population of a city-state should be limited in number, there was no reason why it should not enter into alliances with other states of the same character. The Athenian Empire developed out of a confederation of cities in the face of a common danger, and the position of Rome in Italy during the period of the Punic Wars

was not unlike that which had been occupied by Athens in Greece
during the fifth century B.C. But Rome played the rôle of leading
state in a confederation with greater skill than Athens. She
respected the autonomy of her allies: she imposed no taxes on
them and left them free to manage their internal affairs: all that
she required of them was military assistance in time of war. The
result was very satisfactory. The Italian confederation emerged
successfully from the ordeal of the Hannibalic War, and when
trouble arose the cause was not any wish to be independent of
Rome, but a desire, which would have been almost unintelligible
to the Greeks, for full incorporation in the leading state of the
confederation. Such incorporation, it was realized, would not
involve any serious loss of autonomy. Even states possessing the
full Roman franchise, like Arpinum, the home of Cicero and
Marius, had an active municipal life and a keen local patriotism.
These cities were envied by their neighbours, who felt that if
they could attain to a similar position they would lose nothing
that mattered, and would gain all the advantages which the possession of Roman citizenship brought to cities and individuals.

It might have been expected that when Rome acquired provinces she would apply to them the principles of organization
which were proving so successful in Italy. She might have conferred the citizenship on certain favoured communities and concluded alliances with the remainder on condition that they rendered military service. But for various reasons this policy was
impossible, and it was probably not even contemplated. Although
long before the end of the Republic a large number of individuals
of provincial birth had obtained the Roman franchise as a personal
honour (it was, for instance, granted to a whole squadron of
Spanish cavalry in 89 B.C.[1]), there was a strong prejudice against
the possession by provincial cities of the status of *colonia* or
municipium. The proposal of C. Gracchus to found a colony on
the site of Carthage was unpopular, and the settlement of a
military colony at Narbo Martius in 118 B.C. is an almost unique
example of a policy which was first adopted on a large scale by
Caesar. At a time when the majority of the cities of Italy were not
yet enfranchised, it was unlikely that Roman rights would be
granted to provincial towns.

Again, as was noted in the section on Imperial defence, Rome
was not at this period prepared to recruit her army freely from the
provinces, of whose loyalty she was not without reason doubtful.

----

[1] See C. Cichorius, *Römische Studien*, pp. 130 *sqq.* and the present writer
in *J.R.S.* IX, 1919, pp. 95 *sqq.*

If the Republic had concluded with provincial cities and tribes alliances similar to those which existed in Italy, she would have demanded of them not tribute but military service. It was under such conditions that she recognized as 'friends and allies' the kings of regions like Numidia, Galatia, and Cappadocia which she was not yet prepared to annex, but in the provinces proper the situation was different. Rome undertook (very inefficiently, as has been shown) the task of protecting her provinces from invasion and from internal discord on condition that the inhabitants paid tribute. If then we find the word ally (*socius*) applied freely to provincials, it must be remembered that it was used in a very different sense from that which prevailed in Italy.

The fact is that in the period when the Roman state was acquiring provinces the conception of alliance with individual cities was beginning to be felt as an anachronism. It is true that during the Social War, as Cicero observes[1], there was a party in two Greek cities of Campania which preferred to the Roman franchise 'the liberty conferred by a treaty,' but such an attitude, if typically Greek, was quite out of date. The terms of a treaty which happens to survive between the 'people of Rome' and the 'people of Astypalaea,' a tiny island in the Aegean, are almost ludicrous. The two peoples promise to render to each other mutual assistance in war, and to refrain from assisting each other's enemies. 'The people of Astypalaea shall not publicly permit the enemies and opponents of the people of Rome to pass through its own territory or any territory which it controls so as to wage war against the people and subjects of Rome.... If anyone declare war against the people of Astypalaea, the people of Rome shall assist the people of Astypalaea. If anyone wage war unprovoked against the people of Astypalaea, the people of Rome shall come to its assistance in accordance with this treaty[2].' Rome was by this date (105 B.C.) far more than an ordinary city-state: she was becoming the capital of a nation, citizenship of which was a cherished privilege, and incorporation in which was an object of ambition for individuals and States.

None the less, there existed in the provinces a small number of communities, described as *civitates foederatae*, which stood in theory outside the provincial system and were bound to Rome by sworn alliances. Three such cities existed in Sicily during the rule of Verres, and a few more were to be found in other provinces. It is worth noting that among them were the famous Greek cities

---

[1] *pro Balbo*, 8, 21.   [2] *I.G.R.R.* IV, 1028.

of Athens, Rhodes, and Massilia. The treaties concluded with those States bound them to have the same friends and enemies as Rome, and probably rendered them liable to provide naval, if not military, assistance; but on the other hand they were entirely independent of the authority of the governor, paid no taxes to Rome, and exercised full judicial control over their own citizens and probably, in civil cases at least, over Roman citizens resident in their territory. Almost equal privileges were enjoyed by another and larger group of states known as *civitates sine foedere liberae et immunes*. The position of these states was more precarious, depending as it did not on a sworn treaty but on a law or a decree of the Senate which could at any time be repealed. This status was conferred on many communities which had assisted Rome in war, *e.g.* on seven cities in Africa and many others in Asia Minor which had taken the Roman side in the wars against Antiochus or Mithridates (vol. VIII, pp. 231 *sqq.*, 484, and above, p. 394 *sq.*). The privileges involved in Libertas can be learned from an extant law dealing with Termessus in Pisidia[1]: they include self-government, freedom from land tax and the quartering of Roman troops, and the right to impose customs dues, subject to the exemption of representatives of Rome. A frequently mentioned privilege which probably belonged to free as well as to federate states was that of receiving exiles. Romans like Verres and Milo who were in danger of condemnation by a court could escape the consequences of their acts by taking up residence in Dyrrhachium, Massilia, or Thessalonica.

The chief advantage possessed by these free and federate *civitates* was that they stood outside the provincial system and were not subject to the authority of the governor. That this was regarded as a great privilege is a reflection on the provincial government of the Republic, and it is worth noting that after the foundation of the Principate a complete change of standpoint is to be found. Within a hundred years of the prosecution of Verres the provincial cities which were best satisfied with their status were not those which were independent allies of Rome, but the *coloniae* and *municipia*, outlying portions of the imperial city and fully incorporated in it. This desire for incorporation which we find in Italy under the Republic was during the Principate felt in the provinces.

In what has been said it has been implied that in her relations with the provinces, as distinguished from the client kingdoms,

---

[1] Bruns, *Fontes*[7], 14; Dessau 38.

Rome made her arrangements not with the province as a whole, which had no means of corporate expression, but with the various communities which composed it, and which were enumerated in the *Lex Provinciae*. A province can be best described as an aggregate of States. In Italy, Rome had been accustomed to deal with individual cities, and this fact influenced her provincial policy. She preferred if possible to deal with cities of the familiar Graeco-Roman type, possessing their own magistrates, senates, and assemblies. Pompey's eastern settlement, for instance, was guided by the principle that hellenized and urbanized districts might safely be included in the Empire, while regions like Cappadocia, which had scarcely passed beyond the tribal stage, were left under client kings who recognized the suzerainty of Rome. It was worth while sacrificing a little tribute to escape from the burden of administering backward districts. But if it was absolutely necessary, Rome was prepared in the provinces, as in Italy, to recognize tribes as well as cities and to enter into arrangements with their authorities. This was notably the case in Spain, a region in which city life developed little before the Principate (vol. VIII, p. 307 *sq.*).

This fostering of local government in the provinces was due less to any theoretical attachment to the ideal of autonomy than to very practical considerations. The Republic possessed no Civil Service, and the handful of officials sent out from Rome could not possibly have performed ‘its task without the assistance of the natives. It was therefore very desirable that these natives should be grouped in organized communities with whose representatives the government could enter into relations. The difference between the federate and free cities of a province and the remainder lay mainly in the fact that the latter were required to pay taxes. Their internal organization was very similar to that of the more privileged communities, and they possessed the usual organs of government. The amount of interference to which they were liable was determined by the charter of the province and by the edict of the governor for the time being. The governor was generally entitled to keep an eye on the finances of a city, and his consent was required for extraordinary expenditure on such objects as games, buildings, and embassies. In judicial matters the powers of the local magistrates were determined by the *Lex Provinciae*. Thus in Sicily elaborate arrangements for the settlement of disputes were laid down by the Lex Rupilia. Different procedure was adopted according as the litigants were Sicilians of the same or of different states, or according as they were pro-

vincials or Roman citizens: a claim made by a Sicilian on a Roman
was to be settled by a Roman judge and *vice versa*. Certain cases
had to be referred to a jury drawn from the so-called *conventus
civium Romanorum*. Such Roman citizens as resided in provincial
towns under the Republic, whether they were of Italian or of
native stock, tended to organize themselves in clubs, much
as Englishmen do now in foreign countries. These *conventus*
were recognized by the government and given a certain status.
Cicero makes it a grievance against Verres that in his choice
of jurors he failed to respect the lawful privileges of resident
Romans[1].

The general sketch which has been drawn of the principles of
Roman provincial organization must be supplemented by a study
of the separate provinces; for, as has been said, Rome at no period
made a fetish of uniformity. A provincial charter introduced no
revolutionary changes, and merely provided the machinery for
the administration of justice and the collection of taxes. 'The
very absence of organization,' it has been said, 'betrays the noble
belief that the aggregate of States which formed a province was
rather a confederated suzerainty than an integral part of an
empire[2].'

Under the Republic and during the first three centuries of the
Principate, what distinguished a province from Italy was that its
inhabitants, with the exception of those who had been definitely
granted exemption, were liable to direct taxation. The subjects of
Rome had been accustomed to pay taxes to their previous rulers,
and the existing system was usually taken over with little modification. In Sicily, for instance, Rome adopted the procedure
which had been introduced by King Hiero, and in Macedonia
she left things as she found them, merely reducing by half the
sums which had been paid to the king (vol. VII, pp. 793 *sqq.*,
VIII, p. 273). There is no reason to think that her demands were
excessive. In many provinces at certain periods the revenue can
scarcely have been sufficient to cover the naval and military expenditure involved in annexation. Cicero[3] contrasts Asia with
other provinces as being exceptional in providing a surplus. At
the same time it cannot be denied that the extension of the empire
brought considerable financial advantages to the inhabitants of
Italy, who in the later days of the Republic were extremely lightly
taxed. The only revenue which the state derived from Italy con-

---

[1] II *in Verr.* II, 13, 34.
[2] A. H. J. Greenidge, *Roman Public Life*, p. 329.
[3] *de imp. Cn. Pompei*, 6, 14.

sisted of the proceeds of the harbour dues, of the public lands, and
of a tax on the manumission of slaves. After 167 B.C. the *tributum*,
which at an earlier time had been intermittently imposed on
Roman citizens to meet the cost of wars, ceased to be raised.

In a well-known passage Cicero states that there were two distinct principles on which provinces were taxed[1]. Either a fixed
sum was imposed, which was regarded as a permanent war-
indemnity, or the payment was variable, in which case the right
of collecting it was let out by the censors to *publicani*. The best
known example of the latter procedure was in Asia, where C.
Gracchus introduced a system which brought great gain to the
equestrian order (pp. 64 *sqq.*). In Sicily (vol. VII, pp. 793 *sqq.*)
the tax, which was paid in kind, and varied with the yield of
the harvest, was collected not by the great companies of Roman
publicani but by individuals or companies who had secured the
contract for collecting the tithe in particular districts. There is
no reason why this system should have been a source of grievance
if it had been efficiently administered and if the government had
exercised sufficient control over the tax collectors.

It has been mentioned that in certain provinces at least taxation
was originally regarded as a war-indemnity. As time passed this
conception must have been modified and the view must have
gained ground that the taxes were a contribution made by the
provincials towards the maintenance of the *pax Romana*. 'Peace,'
says a speaker in Tacitus, 'cannot be secured without armies:
armies cannot exist without pay: and payment cannot be provided
without taxation[2].' But only some of the provinces (*e.g.* Spain,
Africa, Macedonia) were conquered in war, and it was impossible
to treat taxation as a war-indemnity in regions like Asia, Bithynia,
and Cyrene, which were left to Rome by the wills of their previous
rulers. Thus we find even under the Republic the beginnings of
a theory, which was formulated definitely by the lawyers of the
Principate, that provincial land was the property of the Roman
State, for the use of which a payment must be made by the
occupiers, whatever their legal status, unless they had received
definite exemption. It is indeed improbable that the view that
taxation was of the nature of rent was consciously accepted in the
period with which this volume is concerned. A sharp distinction
was certainly drawn between those districts within a province
which were *ager publicus populi Romani* and those which were not.
Ownership of provincial land was possible for Roman citizens,

---

[1] II *in Verr.* III, 6, 12.   [2] Tacitus, *Hist.* IV, 74.

and as late as Augustus we find the government paying for land in the provinces on which it wished to settle colonists. At the same time the highhanded methods employed by Sulla and Caesar in dealing with provincial land must have prepared the way for the acceptance of the view that such land was absolutely at the disposal of the Roman State[1].

The fact that in Asia and Sicily the tax was a tithe of the crops suggests that even in the provinces where a fixed sum was exacted the primary object of taxation was the land. It cannot be definitely asserted that the distinction familiar under the Principate between *Tributum Soli* and *Tributum Capitis* (property-tax) was known to the Republic. The references to the census which was periodically taken by the magistrates of provincial towns suggest that it was concerned primarily with the owners of land. At the same time it seems so improbable that wealthy men who were not landowners escaped taxation, that we must suppose that the local authorities were given some discretion in the allocation among individuals of the quota owing to the Roman government.

Although in the provinces which paid a fixed stipendium there was no need for the intervention of *publicani* between the governor's quaestor and the communities, there was probably no province in which they were not to be found—Cicero speaks of their presence in Asia, Spain, Macedonia, Gaul, Africa, Sardinia, and Italy itself. The explanation is that, even if the direct taxes could be collected otherwise, they were indispensable for the collection of the harbour dues, the tax on pasturage, the revenues of the public lands, and for the working of the mines, which were almost everywhere regarded as State-property.

In other chapters attention has been drawn to the political aspect of the rôle played by the *publicani* in provincial administration, especially after the equestrian order had acquired by the Gracchan legislation an important series of privileges (pp. 64 *sqq.*, 75 *sqq.*). It is notorious that in the last century of the Republic no governor could deal firmly with the *publicani* without running the risk of offending the equites, who at most periods possessed great influence in the jury-courts. Here it must be enough to say that the employment of contractors for the collection of revenue was, if undesirable, quite inevitable. The method had been practised in Athens and no doubt in other Greek states. The mines of Laurium were worked and the dues at the Piraeus collected by men who paid the Athenian government for the privilege. Even

[1] See Tenney Frank, '*Dominium in Solo Provinciali*' and '*Ager Publicus*,' in *J.R.S.* XVII, 1927, pp. 141 *sqq.*

in the Hellenistic monarchies revenue was collected not by salaried public servants but by individuals or companies who derived some profit therefrom. But in Ptolemaic Egypt, at least, such strict control was exercised over their activities by representatives of the government that the duty was probably regarded as a burden rather than as a source of profit.

In the Roman Republic the absence of paid officials rendered necessary the employment of contractors. During the Hannibalic War, *publicani* provided food and clothing for the armies in Spain. In his account of Roman institutions in the second century B.C. Polybius emphasizes the number and variety of the public contracts which were controlled by the Senate: 'almost everyone,' he says, was affected by the terms on which these contracts were granted (see vol. VIII, p. 382 *sq.*). The State naturally required guarantees for the fulfilment of a contract, and thus found it convenient to deal not with individuals but with companies possessing accumulated capital. The result was that we find in the later Republic great organizations with their headquarters in Rome and with agents in the provinces. The *magister* (chairman) and no doubt most of the *socii* lived in Rome, and were represented abroad by men who bore the title of *pro magistro*, and had a considerable staff at their disposal. It seems probable that these companies possessed what may be described as a class of shareholders. Certainly large sums were invested in the province of Asia, and in a striking passage of the speech which he delivered in support of the appointment of Pompey against Mithridates, Cicero states that the disastrous invasion of the province in 88 B.C. brought ruin on many. 'We know that at a time when many had incurred great losses in Asia payment was stopped in Rome and credit collapsed. It is impossible for many members of a community to be ruined without dragging many others down with them[1].'

If we may judge by what happened in the province of Sicily, about which we happen to be well informed, the system of entrusting to contractors the collection of a tithe was, in the absence of strict control by the governor, open to very serious objection. It was in the interests of the government to accept the highest offer, and although in strict law the farmer was not bound to hand over more than a tithe of his crop together with 6 per cent., which represented the legitimate profit of the collector, it was almost inevitable that more should be demanded if the latter found that he

---

[1] *de imp. Cn. Pompei,* 7, 19.

had made a bad bargain. It is indeed probable that he was entitled to ask for an *accessio* in cash in addition to the tithe, and under the rule of Verres these *accessiones* amounted to enormous sums.

In the provinces of Syria and Cilicia, and probably elsewhere, the *publicani* entered into agreements (*pactiones*) with the individual communities[1]. This represents a compromise between the system under which they came into direct touch with the taxpayer and the other which dispensed with their services altogether, and made the authorities of each city responsible for the payment of its quota. The gains of the *publicani* were increased by the practice of moneylending: they advanced, often at extortionate rates of interest, the sums which provincial communities owed to the government. Not only companies but individuals found it very profitable to lend money to the provincials. Readers of Cicero's letters will remember Scaptius, the agent of the philosophic Brutus, who tried to persuade him when governor of Cilicia to employ force in order to compel the people of Salamis in Cyprus to pay interest at the rate of 48 per cent. In this, as in other matters, the Senate was well aware of what was happening. In 67 B.C. a Lex Gabinia forbade the lending of money to provincials in Rome, and every governor was entitled to determine by his edict the rate of interest which might be enforced. But it proved impossible to enforce the law, and Cicero was not the only governor who found it difficult to be firm when confronted with the representatives of powerful interests.

There is, however, no reason to think that the Republic imposed excessive financial burdens on its subjects. Macedonia was probably not the only province from which less was demanded than had previously been paid. Much of the money raised was spent on the defence of the province itself, so that it was possible to maintain that Roman rule brought peace in its train. Some attempt was made to equalize the burden of taxation. Immunity was granted to only a few communities, and Roman citizenship did not carry with it any important financial advantages. The moderate dues charged on imports and exports were justified by the care devoted to the upkeep of the harbours. Even the *publicani* were no novelty and were not dispensed with even when the Principate introduced better conditions. If on the whole the system worked badly, the reason, as was said above, must be found partly in the inexperience of the governors and partly in the weakness of the central government.

---

[1] See *e.g.* Cicero, *ad Att.* v, 13, 1; *de prov. cons.* 5, 10.

V. CONCLUSION

In the reign of Nero it was reported in Rome that a certain influential Cretan had been heard to say that it depended on him
whether a retiring governor was to receive or not the thanks of
the province. When the matter came up in the Senate, the Stoic
Paetus Thrasea, a well-known *laudator temporis acti*, delivered a
speech against what he calls 'the new insolence of the provincials.'
'Formerly,' he said, 'not only praetors and consuls but private
persons were sent to inspect provinces and to report what they
thought about each man's loyalty, and whole peoples trembled to
hear the opinion of an individual. But now we court our subjects
and flatter them, and just as a vote of thanks is granted at anyone's
pleasure, so even more eagerly is a prosecution decided on[1].'

Thrasea's words express well the opinion which a later generation held of Republican methods of provincial administration, and
enough has been said to show that they state the facts correctly.
In spite of much legislation in the interests of the provincials, the
welfare of a province depended unduly on the personal character
of its governor, and, as has been shown, upright behaviour on the
part of a governor, if it brought him popularity in his province,
was likely to make him enemies in Rome. At a period when the
standard of political morality was low, few of Rome's representatives abroad were able to make the welfare of the governed their
first consideration. And if Rome was unpopular in the provinces,
the governors were not the only people who were to blame. To
say nothing of the tax collectors, every province was full of
business men (*negotiatores*) who were more concerned with money-
lending than with regular trade. 'No Gaul', says Cicero in a speech
delivered in 69 B.C., 'carries through any business without the
intervention of a Roman citizen: not a penny changes hands in
Gaul without passing through ledgers kept by Roman citizens[2].'
Not many years later one of these Gallic *negotiatores*, P. Um-
brenus, tried to persuade the Allobroges to make common cause
with Catiline in his campaign for the abolition of debt.

The comparatively few Roman citizens who were resident in
the provinces in the period which we are discussing enjoyed undue
consideration. It was fairly easy for any senator who wished to
visit the provinces to obtain what was known as a *legatio libera*,
conferring on him the status of an ambassador of Rome with the
right to make burdensome demands on the inhabitants. Cicero
secured in 63 B.C. the passing of a law limiting these privileges

---

[1] Tacitus, *Ann.* xv, 21. [2] *pro Fonteio*, 5, 11.

to one year, and further restrictions were imposed by Caesar, but
the institution was too popular with members of the senatorial
class to make its abolition possible. Romans were normally regarded in the provinces as foreigners, and provincials who had
obtained the citizenship as instruments of an alien rule. 'If any
Roman governor,' says Cicero, 'is led to restrain himself by respect
for principle, no one gives him credit for integrity because of the
crowd of self-seekers who surround him. It is impossible to find
words to express the hatred with which we are regarded by
foreign peoples because of the greed and violence of those who in
recent years have been sent by us to command armies among
them. Do you imagine that any temple in these lands has been
regarded as holy, any city as worthy of respect, any private house
as safe from attack? No one is fit to be sent to the war against
Mithridates who is not able to keep his hands, his eyes and his
thoughts off the money of our allies, their wives and children, and
the treasures contained in their temples and cities[1].'

It would not however be fair to the Roman Republic to end on
this note. Cicero was not the only senator who had a conscience.
The senatorial class as a whole was well aware of the difficulty of
the problem, and it was probably for this reason that it was normally opposed to annexation. It was well informed about what was
going on in the provinces. Governors were expected to send to
the Senate and magistrates despatches containing an account of
their doings, in which they were allowed to give free expression
to their complaints and criticisms[2]. These despatches were not
pigeonholed in the archives of a Foreign Office, but were widely
read.

Again, the right of provincials to send embassies to Rome
was fully recognized. Representatives of all the cities of Sicily
but two asked Cicero to undertake the prosecution of Verres.
During the month of February the hearing of embassies from
the provinces and foreign kings had precedence over all other
business in the Senate. Although regular provincial assemblies
first make their appearance under the Principate, even under the
Republic the representatives of cities could express the wishes of
the province as a whole. The sending of these embassies was so
popular that governors had sometimes to discourage them in the
interests of economy.

Finally, it must not be forgotten that leading men and leading
families in Rome watched over the interests of particular pro-

---

[1] *de imp. Cn. Pompei*, 22, 64.   [2] See above, p. 446 *sq.*

vinces and cities. Thus the Marcelli were *patroni* of Sicily, which had been conquered by their ancestor. The Fabii were interested in Transalpine Gaul, and the family of Cato in Spain. Marius was patron of Gaetulians whom he had conquered in the Jugurthan War. Cicero frequently mentions the interest felt by public men in particular cities, especially in the province of Asia.

It is therefore quite possible to pass too severe a judgment on the way in which Republican Rome dealt with this very difficult problem. Most of our evidence is derived from speeches delivered in the law-courts, and it would not be fair to treat the careers of Verres and Piso as typical. Many governors, such as Rutilius Rufus[1], were able to gain the confidence and affection of their subjects, and Lucullus was not the only man who took a strong stand against the financial interests. Romans were not fond of fine phrases, and it is therefore significant that Cicero is able to state as a platitude that it is the first duty of a governor to aim at the happiness of the governed[2]. When Augustus remodelled the system of provincial government, he had no need to introduce revolutionary changes. Little more was wanted than to enforce the laws passed under the Republic, to connect provincial government more closely with the task of frontier defence, and to see that Rome was represented in the provinces not by well-meaning amateurs but by men possessing knowledge and experience.

[1] On the legal position and career of Rutilius see above, p. 175 *sq.*
[2] *E.g. ad Q.F.* 1, 1, 8, 24.

CHAPTER XI

ROME IN THE ABSENCE OF POMPEY

I. THE FIRST CATILINARIAN CONSPIRACY

WHEN Pompey was invested with his commands against the pirates and King Mithridates, the political destiny of Rome was transferred from the Forum and the Senate House to his camp. During his absence the dominant issue in Roman affairs was whether he would return to destroy the Republic or to give it a new lease of life. Hence the conflicts which meantime opened in the city were waged under the shadow of his home-coming. But this did not make the battle any the more cool: indeed in domestic politics the period was one of continual storm and stress.

After Pompey's departure the senatorial aristocracy retaliated upon his agents with a counter-attack in the courts of law, where its influence remained strong despite the legislation of 70 B.C. Gabinius escaped prosecution by following Pompey to the East. But a fellow-tribune named C. Cornelius, who had given offence by his measures against jobbery in the Senate and in the praetors' courts (p. 342 *sq.*), was indicted on the conveniently vague charge of 'maiestas' ('contempt of the government'); and Manilius, the henchman of Pompey (p. 348 *sq.*), was implicated in two successive trials for 'res repetundae' (extortion) and 'maiestas' (66–5 B.C.)[1].

Note. By far the most valuable source for the period covered by this and the following chapter consists in the Letters of Cicero. Down to 61 B.C. the flow of his surviving correspondence is slender; from that point its volume grows much larger. Next in order of importance come the Speeches of Cicero, which were particularly plentiful in the year of his consulate. The Commentaries of Asconius and of an anonymous editor known as the 'Scholiast of Bobbio' on the Orations of Cicero, contain excellent historical notes. The *Bellum Catilinae* of Sallust adds little to what is contained in Cicero and is full of errors (p. 889 *sq.*). Suetonius' Life of Caesar is a rich quarry of raw materials. Among the Greek writers Dio Cassius is the most useful; his account goes into considerable detail and provides accurate dates. Plutarch's Lives of Cato Minor, Caesar, Cicero, Crassus and Pompey are of various degrees of historical interest; those of Cato and Cicero are the most important for this period. Appian's *Bella Civilia* is of less value than for the preceding and the following years. See further below, pp. 882 *sqq.*

[1] For a detailed discussion of the circumstances of Manilius' trials, see especially, C. John, *Die Entstehungsgeschichte der catilinarischen Verschwörung*, p. 712–3 n.

These senatorial reprisals did not involve any personage of importance; but they raised the political temperature and led to repeated outbreaks of mob violence. Indeed proceedings against both culprits had to be postponed until a special police force had been enrolled to protect the courts.

A more serious danger than these spasmodic attempts at intimidation arose from an organized plot by discontented aristocrats, the First Catilinarian Conspiracy. This movement was an after-effect of the consular elections for 65 B.C., which left three disappointed competitors with a sense of personal grievance. Two candidates, P. Autronius Paetus and P. Cornelius Sulla (a nephew of the dictator), had stood at the head of the poll, but had been found guilty of bribery under the Lex Calpurnia of 67 B.C. (p. 344), which deprived them alike of their consulships and of their seats in the Senate. A third applicant, L. Sergius Catilina, had not even been admitted to the contest. As this last-named personage will claim much of our attention in this chapter, he requires a few words of introduction.

Catiline was a scion of a decayed patrician family whose tarnished lustre he was firmly set on reviving. As an officer of Sulla in the Civil Wars he had borne himself gallantly, and to many who merely noted his iron constitution and his devil-may-care spirit he appeared a fine type of man. But with this soldierly bearing he combined spendthrift habits and a reckless disregard of human life. In the attractiveness of his outward manner he might compare with Sir Robert Catesby, but his blind instinct of violence degraded him to the level of a Thistlewood. After the Civil Wars Catiline acted as one of Sulla's chief agents in the proscriptions, and rumours, perhaps unfounded but not unnatural, ascribed to his helping hand a series of premature deceases in his own family. For his services to Sulla Catiline received no political reward; but at the purgation of the Senate in 70 B.C. the censors turned a blind eye on his conspicuous record, and in 68 he rose to the praetorship. As propraetor of Africa in 67–6 he caused complaints loud enough to draw remonstrances from the Senate, and on his return to Rome in the summer of 66 he was promptly marked down for prosecution on a charge of extortion. It was probably on account of this impending trial that the consul Volcacius Tullus, who presided over the elections, took counsel with some leading senators and refused to accept his name as a candidate. In so doing the returning officer was acting within his powers; but since at the moment a formal indictment had not yet been presented against

Catiline, his disqualification was not absolute, but depended on the consul's discretion[1]. Volcacius' decision therefore might well appear unfair and arbitrary to the rejected applicant.

The three aggrieved men agreed to seek revenge by murdering the two rival candidates who had slipped in at the supplementary elections, together with a number of personal enemies in the Senate, among whom Volcacius and his advisers were no doubt included. Their plan was to make a sudden assault upon their victims on the first day of 65 B.C., when the incoming consuls would be meeting the Senate on the Capitol, and to seize the fasces of the murdered couple on behalf of Autronius and Sulla. These self-constituted consuls would then repay Catiline for his services by impeding his prosecution and facilitating his candidature for the consulship of 64 B.C. The plot also included a few subordinate members whose motive for participation probably was financial embarrassment. The most notable of these was a dissolute young man named Cn. Calpurnius Piso. According to the historian Sallust[2], it was part of the scheme to procure for Piso the governorship of the two Spains. While this possibility cannot be denied, it is more likely that the mission of Piso to Spain was an afterthought, and was planned by a bigger brain for a more ambitious purpose, which we shall presently discuss. Among the three ringleaders Sulla, who possessed more money than enterprise, probably confined himself to the part of paymaster. Autronius, who was a born rioter and at his recent trial had attempted to disperse the court with a band of gladiators, no doubt cast himself for a more active rôle. But in the subsequent conspiracy of 63 B.C. he was not even second in command. It is therefore more likely that in the present plot he merely followed in the wake of Catiline, in whom we may see the real leader of the movement.

At best the First Catilinarian Conspiracy was a harebrained scheme. It was naïvely optimistic to hope that the Senate, with all the resources of Italy and several experienced generals at its disposal, would tamely acquiesce in the murder of its members by a mere handful of cut-throats with no wider following. But the plotters did not even take the elementary precaution of secrecy. On New Year's Eve Catiline was observed to be making overt preparations for some kind of foul play; the Senate summarily empowered the two incoming consuls to improvise a bodyguard, and on the following day they appeared with an escort sufficient to

[1] On the question of Catiline's first *professio* for the consulship, see especially E. v. Stern, *Catilina*, pp. 31–42.
[2] *Cat.* 18, 5.

deter the assassins from making a move. According to Sallust[1]
the plotters merely postponed their attack until a later session of
the Senate on February 5th; but the reticence of Cicero on this
point is almost conclusive against this view. However this may be,
the threatened consuls outlived their year of office.

II. THE INTRIGUES OF CRASSUS FOR A FOREIGN COMMAND

The rashness of the conspirators in inviting detection was
matched by their luck in escaping punishment. The Senate held
an inquiry into the affair, and despite the nonchalant attitude of
one of the threatened consuls, L. Manlius Torquatus, who pooh-
poohed its suspicions as being based on mere rumour, it should
have had no difficulty in collecting enough evidence to justify proceedings; but in deference to a tribune's veto it hastily abandoned
its researches. But this was not the full measure of the plotters'
good fortune. Not content to forgive and forget, the Senate promoted Piso to be governor of Nearer Spain with the title of
'quaestor pro praetore.' In view of Piso's lack of experience, to
say nothing of his reputation, it cannot be supposed that the
Senate selected him in the belief that he was the best man available,
nor yet, as some ancient writers have suggested, because it was
afraid of him[2]. We are thus driven back upon the explanation
furnished by Sallust[3], that the Senate was acting under pressure
from M. Crassus.

Of all politicians in Rome who looked forward with anxiety to
Pompey's return, Crassus believed himself to have most reason for
alarm. If Pompey's home-coming from a Mithridatic war, like
Sulla's, should be made an occasion for reprisals upon domestic
enemies, might not his head be the first to fall? Under this menace
Crassus directed his restless energy to the throwing up of out-
works in all directions against Pompey's anticipated attack. The
defensive preparations of Crassus in the years from 65 to 63
were the most important, though not the most sensational, event
in the history of that period.

Crassus' first line of defence lay in a provincial command, in
which he might hope to establish a power to match that of
Pompey. Among the available provinces Spain was known to him
by personal acquaintance, for under the Marian terror he had
taken refuge there; and the difficulties which it presented to invading armies had recently been illustrated in the Sertorian War,

[1] *Cat.* 18, 6.   [2] *Ib.* 19, 2.   [3] *Ib.* 17, 7; 19, 1.

when Pompey nearly buried his reputation there (pp. 321 *sqq.*).
Therefore, when Providence early in 65 B.C. offered a vacancy in
Nearer Spain, Crassus snatched at his opportunity. Nevertheless,
policy and personal habit alike prompted him not to show his hand
openly, but to work through agents who might at need be repudiated. Such underlings he always knew how to procure, for he
made a regular practice of attracting broken or compromised men
to his service, and in 65 B.C. the fiasco of the First Catilinarian
Conspiracy gave him a muddied pool to fish in. Nay more, the
means of landing his fish lay ready to his hand. In the Senate
Crassus always exercised considerable influence, for he had many
of its members in his pocket; and in 65 B.C. his hold on that assembly was strengthened by his recent election to a censorship,
which gave him power to expel inconvenient senators. Thus the
mystery of the *dénouement* to the First Catilinarian Plot is resolved.
Crassus, so we may conclude, put pressure upon the Senate to
hush up Catiline's plot and to give unmerited preferment to Piso;
the object of his intrigue was to acquire control of Spain through
Piso's agency.

The patronage exercised by Crassus on behalf of Piso and his
partners has given rise to a confident suspicion that he was their
accomplice from the outset. Some ancient authors went so far as
to assert that the purpose of the conspiracy was not to find consulships for Autronius and Sulla, but a dictatorship for Crassus[1]. If
this was so, the First Catilinarian Plot was a movement of far
greater importance than we have indicated. But the writers who
thus incriminated Crassus were mostly his political opponents,
and their story, even if supported by better authority, would be
difficult to accept. Though Crassus no doubt was unscrupulous
enough, he was certainly not deficient in subtlety, and it does him
injustice to suppose that he would have countenanced, let alone
planned, a crime that would defeat its own purpose. To say nothing
of the absurdity of reviving a discredited office like that of dictator, for Crassus to usurp power by open murder would have been
playing into Pompey's hands: it would have furnished Pompey
with a valid excuse for attacking him, as Sulla attacked Carbo, and
it would have left him without such shreds of moral authority to
mobilize Italy in self-defence as Carbo possessed. In all probability, Crassus was neither the author of the First Catilinarian
Conspiracy nor an accomplice; his part in it was merely to shield
the culprits after its exposure, so as to use them for his own ends.

[1] Suet. *Div. Iul.* 9, citing the annalist Tanusius, the edicts of Bibulus, and
a speech of the elder Curio.

If Crassus did not originate the First Catilinarian Plot, at any rate he made a clear gain out of it. But the fish which he landed was spoilt in the cooking. In selecting a novice like Piso for his instrument Crassus no doubt guarded against immediate detection by Pompey. On the other hand, he invited the risk of failure through the incompetence of his untried assistant. On his arrival in Spain, Piso, whose head had been turned by his good fortune, proved no Sertorius, and instead of conciliating the natives insulted them. For these affronts to Castilian pride he presently paid with his life (late in 65 or early in 64), and thus lost Spain for Crassus. It has, indeed, been supposed that Crassus made an attempt to replace Piso by a half-ruined speculator named P. Sittius, who went to Further Spain in 64 B.C. with an empty purse, and subsequently became a leader of armed bands in Mauretania. But there is no adequate reason for doubting Cicero's assurances that Sittius' interests in Spain were purely commercial[1]. Crassus made no attempt to recover the control of Spain after the death of Piso.

But Crassus did not wait for the loss of Spain before he laid plans for the acquisition of an alternative province in Egypt. As a bulwark against Pompey, this country had an ideal position. Situated on Pompey's flank, it could not safely be ignored by him; yet a resolute defender might hold it against greatly superior forces, as several of Alexander's marshals and successors had found to their cost. A pretext for interference in Egypt lay to hand in the uncertain title by which the reigning king, Ptolemy Auletes, held his throne, and in the existence of a will, presumably spurious but never proved false, under which his predecessor, Ptolemy Alexander II, had bequeathed his realm to the Roman People (see p. 390). Moreover, as a bait to the Roman People to take up its legacy, it was easy to point out that the Ptolemies possessed the largest treasure in the Mediterranean world, and that the surplus grain of Egypt might readily be diverted to the Roman market. To all appearances, then, the bill for the annexation of Egypt which Crassus brought before the Concilium Plebis by means of some friendly tribune had every prospect of success. None the less, it was rejected. This strange rebuff to Crassus was partly due to the opposition of the more resolute nobles under the leadership of Q. Catulus, who upheld the Senate's habitual policy of non-interference in Egypt; but we may believe that the chief credit for it belongs to Cicero. Of this adversary it will be sufficient to say for the present that he considered himself to hold a watching

[1] *pro Sulla*, 20, 56–9.

brief for Pompey, and that on more than one occasion he exposed the hidden purpose of Crassus' intrigues against him. Though the extant fragments of his speech *De Rege Alexandrino* are not sufficient to reveal the complete thread of his argument, yet they show clearly enough that it was directed against Crassus' policy of annexation. The rejection of the Egyptian bill was the first and perhaps the most important of the series of victories which Cicero gained over Crassus in these three years.

III. THE CONSULAR ELECTIONS FOR 63 B.C.

Anticipating the risk of failure in the provinces, Crassus had set about to fit other strings to his bow. In his capacity as censor for the year 65 B.C. he made a bid for the support of the inhabitants of Transpadane Gaul. By a curious anomaly these had not received the full Roman franchise in 89 B.C., but had been put off with the inferior 'Latin' status (p. 196). Crassus now proposed to inscribe them on the censors' burgess-roll. This method of enfranchisement by a mere stroke of the pen would have been invalid even if Crassus' colleague had agreed to it; but the other censor, Q. Catulus, took his usual line of opposition to any change: indeed, he thwarted Crassus with such persistence that not only the burgess-list but also the roll of senators remained unrevised during their term of office. Since Crassus could hardly have failed to foresee this deadlock, his move on behalf of the Transpadanes was plainly no more than a manifesto. But his mere gesture of goodwill was significant, for Crassus did not bestow friendship but invested it for the sake of dividends. His interest in the Transpadanes may be explained in part by their potential voting power. But in view of their great distance from Rome, which would prevent their regular attendance at the Comitia, their vote could hardly have been a decisive consideration. The importance of Transpadane Gaul lay rather in the fact that it was becoming the chief recruiting ground for the Roman armies. Presumably, therefore, the main object of Crassus' manifesto was to secure the military support of the Transpadanes, as Carbo in the civil war against Sulla had won that of the Samnites (pp. 270 *sqq.*). It is probable that a detachment of stalwarts at once came from beyond the Po to Rome to place their strong arms at Crassus' disposal, for in 64 B.C. the Senate found it necessary to expel all Transpadanes then residing in the city. This purgation of Rome was accomplished by means of a tribunician law (the Lex Papia), which made all non-citizens liable to eviction but in practice was mainly directed at the unenfranchised residue of Italians.

In 64 B.C. the duel between Crassus and Cicero, which had opened in the previous year over the Egyptian question, was transferred to the field of the consular elections. Though no less than seven candidates entered, only three were in the running. One of these, Catiline, had been kept waiting for two years before he could secure nomination. The trial for extortion, which in 66 had been deemed too imminent to allow of his candidature, was not actually held until 65, and did not end in time for him to take part in the elections of that year. But if the case had dragged on to an exasperating length, there was never much doubt of its issue. The evidence from Africa, it is true, was extremely damning, but the jury turned a deaf ear to it. According to the usual practice by which the members of the nobility helped each other out in the courts, Catiline's defence was undertaken by the consul Torquatus (who affected to believe that extortion was as foreign as homicide to the defendant's nature) and by other senators of high standing. Better still, the prosecutor P. Clodius opened his perverse political career by a suicidal complaisance in the selection and rejection of jurors. Thus Catiline cleared himself in time for the polls of summer 64 B.C.

Once admitted to the canvass, Catiline bribed on a scale which obviously exceeded his own means. Evidently he was receiving subsidies from some wealthy wire-puller, and we need not hesitate to accept the belief then current that his paymaster was Crassus. In 65 Crassus had done Catiline a good turn in saving him from the consequences of his murder plot; and in view of his later connection with Clodius it is not unlikely that he had a hand in the preconcerted failure of Catiline's prosecution. It would appear, then, that Crassus was at considerable pains to facilitate Catiline's candidature at the elections of 64. But what manner of service did Crassus expect from Catiline in return? For legislation Crassus might confidently reckon on finding a more suitable instrument among the tribunes. We may therefore assume that the part which he reserved for Catiline was military: with or without the sanction of the Senate, Catiline could safely be trusted to make resolute use of his consular authority in an emergency mobilization of Italy. It appears, then, that in supporting Catiline's candidature for the consulship of 63 Crassus was taking precautions against the chance of Pompey's home-coming in that year.

According to a common electoral practice Catiline allied himself with another candidate, C. Antonius, who also was in Crassus' pay. Though of distinguished family—he was a son of the orator

M. Antonius and a brother of the admiral M. Antonius—this personage was of the sort that 'were faithful neither to God nor to themselves.' His one resolute action had been to retrieve his expulsion from the Senate in 70 B.C. by standing for a second praetorship and thus once more qualifying for the consulship. The rest of his career was a record of alternate pilfering and profligacy. It may seem strange that Catiline and Crassus should have leagued themselves with such a good-for-nothing associate. But a nonentity like Antonius could at least perform one negative service; he could hold the second consulship against a third candidate whose election would have neutralized Catiline's victory at the polls.

The third candidate, M. Tullius Cicero, was the best qualified in all respects but one. Unlike most of the young Italians who came to try their fortune in Rome, Cicero was not content with a few minor magistracies, but aspired to fill the highest posts and even to become the leading statesman of the Republic; and his gifts appeared commensurate with his ambitions. His oratorical talents, besides bringing him fame and wealth, had provided him with many influential supporters: though in his leading forensic case, the trial of Verres, he had been counsel for the prosecution, he had specialized in the arts of defence, and had thus laid under obligation many persons of high standing. He had won the favour of the equestrian class, both of the financiers at Rome, of whom he was a recognized spokesman, and of the country squires from whom he was himself sprung. His exuberant wit and his geniality, as yet unclouded by disappointments, had won him friends in many quarters. In the junior posts of his official career he had earned a good name by his industry and integrity. But he was a *novus homo*: his father had not been a senator, but a plain country gentleman. Would his lack of ancestry disqualify him in the eyes of the nobility? So much at least was known to all, that the aristocracy had steadily maintained their hold on the electoral hustings while their other privileges were crumbling, and for the previous thirty years had succeeded in retaining the consulship within their own ranks. Cicero's misgivings on this score are reflected in a surviving pamphlet named the *Commentariolum Petitionis*, or 'Electioneering Manual,' which is usually held to be from the pen of his brother Quintus[1]: its author, while making a brave show of electoral optimism, cannot stifle an undertone of anxiety.

[1] The authorship of the *Commentariolum* cannot be regarded as certain. But its historical value is none the less assured, for the composer, whoever he may have been, was excellently posted up in the circumstances of the election.

In 65 B.C. Cicero, wishing to leave no stone unturned in aid of his candidature, had made a bid for Catiline's co-operation by offering to defend him in his impending trial[1]. But Catiline, who had a full measure of patrician contempt for an *inquilinus* (immigrant) like Cicero, and saw no need of his services as an advocate or a canvasser, rejected his advances. Until the eve of the polling Catiline and Antonius ran against Cicero, and level with him. But Catiline once again proved his own worst enemy. With characteristic recklessness he disregarded the decent precautions with which electoral malpractice at Rome was shrouded, and although on this occasion he probably had no intention of violence, yet his bearing was sufficiently provocative to inspire rumours of a fresh conspiracy. The Senate, suddenly taking alarm, gave instructions for the disbandment of all clubs save those of bona fide craftsmen, and recommended that the existing law on corrupt practices should be stiffened. This proposal, it is true, was vetoed by a tribune among Catiline's supporters, yet it gave rise to a further debate in the Senate at which Cicero seized the opportunity of deepening its sense of danger. The *Oratio in Toga Candida*, which he delivered on this occasion, survives only in fragments; but these remnants suffice to show that Cicero artfully mingled abuse of his fellow-candidates with broad hints of a hidden hand that directed their crimes. Under the impression made by this speech a sufficient number of the votes directed by the nobility was diverted to Cicero to bring him in at the head of the poll. Antonius, whose family name was a good electoral asset, came in an indifferent second, Catiline a very good third.

IV. THE LAND BILL OF RULLUS

When Cicero entered upon his hard-won consulship, he expected, as did Disraeli on breaking into the preserve of the British premiership, to 'rest and be thankful.' As events fell out, he was engaged in a continuous round of battles in defence of the existing political order. On the first day of office he greeted the Senate with a polemic against a tribune named P. Servilius Rullus, and in his first popular harangue he returned to the charge. The subject of dispute was a new agrarian bill, which purported to revive and to extend the land-reform policy of the Gracchi, but in fact had a more dangerous object. Ostensibly Rullus was setting

---

[1] In spite of doubts, it is practically certain that Cicero did not defend Catiline. Had he done so, his action would not have placed a stigma upon him according to the rules of the Roman or of the English Bar.

out to appease existing land hunger by a generous policy of settlement. In Italy he proposed to resume all State domains, including the former territories of Capua and Casilinum in the most fertile region of Campania, and to acquire further acreage at need by purchase out of the public funds. In the provinces he provided for the calling-in of leases on confiscated municipal lands, as at Leontini in Sicily, at Corinth, at Old and at New Carthage, and on the escheated family estates of deposed dynasties in the East. Under this last head he included, in addition to smaller tracts in Macedonia, Bithynia, and Cilicia, the extensive properties of the Attalids and of Mithridates in Asia Minor, and of the Ptolemies in Egypt. For the distribution or sale of these territories he set up a board of ten commissioners. These decemvirs he armed with final judicial authority on all questions of title to land and of compensation, and with powers to amass a purchase fund by calling in outstanding public debts (*e.g.* from the proceeds of Sulla's confiscations and of the sales of recent war-booty), and by drawing upon the prospective new revenues accruing from Pompey's conquests.

On the face of it, this measure had some attractive features. It offered relief to those whom economic pressure or Sulla's evictions had left with insufficient land or none; it respected existing titles of ownership and offered a fair market price for estates acquired by purchase. But on closer inspection it assumed an ugly look. The scale of the decemvirs' operations and the powers entrusted to them exceeded the requirements of even the most ambitious scheme of settlement. The method of appointing the board, by a minority of seventeen tribes as a substitute for the plenary Concilium Plebis, was suggestive of jobbery: the favoured tribes, it is true, were to be selected by lot, but this process did not preclude manipulation. Again, granted the need of feeding the hungry, it was wasteful to replace efficient sitting tenants on the public estates, as at Capua and Carthage, by new and untried cultivators. Above all, it was manifestly unfair to embark on any comprehensive scheme of land distribution in the absence of Pompey, and, as it were, behind his back. Not only had Pompey's conquests provided part of the decemvirs' land and revenue, but the thirty-five or forty thousand soldiers whom he was about to discharge manifestly had a prior claim to the allotments. This general disregard of Pompey's interests was the most significant feature of Rullus' measure, and it provides the clue to its real intentions. Though the Lex Servilia might incidentally serve the purpose of social reform, its chief aim was to hold up the land required by Pompey for his veterans. This object, and the method of achieving it, reveal to us the real author of the bill. Crassus, who in earlier days had amassed wealth by holding real estate against a rise, now planned a 'corner' in allotment-land in order to sell it to Pompey on his own terms. In view of the difficulties which Pompey actually experienced in pensioning off his troops, we may recognize in the Lex Servilia the most typical and the most cunning of Crassus' intrigues: with one harmless-looking move he was about to checkmate Pompey.

But Cicero lost no time in taking the field against Rullus. In his anxiety to discredit his opponent at all costs he piled bad arguments on top of good. He profited by ambiguities in the drafting of the bill to exaggerate *ad absurdum* the powers of the decemvirs and the magnitude of their operations. He awakened an obsolete prejudice in denouncing the reconstitution of Capua as a Roman colony—one of the most praiseworthy provisions in the law. In defiance of his own better judgment he advised the proletariate to live like gentlefolk on the public purse rather than degrade themselves with productive labour. But he also emphasized the essential point that Rullus was merely a pawn in the hand of a more formidable player, and that his bill was in reality aimed at Pompey. Not content with out-arguing Rullus, Cicero outbid Crassus for the support of his colleague Antonius: in place of a seat on the decemviral board he offered him first choice of a lucrative proconsular province. With these counter-measures Cicero was entirely successful; he provided such a chilly reception for Rullus' bill that its author withdrew it without putting it to the vote.

This decisive defeat of Crassus marks the end of his campaign of precautions against Pompey. His time was now running short: Pompey would soon be free to return to Italy, and any further intrigues against him might merely hasten his home-coming. With the failure of Crassus' schemes Rome was freed for the time being from the risk of a fresh civil war. Not that Crassus desired such a war: undoubtedly he would far sooner have struck a bargain with Pompey than have drawn sword against him. Yet Crassus in 65 to 63 B.C. was playing with fire, and he might no more have been able to prevent a drift into war than Caesar's opponents in the years from 52 to 49. It was fortunate for Rome, and probably also for Crassus, that in his game of diamond-cut-diamond with Cicero the edge of his adversary's wits cut the more shrewdly.

V. CAESAR'S PROPAGANDA

Among the associates of Crassus in these three years we have
not yet mentioned the most important of all, C. Julius Caesar.
Born in 100 B.C.[1], Caesar belonged to a patrician family which
could trace back its ancestry to kings of Rome and very gods, but
had never yet produced a person of outstanding ability. Like
Catiline, Caesar believed that his lineage gave him a preferential
claim to political honours, and he showed the same unflinching
determination to win his way to high office. As a young man he
had gained distinction in a minor seat of war (p. 359); but he had
taken no part in the great campaigns of Pompey or Lucullus, and
so had been thrown back on the arts of the Forum for political
advancement. Despite a natural talent for oratory he had failed to
make a name for himself in the law-courts. Greater success attended his courting of the electoral rabble, for to the usual pro-
fuseness of the Roman noble he added unusual abilities as a show-
man: the gladiatorial games and beast hunts which he provided
during his aedileship (65 B.C.) were remembered both for their
sumptuousness and for the artistry of their display. Hence Caesar
was marked out by popular favour for the high honours which he
coveted, and in 63 B.C. he achieved a double success at the polls.
In that year the death of Metellus Pius created a vacancy in the
Chief Pontificate. This post was regarded as a preserve for elder
statesmen, and it was out of the question that the College of
Pontiffs, which since Sulla's time had recovered the right of appointment, should consider a junior aspirant like Caesar. But a
tribune named T. Labienus, who was Caesar's lieutenant on more
than one field, carried an *ad hoc* measure in the Concilium Plebis,
by which the Lex Domitia of 104 B.C.[2] was re-enacted and the
choice of the Pontifex Maximus was transferred to an electoral
college of seventeen tribes selected (ostensibly) by lot. Caesar now
appeared as a candidate and staked his last penny on the contest:
on the morning of the poll he warned his mother not to expect him
back save as Pontifex Maximus, for only so could he face her—
and his creditors. The luck that befriends resolute gamblers attended Caesar in this as in greater ventures, for he won an easy
victory over his two rivals, Q. Catulus and P. Servilius Isauricus,
consuls of 78 and 79 B.C. But the very circumstances of his elec-

---

[1] This date, which is supported by several ancient authorities (Vell. Pat.
II, 41, 2; Plutarch, *Caesar*, 69; Suet. *Div. Iul.* 88; Appian, *Bell. Civ.* II,
149, 620), is plainly preferable to 102 B.C., which has been suggested by
modern scholars on wholly unconvincing grounds.　　　[2] See p. 163 *sq.*

tion are a warning that the functions of the Pontifex Maximus were no longer taken seriously; it is even doubtful whether Caesar recouped his expenses from the perquisites of the office. More important, if less notorious, was Caesar's success as a candidate for a praetorship in 62 B.C., which carried with it the right to a provincial governorship and high military command.

But Caesar's electoral campaigns involved his modest family fortune in debts which gossip estimated at fantastic figures. It is probable that in 65 and 64 B.C. Caesar had already attached himself to Crassus by a cash nexus which bound him for several years to come. Hence we find him at this period acting repeatedly in collusion with Crassus. In 65 B.C. he had been marked out by his patron to play the same part in Egypt as Piso in Spain. Current rumour also proclaimed that in the murder plot falsely attributed to Crassus (really the First Catilinarian Conspiracy) he had been Crassus' principal accomplice, and that in 64 and 63 he had abetted the candidature of Catiline and the legislation of Rullus. On Caesar's behalf we may confidently reject the charge of participation in the First Catilinarian Plot, which is even less plausible than the accusation levelled against Crassus: however drastic Caesar may have been in his political methods, he did not stoop to assassination. But we have adequate evidence that Caesar was in league with Catiline in the year 64 B.C.; we may see his hand in various beneficial clauses of the Servilian Law which anticipated the provisions of Caesar's own agrarian measures in 59 B.C.; and we may take for granted that he supported the campaign on behalf of the Transpadanes, of whom he was a more steadfast, and, as the event proved, a more successful champion than Crassus. But in spite of some casual affinities between Crassus' political views and Caesar's, it cannot be supposed that their alliance was wholly determined by these, still less that Caesar was the managing partner who supplied all the ideas while Crassus merely found the money. On one fundamental point Caesar's personal policy diverged sharply from that of his senior partner. In 67 and 66 B.C. he had been conspicuous in his support of the Gabinian and Manilian laws, and his attitude to Pompey in 63 and 62 B.C. plainly reveals his anxiety to keep on good terms with Crassus' principal enemy. If Caesar nevertheless abetted Crassus' intrigues in 65 and 64 B.C., this was no doubt the interest which he had to pay on his borrowings. We may indeed suspect that he was hardly less pleased than Cicero at the failure of Crassus' schemes.

For a true index of Caesar's political views at this period we must turn to other of his activities in which the influence of Crassus does not show through. From these it appears that Caesar's dominant purpose in these years was to protest against the vindictiveness of Sulla and of other victors in the recent Civil Wars. These protests, it is true, were sadly belated, and their practical effect was negligible, yet they are of interest as showing the trend of Caesar's mind. Though his policy may have been in part inspired by his marriage connection with the house of Marius, it probably had its mainspring in the essential conciliatoriness of his political thought, which rebelled against blind excesses of partisanship.

In 64 B.C. Caesar took advantage of his appointment as chairman of the *quaestio de sicariis* (the court for murder) to invite an information against two of Sulla's executioners, L. Luscius and L. Bellienus, and to press for their condemnation. This prosecution was a legal mistake, in that Sulla's agents were covered by an act of indemnity; a political error, because it uselessly raked up the embers of a dying controversy; and a tactical blunder, for it exposed Caesar to reprisals. A senator named L. Lucceius followed up these cases with a charge against Catiline, who notoriously had been headsman-in-chief to Sulla. Caesar, who at that time was under obligation to Crassus to help Catiline to the consulship, postponed the hearing until after the polling and eventually secured Catiline's acquittal. In so doing he honoured his bond to his creditor but stultified his previous *beau geste*.

In the early part of 63 B.C. Caesar initiated another political trial. His victim on this occasion was an aged senator named C. Rabirius, who was alleged to have taken a hand in the killing of Saturninus in 100 B.C. (p. 171). This prosecution was legally justifiable, for granted that Rabirius had killed Saturninus, his action was a mere application of lynch law and could not be excused by appeal to the *senatus consultum ultimum* which the Senate had issued against Saturninus (pp. 86 *sqq.*). But the affair of Rabirius belonged to an even remoter past than that of Luscius and Bellienus. Moreover Caesar, whose instincts of showmanship here got the better of his discretion, gave the proceedings a dramatic turn which in effect reduced them to a farce[1]. Instead of bringing Rabirius before the *quaestio de sicariis* he resuscitated a court of *perduellio* (high treason), which dated back to the kings of Rome and had become obsolete soon after. At his instigation the handy man Labienus carried a bill in the Concilium Plebis for the

---

[1] Great uncertainty attaches to the details of procedure in Rabirius' case. The account in the text follows generally that of E. G. Hardy (*Journal of Philology*, XXXIV, 1915, pp. 12–39).

appointment of two judges, to be selected by lot from a panel drawn up by the praetor urbanus Q. Metellus Celer. With a discernment which probably surprised no one, the lot happened upon a distant relative of Caesar named L. Caesar (consul in 64 B.C.), and upon Caesar himself. As spokesman of this family party Caesar incontinently condemned Rabirius and ordered him, in accordance with an archaic ritual for the removal of polluted objects, to be tied to a cross and suspended from an 'unlucky' (barren) tree. This sentence was no doubt intended to lead up to a trial on appeal in the Comitia Centuriata; but it was forthwith quashed by Cicero, who induced the Senate to pronounce Caesar's barbarous sentence invalid and vetoed further proceedings by virtue of his consular authority.

But the case was presently brought before the People by an alternative method. Labienus instituted a fresh action by summoning Rabirius before the Concilium Plebis on sundry minor (and probably fictitious) charges, to which he subsequently added an indictment for murder. Hereupon, by an unusual but not unprecedented procedure, he arranged with the praetor urbanus to transfer the case to the Comitia Centuriata. The action now proceeded to its final hearing, but at this stage Cicero re-appeared as counsel for the defence. With doubtful relevance but unquestionable debating skill the consul denounced the 'unpopular' sentence of crucifixion and represented the whole case as an attack upon the *senatus consultum ultimum* and, by implication, upon the consul to whom the Senate in 100 B.C. had entrusted the execution of its decree, to wit Caesar's own relative and hero C. Marius. But before the Comitia could proceed to vote, it was dispersed by Labienus in obedience to a signal from the praetor Metellus Celer (the lowering of a red flag on the Janiculan Mount), which in far-back days had conveyed the message, 'Fall in everybody, the Etruscans are coming.' This last incident, which no doubt had been preconcerted by Labienus and Caesar with Metellus[1], reduced *ad absurdum* a case that throughout had smacked of comic opera. Whatever lesson Caesar intended to convey by the prosecution of Rabirius was lost in the strangeness of its *mise-en-scène*.

If Caesar had to be content with a drawn match in the affair of

---

[1] This collusion has often been denied. Yet it is incredible that Labienus and the People should have allowed themselves to be put off by the flag trick, if they had been in grim earnest. A judge and jury at the Old Bailey would not throw up an important case at the news that the Spanish Armada flares had been lit on Hampstead Heath.

Rabirius, he suffered downright defeat over another issue on which he was undoubtedly in earnest. By means of some friendly tribune he brought in a bill for the reinstatement of the children of Sulla's victims in their political rights. This measure was thrown out at the instance of Cicero, who objected that Sulla's laws must stand or fall together, and that the present was no time for toying with revolution; fourteen years were to elapse before Caesar was able to secure tardy justice for the disqualified. Caesar's plea for the sons of the proscribed is of interest as revealing the germs of his future statesmanship, which was more concerned to heal the wounds of civil dissension than to keep them festering. It is here rather than in the attacks on Luscius, Bellienus and Rabirius that we discern the real Caesar. On the other hand, Cicero in this case was running counter to his normal line of thought, which equally condemned Sulla's reprisals and favoured a conciliatory policy. It has been suspected that Cicero's hands were tied on this point by a compact with the nobility in return for their electoral support. Yet the consul might at this time plead honestly, if mistakenly, that his first duty was to stand fast. His best efforts were soon to be required to obstruct new moves of a kind that might have pushed the Republic over a precipice.

VI. *NOVAE TABULAE*

By his defeat at the elections of 64 B.C. Catiline had lost not only the consulship but the support of Crassus, who could not afford to wait another twelvemonth for the success of his candidate. Left to his own resources, Catiline could not finance another electoral campaign with the same open hand. But each reverse merely strengthened his determination to win a prize which he regarded as his birthright; and if he could not pay for votes in cash, he could issue promissory notes. Accordingly he renewed his candidature in 63 on a platform of *novae tabulae* or a 'clean slate,' offering a general cancelling of debts in return for his election. We may also ascribe to Catiline's instigation an abortive bankruptcy bill which a tribune had introduced earlier in the year, no doubt with a view to testing public sentiment.

In promising relief to debtors Catiline was resuming a policy which had borne good fruit in the early Republic and was supported by the precedent of the Lex Valeria of 86 B.C., by which current debts were scaled down by 75 per cent. (p. 266). But before inscribing Catiline's name on the brief list of Rome's social reformers, we must inquire whose votes he was intent on capturing. His programme was plainly not democratic in the sense of being attractive to the urban proletariate, who had no assets, no credit, and therefore no debts. To the rustic population it offered a real alleviation of burdens. From early times the Italian peasant had lived near the border line of indebtedness. Since the age of the great foreign conquests the influx of alien corn and labour had deprived him of a rise in the price of his work and his products. During the Civil Wars he had been exposed to more or less legalized robbery. When driven to borrow he became the prey of petty usurers, and in the ordinary courts of law he could expect nothing but strict justice. But if the sufferings of this class were evident, its electoral value was highly problematic. In general the small cultivators lived in the more remote and sparsely populated regions of Italy, and their vote in consequence was difficult to organize. It is significant that the only considerable group of rustic adherents to Catiline's cause were old soldiers of Sulla who had been hastily settled on confiscated lands in the Arno valley and had ever since lived on their capital. In all probability the genuine Italian peasant counted for little in Catiline's plans.

It appears, then, that Catiline's propaganda was mainly addressed to the higher grades of Roman society. Among the *equites* he could hope to gain stray supporters who had run into debt through unwary speculation in land or in foreign loans. But in general Roman financiers tempered their enterprise with abundance of caution. For their loans they demanded ample cover, and in their tax-farming operations they distributed risks by parcelling out their capital among several joint-stock concerns. In any case, the *equites* as a class owned rather than owed debts, and so could only have an adverse interest in bankruptcy acts. There remains the senatorial nobility. Individual members of this order had acquired great wealth by inheritance, by warfare, by extortion in the provinces, or, as Crassus, by beating the *equites* at their own game. But the aristocracy in general lacked time and inclination for money-making. On the other hand they stood committed to heavy expenditure in support of their station: frequent bribes to the electors and the upkeep of a permanent army of clients were the self-imposed price of their political ascendancy. Furthermore, the liquidation of debt among the nobility was hampered by a sentimental entail on ancestral estates which disinclined even solvent senators to meet their obligations. Thus in aristocratic circles indebtedness was a recurrent problem: it had exercised the Senate in the days of the younger Livius Drusus, and under the Principate it remained a source of trouble.

It was the nobles, then, that stood to gain most from *novae tabulae*; and for such a measure they could pay in advance. With the disciplined vote of the clients and parasites who were the main cause of senatorial poverty, a handful of aristocratic wire-pullers could carry any ordinary election like an eighteenth-century borough-monger. Catiline's promised debt relief was therefore essentially a piece of class legislation, and was calculated to strengthen the political ascendancy of the nobles by basing it on economic privilege. In effect, it was a reactionary, not a reforming measure.

As election time drew near, Catiline carried himself confidently. He had no formidable competitors on this occasion, and he could count on the tacit support of Antonius, who had a personal interest in a clean slate. But his calculations were again upset by Cicero, who was attached by long association with the creditor element, and indeed held an honest conviction that *novae tabulae* was another name for fraud[1]. In his campaign against Catiline Cicero was assisted by a financial panic which precipi-tated a calling-in of loans and a drain of gold out of Italy. This scare, it is true, was soon allayed by the Senate, which authorized the consuls to prohibit the exportation of gold, and by a long-headed financier named Q. Considius, who set an example by proclaiming an extension of credit to his customers at easy rates; yet the mere occurrence of the alarm gave point to Cicero's polemic. Still more prejudicial to Catiline's chances was a re-newed suspicion of violent designs. With the consulship in his grasp, it is most unlikely that he should at this stage have seriously contemplated a perfectly gratuitous recourse to crime. But he openly indulged in braggadocio, vowing that 'if his fortunes were set ablaze he would quench the fire, not with water, but by pulling the whole house down[2]'—an empty phrase which could serve as a blank cheque to alarmists; and the arrival in Rome of a band of veterans from northern Etruria, though they probably came as voters bona fide, none the less lent colour to the fore-bodings of revolution.

Resuming the tactics which had already won him the consul-ship, Cicero made the most of the prevailing uneasiness. With the Senate's consent he carried through the Comitia Centuriata an impossibly severe law against corrupt practices, which aggravated the existing penalties with ten years' exile. On the eve of the polls he asked leave to recruit a bodyguard and to put off the elections to a distant date, in the hope that in the meantime the contingent

---

[1] *de off.* ii, 24, 84.   [2] Cicero, *pro Murena*, 25, 51.

from Etruria would have dispersed. The Senate, it is true, sorely disappointed Cicero, for it refused him protection and postponed the voting for a few days only[1]. But this respite proved sufficient for the consul. From among the younger *equites*, who willingly rendered such service, he improvised an unofficial escort. On polling day he made a brave show of his stalwarts, and he took care to let the sun catch a highly-burnished cuirass which peeped out from under a loosely draped toga. The electors took the hint, and returned L. Licinius Murena, a former officer of Lucullus, together with one D. Junius Silanus.

VII. THE SECOND CATILINARIAN CONSPIRACY.
THE FIRST PHASE

Catiline's second failure at the polls was the direct cause of the plot which has made him into the stock villain of historical melodrama. Given the pride and the class-loyalty which formed the outlines of virtue in his depraved character, he could not readily resign his aspirations to a consulship, or abandon his debtor-friends after raising their hopes with the promise of *novae tabulae*. Accordingly in the late summer of 63 B.C. he passed from vague bluff to definite preparation of a coup-de-main. Among his confidants he included several other political malcontents, such as his former partner Autronius, and L. Cassius, who had also run at the elections of 64 B.C. But the most notable of his fellow-aspirants to high office was a patrician named P. Cornelius Lentulus, who had held a consulship in 71, had been expelled from the Senate in 70, and in 63 had re-entered that assembly through election to a second praetorship. Not content with this rehabilitation, Lentulus had been lured to extravagant hopes by a stray prophecy that three Cornelii should be kings in Rome— Cinna, Sulla, and (why not?) himself. Altogether, of the sixteen conspirators known to us by name, twelve were of senatorial standing. But Catiline's counsels were also shared by several *equites*, by old soldiers of Sulla, and by a number of women. For the rank and file of the plotters, though not for the ringleaders, the object of the movement lay rather in the remission of debts than in the seizure of political power. The immediate purpose of Catiline's second as of his first conspiracy was to create a vacancy

---

[1] The view that the elections of 63 B.C. were held in September or October rests on quite inadequate evidence, and cannot be squared with the known facts of the subsequent conspiracy. On this point see especially F. Baur, *Zur Chronologie der catilinarischen Verschwörung*.

in the consulship. No doubt Catiline was intent on paying off other political scores, but his chief concern was to get rid of Cicero. For his installation into Cicero's empty seat he counted on the collusion of the surviving consul Antonius. It is uncertain whether he proposed to hold the fasces to the end of 63 or of 62 B.C.; but we may assume that before laying them down he would have satisfied his accomplices by carrying the long-expected measure for *novae tabulae*.

In 63 B.C. Catiline could have no hope, as in 65, of taking his victims by surprise. Therefore, instead of relying on a mere handful of bravoes he made preparations for a considerable expenditure of force. In Rome he requisitioned a disengaged band of gladiators, and in Etruria he commissioned an ex-officer of Sulla named L. Manlius, who belonged to his band of ruined spendthrifts, to raise the veteran colonists. The details of Catiline's dispositions are not clear. But it is probable that the troops from Etruria had instructions to steal along in small detachments to the town of Praeneste, which lay some twenty miles from Rome on the Via Latina (that is, off the main lines of communication between Rome and Etruria), and to concentrate there on October 27th for a night march upon Rome. On October 28th, a date on which public attention would be distracted by the annual games in honour of Sulla's victory, the main action of the plot was to be carried out by the joint forces of the gladiators and of the recent arrivals from Praeneste.

In planning this attack Catiline must have reckoned with the fact that Cicero at any rate could not be caught off his guard. But he had good reason to expect that the Senate would not take the consul's word, and would therefore grant him no protection over and above his unofficial bodyguard, unless definite proof of a conspiracy were laid before it. For his own part, too, Catiline had at last been taught by the results of past indiscretions to keep his hand dark. But, considerable as were his powers of leadership, he was unable to impose silence upon some light-headed associates. The first news of the plot reached Cicero through a demi-mondaine named Fulvia, in whose presence an elated conspirator, Q. Curius, counted his unhatched chickens, not realizing that such women are in request as secret service agents. But her report probably did not go into details. Further information was brought by Crassus, who roused the consul out of a midnight slumber and delivered to him a parcel of letters that had been handed in at his door by an unknown person. These missives were addressed to various members of the Senate, but they all contained the same message, bidding the recipient leave Rome because of an impending massacre. Though several details of this episode remain unexplained, it is fairly certain that the warnings were given in good faith by an accomplice anxious to save his personal friends or protectors, and that Crassus' part in it was the same as Lord Monteagle's in the Gunpowder Plot[1]. On the strength of this message Cicero convened the Senate and announced to it the date of the forthcoming murders. For the present the Senate contented itself with instructions to Cicero to make further inquiries. But a day or two later the consul conveyed to it news that Manlius was on the move and would take up arms on October 27th; and his forecast was confirmed by a private senator who announced suspicious comings and goings in Etruria. At this second session, which took place on October 21st[2], the Senate proclaimed a state of emergency and called upon the consul to take all necessary measures of defence.

Once the *senatus consultum ultimum* was passed, Cicero forestalled Catiline's attack at every point. He removed the gladiators to Capua. He called out the municipal militias and commissioned the praetor Metellus Celer to raise fresh levies in Picenum and the Ager Gallicus. He sent Q. Marcius Rex, who was encamped near Rome with a small force in anticipation of a triumph for his share in the Mithridatic War, to patrol Etruria. With his skeleton corps Marcius was unable to accomplish more than to check and observe Manlius, but in so doing he deprived Catiline of his Italian reinforcements. On November 1st a belated attempt was made by an isolated troop to break into Praeneste, but was foiled by the local defence corps. Not a single Etruscan contingent joined hands with Catiline in Rome. The critical day passed without any worse mishap than a temporary flight of senators who now trusted Cicero's word, but not his powers of self-defence.

Thus Catiline was checked as effectively on October 28th, 63 B.C. as on January 1st, 65; but for a second time he got off

---

[1] It has been suggested that the letters were forged by Cicero and delivered to Crassus by his orders, as a test of Crassus' complicity; or that they were concocted by Crassus with a view to disarming the consul's suspicions. But whatever Crassus might have done with the letters, his action or inaction could have furnished no proof or disproof of his collusion with Catiline. It was not worth while for Crassus or for Cicero to forge them.

[2] This date is certified on the high authority of Asconius (p. 6, c.). In spite of much discussion, the date of the previous meeting of the Senate cannot be fixed.

scot free. For the moment he was protected by a missing link in the chain of evidence, which was not yet sufficient to establish his personal guilt beyond all cavil. In the absence of irrefutable testimony against him, Cicero would not risk his arrest. From the outset of his consulship he had been acutely conscious of an undercurrent of resentment on the Senate's part against the *novus homo* who was saving it despite itself; at the time of the elections he had received an embarrassing reminder of their distrust; and he was repaid for his exertions in keeping Rome quiet on October 28th with accusations of having cried 'wolf.' Foreseeing some such fate as did actually overtake him five years later, if he should presume too far on his powers, he chose the alternative risk of leaving Catiline at large. His wariness was apparently justified by the discomfiture of a young nobleman named L. Aemilius Paullus, who rushed in upon Catiline with a prosecution for breach of the peace. Catiline at once reduced this charge *ad absurdum* by going round to Cicero and other senators with a request to take him into their custody pending the trial; and he succeeded in thrusting himself as a prisoner upon one M. Metellus, who entered into the spirit of the jest.

VIII. THE SECOND CATILINARIAN CONSPIRACY.
THE SECOND PHASE

In selecting his gaoler, Catiline had evidently bargained for the privilege of a latchkey. On the night of November 6th–7th he slipped out to meet his accomplices at the house of one Laeca, in Scythemakers' Row, and there mended the broken threads of his plot. In his revised plan Catiline prepared to attack on more than one front. Not content with murdering some leading senators, he now proposed to distract the government by starting conflagrations in several quarters of the city and by calling out the slaves to loot. If there is any truth in a rumour that he tampered with the crews of a flotilla which Pompey had left to patrol the Tyrrhenian Sea, we may gather that he also intended, like Marius in 87 B.C., to cut off the city's corn supplies[1]. But the most distinctive feature of his reconstructed plot was that he now endeavoured to organize a widespread insurrection on the Italian countryside. He laid plans to enlist the gladiators in the training-schools of Capua,

---

[1] This attempt has sometimes been brought into connection with the conspiracy of 66–5 B.C. But Cicero plainly dates it to the year of his consulship. (*Oratio post Red. ad Quir.* 7, 17.)

the armed herdsmen on the ranches of Apulia (where Antonius owned extensive pastures) and of Bruttium; the discontented peasantry of Cisalpine Gaul and of the hill country between the Central Apennines and the Adriatic. Finally, he arranged to assume personal command of a veritable field force in northern Etruria and from that base to repeat the march of M. Lepidus upon Rome. If Catiline, by keeping his opponents in play elsewhere, had succeeded in occupying the capital, he might for a while have enjoyed a dictatorship like those of Cinna and Carbo. But just as these were swept away by Sulla, so would Catiline infallibly have drawn Pompey upon himself and have gone down before a whiff of his grapeshot. In any case Italy was no longer such a hotbed of rebellion as in the days of the Civil Wars. Besides, whatever chances of initial success stood open to Catiline were once more dissipated by the indiscretions of his accomplices.

Laeca's guests had hardly dispersed before Cicero had word through Fulvia. Her prompt disclosures enabled him to forestall an immediate attack improvised by a knight named C. Cornelius. In this by-plot Cornelius himself with a senator, L. Vargunteius, having gained entrance into Cicero's house at daybreak on November 7th, on pretence of paying him their matutinal respects, were to hold it open for the intrusion of a band of bravoes. Cicero received too sudden notice of his danger to arrange for the arrest of the intruders, but he had time to make his house fast against them. His morning callers therefore had to take at face value the message that he was 'not at home.'

In spite of Fulvia's disclosures Cicero still deemed it imprudent to lay hands on Catiline. On November 8th[1] he convened the Senate for further instructions, and he made the most of the lucky accident that Catiline, in hopes of diverting suspicion from himself by a bold piece of bluff, attended the meeting. In the so-called 'First Catilinarian Oration' Cicero made a pretence of being conversant with Catiline's latest schemes and blackened his character by recounting the details of his criminal career; yet he tamely concluded by inviting, nay begging the convicted traitor to relieve him of his embarrassing presence by leaving Rome. By this calculated anti-climax Cicero probably sought to elicit from the Senate the retort, 'No, no, arrest him at once!' But the Senate

[1] In spite of much controversy on this point, it may be regarded as certain that the First Catilinarian Oration was delivered on the 8th, and not on the 7th of November. See v. Stern, *Catilina*, pp. 166–74; T. Rice Holmes, *The Roman Republic*, vol. I, pp. 461–5.

refused to give Cicero the lead for which he was playing[1]. On the next day Catiline did indeed quit Rome, but not as a penitent sinner to a self-imposed exile: he went as an imperator to his head-quarters in Etruria, to organize his main army of attack. The cries of joy with which Cicero announced Catiline's departure to a popular audience could not conceal the fact that a bird worth caging had flown. Neither did it reduce Cicero's difficulties that the Senate, on hearing of Catiline's arrival at the camp of Manlius, made a belated show of energy by proclaiming both of them public enemies.

Toward the end of November Cicero resumed for a moment his place at the Roman bar in order to defend the consul-elect Murena on a charge of bribery. This diversion was not a mere holiday from his consular duties, for he had marked out Murena to carry on the defence of the Republic against Catiline, in the event of the conspiracy dragging on into the ensuing year. Murena's case was peculiarly awkward, for his guilt was un-deniable, and the statute under which he was being pursued was Cicero's own law on corrupt practices. Moreover the charge was being pressed by a prosecutor named M. Porcius Cato, a de-scendant of the redoubtable censor, who had inherited his an-cestor's integrity and, above all, his dour pugnacity. On other occasions we shall find Cato's obstinacy getting the better of Cicero's opportunism; at Murena's trial his unbending front was turned by a flank attack. Replying to Cato, Cicero made the utmost use of his best weapon, irrelevant but cleverly calculated ridicule; with desperate facetiousness he laughed the case out of court.

Cicero's apprehensions that the conspiracy might outlive his consulship were not realized. Even while he was defending Murena, Catiline's plans were breaking down at every point. In Campania the situation was saved for the government by the vigour of a quaestor named P. Sestius, who unceremoniously expelled Catiline's agitators and by December was able to report all quiet. In the Apennine districts the emissaries were promptly arrested by Metellus Celer, in North Italy they were seized by C. Murena[2],

---

[1] A combination of sections 20–21 of the First Catilinarian Oration with Diodorus, XL, frag. 5 *a*, makes it appear probable that Cicero was actually baited by Catiline into putting a motion for his banishment, but was received in stony silence by the Senate and was hard put to it to explain away this rebuff. The motion, if carried, would have had no legal force, but as a declaration of the Senate's opinion would have strengthened Cicero's hand.

[2] So Sallust (*Cat.* 42, 3). Cicero (*pro Murena,* 41, 89) implies that C. Murena was stationed in Transalpine Gaul. It is not unlikely that temporarily he was governor of both the Gauls.

the brother of the consul-elect. The agent whose mission was to rouse the Apulian herdsmen never reached his destination. Except in Etruria, the expected risings did not take place, or were easily stifled. On the Etruscan sector the issue hung in the balance somewhat longer. After Catiline's arrival there the government troops were reinforced and transferred to the command of the consul Antonius. But Antonius accomplished even less than Marcius, for he failed or never attempted to check the vigorous recruiting campaign which Catiline instituted. It says much for Catiline's driving power, and for his prestige among Sulla's old soldiers, that he contrived to increase Manlius' force from two thousand to some ten thousand men. But not being able to find arms for more than a quarter of these, he could not yet risk an advance upon Rome.

This delay in Catiline's movements cast a new responsibility upon his accomplices in the city, who now had to decide whether they should wait indefinitely for the rebels from Etruria, or should fix a date for their own rising in advance of Catiline's arrival. By the advice of their new leader, Cornelius Lentulus, they resolved to kindle the fires and to call out the slaves on December 17th, the first day of the Saturnalia, and to summon Catiline to march upon Rome in time to consolidate their victory[1]. In itself, this plan was not ill-conceived, for the Saturnalia was a general holiday on which the slave population enjoyed temporary freedom; and in the confusion following upon a nihilistic outbreak in Rome Catiline would have a better chance of slipping through to the city. But once the accomplices had taken to thinking on their own account, they could not let well alone. By a perfectly gratuitous indiscretion they ruined Catiline's last hope of co-operation and fitted a noose round their own necks.

In November 63 B.C. a party of envoys from the canton of the Allobroges in Transalpine Gaul were about to return home from a vain attempt to obtain remedy for grievances from the Senate (p. 545). Lentulus, bethinking himself that their tribe might assist Catiline with mounted forces, made overtures to them through several agents, who threw all reserve to the winds and posted up the Gauls about the whole movement. After some hesitation the Allobroges sold their information to the govern-

---

[1] In our MSS. of Sallust (*Cat.* 43, 1) we read that Catiline's accomplices invited him to arrive 'in agrum Faesulanum' on December 17th. Since Faesulae was distant some 200 miles from Rome, it is agreed that this reading is corrupt. The most probable emendation is 'in agrum Falerianum.' Falerii lay a hard day's march away from the city.

ment, and by Cicero's instructions they exacted from five of the accomplices (Lentulus, Cassius, C. Cethegus, L. Statilius, and P. Gabinius) a sworn and signed covenant. Still acting by the consul's orders, on the night of December 2nd–3rd they left Rome, taking with them the incriminating documents, and accompanied by one T. Volturcius, whom Lentulus had told off to introduce his new allies to Catiline and to deliver a confidential despatch from himself to his chief. As they defiled on to the Pons Mulvius, not far from the city gates, they let themselves be overpowered by an armed patrol which brought back the whole party and all its papers to Rome. Without delay Cicero arrested Lentulus, Cethegus, Statilius, and Gabinius, together with one Q. Caeparius. (Cassius, who had left Rome on another errand, avoided capture.) At a session of the Senate on December 3rd the prisoners were confronted with Volturcius, the Allobroges, and their own signed covenants, and were pronounced guilty by a unanimous vote. By the Senate's orders they were detained in custody, but in deference to their rank (for all except Caeparius were senators) they were allowed the privilege of residence in the private houses of Crassus, Caesar, and other nobles.

From such prisons escape was not impossible; hence in the following night a rescue was planned by clients of Lentulus and Cethegus. But Cicero now had all Rome behind him. By a racy popular harangue in which he described the proceedings in the Senate he had won over the urban proletariate, who might have joined the conspirators in mere looting, but could only feel alarmed at the danger of a general conflagration. The consul accordingly, besides strengthening his patrols, had all the burgesses sworn in as special constables. These precautions sufficed to keep Rome quiet for the rest of the year.

The seizure of the accomplices also relieved Rome of all risk of capture by Catiline's field force. On hearing of the arrest of his associates Catiline at once abandoned all hope of advancing upon the city. His only chance, he now perceived, was to slip away across the Apennines and Alps into Gaul. But Metellus Celer, who had completed the pacification of Central Italy and was free to move northward, headed him off by occupying the exit of the pass from Pistoria to Bononia; and Antonius, whose hand was now forced by the arrival of his masterful quaestor Sestius from Campania, closed in upon the fugitive from the Arno valley. With Manlius and a handful of devoted followers (partly tenants from his Etruscan estates) Catiline stood at bay near Pistoria. In the ensuing battle (January, 62) the first casualty was Antonius, laid prostrate by a premonitory touch of gout. His lieutenant, M. Petreius, who took over the command, annihilated Catiline's forlorn hope, yet not without a hard struggle. Catiline himself fought indomitably and at the last charged single-handed into the enemy ranks. In the words of the *Commentariolum Petitionis*, 'Catiline was afraid of nothing, Antonius trembled at his own shadow.'

IX. THE AFTERMATH OF THE CONSPIRACY

Catiline's conspiracy was not the product of any general discontent, either in Rome or in Italy, and nowhere except in northern Etruria did it receive more than sporadic support. After its suppression Italy finally settled down and forgot the disorders of the Social and Civil Wars. In Rome the economic slate was cleaned as soon as debtors realized that they must not expect relief by legislation. In Cicero's words, 'never were debts greater, yet never were they paid off more promptly, once the hope of fraud was removed'[1].

But on the Forum and in the Senate the plot still gave rise to angry discussions. On the morrow of the accomplices' arrest a squall blew up while the Senate was engaged in the seemingly uncontentious task of voting rewards to the Allobroges and other informers. Fresh disclosures were promised by a professional spy named L. Tarquinius, who offered to produce a message from Crassus to Catiline, calling upon the latter to hasten to the rescue of his accomplices. This denunciation, which was probably instigated by some personal enemy of Crassus, was ridiculous on the face of it. Crassus had parted company with Catiline long before; as a moneylender and property-owner on a large scale he merely stood to lose by *novae tabulae* and schemes for setting Rome on fire; and he must have known that on December 3rd the conspiracy had failed irretrievably[2]. In any event, Crassus' innocence was established beyond the reach of evidence in the eyes of many

---

[1] *de off.* II, 24, 84.

[2] Crassus himself affected to believe that Tarquinius had been suborned by Cicero in order to deter him from salvaging Catiline's second plot in the same way as he had redeemed the conspiracy of 66–5 B.C. But, granted that Crassus could have any interest in befriending Catiline or his accomplices, it would plainly have required something more than a false denunciation by Cicero to prevent him. The rumour that Autronius, who was still at large, had solicited the aid of Crassus, which had been the means of his salvation in 65, is more plausible. But could Autronius have won Crassus by a manœuvre which was tantamount to blackmail?

senators who owed him money. Tarquinius was shouted down and ordered to be kept in chains, in the vain hope that he might disclose who was behind him. But his failure did not deter two personal enemies of Caesar, the ex-consuls Catulus and C. Piso, from pestering Cicero to extract compromising evidence against him from the Allobroges. Though Cicero in later years roundly incriminated Caesar, it is practically certain that he never possessed any valid evidence against him, and that such evidence did not exist. If Caesar stood clear of the First Catilinarian Conspiracy, *a fortiori* he had no share in the more atrocious plot of 63 B.C., at which time he was Pontifex Maximus and praetor-elect. Cicero therefore turned a deaf ear to his mentors. At a subsequent sitting of the Senate in 62 B.C., when Caesar was again attacked by a professional sycophant named L. Vettius, Cicero went so far as to acknowledge that he had actually laid information against Catiline[1].

On December 5th Cicero summoned the Senate to pronounce on the action to be taken against the arrested accomplices. The normal procedure would have been to reserve them for prosecution in the *quaestio* for murder or for breach of the peace. In the following year several plotters or suspects who had escaped arrest were actually brought into court; among those who stood their trial were Autronius, who was driven into exile, and P. Sulla, who was successfully defended by Cicero, now once more appearing as a barrister. But in 63 B.C. the consul Cicero held that a short way with captured rebels might serve as a timely discouragement to those that still stood in the field, and therefore determined on a summary execution of his prisoners by virtue of his magisterial authority, and on the strength of the *senatus consultum ultimum*. In his day the legality of such expeditious methods in times of crisis was generally admitted, but it remained doubtful whether they were applicable to malefactors who, being under lock and key and guarded against a rescue that was threatened, were no longer an instant source of public danger. Foreseeing the dangers which might attend any arbitrary action on his part, the consul hesitated to proceed without a declaration by the Senate which would bind it at least morally to his support.

Despite the fact that Cicero had the proceedings on December 5th recorded in shorthand, ancient writers are not agreed on the

---

[1] It is uncertain whether Caesar made his disclosures in October or December. It is not likely that they were of any great importance, for they are only mentioned quite casually in one of our ancient sources (Suet. *Div. Iul.* 17).

course of the debate. Yet its main outlines are clear. The consul-
elect Silanus, with whom the consultation began, pronounced for
immediate execution, and fifteen other senators of consular standing followed suit. Hereupon, the praetor-elect Caesar cast doubts
upon the legality of summary action, but, instead of reserving the
prisoners for a regular trial, he recommended that they should be
interned for life in various Italian *municipia*[1]. This penalty, though
not wholly unprecedented, was almost as gross an infringement of
personal liberty as sudden death. It is a measure of Caesar's personal magnetism that this utterly unsatisfactory compromise was
echoed by the other members of praetorian rank, and that at a
second consultation the 'consulares' retracted their former
opinions, despite the efforts of Cicero and of Catulus to break the
force of Caesar's speech. Caesar would have carried the day, had
not M. Cato, speaking as a tribune-elect, rallied the wavering
assembly with a typical fighting speech, in which he threw out
unworthy hints of Caesar's complicity with Catiline, and heavily
reinforced Cicero's best argument, that prompt measures would
have a wholesome moral effect. On this last point, which undoubtedly was the crucial factor, the Senate eventually sided with
Cato. Thus Cicero obtained the moral authority for which he had
cast about. Without delay he gave orders for the execution of
Lentulus, Cethegus, Statilius, Gabinius and Caeparius.

In this debate the outstanding feature was not so much the legal
question at issue, for in an age of civil wars (and of *dragonnades*)
this was a comparative trifle, but the antagonism between Caesar
and Cato, which was presently to become a leading factor in
Roman politics. By a curious inversion of their usual attitudes
Caesar now stood for constitutional propriety, Cato for rough
common sense. But this incident may serve as a reminder that it
is an exaggeration to dub Cato a doctrinaire legalist and Caesar a
revolutionist on principle.

But the death of Catiline's associates was not the last word on
that subject. A few days later a new tribune named Q. Metellus
Nepos opened a campaign of popular oratory against Cicero's
illegal conduct, and early in 62 B.C. he introduced a bill into the
Concilium Plebis, inviting Pompey to rescue the constitution

---

[1] According to Plutarch (*Caesar*, 7; *Cicero*, 21) and Appian (*Bell. Civ.* ii, 6)
the imprisonment advocated by Caesar was a mere detentive custody preceding a regular trial. But the evidence of these later writers cannot stand
against that of Cicero and Sallust, who state quite plainly that Caesar
pronounced a life sentence, and confiscation (not sequestration) of their
estates.

from Cicero's 'autocracy.' In this demand he was supported by Caesar, while his fellow-tribune Cato stood by Cicero, or rather against Caesar and Pompey. Metellus made a bad case worse by disregarding Cato's veto and instigating a renewal of mob-violence. The Senate in reply proclaimed a *iustitium*, or suspension of civil government, and when this proved ineffectual passed once more the *senatus consultum ultimum*. Under cover of it the consul Murena would no doubt have prepared for Metellus the fate of Gaius Gracchus or of Saturninus, but that Caesar, who had coolly disregarded the *iustitium*, now dissuaded Metellus from futile heroism. But Metellus' outcry against Cicero was a transparent pretext. His real purpose was to secure for Pompey some new commission which might enable him, as in 71 B.C., to round off his foreign conquests by saving Roman society from enemies nearer home. Metellus' first intention of course was to call in Pompey to suppress Catiline. But when Cicero took the wind out of his sails by disposing of Catiline beforehand, the tribune trans-ferred his sympathies at short notice to the conspirators. The point at issue, therefore, was not whether Cicero was a tyrant, but whether Pompey should come up to Rome with or without his army. For this reason Cato had sued for a tribuneship, hoping to checkmate Metellus with his mere veto; while Caesar, foreseeing the advantage of an alliance with Pompey, made a show of indig-nation against Cicero. Though there is no evidence and small probability of Caesar having at this stage begun actual conversa-tions with Pompey, his attitude and Cato's in the affair of Metellus anticipate the alignment of parties after Pompey's home-coming.

CHAPTER XII

THE FIRST TRIUMVIRATE

I. THE CONCORDIA ORDINUM

THE domestic history of Rome from 65 to 63 B.C. was rich in sensations but barren of achievements. A succession of plots and crises left the Republic almost exactly where it had stood before. Yet this absence of change was significant in itself, for it denoted a rally by the senatorial government against the revolutionary forces that were wearing it down. In particular, the defeat of the Second Catilinarian Conspiracy, though not in itself an event of the first importance, had been of value as a token that the Senate under capable leadership could still hold its own against physical force.

The significance of this victory was at once perceived by its chief organizer. Not content with the ovations of the urban population, the congratulations of the Italian municipalities, and the title of 'pater patriae' with which Catulus and other grateful senators had complimented him, Cicero lost no occasion of glorifying himself with tongue and pen as the saviour of Rome from utter extinction. In this orgy of self-praise personal vanity no doubt counted for much. Yet Cicero had good reason to advertise himself as a conqueror 'in a toga,' for his victories on behalf of civil authority at Rome had been as opportune as Pompey's triumphs over eastern potentates. Furthermore, in the years following his consulship Cicero made a notable effort to consolidate the ground which he had held in 63 B.C. The Catilinarian crisis had brought into momentary alliance all those solid and respectable elements in the commonwealth that stood to lose by gambles in revolution. Why should not this emergency coalition be made permanent as a 'Concord of all Good Men'? In a lasting union of this kind Cicero now saw the means of ensuing the ideal of every patriotic republican, 'otium cum dignitate.' His panacea, it is true, was a woefully inadequate remedy for the ills of the later Republic. It gave no thought to numerous reforms which were dangerously overdue. To mention but a few leading points which Cicero's own experience should have suggested to him: the senatorial aristocracy required a regular infusion of fresh blood from *novi homines* like Cicero himself; the city of Rome needed better protection against rioters and assassins; the economic parasitism by which senators, equites and the urban proletariate in their several ways impoverished the Roman provinces called for drastic remedies.

But Cicero's lack of clear vision into the future was shared by all his chief contemporaries, with the sole exception of Caesar. Besides, if his scheme was no more than a temporary expedient, yet as such it could not have been better chosen. It was no less true of Cicero's day than of the early period of the Principate, that the first requisite of the Roman Empire was a stable government to uphold lawful authority against organizers of riots and military adventurers. An interlude of tranquillity was an essential condition of successful reform to follow. Nay more, on one important point Cicero showed conspicuous sagacity. The worst danger to the Republican government lay not so much in mob leaders and rebels of Catiline's type, as in military commanders to whom the triumphant usurpations of Marius and Sulla were a standing incitement—*Sulla potuit, ego non potero?* The best guarantee against future military coups lay in winning Rome's greatest general, Pompey, to the cause of the Concordia, and this Cicero set himself to accomplish. In view of Pompey's past career, which at first sight might seem to stamp him as the most disloyal and self-willed of Roman *imperatores*, this project of Cicero's might be regarded as mere self-delusion. Yet in forecasting that Pompey might turn conservative and repeat the career of Scipio Aemilianus in politics as in warfare, Cicero displayed true insight into his character. As events were to prove, there was a winning chance that the poacher might wish to turn gamekeeper; and with Pompey's prestige, or if need be, his sword, in the service of the Concordia, the stability of Roman politics might seem assured.

II. POMPEY'S HOME-COMING

In 62–60 B.C. the Concordia Ordinum was tested and found wanting. We shall first pass briefly over two incidents of this period which had effects upon the coalition, but not of decisive importance. In December 62 B.C. a young patrician named P. Clodius, who has already appeared as the collusive prosecutor of Catiline, entered the Domus publica, the official house of the Pontifex Maximus, in female disguise, and broke in upon the worship of an archaic deity named Bona Dea, whose rites were forbidden to men. The Senate at first took up the scandal with a show of vigour and secured the institution of a special court of inquiry by the Comitia Centuriata; but instead of insisting that a special procedure be adopted in selecting the jurors, it allowed them to be drawn by lot from the ordinary panels. In making this concession the Senate played into the hands of Clodius' patron Crassus, who bribed the common jurors in the usual way. The case was also prejudiced by the nonchalant attitude of the Pontifex Maximus. On the mere rumour that his third and penultimate wife (Pompeia, daughter of Pompeius Rufus, consul in 88 B.C.) had been the object of Clodius' gallant adventure, Caesar put her away. Yet he refused to give evidence against Clodius, and when asked why then he had divorced his wife he replied that his family must be above suspicion. In view of Caesar's notorious moral laxity, which was a heaven-sent theme for the wits and epigrammatists of Rome, we may assume that this sally was received with loud laughter. After this broad hint the court acquitted Clodius. (May–June 61 B.C.)

At the end of 61 B.C. a company of tax-gatherers, who had bought the right to collect the revenues of the province of Asia, discovered that they stood to lose by their contract and petitioned the Senate for a rebate off the purchase-price. Their claim was supported by Crassus, yet his influence in the Senate did not avail to overcome the resistance of M. Cato, who saw in the proposal a new form of *novae tabulae* and obstructed it until he killed it. (May–June 60 B.C.)

In a moment of chagrin Cicero lamented that these two episodes had knocked the bottom out of the Concordia. He had hoped that all Good Men would make an exhibition of their virtue at the expense of Clodius, against whom he had brought forward some damaging evidence at the recent trial, and that in the interests of solidarity with the Equites, from which class the petitioning tax-farmers were drawn, the Senate would humour their 'impossible capers[1].' Yet Cicero took his disappointments too tragically. Given the views then prevalent in political circles about the Roman religion, Clodius' escapade could not honestly be exalted into a high affair of State. In the matter of the tax-contracts the Senate probably gained more by its unwonted firmness in the face of jobbery than it lost in the estrangement of the financiers, whose support was never indispensable to any resolute Roman government. But the acid test of the Concordia lay in a reconciliation between the Senate and Pompey. The manner of Pompey's return had been an object of uneasy speculation from the time of his departure, and his attitude to affairs at Rome during his absence had not been reassuring. He had sought by underhand influence to deprive other generals who had recently held command in the East,

1 *ad Att.* I, 17, 9.

Marcius Rex, Metellus Creticus, and L. Lucullus, of their triumphs: it was not until 63 B.C. that L. Lucullus received his trebly-earned reward. In 63–2 B.C. he had employed Metellus Nepos to find a military commission by which he might dominate Italy and Rome itself. By all the tokens Pompey was growing too big for the Republic.

In December 62 B.C. Pompey landed at Brundisium, and there and then disbanded his whole force, save a small escort to attend him pending his triumph. On his arrival at the gates of Rome he at once manifested his desire to come to terms with the nobility. He addressed the Senate in an unfamiliar note of studied respect, and he sought, though in vain, a marriage connection with its protagonist M. Cato. The fears of his principal antagonist, Crassus, he had disarmed beforehand: though Crassus in 62 B.C. had removed himself and all his family from Rome, he had been reassured into a speedy return and for the time being was allowed to maintain outwardly amicable relations with his rival. The cloud that had hung heavy over Rome was thus dispersed of a sudden and gave way to a promise of set fair weather. These surprise moves of Pompey have taken aback modern scholars no less than ancient observers; yet their explanation is not far to seek. Great as was Pompey's egotism, it was tempered by a saving respect for constitutional forms which shrank from undisguised acts of usurpation. In the absence of a colourable pretext for keeping together his army in Italy, he frankly accepted the situation and retired for the time being into civilian life. Besides, the mainspring of his ambition was not so much the love of power as the desire for applause, which Pompey courted no less eagerly, though in a less outspoken fashion, than Cicero. He was therefore not unwilling to pause in his career of conquest in order to bask in the sunshine of public admiration. Finally, since his return from the East Pompey's behaviour showed traces of an irresolution which grew upon him as he advanced in years. As Cicero had divined, Pompey was turning conservative: the time was now ripe for securing him as the champion of the established order.

To this problem Cicero at once applied himself, but he brought to it less than his customary tact. In recent years he had rendered Pompey an undeniable service in safeguarding the home front for him; but in suppressing the conspiracy of Catiline he had purloined a laurel twig out of Pompey's chaplet. And he had added insult to injury by writing letters to Pompey in his absence, and addressing public speeches to him on his return, in which he extolled his own achievements as though they were comparable with those of the great conqueror, and by inviting him to be duly thankful. Yet the annoyance which Cicero inflicted with his untimely self-praise did not cut deep. Pompey was on the whole more amused than angry, and in outward semblance at least seemed disposed to accept Cicero as his political mentor. Indeed the orator half believed that he had captured the general.

But in any case, the crucial question lay not in the attitude of Pompey to Cicero, but in his relations with the Senate. On his return to Rome he held out ostentatiously a hand of reconciliation. The Senate requited this gesture with nagging ill-will. By this sulky attitude it lost the keystone of the Concordia and ruined all hopes of tranquillity in the Republic. For this rebuff, it must be admitted, Pompey had partly himself to thank. In thrusting his way to fame he had pushed aside somewhat rudely other ambitious commanders such as Metellus Creticus and L. Lucullus, and had involved himself in a standing feud with Crassus. But these personal enmities were reinforced by the disinterested opposition of M. Cato, who did not share Cicero's views about Pompey's impending conversion, but went on believing that each move of his was but a prelude to an act of usurpation. For this reason he had taken the lead in resisting the propaganda of Metellus Nepos, and in the summer of 62 B.C. he had persuaded the Senate against its own intentions to refuse special facilities for an officer of Pompey named M. Pupius Piso to stand for the consulship. But, as we have already seen, Pompey overlooked these lesser slights. The Senate's real opportunity to win or to cast away his friendship came when he submitted to it two demands, the ratification of the *acta* or administrative decrees by which he had effected the settlement of the East, and a grant of land to the 35,000 or 40,000 soldiers whom he had recently dismissed. In substance both these requests were perfectly reasonable. Pompey's dispositions in the East had admittedly been judicious, yet until the Senate (or alternatively the Comitia) confirmed them, there was no guarantee that future Roman proconsuls would uphold them any more than Pompey had recognized Lucullus' *acta*. No doubt the Senate in return could claim a right to criticize and amend Pompey's measures on points of detail, but with goodwill on both sides agreement could here have been secured, *e.g.* by the appointment of a commission of decemviri, such as was usually sent out to conquered districts to assist the victorious general in drawing up a provincial charter.

On the question of pensions for Pompey's veterans there was even less ground for dispute. The practice of allotting land to soldiers retiring from foreign service was by then well established, and Pompey's troops, who had followed their commander far more loyally than Lucullus' rascals, had fully earned the customary reward. Besides, there could now be no question of a shortage of funds, for Pompey's conquests had brought in a lump sum of 20,000 talents to the Treasury, and had increased the yearly revenue from fifty to eighty-five million denarii[1]. But Pompey's opponents carried the Senate in a campaign of obstruction. Though they did not venture a point-blank refusal to his request for land, they only allowed it to rank *pari passu* with a similar demand on behalf of Metellus Creticus' troops, and they temporized endlessly over questions of ways and means. In the debate on Pompey's *acta* Lucullus insisted on his tit-for-tat and obtained it in the form of a resolution that Pompey's measures be dissected clause for clause by the Senate sitting *in pleno*.

Thus thwarted, Pompey turned from the Senate to the Comitia. On September 28th–29th of 61 B.C. he had regaled the people with a triumph of unprecedented splendour; with popular support he could hope to carry his point over the Senate's head, as he had done twice before in 67 and 66 B.C. In January 60 B.C. a tribune named L. Flavius introduced on his behalf a land-purchase scheme into the Concilium Plebis. This measure was criticized in a friendly spirit by Cicero, at whose instance it was redrafted so as not to threaten existing tenures. But Pompey's adversaries extended their obstruction to the popular assembly, and the consul Metellus Celer, who now shared the leadership of the opposition with Cato, talked to such purpose that the enraged Flavius marched him off to prison and kept him there, until Pompey sent orders for his release, by placing his tribunician bench athwart the entrance. Moreover, the urban voters were no longer in the mood of 67 and 66 B.C., when they had made short work of the senatorial opposition. As in the days of the Gracchi and of Marius, their enthusiasm for their hero proved a fire of straw that flared up and died without a steady glow of loyalty. In the summer of 60 B.C. Pompey lost heart and allowed Flavius' bill to be dropped. Thus the Senate paid off old scores on Pompey and inflicted a humiliating defeat upon him. Though he could in the last resort have forced the Senate's hand by calling back to his standard the troops whose pensions were being withheld, he shrank from this form of self-help and for the moment stood helpless. But before long the

---

[1] Hence in 60 B.C. a bill to abolish customs duties at Italian ports was carried by the praetor Metellus Nepos.

Senate discovered that it must pay heavily for the luxury of teaching Pompey a lesson.

III. THE FORMATION OF THE FIRST TRIUMVIRATE[1]

But the Senate's worst mistake was yet to follow. In 61–60 B.C. Caesar had held a propraetorship in Further Spain. As a civilian administrator he here made his mark by effecting a settlement of debts (outstanding, no doubt, from the Sertorian War). The compromise which he struck between the opposing parties, assigning two-thirds of debtors' incomes to creditors, recalled the principles of Lucullus' financial settlement in Asia and forestalled his own handling of the debt problem at Rome in 49 B.C. (see below, p. 655). But the chief event of his governorship was a campaign in the mountain country between the lower Tagus and Douro, accompanied by a naval expedition from Gades to Brigantium (Corunna), which completed the subjection of the peoples on the western sea-board of the peninsula. In this warfare Caesar distinguished himself sufficiently to qualify for a triumph, and we may confidently assume that he now definitely discovered his latent abilities as a general. In Cicero's words, the wind was now blowing full into Caesar's sails[2].

In the years following 65 B.C. Cicero and Caesar had frequently been engaged on opposite sides. In 60 B.C. a similar intuition to that which had divined Pompey's trend of thought suggested to Cicero that Caesar too might be won over to the cause of the Concordia. This hope was probably no more than a passing fancy, yet it was less chimerical than Caesar's previous or later career might indicate. As his behaviour in the affair of Metellus Nepos had shown, Caesar was by no means an implacable enemy of senatorial government, and although he could never have consented to rest content with Cicero's policy of 'otium cum dignitate,' it is not out of the question that with Cicero's good offices he might have come to a definite understanding with the Senate. A programme of constructive reform carried out by Caesar with the Senate's co-operation would probably have been the most effective way of rejuvenating the government of the Republic.

On his return to Rome (c. June 60 B.C.) Caesar gave the Senate an opportunity of cultivating better relations with him. His hopes were now centred on a triumph, a consulship, and above all, a

---

[1] This phrase to describe the coalition of Pompey, Crassus and Caesar, though constitutionally unjustified, is used because it is convenient and familiar.

[2] 'cuius nunc venti valde sunt secundi,' ad Att. II, 1, 6.

proconsulship in which he might test his military talents on a larger scale. To the fulfilment of all these wishes the Senate could without loss of dignity have lent a helping hand. Yet once again, as in its dealings with Pompey, it deferred to leaders who would not let old suspicions sleep, and could think of no way of rendering him harmless except by disarming him. Arriving at Rome on the eve of nomination-day, Caesar asked leave to give in his name as a consular candidate by proxy, so as to preserve his right to a triumph, which he would have forfeited if in the meantime he had set foot in the city. The Senate was disposed to grant this request, but it tamely allowed Cato to abuse the members' right of free speech by talking the motion out. Hereupon Caesar threw up his chance of a triumph, and by way of making sure of his candidature appeared at the hustings in person. Having left a lively memory of past exhibitions of generosity in the minds of the electors, and being the only strong competitor in the field, he was from the start a certain winner; but he found himself saddled with a col-league named M. Calpurnius Bibulus, who from being Caesar's friend had become his determined opponent. The return of Bibulus was due to a novel experiment in syndicated bribery on the part of Caesar's principal enemies, to which even Cato sub-scribed 'in the interests of the Republic.' But these manifestations of ill-will could only irritate Caesar without disabling him. A far more damaging attack upon him was made at the eve of the elec-tion, when the time fell due for the Senate to select two provinces for the prospective consuls of 59 B.C. Anticipating Caesar's suc-cess, his adversaries induced the Senate to earmark for him (to be shared with Bibulus, a willing martyr in such a cause) a province whose short title was *silvae callesque* (forests and cattle-drifts). The duties of this department probably consisted in adjudicating rights of user on the State pastures and woodlands in Italy; in any case it was a purely civilian office, and more appropriate to the rank of a quaestor than of a consul. Thus the Senate broke through its usual routine of provincial appointments, and this for no other reason than to ruin Caesar's career.

For the rest of that year the Senate remained free to imagine that it had reduced Caesar to the same state of helplessness as Pompey. But if Pompey in 60 B.C. had begun his political decline, Caesar was only just getting into his stride. To the Senate's last affront he at once replied by entering into secret negotiations with Pom-pey. On the whole, his previous attitude towards him facilitated this new move. Whatever he might think of Pompey's political abilities, Caesar always rated his prestige highly, and he made it a rule to cultivate his friendship. In 67 and 66 he had been a foremost supporter of the Gabinian and Manilian laws; in 63 and 62 he had ostentatiously taken sides with Metellus Nepos, and he had played up to Pompey's vanity by suggesting various small acts of legislation in his honour. It is true that he had allowed himself to become involved in Crassus' intrigues, and he came under suspicion of having been a partner in the unfaithfulness of Pompey's third wife. But for these ill turns Pompey bore him no lasting resentment. On the other hand, when Caesar first made overtures to him, Pompey was smarting over the recent failure of his land law, and he stood in too great need of allies to look closely into their past record. Accordingly he let himself be drawn into a partnership which remained for ten years the controlling factor in Roman politics. By the original terms of this compact Caesar offered, in return for support from Pompey and if need be from his troops, to carry *per fas aut nefas* the measures which the Senate had refused to him. At the same time, or soon after, Caesar made amends to Pompey for his matrimonial mishap by giving him the hand of his only child Julia. This marriage, which took place early in 59 B.C. and lasted until Julia's death in 54 B.C., achieved a far better success than need be expected of dynastic matches, and it materially strengthened the bonds between Pompey and Caesar.

An alliance of these two partners, provided always that each stood firmly by the other, required no further reinforcement. But Caesar in the first instance aimed at a coalition of all those political leaders who were at that time out of humour with the Senate. At the end of 60 B.C. he made an offer to Cicero to include him in the cabal. Though it is doubtful whether Caesar ever attached much importance to Cicero's political wisdom, he knew by experience that his oratory was a formidable power, and that his opinion carried special weight among the Italians outside the capital. To Cicero, who bitterly resented the Senate's refusal to accept Pompey's friendship and his own leadership, an alliance with Caesar held out a prospect of renewed influence and heightened prestige. Yet, while he recognized in Caesar a man of outstanding power, and even when opposing him was at pains not to affront him, he could never shake off a feeling of mistrust in regard to him. Though he had openly discountenanced the rumours of Caesar's complicity in the Catilinarian conspiracies, he would not dismiss a lurking doubt as to his innocence, which in later years gave way to a confident conviction of his guilt. If in the early months of 60 B.C. he had played with the hope of reconciling

Caesar with the Senate, at the end of that year he recoiled from a partnership with Caesar against the Senate. While Cicero continually changed his mind in judging persons and situations, he stood consistently by the principle of parliamentary government, and never wavered in his attachment to existing constitutional usage. Rather than follow Caesar into revolutionary courses, he decided to stand aloof in honourable isolation.

On the other hand Caesar was successful in enlisting Crassus as a third partner in the coalition. This achievement was less difficult than might appear at first sight, for Crassus had his grudge against the Senate for refusing the rebate to the tax-farmers with whom his interests were bound up, and he was better protected against Pompey by joining the alliance than by standing out. But it may be doubted whether Caesar's party gained in strength through the inclusion of Crassus. Since Crassus had advanced large sums to Caesar before his departure to Spain—and it is hardly credible that the proceeds of the latter's campaigns in that country sufficed to clear his debts—we may assume that Caesar was driven by the same financial necessities as forced him to consort with Crassus earlier. Within the new coalition Crassus hardly ever gave overt support to Caesar, and his influence at times proved positively disruptive.

Thus in 60 B.C. died the Concordia Ordinum. In 59 B.C. it was replaced by Caesar's new coalition, or, as it came to be called, the First Triumvirate.

IV. CAESAR'S FIRST CONSULSHIP

In 59 B.C. there was a greater output of legislation at Rome than in any year since the dictatorship of Sulla. Soon after entering upon his consulship Caesar brought forward an agrarian bill which was intended in the first instance to provide for Pompey's soldiers, but had the further object of relieving the general congestion of population at Rome. To this end it earmarked for distribution the residue of the public domains in Italy, with the exception of the Campanian estates; but since the remnant of unappropriated State-land in Italy had been reduced to very exiguous limits, it made arrangements for the purchase of additional private estates in small parcels, at the price entered in the censor's valuation lists. In order to protect the new allotment-holders against themselves Caesar's act further stipulated that their properties should remain inalienable for the first twenty years. The execution of the measure was entrusted to a board of twenty commissioners, from which Caesar himself and all other office-holders were to be excluded[1].

Unlike the agrarian bill of 63 B.C., Caesar's law was modest in its scope and gave no undue privileges to the allotment commission. In providing for Pompey's veterans it met an admitted need, and it was calculated to fulfil its purpose without making an unfair inroad upon the public funds, which had but recently been replenished by Pompey's conquests. Furthermore, Caesar avoided Tiberius Gracchus' cardinal mistake by submitting his bill in the first place to the Senate and inviting discussion and amendment. But his offer was rejected at the instance of Cato, who, in default of any valid objection, denounced Caesar's act as the thin end of the wedge and had renewed recourse to obstruction. This time, it is true, the weapon was wrested out of his hands, for Caesar unceremoniously hauled him off the platform and threatened him with imprisonment; but the Senate played up to him with a passive opposition which defied both argument and force. Hereupon Caesar presented his measure to the Comitia, with the addition of a clause requiring all senators to swear non-resistance to it on pain of exile. For form's sake he invited his colleague to state his objections to the bill in the Forum, but merely drew from him the retort that he would fight Caesar and the whole people into the bargain.

At this stage Caesar unmasked the batteries of the coalition by calling upon Crassus and Pompey, both of whom spoke in favour of the bill. But the real significance of their support was not revealed until the land act was put to the vote. In reply to a veto by three tribunes, and to an announcement from Bibulus that he would 'watch the skies' and thus suspend business whenever the Comitia were summoned, Caesar mobilized Pompey's veterans. Though Pompey himself still refused to use force on his own responsibility, he fulfilled his compact with Caesar by putting his soldiery at the latter's disposal. By 59 B.C. a considerable number of Pompey's men had drifted into Rome, where they were living as best they could on the remnants of the bounty paid to them on dismissal, or on the public doles. Thus Caesar had no difficulty in collecting a strong body of rioters, and with these he swept his opponents out of the Forum. In this affray Bibulus

---

[1] Within the main body of twenty a smaller panel of five officials was also set up. It is tempting to infer that these formed a managing sub-committee; but the fact that a place on this body was offered to Cicero suggests that it was designed to contain the figure-head directors, and that the active members were to be found among the residual fifteen.

began by receiving a basket of refuse over his head and ended by having his fasces broken. Undaunted by this rough usage, he convened the Senate to his own house on the next day and endeavoured to obtain from it a pronouncement, such as had been issued against the laws of Saturninus and of Drusus the Younger, that Caesar's act had been passed in an unconstitutional manner and consequently was null and void. But the Senate had been too well intimidated to carry resistance any farther. So well had the secret of the coalition been guarded that the opposition was completely taken by surprise at the co-operation of Pompey with Caesar. Even Cicero, to whom Caesar had dropped some hints, was unprepared at the new turn of events; the senators in general were so bewildered that they could not think of any counter-move. Abandoned to his own resources, Bibulus shut himself up in his private residence, whence he issued daily notices that he was watching the heavens and rained abusive edicts upon his fellow-consul. The last flicker of opposition was stirred up by Metellus Celer, Cato, and a disciple of his named M. Favonius, who refused to take the oath of obedience to the Lex Julia. But at the last moment Cicero overcame Cato's scruples, and all the non-jurors relented. By April the land-commission had got to work.

But a few weeks of practical experience proved that the new law would not fulfil its purpose. The reason of this failure is not clear, but it is probable that the commissioners, not being armed with powers of compulsory purchase, found themselves unable to obtain the land required in sufficient quantities or at a reasonable price. In any case, toward the end of May Caesar was compelled to bring forward a supplementary bill. In this second act, the so-called Lex Campana, Caesar secured additional land by calling in the leases of the public estates in central and northern Campania. In the re-assignment of these he gave first choice to Pompey's veterans, and among the civilian settlers he accorded a preference to men who were the fathers of three or more children, and therefore more likely to take root. Caesar's second law was open to one serious objection, that it turned adrift many industrious small-holders on the public domains or, if they were allowed to remain as cultivating sub-tenants, saddled them with a rent to the new owners which, it may be presumed, considerably exceeded the amount formerly paid to the State. Yet it met with far less resistance than the previous bill. Cato once more pitted his length of breath against it, but each time he spoke he was bundled off the platform. One senator, M. Juventius Laterensis, actually went into exile rather than swear allegiance to the Lex Campana, but all the rest took the oath without hesitation. The new law had at any rate this merit, that it finally disposed of the problem of Pompey's veterans. Pompey in person went to Capua to draw up the charter of a colony which was now at last constituted upon this site, and it is probable that Calatia and Casilinum were likewise raised by him to the status of colonies. On the other hand the transplantation of civilian settlers to Campania does not seem to have made much headway, for as late as 51 B.C. portions of the Campanian domain remained unallocated.

Though Caesar's two land acts were introduced by the consul himself and stood in his own name, the greater part of the legislation which he initiated in 59 B.C. was formally brought forward by his right-hand man, the tribune P. Vatinius. In accordance with the terms of the bargain between Caesar and Pompey, Vatinius carried a short act by which Pompey's settlement of Eastern affairs was ratified *en bloc*. Resistance was offered, as before, by Lucullus; but a threat of prosecution (presumably for embezzlement of war-booty from his Eastern campaigns) brought him literally to his knees before Caesar. By way of fulfilling Caesar's obligations to Crassus, Vatinius took the question of the Asian tax-contracts before the Concilium Plebis and secured a remission of one-third of the stipulated purchase-price. This truly colossal concession naturally raised the stock of the favoured syndicate to a premium, and Vatinius' commission, which according to a quite credible rumour was paid in its shares, rose proportionately in value. Caesar himself made a show of atoning for this shady transaction by solemnly warning the peccant tax-farmers not to do it again: we may give him credit for having intended this as a joke. There is no evidence of his having received anything for himself from the *publicani*, or that he profited by Vatinius' traffic with various dependent kings in Asia, who wished to confirm Pompey's concessions to them by means of formal treaties with the Roman People and paid Vatinius for the requisite legislation. On the other hand it is certain that he and Pompey jointly exacted from Ptolemy Auletes of Egypt a promise to pay six thousand talents in return for a senatorial resolution and a popular law by which his crown was at last firmly set upon his head. It is difficult to explain on what grounds of policy or business calculation Caesar supported the suit of his future antagonist, the German chieftain Ariovistus, who applied to the Senate for the title of 'friend of the Roman People' (p. 548)

But all the rest of Vatinius' legislation is of slight importance compared with the Lex Vatinia de Caesaris Provincia. By this law, which came before the Popular Assembly in May or June 59 B.C., Caesar's tribune set aside the Senate's selection of consular provinces for 58 B.C. and secured for Caesar the governorship of Cisalpine Gaul and of Illyricum[1]. By the terms of this measure Caesar held his command under specially favourable conditions. He was authorized to nominate his staff of legati without reference to the Senate, and to found colonies at his own discretion[2]. Above all, his proconsulship, instead of being limited to the usual term of one or two years, was guaranteed to him until February 28th 54 B.C. It is not known why this particular date was selected as the legal term of his office; in any event, under the rules of succession then in operation Caesar might confidently expect that he would not actually be relieved before the end of 54 B.C., so that in effect the Lex Vatinia conferred his command for five clear years.

Thus Caesar was furnished with a province which offered him ample opportunities for testing his military skill. Yet the command in which Caesar actually established his fame as a general was bestowed upon him by a later grant and as the result of an afterthought. Soon after the enactment of the Lex Vatinia the governorship of Transalpine Gaul fell vacant by the sudden death of Metellus Celer, to whom this province had been assigned for the current year. At the instigation of Pompey the Senate now made a special grant of this province to Caesar, who thus acquired concurrent authority in both the Gauls. We may wonder that Caesar should have obtained his greatest prize from the Senate rather than from the People. But after its first sharp lesson over Caesar's land laws the Senate fully realized that resistance to the triumvirs was useless, so that henceforward it salvaged its authority by passing the measures which Caesar would otherwise have carried over its head to the popular assembly. We may also suspect an ulterior thought in the Senate's complaisance: Caesar would at all events be removed from Rome during the next five years, and the wider his opportunities of conquest, the greater also would be his chances of a humiliating defeat. It is not unlikely that the Senate banked on his essaying a task beyond his powers, and in this spirit paid out a liberal length of rope for Caesar to hang himself. At all events nobody in Rome, except perhaps the new governor of Gaul, had as yet any ground for suspecting that Caesar might rival Lucullus and even Pompey.

[1] Illyricum appears to have been ordinarily attached to Macedonia.
[2] The town of Comum was reconstituted as a burgess colony under this law (p. 629). It is probable that other such settlements were contemplated at the time when the Lex Vatinia was passed.

Caesar's commitments to Pompey and Crassus obliged him to devote the greater part of his consulship to personal politics undisguised. Yet he found a little time to spare for measures of disinterested reform. At the outset of his term of office he made arrangements for authentic copies of popular laws and of senatorial resolutions, and for bulletins of important news, to be posted up from day to day for public inspection. Apart from its general educational value, this approximation to an Official Gazette was of special service in preventing the garbling of official documents by interested magistrates, a malpractice of which even Cicero had been accused. But the most significant of Caesar's reforming measures was a new act 'de rebus repetundis,' which consolidated past statutes on extortion and closed various loopholes left open to slim plunderers. This law was a durable memorial of Caesar's lifelong interest in the provincial populations. It remained in force so long as the jury-courts functioned, and it accomplished what little could be done by further penal legislation to restrain rapacious governors (see p. 459).

Although open resistance to the triumvirate died down with the passing of the land laws, its adversaries went on making play with the weapons of propaganda and drove their shafts home with considerable success. While Bibulus discharged volleys of edicts, senators with facile pens, such as the encyclopaedist Varro and Scribonius Curio the Elder, assailed the 'three-headed monster' in venomous pamphlets. These manifestos had their effect upon the proletariate and even upon the equestrian class, both of whom joined in demonstrations against the coalition at the public festivals. They also told upon the triumvirs themselves. Pompey made blundering apologies which plainly betrayed his embarrassment. Caesar, for once losing his temper, blurted out threats at the Senate and egged on the rabble with inflammatory speeches against Bibulus. Vatinius, outrunning the constable, proposed to break into Bibulus' house and had to be restrained by his fellow-tribunes from such unexampled violence against a consul.

By midsummer the political temperature had risen near to flash-point, and rumours of intended murder began to fly about. Fortunately the tension was somewhat abated by an incident which foreshadowed a tragedy but ended in broad farce. A professional spy named L. Vettius, who had plied Cicero with information good and bad at the time of the Catilinarian Conspiracy, confided to the younger Scribonius Curio a scheme for the assassination of Pompey. Curio, who had borne a gallant part in the opposition to the dynasts but drew the line at murder, reported the alleged plot to his father, and he to Pompey, at whose instance an investigation was ordered before the Senate. Here Vettius, turning King's evidence, transferred the role of ringleader from himself to Curio and implicated other members of the aristocracy, notably M. Brutus, whose conscience had not yet awakened to the duty of tyrannicide; Bibulus, who had previously volunteered information to put Pompey on his guard against murder; and one L. Aemilius Paullus, who happened at that time to be in Macedonia. The Senate at once recognized that he was at his old tricks and dismissed him with derision. But on the following day Vettius was summoned to undergo a second scrutiny at the hands of Caesar and Vatinius in the Forum. To please Caesar, who notoriously had a weakness for the mother of Brutus, Vettius expunged her son from the record, but to make up he produced from his conjurer's bag a catalogue of fresh culprits, including Lucullus and, by implication, Cicero. Lacking the artistry of Titus Oates, the Roman spy instead of alarming his audiences merely amused them; and far from drawing a fat pension he was packed off to prison by Vatinius and expired under suspicious circumstances. The only clear conclusion from this burlesque is that the plot against the triumvirs was pure fiction; at most we may admit that some hotheads might have sighed suggestively for a new Harmodius or Servilius Ahala. Vettius' mission therefore was plainly that of an *agent provocateur*. But who was his employer? Certainly not Caesar himself, who would have coached Vettius better and would never have suffered the tissue of lies to be embroidered with the name of Brutus. We cannot give an equally clear discharge to Vatinius, whom Cicero afterwards charged in round terms with the whole concoction. On the other hand it is possible that Vettius, like Oates, did not stand in anybody's employ, but invented the plot as a private speculation, in the hope of securing a good price from the triumvirs for inside information. The origin of Vettius' romance and the manner of his death are still unsolved problems.

By the end of 59 B.C. the general indignation against the triumvirs had died away. But Caesar's chief opponents, though foiled for the time being, nursed their revenge for some future day of retribution, and Pompey was filled with misgivings which he stifled again and again, but never fought down completely. As the standard historian of the Great Civil War, Asinius Pollio, pointed out, its seeds were sown 'in the consulship of Metellus[1],' that is, in 60 B.C., when Caesar formed the First Triumvirate.

[1] Horace, *Odes*, ii, i, i. See below, p. 883.

V. PUBLIUS CLODIUS

The First Triumvirate, being based on no common principles, but on a fortuitous convergence of interests among its members, was nothing more than a temporary expedient; like the triumvirate of Antony, Octavian and Lepidus, it offered no durable substitute for the republican administration which it had put out of action. Its essential instability already showed through in Caesar's consulship, for Pompey even then could not conceal his uneasiness at being found in such compromising company. But the very illegality of Caesar's methods in 59 B.C. formed a new bond of union between the dynasts, for in the event of the legislation of that year being subsequently declared invalid, all three of them would suffer. Hence it was in their joint interest to make a common stand against any retrospective attack on the acts of Caesar and Vatinius. The need of such concerted action was at once made manifest after the expiry of Caesar's consulship. At the beginning of 58 B.C. two incoming praetors, C. Memmius and L. Domitius Ahenobarbus, invited the Senate to pronounce Caesar's laws null and void, and a tribune named L. Antistius prepared to impeach Caesar in person. Though nothing came of these attempts, their significance could not be missed. But Caesar at any rate did not require admonition. Foreseeing the need of insurance against his declared opponents, and of re-insurance against Pompey's vacillations, he made it a rule during his proconsulship to attach to himself as many as possible among the magistrates of each year. In this policy, it is true, he met with no great success, for to the very end of the Republic the nobility maintained its hold on the electoral machine. But for 58 B.C. he secured the services of a tribune compared with whom Vatinius might seem a faint-heart.

Vatinius' successor, P. Clodius, has already appeared as the prosecutor and the defendant in two lawsuits, in both of which he cut a sorry figure. Utterly unprincipled in private and in public life, he won his way by sheer audacity, and by his lack of scruples commended himself to several powerful patrons. Though he appears on more than one occasion as a henchman of Crassus, his most important services were rendered to Caesar, who borrowed him in 59–8 B.C. from his fellow-triumvir. In 60 B.C. Clodius, desiring a tribuneship for his own ends, had sought to remove the disqualification of his patrician blood through admission into a plebeian gens, but had been debarred from standing for office by the consul Metellus Celer, who insisted that his adoption, not having been attested and confirmed by the Comitia Curiata, was not legally valid. In the following year, thanks to Caesar's good offices, his *traductio ad plebem* was accomplished with all due solemnity. In his dual capacity as consul and Pontifex Maximus Caesar convened the Comitia Curiata on Clodius' behalf and guaranteed that the apposite ritual had been observed without a flaw: in comparison with this all-important regard for external forms, it mattered little that Clodius' adoptive parent was younger than himself. Thus invested in plebeian status, Clodius stood for the tribuneship of 58 B.C. and secured election. For the present his connection with Caesar was kept as dark as possible. The ceremony in the Comitia Curiata, though nominally performed for the sake of publicity, did not in reality attain this end, for the attendance at this obsolete assembly was usually made up of thirty lictors (one to each curia). Moreover Pompey, who had been invited to take part in the ceremony and to give his word as an augur that the omens were propitious, was not fully enlightened as to the intentions of Clodius and Caesar. To complete the mystification, Clodius pretended to solicit an embassy to the king of Armenia and to bear Caesar a grudge for his refusal.

But on entering his tribuneship Clodius lost no time in showing his colours. On January 3rd 58 B.C. he brought forward no less than four new laws. One of these, which prohibited future censors from expelling senators save after a joint judicial examination, was perhaps intended to safeguard his own position against the risk of some future revision of the Senate-list[1]. The other three aimed at the checkmating of Caesar's opponents and the elevation of his tribunate into a dictatorship. One measure, the only genuine reform among Clodius' acts, repealed two statutes of the second century, the Aelian and the Fufian laws, which facilitated the obstruction of legislative assemblies by magistrates on the pretext of watching the heavens, and it limited this right in future to augurs and tribunes. The immediate purpose of the new law was plainly to prevent a repetition of the manœuvre by which Bibulus in 59 B.C. had endeavoured to thwart and in strict law had invalidated the legislation of Caesar and Vatinius. A second act of Clodius made a bid for the support of the urban proletariate by

---

[1] After the fiasco of Crassus' and Catulus' censorship in 65 B.C. a new pair took office in 64 B.C., but was prevented from holding a *lectio senatus* by some tribunes who feared for their own seats. In 61 B.C. a fresh Senate-list was actually drawn up, but the censors of that year, by way of disarming opposition, waived their rights of expulsion. No appointment of censors took place after this until 50 B.C.

abolishing all payment for public corn. In 62 B.C., after the riots
stirred up by Metellus Nepos, Cato as tribune had sought to
appease the town rabble by a lavish increase in the corn doles
distributed by the State (p. 300 *sq.*). From that year, if we may
judge by the charge which Cato's measure imposed upon the
treasury, a monthly ration of five modii (pecks) of wheat was
delivered to some 320,000 applicants at less than half the normal
market price. This bribe, which Cato no doubt justified by high
reasons of State, was not without effect, for in 59 B.C. the urban
populace had joined heartily in the demonstrations against the
triumvirs. But Clodius now over-trumped Cato by bestowing the
corn free of charge. It mattered nothing to him that this gratuity
absorbed more than one-half of the new revenues accruing from
Pompey's conquests, and that it completed the pauperization of
the Roman proletariate.

The third law of Clodius was at once the most pernicious and
the most important for his own aggrandisement. In 64 B.C., at a
time when plots and rumours of plots followed thick and fast upon
each other, the Senate had placed a ban on all *collegia* or clubs,
save a few artisans' associations of old standing which had kept to
their proper object of common worship and recreation. The effect
of this resolution was to rid the city of a number of recently formed
bodies whose members were drawn from the vagabond population
and were trained to take the lead in the riots fomented by political
agitators. By Clodius' law complete freedom of association was
restored in Rome. In consequence fresh *collegia* sprang up like
mushrooms and provided Clodius with an excellent recruiting
field, out of which he formed a highly organized force of personal
supporters. Thus Clodius, surpassing the highest achievements of
Saturninus, Sulpicius and Vatinius, reduced political hooliganism
to a system. The maintenance of his forces no doubt entailed a
considerable outlay of money. But, to say nothing of his perquisites accruing from sales of titles and immunities, Clodius
could reckon on Caesar or Crassus to provide him with funds. In
effect, he was a domestic *imperator* with a regular army at his beck
and call.

Having thus cleared the field for further action, Clodius introduced two more bills whose object was to deprive the Senate of its
strongest and its ablest leaders, Cato and Cicero.

After his refusal to enter into partnership with Caesar, Cicero
had quitted active politics and was dividing his time between
literary pursuits and forensic practice. But before passing into
retirement he had made an attempt to dissuade Pompey from

tying himself to Caesar's chariot wheels, and when his worst fears of the triumvirate came to be realized, he could no longer restrain himself from a public display of indignation. In March or April 59 B.C., while defending his former colleague Antonius on a charge of misgovernment in the province of Macedonia[1], he blurted out some unguarded remarks about 'the condition of the Republic,' that is, about the illegalities of Caesar and his assistants. After this outburst Caesar decided that it was no longer safe to disregard Cicero. In the first instance he endeavoured to buy off his critic by offering him in turn a place on the land-commission, a post on his proconsular staff in Gaul, or some foreign mission on the orator's own terms. But in anticipation of Cicero's refusal he prepared to render him harmless by a sentence of exile. For the impeachment of Cicero Caesar had a plausible pretext in his execution of Catiline's accomplices, for which the Senate had indeed given him a moral but not a legal sanction (p. 503). In Clodius he had a prosecutor whose past relations with Cicero guaranteed that on this occasion he would not play into the hands of the defendant. After his trial on the affair of the Bona Dea, in which Cicero had tendered incriminating evidence, Clodius had sought to revenge himself on the orator in a contest of repartee before the Senate; but he had merely succeeded in drawing upon himself some telling thrusts of sarcasm—the most formidable weapon in Cicero's rhetorical armoury. Stung to the quick, Clodius never let his desire for vengeance sleep. It was with this end in view that he made his first unavailing attempt to obtain the tribuneship, and when Caesar assisted Clodius into that office it must have been with a full knowledge of the use to which he would apply its powers. It was therefore no mere accident that Clodius' *traductio ad plebem* was accomplished within three hours of Cicero's indiscretion at the trial of Antonius.

As soon as Clodius had consolidated his dominion in Rome, he launched his long-delayed attack. In February or March 58 B.C. he brought forward a law which 'debarred from fire and water' (*i.e.* outlawed) 'anyone who had condemned a Roman citizen

---

[1] The circumstances of this trial have been much disputed. It seems probable that Antonius underwent one prosecution only, and that the indictment was *maiestas*. The current rumour that he had made an underhand compact to share out his Macedonian plunder with Cicero rests on nothing more than some allusions to a payment which Antonius made to Cicero in February 61 B.C. in satisfaction of a long-standing claim. Most probably this transaction was in redemption of a loan made by Cicero in 63 B.C. In spite of Cicero's advocacy Antonius was found guilty and went into exile.

without trial.' Although couched in general terms, this measure
was clearly designed to meet a particular case. Cicero, who had
shown signs of uneasiness in 59 B.C., but had been half reassured
by encouraging answers to anxious inquiries from all three
dynasts, now made frantic efforts to avert the blow. He sent
entreaties to Caesar and cast himself at Pompey's feet; he sought
the aid of the new consuls, of whom A. Gabinius was the trusted
lieutenant of Pompey, and L. Calpurnius Piso the father-in-law of
Caesar since 59 B.C.; he extended his supplications to passers-by
in the streets of Rome; he even played with the idea of rousing all
Italy to a crusade against the coalition. In return Cicero received
expressions of sympathy from every side, and we need not doubt
that most of them rang true. His steadfast friends the financiers
interceded for him; deputations came from all Italy to plead on
his behalf; the Senate, honouring its obligations, invited all
citizens to put on mourning, and was widely obeyed; a tribune
named L. Ninnius undertook to veto Clodius' bill. But all these
kindly gestures went for nothing. In answer to the Senate's
entreaties Gabinius, who had been won over by Clodius with the
promise of a good province to follow his consulship, prohibited
the wearing of mourning; Clodius mobilized his private army and
drew first blood among the more importunate of Cicero's champions. Caesar, who had spent the first months of 58 B.C. in
enrolling recruits for his proconsular army, but as yet showed no
hurry to leave the neighbourhood of Rome, gave significant support to his tribune: while he made an obeisance to his own reputation by putting in a plea for mercy, he cast away his previous
reserve in roundly affirming that Cicero was guilty. Pompey,
who had honestly interceded with Clodius in 59 B.C., but had been
duped by false assurances, still had the wish but lacked the nerve
to renew his expostulations, and evaded Cicero's appeals by retiring from Rome: the story was put about that he had eluded one
attempt at an interview by sneaking out through his back door[1].
Of the senators, Lucullus alone exhorted Cicero to stand his
ground; Cato for once put discretion first and advised surrender.
On the eve of the vote on Clodius' bill (c. March 21st) Cicero
left Rome in self-imposed outlawry. A few days later Clodius
made the ban compulsory (though perhaps not legally valid) by
a second act which forbad Cicero to stay within five hundred
miles of Italy and declared illegal all resolutions in favour of
his recall. In fact, Cicero remained in exile until the summer of
57 B.C.

---

[1] Plutarch, *Cicero*, 31; *Pompey*, 46.

But from Caesar's point of view, if not from that of Clodius, the absence of Cicero was less imperative than the removal of Cato. Unable in this case to find any colourable pretext for a prosecution, Clodius got rid of Cato under the semblance of an honourable foreign mission. In 59 B.C. the triumvirs, having settled the Egyptian question, had left in suspense the kindred problem of Cyprus, where a brother of Ptolemy Auletes held the throne by a similar precarious title, but showed less readiness to pay his footing to them. In the following year, being still disappointed of their bribe, they resolved to disavow him. Accordingly Clodius drew up a bill in which Cyprus was declared a Roman province, and Cato was nominated to take over from the dispossessed king. Though this method of appointment to foreign commands was unusual, its legitimacy was beyond dispute. After a brief demur Cato took his departure and did not reappear in Rome till the end of 56 B.C. In saddling Cato with this bailiff's errand Caesar and Clodius may have nourished a secret hope that he would bring home a damaged reputation. If so, they made a bad speculation, for Cato combined personal integrity with expert knowledge of accounting, and on his return not a flaw could be found in his receivership. Yet if Clodius could not soil Cato's hands, at least he 'plucked out his tongue[1].'

VI. POMPEY'S RALLY

After the departure of Cicero and Cato the triumvirate appeared impregnable by attacks from outside. Clodius' only further task, so it appeared, was to reward himself and his assistants for their exertions. In return for the vigorous support of Gabinius, and the more passive collusion of Piso, Clodius made payment with exemplary promptitude. On the very day on which he carried his first bill against Cicero he also secured the passage of a measure by which Gabinius was invested with Syria and Piso with Macedonia, notwithstanding any alternative arrangements by the Senate. For his own benefit he resumed the traffic in honours with monarchies and cities, his most notorious transaction being the sale of a royal title and the transference of part of Deiotarus' Galatian kingdom to Brogitarus, chieftain of the Trocmi.

But from first to last the chief danger to the triumvirate lay in disruption from inside. This risk had increased since the expulsion of Cicero, for Pompey, who was genuinely uncomfortable at the inglorious part thrust upon him by Caesar and Clodius, soon

---

[1] Cicero, *pro Sestio*, 28, 60.

began to throw out feelers on the subject of his recall (May 58 B.C.).
Clodius, as Caesar's appointed watchdog, was on the alert for
signs of Pompey's defection; but in rounding upon Pompey and
seeking to bury his teeth in him he went beyond his proper part.
With an army of trained rioters at his back, he could safely defy
Pompey, whose veterans had by now been drafted away from
Rome, and his sense of omnipotence overbore his loyalty to
Caesar. In reply to Pompey's first signs of impatience he contrived the escape of the younger Tigranes, son of the Armenian
king, whom Pompey had lodged as a hostage in the house of the
praetor Flavius, and in a skirmish on the Via Appia he defeated
Flavius' attempt at pursuit. He next turned upon his former accomplice Gabinius, who had obeyed Pompey's call for help, and
met his remonstrances by breaking his fasces. In August 58 B.C.
he introduced an armed slave into the Senate, ostensibly to murder
Pompey, and accomplished his real purpose of scaring him so well
as to pen him up for the rest of the year in his private house like a
second Bibulus. In consequence, Pompey's agitation on Cicero's
behalf remained abortive. On June 1st the tribune Ninnius had
raised the question of his recall in the Senate, and in Clodius'
temporary absence had obtained its unanimous consent; but he
did not venture to follow up this resolution with a bill in the
Concilium Plebis. On October 29th a group of eight tribunes
presented a measure to the Comitia, but for fear of offending
Clodius they drafted it with such excess of caution as to stultify
themselves, and the bill was withdrawn.

In 57 B.C., however, the balance of power gradually tilted
against Clodius. Of the new magistrates, the consul Lentulus
Spinther and the tribune Sestius had been useful servants of
Cicero in the Catilinarian crisis and now became his staunch sup-
porters. But the main cause of Clodius' defeat was a rally by
Pompey, who at last devised effective means of counter-attack.
His first step was to assist a free-lance tribune named T. Annius
Milo to collect a corps of retainers for service against Clodius.
Later in the year Pompey made a general appeal to the Italians to
take up Cicero's cause by passing resolutions on his behalf in their
municipal assemblies, or by attendance at Rome, and he paid a
personal visit to his veterans at Capua in order to secure their
co-operation. This enlistment of the countryside Italians was a
winning move, for among them Pompey's prestige still stood
high, and recruits for a decisive tussle in the Forum flocked into
Rome. The visible sign of Pompey's victory was Cicero's return in
September 57 B.C.

In January Cicero's supporters had again brought his case before the Senate, but Clodius prepared an 'eighteenth Brumaire' for the meeting by turning upon it a band of gladiators borrowed from his brother, the praetor Appius Claudius. At the same time a battle in the Forum, where the followers of Clodius and Milo appear to have been the protagonists, resulted in such slaughter that the pavement had to be swabbed clean of blood, and the town sewers were choked with corpses. Soon after this affray Sestius was set upon by Clodius' bravoes and only escaped the finishing blow by shamming dead. But in July, under the joint protection of Milo's bands and of Pompey's stalwarts from Italy, liberty of speech was restored. On the motion of Lentulus Spinther the Senate approved of Cicero's recall with 416 votes against Clodius' solitary dissent, and a few days later, on August 4th, the Comitia Centuriata definitely sanctioned his return[1]. On September 4th Cicero was received back in Rome amid general acclamation.

Henceforward Clodius was politically a spent force. It is true that he kept his bands together and occasionally sprang a surprise upon unwary opponents. In November 57 B.C. he burnt down Q. Cicero's house and all but succeeded in serving Milo likewise. But for these victories he nearly paid with his life, for in one chance encounter he was cornered by Cicero's escort and owed his escape to nothing but a whim of his enemy. His only other claim to our notice is a semi-comic tournament of lawsuits with which he and Milo belaboured each other in 57 and 56 B.C. Early in 57 B.C. Clodius was prosecuted by Milo for breach of the peace, but at one and the same time he proved Milo's case and non-suited him by breaking up the court. At the end of the year, when Milo was in the ascendant, the accusation was renewed, but Clodius evaded it by constitutional obstruction. In 56 B.C. Clodius made Milo a defendant on the same charge, but in his turn was defeated by continual postponements[2].

Three days after his joyous re-entry into Rome Cicero took the lead in a senatorial debate on a new crisis which recalled the worst days of the pirate wars. Rome was afflicted by an unforeseen famine, and an angry mob was threatening the Senate with a general massacre. At Cicero's suggestion the Senate recom-

---

[1] It is not certain whether the Comitia simply overrode the previous acts against Cicero, or whether, as seems more likely, it declared them ineffective on the ground that no banishment could be valid unless it followed upon a proper judicial trial.

[2] The problems in which these lawsuits are involved have been elucidated by Ed. Meyer, *Caesars Monarchie*, 2nd ed. p. 109, n. 3.

mended that Pompey be appointed food dictator, and the consuls
carried through the Comitia Centuriata a law conferring upon him
wide powers to purchase corn and charter transport for a term of
five years. Given this clear lead and ample executive authority,
Pompey showed a flash of his pristine energy and gathered in corn
as vigorously as once he had rounded up pirates. Defying the
elements with a phrase that sailor people still cherish, 'necesse est
navigare, vivere non est necesse,' he made winter voyages to
Sicily, Sardinia and Africa and replenished Rome's granaries
before the next harvest.

If Rome's swift recovery from scarcity may be credited to
Pompey's exertions, its sudden plunge into famine is not so easy
to explain. Indeed only a few days previously the word was going
round that the gods were blessing Cicero's return with bounteous
supplies of food[1]. Was the shortage due to natural causes or to a
preconcerted cornering of stocks? It was openly said by Clodius
that the crisis had been engineered by Pompey for his own
aggrandisement[2]. But Pompey was not Crassus; granted that he
was hankering after a dictatorship, he was utterly lacking in the
experience required for manipulating the grain trade on a worldwide scale. We may rather believe Cicero, who threw part of the
blame on commercial speculators[3]. After the success of the tax-
farmers in squeezing the triumvirs, it would not be surprising if
the corn-dealers organized an artificial scarcity in the hope of
dictating their terms to the food-dictator. But if such was their
aim, Pompey defeated it by his sudden visit to the countries of
supply and his rapid mobilization of transport. In any event, it
seems clear that Pompey took his opportunity rather than made it.

But the main problem of the food crisis turns on a rival motion
which a tribune named C. Messius brought before the Senate. In
addition to the financial powers which the consular bill conferred
upon him, Messius proposed to invest Pompey with authority to
levy troops and warships, and with 'maius imperium' (overriding
control) over all provincial governors. The extravagance of these
terms, which went beyond the wildest provisions of Rullus' land-
law, ensured their immediate defeat. Nevertheless Messius'
motion has often been taken to represent the real measure of
Pompey's ambitions. In that case his proposal was of high significance, for it would mean that Pompey was casting about for a
military command to counterbalance Caesar's power. But had
Pompey desired a new imperium, he would surely have asked for it

[1] Cicero, Oratio post Red., ad Quir., 8, 18.
[2] Plutarch, Pompey, 49.   [3] de domo sua, 5, 11.

on grounds less manifestly absurd. With far better reason he could have drawn attention to the war clouds on the Parthian horizon, or have pressed his own case in the 'Egyptian question' which presented itself in 57–6 B.C. It appears most probable that Messius' kite was not flown by Pompey's orders, but was an unauthorized speculation by a free-lance tribune.

Another test case of Pompey's attitude was presented by the recrudescence of trouble in Egypt. At the end of 58 B.C. Ptolemy Auletes ran away from his irate subjects in Alexandria, who resented the new taxes imposed by the king in order to pay off his debt to the triumvirs. The fugitive monarch came to Rome and pressed his claim for reinstatement upon Pompey. In his wake a deputation of one hundred Alexandrians set out to present a counter-plea to the Senate. But the greater number of these was spirited away on the journey by magic of gold or of cold steel; and the same fate befel their leader Dio, who actually reached Rome and was summoned before the Senate, but was made safe with a bribe, and doubly safe with a dagger. Thus the case went by default in favour of Ptolemy, and the Senate commissioned the consul Lentulus Spinther, who was due to proceed to Cilicia in 56 B.C., to force the Egyptian James the Second back upon his subjects. But at the beginning of 56 B.C. a new situation was created by a flash of lightning which struck the statue of Juppiter on the Alban Mount. The custodians of the Sibylline Books, on being consulted as to the proper means of expiation, opportunely discovered an oracle forbidding the restoration of an Egyptian king 'with a multitude,' which being interpreted meant 'with armed force.' Upon publication of this advice the Senate decided that Roman intervention in Egypt must be purely diplomatic, and reconsidered its previous resolution on behalf of Lentulus Spinther. While Spinther's claims were upheld by Cicero, those of Pompey were now put forward by a few of his friends. Others again suggested that Roman authority should be put into commission among three envoys of equal powers. Lastly, Crassus put out feelers on his own behalf through the agency of Clodius, who made propaganda for his patron in the Forum (January–February 56 B.C.). These conflicting counsels served the Senate as an excuse for shelving the whole question. Ptolemy, who had left Rome in anticipation of a speedy reinstatement, remained on his travels until 55 B.C.

From this Egyptian imbroglio two points of special interest emerge. The first consists in Pompey's failure to obtain for himself the mandate to restore Ptolemy. The king himself made no

concealment of the fact that he expected no less a person to
escort him back, and current opinion in Rome confidently
assumed that Pompey coveted the appointment. Though personal
feuds between Lentulus Spinther and other nobles no doubt influenced its decision, it is probable that the Senate's action in first
demilitarizing the mission to Egypt and finally abandoning it
altogether, was largely inspired by a desire to thwart Pompey's
real or supposed ambitions. Yet Pompey never pressed his claims
during the senatorial discussions of 56 B.C., and what is more
strange, he offered no opposition to the appointment of Lentulus
Spinther in the previous year. Had he made a firm request for a
military command at the outset, it is difficult to see how the
Senate, in view of his manifestly superior qualifications for the
task, could have passed him over. An unprejudiced consideration
of Pompey's demeanour in regard to the Egyptian question must
lead us to infer that, contrary to the prevalent belief, his military
ambitions still lay dormant. It may be assumed that his friends in
the Senate, to whom Pompey never gave any overt support,
followed the example of Messius in making proposals on their own
initiative.

The other important feature in the Egyptian debates is the
recrudescence of conflict between Pompey and Crassus. When
Crassus entered the field of competition for the mission to Alexandria, he treated Pompey as a rival. Thus he renewed hostilities
upon which Caesar had imposed a truce, but not a lasting peace.

VII. THE CRISIS IN THE TRIUMVIRATE

In the triangular pull of forces within the triumvirate, while
Crassus might on occasion be the 'momentum rerum,' the major
influences were the mutual affinities and repulsions between
Caesar and Pompey. In 58 and 57 B.C. the banishment of Cicero
and Clodius' boisterous methods of preventing his reinstatement
had given Pompey reason enough for discontent with Caesar, who
was ultimately responsible for these slights upon his partner.
Hence one of his advisers, Q. Terentius Culleo, prompted him to
divorce Julia and to desert the cause of Caesar for that of the
Senate. But Pompey, who had good reason to believe that if he
were to renew his overtures to the Senate he would merely expose
himself to a second rebuff, was unprepared for such a plunge.
Nay rather, he followed a studiously correct course in his dealings
with Caesar. Though he could safely have forced Caesar's hand on

the question of Cicero's recall, he sent Sestius at an early date
(August–September 57 B.C.) to win Caesar's consent, and he
carried out Caesar's stipulation that some guarantee must be
found for Cicero's future behaviour by exacting a pledge of his
good conduct from his brother Quintus. Thus the triumvirate, in
spite of Caesar's departure, showed signs of continued stability
until the early months of 56 B.C., when Crassus began to exert a
disturbing influence. Though he abstained, as usual, from any
overt opposition to Pompey, he heaped insults upon him through
the agency of Clodius. Nay more, with his patron's connivance or
direct encouragement, Clodius mobilized his bands against Pompey and would no doubt have repeated the incidents of 58 B.C.,
had not Milo's forces been at hand to check him. Under these
affronts Pompey suddenly lost patience. Before the Senate he
accused Crassus of planning his murder, thus overtly proclaiming
a rift in the coalition. This public explosion of Pompey precipitated
an immediate crisis, for it gave the signal for an attack upon the
dynasts from outside.

   This improvised campaign against the coalition comprised a
sapping operation and a frontal assault. The undermining
manœuvre was initiated by Cicero, who had always realized that
the best method of destroying the triumvirate was by disintegrating it, and now staked his career on his chance. After the
first outbursts of exultation upon his return Cicero soon settled
down into a mood of caution and made it his guiding principle in
politics not to offend anybody. But in March 56 B.C., while engaged in the defence of his benefactor Sestius on a charge of
breach of the peace, he went out of his way to make a sustained
attack on Caesar's henchmen Clodius and Vatinius[1]. Soon after this
trial he re-opened in the Senate the question of Caesar's Campanian
land law. Though the terms of his reference to this measure are
unknown, it is fairly certain that they were so framed as to attack
Caesar's interests while safeguarding those of Pompey: in a word,
Cicero was endeavouring to drive a wedge between Caesar and
Pompey[2]. The frontal assault was delivered by a nobleman named
L. Domitius Ahenobarbus, who had taken a leading part against
Caesar in 59 and 58 B.C. Standing as a candidate for the consul-
ship of 55 B.C., Domitius announced that he would use his con-
sular authority to deprive Caesar of his provinces. It is uncertain

   [1] For a full analysis of Cicero's intentions in his speeches Pro Sestio and
In Vatinium, see L. G. Pocock, *A Commentary on Cicero In Vatinium*.
   [2] In December 57 B.C. a partisan of Pompey named Lupus had initiated
an abortive debate on the same issue (Cicero, *ad Q.F.* II, 1, 1).

whether Domitius intended to recall Caesar at or before the expiry of his legal term; in any case, since events in Gaul had shown that Caesar would require an extension of his quinquennium in order to complete the work of conquest, Domitius was threatening the proconsul's interests at a vital point.

There can be little doubt that these moves by Cicero and Domitius were based on the expectation that Pompey in his present mood would connive at the assault upon his colleagues, and that this exhibition of disloyalty would in effect be the death of the triumvirate. Their plan was not ill conceived, but whatever chances of success it might have possessed were set at nought by its being put into execution too soon. At the time when their attack was launched the key of the situation lay not in Pompey's hands, but in Caesar's. According to his usual custom, Caesar had recrossed the Alps at the end of the previous campaigning season and had spent the winter in his Cisalpine province. In April 56 B.C. he was at Ravenna, within a week's journey of Rome, and he had recently been posted up about the coming crisis by Clodius' brother Appius Claudius.

It has been suggested that if Caesar had made a pretext of the situation at Rome to cast Pompey and Crassus aside as disloyal or incompetent, and to fix a quarrel upon the Senate, he could have carried the city in the same manner as Octavian in 43 B.C., and have established his autocracy there and then. We may ask in reply whether Caesar's army, which at that time was still a long way from the perfection which it attained in the days of the Civil Wars, could have coped with a *levée en masse* under Pompey's leadership in defence of the Republic. On such an issue, might Caesar not have played Lepidus to Pompey's Catulus? But such speculations are otiose. It is extremely doubtful whether Caesar in 56 B.C., or even in 49 B.C., had any intention of turning autocrat. On the other hand it is clear that he was firmly determined to complete the conquest of Gaul, and that he had no mind to sacrifice this object to the prospects, however alluring, of a short cut to royalty. Therefore instead of disavowing his colleagues he invited them to a joint conference. Crassus at once went to meet Caesar, but Pompey was more deliberate. To facilitate matters for Pompey, who was about to proceed to Pisa in the course of a voyage to the Sardinian cornfields, Caesar crossed the Apennines to the neighbouring town of Luca, which lay in a transmontane pocket of Cisalpine Gaul, bringing Crassus with him. It is not known whether Pompey's delay arose from a fugitive thought of breaking with his partners or from some more trivial cause. In any case, he eventually went to Luca. In the wake of Crassus and Pompey followed a bevy of lesser politicians: it is said that 120 senators and 200 lictors attached to urban or provincial magistrates were counted in that obscure town. But these hangers-on merely waited on the decisions of the three principals, who held their deliberations in secret conclave. After a brief conference (*c.* April 15th) Caesar hurried back to Gaul, leaving the execution of the new resolutions to Pompey and Crassus.

Immediately after the meeting at Luca Pompey sent a polite message to Cicero, inviting him to postpone his motion on the subject of the Campanian land-law. Cicero at once acknowledged defeat by abandoning his motion altogether. But he was not let off with this prompt surrender. While his brother Quintus was drafted to Caesar's staff as a liaison officer, the orator was required to place his services at the triumvirs' permanent disposal. This captivity proved a severe test of his endurance; yet in response to tactful treatment—for both Pompey and Caesar sugared his pill by conveying their commands in the form of requests—he submitted with outward good grace. On the rare occasions of his return to the political arena Cicero appeared as a spokesman of the triumvirs. In June 56 B.C. he made a notable speech (*De provinciis consularibus*) before the Senate, supporting Caesar's claim not to be superseded in Gaul on the expiry of his legal term; in 54 B.C. he made amends for his earlier outbursts against Vatinius and Gabinius by pleading for them in the courts; in the years from 52 to 49 B.C. he played an intermittent but not wholly abortive part as a mediator between Caesar and Pompey.

Domitius on the other hand was not defeated without a struggle. In order to head him off the consulship, it had been arranged at Luca that Pompey and Crassus should become rival candidates, but the consul, Cn. Lentulus Marcellinus, refused their names on the pretext that they had been given in too late. By way of outflanking Marcellinus, Pompey and Crassus suborned a tribune to veto the elections for the rest of his consulship. In January 55 B.C., under a more complaisant 'interrex,' they were admitted to the polls, and their return was made safe by a strong detachment of Caesar's soldiers on furlough, who canvassed on their behalf with forcible persuasiveness. As a further precaution, Pompey misused his authority as augur to impede the candidature of Cato, who had returned from Cyprus in time to sue for a praetorship. The riots attendant on these elections did not pass without casualties on either side. Returning one day from the Forum with a bloodstained toga, Pompey gave Julia a shock which led to a miscarriage and probably helped to bring about her premature death in 54 B.C.

For the time being the rift in the coalition had been closed, and the opposition had been paralysed no less effectively than in 59 B.C. The road was now clear for Pompey and Crassus to make Caesar's position in Gaul secure and to take their fee for this service, in accordance with the pledges exchanged at Luca. But the fundamental causes of dissension between the partners remained, and the very legislation which was designed to safeguard Caesar and to bind Pompey to him had the eventual effect of rousing their rival ambitions and of kindling their mutual suspicions. The power of Caesar was increased to match his ambition by the completion of his conquest of Gaul, while Crassus, who might have prevented the coalition from becoming a rivalry, was destined to meet his death in Syria. Thus the course of events in the North and in the East became critical for the history of the Republic, and, for the moment, the scene shifts to Gaul and Parthia.

INDEX TO NAMES

Narbonensis was not the official designation of Gallia Transalpina
in this period.

CHAPTER XIII

THE CONQUEST OF GAUL

I. THE CIVILIZATION AND RELIGION OF THE GAULS AND BRITONS IN THE FIRST CENTURY B.C.

THE material civilization of the Celts had entered upon a new phase towards the end of the second century B.C.; this phase, which continues almost to the end of the first century B.C., was the final stage of the La Tène Culture on the continent, though that culture continued to develop in Britain after the Romanization of Gaul. This Late La Tène period was preceded by the arrival in northern Gaul of Celts from the east of the Rhine, the Belgae, who brought to an end the long-established Marne culture; some elements of the older civilization survived in this area, notably certain fashions in pottery[1]. The Belgae practised cremation, which owing to their influence and that of the Romans in the south-east gradually supplanted inhumation as the customary rite in Gaul; in their sepultures they placed the

Note. For sections III–VI of this chapter the only independent authority is Caesar's *Commentarii de Bello Gallico*, books I–VII; the variants from this account in later writers, *e.g.* Dio, are undoubtedly due to critical reconstruction or mere invention, when they are not simply blunders. The dates of composition and publication of the separate books are still disputed; the view here adopted is that Caesar wrote the work as a whole after the campaign of 52 B.C., basing it on his yearly reports to the Senate, which were only partially revised before inclusion in his narrative. The authenticity of the geographical excursuses in the *B.G.* was attacked by Klotz (*Cäsarstudien*, 1910) but has been convincingly maintained by R. Koller (*Wiener Studien*, XXXVI, 1914, pp. 140–163). Caesar's account of events is accepted in this chapter as trustworthy, but the motives alleged by him for his actions have to be carefully examined, and some of the numbers for opposing armies given by him on his own authority or on that of others require revision. Section VII is based on the continuation of Caesar's narrative by his friend Hirtius (*B.G.* VIII); the amount of the tribute imposed on Gaul is given by Suetonius, *Divus Iulius*, 25, 1 and Eutropius, VI, 17, 3. For section I the authorities are Caesar (*B.G.* VI, 13–20 and *passim*), Diodorus (V, 21–22 and 25–32) and Strabo, book IV, supplemented by archaeological evidence. The account in section II is mainly a reconstruction from disconnected passages in Caesar (*B.G.* I, 2–6, 31, 35, and VI, 12). For earlier Celtic civilization see vol. VII, chap. II.

[1] Jullian's view that the Marne burials are to be dated after the arrival of the Belgae and used as evidence for their culture cannot be accepted.

ashes of the dead in cinerary urns of earthenware, some of which resemble a distinctive type of Marne domestic pottery, the pedestal urn. When the Belgae began to penetrate into south-eastern Britain at the beginning of the first century B.C., they took with them the practice of cremation and the use of the pedestal urn, of which specimens have been found at Aylesford in Kent and elsewhere (see vol. VII, p. 70 and below, p. 539, n. 4)[1].

Before the end of the second century B.C. the Celts of Gaul were on the defensive; the Celtic states in south-eastern Gaul had been conquered and annexed by the Romans in 121 B.C., and beyond the Rhine Teutonic tribes were advancing steadily southwards and driving before them the Celts settled to the east of the river. Fresh wounds were inflicted on the resources and prosperity of the Celts by the invasion of the Cimbri and Teutoni (pp. 140 *sqq.*), and their impoverishment is shown by the poor furniture of the burials in this period. The Late La Tène Culture is mainly illustrated by the finds from the various town-sites which have been excavated, especially Alise-Sainte-Reine (Alesia), and Mont Beuvray (Bibracte, the chief town of the Aedui); such sites have yielded a great variety of iron agricultural implements and domestic utensils. The development of town-life and industrial activity in this period is noteworthy, and the previous similarity between the industrial products of the various groups of the continental Celts is now intensified; thus objects from Bibracte are closely paralleled by those found in the Boian settlement at Stradonitz in Bohemia.

As in the previous La Tène periods, the swords and brooches continue to be distinctive and valuable for dating[2]. The typical sword of this period is long and double-edged, as before, but is now rounded at the end, not pointed, and the sword-guard, when it occurs, is usually straight; the scabbard has a straight mouth and a rounded chape. The brooches show a greater variety in details than before, but in all of them the foot is joined to the bow to form a triangular frame, the upper part of which forms a continuous curve with the bow. The use of red enamel for decoration is now common, the enamel being applied to the heads of nails which were then attached to the objects to be decorated; at first the head of the nail was completely covered with the enamel, but in the more developed technique it was crossed by two deep grooves at right angles which were filled with the enamel, making a cruciform decoration; this was probably the origin of the *champlevé* process among the Celts, later carried much farther

[1] See Volume of Plates iv, 14, *a*.   [2] *Ib.* iv, 14, *b*.

in the British Isles. Most of the painted vases which occur at Bibracte and other places in Central Gaul, the decoration of which corresponds with that of vases from Stradonitz, are ascribed[1] to the second half of the first century B.C., after the Roman conquest of Gaul; the abundant common pottery of the period is still mainly hand-made and often rough in execution. Agriculture was now well developed in Gaul, and commerce was facilitated by the excellent natural waterways and by a system of good roads. The commercial activity of this period is attested by the numerous coins; imitations of Roman coins, often with Latin lettering[2], and original Gallic types, sometimes fantastic in design, appear side by side with the older crude imitations of Greek coins[3].

The history of the Celts in Britain before Caesar's invasions is obscure; it is usually assumed that P-Celts had invaded the country before the middle of the fourth century, and that their arrival had been preceded by invasions of the Q-Celts (cf. vol. II, p. 34; VII, p. 53). The chief finds of Early La Tène objects in England come from Wessex (especially Wiltshire) and from burials in Yorkshire; Wessex may have been invaded by settlers from south-west Gaul, but the origin of the people represented by the chariot-burials in Yorkshire is obscure. At the time of Caesar's invasion the interior of the island was held by tribes who were believed to be descendants of the original inhabitants, but the coast districts near Gaul had now been occupied by Belgae from across the Channel. Belgic settlers began to penetrate into south-eastern Britain during the period 100–60 B.C., but there was no extensive displacement of population[4]. A Belgic chief, Diviciacus, ruler of the Suessiones in Gaul, brought part of Britain under his control[5] (c. 80 B.C.); his conquests were lost after his death, but the Belgae of Britain continued to maintain connections in commerce and friendships with their continental kinsmen.

The political development of the Celts is shown in their tendency to unite into larger groups, to combine the various *pagi* into *civitates*. This development was most pronounced in Central Gaul, while the smaller units tended to persist in Aquitania, and also in Britain, where the attempt to form larger unions is only just beginning at the time of Caesar's invasions. The more powerful

---

[1] By Déchelette, *Manuel d'Archéologie*, II, 3, p. 1493; see Volume of Plates iv, 16.   [2] Volume of Plates iv, 10, *k, l, m*.   [3] *Ib*. iii, 16, *f–i*.

[4] This view is based on the distribution of certain types of pottery found in the burial grounds excavated at Aylesford and Swarling; see the report on the Swarling site by J. P. Bushe-Fox (cited in the bibliography).

[5] Caesar, *B.G.* II, 4. 7.

civitates of Gaul, the Aedui and Arverni, moreover, had other
states attached to them in relationships varying from alliance to
subjection, ties summed up by Caesar in the term *clientela*, but
these wider unions were an obstacle rather than a help to the complete unification of Gaul, as they perpetuated on a larger scale the
internal dissensions which were the curse of Gallic political life.
A further sign of the political development of the Gauls is the
transition from kingship to aristocracy; aristocracy had prevailed
in most of the states in Central Gaul, but kingship survived in
Britain and some of the Belgic tribes. Yet the aristocratic governments, usually consisting in a Senate of nobles and one or more
annual magistrates, were unstable and frequently threatened by
the ambition of powerful chiefs; excellent laws were passed to
limit the opportunities of such adventurers, but the governments
were usually quite unable to enforce them.

The insecurity of the state governments was enhanced by the
structure of Gallic society in this period. Wealth and political
power were shared between the nobles (called *equites* by Caesar)
and the Gallic hierarchy, the Druids; the free cultivators and
artisans had been reduced, probably by the establishment of
private property in land and by the substitution of currency for
barter, to a position little better than that of the slaves, and often
bound themselves in a kind of serfdom to the rich, who gave them
in return the benefit of their protection. The nobles vied with each
other in the number of their retainers, slave and free, and were
able to defy the weaker authority of the magistrates.

The military organization of the Gauls was largely influenced
by their social conditions. In the majority of states the most important arm was the cavalry, composed of the nobles and the most
warlike of their retainers; early in the first century Posidonius had
found the war chariot still in use among the Gauls, but it had been
entirely superseded by the cavalry on the continent before Caesar's
arrival, though it retained its former importance among the Belgic
tribes in Britain. The infantry had formed the main strength of
Celtic armies in an earlier period, and in some states, such as the
Helvetii, who were trained in constant border warfare with the
Germans, and the Nervii, who had no cavalry, the infantry was
still formidable, but these two were the only tribes who offered
serious resistance to Caesar's legionaries in the open field. In the
states of Central Gaul the infantry was mainly composed of the
lower classes of society, probably containing a large admixture of
the pre-Celtic population, and had been allowed to degenerate
into an unwieldy and useless mob; the Belgic tribes of the north

were better soldiers, as they were more remote from the enervating influences of civilization. The Gauls in general had declined as a military power during the last two centuries; their armies had been mainly employed in the frequent civil wars between tribes or groups of tribes, which had failed to produce any improvements in weapons or tactics. Their strategy was still of the crudest type; as their temperament was unsuited to the fatigue and delay of a long campaign, their only idea was to force on a pitched battle as soon as possible. When the armies of several states combined for a temporary object, their efforts were largely nullified by the utter inadequacy of their organization, especially in the department of supply, the neglect of which caused the premature dispersion of more than one Gallic army. So the advantage which the possession of a large and warlike population ought to have conferred on the Gauls in the coming struggle was diminished by their decline in the art of war and their inability to place the welfare of the nation above the prosecution of their internecine quarrels.

The religion of the Gauls before the Roman conquest can only be described in general terms, as most of our information about Gallic religion comes from the Roman period, when it had been greatly modified by the assimilation of Gallic to Roman cults. Caesar mentions six important gods in the Celtic pantheon, equated by him with Mercury, Apollo, Mars, Juppiter, Minerva, and Dispater, but the native names of these deities are not given, and it is doubtful whether the equations are more than a very rough approximation. Lucan mentions three gods, Teutates, Esus, and Taranis, as those to whom human victims were sacrificed; they may perhaps be identified as the Gallic Mercury, Mars, and Juppiter, but there is no evidence for the view that they were worshipped as a triad. All identifications are deceptive, as popular ideas about the high gods must have varied from one region to another, though some approach to a uniform theology may have been promoted by the Druids. It seems probable that the Celts had no cult of an Earth-goddess; her place was taken by Dispater, but a native Earth-goddess of the pre-Celtic population of Gaul may be traced in Aeracura, associated in some Gallo-Roman inscriptions with Dispater, or in the cult, so popular later, of the Deae Matres. Various war-gods are identified in inscriptions with Mars, and such war-gods would be popular with the Celts of an earlier period, while the greater popularity in Caesar's time of gods equated with Mercury may be evidence of the progress made by the Gauls in the arts of peace; the two gods may be the same god in different stages of development, as the scholiast on Lucan identifies Teutates with both Mars and Mercury. Apollo is equated sometimes with Belenus, probably a sun-god, sometimes with the gods of healing springs, Grannus and Borvo. Taranis appears to have been a thunder-god, identified as such with Juppiter, while the counterpart of Minerva as inventress of arts and crafts may be found in Brigantia (Brigit), though she was doubtless identified with other goddesses also, such as the mysterious Sul, worshipped at Bath in Roman Britain.

Most of these high gods were probably introduced into Gaul by the Celts; but they adopted from the earlier inhabitants the multitudinous cults of the *genii locorum*, the tutelary spirits of springs, streams, rivers, lakes, and sacred mountains, such as that of the Puy de Dôme, worshipped in Roman times as Mercurius Dumias. The cult of trees was common in Aquitania, and the oak-tree was recognized as sacred by the Celts. It is probable that their religion had once included animal worship; but the animals originally worshipped were later reduced to symbols or attributes of divinity: thus the horse became the attribute of the horse-goddess Epona.

The Gauls did not worship in man-made temples, but in sacred groves. It is doubtful whether they made anthropomorphic images of their deities in pre-Roman times; Caesar's statement that the Gauls had numerous images (*simulacra*) is hard to reconcile with the absence of pre-Roman images in Gaul, and is best explained by a passage in Lucan:

> *simulacraque maesta deorum*
> *arte carent caesisque exstant informia truncis.*

Such *simulacra* were evidently of the crudest type, and it has been plausibly maintained that the religious conservatism of the priests successfully opposed the representation of the gods by anthropomorphic images until the Roman conquest.

The Gallic doctrine of immortality is ascribed in the ancient authorities to the teaching of the Gallic priests, the Druids. The best account of this mysterious priesthood is that given by Caesar; it stresses the political power of the Druids, which they shared with the Gallic *equites*, and their absolute control over religion. In Caesar's time the Druids throughout Gaul (this probably includes the Belgic states, possibly not Aquitania) were all members of one organization headed by a supreme Druid who held his supremacy for life. They met regularly every year in the country of the Carnutes, and there held a high court of justice, at which they decided important cases from all parts of Gaul; their decisions were usually accepted, as they could punish refractory individuals

and states by the imposition of an interdict, which involved religious and political excommunication. The relation of this jurisdiction to that of the Aeduan *vergobret*, who had the power of life
and death in his own state, is not explained by Caesar. The Druids
were exempt from military service and taxation, and their power
and prestige attracted to the priesthood the sons of the nobles,
who sometimes had to serve a novitiate of twenty years before
admission to the order. They controlled education; their teaching
was oral, and included physical and theological speculation. Their
most important doctrine was that of the immortality of the soul[1],
which was regarded as an incentive to bravery and contempt of
death. There is nothing to show that the Druids were a celibate or
monastic priesthood, and the Aeduan Druid Diviciacus was the
father of a family and took an active part in politics and warfare.

On the origin of the Druidic teaching Caesar quotes the belief of
the Gauls in his time: *disciplina in Britannia reperta atque inde in
Galliam translata esse existimatur*[2]; he adds that those who wished to
obtain a more thorough knowledge of Druidism went to Britain
to study it. This belief may be accepted in a modified form as
correct; probably the Celts after their arrival in Gaul had introduced into their religion elements derived from the pre-Celtic
population of the land, elements which were common to the
religion of the pre-Celtic inhabitants of Britain and survived in
Britain to Caesar's time in a purer form than in Gaul[3]. The
hypothesis that *disciplina* in the above passage means 'organization' raises more difficulties than it solves; nothing is known about
the organization of the British Druids, but they seem to hold a
less important position than their brethren in Gaul. If the doctrines taught by the Druids had an earlier origin than the priests
who adopted them, it is possible that the organization of the
Celtic priests as a corporation may date from about 300 B.C.,
when the Celts had established their supremacy over Gaul.
Perhaps their political power grew with the decline of kingship in
Gaul; this would explain the lesser importance of the Druids in
the British states, where monarchy was maintained and the ruler
retained some control over religious observances.

The influence of the Druids on the development of Celtic

---

[1] It is natural to infer from Caesar's description of the doctrine in *B.G.* vi,
14, 5 (*non interire animas, sed ab aliis post mortem transire ad alios*) that the
Druids believed in metempsychosis or reincarnation, but such a conclusion is
contrary to most of the evidence (including that of Celtic literature). See
vol. vii, p. 72.

[2] *B.G.* vi, 13, 11.   [3] See T. D. Kendrick, *The Druids*, p. 204 *sq.*

religion is obscure; if they really held any doctrine of metempsychosis or reincarnation they certainly failed to convert the masses to their belief, for the popular doctrine presumed the continuance of earthly joys and activities after death:

> regit idem spiritus artus
> orbe alio: longae, canitis si cognita, vitae
> mors media est. (Lucan, I, 456–8.)

The world of the dead, situated in another region (*orbe alio*), was probably regarded as subterranean, but quite unlike the Greek Hades, for the life of the dead was a richer and happier continuation of their life on earth. Like the Greeks, the Celts apparently distinguished this world of the dead from their Elysium (sometimes conceived as situated in some island far out to the west), which was only accessible to those who were specially favoured by the gods. In general, the Druids seem to have sanctioned with their approval the multifarious cults and deities of the Celts, though they may have encouraged the worship of the high gods and promoted their identification with local deities. Perhaps their religious conservatism may explain the absence of man-made temples and of sculptured images of the gods, and also the continuance of human sacrifices, with which the Druids are expressly connected by Caesar and other writers, some of whom mention as associated with these sacrifices the practice of divination from human victims. This gruesome aspect of the Druidic religion horrified the Greeks and Romans, who had forgotten their own barbaric past; in Gaul the custom of human sacrifice was mainly confined to the execution of criminals and captives and to the offering of human victims in fulfilment of vows.

The political power of the Druids in the first half of the first century B.C. is attested by Caesar, and there is no ground for the assumption that they had lost it to the secular nobility. If they played any part as a body during the conquest of Gaul, Caesar has said nothing of it. His silence may be a deliberate suppression, to conceal the fact that the national party in Gaul had the support of the national priesthood, but it is more probable that the Druidic organization was unable to agree on any common line of action, and that in the great rising of Vercingetorix the Gallic priests, like the Gallic nobles, were hopelessly divided in their allegiance. The Druidic organization was the nearest approach made by the Gauls to some kind of unity, but when the crisis came the bond of a common organization proved weaker than the selfishness of individual members.

II. THE POLITICAL SITUATION IN GAUL BEFORE CAESAR'S ARRIVAL

The victories of Aquae Sextiae and the Raudine plain (p. 149 *sq.*) had been followed by the restoration of Roman authority throughout that part of Transalpine Gaul which had been annexed in 121 B.C.; but although the independent tribes of Central Gaul had been crippled by the barbarian invasions and owed their deliverance entirely to the Roman arms, no attempt was made to bring them within the Roman protectorate, and the Transalpine province was bounded as before by the Rhône on the north and the Cevennes on the north-west. Beyond this frontier the leading tribes were left to pursue without interference the struggle for supremacy in Central Gaul; the Roman government retained its alliance with the Aedui and later conciliated some of the princelings near the frontier by the formal grant of honorific titles, but it was not committed thereby to any action, and during the next forty years it steadily refrained from any intervention in the affairs of independent Gaul.

During this period the Senate had many distractions elsewhere; moreover the states actually subject to Rome in Transalpine Gaul were still restive, and in 77 B.C., encouraged by the successes won by Sertorius in Spain, the whole province rose in open revolt (p. 321). Pompey severely defeated the rebel tribes on his march through the province to Spain, and the rising was finally crushed by M. Fonteius, whose energetic measures made the province a serviceable base of supplies in money, corn, and auxiliaries to the Roman armies in Spain, but involved ruthless exactions from the wretched provincials and forced them to borrow heavily from the Roman moneylenders resident in the province; the provincials were quite unable to repay these loans, and further troubles ensued when the governors intervened on behalf of the moneylenders. The situation of the Allobroges became so desperate that in 63 B.C. they sent envoys to Rome to appeal for the Senate's protection, but although the action of these envoys materially contributed to the detection of the Catilinarian conspirators in Rome, their loyalty secured no concessions from the Senate, and in 61 B.C. the Allobroges revolted against their oppressors. This revolt was attended with some success at first, and it was not until the following year that it was finally crushed by the governor C. Pomptinus and the province once more 'pacified.'

The revolt of the Allobroges was contemporaneous with a fresh development in the affairs of independent Gaul, where the struggle for hegemony between the leading tribes had entered on a new phase. The hegemony in question was merely that of Central Gaul; the tribes in Aquitania, south-west of the Garonne, more akin to the Iberians than to the Celts in race and language, the maritime (Aremorican) tribes of the north-west, and the states in the loose but powerful confederacy of the Belgae in the north (occupying most of the region between the Seine, the Moselle, the Rhine, and the coast) were not affected by the struggle, though the Belgic Bellovaci had an alliance with the Aedui.

In Central Gaul the two leading states, to which most of the others were attached by ties of alliance or subjection, had long been the Aedui and the Arverni. Their rivalry had been decided in favour of the Aedui by the Roman intervention against the Arverni in 121 B.C., and though there may have been a brief revival of Arvernian power under the leadership of Celtillus, father of the famous Vercingetorix, about 80, it was of short duration, and the Aedui soon recovered their hegemony. The next challenge to their position came from their eastern neighbours, the Sequani, who had frequently disputed with them the right to collect the important tolls on the Saône and now took the dangerous step of calling in foreign aid to overcome their opponents; they appealed to Ariovistus, the leader of a German host beyond the Rhine, who was to be rewarded with the plain of Upper Alsace, part of the Sequanian territory. The date of his first appearance in Gaul is uncertain, but that usually given, 71 B.C.[1], seems too early, as it was not until 61 that the Aedui, after several defeats by the Germans and Sequani, were completely crushed in the battle of Admagetobriga, and compelled to give hostages to the Sequani and accede to their demands, while Ariovistus and his men occupied the promised lands in Alsace.

The sequence of events at this stage is obscure, but it is probable that the battle of Admagetobriga was the decisive factor which produced a chain of consequences leading ultimately to Caesar's intervention in Central Gaul. At first, however, the Senate offered little encouragement to the Aeduan Druid Diviciacus, who came to Rome after Admagetobriga and implored the Senate to give military aid to its Aeduan 'allies'; the Senate merely passed a decree in general terms towards the end of 61 B.C. recommending the present governor of Transalpine Gaul and his successors to protect the interests of the Aedui and other friends of Rome so far as such protection might be compatible with his duty to his province. As the governor was now fully occupied with the

[1] The date is an unjustifiable inference from Caesar, B.G. 1, 36, 7.

Allobrogian revolt, the Senate's decree was equivalent to a polite refusal of Diviciacus' appeal.

Meanwhile another party among the Aedui, led by his brother Dumnorix, was intriguing elsewhere. The four cantons of the Helvetii had been compelled by German tribes some fifty years before to abandon their last possessions on the right bank of the Rhine, and even in their present territory (roughly co-extensive with the modern Switzerland) they were subject to constant pressure from the Germans. It may have been the Aeduan defeat at Admagetobriga and the prospect of Ariovistus' Germans as neighbours on the left bank of the Rhine that induced them to accept the proposal made by Orgetorix, one of their leading men, to emigrate in a body from their land and carve out a new territory for themselves by the Atlantic between the Loire and the Garonne; the preparations were to take two clear years, and the date of the emigration was fixed for the spring of 58 B.C. After this decision was made Orgetorix went on a diplomatic mission to certain states in Central Gaul, during which, in concert with the Aeduan Dumnorix and a Sequanian called Casticus, he formed a plan to make the Helvetian emigration a means to further objects: he was to use his influence to make himself king of the Helvetii; then to assist his confederates to seize the supreme power in their respective states; finally, the three states were to form a close alliance which would ensure their supremacy in Central Gaul. If this scheme had ulterior objects, they can only be conjectured; it may seem clear enough now that the confederates could only establish their supremacy in Gaul by the expulsion of Ariovistus, but it would be rash to assume that this was equally clear at the time, when the designs of Ariovistus may still have been unknown. In any case the scheme was wrecked at the outset, for the Helvetians speedily discovered Orgetorix' plot to make himself their king, and only his sudden death saved him from their vengeance. It is unlikely that the secret plan concerted with Dumnorix and Casticus survived its author, but Dumnorix was careful to maintain good relations with the Helvetii, whose decision to emigrate remained unaffected by the death of Orgetorix.

The preparations made by the Helvetii for their exodus stirred the Roman Senate for a moment from its customary indifference to the affairs of independent Gaul; in February or early in March, 60 B.C., a report arrived in Rome that the Helvetii were in arms and making raids into the Transalpine province. This report, probably exaggerated, roused the Senate to energetic measures; the consuls drew lots for the two Gallic provinces, Cisalpina falling to Afranius and Transalpina to Metellus Celer, troops were levied, and three senators were to be sent to the Gallic states to dissuade them from joining the Helvetii[1]. The alarm subsided as rapidly as it had arisen, for by May Cicero was able to inform his friend Atticus that Gaul was peaceful again and that Metellus was annoyed at this disappointment to his ambitions[2].

Early in the following year, 59 B.C., a new development in the situation ensued: Ariovistus had decided to secure Roman recognition of his position in Gaul, and his representatives now appeared in Rome, bringing gifts to Metellus Celer, who had ceased to be consul but had not yet set out for his province of Transalpine Gaul[3]. The object of their mission was successfully attained, for during this year Ariovistus was formally recognized by the Senate as 'king' and 'friend of the Roman People.' This recognition is ascribed by the secondary authorities to the advocacy of Caesar, who after the sudden death of Metellus secured the reversion of his province from the Senate, and though their testimony on such a point has no independent value it is probably correct. Most of Caesar's own statements about his share in the transaction are strangely vague, but they were made later when his attitude to Ariovistus had changed, and in one place[4] he seems to admit that he was responsible for inducing the Senate to grant Ariovistus' request.

The motives which prompted the grant of recognition to Ariovistus are obscure, and modern attempts to discover them have erred from excessive ingenuity; unless the Romans were prepared to intervene vigorously on behalf of their Aeduan allies there was really no valid reason for refusing to accept the new situation, while Caesar must have thought it worth while to conciliate Ariovistus and to secure his neutrality if not his active support. The recognition actually committed the Roman government to nothing beyond an acknowledgement of Ariovistus' claim to his present territories, for the Roman alliance with the Aedui was still nominally in force, but it completely misled the German leader, who seems to have regarded it as an authorization to extend his power in Central Gaul; he began to treat the Sequani as subjects rather than allies, and when he was joined by fresh bands of Germans from beyond the Rhine he demanded further grants of lands for the settlement of the newcomers. A new westward movement of the Germanic peoples was beginning, but at

[1] Cicero, *ad Att.* I, 19, 2. [2] *ad Att.* I, 20, 5.
[3] Pliny, *N.H.* II, 170. [4] *B.G.* I, 43, 5.

first Roman statesmen seemed ignorant of the interests at stake; their alarm had been excited by the Helvetian menace, but the remoter danger from Ariovistus remained unsuspected.

Such was the situation beyond the Alps when Pompey persuaded the Senate in 59 B.C. (June) to confer on Caesar the Transalpine province left vacant by the death of Metellus, in addition to the provinces of Cisalpine Gaul and Illyricum which he had already received for five years from the people by the Lex Vatinia (in May)[1]. Although the death of Metellus (early in April) probably preceded the introduction of the Lex Vatinia, it is obvious that the addition of Transalpine Gaul to Caesar's command cannot have been contemplated in the original plans of the triumvirs; Caesar must have obtained the promise of a province in his first compact with Pompey and Crassus, though the necessity of satisfying first the demands of his partners delayed the introduction of the Lex Vatinia till May. It is likely, though less certain, that Cisalpine Gaul and Illyricum had been the provinces originally chosen by Caesar; if he held the provinces nearest to the capital he would be able to keep in touch with Roman politics, and as these provinces were to be governed in 59 B.C. by Afranius, a firm adherent of Pompey, there would be no difficulty in securing their transference to one of the triumvirs. It is clear in any case that Caesar could have had no interest in the affairs of Transalpine Gaul until Metellus' death; whether he at once realized the full extent of the opportunity thereby created for him must remain doubtful, as the motives which prompted the triumvirs to secure this addition to his command are unknown. Probably Caesar's designs of conquest beyond the Alps did not develop until he had reached his province and grasped the possibilities of the situation; this is a legitimate inference from the distribution of the four legions under Caesar's command when the operations of 58 B.C. began, three being then stationed in the Cisalpine province, near Aquileia, and only one beyond the Alps at Geneva. At the end of 59 Caesar did not set out at once for his province, but lingered near Rome to support his agent Clodius until the middle of March, when he hurried north in response to an urgent message that the Helvetii were mustering opposite Geneva on the north bank of the Rhône.

---

[1] For this dating of the Lex Vatinia see M. Gelzer in *Hermes*, LXIII, 1928, p. 113. See also above, p. 519.

III. THE MILITARY OCCUPATION OF GAUL

The plan of emigration adopted by the Helvetii was that of a complete exodus of the whole population, including the women and children; such a design might have been frustrated by the reluctance of individuals or groups to leave their homes, but this danger was averted by the destruction of all buildings and all surplus stocks of corn, as soon as the preparations for the migration were complete, and it is unlikely that more than a few stragglers remained behind. The numbers of the emigrants were augmented by the accession of four other peoples, the Raurici, Tulingi, Latovici and Boii, who lived to the north and east of the Helvetii and probably shared their desire to escape from the pressure of the advancing German hordes; the total of the united host reached 368,000, of whom one quarter were fighting men[1].

To convey such a multitude safely across Gaul from east to west would be a difficult undertaking, and it was important that the emigrants should arrive without opposition at their goal, where they would have to dispossess the inhabitants of the land which they wished to occupy. Of the various routes from Switzerland to the west, the passes of Pontarlier would have taken them too far to the north, and the route between the Jura and the Rhône was for the present blocked by the Sequani; they had therefore decided to ask the Romans for permission to go through the Province, and with this aim had mustered opposite Geneva. When Caesar arrived there he demanded time for consideration of their request, used the respite to raise new levies and fortify the left bank of the Rhône below the lake, and then refused to allow the Helvetii to enter the Province; some of them made attempts, probably unauthorized by their leaders, to cross the river in face of the Roman opposition, but were easily repulsed.

The Roman refusal had little result, as the Aeduan Dumnorix persuaded the Sequani to let the Helvetii pass through their country; unless they came into serious collision with the Aedui, the Romans would have no formal justification for further interference with them. Yet Caesar resolved to intervene vigorously in the affairs of independent Gaul; his interference has been severely criticized but was entirely in harmony with an established feature in the Roman foreign policy of an earlier period, which always tried to prevent the growth of any formidable independent power

[1] The figures are given by Caesar, *B.G.* 1, 29, on the authority of lists found in the Helvetian camp, and are now widely accepted as approximately correct.

near the Roman frontier, such as might be created by the foundation of an Helvetian empire in western Gaul. After a hurried
visit to Cisalpine Gaul to bring up the three veteran legions from
Aquileia and two new legions which he had already ordered to be
raised, he crossed the Rhône just above its junction with the
Saône at the head of his united forces. A pretext for intervention
was easily found; the pro-Roman party among the Aedui, which
had recently revived and secured control of the government, now
made a formal appeal to Caesar for protection against the Helvetii,
the greater part of whom had already crossed the Saône into
Aeduan territory. Caesar acted promptly: by a rapid night march
he surprised and defeated the Helvetii who were still on the eastern
bank of the Saône, then crossed the river in pursuit of the main
body. After a futile attempt at negotiation the Helvetii continued
their march; as the direct route to their goal was impracticable,
their column advanced for some distance up the Saône valley
before turning off to the west.

For over a fortnight Caesar followed them at a distance of a few
miles, as the country was unsuitable for an attack and his cavalry,
supplied by the Aedui and led by Dumnorix, was untrustworthy.
When he left the Saône he lost touch with his supplies and the
Aedui failed to make good the deficiency, and though Dumnorix
was soon unmasked and kept under close observation the situation
did not improve. Finally, after a shrewd plan to surprise the
Helvetii had been frustrated by the folly of a subordinate, Caesar
decided to turn aside temporarily from the pursuit and re-provision
his army at the Aeduan capital Bibracte, seventeen miles away to
the north, but he was promptly followed by the Helvetii, whose
desire to force on a battle at this moment is difficult to explain, and
compelled to draw up his army on a line of hills to face the attack.
Caesar's four veteran legions—the rest of the army took no active
part in the battle—had no difficulty in repelling the enemy's first
onslaught, but in their advance the right wing was attacked on the
flank by the Boii and Tulingi, and a stern struggle on two fronts
followed till sunset, when the Romans were at last victorious. The
Helvetian camp was protected by a rampart of wagons and so
resolutely defended by the Boii and Tulingi that it was not taken
until late that night; this resistance enabled the main body of the
Helvetii, now reduced to 130,000, to flee in an easterly direction.
The Roman army was too exhausted for the present to pursue
them, but through the prestige acquired by his victory Caesar
prevailed on the Gauls to deny all supplies to the fugitives, who
were thus compelled to surrender. A section which tried to

escape to the Rhine was recaptured and sold into slavery, but the rest were leniently treated: on the request of the Aedui the Boii were allowed to settle in their territory; the other tribes were compelled to return to their own lands but incurred no other penalty.

The Roman intervention had been brilliantly justified, and deputies came to Bibracte from most of the states in Central Gaul to congratulate Caesar on his victory. He was now informed that the newly-established Roman protectorate in Central Gaul was still on its trial; in a secret meeting the Aeduan Diviciacus, as spokesman of the chiefs, revealed to him the far-reaching designs of Ariovistus, complained about his oppression of the Aedui and other Gauls, and urged Caesar to avert from Gaul the danger which was threatened by the continued immigration of the German hordes from beyond the Rhine. Caesar promised to deal with the situation without delay; he seems to have had no idea until now of Ariovistus' ambitions, but he promptly recognized the danger for Rome in this fresh invasion of Gaul by the Germans, and determined to check it at the outset. It is probable that he expected little success from the diplomatic representations which he proceeded to make to Ariovistus, but as the German had so recently been recognized by the Roman Senate it was important to manœuvre him into a false position; for this purpose, after Ariovistus had refused to meet him, he produced the senatorial decree of 61 B.C. (see p. 546) as justification for an ultimatum, commanding him to leave the Aedui and other friends of Rome in peace and to put a stop to further immigration of Germans from beyond the Rhine.

When these demands were flouted and a report reached Caesar that a fresh horde of Germans had advanced to the right bank of the Rhine, he decided to assume the offensive at once before they could cross the Rhine and reinforce Ariovistus. By rapid marches he reached and occupied the important position of Vesontio (Besançon); here the nearness of the dreaded Germans produced a panic in the army, which threatened to break out into open mutiny. Caesar at once summoned a meeting of officers and centurions, and in a vigorous speech rebuked them for their cowardice and disloyalty: if the rest would not follow him he would go on with the tenth legion only, for he could rely on its fidelity. The success of the speech was immediate; the men of the tenth were delighted, and those in the other legions hastened to show that they were no less devoted to their leader. Never again did Caesar's men waver in their loyalty to him throughout all the hardships of the Gallic campaigns.

From Vesontio the army advanced by a circuitous route to the Belfort gap and the plains of Upper Alsace, where Ariovistus and his people were encamped. The German now consented to the interview which he had hitherto refused. Caesar began by a repetition of his ultimatum, to which Ariovistus replied in a boastful speech that he had entered Central Gaul before the Romans and intended to remain there: he knew that if he killed Caesar he would win the gratitude of the Roman nobles, but if Caesar would leave him alone he would reward him and help him against his enemies. Caesar ostentatiously declined this compromising alliance, and countered Ariovistus' claim of priority in Central Gaul by the contention that the Romans in virtue of their victory over the Arverni in 121 B.C. had established an exclusive claim to the sovereignty of Gaul as against any other foreign power.

After the failure of the conference Ariovistus advanced past Caesar's army, probably along the lower slopes of the Vosges where he would be safe from attack, and cut Caesar's communications with Vesontio. When Caesar had in vain tempted the enemy to battle he resolved to restore his communications by the construction of a smaller camp to the south of the new German position. The attempts made by the Germans to prevent this manœuvre and their subsequent attack on the smaller camp failed, whereupon Caesar by a demonstration in force against the German camp compelled Ariovistus to accept the battle offered by the Romans (middle of September 58 B.C.); the site of the battle was either between Ostheim and Gemar, or farther to the south near Cernay. The Germans were probably superior in numbers and the rapidity of their first charge disconcerted the Romans, who had no time to hurl their *pila*, but the formidable German cavalry seems to have had no effect on the course of the battle (they may have dismounted and fought as infantry), and the vigorous resistance of the German right was overcome by the Roman reserves, which were sent in at the critical moment by young Publius Crassus, a son of the triumvir. This decided the issue of the battle, and the whole German army fled in wild rout to the Rhine, fifteen miles distant, where most of them were caught and slain by the Roman cavalry; Ariovistus himself escaped with difficulty and died soon afterwards.

The immediate effect of this decisive victory was the retirement of the Suebian host which had reached the right bank of the Rhine, but it was obvious that if Caesar withdrew from Central Gaul the German invasions would speedily begin again; the only way to prevent these invasions was that the Romans should assume permanently the protection of the Rhine frontier, and to do this they would be compelled to convert their new protectorate over Gaul into actual annexation. Caesar realized now, if not before, that this course was inevitable, and perhaps he saw also that the effective control of the Rhine frontier would necessitate the conquest of the Belgic confederacy in the north; nothing was said openly about annexation, but the change in Roman policy was clearly indicated by Caesar's decision to fix the winter-quarters of his army at Vesontio, which would form a valuable base for a further advance. The Belgae were naturally alarmed, and they were urged by the anti-Roman malcontents in Central Gaul to intervene; they therefore determined to forestall the anticipated attack, and spent the winter in warlike preparations. In the same winter Caesar raised two new legions in Cisalpine Gaul, and when the campaigning season of 57 B.C. opened he led his army of eight legions from Vesontio to the north; there he was met by envoys from the important tribe of the Remi (round Rheims) who offered their submission and as loyal supporters of Rome played the same rôle in the north as the Aedui in Central Gaul.

The Belgic army at last appeared; it was greatly superior to the Roman, though the figure of 296,000 men, given by the Remi and quoted by Caesar without comment, must be wildly exaggerated, but its commissariat was badly organized and inadequate, like that of most Gallic armies. Caesar's plan was to occupy a strong defensive position north of the Aisne, securing the bridge-head (probably at Berry-au-Bac) with a garrison, and to create a diversion by sending Diviciacus and the Aedui to ravage the lands of the powerful Bellovaci (round Beauvais). The operations of the unwieldy Belgic army ended in complete failure; it did not venture to attack Caesar's position, its attempts to force the crossing of the Aisne were easily defeated, and its supplies were soon exhausted. When Diviciacus' diversion was reported the Bellovaci refused to stay, whereupon the contingents decided to disperse to their homes until the Romans attacked; under the unceasing pressure of Caesar's pursuit their retreat degenerated into a confused rout, and by the unfamiliar menace of the Roman siege-engines the defenders of their strongholds were terrified into submission.

This miserable collapse did not end the struggle: four of the tribes in the north, led by the Nervii, who had an excellent infantry and had planted their country with high hedges to obstruct the operations of hostile cavalry, determined to resist the further progress of the Romans. Late one afternoon, when Caesar's army at the end of the day's march was fortifying a camp on the heights of Neuf-Mesnil above the Sambre, it was suddenly attacked by the enemy, who charged boldly across the river and up the slope to the Roman camp. The surprise was complete, for Caesar had omitted to keep a detachment under arms during the construction of the camp, and only his desperate energy and personal example averted a catastrophe on the right wing, which had temporarily become isolated by the victorious advance of the Roman left and centre and exposed to the main attack of the Nervii; by his intervention Caesar encouraged the right to hold out until the arrival of help from the victorious left enabled him to turn the tables on the enemy, who fought bravely to the end. After their heavy losses in this battle the Nervii surrendered; the Atuatuci tried to resist in their chief stronghold (? Mont Falhize) and after offering to submit made a treacherous night-attack on the Romans, in punishment for which they were all—to the number of 53,000—sold into slavery.

Meanwhile P. Crassus had been sent with a legion against the maritime tribes of Normandy and Brittany, which submitted without a struggle and gave hostages, and thus the whole of Gaul from the Garonne to the Rhine, except the Morini and Menapii in the far north, had been brought under Roman control. At the end of the summer an attempt was made to open up the route over the Great St Bernard, which would have facilitated communications between Italy and Northern Gaul, but the force sent was too small to achieve its object. Elsewhere the Roman arms had been completely successful, and the greatness of the achievement was suitably recognized by a thanksgiving of fifteen days at Rome. But the conquest was far from final; the Gauls had been paralysed by the rapidity of Caesar's movements and hypnotized by the deceptiveness of his professions, and the realization of their true situation was bound to be followed by attempts to recover their lost independence.

IV. THE FIRST REVOLT AND THE MASSACRE OF THE GERMANS

The Roman hegemony had no sooner been established in Gaul than Caesar began to plan an expedition against Britain, and in the late summer of 57 B.C. P. Crassus was sent across the Channel from Brittany to the opposite coast on a voyage of exploration[1]. These designs aroused the resentment of the Veneti, the most

[1] This statement is an inference from Strabo III, 176; see T. Rice Holmes, *Ancient Britain*, pp. 494–7.

important of the Gallic maritime states, who controlled the trade
between Western Gaul and Britain and disliked the prospect of
Roman competition[1]; they disowned their recent submission to
Rome and arrested some Roman officers in the hope of exchanging
them for their own hostages. The example of the Veneti encouraged
most of the north-western states to join the revolt, which was supported by the still unconquered Morini and Menapii; signs of
unrest appeared among the Belgae, and a fresh German invasion
of Gaul was impending, this time on the lower Rhine. After
Caesar had secured the continuance of his command by the conference at Luca (p. 534 *sq.*) he hastened to Gaul in the spring of
56 B.C. to deal with the various dangers which threatened his
conquests. Confident of easy success, he detached twelve cohorts
and some cavalry under Crassus for an unprovoked invasion of
Aquitania on the frivolous pretext that the tribes of that region
might aid the revolt; this expedition was brilliantly successful, and
many of the tribes between the Garonne and the Pyrenees were
conquered. Labienus, the greatest of Caesar's lieutenants, maintained order with a force of cavalry throughout the year in the
north-east, where the German invasion was fortunately deferred,
and Q. Sabinus with three legions crushed the resistance of the
tribes in Normandy.

The operations against the Veneti were directed by Caesar in
person. He had realized from the beginning of the revolt that he
would have to destroy their maritime supremacy if he wished to
reduce them to submission; as the Romans possessed no fleet in
the Atlantic he determined to create one, and in the winter of
57–6 B.C. warships were constructed in the Loire. The new fleet,
manned by sailors from the coast-towns of the Province, was augmented by squadrons from the maritime tribes between the Loire
and the Garonne; Decimus Brutus was made admiral of the combined fleet, and the separate ships, on which Roman legionaries
served as marines, were commanded by Roman tribunes or centurions. When the campaigning season opened the fleet was
probably not yet ready, and it was further detained by contrary
winds; meanwhile Caesar started operations on land against the
enemy, but the absence of his fleet frustrated all his efforts. The
Veneti had taken refuge in their coast-towns, which were situated
on peninsulas only accessible at low water, and even when the
besiegers had overcome the natural difficulties the defenders could
sail away with their possessions to the next fortress to renew the
struggle there under the same conditions. Finally Caesar decided

[1] Strabo IV, 194.

to wait for his fleet, but the summer was well advanced before it appeared, whereupon the Venetian fleet of 220 ships sailed out to meet it; the size of the Roman fleet is unknown.

The ensuing battle off Quiberon Bay was the first fought by a Roman fleet in the Atlantic, and has the additional interest of a conflict between a fleet of sailing-ships and one composed mainly of galleys. The usual Roman tactics were useless against the great oak-built sailing-ships of the Veneti, which were too strong to be rammed by the lighter galleys, while the greater height of their decks made boarding difficult and javelin-fire ineffective. These disadvantages had been foreseen by the Roman leaders, who had devised a simple means of circumventing them. When the ships of the two fleets came to close quarters, the Romans by means of sharp sickles attached to the end of long poles cut the ropes which fastened the sail-yards of the Venetian ships to the masts; as the ships had no oars the collapse of their sails left them a helpless prey to the attacks of the Roman marines. After several ships had been captured in this way, the rest of the fleet turned in flight, but their escape was frustrated by a sudden calm, and when night came all but a few ships had been captured.

This overwhelming victory transferred the naval supremacy in the Bay of Biscay and the Channel to the Romans, and ended the resistance of the maritime tribes in Brittany. But Caesar's glory was sullied by his treatment of the conquered; on the shallow pretext that the requisition-officers arrested by the Veneti were ambassadors and that their arrest was a violation of international law which must be severely punished, the chiefs who formed the Venetian senate were executed and the rest of the population sold into slavery. Probably this act of terrorism was intended to be a warning to the rest of Gaul that Caesar's clemency had its limits and that further revolts would be followed by ruthless vengeance.

The Morini and the Menapii still refused to submit, and though the summer was almost over, Caesar led his army against the Morini, who controlled the harbours nearest to Britain. But they took refuge in their forests and adopted guerrilla tactics, until the difficulties of the campaign combined with the lateness of the season compelled Caesar to defer their subjugation until the following year.

The security of Caesar's conquests was now threatened by a new danger. He had not yet established effective Roman control over the left bank of the Rhine below Cologne, for the Menapii who dwelt there on both banks of the river were still unconquered, and in the winter of 56–5 b.c. the entire population (estimated by

Caesar at 430,000)[1] of two tribes, the Usipetes and Tencteri, who had been driven from their homes by the Suebi and had wandered about Germany for three years, crossed the lower Rhine at or near Xanten and expelled the Menapii from their lands. Their permanent settlement on the Gallic side of the Rhine could not be tolerated by the Romans; already the anti-Roman parties in the Gallic states had attempted to secure the support of the new-comers, and some of the Germans had advanced south beyond Liège. Caesar on his return to Gaul, after calling a formal council of the Gallic chiefs and securing the aid of their contingents for the coming campaign, marched against the invaders, who tried in vain to obtain his permission to remain in Gaul. Caesar offered to obtain lands for them on the right bank of the Rhine, but he refused their request that he should stop his advance, and moved up his army until he was within eight miles of the main body of the Germans, who were still encamped between the Rhine and the Meuse, only a few miles from Xanten[2].

The proximity of the two armies made the avoidance of hostilities almost impossible, and a further advance by the Gallic cavalry provoked a German attack in which the Gauls were routed. Caesar chose to regard this incident as a decisive proof that the barbarians were not to be trusted; when their chiefs came next day to explain he arrested them, and at once led his army against the German camp. The men, taken by surprise and deprived of their leaders, made little resistance, and those who escaped were drowned in the Rhine. The fate of the rest may be told in Caesar's own words: 'at reliqua multitudo puerorum mulierumque ... passim fugere coepit; ad quos consectandos Caesar equitatum misit[3].' The barbarians were utterly annihilated, and Caesar adds complacently that the only Roman casualties were a few wounded. This deliberate massacre is the most disgraceful of Caesar's actions and the worst example of the atrocities which have often been perpetrated in collisions between civilized and barbarian races; it has been excused by the greatness of the peril threatening the Romans, but this assumes that the estimate given for the German numbers by Caesar is approximately correct. Caesar's arrest of the envoys was a clear breach of that rule of international

---

[1] *B.G.* iv, 15, 3. The correctness of the estimate is doubtful; see p. 537 *Note*.

[2] Not far from the *confluens Mosae et Rheni*, *B.G.* iv, 15, 2; some think Caesar wrote or meant to write *Mosellae* for *Mosae*, and prefer a site near Coblenz, but it is unlikely that the whole multitude had advanced so far to the south.   [3] *B.G.* iv, 14, 5.

law which he had so recently claimed to vindicate by the punishment of the Veneti; but the proposal of Cato to surrender the perfidious general to the Germans was inspired by political antipathy rather than by any genuine indignation, and was disregarded in Rome (p. 620).

After the extermination of the immigrants Caesar resolved to ensure the security of the Rhine frontier by a demonstration of Roman power on the right bank, to make the Germans realize that interference by them west of the river would provoke prompt retaliation; moreover, some German tribes on the east bank, especially the Ubii, who had come under the influence of Celtic civilization, had already offered to put themselves under Roman protection. When the Roman army had marched up the west bank to a point a little below Coblenz, it was ordered by Caesar to construct a bridge of piles across the Rhine, a monument of Roman engineering skill which was doubtless intended to impress the barbarians, and in ten days the work was completed. The army crossed and ravaged the territory of the Sugambri, neighbours and enemies of the Ubii, but the more formidable Suebi refused to be tempted to a battle and retired into the interior, whither Caesar did not venture to follow them. He had achieved the main purpose of his demonstration, for he was satisfied with the Rhine frontier and had no desire to extend his direct control beyond it, and after spending eighteen days beyond the Rhine he returned to Gaul.

V. THE BRITISH EXPEDITIONS AND THE SECOND REVOLT

After his return from Germany Caesar prepared to carry out his long-projected invasion of Britain; as the campaigning season of 55 B.C. was now far advanced, he planned an expedition on a small scale to reconnoitre the country which he proposed to invade with a larger force in the following year. He tried to justify his policy by the alleged necessity of preventing British interference on behalf of the Gallic malcontents, but such interference was of little importance since the control of the Channel had passed to the Roman fleet. No military or political interests of the Roman Empire were served by this attempt to extend it beyond its natural boundaries, but Roman greed exaggerated the wealth of the unknown island, and a victorious expedition to Britain would be a spectacular success more likely to impress the imagination of Caesar's contemporaries than his great achievements on the continent.

There had been frequent intercourse between the Belgic tribes of southern Britain and those of northern Gaul, and some of the Gallic chiefs had connections and influence on the other side of the Channel; the most important of these was Commius, whom Caesar had made king of his own tribe, the Atrebates (round Arras). Commius was sent on beforehand to Britain to induce the tribes to submit to Rome, but his mission was a failure and he was imprisoned. Soon afterwards Caesar sailed from Boulogne with an army of two legions, and on the following morning (August 26th, 55 B.C.) anchored off the British coast opposite Dover; late in the afternoon of the same day he sailed on and, despite fierce opposition from the British cavalry and war-chariots, effected a landing on the east coast of Kent, probably at Walmer. After this defeat the Kentish tribes released Commius and made offers of submission, but changed their attitude again when many of Caesar's ships were wrecked by a high tide four days after his arrival. His cavalry transports had been dispersed by a gale and driven back to Gaul, and without cavalry he did not dare to advance far from his base. The Roman misfortunes encouraged the Britons to attack the Roman camp, but they were decisively beaten; this success and the renewed submission of the Kentish chiefs restored Roman prestige and enabled Caesar to leave the island without discredit about the middle of September.

The comparative failure of the first expedition necessitated a more convincing demonstration of Roman power, and during the winter Caesar ordered the construction of 600 new transports. Preparations were made on a scale which left no doubt that the definitive conquest of southern Britain was intended, and expectations ran high in Rome, for at the same time Crassus was preparing his great expedition against Parthia. But the new Roman imperialism, inspired by ambitious generals, was losing all sense of proportion. Caesar was pushing on the conquest of Britain while his hold on Gaul was still insecure. The British expedition was unpopular with many of the Gallic chiefs, and some of them planned to stir up trouble in Gaul during Caesar's absence beyond the Channel. Valuable time had to be lost in the re-establishment of Roman influence among the Treveri (round Trèves), where the anti-Roman party had been reviving under the leadership of Indutiomarus. Caesar saw that he would have to take the Gallic chiefs to Britain as virtual hostages, and when his old enemy the Aeduan Dumnorix tried to evade the necessity by flight from the Roman camp, he was pursued and cut down, protesting with his last breath against the violation of Aeduan independence.

These distractions and adverse winds delayed the departure of the expedition until early in July 54 B.C. The army of conquest, five legions and 2000 Gallic cavalry, sailed from a harbour called by Caesar *portus Itius*, probably Wissant, and landed on the Kentish coast (between Sandown and Sandwich) without opposition. The Britons had taken no steps to secure a unified resistance to the Roman attack, and Caesar hoped to crush their scattered forces by the rapidity of his advance; within a few hours of his arrival he marched westward by night with the greater part of his forces, and on the next day defeated the Kentish levies on the Great Stour near Canterbury. But on this occasion Caesar's impatient haste ruined his plan of campaign; to save time he had left his fleet at anchor instead of hauling it up on shore, despite his disastrous experience in the preceding year. On the night after his victory a great storm arose which destroyed forty ships; this mischance compelled Caesar to lead his army back to the coast, where they worked strenuously, drawing the rest of the ships ashore and protecting them by fortifications. This delay was serious, as it left only two months of the campaigning season available and also gave a valuable respite to the Britons, who at last decided to combine against the invaders.

The leader chosen by the British chiefs was Cassivellaunus, king of the region north of the Thames and west of the Lea, who had recently extended his rule over the Trinovantes of Essex, driving Mandubracius, the son of their former ruler, to seek refuge with Caesar. The insular Celts still retained the war-chariots which their continental kinsmen had long abandoned, but though these chariots harassed Caesar's Gallic cavalry and gained some success even against the legionaries on one occasion when their ranks were already in disorder, a frontal attack on the legions was decisively routed. After this reverse the British leader decided to avoid pitched battles and to hamper Caesar's advance by guerrilla warfare; cattle and men were removed from the countryside before the Romans arrived, and their march was dogged by a picked body of charioteers, whose frequent attacks compelled the auxiliary cavalry to keep in close touch with the legions. Despite these difficulties the Roman army advanced steadily until it reached the lower Thames at an important ford (which cannot be identified); the Britons were drawn up on the farther bank to prevent the crossing but were easily driven off.

So far the strategy of Cassivellaunus had been fairly successful, but Mandubracius now brought the Trinovantes over to the Roman side, and their example was followed by several other tribes. On the advice of his new allies Caesar attacked the principal stronghold of the British leader, but though he easily stormed the rude fortifications of the place and captured large herds of cattle which had been placed there, most of the men escaped. Meanwhile Cassivellaunus had ordered the Kentish chieftains to attack Caesar's naval camp in the hope of compelling him to retire by this threat to his base; when the attack failed he consented to open negotiations with Caesar, who had received alarming news from Labienus about the situation in Gaul and therefore wished to liquidate his British enterprise as quickly as possible. By the terms of the settlement Cassivellaunus acquiesced in Caesar's retention of the captives taken by the Romans in Britain, undertook to leave Mandubracius and the Trinovantes unmolested, gave hostages and promised an annual tribute. The Roman army returned to Kent, and from there sailed back to Gaul shortly before the autumn equinox.

No Roman troops had been left behind in Britain to secure the fulfilment of the peace-terms, and it is doubtful whether the tribute was ever paid. Caesar's attention was soon fully occupied by repeated revolts in Gaul, and the Britons could then ignore the settlement with impunity. Although Caesar's British expeditions have a romantic interest for us, they must be regarded from the Roman point of view as mistaken, and Augustus, whose popularity required no such adventitious aids, rightly disregarded all demands for an extension of the Empire beyond the Channel, preferring peaceful penetration to annexation.

Soon after Caesar's return from Britain, in the autumn of 54 B.C., the second revolt broke out in Gaul, where the discontent against the Roman rule had been steadily growing. The earlier gratitude for the expulsion of the Germans had been changed into resentment when the Gauls found that they had to maintain a large Roman army permanently in their country and at the same time to satisfy the rapacity of Caesar and his officers; by 54 B.C. Caesar had already amassed enormous wealth, which cannot have been entirely acquired by the sale of captives, and every needy adventurer in Rome who could win Caesar's favour went to Gaul to restore his fortunes. Moreover, the old inter-tribal quarrels were forgotten under the general grievance of alien oppression, and the prospect of uniting all the Gauls in a war of liberation became more hopeful. All turned on the attitude of the states in Central Gaul, which had been cajoled into submission rather than conquered; but they were not yet ripe for rebellion, the second revolt failed to produce any leader who could attract their support, and

the refusal of all except the Carnutes and Senones to participate in
the movement was largely responsible for its failure.

Although Caesar was expecting a Gallic rising, the occasion of
its outbreak seems to have taken him by surprise. The first sign of
the coming storm was the assassination by the Carnutes (round
Orléans) of their king, who had been imposed on them by Caesar.
This was soon followed by the revolt of the Eburones on the
Meuse, instigated by the restless Indutiomarus. Under Ambiorix,
one of their two kings, they attacked the Roman winter-camp at
Atuatuca[1]; when force failed, Ambiorix opened negotiations with
the Roman commander Sabinus, offering him and his men a safe
conduct to the nearest Roman camp. Despite the vehement opposition of L. Cotta, Sabinus' junior colleague, the treacherous offer
was accepted and the fifteen cohorts of the garrison evacuated
their fortified camp. Ambiorix had posted his Eburones in ambush at either end of a valley two miles from the camp, and when
the greater part of the Roman column had entered the valley he
gave the signal to attack. The Romans, rallied by Cotta, fought
bravely, but were unable to come to close quarters with the light-
armed Eburones, who from a safe distance thinned the Roman
ranks with their missiles. The battle had raged for seven hours
when Sabinus decided, against Cotta's advice, to seek an interview
with Ambiorix, who first disarmed and then murdered the Roman
commander and those who were with him. The triumphant barbarians now overwhelmed the Romans in a combined attack, in
which Cotta and most of his men were slain. Some made their
way back to the camp and there in despair committed suicide;
only a few survivors escaped through the forests to bring the
disastrous news to Labienus.

After this success Ambiorix at once rode southwards and induced the Nervii to revolt and attack the legion encamped in their
country. Its commander was Quintus Cicero, the younger brother
of the famous orator. Though he was in feeble health, he hurriedly
organized the defences of the camp, refused to listen to the in-
sidious offers of the enemy, and successfully beat off all attacks.
His messages to headquarters asking for help were intercepted,
until at last the Gallic slave of a loyal Nervian chief got through to
Caesar, who was at Samarobriva (Amiens), entirely ignorant of the
recent disaster. On hearing the news he hastily collected a force of
7000 men and marched north to relieve Cicero. A messenger sent
on ahead with a letter for Cicero was compelled to tie it to a javelin

---

[1] The site of Atuatuca is unknown; the usual identification with Tongres
is open to serious objections, but no satisfactory alternative has been proposed.

which he hurled over the ramparts of the camp; the javelin stuck unobserved in a tower, and it was not until two days later that the letter was discovered. The worst anxiety was now over, and soon the garrison saw in the distance clouds of smoke which heralded Caesar's approach. The besiegers raised the siege and departed to meet the relieving army, but they were easily outwitted by Caesar and completely defeated, and on the same day Caesar entered Cicero's camp and congratulated the garrison and its commander on their heroic defence.

The catastrophe at Atuatuca, due to barbarian treachery and to the almost incredible folly of the Roman commander, had nevertheless destroyed the spell of Roman invincibility throughout Gaul, and Caesar admitted that every state except the Aedui and the Remi was shaken in its loyalty to Rome. The Senones (round Sens) expelled their king, another of Caesar's nominees, and defied the Romans, while symptoms of unrest appeared among the Aremorican states. Yet the immediate results of the disaster were slight; the energy and vigilance of Caesar, who for the first time wintered in Gaul, prevented the further spread of the revolt in the central states, and the movement in the north-east was checked by Labienus. Indutiomarus had raised an army among the Treveri, augmented by desperadoes from the whole of Gaul, but he wasted time in futile demonstrations outside Labienus' camp. Meanwhile the Roman general had ordered the neighbouring states to send a large force of Gallic horse, which he smuggled into his camp by night without the enemy's knowledge; late in the following afternoon they made a sudden sortie against the Treveri, who were completely surprised and routed. In the pursuit the Roman cavalry, following Labienus' instructions and stimulated by the offer of a large reward, ignored the rest and concentrated on the pursuit of Indutiomarus, who was intercepted and killed; his death removed the only leader of the revolt who had sufficient influence to win over the states of Central Gaul.

During the winter Caesar replaced the cohorts lost at Atuatuca by three fresh legions (including one borrowed from Pompey), thereby raising his total force to ten legions, and compelled the Nervii to submit. In the spring of 53 B.C. he brought back the Senones and Carnutes to their allegiance by a display of force, and for the first time subdued the Menapii in the far north, while Labienus again defeated the Treveri.

By these operations Caesar had completely isolated Ambiorix and his Eburones, but he deferred his revenge until he had made a fresh demonstration against the Germans, which was as fruitless as it had been two years before; the Rhine was again bridged and the Suebi again retired into the interior. Caesar had doubtless hoped to bring the Germans to battle and to win a decisive victory, but he did not intend to incur unnecessary risks in pursuit of an aim which was only incidental to his main design, and so withdrew once more to the left bank, leaving part of the bridge standing, with a fort and a garrison of twelve cohorts to protect it. After this interlude the Roman army marched against the unlucky Eburones, who made no attempt at organized resistance; their country was systematically devastated to ensure the death by famine of all who escaped the sword. Extraordinary efforts were made by the Roman cavalry to catch Ambiorix, but he evaded them all, protected by the devoted loyalty of four trusty companions, and the inglorious man-hunt ended in fiasco. Caesar tried to terrorize the patriotic Gauls in another way; at the end of the summer he held a court of enquiry into the causes of the revolt among the Senones and Carnutes, at which Acco, the leader of the anti-Roman party among the Senones, was condemned to be scourged and beheaded, and other patriots who escaped punishment by flight were formally outlawed. In these proceedings Gaul was for the first time openly treated as a conquered province and its inhabitants as Roman subjects; but the demonstration was ill-timed: the chieftains of Central Gaul were not intimidated but roused to action, and as soon as Caesar departed beyond the Alps they began to concert plans for a general revolt.

VI. THE THIRD REVOLT: VERCINGETORIX

The great Gallic revolt of 52 B.C. was mainly confined to the states of Central Gaul; the Aquitanians held aloof, and the Belgic tribes played little or no part in the movement until it was too late. Commius, who had now joined the anti-Roman party, had undertaken to secure the support of the Belgae, but Labienus, who had as usual been left in charge of Gaul during Caesar's absence, discovered his intrigues and devised a treacherous plan to assassinate him; Commius escaped with a severe wound which incapacitated him for several months, and no other Belgic chieftain was influential enough to induce the northern tribes to revolt. The conspiracy in Central Gaul received further encouragement from the news of the anarchy prevailing in Rome after Clodius' death (p. 624). The patriots decided to provoke a general rising before Caesar's return so that he could not rejoin his army, the greater part of which, six legions, was stationed under Labienus at

Agedincum (Sens); there were also two legions among the Treveri and two among the Lingones (district of Langres). A young and inspiring leader for the war of independence was found in the Arvernian Vercingetorix, son of Celtillus, and the Carnutes volunteered for the dangerous honour of being the first state to start the revolt.

The early stages in the execution of the plan were successful; the Carnutes massacred the Roman officials and traders in Cenabum (Orléans), and Vercingetorix, after an initial rebuff, drove out the oligarchical government of his own state, including his uncle, and was made king of the Arvernians by his enthusiastic partisans. Most of the states between the Loire and the Garonne, as well as the maritime tribes of the north-west, now openly joined in the revolt, and Vercingetorix himself secured the adhesion of the Bituriges, whose principal town was Avaricum (Bourges). A second force under Lucterius had marched south, won over the Ruteni and Nitiobriges to the patriotic cause, and prepared to invade the Province in the region of Narbo. During all this time Labienus seems to have remained inactive, possibly because his supplies had been intercepted by irregular bands organized by the Senonian Drappes.

As soon as he was able to leave Italy, Caesar hastened to Narbo, and rapidly organized on the old frontier a chain of posts through which Lucterius was unable to penetrate. Although the Cevennes were still covered with snow, which lay six feet deep in the passes, Caesar determined to cross them and create a diversion in the Arvernian country; by great exertions he and his men made their way over the mountains and began to ravage the Auvergne. This unexpected attack deranged the plans of Vercingetorix, who was compelled by his men to return home; meanwhile Caesar hurried through the Aeduan territory to the two legions wintering among the Lingones, and with them soon after rejoined the rest of his army.

Thus the patriots had been foiled in their main object, but Caesar was not ready for an immediate campaign; the season was so early that it would be difficult to maintain the transport of supplies, and the revolt had deprived him of most of his cavalry, which he now began to replace with German mercenaries. But Vercingetorix compelled him to move by besieging Gorgobina, a town of those Boii who had been settled among the Aedui in 58 B.C. (p. 552). Caesar could not abandon it without a serious blow to Roman prestige, so he marched to its relief by a circuitous route, capturing on the way Vellaunodunum (Montargis) and

Cenabum, which was sacked to avenge the massacre of Roman citizens there at the start of the revolt. On Caesar's approach the siege of Gorgobina had been abandoned, and from Cenabum the Roman army advanced southwards against Avaricum.

Vercingetorix wished the Bituriges to evacuate the town; recent events had proved the inability of the ordinary Gallic fortress to resist Roman attacks, and had induced him to adopt a new strategy, derived perhaps from that of Cassivellaunus; the Gauls were to starve out the Roman army by cutting off its supplies, and to facilitate this object the countryside was to be turned into a desert and all the towns and villages destroyed. Such a policy involved greater hardships for the Gauls than for the less civilized Britons, and the proposal to abandon and destroy Avaricum provoked vigorous opposition, to which Vercingetorix had to yield; he took up an impregnable position to the north-east of the town from which he maintained communications with the garrison and sent out his cavalry to intercept the Roman supplies. The besieged conducted the defence with great energy, but the determination of Caesar's veterans triumphed over all difficulties; within a month they constructed a gigantic siege-mound, which enabled them to storm the town by a surprise attack; all found within, men, women, and children, were slaughtered without mercy. Ample supplies were found in Avaricum, and the army rested there for several days.

This success had little effect on the course of the rising, for the drooping spirits of the Gauls were soon revived by the inspiring speeches of their leader, whose influence was more firmly established by the disaster which he had predicted; he raised fresh levies, especially of cavalry and archers, and made great efforts to win over the states which had not yet joined the revolt, above all the Aedui, whose ambiguous attitude was not the least of Caesar's anxieties. The spring was now beginning, and Caesar decided to extend the scope of his operations by dividing his army; Labienus was sent north with four legions against the Senones and Parisii, while Caesar himself took the remaining six south to attack the Arverni. Vercingetorix tried to prevent the Romans from crossing to the left bank of the Allier, but when by a stratagem they repaired one of the bridges which he had broken down, he hurried on before them to Gergovia.

Gergovia was a fortified town strongly situated on a plateau raised more than 900 feet above the surrounding valleys; this plateau extends for nearly a mile from east to west and about one-third of a mile from north to south. The slopes on the north and east sides of the plateau are steep, but the southern slope, which is intersected by ravines, is more accessible, and on the south-west a saddle, the Col des Goules, gives access to a hill called Risolles, little lower than Gergovia itself. Between the plateau and the Auzon, a stream running parallel to the plateau on the south side, is a hill called La Roche Blanche. This hill and Risolles had been occupied by Vercingetorix, whose forces were not confined to the town but occupied camps on the higher parts of the slopes to the south and west of it, where he naturally expected Caesar to attack.

As soon as Caesar saw the natural strength of the position he recognized that Gergovia could not be stormed, but he professed to believe that a blockade would be more successful; he surprised the Gallic outpost on La Roche Blanche, took the hill, and built there a small camp, connected by entrenchments with the main camp to the east. His operations were interrupted by disturbances among the Aedui, whom his personal intervention recalled to an insincere allegiance. Meanwhile Vercingetorix had countered the threat of blockade by strengthening his positions on the Col des Goules and Risolles; so long as the Gauls retained these, the area occupied by them was too large to be blockaded by a force of only six legions.

Caesar was preparing to admit his discomfiture by withdrawal, when an alteration in the disposition of the Gallic forces seemed to offer an opportunity for a bold stroke. According to his own statement, the object of his new plan was merely to capture the Gallic camps on the south slope outside the town; this may be true, as such a success would enable him to retreat with some credit, but it is quite possible that he had formed the hazardous design of attempting to take the town itself by escalade. He skilfully induced his opponent to concentrate his forces on Risolles by various movements which seemed to threaten a Roman attack in that direction, and then rapidly led his main force up the centre of the southern slope, while the Aeduan infantry ascended the hill by a circuitous route on the right. The three Gallic camps were surprised and captured; then the soldiers, contrary to their orders if Caesar is to be believed, pressed on to the town wall. But though some of them actually climbed it, Vercingetorix soon hurried to the rescue, the sudden appearance of the Aedui, who were mistaken for enemy reinforcements, threw the Romans into a panic, and they were driven down the hill with a loss of nearly 700 men, including no less than 46 centurions.

This was the first time that Caesar himself had been defeated by the Gauls, and the effect of the disaster was immediate. The

Aedui thought that they could now safely join the revolt; they captured Caesar's depôt at Noviodunum (? Nevers), which contained his stores, remounts, and the hostages of the Gallic states, and tried to intercept his retreat across the Loire by breaking down the bridges. But Caesar crossed the river and hurried north to rejoin Labienus, who had secured his retreat by a decisive victory over the army of the northern insurgents on the left bank of the Seine, opposite Lutetia, the town of the Parisii, situated on what is now the Île de la Cité in Paris.

For a few weeks the Roman army rested among the Lingones (who with the Remi remained loyal to Caesar), where it was reinforced by cavalry and light-armed infantry from the German tribes beyond the Rhine. During this period the Aedui attempted to secure control of the Gallic army, but a general council at Bibracte confirmed Vercingetorix in the supreme command; he then increased his cavalry to 15,000 and tried to promote a revolt in the Province, but the attempt was foiled by the resolute opposition of the Allobroges. When Caesar at last began to march towards the Province, Vercingetorix decided to launch his cavalry against the Roman column, apparently in the hope of compelling it to abandon its baggage. The Romans were completely surprised, but their German cavalry routed the Gauls (on or near the site of Dijon) and Vercingetorix was compelled to retire north-west to Alesia with the infantry, which had taken no part in the battle. Caesar pursued them vigorously, and on his arrival at Alesia again defeated the Gallic cavalry; Vercingetorix saw that he would have to stand a siege, and sent away his cavalry to summon a general levy to his aid.

The hill on which Alesia stood, now Mont Auxois, is almost isolated, as it is cut off from the surrounding hills on the north and south by valleys and on the west by the plain of Les Laumes; the area to be invested was smaller than at Gergovia, and Caesar now had ten legions at his disposal. As it was almost certain that a fresh Gallic army would arrive before the garrison of Alesia could be starved into surrender, Caesar constructed a double line of trenches and ramparts, the inner to invest the town and the outer to resist the relieving army. These lines occupied the slopes of the hills facing Alesia except on the west, where they were carried across the open plain; the defences in this section were strengthened on the inner side and protected by a zone of obstacles to hinder the sallies of the besieged.

At last the relieving army, estimated by Caesar at 250,000 infantry and 8,000 cavalry, appeared and encamped on the hills west of the plain; some critics have thought that the Gallic leaders ought to have brought up every available man, so that Caesar's lines could have been overwhelmed by sheer numbers, but it would have been impossible to feed or manœuvre such enormous masses. Bad leadership decided the fate of Gaul; there was no unity of command, and valuable time was wasted, first in an attack by cavalry and archers alone, and then in a night-attack on Caesar's lines in the plain. When both these failed, a more formidable attack by 60,000 men under Vercassivellaunus (Vercingetorix' cousin) was directed against the north-west angle of the Roman lines, but though Vercingetorix and the besieged ably supported them by a vigorous offensive against the Roman positions south of Alesia, the rest of the relieving army did little or nothing to help, and Caesar was able to concentrate most of his men in the two sectors where the enemy had broken through. A fierce struggle followed; finally Caesar repelled the attack of Vercingetorix, and hurried to aid Labienus against the relieving army. The enemy from the heights observed his approach, for he was wearing the crimson cloak which marked the Roman general in action, and made a desperate effort, but the Roman troops stood firm, and at last the Roman cavalry, previously sent by Caesar, took the division of Vercassivellaunus in the rear and routed it. In the same night the great Gallic army dispersed, and on the next day Vercingetorix gave himself up to the Romans to save the lives of his men; according to Plutarch[1] he came to Caesar alone, mounted and in his finest armour, rode once round Caesar's tribunal, then dismounted, took off his armour, and sat down in silent submission at the feet of his conqueror. For six years he was kept in captivity, to be led through the streets of Rome at Caesar's triumph and then put to death, but he had earned that imperishable renown which is always assured to the heroic leader of a great nation's struggle for independence. Had he succeeded at Alesia, he would soon have found that the permanent unification of Gaul was a vain dream, and his defeat may have spared him the bitterness of an end like that of the German hero Arminius, who liberated his country from the Romans but fell a victim to the jealous ingratitude of his own people.

VII. THE RECONQUEST OF GAUL: CONCLUSION

The great revolt had received a severe blow at Alesia, but some of the Gallic patriots refused to accept it as decisive. There were

[1] *Caesar*, 27.

many homeless and desperate men in Gaul, who regarded warfare
and brigandage as their livelihood; such troops could not face the
legions in battle but they might maintain a troublesome guerrilla
warfare, and the surviving anti-Roman chiefs seem to have hoped
that they could prolong the struggle on these lines until Caesar's
command terminated, and that in the ensuing confusion the Gallic
states might recover their independence.

For Caesar the speedy suppression of the revolt was a necessity;
he remained in Gaul for the winter of 52–1, during which he re-
established the Roman supremacy over most of Central Gaul, the
Aedui and Arverni having already been induced to submit in the
autumn by the restoration of their men captured at Alesia. But
the Bellovaci rose against the Romans under an able leader,
Correus, and were joined by many other Belgic tribes; this rising
was formidable and for a time Caesar was foiled by the steadfastly
Fabian strategy of Correus, ably seconded by Commius. Even
when Caesar had concentrated seven legions in this region he
made little progress until Correus was killed in an ambush, whereupon the stubborn resistance of the Bellovaci abruptly collapsed.

Meanwhile a Celtic army had been operating in the west, in the
country south of the Loire, but after the submission of the
Bellovaci Caesar detached a force sufficient to crush it; 2,000 men
from the beaten army fled south, under Drappes and Lucterius,
and occupied the impregnable hill of Uxellodunum (probably the
Puy d'Issolu, near the north bank of the Dordogne). It was
promptly invested by the Romans, but the blockade was incomplete, and Drappes and Lucterius left the town to collect fresh
supplies for the besieged from the surrounding country. On their
return they were intercepted; Drappes was captured, and later
committed suicide by self-starvation. Lucterius escaped for a
time, but was finally surrendered to the Romans by an Arvernian
chief with whom he had taken refuge. Despite the loss of its
leaders the garrison of Uxellodunum held out and the Roman
blockade dragged on without result, so that Caesar was compelled
to intervene in person. He at once saw that the only hope of
success was to cut off the water-supply of the besieged; their access
to an adjacent stream was rendered almost impossible, so that they
were reduced to dependence on a single spring just outside the
town wall, whereupon Caesar ordered his engineers to divert the
spring by a mine. A desperate sortie of the Gauls had already been
repelled, when the failure of the spring made them believe that
even their gods had deserted them, and compelled them to surrender. As the garrison was largely composed of the desperadoes

who were a menace to the peaceful settlement of Gaul, Caesar ordered their hands to be cut off as a terrible warning to the rest (? August 51).

In what remained of the summer Caesar visited Aquitania and received the renewed submission of the tribes there. By a judicious mixture of clemency and firmness he rapidly restored peace in Gaul; even Commius, who had been attacking the convoys in the region of Arras, finally came to terms with the Romans. But he soon regretted his submission, and in 50 made good his escape to Britain, where he established a kingdom in the country south of the Thames, and the last defender of Gallic independence ended his days as a free and powerful ruler in the land which as Caesar's agent he had once tried to enslave to Rome.

Caesar's conquest of Gaul was complete and the country gave little trouble for many years. The suppression of the great revolt had contributed to this result, for the Gauls would never have submitted to the loss of their liberty without one last great effort to recover it, and when that effort had been defeated by Roman skill and resolution they acquiesced in their destiny. But the subsequent peacefulness was partly due to Caesar's conciliatory policy after the revolt; the struggle with the Senate was impending, and it was important that if civil war broke out there should be no trouble in Gaul requiring the presence of the legions; accordingly no efforts were spared to win over the leading chiefs in the various states, and the yearly tribute imposed on the country was fixed at 40,000,000 sesterces, a moderate estimate which recognized the severe exhaustion of Gaul after eight years of warfare.

The year 50 passed peacefully in Gaul; in the course of it Caesar surrendered two of his legions when they were demanded by the Senate for the Parthian War, but he had raised another legion in Transalpine Gaul in 51 (afterwards famous as the Alaudae), and when the Civil War broke out he had eight legions in Transalpine Gaul (four under Trebonius among the Belgae, four with Fabius among the Aedui), as well as one (the 13th) in Cisalpine Gaul, at Ravenna[1].

The conquest of Gaul was an undertaking which had enabled Caesar to combine the attainment of many different objects: he had acquired a renown which overshadowed the successes of Pompey, he had trained a large army and secured its absolute devotion, he had amassed great wealth with which to reward his supporters and bribe his opponents, and he had added a vast

---

[1] *B.G.* VIII, 54, 3–4. The Alaudae are perhaps not included in the nine legions enumerated by Hirtius: see below, Note 5, p. 898.

province to the Roman Empire. If his assumption of the task was not entirely due to that disinterested appreciation of the Empire's needs to which his panegyrists attempt to ascribe it, in its completion he contrived with rare success, except in the two expeditions to Britain, to reconcile the interests of the Empire with his own. Yet the personal motives which partly influenced Caesar, although they did not hinder his effective prosecution of the work of conquest, undoubtedly affected the manner in which the conquest was accomplished. The total of human suffering and misery occasioned by Caesar's Gallic campaigns is terrible to contemplate, and it is certain that much of it was unnecessary; in this and in his ungenerous treatment of Vercingetorix the conduct of Caesar contrasts unfavourably with that of Pompey. His severity tended to defeat its object, and the final pacification was due no less to his tardy measures of conciliation than to the ruthless cruelties by which they had been preceded.

The sufferings of the Gauls during the conquest and the heroism of their final struggle must not obscure the fact that their subjugation by a foreign conqueror was largely due to their own errors; they had had long enough to work out their own salvation, but the fratricidal jealousies of the larger states were only aggravated by time, and triumphed over the weaker influences which tended towards the promotion of national unity. When Caesar arrived in Gaul there was no future for the Gauls but submission to a stronger power, and they were fortunate that the German hordes were forestalled by the legions. The Roman conquest of Gaul conferred on its inhabitants the benefits of the Roman civilization and the *Pax Romana*; to the Romans it gave the security of the Rhine boundary, and facilitated that great work of providing the Empire with a scientific frontier on the north, the completion of which was reserved for Caesar's heir.

CHAPTER XIV

PARTHIA

I. THE EARLY KINGS

WHAT passes for the history of Parthia as derived from classical writers has been truly called a conventional fiction. The Parthian Empire has left no records, except an abundant coinage; but as the coins, before Mithridates III, call every king Arsaces and have to be interpreted from the literary texts, they raise more problems than they solve. Until we reach the history of Rome, an account has to be put together as best it may from scraps collected from many diverse sources, and the margin of uncertainty is considerable. The traditional list and numbering of the Parthian kings during this period, as generally used by numismatists, is unsatisfactory, for it is derived from the classical authors and from conjecture and takes no account of the cuneiform evidence; the list used in this chapter is printed on p. 613, with the traditional list beside it for reference.

The steppe country north of Hyrcania was occupied by a confederacy of three tribes collectively known to Greeks as Dahae; doubtless, like most of the steppe peoples we know, they were a mixed horde, but their leading clans were apparently Iranian and presumably spoke a North Iranian dialect akin to Sogdian. They were not pure nomads, though they had furnished horse-archers

Note. For Parthia, the best contemporary evidence consists of the coinages of Parthia, Elymaïs, Characene, and Persis; astronomical and business documents from Babylon and Uruk; information in Ssu-ma-ch'ien, *Shi-Ki*, ch. 123, which embodies Chang-k'ien's Report; and, in Greek, a few inscriptions, the first parchment from Avroman, the document on which Isidore's *Parthian Stations* is founded, and notices preserved by Strabo. Among later material, Trogus-Justin and the fragments of Diodorus supply a kind of narrative, of uncertain value. For the invasion of Crassus two accounts are extant: Dio Cassius, XL, 12–30, which represents Livy's lost narrative, and Plutarch's *Life of Crassus*. Dio's account of Carrhae is rhetoric, and the battle must be reconstructed from Plutarch alone. Plutarch occasionally uses Livy; but his main source, which is excellent, is a well-informed Greek of Mesopotamia or Babylonia, who impartially dislikes both Rome and Parthia; his identity is unknown. See further the Bibliography.—For the history of the Graeco-Bactrian and Indo-Parthian kingdoms see the *Cambridge History of India*, vol. I, chaps. xvii, xxiii.

See Map 14, facing p. 612.

to Alexander; they occupied some oases, one of which, Dihistan, possibly long bore their name, and were known as good fighters on foot. Part of one of their three tribes, the Parni, led in the tradition by two brothers, Arsaces and Tiridates, had before 250 B.C. separated from the rest and moved to the lower Ochus (Tejend); the powerful and semi-independent satrap of Bactria, Diodotus, attempted to bring them under his rule, and to escape him they migrated into the Hyrcanian-Parthian satrapy; there they came into conflict with, and killed, the Seleucid satrap Andragoras (not the Andragoras of the coins), whose name is variously given. Arsaces, afterwards reckoned the founder of the dynasty, is a legendary figure; the founder of the kingdom was Tiridates, who took the name Arsaces, subsequently borne as a family name by all his descendants. Tiridates and three other shadowy monarchs— Artabanus I, Phriapitius, and the son of the latter, Phraates I— fill the period till Mithridates I. Tradition makes Tiridates, perhaps with further support from his tribesmen, reduce part of the Hyrcanian-Parthian satrapy, that is, the later provinces of Astauene, Apavarktikene, and Parthyene. Astauene was seemingly the first conquest; it was the country of the eastern Tapuri, one of the pre-Iranian peoples displaced and broken by the original Iranian invasion; they may have made common cause with the Parni, for Astauene became the homeland of the dynasty. Tiridates' first capital was the fortress of Dara (Dareium) which he built, probably near Abivard in Apavarktikene, facing the desert whence he had come. But the kings of his line were buried at Nisa in Parthyene, a district well known in the Persian sacred books as Nisaea; and he himself was crowned at a town near Kushan in Astauene (also part of the old Nisaea) which afterwards bore his name, Asaak (Arsacia). This marks a certain progress in ideas; to the connection with the desert is added the conciliation of the Mazdean religion of the settled lands. For at Asaak the holy fire, used at the coronation, was kept burning for ever; undoubtedly (though it cannot be said which derived from which) it was connected with the Farmer's Fire, Adar Burzin Mihr on Mt Ravand, one of the three sacred and eternal fires of later Zoroastrianism, the others being the Warrior's Fire in Atropatene and the Priest's Fire in Persis. They correspond to the three aspects of the Mazdean Glory which descended upon the king; and the Farmer's Fire was no bad omen for the commencement of a state whose background was to be the revolt of the countryman against the Greek and Graeco-Babylonian city.

The origin of the name Arsaces is unknown. The Arsacids,

possibly in imitation of the Seleucid pedigree[1], subsequently claimed descent from Artaxerxes II, whose personal name had been Arsaces; but Arsaces may well have been the first king's family name. Another doubtful matter is the date of Tiridates' coronation, that is, of the formal establishment of the kingdom. The so-called Arsacid Era (p. 592), as used later in Babylonia, was based on the belief that the coronation took place in the year preceding 1 Nisan 247 B.C. (*i.e.* in 248–7), so that this date, from which the Arsacid Era was reckoned, would have been the new king's first New Year festival had he been master of Babylon. We cannot go behind this, and it is difficult to believe that the kings did not keep some sort of record, on the lines of a Hellenistic king's *Journal*; indeed, later tradition speaks of Parthian annals destroyed by the Sassanians.

The establishment of the new kingdom had been favoured by the troubles of Seleucus II (vol. VII, pp. 717–20); but, once his hands were free, Seleucus made an expedition eastward, and Tiridates fled to the Apasiacae (Apa-saka, 'Water-Sacas') of the Caspian steppe, a branch of the great Saca confederacy called Massagetae. Seleucus, however, was recalled by a revolt in Antioch, and Tiridates, allied with Diodotus II of Bactria, recovered his kingdom, although his traditional great victory over Seleucus does not belong to history. The kingdom cannot have expanded farther till after 217, as Antiochus III still had access to the Dahae; but, after the Syrian disaster at Raphia, Tiridates conquered Hyrcania proper, the warm fertile lands along the south-east Caspian, and Comisene, and made the Seleucid city of Hecatompylos his capital. This marks a further progress in ideas: the work of the Greeks was to be used, not destroyed. Either Tiridates or his son Artabanus I then conquered Choarene, and Artabanus for a time perhaps held Ecbatana; but when Antiochus III was able to turn eastward (vol. VIII, p. 140 *sq.*) he easily recovered the country west of Comisene. The Parthians however, whether by conquest or friendship, had secured Tapuria, the eastern Elburz, and the Tapuri fought valiantly against Antiochus; but he reconquered Comisene and Hyrcania, which he held till after his defeat by Rome. He left Artabanus the rest of his kingdom as a subject ally, useful against Bactria if required. But at some unknown period, probably after the retirement of Antiochus, Parthia was attacked from the east by the powerful Graeco-Bactrian monarchy, and lost Astauene; the Bactrians made two satrapies of the

---

[1] The writer in *C.Q.* XXIII, 1929, p. 140.

conquered territory, Tapuria, the upper Atrek, and Traxiane, the valley of the Kashef-Rud[1]. The loss of Astauene must have entailed that of Apavarktikene also, which was presumably included in the two Bactrian satrapies; and the ruling Arsaces (? Phriapitius) was reduced to Parthyene alone. But the exhaustion of Syria after Magnesia was again Parthia's opportunity; the Arsacids threw off the Seleucid suzerainty, recovered Hyrcania, Comisene, and Choarene, and carried their boundary to Charax, west of the Caspian Gates. Tradition attributes part of this to Phraates I, and adds that he 'conquered' the Mardi of the central Elburz and settled some of them about Charax to guard his frontier; but Mardi also appear later as military settlers in Armenia and Atropatene, and Phraates may have known how to win the goodwill of the pre-Iranian peoples, as did the kings of Elymaïs. The belief that some Arsaces held Babylon in 180–79 arose from a mistake[2].

The first Arsacids, though wedged in between the Seleucids and the Graeco-Bactrians, had thus made a kingdom; and as their own Parni cannot have been numerous, this implies considerable support from the native inhabitants. Their early conquests, often in hill country, were certainly not made solely by horse-archers. The Dahae were partly footmen, and the Parni were joined by vagrant or deserting mercenaries and by skilled workmen, who made arms for them. Their armies at first probably differed little from Seleucid armies, except for a greater proportion of cavalry; and many who fought for them had learnt their business in Seleucid service.

Their kingdom was universally known to Greeks and Romans as Parthia and its rulers as Parthians; what they called themselves is unknown. The Parni were probably not the first invaders from the desert who settled in Iran[3], as they were not the last; and it has been suggested that the Parthava of Darius I's inscriptions also might have been recent settlers—they are not mentioned in the Avesta—and that the Parni recognized some kinship with them. But the appellation 'Parthia' for the kingdom is Greek, not native, and merely means that, when Greeks first observed it, the face it turned towards them was that of the old Parthian satrapy; indeed, the homeland of Astauene had probably belonged, not to Parthia, but to Hyrcania.

---

[1] See W. W. Tarn, *Seleucid-Parthian Studies*, cited p. 582 n. 1.

[2] J. N. Strassmaier, *Z.A.* VIII, p. 110 (cf. vol. III, p. 247), on which see F. X. Kugler, *Sternkunde*, II, p. 448, n. 1; *Von Moses bis Paulus*, p. 339.

[3] For a possible earlier settlement of Parni, see vol. III, p. 81.

II. MITHRIDATES I AND PHRAATES II

Phraates I was succeeded by his brother Mithridates, the creator of the Parthian Empire. The date of his accession is quite uncertain; it has been put as early as 174, as late as 160. It is hardly material, for in any event his activity did not begin till well after the death of Antiochus Epiphanes in 163[1].

The defeat of Antiochus III at Magnesia in 189 worked considerable changes in Asia. The two Armenian kingdoms, and Atropatene, threw off any suzerainty which he may have exercised. Elymaïs also revolted under one Kamnaskires, whose affinities are unknown; his capital was the semi-Greek Susa and his coinage as king was purely Greek, but his fighting strength lay in the pre-Iranian Elymaei of the Zagros, unconquered hillmen, who had kinsfolk in the Elburz. Antiochus III, in need of money, attacked Elymaïs and met his death trying to plunder the temple of Bel. Antiochus Epiphanes subsequently attempted to restore the position in the east, but his attack on Elymaïs also failed, and on his way to reduce Parthia he died at Gabae (vol. VIII, p. 514). Kamnaskires annexed Gabiene and took the title 'Victorious'; on the south his kingdom touched the Persian Gulf, which probably means that he held Seleuceia on the Erythraean Sea. Hyspaosines son of Sagdodonacus, Epiphanes' Iranian governor in Mesene (Chaldaea), also revolted on his death and made a little kingdom, Characene, at the head of the Persian Gulf, which extended up the Tigris to Apamea and embraced the Greek cities on the west of the Gulf (the 'parts about the Erythraean Sea'), with some suzerainty over the neighbouring Mesenite Arabs. He also refounded Antioch at the Tigris mouth, damaged by floods, as his capital Charax (Kerak), rebuilding it on an artificial embankment. He must have claimed to be in the Seleucid succession, for during his brief rule in Babylon that city, though it naturally dropped the Arsacid Era (p. 592), dated, not by his reign, but by the Seleucid Era alone[2]. On the death of Antiochus Eupator in 162/1 Timarchus, satrap of Media, revolted and declared himself independent, and Persis also broke away from the Seleucids, if it had not done so earlier. Dim stories of fighting in Persis remain; the result was that the priest-kings of Persepolis, who had retained some quasi-autonomy under the Seleucids

---

[1] As Timarchus in Media copied the coinage of Eucratides of Bactria (*Cambridge History of India*, I, p. 457; cf. Volume of Plates iii, 14 *a*), Parthia in 162 was no serious obstacle to inter-communication.

[2] Tablet published by Pinches, *Babylonian and Oriental Record*, IV, p. 131.

and had coined from about 250, made themselves kings of
Persis with the title of Malik (Shah). Whatever Power held
Media and Babylon was now cut off from the Persian Gulf by a
ring of states, Characene, Elymaïs, Persis.

This was the position when, somewhere before 160, Mithridates began his career of conquest. He first took Media up to
the Zagros from Timarchus and annexed it to Parthia, making
his general Bagasis satrap and doubling his own strength; Timarchus he left to be finished off by Demetrius I of Syria (vol. vɪɪɪ,
p. 519). Then he attacked Eucratides of Bactria, now weakened
by his long duel with Demetrius of the Punjab[1], and retook the
lost provinces, Tapuria and Traxiane, bringing his frontier back
to the Arius. His next conquest was Elymaïs, where he secured
10,000 talents from the temples of Athena and Nanaia; as he had
to take Seleuceia on the Hedyphon, the Greek element probably
supported Kamnaskires. For two generations Elymaïs unwillingly
remained a Parthian fief; as her coinage was in abeyance, it
is not known how she was ruled. Persis became, and for nearly
four centuries remained, Parthia's vassal, and Parthian influence
is reflected on her coinage; the reason why her monarchy was
never abolished is unknown. Eastward Mithridates extended his
rule to the Hydaspes in Gedrosia (? Purali), Virgil's *Medus Hydaspes*, a name which gave rise to a legend that he made conquests in
India. It is not known what happened to the southern provinces
of the Bactrian kingdom; but if he held Gedrosia he must at least
have taken Seistan and so much of Aria as gave him the great road
northward from Seistan by Herat to Parthyene.

The conquest of Elymaïs brought him to the gates of Babylonia,
a land of ancient cities, where the wealth of the eastern trade-routes
poured into Seleuceia and the prestige of old renown clung to the
name of Babylon; though Antiochus Epiphanes had refounded
Babylon as a Greek city, the native element, whose centre was
E-sagila, still kept continuity with the past. The Seleucid Demetrius II was fighting for his crown against the usurper Tryphon,
and late in 142 Mithridates annexed Babylonia, though perhaps
not Seleuceia. His conquest, on the strength of an astronomical
table, has been put in July 141[2], the first dating in the Arsacid
Era being believed to be 108 Ars.[3] (140–39 B.C.); but a contract exists dated 107 Ars.[4] (141–40 B.C.), and Mithridates must

---

[1] See *Cambridge History of India*, ɪ, p. 446.
[2] See F. X. Kugler, *Von Moses bis Paulus*, p. 339 (S.H. 108); W. Kolbe,
Syrische Beiträge, p. 38.   [3] F. X. Kugler, *Sternkunde*, ɪɪ, p. 446.
[4] O. Schroeder, *Kontrakte der Seleukidenzeit*, no. 37; dated 107 Ars.
= 171 Sel.

therefore have been master of Babylon some time before 1 Nisan (March–April) 141 B.C., the day on which 107 Ars. began (p. 593); Demetrius' last known date in Babylon is in February 142. Mithridates subsequently annexed Adiabene (Assyria), returned thence to Babylonia, and early in July 141 entered Seleuceia (if the broken name we have be Seleuceia), whether peaceably or otherwise is unknown. He now held Babylonia and the Tigris frontier to the northward, though northern Mesopotamia remained Seleucid, and in 140 he appears in a Babylonian document as 'King of Kings[1],' a revival of the old Achaemenid title (vol. IV. p. 185).

Mithridates is represented as a moderate and conciliatory ruler, and his assumption after he conquered Babylonia of the title Philhellene—a regular title of his successors after Phraates II—shows that he recognized the value of Greek co-operation; but the Greek cities remained loyal at heart to the Seleucid, and called on Demetrius for help. Demetrius could not relinquish Babylonia without a struggle; also its reconquest might strengthen him for the civil war in Syria. He secured Bactria, Elymaïs, and Persis as allies, which took time, for his envoys must have gone across Parthia in disguise. In December 141 a Bactrian invasion had already caused Mithridates to fly to Hyrcania, while the Elymaeans were marching on Apamea on the Silhu[2]; these dates are further evidence that Mithridates took Babylonia much earlier than July 141. Demetrius himself, leaving his competent wife Cleopatra Thea to hold Antioch against Tryphon, invaded Babylonia late in 141 or early in 140; he won some victories and recovered Babylon. But Mithridates was too strong for the coalition, and, having first driven out the Bactrians, he defeated and captured Demetrius (late 140 or early 139); he recognized his captive's value, kept him in honourable captivity in Hyrcania, and married him to his daughter Rhodogune. Elymaïs and Persis again became Parthia's vassals; whether Mithridates also subdued Characene is not known.

This was his last exploit; he must have died about 138, as 139–8 is the last date on his dated tetradrachms. The man who found a little kingdom and left an empire extending from the Caspian to the Persian Gulf must have had qualities; Greek writers schedule his virtues, and Arrian gives him a small list of superlatives

---

[1] J. N. Strassmaier, Z.A. III, p. 129, no. 1 = J. Kohler and A. Ungnad, *Hundert ausgewählte Rechtsurkunden*, no. 94; dated 108 Ars.

[2] See F. X. Kugler, *Von Moses bis Paulus*, p. 342 (S.P. 1, 176).

modelled on his famous eulogy of Alexander[1]. He is said to have
collected the best laws from every people in his empire, which may
point to an attempted codification of Iranian law, after the pattern
of Hammurabi's code; whether he began that reorganization of
the provinces which appears under Mithridates II is unknown.

His son Phraates II was a minor, and his mother Ri..nu became
regent[2]; he took the Persian title 'King of the Lands,' but not
apparently that of 'King of Kings.' Nothing is known of his reign
till the year 130, when his kingdom had to encounter two great invasions simultaneously. The reigning Seleucid Antiochus Sidetes,
brother of Demetrius II, had shown himself a strong and
tolerant ruler; and, after disposing of Tryphon, recovering Judaea,
and settling Syria, he set out to reconquer the East. He started
early in 130 by the route east of the Tigris; Phraates was presumably in Hyrcania, but Antiochus, who had with him his son
Seleucus and a daughter of Demetrius, defeated Phraates' generals
in three battles and recovered Babylonia; the last known cuneiform document from Seleucid Babylon is dated in June 130. Unfortunately we know nothing of the cause of his success, the
tradition only supplying some absurd figures; but the Greek cities
would keep him well-informed, and Mithridates' conquest of
the hill state of Elymaïs shows that the Parthians were not yet
a people of horse-archers, though doubtless they were stronger in
cavalry than the Syrian king. Antiochus next recovered Media,
and demanded from Phraates tribute and the cession of everything
except the old Hyrcanian-Parthian satrapy; it seemed as if he
was to restore the empire of Antiochus III. But the winter was
fatal to him. He wintered at Ecbatana, and had to divide his
army among the neighbouring towns, mostly native; they disliked
the burden and resented the conduct of his general Athenaeus;
Phraates was able to arrange a simultaneous rising against the
Syrians, and Antiochus, hurrying to the help of the nearest detachment, was defeated and killed. Phraates sent home his body in
a silver coffin, and Syria mourned her last great king. Seleucus
remained in honourable captivity in Parthia, and Phraates married
Demetrius' daughter; but in the stress of the conflict he had released Demetrius to raise trouble as a pretender in Syria (see vol.
VIII, p. 530 sq.). Phraates' absence from the seat of war in 130 must
mean that the Sacas had crossed his frontier; tradition says that he
staved off the invasion for a moment by taking their vanguard into

[1] Assuming that Suidas, *Arsaces*, refers to Mithridates I.
[2] On the date of this document (A. T. Clay, *Babylonian Records*, ii,
no. 53) see E. H. Minns, *J.H.S.* xxxv, p. 34.

his pay, which is possible. But after Antiochus' death he had to meet them seriously; he attempted to use Antiochus' mercenaries, who turned against him, and in 129 or 128 he fell in battle with the Sacas, and his kingdom lay open to the nomad hordes.

III. THE SACAS AND MITHRIDATES II[1]

The various tribes collectively called Sacae by Persians and Greeks (though Greek writers often wrongly use the term 'Scythian') were at this time a very numerous people; it seems that their countries were over-populated and in a condition of unstable equilibrium. Three main bodies of the race have been made out. The Amyrgian Sacas of the Pamir, who had once held, but had lost, Ferghana, the 'Amyrgian plain' of Hecataeus, do not come into this story. The Sacaraucae (Saka Rawaka) lived north of the Jaxartes; possibly their original seat was the Ili valley. The great Saca horde or confederacy called Massagetae held the Caspian steppes north of the Dahae, including the lower Oxus and Chorasmia; they extended northward to the country of the Aorsi, who from the Ural river stretched eastward round the Aral, probably to the Jaxartes. The Sacas themselves, who spoke a North Iranian language, were probably of Iranian origin; but the Sacaraucae, if they be Chang-k'ien's Kang-k'iu, as is likely, seem also to have contained Turki elements, while the Massagetae were thoroughly mixed; their Saca clans were ruling agricultural peoples in the oases and primitive fish-eaters in the river deltas (vol. III, p. 194).

The nomad invasions which destroyed the Graeco-Bactrian kingdom and transformed Parthia were the end of a movement of the peoples of Central Asia which started in Kan-su (Northwest China) in the early part of the second century, when the Hiung-nu (Huns), a Turki horde with a blonde admixture, finally defeated and drove out a rival horde, the Yueh-chi. The Yueh-chi were largely the Indo-European Tochari, a blue-eyed people whose speech was akin to Latin and Celtic and whose journey from Russia to China can perhaps be traced by grave-mounds; but they were ruled by Turki clans, the Arsi (Greek Asii) and the Kuṣi (Kushans) being known. The trek across Asia of the defeated Yueh-chi has often been described; it suffices here to say that on the way they displaced a people called Sak or Sok in the Chinese accounts, doubtless the Sacaraucae, and drove them west and south; in 128 the Yueh-chi were in the Samarcand country, and

[1] The references and reasons for much in this section are given in the writer's *Seleucid-Parthian Studies*, Proc. Brit. Acad. 1930.

those of the Sacaraucae (Kang-k'iu) who had not invaded Parthia
were strung out through western Sogdiana and across the Jaxartes,
the northern branch being subject to the Huns and those in Sogdiana to the Yueh-chi. These movements had set the whole steppe
country in motion; Greek rule in Bactria ended about 135, and
the nomads subsequently invaded Parthia. The invaders of Parthia
included part of the Sacaraucae, but the larger body must have
been furnished by the Massagetae; doubtless they swept along
with them parts of other peoples, as (from their geographical
position) the Dahae; it was a general upheaval, but we can only
refer to the invaders collectively as Sacas. All the nomad peoples
mentioned here were horse-archers, and the Chinese reckoned
that each family supplied one horseman to the general levy; even
if the Chinese figures be high—the Sacaraucae (Kang-k'iu) have
90,000 horse, later 120,000—their military strength in proportion to population was far greater than that of the settled peoples.
The Yueh-chi, who soon after 128 occupied Bactria proper and
subsequently faced towards India, took no part in the invasion of
Parthia; but it was the visit paid to them in 128 by the Chinese
Chang-k'ien, general and diplomat, which gave that shrewd observer his first knowledge of Parthia, a knowledge supplemented
by the reports of the lieutenants he sent out in 115.

The death of Phraates II left Parthia open to the nomads; of
the brief reign of his uncle and successor Artabanus II nothing
is known, save that it must have consisted of efforts to check the
invasion. The Sacas entered Parthia proper and occupied Tapuria
and Traxiane; here they must have divided, as the Persian desert
and the great roads dictated, one body going westward, north of
the desert, and one going southward, east of it. The former body
presumably overran Hyrcania and Comisene[1]. Tradition mentions a Saca raid west of the Tigris, and a dark-skinned community
of idolators (? Indians) existing in Armenia in A.D. 304 believed
that their ancestors had fled thither before the (Saca) chief Din-
ashké. Beyond this, however, the westward invasion did not go;
Artabanus may have been successful in checking it, and may even
have recovered parts of Hyrcania-Parthia. But the larger body
of the invaders went south, following the road by Herat to the
Hamun lake and occupying Aria and Seistan; they founded a
kingdom on the lower Helmund (Sacastene) in what had been

---

[1] Isidore's source says there was no city in Comisene, which probably
means that Hecatompylos was destroyed (it was rebuilt later), while the
nomenclature of Hyrcania in Ptolemy is completely different from that of
the earlier period, and a Saca town occurs there, Ptol. iv, 9, 7.

the Seleucid province of Paraetacene, and occupied Candahar; later this flood was to pour eastward into India[1].

Such roughly was the position when about 124 Artabanus fell in battle with the invaders and his place was taken by his gifted son Mithridates II; probably the Parthia which Rome knew was more his creation than that of his uncle Mithridates I. His first preoccupation, apparently, was less with the Sacas than with affairs in Babylonia; probably, as will be seen, he entrusted the situation east of the desert to other hands till his rear was secure. When Phraates II went eastward to meet the nomads he had left as his governor in Babylonia one Himerus, a Hyrcanian, represented as cruel and vicious. Phraates himself had threatened Seleuceia with savage punishment for something done to his general Enius during Sidetes' invasion, a threat never carried out; but Himerus' business was to reduce Babylonia to order again after the disturbance, and he inflicted great damage on Babylon and sold many Babylonians as slaves in Media. This reference to Media implies that he had some authority there; and this, added to Diodorus' statement that he was king of the Parthians, may mean that during the troubled reign of Artabanus he was a rival king in the west. Numismatists assign to him a coin dated in 124/3[2] (which *might* belong to Mithridates II) and believe that he adopted the title 'Victorious,' presumably with reference to the capture of Babylon. The one thing certain is that he had a war with Hyspaosines of Characene and that Hyspaosines was king in Babylon in 127 and 126[3]; possibly the Greek element invoked his aid against Himerus, but it is difficult to see whence he obtained the necessary military strength, unless Elymaïs aided him. Whether Himerus' capture of Babylon preceded or terminated Hyspaosines' rule cannot be said. But if he was king at Mithridates' accession Mithridates made short work of him, for by 122 he had recovered Babylon and reduced Characene to vassaldom; a series of bronze coins of his dated 122/1 are overstruck on Hyspaosines' money, which with Parthian kings signifies military conquest[4].

This left him free to turn eastward. The broad outline is that the Parthians recovered Seistan, making Sacastene a vassal province, and took and ruled Candahar, perhaps another Saca state; they recovered Aria, and all Parthia up to the Arius boundary; finally they captured Merv, which was to remain Parthian. Chang-k'ien's Report, which incorporates the information he collected

[1] E. J. Rapson in *Camb. Hist. India*, 1, p. 567; E. Herzfeld, *Paikuli*, p. 38.
[2] Volume of Plates iv, 8, *g*. [3] Tablet cited p. 578, n. 2.
[4] Volume of Plates iv, 8, *h–k*.

in 115, makes Mithridates' kingdom stretch along the bank of the Oxus and border to the north on the An't-sai (Aorsi) of the Aral, which doubtless means that he was overlord of the Caspian steppes up to where the Oxus entered the Aral, that is, of the Massagetae. One might guess that the Parthian arms struck at the centre of the long line held by the Sacas and rolled up the two ends, towards Candahar and towards Merv; the northern body were driven back on the steppes, the southern eastward to India. The northern campaign can be followed in the 'campaign' coins, a series unlike any other Parthian coins; five are known, two with the legend ΚΑΤΑΣΤΡΑΤΕΙΑ[1] and three bearing the names of Aria, Traxiane, and Merv—medals of conquest—which illustrate the Parthian progress northward[2]. Numismatists seem certain that these coins were not struck by Mithridates II and cannot be earlier than his reign, and so assign them to a mythical successor 'Artabanus II'; but as this Artabanus is unknown alike to Greek tradition and Babylonian records[3], and as Merv was Parthian by 115, the solution seems to be that they were struck by a joint-king: Mithridates, whose reign began with war on two fronts, copied the Seleucid practice and appointed a joint-king in the east, while he dealt with Babylonia. Doubtless the two subsequently co-operated. The coins of the joint-king are not part of the Parthian regal coinage, but were struck to pay his troops and record his victories.

Parthia deserved well of western civilization for damming the nomad flood. The result of these campaigns was that the Massagetae were broken, their strongest elements having passed on into India; they partially recovered, but their fate was to be absorption by the Aorsi and thus ultimately to become part of the Alan horde. But the Sacaraucae who had remained in Sogdiana gained an accession of strength, probably from their returning tribesmen; they were able to free themselves from the Yueh-chi and establish their capital at Bokhara, and a generation later could again interfere in Parthia. But for the rest of Mithridates' reign Parthia had peace in the east; he received, with much pomp, an embassy from the Han emperor Wu-ti, and the road was opened for the inflow into Parthia of caravan trade from China through Chinese

[1] Dr G. F. Hill has suggested that this is not κατὰ στρατείαν, 'on campaign' (cf. O.G.I.S. 225), but is the substantive of καταστρατεύομαι, 'offensive campaign.'   [2] Volume of Plates iv, 8, c, d.

[3] Because of an error in a proper name (Tigranes for Mithridates) Gutschmid shifted part of Trogus' Prol. XLI to XLII, thus making the Artabanus there named the successor, not of Tiridates I, but of Mithridates II.

Turkestan along the subsequently famous Silk Route, a development for which the main credit belongs to Chang-k'ien. Parthia now became of international importance, for in 92 B.C. Mithridates sent an envoy to Sulla; his reign thus saw touch secured with both China and Rome. In the south he drew tighter the suzerainty over Persis, and the great Zoroastrian fire-altar was replaced on her coins by the little altar of Parthia, known from Arsacid seals[1]. In the west he secured Mesopotamia and carried his boundary to the Euphrates, but a war with the queen of some Arab tribe, Laodice, who was supported by Antiochus IX Cyzicenus, is all that is known of the conquest; in 87 his governor intervened in the chronic civil war in Syria and captured Demetrius III Eukairos. His Mesopotamia included three vassal kingdoms: Adiabene and Gordyene (the Carduchi), which had probably asserted their independence during the general Seleucid break-up, and Osrhoëne, a little principality round Edessa; it had been formed in 132 by an Iranian, Osrhoës, probably a Seleucid governor, who in 127 had been succeeded, or ousted, by an Arab, Abdu bar Maz'ûr, ancestor of a long line. Probably from Zeugma to Nicephorium the Euphrates was Mithridates' frontier, but from Nicephorium to Babylonia he held the Peraea west of the river (Parapotamia), his boundary towards Syria being the desert. By 108 he had taken the title 'King of Kings,' which he used regularly; in 88 he had three queens, his paternal half-sisters Siake and Azate, and Automa daughter of Tigranes of Armenia[2]. He carried out, or completed, the Parthian provincial organization, and made a survey of his kingdom on the lines of the Seleucid survey, the 'Asiatic Stations' mentioned by Strabo[3]. Mithridates' dealings with Armenia will be noticed later.

But the end of his reign saw troubles in his kingdom. He was alive in 87, for Demetrius Eukairos was sent to him as a prisoner,

[1] Volume of Plates iv, 8, *m, n*.

[2] Professor Rostovtzeff has suggested in *Yale Classical Studies*, ii, 1930, pp. 41 *sq.*, that the Avroman parchments are dated by the Arsacid Era. There are strong arguments for and against this view; it seems best to retain the Seleucid dating until a Greek document be found certainly dated by the Arsacid Era alone.

[3] xv, 723; see Kiessling, *s.v. Hekatompylos* in P.W. col. 2794. Bits of the Seleucid survey may be imbedded in the Peutinger Table; cf. Tomaschek, *Wien S.B.* 1883, p. 145. The Parthian survey was the basis of Isidore's 'Parthian Stations,' for though Isidore introduces later historical notices he is using a survey made after Parthia acquired Merv and before she lost Candahar, *i.e.* between 115 and somewhere about 75; the variant distances between Isidore and earlier writers given in Pliny may reflect the two surveys.

and Demetrius' last dated coin is 88/7; but in 89 Gotarzes I was king in Babylon, which probably means that he had seized power there in 90, though as Mithridates was king in Kurdistan in November 88 we may suppose Gotarzes only held Babylonia, especially as his wife Asibatum is only called *bilit* (Lady) instead of the usual *sarrat* (Queen). Possibly Mithridates had never really secured Babylonia's willing allegiance. A period of considerable disturbance followed. Gotarzes' known dates are 89, 88, and 87; in 86 and perhaps 85[1] an unknown Arsaces, who *might* be Orodes I, is king in Babylon; by 80 the crown has passed to Orodes I (really Hyrodes), but whether he called himself 'King of Kings' has been doubted[2]. About 77 the Sacaraucae again intervened in Parthia and brought to the throne an old man, Sinatruces, who reigned till 70; again there is a doubt if he was 'King of Kings.[3]' This disturbed period ended with Phraates III, but the classical tradition has two well-attested dates for his accession, 70 and 66. There was however in 68 an Arsaces ruling in Babylonia whose wife Pi-ir(?)-us-ta-na-a is seemingly called Lady, not Queen[4], and whose position therefore was presumably similar to that of Gotarzes; and the explanation of the *two* classical dates may be that Phraates was crowned in 70 but was not king in Babylonia, *i.e.* master of his Empire, till 66. In 64 Phraates is 'King of Kings,' and we again have an established line.

Plutarch calls this period one of civil war, and the disturbance was reflected in large territorial losses. Elymaïs had by 82 secured absolute independence under Kamnaskires II, an independence which his dynasty long maintained. The suzerainty over the Caspian steppes and the Massagetae was not held, though the Oxus was still the boundary between Parthia and the Sacaraucae (Bokhara) and Merv remained Parthian. More important was the loss of Seistan and Arachosia, where somewhere about 75 there was formed that 'Indo-Parthian' kingdom which Chinese writers call Woo-yi-shan-li; its kings ultimately ruled on both sides of the Indus and attained considerable power. Further movements in the East lie outside the scope of this chapter, and with Phraates III the story of Parthia shifts to the western front.

[1] If the *Arsacid* dating in Reissner, Hymn 55 = no. 4 in M. I. Hussey, *A.J. Sem. Languages*, XXIII, p. 142, be the correct one.

[2] J. N. Strassmaier, *Z.A.* III, p. 129, no. 9, read *Sar Sarrani*; E. Schrader, *S.B. Berlin*, 1890, p. 1326, doubted the reading, cf. Minns, *J.H.S.* XXXV, p. 35. Kugler, *Sternkunde*, II, p. 447, no. 26, now supports Strassmaier.

[3] If the Arsaces of the document dated 172 Ars. = 236 Sel. in Strassmaier, *Z.A.* VIII, p. 112, *be* Sinatruces. Minns and Kugler, *ll.c.*, differ as to the title.

[4] Following Kugler's reading, *l.c.* no. 30.

IV. THE PARTHIANS AND THEIR EMPIRE

The stages by which the nomad Parni became the Parthian aristocracy are unknown; they brought nothing with them from the desert but their military ability and their own tolerant indifference, which occasionally recalls the great Mongols. It is however fairly certain that they were Iranians. Their kings' names, with the possible exception of Sinatruces, were all Iranian, drawn from figures of the Mazdean religion; no trace of Turki speech occurs; and even the Sassanids, while on religious grounds they attempted to forget the Parthian interlude and go back to the Achaemenids, nevertheless honoured as an old aristocracy the seven great 'Pahlavi' families, notably the Surēn, Karēn, and Aspahbed, perhaps because these were copied from the seven Persian families. But the Parni were definitely North Iranian, perhaps nearer akin to the Sacas than to the Persians. Their kingdom represented the triumph of the north over the south; but the south they could neither absorb nor really hold, and it was ultimately to overthrow them.

The Arsacid kings were absolute rulers, but the devotion of their followers was devotion to the family, not the individual. The monarchy was elective in the Arsacid house. There were two councils, one of the aristocracy, called by Greeks *probouloi*, and one of wise men and Magi; the councils jointly chose the king, who was by no means always the eldest son. Next to the king stood the seven great families, the right of crowning him being at this time vested in the Surēn[1]; by the first century Greek court titles like Kinsmen, Friends, Bodyguards had been adopted; great feudatories were called *skeptouchoi*. That the principal nobles, who supplied the provincial governors, were called Megistanes is only a deduction from analogy. In Armenia, which was a copy of Parthia, there stood above the governors the four great Wardens of the Marches, representing the four cardinal points; as a relief remains of the four quarters of heaven doing obeisance to Mithridates II[2] (which may mean that, like Cyrus, he took the Babylonian title 'King of the Four Regions'), there must have been similar Wardens in Parthia, representing upon earth the four 'Regent' stars of the Avesta who guarded the four quarters of heaven; they were seemingly called *batesa* or *bistakes*, the same word[3]. The kings had provided their Parnian

---

[1] Surenas is not a title, but a family name like Arsaces.

[2] Fr. Sarre, *Die Kunst des alten Persien*, p. 26.

[3] See M. Rostovtzeff, *op. cit.* pp. 51 *sq.* on this title.

followers with estates—that of the Karēn was near Nihawand in Media—but part of the aristocracy of the Empire must have been the original Iranian landowners; whether any discrimination was made between the two classes is unknown.

Of their society we know little. Polygamy was practised; the kings married their paternal half-sisters, as even some Greek laws permitted, or princesses of other lines, and their queens are sometimes named with them in the dating of documents, and could act as regents; the Greek statement that the Arsacids were sons of Ionian courtesans merely shows that the usual term of abuse in the East is two thousand years old. The queens with non-Iranian names might be daughters of hill-chieftains, another link with the pre-Iranian peoples. Art shows the king's headdress changing from the pointed Saca cap to the domed tiara broidered with pearls[1]; we see the nobles with frizzed hair and long coats of mail, the women with elaborate coiffures[2]; the royal ointment used at the coronation contained 27 ingredients. The nobles ate sparingly and drank heavily, palm wine being favoured; the spacing out of Parthian houses at Babylon, and a chance fragment of Apollodorus, may indicate a fondness for gardens. They kept certain traits of the desert, like blood-brotherhood, and lived largely on horseback. The occupations of a gentleman were hunting and fighting; if a king lived otherwise, he found little favour. Roman authors naturally accuse them of faithlessness, while Josephus (*Ant.* xviii [9, 3], 328 *sq.*) says they always kept solemn engagements; history rather justifies the Jewish writer.

They were a silent race, quicker to act than to talk. Whatever their original dialect, they adopted that form of middle Persian called Pahlavik (Parthian Pahlavi), an ideographic system written in Aramaic, its ideographic methods being borrowed from cuneiform; it was akin to Parsik (Sassanian Pahlavi), and the roots of both systems have been traced to Achaemenid times. Parsik was represented at this time by the legends on the Persis coinage, and definitely belonged to South Iran, while Pahlavik faced northward; both Armenian and Sogdian borrowed freely from it. A lease from Avroman has now supplied a specimen of Pahlavik of the first century B.C.; a later example is the long inscription from Paikuli. The Arsacid records, if there were any, have perished; the Parthians were not literary, and have not left a line or an inscription about themselves; but the influence of Parthian writing on other languages and its effect on the *machinery* of literature shows there was more actual writing than we should suppose.

---

[1] Volume of Plates, iv, 8, *a*; 10, *e, f.*   [2] *Ib.* iv, 18; 22, *a.*

Their writing material was parchment; the mass production of the Pergamum slave factories at first helped here, but later they must have manufactured for themselves; several parchments from Doura and Avroman are known. Parchment penetrated Babylonia and ultimately killed the cuneiform; a 'parchment scribe' is recorded at Uruk. (See also vol. VIII p. 665 n. 1). But more important was the effect on China. The first thing Chang-k'ien noticed about Parthia was that the people wrote on parchment from left to right; the convenience of this made the Chinese dissatisfied with their own writing materials, silk and split bamboo, and perhaps led to the achievement of Ts'ai Lun in A.D. 105—the invention of paper.

The Arsacids entered a ready-made kingdom, and had only to take over the Seleucid administration; and as their peculiar tolerance made them content to utilize Greek work they never created a really strong administration of their own. When the rest of the Seleucid Empire dissolved into a number of Succession States they were satisfied with exercising a loose suzerainty over the others as vassals; later times called the Arsacids 'kings of the sub-kingdoms.' What Parthian suzerainty meant is unknown; neither military contingents nor tribute from their vassals are heard of, though tribute there must have been. Beside the great vassals, there were petty dynasts in the Zagros and doubtless elsewhere. The provinces not under vassal kings were governed directly as satrapies, but the governor's title is unknown; possibly these provinces too were officially called 'kingdoms.' Their number varied with the fluctuations of the empire's boundaries; Pliny's eighteen belongs to a given moment only. The big Seleucid satrapies were broken up into smaller units; thus Parthia-Hyrcania became five provinces, Apavarktikene, Astauene, Parthyene, Hyrcania, Comisene; Media became five; and so on. This subdivision was common to every Succession State, with the possible exception of Persis. Elymaïs contained several eparchies, Bactria several satrapies, Cappadocia ten generalships; the subdivision in Armenia was drastic; even kingdoms like Adiabene and Characene, themselves only fractions of a Seleucid satrapy, exhibit the same phenomenon. Possibly all this subdivision went back to a common source in Seleucid organization; the provinces of Parthia and Elymaïs may represent pre-existing subdivisions of the Seleucid satrapies, administrative units intermediate (contrary to the usual belief) between satrapy and hyparchy[1]. The Parthians kept the Seleucid hyparchies, and the land-registers based on the hyparchy. For registration purposes a hyparchy might contain so

[1] See *Seleucid-Parthian Studies* (above, p. 582).

many *stathmoi*, post-stations on a main road, possibly fortified, with the villages grouped round the *stathmoi*; a vineyard in Kurdistan is described as in the village of Kopanes belonging to the *stathmos* Baithabarta in the hyparchy of Baiseira; in a Mesopotamian hyparchy later no *stathmos* occurs. The Parthians planted military colonies, as, for example, the Mardi at Charax in Media and the Romans at Merv; the Avroman leases, in which non-Iranian names occur, pre-suppose a planned settlement.

The kings must have had officials and secretaries who understood Greek, if only for diplomatic purposes; besides, they had many Greek subjects, and Greek was a common medium of commerce. Doubtless some Parthian nobles and governors knew Greek; Crassus' opponent Surenas spoke Latin[1]; an occasional Greek word may have been used, like 'diadem', which passed from Parthian into Sogdian and later into Mongolian[2]. But to speak a language for purposes of utility does not imply the adoption of the things that language represents, and there is no sign that kings or nobles were really touched by Greek culture; they never even took Greek names, and the hard-worked story that Greek plays were acted at the court is a mere mistake. They were simply ready to take what their Greek subjects could give—to use them as engineers and artists, purveyors of amusements, creators of wealth. The coinage illustrates this[3]. It is a Greek coinage, on the Attic standard like the Seleucid, which uses (though it alters) Seleucid types, dates by the Seleucid Era and (later) by the Macedonian month, employs the Greek language, and gives the kings masses of Greek cult names drawn from the coinage of Syria or Bactria; the persistence, for example, of the Seleucid elephant as a type shows that it was struck for the government in Greek city-mints, for Parthians never used elephants. But things like the adoption by Mithridates I of a *new* title, Philhellene, must be due to the king, who therefore exercised a certain control. The drachmae bore the king's portrait on the obverse, and on the reverse an archer, beardless and wearing the well-known Saca cap, seated on the omphalos like the Seleucid Apollo; the early kings are beardless, but from Mithridates I all the kings have beards, and under Mithridates II the golden throne of the Arsacids replaces the omphalos as the archer's seat; tetradrachms first appear with Mithridates I. The view has indeed been advanced[4] that no king

---

[1] This seems to follow from Plutarch, *Crassus*, 30.

[2] B. Laufer, *Sino-Iranica*, p. 573.   [3] Volume of Plates iv, 8, *a–l*; 10, *a–f*.

[4] J. de Morgan's view (see Bibliography) is supported by M. Dayet, *Aréthuse*, 1925, p. 63, and A. de la Fuye, *Délégation en Perse*, xx, 1928, p. 55.

coined before Mithridates I; but the supposition that the early
coins are a sacerdotal issue of his reign made by a hypothetical
'Scythian' priesthood is, historically, too fanciful to accept, while
the more worn condition of the 'beardless' coins in the Mandali
hoard witnesses to their earlier date. The coinages of Elymaïs and
Characene both begin with kings clean-shaven in the Hellenistic
fashion, and the Iranian beard only appears as Greek influences
weaken; either the early Parthian kings also shaved in imitation
of the Seleucids, or their Greek artists thought it proper so to
represent them.

The centre of Parthian power was populous Media, and during
this period Ecbatana was the capital and summer residence; the
kings wintered in Babylonia, but the foundation of Ctesiphon as
a capital is later. Rhagae-Europus was renamed Arsacia, as was
some town (Asaak) in Astauene; but probably the Parthians had
already too many towns for their liking, and during this period
they built nothing but Hatra in the desert, if indeed they did
build it. The first style at Hatra approximates to the dated Parthian building at Ashur (Libba) of 88 B.C.; it was built as the
frontier town on the route from Babylonia to Nisibis after Nisibis
and Singara became Armenian. There was no Hellenistic planning
about the city of Sanatruk the giant; it was an Arab town, in the
centre of which stood a walled quadrangle, probably fortified,
containing the Parthian buildings and palace; a similar quadrangle
enclosed the Parthian buildings at Ashur. Building inscriptions[1]
assign the palace at Hatra to 'King Orodes'; whether this means
Orodes I or II of Parthia, or a vassal king, is an unsolved riddle.
The buildings at Hatra and Ashur explain why the Arsacids never
made Seleuceia their capital; there was no room for their quadrangle
in the densely populated great city.

The calendar was complicated by the use of two eras, the
Seleucid (in both its forms) and the so-called Arsacid. The Arsacid
kings on their coinage employed the Macedonian Seleucid Era
beginning 1 Dios and the Macedonian months, as seemingly
did Elymaïs, Characene, Adiabene, and Seleuceia; the Pahlavik
parchment from Avroman shows, however, that the Persian months
remained in use in the country districts, as they did in Cappadocia
and Armenia. Babylonia had her own version of the Seleucid
Era beginning 1 Nisan, with the Babylonian months; to this,
after the Parthian conquest, was added the Arsacid Era. This
era assumed that the first full year of the first Arsaces had begun

---

[1] See E. Herzfeld, *Z.D.M.G.* LXVIII, 1914, p. 661.

1 Nisan Sel. 65 (247 B.C.), and was calculated from that date; thus the first full year of Mithridates I at Babylon, beginning 1 Nisan Sel. 171 (141 B.C.), was called Ars. 107. This year, 107, is the first known dating in the Arsacid Era, and, except for one cuneiform document (p. 580, n. 1), possibly due to a scribe's omission, that era never occurs alone but always as a double dating with the Seleucid, usually in Babylonia; a double dated loan contract is now known from Doura[1], but the Seleucid dating governs the transaction. The origin of the Arsacid Era is unknown; for though Greek documents sometimes call it 'as the king reckons,' no instance of its use by any Arsacid king has so far come to light. Nothing prevents the belief that these kings may have used it from the start for their official records, if they kept any; but it also seems possible that it was merely invented at Babylon after the Parthian conquest, to enable Babylon to preserve her old custom of dating each year by the ruler who actually had the power to take the hands of Bel at the New Year festival without having to abandon her newer custom, so convenient for commerce, of dating business documents by the Seleucid Era.

For the country people of Iran the Arsacids signified little but a change of rulers. 'Parthian' art or trade means the art or trade of their subjects; the Parnian nobility did not carve reliefs or bargain with merchants; indeed their total indifference to the sea, which (except the Caspian) they never effectively reached, is most striking. In one way only was the common man affected. He now had rulers who were ready to profess his own Mazdean religion; doubtless this wise policy accounted for much of the support the kings gained at the start. What the Parthian religion really was is hard to say. They brought with them from the desert household gods for domestic worship; they probably, like the Massagetae, worshipped the Sun (subsequently identified with Mithras), whom they invoked before battle; the king was 'Brother of the Sun and Moon[2].' He was nearer heaven than his subjects, and none dined at his table, but that he was a god himself, as some believe, seems more than doubtful. The title *Theos* on some coins may only be the common Greek attitude of the time towards one whom it was politic to honour; nothing shows that the king was a god to his own people, though his *daimon* (*i.e.* his *fravashi*) may have been venerated[3]. Whether the beardless archer on

---

[1] M. I. Rostovtzeff and C. B. Welles in *Yale Classical Studies*, II, 1930, cited above. It is dated A.D. 121.

[2] On many coins the king's head is set between sun and moon.

[3] Inscription from Susa; see Fr. Cumont, *C.R.Ac.I.* 1930, p. 216.

the coins[1] represents the deified Arsaces (Tiridates' brother), founder of the dynasty, or some Parnian god, has been much debated; the earliest Chinese visitors took this figure for a woman, which may mean that they too could get no explanation. It might merely be the Achaemenid archer in Parthian guise on the Greek omphalos, the usual attempt to claim the heirship of both civilizations, as seen in Commagene and Elymaïs (p. 597).

The Arsacids certainly did not follow the teaching of Zoroaster himself, and the Sassanids refused to consider them true believers. They adopted popular Mazdaism, from motives of policy; but they only took what they chose, and the amount grew less with time. The Magian prohibition of pollution of the sacred elements, earth and fire, was not observed, except by pious *individuals*; bodies of enemies were sometimes burnt, and the numerous Parthian coffins, constructed to hold the body, not bones, prove that the Parthians did not habitually expose their dead to the birds; the kings themselves were buried like the Achaemenids. Sinatruces, the one king with a name possibly non-Iranian, *perhaps* married his full sister[2]—the Magian custom; no other case is recorded. The Magi maintained the holy fires, and at Ecbatana sacrifice was offered daily to Anaitis; conceivably they would have been intolerant had they dared, for (whatever its actual date) the fable in which the Persian goat triumphs rather brutally in argument over the sacred tree of Assyria may exhibit their spirit[3]. But the kings, though they honoured the Magi and called them to council, were ready to respect every religion[4]. Greek deities appear on their coins; the Jews regarded them as friends, and proselytized freely; the religion of Babylon spread as it pleased; no local cult was disturbed. But their catholic tolerance may have been due to indifference rather than to enlightenment. One gathers the impression that they thought all religions useful, none material; what mattered to a man was his horse, his bow, and his own right arm.

It was the kings of Persis, ancestors of the Sassanids, who considered themselves guardians of the true Zoroastrian faith. On their earlier coins the priest-king, the 'Fire-kindler,' ministers

---

[1] Volume of Plates iv, 8, *a*.

[2] J. N. Strassmaier, *Z.A.* VIII, p. 112 (= F. X. Kugler, *Sternkunde*, II, p. 447): 'Arsaces, King, and Ishbubarzaa his sister, Queen'; 76/5 B.C. She was possibly however a half-sister.

[3] See Sidney Smith in *Bull. School of Oriental Studies*, IV, 1926, p. 29.

[4] The first great translator of the Buddhist scriptures into Chinese, in the second century A.D., was an Arsacid prince living in China: P. Pelliot, *Rev. d'hist. et de litt. relig.* 1912, p. 106.

before a great fire-altar above which hovers Ahura-mazda[1]; beside it stands the sacred banner of the smith Kava, the Sassanian standard, under which some believe Darius III had fought at Issus. But Persis did nothing to spread the faith, even if the Persian gods on the Kushan coinage in India may have come from her, not from Parthia[2]. Mazdaism was expanding of itself in the western borderland, in Pontus, Cappadocia, Armenia, Commagene, and among the pirates of Cilicia; but what was spreading was essentially the popular belief and its gods, notably Mithras. Whether the later movements of Persian religion and nationality ever began to stir beneath the surface in Parthia is unknown.

The Greek cities of the east had been loyal to the Seleucids while they could be, but when the Seleucid Empire broke up they became enclaves, without any political background; perhaps after Sidetes' death they accepted the position, for in the first century they often contained pro-Parthian parties. Their cultural background, however, remained, and there was no break in their life. They retained their constitutions and magistracies, and probably had just as much autonomy under the Parthian *epistates* (city governor) as under the Seleucid; he was now sometimes not a foreigner but a citizen of the city, even a magistrate, and had certain judicial powers; possibly the 'tyrants' of some Greek cities were really the Parthian *epistatai*[3]. Doura shows that the city registries of deeds still functioned. Mixture of blood had begun, but some Greek communities, like that of Seleuceia, kept themselves purely Greek. Seleuceia, whenever her factions chose to unite, could defy the Parthians; in the confusions of 89/8 her Council began to issue autonomous coins, and apparently some other cities followed. Greek remained a dominant and even aggressive language; inscriptions and coins show that it did not begin to become ungrammatical much before the second century A.D., despite the blundered legends on some coins of Orodes II, due to oriental workmen; the Greek leases from Avroman of the first century B.C., made between natives and drawn up by a local scribe, illustrate its grip even on remote country districts; the law of the Greek cities was never superseded by anything Asiatic. In Babylonia during this century Babylonians continued to take Greek names; there are tablets on which the Babylonian words have been written in Greek for the use of learners[4]; very striking

[1] Volume of Plates iv, 8, *m*.   [2] *Ib.* iv, 10, *g*.

[3] A city might also be under an hereditary feudal governor or *arkapat*; see M. Rostovtzeff, *op. cit.* p. 55.

[4] See vol. III, p. 247 (cf. p. 720 [5]).

is a Babylonian dedication, a living document issuing from a priestly circle, written, not in cuneiform, but in Greek letters[1]. A Greek diptychos from Doura with folded wooden leaves may be the ancestor of the first true book.

Throughout the first century Greek literary activity continued. Apollodorus of Artemita wrote that *History of Parthia* whose loss we deplore. Isidore of Charax compiled a description of the Parthian empire, while his *Parthian Stations* is our best literary authority for the time; Augustus drew on the knowledge of the East possessed by Dionysius of Charax, if indeed Dionysius be not Isidore himself. Archedemus of Tarsus, a pupil of the famous Stoic Diogenes of Seleuceia, set up a school in Babylon. Diogenes the Epicurean visited Seleuceia, as did the rhetorician Amphicrates of Athens; the Seleuceians begged Amphicrates to set up a school among them, but he said that a dish would not contain a dolphin. Herodicus of Babylon, critic and grammarian, interested in the warfare of literary cliques, recorded that he had two homes, Hellas and 'Babylon child of the god'—a recondite allusion to the nymph Babylon as Bel's supposed daughter; Herodorus of Susa wrote the poem whose language and elaborate metre show the vitality of Hellenism in his city[2]. Some Greeks learnt Babylonian; Isidore knew Aramaic; the numerous half-breeds supplied interpreters. No doubt Hellenism was weakening, but in spite of mixed marriages it was not as yet dying. It was probably on the religious side that the Oriental reaction affected Greeks most. At Uruk and Susa Greeks dedicate girl children as hierodules in native temples[3]; in Herodorus' ode to Apollo, addressed by the Semitic name Mara, the tendency appears to merge all gods in the Sun as the sole and supreme object of worship; in the first century A.D. names at Doura are freely drawn from among all the gods and goddesses in the Near East.

The revival of Babylonia under the first Seleucids was working itself out to its conclusion, but Babylonian culture still showed some living strength. Cuneiform writing long held its own against more modern scripts; the last known cuneiform is dated 6 B.C.[4] The astronomical schools were still at work, and the famous Seleucus may have lived into Parthian times; a table for the moon's positions, calculated on the formulae of the older astronomer Naburian, whose name was known to Greeks, was drawn up as

---

[1] W. G. Schilieco, *Arch. f. Orientforschung*, v, 1928, p. 11.
[2] Other Greek poems from Susa of this time are now known.
[3] A. T. Clay, *Babylonian Records*, ii, no. 53; Fr. Cumont, *Délégation en Perse*, xx, p. 84, no. 4, *C.R. Ac. Inscr.* 1931, p. 278.   [4] See vol. iii, p. 247.

late as 49 B.C.[1] Babylonian astrology flooded the world; two first-century Babylonian writers treated of the effect of precious stones on human destinies; about the Christian era the book of Teucros of Babylon, whether a Greek or a native, gave shape to a mass of astrological constellations which for long ruled the skies of Asia[2]. The elaborate ritual of the old gods was still celebrated at Uruk, and they still possessed some activity. Adad and Nanaia became the chief deities of Doura; if Beltra of the Peutinger Table be Adrapana, Bel reached Ecbatana; he did reach Palmyra, and also Cappadocia, where an Aramaic inscription[3] shows the Mazdean religion personified as Bel's sister and spouse—a true allegory, for popular Mazdaism had been much affected by Babylonian ideas, and there was a tendency to equate Ahura with Bel no less than with Zeus. It is believed that the Babylonian New Year festival was even celebrated at Ashur. Certainly to Parthia Babylonia remained a strange foreign land, as Chinese observers noticed; of the things she could give—learning, wealth, prestige—only the two latter would attract the Arsacids. But even Parthia could not entirely resist Babylonian religion; there has been found, attached to the temple of Anu at Uruk, a Parthian chapel intended for some Babylonian cult.

Of Elymaïs little is known. Her symbols, the star and crescent and the anchor (if it be an anchor), may suggest that, like Commagene, she claimed to represent both Achaemenids and Seleucids; a mausoleum discovered at Susa may be the tomb of one of her kings. Her goddess Nanaia, often equated with Anaitis, was one of the most popular deities of western Asia; in her great temple at Azara in Elymaïs tame lions lived in the precinct, as in that of Atargatis at Bambyce. Characene was little but the background of her cosmopolitan trading port, Charax; her kings' names reveal a very medley of tongues and cults, Babylonian, Persian, Elamite, Arab; the Greek element is certain. But if Charax was cosmopolitan, a community farther up the Tigris kept themselves apart—the Assyrians at Ashur. The Aramaic inscriptions found there, largely of the Christian era, show a little body of people, among them perhaps a family of temple priests, still carrying on the worship of Ashur and his consort Serui at the accustomed spot, though the old Ashur temple had been replaced by a Parthian building; save for Nanaia, they worship no other god; their names are purely Assyrian, and Greece and Iran have

[1] P. Schnabel, *Berossos*, p. 244.
[2] Fr. Boll, *Sphaera*; Fr. Cumont, *Rev. Arch.* 1903, I, p. 437
[3] M. Lidzbarski, *Ephemeris*, I, 69.

alike left them untouched; in the third century A.D. there appears among them the name Esarhaddon. It is a pathetic survival of one of the toughest peoples of antiquity.

The revenue of the Arsacids is unknown, but they grew wealthy on their subjects' trade; customs houses and *octroi* stations are mentioned, and there were some very rich men in Babylon. At a later time both Roman and Chinese writers complained that Parthia jealously blocked trade between them, but during our period there seems to have been remarkable freedom of movement; Greek literary men might be at home both on the Ilissus and the Euphrates, and the eastern Jews had free intercourse with Palestine; in Hyrcanus' reign the President of the Sanhedrin was Nitai of Arbela[1]. The mass of Seleucid coins in the Teheran and Mandali hoards attest much trade with Syria, even in its decline; in 55 B.C. Seleucid gold still circulated in Babylonia[2]; the Samaritan trader Eumenes, whom his wife Arsinoe buried near Conchobar in Media, may belong to this time[3]. Chang-k'ien was struck by the keenness of the people to trade, and after 115 trade with China became active; silk came to Parthia, and Chinese figured silks may have appeared in Egypt[4]; Syrian textiles reached Urga in Mongolia[5], and coins of Mithridates II made their way to Karghalik in Turkestan[6]. Parthia began to import from China the famous Seric iron, called Margian because it came in through Merv[7]—a fact very damaging to the theory that it came from the Cheras of southern India. Chang-k'ien took to China seeds of the grape-vine and the Median lucerne; China sent to Iran the apricot and the peach, and subsequently received the 'Parthian fruit,' the pomegranate[8]. The one-humped Arabian camel, domiciled about the Persian desert before Alexander's day, was now used by the Yueh-chi in Bactria; the great Nesaean chargers travelled to Ferghana and thence in 101 B.C. passed to China, where they were called 'heavenly horses'; somewhat later China imported ostriches—'Parthian birds'—from Babylonia. China had long since got her constellations from Babylon[9]; she now

---

[1] M. Mielziner, *Introduction to the Talmud*, 2nd ed. p. 22.

[2] A. Dumont, *Mélanges d'archéologie et d'épigraphie*, 1892, p. 134.

[3] Fr. Sarre and E. Herzfeld, *Iranische Felsreliefs*, p. 226.

[4] Sir A. Stein, *Burlington Magazine*, 1920, p. 3.

[5] W. P. Yetts, *Burlington Magazine*, 1926, p. 168; M. Rostovtzeff, *The Animal Style in South Russia and China*, 1929, Pl. xxiv A, and p. 85.

[6] Sir A. Stein, *Serindia*, III, p. 1340.

[7] Combining Orosius, VI, 13, 2 with Plutarch, *Crassus*, 24.

[8] B. Laufer, *Sino-Iranica*, pp. 190, 284, 539.

[9] C. Bezold, *Ostasiat. Zeitschrift*, VIII, p. 42.

took from Sogdian the names of the planets[1]. Traders too brought their gods; Ma of Comana reached Susa, Isis (seemingly) Uruk. In the first century there must also have been trade communication between Parthia and India, though most of the evidence is later; but the round omicron changes to the square form on coins of the Saca Azes in India in correspondence with the similar change on the coins of Orodes II, and some of Orodes' coins were stamped for re-issue by some Indo-Parthian king[2]. Parthian silver coins remained of good value till after Phraates IV, even while the Hellenistic currencies were depreciating[3].

Whether any bulk of trade passed by the Caspian-Euxine route, at any rate till Roman times, is very doubtful. The main trade road, described by Greek and Chinese writers, came from China through Chinese Turkestan and the mart at Lan-che (Bactra) to Merv, and thence ran Hecatompylos-Ecbatana-Seleuceia; the eastern section has recently been explored[4]. By the first century B.C. the disturbances along the Euphrates due to the Seleucid break-up were over, and from Seleuceia Parthia possessed two main roads westward. One went north through Ashur and Hatra to Nisibis, whence branches ran to Zeugma and into Armenia; the wealth of Hatra, which may be the unidentified Ho-tu of the *Annals of the Later Han*[5], attests the commerce which passed. The other crossed the Euphrates at Neapolis, followed the west bank by Doura to Nicephorium, and thence went up the Belik to Carrhae and Zeugma; the inscriptions on Iamblichus' tomb at Palmyra may suggest that the short cut from Doura to Syria via Palmyra began to come into use about 100 B.C. Between these two roads ran the desert road of the Skenite Arabs, noticed later. In the south, Persepolis became 'the mart of the Persians,' and Persis, which now ruled Carmania and could exploit its mineral wealth, grew rich and luxurious; but there is no direct evidence that the route Persepolis-Carmania-Seistan to India carried much trade, and the omission of this road by Strabo, though he thrice mentions the Persepolis-Carmania section, may be against it. Communication between the Euphrates and Indus is well attested later; but there are indications that, even at this time, trade was taking the sea route to India from Charax and (for Persis) from the Gulf of Ormuz. Some one indeed had tried to improve

[1] R. Gauthiot, *Mém. Soc. Linguistique*, 1916, p. 126.
[2] E. J. Rapson, *J.R.A.S.* 1904, p. 677. See Volume of Plates iv, 8, *l.*
[3] J. Hammer, *Z. Num.* xxvi, 1907, p. 86.
[4] Sir A. Stein, *Innermost Asia.*
[5] Unidentified: E. Chavannes, *T'oung Pao*, VIII, p. 177.

this sea route by establishing agriculture on the Gedrosian coast, the fact hidden behind Pliny's story (*N.H.* vi, 95) that 'Alexander forbade the Fish-eaters to eat fish.'

Art in the Parthian period has now definitely come into view, and some would even assign it a character of its own; there are statuettes, terracottas, and the characteristic glazed sarcophagi. Possibly it meant two distinct streams. One was decadent Hellenistic with oriental elements, like the plaster and painted Victories from Doura[1] and the Ashur steles; the other was a rude native art struggling for expression, as in the figures of the Parthian nobles with frizzed hair. One such noble on a clay mould stands before a definitely Hellenistic goddess (? Anaitis)[2]; the same hand never made both figures. Achaemenid art had been a king's art which died with the dynasty; the Iranian people had to make a fresh start. Where better work is found it is simply Greek, like the coin-portraits of Artabanus II; that of Tiraeus I of Characene in old age[3] and the fine Graeco-Assyrian head of Mithridates I stand alone[4]. Far better than the statuary, seemingly, was the ornamental metal work of the period, as illustrated by the gold and silver vessels of the Treasure of the Karēn, most of them unfortunately dispersed and melted down, which show Greek and Achaemenid influences[5]. For architecture, we now have temples at Ashur and Uruk, palaces (or halls) at Ashur and Hatra[6], a peristyle house at Nippur; in the usual view it is decadent Hellenistic work moulded by Iranian influences; all three orders occur, with a fondness for engaged columns. Parthian tombs, built of brick and barrel-vaulted, have been discovered at Ashur, Ctesiphon, and elsewhere. Persis exhibits a style of its own, said to have been traced right across Asia—square buildings with flat roofs and cupolas. Scanty as are its remains, the art of Iran in the Parthian period was destined, in the view of some scholars, to have no small historical importance. To Professor Strzygowski, who refuses to see in it Hellenic influences, it was destined to play a large part in history through its decisive influence on the art of Armenia; Professor Rostovtzeff believes that its influence can be traced alike in the arts of Palmyra, of South Russia, and of China in the Han period.

This sketch of the empire must end, as it began, with the Parthian aristocracy themselves, for they had one accomplishment of their own—war. It speaks well for a military people that they were not more aggressive; and indeed Parthia was always stronger

[1] Volume of Plates iv, 18, *a, b*.   [2] *Ib.* iv, 22, *a*.   [3] *Ib.* iv, 10, *a, b*.
[4] *Ib.* iv, 24.   [5] E. Herzfeld, *Burl. Mag.* 1928, p. 21.
[6] Volume of Plates iv, 20, *b*.

in defence than in attack. Judging by the Sacas, the Parni brought from the desert two modes of fighting on horseback; the wealthy wore armour and used swords or spears, and their horses had metal breastplates; the common people, when mounted, were light-armed horse-archers. The armoured rider was conditioned by the power of his mount, but once the Parthians had acquired Media and the Nesaean horses this arm developed rapidly. The Nesaean horses had always been a large breed, and the Parthians bred them bigger and bigger till they became the magnificent chargers of the Sassanian reliefs, prototypes of the huge German and Flemish war-horses of the Middle Ages; they had, says Strabo, 'a shape of their own,' and popular literature compared them to elephants[1]. The riders developed their armament to correspond, and by Crassus' time differed little from medieval knights; they wore long coats of mail to the knee, helmets, and mailed greaves; they are described as built into their armour, and rather helpless if knocked off their horses[2]. The horses, too, were armoured, and the spears, which Greeks called 'barge-poles,' had grown enormous. Unlike the medieval knights, however, these 'cataphracts' had one vulnerable spot; as they rode without stirrups, their thighs were left unarmoured to ensure a good grip, and they could be attacked from the flank. Antiochus III, after meeting Parthians, had experimented with cataphracts at Magnesia; the Armenians copied Parthia after Tigranes had raided Media for horses; the heavy armament reached China[3], and Wu-ti sent two armies to Ferghana to obtain a few of the coveted Nesaean chargers; in the hands of the Sarmatians and the Sassanians the mailed cataphract cavalry became the weapon of Asia. It was the arm of the aristocracy, as in the Middle Ages; and the frequent recurrence of one number, 6000, when cataphracts are mentioned in other countries in this period suggests that 6000 was really the full force of Parthia.

But in the first century B.C. it looked as if the weapon of Asia was to be, not the cataphract with his heavy horse and great spear, but the horse-archer with his light horse[4] and bow shortened below the grip for use in the saddle. At some period unknown— it is difficult to dissociate the process from the Saca invasion—

[1] W. W. Tarn, *Hellenistic Military and Naval Developments*, pp. 77 *sqq.*, 156 *sqq.*

[2] See Volume of Plates, iv, 26, *c.*

[3] B. Laufer, *Chinese Clay Figures*, p. 217; M. Rostovtzeff, *Mon. Piot*, XXVI, p. 135; *The Animal Style in South Russia and China*, p. 107.

[4] See Volume of Plates iv, 8, *c*; 26, *b.*

the Parthians abandoned the mixed Hellenistic type of army for the horse-archer; they used no more mercenaries and hardly any footmen, and had no standing army. Their horse-archers, like the Achaemenid cavalry, consisted of the retainers of the landowners and nobles, who followed their lords to battle; the Parthian innovation was to abolish javelin and short spear alike, and arrange that the whole nobility, Parthian and Iranian, should arm their retainers with the bow. From youth up they were trained in shooting; and their method, brought from the desert, of pretending to fly and firing back over the crupper—the 'Parthian shot'—became famous. Greeks called some of these retainers 'slaves,' which has led to the suggestion that the Parthians used Janissaries; more probably it was merely the same misunderstanding which had caused Greeks to call even Achaemenid satraps or princes 'slaves' of the Great King[1], helped by Greeks translating some Parthian term for 'aristocrats' as ἐλεύθεροι, free men (Josephus, *Ant.* xiv [13, 5], 342). By Crassus' time the re-arming of Asia was complete, and a Parthian army consisted of just two formations, the mailed knights and their retainers the horse-archers. It meant that the walls of Seleuceia or the mountains of Elymaïs could defy them; but they were not thinking of Elymaïs, and against walls Greek science might be used. Tradition puts the total Parthian levy of horse-archers at 40,000. The West had small belief in horse-archers; Alexander had not been much impressed by those he met, Lucullus had had little trouble with those of Armenia, and Parthians, it was said, could not fight for long; it was apparently an axiom that horse-archers soon ran out of arrows. But Parthia was to produce a man who realized the possibilities of the long-range weapon if sufficiently munitioned.

V. PARTHIA AND ROME

Armenia has already entered into the history of this period in the Mithridatic Wars (pp. 356 *sqq.*). The story of her rise cannot be told, because it had perished before the Armenians began to write history; the line of Arsacid kings with which their annalists filled the blank is fictitious. Armenia had apparently never been subject to the Seleucids till Antiochus III compelled Artaxias and Zariadris, rulers of Armenia proper and Sophene, to accept his suzerainty and govern as his generals; but they recovered their independence after Magnesia (vol. VIII, p. 514). The country was one of those in which an Iranian aristocracy

---

[1] See A. S. F. Gow, *J.H.S.* XLVIII, 1928, p. 134.

ruled over the native population, as in Pontus, Cappadocia, Commagene, and Atropatene. In the course of the second and first centuries it had close relations with the growing power of Parthia, from whom it borrowed much; it became a copy of Parthia in many things besides military organization.

Mithridates II after his conquest of Mesopotamia attacked Artaxias' descendant Artavasdes, took his son Tigranes as hostage, and ultimately put Tigranes on the throne, taking seventy valleys in payment and marrying his daughter. The confusion in Parthia after Mithridates' death was Tigranes' opportunity; having united Armenia by the conquest of Sophene, he recovered the seventy valleys and took Gordyene, Adiabene, and Nisibis, bringing his Mesopotamian frontier south of Singara; then he invaded Media, burnt the palace at Adrapana, and presumably secured a supply of Nesaean horses (a breed he may have already possessed) for his cataphracts. Parthia was now confined to the Euphrates route to Osrhoëne and Zeugma, until Hatra was built; and Tigranes, for commercial reasons, secured the submission or goodwill of the Skenite Arabs and the advantage of their trade route, which, avoiding cities, ran from Babylonia through the Mesopotamian desert, crossed the Belik between Ichnae and Carrhae, skirted Anthemusias to the southward, and reached the Euphrates opposite Bambyce. Tigranes also made Atropatene subject, conquered northern Syria (in 83), and called himself 'King of Kings'; conceivably this or that Arsaces was even his vassal. He had grown great, and had effectually humbled Parthia.

In 92 Parthia came into contact with Rome: Sulla was on the Euphrates, having settled Cappadocia, and Mithridates II sent an envoy to him with a request for friendship and alliance; both saw with concern the growing power of Pontus. The first relations of Rome and Parthia were consistently friendly; in 73 Sinatruces refused an appeal for help from Mithridates of Pontus, and in 69, after the battle of Tigranocerta (p. 368), Phraates III again sought friendship and alliance from Tigranes' conqueror Lucullus, who recognized the Euphrates as Parthia's boundary. Tigranes now appealed to Phraates for help against Lucullus and offered to restore Gordyene, Adiabene, Nisibis, and the seventy valleys. It was tempting; Phraates hesitated; Lucullus would have attacked him, but his troops practically mutinied; finally Lucullus' successor, Pompey, offered Phraates the same territory and also recognized the Euphrates as boundary. Phraates thereon decided for Rome, accepted Pompey's offer, and invaded Armenia; but he failed to take Artaxata and went home again, and it was to Pompey that

Tigranes surrendered. Phraates proceeded to occupy the promised territory. But Tigranes was now Rome's friend; probably, too, Pompey thought that Phraates had shown insufficient zeal[1]. He ordered him out of Gordyene, and without waiting for a reply sent his general Afranius to expel his men; Afranius gave back Gordyene and Nisibis to Tigranes and marched home through Mesopotamia. Parthia never forgot Pompey's double-dealing; it was the breach of faith of which Surenas afterwards reminded Crassus. Phraates sent Pompey a protest, and received an insolent reply; he thereon again attacked Tigranes. But both kings saw that their quarrel could only advantage Rome; they accepted Pompey's arbitration and made peace; seemingly Tigranes kept Gordyene and Nisibis and Phraates Adiabene. Phraates also lost part of western Mesopotamia, where the king of Osrhoëne, Pompey's friend Ariamnes or Mazares (*i.e.* Maz'ûr), officially called Abgar II, became Rome's ally, as did Alchaudonius (or Alchaedamnus), an Arab dynast west of the Euphrates. It is said that, after Phraates' protest, Pompey thought of invading Parthia, but considered it too hazardous; but the idea, once started, bore fruit later.

About 57 Phraates was murdered by his sons Orodes and Mithridates, and the elder became king as Orodes II. Mithridates soon revolted, drove out Orodes, and struck coins which bore his name, the first Arsacid to do so[2]. The general Surenas however restored Orodes with his private army (p. 607), and Mithridates fled to Gabinius, proconsul of Syria, and persuaded him to reinstate him (55); Gabinius had actually crossed the Euphrates when a more lucrative undertaking presented itself. Ptolemy XI (Auletes) of Egypt had in 58 been virtually expelled from Alexandria on account of the loss of Cyprus and had gone to Rome; there he had gained Pompey's ear, and Pompey recommended him to Gabinius, to whom he promised 10,000 talents as the price of his restoration. Though unauthorized by the Senate, Gabinius invaded Egypt, restored Ptolemy to his throne, and returned to Syria; he was subsequently condemned for his action and fined the 10,000 talents he had received (p. 621 *sq.*). Mithridates returned to Parthia and raised his partisans, but Surenas shut him up in Seleuceia and ultimately (in 54 B.C.) took the city, doubtless with help from within the walls; on Orodes' coins Seleuceia kneels to him[3], and he secured his throne by putting Mithridates to death.

[1] Dio shows that Pompey had attached no conditions to his offer, beyond alliance (XXXVI, 45, 3; 51, 1; XXXVII, 5 and 6).
[2] H. Dressel, *Z. Num.* XXXIII, p. 156. See Volume of Plates iv, 10, *c.*
[3] *Ib.* iv, 10, *d.*

We must turn for a moment to Rome. The conference of the triumvirs at Luca (p. 535), which had arranged that Pompey and Crassus were to be consuls for 55, had perhaps also decided on the conquest of Parthia, to be carried out by Crassus as proconsul in Syria; what passed is not known, but the idea may have been due to Caesar as much as to Crassus, though Crassus welcomed it. Crassus had now turned 60, but was old for his age and rather deaf. He had always followed where others led; he had amassed wealth, but had not achieved either the renown or the popularity of his two colleagues; he had an unhappy sense of inferiority. It has been suggested that his object was the control of the silk trade[1]. The master of Seleuceia would control most things coming from China or India; but, though Parthian gold doubtless attracted him, his principal aim was nevertheless conquest for itself, fame in the field which should put him on a level with Caesar and Pompey in the popular mind. Tradition, right or wrong, says he desired even more than this; he hoped to reach the Eastern Ocean and surpass Alexander. He had read some history, but he probably knew little about Parthia; he thought Parthians were like Armenians, and, misled by Lucullus' victories, looked forward to easy and well-gilded laurels; his one fear was that success might be too easy, thus diminishing the coveted glory.

He began to prepare during his consulate. The Trebonian law of 55 gave both consuls the power of recruiting troops, not only in Italy but in the provinces; but Pompey and Caesar had already had their pick of the youth of Italy, and Crassus had to employ press-gangs and got some second-rate material. His project was unpopular: the Optimates fought him with the cry that Parthia had done no wrong and that to attack her was unjust; Cicero wrote later 'We had no pretext for war,' and indeed all the grievances were on Parthia's side. On the earliest legal day, the Ides of November 55, Crassus left Rome in his uniform (p. 618). The temper of the crowd, led by the tribune C. Ateius Capito, was so ugly that Pompey had to throw the cloak of his own popularity over Crassus to get him away without trouble; and as he passed out of the city Ateius sat in the gateway beside a brazier and with the solemn curses of an ancient ritual devoted him to the infernal gods, the first of many evil portents which, so men believed, attended the ill-starred expedition. He embarked at Brundisium for Dyrrhachium, lost some ships crossing, marched to Syria, and in the spring of 54 took over the province and the troops there from Gabinius. There was still civil war in Parthia, and Mithridates still held out in Seleuceia.

[1] P. Giles, *Proc. Camb. Philol. Soc.* 1929, p. 1.

VI. THE INVASION OF CRASSUS

With the troops taken over from Gabinius, Crassus had seven legions in Syria, with their quota of cavalry and light-armed; it has been suggested that he must have had an even number, eight[1], and left one behind in Syria, but there seems no reason to discredit the tradition. His legates were Octavius, Vargunteius, and his son Publius Crassus, the conqueror of Aquitania, whom Caesar had sent to him with 1000 picked Gallic horse, the best corps he had; C. Cassius Longinus, afterwards Caesar's murderer, was quaestor. Roman cavalry was seldom effective and Crassus knew that he would need more than he had, but for this he relied on Rome's allies; Abgar and Alchaudonius could bring light horse, and Artavasdes of Armenia, who had recently succeeded his father Tigranes, could supply a considerable force. He began operations at once by invading Mesopotamia; the Parthian governor, Sillaces, had only a few men and was easily put to flight, and Crassus occupied the towns along the Belik down to Nicephorium. Most accepted his garrisons, but at Zenodotium, a little place, his men were killed and the town thereupon was stormed; for this exploit his troops hailed him Imperator, a fact which illumines the mentality of both army and general. He left 7000 foot—two cohorts from each legion—and 1000 horse to garrison the cities, and returned to Syria to winter; whether he was training his troops, or whether he desired western Mesopotamia as an advanced base, cannot be said. He has been blamed for not making straight for Seleuceia while Mithridates still held out; but merely to substitute Mithridates for Orodes on the throne was not at all what he wanted.

Crassus was a general of a type which had been common in Roman history—brave enough, obstinate, ordinarily competent, perfectly conventional; he seems to have believed that his business was to bring the legions into contact with the enemy, and the legions would do the rest. His men as yet felt no devotion to him, and he did not understand how to win it. It was his misfortune to meet, late in life, an opponent who had all the imagination which he lacked. Surenas—his personal name is unknown—was a tall young man, not yet thirty, who dressed elaborately and painted his face like a girl; but he feared nothing and had an idea, a dangerous combination. It had occurred to him that archers

---

[1] E. Meyer, *Caesars Monarchie*, 2nd ed. p. 170; M. Gelzer, *Licinius (Crassus)*, no. 68 in *P.W.*

were useless without arrows; this does not seem to have occurred to anyone before. As he was the second man in the empire, and very wealthy, the number of his retainers was limited only by his wishes; and from them he had formed a body of 10,000 horse-archers, the largest force he thought he could munition. They 'always accompanied him,' that is, they had constant training; but the vital matter was his corps of 1000 Arabian camels, one to every ten men, who were an integral part of his army and carried a huge reserve of arrows. For the first time in history, so far as is known, there had appeared a trained professional force depending solely on long-range weapons and with enough ammunition for a protracted fight. Crassus had not the least idea of what he was going to meet; but many Greeks must have known, and the most serious count against him is his neglect of Greek sources of information.

During the winter Crassus recruited some cavalry in Syria, but he did not give his troops the hard training which might perhaps have saved him; he spent the time instead plundering the temples at Bambyce and Jerusalem. In the early spring of 53 Orodes, whose hands were now free, sent an embassy to enquire if it was Rome's war or Crassus' private adventure; if the latter, he was prepared to let Crassus off lightly, as he was an old man. Crassus replied that he would give his answer at Seleuceia, whereon the Parthian envoy held his hand out and said 'Hair will grow on my palm, Crassus, before you see Seleuceia.' Artavasdes also came, with the offer of the Armenian cavalry if Crassus would invade Parthia through Armenia, *i.e.* substitute Ecbatana for Seleuceia as his objective; Crassus naturally refused, for he would merely have been committed to a distant route with an uncertain ally between him and his base. He seems however to have believed that, notwithstanding this refusal, Artavasdes would still fulfil his obligations as Rome's ally; he may have been right, for Orodes believed it also; as he saw it, Parthia was threatened with war on two fronts. He decided that he himself with the Parthian levies would conduct the offensive against Armenia, while he entrusted the defence of Mesopotamia against Crassus to Surenas and his private army, which he reinforced with 1000 mailed knights. Probably the plan was Surenas' own; it ensured easy glory for Orodes, while he himself was safeguarded by his instructions, which were to keep Crassus busy and see what he could do. Doubtless he knew very well what he could do. He took up a position on the Belik between Carrhae (Harran) and Ichnae, where the Parthian and Arab roads to Babylonia intersected; he also flanked the road by Carrhae and Nisibis to the Tigris on the north and the Euphrates line to the south-west, and could intercept Crassus if he came by either route. He had his 10,000 archers, 1000 cataphracts, and a few men brought by Sillaces, who joined him. Even Roman writers, with one unimportant exception[1], never ascribe a large force to the Parthians; as they usually represent Livy, this is greatly to Livy's credit.

Crassus crossed the Euphrates below Zeugma on his own pontoons in a great storm; more portents occurred, and one eagle tried to turn back. He had with him 7 legions, now of 8 cohorts apiece—28,000 men—4000 horse, and 4000 light-armed; after crossing he was joined by Abgar and Alchaudonius with their cavalry. He went down the Euphrates to where the Arab road (p. 603) reached the river opposite Bambyce; there scouts reported the tracks of horsemen going eastward, and he held a council to decide on the next move. Cassius advocated keeping to the Euphrates and carrying their supplies by water, but Crassus was anxious to follow what he believed to be the retreating enemy, and accepted Abgar's offer of guidance. In the tradition Abgar appears as a traitor who led Crassus through the desert to deliver him to Surenas, but his treachery cannot be substantiated. He had been Pompey's friend, and probably lost his own kingdom after Carrhae; certainly he deserted before the battle, but he had learnt by then that the army, being what it was, must be defeated; and he was not dishonest over the route, for he merely took Crassus along the Arab road[2] which the retiring Parthian scouts had followed. It was a regular trade route, in places equipped with cisterns; but it was meant for Arabs and their camels, and it went through desert country for a day and a half before reaching the Belik. The real problem of Crassus' march is why he did not follow the ordinary Parthian road from Zeugma to Nicephorium.

Crassus has been blamed both in ancient and modern times either for not keeping to the Euphrates or for not going through the Armenian mountains, where cavalry could not attack him. Such criticism is idle. If his objective was Seleuceia, it mattered nothing what way he took; by any route he had sooner or later to cross open ground, and Surenas, with greatly superior mobility, could choose his own battlefield. If a general can only invade a country by avoiding contact with its armed forces, he cannot invade that country to much purpose.

Soon after Crassus quitted the Euphrates he met envoys from

---

[1] Vell. Pat. II, 46.   [2] Plut. *Crassus*, 22, Νομάδι λῃστάρχῃ προσήκουσαν, identifies it with the road of Strabo XVI, 748.

Artavasdes, who told him that Artavasdes could send no help, as Orodes was invading Armenia; indeed he begged help from Crassus. Crassus merely remarked that he would punish him later, and pushed on fast, for more tracks of horsemen had been seen. The army grumbled at the hardships of the march; they were soft, and Abgar's sarcasm 'Did they think it would be a route-march through Campania?' was perhaps not unjustified. They were soft, too, in mind as well as in body; every fresh story of the strength of the Parthian bows went home. Finally came the desert belt before the Belik, which tried them severely, and when at midday on 6 May 53 they reached the river between Carrhae and Ichnae they were hungry, thirsty, and weary. No enemy had been sighted, and his officers advised Crassus to form camp by the river, rest the men, and reconnoitre; but his one thought was that the flying foe might escape him. He made the men take a hasty meal in their ranks, and had started southward towards Ichnae when his scouts came in with the news that the Parthians were upon them. Abgar and Alchaudonius promptly deserted with their cavalry and went home.

Crassus had started down the river in line, Cassius commanding on the left and Publius on the right, but he now began to form 48 of his cohorts into square, with small bodies of horse between the cohorts; the left rested on the river, while the right was to be protected by Publius' force—his Gauls and 300 other horse, 500 light-armed, and the 8 cohorts not in the square—which was left free to manœuvre[1]. The other light-armed were thrown forward. But he was in awkward formation, with the square not yet completed, when over rising ground the Parthians came into sight, heralded by the crash of kettledrums, while on their silken standards alien eagles faced the eagles of Rome. Their mailed lancers made one charge, to drive in the light-armed; then they retired behind the archers, and the hail of arrows began. The shield of a legionary was supposed to stop an arrow; but while the Parthians in front maintained direct fire, those behind used high trajectory, and one shield would not meet both. Cavalry and light-armed alike proved useless in counter-attack, and men began to fall; but the army comforted itself with the thought that (as they had been told) the quivers would soon be empty and it would be their turn. But the camel train had already come into action, and the enemy could be seen retiring on it by squadrons for fresh arrows; the army began to lose heart. Crassus had not the cavalry to attack the camels; but what seemingly troubled him

[1] This is F. Smith's arrangement of Crassus' army. There is no certainty.

more was that the enemy, though outnumbered thrice over, were threatening to turn his right flank, and the square was not yet formed. It was vital to complete it, and he ordered Publius to charge and give him room. Publius charged; the Parthians fled, and his eight cohorts followed him cheering for victory; the dust-cloud swallowed up pursuers and pursued, and Crassus was able to complete the square. But once the Parthians had drawn Publius away from the main body they turned on him; his light-armed Gauls, though they fought with desperate bravery, were ridden down by the cataphracts with their great spears, and the rest of his force was then ringed in and shot to pieces. A few escaped and told Crassus that his son was fighting for his life; he moved forward to his support, and met the returning Parthians bearing Publius' head on a lance, a sight which did nothing to restore the army's morale. Crassus himself took the blow with dignity and courage; he went down the ranks, telling the men that the sorrow was his alone: they must stand fast for Rome. Stand fast the square did till dark despite heavy loss, for indeed there was little choice, and with the dark the Parthians drew off; they could no longer see to shoot. Parthians usually camped at a distance from their enemy, for at night, dismounted and unable to shoot, they were very helpless; but this time they bivouacked near at hand. The ancient world had seen generals who, somehow or other, would have attacked that bivouac in the dark and settled the matter while the weary horses grazed; but Surenas had understood his opponents. No one in the Roman army thought of anything but flight. Once the strain was off, Crassus broke down; Octavius and Cassius ordered the retreat, abandoning 4000 wounded to the Parthians, and by dawn most of the survivors were within the walls of Carrhae.

But Carrhae offered no real security, for it was not provisioned and there were no troops in Syria to relieve it. Surenas, whose horses were tired, spent the next day collecting stragglers and destroying four cohorts under Vargunteius which had strayed from the main body; but though he did not appear before Carrhae till the 8th he had ascertained that Crassus *was* there, for he desired now to round off his victory by sending him alive to Orodes. Crassus dared not attempt to reach the Euphrates; he decided on a night retreat to the town of Sinnaca[1] at the foot of the Armenian mountains; once in the hills they were safe from the horsemen. Unfortunately he trusted the wrong man, Andromachus, leader

---

[1] A town (Strabo XVI, 747), not a mountain, as the form of the name shows. Another town called Sinnaca in Hyrcania, Ptolemy, VI, 9, 7.

of the pro-Parthian party in Carrhae, whom Orodes afterwards rewarded with the tyranny; and when he started[1] Andromachus guided him astray, intent on wasting time till daylight. The army, too, was ceasing to be a disciplined force, and was breaking up; even Cassius that night deserted his general and with 500 horse rode for Syria; we may believe that he was thinking not of himself but of the Republic. One officer in that retreat kept his honour, the legate Octavius. He held 5000 men together and reached Sinnaca at daybreak, where he waited for Crassus; but when Crassus presently came into sight on a low foot-hill two miles away, with only four cohorts and the enemy swarming about him, he left the walls and went back to his help. But the expected attack never came. Surenas feared that Crassus might even yet escape; he rode forward with outstretched hand and bow unstrung and spoke to the Roman troops. They had seen, he said, that Parthia could fight; now they should see that she could forgive; let Crassus come down and make a covenant with him, and they should go home in peace. Crassus saw the trick, and begged the men to hold out for two short miles more. But Surenas' offer of safe conduct had destroyed the last traces of discipline or shame; they turned on Crassus, reviling him and even threatening his life; they would not face the arrows again for one who dared not face Surenas unarmed. Crassus knew it was the end, and met it like a man. He went out alone to Surenas; one likes to believe that, as he went, he did say to Octavius 'Tell them at home that I was deceived by the enemy and not betrayed by my own men.' Surenas greeted Crassus and ordered a horse to be brought for him, saying that the definite treaty must be signed on the Euphrates boundary 'since you Romans are a little apt to forget your treaties.' But Octavius and some officers had followed Crassus down, and when the horse was brought they guessed that the Parthians meant to carry him off; there was a scuffle which became a fight, all the Romans were cut down, and in the confusion Crassus too was killed; none ever knew how he died.

So ended one of the worst disasters which the Roman arms ever suffered. Of Crassus' 44,000 men, including his garrisons, some 10,000 ultimately reached Syria and were formed into two legions by Cassius for the defence of the province, and another 10,000 were made prisoners and settled at Merv to keep the Parthian frontier; the rest perished. Plutarch's informant, who loves Parthia as little as he loves Rome, relates that Surenas staged at Seleuceia a parody of a Roman triumph, in which a prisoner

[1] The possible evenings are May 8th, 9th, 10th, or 11th.

who resembled Crassus was paraded in women's clothes and mocked by the rabble as Imperator. Crassus' head and hand were cut off and sent to Orodes, who was at the Armenian capital Artaxata; for his invasion of Armenia had induced Artavasdes to change sides and become his ally, an alliance confirmed by the marriage of his son Pacorus to Artavasdes' sister. Plutarch's story goes that after the wedding feast Artavasdes, who cultivated literature and wrote Greek tragedies, had the tables removed, and a strolling company of Greek actors began to give the last scene of Euripides' *Bacchae*, the death of Pentheus, the part of Agave being taken by Jason of Tralles, a city which had recently suffered much from the Roman publican Falcidius. As Agave came forward with Pentheus' head, Sillaces entered the hall, saluted, and flung down the head of Crassus; Jason laid aside Pentheus' mask, took the head of Crassus in his arms, and began to chant as one inspired 'Blest is the prey that I bear, new-shorn from the trunk'; and when the chorus asked 'Who slew him?' and the answer came 'Mine was the honour,' a Parthian named Pomaxathres sprang forward and seized the head, shouting that the honour was his. The pointed alteration by the chorus of one of Euripides' lines may suggest that the whole savage scene was pre-arranged, while the very different treatment accorded to the bodies of Crassus and Antiochus Sidetes serves to illustrate the hatred which Rome evoked.

Surenas did not long survive his opponent; Orodes put his too successful general to death lest he should aspire to the diadem. The Parthians of course recovered Mesopotamia up to the Euphrates, doubtless including Nisibis and Gordyene, but Surenas' death disorganized the plans for the expected invasion of Syria in 52, and though a Parthian force under Pacorus did enter the province in 51 it was no longer Surenas' army. The horsemen swept through the open country, rousing the discontented, but broke helpless against the walls of Antioch; and when they attempted the small city of Antigoneia Cassius ambushed and defeated them. The new proconsul of Syria, Bibulus, with the help of a disaffected Parthian governor, then managed to render Pacorus suspect to his father, and he was recalled; but part of the army wintered in Cyrrhestice, and it was not till July of 50 B.C. that their last horseman recrossed the Euphrates. But the outbreak of the Roman civil war next year precluded any thought of revenge for Crassus' death; and for thirty years yet the Parthian was to keep his captured eagles.

LIST OF PARTHIAN KINGS

List used in chapter XIV	*The traditional list (from Wroth)*
[Arsaces]	Arsaces? 250–248
Tiridates I. 248/247–after 227	Tiridates I. 248/247–211/210
Artabanus I. Before 208– ?	Arsaces. 210–191
Phriapitius. ? [15 years reign] ?	Phriapitius. 191–176
Phraates I. ? –before 160	Phraates I. 176–171
Mithridates I. Before 160–138	Mithridates I. 171–138
Phraates II. 138–129 or 128	Phraates II. 138–128/127
Artabanus II. 129 or 128–124	Artabanus I. 128/127–123
Himerus. ? 128–? 124 or 123	Himerus. 124–123
Mithridates II. 124–87	Mithridates II. 123–88
Gotarzes I. 90–87	Artabanus II. 88–77
Unnamed Arsaces. In 86 and ? 85	
Orodes I. In 80	
Sinatruces. 77–70	Sinatruces. 77–70
Phraates III. 70–57	Phraates III. 70–57
? Unnamed Arsaces. In 68	Unknown king. Before c. 57
Orodes II. 57–56	
Mithridates III. 56–55	Mithridates III. 57–54
Orodes II. 55–38/37	Orodes I. 57–38/37

Note. Wroth's list, based on von Gutschmid, is merely repeated in the latest numismatic study (that of J. de Morgan in Babelon's *Traité*) with the omission of the 'Unknown king.' The list used in chapter XIV owes much to E. H. Minns, *J.H.S.* xxxv, pp. 22 *sqq.*

CHAPTER XV

FROM THE CONFERENCE OF LUCA
TO THE RUBICON

I. THE COALITION IN POWER AT ROME

WITH the completion of the elections for the year 55 B.C. (see above, p. 535) the control of Rome by the coalition seemed complete. Cicero wrote as much to his brother Quintus, and to Lentulus, the governor of Cilicia. The old unrestricted aristocratic competition for power and profit which seemed liberty was past, but Rome might have internal peace if only the new régime was patiently endured. Cicero himself was for seeking consolation in the study of rhetoric, now that the practice of it in the Senate House, if not the courts, was ineffective or even dangerous. But there were others who were not so resigned, and who saw as little as Cicero did that the interests both of Rome and of the provinces were better served by a strong central control, whatever its origin and methods, than by the abuse of Republican institutions in the name of the Republic. Cato had returned from Cyprus more influential than ever and no less determined to oppose the coalition by all constitutional means. A majority of the Senators acquiesced at least in the predominance of Pompey, the equites believed that Crassus' consulship made the world safe for plutocracy, and the more vocal part of the Roman People were ready to shout and fight as Clodius bade them, but there remained an aristocratic *Fronde* which found its ideals, its self-respect, its ambitions or its feuds irreconcilable with the rule of the coalition and discovered in Cato a spirited leader.

For a time the Opposition had little success. Pompey and Crassus were determined that Rome's government should be carried on, and instituted a series of practical reforms. A law against malpractices at elections was announced, but a proposal, that the praetors at last elected for 55 should not enter office for sixty days so that they might be indicted for bribery, was disregarded by the consuls. Violence and no doubt bribery had been

Note. For this chapter the most valuable evidence is supplied by Cicero's own letters and those of Caelius to Cicero, together with Cicero's speeches and the material provided by the Commentaries of Asconius. On the secondary authorities, Dio and Appian, and the biographical tradition in Suetonius' Life of Caesar and Plutarch, see below, pp. 885 *sqq.*

employed in the interests of the coalition, and what Rome needed
at once was praetors not prosecutions. The appointment of *iudices*
from the three classes of senators, *equites* and *tribuni aerarii*[1] was
removed from the caprice of the *praetor urbanus* and the quaestors of each year. The *iudices* were chosen from among the richest
of each class, who would, on a sanguine view of human nature, be
least corruptible[2]. This led the way to the Lex Licinia de sodaliciis,
in which Crassus imposed penalties on the employment of political
clubs in the interests of candidates for office and did something
to make convictions for bribery more possible. In trials for this
and like offences the accuser was empowered to name four tribes
to supply the *iudices*, and of these four the defendant might
only reject one. Thus a candidate who was not able or willing to
bribe all the tribes, might be tried by men who had not enjoyed
his money. The consuls also arranged for Clodius a *libera legatio*
to enable him to collect bribes due to him at Byzantium and in
Galatia instead of troubling the streets of Rome[3]. A Lex Pompeia
de parricidis, which may be set in this year, further defined the
crime and admitted the penalty of exile for this as for other
offences judged by the *quaestiones* (p. 880).

Nor was the problem of provincial government disregarded.
Pompey raised in the Senate the question of extending the scope
of Caesar's law *de rebus repetundis* (p. 520). But here he could not
well count on Crassus' support, and the declared opposition of
senators and of *equites* prevailed[4]. On the other hand, both consuls
met at Pompey's villa at Alba to discuss financial arrangements
to be made at Rome with the representatives of the tax-farming
companies[5]. What came of the meeting is not recorded; and there
is no ground for believing that the provincials gained by it. The
very scanty evidence is, however, enough to show that the two
dynasts were prepared to work together for a programme of reform, even if that was limited by their own employment of methods
which they condemned and by their pre-occupation with the
careers of themselves and their partner in Gaul.

To Cicero Pompey was plainly the leading man in the coalition,
and probably all men in Rome, except Crassus, thought the same.
The Campus Martius had witnessed the rise of the first stone
theatre at Rome, the gift of Pompey's munificence from the
spoils of Asia. This was now dedicated with games which cul-

----

[1] See above, pp. 338 *sqq.*   [2] Asconius, p. 17 c.
[3] Cicero, *ad Q. F.* II, 7 (9), 2. It is doubtful, however, if in the end
Clodius accepted it. He was in Rome in the summer of 54 B.C.
[4] Cicero, *pro Rab. Post.* 6, 13.   [5] Cicero, *ad Att.* IV, 11, 1.

minated in the slaughter of 500 lions and the chase of 17 elephants. 'What pleasure,' wrote Cicero, 'can it give to a civilized man to see a feeble human creature torn by a powerful wild beast or a splendid animal transfixed by a hunting spear?'[1] Even the brutal rabble at Rome had moments of pity at the spectacle. Adjoining the theatre was built a portico containing a meeting-place for the Senate in which Caesar was to fall at the feet of Pompey's statue. Finally, there was begun a temple to that Venus Victrix who had watched over Pompey's battles and was to be Caesar's battle-cry at Pharsalus.

Caesar, meanwhile, had found that Gaul was not quickly to be conquered, and planned a demonstration in Britain which would impress Britons and Romans alike (p. 559). He was not the man to return home without clearing up the position beyond the Alps, and at Luca he had stipulated that his governorship of Illyricum and Cisalpine Gaul should be prolonged, and that his position in Transalpine Gaul should be made equally secure. At the moment the latter rested only on a *senatus consultum* and in the previous year Cicero had not been able to deny the legal possibility of its transference to another magistrate[2]. Accordingly, Crassus and Pompey proposed a law which conferred on Caesar the governorship of both Gauls and of Illyricum for a period of five years.

Whether this period began before Caesar's first tenure of Cisalpine Gaul and Illyricum expired, and, if so, till what date it ran, is much disputed. There should be no doubt that his first tenure of Cisalpine Gaul and of Illyricum was originally to continue till the last day of February 54 B.C. So far as these provinces are concerned, a law conferring on him a new *quinquennium* beginning 1 March 54 would meet the needs of the moment, but it left the position as regards Transalpine Gaul unsecured until that date. So long as Pompey and Crassus were consuls, they could prevent any proposal to take this province away from Caesar, but in the interval between the end of their consulship and 1 March 54, Caesar's command in Transalpine Gaul might be attacked in the Senate. That the attack would fail was fairly certain in view of Caesar's successes, but it was poor politics not to prevent it, the more as it was known that a possible consul for 54 was L. Domitius Ahenobarbus, who had openly declared his intentions in this very matter[3]. It is, therefore, not improbable that it was arranged at Luca that Caesar should begin his second *quinquennium* in all three provinces before his first *quinquennium* in Cisalpine Gaul and

---

[1] *ad fam.* VII, I, 3.   [2] *de prov. cons.* 15, 36.
[3] Suetonius, *Div. Iul.* 24.

Illyricum had expired. By such an arrangement it would be possible to make the provincial commands of all three dynasts end at the same time. There is no doubt that Crassus left Rome as governor of Syria about the Ides of November 55 B.C.[1], and that date five years hence is the latest date that can plausibly be assigned for the termination of the provincial commands of Crassus and Pompey as secured to them by the Lex Trebonia. From this it would follow, on the above assumption, that the *quinquennium* conferred on Caesar by the Lex Pompeia Licinia ended in the year 50 B.C., possibly on the Ides of November (p. 632)[2]. The two laws were passed almost simultaneously, probably earlier in the year (for there was no good reason for delay), though there is no means of fixing the date precisely. The opposition was not inactive: two tribunes, C. Ateius Capito and P. Aquilius Gallus, were ready to interpose their veto and Cato was prepared to hear interrupting thunder at any moment, but a combination of violence and chicanery defeated their intentions.

The powers given to all three dynasts were very wide, including the right to make war and peace, and to maintain armies of seven to ten legions[3]. This was reasonable as regards Caesar, who had found his present forces none too large, and Crassus, who intended to complete Pompey's settlement by a campaign against Parthia. In Spain there had been trouble with the Vaccaei, but it may be doubted whether Pompey needed so great an army for Spain, so that we may suppose that his establishment was raised beyond his needs in order to put him on an equality with his partners. The duration of the coalition might well seem better secured by equality of strength and of tenure than by the mutual trust and regard of three men of diverse temperaments and divergent ambitions. Caesar desired to finish with Gaul and then return to a triumph and a second consulship, Crassus to win military glory and wealth in the East, Pompey to control Rome by his care of its food-supply and the existence of an army in Spain. Neither Caesar nor Crassus probably expected to spend all the next five years abroad, and we may well suppose that they each felt that they were conquering against time. But whenever either was

[1] Cicero, *ad Att.* IV, 13, 2.

[2] On the vexed question of the term of Caesar's command see the works cited in the Bibliography. Reasons for the view here adopted are given in the *Class. Quarterly*, XXVI, 1932, pp. 14 *sqq.*

[3] Pompey in 49 had seven legions in Spain apart from one previously lent to Caesar, Crassus probably had seven (p. 606). The increases of Caesar's army suggest that he was authorized to maintain ten regular legions in all.

ready to return, he would find Pompey at the gates of Rome if not perhaps in the city itself.

It was true that Caesar could not, without senatorial dispensation, be consul a second time until 48 B.C., but so long as Pompey held by the coalition, such a dispensation could be secured. That Caesar seriously contemplated a period of inaction between his conquering of Gaul and his second consulship at Rome, is most improbable, for with power had come a persistent itch to use it. For this reason it appears to the present writer improbable that the Lex Pompeia Licinia contained a special clause prohibiting the discussion of a successor to Caesar before 1 March 50, which combined with the existing Lex Sempronia de provinciis consularibus might enable him to continue in Gaul until the very end of 49 B.C. (see also below, p. 629, n. 2). This Caesar would not wish to do unless he had much to fear at Rome, and therefore such a clause would have envisaged the complete breakdown of the coalition in a way which is psychologically improbable in a compact made at the moment of its triumphant renewal. It is at least possible that provision was made for land allotments to Caesar's troops when the time came by a law proposed by a group of tribunes which supplemented the land legislation of 59 B.C. (pp. 515 sqq.)[1].

During the summer of 55 both Crassus and Pompey were busy raising troops, and Crassus sent a *legatus* to Syria to take over the province. The levies were unpopular, and their legality was challenged by the opposition tribunes who set on foot prosecutions against the *legati*, whereupon Pompey carried them on outside the tribunes' jurisdiction, and Crassus threatened to use force, until the tribunes abandoned their resistance. Gabinius in Syria refused to hand over to Crassus's *legatus*, a fact which suggests that in this, as possibly in the levy, the consuls were anticipating the date at which the authority granted them by the Lex Trebonia in fact began. But by November Crassus, with his son Publius, seconded from Caesar's army, was ready to set out to make war on Parthia. He solemnly assumed the *paludamentum* which marked the beginning of his command, in the face of the

---

[1] By the Lex Mamilia Roscia Peducaea Alliena Fabia (Bruns, *Fontes*[7], 15). See P. Willems, *Le sénat de la république romaine* 1, p. 498, n. 5, and M. Cary in *Journ. Rom. Stud.* XIX, 1929, pp. 113 *sqq.* This theory appears more probable than that of a praetorian law in 49 B.C., and the law cannot well be no more than a *lex data* of Caesar's land commission of 59. The date (109 B.C.) suggested by E. Fabricius is refuted by E. G. Hardy in the *Class. Quarterly*, XIX, 1925, pp. 185 *sqq.*

obnuntiatio of the tribune Ateius, who had previously declared it *nefas* to begin the war without provocation. The proposal of the tribune to arrest Crassus was blocked by the other tribunes and the new governor of Syria rode out of the city, while Ateius, in one comprehensive imprecation, consigned him with all his army to destruction.

With the departure of Crassus and the end of Pompey's consulship there was more prospect of independent action by Cato and his friends. Cicero was not to be moved from his cautious retreat. The fears begotten of his exile lamed the ambitions born of his consulship, and he had learnt how little real support and sympathy he could look for in the aristocrats. In the courts he was still a power if he used his eloquence to serve the friends of the coalition, as by his defence of Caninius Gallus, a protégé of Pompey and, in the previous year, of Cornelius Balbus, who had enjoyed the patronage of Pompey and now enjoyed the confidence of Caesar. He shunned the Senate except when he went to witness the humiliation of Calpurnius Piso, who had returned from Macedonia after an unsuccessful governorship and did not venture to demand a triumph. Piso had not forgotten Cicero's onslaught on him in his speech on the consular provinces, and gave vent to his resentment in the Senate House. Despite Piso's close relations with Caesar, Cicero indulged in one of those tirades which injured his own reputation more than his victim's. Later Cicero published the speech which we now possess, in which he sought to injure Piso without giving too great offence to Caesar. A retribution quickly followed in the biting pamphlet of which a part survives under the name of Sallust, who may possibly have lent his pen to the service of Piso[1]. In this curious work Cicero's political inconsistencies and instability were assailed with a cold venom which must have delighted those who had been stung by Cicero's sharp epigrams or wearied by his self-praise. A second miscalculation was an attempt to attack Gabinius at the moment when Crassus was alienated from him by the treatment of his *legatus*. Gabinius sent to Rome part of the reward received from Ptolemy, and doubtless made his peace with Crassus. Cicero, who had no love for the triumvir, probably betrayed his feelings and in return Crassus cast

---

[1] See E. Meyer, *Caesars Monarchie*, 2nd ed. p. 164, n. 1, with the literature there cited. Cf. Funaioli in *P. W. s.v.* Sallustius, col. 1934 *sq.* The reference to Cicero's house (2, 2) presents a difficulty (see Th. Zielinski, *Cicero im Wandel der Jahrhunderte*, p. 348), which, however, hardly outweighs the probability that the work belongs to the year 54 or removes the possibility that its true author is Sallust.

in his face the bitter taunt of exile. Estrangement from the coalition at this moment was more than Cicero dared to face; he swallowed the insult and on the eve of Crassus' departure entertained him to a farewell dinner, which perhaps he hoped would deserve its name. Once Cicero set out on the path of reconciliation, no one could be more tactful, and a letter which he sent after Crassus to Syria betrays the careful skill with which he sought to win the protection of the coalition leaders without sacrificing his self-respect[1].

Cicero, then, was not willing to sacrifice himself, perhaps in vain, for political principles which he laid to heart more than he admired those who practised them. Cato succeeded in being elected praetor for 54; one of the new consuls was Caesar's enemy, L. Domitius Ahenobarbus, who was not a leader whom a man of intelligence would readily follow. The other consul was Appius Claudius, a connection of Pompey by marriage, who partly cancelled out his colleague. Pompey was busy with the Roman corn-supply and took little interest in the factious quarrels that filled the courts at Rome with prosecutions. Caesar had disgraced himself and Rome by his treatment of the Usipetes and Tencteri, so that Cato, with rare courage, declared that the honour of the Republic should be cleared by his surrender to his victims (p. 558 *sq.*). But Rome had not conquered the world by punishing successful generals, and Caesar's despatches, wreathed in laurel, were honoured by a formal thanksgiving of twenty days. Caesar, who was no brutal proconsul, eased the smart of his conscience by indulging a hatred of Cato which vented itself in a vehement attack on him sent to be read in the Senate.

II. GROWING ANARCHY

The consuls for 54, Domitius and Claudius, were no friends of the coalition. Indeed early in the year Cicero wrote to Crassus declaring that he had defended him in the Senate against attacks by the consuls. But against Pompey at the gates of Rome and Caesar, who knew well how to transmute his patronage and his wealth into political power, they could achieve nothing. On the other hand Pompey, pre-occupied with the organization of the food-supply and debarred from entering the city by his proconsular command, allowed affairs to drift towards confusion and anarchy, which at the worst would only make his strong hand necessary. Of the more reputable senators Cato alone worked whole-heartedly for good government. His probity earned him

[1] The fact that this letter presents us both the first draft and the finished product was first seen by C. Bardt (*Hermes*, XXXII, 1897, pp. 267 *sqq.*).

the striking compliment that the candidates for the tribunate each deposited with him 500,000 sesterces to be forfeited if they resorted to malpractices, and left him to be judge[1]. Cato's integrity was admired but was not imitated. The four candidates for the consulship were so active in mobilizing the means of bribery that the rate of interest suddenly rose from 4 to 8 per cent. No one of the four enjoyed the active support of both Pompey and Caesar, and the revelation of a scandalous compact made between the consuls and two of the candidates, Domitius Calvinus and Memmius, discredited both the consuls and Memmius, who at Pompey's instigation turned informer about the bargain. A third candidate, M. Aemilius Scaurus, was brought to trial for extortion in Sardinia and it needed all Cicero's eloquence to secure his acquittal. The consular elections were time after time delayed by the intervention of political-religious devices, until it was suspected that Pompey wished no one to be made consul in order that he might himself be made dictator. To the Roman aristocracy domestic politics had become little more than a battleground for ambitions and feuds. The courts remained active, if only because Pompey cared for justice, or at least for the administration of it. Cicero defended his friends or his past or prospective benefactors, C. Messius, M. Livius Drusus, Scaurus, C. Plancius, and glorified himself. He even under pressure from the dynasts spoke for two old enemies Vatinius and Gabinius.

Gabinius had led his army outside his province of Syria in return for the promise of an enormous bribe from Ptolemy and so had brought himself within the scope of Sulla's law of *maiestas* and Caesar's law *de repetundis*. Ptolemy was restored but he failed to pay the whole of the 10,000 talents and earlier loans raised from Roman capitalists, despite the appointment of a Roman C. Rabirius Postumus as *dioiketes* or finance minister to extract from the wretched Egyptians the price of that doubtful boon, the King Ptolemy. The king probably tricked his benefactors or else secretly conveyed the money he had promised, for he later denied that he had paid anything more than the costs of the military operations. Rabirius, this bailiff-chancellor, was, either in reality or in appearance, sacrificed to the resentment of the Egyptians and returned to Rome, in reality or appearance, a poor man and a pensioner of Caesar. Gabinius was placed on his trial for *maiestas*, but by the influence of money and the dynasts was acquitted. He was then indicted *de repetundis*; and Cicero yielded to the insistence of Pompey and defended the man whom he had

[1] Cicero, *ad Att.* IV, 15, 7.

vilified for the last three years. His eloquence may have been half-hearted and it was in vain. Gabinius was condemned, but the balance of the enormous bribe was not to be found and he went into exile. Rabirius was then put on his trial, it being alleged that he had received a part of the bribe which it had been his business to collect. Cicero defended him with better heart, for he had old cause to be grateful to him. To all appearance Rabirius was acquitted and lived on in Rome under Caesar's patronage, appearing as a correspondent of Cicero under his original name of C. Curtius[1].

But Cicero was a disappointed man, and his disappointment might make him dangerous to the triumvirate which had really eliminated him from Roman politics. Caesar had some hold upon him through the employment of his brother Quintus as a *legatus* in Gaul, and through a loan which Cicero later found it difficult to repay and dishonourable to forget. Pompey apparently pressed on him a post in Spain, but the offer did not commend itself to Caesar, and it came to nothing. Nor, if it had become a fact, would Cicero have been long contented. Less important were the two young men of letters, Licinius Calvus and Catullus, who wrote fiery epigrams which stung Caesar but did not move him to lasting resentment.

It was no doubt the fashion in aristocratic circles to belittle the dynasts, but the populace at Rome were easily won to admire the victories of Caesar and the munificence of Pompey who secured them *panem et circenses*. In the summer of 54 Caesar set in hand the reconstruction of the Basilica Aemilia[2], a great work to match the buildings of Pompey. In September the people had an occasion to display their feelings. Julia, Caesar's daughter and the beloved wife of Pompey, died after giving birth to a daughter. Pompey wished to bury her on his Alban estate, but the people carried the body to the Campus Martius and gave it a great funeral. She was to them even more than Pompey's wife and Caesar's daughter: she was the one being who had linked together the two dynasts by a bond stronger than public policy, calculating self-interest, or mere scruples of conscience.

If Caesar and Pompey ceased to be friends, they would become rivals unless they were held together by distrust of the third partner Crassus. This strange bond was soon broken. In July 53 came the news that Crassus and his son Publius lay dead in the

---

[1] H. Dessau in *Hermes*, XLVI, 1911, pp. 613 *sqq.*; E. Ciaceri, *Processi politici*, pp. 197 *sqq.*

[2] *ad Att.* IV, 16, 8.

deserts of Mesopotamia and that a Roman army had been destroyed by the Parthians. Syria itself was in grave danger, although the energetic quaestor of Crassus, C. Cassius, was diligent in organizing its defence. But the *patres* had little time to spare for the needs of the Empire. After a year of intrigues and riots consuls for 53 B.C. had been elected, Cn. Domitius Calvinus and M. Valerius Messalla. Pompey, belying for the moment his alleged intention of being dictator, had induced a moment of order so that elections were held (July 53 B.C.). During the previous winter he had lent Caesar a legion, and he may have scrupled to take for himself alone the open control of affairs at Rome. Caesar himself was no less anxious to keep up good relations with the other dynast, and now, being as willing to sell his hand as to give his heart, he proposed a double marriage of policy. This however Pompey declined, and married some time later P. Crassus' widow, Cornelia, an alliance which brought him nearer to the aristocratic party in the Senate, though his wife's devotion to him to the last suggests that the marriage was one of affection rather than of policy.

Cicero was at this time busy with constitutional theory as set out in his *de Re publica* and *de legibus*. In the former of these works Scipio Aemilianus speaks of the three simple constitutional forms, monarchy, aristocracy and democracy and applauds the equilibrium of them in the consuls, the Senate and the populus Romanus with their several watchwords—potestas, auctoritas, libertas. Laelius urges that to preserve this equilibrium is needed the watchful care of one man, the first man in the State. There had been a time when Cicero had hoped to find the protector of equilibrium in the Concordia Ordinum or the consensus of *boni cives* (p. 506 *sq.*). Now he looks to the presence in the State of a single man—the *rector* or *moderator rei publicae*. It has been urged that this man was in Cicero's eyes Pompey himself. Cicero began to write in May 54 and, after two changes of plan, had finished the work just before he set out to Cilicia in 51[1]. During that period he found much in Pompey to disillusion him, and it is not easy to imagine that the strong hand of Pompey restoring order by force was to him the hand of the *rector rei publicae* guiding the State by wisdom. There is nothing to show that Cicero's *moderator* was to possess military power: he was to be a statesman and a philosopher, and we may not be doing him an injustice if we

---

[1] Cicero, *ad Att.* IV, 14, 1 and *ad Q. F.* III, 5 and 6, 1; *ad Att.* V, 12, 2; Caelius, *ad fam.* VIII, 1, 4.

suppose that this figure, so far as it is not a thing of theory alone, is the figure of Cicero himself[1].

Before the *de Re publica* was finished, Cicero had taken in hand his *de legibus*, most of which was written in the year 52 B.C., though the treatise was probably finished after his return from Cilicia. Defective as is the work that has come down to us, it displays the Roman instinct for law and the balanced judgment of institutions which Cicero possessed, once his egotism and vanity were set aside. It is one more piece of evidence for the fact that the last sixty years of the Republic were not simply the scene for personal ambitions and partisan policies but an age in which the outstanding figures, Sulla, Pompey, Cicero and Caesar concerned themselves with practical questions of reform.

III. POMPEY'S THIRD CONSULSHIP

The election of one pair of consuls was immediately followed during the autumn and early winter of 53 by a long-drawn struggle about the choice of their successors. Cornelia's father Q. Caecilius Metellus Scipio and P. Plautius Hypsaeus, who had served under Pompey in the East, were candidates, and both doubtless enjoyed the support of the coalition. But they had a formidable rival in T. Annius Milo, a hot-blooded nobleman of Samnite descent who loved violence and enjoyed, for what it was worth, the support of Cicero, who could not forget that Milo had proved his friend by proving himself the enemy and rival in violence of Clodius. Cicero's zeal was whetted by the fear that Clodius would be elected praetor and pursue his vendetta from the seat of justice. Unwilling to use force without a formal commission and not unwilling to see himself once more indispensable, Pompey allowed the elections to be made impossible by riots until on 18 January 52, Milo had Clodius killed after an affray on the Via Appia. Clear-sighted in his appreciation of the directest methods of Roman politics, an aristocrat clever enough to match Cicero yet ridden by a perverse desire *s'encanailler*, Clodius was not born to die in his bed, yet his death shook the Republic. The Senate House itself was burned as a pyre for his body. No ordinary consuls could restore order between the bands of partisans, and the extremist aristocrats no less than the mass of the people perforce turned to Pompey. The Senate called upon the interrex, the tribunes, and the proconsul Pompey to save the State. At the word Pompey's indecision fell from him: he raised

[1] E. Ciaceri, *Il Trattato di Cicerone 'De republica,'* etc., Rend. d. R. Accad. dei Lincei, XXVII, 1918, p. 312.

troops and prepared to enter the city. Rome wanted order, not a new Sulla: that most rigid constitutionalist Bibulus proposed that he should be made not dictator but consul without a colleague, and Pompey was content.

The trial of Milo, if conducted by the usual procedure, was certain to provoke long-drawn disorder. Pompey, therefore, with the approval of the Senate promulgated a law *de vi*, in which not only the killing of Clodius was mentioned but also the scenes of violence which had followed it. He also put forward a law *de ambitu* which was to punish the wholesale bribery which had preceded the murder[1]. The effect of both measures was to shorten trials and to make bribery almost impossible. The laws were passed, and on 4 April Milo was brought to trial. Pompey had taken measures to ensure that the jury should consist of men of known probity, and, on the closing day, on which Cicero's eloquence was to defend Milo, the shouts of Clodius' followers were followed by the disciplined violence of Pompey's soldiers. Inter arma silent oratores. Cicero did not wholly fail his client, but the speech which he delivered was far less impressive than the oration which he had prepared and which he afterwards published. It was easy to prove that Milo had no more intention of killing Clodius on 18 January than on any other day and that Clodius would not for a moment have hesitated to kill Milo, but constructive self-defence could hardly cover the slaughter of a man already defeated and wounded, and, given a fair trial, no eloquence could have averted the verdict of condemnation. Out of 51 judges only 13 were for acquittal and Milo went into exile at Massilia to enjoy the culinary resources which even then that city boasted, while his enemies and his creditors continued to wrangle over his other misdeeds and his estate. The young Brutus did not hesitate to defend Milo's act as defending not himself but the State—a defence that must have moved his client to the same cool irony with which he thanked Cicero for sending him the speech which he would have delivered.

Other trials followed. Milo's lieutenant Saufeius, charged with having led the band which actually ended Clodius, was acquitted by a single vote on that charge, and, later on, another together with M. Terentius Varro Gibba. Both owed their escape to Cicero, who showed great constancy and no small courage. Gratitude

---

[1] This law cannot well have been retrospective as far back as 70 B.C., so as to include the elections for 59 (and 55), despite the statement of Appian, *Bell. Civ.* II, 23, 87, and a possible inference from Plutarch, *Cato min.* 48, 2. See A. C. Clark's *Cicero, pro Milone*, pp. xii *sqq.*

with him outweighed the risks of unpopularity and alienation from Pompey. Pompey, having dealt with Milo, was no less coldly just to the supporters of Clodius who had filled Rome with riot and arson. The most notable, including Sextus Clodius, Hypsaeus, and the two tribunes, Q. Pompeius Rufus and T. Munatius Plancus, were condemned. Among these were men who had served Pompey well, but for only one of them, Plancus, did he intercede, and that in vain.

The position of Pompey during these months, the combination of consular power with the proconsular *imperium*, has justly been compared with that of Augustus between the years 27 and 23 B.C.[1] But although there is enough likeness to supply a kind of precedent, it must be remembered that both to the Senate and to Pompey the combination was transient and without any deep constitutional meaning. The power of Pompey in Spain was, in practice, matched by that of Caesar in Gaul, and the fact that before the year was over the Senate re-affirmed Pompey's government of the two Spains suggests that the incompatibility of his two offices was not overlooked. Rome had what it needed, a strong hand restoring order and removing abuses, not an autocrat: neither in theory nor in fact did the Republic witness a *Pompeianum regnum*. It was Pompey's task to protect the normal machinery of State from paralysis, and his success in achieving it made him the possible refuge of constitutionalists.

In July or August Pompey had associated with himself as colleague in the consulship his father-in-law, Metellus Scipio. During the summer Caesar had been fighting hard in Gaul, until at last, after a serious reverse before Gergovia, he had besieged Vercingetorix in Alesia, beat off a relieving army and compelled his surrender. Not even Caesar could have found much time to give to Roman politics, and in general Pompey acted with little regard for his interests. During the previous winter the way had been prepared for a special law to allow Caesar to be a candidate for the consulship *in absentia*, and in the first half of 52 B.C. the measure was passed on the proposal of the whole college of tribunes. Cicero smoothed its path at the request both of Caesar and of Pompey. As the law was prepared at a time when Caesar undoubtedly expected to be soon secure in the control of Gaul, it may fairly be assumed that it was applicable in any of the following years, and not only in 49 B.C. when the regular decade since his last election to the consulship expired. Possibly it remained necessary to secure a dispensation from the Senate of the usual ten

[1] Most recently by W. Kolbe in *Aus Roms Zeitwende*, p. 53.

year rule, but that Caesar might fairly count upon if the coalition continued to exist, and its breakdown was as yet not certain[1]. A question, however, of the validity of the law of the Ten Tribunes soon arose. Pompey passed a measure *de iure magistratuum* which contained a clause re-enacting the obligation of a candidate for office to attend in person. The point was taken that this law cancelled the special right conferred on Caesar, whereupon Pompey, alleging forgetfulness, inserted in the law after it had been passed and placed in the State archives a special exception in favour of Caesar's right. It may be that Pompey's forgetfulness was after Gergovia and his repairing of it after Alesia, though there is no independent evidence of the coincidences in time, and it is more probable that Pompey had never intended to invalidate Caesar's *privilegium*, to which he himself had given his support. It might fairly be urged that if the *privilegium* had been valid against the existing law, it continued valid against a later repetition of it.

Pompey further passed a law to implement a resolution of the Senate in the previous year[2], providing that ex-consuls and ex-praetors should not proceed to provinces until five years had elapsed since their term of office at Rome. The senatorial resolution had been intended to reduce the avidity with which men bribed their way into office as a speedy passage to a rich province, and there is no need to suppose that Pompey had any other motive. It is true that incidentally it repealed the Lex Sempronia of Gaius Gracchus which provided that the consular provinces should be named by the Senate before the election of the consuls who were later to govern them (p. 63 *sq.*). The repeal was amply justified by the needs of the State. With the constant possibility of serious warfare with Parthia and the existence of a new power in Dacia the leisurely machinery of the second century was out of place. Furthermore, the Lex Sempronia had exempted the action of the Senate in respect of consular, though not praetorian, provinces from the tribunician veto. That exemption was a practical necessity if the Senate were to be able to make their decision before the elections (the more as the consideration of the provinces could not well begin until after February, the month reserved for the hearing of foreign embassies). The need for reaching a decision before the elections had now disappeared, and in the new law the tribunician veto was not ruled out. There is no good reason to suppose that the law was directed against Caesar. It is true that it made

[1] It might further be argued that, since Caesar's command in Gaul was due to end before the election of 49 B.C., the leave to be candidate *in absentia* implied permission to be candidate in an earlier year.   [2] Dio XL, 46.

possible the sending out of a successor from the *consulares* as soon as his legal term expired, but only if no tribunician veto was interposed, and this same veto was already Caesar's only protection, once his term of government expired, if the Senate decided to make his provinces praetorian.

The passage of this law left a hiatus in the succession of governors, and to fill this the Senate called on the services of ex-magistrates who had not proceeded to provinces. Cicero, much against his inclination, was made governor of Cilicia for a year from the summer of 51. Cicero's reluctance is no proof that the Senate was unwise in thrusting this task on him. He found a competent soldier, C. Pomptinus, to assist him in warfare, and otherwise his administration proved competent as well as honest. At the same time Caesar's old colleague and opponent Bibulus was appointed to Syria to relieve Cassius (p. 612).

Pompey, meanwhile, by being consul at Rome had, according to strict practice, ended his proconsular government in Spain and so the Senate, to make an honest proconsul of him, voted his command in Spain, not for the remainder of his term but for a further period of five years beginning apparently in 52 B.C. This act put him at a possible advantage over Caesar and upset any parity of command that may have been arranged at Luca (p. 616). On the other hand, Caesar had no desire for a further prolongation in Gaul, except so far as would cover him until after the election of 49 B.C., when, if not before, he intended to be a candidate for the consulship *in absentia* by virtue of his *privilegium*. To secure this prolongation he needed the active support of Pompey, who however was drifting away from the coalition and towards the senatorial leaders, who had at last recognized his merits as the protector of order and good government. These in turn saw an opportunity to weaken the coalition by playing on the selfishness of Pompey, who must by now have grown jealous of the rise of a second military reputation of the first order, emphasized by the vote of yet another thanksgiving for victory in Gaul. A sudden *volte-face* was alien to Pompey's character: it would be long before he could be brought to an open breach with Caesar, but those who did not look forward to a year like 59 B.C. and regarded Caesar as the leader of disreputable careerists began to hope that they could bring him down between the time that he was governor in Gaul and his election as consul. For it was apparently taken as certain that his electioneering skill backed by the wealth of Gaul and the votes of North Italy would secure him the consulship if he got as far as an election.

IV. THE BREAKDOWN OF THE COALITION

At the consular elections for 51 M. Claudius Marcellus and Ser. Sulpicius Rufus were elected, the latter a mild jurist, the former a violent conservative. Cato, who was a candidate, failed to be elected. When the next year began Caesar asked for a brief extension of the term of his command, and the Senate refused it[1]. Pompey, it is to be presumed, remained silent. Encouraged by this, the consul Marcellus ventured to propose to the Senate the question of superseding Caesar and terminating his command[2] on the plea that the war in Gaul was over and the veterans in his legions could fairly claim their discharge. The action was not justified by the military situation, and to approve it violated the Lex Pompeia Licinia unless a new law was passed to shorten the term there provided. He further challenged the validity of the law of the Ten Tribunes, asserting that Pompey's law made it of no effect[3]. This was going too far: his colleague declared that a governor who committed no crime could not be deposed from his command before his legal term had expired, and the tribunes who were on Caesar's side interposed their veto. Pompey himself opposed Marcellus and hinted his intention of going to Spain. This caused perturbation to Cicero in Cilicia[4], and presumably to the Optimates at Rome. Pompey was further put out of humour by the aggression of Marcellus in scourging a citizen of Novum Comum to show his contempt for Caesar's establishment of citizen colonies in the Transpadane area[5]. Pompey might well take umbrage at this act, for his family had been responsible for the partial enfranchisement of that region (p. 195 *sq.*).

To go further might well lead only to a second conference of Luca, and even the most hot-headed of Caesar's enemies practised patience. As Caelius wrote to Cicero—'Marcelli impetus resederunt, non inertia sed, ut mihi videbantur, consilio'[6]. But Pompey's growing reluctance to make smooth the path of Caesar had not removed his unwillingness to be actively disloyal to his old political ally, and the result was a compromise. A resolution of

---

[1] Appian, *Bell. Civ.* ii, 25, 97; Plutarch, *Caesar*, 29.

[2] Apparently on 1 March 50. *ad Att.* viii, 3, 3; Hirtius, *B. G.* viii, 53; Suetonius, *Div. Iul.* 28; Dio xl, 59, 1. The assumption often made that in March 51 Roman politicians were pre-occupied with what might happen in 49 does more or less than justice to their methods. The fact that Marcellus repeatedly brought the question before the Senate in 51 is sufficient proof that the Lex Pompeia Licinia did not forbid its discussion before 1 March 50.

[3] Suetonius, *loc. cit.*   [4] *ad fam.* iii, 8, 10.

[5] *ad Att.* v, 11, 2.   [6] *ad fam.* viii, 2, 2. (June 51.)

the Senate was passed on the last day of September advising the consuls of the next year to raise the question of a successor to Caesar on 1 March, the earliest date on which the provinces and their future governors would normally come under review.

It was hoped that when the time came a successor to Caesar might be appointed at once, who would take over his provinces as soon as the term set by the Lex Pompeia Licinia expired. But there was one hindrance to the programme: it was not that Caesar would refuse to make way for a legally appointed successor, for that would bring him within the scope of the law *de maiestate*, it was that a tribune would be found to prevent the Senate from making the appointment. What tribunes could do had already been shown by the failure at that very session to pass three decrees, the first that tribunes should not interfere with the allotment of provinces, the second to permit soldiers in Caesar's army to apply to the Senate for their discharge, the third to send ex-praetors to Cilicia and the other provinces with the exception of those held by Pompey, Caesar and Bibulus as consular[1]. Pompey's statement that it was the same thing for Caesar to disobey a decree and prevent the Senate passing a decree can have convinced few who did not wish to be convinced. Nor was his reply to another suggestion more satisfactory. 'What if Caesar wishes to be consul and to retain his army?' And he replied mildly 'What if my son raises a stick to strike me?'

What was believed was that Pompey's attitude would cause Caesar to acquiesce in an arrangement either to remain in Gaul and not be a candidate in the year 50 or, if he could be elected consul for 49, to leave his province[2]. This amounted to an offer that if the candidature *in absentia* granted him by the law of the Ten Tribunes was accepted and was successful, he would take no steps to obstruct the appointment of a successor to his provinces and would hand them over in order to return to Rome shielded from his enemies by his position as consul designate. If the Senate refused to supplement the law with a dispensation of the rule about the interval between the consulships to enable Caesar to be candidate in 50 B.C., they would find that the appointment of a successor could not be carried through.

The issue indeed was becoming plain. Caesar claimed that the constitution should be worked in his favour, as it had been worked

---

[1] *ad fam.* VIII, 8, 6–8.

[2] 'Ut aut maneat neque hoc anno sua ratio habeatur aut, si designari poterit, decedat,' *ad. fam.* VIII, 8, 9—'hoc anno' must, in the present writer's view, refer to the elections of the year 50 B.C.

in favour of Pompey; Caesar's enemies were resolved to make no concession; Pompey, though too scrupulous to go back upon his open obligations to Caesar or to allow any abrogation of the law which bore his name and that of Crassus, was willing to see Caesar's plans for a second consulship thwarted. This willingness he revealed just sufficiently to prevent Caesar's implied offer from being accepted. There were men who hoped that an arrangement would be reached. In December 51 Cicero, who had by now received news of the Senate's session, wrote to Atticus in terms which suggest that that shrewd observer had expressed hopes that Caesar would give way[1]. But Caesar had no intention of doing any such thing. If he was not allowed to be candidate in 50 B.C., a candidature for which he had already made some preparations in Cisalpine Gaul[2], then he would resort to tribunician obstruction. For that he needed the services of a tribune who would not be daunted either by the dominant party in the Senate, or, if it came to that, by Pompey, and who would be able to keep before the *patres* (many of whom wanted the preservation of peace far more than the destruction of Caesar) the reasonableness of his demands. He therefore offered a career to a tribune hitherto hostile, C. Scribonius Curio, a young man who rivalled his own youth in debts and ambitions. The choice was shrewdly made: though several of the other tribunes were in Caesar's interest, it was Curio who bore the brunt of the battle. Of the two consuls elected for 50 C. Claudius Marcellus C.f., although married to Caesar's great-niece Octavia, was firmly opposed to him. His colleague L. Aemilius Paullus was less stalwart, and finally Caesar's offers reached the high value which this nobleman placed on his political integrity.

Early in the year 50 Curio went over openly to Caesar. During the winter Cicero had hoped that Pompey would be sent out to command in Syria against the Parthians. What the proconsul was anxious about was his own return from his province, and, clearly with some qualms of conscience, he prepared to leave Cilicia as soon as his year was up in July 50. The activities of Curio in preventing discussion of the provinces, of which news reached him sent from Rome at the end of March or soon after, troubled him, but he apparently thought that there would not be a dangerous crisis if Pompey stood firm[3]. The question of the provinces and of a successor to Caesar should have come up on

---

[1] *ad. Att.* v, 20, 8. 'Iucunda de Caesare et quae senatus decrevit et quae tu speras; quibus ille si cedit, salvi sumus.'

[2] *ad Att.* v, 2, 3; *ad fam.* VIII, 1, 2.

[3] *ad Att.* VI, 3, 4.

1 March, but Curio prevented any decision, and in April or early in May Caelius wrote to Cicero to explain the political situation as he saw it[1]. By this time it had become clear to Caelius that either Curio would be allowed to maintain his veto, which meant that Caesar would remain in his province as long as he wished, or that if pressure was put on Curio Caesar would defend him. Pompey and the Senate united to insist that Caesar should leave his province on the Ides of November of the current year[2]. Curio was firm in opposing this. Pompey affected to be acting fairly by Caesar, but it was clear that he was anxious to prevent him from retaining his army and provinces until he was elected consul (*i.e.* the summer of 49 B.C.).

Meanwhile Caesar was in winter-quarters in Gaul, well satisfied, we may assume, that Curio's action made his interests secure. It was, however, important that when Curio's tribuneship expired on 9 December 50 another strong tribune should take his place. Caesar's candidate was Antony, who left the army in Gaul in good time to present himself for the elections. For the consulship Caesar now put forward Ser. Sulpicius Galba and mobilized in support of both voters from the townships of Cisalpine Gaul. Meanwhile the orator Hortensius fell ill and died, causing a vacancy in the college of augurs, whereupon Antony decided to be a candidate. The extreme aristocratic party which was opposed to Caesar and Caesar's lieutenant prepared to support energetically L. Domitius Ahenobarbus at the augural election, which would follow those for the tribunate and the consulship. At the same time the news from Syria was bad and a serious Parthian invasion of the province was feared. The governor Bibulus plainly might need reinforcements, and, probably in May, the Senate voted that Caesar and Pompey should each contribute one legion to be sent to Syria. The action was in itself justified. Caesar's war in Gaul was over; Pompey's war in Spain had not even begun. Nor could Caesar complain when Pompey offered as his contribution the legion which he had lent to Caesar two years before. Without undue delay the two legions were detached, the First from Southern Gaul, the Fifteenth from Cisalpine Gaul, and sent south so that they reached Rome in the autumn. The threatened Parthian invasion came to nothing, and the two legions were not restored to Caesar but were sent to winter quarters in Campania.

---

[1] *ad fam.* VIII, 11, 3.

[2] It appears to the present writer probable (though not certain) that this was the date up to which Caesar's governorship was explicitly secured to him by the Lex Pompeia Licinia; see above, p. 617.

V. THE FINAL CRISIS

In Gaul, meanwhile, Caesar had good reason to believe that order was secured and, presumably on receiving word from Antony of his candidature for the augurship and the gathering opposition to it, he decided to hasten to Northern Italy. The election to the augurship was to be a trial of strength, and he was also anxious to help his lieutenant, on whose zeal and courage much would depend later. Moreover, if all went according to plan, Cisalpine Gaul would be the base of his own political campaign for the consulship elections in the year 49. The elections were held by the end of July[1], and before Caesar reached North Italy he was met by the news that Antony was successful in both his elections but that Galba had failed, and the new consuls-elect L. Lentulus and C. Marcellus M.f. were his declared enemies. It was clear that Pompey had not bestirred himself to assist Caesar's nominee in that election, and accordingly Caesar devoted himself for a while to the confirming of his popularity in Cisalpine Gaul. He then left Labienus in charge of that province and recrossed the Alps to rejoin his legions, which were concentrated for a review which was a farewell if all went to their general's liking and a pledge of their support if he had to face the Roman State in arms. The Thirteenth legion was ordered to Cisalpine Gaul to replace the Fifteenth and to be at hand in a crisis. By the middle of November 50 B.C. Caesar had posted his other regular legions in winter quarters, four under Trebonius among the Belgae, four under C. Fabius among the Aedui. This distribution, though not unprovident, was unprovocative. Caesar was careful to avoid the appearance of leaning upon armed force, for he had no desire to precipitate a crisis, the more as he knew that Rome was the prey to rumour; indeed, in September there had been a scare that he intended to occupy Placentia with four legions on 15 October[2].

It was indeed true that the situation had steadily become more dangerous. Curio had firmly maintained his veto, and in June the consul C. Marcellus had failed to secure a vote of the Senate to put moral pressure upon him. Pompey, who had earlier been unwilling to allow to Caesar anything more than the law which bore his name granted him, wavered from day to day. The consul-elect Lentulus was suspected of intending to serve Caesar's

---

[1] See F. W. Sanford, *Nebraska Univ. Studies*, XI, 1911, no. 4.
[2] Cicero, *ad Att.* VI, 9, 5.

interests. The summer might have seen a new conference of Luca, which would impose on Rome Caesar as consul in 48 with Pompey abroad in Spain or in Syria. But the time for that passed, and with the Ides of November came what is here assumed to be the expiry of Caesar's term as defined in the Lex Pompeia Licinia. Yet, according to the practice, he remained in his province as governor so long as no successor was appointed, against Curio's veto the Senate were helpless, and when 10 December came there was Antony ready to take Curio's place. In May Pompey had fallen sick and lay ill in Campania where he was restored to confidence before he was restored to health by public expressions of goodwill.

By this time Curio had added a refinement to his tactics. Whether with Caesar's approval or not[1], he constantly proposed that the Senate should pass a resolution that both Caesar and Pompey should give up their armies. The proposal commended itself to that great majority who wished to avoid a civil war at all costs. But Pompey could not bring himself to make a firm declaration of acquiescence, and the anti-Caesarian party plainly suspected a trap. In August[2] Caelius believed that within a year it would come to an open war between the two dynasts unless one of them went off to fight the Parthians, though he also believed that there was still time to wait and see which side would prove to be the stronger. In October Cicero, now at Athens on his return journey, began to fear that he would return to a civil war and found little to comfort him in the letters which he received both from Caesar and Pompey.[3] Caesar's claim was that the law of the Ten Tribunes gave him the right to be a candidate for the consulship *in absentia*, to which he apparently added as a corollary that he could retain his governorship and his army until he had exercised that right. Such a claim was plausible but it was no more[4].

When his governorship under the Lex Pompeia Licinia expired, his right to be a candidate *in absentia* could not deter the

---

[1] The fact that Hirtius, *B. G.* VIII, 52, 4, writes as if Curio was making this proposal at Caesar's instance is not proof. It was, perhaps, a dangerous offer to make. If Pompey had openly accepted it, Caesar was somewhat awkwardly placed. It looks more as if Curio got Caesar's approval later; see also *B. C.* I, 9.

[2] See Sanford (*op. cit.* p. 35), who establishes a date early in August for *ad fam.* VIII, 14.

[3] *ad fam.* XIV, 5, 1; *ad Att.* VII, 1, 3.

[4] The soundness of Caesar's contention is not proved by Cicero's laments that he had been granted so much already—'Quid ergo? exercitum retinentis, cum legis dies transierit, rationem haberi placet? Mihi vero ne absentis quidem; sed cum id datum est, illud una datum est.' *ad Att.* VII, 7, 6.

Senate from appointing a successor or debar that successor from
taking over his army and his provinces. The bar to that lay in the
persistent use of a tribune's constitutional right to prevent by his
veto the Senate from doing its constitutional duty, and, once the
last day of Caesar's legally secured term had passed, this tribunician obstruction was really a challenge to the constitution. The
interests of the Republic did not require Caesar to remain in command in Gaul and were injured by the failure to appoint governors
for other provinces. On the other hand, Caesar was unwilling to
give up some military command until the day he became consul
designate because he feared his enemies at Rome, and he was
prepared to protect, by force if need be, the tribune who protected
him. His enemies, in turn, could only bear down tribunician obstruction by declaring that Caesar's army threatened the safety of
the State. Yet they dared not conjure up the vision of war without
the means and, above all, the leader to face it if the vision became
reality. Thus all turned on Pompey, whose reputation and military
following alone could match the conqueror of Gaul with his
veteran legions at his back. He had indeed little choice. He had
gradually committed himself against Caesar's widest claims, and if
now he stood aside he would seem to Caesar one 'willing to wound
and yet afraid to strike' and to Caesar's enemies he would seem
Caesar's lackey. If he turned to Caesar it would be no longer as
an equal partner. He would not be going to Luca, but to Canossa.

He cannot have faced the struggle with a light heart—he was
too good a soldier to believe that he had the overwhelming advantage which he ever sought—but he spoke boldly, and Caesar's
enemies felt sure of him. Under the shadow of war Curio contrived to force his proposal to a decision, and on 1 December the
Senate by 370 votes to 22 voted that both generals should lay
down their commands. But the vote was denounced as really a
surrender to Caesar and the motion was vetoed. On the next day
the consul Marcellus called on Pompey to take command of the
Republic's forces in Italy, and Pompey accepted the commission.
In the meantime Caesar had come into Cisalpine Gaul. He had
good reason to suspect that his lieutenant Labienus, who may have
overrated the rewards due to his success or resented the advancement of Antony, had been won over by his enemies and, besides,
he could from there keep in touch with his agents in Rome. He
still hoped to gain his ends without open war. He was now willing
to be content with Cisalpine Gaul and Illyricum and two legions,
or perhaps even with one legion and Illyricum, and he sent his
lieutenant Hirtius to negotiate by means of Pompey's father-in-law

Metellus Scipio[1]. On 6 December Hirtius reached Rome only to find that Pompey had been named general to protect Italy against invasion, and, presumably believing that negotiation would be fruitless, he left Rome without seeing him. This naturally convinced Pompey that peace was out of the question, and events moved swiftly to the final break[2]. There were already rumours that Caesar's legions were preparing to attack, and if Italy was to be defended the government must act quickly. Nor could Caesar himself remain inactive. No sooner had the news come of the action of Marcellus than his couriers rode off to Southern Gaul with orders to the Eighth and Twelfth legions to break camp and march at speed to Italy[3].

Curio made one more effort. He went to Ravenna and received from Caesar an ultimatum with which he posted back to Rome in time to deliver it to the consuls before the meeting of the Senate on the first of January. It was Curio's previous proposal, backed by a threat if it was not accepted in its entirety. Less than ever could Caesar resign his command unless Pompey did the same. It was for the Senate to make effective the bargain which so great a majority had endorsed a month before. But the consuls would not permit a vote on the precise offer but raised a debate on the general situation. Pompey, whose military command prevented him entering the city, let it be known that the Senate must stand firm or forfeit his services. After various debates and proposals Metellus Scipio was allowed to put the deadly motion that Caesar should lay down his command by a date to be fixed[4], and that if he refused he should be treated as a public enemy.

Such a proposal implied, what in the view of the present writer was the fact, that Caesar's legally secured term was at an end. Until the command conferred on him by the Lex Pompeia Licinia was at an end it was idle to raise as a vital issue whether Caesar would lay down his command. But now he must face the question whether, if the Senate fixes a date by which he must cease to hold his provinces, he will obey the Senate. In the absence of an over-ruling vote of the People it was, by constitutional practice, a matter for the Senate to decide, and if Caesar refused obedience he was

---

[1] Appian, *Bell. Civ.* ii, 32, 126; Suetonius, *Div. Iul.* 29; Vell. Pat. ii, 49, 4. This offer may have been made at this time. See Rice Holmes, *op. cit.* pp. 331–3.

[2] Cicero, *ad Att.* vii, 4, 2.

[3] The legions must have started about Dec. 18. Sanford, *op. cit.* p. 18.

[4] *ante certam diem.* The interpretation of these words by E. T. Merrill in *Class. Phil.* vii, 1912, pp. 248 *sqq.* is here accepted.

setting himself against the Republic. Even Gaius Gracchus had exempted the assignment of consular provinces from the veto of the tribunes, and it was not for one of the tribunician college to obstruct for ever the action of the Senate.

Caesar's answer had already been given by his announcement that he would only lay down his command if Pompey did the like, and it was given again when his agent the new tribune Antony interposed his veto and prevented the resolution from having effect, after a large majority had voted for it. Pompey set to work to mobilize more troops, and the tribunes Antony and Q. Cassius were warned to leave the Senate House if they would escape violence. They left Rome, taking with them the one constitutional battle-cry with which they could supply their master, that the rights of the tribunes were being overborne. The Senate then, as though Caesar was a second Lepidus or Catiline, empowered the consuls, proconsuls, praetors and tribunes, to take measures to protect the State against the common enemy. Late on 10 January the fugitives reached Ariminum.

They brought to Caesar his battle-cry before the battle, but after the declaration of war. It had already become amply clear that the time for action had come. The Thirteenth legion had been moved to Ravenna, and there Caesar, with the knowledge of the debates in the Senate, had made his decision. On the night of the 11th the troops had been ordered across the Rubicon which divided Cisalpine Gaul from Roman Italy. Caesar dined quietly with his staff and then rode off across the river. There was to be no going back. The Civil War had begun.

CHAPTER XVI

THE CIVIL WAR

I. THE SEIZURE OF ITALY

CAESAR had one legion at Ariminum and no prospect of reinforcements from his provinces for a fortnight. It was early in winter, for the current Roman calendar was some seven weeks in advance of the seasons[1], but once Caesar had crossed the Rubicon it was clear that he had no intention of waiting for the spring. It was in his interest to act at once, so that he can only have been thankful to his enemies for forcing the pace. Great as was the risk of invading Italy with a single legion, it was smaller than that of waiting till the defence of the peninsula was organized. It is true that until the Senate proclaimed a state of war, the levy could not be begun, but it would have been possible, under the pretext of the Parthian war, to transfer to Italy the legions from Spain, which could have covered the mobilization even against the legions from Gaul, if Caesar decided to make war. If it was possible to leave Caesar governor of Gaul till the end of February[2] without compromising the whole question of his right to retain his governorship until his election, the precipitate decision of the Senate was simply due to a military miscalculation. The reason for the miscalculation was apparently the belief that Caesar's legions would not follow him in open war against the government. The information on which this belief rested was false, but it came from a good source, Labienus, who now left Cisalpine Gaul to join what he believed to be the winning side. Pompey declared that he had ten legions ready to take the field[3], and, since the first

---

Note. For the main narrative the sources are Caesar's *Civil War* and the *Bell. Alexandrinum*, the *Bell. Africum* and the *Bell. Hispaniense*. The correspondence of Cicero adds something, as do secondary sources (Suetonius, Plutarch, Appian, Dio), which preserve some traces of an independent tradition derived from Pollio. See below, p. 883.

[1] In this chapter, since the time of the year is important for the understanding of military operations, the dates are given as corrected to the Julian calendar, 10 January, 49 B.C. being 22 November, 50 B.C.

[2] By the current calendar.

[3] Caesar, *B.C.* 1, 6, 1. 'Pompeius...copias suas exponit; legiones habere sese paratas x.'

concern of his hearers was the defence of Italy, it may be assumed that he meant legions available for that purpose. In Italy he had the two legions withdrawn from Gaul ostensibly for Parthia and no doubt some other troops raised in 52 and 51 B.C. ostensibly to reinforce Spain. But to reach the total of ten legions he must have reckoned upon transferring part at least of the Spanish army to Italy. No one at the time can have doubted Caesar's daring, but if he was not able to persuade his legions to move until he had concentrated his whole army, the government's mobilization might be completed. For this purpose Italy was mapped out into districts and the troops from each were enrolled in cohorts. A large proportion of the soldiers would be men who had seen service, and, once cohorts of experienced men were collected, they could then be organized into legions which would soon be ready to take the field. Raw recruits could be drafted to depots out of Caesar's reach to be trained at leisure.

By 26 November the news reached Rome that Caesar had entered Ariminum. This showed that he had, at any rate, one legion that would follow him even alone. Pompey, who had already realized what it would mean if Caesar was able to strike at once[1], sought to gain time by negotiation. Despite the efforts of Cicero, who since his return from Cilicia had laboured hard in the cause of peace, the consuls persuaded the Senate to send to Ariminum two envoys, the praetor L. Roscius and L. Caesar, to inform Caesar of the decrees that the Senate had passed. Pompey, the victim of his own brave words, could not openly advocate negotiation, the less as, despite a sensible proposal of Cato to that effect, he was not given overriding powers as Commander-in-Chief. But he sent a private message, which, according to Caesar[2], was no more than an appeal to subordinate his private wrongs to the public good and to think no ill of Pompey for acting as he had done. It is impossible not to suspect both that something more seductive was suggested and that the suggestion was intended to gain time by delaying Caesar's advance. Caesar's reply was to repeat his offer to disband his army if Pompey would do the same; if Pompey would countermand the mobilization and proceed to Spain, he was prepared to hand over his provinces to his successor and to present himself in person at the election for 48, waiving the right granted to him by the law of the Ten Tribunes. Thus the normal constitutional machinery could work freely and under no compulsion of force. This agreement was to be ratified by an

---

[1] Cicero, *ad Att.* VII, 10; 11, 3–4; 12, 4.   [2] *B.C.* I, 8.

interchange of solemn pledges taken at an interview between himself and Pompey[1]. Caesar, it may be assumed, added that until he received a reply agreeing to these proposals he would continue to act as his military interests dictated.

The offer was sincerely meant. If Pompey agreed to it, thus sacrificing, for the present, his personal ascendancy at Rome in the cause of peace, Caesar and he could, no doubt, contrive that Caesar would be safeguarded until the elections and then be elected. The effect would be the restoration of the coalition, but with Caesar as the dominant partner. The reply was received in due course by Pompey and submitted to the consuls and to the senators who had by then left Rome and removed to Capua. An answer was sent promising Caesar the consulship and a triumph if he would withdraw to his province and disband his army, but declaring that until he gave a pledge to abide by his own offer the levy must proceed. Pompey would go to Spain but a date for his departure was not fixed. On the other hand he was not prepared to meet Caesar, at least at this point[2]. We may suspect that both the Senate and Pompey were not sure that they could trust Caesar, that the Senate was not sure that it could trust Pompey once he met Caesar, and that Caesar was not sure that he could trust either Pompey or the Senate if the mobilization was allowed to continue undisturbed. Caesar refused to be content with the partial acceptance of his offer, and, little as any of the combatants can have felt confident of victory, the war went on its course.

The first operation of Caesar was to seize Pisaurum and Fanum on the coast road[3]. This gave him control of the north ends of the Via Flaminia. At the same time, Antony with five cohorts was sent to occupy Arretium on the Via Cassia. Next, while one cohort held Ancona, Curio with four others marched south and secured Iguvium. It was significant that the townspeople showed such goodwill towards Caesar that five Pompeian cohorts, which had been stationed there, were withdrawn by their commander and then dispersed to their homes. The occupation of Arretium and Iguvium secured Caesar against a sudden advance by the enemy and threatened a march on Rome by one or other of the two great roads. But Pompey was too good a soldier to attempt to hold the capital which would be the prize of victory, and Caesar had in view another objective, Picenum, where the local influence of the Pompeian house might prove strong. Accordingly, he ordered Curio and Antony to transfer their forces to Ancona, which

[1] B.C. i, 9, 5–6. Cicero, ad fam. XVI, 12, 3.
[2] Cicero, loc. cit. Caesar, B.C. i, 10, 3–4; 11, 1–3.   [3] Maps 4 and 6.

they both reached by 11 December. Meanwhile Pompey, the consuls and most of the senators had withdrawn to Capua. Here they considered Caesar's reply to the first envoys and sent the answer that has been described. On receiving it Caesar replied, and then, knowing that the Twelfth legion was at hand, pushed on south along the coast road, turning aside on the way to make sure of Auximum. In a week he had reached Castrum Truentinum, and had received news that Cingulum, despite the fact that it owed much to Labienus, was on his side. It was not safe to advance farther without being secure of the strong town of Asculum, which was held by Lentulus Spinther with ten cohorts. But the newly raised troops were not disposed to face Caesar's veterans. The Pompeian commander Attius Varus, who had been sent to conduct the levy in Picenum, had found it impossible to prevent his troops deserting as they retreated from Auximum and was equally unable to offer resistance. Vibullius Rufus, an officer in Pompey's confidence, arrived at this point, and, no doubt acting on instructions given in case things were going badly, contrived to collect 13 cohorts from the remains of the levy in Picenum and fell back on Corfinium, where eighteen cohorts had been concentrated[1]. Caesar had now two veteran legions, and behind him his officers were busy turning Pompeian deserters into Caesarian recruits.

In the meantime, Pompey had moved from Campania to Apulia, where he lay at Luceria with fourteen cohorts from his two legions. He realized that it would be necessary to abandon not only Rome but Italy. Indeed, the remainder of his troops were already at Canusium and Brundisium. The levies from the important recruiting ground of Campania and the south were to march to Canusium. They amounted in the end to thirty cohorts, and if the like number joined him from Corfinium he would have the makings of a strong army. But at Corfinium there was L. Domitius Ahenobarbus, the new governor of Transalpine Gaul. He was formally not subordinate to Pompey and he believed himself to be a general. About 19 December he received an urgent message from Pompey begging him to march south while there was time and he prepared to do so, but then with a flash of strategic folly he decided to stand his ground. He had heard that Caesar had

---

[1] Domitius had brought 4000 men from Rome (Appian, *Bell. Civ.* ii, 32, 129; 38, 149), apparently 12 cohorts, the remaining 6 had been recruited by Hirrus in Pompey's name. The 4000 men may be Pompeian levies raised in 52 B.C.; Lucan ii, 478–9 and cf. A. v. Domaszewski in *Neue Heid. Jahr.* iv, 1894, p. 163, n. 4.

advanced along the coast road to Castrum Truentinum. It appeared to him feasible to hold up the enemy's advance if they turned against him, and to join Pompey later if they continued to press on to the south. Pompey pointed out the dangers of this plan before it was too late, but on 27 December he received from Domitius a letter which reiterated the intention of holding his ground and a second message urging an advance north from Luceria. Pompey replied at once in a despatch which showed how clearly he realized the situation[1].

But it was now as impossible for Domitius to retreat as it was unwise for Pompey to advance. Caesar had seized his opportunity with both hands, and on 26 December he had secured the bridge over the Aternus near Corfinium and was preparing to invest the town. Domitius' dispositions were faulty. He had weakened his forces by posting six cohorts at Alba and seven at Sulmo, and he sent troops just too late to destroy the bridge[2]. Two days later Caesar was joined by the Eighth legion and twenty-two cohorts of recruits, so that even if Pompey had advanced with his two doubtful legions it would only have been to certain defeat. The investment rapidly proceeded while Domitius meditated his own escape, until on 1 January the garrison surrendered. Domitius, Lentulus Spinther, Vibullius and other men of rank were set at liberty, the troops comprising eighteen cohorts were enrolled in Caesar's army and, together with their comrades from Sulmo, who had surrendered, were sent to take possession of Sicily. With the rest of his army Caesar, that afternoon, marched against Pompey.

Four days after Corfinium fell Pompey reached Brundisium. The consuls had followed his instruction and brought the levies along the Via Appia, and within some ten days the whole available Pompeian army was concentrated at the port. Transports had been collected, and on 12 January the consuls with more than half the troops sailed to Dyrrhachium. Five days later came Caesar. His troops, incited by great promises, had marched twenty miles a day to prevent Pompey's withdrawal, and Pompey with 20 cohorts was still in Italy. Ahead of the army had travelled an envoy, Numerius Magius, an officer whom Caesar had captured and sent on with a message inviting Pompey to an interview at which proposals for peace would be made. What these would have been, we cannot say, for Magius was sent back with an answer which Caesar does

---

[1] For this correspondence see the enclosures A–D in *ad Att.* VIII, 11.

[2] Sulmo opened its gates to Antony and the cohorts posted at Alba subsequently deserted to Caesar. See O. E. Schmidt, *Briefwechsel des M. Tullius Cicero*, p. 133 and G. Veith in *Klio*, XIII, 1913, p. 21.

not care to reveal[1]. We may assume that Pompey's conscience
and vanity alike forbade him to be seduced into deserting his new
friends in order to become the adjutant of his old partner. But
Caesar did not despair. Magius took back some kind of message,
presumably more definite temptation, to Brundisium, where
Pompey was waiting for the return of the transports from Dyrrhachium. Caesar arrived and while he strove to block the harbour
to prevent Pompey's sailing, he tried once more through an
intermediary to bring about an interview. If he could capture
Pompey either by war or by words, the game was in his hands.
But Pompey returned the correct answer that he could not
negotiate without the consuls[2], and then skilfully contrived to
embark his army and sail away.

With Pompey's escape went the hope of a speedy peace. It was
not by Caesar's choice that the war went on. In sixty-five days he
had made himself master of Italy. During that time he had
displayed a clemency and generosity unknown in civil war. His
troops had been kept firmly in hand, and to the indignant amaze-
ment of men like Cicero, the Italian municipalities had been
ready to see in him anything rather than a Catiline or a vindictive
Sulla. He remained in correspondence with members of the
aristocracy, and his letters were skilful as well as sincere in making
plain his readiness for a peaceful settlement provided always that
he was allowed to reach the consulship without having to trust his
enemies any farther than they were willing to trust him. The only
peace that could have been made would have ensured him his
career and the opportunity of carrying through reforms, and there
is so far no evidence that such a peace or Caesar's use of it would
have destroyed the framework of the constitution. Caesar was a
reformer and ambitious by nature, a revolutionary only by force
of circumstances.

Pompey left Brundisium on 25 January. Two days later
Caesar started for Rome. Most of the magistrates had left the
city with the consuls, but one of those who remained, the praetor
L. Roscius, had proposed and passed a bill which at one stroke
conferred the full Roman franchise on the population of Cisalpine
Gaul. This measure, which became law on 19 January, placed
beyond cavil any grants of citizenship which Caesar had made,
and completed the full enfranchisement of Italy. The Transpadane
Gauls had deserved well of Caesar but this was more than the

---

[1] See the letter of Caesar to Oppius and Balbus (*ad Att.* IX, 13 A) and
B.C. I, 24, 5; 26, 2.
[2] B.C. I, 26, 3–5.

payment for their services, it was an act of wise statesmanship. On two tables found at Veleia and at Ateste are recorded parts of a Lex Rubria which covers the transition in Cisalpine Gaul from Latin rights to citizenship so far as legal procedure is concerned[1].

Caesar sought to collect a Senate, and notices were put up in the towns calling on senators to attend a meeting convened by the tribunes Antony and Q. Cassius on 9 February. On his way to Rome he had an interview with Cicero at Formiae and tried without success to prevail on him to attend. At the meeting, held outside the city since Caesar could not enter it without forfeiting his proconsular *imperium*, he tried to secure the co-operation of the *patres*, who were not willing to commit themselves so far as to take proposals of peace to Pompey. In Rome there was the treasure in the Aerarium which the consuls had failed to remove. This money Caesar needed, and apparently the Senate was brought to vote that he might draw from it. But a tribune Metellus vetoed the proposal and sought to secure the treasure by interposing his sacrosanct person. But Caesar, who did not intend to be hindered by the fact that he championed the cause of the tribunes, told Metellus that it would be easier to put him to death than to threaten him and he set smiths to break open the Aerarium and had carted away 15,000 bars of gold, 30,000 bars of silver and 30,000,000 sesterces[2].

Such a prize was worth the doubts of Caesar's mildness which his action aroused[3]. Some kind of government had to be left in Italy: the praetor M. Aemilius Lepidus acted as *praefectus urbi*, while Antony, although tribune, was placed in general charge of the peninsula, which was full of troops being trained for the war. Two squadrons of newly built galleys were formed to patrol the Adriatic and the Tyrrhene sea. Antony's brother Gaius was sent as *legatus* to Illyricum to hold the tribes in check and to guard the north-eastern borders of Italy; M. Crassus replaced Labienus in Cisalpine Gaul. Then after about a fortnight's stay in Rome Caesar himself set off on his way to his next campaign.

Pompey's decision to abandon Italy to Caesar was, beyond doubt, correct. He had only two legions that were trained to the necessary cohesion for battle, and these he could not trust to

[1] Bruns, *Fontes*[7], 16 and 17. For the view here taken on this vexed question see E. G. Hardy in *Eng. Hist. Review*, XXXI, 1916, pp. 353 *sqq*. For a different view of the *fragmenta Atestina* see Mommsen, *Gesammelte Schriften*, I, pp. 152, 192 *sq*.

[2] Pliny, *N.H.* XXXIII, 56. Orosius VI, 15, 5 gives 4135 pounds of gold and 900,000 pounds of silver.

[3] Cicero, *ad Att.* X, 4, 8; Caelius, *ad fam.* VIII, 16, 1.

fight against the general whom they had so recently left victorious. The reproaches of Cicero were justified in so far as Pompey had been over-optimistic about his mobilization of Italy, but nothing else in Cicero's letters on this point is justified, despite the fine heading *M. Cicero imp. s.d. Cn. Magno procos.*[1] Granted that it was necessary to evacuate Italy, Pompey's choice lay between Africa, Spain and Greece. To go to Africa was to place the Senate's cause at the mercy of a single barbarian king, who might see fit to make terms with Caesar. How readily Africa might be fatal to a losing cause Pompey himself knew well. In Spain there was a Pompeian army, but with Gaul firmly Caesarian, Spain was a prison. It offered no hopes of a second Hannibal, only of a second Sertorius. Nor was the winter the time to trust all the fortunes of the Senatorial cause to a longish voyage. Finally, to go either to Spain or Africa was to forfeit the chance of using the resources of the East. It was a short voyage to Greece and an easy voyage back to Italy, if the moment came. The moment might come for Pompey as it had come for Sulla—*Sulla potuit, ego non potero?*

But though Pompey adopted the course which gave the most chances, these chances were not great. In the East he could find money and specialist troops such as archers and light cavalry, but between the Adriatic and the Euphrates he could not raise more than some half-dozen legions. In a pitched battle, legions would decide the issue, and they were to be found in Italy and Gaul this and that side of the Alps. When Caesar crossed the Rubicon he was the master of ten legions (including the Gallic formation called the Alaudae) and twenty-two cohorts; on the day of Pharsalus, eighteen months later, he had some thirty legions under arms[2]. But although that fact made a Pompeian invasion of Italy in the face of Caesar's armies out of the question there were factors which Pompey could take into account. The fleets of the Republic were in his hand, and if Caesar went overseas to meet him he had to risk the intervention of Pompey's galleys. Further the size of the army that Caesar could bring with him across the Adriatic was limited by the deficiency of transport. This was particularly true of cavalry, and so far discounted the fact that the troopers of Gaul and Western Germany were superior on the battlefield to any horsemen west of Parthia. Finally, if Caesar operated in a country that held by the Senate, his army would be limited by difficulties of supply.

But Caesar's veteran legions, thin as their ranks were, were each of them at least a match for the strongest Pompeian legions,

---

[1] *ad Att.* VIII, 11, B, D.   [2] See p. 572 and Note 5, p. 898.

and the problem of supply could be solved partly by the fighting power of Caesar's ration strength and partly by the willingness and ability of his legionaries to suffer hunger for their general. Caesar's daring, his impatience of the long game, and the skill of his opponents brought moments of danger, but the story of the Civil War is the story how his skill and the devotion of his men triumphed over the difficulties that beset the application of his superior man-power.

There are factors in the military problem which remained constant throughout the war. Cavalry, such as Caesar's heavy Gallic and German horse, could defeat other cavalry, bring infantry to a standstill, drive off light-armed troops and, of course, cut up a broken enemy. But it had small value for shock tactics against steady experienced infantry, which indeed might be used to support weaker cavalry against stronger with effect. The pilum, though its range was short, was an effective missile, and it could, at need, be used as a thrusting spear against horsemen. On the other hand, the pilum was outranged by the arrow and the sling bullet, and though legionaries were skilful in the use of their shields they might be worn down by the combined attack of light cavalry and light-armed troops. In a battle between infantry the skill of veterans told with the utmost effect. Their volleys of pila were more crushing and their handling of sword and shield more adroit, so that they could account for superior numbers of less experienced troops. On the other hand advantage of ground was of the first importance and especially if it was on the side of superior numbers it would compensate for inferior fighting quality. To the comparative immunity conferred by superior terrain may be added the speed with which troops could protect themselves by field fortifications which could not be carried except under heavy losses. Both sides showed great adroitness in this and especially in the combination of entrenchments with walled towns. On the other hand, siegecraft had been so developed that it was no longer impossible to take a fortress except by the lavish use of greatly superior numbers or the slow process of blockade. With operations thus protracted supply was a constant problem, especially to Caesar who, except in Spain, was always weaker in cavalry than his opponents.

It may be said that in general the interest of these campaigns lies in strategy rather than in tactics, for when the battle was once joined the issue could generally be foretold. Only once, at Pharsalus, did Caesar's opponents deliberately offer battle on open equal ground, and that was in the mistaken belief that cavalry could win the day before infantry lost it. Only once, at Munda, did Caesar attack in full force against definitely superior ground, and then he came within an ace of defeat.

The Civil War is disconcerting to students of naval strategy. In the most critical campaign Pompey trusted to sea-power, Caesar to the sea; and, despite exciting moments, the sea won. The cruising capacity of the fleets was small; Caesar was not afraid of campaigning in bad weather; and though his soldiers cannot have enjoyed their crossings they were obedient and patient. Naval construction had turned from speed towards solidity with the result that sea fights had become more and more affairs of boarding and in these the fighting power of legionaries counted for more than dexterity of manœuvre. The large crews were not easy to pay and to maintain, and after Pharsalus the naval superiority of the Pompeians disappeared.

There were more good generals among Caesar's enemies than in his own armies. Pompey was an able organizer and a fine strategist, Afranius displayed subtlety at Ilerda, Petreius was at the least a hard-bitten fighter, Labienus as a tactician was in Caesar's own class. On the other side, Antony's march to join Caesar after his landing in 48 was an earnest of his later exploits as a master of retreat; Decimus Brutus proved himself competent as did C. Fabius; Vatinius displayed enterprise. Apart from Romans, the cause of Pompey was well served by Saburra the Numidian general and the cause of Caesar by Mithridates of Pergamum and Bogud of Mauretania. But it is roughly true to say that when Caesar himself was not present, his lieutenants constantly had the worst of it. On the other hand, he had an advantage in his more numerous centurions. The greater part of the middle-class professional skill of Rome was on his side, and his legions of recruits could be officered by soldiers from among his veterans who had a knowledge of the art of war which they were ready to assert even in the face of their admired commander. Finally, to the troops themselves the war was not a war about high principles. The legionaries, it is true, were no mere mercenaries ready to sell their swords to the highest bidder. Their soldierly conscience kept them loyal to their commander so long as success was reasonably possible, but they fought for their generals, and in the magnetism which inspires troops to fight to the death for their leader Caesar had not to fear a rival in the enemy camp.

II. ILERDA AND MASSILIA

Caesar had to provide for the defence of Italy from starvation. On the day that Pompey had left Brundisium Cicero[1] had written of the possibility that his fleet would blockade Italy and seize the provinces on which Rome drew for food. Roman Africa, in particular, might be dominated by the Pompeians with the help of Juba, the king of Numidia. Accordingly Curio was sent to make sure of Sardinia and Sicily and thence to cross to Africa. It was possible that Pompey might advance north against Illyricum and with the help of the revolted tribes even threaten the north-eastern borders of Italy. Rome and Italy themselves were in no great danger. Pompey could not venture a serious invasion for the present, and in the meantime Caesar's officers were busy turning cohorts into legions.

There remained Spain, a natural objective which Caesar could reach without needing transport which he did not yet possess; and thither Caesar set out to eliminate the Pompeian army of the West. In order to secure a rapid, decisive and inexpensive victory he detailed for the campaign six legions from Gaul and brought with him from Italy three more, together with 900 cavalry. The last three legions were intended for the siege of Massilia and were left to conduct it under C. Trebonius[2], while with his cavalry Caesar rode on towards the Pyrenees. It had been the task of his lieutenant Fabius with the legions of Gaul to advance through the passes and to keep the Pompeians in play until his arrival. This had been achieved, and Caesar joined his army before the city of Ilerda.

Despite the superiority of Caesar's veterans in a pitched battle, the problem taxed even his genius. The Pompeian army of seven legions had been divided into three parts. Three legions under Afranius had been posted in Nearer Spain, in the eastern half of Further Spain Petreius had two legions, in the western half Varro another two. The legionaries were trained both in Roman and in Spanish methods of warfare; Afranius, who had fought against Sertorius as well as in the East, was an experienced and skilful general; Petreius, who had crushed Catiline, was a tough soldier. These two joined forces at the beginning of 49 B.C. and, with their five legions and a large number of Spanish auxiliaries, had troops enough for the strategy which they had determined upon after consultation with Vibullius, whom Pompey had sent to Spain. Varro, a man of letters rather than of war, was left in Further Spain,

---

[1] *ad Att.* IX, 9, 2.　　　[2] T. Rice Holmes, *The Roman Republic*, III, pp. 384 *sqq.*

doubtless to organize reinforcements. The Pompeian strategy was to avoid defeat during the campaigning season of 49, to offer battle only at a great advantage. Caesar's strategy was the converse of this: he sought to dispose of the Pompeian armies in Spain without exposing his own legions to the losses inevitable in a pitched battle fought at a disadvantage of position. The day had not come when he could venture upon a battle like Munda (p. 703). He had to curb the impetuousness of his own troops confident from years of victory and to overmatch the patient skill of his opponents schooled in years of war. In one arm alone he had a definite and constant superiority—in cavalry, which he must use, not to win a victory—indeed Caesar never was a cavalry general like Alexander —but to secure himself the advantage in terrain. In this he at last succeeded in the course of a campaign which is a model of its kind.

Fabius had done his part well, and was by now encamped north of Ilerda which lies on the western bank of the river Sicoris (Segre). Here Afranius and Petreius had taken up their position. The city itself, strong on its hill, was garrisoned, but the main forces held the high ground of Gardeny, less than half a mile to the south-west. Their camp was too strong to be stormed, the city covered the stone bridge which crossed the river, the river itself covered their communications and secured their supplies, and Afranius could count on one ally more—the spring rise of the Spanish rivers, which he knew better than his antagonist. Even before Caesar's arrival on 2 May, there had been a sudden flood which swept away one of the two bridges which Fabius had built north of Ilerda. It was only Fabius' promptness in realizing his danger that saved from destruction two of his legions, which were for a moment isolated on the southern side of the Sicoris.

Caesar now came and offered battle, which Afranius more than half refused by ranging his army on the slopes of Gardeny. It was no part of Caesar's purpose to throw his legions into an uphill struggle in which his 7000 cavalry would take little part, but he skilfully contrived to form a camp within striking distance of his enemy. Between Gardeny and the town there was a low eminence which the Pompeian generals had left unfortified. Caesar tried by a surprise attack to capture it and then force the enemy to fight a pitched battle or to forfeit Ilerda and the all-important stone bridge. The attack failed, and Afranius established a force strongly entrenched on the knoll, which perhaps he had left open as a lure.

Next day the river rose in spate; Fabius' pontoon bridges were broken, and Caesar found his army short of supplies in the peninsula formed by the rivers Sicoris and Cinca. A convoy approaching from Gaul was only saved from destruction by the gallantry of its escort of Gallic cavalry. The Pompeians must have thought Caesar was trapped, as the Austrians were to think Napoleon was trapped before Aspern. After ten days Caesar contrived to pass troops across the river some twenty miles north of Ilerda by the use of coracles such as he had seen in Britain; a bridge was built, the convoy reached his camp, and his cavalry was able to act against the Pompeian communications. But its effect was diminished by the distance of the bridge, so that when the river began to run down Caesar prepared to divert part of the stream just above Ilerda so as to make a ford. Once this was made, the Pompeian supplies would be exhausted without the means of replenishment and retreat would be impossible. Accordingly, Afranius decided to fall back on a new position south of the Ebro, and a bridge was begun at the town of Octagesa[1]. In the night of 1–2 June the retreat began. Caesar's cavalry had got across at the ford, but it was barely practicable for infantry. None the less, as the legions saw the enemy escaping them, they begged leave to take the risk, struggled across, and then set off to march down the Pompeians, who had been delayed by repeated charges of cavalry. By the middle of the afternoon the two armies were in touch, and the retreat was checked. There followed a week of manœuvring, after which, despite the skill of Afranius and the resolution of Petreius, the Pompeian army, cut off from food and water, was forced to capitulate. Caesar's immediate purposes were met by its disbandment; Afranius and Petreius were spared to fight another day; before two months had passed, Varro had abandoned an unequal struggle and Further Spain was in Caesar's hands.

On his way from Spain Caesar found Massilia at his mercy. C. Trebonius had been left to conduct the siege, helped by Decimus Brutus in command of a fleet of twelve ships that had been built in haste at Arelate. The traditional seamanship of the Massiliotes failed before the resource of Brutus and the fighting of the picked legionaries who manned his galleys. Pompey, who knew the value of sea-power, sent a squadron to help the besieged, but it was feebly led and did no more than watch Brutus win a second victory. In the siege by land both attack and defence exploited the utmost resources of the times until at last a whole bastion was undermined. The moment had come for a grand assault which

---

[1] Octagesa cannot well be Mequinenza (see Rice Holmes, *op. cit.* pp. 399 *sqq.*), but the present writer, after travelling over the ground, believes that it is not possible to decide between the claims of Ribarroja and Flix or of some place in their immediate neighbourhood.

would end in a massacre. This Caesar had forestalled by sending instructions that the city was not to be stormed, and Trebonius made an armistice with the inhabitants pending the arrival of Caesar himself. Trusting too much to their good faith and wisdom, he left to the citizens the means of defence, which they used to surprise his army and burn part of his siege works[1]. But the respite was brief: Caesar's engineers contrived new means of attack, and a great terrace was built up to the city walls and again on the eve of assault the Massiliotes surrendered. That their surrender was accepted—though this time it was made surer by the handing over of arms and war-machines, ships and treasure—bears witness to the obedience which Caesar could exact from his officers and men. Presently he came himself to give sentence. The city was saved by its ancient repute, but it was stripped of most of its territory and dependencies and ceased to possess any political importance. For over two centuries Massilia had prospered, largely through her shrewd fidelity to Rome. She might be forgiven for accepting Domitius as the legitimate governor of the province and for doubting the fortune of Caesar, nor can a single act of treachery wholly discredit the bravery and determination of her defence.

III. CURIO IN AFRICA

In Africa P. Attius Varus had two legions at Utica and one at Hadrumetum and, what was more important, the promise of help from Juba, king of Numidia, whose father owed his kingdom to Pompey and who had a grudge both against Caesar for protecting a rebellious subject against him and against Curio who as tribune had announced a law to make his kingdom a Roman province. Underrating the enemy, Curio invaded Africa with only two of his four legions and 500 cavalry. He had with him as *legatus* C. Caninius Rebilus, an experienced soldier. At first all went well. Landing not far west of Cape Bon[2], he marched to the Bagradas and then went forward with the cavalry. He captured the goods that were being hurried into safety and won a success in an affair of horse, while his fleet caused 200 merchantmen off Utica to

---

[1] Caesar, *B.C.* II, 14, 1. Dio (XLI, 25, 2) refers to an abortive night attack by the besiegers during the truce. Caesar (or Trebonius) might conceal this, but there is no doubt that the townspeople destroyed the siege works by a surprise, and a surprise would be impossible if either side had previously broken the armistice.

[2] Stoffel's placing of Caesar's Anquillaria. This is doubtful, but no alternative as good has been suggested. See Rice Holmes, *op. cit.* pp. 424 *sqq.*

transfer themselves and their cargoes to his side. Rejoicing in these successes his troops hailed him *imperator*. Curio then advanced before Utica and defeated an advance force from Juba. But his army had already begun to suffer from sickness, which some attributed to the poisoning of the water-supply[1], there were some deserters and Curio's two legions were troops who had changed sides at Corfinium and might change sides again. Curio decided to make an appeal to his army and then to try to defeat Varus before he and Juba could join forces. Varus drew up his army outside Utica perhaps in the hope that Curio's men would desert wholesale, but when it became clear that this would not happen, he evaded a pitched battle and retired within the town. Curio, who had not the means to batter down the walls of Utica, began siege lines in the hope that the townspeople would force Varus to surrender. But their resistance stiffened at the news that King Juba was marching to their relief.

The news was true. Undeterred by the intelligence of Caesar's successes in Spain, the king was advancing, and when Curio became convinced of his approach he fell back on the Castra Cornelia, where he made a strong base with communications by sea. He sent for his other two legions and the rest of his cavalry; Caninius, of whom we hear nothing further, was perhaps dispatched to Sicily. All might have gone well, but, in an unlucky hour, false news was brought that Juba had turned back to repress a rising at home, and had sent on only weak forces under his general Saburra. Curio resolved to strike a crushing blow with his own army. He marched in the night with his legions, and dawn found him within the grasp of his enemy, who with the traditional strategy of the country led him on with a feigned retreat. Curio's cavalry had been sent on and had won a victory which convinced their general that he was right, and part of it was in no case to accompany the infantry in its advance. Everything from Curio's confidence to Saburra's skill worked together to bring about a complete disaster. The tactics rather than the overwhelming numbers of the Numidians[2] wore down the legionaries, and when Curio tried to break through to higher ground it was only to find that the enemy

---

[1] Appian, *Bell. Civ.* II, 44, 178. The fact of the sickness (which Caesar does not mention) may be accepted; its cause is very doubtful. See A. Ferrabino in *Atti della Accad. di Torino*, XLVIII, 1912–13, pp. 499 *sqq.* and S. Gsell, *Histoire ancienne de l'Afrique du Nord*, VIII, p. 14.

[2] The forces of Juba in the campaign of Thapsus after two years of preparation suggest that his infantry was 10,000 and his cavalry perhaps 3000. The figures of Veith, *Antike Schlachtfelder*, III, p. 759 seem too high.

cavalry had forestalled him. Curio refused a chance to escape and died with the legions which Caesar had entrusted to him. The soldier historian, Asinius Pollio, escaped from the battle to warn the five cohorts that held the Castra Cornelia. But the warning proved vain. Part of the ships sailed at once, part were swamped by the troops that pressed on board, and the survivors who could not get away by sea surrendered to Varus, who did no more than protest the injury to his honour when the Numidian king claimed the right of a victor and had them massacred.

In Curio there perished a brilliant young nobleman who, in war at least, repaid with more loyalty than skill the admiration and confidence of Caesar. More deserving of pity are his legionaries— more important is a defeat which promised a hope of victory over Caesar's legions, and left Africa to be a rallying-point for the Pompeians after Pharsalus.

In the meantime the Pompeians had succeeded, for once, in profiting by their superiority at sea. Dolabella with a squadron had been set to guard the Adriatic. His task was to protect the coast of Italy and of Caesar's province of Illyricum. Pompey's admirals M. Octavius and L. Scribonius Libo drove him on to the Dalmatian coast and there defeated him. He fell back on Illyricum in the hope of being covered by Caesar's troops under C. Antonius, who thereupon rashly posted part of his army on the island of Curicta (Veglia)[1]. When Dolabella had been driven off this force was besieged while two legions under Basilus and the historian Sallust watched helplessly from the mainland. Some of the troops escaped on two great rafts, but a third was entrapped by the enemy, and the Gallic auxiliaries on board after a heroic resistance against overwhelming numbers killed themselves rather than surrender. The rest of Antonius' force, fifteen cohorts strong, were driven by starvation to capitulate and were carried off to Pompey who drafted them into his newly formed legions. Besides these, Caesar had lost forty ships and what slight hope he had of disputing the command of the Adriatic. Octavius tried to follow up his success by reducing Salonae, but the Romans in the town held out stoutly until by a sudden sally they drove the besiegers to their ships. But although the coast of Illyricum was firmly held, it became to Caesar a source of anxiety rather than of strength.

[1] The fact that Lucan mentions Salonae (and Iader) is not evidence for the MSS. reading in Caesar B.C. III, 10, 5 'Corcyram' (which would be Corcyra Nigra) as against Mommsen's 'Curictam,' for Lucan (IV, 406) places Antonius on Curicta. For the topography see Kromayer-Veith, Schlachten-Atlas, Röm. Abt. III, Bl. 21 and text, and G. Veith in Strena Buliciana, pp. 267 sqq.

IV. THE CAMPAIGN OF DYRRHACHIUM

After the surrender of Afranius those of his legionaries who were not domiciled in Spain were conducted by four of Caesar's legions to the south-eastern border of Transalpine Gaul, whence they could disperse whither they would. The legions were then stationed at Placentia to wait for Caesar himself. They had served him well, but they were tired and disappointed of the bounties which had been promised them, and while they waited they showed signs of mutiny. The Ninth legion supplied the ringleaders, who may have hoped to force their general to allow them licence to find their compensations in the plunder of the civil population. They were soon undeceived. Hastening to Placentia, Caesar paraded the legions and announced his intention of visiting the Ninth with decimation. His masterful action sufficed to bring them to their obedience, and on the entreaties of the tribunes, he contented himself with the execution of twelve of the ringleaders and forgave the rest. The legions then set out on the march to Brundisium for a campaign in which their devotion was to stand every test of hardship and danger.

During Caesar's absence in Spain he had been concerned with his position in the State. It was no part of his purpose to challenge the rights of the existing consuls so long as they could not exercise them, but it was all-important to secure his own election for 48 B.C. It was the prize for which he had taken up arms, and when the application of force had secured that the 'beneficium populi Romani' should not be made of no effect, we may assume that he would have been content. With the consulship went security for himself and his career. But the absence of the consuls put out of action the normal machinery for his election. First he sought to have it ruled that the praetor Lepidus might conduct the consular comitia[1], and it was not until this project failed that he caused the same praetor to propose a law creating a dictatorship and appointing him to it. The definition of his dictatorship has not survived in the Fasti, but the fact that it rested on a law suggests that it followed the precedent of Sulla and conferred upon him the widest powers and not merely the competence to conduct elections and celebrate the Latin Festival. The greater his powers the more striking would be their abdication, which he intended as soon as he entered on the consulship. The wider powers had the additional advantage that he could appoint officers with a legal status, whose

---

[1] Cicero, *ad Att.* IX, 9, 3.

authority however would lapse upon his abdication. Finally, as dictator, he was raised above the veto of hostile tribunes which had embarrassed his first visit to Rome (see below, p. 729 n. 1).

He had showed that he was more clement than Sulla; it remained to show that he was no Catiline despite old fears due to his past and to the present character of many who were in his camp, the men whom Atticus neatly described as the *Nekyia*[1], ghosts emerging from the shades to regain the show of life by draining the blood of a Rome sacrificed to them. The war and the fear of it had led to a scarcity of money, creditors unwilling to lend and debtors unwilling to pay. Caesar thereupon, presumably by an edict, allowed debtors to discharge their obligations at once by surrendering property estimated by arbitrators at its pre-war value and, though of this Caesar himself says nothing, deducting the amount already paid by way of interest. It was estimated that the average loss to creditors was a quarter of the principal[2], but it was better to be paid that than to be paid nothing. A further danger was hoarding, and Caesar forbade the holding of more than 60,000 sesterces in cash. Such a prohibition could only be made effective by rewarding informers, but Caesar was careful not to admit slaves to the benefit of this. For he scrupulously avoided giving rise to nervousness about the established social order, and he had his reward in the growing confidence of the Roman financiers[3].

If Caesar thus belied the suspicions due to his earlier career, he gave effect to a policy which he had always urged (p. 489). He reinstated in their civil rights the descendants of those whom Sulla had proscribed and with more doubtful clemency he reversed the exile of those who had been condemned under Pompey's laws. The general recall of exiles was always the prerogative of the highest legislative bodies in ancient states and it was practically desirable to place it beyond all legal question. Caesar, therefore, even if his dictatorial competence absolved him from the necessity of doing so, was careful to have each exile restored by a law passed on the proposal of a praetor or a tribune.

Meanwhile he had been elected consul in due form together with a respectable but pliant aristocrat P. Servilius. The other magistracies were then filled with his partisans and governors were appointed for those provinces which were in Caesar's control, Lepidus to Nearer Spain, A. Albinus to Sicily, Sex. Peducaeus to Sardinia and Decimus Brutus to Gallia Transalpina. Q. Cassius

---

[1] Cicero, *ad Att.* IX, 18, 2.   [2] Suetonius, *Div. Iul.* 42.
[3] Caelius to Cicero, *ad fam.* VIII, 17, 2.

was already governor of Further Spain. The Latin Festival for 49 was at last celebrated, and after eleven days in Rome Caesar set out to join his army at Brundisium.

Pompey had under his immediate command nine legions. Of these two had once been lent to Caesar; three had been formed from the Italian levies which escaped from Brundisium; one came from Cilicia, being formed from the two very weak legions which Cicero had found there; one was of time-expired soldiers who had settled in Crete and Macedonia and two had been formed in Asia by the consul Lentulus. Into these nine legions he had drafted recruits from Greece and Epirus and the troops captured from C. Antonius. We may assess the average strength of these legions, thus reinforced, at some 4000 men[1]. Pompey had therefore about 36,000 legionary infantry partly veteran and only very slightly adulterated, if at all, by non-Italians. On the other hand his legions in training and cohesion remained inferior to Caesar's best troops. This inferiority would however disappear with time, and Metellus Scipio was on his way with two more legions from Syria, which were largely veterans and which, by the incidents of their march, showed themselves to be of good quality. Pompey had besides 3000 archers and 1200 slingers, all doubtless professional troops, and 7000 cavalry, which included 1100 excellent Galatian horse. During the summer of 49 great stores of food and munitions had been collected and placed in depots. The squadrons of Pompey's fleet under the general command of Bibulus reached at least 300 ships. Every month that Pompey was left unassailed made him stronger. Thus Caesar must strike at once. He had 12 legions under his hand in Italy, and though they were far below strength (perhaps 2500–3000 men each), they would win a pitched battle. He must therefore seek out Pompey. But Pompey was no novice in war and would refuse to play into his hands. Caesar must then force him to fight by threatening a vital point. The vital point most within reach was the connection between Pompey's army and his fleet, that is, the naval bases on the east coast of the Adriatic[2]. If Caesar could succeed in placing his army on that coast he might either seize it all or bring on a decisive battle. To march round through Illyricum would take too much time, expose

---

[1] There are signs that Caesar overstated slightly Pompey's actual fighting strength at Pharsalus, which in legionaries may be set at somewhat under 40,000 men (p. 899). When allowance is made for the accession of the *cohortes Afranianae* (apparently seven in number) and the losses earlier in the campaign, the estimate squares with that made above.

[2] See Map 3, facing p. 107.

his army to losses from the tribes of the hinterland and present the gravest difficulties about supply. The alternative was to cross by sea, and that meant dividing his army, for he had only transport for some 20,000 men, and risking destruction from the Pompeian fleet. But great as were the dangers, they must be faced.

Caesar hastened to Brundisium and no doubt news of his arrival there went across to Pompey, who marched westwards along the Via Egnatia from his training grounds in Macedonia. He might well trust his squadrons at Dyrrhachium, Apollonia, Oricus and Corcyra to give him timely warning, but there was no harm in being within striking distance of the coast. The Pompeian fleet failed him; Caesar put seven legions on board his transports, and a northerly wind carried him across the Adriatic, so that he was able to land on the open coast south of the Acroceraunia. If now the rest of his army which had been left under Antony could follow in the transports which he sent back for them, the first step to victory was secured. But Caesar's good fortune here deserted him for a time. The transports were either destroyed at sea or blockaded at Brundisium by Bibulus, raging at his missed opportunity; and though, by forced marching, Caesar secured the surrender of Oricus and Apollonia, he failed to consummate his success by taking Dyrrhachium.

After landing he sent his prisoner Vibullius Rufus to seek out Pompey with proposals for peace. Caesar may have hoped to induce in his antagonist a moment of indecision which might be turned to military profit, but, if so, the manœuvre avenged itself. Pompey was nearer than Caesar can well have realized, and Vibullius hastened to bring the news to him that Caesar had landed. By exertions which went near to turning his army into a rabble, Pompey reached the high ground where the north-west branch of the Via Egnatia leads to Dyrrhachium. It was a critical moment: had Dyrrhachium fallen, the coast was Caesar's: as it was, he was not strong enough with only seven legions to force his way through, and there was nothing for it but to call a halt. He took up a position south of the Apsus (near Kuči[1]) and Pompey with his troops now well in hand faced him on the opposite bank.

The position was now in favour of Pompey. Until reinforced,

---

[1] Though not all Veith's arguments are cogent, he has made it highly probable that Kuči is the spot, lying as it does on the road north-east from Apollonia with suitable positions on the side of the river and at the northern edge of what we may suppose to be Apolloniate territory. The plain to the west of it is waterlogged in winter.

Caesar could not advance. Nor could he retreat without abandoning Apollonia and Oricus and their neighbours Amantia and Byllis, which had declared for him; indeed, if he retreated far, he would lose all chance of contact with the rest of his army. Pompey could draw supplies by sea and watch his opponent slowly exhaust the resources of the country behind him. With such prospects in view, it is improbable that Pompey seriously sought to bring on a general engagement, and though Dio[1] and Appian[2] suggest something of the kind, we may suppose that Pompey did no more than attempt to get cavalry across the river to hamper Caesar's foraging. The two armies began to fraternize across the stream which divided them, and Caesar tried to bring about a conference through Vatinius, but it was prevented by the sudden violence of Labienus. Earlier than this Vibullius had failed to break down Pompey's unwillingness to accept a compromise which put him, apparently and perhaps in reality, at Caesar's mercy.

For a time—exactly how long we cannot say—Caesar waited in vain for the rest of his army, which he ordered to make for Apollonia or, if that proved impossible, for a landing place well to the north of Dyrrhachium[3]. In his anxiety he even tried to cross himself from Apollonia[4], but failed, despite his brave words about the boat bearing Caesar and his luck. The failure is not recorded in the *Commentaries*, for he was not the man to think that an epigram made it good. Bibulus had died, a martyr to hate and duty, but a Pompeian squadron under Libo strove hard to maintain a blockade of Brundisium based on an island off the harbour mouth. Antony, however, was a soldier of resource, and prevented it. None the less Caesar had good reason to send the most stringent orders to his lieutenant. The season of winter storms was passing, and in good weather the Pompeian galleys could keep the sea, while the sudden calms of the Adriatic in the spring would expose to destruction the sailing ships that were Antony's transports. At last towards the end of February[5] with a southerly wind Antony slipped away with four legions, some slingers, and 800 cavalry. He was carried north past Apollonia and then past Dyrrhachium

[1] XLI, 47, 3.

[2] *Bell. Civ.* II, 58, 241.

[3] Reading with Hofmann 'sive ad litora Apolloniatium ⟨sive ad Labeatium⟩,' in *B.C.* III, 25, 4.

[4] See Veith, *Der Feldzug von Dyrrhachium*, pp. 108 *sqq.*

[5] Caesar, *B.C.* III, 25, 1. 'Multi iam menses erant et hiems praecipitaverat' implies a date not earlier than February (Julian). Pharsalus was fought on June 6 (Julian). Caesar must have retired from before Dyrrhachium

under the eyes first of Caesar and then of Pompey. Sixteen galleys from Dyrrhachium all but caught the transports during a drop in the wind, but in the nick of time the breeze freshened and the chase went on. Antony made the harbour of Nymphaeum (S. Giovanni di Medua) but it was exposed to a south wind. But as the transports came up, the wind—'incredibili fortuna'—veered to the south-west, and they were able to enter the haven, while the Pompeian galleys with tired rowers were broken on the lee shore.

The next problem was the junction of the two parts of Caesar's army. Antony had no doubt precise instructions in the event of his having to land north of Dyrrhachium and his natural march would lead him to the east of Pompey by the pass near Elbasan. The news of his landing reached Pompey, who divined what he would do, broke camp at night and marched to waylay him. The next day Caesar had the news, and himself marched north-east. Pompey reached a suitable spot, apparently Ciberak[1], and waited for Antony to march on him. But in vain was the net spread. Warned in time, Antony halted and when Caesar came up, Pompey, who could not afford to fight a pitched battle, marched off west and encamped at Asparagium (near Rogozina) north of the river Genusus. The enemy armies joined hands and followed him, crossing to the south bank of the river perhaps near Clodiana, where there are remains of an ancient bridge. The reason for the crossing may be that the other road had been blocked by Pompey or simply to have the river to guard their flank. Caesar with his united army offered battle, which naturally was refused.

He then determined to manœuvre his opponent out of his position by striking at Dyrrhachium. Accordingly he marched east. Pompey could not well move till he knew what his opponent had in mind, and when his scouts next morning informed him of Caesar's probable objective, he might well hope to reach Dyrrhachium on the straight road in time. But he had underrated the marching powers of his opponent's veterans and when his advance guard reached the coastal plain south of Dyrrhachium, Caesar was already before the city. It was a near run thing, but Pompey had time to seize the high ground of Petra (Sasso Bianco) some six miles below the town, and his presence made a regular siege

about a month before that (c. 9 May Julian). This leaves little more than two months for the operations before Dyrrhachium and Suetonius' statement (*Div. Iul.* 35, 1) that the blockade of Pompey lasted nearly four months must be rejected. The other indications of date are reconcilable with the above chronology. See Rice Holmes, *op. cit.* pp. 477 *sqq.*

[1] Veith, *op. cit.* pp. 117 *sqq.*

impossible. He might indeed be not dissatisfied. Near both the sea and Dyrrhachium he had his supplies better secured than at Asparagium: on the other hand, though Caesar now had behind him a fertile plain, the food reserves of that plain had been systematically swept clean by Pompey's cavalry and it would be two months before the harvest was ripe. His position was the worse for the fact that the younger Cn. Pompeius had captured or burnt his ships of war in the harbour of Oricus and had destroyed thirty of Antony's transports, which had been posted at Lissus.

The immediate problem for Pompey was to make himself secure and to exploit his superior numbers not in battle but in the art of field fortification. This he did until his lines ran from fort to fort along the semicircle of hills which lies south or south-east of Petra. Caesar tried by a brusque attack to capture a hill (Paliama) which would have enabled him to bring his lines to the sea only three miles south of Petra; but Pompey realizing the danger defeated the attack. Finally, although Caesar succeeded in drawing his lines right round Pompey's position so that the south end rested on the sea, they were no less than fifteen English miles long, and to hold them Caesar had no more than a man for every yard. This grandiose operation, the attempt to imprison an army superior in numbers, is condemned by Napoleon, but it is to be remembered that the critic lived at a period in which trench warfare on a great scale was not in vogue. And, indeed, it is not easy to see what other course offered greater chances, granted that Pompey was not willing to accept a pitched battle. For perhaps six weeks the two armies watched each other while constant warfare along the two lines practised Pompey's recruits. Caesar's army had to support a severe shortage of their regular rations, and it was further weakened by the detachment of one legion and 200 cavalry to Thessaly, five cohorts to Aetolia and two veteran legions and 500 cavalry to Macedonia. These detachments took from Caesar his margin of superiority and it is probable that they were forced on him very largely by difficulties of supply[1]. But if the lines could hold, the future for Caesar was slowly becoming brighter. Though Pompey's troops could get their rations regularly by sea, fodder for his horses began to fail, and the one arm in which he was definitely superior began to be ruined. Even more dangerous was the threat of pestilence and the certainty of malaria as the season advanced. On the other hand, as the corn in the plain behind Caesar's lines began to ripen, the days of his privation would soon be over.

[1] Veith, *op. cit.* p. 245 *sq.*

Pompey now had to face the task of breaking through the enemy lines. His first plan was subtle and complicated. He was well aware that Caesar himself was worth a legion, and he contrived to draw him away by having offers made to betray to him Dyrrhachium itself. Leaving P. Sulla in command of the main reserve, Caesar with a small force embarked on the offered adventure and was then cut off by a sudden landing of Pompey's troops and only by hard fighting escaped with his life. Meanwhile three attacks were launched, a slight demonstration and two heavy attacks on positions in the centre of Caesar's lines. Only the heroism of a cohort which withstood the onset of four legions saved the situation until Sulla with the reserves came into action. It taxed even Pompey's skill to disengage his troops, so that Caesar's veterans, who were connoisseurs of warfare, believed that a victory might have been won if Sulla had taken the responsibility of driving home his counter-attack. Caesar defended his lieutenant, but the defence only shows how well advised Pompey had been to lure his great opponent from the scene of the battle. In the meantime an attempt had been made to save the Pompeian cavalry by transferring it to the land just north of Dyrrhachium, but this move was blocked by Caesar, who sent detachments to hold the two isthmuses which join the city to the mainland, but at the cost of a further slight weakening of his reserve[1].

Pompey then made a second plan, less far-reaching in scope but more sure in execution. Two Gallic notables had deserted to him bringing precise information about Caesar's dispositions. At the point where his lines approached the sea on the south a second wall had been built to guard it against troops landed behind it, but there was no cross wall to prevent an enemy from penetrating between the two. The end of the line was guarded by the quaestor P. Marcellinus, who was ill; next to him was Antony with the Ninth legion; Caesar and the headquarters were at the northern end of the lines. Here then was a weak spot, and Pompey struck at it in full force. No fewer than six legions and boat-loads of light-armed troops were used, and the attack succeeded for a time until it was held up by Antony, who signalled to Caesar. Presently came the reserves and the counter-attack, aimed at regaining the lost ground before Pompey could organize it and so make permanent the breach in the lines. With 33 cohorts Caesar attacked;

---

[1] The precise scope of these operations is rendered uncertain by a lacuna in the text of the *Civil War*. It is possible that in the lacuna has been lost an account of the arrival of *Afranianae cohortes* from Africa to reinforce Pompey. See N. Menegetti, *Quel che Cesare non dice nel suo capolavoro*, pp. 44 *sqq*.

for a time all went well and an advanced Pompeian legion was hard beset, but Pompey brought up reinforcements and the attack miscarried among the network of trenches and fortifications. There was a panic, and it was only the complications of the terrain that prevented the defeat from being turned into a great disaster.

Even so, Pompey might be well content. The renegade Labienus asked to dispose of the prisoners, and taunted them before their death with the question whether it was the habit of veteran soldiers to run away. Pompey's troops had at last seen the backs of Caesar's veterans. The sight was to be too well remembered a month later before Pharsalus. In their newly won confidence the nobles ceased to fear the one thing they had still to be wary of—a genius commanding an army that had a defeat to avenge. Pompey, on the other hand, lacked the fiery energy needed to drive home his success. Method, calculation and dexterity had done their work, and to these he still trusted. His troops, as will be seen, were partly out of hand: whereas, shaken as they were, his opponents were still veterans. With consummate skill Caesar withdrew them from the lines and concentrated them at a point a few miles to the southwards. There he made to them speeches with the pregnant message 'ut acceptum incommodum virtute sarciretur.' Pompey was by this time encamped opposite him but in the night Caesar's army slipped away and the Pompeian cavalry failed to bring it to a standstill. In the morning he had reached his former camp at Asparagium and both he and his opponents occupied their old positions. Part of Pompey's troops who had started in haste went back to the camp of the previous day to collect their belongings, and at noon Caesar made a second march which Pompey could not follow. This start he maintained, and after four days the pursuit was abandoned.

V. PHARSALUS

Both commanders had for the moment some freedom of action, both, if we may trust Caesar, were largely swayed by a care for their other forces. Metellus Scipio was leading two legions and a strong force of cavalry from Syria. His march had been long and difficult, even if mitigated by plunder[1]. The self-conferred title of *imperator* commemorated the reverses he had suffered from the mountaineers of the Amanus. The news of Caesar's landing in Epirus had reached him while he was requisitioning the treasures of Diana of the Ephesians, and with laudable zeal he pressed on

---

[1] *B.C.* III, 31–2. Roman Asia Minor was no doubt subjected to heavy exactions, even if these are more exaggerated than is usual with Caesar.

into Macedonia, where Domitius Calvinus was waiting to intercept him with two veteran legions. Scipio swerved aside in the hope of surprising Caesar's other lieutenant Cassius in Thessaly but failed to bring him quickly enough to battle and marched north again just in time to secure his valuable baggage from the advance of Domitius. The two generals manœuvred on the Haliacmon until Domitius, running short of supplies, retired westwards along the Via Egnatia[1]. By this time the reverse before Dyrrhachium had caused Caesar to send to him instructions to march to Thessaly, but the messages failed to get through, so that he was all but caught by Pompey. Only a lucky meeting of his scouts with Gallic deserters to Pompey saved him: he slipped away with four hours start, and marching south, joined Caesar at Aeginium. Scipio in turn, on instructions from Pompey, marched into Thessaly and occupied Larissa.

Thus the need to save Domitius' army from destruction had practically compelled Caesar to march towards Thessaly. Pompey was not so limited in his choice. His first movement to entrap Domitius would have enabled Scipio to join him by marching west along the Via Egnatia, and he could then decide whether or not to follow Caesar into Thessaly. But he had in fact already decided. At a council of war after Dyrrhachium Afranius had urged him to invade Italy, leaving Caesar in Greece. He could return, like another Sulla, to find Rome at his mercy. But that meant the abandonment of his Greek and Eastern allies and the appearance of flight before a defeated enemy. It would be no easy task to recover Spain without first mastering Gaul, which would hold by Caesar; to maintain large forces under arms but inactive in Italy would be burdensome; the senatorial leaders might forget the war in their revenge. Until Caesar had been decisively defeated and his army destroyed, there could not be peace; the Pompeian army had gained confidence and must win before losing it again. Pompey, therefore, chose the best course open to him and marched to Larissa, where he found Scipio.

If Pompey was bound to fight in the end Caesar was by now ready to fight at once. He had joined Domitius at Aeginium and seized upon the resistance of Gomphi in Thessaly to hearten his troops with wine, loot, and massacre. This terrorism, followed by

[1] The account in *B.C.* III, 36–8, based presumably on the report of Domitius, seems to do less than justice to the energy and resource of Scipio. See G. Veith, *Ant. Schlachtfelder*, IV, pp. 534 *sqq.* The scene of these manœuvres on the Haliacmon was probably near Kesaria. Veith (*loc. cit.*) has added new arguments in favour of this theory, which is that of Heuzey.

clemency to towns which submitted, gave him the control of the
fertile western basin of the river Peneus. The corn was not yet
ripe, but the army that had endured before Dyrrhachium would
not be defeated by hunger in Thessaly. The precise manœuvres
which brought the two armies face to face are not revealed to us.
At some point near the town of Palaeopharsalus[1] Caesar encamped
and presently Pompey cautiously approached and established himself on higher ground so that he could not be forced to fight except
with the slope greatly in his favour. Caesar offered battle on
several days and then decided to move off, hoping to manœuvre
his opponent out of his position, perhaps by striking at his communications. In a war of movement the superior nimbleness of
his army might offer him a chance of battle at an advantage.
Whether Pompey could have afforded to stay where he was we
cannot say, but on the very day that Caesar ordered his army to
move, he decided to offer battle. As the head of the column was
leaving the camp, he saw that the Pompeian army was forming
for battle near the foot of the slopes. His chance had come: the
legions were deployed into line with orderly speed and Caesar
rode forward to discover the dispositions of the enemy.

That Pompey offered battle wholly against his own military
judgment and because of the impatience of the nobles in his camp
is improbable. It is true that his decision was apparently taken
before Caesar set his troops in motion, so that it was not due to any
threat at his communications. Nor so long as he kept in touch
with Larissa was his present position such that he was compelled
to fight at once at all costs. But granted the chances of victory
were on his side, it was wise to offer battle before his army forgot
Dyrrhachium. Nothing in Pompey's career hitherto as a general
suggests that he would have permitted his calculations to be influenced by the clamour of mere impatience. He must, therefore,
be credited with the belief that the chances were on his side, and
that he could not expect in the near future a more favourable
opportunity. In his camp was Labienus, who had been a successful
leader of cavalry in Gaul[2], and we may fairly assume that he had

---

[1] The site of Palaeopharsalus cannot be decided with certainty. F. L.
Lucas (*B.S.A.* XXIV, 1919–21, pp. 34 *sqq.*) places Palaeopharsalus at Koutouri,
the battle below Mt Dogandzis, the Pompeian retreat to the north; Caesar is
facing west, hence his movement towards Scotussa. This theory appears to
the present writer the most probable, despite the objections advanced by
F. Stählin in *Das Hellenische Thessalien*, p. 142, *Philologus*, LXXXII, 1926–7,
p. 115 and J. Kromayer, *Antike Schlachtfelder*, IV, pp. 637 *sqq.*
[2] Caesar, *B.G* III, 11; V, 56–8; VI, 7–8; VIII, 45.

convinced Pompey that in the plain of the Enipeus his cavalry could decide a battle while his infantry withstood the attack of Caesar's legions. Caesar states that Pompey had 110 cohorts in the line at Pharsalus, rating them at 45,000 or 47,000 men in all, and that he himself had 80 cohorts amounting to 22,000 men. The number of his own men is no doubt roughly true, the number of the Pompeian infantry is almost certainly exaggerated. But that the average strength of a Pompeian cohort was greater than that of a Caesarian may be taken as certain, so that Pompey had a definite advantage in numbers. His troops, however, were not of the same quality as those of Caesar, and two of his eleven legions had fought in Gaul. It was in his cavalry that Pompey trusted, and his cavalry failed him. Its mission was to attack the enemy legions in the flank and rear after having swept away the thousand cavalry of Caesar. Its effects would be felt when the whole of the infantry was engaged. Caesar met this danger by withdrawing eight cohorts from his normal reserve and forming them into a separate reserve, placed obliquely behind the line.

The Pompeian infantry were ordered to stand and not advance to meet the Caesarian legions when they charged, so that the enemy might arrive out of breath and in disorder. But the experience of years of fighting had not been wasted. Of their own accord the veterans halted half-way, rested a moment, and then, hurling their pila, charged home. But though the Pompeians had lost the physical advantage they had hoped for and the moral advantage of the attack, they stood their ground. But on their left the cavalry lost the battle. They had thrust back Caesar's horse and were wheeling to envelop his infantry when the eight cohorts, holding their pila as stabbing spears, sprang forward. Caesar had said that all depended upon them, and they did not fail him. The cavalry broke and galloped off, the eight cohorts in their turn outflanked the enemy infantry, Caesar's third line was thrown into the battle and the Pompeian legions gave way and fled to their camp. Despite the heat and their exertions, Caesar's troops responded to his order to storm the camp, and the enemy infantry streamed in flight northward. When Pompey saw his cavalry turn he rode to his tent where he stayed a while, 'summae rei diffidens et tamen eventum exspectans.' Then as the enemy broke in over the ramparts, he laid aside his general's badges, found a horse, and fled.

While Antony with the cavalry hunted scattered fugitives, the main body of the Pompeian infantry retreated along the ridges to the north. By dusk Caesar with four legions had headed them off, and that night, after a day of fighting and marching, his tireless infantry drove an entrenchment between the hill on which the enemy had halted and the stream that flowed beneath it. By daybreak the remnants of Pompey's infantry surrendered. They had fought as well as their cavalry had fought badly, and Caesar and his troops treated them as brave men deserved to be treated. From first to last more than 24,000 men surrendered; the remainder were dead or scattered in flight, and Pompey's army ceased to exist. Labienus, who had sworn not to leave the field except in victory, brought the first news of the defeat to Dyrrhachium. L. Domitius had fallen, a few other senators escaped, and, at Larissa, Caesar burnt unread the correspondence of Pompey and Scipio. Then within three days of the battle, he rode out in pursuit of his rival.

While Pompey and Caesar manœuvred in the Balkans, the Pompeian fleet had not been idle round Italy. Even before Pharsalus D. Laelius had imitated Libo in establishing a naval blockade of Brundisium, where Vatinius had been left in command. Vatinius contrived to capture three of his ships and used cavalry patrols to prevent the enemy from obtaining water on the mainland. Corcyra and Dyrrhachium, however, sent supplies to the blockading squadron, which was based upon an island that lay off the harbour. Laelius' object was to prevent reinforcements crossing the Adriatic, but with the news of Caesar's victory he had no good reason for maintaining the blockade, the confusion of the Pompeians disorganized his supplies, and there was nothing for it but to withdraw. Another Pompeian squadron raised in Syria, Phoenicia and Cilicia boldly attacked the fleets which Caesar had posted at Vibo and Messana, presumably to protect the corn convoys from Sicily and Sardinia to Rome. Neither of Caesar's admirals was on his guard: a surprise attack by fireships destroyed the 35 galleys stationed under M. Pomponius at Messana, and the squadron of Sulpicius Rufus off Vibo would have met the same fate had it not been for the promptitude of the invalided veterans who had been left there. Five of Sulpicius' ships had already been destroyed when the legionaries without waiting for orders embarked in the remainder and beat off the enemy with the loss of two quinqueremes and two triremes. The Pompeian admiral C. Cassius escaped from his flagship, which was captured. Soon after he too received information of the news of Caesar's victory and withdrew with the fleet.

A third objective for naval action was the Adriatic, where hitherto the Pompeians had had successes. The events of 49 B.C. had emboldened the inland tribes against the Romans in the coast towns who adhered to Caesar. With the southernmost of these tribes, the Delmatae, M. Octavius allied himself after Pharsalus. Caesar in the spring of 48 B.C. had sent two more legions from Italy under Q. Cornificius, who had also raised a few ships from the coast town of Iader with which he made head against Octavius. But the war by land was difficult, and Caesar feared that the tribesmen would be reinforced by scattered Pompeians or even that Pompey himself would find means to revive the war in Macedonia. Gabinius was ordered to bring reinforcements. Presumably because the Pompeian squadron still held the sea he marched by land and did not reach the theatre of war until late in October. Even then his force suffered reverses and at last with only a remnant of his army he took refuge in Salonae, where disease ended his varied career.

By this time Caesar was far away and the veteran legions in Italy would not readily have left their quarters in Campania for a thankless and inglorious war in the mountains of Illyricum. But at Brundisium there were veterans who had been on the sick list when Caesar had crossed and were now fit and ready for action. In command was Vatinius who, for all Cicero's epithets, was a man of energy and resource. Cornificius wrote urgently for help, whereupon Vatinius improvised a fleet, put his veterans on shipboard and boldly set out to challenge Octavius who was blockading Epidaurum. Puzzled by this fleet from nowhere, Octavius retired northwards, but when he learnt the forces of his pursuer, he turned to fight off the island of Tauris (Torcoli, Ščedro). In an engagement, which has not unjustly been compared with the battle of Lissa in 1866, the boldness of Vatinius had its reward. His fleet came up piecemeal, but as each ship reached the battle its legionaries took charge of the event. With the remnant of his squadron Octavius disappeared, Vatinius returned to Italy in triumph, and Cornificius, with better hopes, resumed the task of pacifying Illyricum[1].

VI. CAESAR AT ALEXANDRIA

After his defeat at Pharsalus Pompey had ridden off and escaped by sea to Amphipolis, thence to Mitylene, where he joined his wife. Neither in the Aegean islands nor Asia Minor nor in Syria could he find strong friends. The legend that he meditated flight to Parthia may be disregarded. There remained two reasonable places of refuge, Africa and Egypt. Africa offered the better

[1] See Kromayer-Veith, *Schlachten-Atlas*, Röm. Abt. iii, 4, Bl. 21 and Text and G. Veith, *Strena Buliciana*, pp. 271 *sqq.*

chance of restoring the balance of the war. Covered by a concentration of his fleet, he might yet build up a second army and by the constant threat to Italy force Caesar to some kind of peace. But he decided against this project. His pride may have revolted from enduring the insolence of King Juba, and he may have doubted whether his authority would survive defeat. For whatever reason, in an evil hour, he sailed for Egypt.

Three years before, Ptolemy Auletes had died: his will named as his successors his eldest surviving daughter Cleopatra and his elder son, a lad of nine or ten years, and entrusted them to the protection of the Roman People. Around these two had gathered a group of adventurers, Pothinus, tutor of the young Ptolemy XII, Theodotus, who was to teach him rhetoric, and an Egyptian or half-breed soldier, Achillas. The throne was guarded by a small 'army of occupation' left by Gabinius, which had no intention of leaving Egypt and had gathered to itself the foreign mercenaries of the royal house. Many of the Roman troops had served under Pompey, and if the new monarchs of Egypt forgot what their father owed to him, they might take up his cause. In the previous year the young Cn. Pompeius had been able to collect a fleet of 50 ships from Egypt, corn and 500 men, though this reflected a speculation on the chance of the war rather than any true friendship. For Caesar, no less than Pompey, had had a hand in the restoration of Auletes. In the previous few months Cleopatra had been driven from the country by a rising in Alexandria promoted in the interest of her brother or rather of his advisers. With the undaunted energy of a Macedonian queen, she had raised an army and now at Pelusium faced in arms her brother. At such a time, the advent of Pompey was unwelcome. 'Dead men do not bite' said Theodotus, and as Pompey stepped on shore he was stabbed by Achillas and two Roman officers. It was the 28th of September[1], the day on which, thirteen years before, he had entered Rome in triumph over the pirates and Mithridates. That day had marked the zenith of his fame, this ended the agony of defeat, and who shall say which day was the more fortunate?

His death excited the pity of the world and won for him a constant loyalty which in life he had enjoyed from few but his soldiers. The fame of his rival suffers no detraction by a fair estimate of Pompey's qualities. It is true that as a politician he was selfish, tortuous in word, ungenerous, greedy of praise. Yet he cared for good government and would give the State unwearying service in return for confidence and compliments. Set

[1] By the current Roman calendar.

to a task within the ambit of his powers, he was clear-headed, swift
and single-minded. Once the task was done virtue went out of
him. His nature forbade him to grasp openly at power and
rendered him maladroit in seeking it. An excellent organizer, a
skilful tactician, a wary yet bold strategist, he was in the field no
unworthy opponent of Caesar himself. Yet at Dyrrhachium
Caesar had been the last soldier in his army to be defeated: at
Pharsalus Pompey was the first. Herein lay the difference between
them, not in technical skill or judgment or resource, but in that
Pompey lacked that fusing together of spirit and intellect that
marks off genius from talent.

Three days after Pompey's death came Caesar. He had marched
to the Hellespont and crossed to Asia Minor, protected by the
news of his victory. There was a story that as he crossed the Straits
his flotilla of small merchant craft was at the mercy of a Pompeian
squadron under one L. Cassius, who surrendered to him. The
story is disproved by the fact that Cassius' galleys do not appear
to be reckoned in the fleet with which Caesar reached Alexandria[1].
Caesar's arrival in Asia saved the treasures of Ephesus which
were on the point of being commandeered by the enemy. For the
moment, since he needed goodwill and cared for good government, he remitted some taxation and made a beginning with an
arrangement by which he improved upon the reforms of Pompey
(see p. 395 and below, p. 712). It could only have been a beginning, for such an arrangement would take a long time. Hearing that
Pompey had been seen at Cyprus, he deduced that he was making
for Egypt, and with a small fleet he set out, taking with him his
800 cavalry and Sixth legion, together with a legion under Calenus
ordered from Achaea. The two legions together only numbered
3200 men.

Off Alexandria he was met by Theodotus bearing the embalmed
head of Pompey and his signet ring. A man of Caesar's generosity could not but be moved by the death of Pompey at the hands
of renegades and aliens. But his sympathy must have been tempered by relief. After Pharsalus no composition was possible.
Pompey stood too high even for Caesar's clemency, and his death,
by his own hand or another's, was necessary. Now Caesar's good
fortune had removed his rival without Caesar's act. After due
respect had been paid to the past greatness of the dead, he might
now take in hand the destruction of the remaining Pompeian
forces. He was free to choose whether he would himself clear up

[1] To judge by Caesar's own statement, *B.C.* iii, 106, 1, 'navibus longis
Rhodiis x et Asiaticis paucis.'

the situation in the East or, sending his army to reinforce Domitius Calvinus who had been dispatched to Asia, go to Italy, transfer his veteran legions to Africa, avenge Curio and prevent a rally of the enemy. Whether he struck first east or west he could count on finishing the war by the next summer, and no one knew better than he the importance of following up a victory. On the other hand, during the next month the etesian winds made it difficult to sail north from Alexandria, and in that short interval it would be profitable to settle the Egyptian succession and exact the money still due to the Triumvirs for the restoration of Auletes.

His force was small, but as he tells us himself he was in the mood to trust to the prestige of Pharsalus. With the contempt of a Roman magistrate for a Hellenistic monarchy he landed with his lictors going before him and announced his intention, as consul, of deciding the fate of the Egyptian throne in the name of the Republic. This insult to a State which was still in name the ally not the servant of Rome, combined with the knowledge that Caesar had in the past sought to bring about the annexation of the country, aroused the populace of Alexandria, which was long accustomed to settle dynastic questions in its own way. The so-called army of occupation—a military Alsatia—was easily roused to resist an intruder by Achillas and by Pothinus, who, whatever his motives and method, sought to maintain the independence of the royal house. Before the etesian winds had ceased to blow, Caesar and his small army found themselves threatened by a siege in the royal quarter of the city.

The king, who had come to Alexandria at his summons, was with him in the palace and it might be possible to extricate himself by pronouncing in Ptolemy's favour and leaving Pothinus to rule in his name. Such a course would not easily commend itself to Caesar, who had already sent to Domitius for reinforcements, but it was quickly prevented. Cleopatra had a right to be heard if Caesar was to be judge, and she contrived to reach the city and to find a boatman to take her to him. She came, saw, and conquered. To the military difficulties of withdrawal in the face of the Egyptian army was added the fact that Caesar no longer wished to go. He was past fifty, but he retained an imperious susceptibility which evoked the admiration of his soldiers. Cleopatra was twenty-one, as ambitious and high-mettled as Caesar himself, a woman whom he would find it easy to understand and admire as well as to love. The path of safety and of self-denying statesmanship led away from Alexandria, but only those who underrate the daring and the egotism of Caesar will be surprised that he did not follow it.

Installed in the palace with Cleopatra as his mistress, he was now bound to maintain himself until he had placed her securely on the throne. The short war which followed taxed his genius to the utmost. The quarter of the city which contained the palace and the theatre had been organized for defence. By a *coup de main* he seized the great lighthouse at the eastern end of the island of Pharos which stretched across the main harbour. The Alexandrian fleet of 72 ships which lay at the quays was burnt and the flames consumed stores of books which legend promoted to be the great Library itself. Caesar had now opened the way to the sea and commanded it with his fleet of 34 ships. But his enemies were neither daunted nor incompetent. The western side of the main harbour was closed by a great mole, the Heptastadium, which they controlled, and beyond it in the Eunostos harbour a new fleet was built. In the meantime Cleopatra's younger sister Arsinoe had escaped from the palace and proposed to play queen to Achillas's general. Achillas was probably anxious to sell his sword to the highest bidder. At least Pothinus sent messages to him from the palace, urging him to hold by the king. The messages were intercepted by Caesar, who put Pothinus to death. Achillas soon after was killed by Arsinoe, who made her own tutor Ganymedes commander-in-chief. The change was of no advantage to the Romans. Their water supply came from cisterns fed by conduits from the higher parts of the town. Ganymedes contrived to raise sea water so as to spoil the water in these conduits. This new form of attack shook the courage of Caesar's legionaries until he set them to dig wells. A night of digging ended in the discovery of a fresh supply.

The day after this danger was averted came a fleet of transports bringing the Thirty-Seventh legion from Syria. Once Caesar had determined to stay at Alexandria he had dispatched a more urgent message to Domitius to send what troops he could by sea and to march himself with the remainder through Syria. Domitius was busy with Pharnaces (see below, p. 676 *sq.*) and though he sent two legions, had to remain himself in Asia Minor with the third. But Caesar had not trusted to Domitius alone. Besides sending messages to the ports of the Levant demanding ships and to Malchus, king of the Nabataeans, for cavalry, he had commissioned a well-born adventurer, Mithridates of Pergamum, to raise any troops he could in Cilicia and Syria and march to Egypt. Mithridates collected a small army from people who had a grudge against Pompey or Egypt, or a sense of the wisdom of backing Caesar. The shrewdest of these was the Idumaean Antipater who had changed sides on the news of Pharsalus (p. 404). The second of

Domitius' legions apparently got no farther than Syria, but before the end of 48 Mithridates was within striking distance of Pelusium, the eastern gate of Egypt. Meanwhile, Caesar had brought in the transports, which had been driven by a south-east wind past the entrance to the Great Harbour. He had set out with his fleet without taking on board the legionaries who were needed to hold the land defences, and he was in some danger from the new Alexandrian fleet which Ganymedes dispatched to cut him off. But the skill of the Rhodian galleys won for him a naval victory, and the transports were towed in triumph into port.

The naval victory was not complete, for darkness had prevented a pursuit of the defeated enemy. By great exertions Ganymedes managed to get ready for sea a considerable fleet including five quinqueremes and twenty-two quadriremes. It was a medley of old and new ships with many improvised oars and, perhaps, ill-trained oarsmen, but Ganymedes made a bid for the command of the sea. Caesar accepted the challenge and advanced against the Eunostos harbour. His fleet was thirty-four ships, six of them quinqueremes and ten quadriremes, manned for this critical engagement with every soldier who could be spared. Between the two fleets were shoals pierced by a narrow passage, and neither for a time ventured to risk the advance which might mean defeat before the supporting ships could deploy. But the Rhodian Euphranor, who acted as admiral, was as bold and skilful on sea as Caesar was on land. Four of his galleys darted through the passage and by a dexterous manœuvring made sea room for the rest. Once Caesar's fleet had got into the harbour, the sailors' battle became a soldiers' battle in the narrow space, and the Alexandrians were driven in flight to the shelter of the Heptastadium and the buildings of the harbour, which were equipped with every kind of artillery.

This victory, too, was incomplete. What was needed was to capture the Heptastadium, and this Caesar now attempted to do. By a surprise attack he captured the whole island of Pharos and secured a footing on the north end of the mole. Next day he launched an assault on the mole itself supported by his fleet. But the impetuosity of his marines and sailors, first in attack and then in flight, ruined Caesar's plans. The Alexandrians fought well, and the assault proved a complete fiasco. Caesar had to swim for his life, and 400 of his precious legionaries perished. He had now no longer men enough to do more than defend himself, and the sea remained disputed by the two fleets. Indeed, in an engagement off the western mouth of the Nile, Euphranor alone distinguished himself. His reward was to be left unsupported so that his ship was sunk with all on board. Caesar had placed in command of the fleet the quaestor Tiberius Nero, the father of the Emperor, whose family believed that he won a victory[1].

In the meantime, Caesar had sent the king to join his subjects. A party among the Alexandrians was weary of the war and of the rule of Arsinoe and Ganymedes; the king would be a rival to their authority and a means of reaching a peace with Caesar, if reinforcements, which were already expected, made him too strong to drive out. Accordingly they requested Caesar to allow the king to leave the palace. This Ptolemy was very ready to do: he hated Cleopatra and Caesar, feared that he would be supplanted by Arsinoe, and hoped to lend his name to a victory over all three. Caesar in turn had good reason to accede to the request, besides the gentlemanly preference for fighting against a king which is adduced by the author of the *Bellum Alexandrinum*. That he can have believed that the king would work for peace is hardly probable, but it was clear that Ptolemy's presence in the enemy's camp would do them little good, and would make Caesar's liaison with Cleopatra pass more smoothly. At an interview rich in dissimulation in which Caesar shrewdly played the dupe, they parted. 'With such alacrity did the king begin to make war against Caesar, that his tears at the interview seemed to have been tears of joy'[2].

It was not long before the war was transferred to the open field. Mithridates had taken Pelusium after a day of hard fighting, and now marched down the eastern branch of the Nile rather than entangle himself in the streams and canals of the Delta. Ptolemy, who appears to have lacked neither energy nor an instinct for war, sent a force to check the advance and then moved the rest of his army by water down the Canopic Nile in the hope of crushing Mithridates before he could join hands with Caesar. But the news had reached the Romans at the same time. Caesar embarked the main part of his army and sailed eastwards as though to reach Mithridates from that side; then with lights out his ships turned and slipped along to the Chersonnesus promontory. Here the troops landed and by a forced march reached the relieving army. Ptolemy posted his forces skilfully and made a stout resistance. Caesar's German cavalry contrived to cross an arm of the Nile which protected one side of the king's position, and the legionaries, making bridges of felled trees, followed their example. The

---

[1] Suetonius, *Tib.* 4; Dio XLII, 40, 6.
[2] *Bell. Alex.* 24, 5.

advanced forces of the Alexandrians were routed, but the main camp of the king held out firmly. The defence seemed to prevail, and most of the troops stationed to guard the rear of the Alexandrian position crossed to the main front to assist or applaud the defenders. This movement on higher ground was detected by Caesar, who promptly sent an experienced officer, Carfulenus, with three cohorts to assault the weakened place. He carried out his task to perfection: the sudden inrush of his troops caused a panic, the Alexandrians broke down the wall of their camp in order to escape by water. In the rout Ptolemy met his death. Leaving the infantry to follow, Caesar rode off to Alexandria, where he was greeted by a population of suppliants, bearing with them the images of their gods, who having failed to bring victory were now mobilized to secure forgiveness for their worshippers. Once more Caesar's skill and good fortune had served him well, though little better than Mithridates of Pergamum.

Caesar passed in triumph through the enemy barricade to greet the handful of men he had left to hold his improvised fortress in Alexandria. He brought to Cleopatra the welcome news of her brother's death, sent Arsinoe to Italy, and proceeded to give effect to the will of Ptolemy Auletes. There survived a younger son, a lad of ten or eleven who was proclaimed the royal consort of Cleopatra as Ptolemy XIII. It is to be assumed that the royal debt to the Triumvirate was paid to its surviving member. It is possible that Caesar promoted in some way the interests of the local Jewish community[1]. The part of the city in which they lived adjoined the royal quarter, and they may well have been of service to Caesar in the siege[2]. Their fellow-countrymen had also been the most forward to supply troops and supplies for the relieving army. All this was for Caesar a few days' work at most: for the next two months he enjoyed the company of Cleopatra and the sights of Egypt. A State barge conveyed him and his mistress up the Nile, while both general and soldiers enjoyed a well-earned holiday.

Yet Caesar's presence was badly needed elsewhere. It was more

[1] On the position of the Jews in Alexandria see above, p. 431, n. 1. Josephus (*Ant.* XIV [X, 1], 188; *c. Apion.* II, 37) declares that a stele attested the right of citizenship granted to them by Caesar. But it is not easy to see how Caesar could have changed whatever civic status they possessed in a kingdom legally independent of Rome. It is perhaps more probable that the stele recorded an act of Augustus. See Th. Reinach in *Rev. des études juives*, LXXIX, 1924, p. 123.

[2] A. Bouché-Leclercq, *Histoire des Lagides*, II, p. 214.

than a year since he had left Rome to take the field against Pompey and during that time things had not gone too well. As has been seen, he had refused to act like a Sulla, or a Catiline, and some of his greedier followers soon showed their disappointment. Above all, Caelius, who had fought in Spain and had been rewarded by election to the office of *praetor peregrinus* for the year 48, had set himself to thwart the administration of the new law of debt by the *praetor urbanus* Trebonius. He soon passed from legal obstruction to rioting, until Servilius, Caesar's colleague in the consulship, invoked the authority of the Senate and put an end to his activities at Rome. Thereupon, after a vain attempt to raise a party in Campania, he joined Milo in the south of Italy. Milo, who had returned from exile in order that his talents in disorder might not be wasted, gave out that he was acting under Pompey's orders while Caelius alleged that he was on his way to join Caesar. Milo tried violence at Cosa, and Caelius tried bribery at Thurii, and both met their death.

After this there was quiet while all men waited for news from beyond the Adriatic. At last came, first rumours and then the certainty of Caesar's victory, presently followed by the arrival of Antony with the legions sent home after Pharsalus. There had been no consular elections for 47 and it was now the end of October according to the calendar in force. Any doubts about the future were soon set at rest. Antony brought word that Caesar wished to be dictator on the same terms as before with himself, Antony, as Master of the Horse. No term was fixed for the dictatorship. The augurs protested against Antony's appointment as not being limited to six months, but the protest was probably bad law and certainly bad policy. At least it was ineffective, and Antony, as Caesar's deputy, assumed control of the administration. His task was not easy: he had to maintain order, to keep Caesar's veterans in a good temper until Caesar returned, and to pursue towards the supporters of Pompey a policy of clemency combined with precaution. During the crisis in Alexandria nothing was heard of Caesar, then came the news that he was victorious but in no hurry to leave Egypt, and then that he had embarked upon a new campaign of uncertain duration. During such time as he could spare from riotous self-indulgence, Antony struggled against difficulties with fair success.

The unextinguished rights of the tribunate were exploited by Cicero's worthless son-in-law Dolabella, who proposed to legislate about debt to the disadvantage of his own creditors and those of other men. He was held in check by his colleague Trebellius, while the Senate passed resolutions that no new laws should be proposed until Caesar returned and, later, that Antony might keep troops within the city. The tribunician opposition to Caesar was becoming serious in his absence; and in the early summer of 47 Antony found it necessary to descend upon the Forum in full force to prevent Dolabella's proposals from being passed into law. Even more troublesome were the legions, who resented the delay in their triumph and discharge. They became a danger to the State and a curse to the townships in which they were billeted. Antony had the prestige born of his own achievements and Caesar's favour, but as the year 47 advanced, even he began to lose his control over troops who were well conscious of their deserts and their own power to enforce their claims[1]. Finally, there were the Pompeians, the possible danger of a sudden stroke from Africa against Italy or the provinces which sent food to Rome, and the difficulty of handling men of position who measured Caesar's mercy by their own and might be driven by fear and a bad conscience to join the enemy in the field or to provoke trouble in Italy or the provinces. The anxieties of such men may be deduced from the letters of Cicero, who added to them estrangement from his wife, quarrels with his brother and disapproval of his son-in-law.

VII. NICOPOLIS AND ZELA

But before Caesar could return to Rome he had a task before him in Asia Minor and Syria. The chief client kings, Ariobarzanes of Cappadocia and Deiotarus, who ruled most of Galatia and Lesser Armenia, had helped his opponents. They were anxious to show their loyalty to the Senate and their gratitude to Pompey. One other, Pharnaces, the son of Mithridates Eupator, preferred to play for his own hand. His rule in the Bosporus was not so much the reward of loyalty to Rome as of disloyalty to his father; now he sought to exploit the absence of Ariobarzanes and Deiotarus by overrunning and annexing Cappadocia and Lesser Armenia. After Pharsalus the two kings hastened to buy their peace from Caesar by engaging to pay subsidies, and Cn. Domitius Calvinus with three legions formed from Pompey's troops was sent to settle the affairs of Asia Minor. Two of these legions were, however, dispatched to help Caesar at Alexandria so that Domitius was left with insufficient forces to deal with Pharnaces, who had withdrawn from Cappadocia, but now was not disposed to

---

[1] Signs of discontent had appeared during the winter 47–46. Cicero, *ad Att.* XI, 10, 2.

evacuate Lesser Armenia. Domitius, who knew that his duty was to reserve for Caesar the profits of Deiotarus' fall from grace, concentrated at Comana in Pontus the best army that he could muster. He had one legion of good troops, the Thirty-Sixth, two of Galatians whom Deiotarus had had trained and armed in the Roman fashion, one hastily raised in Pontus and a modest force of cavalry[1]. With these he advanced as far as Nicopolis, disregarding the embassies and royal presents with which Pharnaces sought to stay his progress, and halting just before an ambush which was prepared to entrap him.

Domitius apparently hoped for a time that Pharnaces would in the end abandon his claims to Armenia, but the king was emboldened by intercepted despatches which told of Caesar's straits at Alexandria and urged Domitius to march to Syria and Egypt. Caesar's instructions were in some way let through to his lieutenant, and Pharnaces in a well-chosen position before Nicopolis waited to see his opponent retire or offer terms. Resolute to do neither, Domitius offered battle. His Pontic and Galatian troops were defeated by the shrewd tactics of the enemy, and only the steadiness of the Thirty-Sixth saved it from destruction[2]. The remnant of the army and the advent of winter protected Western Asia Minor, while Pharnaces overran Pontus, taking town after town, satisfying his avarice with plunder, his cruelty and lust with the castration and dishonour of Roman youths, and his pride with a comparison between his father's fortunes and his own.

One thing was needed to complete the comparison: Mithridates had had to face Sulla, Lucullus and Pompey, Pharnaces had to face Caesar. Late in March, when the season for campaigning in Asia Minor was at hand, Caesar broke off his holiday and sailed from Alexandria for Ptolemaïs Ace in Syria. To protect Cleopatra and her new child-consort he left behind three legions with the son of a freedman[3] to watch his interests. With Caesar went only the Sixth legion barely a thousand strong, but he had at call

[1] *Bell. Alex.* 34, 3–5. The MSS. give 100 cavalry from Deiotarus and as many from Ariobarzanes. The number is reasonably suspect as too small. Domitius also sent for troops from Cilicia, but either Mithridates of Pergamum had already collected the available forces or they had no time to reach Domitius before Nicopolis.

[2] On the topography and the tactics of the battle see Kromayer-Veith, *Schlachten-Atlas*, Röm. Abt. iii, 4, Bl. 21 and Text, on the chronology see Judeich, *Caesar im Orient*, pp. 63 *sqq.*

[3] Rufio or Rufinus, according to the reading in Suetonius, *Div. Iul.* 76. The choice of one below senatorial rank is perhaps an anticipation of the policy of the principate towards Egypt.

the forces of Mithridates and the second legion sent by Domitius, which was still in Syria. The victory at the Nile had restored his prestige so that he could quickly enforce his will wherever he would.

The Jews had deserved well of him and he reversed the arrangements of Gabinius (p. 403) and restored Jerusalem to its predominance, confirming Hyrcanus as High Priest and promoting Antipater to be administrator of Judaea. The walls of the city were to be rebuilt and Joppa, its natural seaport, was restored to the Jews, who were freed from providing winter quarters for Roman troops and for a time at least exempted from paying tribute to Rome. Though these arrangements were referred to the Senate for formal ratification and modified later by Caesar himself, they were practically effective and won for Caesar the goodwill of the Jewish Diaspora, which still cared for the fortunes of their homeland.

From Judaea he passed on to Antioch. Here he rapidly completed his arrangements for Syria and left the province in the charge of Sextus Caesar. He himself sailed from Seleuceia to Tarsus, where he received the representatives from the several communities of Cilicia and also C. Cassius, whom he pardoned; then with the Sixth legion he marched rapidly northwards to Mazaca and thence to the borders of Pontus, where he joined forces with the Thirty-Sixth and the Pontic legion together with a legion and cavalry furnished by Deiotarus.

Pharnaces, divided between fear and the desire to keep what he had won, sent envoys to Caesar, who made a reply which would keep the king within striking distance. He hinted that submission and reparation—so far as reparation was possible—might earn him pardon, and left him to imagine for himself that his opponent was more anxious to leave Asia Minor for Italy than to crush him. Thus Pharnaces lay at Zela, the scene of his father's victory over Triarius, and temporized with growing confidence in his fortune and his subtlety. Caesar drew nearer to his prey, until with a sudden night move he brought his legions within a mile of the enemy. While the legionaries were making their camp on an eminence which faced Pharnaces' army across a narrow valley, the king, who had drawn out his troops in line, suddenly decided that the moment was propitious to attack. The scythed chariots which led the charge were on the Romans before their ranks were formed, but the pila drove them off and the royal infantry as it followed soon met Caesar's men advancing down the slope. The Sixth legion on his right presently bent back the enemy's line, and after some hard fighting the king's army reeled in confusion into the valley and scattered as Caesar's line in turn pressed up the opposing hillside. Pharnaces' camp was stormed and he himself fled in defeat. To the writer of the *Bellum Alexandrinum* the battle was a crowning mercy vouchsafed by gods who intervene most at those crises of war where skill could not decide the issue. Caesar himself summed up this five days' campaign in the famous inscription carried in his triumph—*veni, vidi, vici*. Pharnaces, the dupe of his ambition, his superstitions and his cunning, found in the Bosporus a rebel governor Asander, who treated him as he had treated his father. The kingdom left vacant by his death was granted by Caesar to Mithridates of Pergamum, but the short day of that adventurer's brilliance was soon ended, for in the attempt to establish himself in possession of his new kingdom he was defeated and killed.

Mithridates, furthermore, had a claim which Caesar after Zela satisfied at the expense of Deiotarus. A few years before, that aged intriguer had succeeded in seizing Eastern Galatia, which had belonged to Brogitarus his son-in-law, a friend of Clodius. The Senate had acquiesced in this to the exclusion of Mithridates, the sister's son of Brogitarus, who according to Galatian practice had a claim to succeed. Deiotarus, realizing his danger now that Mithridates had earned Caesar's gratitude, had been diligent in his protestations before Zela and, after all, his troops had shared Caesar's victory as well as Domitius' defeat. But though he was confirmed in his royal title and apparently allowed to retain territory in Central Galatia recently acquired by the killing of another son-in-law Castor, he was compelled to cede Eastern Galatia to Mithridates and to surrender his claim to Lesser Armenia to Ariobarzanes of Cappadocia. If we may trust the son of Castor and discount the advocacy of Cicero, he ventured to meditate the murder of Caesar[1]. It is idle to debate the probability of a charge which does no injustice to Deiotarus' character, but which would be readily invented for that very reason. If the plot was made, it failed. Caesar left Domitius to complete the details of the settlement, entrusting the Thirty-Sixth and Pontic legions to a *legatus*, Caelius Vinicianus, and hastily collected fines and presents to replenish his war-chest, until, about the end of June, he embarked at last for Italy[2].

[1] Cicero, *pro rege Deiotaro*, 5, 15 *sqq.*
[2] He may have intended to go direct from Greece to Sicily for the African campaign and have been deflected to Rome by news of the dangerous feeling of the army. Cicero, *ad Att.* xi, 20, 2.

VIII. THE CAMPAIGN IN AFRICA

By the middle of July Caesar reached Italy and Rome. Civil disorders disappeared, but the mutiny among the legions in Campania had become dangerous. Sallust, sent with promises of 1000 drachmae a head, was answered by volleys of stones and barely escaped with his life. The troops marched on Rome and bivouacked in the Campus Martius demanding their rewards or their discharge. But the sudden appearance of Caesar before them, the old habit of discipline, an appeal veiled in apparent acquiescence and promises, the threat that they should not share Caesar's triumph and the final allocution as 'citizens' brought them to repentance. Eleven years before Caesar had faced discontent by the avowal that he would march against Ariovistus with the Tenth legion only; now he offered to retain all but the Tenth as his soldiers. At last even that legion was restored to his service but not to his real forgiveness. It was to lead the charge at Thapsus and sustain the day at Munda and only then did a remnant of it at last receive its discharge and grants of land in North Italy or Transalpine Gaul. The legions were ordered to prepare for the campaign in Africa and as occasion served the ringleaders were quietly removed.

For Antony who had failed to keep order and Dolabella who had troubled it, Caesar had forgiveness but not favour to bestow. They were compelled to pay the sums they had bid for the confiscated estates of Pompeians and it was over a year before Antony regained Caesar's confidence. Yet the troubles about debts which had caused the disorders were not wholly without ground; and a remission of rents for one year up to 500 denarii at Rome and 125 denarii in the rest of Italy[1] and of interest which had accrued since the outbreak of the war or since the beginning of 48 B.C. was granted. This, together with the effect of his previous edict (p. 655), alleviated the crisis, and at the same time, by Caesar's refusal to go farther, helped to secure the goodwill of those who had had money to lend. While prominent Pompeians received pardon in return for submission, prominent Caesarians received all the rewards which the Republic could offer. Calenus and Vatinius were elected consuls for what remained of the year 47, two additional praetors were chosen for the next year and the colleges of pontifices, augurs and *Quindecimviri sacris faciundis* each received an additional member. The Senate was far below

---

[1] Suetonius, *Div. Iul.* 38; *Fasti Ostienses* (*C.I.L.* xiv, *Suppl.* 4531); Cicero, *de off.* ii, 23, 83; Dio xlii, 51, 1.

strength as a result of the war (see below, p. 730 *sq.*) and new senators were appointed from *equites* and even centurions who had served Caesar well. Reforms had to wait till the formidable forces in Africa were crushed, and Caesar, who still retained the dictatorship and had been elected consul for 46, took the field once more at the end of September.

The danger from Africa had become serious. In the summer of 49 Curio had met with disaster (p. 653). All that Caesar could do at the moment was to have Juba declared a public enemy and to have Bogud and Bocchus, the two kings of Mauretania in the west, recognized as friends and allies of the Roman People. Allied with Juba was Masinissa, who ruled over the part of Numidia which lay between Juba's kingdom and Mauretania. The Roman province of Africa remained in the control of Varus, and both he and Juba were diligent in preparing to defend themselves. In particular the Numidian had part of his native soldiery trained in the Roman fashion and formed into four legions. In the spring of 48 Caesar sent orders to Q. Cassius, his general in Spain, to invade Africa. Cassius began to collect a fleet and was about to set out with four legions when part of his army mutinied and the expedition came to nothing. Indeed Cassius was compelled to call on King Bogud for help in Spain, and at no time during the next three years was there a Caesarian army in Spain sufficiently strong and secure in its hold on the country to detach a force to Africa.

In the autumn of the year 48 came fugitives from Pharsalus and remnants of Pompey's forces, Cato with fifteen cohorts from Dyrrhachium, Labienus with Gallic and German cavalry, Afranius and Petreius, Faustus Sulla, Sextus and Cnaeus, sons of Pompey, and the consular, Q. Caecilius Metellus Pius Scipio, a constellation of names and reputations. The disinterested commonsense which distinguished Cato in the whole war enabled him to secure for Scipio as consular and *imperator* authority over Varus and his own companions in misfortune and perhaps taught Scipio not to neglect the talents of Labienus, the bourgeois renegade. For there are good grounds to suppose that, in the campaign which followed, the skill which so long foiled Caesar and twice brought him within an ace of defeat was the skill of Labienus. The defeat of Curio had shown what Numidian fighting could achieve in Africa, Labienus had always practised the use of cavalry, and with the unconventional resourcefulness in which he rivalled Caesar and surpassed Pompey, he now set himself to perfect combined tactics with his heavy cavalry, Numidian horse and light infantry.

There remained King Juba, *homo superbissimus ineptissimusque.*

Faithful perforce, he made fidelity his sole virtue. From Saburra's victory with cavalry and light-armed troops over legionaries, he had learnt to train Numidians as legionaries and to believe himself a conqueror. His arrogance and the cruelty with which he inspired terror instead of confidence, went far to neutralize the value of his assistance. His forces indeed were considerable. His household troops were a corps of Gallic and Spanish cavalry, his Numidian horse and foot may have amounted to 30,000 men, and he boasted the possession of rather more than sixty elephants. In the end, these animals were to prove a disastrous possession, but in the early stages of the campaign Caesar had to treat them with respect. Masinissa, the ally of Juba, was also not negligible in the field. Even more formidable were the forces which the Pompeians had collected by the end of the year 47—ten legions (perhaps 35,000 men), light-armed troops, archers, javelin men and slingers, and nearly 15,000 cavalry of all kinds. The infantry was in part of good quality; even without Juba's help the cavalry greatly out-numbered any mounted troops that Caesar could hope to raise and transport to Africa.

The invasion of Africa had thus become an enterprise which demanded the attention of Caesar himself and his veterans. It was not a task for recruits only; but the use of the veteran legions who had already shown their desire for triumph and discharge, meant a speedy beginning. Nor was delay Caesar's habit, and, so far as personal feelings affected his calculations, he must have been eager to take revenge for his friend Curio. The Pompeians had collected a fair-sized fleet, some fifty or sixty ships of war, and Caesar had not the means or the time to secure to himself the decisive superiority by sea. Nor had he the transports to bring across from Sicily, his advanced base, the whole of his army. He designed to use ten legions in all, five of them veteran reinforced by drafts, five of them recruits, some 2500 men who had been left behind as invalids when he crossed to fight Pompey, something less than 4000 cavalry, perhaps 3000 light-armed troops whom he reinforced from the crews of his fleet. These forces were none too large, and it was to be three months from the opening of the campaign before they were all concentrated in Africa. In Africa itself Caesar could look for some help. The kings of Mauretania could be trusted to attack their eastern neighbours Masinissa and Juba at the right moment, and draw off perhaps half their strength. One ally more there was, an adventurer from Nuceria in Campania, P. Sittius, who had left a Rome full of creditors to mend his fortunes in Spain and then, for nearly twenty years, to serve the princes of Mauretania with a private army and tiny fleet of his own. Caesar's necessity was to be his opportunity, and he seized it with both hands. Finally, there was the effect on the communities of Africa of the harsh tactlessness of Scipio, the fear of the barbarian Juba, and the prestige of Caesar's victories, which lured over deserters even when his prospects seemed darkest.

The Pompeians could not be taken by surprise; they had garrisoned most of the seaports, strengthened many of the towns and accumulated vast stores of provisions. As early as January 47 Cicero believed in their strength and preparedness[1]. The need for haste meant that the enemy's convoys must cross amid the storms of the late autumn and winter. But Caesar had, before now, trusted the chances of the sea and the caution of his opponents. On 8 October he sailed from Lilybaeum with the troops then available, six legions and seven cohorts, 2600 cavalry[2], and a small force of light-armed troops. Of these legions one only, the Fifth, was veteran; the great adventure began without the most famous of his soldiers, the Ninth, the Thirteenth, the Fourteenth and the Tenth. His objective, known to himself alone, was probably Hadrumetum[3], where he arrived after coasting south from Cape Bon, but with only a small part of his ships. The remainder were scattered by a storm and were seeking safety and their secretive general. With only 3000 infantry and 150 cavalry under his hand he could not hope to take Hadrumetum, which was held in force, and he moved on to Leptis some seven miles to the south. The city went over to him and gave him a harbour, where indeed there arrived at once galleys and transports which increased his infantry to some 5000 men. Leaving six cohorts in Leptis, he decided to occupy the plateau near Ruspina some four miles to the north. Rabirius Postumus was dispatched to Sicily to hasten the embarkation of the rest of the army and the historian Sallust to raid the island of Cercina where the enemy had deposited stores of corn.

Of the campaign which followed there has survived, in the *Bellum Africum*, a plain tale. The writer, a trained soldier but not in Caesar's immediate confidence, has written an account in straightforward Latin which is what presumably it was meant to be, excellent raw material of history. The defects are few compared with those of most ancient accounts of warfare. Events are dated and distances are given: it is not the writer's fault that the manu-

---

[1] Cicero, *ad Att.* xi, 10, 2.   [2] Rice Holmes, *op. cit.* iii, p. 534.
[3] Gsell, *op. cit.* viii, p. 61. Clupea and the coast near Utica was strongly held by the enemy.

script tradition has dealt hardly with them. This fact, however, and a certain parsimony in the points of the compass have caused some topographical perplexities which no research can wholly resolve[1]. Here and there, as in the description of the battle of Thapsus itself, the writer has been content to limit his account to the events at which he was present. Far more important than any defects of detail is the merit of its sobriety which enhances the picture of the greatness of Caesar, the faith which he inspired in his men, his unfailing resource and courage, the peculiar blend of aristocrat and democrat which made him the greatest soldiers' general of history. Granted the final result, the details of the campaign have little importance for general history and will not here be set out at length.

The distribution of the enemy forces was as follows. Cato was in command at Utica where his firmness and fair dealing held in check the Caesarian sympathies of the city. Here, too, was General Headquarters with Scipio at the head of eight legions and most of the cavalry. Considius at Hadrumetum had two legions; the remaining Pompeian forces were in garrison; Juba was still in Numidia. It was all-important to crush Caesar's advance guard, and on the news of his landing Labienus set out with cavalry and light infantry from Utica, closely followed by other forces of the same type under Petreius and Calpurnius Piso. From the north came Scipio, from the west Juba. Caesar was half surprised and almost defeated by Labienus and Petreius as he sought to collect provisions. A brilliantly bold manœuvre in which his alternate cohorts faced about so as to attack simultaneously on both fronts saved him. Then came three weeks of waiting behind fortified lines while Caesar on the plateau of Ruspina trained his recruits and was slowly strengthened by the arrival of ships from his first convoy. Juba had been compelled to return to Numidia by the timely intervention of Bocchus of Mauretania and Sittius, but he left behind him some cavalry and thirty elephants. Even without his help, Scipio was too strong for Caesar to venture on an offensive. At last the second part of the expedition arrived bringing the Thirteenth and Fourteenth legions, 800 cavalry and 1000 archers and slingers.

[1] All previous studies of these problems are superseded by the masterly discussion of them by Veith in *Antike Schlachtfelder*, III (to which should be added *ib.* IV, pp. 647 *sqq.* and *Schlachten-Atlas*, Röm. Abt. III, 4, Bl. 22 and text). Even Dr Rice Holmes *op. cit.* and M. Gsell have been able to add little. The few points of topography in which this account differs from the evidence of Veith will be seen by a comparison of Map 16 with *Schlachten-Atlas*.

With their arrival the initiative passed to Caesar. He had now concentrated eight legions, three of them veteran, and might hope for victory in a pitched battle if the enemy had no advantage in position, and if a battle could be brought about before Juba returned to reinforce Scipio. Furthermore the *place d'armes* at Ruspina was not easily provisioned and Caesar's horses had begun to suffer from lack of fresh fodder, like those of Pompey at Dyrrhachium. Accordingly on the night of 7 November Caesar moved out and posted himself on a group of low hills six or seven miles to the south. This movement extended the area from which he could draw supplies but it failed of its main purpose. Scipio encamped so as to be able to use the town of Uzita to strengthen his position, and could not be brought to offer battle except at an advantage. Juba left Saburra to make head against Sittius and joined Scipio, even though his pride compelled him to keep his forces in a separate camp. It is alleged by Dio[1] that he was promised the Roman possessions in Africa as the price of his help. Such a promise was of little value, but it would not be made except in straits worse than those in which Scipio found himself. Caesar, now further reinforced by the arrival of the Ninth and Tenth legions, sought to force on a battle by extending his lines so as to threaten Uzita, but again he was foiled by the skilful use of the terrain by his opponents. Labienus was indefatigable in hampering the collection of supplies, and despite a success against him Caesar once more decided to move his ground. Varus with a fleet of fifty-five ships had attempted to dominate the coast from Hadrumetum, whereupon Caesar, turning admiral, had hunted him home again. He might now leave Acholla, Ruspina and Leptis to the protection of garrisons and of his ships, and himself march farther south, where in a war of manœuvre he might again try to bring on a decisive battle. His troops, in particular the Fifth legion, had been carefully trained in anti-elephant warfare at the expense of beasts brought from Italy.

The campaign now enters its third phase. Ten weeks after leaving Ruspina[2], Caesar set fire to his camp and marched to a place called Aggar, which lies about twenty miles south south-east from Uzita. In this region he might hope to entice the enemy to a general engagement or force them to fight to cover some town which held supplies. But Scipio would not gratify him. What with spies, deserters and cavalry vedettes, both sides received as much

---

[1] XLIII, 4, 6.

[2] 26 Jan. to about 15 March by the uncorrected calendar. There is to be reckoned in an intercalary month of 23 days.

intelligence as was good for them. A sudden stroke at the town of Zeta was countered by an attack on Caesar's legions as they marched wearily home again and a second time the tactics of Labienus nearly triumphed. Caesar then moved on Sarsura, where he massacred the Numidian garrison and seized the supplies of wheat collected in it. Rather more than ten miles to the south lay a greater prize, Thysdrus, where the concentration of 300,000 modii (75,000 bushels) of corn was reported. But Caesar found the town strongly held by Roman troops and hard to besiege from lack of water in the neighbourhood. There was nothing for it but to return to Aggar. Four months of warfare had yielded no decisive advantage. A few towns offered their services to Caesar but each offer contained the request for a garrison, and there were few troops to spare. To one place, Vaga, help was sent too late and Juba had massacred the inhabitants. Now came envoys from Thabaena fifty miles south along the coast. The inhabitants had begun by killing the royal garrison and this *fait accompli* forced Caesar's hand, so that he sent three cohorts, archers and war machines to protect them.

Drafts amounting to 4000 legionaries, 400 cavalry and 1000 archers and slingers had arrived from Sicily. It was the moment to strike a decisive blow. Hitherto strategical prudence and tactical resource had baffled Caesar's skill. Only in a pitched battle on equal ground with a limited front could the fighting power of his infantry overcome the superior numbers of the enemy and neutralize the effect of their cavalry. To bring about this battle needed a dangerous master-stroke, and Caesar's daring and genius rose to the emergency. Fifteen miles to the north of him lay Thapsus, on the sea, approached by the necks of land either side of a wide lagoon. The city was in sympathy hostile to Caesar and was held by a strong garrison. By a night march Caesar reached the eastern of the two isthmuses, organized a line of defence near the southern end of it and advanced on the city. What was Scipio now to do? He might stay where he was—like Dogberry. He might advance to his previous position near Uzita and thus circumscribe the area of Caesar's supplies in the hope that they would give out before the city fell. He might move his whole army as near as he could to the city and thus hamper the siege. The first course would destroy his prestige, the second and third might save Thapsus but would leave Caesar free to march away. For that he would offer battle at a disadvantage was not to be hoped. There remained one other strategy: to pen in Caesar by holding the two necks of land until he starved. This promised victory, but it meant a division of forces which was dangerous. However, if all went well, the skill of legionaries in field fortification might neutralize the danger. For the prize the risk was worth taking. Scipio marched to the eastern isthmus and was held up by Caesar's line of defence. He thereupon halted and leaving the consular Afranius and Juba to block that way, he made a night march with the greater part of his own army round the western side of the lagoon and at dawn he was no more than a mile from his opponent, who had moved to the west side of the city (6 February).

This was the moment for which Caesar had looked so long. His enemy lay with the sea on one flank, the lagoon on the other, too near to retreat to safety. The temptation to advance to the narrowest part of the isthmus had been too strong for Scipio to resist, or he had forgotten that Caesar might have divined his movements. Leaving two legions to secure him against a sortie from the city, Caesar advanced with the remainder, sending his ships on ahead to demonstrate at the right moment against Scipio's rear. The main body of the enemy army was drawn up to cover the work of entrenching, the elephants on the wings, the legions in the centre. Caesar had four of his veteran legions in line and the Fifth with light-armed troops divided so as to deal with the elephants. Their special training was not to be wasted. On the left his advance had been through marshy ground and Caesar waited for that wing to come into alignment before he gave the signal for attack[1]. As each corps came into line he addressed it—in what terms of confident triumph may be imagined.

There was time to spare: the enemy could not disengage themselves and the blow would be heaviest if it fell all along the line. But the fighting spirit of his veterans was impatient. Their general had given them a battle, and they would wait no longer for the perfection of his art. On the right, where the Tenth legion stood, a trumpet sounded the charge and the line moved forward sweeping with it the centurions as they struggled to hold back their men. Caesar mounted and led the charge. The elephants on the enemy left crushed their way back towards their own camp; the Fifth legion dealt with the remainder. With the left wing broken, the army of Scipio was soon swept away in flight. While part of his troops kept up the pursuit Caesar, apparently with the remainder, marched past the city along the eastern isthmus and appeared before the camp of Afranius and Juba. The consular and the king had already fled at the news of Scipio's defeat. Caesar had now headed off part of the fugitives from the battle who had streamed

[1] See Veith, *Antike Schlachtfelder*, III, p. 841, IV, p. 653.

back along the route on which they had marched the night before. They gathered on a hill, laid down their arms and asked for quarter. But Caesar's troops, exasperated by weeks of fruitless marching and fighting, were in no mood for the decencies of warfare. Despite the efforts of their general and his officers they killed their helpless enemies to the last man.

The strategy by which Caesar had brought off the battle of Thapsus was his crowning masterpiece. The campaign was over; in three weeks all Roman Africa was in his hands. In Numidia Sittius had defeated Juba's general Saburra. The king himself with Petreius had reached his capital Zama. Before he marched he had prepared a vast pyre on which, if he was defeated, he proposed to immolate his wealth, his subjects, his family and himself. In this high act the people of Zama were unwilling to play their part and closed the gates against him. He and Petreius decided to die: one killed the other and then himself. Masinissa vanished from the scene, and his son Arabion escaped to Spain. The greater part of the kingdom of Juba was annexed to make a province of Africa Nova, while the western dominions of Masinissa were given to Bocchus, the eastern to Sittius, who added to them a strip of territory that had belonged to Juba.

Gnaeus Pompeius, after failing to gain a footing in Mauretania, had long ago established himself in the Balearic Islands whence, about this time, he moved to Spain, and his brother Sextus, Labienus and Attius Varus escaped to join him. Afranius and Faustus Sulla fell into the hands of Sittius who brought them to Caesar. Whether at his order or not they were put to death. Scipio attempting flight by sea fell in with the fleet of Sittius and stabbed himself. As the enemy sailors hunted for him on his ship, they found him dying and asked him where was the *imperator*. His answer was—*imperator bene se habet*. His generalship may have been borrowed from Labienus, his faults and his courage were his own. There remained Cato in Utica. He strove first to make good the defence of the city while there was any hope, and then to save the inhabitants from the cruelty of the desperate fugitives from the battle. By 10 February the cavalry of Caesar's advance guard were within two days' march of Utica and all was lost. Then with the calm of a Stoic and a Roman noble Cato took his life.

The death of Cato was justly regarded as the end of the Civil War, so far as that was a conflict in arms between Caesar and the traditions of the Republican constitution. However little Cato's abilities and opinions matched the needs of Rome, he stood alone among his generation in devotion to a cause and an ideal without any thought for his own advancement. In the war itself he had shown not only courage and capacity but a rare willingness to subordinate himself loyally even to Pompey, whom he must have distrusted. The Republic had come to need great men and had to pay them their price, which Cato would never have paid. The gods were right in preferring the winning cause, but Cato did not die in vain. The idea of the Republic was kept alive by the death of a martyr. Vastly superior as Caesar was to Cato in intellectual power and breadth of vision, he saw in him a man before whom his genius was rebuked, as was Macbeth's by Banquo; and knowing that Cato was more dangerous dead than living, he pursued him, alone of his opponents, with rancour and calumny until he himself perished, the victim of the ideas for which Cato had died.

There remained Caesar's triumph for which his legions had fought so many years. It was to eclipse the memory of Pompey and to show Caesar not as the victor in a civil war but as the man who had defended and advanced the frontiers of the Empire. On four several days, for Gaul, for Egypt, for Pontus and for Africa, the procession passed on its way to the Capitol, with senators and magistrates, trumpeters, spoils and pictures, prisoners, Arsinoe, a princess of Egypt, Juba, a prince of Numidia, and Vercingetorix, who was to be led away to be strangled, for Caesar had for a barbarian who had been dangerous no more mercy than any other Roman of his day. After the prisoners came Caesar himself, and then the legions, those incomparable veterans, singing ribald songs about their baldheaded general. A train of waggons, laden with gold and golden crowns, carried their reward, for every legionary five thousand denarii, for every centurion ten thousand. Even after these bounties were distributed and after each of the spectators had received a hundred denarii, there remained a great treasure[1]. When the last day was over, Rome abandoned itself to a feast at twenty-two thousand tables; the dictator was escorted to his house with elephants carrying linkmen on either side. His daughter, Pompey's wife, at last received commemoration in shows of plays, a mimic naval action, a battle between prisoners of war and criminals, a hunt of four hundred lions and of giraffes. A Basilica Julia and a Forum Julium, both of which Augustus was to complete, were solemnly dedicated and with them a temple of Venus Genetrix. During the triumph

---

[1] The plentiful *aurei*, each of the value of 25 denarii, which were issued in this year, attest the distribution of these donatives. See Volume of Plates, IV, 12 d.

Caesar's chariot had broken down before Lucullus' temple of
Fortune, and his 'old grumblers' had rioted because there was
lavished on shows money that might have been given to them.
Caesar himself seized a ringleader and had him led to execution.
If Dio is to be trusted, two others were solemnly sacrificed in the
Campus by the priest of Mars. In accordance with custom,
Caesar had ascended the steps of Juppiter's Temple on his knees
each day of his triumph to lay his laurels on the altar of the god.
The awnings which protected the people were of the silk which
had begun to come from the East to be the standard luxury of
Rome under the Empire. In such a setting of the old and the new,
of open triumph and inward resentment, the Civil War ended.

CHAPTER XVII

CAESAR'S DICTATORSHIP

I. CAESAR AND CICERO

ALTHOUGH Caesar's triumph was to mark his services to the State, pictures were carried showing the deaths of Scipio, Petreius and Cato, to point the moral that Caesar's enemies had fought for an enemy of Rome. No mention was made of Pompey or Spain or of Pharsalus, just as Pompey refused the antecedents of a triumph after his success before Dyrrhachium. But to the old governing class at Rome there was a distinction. Although the Optimates, preferring King Log to King Stork, had fought with Pompey, they did not wholly forget that in one aspect the Civil War was between two great military chiefs both of whom had made their name in defiance of the traditions of the Republic. To them the men who fought in Africa stood more clearly for the good cause than Pompey had done. The harassing doubts which filled Cicero's letters to Atticus in the early months of 49 were not merely native vacillation and the desire for *otium cum dignitate*: they were in part due to the realization that the victory of Pompey might mean proscriptions and a time like that of the *Sullanum regnum*[1].

Cicero decided that he ought to be grateful to Pompey and in the end followed his fortunes till Pharsalus. He then saw that there was a choice, between the acceptance of defeat in the hope that Caesar would take the fruits of his victory and then leave the Republic intact, and the renewal of war in Africa in the hope not so much of victory as of forcing Caesar to a compromise. Caesar's year in Egypt and Asia Minor made an opening for the second alternative[2] so that the growing power of his enemies in Africa prevented the general submission which he might have achieved had he returned to Italy in 48. Moreover, the uncertainties and disorders during Caesar's absence prevented the realization of peace and economic stability and enhanced the doubts of Caesar's intentions which throughout his career had hampered him. When

---

[1] *ad Att.* IX, 7, 3; 10, 2; 10, 6; 11, 3; X, 7; XI, 6, 2; 6, 6; cf. *ad fam.* IV, 9, 3; V, 21, 3; VII, 3, 2.
[2] *ad fam.* XV, 15, 2.

he did appear in the summer of 47 he had no time to do much more than prepare for the African campaign, and the respectability of his opponents imposed on him the character of a revolutionary. But when he returned after Thapsus there was the chance of some kind of a reconciliation.

In 49 Caesar's clemency had been doubted; by 47 no sane man could doubt it any longer. Cicero realized that the troubles of the State were not all Caesar's fault: the danger was that he would be the prisoner of his victory and be obliged to give way to the group of adventurers who had helped him[1]. As early as March 48 Caelius had written to Cicero of his dislike for Caesar's followers[2]. Caesar himself had realized the desirability of working with the Senate during a time when it was not yet flooded by his adherents, that is if we may suppose that Antony during the year after Pharsalus acted in the general spirit of instructions from his leader. Cicero was inclined to abandon himself wholly to letters, but he felt it his duty to miss no opportunity of assisting a reconciliation which would mean the end of Caesar's autocracy[3]. It was impossible for the ordinary Roman of the governing class to accept the abstinence or exclusion of the members of the *nobilitas*, who through the Senate had come to mean Rome more definitely than the Populus Romanus itself. It is true that Cicero's own writings betray a consciousness that the Republic, if it meant simply free play for the rival ambitions of the nobles, was outworn: he had hoped for a closing of the ranks, including the bringing in of the Equites and a general effort for government by consent between the governors. This was the Concordia Ordinum, and it had failed. The State needed a great servant who, without replacing the traditional government by the Senate, would keep it steady to its task.

In the *de Re publica* he may have thought that this could be done by persuasion by such a statesman as he believed himself to be, but the Civil War had shown that arms went over political wisdom. He may have hoped (though his letters give no hint of it) that Pompey with the prestige of his victories would be this servant of the State if Caesar was defeated. Now he saw clearly how great Caesar's dominance had become, and he must have realized that Caesar was not the man to resume his place as one among a ruling aristocracy. His hope, then, was that Caesar would be induced to content himself with the position, not of an abdicated Sulla but of the armed protector of a free Republic. Caesar's control of the armies of the State would at least prevent

---

[1] *ad fam.* IV, 9, 3.   [2] *Ib.* VIII, 17, 2.   [3] *Ib.* VII, 33, 2.

the ambitions of others from taking that turn, and he might be willing to 'restore the Republic' in this sense, and then satisfy himself by warfare in the East as Pompey had done. The symptoms would be a readiness to employ the *nobiles*, to win them to employment by further pardons and to carry through needed reforms at once. In September 46 Cicero believed that he descried these signs of hope. He engaged in correspondence with those who were not reconciled to Caesar or who feared him. When Caesar was moved by the entreaties of the Senate to grant safe return to M. Marcellus, one of the bitterest and most intransigent of his opponents, Cicero delivered a splendid speech. It is addressed both to the aristocracy and to Caesar. The Optimates are not to sacrifice their self-respect. The conflict had been a great visitation; and the accounts of right and wrong were closed. Caesar's way of victory had taken the sting from defeat. Caesar had a great task of social reform: he had to heal the wounds of the State; and beyond that he had a great duty—to give stability to the State. It is not an invitation to live to be an autocrat, but to restore the Republic first to health and then to activity under his protection.

Cicero was not alone in urging upon Caesar a programme of social and economic reform. To the same year belongs a pamphlet which is possibly the work of the historian Sallust, who had been employed by Caesar in Illyricum in 49 and was appointed to govern Africa after Thapsus. The writer seeks to show that the less reputable followers of Caesar had left him, adjures him to be deaf to those of the remainder who urge him to be as cruel as his enemies would have been, and to establish harmony in the State. He points out the uselessness of the attempt to set up again old standards of conduct by forbidding people to spend beyond their incomes. He sees the root of all evil in the worship of wealth. There are a few definite proposals: the equalization of military service, the extension of *frumentationes* to municipia and colonies for the benefit of time-expired soldiers. Small as is the value of the pamphlet as evidence of the wisdom of its author, and little as it befits the character of Sallust—if it is indeed his work—it is an indication that among Caesar's followers there were those who advocated reforms or, at the least, believed that such advocacy would be welcome to him.

But Caesar was not the man to be guided by pamphlets or even by Cicero's political philosophy. Cicero was a man of the city, trained in the practice of Roman domestic politics, the theory of the Greek city-state and of the ancient tradition of the Republic. For a year he had governed Cilicia with a care for the provincials which deserves far more credit than his complacency makes it easy to give. But for him government meant government guided by speeches in the Curia. For nine years Caesar had conquered Gaul with the autocracy of an *imperator* in the field, and for nearly four years he had won victories while his lieutenants suffered reverses. Such a man, conscious that there was much to do and little time to do it in, was not likely to content himself with playing protector to lesser men or to see others fumble where his own sure hand could guide the event. In the sphere of thought or letters he knew Cicero for at least his equal, but in the world of action he knew that he stood alone. He was not a fatalist nor a theorist. The fatalism which led Sulla to abdicate, the waiting on events which hampered Pompey's statesmanship, the illusions which beset Cicero's judgment of situations if not of men, the inflexible Stoic ideals which made Cato a citizen of Plato's Republic not of 'the dregs of Romulus' found no echo in his positive active spirit. The ancient tradition that Rome was greater than Rome's greatest man meant nothing in such a Rome to such a man. Men and fortune, the only things that existed for his philosophy and his adventurous spirit, had so far yielded to his genius; and his genius would dominate them still or fall greatly. Against both his armour had been not longdrawn calculation but the swift unerring exploitation of the moment, the realization of the probable immediate consequence. He had become what Cicero had once ruefully called him, 'a portent of incredible speed, application and insight.'

As the year 46 ended it became clear that he was in no hurry to 'reconstitute the Republic.' He was consul and dictator. No elections had been held for the ordinary magistracies for 45, and now he set out for Spain, leaving Rome and Italy to be governed in his absence by Lepidus, his colleague as consul and his *magister equitum*, and by eight *praefecti*, who enjoyed praetorian rank. The wishes of the dictator were known during his absence mainly from the unofficial pronouncements of his confidants Oppius and Balbus, with whom he corresponded in a simple cypher. Envoys from foreign States waited for Caesar's return, and while the day to day administration could be carried on, no policy could be initiated, and apparently, as during his absence at Alexandria, it was not possible to hold elections or to pass laws.

Nothing made Caesar's autocracy more apparent and more galling than the paralysis induced by his absence. Cicero's letters show a rapid change of feeling. This is partly due to misery because of the death of his daughter but partly to political disillusionment. He recognized that it would be disastrous to see the young Pompey victorious, to exchange a gentle old master for a savage new one. But it was already known that Caesar's victory in Spain would only be the prelude to a war in the East. A message was transmitted to Cicero that the dictator meditated 'reconstituting the Republic,' before he launched this great adventure, and the orator prepared to send to Caesar such political advice as, he thought, Aristotle or Theopompus might have addressed to Alexander. But it was soon made clear to him that Caesar would not welcome counsels that did not echo his true intentions[1]. Nor was even Caesar's clemency without an exception. Laudations of Cato drew from him a pamphlet in which he sought to blacken the memory of the man who, secure in his grave at Utica, seemed to embody the ideals of the Republic. When Caesar returned from Spain in September 45 to celebrate a triumph over the sons of Pompey it was soon apparent that the day for the adaptation of his power to the practice, if not the forms, of the Republic was past.

II. CAESAR'S LEGISLATION

The hope that Caesar would stand aside was vain. On the other hand he needed no exhortation from Cicero to take in hand the remedying of abuses, and the improvement of public efficiency.

The legislation for which Caesar was responsible down to his return from Africa, whether by edict, instructions to praetors, laws passed in his own name or under the name of others, was either the implementing of an old programme or the meeting of a financial emergency. The Transpadane Gauls and any non-citizens in the Cispadane area had been granted the full franchise which Crassus and Caesar had intended they should have twenty years before (p. 481). It was the completion of the work of the Social War justified by the Romanization of that region. The restoration of political exiles was an old feature in Caesar's policy, though the need of attracting adherents extended it to characters who had been justly punished, even when justice was not in the minds of their judges. The measures about debt and house-rents were a mitigation of the effects of the Civil War and of the uncertainty that immediately preceded it. The legislation which followed Thapsus was in the main the rapid removal of existing abuses or inconveniences. Caesar had a keen eye for abuses and a quick hand in removing them. We may suppose that during

[1] *ad. Att.* XII, 40, 2, 51, 2; XIII, 26, 2, 27, 1, 28, 2–3, 31, 3. Cf. Ed. Meyer, *Caesars Monarchie,* 2nd ed., pp. 438 *sqq.*

his brief stay in Rome in 47 he laid down the general lines of legislation which were filled in by the activities of his agents and helpers at Rome. Even so, all admiration is due to the speed of his reforming activity.

Between the solar year which had been calculated by Alexandrian astronomers and the Roman calendar year of 355 days there was a hiatus of $10\frac{1}{4}$ days which was from time to time closed by the intercalation of a month at the discretion of the *pontifices*. But their discretion was governed by all manner of motives and its application or neglect alike caused inconvenience. Nothing more strikingly attests the Romans' tolerance of traditional abuses than the fact that since 52 B.C. there had been only one intercalation, and that the calendar was still two months in advance of the seasons. The blame for this must rest mainly on Caesar as Pontifex Maximus. Now he was also dictator, and he added two months, amounting to 67 days, between the last day of November and the first day of December. This, together with an intercalation earlier in the year, caused the kalends of January 709 A.U.C. to coincide with the 1st of January in the solar year which we call 45 B.C.[1] The ten additional days were distributed over the months, and the quarter of a day was provided for by the intercalation of a day every four years after the 23rd of February[2]. In the addition of the days care was taken to avoid disturbing the incidence of Roman festivals. Thus was constructed the Julian year which apart from a slight correction made in the Middle Ages has ruled Europe from Caesar's day to this.

Less admirable was Caesar's activity in the restraint of luxury and ostentation. The reckless profusion of his triumph did not seem to Romans inconsistent with the attempt to impose a check on private extravagance; and Greek and Roman alike, Sulla no less than Plato, believed that sumptuary laws were both enforceable and worth enforcing. To this illusion Caesar fell a ready victim. The wearing of pearls and purple, the riding in litters, the cost of sepulchral monuments, the sale of various comestibles were subjected to regulation or prohibition. Lictors and soldiers were

---

[1] Mommsen's view (*Staatsrecht*[3], i, p. 600), that it was Caesar who finally made the calendar year begin on Jan. 1 (thus agreeing with the consular year) is definitely disproved by the fragments of the pre-Caesarian Calendar of Antium (published by G. Mancini in *Notizie degli Scavi*, 1921, pp. 73 *sqq*).

[2] Possibly because of a misunderstanding of the phrase 'quarto quoque anno,' there were three too many intercalations in the first 36 years of the new system. This was put right by Augustus, who omitted the intercalations of 5 and 1 B.C. and A.D. 4.

active in guarding markets and invading dining rooms, until Caesar
went off to Spain and Roman society returned to practices which
public sentiment did not condemn. Of more practical advantage
to the State were measures aimed at securing public order in Rome
and Italy. The existing law against the promotion of violence was
strengthened by the introduction of the penalty of outlawry[1], and
the *collegia*, which since the tribunate of Clodius had been the
instruments of factious violence, were abolished with the exception
of those which were of ancient origin and of those of the Jews who
enjoyed Caesar's favour for their services and whose associations
had presumably no political complexion. More efficacious for the
time being was the readiness to use troops to reinforce the lictors,
the only civil police force known to the Roman State. Finally, as
will be seen later, Caesar took steps to reduce the ill-occupied
rabble that filled the city.

In Italy, especially in the south, there were bands of rough
herdsmen on the great estates from among whom Pompey had
raised troops of cavalry and Milo had sought to collect insurgents
during the troubles of 48 B.C. Where such bands were slaves they
might be encouraged to rise in rebellion either for or against their
masters. On the other hand, it was not possible to destroy the
only practicable method of ranching without striking at private
property in a way which Caesar was careful to avoid. As a pallia-
tive of this possible evil he passed a law that one-third at least of
these shepherds and herdsmen should be recruited from among
men of free birth. For such a measure there was precedent in
earlier legislation, and the law had the further advantage that the
provision of employment for free citizens could not but benefit
both society and the State. From such hardy rustics legions could
be raised, and, if Caesar contemplated the disbandment of the
over-numerous soldiers who had not as yet earned land allotments,
it was important that they should find a means of livelihood. The
re-imposition of the customs duties which had been abolished in
60 B.C. may have had some slight effect in encouraging Italian
industries, but it is not probable that they were intended for this
purpose, for they were small and levied also on exports.

There is one other measure attributed to Caesar which is not
alien to the spirit of his legislation. In the legislation of his first
consulship in 59 B.C. he gave a precedence among civilian settlers
to men who were the fathers of three or more children (p. 517).
Though there were good practical reasons for this, apart from the
desire to see a prolific citizen population, he may have detected

---

[1] Cicero, *Phil.* 1, 9, 23.

the danger of a falling Italian birthrate. Now, in his dictatorship, if we may trust Dio[1], he offered privileges to the fathers of large families. But his action is described as consequent on a general census which it is certain that he did not carry out, and it appears not improbable that either Dio or some authority which he is using has credited Caesar with what is an anticipation of the lawgiving of Augustus[2].

In the sphere of criminal law Caesar carried farther the work of Sulla. The sanctity which hedged the life of a citizen was a tradition too strong to break, but if we may accept a statement of Suetonius, who cites the authority of Cicero, those guilty of *parricidium* forfeited the whole of their property, those guilty of other offences the half of it[3]. Of crimes against the State *maiestas* as well as the promotion of violence was punished by outlawry. Consistent with this and in the spirit of Sulla was the enactment of a law which limited governorships in consular provinces to two years, in praetorian provinces to one. At the worst, this was the extension of patronage and a concession to avarice, even if Caesar might hope to curb the worst excesses of governors by the enforcement of his earlier law *de repetundis*; at the best, it was the sacrifice of the provincials to the security of the home government. As the Empire was to demonstrate, what the provinces needed was government by men who were adequately paid and allowed to remain in provinces after they had acquired a knowledge of them. The salutary law of Pompey that no consular should proceed to a province until five years after his consulship was allowed to lapse. But in defence of Caesar it should be said that the Optimates had set the example of disregarding it at the outbreak of the Civil War, and that the immediate purpose of Pompey's law was to hinder bribery, which was less a danger now that office went more by Caesar's favour than by that of the Roman People.

It is not certain whether all these laws were passed before Caesar went to his last campaign in Spain, but enough was done to prove, if it needed proving, that he was whole-heartedly bent upon reform as he understood it.

Finally, it is convenient to take account of the laws which were still being prepared at the time of Caesar's death. A bronze table found at Heraclea in the south of Italy[4] contains drafts of four

---

[1] XLIII, 25, 2.

[2] See J. S. Reid in *J.R.S.* v, 1915, p. 215.

[3] Suetonius, *Div. Iul.* 42, 3, 'ut Cicero scribit.' The passage of Cicero, which we may fairly suppose to have existed, has not survived.

[4] Bruns, *Fontes*[7], 18; E. G. Hardy, *Six Roman Laws*, pp. 149 *sqq.*

measures which were produced from among Caesar's papers and which, although they still lacked final revision, were given the force of law in June 44 B.C. by the Lex Antonia de actis Caesaris confirmandis[1]. It is possible that the last of the four, which is the confirmation in advance of amendments in the charter of Fundi in Campania, was interpolated by Antony[2].

The first draft relates to the registration of those of the *plebs urbana* who received corn from the State. An inquiry conducted by a visitation of the blocks of tenements at Rome had reduced the number of recipients from 320,000 to 150,000, and provision had been made to fill vacancies by death in this reduced list from applicants of the necessary poverty who had not been included in the inquiry. More than this was needed, and the draft law required a return from those on the list whose property or income rose to an amount which excluded them from the privilege. In connection with this Caesar in 44 B.C. provided that two additional aediles should be elected with the duty of controlling the distribution of corn.

The second draft was of a measure to regulate the upkeep of roads in Rome and the suburbs, the control of traffic and the use of public open spaces and buildings. The congestion of Rome, even when relieved by the emigration to colonies, was no doubt severe, and was one reason for the building projects which Caesar had had in mind for a decade. Two of the provisions in the law are significant: the ancient privilege of Roman matrons to drive in the city disappears, but there is a definite assertion of the rights in this matter of the Vestals, the *rex sacrorum* and the *flamines*. Whereas the general regulations may be suggested by the laws of Greek cities (though Caesar was capable of detecting and removing an inconvenience without a model to help him), we here see the dictator's inclination to sumptuary laws and his care as Pontifex Maximus for the privileges of the State religion.

The third draft is of more importance. It regulated the right to membership of the governing councils in communities of Roman citizens outside the capital itself. It defines a limit of age for magistracies in these communities, provides for the exception from this limit of those who had served six years on foot with the

---

[1] As is shown by A. von Premerstein in *Zeitschrift der Savigny-Stiftung, Rom. Abt.* XLIII, 1922, pp. 45 *sqq.*

[2] M. Cary, *Notes on the legislation of Julius Caesar*, II, in *J.R.S.* XIX, 1929, pp. 116 *sqq.* Von Premerstein (*loc. cit.*) has shown that this draft refers to the 'municipality of Fundi,' and that all attempts to invent a class of 'municipia fundana' are unnecessary.

legions or three years in the legionary cavalry or of those who have exemption from service, and excludes from office those who are engaged in the occupation of auctioneer, beadle or undertaker. What is here noteworthy is that this disability had apparently also rested upon those who had once followed these callings but that it is now removed from such as had retired from these pursuits. Membership of the councils of these communities was denied to persons who had been convicted of various offences, to gladiators, bankrupts and those under certain civil disabilities. Significant of Caesar's own mind is the exclusion of those who had been cashiered from the army or had been the servants of a proscription, and the inclusion of exiles who had been restored to their former status. There is no indication that freedmen were debarred from any municipal office. Finally, it is provided that when the censor or any other magistrate at Rome takes a census, the highest magistrates of all such communities as are within Italy shall do the like and send forward the results to Rome.

This third law had been in preparation since before February 45 B.C.[1], and its position after one law and before another on the Table of Heraclea suggests that it is the whole of Caesar's draft legislation under this head. It does not appear probable that the fourth draft, that about Fundi, would follow or be interpolated except after the last clause of the draft about municipalities in general. We may further deduce that Caesar had not already passed a general law governing municipia, since such a law would have dealt with some if not all of the topics covered by this draft. It is true that there is one single citation of a Lex Julia Municipalis at Patavium[2]. This is, however, presumably cited because it governs an appointment in some abnormal circumstances[3]. It seems most reasonable to assume that it is a *lex rogata*, passed by Caesar or some other Julius, which had especial reference to the municipality of Patavium. In this draft law we find Caesar imposing uniformity of institutions where uniformity is convenient or desirable in order to facilitate the census. That he had any general policy of extending or curtailing the normal self-government of municipalities or colonies cannot be affirmed. Still less do these drafts entitle us to say that Caesar had any intention of reducing Rome to the position of a municipality. So long as scholars adhered to the opinion that the Table of Heraclea con-

---

[1] Cicero, *ad fam.* VI, 18, 1.　　　　　　　[2] Dessau 5406.

[3] A parallel would have been the law about Fundi and perhaps the Lex Cornelia, which apparently governed appointments at Petelia (Dessau 6468–9). On the whole question see Cary, *loc. cit.* p. 116.

tained parts of one law about municipalities which embraced Rome in its scope, it was not unreasonable to see in it evidence of such an intention. But with the refutation of that opinion, the evidence disappears. Such of Caesar's legislation as survives, gives us, in fact, no reason to suppose that Caesar did not regard Rome as the city which ruled the Empire, the Populus Romanus as the whole body of citizens of that city, and himself as the man to whom these citizens had entrusted an exceptional office of authority in their State.

Caesar's especial care for Rome and Italy is further attested by a number of projects which were attributed to him, for which perhaps it was known that preparations were afoot. He intended to have the Pomptine marshes and the Fucine Lake drained in order to increase the arable acreage of Italy. A new road was to cross the Apennines to the Adriatic. The harbour at Ostia was to be deepened so as to become the Piraeus of Rome. The artificial lake which had been the scene of the naval display at his first triumph was to give place to the site for a great temple to Mars. The Tiber was to be curbed by a new channel. There were to be public libraries with the learned Varro as their director; a new theatre was to stand on the Tarpeian rock. Finally, what Sulla had done for criminal law was to be more than done for civil law in the shape of a codification. This last Pompey is said to have planned and abandoned: the task from which Pompey had flinched Caesar intended to achieve. These masterful plans were cut short by his death: it was reserved for Augustus, for Claudius and for Justinian to accomplish part of them.

The notable features of Caesarian legislation, so far as time has spared it, are its direct and radical removal of acknowledged abuses, its insistence on order and good administration, its resource in dealing with present perplexities. At the same time, it is difficult to discover anything which is a marked breach with the past or anything which looks far beyond the present. Historians who have seen in Sulla nothing more than a reactionary have been apt to see in Caesar nothing less than a revolutionary. But if the work of the two men in the field of social and administrative legislation is compared, the likenesses are far more striking than the differences. For the future Sulla had trusted in fortune and a Senate unhampered by the presence of its enemies, Caesar trusted in fortune and in his own autocratic power despite the presence of its enemies. The lessons which Caesar had learnt from Sulla were that the ruthless exploitation of victory was unworthy and that Sulla had been an ignoramus when he abdicated.

III. MUNDA

The beneficent activities of Caesar since his return from Africa suffered one serious interruption—the campaign of Munda. Since the year of Ilerda misgovernment and mutinies had so destroyed the goodwill of the Romans resident in Spain that they had showed themselves ready to welcome Caesar's enemies. Even before Thapsus the younger Gnaeus Pompeius had landed in the Peninsula, where he was joined by his brother Sextus and by fugitives from Africa. The legions that had mutinied feared punishment, and the troops of Afranius, who had been allowed to go to their homes in Spain, returned to the trade of arms. After Thapsus Caesar sent troops under Q. Pedius and Q. Fabius but they failed to prevent the spread of the revolt, and before the year 46 was out Gnaeus Pompeius had under his command thirteen legions[1]. Two of these garrisoned Corduba, the chief city of Further Spain. Of the eleven which formed the field army four were of good quality; the remainder, in part native Spaniards, were inferior in training though not in courage. He had 6000 cavalry and light-armed troops and as many auxiliaries: he brought a great name and embittered resolution, and with him was Labienus.

It was true that the young Pompeius, cruel and arrogant, was no Sertorius, but if Spain was left to itself, its re-conquest would be long and difficult. There was no one of Caesar's lieutenants able enough to cope with the skill of Labienus, which in Africa had for so long baffled the master himself. The only means of achieving a rapid victory was for Caesar to take the field, and the dictator was not tired of being a general. Reforms, reconciliation, restoration of the State must wait their turn. Early in November 46 he drove out of Rome and in twenty-seven days he was at the Spanish front.

In Corduba there was a party ready to go over to Caesar, otherwise the Baetis valley apart from the single town of Ulia was on Pompeius' side. But his very success pinned him down to a narrow theatre of war. Caesar succeeded in throwing reinforcements into Ulia and, after vainly threatening Corduba, embarked on a war of sieges and marches in order to bring Gnaeus to battle on equal ground. With the reinforcements that presently arrived he had eight legions, four of them veterans, 8000 cavalry, together with auxiliary troops, and even if outnumbered in infantry he could trust his army to win a decisive victory. For more than two months Pompeius evaded the issue but gradually lost ground

[1] See Rice Holmes, *op. cit.* p. 542 *sq.*

and was compelled to abandon first Ategua then Ventipo to Caesar[1]. These failures to protect his adherents produced their natural effect, and Pompeius retreated still farther south to the neighbourhood of Urso. There he proposed to make a stand in a strong position between that city and the town of Munda and promised his friends the encouragement of seeing Caesar refusing to attack him. But Caesar did not refuse. On March 17 the Pompeians, already in array on the high ground, saw the enemy advance in line of battle, cross a stream that lay before their position, and then stand fast. Thus Caesar offered a battle in which the Pompeians would fight with the slope in their favour, and Gnaeus could not refuse the challenge. He had moved down the hill on Caesar's approach, and at the foot of it the battle was joined.

Caesar placed the veteran Third and Fifth legions on his left and the Tenth on his right, for he must aim at turning one or other of the enemy's flanks. His cavalry presently swept away the Pompeian horse and was then withdrawn under the general command of the Mauretanian prince Bogud to wait until the enemy's reserves were all engaged, for Pharsalus had shown how good infantry could repulse the shock of horse. The soldier, perhaps one of the Tenth legion, who has written the *Bellum Hispaniense* has placed on record that it was a very fine day for a battle. But victory was slow in coming. For hours the two armies struggled with charge and countercharge: in courage they were well-matched, the slope neutralized the training of Caesar's troops. Even the veterans began to waver at last, and Caesar threw himself into the fray as thirteen years before in the battle with the Nervii. The Tenth legion did not fail him, but by a crowning effort thrust back the enemy's left. Now was the moment for the cavalry, and Bogud with his Moorish troopers rode to strike at the enemy's flank and rear. Labienus saw the danger and succeeded in withdrawing troops from the opposite wing to make a flank guard. But as they moved behind their own line the hard-pressed Pompeians believed it was the beginning of flight; at last their hearts failed them and they broke. Wearied with hours of conflict, they were in no case to escape and were killed and ridden down until the last army of Caesar's enemies was utterly destroyed. Labienus and Varus fell fighting and were given honourable

[1] On the topography and operations see the works cited in the Bibliography. For the position of Munda, as, in the main, for the battle itself, the conclusions of Veith in *Antike Schlachtfelder*, iv, pp. 552, 599, are adopted. See Map 10, facing p. 319.

burial. Cn. Pompeius, who escaped, failed to get away by sea and was hunted down: three weeks after the battle his head was brought to Hispalis and displayed to the people. His brother Sextus found refuge among the tribe of the Lacetani, who cherished the memory of his father, and lived to revive for a time the cause in Spain and then to trouble the peace of the Mediterranean for nearly a decade.

With the field army of the enemy destroyed it was an easy task to reduce Further Spain to obedience. Caesar in need of money for his wars and of land for his colonies had now no clemency. The war had since its very start been savagely conducted on both sides, and partisan rancour within the cities helped to induce massacres which suited Caesar's purposes, little as they accorded with his nature. The Spanish war was held to be rebellion helped by traitorous Romans, and, after the ruthlessness which was traditional in the Roman coercion of Spain, Caesar did not hesitate to celebrate a triumph and to allow, with small enough cause, a like honour to his lieutenants Pedius and Fabius.

With Munda Caesar's career in the field ended. What remains is an indication that in planning his campaign against the Parthians he set himself to learn by the disaster of Crassus, and his strategy was not refuted by the ill-success of Antony—if we may suppose that his lieutenant was seeking, with more haste than skill, to carry it out. At Munda, it is true, the issue hung in the balance, and it is at least probable that the manœuvre of Bogud which precipitated victory was not at Caesar's own direction. But a soldiers' battle in which he strained to breaking point the endurance of his veterans was not an unworthy end to his fighting career. He shared with Alexander and Hannibal the skill to fashion an instrument of war which fitted his own genius as the blade the hilt. Few students of war have doubted that Caesar's is the greatest name in the military history of Rome. His own *Commentaries*, the account of the Alexandrian War, and the soldierly if ungraceful narratives of the campaigns in Africa and Spain make us able to judge best of the best general of antiquity.

The appreciation of Caesar as a general has a significance for more than the history of the art of war, if we may make the reasonable assumption that the instincts and qualities of Caesar in war were his instincts and qualities in politics and statesmanship. His most striking quality was his entire faith in his own genius. From the day that he marched to see what he could do with the Helvetii and with Ariovistus to the day when he ordered the advance at Munda he never hesitated to accept the challenge of the moment. The cold prudence that warns against following opportunity too closely at the heels had little meaning for him. It was not that he lacked wariness: until his hour came his patience was iron. If inaction was the certain road to victory as at Berry-au-Bac he could be patient, but only if that was the certain way. No critic has detected a moment when he missed his chance. A few times he struck too soon, at Gergovia, Ilerda, Dyrrhachium: he never struck too late, and when he struck home, the blow was mortal. No army that he defeated escaped destruction or surrender.

He preferred to operate with comparatively small forces of the highest quality. This was partly because he understood, as the Romans understood so well, the importance of supply. But it was also because he trusted his own skill to make every man tell. When he confessed that fortune plays a great part in war, he was claiming victory as his own, for a nimble wit and an unclouded courage were the only weapons against fortune. Thus, while his strategy was often patient where defence was needed, it bears little signs of profound calculation. The conditions of his day did not permit the far-ranging manœuvres of Napoleon before Ulm. But when it came to battle he would subscribe to the maxim of Napoleon, *je m'engage, et puis je vois*. His triumphs were so much the product of his own personality that he left behind him no single advance in the art of war. He bequeathed to the generals who followed him no recipe for victory except one beyond their reach—to be Caesar. As an excellent critic and an experienced soldier has pointed out, he made no single innovation in the technique of Roman soldiering[1]. In that respect he was not the rival of Marius and perhaps not the rival of Sulla. He had not Pompey's instinct for amphibious warfare, he had not Alexander's appreciation of cavalry as a striking force; the traditional Roman art of war was sufficient for him because he handled it with a virtuosity and a drastic application which marked his genius.

IV. COLONIES AND CITIZENSHIP

Both before and after Munda Caesar was concerned not only with reforms at Rome but with problems of colonization, in part made urgent by his own career.

The first of these was the provision of lands for the veterans

---

[1] G. Veith, in Kromayer-Veith, *Heerwesen und Kriegführung der Griechen und Römer*, p. 465.

who had fought under him in Gaul and might fairly demand their release and their reward. As early as 51 the Senate had, with some plausibility, considered the claims of Caesar's legionaries; in 49 the Ninth legion had demanded its discharge. After Pharsalus Caesar had sent back to rest in Italy all the legions that had fought in Gaul, except the Sixth[1]. Idleness in Campania did not induce content: in 47 there was the mutiny in which the Twelfth and Tenth legions took the lead. It is noteworthy that of the veteran legions apart from the Sixth, two, the Eleventh and Twelfth, were not taken to Africa, and possibly Caesar made a start at once with the allotments for these legions. At the close of his African campaign he assigned land there to a number of his troops, perhaps to those who preferred to settle down at once; and during his absence his commissioners were busy completing the necessary survey of land available in Italy. Whether from fear or favour, the Italian communities had done nothing to hinder Caesar's advance in 49, so that he had no good ground, even if he had the mind, for confiscations like those of Sulla. But short of that, his commissioners were active enough in enforcing the claim of the State to lands, even lands dedicated for religious purposes.

The agrarian law of 59, after fulfilling its immediate purpose, had left some land available, if it is right to suppose that the Lex Mamilia was a supplementary measure passed in 55 to prepare the way for settlements of Caesar's veterans (see above, p. 618). It should be added that most of Pompey's veterans who had rejoined the eagles in 49 had gone over to Caesar, and it may have seemed bad policy to disturb the allotments of the remainder. Caesar was careful to announce that the Sullan allotments would be respected, and it would belong to his politic clemency to respect the claims of Pompey's soldiers who had done no more than fight again under their old general. The survivors of Caesar's Gallic army may be estimated at 20,000 men, and to these should be added soldiers in other legions who had had long service in the decades preceding the Civil War and who had a claim to good treatment and discharge. A part of these were settled in Africa and a number joined in the colony that was sent to Corinth[2]. For the remainder, land seems to have been found in Italy except for the Sixth and Tenth legions. The Seventh and Eighth, and possibly others, were settled in Campania[3].

The Tenth legion, whom Caesar could neither forgive nor dispense with, and the Sixth, which had probably been raised in 52

---

[1] See Note 5, p. 898.   [2] Strabo XVII, 833.
[3] Cicero, ad Att. XVI, 8, 2; Nic. Dam. XXXI, 132; C.I.L. X, p. 369.

at earliest, fought at Munda. By that time the Tenth, on which Caesar had possibly drawn for the training of his recruit legions[1], had shrunk to very few men[2], and the Sixth, which had fought with Caesar in the Civil War from Spain to Asia Minor, was at Zela less than a thousand strong[3]. These two legions were now disbanded and settled in the part of the world outside Italy which was most Italian in character and Italianized in tradition, in the old province of Transalpine Gaul, the Tenth at Narbo Martius, the Sixth at Arelate. The *territorium* assigned to this last colony extended as far as Toulon[4], and we may assume that the allotments were on a very generous scale. Land in this region could be supplied at the expense of Massilia. How land was procured at Narbo must remain unknown, but it is possible that Hirtius was employed there immediately after Munda[5]. Thus Caesar had provided for the army of Gaul, but since at the time of his death there were some thirty-five legions under arms, the future contained a still more formidable problem (see further below, p. 712).

The second kind of colonization had economic and political purposes. There were in Italy, above all in Rome, a great number of people who had lost the taste or the opportunity for employment. They were a burden to the Treasury, and their disorder, indeed their very presence, was a nuisance in politics. Caesar's enfranchisement of Transpadane Gaul was not accompanied, so far as we know, by the attempt to bring about any representative system, and, so long as Caesar himself dominated elections and legislation, this may not have seemed an immediate problem. But, in any event, the concentration in Rome of so many idle voters was a political problem. Thus, both on economic and political grounds, it was desirable to draft off a large proportion of the urban proletariate. Agrarian colonies alone would not suffice, for many of these people could not dig. Accordingly, Caesar planned colonies offering industrial and mercantile opportunities.

It was in this side of his colonial policy, and perhaps this only, that Caesar was the heir of Gaius Gracchus. The statecraft or fears or impatience of a politically-minded Senate had destroyed two of the great commercial centres of the ancient world, Corinth and Carthage. Gaius Gracchus had taken great risks to set on foot a colony at Junonia in the near neighbourhood of Carthage (p. 73). This enterprise, which was only in part achieved, Caesar determined to carry through. The new Carthage was to be, as it

---

[1] *Bell. Afr.* 16, 1–2.   [2] *Bell. Hisp.* 31, 4.
[3] *Bell. Alex.* 69, 1.   [4] *C.I.L.* XII, p. 84.
[5] Cicero, *ad Att.* XII, 37, 4.

became, a centre for agriculture as well as trade; Corinth was dedicated by nature to commerce. Caesar is credited with the intention of cutting a canal through the Isthmus; and the colonists who were sent to Corinth, whether before or after Caesar's death, contained many freedmen who, it may be assumed, had largely bought their freedom by their skill in industry. These, who had presumably failed at Rome, were to make a new start.

Parallel with the colony at Corinth is that at Sinope. That Sinope is a Caesarian foundation may be deduced from its Era, which dates from 47 in place of that which had run from 70 B.C., the year of its capture by Lucullus (p. 365). The city had offered only a brief resistance to Pharnaces[1], and we may assume that Caesar took from it part of its territory to provide for new colonists. It appears more probable that it was a commercial colony of the same kind as Corinth than a soldiers' settlement, since the only veteran troops with Caesar in Asia Minor were the Sixth legion, which was sent back to Italy.

With the new Carthage only a beginning was made in Caesar's lifetime: the nascent Caesarian settlement at La Malga can be distinguished from the later additions of Octavian and the city that grew up during Imperial times. In Africa Vetus there were also planted colonies on the coast at Curubis and Clupea and, probably also Caesarian, at Carpis and Hippo Diarrhytus, possibly Caesarian, at Thysdrus and Neapolis. In this African group were settled some of those veterans whom Caesar left behind after Thapsus, men who preferred urban life to being small landowners in separate homesteads. In the territory held for the moment as a reward by Sittius, there were colonies at Cirta and probably at Rusicade, Chullu and Milev which were perhaps intended to make good Roman citizens out of the broken men who had followed the fortunes of that adventurer.

Equally, if not more, important were the foundations in Spain. Here in both provinces there were, besides some earlier foundations, *conventus* of Roman citizens. Some of these were raised to the dignity of a colony as a reward for fidelity, such as Ulia, which alone in the Baetis valley had held by Caesar (p. 702). In Nearer Spain this status was given to Nova Carthago[2], Tarraco and Celsa[3]. In the Further province Hispalis, Urso, Ucubi and Itucci forfeited land which was granted to colonists, and no doubt these were not all. Thus a beginning was made with the Romanization

---

[1] Appian, *Mithr.* 120.
[2] It resisted Cn. Pompeius. Dio XLIII, 30, 1.
[3] Celsa was perhaps not formally a colony till the government of Lepidus.

of the south and south-east of Spain which it was one of Augustus'
greatest achievements to carry through.

For the character of these colonies some evidence is afforded by
the extant chapters of the Charter governing the colony of Genetiva
Julia established at Urso in Spain[1]. The Charter shows imperfection in drafting and the evidence of at least two hands. Part of
its provisions are doubtless tralatician[2], but there are signs of
Caesarian innovations. The dictator has apparently appointed the
first set of magistrates and reserves to himself the right to make
appointments in future[3]. In future no Roman Senator or son of
a Senator may become *patronus* of the colony unless he is a private
person in Italy without the *imperium* and is approved by three-
quarters of the local council of *decuriones*[4]. There is a rigorous rule
against bribery in money or in kind at elections, perhaps based
upon Cicero's law *de ambitu*[5]. An indication that Caesar wished
to maintain industrial life in his colony might be seen in the provision that no one might possess within the town works which
could produce more than 300 tiles a day[6], were it not that one
such factory could perhaps suffice for the needs of Urso and the
district, if a house dignified enough to be the residence of a local
magistrate at Tarentum might be roofed with so few as 1500
tiles[7]. Careful provision is made for the practice of the Roman
State religion with augurs and pontifices[8]. The Capitoline Triad,
Juppiter, Juno and Minerva, are to be honoured for three days,
Venus for one[9]. The name of the colony and the provision for
Venus combine to attest Caesar's emphasis on his patron goddess,
but it is to be noted that there is no trace in the Charter of any
Caesarian religious policy inconsistent with the normal practice
of the Roman State.

Of more importance is a phrase which prescribes that no objection may be lodged against the right of a *decurio* on the ground
that he is a freedman[9]. This phrase appears to be the negation of
a lost tralatician clause by which *ingenuitas* was required, and it is
reasonable to suppose that we have here a trace of a Caesarian
innovation in favour of freedmen, and we find it also in Caesar's
colonies of Curubis and Clupea in Africa. The innovation is

---

[1] Bruns, *Fontes*[7], 28; E. G. Hardy, *Three Spanish Charters*, pp. 23 *sqq.*
[2] *E.g.* the reference to Italian or Gallic *tumultus* (cap. LXII).
[3] Cap. CXXV.
[4] Cap. CXXX. This is apparently a later modification of the previous
practice given in the tralatician chapter XCVII.
[5] See above, p. 493.   [6] Cap. LXXVI.
[7] Bruns, *Fontes*[7], 27, l. 28.   [8] Cap. LXVI–VIII.   [9] Cap. LXX–I.

natural in making laws for colonies intended to draw off the urban proletariate, in which many freedmen would be found[1]. But it appears to be a fair deduction from the Table of Heraclea that in the last year of his life Caesar was proposing to place freedmen on a level with *ingenui* for all purposes in all municipia and colonies. A liberal attitude towards freedmen had long been a touchstone of progress in Roman political thought, and this legislation is one more piece of evidence which reveals Caesar as following the most broadminded tendencies in Republican state-craft.

Apart from the settlements of veterans these colonies appear to have been intended to relieve overpopulation in Rome rather than to deprive the Italian peninsula, including the enfranchised region in the north, of its privilege and duty to be the recruiting ground of the Roman armies. The statement of Suetonius[2] that Caesar settled 80,000 citizens overseas is in a context which suggests that the figure refers to people drawn from the urban proletariate, and he goes on to credit Caesar with forbidding Italian citizens of military age to be absent abroad for more than three years except as enlisted soldiers[3]. Caesar's own army of Gaul had been recruited in Italy though largely from a part of Italy which had not yet received the full franchise. The famous Alaudae, recruited in Transalpine Gaul, do not appear to have been recognized as a regular legion with a number until after the Civil War had begun. For cavalry and for the light-armed troops that acted with cavalry he had followed the usual practice of Roman commanders and looked outside Italy. But there is no good reason to suppose that the legions contained any considerable proportion of soldiers who were not of Italian birth. There were certainly more legions in the world at the time of Pharsalus than at the time of Caesar's death. The admixture of non-Italians in Pompey's army was, to all appearance, very small; whereas by then Caesar had had little opportunity to draft non-Italians into his army[4]. During the years 46 and 45 nine veteran legions had been disbanded; on the other hand part of Pompey's legionaries had passed into Caesar's service, and it was Caesar's practice to allow legions to shrink rather than to replenish them by drafts of re-

---

[1] The name of this colony is given by Pliny (*N.H.* III, 12) as Gen⟨eti⟩va Urbanorum, if this is not a textual corruption for Ursaonum.

[2] Suetonius, *Div. Iul.* 42, 1.

[3] *Loc. cit.* The lower limit of age is 20 years; the MSS. reading for the upper limit (*decem*) is corrupt, but plainly age limits for military service are implied.

[4] See below, Note 5, p. 898.

cruits. Despite the losses of the wars it is not necessary to assume any extensive recruitment in the provinces between Pharsalus and the Ides of March. Caesar's opponents in Spain and in Africa were driven to enlist provincial non-Italians, but this was not, so far as can be conjectured from the scanty evidence, the practice of Caesar or the policy of the Roman State.

The enfranchisement of Italy north of the Po satisfied, for the present at least, the need for citizen soldiers, but it was not inconsistent with Roman liberal statecraft to prepare the way for further enfranchisement in regions that became Romanized. Sicily was geographically almost a part of the peninsula, and there is nothing improbable in the statement that Caesar at least meditated conferring on the whole island the Latin right that was a half-way house to citizenship[1]. It required more imagination to pass beyond the Alps and do the same for Romanized urban communities of the old province of Transalpine Gaul and of Spain. Within the Alpine region itself, where Latin culture had made its way, similar rights followed. There is no doubt that Caesar made free use of the right to grant citizenship to individuals which belonged to the patronage of Roman generals. On those of alien birth who followed the practice of medicine or of letters at Rome he conferred the franchise. But when due allowance is made for Caesar's respect for culture and care for the social well-being and status of those who shared Italian civilization, it is not to be concluded that he had abandoned the idea of the predominance of Italy through its rights in Rome.

V. THE FINANCIAL AND FOREIGN POLICY OF CAESAR

The financial policy of Caesar had been to make war support war. He confiscated the estates of avowed Pompeians so far as that did not conflict with the clemency which seemed to him politic and natural. But as the war went on, his need became greater and his conduct, of necessity, harsher. In Africa after Thapsus he imposed enormous fines and contributions, and in Spain he punished by confiscation of land the cities that had taken the side of his enemies. Part of the land confiscated in Africa he used to raise money; most, if not all, of that taken in Spain apparently went to colonies. Thus his policy of colonization, apart from the allotment of lands to veterans, was a charge on the State in the sense that land was given to colonists which might have been sold

---

[1] Cicero, ad Att. XIV, 12, 1.

for the benefit of the Treasury. A partial set-off was the drastic limitation of the distribution of corn. The citizen population resident in Italy was immune from direct taxation, and his extension of the franchise to Transpadane Gaul meant a loss to the Treasury. On the other hand the re-imposition of the customs duties at the harbours of Italy abolished in 60 B.C. (p. 511, n. 1) was an indirect taxation of the citizen body in addition to the *vicesima libertatis*[1]. Gaul with a tribute of forty million sesterces could more than pay for its government, but for the moment most of the other provinces must have been exhausted. In the Greek East Caesar had remitted some taxation and, to judge from the scanty evidence, had fixed the amounts due from communities and permitted them to collect it themselves without the unwelcome assistance of *publicani*. Governors, too, were to be strictly watched, but it would be some time before the prevention of extortion for private profit would have its full effect in benefiting the State treasury.

Towards expenditure Caesar preserved the genial attitude of one to whom other men's money had come easily. His triumphs were so costly that the greedy veterans complained that money was being taken from them, despite the donatives with which they were rewarded. In building and in public works he spent and was planning to spend freely, though those who would win his favour were encouraged to assist. He had many needy friends and allowed some of them to enrich themselves indirectly at the State's expense. Much of his expenditure was on valuable public services and would have good economic effects. That Caesar had any serious intention of seeking a seat of government elsewhere than in Rome is rendered improbable by his plans for making the city more splendid. It was certainly good statesmanship to follow and surpass the policy of Sulla, the first great master-builder of Rome as a world capital. But that was not all. The existence of some thirty-five legions, which every year involved the State in present expense and future liability was a financial problem of the first magnitude. The present expense was increased by the virtual doubling of legionary pay which Caesar introduced, even if that made possible savings which reduced the needs of the soldiers at discharge. The natural solution was to disband all but the formations necessary for the establishment and maintenance of security within the Empire and on its borders. With peace assured, the provinces that had been visited by war and drained by requisi-

---

[1] The tax on manumission, which was, however, freely evaded by the practice of *manumissio minus iusta*.

tions would be able to make a contribution justified by the protection which they received. Those of the legionaries who could demand allotments might be provided for by purchase without further confiscations of provincial land if Rome annexed Egypt. In Egypt was the famous treasure of the Ptolemies, and if Rome gave to the Egyptians peace and security, though not the freedom which they had never enjoyed, it would be no injustice to use a part of the wealth of the country for the needs of Rome. The Ptolemaic dynasty had outlived its usefulness, and the machine of government could be readily adapted to serve a new master. All this the future was to show, but the possibility must have been plain for all men to see.

The one thing which stood between the Ptolemaic dynasty and its extinction was the queen Cleopatra. She had been Caesar's mistress and was the mother of his son. The fate of Egypt hung in the balance at Rome, and with good reason the queen left Alexandria to conjure the danger to her power. How far she kept a hold on Caesar's affection we have not the evidence to tell. He placed her statue in his new temple of Venus Genetrix, and provided her with a residence in his gardens beyond the Tiber. As at least the guest of the dictator she seems to have fretted the pride of the Roman aristocrats. After Caesar's death Cicero made bold to write how he resented her arrogance[1]. Whether Cleopatra hoped to see Caesar do more for her than to leave Egypt a Ptolemaic kingdom we cannot tell. But so much she achieved, and after the Ides of March her boy husband vanished from the scene, and she set her son by her side as Ptolemy Caesar. It was reserved for Caesar's heir Octavian to put an end to her dynasty and to Caesar's son.

The task of Cleopatra was perhaps made easier by Caesar's preoccupation with a more splendid enterprise. Even before he left Asia Minor in 47 he is credited with the project of a Parthian campaign, and it may be conjectured that, if Caesar had been permitted to gain in peace his consulship for 48, he would have used it to secure the command in the East. Revenge for the defeat of Crassus was already overdue, the claim of prestige, the need to make secure the Roman East and possibly a calculation that war could be made profitable were motives enough to justify to Roman statecraft a great effort to defeat the Parthians if not to conquer their country. On the other hand, it must be admitted that, as events showed, the effort could safely have been postponed, had the dictator cared to give himself to the completion

[1] *ad Att.* xv, 15, 2.

of a greater task, the reconstruction of the Roman State. It was true that a resounding victory in a war in which Roman pride was so deeply engaged might be the crowning justification of his autocracy. But when after the fall of Alexandria Octavian renounced the project of a war with Parthia and turned back to the hard task awaiting him at Rome, he proved himself a greater servant of the State than Caesar could bear to be.

Whether indeed Caesar was moved by a profound political calculation is a matter for conjecture. A readier explanation is that for him war had become 'une belle occupation,' and that, as his health began to fail, he was filled with the desire to make sure of one more great campaign. To this desire considerations such as those which moved Octavian would yield, and further it could not be denied that there were good grounds for other military operations which might conveniently be associated with a far-reaching enterprise in the East.

In Syria there had been and still was trouble. In 47 Caesar left his young kinsman Sextus Caesar with a legion to look after that province. Sextus enjoyed the support of the Jews and, more important, the prestige of Caesar's victory. But in the first half of 46 B.C. a follower of Pompey, Q. Caecilius Bassus, tampered with some troops at Tyre, spreading a rumour that Caesar had been defeated and killed in Africa, and fomented a mutiny in which Sextus lost his life. The part of the Caesarian garrison which remained loyal retreated into Cilicia, while Bassus made Apamea on the Orontes a formidable *place d'armes*, since he expected a punitive invasion from the neighbouring province. The governor of Cilicia, Q. Cornificius, held him in play until a new governor of Syria arrived, C. Antistius Vetus. He advanced and besieged Bassus, who had turned to Parthia for help and was relieved by a Parthian raid under Pacorus, which, however, ended with the advent of the winter of 45. Bassus had the support of Alcaudonius, who had deserted Crassus before Carrhae (p. 609). L. Staius Murcus, the successor of Antistius, had three legions under his command at the beginning of 44 and three more were ordered to Syria from Bithynia. These were to clear up the situation during that year and then to play their part in Caesar's campaign.

The Romans had also grounds for disquietude from the power of the Dacians. A great king Burebista had arisen, who with the help of a kind of prophet Dekaineos had reformed the habits of the people so that they were able to win back from the Celtic Boii the plain of the Theiss, which they had recently invaded. This he accomplished by a victorious war against them and the Taurisci, and the dislocation of people caused by this had given rise to uneasiness on the borders of Illyricum about the time that Caesar became governor of that province. The Greek cities of the western coast of the Black Sea had now to reckon with a formidable neighbour, who by 50 B.C. had succeeded to the menacing power of the Bastarnae. With Rome preoccupied the Greek cities seem to have acknowledged some kind of Dacian suzerainty[1], and Burebista even began to negotiate with Pompey just before the battle of Pharsalus. This action cannot have commended itself to Caesar, and he may have feared a coalition between the Dacians and Asander the ambitious usurper of the Bosporan kingdom. Moreover the raids of the Dacians troubled the borders of Macedonia[2]. It was therefore desirable to clear up the situation in that corner of the Empire and Caesar decided to make war on Burebista as a prelude to his invasion of Parthia.

Caesar had intended to use a striking force of at least six legions against the Dacians in a summer's campaign. Burebista, it is true, fell victim to a conspiracy, whether shortly before or after Caesar's death cannot be said with certainty. But it may fairly be assumed, in either case, that the plan was to make a formidable demonstration of Roman power in the North-East while the situation in Syria was being secured. The formal allotment of the provinces of Macedonia and Syria to the consuls of 44, Antony and Dolabella, was made after Caesar's death, but in view of the importance of Syria to a Parthian campaign and of Macedonia, if the Dacian question needed further settlement, it is reasonable to suppose that Caesar had given some indication of his wishes about the governorships of these provinces during 43 and 42. It was important that they should be consular so that they might be in charge of the same trusted governors for both years. While the proconsul in Syria held that province against a Parthian counter-stroke, the proconsul in Macedonia could carry through any settlement required on the borders of his province and convert into security the results of Caesar's campaign.

The question of Illyricum was linked up with that of the Macedonian frontier. The Delmatae had long been hostile to the coastal districts held by *conventus* of Romans and Italians. During the civil wars which preceded Sulla's dictatorship they had made bold to capture Salonae and were only driven back after two years' campaigning by C. Cosconius, a general who had proved himself in the Social War. It is possible that the rising spread as far north

---

[1] Ditt.[3] 762.   [2] Strabo VII, 304; Suetonius, *Div. Iul.* 44, 3.

as the Iapudes, the people of the Carso. For a time, possibly because of the successes of M. Lucullus on the Macedonian borders, the tribes appear to have been quiet, but Mithridates' project to march on Italy by land (p. 391) was not madness except in a king who had outlived the self-sacrifice of his subjects. Caesar's original choice of Cisalpine Gaul and Illyricum as his proconsular provinces can be explained without any hypothesis except the desire to be within reach of Rome (p. 549), but it may be conjectured that he intended to settle the Illyrian question by war had not Gaul offered a greater theatre for his genius. But as a clash between Caesar and the Roman government became more probable, the Iapudes and Delmatae began to threaten both the loyal coast-towns and their neighbours the Liburnians. Thus during the first years of the Civil War Caesar's lieutenants had not only to cover the eastern borders of Italy against a possible Pompeian invasion from the Western Balkans but to fight the tribes which wished to be rid of Rome once and for all. There is not direct evidence that the Delmatae had leagued themselves with Burebista, but, if we may trust Appian[1], they feared that Caesar would attack them as a preliminary to his Dacian campaign and sent envoys to Rome. To convert into fact this gesture of submission Vatinius was made governor of the province for 45 and 44 B.C. with an army of three legions. By the winter of the former year he had achieved successes which merited a *supplicatio*. But the country was difficult, the climate unfriendly, and even Vatinius' proved energy and resource were almost baffled. In letters to Cicero he complained of his hard task and his fear that Caesar expected of him more than any general could achieve. But the dictator may have calculated that the display of Roman power farther east would intimidate the Illyrian tribes, and that during the second year of his government Vatinius might complete the subjection of his province. His army would then be at the disposal of the governor of Macedonia.

The Roman provinces in Asia Minor were for the moment important chiefly as bases of supply for the Parthian expedition. Bithynia was to be entrusted during 44 to L. Tillius Cimber who enjoyed Caesar's confidence, while the experienced Trebonius was to govern Asia as consular during 44 and 43. It is not known who was to be responsible for Cilicia.

In the West there were fewer pre-occupations. In 46 B.C. there had been a rising of the Bellovaci, which Dec. Brutus had put down, but there were no grounds for fearing an attempt to recover

[1] *Ill.* 13.

Gallic independence. The events of the Civil War must have weakened Roman Spain, and it was arranged that Lepidus, who had governed the Nearer province in 48, should take charge of that region together with Southern Gaul in 44, while Asinius Pollio with three legions held Further Spain and dealt with Sextus Pompeius. The remainder of Gaul was entrusted to Munatius Plancus, who had served under Caesar in Spain and Africa. In Cisalpine Gaul, which would be the base of reinforcements if there was a war in the West, and in which the Alpine tribes might give trouble, Decimus Brutus was to be posted. In Africa Nova there was an army under T. Sextius, who had served as *legatus* under Caesar in Gaul and throughout the Civil War.

Apart from the forces which would be grouped under Caesar's own immediate command, eighteen legions were ranged in a ring from Africa to Illyricum. In Egypt yet another legion had been enlisted from the soldiers there, so that there were now four in all. The distribution of forces took account both of the needs of the Empire and the desirability of balancing against each other any possible ambitions of army commanders, no one of whom was to control too formidable a force or to control any force for too long. The provinces which needed armies were to be governed during 44 B.C. by men whom Caesar trusted, and he intended that during 43 the key-province of Nearer Spain and Southern Gaul should be in the hands of Lepidus, Macedonia Syria and Asia in the hands of Antony, Dolabella and Trebonius. The remaining provinces would be distributed among the praetors of 44 B.C., in whose election Caesar had had a say. Whereas the Julian law about provincial commands and the share of the Senate in distributing them remained in force, we may assume that during the dictator's absence the legions other than his own field army would be grouped under Caesarian generals in provinces in which their presence could reasonably be justified. The candidates for the consulships of 43 approved by Caesar were C. Pansa and A. Hirtius, for 42 Dec. Brutus and L. Munatius Plancus, who thus had an interest in the maintenance of Caesar's predominance. Lepidus was to be Caesar's *magister equitum* until at some future date, which we cannot fix, he took over his provinces. He was then to be followed by Cn. Domitius Calvinus (p. 725 *sq.*). A reason for keeping Lepidus for a time in Rome may be found in the mutual hostility of the consuls Antony and Dolabella, which it would be the task of the dictator's deputy to compose.

The confusion which followed Caesar's death naturally obscures the shrewdness with which he had provided for the first year or more of his absence from Rome. This is characteristic of him, but equally characteristic is the fact that he left for his own future decision or to the Senate guided by the consuls most of the provincial arrangements for 43 and 42. But he had not divined that among the generals whom he trusted were men who were ready to plot against his life. Further, the past had shown how reform and the processes of government might be paralysed by his absence[1], and that his dictatorship might be doubly galling if exercised from beyond the Euphrates. To the governing class Caesar was after all one of themselves: there was a world of difference between an absent autocrat and the first gentleman in Rome. While the people rejoiced in a declaration of war against the Parthians, the Roman nobles set themselves to face the question whether Caesar's position in the State was to be endured.

VI. CAESAR'S POSITION IN THE STATE

Caesar has been credited with a religious policy which aimed at anchoring in the next world a monarchy in this. The truth about it is not easily discovered. The emotion aroused by Caesar's sudden death, which so quickly plunged the Roman world back into civil war, made him accepted as a god. A decade of propaganda which appealed to Caesar, now in the interest of Antony now in the interest of Octavian, must have clouded the memory of what happened before his death. The desire of rhetorical writers to heighten a tragedy by the stage-properties of greatness and to make an imposing gesture to Nemesis, the moralizing simplification that only pride goes before a fall, confuse the ancient biographical tradition. Finally Dio, the writer who has most to say about honours voted to Caesar, admired the monarchy of his own day and was peculiarly at the mercy of any tradition which wrapped up the body of Caesar in the autocratic trappings which he believed to go with the office of emperor. The mere fact that so much in Dio does not appear in Suetonius' life of Caesar should give a historian pause, and no historian will be easy in mind when he has to use Suetonius as the touchstone of truth. There are a few hints in Cicero's letters which are invaluable, partly because their fewness should teach us to be on our guard. On the other hand, the historian has to remember how tremendous must have been the effect of Caesar's personality, towering above

---

[1] There are signs in the Table of Heraclea (Bruns, *Fontes*[7], 18, 89, 98) that it was intended to have some at least of Caesar's drafts passed into law after he left Rome.

his followers and his enemies and even above the State. Fortune, which the Romans counted a part of greatness, had been as faithful to him as she had been to Sulla, and to the glamour of past success he had added a clemency which scorned to fear the future. In the Senate, the fountain of honours, there was a majority of men who would naturally seek to express their devotion to their leader, to emphasize the triumph of their party, together with a minority who wished to exaggerate and transmute triumph and admiration into flattery which would only injure its object until, in the drastic phrase of Florus, 'they decked him with fillets like a victim to the sacrifice.'

To accept the statements of Dio and Suetonius without question is to abdicate the office of a historian; but to discover precisely what was offered to Caesar before his death and accepted by him is hardly possible. In the six months that followed Caesar's death Octavian was active in stressing his divinity, and it may be suspected, if not proved, that there has been some confusion between what preceded and what followed the Ides of March. Dio asserts that Caesar not long before his death was promoted to be Juppiter Julius and that Antony was appointed his priest 'like a *flamen dialis*[1],' Suetonius that Caesar accepted the appointment of a *flamen*[2]. In the *Second Philippic*[3] Cicero declares that Antony is *flamen* of Divus Julius, as there are *flamines* of Juppiter, Mars and Quirinus. The absence of any other evidence for Caesar as Juppiter Julius makes Dio's statement more than suspect, and without further evidence, the appointment of a *flamen* in his lifetime may be in Caesar's honour like that of the Luperci Julii rather than for his worship. Dio[4] and Appian[5] state that a temple was ordered to Caesar and to his clemency: a coin shows a temple accompanied by the legend CLEMENTIAE CAESARIS[6]. It appears that what was ordered was a temple to Caesar's clemency in which his statue would be placed as it had been in the temple of Quirinus.

But when due allowance is made for confusion and exaggeration there remain a group of less mundane honours which were voted to Caesar and which he accepted. What is important is to estimate how nearly Caesar was officially deified and how far these honours are to be ascribed to deliberate policy on his own part. A distinction must be drawn between the expression of enthusiasts in a cosmopolitan city such as Rome was becoming,

[1] XLIV, 6, 4.   [2] *Div. Iul.* 76.
[3] 43, 110, cf. *Phil.* XIII, 19, 41; 21, 47.   [4] *Loc. cit.*
[5] *Bell. Civ.* II, 106, 443.   [6] Volume of Plates iv, 12, *e.*

and deification as a recognized device of statecraft. Sulla had been dictator with the duty of drafting a new constitution: Caesar was a dictator of the same kind. It was a pardonable exaggeration to describe him as the re-maker of Rome, and after his victory at Munda had been interpreted as the salvation of the State from servitude he was offered and accepted the designation of *parens patriae*[1]. It is this view of Caesar which explains the placing of his statue in the temple of Quirinus, whom it was fashionable to regard as the deified Romulus, founder of Rome. The same meaning may be assigned to the placing of his statue along with the Kings of Rome. The setting-up of his chariot opposite the temple of Juppiter is the symbol of his triumph; a statue of him with the globe beneath his feet commemorates victories from one end of the Mediterranean world to the other. If this statue bore an inscription describing Caesar as a demigod, Caesar had the word erased. The statue in the temple of Quirinus is said to have been inscribed 'to the unconquerable god.' The evidence for this comes from Dio[2], but it may be true, and it is possible that a phrase applied to Alexander[3] was used of Caesar. It is also possible that the inscription was added after Caesar's death. The intention to build a temple to Caesar's Clemency is natural enough without any assertion that Caesar was a god. His statue was to be set up greeting Clemency, but the placing of a man's statue in a temple need not mean that he was regarded or worshipped as a god[4]. Thus the decree (if it was passed) that Caesar's statue should be set up in the cities and all the temples at Rome does not amount to a general deification[5]. The addition of a group of Luperci Julii set his *gens* by the side of the Fabii and Quinctii or Quintilii, from whom the existing Lupercal colleges drew their name. The change of the month Quintilis to Julius was a similar honour, not inappropriate to the reformer of the Calendar, and need have no more theological implications than the later change of Sextilis to

---

[1] Confirmed by the legend on coins of the year 44 B.C. See Volume of Plates iv, 12, *f*. The news of Munda arrived on the eve of the Parilia, and the association of Caesar with the celebration of this festival reflects this idea. Drumann (Drumann-Groebe III, p. 580 n. 3) compares the proposal to call the day on which Gaius became Emperor by the name Parilia 'velut argumentum rursus conditae urbis,' Suetonius, *Caligula*, 16, 4.

[2] XLIII, 45, 3.

[3] Hypereides I, 32, 5. See H. Berve in *Gnomon*, v, p. 376 n. 2.

[4] A. D. Nock in *Harvard Studies*, XLI, 1930, p. 3.

[5] Dio XLIV, 4, 4. This may be an anticipation of the Lex Rufrena of 42 B.C. What may be the similar recognition of Octavian as a national hero in 36 B.C. may be deduced from Appian, *Bell. Civ.* v, 132, 546.

Augustus[1]. When he was still absent in Spain his statue was carried with that of Victory at the games to celebrate his success at Munda. The substitution of his statue for himself is natural enough, and Cicero's gibe that the people thought poorly of the goddess in such company[2] is not to be taken seriously. The celebration of Caesar's birthday and the offering of prayers for his long life, even the taking of oaths by his *genius* had in antiquity no more implications of divinity than in modern times. On the other hand, it must be admitted that it was a short step from such honours as these to a kind of quasi-deification. The carrying of a statue of Caesar in the procession at the games for Munda was followed by a like order for other *ludi circenses*. It might become difficult to distinguish the humanity of Caesar's statue from the divinity of the statues of the gods in its company. Possibly before Caesar's death, Antony carried a law to add a day to public festivals in his honour. A gable, which had hitherto been the distinguishing feature of a temple, was added to his house, though the precise interpretation of this must remain in doubt so long as it cannot be told whether or not the house in question was Caesar's official residence as Pontifex Maximus.

Many men in Rome, especially those who inherited Hellenistic traditions, were no doubt very ready to treat Caesar as more than human. To them deification meant little more than the expression of gratitude and admiration. When they had seen Caesar's triumph move up to the Capitol, it was a small thing for them to continue the procession to Olympus or wherever else gods might dwell. But it remains true that the evidence falls short of attesting the official admission of Caesar in his lifetime to a place among the gods of the Roman State[3]. Almost all the honours paid to him can be explained as due to an extravagant form of recognition of what he had done. It is therefore hazardous to attribute them to any deliberate religious policy of his own. Amid the honours paid to him he presumably remained coolly detached. He might none the less have used the confused thinking of others to promote his plans. But if that theory is not forced upon us it may

---

[1] The statement of Dio (XLIV, 5, 2) that the name Julia was conferred on one of the Roman tribes in Caesar's honour appears to be untrue.

[2] *ad Att.* XIII, 44, 1.

[3] Dessau 72, 73, 73 *a* are not evidence for Caesar's lifetime. Dessau 6343, 'M. Salvio Q. f. Venusto decurioni [be]neficio dei Caesaris (Nola),' does not prove that Caesar was described as *deus* at the time when he conferred this *beneficium*, and, in any event, the phrasing of a private dedication is not to be pressed too far.

be rejected as little suited to what we know of Caesar's own acts and of his attitude of mind. As Pontifex Maximus he undoubtedly cared for the State religion of which he was the head. It was to him, we may assume, as to other cultivated Roman aristocrats of the day, at least the symbol of the Republic's greatness. When his head appears on the coins of the State it bears either the laurel wreath of a *triumphator* or the veil of the Pontifex Maximus[1]. He was careful to secure the ancient rights of the Vestals, *rex sacrorum* and *flamines* in the city, and in his charter for the colony of Genetiva Julia he provides for the establishment and performance of public worship on the Roman model. It may be imagined that his own instinct would be against innovations in the State religion, but though he declined some honours, he could not be always refusing distinctions which he valued at their true worth, even if he suspected that they were prompted by malice as well as by enthusiasm.

We may, then, attribute to Caesar at Rome no more than a policy of *laissez-faire* in religious matters. The same is even more true of Caesar in the provinces. Hellenistic States had hailed him as a god after Pharsalus, as they would have hailed Pompey if the day had gone for him[2]. Since the time of Flamininus they had shown gratitude for favours, respect for power or fear of punishment by this language of compliment, and their readiness to offer to Caesar divine honours does not mean that he claimed them. It is true that these honours would have smoothed Caesar's path if he sought to make himself a monarch of the Hellenistic type; but they are equally consistent with the absence of any such intention.

It is not, in fact, easy to attribute to Caesar any such serious design. The philosophical justification of the Hellenistic monarchy, with its insistence on the duty of promoting common goodwill

---

[1] Volume of Plates iv, 12 *f, g, h.*

[2] Carthaea (Ceos), *I.G.* xii, 5, 557; Lesbos, *Ath. Mitt.* 1881, 61; Mitylene, *I.G.* xii, 2, 165 *b*; Ephesus, Ditt.[3] 760. Cities also give him the titles of Soter, Euergetes or Ktistes, Athens, Ditt.[3] 759; Thespiae, *I.G.* vii, 1835; Carthaea, *I.G.* xii, 5, 556; Mitylene, *I.G.R.R.* iv, 57; Pergamum, *ib.* iv, 303, 304, 305, 307; Chios, *ib.* iv, 929. In 48 b.c. Pergamum calls Metellus Scipio Soter and Euergetes, Ditt.[3] 757. The language of these inscriptions falls short of attesting the recognition of Caesar as the prospective founder of a world-monarchy reconciling East and West. The striking phrase of the inscription at Ephesus (Ditt.[3] 760) 'god manifest and common Saviour of the life of man' belongs to the months immediately following Pharsalus, when Caesar's policy cannot have been declared, if indeed it ever was. There is no evidence for the precise date of the similar inscription of Carthaea.

and its conception of the responsibility of the monarch towards his subjects, might well appeal to the best sides of Caesar's character. Yet the great days of those monarchies were over: the last of them was a precarious survival in which the divinity that hedged a king was slight protection against an Alexandrian riot or an insurrection of fellahin. Despite real services to civilization and to the economic development of their subjects the Hellenistic monarchies had proved in the end a political failure. It is true that the Roman Republican constitution was ill adapted to govern the Mediterranean world. The task was too great to be left to the interplay of Senatorial coteries, to the rivalries of ambitious nobles who used their short reign in the provinces to secure power or wealth, to improvised armies, to irresponsible taxation bringing profits to Roman capitalists. None the less, when compared with the Hellenistic monarchies, the Roman system of the radiation of power from a city-state had proved a great success.

Caesar himself had led the armies of the West to victory in the Hellenistic East. In a military sense the centre of gravity of the Mediterranean world still lay in Italy, as the Civil War had proved, and the potential sea-power and the specialist troops of the Greek East cannot have counted for much with a soldier who had always put his faith in the legions. Hellenistic monarchy had become a shadow, and a realist, such as Caesar's writings and whole past career show him to have been, was not likely to sacrifice the substance of power for the shadow. That by the last year of his life Caesar had determined to enjoy autocratic power for the remainder of his days is plain. But to suppose that this autocratic power would be fortified by abandoning the traditions of the West in favour of those of the Greek East would have argued political blindness almost unthinkable of Caesar. Italy and the West might endure autocracy for the sake of a beneficent autocrat or to be secured from civil war. But to break autocracy loose from the sentiment of what was still the strongest political and military complex in the world was to root it up. The care which Caesar had taken to be sure of the West during his Parthian campaign shows, if it needs to be shown, that this almost self-evident fact had not escaped him.

The cure for the weaknesses that beset Rome's government of the Mediterranean world was, beyond doubt, some kind of autocracy or, if not precisely that, the entrusting to one man of the solution of its recurrent problems. For a generation Roman political thought had been inclining towards such a constitutional change in theory at least, though the memory of the time when the Senate embodied a steady control presented a constant rival. Augustus sought to reconcile the two ideas in an apparent compromise. Caesar was not the man for compromises, but he may have believed that in what remained of his life he might work out a permanent form of autocracy which would reconcile the traditions of East and West. But into what his autocracy might have been transformed we cannot say. He was killed because of what he was, not because of what he might be; and even the assertion that he had formed any clear plan for the future of the Roman State goes beyond the evidence and is not made necessary by his character. We have seen that as a general he trusted his genius to find a triumphant way out of the problems which war presented. He may well have postponed the problem of a final constitutional settlement until after his return from Parthia. One thing he did not do, he did not mark out anyone to be a successor to his power.

On the Ides of September 45 Caesar had made a will which was deposited with the Vestal Virgins. Up to the beginning of the Civil War Pompey, who had been his son-in-law, stood as his heir. The new will named Octavius, grandson of his younger sister Julia, heir in respect of three-quarters of the estate, L. Pinarius and Q. Pedius, who were grandsons of his elder sister, in respect of the remaining quarter. A number of persons were to be second heirs in default of the above three; among them were Decimus Brutus, and Antony, who was a connection of Caesar's on his mother's side. Guardians were appointed for a son in case one should be born to him. At the end of the will Octavius was adopted Caesar's son. The adoption of a son was in itself no more than what would be expected of a Roman noble with a high sense of the dignity of his family. Caesar might still hope to have a son born of his body, and the fact that he had not divorced Calpurnia suggests that he had not despaired of her motherhood. But his health was not good, and he was already determined to leave Rome on a distant campaign, from which he might not return[1].

[1] The will is concerned with three possibilities: that Caesar might die in the East, that Calpurnia might bear a child to him in his absence, and that one or all of the first heirs might die and so make way for the second heirs. It affords no evidence of any further intentions by Caesar, least of all the intention to marry Cleopatra and legitimatize his son by her. At the moment Cleopatra was in law the wife of Ptolemy XIII and reigned in Egypt as his consort. Clearly a legal Roman marriage with Cleopatra would be preceded by the death or divorce of Ptolemy and the divorce of Calpurnia,

Octavius both by bequest and adoption was preferred over Pinarius, in whose career Caesar appears to have taken no interest, and over Pedius, who had been a *legatus* in Gaul from 58 to 56 B.C., without being entrusted with any important command, and after that had shown no great capacity in Spain, where with Fabius he had failed to repress the movement in favour of Cn. Pompeius. What success was achieved might be set down to Fabius, who was a good soldier, and it is possible that the triumph which Pedius as well as Fabius was allowed to celebrate was a consolation prize. Little as Octavius' character resembled that of the dictator, we need not doubt that Caesar regarded him as definitely the most promising of his younger kinsmen. During the last four months he had been in Spain; and Caesar must have seen in him capacity. In the triumph after Thapsus he had been permitted to follow Caesar's chariot as though he had been *contubernalis*, and he had been made a patrician and a member of the pontifical college. More than that cannot be said. He was only ten days over eighteen, and Caesar cannot have dreamt of this young man's succeeding to his own autocracy, should any mishap befall him on his Parthian campaign. The very fact of his adoption was apparently kept a secret and would presumably have been kept a secret for years had Caesar lived, if only because the hope of being Caesar's heir was a useful hold on Antony[1]. For the time being Octavius was sent to pursue his studies at Apollonia until the time came for him to begin his apprenticeship in the art of war in the Dacian and Parthian campaigns.

It is stated by Dio[2] that Caesar intended Octavius to be a *magister equitum* and by Appian[3] that he had actually been made so for one year. It is possible that Appian only means that he had been designated for the office and is repeating the same tradition as Dio. According to Pliny[4], Octavius asked Caesar to make him *magister equitum*, and despite his request Lepidus was preferred to him. It is possible, though not necessary, to restore the Fasti so as to bring in Octavius as successor to Lepidus when he set out to Spain. Octavius would then be *magister equitum* for the remainder of the year 44, and be succeeded in 43 by Domitius

accompanied by the making of a new will. The alleged intention of Helvius Cinna (Suetonius, *Div. Iul.* 52, 3; cf. Dio XLIV, 7, 3) to propose a law at Caesar's instance to allow him to marry as many wives as he pleased in order to beget children does not deserve discussion as a serious proposal.

[1] M. E. Deutsch, *Caesar's Son and Heir*, Univ. of California Publ. in Class. Phil. IX, no. 6.

[2] XLIII, 51, 7.

[3] *Bell. Civ.* III, 9, 30.

[4] *N.H.* VII, 147.

Calvinus. But the silence of Suetonius in his lives of Caesar and of Augustus and still more the silence of Cicero seem to be decisive against the designation of Octavius. It appears far more probable that it was Caesar's intention to take Octavius with him on his campaign as *contubernalis* and to have Lepidus *magister equitum* at Rome for part of 44 B.C., and Calvinus *magister equitum* at Rome on Lepidus' departure. The tradition in Dio, and perhaps in Appian, is then to be explained as belonging to that war of propaganda which has done so much to confuse the history of Octavius' rise to power[1].

It is conceivable that Caesar might violate practice so far as to have one *magister equitum* at Rome and another with him in the East to act as second in command. But there is no hint of this in any ancient authority, and if Caesar had to choose a lieutenant in the field, his choice would hardly fall on a young man who had never seen a pilum thrown in anger. In fact, though Octavius enjoyed such promotion as was suitable to his years, it is not possible to show that Caesar had so far acted as though he intended to mark him out as a kind of crown prince[2]. At the news of Caesar's death Octavius returned to Italy, but it was the news of Caesar's will, hitherto unknown to him, that roused him to his great venture: it was the fact that Caesar had been murdered and that his lieutenant Antony was apparently consorting with his murderers that made the veterans follow a young man who now bore Caesar's name. No one in the summer of 44 B.C., to judge from the contemporary literature, saw in Octavius the man whom Caesar had chosen out to be the heir to the autocratic position which he himself had held. There was, then, no known evidence that Caesar aimed at establishing a dynasty, and the terms of his will afford no presumption that that was his intention. Nor were honours especially reserved for his descendants. It is said that the office of Pontifex Maximus was conferred in advance on his son or his adopted son[3]. But it will not readily be believed that, if the office fell by right to Caesar's heir, Octavius would not have taken even more credit in the *Res Gestae* for having left Lepidus Pontifex until his death.

[1] See below, Vol. x, chaps. I–III.
[2] Dio (XLV, 1, 2) declares that Caesar intended Octavius to be the heir to his power as well as to his name, but this appears to be no more than a deduction from Caesar's behaviour towards him and from a collection of myths about Octavius' birth and boyhood which were not known to Nicolaus of Damascus and Suetonius, or did not impose upon them.
[3] Dio XLIV, 5, 3.

We may now return to Caesar's own position in Rome. It was no more royal than it was divine. It is true that Caesar claimed descent from kings as well as gods, and sometimes wore high red boots which tradition associated with the kings of Alba from which the Julian *gens* claimed to have sprung. But much more than that was needed to make him king in Rome. Caesar's right to wear a laurel wreath and a purple robe and to sit upon a gilded chair, marked him out as *triumphator*, not as king. Pompey, too, had worn his robe after his last triumph[1]. That these insignia were complimentary and not the evidence of a constitutional position is shown by the fact that the occasions on which Caesar was invited to make use of them were first few, then many, then unlimited. One piece of evidence which cannot be lightly dismissed is the decree to place Caesar's head on the coins of the State during the last year of his life[2]. This was an innovation which might be regarded as admitting a claim to kingship. It might be thought that Rome had become a monarchy like those States which issued coins bearing the heads of their rulers. Yet if the Senate had decreed the issue of coins that meant to the Romans that Caesar was their king, it is hard to see why the imputation that he aimed at monarchy remained to be made. Faustus Sulla had issued coins bearing the head of the dictator Sulla within a generation of his death; the quaestor of Cn. Pompeius in Spain had struck coins with the head of Pompey the Great. The difference lay in the fact that Caesar was still living, but adulation might bridge that gap. It may fairly be supposed that the Senate were adding simply one compliment more to those paid to the dictator. Nor is it easy to suppose that the appearance of Caesar's head was thought to mark the end of the Republic. Within two years of Caesar's death Brutus allowed his head to be placed on coins which, though struck in the provinces, purported to be coins of the Roman State and bore, in one issue, the daggers and cap of liberty of the Ides of March[3]. The autocracy of Caesar, like that of Sulla, might be described as a *regnum* by those who felt that it curtailed their freedom or went beyond the normal practice of the Republic, but the word has not the force of a legal or constitutional definition. It is intended to convey the reproach of tyranny: so far as it looked back in Roman history, it looked back to the last Tarquin and that is all.

---

[1] Vell. Pat. ii, 40, 4; cf. Cicero, *ad Att.* i, 18, 6.

[2] Volume of Plates iv, 12, *f, g, h*.

[3] *Ib.* iv, 12, *j*.

Nor was Caesar's position simply military. The statement of Suetonius[1] and Dio[2], whatever its source, that he was granted and accepted the use of *imperator* as a praenomen is proved false by coins which till Caesar's death give him the praenomen of Gaius. It is equally certain that the name which Octavius received as adopted son of Caesar did not include the word *imperator*[3]. It is true that the legions would all of them obey Caesar, but a proconsul at the head of an army in his own province was not Caesar's *legatus*, and did not stand to him in the same relation as that in which, for example, Afranius in Spain stood to Pompey. His lieutenants, Pedius and Fabius, had celebrated triumphs, presumably in their own right, and Vatinius, the proconsul of Illyricum, was looking forward to doing the same. There is no sign that Caesar anticipated the Imperial monopoly of the triumph. He was not in fact any more or less an *imperator* than any other successful Roman general. The position of Caesar in the State cannot be equated with that of the first Dionysius as *strategos autokrator* of Syracuse.

Still less was Caesar's autocracy 'broad based upon the people's will.' It has been argued that he was the heir to the Gracchi, but he had no intention of imitating the shortlived power of Gaius Gracchus, which rested on the vindication and exaggeration of the power of the Populus Romanus against its partner by convention, the Senate. For the *faex Romuli* the new Romulus had no respect. He had no scruple in reducing the number of the mouths that ate the bread of the State, and though he could play the demagogue at a pinch, he cared little for the tongues that shouted praise or blame. His liberality with the citizenship showed how little he was bound by narrow traditions that were popular as well as senatorial, and while he provided for efficient local self-government, he neither made nor intended to make, so far as we can see, any provision for the government of Rome by representatives of a widened and widening citizen-body. Nor did Caesar stand for that ancient democratic power, the tribunate. In the past he, like other Roman politicians and generals, had found tribunes useful pawns in the game of politics. He had been compelled to use the tribunate to immobilize the machine of government when his

---

[1] *Div. Iul.* 76.   [2] XLIII, 44, 2; cf. LII, 40, 2; 41, 4.

[3] That Caesar did not take Imperator as a permanent or distinctive title has been proved by D. McFayden in *The History of the title Imperator under the Roman Empire*, pp. 15 *sqq.* The one respect in which Caesar went beyond Republican practice was in retaining the title though he entered the City before his triumph in 46 B.C.

enemies sought to use it against him. Thus he assumed the rôle of protector of the tribunes' rights, and so long as his dictatorial powers exempted him from their veto[1], he had no need to brave the ancient imprecations against those who left the Plebs without their leaders. Indeed the only effective, though spasmodic, opposition which Caesar had to face during his dictatorship came from the independent action of the tribunes[2]. In 44 B.C. there was conferred on him a tribunician sacrosanctity[3] and its outward manifestation, the right to sit upon the tribunician benches at the games. But he did not seek, or else he failed to find, a remedy for the deep-seated malady which the tribunate had become in the body politic. The tribunician veto was powerless against the dictator, but when tribunes acted independently of his approval, his remedy was to have them deposed by a bill put forward by another tribune (p. 737), a remedy which presumably he would not have invoked had any less unpopular course lain to his hand. And when he was affronted by the tribune Pontius Aquila, who refused to rise as he passed in triumph after Munda, his remedy was an angry phrase and a repeated sneer at the veto from which he was protected—'si tamen per Pontium Aquilam licuerit.' The disease was to be cured by homeopathic means, in the shape of the overriding active *tribunicia potestas* which was one of the greatest contributions of Augustus to Roman statecraft.

It is not easy to tell what future Caesar intended the Senate to enjoy. During the last twenty years it had generally been swayed by his enemies, although 120 senators had thought fit to travel to the conference of the triumvirate at Luca and 370 had voted for Curio's motion that Pompey, as well as Caesar, should lay down his command. The Civil War had removed part of the Senate hostile to him and most of the remainder, like Cicero, had removed themselves. The Senate had, by Caesar's act, the duty of providing half the members of the juries in the *iudicia publica* instead of only one-third. This, together with the need of providing for particular transactions a high quorum, made it reasonable to increase its numbers; and in adding new members Caesar had borne his own adherents in mind. There is no need to take too seriously lampoons about Gauls exchanging their trousers for the

---

[1] On the relation of the veto to the dictatorship see Mommsen, *Staatsrecht*, II³, p. 165 *sq.* But it may fairly be assumed that if Caesar's dictatorship was modelled on that of Sulla, it was exempt from the tribunician veto which would hinder precisely the task assigned to the dictator.

[2] See E. Pais, in *Atti della r. Accad. di Napoli*, N.S. II, 1913, pp. 149 *sqq.*

[3] See Note 6, p. 900 *sq.* on Caesar's *tribunicia potestas*.

toga or not knowing the way to the Senate House. He no doubt
added men of provincial birth and his own officers, even centurions,
but how readily this might be exaggerated by partisans is shown
by the fact that Sallust did not hestitate to attribute to Sulla the
appointment to the Senate of *gregarii milites*. The increase in the
number of magistrates who passed into the Senate was an administrative necessity, but it meant that the specifically Roman character of the Senate would be maintained. The sons of Senators
were indeed forbidden to leave Italy except on the service of the
State. The majority of the Senate was, and would be, Caesarian in
feeling, for the dictator's influence was bound to be strong in the
elections of these magistrates. Only if the remnant of unreconciled
Optimates gave the Senate a lead and evoked in it the old tradition
would it be more than a body ready, even too ready, to anticipate
Caesar's wishes or to go beyond them in adulation. When the
Senate took an oath to guard Caesar's life we may assume that
most of the *patres* meant it honestly.

There are no signs that Caesar meant to restore to the *patres*
the initiative in policy, or to give to them a large share of real
power in order to win over the discontented section of the
aristocracy. But the prestige of the Senate still persisted in the
provinces and client kingdoms and it was the one permanent
organ of the Roman State that could, in practice, bind it in day-
to-day policy. This was especially so in the region of foreign affairs.
As regards provincial commands, the assignment of particular
provinces to particular ex-magistrates, Caesar had no doubt only
to express a wish to see it fulfilled, but he appears to have left to
the Senate the assignment of praetorian provinces for 43. The
consuls, acting on Caesar's instructions, would naturally give a
lead, but the powers of the Senate were not taken away. So too
with the transaction of the multitude of foreign affairs, the embassies which (particularly in February) came to Rome. In the
year 45 envoys from Mitylene and from Cnidos were put off till
Caesar returned from Spain and then waited on his pleasure so
that it was not till the late autumn that their affairs were settled[1].
But while this shows how far the business of the Senate might be
delayed by the need to know the dictator's mind, in the case of
both these embassies, which deal with the formal ratification and
the making of alliances, the Senate plays its traditional part. The
same deduction may be drawn from the examination of the decrees
cited by Josephus about Rome and the Jewish community in

[1] C. Cichorius, *Ein Bundnisvertrag zwischen Rom und Knidos*, Rh. Mus.
LXXVI, 1927, p. 327.

these years. Caesar had in Syria made decisions in 47 B.C., but any permanent privileges of the Jews needed a decree of the Senate[1]. On the other hand, it has been argued with some force that the Senate did no more than register the decisions of Caesar by acclamation and not by consideration before the passing of a *senatus consultum*—that the Senate came in merely as a means of record and publication[2]. Cicero's complaint that his name was entered as attesting the drafting of decrees at meetings at which he was not even present may bear this out[3]. But it is to be remembered that there was a considerable body of decrees to pass which could do no more than register executive decisions taken by Caesar in the Greek East in 47, and that it would be rash to assume that during the years in which he expected to be fighting far from Rome he did not intend the Senate to carry on its traditional functions. Finally, it may be added, that the statement of Dio that Caesar was invested in 48 B.C. with the power to declare war and make peace in the name of the Roman People is not borne out by the facts so far as we know them[4].

Caesar's reforms had been carried through by virtue of his power as dictator, reinforced or rather emphasized in one direction by the *praefectura morum* which was conferred upon him after his victory at Thapsus[5]. Although the ordinary magistrates held office, they had no power to hinder his legislative activity, whether this took the form of laws passed through the Assemblies or of laws issued on the strength of his commission

[1] Josephus XIV [8, 5], 143 *sqq.* and [10], 185 *sqq.* and the discussion in E. Täubler's *Imperium Romanum*, pp. 159 *sqq.* It may be doubted if Josephus' presentation of these documents is sufficiently trustworthy to justify the exacting analysis to which Täubler subjects them.

[2] Täubler, *op. cit.* p. 171.   [3] *ad fam.* IX, 15, 4.

[4] XLII, 20, 1. See L. Wiegandt, *Zur staatsrechtlichen Stellung des Diktators Caesar: Das Recht über Krieg und Frieden* in *Jahresb. d. Kgl. Gymnasiums zu Dresden-Neustadt*, 1898.

[5] Cicero's reference to Caesar as 'praefectus moribus' (*ad fam.* IX, 15, 5) may not be technical, but the statements of Suetonius (*Div. Iul.* 76, 1) and of Dio (XLIII, 14, 4) may be accepted. The statement of Dio XLIV, 5, 3 that Caesar was appointed sole censor for life in 44 B.C. is suspect because of the silence of other authorities. It may receive some slight support from Velleius (II, 68, 5) who says that Caesar punished the two tribunes Flavus and Marullus, 'censoria nota potiusquam animadversione dictatoria,' but the support is slight. It would appear that Caesar could have acted in virtue of his powers as dictator or *praefectus moribus* and Velleius' phrase may be no more than a literary turn to provide a stylistic balance. If the offer was made, it was at an inopportune moment, just before Caesar was to set out from Rome for several years.

'*legibus scribundis.*' For the curule magistrates must bow to his superior *imperium*, and his dictatorship was not subject to the veto of the tribunes. The Senate might in theory refuse to pass *senatus consulta* to meet his wishes, and apart from overriding laws in the Assemblies, it had a constitutional right to decide upon the assignment of provinces. But the dictator's powers, following those of Sulla, had enabled him to nominate so many Senators as would secure a majority in the curia, even if opposition was declared. Thus in practice the appointment to provinces lay in his hand. For domestic administration he had the right of appointing *praefecti* who, as appointed by a dictator, wore the insignia of office and were clothed with an authority borrowed from his own. And to support and co-ordinate their activities he had the right to nominate a *magister equitum*, who could take his place at Rome while he was in the field, and could exercise his own overriding powers. Abroad Caesar might appoint *legati* and grant them praetorian rank. So comprehensive and so firm was the grip upon the State which with remorseless logic Caesar derived from his dictatorship.

The cumulation of the consulship with the dictatorship had a precedent in Sulla, the continuous iteration of consulships a precedent in Marius, the position of sole consul for a time a precedent in Pompey. The command of Pompey against the pirates followed by his governorship in Spain had pointed the way to the wide delegation of powers dependent on a single *imperium* (see above, p. 347 *sq.*). It might be argued that the needs of the Republic were forcing it to gravitate towards such a central power as Caesar possessed. The right granted to Sulla to make laws as dictator, whether Sulla used it or not, involved a temporary abdication of the sovereign right of the Roman People, and this abdication was repeated with Caesar, although he appears to have taken little or no advantage of it in important matters. But Caesar was permitted, in fact though probably not in theory, to control elections to the curule magistracies. After Munda the Senate offered him the right of nomination to a part of the great offices of State, and though Caesar contented himself with commendations to the electors, there was set a new precedent which went far to eliminate the Roman People from the government of Rome. In 44 B.C. a *plebiscitum* proposed by Antony's brother Lucius permitted the elections in advance of magistrates for future years and, so far as Caesar availed himself of this permission, his nomination in fact governed the choice of the electors not only in the present but for the future. The old forms remained.

Antony as augur prevented the election of Dolabella in 44 B.C. as *consul suffectus* to Caesar himself. On the last day of December 45 the consul Q. Fabius died, and the dictator caused a new consul to be elected in his stead for the remaining hours of that year. Needless to say Cicero made this the occasion for bitter jests[1], and though it is reasonable to suppose that Caesar was moved by formal correctness rather than by the desire to make the consulship ridiculous, his action showed how little he cared what construction might be placed upon it. In fact the dictator's patronage extended throughout the State with the possible exception of the tribunate.

Of less moment, but not without some significance, was the right conferred on Caesar to create, or nominate for creation, new patricians. Some reinforcement of the patriciate had by now become practically necessary, and it was natural to entrust the task to the *dictator rei publicae constituendae*. But Caesar's enemies might well point out that for a precedent it was necessary to go back to the traditions of the ancient monarchy. Increases in the number of magistrates—the quaestors to forty, the praetors first to ten, then to fourteen, then to sixteen—justified as they were by the needs of Rome and of the provinces, added in effect to the dictator's patronage. The priestly offices which Roman nobles coveted as social distinctions became the rewards of Caesar's favour. Although it would be too much to say that he formed out of the few men in his confidence an *imperium in imperio*, it was galling for men like Cicero or still more for aristocrats with centuries of consulships behind them to wait in Caesar's ante-room or address themselves to men like Oppius and Balbus who had the ear of their patron. The flood of compliments poured on Caesar washed away some of his defences. Although in general he was possessed of rare tact and polished manners, servility aroused in him moments of arrogance. When early in 44 B.C. the *patres* went in procession to announce to him a new grant of honour, he failed to rise at their approach, and the excuses advanced for this behaviour cannot have satisfied those who were ready to be affronted. His ceaseless clear-headed activity till the end disposes of the legend of him as the pathological study in diseased greatness which Shakespeare has read out of his Plutarch, but in small matters he yielded now and then to vanity which would have been harmless except in one whose position challenged the traditional pride of an aristocracy. An enemy attributed to him the saying that the Republic had become a form without substance; and it was perilously near the

---

[1] *ad fam.* VII, 30, 1–2.

truth. He had drained the life-blood of the State into his dictator-ship—'dictaturam' wrote Cicero 'quae iam vim regiae potestatis obsederat[1].'

But in the fact that he vested his power, present and future, in the dictatorship lay his danger. The dictatorship of Sulla had always been an offence to constitutionalists, but his abdication had con-firmed the tradition that the office did not last beyond the emer-gency which made it necessary. For this doctrine Caesar showed less and less respect. He had been dictator and had abdicated on becoming consul for 48. He had been made dictator again after Pharsalus and had been slow to surrender his powers. Then came the conferment of the office for ten years: that was going far enough. But when his friends in 44 B.C. voted in the Senate that he should be dictator in perpetuity they did him an ill turn, and he did himself an ill turn when, as his coins show, he accepted what was offered him[2]. Powers which strained the content of the dictator's office combined with permanence which violated its very nature were enough to make good constitutionalists see in Caesar a tyrant. Finally, as the dictatorship was an emergency office, it was not so woven into the fabric of the State that it could not be removed without destroying it. With the abdication of a dictator the State simply resumed its normal course. The officers who depended directly upon him vanished at once, and all was as before. Thus those who saw in Caesar's dictatorship the cessation of traditional government believed that one thing only was needed to restore it, and that was to remove the dictator, since he would not remove himself.

How far Caesar realized the danger to his life, it is hard to divine. Subtle as he had been where intrigue was the only way, it was not in his nature to cloak his power once he possessed it. In his first consulship he had at last broken out into open triumph over his enemies. To his sense of power, the prize of his genius, he would not be untrue. There is much self-revelation in the phrase he used to explain his clemency to his opponents—'I wish for nothing more than that I should be like myself and they like themselves[3]'—a phrase which finds an echo in the letter of the faithful Matius after Caesar's death[4]. And with the sense of power came an impatience with indirections. Once in the saddle he would ride hard, even if it meant riding for a fall. He was conscious, too, of the services which he could render to the State, and it may have been hard for him to realize how blind men

[1] *Phil.* I, 1, 3.   [2] Volume of Plates iv, 12, *h*.
[3] *ad Att.* IX, 16, 2.   [4] *ad fam.* XI, 28, 8.

could be to the need of him. That he was not loved by the
Roman aristocracy he knew well enough, and he was well aware
that proud men are not often won by pardon. Though he had
proclaimed an amnesty, defeat still rankled. But it might have
seemed to him unreason to exchange a Caesar for a competition
for power between an Antony, a Lepidus, a Brutus or a Cicero.
Moreover, the Senate had voted him the sacrosanctity which
belonged to the tribunes and the Senators had bound themselves
by an oath to protect him from hurt. He dismissed the Spanish
horsemen that had been his military bodyguard, and moved freely
about the city in apparent confidence and security. For if he was
to be treated as a tyrant he would not suffer the tyrant's punishment, to live in fear.

VII. THE CONSPIRACY AND THE IDES OF MARCH

How long before the Ides of March there was a conspiracy
against Caesar's life it is hard to say. Cicero's letters show that
the Roman aristocracy was a whispering gallery, and yet, though
more than sixty men were in the plot, the deadly secret was kept.
In the summer of 45 Brutus was ready to defend Caesar, and it
would take time to make Brutus forget his benefactor in remembering the Brutus who had overthrown the Tarquins. It is reasonable to assume that it was not till after Caesar's return in triumph
over Pompey's blood that the plot was begun. The beginning of
the year 44 was filled with preparations for Caesar's departure to
the East. It is possible that along with Caesar's other motives
went the desire to exchange the air of Rome heavy at once with
exaggerated compliments and with suspicion and ill-will for the
camp and the legions that he knew he could trust. His enemies
knew that the time was short if they would strike while the blow
could be sure and might be safe.

To analyse precisely the motives of the conspirators is a thank-
less task. Cassius was a man of capacity and determination whose
pride would not brook the most honourable subordination. Brutus
was a compound of tradition and philosophy set in a rigid nature
which imposed on Cicero by the attraction of opposites. That he
had been Caesar's decoy for the aristocracy is not proved, nor
that he was swayed by a sense that his services had been in-
sufficiently rewarded. But he had no eyes for anything beyond the
negative duty and the dull simplification of tyrannicide. What
motives of pride, of thwarted ambition or vulgar envy were mixed
in the natures of other of the conspirators it is unprofitable to

inquire. That there was much honesty and idealism, however perverted, cannot be denied. Men like Trebonius and Decimus Brutus owed everything to Caesar and were marked out to high distinction by his favour. Caesar was marked down for death, and he alone. The decision of the conspirators to leave Antony untouched is capable of more than one explanation. To remove the dictator and leave the consul suited constitutional theory; Antony was ambitious enough to sacrifice Caesar's memory to his own advantage, and the legions might listen to Antony; to kill any man but the tyrant was to turn a sacrifice into an assassination. Of the young Octavius in Apollonia no one thought.

What followed during the last three months of Caesar's life was preparation for the act. If Caesar was tyrant he was a beneficent tyrant. The Roman People, in whom the conspirators too readily saw the source of power, might resent Caesar's removal more than they resented his rule. Yet among the populace at Rome, by the side of an idolatry of Caesar which broke out after his death, there was the ancient hatred of monarchy born of historical tradition and fed by the spectacle of client kings, whose kingship meant to the Romans the denial of freedom to their subjects. That, at the moment at least, Caesar aimed at converting a Republican autocracy into a formal monarchy is a hardy hypothesis. Napoleon, who was no bad judge, has pointed out that the eve of a prolonged absence is not the moment to subvert a constitution. But to insinuate the design and at the same time to bring the dictator into collision with the tribunes, the traditional guardians of liberty, was a game worth playing. To ancient theorists and moralists who believed that the art of the statesman is dissimulation it was natural to suppose that Caesar inspired the tragicomedy that followed, but we are entitled to place a more reasonable interpretation upon the facts.

First came the placing of a diadem on Caesar's statue and its prompt and ostentatious removal by the tribunes, Flavus and Marullus, as an outrage on democratic liberty. Then, as the dictator was returning on January 26 44 B.C. from celebrating the Latin festival as consul the cry of 'rex' was raised. Caesar tried to turn it off with an easy phrase—'non sum rex sed Caesar' —which might seem no more than a casual half-jesting evasion, but perhaps betrays Caesar's scale of values. The tribunes hastened to arrest the man who was said to have raised the first cry. Their action made the cry more dangerous, and there is no reason to doubt that Caesar was more than displeased. He had renewed ground for anger when they issued an edict declaring that their prerogative of free action had been infringed. Thereupon Caesar attacked them in the Senate and the tribune Helvius Cinna proposed and carried their deposition. Two new tribunes were elected to take their place. Thus the insinuation that Caesar aimed at becoming *rex* was emphasized, and with it the clash between the dictatorship and the tribunate.

Three weeks later came the Lupercalia, when the consul Antony offered Caesar a diadem which he ostentatiously and repeatedly refused before dedicating it to Juppiter Capitolinus, the only king of the Roman People. More than this, he caused to be inscribed in the Fasti that M. Antonius, consul, at the People's bidding had offered kingship to C. Caesar, dictator in perpetuity, and that Caesar had refused to accept it. Of this incident the simplest explanation seems to be the truest, that Caesar had realized the danger and decided to conjure it once for all. Had he planned a *coup d'État* the Lupercalia would have ended otherwise. The Roman People, as their later behaviour showed, were not convinced that when Caesar fell he would not fall as a would-be Tarquin. One device remained—the Sibylline books.

Twelve years before, when Pompey was credited with a desire for the profitable task of restoring a Ptolemy to Alexandria, his enemies had produced an oracle that the king of Egypt must not be restored 'with a multitude,' that is 'with an army' (p. 531). In February 44 B.C., two things were public knowledge, that Caesar intended to march against Parthia, and that he had definitely refused an offer of kingship. A vague phrase in the Sibylline books was found, and the Quindecimvir L. Cotta was ready with the interpretation that the Parthians could only be overcome if the Romans were led by a king. It was a dilemma. That Caesar would forgo his campaign was out of the question, but if he disregarded the interpretation of the Sibylline books, its publication would arouse the superstitions of the people and perhaps of the soldiers. Ten years before, Crassus had set out against Parthia; he had left Rome under the solemn imprecations of a tribune, and he and his army had met with disaster. Until the interpretation was reported to the Senate it was a secret of State which could afterwards be dismissed as an idle rumour, but it was an open secret, and known to the dictator[1]. He found a

---

[1] Cicero, *ad Att.* XIII, 44, 1 (July 45 B.C.) 'Verum tamen scire omnia non acerbum est, vel de Cotta' has been adduced as a reference to the interpretation of the Sibylline books. If that is so, then the idea was not first conceived in February 44. But in that letter (3) come the words 'Cottam mi velim mittas' in which Cotta presumably means 'a book by Cotta'

solution: he would march against Parthia as a king but would not go back on his solemn refusal at the Lupercalia: he would bear the title of king not in Rome, but in the Provinces and client-states. That was the answer to be given when the interpretation was reported to the Senate. All that remained was to spread the rumour that Caesar would make Ilium or Alexandria his capital[1]. The battle of wits was over, the conspirators were forced to strike at once, and the comedy was turned into tragedy on the Ides of March.

On the evening before the Ides Caesar dined with Lepidus, and as the guests sat at their wine someone asked the question 'What is the best death to die.' Caesar who was busy signing letters said 'A sudden one.' By noon next day, despite dreams and omens, he sat in his chair in the Senate House, surrounded by men he had cared for, had promoted or had spared, and was struck down, struggling, till he fell dead at the foot of Pompey's statue.

Caesar died the martyr of his own genius. The versatility of his intellect matched the steadiness of his will. A fine gentleman free from the less elegant vices, an antiquarian, a purist in language, a man of letters, a consummate politician, an administrator and a soldier, he was all these as the moment demanded and was each of them with easy mastery. The chances of time have denied us any portrait made of Caesar in his life, but Suetonius has left on record

possibly not the Quindecimvir. It seems difficult to suppose that 'Cotta' has not the same meaning in both sentences and has no reference to the Sibylline oracles. It is also *a priori* improbable that a discovery of importance to the State would not be reported to the Senate before the Ides of March 44 if it was made in July 45. Apart from that, the ancient authorities refer to the rumour of the oracle in connection with the events of the six weeks preceding Caesar's death. This may only be in order to support the tradition (here rejected) that it was part of a plan by Caesar or his friends to procure for him the title of king, but it suggests that there was no rival tradition about the date of the discovery of the oracle.

[1] Similar rumours, with equal ground, were spread abroad under Augustus (cf. Horace, *Odes*, iii, 3). Nicolaus asserts that the rumour about Alexandria was refuted by Caesar's will. Unless Caesar intended to make a new frontier much farther East—and of this there is no evidence—there was no advantage to be gained by moving the capital. And indeed the mention of Ilium along with Alexandria goes far to remove the allegation from actuality. When Cicero (*ad Att.* xv, 4, 3), in a moment of depression, was inclined to regret the Ides of March—'ille enim numquam revertisset'—we may suppose that he had not in mind Caesar's governing Rome as an autocrat from Alexandria, but an optimistic hypothesis that he would never come back from his campaign.

his tall figure, his clear complexion, his dark eyes with their quick glance, the studied, almost foppish, elaboration of his dress. His mind is mirrored in his acts and in his words. His culture, his ideas were Roman not borrowed from the Greeks. Hard-headed as his race, practical, positive, he was no dreamer nor ideologue. Among his exploits he lived intensely, as his writings show, an artist of action, alert with a *vivida vis animi*. No man has ever been so determined to impose his will on others and no man has been so gifted by nature for the achievement of his purpose.

Alexander alone in antiquity rivals Caesar in the range and speed of his exploits:

> *fu di tal volo*
> *che nol seguiteria lingua nè penna.*

It was inevitable that he should be compared with Alexander because of his victories and because of his death, cut off as he was in the plenitude of his power as was Alexander in the midst of his days. Yet the likeness between them belongs to rhetoric rather than to history. The story went that as praetor in Spain Caesar had lamented that he had achieved so little by the age at which Alexander had died. Beyond that, there is no evidence that Caesar set Alexander before himself as his model. There are no good grounds for supposing that his project to march against Parthia was in imitation of Alexander's conquering invasion of the Persian Empire. Gossip that Caesar dreamed of returning from Parthia past the Caspian to Scythia and then through Germany back to Gaul may be evidence that the Alexander-legend was strong, but it is evidence of nothing else. In judging Alexander it must not be forgotten that he was not the heir to Greek tradition. The old Greek advice of Aristotle to be a leader to the Greeks, a master to the barbarians, fell on deaf ears. The Greek ideas of Alexander were new ideas, the ideas of the unity of mankind. Caesar was a Roman aristocrat, steeped in the Roman tradition of reasonable, calculated, but inflexible domination, the belief in power rather than in conquest, in the extension of Rome to the Romanized, in steady progress but in continuity of policy.

His ambition was compounded of the Roman desire to achieve the distinction which his birth and genius claimed for him and of an unresting zeal for good administration and the greatness of Rome. In his clemency there may have been a touch of contempt, a masterful challenge of the future. The cold prudence of the maxim 'Stone-dead hath no fellow' would have belittled him. For men of his own aristocratic stamp or for men who followed the trade of arms, which was nearest to his heart, he had a generous sympathy. But he did not hesitate to requite craft with deeper craft or to strike terror by cruelty if barbarians crossed him. There can be no doubt that in his *Commentaries* he was an advocate for Caesar. But he deceived others as little as might be, and deceived himself not at all. The politicians of his day found him hard to trust, because they could not but see that his appetite for power grew with eating, and they judged him by themselves. To the end he remained to them incalculable. Yet his genius was the hard practical genius of Rome raised to the highest power: he was a keen edge on the old blade.

But he reached power late, too late for patience. The impulses of fifteen years of tremendous activity still spurred him, but he was tiring; 'satis diu vel naturae vixi vel gloriae[1].' His health was breaking, he had few friends and no one whom he would trust to help him bear the burden as Octavian was to trust Agrippa. For this reason he could not admit Time to his counsels, nor share them with others. Thus he became, in a sense, un-Roman in the last year of his life. There came the clash between his genius and the Roman steady tradition, and in the clash he was broken, with plans unachieved and plans unmade.

He had shown the world the greatest of the Romans, but he was not the creator of a new epoch. Whatever he might have done, he had as yet neither destroyed the Republic nor made the Principate. His life had set an example of autocracy which his death converted into a warning. The civil wars that followed the Ides of March prepared the way for a statesman who was the heir to Caesar's name, the avenger of Caesar's death—but no Caesar. The aristocracy was almost destroyed, the legions became the servants of a man who was not a soldier first. The Roman world became ready to welcome the Empire that was peace. Caesar had done much for the State in his reforms, but he did Rome no greater service than by his death. The cruel years during which Octavian fought his way to undivided power were the last blood-letting of the body politic. A spark of Caesar glowed smokily in Antony and was extinguished: there remained Octavian.

[1] Cicero, *pro Marcello*, 8, 25.

CHAPTER XVIII

LITERATURE IN THE AGE OF CICERO

I. GENERAL

IN histories of Latin literature, the last century of the Republic is often described as the Ciceronian age; and the great orator has perhaps as much right to furnish an eponymous title as Chaucer or even Shakespeare. Prose and poetry had long ceased to depend on the freedmen attached to some man of rank; the nobles and knights had taken Roman literature into their own hands. In the sphere of oratory, there was no doubt a practical incentive—Cicero himself, in his early years, treated other forms of art as a preparation for a political career—but his interest in poetry, history and philosophy was also the mark of a culture shared by Roman society in general. This literary circle was, in fact, a close and fairly small corporation of which Cicero became the acknowledged head. Rival orators, like Hortensius and Calvus, were of course known to him professionally; but literature was the chief—perhaps the only bond—which bound him to such men as Varro and others whose connection with State affairs was slight. The respect paid by Caesar to Cicero as well as to the Pompeian Varro is not only a proof of the dictator's personal magnanimity, but an honour duly paid to literature through its two chief representatives.

During Cicero's lifetime there were many special developments in the style and composition of both poetry and prose, which can best be studied under particular names; but there are certain general considerations that apply to the writers of the period as a whole. The main point at issue was to decide whether literature should stand on the ancient ways: whether Ennius, in verse, and Cato, in prose, should be the models of a generation, which had moved beyond the ideals and even the language of those 'examples.' The spirit of antiquarianism may have been, in part, a legacy of Alexandria; but it was thoroughly congenial to the Roman, and indeed—in a sense—was native to Rome. For the Republic was now old enough to be interested in its own origins, and the erudition of Varro had a double significance. It implied not only that Romans should be proud of their birthright, but that they should imitate the *exempla maiorum* by carrying on the tradition of the Latin language. If the style of the Twelve Tables was too archaic for even the most enthusiastic purist to follow, the speech of Ennius and Cato might still be maintained—or recovered. Terence, in particular, became the norm of purity (*elegantia*) for those who, with Cicero and Caesar, rejected the severer forms of archaism. The problem of style was further complicated by the insistent claim of Greek words to be naturalized for poetical and philosophical needs. It is true that oratory—the most important and successful form of literature in the age—was little troubled by questions of archaism or Graecism: the speaker was obviously required to conform to *usus*, the language of the day. But, throughout the century, historians and other prose writers, as well as poets, were more or less sharply divided on the subject of linguistic propriety.

In spirit, the division was equally marked. To Cicero and other patriots, oratory, history and philosophy, however much the arts or sciences might owe to Greece, were now to be valued in terms of Roman culture. The Rome of Cicero had become the engrossing theme of literature not less than the Rome of Augustus, although the Republic, as a symbol, may have lacked the glitter of the imperial name. On the other hand, there were still some (especially among the poets) whose interest in Greek literature was almost wholly divorced from Roman values. During the protracted agony of the Marian and Sullan struggle, the detachment of a Lucretius, the self-absorption of a Catullus, are signs that Greek poetry was still able to command the undivided allegiance of many who thought most acutely or felt most profoundly.

II. POETRY

The names of Lucretius and Catullus are a sufficient reminder that the age of Cicero was not merely prosaic; but the wide interest in poetry is best indicated by the fact that few of the many orators and prose writers in the period were not also practitioners of verse. No doubt the practice had its dangers: Julius Caesar was deemed more fortunate than Cicero because (like Brutus) he wrote not better but fewer verses; and Augustus was perhaps wise in suppressing these indiscretions[1]. But Varro, Sisenna, Sulpicius Rufus (the great jurist), Q. Cicero—more persistent than his brother—Hortensius and Cornelius Nepos are only some of those who included poetry with other forms of literature. The chief influence was drawn from Alexandria. This was inevitable, since

---

[1] Tacitus, *dial.* 21; Suet. *Div. Iul.* 56.

the social and political conditions of the Greek city-state were now remote, whereas the art of the Ptolemaic kingdom could be readily assimilated by Romans. Scholars, such as the two Ciceros, of course admired and translated or imitated the Attic tragedy; but the classical play gave little satisfaction to the popular taste. Although Aesopus, in tragedy, and Roscius, in comedy, won high reputation as actors, the age produced no rival of Accius. Indeed, the Roman stage was occupied by revivals of the plays of Ennius, Pacuvius and still more of Accius himself[1]. Much has been written to account for this decline in drama between the periods of Accius and the Augustans, the simplest explanation being that, while poetic genius was certainly abundant, it was diverted— as in the Victorian age—into more congenial paths, until the *Thyestes* of Varius and the *Medea* of Ovid attempted to recapture the form, if not the spirit, of Sophocles and Euripides. In any case, there was little to encourage serious drama at a time when acted tragedy was tending to be supplanted by the later pantomime in which a silent actor 'danced' his part.

Only a single form of drama—the Mime—found favour in this period. Here DECIMUS LABERIUS (105–43 B.C.), a Roman Knight, and PUBLILIUS SYRUS, an enfranchised slave who became an actor, gained distinction in a *genre* which, although cultivated by Herodas and other Alexandrians, seems to have been completely Romanized. Unlike the Atellan play which it superseded[2], the Mime dispensed with stock characters and masks; and—an even more notable innovation—feminine parts were taken by actresses. According to Ovid, the plots were drawn from love-intrigues, and the author of the *Art of Love* complained that he had been punished for a licence permitted to the Mime[3]. It may seem surprising that these musical farces—they were often acted as interludes—should have won their way into literature; but Laberius gave them at least a passing dignity. Commanded by Caesar to play in his own mime, as a penalty for some slighting allusion to the autocrat, he expressed, in a prologue of great force, his feeling of shame at the insult of compelling a Roman Knight to return home an actor:

> Citizens, henceforward Liberty is lost.

In these lines his Latinity is impeccable, but we know that Laberius often had recourse to the plebeian vernacular which was afterwards exploited by Petronius. His diction, no less than his

---

[1] See Tenney Frank, *Life and Literature in the Roman Republic*, p. 60 *sq.*
[2] Cicero, *ad fam.* IX, 16, 7.   [3] Ovid, *trist.* II, 497 *sq.*

anti-Caesarian politics, was doubtless the ground of Horace's contempt[1].

His successful rival, Publilius, being a freedman, was not too proud to act; but he was also a writer, celebrated for his moral apophthegms (*sententiae*); and numerous fragments, of which the greater part are accepted as authentic, have been preserved from a collection made in the first century of the Empire, and much used in schools. Verses like

iniuriarum remedium est oblivio

and

numquam periclum sine periclo vincitur

with many others after the model of Menander and Terence, suggest that Publilius, at least, was no party to the later degradation of the Mime.

The age of Cicero produced two poets who would give distinction to the literature of any nation. To add the name of Cicero himself may well seem a bathos, since the orator became a by-word for his *ridenda poemata*. Possibly this criticism (which became common form among the writers of the Empire)[2] was mainly due to a couple of lines, one of which—*o fortunatam natam me consule Romam*—may well deserve the ridicule of Juvenal and Martial. But a critical method relying on 'the worst lines in poetry' would debar Wordsworth or Tennyson from the rank of a poet; it is fairer to recall Plutarch's observation that for a time—presumably before Lucretius and Catullus—Cicero was held to be the best poet, as well as the best orator, of Rome[3]. This remark is often regarded as a condemnation, in effect if not intention, of Roman poetry at the time; but Cicero's own achievement by no means warrants the censure. Formally, he did conspicuous service in refining the roughness of Ennius—his fault, indeed, was rather in a certain smoothness tending towards monotony, as may be seen from his early translation of Aratus' *Phaenomena*, followed by that of the *Prognostica*. A style that influenced Lucretius is not lightly to be despised[4]. In later years his poetry became the self-glorification of his own consulship (*de suo consulatu* and *de temporibus meis*); and it was these poems, in particular, which injured his reputation. Even when he suppressed his own deeds, in eulogies of Marius

---

[1] Horace, *sat.* I, 10, 5.

[2] Seneca (rhetor), *exc. contr.* 3 *praef.* 8; Seneca, *de ira*, III, 37, 5; Quintilian, XI, 1, 24; Tacitus, *dial.* 21; Martial II, 89; Juvenal X, 124.

[3] Plutarch, *Cic.* 2.

[4] See Munro's ed. of Lucretius, vol. II, p. 2, and on book v, 298, 619. His imitation of Cicero seems certain; see W. B. Sedgwick in *Class. Rev.* XXXVII, 1923, p. 115 *sq.*

and Caesar, it is clear that he suffered from the fatal Roman habit
of viewing poetry as a species of history. But Cicero, if never
inspired as an original poet, was at all events an extremely competent translator. And he has the great credit of getting beyond
Aratus to the masterpieces of earlier Greece. His renderings,
starting chronologically with Homer's Siren-song, include passages
from all the three great tragic poets. Among these translations,
we no longer possess the original of the *Prometheus Unbound*; but
Cicero's version beginning

Titanum suboles, socia nostri sanguinis

has a vigour and directness of language which gives the impression
that his verses, although they may lack the delicacy of the original,
are a faithful rendering of the Aeschylean grandeur. His translation of Aratus was no doubt the work which brought him the
recognition mentioned by Plutarch; and sufficient of this remains
to justify Cicero's place among Roman poets. Aratus, who has
ceased to interest the modern world, had a peculiar appeal to
ancient readers, as Virgil bears witness in the *Georgics*; and, while
Cicero does not reach the height of Virgilian charm, he has a
strength and beauty of his own which compares very well with the
rather tame facility of his original.

An admirer of Ennius and Pacuvius, as well as of Plautus and
Terence, Cicero was before all things a traditionalist in poetry.
Nevertheless he was writing—as he spoke—not for antiquity, but
for his own day; and he avoids the sometimes excessive archaism
of Lucretius. His aim was obviously to carry on the inheritance of
Ennius, without copying the uncouthness of the old school. On
the other hand, he had no sympathy with the new Alexandrian
fashion which Catullus and his friends were now imposing on
Latin verse. No stress can be laid on the fact that he never
mentioned the rising poet of Verona, who had thanked him, for
some service, in a few graceful lines of acknowledgment—it was
not Cicero's way to talk much of contemporary poets. But he was
sarcastic about the affected cadences for which the 'echoers of
Euphorion'—*cantores Euphorionis*—were notorious[1]. The leader
of this 'neoteric' school was P. Valerius Cato, who, like Catullus,
was a Cisalpine. Of his own poetry, no undisputed fragments
remain; but his influence as a teacher in fostering the spirit and
technique of Alexandria is attested by the eulogy of a friend or
pupil—possibly M. Furius Bibaculus—who calls him 'the Latin
Siren, the only reader and maker of poets.'

Cicero himself, as the translator of Aratus, could not have

---

[1] Cicero, *Tusc.* II, 10. For the 'Neoterics' see further, p. 751 *sq.*

resented the chief feature of the Alexandrians—their didactic erudition. But he had no sympathy with their affectations, which ill accorded with the dignity of the Ennian hexameter. Whatever may be our view on Cicero's own poetic powers, it is clear that his appreciation of poetry was neither deficient, nor, in the main, unsound. If his strong patriotism led him to undervalue the neoterics, he seems to have done justice to Lucretius as an example of genius combined with art[1]. In his enthusiasm for 'the studies which educate the young, and delight the old; which adorn prosperity, and give a refuge and a consolation to adversity'— *pernoctant nobiscum, peregrinantur, rusticantur*[2]—Cicero is speaking on behalf of a poet; and he seizes the occasion for a splendid defence of his client's profession, before an educated jury who may well have excused a peroration so foreign to the atmosphere of a modern court. His patronage of poets, attested by Pliny (*ep.* III, 15), is not the least pleasing feature in the great advocate who held that the orator and poet were kinsmen.

The life of the most famous poet in this period, T. LUCRETIUS CARUS, is practically unknown. Our chief authority is a passage in Jerome's continuation of Eusebius' Chronicle (apparently derived from Suetonius), where he is said to have been born in 95 B.C., and to have died 52–51 B.C. Other late evidence is conflicting; but it seems probable that the poet's lifetime falls within the limits of 99–54 B.C. His parentage and birthplace are nowhere stated; but he was no doubt a patrician, as the *gens Lucretia* was among the noblest—though some of its families seem to have been plebeian—and his tone towards Memmius, the praetor to whom he dedicates his poem, is that of an equal rather than a client. Jerome adds that Lucretius wrote in the intervals of madness induced by a love-potion; that this was followed by suicide, and that his poem was afterwards 'emended' by Cicero. These statements are possible, but suspect: the *de Rerum Natura* bears no traces of insanity, although it ends abruptly and needs revision throughout. The charge of madness may well be due to a dislike of Epicureanism—the *insaniens sapientia* of Horace's recantation —aided perhaps by a confusion between two senses of *furor*, which may mean either poetic inspiration or physical madness. In Statius (*Silvae*, II, 7, 76)

et docti furor arduus Lucreti

the former sense is of course intended, and this criticism—that the poet showed both learning and genius—is borne out by

---

[1] See below, p. 747.   [2] Cicero, *pro Archia*, 7, 16.

Cicero's one reference to Lucretius. In a letter written to his brother (54 B.C.), the poem is described as *multis luminibus ingenii multae tamen artis*. The compliment is high: Lucretius is allowed the genius of the old school represented by Ennius, while he nevertheless (*tamen*) has more art than Ennius, who was proverbially 'rude.' As Cicero had himself refined this rudeness, he naturally welcomed the Lucretian improvements, which largely followed his own technique. Owing to the habit of contrasting genius and art, a poet was more often placed in one of these two categories than allowed an equal share in both. With this appreciation, it seems not impossible that Cicero—in spite of his dislike of Epicurean philosophy—may have lent his name (or his slaves) to the publication of the book.

In the middle of the century, Epicureanism was certainly fashionable among the ruling class, and was adopted by such men as Piso, Atticus, Pansa (Caesar's general) and—at least unofficially —by Caesar himself. The school counted two distinguished Greek teachers, Phaedrus and Philodemus, and its principles had been expounded in the prose of Amafinius and others. But an Epicurean poem was a new experience, not attempted by the Greeks themselves, who had followed the severe prose of their own master. Even Lucretius found it a hard task to extract poetry from the atomic theory, and must have been hindered rather than helped by the bald style in which Epicurus revealed his 'divine discoveries.' As a poet, he went back to the Greece of the fifth century—to Empedocles, for whose poem on Nature he expresses the warmest admiration (i, 716 *sq.*), although the philosophy of the great Sicilian could not be reconciled with his own. His more immediate model was naturally Ennius; and in fact he may be called the last adherent of the true Ennian tradition. Compared with Virgil, and even with the verse of Cicero, his archaisms, both in language and grammar, are very striking. He was obliged, like Cicero, to neologize—*propter egestatem linguae et rerum novitatem* —in translating philosophical terms; but his normal idiom is far older than contemporary use, nor had he any sympathy with the Alexandrian movement. In his treatment of the hexameter, he shows more variety than Catullus, although (with all pre-Augustans) he is too apt to make the sense coincide with the line, while his rhythms are often loose and jagged.

The whole history and criticism of Greek poetry from Hesiod to Aratus had supported the poet's claim to teach; and the *De Rerum Natura* is frankly and proudly didactic. Lucretius is only concerned to teach delightfully, offering a honied cup to conceal the taste of the medicine (1, 936). Some part of the draught is 'bitter' enough. The reader is not spared the *minutiae* of atomism in the first two books; of psychology, in the third; of sense-perception, in the fourth. It is not until the middle of the fifth book—after some very primitive astronomy—that the subject becomes humanistic, in the wonderful description of man's origin and progress from savagery to civilization. Yet, in spite of this unpromising material, the poetry is never, for long, in abeyance. His 'digressions' are much more than the quiet resting-places that they have sometimes been called. They are rather the very essence of a poem in which physical details have only value in terms of humanity. Lucretius knew that man, if not the measure of all things, is at least the measure of all poetry.

Epicurus himself had regarded a knowledge of the Universe as important only for its ethical significance. His follower, being a poet, goes deeper. Although no Epicurean approached the conception of science for its own sake, Lucretius is plainly awed by the 'majesty of things'—by the grand phenomena of

> Moon, day and night, and the austere signs of night,
> Night-wandering fires and rushing flames of heaven.

> *luna, dies et nox et noctis signa severa*
> *noctivagaeque faces caeli flammaeque volantes.*   (v, 1190–1.)

And, from contemplating the *flammantia moenia mundi*—the fiery ramparts of the Universe—he can pass, with equal insight and enthusiasm, to the nearer aspects of Nature. The bare philosophic statement—'nothing returns to nothing'—is vivified by a picture of Nature's eternal restoration, seen in the growth of crops, the singing of birds, the lambs frisking in the fields[1]. The differences of atomic structure are illustrated by the shells 'that paint Earth's bosom, where the sea with lapping waves beats on the thirsty sand of the curven shore[2].'

But, although every phase of Nature, great or small, has an interest to Lucretius, his real concern is philosophic—to explain man's relation to the Universe; and his place as a poet must ultimately be judged by his power of reconciling the ancient quarrel between poetry and philosophy. The first object of the *De Rerum Natura* is to dispel man's fear of angry or capricious gods during life, and of their vengeance after death. The Epicurean theology, with its gods far removed from all participation in human affairs, might well have seemed an unfruitful subject

---

[1] I, 250 *sq.*   [2] II, 374–6.

for poetic imagination; but, at least negatively, it inspired
Lucretius with a burning hatred of superstition, summed up by
his indignant comment on the sacrifice of Iphigenia, in the famous
line

tantum religio potuit suadere malorum.   (I, 101)

But the magnificent passage containing this line is not merely
negative. It stands in the very forefront of the whole book, as an
invocation to Venus—not, of course, the goddess of popular cult,
but (as Tennyson saw) the personification of Nature in her
unifying and creative power, contrasted with the disruptive
agency of Mars, the god of strife. In strict logic, no doubt, this
invocation is unphilosophical; but here, as often, Patin's phrase—
L'anti-Lucrèce chez Lucrèce—is to the point, and we need search
no further for a parallel than the Miltonic Urania.

Just as we have no reason to fear angry or capricious gods, so
we can meet death without apprehension. Nowhere, perhaps, in
the whole poem, does Lucretius rise to a higher flight of poetry
than in the third book, when he fights against the fear of annihilation—not, as is sometimes thought, with a desperate fortitude,
but rather with a fervour which may be called triumphant,
reminding us of Walt Whitman's apostrophe to Death, but without the exaggeration of that 'low and delicious word.' The tone of
Lucretius is stronger, more virile, than that of his master, whose
attitude has been well described as that of placid indifference, not
unfairly represented by Swinburne's famous lines in the *Garden of
Persephone*. Briefly, his argument is that where we are, death is
not; where death is, we are not: *nil igitur mors est ad nos, neque
pertinet hilum*—itself a commonplace of the school. But the
splendid Consolation (as it may be called) which this line introduces must always remain one of the greatest achievements of
poetry. The theme itself is simple: each man has his day, and
must be content to leave, in due time, like a banqueter well-sated
with his feast: but no translation can do justice to the poetry with
which this idea is clothed. Lucretius can be hard on the coward
who clings to life; still harder on the rich idler, bored in turn by
his town-mansion and country-house, and unable to enjoy aright
his allotted years. Yet, in spite of his rigid Stoicism (for here the
rival schools agree) he does not forget the sadness of death—but
the sorrow belongs to the living mourners, not to the dead:

> No longer will thy home and loving wife
> Welcome thee back, nor will thy children dear
> Hasten to snatch a kiss, filling thy heart

With silent gladness. Gone thy fortunes, gone
The safety of thy house! O wretched man,
One luckless day hath stolen utterly
The prizes of thy life. So men complain,
But add not 'And for thine unhappiness
No yearning doth beset thee any more.'   (III, 894–901.)

Lucretius is no Leopardi; and to call him a pessimist is simply a misuse of language. The lines just translated shew that, no less than Virgil, he can feel the tears in mortal things; and there are other passages which stress the sorrows and dangers of human existence in a decaying world. But much of the sorrow is of man's own making, and his unsparing comment on human frailty marks the satirist as well as the poet. The evils of luxury and ambition, the base dominion of a worthless love, in which *surgit amari aliquid quod in ipsis floribus angat* (IV, 1134); the whole picture of a mistress concealing from her lover what 'is behind the scenes' —*vitae postscaenia*: all this is drawn in a spirit worthy of Juvenal. None the less, Lucretius never wavers in his belief that life may be well lived, by following the precepts of Epicurus; and, if enthusiasm is not in itself sufficient to create a poet, still the fervid energy infused into a rather flaccid creed is not the least sign of that 'divine fury' which has raised Lucretius to the rank of Dante and Milton.

In style, subject-matter and outlook on life, no poet could differ more entirely from Lucretius than his younger contemporary, C. VALERIUS CATULLUS (87 or 84 to 54 B.C.). Like Virgil and several other poets of the time, he was a native of Transpadane Gaul, which did not receive the rights of Roman citizenship until some years after his death. But except in political status, Verona and Mantua had long been completely Roman, and Catullus spent most of his short life in the capital. His father was the friend and host of Caesar, and Catullus must have inherited his wealth, as—although he makes the fashionable complaint of poverty—he owned at least two villas, and his Roman associates, as well as his mistress, were of high rank. He was on more or less friendly terms with the leading statesmen of the older generation —including Cicero and Hortensius—but he seems to have felt no ambition for a public career, although he served on the staff of Memmius the governor of Bithynia (57–56 B.C.). In spite of the family connection, he was opposed to Caesar, whom he attacked both directly and through his favourite, Mamurra. But Caesar thought it worth while to make advances, and a reconciliation took place shortly before the poet's death.

On the formal side of his art, Catullus must be classed as an Alexandrian. The school was well established before the middle of the century; and the verse of Lutatius Catulus (about 100 B.C.) was modelled on one phase of Alexandrianism—the erotic epigram. More important, in this vein, were the love-poems of Laevius, whose activity belonged to the beginning of the century. His chief poem—the *Erotopaegnia*, in various lyric metres—may have influenced the generation of Catullus, which included several poets of considerable fame in their own day. Of these, two at least deserve mention: C. Helvius Cinna and C. Licinius Calvus —both intimate friends of Catullus. Cinna was perhaps the most 'Alexandrian' member of the school, if we may judge by the references to his celebrated poem, *Zmyrna*. We are told that he spent nine years on polishing this piece of erudite affectation, which gave material for commentators as soon as it was published. Much more regrettably, the poems of Calvus have also been lost. Although he was perhaps better known as an orator than poet, his fame in poetry was sufficient for Ovid to bracket him with Catullus; and these two are always named as the leaders of the new school.

It was mainly by virtue of mythological learning that Catullus earned his title of *doctus*, although the epithet was appropriate to any poet both as 'teacher' and artist. His longest work, in this kind, was the *Marriage of Peleus and Thetis* (LXIV), a rather involved and mannered poem in hexameters. The subject, in part, is a description of tapestry—including the story of Ariadne—and the whole treatment suggests a study of wall-paintings in the Pompeian style. Even so, there are signs that Catullus could observe Nature at first-hand. There is real beauty in his picture of a Mediterranean scene, 'when the morning west-wind stirs the smooth water into ridges; slowly, at first, the little waves move on, and their laughter rings with light plashing; then, as the wind freshens, they crowd together, and, as they float far off, reflect the purple light[1].' This may be Alexandrian, but it is poetry. The rhythm of the verse has often been criticized, as lacking the variety and dignity of Virgil; it would indeed be monotonous, if the poem were as long as the *Aeneid*; but the short 'epic idyll' (*epyllion*) cannot be judged for what it does not pretend to be. The hexameter has not yet been slowed down to the sober Roman majesty, but still moves with the lightness of the Homeric (not merely Alexandrian) dactyls. Lines such as

> ne labyrintheis e flexibus egredientem
> tecti frustraretur inobservabilis error

[1] LXIV, 269–75. Ultimately, the simile is not Alexandrian, but Homeric (*Iliad*, IV, 422–3).

may miss the authenticity of the Virgilian note, but their lilt has a charm (perhaps, a little exotic) of their own. Another poem— the *Attis* (LXIII)—is even more un-Roman, judged by the standards of Virgil. The theme (dealing with the self-mutilation of Attis) was no doubt Alexandrian, and, although it appealed to such different Romans as Varro and Maecenas, its treatment by Catullus, in the difficult galliambic metre, makes his poem unique in extant literature.

So far, Catullus belongs to the Neoterics. But he is too great to be labelled, least of all as an Alexandrian, in the usual connotation of the term. Indeed, his essential qualities are directly opposed to the ideals of that school. The characteristic poetry of Apollonius and Callimachus is an escape from contemporary life; to Catullus, it is a passionate expression of his own life (Vol. VII, p. 272). His spiritual home is not the kingdom of the Ptolemies, but the Lesbos of Sappho. The loveliest of his marriage-songs (LXI) recalls the *epithalamia* for which Sappho was noted; and Catullus acknowledged his debt not only in the translation of her great lyric —*ille mi par esse deo videtur*—but, more subtly, in the choice of the pseudonym Lesbia for his mistress. The details of his intrigue with Clodia need not concern us, except in so far as they illustrate his poetic life, which may be summed up in his own words—*odi et amo*:

> I hate and love; wherefore, I cannot tell,
> Knowing but this: I feel the fires of Hell.   (lxxx)

It is in the record of this passion that Catullus may count as the peer of Sappho, and pre-eminently the love-poet of the Roman world. Compared with Catullus—and here, at least, a comparison between two such dissimilar poets may be permissible—Horace only loved Cinara 'in his fashion,' while Tibullus and Propertius, though 'great lovers,' do not attempt the lyric note which lifts the devotion to Lesbia above the level of an unlucky affair with a doubly unfaithful Clodia. The early history of the intrigue is revealed in poems too well known to need discussion—ranging from the light 'Sparrow-song,'

> *Passer deliciae meae puellae*

and its pair

> *Lugete o Veneres Cupidinesque*

to the verse in which the poet bids his mistress live and love (*vivamus, mea Lesbia, atque amemus*)—lyrics, like those of Sappho herself, 'few but roses,' which have been a constant source of inspiration and admiration from Ovid and Martial to Ronsard and du Bellay, from Jonson and Campion and Herrick to Landor and Tennyson.

The journey to Bithynia, subsequent to the rupture with his mistress, at least diverted Catullus into other themes, and suggested several delightful poems, of which the famous address to Sirmio, written after his return, has its nearest equivalent (both for length and spirit) in the modern sonnet-form:

> Gem of the isles and forelands, on the breast
> Of liquid lake or on the unbounded main
> —Children of Neptune in his two-fold reign—
> Is it a dream? Or am I truly blest
> For joy of thee, dear Sirmio, manifest
> To tired eyes gazing on the Thynian plain?
> Oh happy day, when Care's unquiet strain
> Ends, and the longing wayfarer has rest
> —Rest in familiar bed, with quittance due
> To labour past, to perils overcome.
> Hail, lovely Sirmio! For thy master's sake
> Rejoice! And be thou joyful, Garda lake,
> Greeting him; and ye wavelets, merry crew,
> Laugh, every Laughter in our Lydian home!   (xxxi)

The words *odi et amo* could be taken as the keynote of the poet's character in a wider sense than its original application to Lesbia. Catullus was passionately devoted to his friends, as is shewn by the warmth of his feeling towards Veranius (ix) and Calvus (xiv, L, LIII) and especially by the touching references to his brother's death in several of his elegiac poems, one of which—in commemoration of his visit to the tomb in the Troad—can hardly be matched as an expression of the most poignant grief (ci). On the other hand, Catullus could be unsparing to his enemies, whether political, such as Caesar and Mamurra, or personal, like the Gellius and others who lost his friendship by becoming rivals in Clodia's unstable love. On these, the poet is outspoken in his invective, not remarkable, when we remember that the fashion of the times admitted, or expected, a licence of language which included even friends in playful charges of indecency. Here Martial, who could not follow Catullus as a lyric poet, could at least equal him as an epigrammatist. As such, the older poet was no professional. He wrote his epigrams, not on a theme but on a real person, and was not careful about the 'point' which the modern epigram owes to Martial.

In any case, the fame of Catullus does not depend on these by-products of his pen. His real genius lay in the lyric expression of his own personality, untrammelled by limitations which, both for good and evil, the Augustan attached to self-revelation. He is first and foremost a 'subjective' poet, although not so much engrossed in self as to confine his lyrism to his own circumstances. It is true that he was not expected, like Horace, to put his lyre at the service of the State; but some of his finest songs are inspired, not by his own love, but by that of others—notably the love-idyll of Acme and Septimius (XLV) and the beautiful song for the marriage of Torquatus and Vinia (LXI). On one occasion, at least (XXXIV), he anticipated the Horatian hymns to Apollo and Diana, by a little poem in glyconic metre which seems likely to have been sung by a choir of boys and girls at a festival in honour of Diana:

> Dian keepeth us secure,
> Girls and boys unblamed and pure
> Boys and maidens pure, upraise
>   Dian's hymn of praise.
>
> Daughter great of greatest Jove,
> When, beneath the Delian grove,
> Leto grasped the olive-tree,
>   Travailing for thee—
>
> Born the holy mountain-maid
> Haunter of mysterious glade,
> Queen of leafy grove, supreme
>   Over sounding stream.
>
> Thou art Juno, who dost bring
> Succour to women suffering,
> Guardian of the Triple Ways,
>   Moon of foreign rays!
>
> Month by month is thy course bent
> Toward the year's accomplishment,
> Till each barn is filled with hoard
>   Bountifully stored.
>
> Whatsoever name hath grace
> To win thee, Lady, let the race
> Of Romulus, as then, be still
>   Safe in thy goodwill!

The special title of *doctus* seems to imply that the Romans themselves laid more stress on the 'art' than on the 'genius' of Catullus. Modern criticism, while rightly refusing to make a sharp distinction between Form and Spirit, would rather empha-size the natural quality of the 'tenderest of Roman singers.' Nevertheless, we should do him grievous wrong by underrating his formal excellence. Some of the Alexandrian artifices may not please us more than they pleased Cicero; but the enduring merit of the Catullan school was to rescue Roman poetry from the harshness of the Ennian tradition, and to prepare the way for the polish—perhaps the over-refinement—of the Augustan age. Catullus was not, indeed, equally successful in every metrical form. His elegiacs are rougher than the graceful couplets of Tibullus and Propertius; but his favourite metres, the hendecasyllabic and choliambic, are perfect vehicles for the expression of feelings which range from the highest lyric sentiment to comments on daily life and manners. In pure lyric, his language is the educated speech of the day, with scarcely any archaism. It is even colloquial, as in the numerous diminutives which later purism severely restrained. The colour of his style was heightened by an effective use of assonance and alliteration, not unduly prominent, as in earlier verse and in Lucretius, but producing very subtle and calculated effects. For example, in the poem to Sirmio (translated above) the liquids give a unity to the whole piece, from the opening note— *liquentibus, libenter, laetus*—to the beautiful close of *Lydiae lacus*. However passionate and unrestrained he may seem, his emotion has always been recollected in the tranquillity of a perfect art.

III. CICERO AND THE ORATORS

From his boyhood, CICERO seems to have planned a political career, which could only be gained by oratory. For, although the art of rhetoric as the staple of Roman education was an end in itself, the ultimate prize of a barrister was not, as in modern life, a judgeship, but the consulate, even if the need of oratory did not stop with the attainment of that office. His early youth was occupied with the usual literary training of the times, which, we have seen, included the study and practice of poetry, and translations from the Greek. As a young man he frequented the Forum, and listened to the speeches of Crassus and Antonius, the leading orators of the day (vol. VIII, p. 421 *sq.*), and it would be interesting to know more fully how far Cicero profited by their example. Unfortunately, our chief knowledge of their style depends largely on Cicero's own account, since Antonius published nothing and Crassus very little, of which only a few passages have survived. It is clear that the orators of this period improved on the comparatively unstudied manner of C. Gracchus, whose tumultuous eloquence failed to reach the polish expected in the age of Cicero[1]. What is not so clear is the precise improvement effected by Cicero himself, apart from the periodic structure which he developed. It might well be claimed that he united the very different excellences

---

[1] Cicero, *Brutus*, 33, 126; Tacitus, *dial.* 18.

of Antonius and Crassus, the former being famed for general eloquence, while the latter was praised for a lively wit adorning a simpler style. When about twenty-two years of age, Cicero planned a work on rhetoric, of which he completed the two books that survive under the title *de Inventione*—a dull and rigid composition which he lived to regret. One of his models—for he claims to have followed the example of Zeuxis in selecting from the beauties of several—was the treatise addressed to Herennius, a work of uncertain authorship; but Cicero's own work goes no further than 'Invention,' the 'finding' of the material proper to his subject[1].

His first appearance as a pleader dates from 81 B.C., when he delivered a speech *pro Quinctio*. The suit itself was of little importance, and its chief interest is negative, shewing how far Cicero was yet to travel on his way to the eloquence of later years. The next case—*pro Roscio Amerino* (80 B.C.)—was more important in itself, as a defence against the charge of parricide. Cicero won, and although his speech bears some traces of the rather hard and scholastic style inherited from the rhetorical schools, it gained him an established position at the bar. But his health caused anxiety, and he was persuaded to leave court-practice for two years (79–77 B.C.) which he spent in Greece and Asia Minor, studying philosophy at Athens and rhetoric under Molon at Rhodes. To this vacation he owed a double debt. Not only was his health restored, but his oratory was improved by the criticism of a teacher who, as he acknowledged in the *Brutus*, pruned the redundancy of his periods. After his return he could meet his chief rival, Hortensius, on equal terms; and, in 70 B.C., the great trial of Verres gave him acknowledged supremacy in the Forum. Meanwhile he was passing through the *cursus honorum*; but though, during and after his consulship, his speeches were more often political than purely forensic, he continued to plead at the bar (with a break caused by his exile) until at least the year 52 B.C. (*pro Milone*); and his activity, as a political speaker or writer, culminated at the very end of his life, in the famous *Philippics* of 44 and 43 B.C.

It is well known that some of his speeches (as that for Milo) were more or less completely revised before publication, while others, such as the greater part of the *Verrines* and *Philippics*, were not actually delivered. But these political documents are so entirely oratorical that no distinction can be drawn between the spoken and written speech. By the time of the *Verrines* Cicero had found his style; and, even in his later philosophical works, he does

---

[1] See T. Petersson, *Cicero*, p. 373 *sq.*

not essentially modify the manner which he used as an actual
speaker. The formal distinction between oratory and other forms
of prose was unimportant at a time when all prose—as well as
verse—was intended to be read aloud.

Technically, Cicero's style was intermediate between two extremes. Greek rhetoricians had divided all forms of literary composition into three categories; and their Roman pupils adopted
the classification of *eloquentia* as 'austere' or 'simple' (*tenuis,
exilis*), ornate (*grandis, ornata*) and 'middle' (*media*). The simple
style was ultimately derived from Lysias, the first and most
typical Greek exponent of an art which excluded almost every
ornament, relying mainly on the virtues of brevity, directness and
lucidity. The Roman imitators of Lysias claimed the title of New
Atticists (*novi Attici*), although Cicero remarked that the greatest
Athenian orators were by no means Attic in this narrow sense[1].
It is obvious that such a style, except in the hands of a master, was
likely to be frigid and uninspiring; its chief practitioners, in
Cicero's own age, were C. Licinius Calvus and M. Brutus; and,
of these, the former—though still admired, in the time of Tacitus,
for his prosecution of Vatinius—had been otherwise forgotten,
while Brutus, always too philosophic to be a force in oratory,
seems never to have aroused popular enthusiasm[2]. Cicero had
great hopes of Brutus, who plays so large a part in his oratorical
treatises; but his private letters to Atticus show that he could not
admire the style of a speaker whose school 'was apt to make not
only the gallery stampede but the bench itself[3].'

At the other extreme stood the Asiatic school, who failed to
commend themselves to Cicero during his stay in Asia. None of
their speeches is preserved; but we have a fair notion of their
Roman followers from Cicero's own criticism. The Asiatics relied
on neatly turned antithesis and verbal conceits, in florid ornament
and a rapid high-flown torrent of language, delivered in a sing-
song manner, with emphasis on rhythmical effect. They have been
called the euphuists of antiquity. Their style, or styles (Cicero
distinguishes two) appealed to, and suited, the youthful beginner,
and the orator attributes the decline of Hortensius' popularity to
his persistence in a fashion undignified for a consular[4]. It has

---

[1] *Brutus*, 82, 285. Historically the New Atticism was a reaction from
Asianism.

[2] Tacitus, *dial.* 21, 10; Cicero, *ad Att.* XIV, 20 and XV, 1.

[3] *Brutus*, 84, 289.

[4] *Ib.* 95, 325–7. On the Asiatic style see E. Norden, *Antike Kunstprosa*, I, pp. 131 *sqq.*; J. F. D'Alton, *Roman Literary Theory*, chap. 2.

sometimes been thought that Cicero had himself fallen under the Asiatic influence, as his reference to Molon may possibly suggest. His speeches at least indicate one feature, generally held to be a fault of the Asiatic school—a tendency to wordiness, which he never completely conquered. But it is only fair to add that Cicero's exuberance was often intentional. Sometimes, no doubt, a cloud of words could conceal a weak argument or doubtful case; far more often, the style was the man—who needed an ample sweep for the swelling period which he perfected. His praise of Hortensius applies with more force to himself: 'no one could be more terse and pointed, when he wished to raise a laugh; no one could better move the judges to anger or tears; no one, in fact, could better achieve the supreme aim of the orator—to convince[1].'

Cicero's model (as far as he was conscious of a single model) was the highest in classical oratory—Demosthenes; but he knew that the genius of the Latin language, as well as temperamental differences between Greeks and Romans, needed a style that can be at least as easily contrasted as compared with the Demosthenic. In form, his greatest achievement was the final development of the 'period,' to which the rhetorician Isocrates had devoted infinite pains, both in theory and practice. The *Orator* is largely concerned with the structure of the sentence and particularly of its conclusion (*clausula*), and Cicero acutely analyses the effect of a prose style which (as Aristotle had long since noted) must be rhythmical but not metrical. He points out, for example, the charm (to Roman hearers) of a double trochaic ending ($-\cup-\cup$); but, curiously enough, he was hardly conscious of a rhythm exhibited by a very large number of his own endings—a cretic base followed by this or other (mainly trochaic) cadences (*maximis consecutus*)[2]. The ancient precept *ars est celare artem* was here so strong that the art eluded the artist himself.

Cicero had practised for more than twenty-five years, before he turned seriously to this theoretic discussion of orators and their styles. His form was the dialogue, especially of the 'Aristotelian' type, in which the author was the chief speaker. In 55 B.C. he published the *de Oratore*, a dialogue between Crassus, Antonius and other distinguished speakers of the last generation. The three books of this treatise deal with the ideal orator's education and training, the treatment of his material and the delivery of his

---

[1] *Brutus*, 93, 322; *cf.* 84, 290.
[2] The modern study of Latin prose and rhythm by Zielinski and others is too technical for discussion here; see H. D. Broadhead, *Latin Prose Rhythm*, and Fr. Novotný, *État actuel des études sur le rhythme de la prose latine*.

speeches. Nine years later (46 B.C.) Cicero returned to the subject, adding the *Brutus* and the *Orator*, as the fourth and fifth books of his great treatise. The *Brutus* is mainly historical, the *Orator* more personal, concerned (like the *de Oratore*) with the ideal orator, but differs in substituting the first person for the dialogue. The *Orator*, in fact, is largely autobiographical. Cicero here admits us to his private workshop, analysing the technique, both verbal and rhythmical, of his own speeches.

These two treatises belong to the last years of Cicero's life, when the state of politics had debarred him from the full exercise of his proper function: such speeches as he delivered in 46–45 B.C. were written under the shadow of autocracy. Thapsus was followed by Munda, and his oratory was crushed until the final and fatal outburst of the *Philippics*. During the year 45–44 B.C. his energy, excluded from public life, found an outlet in writing. The death of his daughter Tullia had been the heaviest blow in his life, and he sought distraction by plunging feverishly into philosophic study. It has been said with justice that this year 'is, in mere quantity of literary production, as well as in the abiding effect on the world of letters of the work he then produced, the *annus mirabilis* of his life[1].' His personal grief was expressed by two (lost) essays—the *Consolatio* and *Hortensius*, the latter of which changed Augustine's whole scheme of life—he had begun to read Cicero as an orator, and found him a guide to philosophy and religion[2]. These works were followed by a series of philosophical books including (amongst others) the *de finibus* and *Academics* (45 B.C.), the *Tusculan Disputations*, *de Natura Deorum* and *de officiis* in 44 B.C. Besides these, Cicero found time to write two essays of a less technical kind—the *de Senectute* (*Cato major*) and *de Amicitia* (*Laelius*)—both, perhaps, better known than his more 'philosophic' books.

As a philosopher, Cicero neither claimed nor possessed great originality. In a letter to Atticus he frankly confessed that some, at least, of his treatises are simply ἀπόγραφα, transcripts or paraphrases: 'I only contribute the words which I have in abundance[3].' The admission of 'abundance' is patently true, though in jest, and the whole statement is modest enough, even if we remember that the credit of a translator stood much higher in Roman than in modern times. By Roman literary convention it was always a recognized ground for self-praise to claim priority in adapting a Greek original. This habit has puzzled or offended many moderns

---

[1] J. W. Mackail, *Latin Literature*, p. 72.
[2] *Confess.* III, 4, 7.   [3] *ad Att.* XII, 52, 3; cf. *ad fam.* XIII, 63, 1.

who are apt to lay more stress on Content than on Form. To the classical critics, Thought was rather to be regarded as common property, whereas Form was personal expression; and the transference of a literary *genre* from one language to another was sufficient proof of originality. The proof would have been more convincing if the Romans had emphasized their real achievement in literature—the distinctive Roman cast which the greatest of their own authors (Cicero as well as Virgil) succeeded in giving to their Greek exemplars.

Cicero's own debt to the Greeks varied according to the subject. It is obvious that in his political philosophy, as developed in the *de Re publica* and *de legibus* (works belonging to the years immediately before his proconsulate in 51 B.C.); he was far more 'original' than in his view on metaphysics or ethics. If his model was Plato, the application was entirely practical; Plato's Utopia was transmuted into the reality of Rome. That city was far enough from the ideal Republic whose pattern was laid up in heaven; but Cicero was no political pessimist and, even if in his last years he seems to despair of the State, he had still confidence in the character—the *mores antiqui*—by which Rome had outgrown the actual Greece of Plato.

In pure philosophy, Cicero, like other Romans, was wholly dependent on the Greeks. As a boy, he had been taught the principles of Epicureanism by Phaedrus, but he was by no means converted. His objections to the school were radical: he was repelled by its reliance on the senses; by its physics—the swerve of atoms was ridiculous—by its gods, who were useless; by the negation of Providence, which left the world to the blind forces of Chance; by the doctrine of Pleasure, which (at least in theory) dethroned the higher values of life; and, not least, perhaps, by an abstinence from public affairs which a Roman statesman was bound to condemn. At the same time, he could not wholeheartedly ally himself with the great opponents of Epicurus. He had studied Stoicism under the Greek teacher Diodotus, with whom, as with Phaedrus, he remained on terms of affection. Later, during his visit to Rhodes, he was attracted by Posidonius, the most prominent—if not the most orthodox—Stoic of the day. Posidonius himself had been a pupil of Panaetius (vol. VIII, pp. 459 *sqq.*); and, although Posidonian influence on Roman Stoicism has been exaggerated, there can be no doubt that Cicero's admiration for Stoic ideals was largely inspired by his own master, as well as by Panaetius. In the *de officiis*, for example, Cicero was a follower of both philosophers; but in the second book of the *de finibus*, as also in the *de divinatione* and *de fato*, his chief authority was Posidonius. That philosopher, for a Stoic, was singularly broad-minded; and Cicero's esteem was readily won by a teacher who knew how to soften Stoic asperities by some admixture of Platonism. Whereas the orthodox dogma regarded the soul as a unity, with no irrational part, and therefore demanded that the emotions should be wholly suppressed, Posidonius returned to the tripartite psychology of Plato, and so modified Stoic 'apathy': the passions must be controlled by reason, but need not be extirpated. Here and elsewhere, in fact, he was something of an eclectic, believing that all the schools (except their common enemy the Epicurean) were often in unsuspected agreement.

But Cicero could not wholly subscribe even to the less rigid demands of the Posidonian sect. He was not one to wrap himself in his own virtue, nor, as a practical lawyer, could he approve of an uncompromising creed that held all sins to be equal. He admired (with reservation) the stern inflexibility of the Catos, but his own character—intensely human and emotional—was not built on the lines of apathy. Moreover, any form of dogmatism was repugnant to one whose training had taught him that Truth, in philosophy as in the courts, is not easily discovered. Apart from this, Cicero was a real, if not always an understanding lover of Plato; and the school which at least claimed to be in lineal succession to the Master, was his natural affinity.

The New Academy had not stood still with Carneades (vol. VIII, pp. 455 *sqq.*). It was at least saved from stagnation by a healthy disagreement between its later professors. Cicero's introduction to Academic theory dates from his youth (88 B.C.) when he attended lectures given by Philo, then head of the sect. In 79 B.C. he heard Philo's successor, Antiochus, in Athens; the *Academics* is the result of this joint tuition. But the two teachers disagreed, and Cicero followed the general doctrine of Philo. Briefly, the difference turned on the place of the senses in relation to absolute knowledge. The Stoic position was to admit the fallibility of the senses, but to correct them by reason. Absolute knowledge was therefore possible. Antiochus adopted the Stoic view, thereby deserting the dogma of strict scepticism, which Philo upheld. Hence the absolute certitude of the Stoics must be superseded by Probability. But even Philo made concessions to the Porch. So far from maintaining a purely negative position, he was anxious to show that probability is a safe guide, both in theory and practical life. Cicero has been called a pragmatist[1]; and the

---

[1] Petersson, *op. cit.* p. 546.

New Academy of Philo, which allowed not only freedom of opinion but change of opinion, was an easy refuge not only for his temperament but for his time.

If we know more of Cicero than of any other personality in ancient life, our knowledge is chiefly due to his letters. It is impossible to discuss them adequately in a short compass, and all that can be now attempted is a bare outline of their literary significance (see further, pp. 773 *sqq.*). Here, at least, no dispute about 'originality' arises—nowhere is it truer to say that 'the style is the man himself.' The whole correspondence—including letters received by Cicero—extends over a period of about 25 years (68–43 B.C.), but only a few belong to his pre-consular years and none to that of his consulship. Nothing is more remarkable than the infinite variety of the letters in scope and style. The correspondents themselves range from the most eminent persons in the political world to Cicero's own family, including his freedman Tiro. The subjects vary from high politics to the details of business and domestic life and letters of introduction; and the style is perfectly adapted to the different degrees of intimacy between the writer and his various friends. Some of these *familiares* are not 'friends' at all, even in the political sense; and it is interesting to see that, in his letters to Pompey and Caesar, Cicero's style is almost as carefully oratorical as in his speeches or essays. When standing on his dignity or uncertain of his ground he is precise in his periods and cadences. But all this technique is dismissed in letters to real friends—to Caelius or Trebatius, and especially to Atticus.

While his dialogues show complete command over the ordinary talk of educated men, these intimate letters are far less 'literary.' Cicero 'talks to his friend as to himself'—*ego tecum tamquam mecum loquor*—and the talk is terse, allusive, often elliptic. Nevertheless, it is never slipshod. Even when he uses the common words which, as he says, distinguish letter-writing from oratory, he never fails to be *elegans*, a stylist. His colloquialism often reminds us of the language of Plautus, whom, unlike Horace, he greatly admired, and there may be some conscious imitation. But, in the main, his language must have been current in his own day[1]; and, if it happens to agree with Plautine usage, the coincidence is due to the conservatism of popular speech. A love of quotations, from Greek poets and—much more often—of Greek words and phrases, is a marked feature of his letters. It has been called the

---

[1] *ad fam.* IX, 21. Epistolas vero quotidianis verbis texere solemus.

argot of literary Rome[1], and serves more than one purpose. A Greek phrase is often used (as a French word in English) for a *nuance* of which Latin was not capable—the *egestas linguae* did not stop at philosophy. Sometimes (like French on an English post-card) the Greek made for a secrecy which, in dealing with politics, Cicero felt desirable, especially as his letters were mainly dictated: βοῶπις—Juno—was safer than Clodia. But Cicero is fond of a humorous nickname, even when there is no need of secrecy; and, in his general practice, the choice of Greek has apparently no motive more particular than the Latin quotations once admired in English society. Modern fashion—or education—has here changed; but Cicero was writing to Atticus and other cultivated men, for whom Greek was not so much a 'second language' as almost their own.

The letters were certainly not published in Cicero's lifetime. Most of them, indeed, could hardly have been written with a view to publication. Nevertheless, towards the end of his life, Cicero was thinking of a collection of at least some letters, and wrote to Atticus about correcting them[2]. Did he, when writing his private thoughts, have an eye on the public more often than we should naturally expect? It is difficult to believe that he would have wished to unlock his heart so openly, and often so danger-ously, during his life. But the 'political letter' was at least as old as Plato, and Cicero may well have desired to follow here, as elsewhere, the founder of the Academy.

IV. C. JULIUS CAESAR

In itself, there is of course nothing surprising to find Caesar among the authors. Even in much less 'literary' ages, there have been many generals who have used the pen to explain their success (or failure) with the sword; but Caesar's *Commentaries* are surely unique as the record, by a statesman and commander of the highest order, which has also outstanding literary merits of its own. If Caesar regarded the arts of speaking and writing as ancillary to a public career—the *Commentaries* have themselves a political purpose—there can be no doubt that, like Cicero, he had also a disinterested love of his own language. His treatise on Analogy—written apparently in 53 B.C. when he was crossing the Alps—would be at least an unusual performance for a modern general. In oratory he was second to Cicero alone: if Cicero's own

---

[1] Tyrrell and Purser, *The Correspondence of M. Tullius Cicero*, I[3], pp. 85 *sqq.*   [2] *ad Att.* XVI, 5; *ad fam.* XVI, 17.

praise in the *Brutus* may be suspect for reasons of State, there is
abundant evidence in the consensus of later writers—among them
Tacitus and Quintilian—that, after his prosecution of Dolabella
(77 B.C.), Caesar ranked with the most eminent of the orators.

Now that his speeches and letters have been lost, his fame as a
writer depends solely on the *Commentaries*. Of these, the seven
books on the Gallic War were published in 51 B.C. The title—
'notes' or 'records'—is modest; Caesar does not claim to be
writing history but providing materials for a future historian.
Even so, Cicero's eulogy in the *Brutus* (75, 262) is very much
to the point: the *Commentaries* could, no doubt, be embellished;
but their 'clear brevity' will deter a prudent historian from the
attempt. Here, again, Cicero's motive in praising may be suspect,
but the praise itself is justified: the *Commentaries*, as he says, are
nudi, recti, venusti, charming in their bareness and directness. We
know from the fragments of his *de analogia* that Caesar was an
Atticist aiming at purism in Latinity. From Aristotle onwards,
the 'choice' of words had been one of the main studies of Greek
rhetoric; and, in Latin, 'elegance' implied a Wordsworthian
'selection' of common (but not rustic) language: in Caesar's well-
known precept, a writer must avoid an unknown or unusual word
like a rock at sea[1]. It is not surprising that he, no less than Cicero,
admired Terence as *puri sermonis amator*, in a metrical criticism
which shows that if Caesar was a poor poet he was a good critic,
who could follow the Terentian virtues of absolute simplicity of
diction and lucidity of expression. If the *Gallic War* never became
a school-book in Rome, as it has become in the modern world[2],
the reason may well be that it contains practically no rhetoric in
itself, nor does it suggest any theme for rhetoric in others.

Beneath the artistic simplicity of style, the *Commentaries* have
a purpose as artfully concealed. Caesar was writing not so much
for his admirers as for those who feared that the Gallic Wars were
only a stage towards his complete conquest of Rome. In particular, he had to defend himself against the charge of waging war
sua sponte, without the Senate's permission; and his chief concern
was therefore to prove that his wars were inevitable. The expeditions to Britain, at least, required some special pleading. This
political need colours the whole conception of his work: Caesar
was proconsul for peace as well as war, but he has almost nothing

---

[1] *ap.* Gellius, *N.A.*, 1, 10, 4. Pure Latin implied *urbanitas*, the
educated speech of the Capital, without 'low' diction, unusual constructions
and provincialisms.

[2] See E. G. Sihler, *Annals of Caesar*, p. 265.

to say about the normal government of his provinces. He permits himself but one considerable digression from the proper scope of his military despatches—the sketch of the Gauls and Germans in his sixth book, at a point when there is a pause in his campaigns (p. 537, *note*). Even while otherwise keeping strictly to the point, a general may be expected to give some account of his opponents; and the Gallic and Germanic nations were always interesting to the Roman mind. Caesar makes this concession to popular taste; but he is not one to idealize his enemies, and the spirit of Tacitus in the *Germania* is quite remote from a conqueror who, for all his magnanimity to Romans, had no mercy for a Vercingetorix.

His other work *On the Civil War* was never finished, stopping at the commencement of the Alexandrian campaign in 48 B.C. Caesar was no longer an aspirant, but dictator. Yet the general tone of detachment, of objective writing, so characteristic of the former work, is still maintained. There is no suggestion of personal triumph. Pharsalus calls for only a single comment—on the luxury of the Pompeian camp in contrast with the Caesarian, where even necessaries were absent. The news of Pompey's death is dismissed in the baldest phrase: *Alexandriae de Pompeii morte cognoscit.* Lucan's rhetoric finds no support from the chief actor in the *Pharsalia*.

Caesar's example, or command, inspired more than one of his subordinates to continue his notes. Chief of these was A. Hirtius (consul in 43 B.C.), who had been commissioned to collect material for the *Anticato*, an answer to Cicero's *Praise of Cato*; and, immediately after the dictator's death, Hirtius added an eighth book to the *Gallic War*, in order to supplement the broken record left by Caesar himself. The preface shows that the work was a labour of love, although the writer is anxious to disclaim any rivalry with his old commander. The book is not unworthy of Caesar—a compliment which may possibly apply also to the extant *Bellum Alexandrinum* (probably, but not certainly, by the same Hirtius), and to the *Bellum Africum* (written by an unknown author of considerable ability); but it would be grossly excessive as a description of the *Bellum Hispaniense*, which completes the record of Caesar's campaigns. Apart from its—not very considerable—value to the historian, the *Spanish War* is mainly interesting from a negative point of view, as an unconscious warning (if warning were needed) that Caesarian prose is not easy to write. Its author was obviously a military man who had served with Caesar in Spain; but his inexperience in writing does not suggest that he was an officer of high rank. We need not pause to consider whether he was a tribune or merely a centurion, but his Latinity, at least, would not have been surprising in a common soldier. He certainly drags in some culture by the heels, not realizing that Caesar's exploits do not need quotations from Ennius, or imitation of Greek idioms. His colloquialisms—he is fond of expressions like *bene magnus*—have an interest to students of the *sermo vulgaris*, but would have shocked his master not less than his occasional excursions into rhetoric. The latter fault, together with a certain delight in horrors, is familiar enough in the generation of Seneca and Lucan, but is happily alien to the severe style of other Caesarian writing.

V. THE HISTORIANS

In the generation preceding that of Cicero several historians carried forward the traditions of Asellio and Coelius Antipater (vol. VIII, p. 419 *sq.*). Four of these, at least, deserve mention, as authorities immediately leading up to the historical methods of Sallust and Livy.

Q. CLAUDIUS QUADRIGARIUS (vol. VII, p. 317 *sq.*) began his Annals with the Gallic invasion, disregarding the legendary accounts of Roman origins, as being unsupported by documents—a remarkable attitude for an ancient historian[1]. He lived to see the dictatorship of Sulla and certainly extended his history to that date. But, although he may be called an early Ciceronian in chronology, he belonged in style to the time of Cato. His curt sentences and archaic diction could not have appealed to Cicero, and it was not till the age of Fronto and Gellius, in the general revulsion from Ciceronian prose, that he is quoted with admiration as an example of 'ancient sweetness.' His longest fragment—an account of the duel between Manlius and the Gaul—is certainly not devoid of charm, but the simplicity—intended no doubt to be Herodotean—is too archaistic to seem natural[2]. Livy quotes Claudius not infrequently, and not always with approval: but the Augustan historian is much more often concerned with the contemporary of Claudius, VALERIUS ANTIAS, whom he seems to have followed without discrimination in his earlier decades. Later, however, Livy discovered that Valerius was often incredible, especially in his numerical statements. His style was less archaic, apparently, than that of Claudius, and so found no favour with the Antonines; and, in substance, his work (the very title is uncertain), in more than seventy books, was of course superseded by Livy himself.

[1] Peter, *Hist. Rom. Rel.* p. cclxxxvi.   [2] Gellius, *N.A.* IX, 13, 4.

While Valerius started, in the usual way, *ab urbe condita*, his contemporary L. CORNELIUS SISENNA (119–67 B.C.) seems to have confined himself to his own age, and his history of the Sullan period is praised by Sallust. Cicero, too, speaks highly of his learning, but was not greatly impressed by the history[1]; while Sisenna's archaisms and use of uncommon words did not commend themselves to the orator. According to Varro, Sisenna was distinguished for his affectation of *adsentio* (for *adsentior*, 'yea' for 'yes') in the Senate; and his other curiosities of language were more interesting to late grammarians than to his own generation.

There remains C. LICINIUS MACER, father of Calvus the orator and poet familiar to readers of Catullus. Macer himself, like his friend Sisenna, was a praetor; but less fortunate or honest than Sisenna, he was condemned for extortion in his province, and committed suicide. Cicero, who presided over the court, not unnaturally disliked him and characterized his writing as mere loquacity[2]. His *Annals*, according to Livy, were untrustworthy when the honour of his clan was involved; but he had the credit of using original authorities such as the *libri lintei* (the lists of the Magistrates), at a time when 'sources' were generally neglected. Several other annalists of the Sullan age are recorded, including Sulla himself, whose memoirs or commentaries seem to have been of small historical importance, except, no doubt, in military matters, where Plutarch (in his Life of Sulla) must have found his writings to be valuable. The list of such writers shows that there was a wide interest in the origins and later development of Rome, although the annalists of this period were largely superseded by those of the next two generations—by Varro and Caesar, among Cicero's coevals, and by Sallust and Nepos, among his juniors.

C. CRISPUS SALLUSTIUS (86–35 B.C.) born, like Varro and Horace and other distinguished writers, in the Sabine territory, was a plebeian and a member of the popular party, and (after being expelled from the Senate) was reinstated by Caesar. He rose to the praetorship and became proconsul in Africa, where he amassed enough wealth to retire in 45 B.C. His famous Roman villa—the 'Gardens of Sallust,' afterwards the favourite residence of several emperors—does not suggest that its owner practised the virtues of austerity and simplicity which he admired in ancient Rome[3], even if he outlived the scandals of his earlier life. The later Romans were quick to notice the inconsistency; Macrobius tersely describes Sallust as a grave censor of others' luxury. All his literary

---

[1] Cicero, *de legibus*, I, 2, 7, *Brutus*, 64, 228; 74, 259.
[2] Cicero, *de legibus*, I, 2, 7.   [3] Sallust, *Cat.* 12.

work belonged to the years of his retirement, when he was prudent enough to take no part in the troubles following Caesar's death. But the choice of subject in his first work—the *War of Catiline* —shows his fidelity to Caesar, and his democratic leanings are apparent throughout his writings. Caesar had been suspected of complicity with the Catilinarians, and Sallust undoubtedly wished to clear his leader's memory from the charge. In the main, however, his object was much wider. He was probing the deep-seated causes of the political disease which produced a Catiline, and found that the only remedy lay in a Caesar. He claimed to be impartial, and his fine characterization of Cato, as well as of Caesar[1], is proof of a broad outlook; but his rather faint praise of Cicero (whom he could not entirely neglect) does not suggest that Rome was 'fortunately born in that statesman's consulship[2].'

The *Catiline* is not free from inaccuracies (see p. 889 *sq.*); but, as a work of art, it seems to justify the reputation of its author in later Roman criticism, although Livy and others were dissentients. In the early Imperial age, Sallust was accused of 'pilfering Cato'; and his diction, as a fact, has a decided tinge of the archaism so much affected by many writers of his time. His chief literary influence, however, as Roman critics observed, was the style of Thucydides, who was second to Lysias alone in favour with the Atticists. The famous Sallustian 'brevity,' which Tacitus followed, is the most striking outcome of this imitation. But Thucydides was his model for thought as well as style. Numerous 'reflections'—whether in prefaces or interspersed in the body of his narrative—are on Thucydidean lines; his vivid descriptions are sometimes modelled on the *Peloponnesian War*[3] and, negatively, he follows the rationalistic Greek historian, by his silence in regard to omens and other supernatural phenomena which Livy so carefully records.

Sallust's second monograph—the *War with Jugurtha*—was no doubt suggested by his knowledge of Africa. But one of his reasons for the choice of subject was political: in his own words, 'the pride of the nobles was then for the first time opposed.' The conquest of Numidia ends with the triumph of Marius, but is the beginning of a struggle which led to the devastation of Italy[4]. Although Sallust favours the popular party, he recognizes faults on both sides: the oligarchs abused their high position, the people their liberty[5]. Except for these incidental comments, the *Jugurtha* is objective history; and, as such, (if inaccurate in detail) it

[1] Sallust, *Cat.* 54. [2] *Ib.* 26, 31, 43.
[3] As in *Bell. Jug.* 60 (Thuc. VII, 71).
[4] *Ib.* 5. [5] *Ib.* 41.

may be considered even superior to the *Catiline*[1]. But the claim of Sallust as a historian seems mainly to have rested on the *Histories*—a continuation of Sisenna's work—of which only four speeches, two letters, and some fragments remain[2]. His speeches, though not to be regarded as more authentic than those of Thucydides, are always in character, even if their rhetoric is that of the schools—indeed, the speeches from the *Histories* were apparently preserved as being models of rhetorical art. They are naturally more periodic, more Ciceronian, than Sallust's narrative style; but the rhythm is different; and here as in the biographies, certain cadences (for example, the hexametric ending) are admitted which Cicero would have carefully avoided. It would seem that Sallust disliked the great orator as much for his periods as for his politics.

The only other historian who need here be mentioned is CORNELIUS NEPOS. Little is known of his life beyond the fact that he was born in Cisalpine Gaul, and belonged to the inner circle of Cicero and Atticus. He seems to have been slightly younger than Cicero, and probably a little older than Catullus, who dedicated his book of poems to his friend and countryman. The date of his death is uncertain, but was later than 32 B.C. Catullus mentions his *Chronica* as 'a learned and laborious' work: it was apparently a chronological digest of Greek and Roman history, but its scope and method are uncertain. His main interest was in biography, and here the loss of a panegyric on Cicero is to be regretted. His extant biographies are part of a larger collection 'On illustrious men'—parallel lives of Romans and foreigners—together with two lives (*Cato the Elder* and *Atticus*) from the *de Latinis historicis*. In the Life of Pelopidas Nepos makes the disarming remark that he is writing a biography, not a history; but even this excuse does not palliate his disregard of chronology, and his carelessness in the use of authorities. The biographer seems to have genuinely admired his illustrious men, with the doubtful merit of concealing their defects. This hero-worship is certainly excessive in his treatment of Atticus, to whose faults his friend is more than reasonably blind. His style, if undistinguished, is at least clear and succinct; but he sometimes attempts a longer periodic manner without conspicuous success. A link, in point of time, between the prose of the Republic and the Empire, Nepos has neither the force of Caesar nor the splendour of Livy. The great chain of authors in either age might well deserve a stronger connection.

---

[1] On the composition of the *Bellum Jugurthinum*, see above, pp. 113 *sqq.*

[2] On the brochures *ad Caesarem senem* attributed to Sallust see below, p. 890.

VI. VARRO

While the highest culture of the Ciceronian age may be fairly represented by Cicero himself, the whole range of literary and intellectual pursuits is even better shown by M. Terentius Varro (116–27 b.c.), the most comprehensive scholar of this, or any other Roman period. Born ten years before Cicero, he outlived the orator by over fifteen years; and if Cicero, writing in 45 b.c., thought his 'polygraphy' a marvel, Varro added extensively to his writings in old age—the work on Husbandry belongs to his eightieth year. Like most authors of the time, he was a politician and a soldier, important or rich enough to be proscribed by Antony, though his life was actually spared.

Varro's recorded works include practically all branches of Roman knowledge in literature and philosophy, in geography, law, grammar and history. If his encyclopaedic interests can be narrowed to a single term, he may be classed as an antiquarian, his most famous work being the *Antiquitates rerum humanarum et divinarum*, a systematic account of Roman civil and religious history, in over forty books, much quoted by Augustine and other Christian apologists. Servius described him as *expugnator religionis*, and Augustine attacked his rationalism[1]. In the sphere of history, he chiefly affected the biographical form, which was now becoming popular, and his *Portraits* (*Imagines*) of 700 celebrated characters—both Greek and Roman—may be (as Pliny states) the first example of an illustrated book. Of this enormous output, only two works survive in more than fragments; and one of these (*de lingua Latina*) is mutilated. The whole treatise, in twenty-five books, covered a wide ground—etymology, grammar and syntax, poetical and ordinary diction, and a discussion on the theories of Language (Analogy and Anomaly) which divided ancient scholarship into two camps.

Far more interesting are the three books on Agriculture (*rerum rusticarum*). The form is that of a dialogue—a *genre* which seems almost as inevitable in the Ciceronian age as the novel 'with a purpose' at the present day. The persons (besides Varro himself) appear to have been mainly chosen for their names, *e.g.* Scrofa (sow), who, however, was a noted agriculturalist; and, in the last book, a number of persons bearing birds' names (Merula, Pavo, Pica, Passer) are in keeping with the subject of that book, which is mainly concerned with birds and aviaries. The scene changes in the different books, from a temple of the Earth goddess—the first

---

[1] Servius on *Aen.* xi, 787; Augustine, *de civ. Dei*, vii, 35.

book ends, rather unnecessarily, with the murder of the priest—
to Epirus, in the second book, and back to Italy, in the third,
where the company are waiting for the issue of an election. Crops,
stock, bees, tame and wild preserves, are all included in Roman
agriculture, and their treatment is on the princely scale to which
the senatorial class were by now accustomed. The simple estate
of Cato has grown almost beyond recognition, just as Varro's
learning is infinitely greater than the practical common sense of
his predecessor. His own style is not unattractive, midway between the terse staccato sentences of Cato and the periodic structure of Cicero. It is not 'literary talk,' but the plain speech of an
old-fashioned Italian gentleman, well-educated, but more interested in farming than politics. In the year 36 B.C. (when the book
was published) Virgil had already begun the *Georgics*, to show an
aspect of country life with which we find no sympathy in Varro.
The poetry of Agriculture had no place in the work of a scholar
who, none the less, could write very respectable verse, as appears
in the fragments of his Menippean Satires.

This literary form takes its name from Menippus of Gadara, a
satirist of the third century, when it had become the fashion for
Cynic comments on philosophy and ordinary life to be expressed
in humorous or caustic language (vol. vii, pp. 264, 274). Menippus was the first, or among the first, to use the form, and his subjects were themselves a medley, corresponding to his mixture of
prose and verse. To the Romans, with their natural trend towards
satire, this species of their own *satura* must have been welcome;
and, although the distinctively Roman satire, from Lucilius to
Juvenal, was mainly confined to verse, Petronius is in lineal
descent from Varro. Our direct knowledge of his satires depends,
very inadequately, on the titles and on about 600 fragments. The
titles are in Greek and Latin, sometimes in both languages, and
several suggest a popular treatment of Cynic philosophy. This
accords with Cicero's reference to the scope and character of
Varronian satire: Varro is reported as claiming to imitate Menippus 'with a certain humour,' in order that the less educated may
be attracted to philosophical study; and Cicero, speaking in his
own person, then congratulates the satirist on the variety and
elegance of a work 'in nearly every metre' which suggests rather
than teaches philosophy[1]. The longest prose fragment, from a
satire entitled *Nescis quid vesper serus vehat*, gives advice on entertaining at dinner. It is written in an ordinary conversational style,
with frequent verbal puns and a sprinkling of Greek words. The

[1] Cicero, *acad. post.* 1, 2, 8 *sq.*

latter habit may well be due to the example of Lucilius, whose influence on Varro must have been considerable, but, as we see from Cicero's letters, it was also a general fashion of the times. There is no archaism apparent in this fragment; but it is clear from others that Varro often harks back to the language as well as the ideas of his great predecessors, Pacuvius and Lucilius. We must, however, bear in mind that the fragments are a very small portion of the original books; and, having been mainly preserved by Nonius for their peculiarities of diction, they do not necessarily represent the style as a whole. Nevertheless, enough is extant to make us wish for more: as a comment on contemporary life and thought, and a criticism of Roman morals, written in popular language, but by the most distinguished scholar of the age, these Menippean satires represented a type of ancient literature whose almost total loss is deplorable.

From a wider point of view, the mutilation of Varro's works is less regrettable. In his own life, the great 'polymath' might be classed with Cicero as almost equally representative of the period. But later ages clearly distinguished their permanent values. Varro, though never neglected, left but little impress on the sum-total of Latin literature, whereas Cicero, who had been merely *primus inter pares* to his contemporaries, became as unique in prose as Virgil was to become in poetry—a symbol, both for thought and style, of the highest Roman achievement. Himself no great philosopher, he preserved and handed on to his later countrymen and to the Middle Ages all the Greek learning which they could readily assimilate. And the debt of Christian Fathers and churchmen is only part of his service to Western civilisation. Although his own age was intensely active in so many spheres of literature, this activity, as we have seen, was centred in Cicero's outstanding genius. It was a true instinct that gave him chief credit for the final development of a language which survived for more than a thousand years as the *lingua franca* of Europe; and, still later, the same instinct guided the scholars of the Renaissance in recognizing the Ciceronian idiom as the supreme model of Latinity.

CHAPTER XIX

CICERONIAN SOCIETY

I. INTRODUCTION

IN the ancient world, before the Roman Republic passed through its final phases, there had existed societies characterised by notable refinement. But the society of Periclean Athens, of the courts of Alexander's successors, or of Rome itself in the days of the Scipionic Circle cannot be recreated so fully as the environment of Cicero. Its unique interest and the justification for calling it Ciceronian society lie largely in the fact that Cicero was at once a great political and social figure, and that our best evidence for the period is derivable from his orations, treatises and extraordinarily vivid correspondence. The extreme range among its personages is from Marius, Sulla and their myrmidons through Pompey and Caesar to Antony, Octavian and to others of Cicero's correspondents who, like the lawyer Trebatius or the literary ex-governor Asinius Pollio, lived to take a part in Augustan society. Nepos suggests its limits in time by the remark that the same Atticus (109–32 B.C.) made himself agreeable as a youth to the aged Sulla and as an old man to young M. Brutus. Cicero's life (106–43 B.C.) was, then, coeval with two generations—from the Cimbric peril averted by his fellow-townsman Marius till the ascendancy of the triumvirs whose duty was nominally to restore the Republic but who by historic irony made away with some of its most patriotic defenders.

The orations go farther back than the letters as social documents. An early speech, that for Roscius of Ameria in 80 B.C., presents the youthful advocate in brave antagonism to scandalous injustices plotted under the auspices of one of Sulla's powerful freedmen, and illustrates a deeply disturbed state of society when confiscation of land was rife in the country and murder easy in Rome. No letter is earlier than 68 B.C., when Cicero was a man of thirty-eight: the first eleven letters which survive do not bring us beyond 65 B.C. and there are no letters from the year of Cicero's canvass for the consulship or for that year itself, 63 B.C. Yet we are abundantly and brilliantly supplied for the period as a whole. The correspondence, if we accept the letters to Brutus as genuine, comprises over 900 epistles, of which one in ten were written to Cicero.

What increases their value is their frank spontaneity. Written until nearly the end without a thought of preservation for a reading public[1], they possess the combined attraction of a chronicle of thrilling events and purely personal, sometimes even trivial, concerns. They are alive, whether they record judgments on contemporary makers of history, or show the writer's interest in a book, a business transaction, a country house, a work of art, a lady's rheumatism or a menu. Viewed solely as a gallery of human portraits, the correspondence is unsurpassed: and it has the advantage of reflecting a vital age in civilization. The society of the final century of the Republic did not lack variety. What Cato the Censor and other anti-Hellenes had foreseen in fact took place. New wealth, new tastes, new manners acted as inevitable solvents of the old well-disciplined and rather unimaginative Roman character. Force of circumstances made men critical of tradition; and the adventurous flouter of the *mos maiorum* became a law to himself, so that at no Roman epoch is such an individual divergence of personality discoverable. If some periods are stamped with homogeneity, here the protagonists were fashioned after no one pattern. Political, social and literary movements alike intertwined audacious novelties with revered convention, making the potentiality and promise of the age incalculable. Much looked like decay and ruin: much proved to be virility and accomplishment. Like all eras pregnant with fresh development it produced anomalies: alongside of impetuously unstable figures like Catiline, Clodius, Caelius, Curio and Dolabella there stood out rigidly unimpressionable aristocrats like Cato; some men, like Atticus, strictly attentive to business; others, like Varro, who combined scholarship with official duties; many who found the times too distracting to understand; and one only who could bend everything to his will, Caesar.

To Cicero everyone worth knowing was known. We owe it to his sensitive keenness in observation and to his marvellous control over words that we see this society not at the supposed distance of ancient history but at close range. Interest in his fellow-man never deserted him: isolation gave him pain. However much Rome might have altered in constitution and atmosphere, it remained the centre in whose radiant life he loved to bask. 'The city, the city, my dear Rufus' he writes from abroad to his young friend Caelius Rufus 'is what you must make the object of your devotion: live in the sun you have there[2].' Hence the pang of emptiness

---

[1] *ad Att.* xvi, 5, 5, July 44 B.C., habet Tiro instar septuaginta.
[2] *ad fam.* ii, 12, 2.

caused by his exile, by his residence in Cilicia where no administrative duties availed to make up for the capital[1], and by his weary months of waiting as a ruined Pompeian at Brundisium until Caesar saw fit to lift the embargo and let him return. Thoroughly as Cicero could at times concentrate on the solace of studies and literary work, much as he enjoyed a tour among his country and seaside villas, it was an imperative law of existence for him to enter into the activities of the city. When in later days political life was barred to him, social life offered compensations. Certainly he could not complain of neglect. He was sought out: his receptions were attended by Caesarians who were encouraged to repeat his witticisms to Caesar. In fact Caesar had become such a Ciceronian connoisseur that he could distinguish a spurious *bon mot* from a genuine one of the old Lucilian stamp which Cicero tells his sunny Neapolitan friend Paetus is his particular preference[2]. Characteristically Cicero's own moods alter: now beneath his banter runs an undercurrent of melancholy regret for a lost Republic[3], and now he bubbles over with the recollected enjoyment of a dinner-party and its conversation in which the old orator knew how to shine[4].

But if Cicero loved to hear himself talk and to write letters, he was also a begetter of talk and letters in his fellows. Out of Rome he pined for news, even for gossip. 'Write, if only to say that you've nothing to say,' he implores Atticus[5]. In 59 B.C. he writes 'I seem absolutely exiled (*relegatus*) since I came here to Formiae: at Antium there never was a day when I didn't know about occurrences at Rome better than people in Rome ... so do send me a bulky despatch' (*ponderosam aliquam epistulam, ad Att.* II, 11, 1). When Cicero went to his province in 51, Caelius, a lazy correspondent as he called himself, deputed someone else to compose a budget big enough to satisfy Cicero not merely with political items like *senatus consulta* but with the tittle-tattle of town (*fabulae, rumores* or *rumusculi: e.g. ad fam.* VIII, 1). Caelius was, however, equal to reporting the latest engagement or divorce and the spiciest bits of scandal: once in a spirit of mischief he withholds details, adding 'I just like the notion of a victorious proconsul prowling to find out who is the lady so-and-so has been caught with![6]'

---

[1] *ad fam.* II, 11, 1, mirum me desiderium tenet urbis...satietas autem provinciae: cf. *ad Att.* v, 15, 1 (from Laodicea), haec non desidero: lucem, forum, Urbem, domum, vos desidero; v, 11, 1 (from Athens), non dici potest quam flagrem desiderio Urbis.

[2] *ad fam.* IX, 15.   [3] *Ib.* IX, 17.   [4] *Ib.* IX, 26.
[5] *ad Att.* XII, (44, 4), 45, 1.   [6] *ad fam.* VIII, 7, 2.

Curiosity, then, operated along with patriotism among Cicero's motives, but family affection as well; for in the nerve-racking year of 49 he appeals for constant letters from his beloved women-folk at home (*vos, carissimae animae, quam saepissime scribite*). This passion for getting and sending letters contributes a news-paper-like freshness to the correspondence: he would write at times in jerky sentences scribbled before starting on a journey when it was scarcely dawn, or dictated to an amanuensis in hot haste. But if very many letters were hurriedly written, others were designed to convey explanations or comments in a full and serious way; for Cicero, as a great artist in words, remained master of at least two manners—the urbane and polished style of a man as deeply versed in affairs as he was cultivated in literature, and the other that lighter easy-going and on occasion flippant style which, with the writer's sympathetic discernment into all types of humanity, fitted the tone of the missive to the recipient. Cicero is seldom stilted in his letters; but there is a world of difference between his formality in addressing *grands seigneurs* like Metellus Nepos or Appius Claudius and his unrestrained freedom in writing to his life-long friend Atticus or exchanging jokes with Trebatius, Paetus and Eutrapelus. When he chose, he used his learning and his Greek, but equally when he chose, he drew from colloquial Latin and from the kindred diction of Roman comedy. Behind all is the creative genius which gives life to literature by flashes of revealing light upon contemporary events, whether great or small, and upon the persons concerned. It is impossible to escape a thrill from words written to Cicero by Caesar, Antony and Cassius, or to miss the interest of the description of a call from Pompey or from Caesar; but we meet flesh and blood as really in letters with no political bearing, where, for example, Cicero dines out, or comes home mellow at night to look up a legal point just discussed with Trebatius, or sympathizes with his freedman Tiro's illness, or reprobates the cruelty of the games, or chronicles the books he has been reading or writing, or reports a squabble between Atticus' sister Pomponia and her husband Quintus Cicero, who was so much freer with his hot temper in his province than in his own house.

Cornelius Nepos regards the sixteen volumes of the epistles sent to Atticus as furnishing an almost complete history of the times[1]. Here it is proposed to illustrate the social phenomena which made the background to them and Cicero's other writings.

---

[1] *Atticus*, 16: quae qui legat non multum desideret historiam contextam illorum temporum.

II. THE SOCIAL GRADES

The political significance of the three ranks in the state—the senatorial order or *optimates*, the equestrian order and the commonalty—is written large in the history of Rome. They must now be glanced at from a social angle, though it is impossible wholly to separate Cicero's relations to them from his political watchwords of *Senatus auctoritas* and *Concordia Ordinum*, indicating a commonwealth in which all good citizens and especially the moneyed middle class should unite with the aristocracy in maintaining the *optima causa* against revolutionary schemes. But if such co-operation appeared to be temporarily realized in the suppression of the Catilinarians, there were occasions when his mind was painfully divided between merits and faults in the time-honoured ruling caste. Certainly there was much in the patricians to impress an ambitious *novus homo*. The old families, originally of varied local provenance[1], but by age-long association and service Roman to the core, shewed, however much some fell short of the best traditions of their order in character and in governing ability, that they were still animated with the consciousness of inheriting a great past and still jealously resentful of any infringement either on their caste privileges or on the glory of the ancestral name. In this spirit Metellus Celer stiffly reminded Cicero that *familiae nostrae dignitas* should have been a check upon his free language about a Metellus[2]. In the same spirit, long after, a mistake made by Metellus Scipio about an ancestor affecting the inscription on a statue is reprobated by Cicero himself as discreditable[3]. Some old names, it is true, suffered eclipse; for the civil wars and physical degeneration wrought irreparable havoc in spite of attempts to perpetuate families by the female line or through adoption; but there were still prominent in Rome bearers of fair-sounding names like the Cornelii, Claudii or Sulpicii.

Respect was by custom due to an Optimate—it was due to such external reminders as his distinctive dress, his imposing retinue, his seat in the theatre, due also to his very bearing, but above all to the prestige of his standing in the State as the holder of high office at home or abroad. Kings and potentates found advantage in paying court to a Roman governor. To maintain a social position so exalted, to be prepared to bribe electors or jurors, wealth was essential; and, though senators were forbidden to make money by trade, it was possible to have the finances of an estate controlled by an agent, whether Roman knight or oriental freedman; possible

---

[1] See F. Münzer, *Röm. Adelsparteien und Adelsfamilien*, pp. 408–413.
[2] *ad fam.* v, 1.   [3] *ad Att.* vi, 1, 17.

likewise to be secretly behind some capitalist company in a commercial venture; and only too possible to raise a fortune by extortion in a fat province. One indication of a senator's importance might be seen in the attendance of clients from the country as well as from the city in his *atrium* at the morning *salutatio* with which the *patronus* opened his day's work. Sometimes these receptions were extended on a smaller scale to the rural and seaside mansions of public men: hence Cicero in his villa at Cumae claimed to have been entertaining a miniature Rome (*habuimus in Cumano quasi pusillam Romam, ad Att.* v, 2, 2).

Though there were notorious exceptions in the shape of voluptuaries, adventurers, and oppressors, many of the nobility maintained honourable traditions of patriotism and a high standard of literary culture. Thus it was not inappropriate that Cicero should compliment the critical taste of Lentulus Spinther by promising to send him some of his poems out to Syria besides copies of certain speeches and his *De Oratore* to help his son's studies[1]. Yet he was often in the guise of spokesman for a privileged class which he could not unreservedly admire. He might in politics be with them: he was not of them. Backbiters did not confine their sneers within aristocratic *circuli* and *convivia*, but openly shewed disdain for the successful pleader from Arpinum. With a lurking sense of inferiority and perhaps a touch of envy tempering the pride of a self-made man, Cicero complained that honours were thrust on nobles even in their sleep, while others less lucky had to toil for them[2]. The *rapprochement* which intervened in 63 was followed by disillusion in 60, when a recurrent theme in the letters is aristocratic jealousy of himself and the selfish love of luxury on the part of careless fools for whom a scandal like Clodius' outrage on the ritual of the Bona Dea or the very safety of the State counted nothing provided their fishponds were unharmed[3]. These 'Tritons of the fish-ponds,'[4] as the ex-consul dubs them, were but lamprey-breeders: 'they're in paradise, they fancy, if there are bearded mullet in their tanks to come to their hands for food[5].' So the future author of the *De Amicitia* realized the want of heart in the attitude of high society towards him: lonely amidst a crowd of acquaintances and clients he wrote from Rome to Atticus in Epirus, longing for him as a confidant: 'These showy and gaudy friendships of ours enjoy a certain lustre in the world outside, but they don't possess any homelike value[6].'

---

[1] *ad fam.* I, 9, 23.   [2] II *in Verr.* v, 70, 180.
[3] *ad Att.* I, 18, 6: cf. I, 19, 6; 20, 3.
[4] *ad Att.* II, 9, 1.   [5] *Ib.* II, 1, 7.   [6] *Ib.* I, 18, 1.

With the equestrian order, the moneyed as contrasted with the landed aristocracy, both in Rome and in the townships of Italy, Cicero felt himself in essential harmony. He belonged to the class by birth, and regularly proclaimed his devotion to its interests[1]. Though the term *equites*[2] occurs as an expression for the eighteen centuries of military knights drawn from the Roman *jeunesse dorée* like Caelius Rufus and Curio, it usually at this period means the wealthy class who owned capital enough to enable them to contract for farming the public revenues, the collection, that is to say, through agents of provincial tribute or the tax on pasturelands or the *portoria* levied on exports and imports; or, again, the management of commercial enterprises through joint-stock companies (*societates*). The equestrian census was 400,000 sesterces, and those who belonged to the class were accommodated in the theatre and at public spectacles in fourteen rows of seats behind those allotted to senators. With their rights on juries and their financial interests Cicero was in active sympathy. Consequently it is one of his chief objections to Cato, whose firmness and integrity distinguished him from the majority of the nobles, that an impracticable idealism made him ready to offend the equestrian order by insisting too literally upon the terms of a contract.[3]

Atticus, Cicero's greatest friend and most regular correspondent (though none of his answers to Cicero have come down), was a shrewd and cultured member of the order, avoiding on Epicurean principles any entanglement with political sides, cultivating his taste through literature and art, while all the time he knew how to make money by purchasing and developing an estate in Epirus, lending sums at interest, negotiating bills, keeping slaves to copy books, and training gladiators to fight. Though he inherited most of the ten million sesterces left by a skinflint uncle, Atticus was far more than a prosperous merchant in agricultural produce, in money and in human lives. Long residences abroad gave him considerable Hellenic learning; and, strictly economical as his inclinations were, it was a feast of intellect rather than of expensive dishes that he provided for literary guests in his artistically adorned mansion on the Quirinal. A well-read amateur without being a

---

[1] E.g. *pro Rab. Post.* 6, 15: nunc vos, equites Romani, videte: scitis me ortum a vobis; omnia semper sensisse pro vobis.

[2] E.g. *ad Att.* 11, 19, 3. This is the 'manus Curionis' of Cicero's correspondence. Cf. H. Hill, *Livy's Account of the Equites*, Class. Phil. xxv, p. 244.

[3] *ad Att.* 1, 18, 7; 11, 1, 8, dicit (sc. Cato) tamquam in Platonis πολιτεία, non tamquam in Romuli faece, sententiam; 11, 5, 1, Cato ille noster qui mihi unus est pro centum milibus.

Varro, he was a critical adviser as well as a publisher. Cool and self-centred in the regulation of conduct, he possessed an indefinable personal charm which was the secret of his success in winning a surprising number of different friends. Discriminating and adroitly calculating in his judgment of character, he laid himself out to please: and an astute adaptability made him all things to all men. While he could thus, as a proved adept in neutrality, be a social and sociable reconciler of opponents, Atticus never stood in the fighting line of his country's politics where some of his friends felt bound to serve.

The plebeians, or third estate, were still in the Ciceronian age voters and therefore the objects of political flattery and State generosity. Candidates for their suffrages addressed them in *contiones*, canvassed them privately or otherwise, and entertained them with expensive shows consisting of gladiatorial combats or *venationes* of wild beasts. The ranks of the needy urban *multitudo* had been swollen by a stream of Italian peasant proprietors dispossessed by re-allotment of lands or ruined by changed conditions of agriculture. When Caesar reformed the corn-distribution, the 'masses' in receipt of a free corn-grant numbered 320,000[1]. Included in this class were not only the ruffianly loafers who could readily join a gang of Clodian rioters but also the small tradesmen and artisans; for slave labour in big houses had not wholly ousted the free citizen from manual production. From one standpoint these were a fraction of the State with claims long since asserted and constitutionally defined, but from another standpoint they seemed largely a wretched mob not yet, as under the Empire, deprived of the chance of selling their votes, but already fatally dependent upon a State dole and public amusements. For the city proletariate Cicero shows little regard. He writes in 61 B.C. that his influence was the same as ever with loyalists (*boni*) and had improved 'with the scum and dregs of the town' (*apud sordem urbis et faecem*[2]), and continues with scathing irony: 'the public that like a leech sucks the blood of the treasury, the miserable starveling rabble (*illa contionalis hirudo aerarii, misera ac ieiuna plebecula*), takes me to be high in Pompey's favour'; then, with a chuckle over 'the chin-tufted blades' who had nicknamed him 'Gnaeus' Cicero, he adds 'I have had marvellous ovations in the circus and at gladiatorial shows.'

---

[1] Suet. *Div. Iul.* 41. Corn previously available at cheap rates owing to State-purchase was given gratis during the later Republic from the time of Clodius, 58 B.C. (see p. 524).

[2] *ad Att.* I, 16, 11; cf. 'in Romuli faece,' *ib.* II, 1, 8.

While some of the homes of the lower population were on the Aventine, the Caelian, and on parts of the Esquiline, the principal quarters for the poorer classes were in the natural depressions leading down from the heights towards the Forum, such as the Subura between the Esquiline and the Quirinal,—a swelteringly hot trading district in summer—and, closer to the Forum, the Argiletum where shoemakers and booksellers carried on business. Their accommodation in common lodging-houses or tenement blocks (*insulae*) several storeys high (such as have been restored in recent years at Ostia) made a striking contrast to the fine mansions or parks of the rich on the Palatine and other elevated sites. The contrast was as great in the sphere of food. While the staple dietary of humbler Romans consisted mainly of wheat, vegetables, fruit, oil and wine, the fare of the wealthy was anything but strictly vegetarian. It drew upon all the resources of land and sea to provide an astonishing variety of cuisine.

For the *municipales*, or country voters throughout Italy, Cicero entertained kindlier feelings than for the urban populace. His own origin partly explains the breadth of vision with which he extended his ideal of Concordia Ordinum outside Rome. To such Italian voters he felt grateful for supporting his recall from exile; but their attitude in 49 after the outbreak of civil war seriously chagrined him. When Caesar's clemency had won them over to put economic safety first, Cicero writes angrily about the *municipales homines* and *rusticani* with whom he has been talking a great deal: 'they care only for their lands, their farm-houses (*villulas*), their cash' (*nummulos, ad Att.* VIII, 13). Clearly, then, the class included persons of substance; and we find Cicero in 46 B.C. anxious to help his townsfolk at Arpinum by forwarding to M. Brutus, whom Caesar had made governor of Gaul, a request to secure payment of rents from lands belonging to the corporation[1]. In a similar spirit he applied to Valerius Orca as a land-commissioner on behalf of the people of Volaterrae[2].

III. WOMEN OF THE DAY

The Roman matron had for long held a dignified position in the community. Free from that seclusion which hampered the Athenian wife, she was honoured in the home much as the Vestal was by the State. Behind the political scene, if of high family, she could exert considerable influence on public affairs. Curiosity, indeed, had sometimes led her too far, as shewn in the incident of

---

[1] *ad fam.* XIII, 11. [2] *Ib.* XIII, 4.

the boy who was over-inquisitively cross-examined by his mother about proceedings in the Senate which he had been privileged, as one of the *praetextati*, to attend[1]. But even such curiosity implied intelligent concern and the potentiality of influencing policy. In fact, the wives of prominent *optimates* exercised a power comparable to that of princesses at the courts of Alexander's successors. There are in the Ciceronian period many illustrations of the recognition of woman as a political no less than a domestic factor. How Cicero tried to mitigate hostility to himself at the close of his consulate by craving the good offices of Clodia, who was sister-in-law to Metellus Nepos, and of Mucia, who was then Pompey's wife; how Pompey, returning from the East, made more than one overture for a marriage-connection with the Cato family and scandalized the eligible young women by overdoing the bribery of voters in his gardens; and how Caesar diplomatically sent presents from Gaul for ladies of importance are instances familiar to students of the age[2]. Though Pompey's contemplated matrimonial alliance with the Catos fell through, he succeeded in securing the hand of Caesar's daughter Julia just when she was to have married Caepio (Plutarch, *Pomp.* 47). The disappointed bridegroom was consoled with Pompey's daughter, although she had been promised to Sulla's son, Faustus. These *mariages de convenance* (sometimes with mere girls) did not necessarily exclude affection. For a time Pompey was so devoted to his new wife that he kept her assiduous company in his gardens to the neglect of public affairs[3]. Her death in 54 B.C. ended a connection which veiled rather than checked the ambition of two powerful men: as Lucan says, Julia took away with her the pledges of a family union (*pignora iuncti sanguinis*, I, 111–112). Pompey's next bride was Cornelia, daughter of Metellus Scipio, and widow of Crassus' son, Publius. She had literary tastes, studied geometry and philosophy, played the lyre, and made a pretty and accomplished wife, though too young, people remarked, for Pompey[4]. But the value of such marriages depended as much on the lady's gentile connection[5] as on her suitability in years or her gifts of mind or looks.

Though the correspondence contains no letter from a woman, we hear constantly of the part played by some highborn dame at

[1] Gellius, *N.A.* I, 23, cited from Cato.
[2] *ad fam.* V, 2, 6; Plutarch, *Cato min.* 30; *Pomp.* 44; 51, 2.
[3] Plutarch, *Pomp.* 48 and 53.   [4] *Ib.* 55.
[5] This point is intelligible from the genealogical tables in Münzer, *op. cit.*: for relationship among Caesar's assassins see the table in Shuckburgh's translation of the *Letters of Cicero*, vol. IV, Introd. p. xxxviii.

a critical juncture. Cicero acknowledges gratefully support given during difficult times by Junia, the wife of C. Claudius Marcellus, when he assures her son that 'from your revered and excellent mother ... I have received greater services than were to be expected from a lady[1].' Calpurnia's marriage to Caesar led to her father's consulship, though against such intolerable traffic in the chief magistracy and against women's interference in the assignment of armies and provinces Cato protested in the spirit of Napoleon's question: 'Since when did the Council of State meet at Madame Récamier's?' Postumia, the energetic wife of Servius Sulpicius Rufus, was probably the inspirer of young Sulpicius' wholehearted support of Caesar, though his father was a Pompeian, if only a lukewarm one[2]. On the other hand, Porcia, Cato's daughter and Bibulus' widow, whom M. Brutus married on divorcing Claudia, must have deepened her husband's republican sympathies. Along with Cassius' wife Tertia or Tertulla, who was Brutus' half-sister, and with Brutus' mother Servilia, Porcia made an influential trio of women in an interview at Antium, when Cicero advised Caesar's assassins, Brutus and Cassius, to accept corn-purchasing duties in Asia and Sicily[3]. Servilia's position here should be noted. She undertook to get the corn appointment cut out of the senatorial decree[4]; and elsewhere we find her objecting to a proposal made by Cicero in the Senate[5]. The mother of M. Junius Brutus by her second husband, Servilia was step-sister to Cato of Utica, so that her son's wife Porcia was her step-niece. One daughter by her first marriage was Junia, who married the triumvir Lepidus: another, Tertia, had, as mentioned, married Cassius. Though M. Brutus was credited with purity of life, the attachment of his mother, Servilia, to Caesar occasioned much talk, nor did scandal spare the daughters. Comment arose when Junia's portrait was found with those of other married ladies among the baggage of the hare-brained Vedius whom Cicero met on a road in Asia Minor travelling with two chariots, a carriage and two horses, a litter, a huge band of slaves, a dog-headed baboon and some wild asses[6].

Matches were also contracted with an eye upon worldly gear. The fortune-hunter was at work. It is significant to read of Thalna's proposal to Cornificia, 'an old dame of many marriages,' and of his rejection because his property did not amount to 800 *sestertia*[7]. Cicero's re-marriage late in life to his young ward

---

[1] *ad fam.* xv, 7.   [2] *ad Att.* ix, 18, 2; 19, 2; x, 3*a*, 2; 7, 2.
[3] *Ib.* xv, 11.   [4] *Ib.* xv, 11 and 12.   [5] *ad fam.* xii, 7.
[6] *ad Att.* vi, 1, 25.   [7] *ad Att.* xiii, (28, 4), 29, 1.

Publilia was not without mercenary motives. Not unnaturally many unions proved loveless. Divorces grew frequent for infidelity or for capricious reasons. Not everyone found such flagrant cause to repudiate a wife as the younger Lentulus Spinther in 45 B.C.; Caesar had simply justified the dissolution of his marriage to Pompeia with the famous dictum that his wife must be above suspicion[1]; and Cicero tells of Paulla Valeria divorcing her husband without grounds alleged[2]. Indeed the unconcern with which marriage-ties were broken is nowhere better shewn than in Cicero's amazing professions of regard for his ex-son-in-law Dolabella, who had been divorced by Tullia for unpardonable misbehaviour. The frequency of re-marriage was a largely consequential feature. Cicero's daughter had three husbands; and Fulvia, before she married Mark Antony and so controlled the affairs of Galatia from her boudoir, had been the wife of Clodius and of Curio.

Without romantic qualities, some women proved themselves good housewives or diligent students. Terentia, Cicero's wife, had great capacity in handling property and accounts—a managing person in many ways; for, on the eve of the debate about the punishment of the Catilinarians, had she not, according to Plutarch, urged her husband to take an uncompromising line? The breach with his wife after thirty years of wedlock is one of the psychological puzzles in the chronicle of marital separations. Cicero's marriage could not be pictured, like Byron's, as foredoomed to failure: no sudden realization of incompatibility in temper accounted for the estrangement. Terentia's cool complacency may have been a foil to his oratorical impetuosity—exasperating qualities in her, no doubt, at certain junctures, and yet admirable in a matron entrusted with the control of business matters during his absence. Slowly a gulf widened between them, and the letters grow colder, till they end in domestic instructions not courteous enough to send to a housekeeper. Atticus' sister, Pomponia, with all her shrewishness, was a thrifty housewife, for her son records her careful way of checking wine-jars to prevent pilfering by slaves[3]. Caerellia, Cicero's most learned lady-friend, was of a different stamp. Keen on philosophy, she copied books by Cicero from Atticus' *librarii* and took pains to obtain early copies of his treatises[4]. The malice of Dio Cassius sought to besmirch the innocence of her relations with Cicero: perhaps the best disproof of his libel is the fact that she was an emissary sent

---

[1] Plutarch, *Caesar*, 10, 6; Suet. *Div. Iul.* 74.   [2] *ad fam.* VIII, 7.
[3] *ad fam.* XVI, 26.   [4] *ad Att.* XIII, 21, 5; 22, 3.

to induce Cicero to re-marry Publilia[1]. It was an age when reputations were readily assailed: Attica, the daughter of Cicero's friend, studied privately under Epirota, and gossip made free with their names.

Often there was ample provocation for talk. Some women were in league with extremists. As supporters of Catiline Sallust[2] mentions women whose extravagance and debts pointed them towards revolution as a way out. Among them is described Sempronia, a good-looking married lady, well read in Greek and Latin, musically accomplished, too fond of gaiety to consider her honour and too clever a dancer to be virtuous. Talented in the use of language, she wrote verses, and could both charm and shock by her conversation. To her husband, who had opposed Saturninus and was consul in 77, she bore D. Junius Brutus, one of Caesar's murderers. Dangerous women, too, came from overseas. Cicero watched the *liaison* between Caesar and Cleopatra with anxiety lest this over-attractive Eastern woman might become a sort of empress in Rome. 'I loathe Her Majesty' (*reginam odi, ad Att.* xv, 15, 2), says he, detesting her agents and her promised gifts to himself. Her airs had been insufferable when she stayed at Caesar's trans-Tiberine villa, and so he hopes that Cleopatra and her brat Caesarion have come to grief since leaving the city after the Ides of March[3].

But among Roman women of birth who gave themselves to a life of pleasure among the fast set in the period following Cicero's consulate, the most notorious was Clodia, wife of Q. Metellus, and the 'Lesbia' of Catullus' love-poems. A gifted woman, reckless in extravagance and generosity, Clodia, both as wife and widow, bade defiance to convention. Her appearances in public with male friends, her garden-parties by the river, her boating excursions at Baiae, her ceaseless round of revelry and music among a succession of amorous admirers gave her a bad name which Cicero avidly took occasion to emphasize and exaggerate when summoned to defend Caelius on certain criminal charges, including one of attempting to poison Clodia. This smart dandy, of equestrian family from Puteoli, had been a diligent pupil in oratory under Cicero, who liked his talent in clever speech and racy letter-writing. One of the wild roysterers about town, Caelius was also a social success, and, entering the circle of Clodia's gallants, ousted Catullus from her favour. The subsequent cooling of Caelius' passion stung Clodia into the charges which it fell to Cicero, as counsel with Crassus, to rebut in his

---

[1] *ad Att.* XIV, 19, 4.   [2] *Cat.* 24–5.   [3] *ad Att.* XIV, 20, 2.

devastating counter-indictment of 'this Palatine Medea.' He
launches his main onslaught with the ironical innuendo: 'I never
thought it desirable to be on bad terms with ladies, especially with
one who has the character of being lady-friend to everybody.'

The implication here, the additional allusions to her *meretricia
vita*, and the epithet *quadrantaria* force upon our notice the class
of women who served the lusts of Rome for money. The comparative freedom in social intercourse between the sexes which
Nepos in his Preface illustrates from the Roman habit of taking a
wife to a banquet, in contrast with Greek seclusion, tended to
accentuate the dishonour attached to furtive amours with loose
women. Prostitution was, according to Roman sentiment, a disgrace for both parties, although Cicero, holding a brief for Caelius,
propounds an indulgent 'wild oats' plea out of keeping with the
respect which as a moralist he shews for the family[1]. Elsewhere
it suits him to stigmatize Catiline, Clodius and Antony in turn for
irregular attachments[2]; and he is nervously apologetic in his confession that he had met at dinner the *mima* Cytheris who became
Antony's mistress[3]. It is but right to say that courtesans in Rome
held no such elevated position as the educated *hetaerae* in Greece[4].
Moral rigidity kept the Roman from granting them too many
privileges. Women adopting a career of shame were obliged to
take out a licence at the aedile's office[5]: once registered, a name
could never be erased. Distinctive dress, dyed hair, and civil disability were further marks of outward reprobation. But this did
not prevent their appearance, flaunting their finery, at circus,
theatre, or banquet: they might thread the narrow streets, lolling
in a litter, bejewelled, scented, and fanned by slaves. There is only
too clear evidence of the harm they wrought. Rapacious wantons
of what Catullus calls the *salax taberna* figure in his poems; and
Lucretius has them in view when, treating the frenzy of love, he
declares that a concentrated passion may cost more mental pain
than *Venus volgivaga*[6]. Entanglement with a fashionable mistress
might mean a noble patrimony squandered on dress, emeralds,
feasting and drinking[7]; but 'from the midmost fountain of de-

---

[1] *pro Caelio*, 12, 29–30; *de off.* i, 17, 54.

[2] *in Cat.* ii, 10, 22–3; *pro Mil.* 21, 55; *Phil.* ii, 28, 69; 41, 105.

[3] *ad fam.* ix, 26; *ad Att.* x, 10, 5; *Phil.* ii, 24, 58; 31, 77.

[4] Lombroso and Ferrero in *La donna delinquente*, Torino, 1894, p. 239
overstate the facts: 'esse, come le etere in Grecia, esercitavano a Roma un'
influenza grandissima.' Havelock Ellis, *Studies in the Psychology of Sex*,
vol. vi, p. 239, takes a more guarded view.

[5] Tacitus, *Ann.* ii, 85.   [6] iv, 1071.

[7] *Ib.* 1121–1140.

lights rises something of bitter to vex among the very flowers'—
remorse over 'the misuse of time and damnation of the brothel'
(*desidiose agere aetatem lustrisque perire*). Alongside of the relaxa-
tion of the marriage bond, the prevalence of such vice was a
symptom of the social disintegration which Augustus and his
advisers endeavoured to arrest.

IV. SLAVES AND FREEDMEN

Strictly, slaves formed no part of Roman society: they were not,
in law or in the common view, persons but chattels. They did,
however, perform indispensable services as members of the
familia urbana or *familia rustica*. In town, they were not confined
to menial domestic duties like cleansing, waiting or cooking: they
acted as messengers or attendants on travel, and educated slaves
were employed as secretaries, copyists, librarians, *paedagogi* for
children, or as physicians. Capitalists who owned palatial mansions kept in some instances staffs to produce materials rendering
them largely independent of purchases from without, while some
servile labour was absorbed in factories for bricks, pottery and
metal implements. Rome's wars were the most fertile source of
slaves: a single victory of Caesar's yielded 53,000 saleable captives (p. 555), and Cicero's little hill war in Asia involved loss of
liberty for his prisoners (*mancipia venibant Saturnalibus tertiis, ad
Att.* v, 20, 5). Piratic kidnapping, breeding of home-born slaves
(*vernae*), and forfeiture of freedom under debt-laws had raised the
servile population in Rome to well over 200,000. In the country,
too, Varro's evidence is that skilled slaves were needed on a productive estate for its olives, vines, fields and game; while bondsmen
of a rougher and more dangerous sort were on the wild pastures.

Though a kind master, Cicero accepted the customary theory
of slavery. Feeling short-handed at Rome and on his estates, he
gladly accepted his brother's promise to get him Gallic slaves[1].
He wanted a friend's runaway slave traced in Asia[2]; and in 46 B.C.
he urged the governor of Illyricum to arrest Dionysius, his own
slave, with whom he was angry for purloining books[3]. The hue-
and-cry after this defaulter was being kept up the year after by the
next governor (*ad fam.* v, 9). In the correspondence slaves cross
the scene repeatedly. They are the *pueri* who carry letters: they
are discussed—to be sold or not—when Cicero writes to Terentia
about their possible confiscation consequent on his exile and about
the expediency of declaring some of them free. Again, they are

---

[1] *ad Q.F.* III, 9, 4.   [2] *Ib.* I, 2, 14.   [3] *ad fam.* XIII, 77, 3.

the copyists in Atticus' service, completing the manuscript of the *Academica*[1]. In one case three of them, Pharnaces, Antaeus and Salvius, are specifically asked to delete an erroneous name from copies of the *Pro Ligario*[2].

Usually Cicero is conscious of a social gap severing him from bondsmen. He is half apologetic over showing grief at the decease of an attractive young servant who used to read to him (*puer festivus, anagnostes noster*): 'it affected me more than it seemed the death of a slave should[3].' Yet the incident supplies the key to his attitude. It was culture and community of literary interests that bridged the gap, and the great example of this is the delightful relationship subsisting between Cicero and Tiro. To this faithful servant there fell difficult and easy tasks alike—from tangled business problems to mere household routine. As Cicero's chief secretary, it was his duty to deal with correspondence and accounts, and execute responsible commissions such as negotiating a loan or demanding arrears of interest. Domestic economy also came under his purview—arrangements for a dinner-party, building projects, improvements in the garden. His literary powers fitted him to help Cicero in his writings, and, long surviving him, he edited the greater part of the correspondence. To qualities of brain he added mechanical skill in shorthand: 'Tiro can take down whole periods as you say them,' remarks his master, explaining by way of contrast that a letter to Varro, which needed careful phrasing, was dictated syllable by syllable to an under-clerk[4]. Little wonder then that the letters to him are as affectionate as they are confidential. When Tiro grew seriously ill and was left at Patrae on the homeward journey from Cilicia, Cicero showed acute distress. One day in anxiety he wrote three times to Tiro entreating him to take the greatest care of his health. 'Your services to me are beyond reckoning—at home, in the forum, in the city, in my province: in private and public affairs, in my studies and compositions. You will surpass all this by letting me see you, as I hope, well and strong[5].'

No slave ever better deserved emancipation. When Cicero rewarded Tiro with liberty, he got a letter from his brother Quintus thanking him for a new friend. Tiro thus makes a transition between the classes of slaves and freedmen. By purchasing a small farm he acted in a typical way; for the freedman, in virtue of his saved *peculium* or his master's bounty, was regularly enabled to own property or start business subject to the customary observance

---

[1] *ad Att.* XIII, 23.   [2] *ad Att.* XIII, 44, 3.   [3] *ad Att.* I, 12, 4.
[4] *ad Att.* XIII, 25, 3.   [5] *ad fam.* XVI, 4, 3.

of *officium et obsequium* and the performance, in certain cases, of specified services (*operae officiales vel fabriles*). He might or might not leave his patron's house, but many avenues lay open in commerce or industry. Some freedmen remained confidential secretaries and literary advisers like Tiro: some were financial agents like Philotimus, Terentia's servant, so much distrusted by Cicero that he wrote cryptically in Greek to Atticus about his faults; and some were political agents like Caesar's Diochares or Pompey's Theophanes. Success turned the heads of some; for another of Pompey's freedmen, Demetrius, would impudently take his place at table before his master received his guests[1]. He got possession of agreeable pleasure-grounds in the suburbs. A man of different tastes was Apollonius, once Crassus' *libertus*, and engaged on a Greek account of Caesar's exploits when Cicero commended him to Caesar in 45[2]. We should not leave this subject without calling attention to the continuous infiltration of foreign blood into the citizen-body as the result of unfettered manumission.

V. SOURCES OF LIVELIHOOD

No one could have called the Romans a nation of shopkeepers: there was more truth in the epigram that their main industry was war. In great measure Rome lived on her conquests, growing rich at the expense of her dominions, especially in the East. Her stock of capital had accumulated out of plunder as the fruit of victory and tribute as the price of administration. Governors and *publicani* amassed riches by unscrupulous exactions, and the operations of bankers yielded handsome profits. This flow of wealth into a city no longer the chief town of an agricultural people, but a cosmopolitan caravanserai, made Rome independent of the economic fact that her imports in foodstuffs, raw materials, luxuries and art vastly surpassed in value her visible exports. For, despite a conventional disdain for trade, her commerce steadily increased. It was in accord with the old prejudice of a landed aristocracy that Cicero summarized the antipathy to manual labourers and retail vendors—the former were not artists and the latter 'would get no profits without a good deal of lying[3].' Senators were forbidden by law to trade or to own large ships: their fortunes were understood to be derived from estates or oftener from such extortion in the provinces as Cicero charges against Verres. Heavy debt encumbrances were very frequent. If,

---

[1] Plutarch, *Pomp.* 40.　　　[2] *ad fam.* XIII, 16.
[3] *de off.* I, 42, 150–1.

however, a nobleman had money to invest, he might be a hidden partner in a company venture or money-lending firm. Cicero, when governor of Cilicia, discovered that M. Brutus, 'an honourable man' as literature assures us, had invested money widely on loan in Cyprus, and, in defiance of Brutus' imperious tone, he declined to enforce to the uttermost the shamefully oppressive contracts made with the provincials: in particular, he objected to agents of this philosophic gentleman starving defaulting debtors to death. In Rome, Crassus added to his notorious and unpopular wealth by emergency purchases of properties on fire or of adjoining properties. The sources of Cicero's own wealth have often been investigated. He inherited a moderate patrimony: then his practice as advocate brought considerable returns, not in fees (which were illegal) but in presents and in legacies from grateful clients. We know of his accepting a library as a gift, and in the last year of his life he acknowledges having received in legacies the sum of twenty million sesterces[1]. Such bequests might spring from gratitude, but the motive of sheer vanity also prompted citizens to associate their names through their wills with prominent people. Thus on one occasion Cicero found himself co-heir with his arch-enemy Clodius, and on another with Caesar. In administering Cilicia he set his face against rapacity: even so his year yielded him over two million sesterces in the current *cistophori*. These savings, placed with companies of *publicani* in Asia, were largely wasted on a loan to Pompey. Cicero drew rents from properties in Rome, and earmarked some of these for the allowance which young Marcus frittered away in his student days at Athens[2].

Equestrian wealth, as previously noted, brings before us the handling of money, tax-farming, and management of businesses either by companies for the benefit of shareholders or by an individual for personal profit. Atticus has appeared in another connection. The Roman knight Oppius was a sort of junior partner with L. Cornelius Balbus (to be distinguished from the devoted Pompeian T. Ampius Balbus). Of good Spanish stock, Balbus received citizenship from Pompey. When propraetor in Further Spain, Caesar had discerned his ability, and he appointed him a confidential agent in Rome during the Gallic campaigns. His power in the city excited jealousy and an attack on the legality of his citizenship. Put on trial, he was championed by Pompey, Crassus and Cicero, whose *Pro Balbo* won a favourable verdict. Oppius and Balbus both tried to keep Cicero from

---

[1] *Phil.* II, 16, 40.   [2] *ad Att.* XV, 20, 4.

joining Pompey and they financed prominent Romans, without interest, to make them Caesarian. They had also a turn for intellectual things—Balbus for philosophy and Oppius for biography. C. Matius Calvena, a financier, and a friend of Cicero, though not in agreement with his politics, was representative of the moderate men in business who rested their hopes of security on Caesar and were incensed against his assassins. Matius' letter after the murder claiming the right to grieve openly for one whom he considered a friend is deservedly admired for its unaffected frankness[1]. His share in financing public games to be given by Octavius met with Cicero's disapproval.

Without examining in detail the economics of the age, it is desirable to avoid certain misconceptions. We must not underestimate the rural prosperity of Italy or the free labour in town and country or the volume of industry and trade. From the country war-service had drawn away many small proprietors never to return: they met their death or settled in Rome or emigrated, thereby contributing to the Romanization of the provinces[2]. But the peasant had not entirely died out, and much of Italy, despite ravages, re-allotments, and the increase of pasturage and stock-breeding over corn-growing, was in a fair state of cultivation. It should be made clear that the Sullan and post-Sullan periods were not periods of decay either in an economic or in a cultural sense. The affluence of a town like Pompeii had more than begun, and this interests us, as Cicero owned a residence there. Once a poor little place, it now possessed shops and elaborate houses reflecting the flourishing condition of Campania especially in wine-production. Varro, writing his *Res Rusticae* soon after Cicero's death, and Virgil in the *Georgics*, though the one may have in view capitalist villa-owners and the other ordinary farmers, alike bear witness to the natural resources of the land.

In Rome, alongside of workless and often worthless proletarians, there were hundreds of free shopkeepers and busy artisans. Evidence from inscriptions is much fuller for the imperial period, but many trades and industries had their foundations firmly laid before the Republic ended. The financial heart of all was the Forum, the central piazza, where men carried on traffic in shares and security-bonds, and made purchases, for ready money or credit, of dwellings, shops, warehouses, farms, estates, slaves,

---

[1] *ad fam.* XI, 28.
[2] See M. Rostovtzeff, *A Social and Economic History of the Roman Empire*, p. 33 and p. 495. He believes, contrary to Heitland, that peasant emigrants and peasant agriculturists were numerous.

cattle, ships and cargoes. To satisfy the wants of an urban population in food, clothes, housing, tools, furniture, ware, and adornment of homes mean and great, to furnish material for public
edifices and road-making, to meet the requirements of army, navy
and mercantile marine, and to render possible the work at farms
and villas, specialized industries inevitably multiplied. Trade
made corresponding progress[1], aided by a network of better roads
and safer sea-routes. But there were troubles, as recurrent
financial crises showed. Ancient means of supply or of demand
involved losses only to be covered by contracting loans at ruinous
rates. An example of fluctuating fortune is seen in Rabirius
Postumus, the enterprising merchant-adventurer whom Cicero
defended in 55 B.C. His father was a knight who did well in
business, and he himself advanced loans to many cities abroad and
to Ptolemy 'the Flute-player,' who needed money to recover the
Egyptian throne. When, thanks to the collusion of Gabinius, proconsul of Syria, Ptolemy at last returned to Alexandria, Rabirius
became financial controller of Egypt, and despatched a flotilla to
Puteoli with cargoes of such products as cloth, glass and papyrus.
Though failure in this scheme was punished by imprisonment for
a time in Egypt, Rabirius typifies the imaginative man of business
whose operations in banking and trading were conducted on an
almost international scale.

VI. EXTERNAL CONDITIONS OF LIFE

In high society the parade of wealth was an obvious characteristic of the day. Historians, orators, moralists and poets comment
on the perniciously extravagant fashions then prevalent. Marius
had made a spirited attack on the self-indulgence of the nobility;
and luxury during Cicero's youth may be illustrated from Sulla's
household, rich in oriental furniture and art, and manned by
slaves who ministered to aesthetic and often immoral tastes.
Sulla's well-groomed freedman, Chrysogonus, throve on the purchase of forfeited estates, and amassed a rich collection of paintings
and of marble or bronze statues. Cicero enables us to picture his
vulgar display. He specifies along with his Corinthian and Delian
treasures, a 'self-cooker,' *authepsa*[2], which the upstart bought for
such an outrageously high price at a sale that bystanders, ignorant

---

[1] J. Toutain, *The Economic Life of the Ancient World*, pp. 227–250, argues
that Tenney Frank in *An Economic History of Rome* (ed. 2) underestimates
the industry and trade of the period.

[2] *pro Rosc. Amer.* 46, 133.

of the Greek word, thought some enormous estate was being
knocked down to him. In the time of Cicero's manhood the pro-
fuse expenditure of his noble friend Lucullus on banquets, residences and gardens made his name proverbial[1]. After his Mithridatic campaigns Lucullus gradually withdrew from public life,
preferring to spend his Asiatic wealth ostentatiously on his villas
at Tusculum and Naples. His gigantic schemes to lay out parks
and fishponds appear to have involved levelling hills and invading
the sea. To the lavish pleasures of his table, however, he added
intellectual interests: he offered warm hospitality to philosophical
and literary Greeks, and generously put his valuable library at the
disposal of consultants. Lucretius, ascetic in his Epicureanism,
contrasts the magnificent splendour of such luxurious mansions
unfavourably with the truer enjoyment of reclining on soft grass
in the flowery springtime: simple needs are satisfied

> Though no gold statuettes of youths indoors
> May in the right hand hold the flaming lamps
> To serve the nightly feast with brilliancy—
> Though gold nor silver set the house agleam
> Nor harps make roofs with panels gilt resound.　(II, 24–28)

There was no more significant feature of private life than what
we may call the villa-habit. The passion for possessing residences
in the country and by the sea in addition to sumptuous town
houses was symptomatic of both luxury and restlessness. Lucretius illustrates the vain attempt to escape from self in the
feverish dash from town to the rural villa:

> Oft from his mansion vast forth fares the man
> Who has grown sick of home: then straight returns,
> Finding no better luck abroad. Full-speed
> He drives his jennets to his country hall,
> As if he rushed to help a house on fire!
> He yawns the moment he has reached the door,
> Or sinks asleep and woos forgetfulness,
> Or e'en makes hurriedly again for town.　(III, 1060–1067)

But other motives operated more laudable than mere restlessness.
Cicero had eight villas—one, nearest to Rome, at Tusculum, one
at Arpinum among his native hills; the remainder on the coast, at
Antium, Astura, Formiae and in the Neapolitan district at Cumae,
Puteoli, and Pompeii. He visited them for sound reasons of
physical and mental health. 'No place,' he writes, 'gives me complete rest like Tusculum after all worries and hard work[2].' Once

---

[1] Plutarch, *Lucullus*, 39–42.　　　[2] *ad Att.* I, 5, 7.

an internal illness drove him out there to recuperate. There were times too when he longed to study and think in quiet—but he knew some villas were more liable than others to the intrusion of callers and bores. Crowds of visitors at Formiae, for instance, hindered literary work[1], and the garrulity of Philippus, Octavian's step-father (nicknamed 'son of Amyntas' as if a Macedonian king!), could spoil the sweet solitude of Astura. Usually, however, his delight is unmixed: 'why am I not looking at my pretty villas—sweet gems of Italy?' (*ocellos Italiae, villulas meas, ad Att.* XVI, 6, 2), he asks; and he cannot bear to depart for Cilicia without taking leave of them in turn. Similar feelings recur at the outbreak of the Civil War—he may never see them again, he fears[2].

If Cicero has not, like the younger Pliny, left a description detailed enough to furnish a ground-plan of a villa, we can at least follow his practical interest in his own houses and in his brother's. He arranges for improvements: he adds *exedrae* for holding discussions with friends: he criticizes architects freely when structural alterations are in progress. We catch glimpses of a pleasant country house bought for Quintus with fishpond, playing fountain, palaestra and shrubbery. Already comforts like the heating of floors by hot air had come in[3]. Nor was the appeal to taste and intellect overlooked. Books well arranged, Cicero felt, gave a house soul (*mens*): his library was an *Academeia*, as Atticus had an *Amaltheum*, Brutus a *Parthenon*, and Varro a *Museum*, where he wrote. Art too claimed consideration. There are repeated appeals to Atticus to choose articles of *vertu* for a gymnasium at Tusculum; Cicero wants Hermae of Pentelic marble with bronze heads sent him; and, when certain statues are landed at Caieta, he eagerly arranges for their transport inland. He needs pictures also for sitting-rooms. We get a realistic peep at him writing to Quintus beside the carved lampstand which he liked because his brother got it made in Samos. Naturally, not every work gave satisfaction: once Fadius Gallus bought for Cicero more statues than he wanted—unsuitable ones too; and an amusing letter[4] tells him that the money would have been better spent on a place of call at Tarracina to afford a rest overnight on the journey along the Via Appia to Formiae.

Varro[5] draws the contrast between the fashionable villa and the older farm-steading built to meet agricultural needs. 'Nowadays,' he remarks, 'size and adornment in the villa urbana is the main object: men vie with the country houses of Metellus or Lucullus

[1] *ad Att.* II, 14.   [2] *Ib.* VIII, 9, 3.   [3] Val. Max. IX, 1, 1.
[4] *ad fam.* VII, 23.   [5] *Res Rust.* I, xiii, 6–7.

—the building of which has been a national disaster' (*villas pes-simo publico aedificatas*). Elsewhere he touches on different sorts of villas[1]. In some we see business premises for securing profits from land and from live-stock in accordance with the advice in his handbook: others are rich in furniture of citrus-wood, gay in gold and vermilion, and tastefully floored with a tessellated pavement (*emblema*). A wealthy landowner like Varro combined the practi-cal with the ornamental. He was keen on stock-rearing within the precincts of the villa (*de villaticis pastionibus*)—rearing, that is, not sheep, but birds like peacocks, field-fares, pigeons, ducks, besides game, snails, bees and fish. His aviary at Casinum was renowned; but his garden and still more his library stirred the envious admir-ation of Cicero.

The prominence of villas directs attention to conditions of travel and the transmission of letters. Journeys by road, whether by horse or mule, whether in light *cisium* or four-wheeled *reda*, whether with few or many attendants, were, judged by modern standards, painfully slow. Still slower progress was possible in a *lectica* borne by poles on the shoulders of slaves: at times, as on the bay of Naples, recourse might be had to a boat[2]. Since breaks of journey were often unavoidable, *deversoria*, or lodges, were arranged for as places of call, some of them little more than night-shelters for the retinue of an important personage. An alternative was to stay with friends, as Cicero did on the Via Appia when he was put up in Philemon's villa at Ulubrae, and listened to the frogs croaking in the marshes[3]. While the main roads were under public control, some country ones were left to local proprietors, and might be bad and fatiguing, as Cicero found the road to Aquinum[4]. The speed attained depended on many factors. Cicero instances a man who travelled 56 miles in 10 hours during the night from Rome into Umbria in a light vehicle of the sort kept for hire at stages along the chief roads (*cisiis pervolavit, Pro Rosc. Amer.* 7, 19). Ordinary couriers and travellers averaged five Roman miles an hour, or a modest rate of about 50 miles a day. This was eclipsed by imperial despatch-bearers who could in cases of urgency cover 160 miles in 24 hours[5]; and it is recorded that Caesar travelled 100 miles a day for some days in succession, driving in a hired *reda*[6].

The absence of regular postal facilities in Cicero's day obliged

---

[1] *Res Rust.* III, ii.   [2] *ad Att.* XIV, 20, 1.
[3] *ad fam.* VII, 18, 3.   [4] *ad Att.* XVI, 13a.
[5] Friedländer, *Sittengeschichte der röm. Kaiserzeit*[8], II, p. 22 *sq.*
[6] Suet. *Div. Iul.* 57; cf. Plutarch, *Caes.* 17.

ordinary correspondents to employ slaves or freedmen to carry letters. If lucky, they might get the expeditious service of the *tabellarii* of *publicani* travelling with business documents between Rome and the provinces. There were hazards to face—carelessness, interception, brigandage. A letter might never be delivered, or might be spoilt by rain[1]. The conditions of travel and correspondence come home vividly, as we read[2] of the dark November morning on which Cicero took the road from Sinuessa by torchlight, and had just sent away his torchbearers when he was met by a letter-carrier bringing a note which as yet there was not enough daylight to read. It is interesting to observe the time taken by letters on the way. At Puteoli Cicero might expect letters from Rome dated from two to four days earlier[3]. One letter took the unusually long time of six days to Puteoli[4]: by way of contrast we have a letter from Rome acknowledged which travelled fast to Pompeii in two complete days[5]. Despatches from Gallia Narbonensis reached the city in ten days. Longer distances involved additional risks from bad weather or a sea voyage. Caesar wrote twice to Cicero from Britain: the first letter took 26, the second 28 days to reach Rome. Similarly a letter from Cilicia to the capital would take a month in favourable circumstances. At the beginning of May Cicero received in Laodicea a bulletin of Roman news up to March 15th: his letters *via* Tarsus arrived about two months old.

VII. SOCIAL AND INTELLECTUAL CULTURE

Cicero is in the fullest sense typical of the social culture of his day—its education, learning and literature, language, manners and outlook on mankind. His education, planned by his father when he came from Arpinum, ensured wide acquaintance with Greek and Latin literature, with rhetorical principles, and philosophic thought. Earnestness and wellnigh unbelievable diligence marked his multifarious studies. Above all, he took daily exercise in private declamation.[6] He attached himself to the orators of the previous generation, Antonius and Crassus, as Caelius afterwards became his apprentice. When he was about 21, a lull in the storm of civil strife opened up a valuable stretch of advanced study (*triennium fere fuit urbs sine armis*). After two years at the bar, he went in 79 on an eastern tour to follow 'post-graduate' courses in the thought and oratory of Athens and Rhodes. But Cicero's

---

[1] *ad Q.F.* II, 10, 4.   [2] *ad Att.* XVI, 13a.   [3] *Ib.* XIV, 20.
[4] *Ib.* XIV, 13, 1.   [5] *Ib.* XIV, 18, 1.   [6] *Brutus*, 90, 308–9.

education in reality never ended. Again and again he gladly fell back on study, eager to learn from Greek speculation and to transmit it to his countrymen. He was, indeed, a teacher as well as a learner, and would have welcomed even the Persius whom Lucilius deemed too erudite to be a sympathetic reader[1]. Similar methods of training were handed on to the younger generation. The Cicero cousins, Marcus junior, and Quintus junior, had great pains expended on them, and were initiated into foreign travel when Cicero took them to his province and arranged for their residence at the court of King Deiotarus and for the continuance of their lessons under Dionysius[2]. The one needed a spur, the other a bridle[3]. Later they were students at Athens, where Marcus, given to festive company, outran his fond parent's allowance. Both son and nephew in many ways disappointed Cicero's hopes.

The intellectual standard attained is evident from Cicero's own learning, the literary achievement of the age, and the spread of culture. Speeches, treatises and epistles alike show his passion for Greek classics and old Latin literature. A wonderful memory guaranteed a power of copious and apt quotation from the writers of both languages. Admiringly conscious of the triumphs of Hellenism, Cicero turns with loving patriotism to the earlier Latin poets, citing them with an affection which is most noticeable in the case of Ennius. He insists on knowledge of Latin literature and even of Latin translations from Greek as essential to Roman culture[4]. Some quotations run in his head as favourites and recur in different parts of his works, such as Naevius' *laudari a laudato viro*, Ennius' *unus homo nobis* and Accius' *oderint dum metuant*. But literary history owes to Cicero alone the preservation of a large variety of fragments from primitive Latin authors—many of them passages of considerable length quoted for their thought or merit instead of those linguistic curiosities which attract grammarians and lexicographers. Just as he delighted in quoting an old play, so he maintained his interest in contemporary drama. He had met the aged Accius; he knew the chief actors of the day, Aesopus and Roscius; and it is from personal acquaintance with the theatre that he mentions witnessing mimes by Laberius and Publilius, records the quickness of audiences to read political allusions into dramatic lines, instances the elocutionary power of an actor, and condemns the overdoing of scenic display in plays like Accius' *Clytem(n)estra* or Andronicus' *Trojan Horse*[5].

[1] *de fin.* I, 3, 7. [2] *ad Q.F.* II, 12, 2; III, 3, 1 and 4.
[3] *ad Att.* VI, 1, 12. [4] *de fin.* I, 2, 4–10.
[5] *ad fam.* VII, 1, 2; XII, 18, 2; *pro Sestio* 56, 120–123.

With most of the great figures in contemporary literature Cicero had some contact. How much he knew about Catullus' infatuation for Clodia, in whose graces Caelius supplanted him, and how far he classed the poet with Alexandrine imitators (*cantores Euphorionis*) we cannot tell: he seems once at least to echo a phrase of his ('softer than the tip of the ear,' *ad Q.F.* II, 13, 4), and there survives one little poem of thanks addressed to 'Mark Tully' for a kindness done to Catullus, who subscribes himself

> Of poets all as much the last
> As you're a pleader unsurpassed.   (xlix, 6–7)

Cicero's acquaintance with Memmius, the dilettante noble on whose staff Catullus went to Bithynia and to whom Lucretius addressed his work, may have brought him into touch with both poets. Lucretius, at any rate, was influenced by Cicero's *Aratea*, and we know that Cicero and his brother were reading and criticizing his poem in 54 B.C. (p. 747). The correspondence constantly shows interest in literature old and new. We can picture him fingering lovingly the volumes in his library after their rearrangement by Tyrannio[1], or 'browsing on' an Aristotelian library, as he writes from Cumae[2], or absorbed in Dicaearchus' *Constitution of Pallene* till the unwound roll is piled up in a huge heap on the floor[3]. Copies of his speeches go to Atticus to be criticized and copied; and his account of his consulship in Greek prose is submitted with the promise of a poem to follow (*ad Att.* I, 19, 10; I, 20, 6). In return, Atticus' history of the consulship is acknowledged—plain in style, the orator recognizes, beside his own florid handling (*ib.* II, 1, 1–3). Verses also go through Quintus to Gaul for Caesar's opinion (*ad Q.F.* II, 15, 5).

Such exchange of views by correspondence formed a parallel to those oral discussions with friends which made it easier for Cicero to adopt a dialogue frame-work for a treatise. He approaches Lucceius, then engaged on a history of the times, with a request for a eulogy on his consular services: he propounds the alternatives of weaving the consulate into the narrative or of composing a separate monograph. Even over-statement would be an acceptable tribute; for with cool assurance he remarks 'a letter doesn't blush[4].' Facing Varro, the great polymath whose canonic authority was evidenced in his collection of genuine Plautine plays, Cicero feels less confident. When occupied on the *De Republica*, he asks leave to use Atticus' library with the specified object of consulting Varro's writings. To him a letter, as mentioned, had to be dic-

[1] *ad Att.* IV, 4*a*, 1.   [2] *Ib.* IV, 10, 1.
[3] *Ib.* II, 2, 1.   [4] *ad fam.* V, 12, 1.

tated with scrupulous care, and no doubt Cicero took it for as high
an honour to be permitted to dedicate the *Academica* to him as to
accept the dedication of Varro's *De Lingua Latina*. The presentation copy of the *Academica* was prepared as an *édition de luxe*[1].
Here a certain severity in Varro overawed Cicero into a bashful
nervousness about its possible reception, and a Homeric verse
crosses his mind: 'a dread man he is, who might easily blame one
that is blameless.' Other writers in the Ciceronian circle were the
biographer Nepos, and Asinius Pollio. Next to Varro the most
distinguished *littérateur* among Cicero's correspondents, Pollio
wrote from Corduba about a *praetexta* by his fraudulent quaestor,
the younger Balbus, dramatizing his adventure into Pompey's
camp. Cicero is told he can, if interested, borrow the play from
Pollio's literary friend, Cornelius Gallus[2]. It will be realized that
just as Caesar himself could be orator, historian and philologist at
choice (he dedicated his *De Analogia* to Cicero), so the diffusion
of culture among his staff was marked. Business men, we have
seen, had literary tastes; and houses of standing gained intel-
lectually by the presence of Greek freedmen like Tyrannio, Tiro
and Dionysius.

The language of refined society is well represented in the
letters, though, as indicated, Cicero had more than one manner
and ranged with ease from a formal to a conversational style,
dotted here and there with the teasing or affectionate diminutives of spoken Latin, and sometimes as abrupt and elliptic as
utterances overheard at one end of a telephone. In verbal mastery
he far surpassed most of his correspondents; for it is exceptional
to meet anything so good in their portion as the consolatory letter
from Sulpicius on Tullia's death. From the license of foul abuse in
such a speech as that against Piso (*e.g. belua, caenum, lutum, sordes*),
it is clear that society on occasion tolerated a freedom of language
in striking contrast with the polished diction of a philosophic dialogue. Some people, indeed—Stoics and others—made a parade
of plain speaking, whether it outraged decency or not: it is, therefore, instructive to note Cicero's revulsion from words or phrases
which, even if innocent in themselves, might by their very sound
raise an obscene suggestion[3]. In one attractive passage he advocates a science of polite conversation, sketching principles calculated to save a social situation from tactless bores[4]. Much might
be written on the pleasantries with which Cicero enlivened a trial,
a debate, a dinner-party or the letters in which he plays up to the

---

[1] *ad Att.* XIII, 25, 3.   [2] *ad fam.* X, 32.
[3] *Ib.* IX, 22.   [4] *de off.* I, 37, 132–5.

jocular style of Trebatius or Paetus. He plumed himself on his wit. He studied its very foundations in the *De Oratore*. It was not always in the best taste, nor always very funny; but he won a reputation for it. 'What an amusing consul we've got!' said Cato with a smile at Cicero's bantering of Stoicism in the *Pro Murena*[1]. To Clodius he seemed rather a 'Cynic' consular who could bark and bite. Men frequented his receptions to hear his smart sayings and ready repartees, and enthusiasts made anthologies of them.

The manners pervading this complex society can only be glanced at. Nothing can restore its atmosphere so well as Cicero's pages, which recreate the etiquette of *salutatio, clientela,* electioneering and private life. 'I like a dinner-party,' he tells Paetus, 'I talk about whatever crops up, as the phrase goes, and I change sighs into loud laughter[2].' The manners sketched for 129 B.C. at the country house of Scipio[3] may serve as an index to the usages for some succeeding generations: there we observe the courteous welcome extended to guests, the announcement of visitors by a slave, the greetings exchanged among members of the company, and the formal guidance of late arrivals to a comfortable seat. The letters bring before us ceremonial calls like Pompey's at Cicero's Cuman villa in 55 B.C., when his political declarations had to be taken with needful caution; or Cicero's after-dinner call in his *lectica* at Pompey's park-residence to talk over Quintus' release from duty in Sardinia; or again Caesar's call on Cicero when serious business was ignored in favour of scholarship (φιλόλογα, *ad Att.* XIII, 52).

In theoretical ethics the ideal stood high, but the correspondence reveals laxities in the code of honour. Its flatteries and protestations of friendship contain much that is disingenuous. The testimonials in the *litterae commendaticiae* do not mean all they say; and apparently no shame is felt in opening and resealing letters intended for others, in forging complimentary letters to produce a favourable impression, or in disowning the authorship of a speech which has given offence in awkward directions. There are, however, indications of the spread of kindlier feelings towards misfortune and suffering. Consideration for slaves, as noted, was on the increase. The same Caesar who was responsible for inexorable massacres in Gaul and who wasted no chivalry on Vercingetorix showed broadminded mercy to his opponents in the Civil War. The same Cicero who, in describing his own opera-

---

[1] Plutarch, *Cato min.* 21.　　　　[2] *ad fam.* IX, 26, 2.
[3] *de Rep.* I, xi–xii.

tions, records without any sign of pity the slaughter or enslavement of Cilician mountaineers, expresses a tender compassion for the pain inflicted on fine animals and especially on elephants butchered to make a Roman holiday in 55 B.C.[1]; and he was horrified at the bloodthirsty threats of Pompey's supporters against their fellow-citizens.

A few words are due to a great force in Roman life—the strangely conglomerate fabric of domestic and public religion. There is no space for weighing it as an amalgam of primeval rural spirits with anthropomorphic Greek gods or as a set of beliefs concerning which, in an age of unrest, educated Romans harboured a profound scepticism[2]. *Religio* implied not so much sincere reverence at heart as scrupulous observance of prescribed ritual with a semi-timid apprehension of an incalculable Power and a semi-speculative eye on the chance of ultimate benefit. As in ancient times the farmer offered sacrifices expectant of divine favour in repayment, so the statesman valued ritual as a protection for the whole community. Romans seldom got rid of a bargaining tendency in their *pietas*, which for Cicero himself meant justice towards the gods. His petulant letter to Terentia at the beginning of his exile suggests that she has been shabbily treated for her feminine devotions: 'I wish, my love, to see you as soon as possible and die in your arms, since neither the gods whom you have most devoutly worshipped (*tu castissime coluisti*) nor men, whom I always served, have made us any return.' His interest in religious practices was confined to ceremonials of political importance. Himself an augur, he was proud of his office: to him, however, the study of the sky for omens seemed just a serviceable bit of State machinery, and the *ius divinum* a portion of the *ius civile*. The *De legibus*, in handling the religious aspect of constitutional law, contemplates a religion State-worked to maintain salutary relations between citizen and deities and so give the community the blessing of the *pax deorum*. It was thus an insurance against danger.

This strict adherence to formalism in religion was compatible with full liberty in probing the bases of such religion. Freedom of question about the gods remained permissible so long as they were outwardly worshipped. Some gave a sceptical or an atheistic answer. Cicero, in this respect like Varro, accepted the Stoic theory of a world-soul identifiable with Juppiter, the ultimate sanction for law and morality[3]. While he can denounce super-

---

[1] *ad fam.* VII, 1, 3.   [2] See above, vol. VIII, chap. XIV and below, vol. X.
[3] *Phil.* XI, 12, 28; *de legibus*, I, 6, 18; II, 4, 10; *de Rep.* III, 22, 16; *de nat. deor.* I, 15, 40.

stition, he does not deny the gods, but sees a divine hand in Roman history, in his own consulate, and in the foiling of Catiline[1]. Yet in all this there is no heavenly call upon the individual to live a good life, nor any clear sense of responsibility to a Supreme Being. On the question of immortality he wavers. Sulpicius, consoling Cicero on Tullia's death, states guardedly the hypothesis 'if the dead have consciousness[2],' and the phrase is curiously echoed in Cicero's speech about the same Sulpicius after his death[3]. Long before, speaking for his poet-friend, he had argued for human confidence in something to follow death[4]. The blow of his beloved daughter's death in February 45 B.C. forces the problem back upon him. His 'pet Tulliola,' as he calls her in one of the earliest letters when she was a girl of eleven, was always a joy and comfort to her father, who thought highly of her abilities. She had not failed him, as her mother did; and now, soon after bearing a son to Dolabella, she had passed away. He shut himself up at Astura, to spend long days alone in the woods thinking and mourning[5]. So noble a soul as hers could not perish, and for over a year he considered one plan after another for the erection not of a mere monument to her memory but of a shrine to her immortal spirit[6]. In this design to honour her sanctity he found a spiritual solace which aided the healing that came from friends' condolences, from the elaborate *Consolatio* composed by himself, and from his resolute immersion in those studies which invariably brought him peace.

[1] *Phil.* IV, 4, 10; *ad Att.* I, 16, 6; *in Cat.* III, 9, 22.
[2] *ad fam.* IV, 5, 6.
[3] *Phil.* IX, 6, 13.   [4] *pro Archia*, 11, 29.
[5] *ad Att.* XII, 14 and 15.
[6] *Ib.* XII, 36, 1; 37, 2; 37a.

CHAPTER XX

THE ART OF THE ROMAN REPUBLIC

I. INTRODUCTORY: THE PROBLEM OF ORIGINS: ITALICS, ETRUSCANS AND GREEKS

TILL about forty years ago no serious attempt had been made to give Roman art its proper status as an original and vital expression of the Roman genius and civilization. The subject had long been obscured by doctrines traceable to Winckelmann and his disciples, who looked upon Rome solely as the heir of Greece, and ignored the native elements in her culture and her art. Even now that its merits have won recognition, they are more frequently attributed to the skill of Greek artists in adapting themselves to Roman conditions than to any artistic instinct inherent in the Roman people. Though it is impossible to deny the deep impress which Rome received from Greece and its effect upon her art, the forms and motives freely adopted from the Greeks no longer blind us to the underlying Roman and Italic strains, or conceal the creative instinct which turned borrowed material to new purpose. Roman art may be the result of a slow and painful elaboration rather than of spontaneous growth, but it is becoming evident that, like every great civilization, that of Rome produced in time an art peculiar to itself, receptive of contribution from other races, but preserving intact its own spiritual content.

Recognition of this truth is of recent date. The interest in Roman art which was first aroused by Wickhoff's theory of a Roman *Reichskunst* was concentrated on the art of the Empire. That of pre-Imperial Rome, on the other hand, continued to be represented by a few portraits and friezes of late Republican date, and few attempts were made to trace it back to its origins in the racial circumstances of the Italic peoples. Pliny's express statement as to the existence of a very ancient Italic art was virtually ignored and, though affinities were admitted between Roman and Etruscan art, little progress was made along that line of enquiry so long as the Etruscans were represented as rudely breaking into the old Italic civilization, and destroying its essential unity.

The difficult question of origins began to open out to its true proportions with a clearer knowledge of the cultural conditions of the peoples of ancient Italy. When once the two great pre-Etruscan civilizations—that of the *terremare* and that of the Villanovans—stood revealed in their full extent and significance, it became imperative to revise the opinions currently held of the Etruscans.

Whatever view is held of their provenance as a ruling caste, it is now generally admitted that their domination did not obliterate the Italic civilization of the Villanovans, and that Etruscan art stands out as merely one phase of a development which is continuous from the period of the *terremare* to that of Constantine. Its more progressive character was due to the early commercial contacts which, in virtue of the natural advantages of their soil, the Etruscans were able to establish with Oriental and Greek civilizations. This Etruscan art, which has already been described (vol. IV, pp. 421 *sqq.*), was largely indebted to Greece for its form and its subjects, but even in the sixth century B.C. when the spell of Ionia was strong upon it, it remained faithful to its Italic origins. From this fidelity it derived strength to stimulate to more active production the latent artistic currents in the more backward parts of the peninsula. Its influence, however, was by no means towards uniformity; on the contrary the archaeological material shows that it was modified according to the culture with which it came into contact. In Etruria itself local differences are as evident as common characteristics; while in Campania, in succession to the earlier culture of Etruscans and Greeks, there developed that Osco-Samnite variety of Italic art which eventually competed with the Etruscan in the formation of Roman art. One result of the better arrangement of the rich material contained in the many local museums of Italy is to demonstrate that there were differences as marked between the various art centres of ancient Italy, as between those of the Italy of the Middle Ages and of the Renascence.

In Rome Etruscan influence remained paramount till the changes which followed the expulsion of the Tarquins at the close of the sixth century. After these, Rome's cultural outlook expanded, and fresh contacts with Samnium and Campania, with Magna Graecia and later with Hellenistic Greece, contributed to enrich the old Italic stock and helped in the formation of Roman art, though three centuries and more went by before it blossomed out into a genuine expression of the national genius. This could only happen after a long struggle between the native and the borrowed Greek elements in the nascent art of the Republic. It was inevitable that Rome should feel the perennial attraction of the Greek mind

—of the beauty of Greek art with its perfected technical methods and sureness of aesthetic aim. Nevertheless, the underlying Italic factor remained constant and informing; it was too deeply rooted in national and religious life to be more than superficially affected by Greek influence. The question of Greek versus Roman was, it is true, transformed for a time into one of acute political partisanship; an advanced philhellenic party who welcomed and encouraged every form of Greek culture—its art, its philosophy, even its religion and its ritual—was violently opposed by a conservative party who feared, perhaps with reason, the disintegrating effects of foreign fashions.

The conflict was long protracted. When Virgil makes Anchises say that others are welcome to produce works of marble or of bronze, but that a just and peaceful rule will prove the basis of Rome's future greatness, he is giving an exalted and poetic form to a sentiment which may be traced back to Cato's fine scorn of the enthusiasm for those Greek statues which turned the Romans away from the traditional art of Italy. The opposition of men of Cato's stamp, and there were many[1], has too often been looked upon as a proof of barbarian insensibility on the part of the Romans to the charms of art. But it represented something deeper. It was originally inspired not so much by ignorance and prejudice as by a desire to stem the unmeasured adoption of foreign standards. The monuments themselves bear witness to a long period of oscillation between Italic traditions and Greek principles. Towards the end of the second century B.C., and more especially in the Sullan period, there were moments when Roman art might have succumbed to the fashionable Hellenism of the day, and petered out into futile imitations of the Greek. Roman commonsense soon began to readjust the balance and in the time of Caesar a reaction had already set in, though the Italic element was only restored to complete ascendancy under Augustus, whose life-long policy was to present the culture of the Roman Empire—whether expressed in art, religion or literature—as being one with that of ancient Italy[2].

This Italic element is appreciated very differently according to the angle from which it is viewed. What some regard as merits others judge to be gross errors and mere deformations of the

---

[1] On this intransigence see Furtwängler, *Die antiken Gemmen*, III, pp. 271 *sqq.*; E. Strong, *Art in Ancient Rome*, I, p. 74; F. Goethert, *Zur Kunst der Römischen Republik*, p. 27.

[2] G. Snijder in *Tijdschrift v. Geschiedenis*, XL, 1925, pp. 1 *sqq.*; *ib.* XLII, 1927, pp. 113–143. Cf. Ch. Picard, *Rev. E. L.* 1928 (Bull. Bibl. p. 7 *sq.*).

aesthetic principles early put into practice by the Greeks. The question, however, is not one of academic standards, but of discovering without aesthetic bias what were the special qualities of Italic and Roman art and wherein and for what reasons its canons differed from the Greek. It is usual, for instance, to point to a fundamental difference between Italico-Roman 'realism' and Greek 'idealism,' between the Roman preference for individual traits and the more generic character of Greek art. Roman 'realism' arises out of the same interest in human individuality and its varied experiences that colours the Italic art of all periods; hence its inherent passion for portraiture, and for the representation of those res gestae, official or domestic, in which the Romans eventually attained to supreme excellence. On the other hand, owing to their cruder artistic vision, the Italics were apt to indulge their love of reality at the cost of plasticity: their harsh linear systems of form, their partiality for cubic and frontal effects, often contrast unfavourably with the more organic modulations of Greek art, while their desire to realize the third dimension in space led them in their reliefs to break into the surface of the background in a manner scarcely, if ever, tolerated by the Greeks.

Such instances of an aesthetic sensibility inferior to the Greek could be infinitely multiplied, yet it would be unfair to put down all Italic deviations from the Greek canons to mere incapacity or to a misunderstanding of classic models. Owing to his realistic instinct the Italic artist felt impelled to discover means of expressive movements and situations which Greek art would undoubtedly have rejected but, to quote a recent criticism[1], this very indifference to purely aesthetic problems gave the Romans liberty to sin against the canons and rules imposed by the Greeks and thus to produce works which transcend in boldness anything that Hellenism had dared to attempt.

II. EARLY ETRUSCO-ITALIC ART

After what has already been said of Etruscan art in earlier volumes, this need only be touched upon here in so far as it affected the formation of that of Rome. Owing to the obscurity which envelopes the origins of the city and its early history it is difficult, however, to lay down with precision the date when Etruscan influence was first operative. So closely ringed was the Roman territory by great Etruscan or Etruscanized centres—Caere and Veii, Falerii and Fidenae, Praeneste and Tusculum—that

---

[1] G. Kaschnitz-Weinberg in *Formes*, October 1930, p. 7.

we might expect Etruscan culture to have reached Rome long
before the period of the Etruscan rule. Of this there is little or no
trace. The finds made in the *Sepolcreto*—the old burial ground in
the valley of the Forum—show affinity only with the material from
the cemeteries of the Alban hills, and almost nothing has been discovered on Roman soil to betray kinship with the rich civilization
disclosed in the princely tombs of Caere or Praeneste[1]. As it is,
the earliest work of art that can be safely connected with Rome
belongs to the advanced Etrusco-Italic phase of the closing years
of the sixth century. This is the famous terracotta group in
the Museo di Villa Giulia known as 'the Contest for the Sacred
Hind,' which was found in the Capitolium of Etruscan Veii and
which it is therefore reasonable to attribute to the school of
that same Volca of Veii who made the cult statue of Jupiter
for the Capitoline temple and other works in Rome (see above,
vol. IV, p. 424 *sq.*).

The group can thus teach us what the early Roman statues were
probably like, which were executed by Etruscan artists or under
their immediate influence. Technique and composition evidently
derive from Ionia, but in the Apollo, to take the outstanding
figure of the group, the Italic love of accentuation is evident in
the heavy modelling of the face, in the full lips and chin, in the
thick twisted curls and the deep groovings of the hair[2]. Italic also
are the intensity of the glance and the jubilant fierceness of the
expression, the savagery of the stride and the almost clumsy prominence of the muscles on the sinewy legs and arms. The same
violent effects recur in the antefixes in the shape of Gorgon masks,
of the same Veientane temple[3]. Here again conception and
form doubtless derive from Greek prototypes, but a new terror
has been imparted to this Italic Gorgon by the deep modelling of
the furrows around the mouth and of the writhing snakes that en-
circle the face. The artist attempts to differentiate expression,
as in the group itself where the Hermes wears the tranquil
smile of an amused spectator in fine contrast to the passionate
eagerness of the Apollo[4].

In the utter dearth of any Roman statuary of very early date a
curious and little known head, in the Villa Giulia, from Civita Castellana (Falerii Veteres) may throw light on the *ars statuaria vetustissima*,
examples of which were still known to Pliny[5]. Whether Etruscan
or purely Italic, it belongs to an earlier stage of art than the 'Contest for the Sacred Hind.' It was found on the site of the venerable

---

[1] Volume of Plates IV, 32, *a*.   [2] *Ib.* 34, *a*.
[3] *Ib.* 34, *c, d*.   [4] *Ib.* 34, *b*.   [5] *N.H.* XXXIV, 33.

temple of *Juno Quiritis*, and, being over life-size, probably belonged to the ancient cult image of the temple, preserved by the piety of successive generations. The low forehead, the large and bulging eyes, the prominent chin and the thick rolled strands of hair are familiar Italic traits[1]. The unattractive spongy material—a tufaceous stone known as *nenfro*—was possibly coloured, the effect of the colouring being further enhanced by the wreath of burnished or gilt bronze, fragments of which still adhere to the hair. We may gain an idea of the general effect from the alabaster statuette of a goddess in the British Museum, which still retains traces of colour and can only be very little later in date than the Falerii fragment[2].

It is not, however, in the rendering of divine but of human beings that Italic art excelled from the first. Its power of individualization which was destined to triumph in Roman portraiture had early set its mark on that of pre-Roman Italy; witness two uncouth terracotta heads of the mid-sixth century, from sarcophagus lids, in the Museo Gregoriano of the Vatican[3]: the woman with the redundant cheeks and chin of placid middle age, the man—the more closely studied of the two—with keen eyes, lips tight closed like a trap, large inquisitive ears, and soft felt cap pushed back from the forehead. In spite of the inadequate technique this is already true portraiture, as distinct from the exalted Greek conception of type or from mere vulgar likeness.

The portrait instinct was doubtless fostered in ancient Italy by the religious conviction that the ultramundane life of the individual depended on fixing his image for the survivors. Hence those strange anthropoid urns with portrait lids known as *canopi*, which are a humanized version of the Villanovan type of burial vase. They are peculiar to Chiusi, where the Villanovan culture admittedly survived almost to the historic period. The very shape of the Villanovan vase lends itself to the human form: the lid, an inverted cup, often receives a crest-like ornament, sometimes further transformed into a helmet; a human face or mask[4] is next suspended from the neck; soon the whole lid becomes a head, while the handles turn into arms, and breasts are sometimes indicated on the body of the vase. We have here the germ of the later Roman portrait bust—a shape practically unknown to the Greeks, except

[1] Volume of Plates iv, 32, *b*.   [2] *Ib.* 32, *c*.   [3] *Ib.* 36, *a*.
[4] The canopic portrait-head is often looked upon as the humanization of these masks, which are themselves of singular interest, no two of them being alike. See H. Mühlestein, *Die Kunst der Etrusker*, p. 227 to plates 147, 148.

as terminal shaft, until a quite late period. One of these urns at Arezzo[1] is an astonishing piece of portraiture: skull and facial oval form an harmonious whole, the mouth is well drawn, the eyes large and far-seeing, the planes of the face sharply defined. These Italic characteristics persisted for centuries and recur with new force in the Imperial portraiture of the fourth century A.D.— in the Constantine of the Basilica Nova, for instance, which shows the same architectural structure of the head, the same wide-open eyes with the far-off gaze that befits alike the ruler and the dead. Other Chiusine urns are executed in a brilliant dashing style, such as the portrait of a youth whose proud bearing and aristocratic insolence anticipate Pollaiuolo's portrait, in the Bargello, of a young *Condottiere*. The head is of stone and the body of metal; the whole effect is heightened by the beautiful high-backed chair with carved griffins on which the urn sits as on a throne[2].

Like the portrait bust, the portrait statue also seems to derive from the canopic urn. The lid of a Chiusine *canopus*, for instance, might be used as the base to support one or more figures[3]. Good instances are the well-known group in Florence of a man seated at table and waited upon by his servant ('Banquet of the Blessed')[4], and the half-figure at Chiusi of a goddess or deified mortal[5], a powerful work, curiously modern in feeling, in which the cubic build, the heavy plaits and the fervour of the crossed hands suggest comparison with some Madonna by Epstein.

So intimate was the connection between the dead and his urn, so strong the anthropomorphic instinct, that the whole cinerary recipient might be transformed into a statue. To this class belong two interesting male effigies in the British Museum, one with a removable head for the insertion of the ashes[6] and the other seated in the round-backed chair familiar from Etruscan tombs[7]. These bearded aristocrats might be the elder brothers of our Chiusine *Condottiere*, not unworthy to rank as portraits of ancient Villanovan rulers or their immediate descendants.

During the later part of the fifth century and most of the fourth Etruscan art ceased to be creative, owing probably to the political depression brought about by the unequal contest with Rome. Towards the close of the fourth century, however, a new spirit was stirring, due to the influence which Rome, now mistress of Etruria, was beginning to exert upon its culture. The portraits of the

---

[1] Volume of Plates iv, 36, *b*.　　　[2] *Ib*. 36, *c*.　　　[3] *Ib*. 38, *a*.
[4] L. Milani, *Museo archeologico di Firenze*, ii, plate 76.
[5] Volume of Plates iv, 38, *b*.　　　[6] *Ib*. 38, *c*.　　　[7] *Ib*. 38, *d*.

sarcophagi and urns of the third and second centuries B.C. provide excellent material for the study of this new phase.

The figure on the Chiusine sarcophagus now in Florence, called, out of compliment to Catullus, the *obesus Etruscus*, is a remarkable study of a man overtaken in middle life by a monstrous corpulence[1]. There is poignant, if unintentional, irony in the rendering of the flabby paunch, the shapeless waist, the inert right arm, too fat and heavy to detach itself from the body. The execution is summary and without much detail; a finer finish, a greater care expended on realistic features, might have made the whole work repulsive or turned it into caricature; as it is, the discreet handling invests this mountain of flesh with a certain dignity; the artist finds in the subject an outlet for the *humanitas*, for the interest in the individual which survives as a distinguishing trait of Roman art.

The female counterpart of the Florentine *obesus* may be seen in the 'Seianti Hanunia wife of Tlesna' from Caere, now in the British Museum, and in the *Larthia Seianti*, from Chiusi, in Florence—both datable to about 150 B.C. Were it not for the Etruscan inscriptions these might be the portraits of Roman ladies of rank. Both recline with nonchalant grace, lazily raising themselves upon a cushion to gaze into their mirror with a seriousness which indicates that, according to Etruscan lore, the mirror also reveals the secrets of the future life—a theme taken up by the rosettes of the sarcophagus, symbolic of the flowers of resurrection. The connection with Rome of this later Chiusine portraiture is evident from the likeness of the head of the *obesus* to the portrait, now in the Vatican, found in the Tomb of the Scipios, and from the striking similarity which the head of a middle-aged man with striated hair and well-defined facial planes from a Chiusine sarcophagus offers to certain portraits of Augustus, including the one which was discovered at Chiusi itself[2].

By the side of the Roman strain we may notice a more distinctly Hellenistic one in the graceful figure of *Larth Sentinate Caesa* found in the recently opened tomb of the *Pellegrina* near Chiusi[3]. Scopadic influence is claimed for the head, and rightly; but it is only necessary to look at it closely to perceive that the forms have been transposed to the key of Italic naturalism; the softer Italic note, so marked in Campanian art (p. 823), is more apparent here than the austerer Etruscan or Roman.

The ash-chests peculiar to Volterra, a quaint compromise

---

[1] Volume of Plates iv, 40, *a*.   [2] *Ib.* 44, *a, b*.
[3] *Ib.* 40, *b*.

between urn and sarcophagus, upon which the effigies of the dead, made too big for the lid, were squeezed as on to a bed of Procrustes, afford further interesting examples of the portraiture of the second and first centuries B.C. Owing to the number of these chests—600 exist in the museum of Volterra alone—we are apt to pass by even the finer pieces in weary indifference. The best-known group is the one of a man and his wife[1] in which Italic naturalism almost becomes Roman realism. The man's wrinkled and rugged face, his stupefied look, his pendulous cheeks and tired, sunken body contrast with the alert movements and expression of his shrewish wife, who turns towards her spouse with relentless intensity. This head, unique at this early date, scarcely has its match among the many Roman portraits of ageing female autocrats; its sentiment is baroque rather than classic; in her determination not to abdicate an inch of her power the old Volterran shrew anticipates certain Italian portraits of the seventeenth century; nowhere has the contrast between decaying physical form and persistent vitality been more forcibly expressed. It must be borne in mind that the greater number of these sarcophagi being in terracotta or in the local tufaceous stone—both of them unsympathetic materials—have lost much of their beauty with their colour.

III. TRANSITION FROM ITALIC TO ROMAN POR-TRAITURE IN THE LAST CENTURIES OF THE REPUBLIC

Etrusco-Italic portraiture is not limited to urns and sarcophagi: many interesting and attractive pieces may be looked upon as genuine portraits of the living. Conspicuous among these is the bronze head of a young boy, long known as a treasure of the Museo Archeologico in Florence[2] in which, as has been pointed out[3], the transition from boy to adolescent is expressed with the same understanding as in the boys of Donatello or Luca della Robbia. The long meshes of hair are rendered by groovings, as usual in Italic art; 'the simple naturalism of the forms and the candid expression suit the childish face, which nevertheless exhibits, beneath its external softness, a strong almost masculine structure of the brow, cheek-bones and jaw.' With this masterpiece

---

[1] Volume of Plates iv, 40, *c*. [2] *Ib.* 42, *a*.
[3] By G. Kaschnitz-Weinberg, *Studien zur Etruskischen und Frührömischen Porträtkunst*, Röm. Mitt. XLI, 1926, p. 137.

may be connected a bronze head of great beauty in the British Museum, of a young man wearing the Etruscan *tutulus* or cap[1].

Many portrait heads occur among votive terracottas such as the head of a girl in the Museo Gregoriano[2], which has all the simplicity and grace which we shall find again in the women of Campanian wall-paintings. Other examples are the head of a young man in Munich[3]; a similar head in the British Museum, which in spite of its beauty and finish has so far escaped attention[4]; and the well-known Boston head of an elderly man[5], possibly the finest of the group. So intensely lifelike are the majority of these that we must imagine them to have been rapidly worked in clay from the living model.

Closely connected with the Italic group are two heads, one in hard limestone from Praeneste, now in Berlin[6], of an elderly man with a high, pear-shaped skull and long wavy wisps of thin hair; the other a bronze head from Fiesole in the Louvre[7], which resembles the Praenestine example in the treatment of hair and features, though the outline is fuller and firmer to suit the more youthful subject. These are examples of naturalism untouched as yet by Greek idealism or by the Roman insistence upon detail.

On the other hand there is a strong tendency towards Roman 'realism,' mixed with an Etruscan element which recalls the Florence boy, in the celebrated bronze of the Museo dei Conservatori once supposed to be a portrait of the elder Brutus[8] and a work of the late Republic or the early Empire. But the rigid three-dimensional construction, the long, lanky hair, pointed at the tips, the intensity of the gaze, the sharply set-off planes of the face and the tightly-closed lips, point to an earlier date. The type of statue to which the head belonged is unknown, though an equestrian figure has been surmised; the identity of the personage is equally uncertain, but it might, as formerly supposed, be an imaginary portrait of the elder Brutus, put up at a time when the historic spirit was stirring and the Romans were beginning to honour the memory of their great men. It might in fact be the translation into bronze of an ancestral *imago* set up by the descendants; there can be no question here of absolute transcription of a wax mask (p. 814), but the almost

---

[1] Volume of Plates iv, 48, *a*.

[2] *Ib.* 42, *b*.   [3] *Ib.* 42, *c*.   [4] *Ib.* 42, *d*.

[5] A. Hekler, *Greek and Roman Portraits*, Pls. 144, 145.

[6] Arndt-Bruckmann, *Porträts*, 73, 74; A. W. Lawrence, *Later Greek Sculpture*, Pl. 103.

[7] Volume of Plates iv, 48, *c*.   [8] *Ib.* 46.

supernatural intensity of the expression may emulate that of those life-like *imagines maiorum* so vividly described by Polybius (VI, 53). A bronze head in Paris[1] found at Bovianum Vetus in Samnium, comes close to the Brutus in style; it has the same intense gaze, tightly-closed lips and finely-modelled nose, though the harsher lines of the Paris head and the fact that it was found in the capital of Samnium incline one to see in it an example of the Samnite variety of Italic art (see p. 822). The hair on the other hand is more animated than in the Brutus, and seems to be imitated from some Polyclitan model, while the *pointillé* on cheeks and lips would seem to represent with almost unpleasant realism the nearest approach to clean shaving allowed by the ancient razor.

The famous portrait statue in Florence[2] inscribed *Aules Metilis* (Latin *Aulus Metilius*) and known from its gesture as the 'Orator' or *Arringatore* is almost entirely Roman in character. It may be dated towards the end of the second or the beginning of the first century B.C., the short toga being that of the Sullan period or of the one immediately preceding it. The folds are stiff and linear with few transitions; the concentrated expression (compare the Brutus) and the quivering lips betray a growing attention to detail due possibly to the influence of an *imago*.

The *Aules Metilis* is inscribed in Etruscan characters, but its Roman quality is further proved by its analogy to certain sepulchral effigies of the period of the Social Wars when Roman characteristics began to predominate. The *Aurelius Hermia* in the well-known *stele* of himself and his wife, in the British Museum[3], resembles the *Aules Metilis* in the furrowed face—crumpled rather than wrinkled—the shape of the skull, the movement and the cut of the toga. Only a little later—datable possibly to about 60 B.C.—comes the fine *stele* of a man and his wife from the Via Statilia, in the Museo Mussolini[4], in which the man's effigy has much in common both with the Florence bronze and with the *Hermia*, while the small eyes that peer keenly from beneath the bushy brows and the thin lips are in the Italico-Roman tradition of the Brutus. Both *stelae* offer a further interest in the curiously mixed character of the composition. Hermia—a Roman figure of Italic descent—is turned in profile towards his wife as on an Attic *stele*: on the other hand the figures of the Via Statilia relief are fully frontal, but the man's sturdy Roman bearing is in amusing contrast to the Hellenic graces of his wife, who stands in

---

[1] Volume of Plates iv, 48, *b*.   [2] *Ib.* iv, 48, *d*.   [3] *Ib.* 52, *a*.
[4] *Ib.* 52, *b*; 54 *a*, *b*.

the pose of the Greek *Pudicitia*—itself originally a grave statue. Here again we find conflicting elements, for she shows an amount of facial expressiveness rare in the female portraits of the time. The figures of a third *stele*, that of the baker *Vergilius Eurysaces* and his wife *Atistia*[1] from their tomb near the Porta Maggiore (p. 822 and p. 830), show a return to an Italic rigidity of form and outline not uncommon in the portraiture of the second half of the first century B.C.

Roman realism found another outlet in the portraiture— mainly of old men—modelled apparently with the help of a death-mask. The custom of the wax mask placed on the face of the dead to conceal the unavoidable decay during the long cere- monial lying in state, was doubtless of great antiquity, but so far no exact copies of these masks in stone or bronze are known earlier than the period of Sulla—or, according to others, of Caesar. A curious piece in Turin[2] is apparently the accurate transcription of a death-mask in which the eyes have been worked up into a sem- blance of life. Three similar portraits in Aquileia[3], Dresden[4] and Leipzig[5] are almost as startling as the Turin example in a crude realism which does not shrink even from the physical blemishes of age or death. These a Greek would have rejected as conflicting with an ideal conception, and the earlier Italics and Etruscans might have partially ignored them as unnecessary to a naturalistic portraiture based on impression rather than on searching obser- vation of characteristic detail.

A death-mask gravestone now at Ny Carlsberg inscribed with the name of C. Septumius, a magistrate (*iv vir iure dicundo*) of Vulci where the relief was found[6], shows that the new realism was not slow to spread from Rome to the provinces: the bust of the dead man is placed in just such a shrine as held the wax portraits in the *atria* of Roman houses; the frontality is absolute; the im- mobility of the features has become rigidity; the sunken cheeks, the denuded vocal chords, are shown with unflinching accuracy. From the thick folds of the *balteus* upon which the right hand rests, it is evident that the toga of Septumius is of the ampler proportions that came into fashion at the very end of the Republic. Many an in- teresting Roman portrait comes from gravestones of this type, and though not by any means always moulded from the death-mask, imi- tates its severity and the arrangement within the shrine or *armarium*. Sometimes they are isolated, at others several members of one family

---

[1] Volume of Plates iv, 52, *c*.　　[2] *Ib.* 50, *b*.　　[3] *Ib.* 50, *c*
[4] A. Hekler, *op. cit.* Pl. 138.　　[5] *Ib.* Pl. 143 (Bust of Vilonius).
[6] Volume of Plates iv, 50, *a*.

—men, women and children—appear stiffly aligned within the same frame. From the coiffure of the women on the earliest of these stones, which is that on the coins of Octavia sister of Augustus[1], they cannot be dated very much before the Principate.

Sepulchral portraiture, however, is far from affording the measure of what was achieved in the honorary and other portraits of the time of the Republic. In these, strong Hellenistic influence is undeniable—especially in the Sullan period—though it rarely affected the Roman conception of the individual. We have a fine example of this Romano-Hellenistic manner in the portrait from Tivoli in the Terme of a general of about 100 B.C.[2] Owing to the combination of an elderly face with a semi-naked body and Zeus-like drapery, the statue as a whole affects one at first sight as unpleasantly as do all the Roman combinations of a Greek ideal figure with a realistic portrait head; but the head taken alone is a masterpiece and, as such, has been claimed as Hellenistic. Hellenistic assuredly are the fine technique, the graded transitions, the absence of all angularity and the parted lips; yet at the back of these Hellenistic traits and dominating them is the purely Roman structure of the head with the accent strongly laid on the full-face view to the neglect of the profile. Like the Tivoli statue, the fine Pompey at Ny Carlsberg[3] has also been claimed as Hellenistic, and not unjustly so if we look only to the faultless technique and the fluid modulations of the surface; at the same time nothing could be more Roman than the general design, the insistence on the full-face frontal view already noted in the Tivoli statue, and the almost cruel insistence on detail: the small and anxious eyes which reveal a strain of vanity and weakness, the loose untidy hair, the nerveless flesh, the snub nose all cartilage and fat without real bony structure. In the Pompey as in the old Volterran couple noted above (p. 811) for its Roman quality, every defect asserts its right to be represented, in direct negation of the principles of Greek idealism. The contrast is evident if we compare the Tivoli and Ny Carlsberg heads with the head at Munich of about the time of Sulla[4], in which a Roman is portrayed in the Greek idealizing manner, or to the magnificent *Mithridates VI Eupator* in the Louvre[5], whose exalted expression is imitated from that of Alexander. As to the authorship of the Pompey it is

---

[1] Volume of Plates iv, 56, *k*.

[2] R. Paribeni, *Terme di Diocleziano*, No. 104. For the head alone see L. Curtius, *Die Antike*, VII, 1931, p. 240.

[3] Volume of Plates iii, 162, *c*, *d*.   [4] Hekler, *op. cit.* Pl. 135.

[5] Volume of Plates iv, 44, *c*, *d*.

difficult to pronounce an opinion. It is clearly neither purely Hellenistic nor entirely Roman; perhaps an old attribution to Pasiteles[1], an Italianized Campanian Greek who was a distinguished sculptor working mainly in Rome and of whom it is expressly said that he lived *circa Magni Pompei aetatem*, shows in what quarter we may discover the school to which the Pompey should be attributed.

The portrait of Cicero, known from somewhat commonplace copies at Apsley House, the Vatican and elsewhere[2], must likewise have been a powerful study of the individual, in style not unlike the Pompey. Of Caesar we have no contemporary portrait save on his coins, though the colossal Farnese head in Naples[3], which is perhaps Augustan, has an Italic severity of form which doubtless reproduces the character of the original and shows the reaction that took place at the time of Caesar from the softer modulations introduced by Hellenistic art. The same change affects the portraiture of women—as in the attractive head in the British Museum often called Cleopatra, though the absence of any diadem makes the identification doubtful; but it may well be a lady of her court, whose Semitic features were reproduced by a severe but not ungracious chisel during the queen's residence in Rome[4]. That the portraiture of women continued to develop individuality—in anticipation of the magnificent female portraiture of the Empire—is evident from the numerous portraits having the front hair raised in a little bun as in those of *Octavia*[5]. From the second century onward Rome was crowded with portraits, honorary statues and groups, as well as with genuine copies of Greek statues, but most of these are known only from the authors and cannot be discussed here. Further admirable examples of portraiture occur on Republican coinage[6]. The coins of Caelius Caldus and of Restio, for example, if translated into the round, might surpass any contemporary marble and bronze heads for sobriety of line and realistic intensity.

So arresting is the Roman portrait-head that one is apt to lose sight of the portrait-statue; yet, unless composed as busts, the majority of the heads we have been studying must have belonged to togate figures which are more or less uniform in type. Whereas the Greek diffuses expression throughout the body, the Roman concentrates it in the head. Hence the comparative indifference of

---

[1] W. Klein, *Vom Antiken Rokoko*, p. 173.
[2] Hekler, *op. cit.* Pl. 159.   [3] *Ib.* Pl. 157.
[4] Volume of Plates iv, 54, *c*.   [5] *Ib.* 54, *d*.   [6] *Ib.* 56.

the one to facial expression and of the other to the movements of the figure. The Roman *togatus* is often invested with a stern and impressive majesty, but the primary function of the heavily draped body is to afford life-like support and carriage for the head and with that the Roman artist is satisfied. The so-called Cicero at Naples[1] is a togate figure of Republican date in which a rigid effect is produced by sharply cut and deeply furrowed folds with the absence of plasticity common to Italic figures. This essentially Roman theme underwent further modification at the hands of Greek artists. The heavily draped *togatus* in the British Museum[2], from which the later Flavian head should be removed, and the well-known statue in the Vatican of a Roman sacrificing[3], both probably of Greek execution, show how a Greek chisel could impart a new animation and variety to the folds by introducing a suggestion of bodily form beneath the voluminous draperies. The possibilities of the togate effigy were explored throughout the last century of the Republic, though it was not until the time of Augustus that it found its full expression in the rhythmical *gravitas* of the Imperial processions of the *Ara Pacis*.

IV. ETRUSCO-ITALIC INFLUENCE IN ROMAN RELIEF AND PAINTING

The principles of Roman composition, whether in relief or in painting—and in the earlier periods the two can scarcely be dissociated—derive from Etrusco-Italic models, tempered by influences from Southern Italy and Greece. Roman relief owes as much to the carvings on Etruscan ash-chests and sarcophagi as does Roman portraiture to the figures of their lids. This is especially clear after the third century B.C. The subjects are largely drawn from Greek mythology, and as often as not the scheme is Greek, but the interrelation of the figures and the tendency to transform the background into space by bringing it into the composition are alien to the Greek conception of the background as a rigid screen against which the action is displayed two-dimensionally. The Italic method may be studied on numberless Etruscan ash-urns. One of the finest, in Florence, has been analysed for the clue it affords to the subsequent development of Roman relief[4]; it represents, in finely ordered turmoil, the Italic legend of the raid in the grove of the

---

[1] Volume of Plates iv, 58, *a*.
[2] *Ib.* 58, *b*.   [3] *Ib.* 58, *c*.
[4] By J. Sieveking, *Festschrift für P. Arndt*, p. 20, fig. 1.

Seer Cacus, who, drawn in three-quarters view, sits serene in the midst of the combatants[1]. Here figures are boldly foreshortened and made to cut diagonally into the background or to issue from its depths. This system of design, though modified for a time in Republican Rome in favour of the more orderly sequences of Greek relief, inspired the crowded compositions of the Empire and appear outside Italy in the first century B.C. on the Arch of Orange and on the tomb of the Julii at St Rémy[2]. At St Rémy especially, there is a forward movement from back to front which it would be difficult to parallel in Greek art, though secondary details may be of Hellenic importation. These Gallo-Roman and Etruscan reliefs are in strong contrast to those of the 'sarcophagus of Alexander,' or to the larger frieze of Pergamum. In the Greek examples, also, the subjects demand a crowded grouping; but in the tumultuous hunting and battle scenes of later Hellenic art the overlapping is less dense than in contemporary Italic reliefs, and the unity of the background remains intact.

Among the subjects which the Etruscans borrowed from the Greeks none proved more attractive than the expiatory slaying of the Trojan prisoners at the Tomb of Patroclus, owing doubtless to its mystical possibilities as a symbol of retribution. Three especially fine versions occur, one on a still brilliantly coloured sarcophagus at Orvieto (where the scene has its sequel in the 'Sacrifice of Polyxena' of the reverse)[3]; another on a *cista* from Praeneste in the British Museum[4], which is perhaps more Latin in spirit than Etruscan (p. 821); a third among the paintings of the François tomb at Vulci[5]. They all doubtless derive from one or more Greek originals; but the crowding up of the figures and the bold foreshortening of the seated or crouching prisoners, bear witness to the Italic striving towards the conquest of the third dimension.

It is true that the frieze-like arrangement of figures and groups in the Vulci painting has the wider spacing of its Greek prototype—but the corporeity of the figures and above all the resigned expression of the prisoners in this and other Italic versions of the myth introduce a note foreign to the Greek models. Whether on the Orvietan sarcophagus, or on the Praenestine *cista* at Vulci, they stand with the same patient resignation as the 'Christ at the Column' or the 'St Sebastian' in pictures of the Renascence.

---

[1] Volume of Plates iv, 60, a.   [2] *Ib.* 60, b.
[3] A. Della Seta, *Italia antica*, 2nd ed. 1928, p. 267, fig. 289 (after *Mon. Ant. Lincei*, 1916, tav. i–iv).
[4] Volume of Plates iv, 60, c.   [5] *Ib.* 62, a; 64, a.

This compassion, this sense of pity, spring from that interest in the individual already noted in Etrusco-Italic portraiture. We find it again in the rendering of the death-goddess Vanth, as with sorrowful expression and gesture she watches over the Trojan captives in the Vulci paintings, or as she sits in stately resignation beside the dead on his funeral couch on a sarcophagus at Florence[1], or guards a sepulchral chamber on an urn in the British Museum[2]. Some of the most impressive conceptions of the spirits of Death and Resurrection come to us from Etruria: to wit, the Michelangelesque figures that guard the entrance to the other world on a sarcophagus in the tomb of the Volumni near Perugia[3] or the Vanths that float with protecting wings above the group of a mother and child as they part from husband and father, on an ash-urn at Berlin[4]. For tenderness and religious feeling this last composition can bear comparison with the Holy Families of the Quattrocento. This same *humanitas* gives new meaning to many a subject borrowed from the Greek: such as the delightful group at the Louvre—presumably the entry of Heracles into Olympus[5], in which Athena ministers to the weary seated hero, as might an old Italian *contadina* to a worn-out fellow-worker. This is no longer the condescending pity of the Greek gods; it is the compassion of one human being for another[6]: the interest centres in the weariness of the hero, rather than in his triumphant reception among the Olympians. There could be no better instance of the transformation or rather the transmutation of a theme from an ideal to a popular key. This spirit never died out of Italian art. Under the Empire, human themes—women with their babies, fathers carrying their children shoulder-high, soldiers tending wounded comrades, and other minor episodes of camp-life— provide the necessary relief to official scenes of battle and ceremonial on columns and on arches.

Almost every subject afterwards found in Roman reliefs— triumphal or other—can be discovered in the Italic art of Etruria, or in that of Latium and Campania. A first attempt at historical painting, for instance, occurs in the François tomb at Vulci where it faced the 'Sacrifice of the Trojan prisoners' and represented episodes doubtless taken from some ancient chronicles glorifying

[1] L. Milani, *Museo archeologico di Firenze*, ii, Pl. 86.
[2] B.M. Cat. of Sculpture, vol. i, pt. ii, No. 19, fig. 35.
[3] Volume of Plates iv, 66, *a*.   [4] *Ib.* 66, *b*.   [5] *Ib.* 66, *c*.
[6] The vase picture of Achilles binding the wounds of Patroclus shows that Greek art could give unrivalled expression to such themes, but it remained indifferent to many of its possibilities.

the ancestors of the occupants of the tomb. The series begins on the left, on the return wall, with the group of *Caile Vipinas* cutting the chains of *Macstrna* (all the names are inscribed) who had been taken prisoner[1]; the three groups of the long wall show Etruscan warriors massacring their enemies; on the right, round the corner, depicted on a larger scale, and in a different style from the rest of the series, comes an Etruscan chief who grasps *Tarchu Rumach* (*i.e. Tarquinius Romanus*) by the hair, preparatory to slaying him. These wall-paintings mark the beginning of that narrative or epic style which the Romans were later to bring to perfection, though here the episodes are simply strung together, as they might be on a Greek vase, without the continuity of Roman narrative representation.

The beginnings of the 'continuous style,' involving the recurrence at intervals of the same person or persons, may, it is now thought, be traced back to the Italic art of the pre-Roman period. Dr Van Essen, for instance, detects it in a number of Etruscan urns and sarcophagi, of which a Volterran urn with its twice repeated figure of Orestes—once carrying away the *xoanon* of Artemis, and the second time approaching the temple with the *xoanon* in his arms—is a striking instance[2]. Similar tendencies towards continuous representation occur on an Esquiline fresco in Rome (p. 825), and, as Dr Van Essen again points out, on Apulian vases, on the little frieze set up at Delphi for the victories of Aemilius Paullus, which is strongly under Roman influence[3], and in the Odyssey landscapes from a house of Republican date on the Esquiline (p. 827).

A definitely historical theme appears on a Praenestine *cista* at Berlin[4] representing the triumph of a general who is the very prototype of the victorious Emperor of countless Roman reliefs. The triumph represented is assumed to be Latin, but from Latin to Roman was but a step. It must be remembered that Novios Plautios, the artist of the famous Ficoroni *cista*, expressly states that he made it at Rome (*Novios Plautios med Romai fecid*), and he and other of his colleagues may have had workshops in Rome

---

[1] Volume of Plates iv, 62, *b*; 64, *b*.

[2] Dr Van Essen has courteously permitted the present writer to quote from the MS. notes of his still unpublished lecture, in which he divides the examples of the Italic continuous style according to the three classes, Italic, Etruscan and Roman. The Volterra urn is given by Robert, *Archäolog. Hermeneutik*, Fig. 219.

[3] S. Reinach, *Répert. reliefs grecs et romains*, i, p. 118.

[4] Volume of Plates iv, 68, *a*.

and drawn inspiration from Roman subjects. Comic or humorous episodes, Latin perhaps rather than Etruscan, are common in Praenestine *cistae* and mirrors. The Silenus of the Ficoroni *cista* drumming on his paunch, in droll imitation of the movements of one of the Dioscuri who is exercising himself at punch-ball near by[1], is an example of the same homely fun that often enlivens Latin terracottas. Whatever the exact meaning of the Greek original from which the familiar groups of Satyr and Maenad are imitated, there is no doubt that the drollness of the Satyr and the coy reticence of the Maenad in the versions from Satricum are purely Italic in spirit[2].

To the same category belong the domestic scenes which make a first appearance in Etruscan tomb-paintings after the fourth century B.C. and pass later into Roman art; one of the paintings of the Tomba Golini at Orvieto, of which there are good copies in Florence, introduces us to the kitchen, the larder and the pantry, where the 'heavenly banquet' is being prepared by the very human agencies of the cook, the butler, and their assistants[3], the purpose of the painting evidently being to secure to the dead the same excellent food and good service which they enjoyed in life. The whole is treated with indescribable freshness and humour; see the energy with which a young slave scrubs the kitchen table, or possibly kneads flour for the pastry, to the rhythmic accompaniment of the flutes. Behind the flute-player a woman is busy at a side-board well laden with dishes ready for the table. At other side-boards servants are displaying a well polished dinner service, handsome drinking vessels, elegant candelabra in which candles are already burning, all having probably been brought out for the occasion from the family plate chest. A man is seen chopping wood, and there is much activity in the kitchen, where one stokes the range and others stir the meat and the soup in the saucepans. These cooking operations, the hurrying servants, the well-stocked larder in which hang poultry, venison and beef, are already in a purely Plautine mood and bring to mind the speech of the parasite Ergasilus in the *Captivi* as he bustles about making the preparations entrusted to him for the coming banquet:

So he's gone off and left all the catering to me. My God, now for some executions! Off with his head! Bacon's doom is sealed, and ham's last hour has come. Trouble for tripe and peril for pork. No time now to mention every item that goes to replenish the belly. I must be off to the courts to sentence bacon and help through hams that are still hanging in the balance.

Plautus, *Captivi*, 901–8.

---

[1] Volume of Plates iv, 68, *b*.   [2] *Ib.* 68, *c*.   [3] *Ib.* 70.

In Rome similar subjects occur on the tomb of the baker and contractor Vergilius Eurysaces outside the Porta Maggiore of about 50 B.C. Vergilius wished to commemorate himself, his bakery and his men at their work, in the little frieze that crowns the monument. The front to which belonged the portrait stele already mentioned (p. 814) was destroyed when the tomb was incorporated within the new gate-bastion of the Aurelian wall, but on the friezes of the remaining sides we see the sifting, cleansing, and grinding of the wheat, the kneading, rolling and baking of the bread, and finally the delivery and weighing of the loaves in the presence of the magistrates who employed Vergilius as contractor[1].

V. OSCO-CAMPANIAN INFLUENCES IN ROMAN ART

During the second half of the fourth century B.C. the slow advance of Rome's policy brought her into close connection with Campania (vol. VII, pp. 584 *sqq.*). Here the Sabellian peoples of the high Apennines had descended a century before on a civilization that was in part Greek, in part Etruscan, and had rapidly developed an art which may claim to be national in character. The spread and depth of this Osco-Samnite culture it is hard to assess, for apart from the excavations of Pompeii and the more recent ones of Herculaneum and Cumae, there are as yet few archaeological data available, especially for the mountain hinterland. In this region we may hope to find evidence for the art of the Samnites who at the beginning of the third century B.C. disputed at Sentinum the mastery of Italy. Among the few objects which we have is a significant bronze statuette, in the Louvre, of a warrior in armour with holes in his helmet for the high Samnite plumes and crest[2], a bronze breast-plate, adorned with three bosses, a bronze belt, leather apron and greaves. This is the evident ancestor of those Samnite or Oscan knights of the fourth century painted in Capuan tomb-chambers. The attachments of the arms are crudely naïve, but the figure stands firmly on its large flat feet, and the boorish expression of the warrior-peasant, called upon to relinquish the plough for the sword, is admirably rendered. The bronze head from Bovianum Vetus has been mentioned as an Italic work of the third century whose harsh structure may be due to a Samnite origin though expression, hair, and rendering of flesh betray Hellenistic influence.

We possibly have another example of the same art in the spirited equestrian statuette in the British Museum found at

---

[1] Volume of Plates iv, 72.   [2] *Ib.* 74, *a.*

Grumentum in South Lucania[1]. This may be the distant imitation of an archaic Greek model—but the steed's bovine hindquarters suggest the art of a people more familiar with cattle than with horses. On the other hand, the rider sits with easy balance, his body is well modelled and his hair, which flows down his back in V-shape, is treated with the same draughtsman-like precision as the fore- and sidelocks of the horse's mane. The high crest of the helmet is missing, but the whole accoutrement again recalls the Osco-Campanian knights.

A good notion of later Samnite art as it flourished in Campania can be gathered from a small group of sepulchral paintings ranging from the fifth to the third centuries. Though shockingly mutilated, they afford evidence only second in value to the Etruscan for the history of painting in pre-Roman Italy[2]. One of the earliest of these paintings, representing a dead woman enthroned as Persephone, has long been known for its stately beauty and its vigorous draughtsmanship[3]. No less attractive is a somewhat later picture at Naples, from Cumae, almost Chinese in its delicacy, where the 'Lady of the Pomegranates' is seen approached by a young girl bearing a basketful of the same golden fruit[4]. Here the artist has been eminently successful in his effort to render, both in face and dress, the softness and seriousness of a typical Campanian woman[5]. That the Pompeian painters themselves owed not a little to their Osco-Samnite predecessors, is evident from the Campanian types which the painter of the now famous frieze[6] in one hall of the Villa of the Mysteries at Pompeii has substituted for the Greek originals[7].

Many South Italian terracottas have the same popular character; a girlish Athena from Pompeii, which the compiler of the Naples catalogue[8] compares to a *contadinella*, has no more in common with the idealized Greek Athenas—even when these are shown as very youthful—than have certain peasant girl Madonnas of the Renascence with the stately Theotokos of Byzantine art. A still homelier vein is apparent in a numerous class of gems long ago separated by Furtwängler as Italic from the purely Etruscan. In several instances, as he pointed out, these gems apparently reproduce votive pictures set up as thank-offerings in popular temples or pilgrim shrines. One of the most interesting[9], datable

[1] Volume of Plates iv, 74, *b*.　[2] A. Maiuri in *Historia*, 1930, p. 66 *sq.*
[3] Volume of Plates iv, 76, *a*.　[4] *Ib.* 76, *b*.　[5] Maiuri, *op. cit.* p. 67.
[6] Volume of Plates iv, 76, *c, d*.　[7] A. Maiuri, *Villa dei Misteri*, p. 171.
[8] A. Levi, *Terrecotte figurate del Museo di Napoli*, No. 818, fig. 141.
[9] Volume of Plates iv, 56, *e*.

to the third century B.C., is thought to copy a picture dedicated
by some grateful devotee who had successfully passed through
the traditional test of virginity imposed upon girls in the ancient
temple of Juno at Lanuvium. The fulness of the forms is
Campanian, the heaping up of details Italic.

The splendid Samnite horseman at Capua—originally, no
doubt, part of a procession of young knights—who proudly sits
his spirited stallion, is a fine example of Oscan painting of the
fourth or early third century[1]. His gold helmet has a red crest,
black horse-hair tail, and two white upstanding aigrettes, one at
each side—an adornment also given to the horse above its golden
frontlet—and all details of armour and harness are picked out
in vivid colour. The same accoutrement appears in a painting of
somewhat later date from Paestum, now at Naples, representing
the 'Homecoming of the Warriors[2],' but of similar style. Another
picture less well known is that of a groom at the head of his horse[3].
The motive of a knight plunging forward, often found on
Roman gems, possibly originated in Campanian art[4]. It is familiar
on Roman lamps and was adopted about the time of Sulla for
the Mettius Curtius leaping into the chasm, on the slab of the
Museo Mussolini[5], that once adorned a balustrade round the
lacus Curtius in the Forum. The drawing is faulty in the extreme,
but the movement of horse and horseman is full of vigour; the
marshy region of the *lacus* is picturesquely indicated by tall waving
reeds; like the Italic gem, the slab strikes a romantic note.

A fragment in the Museum of Capua[6] showing two gladiators
attacking one another with fury, in spite of their grievous wounds,
is important for the genesis of similar themes among the Romans.
We can trace the influence of these pictures in the Roman Gladiator relief now at Munich (p. 830), and it reappeared in a debased
form in the poster art announcing gladiatorial shows, which
aroused the enthusiasm of Horace's servant (*Sat.* II, 7, 96).

A scientific exploration of Central and Southern Italy would
probably reveal the fact that every region had its local school of
painting. At Ruvo in Apulia, for instance, where a magnificent
example of vase-painting in the Greek style was discovered in the
Talos Vase, we also find tomb-paintings in the Osco-Samnite style,
such as the delightful group of dancing women now in the
Museum of Naples[7].

[1] Volume of Plates iv, 78, *a*.   [2] *Ib.* 78, *c*.   [3] *Ib.* 78, *b*.
[4] Cf. P. Couissin in *Rev. Arch.* 1930, p. 265, p. 269, p. 278.
[5] Volume of Plates iv, 80, *a*.   [6] *Ib.* 80, *b*.
[7] *Ib.* 80, *c*.

By the first half of the third century Campania, with all its artistic treasures, had finally come under the dominion of the Romans, who found here a fresh, vital source of inspiration, not inferior to that of Etruria or Latium. The strong Osco-Samnite strain which permeates her art in the later Republican period shows that Rome had not been slow to avail herself of the advantages accruing to her from her new position as capital of Italy. The foundations of a national Roman art were now definitely laid.

VI. ROMAN PAINTING AND RELIEF TO THE CLOSE OF THE REPUBLIC

One of its first manifestations was in those 'triumphal' panel pictures, which were amongst the earliest recorded paintings in Rome. They were put up in public places by victorious generals in commemoration of successful campaigns, and afterwards dedicated in the temples as *ex-votos*. The pictures of their campaigns exhibited in 263 B.C. by M'. Valerius Maximus Messalla outside the Senate House, and by L. Hostilius Mancinus in the Forum after the fall of Carthage, are classic examples. The panels were of much the same character as the pictures and groups carried in triumphal procession, and like these they were a commentary on reality rather than an artistic endeavour[1]. We fortunately possess a copy of a picture of this type in the fresco in the Museo Mussolini, which comes from a chamber tomb on the Esquiline[2] datable to the end of the third century B.C. The varied incidents of a campaign are arranged in superposed bands; the fore-shortenings, the lively movements, the varied gestures, the animated battle scene, exhibit a blend of Etruscan and Samnite influence, which recalls both the François tomb warriors and the knights of Capua. The parley between the commanders, twice repeated, marks the first appearance of the 'continuous' style on a Roman monument, and the group of soldiers disposed in serried tiers on the second frieze, in the manner familiar from later Roman reliefs, possibly derives from Etruria[3]. On an ash-chest in the British Museum, for instance, the mounted knights who take part in a funeral procession are similarly arranged. Picturesque details were doubtless introduced; but of these there only remains the fortress along whose battlements two sentinels are pacing.

[1] P. Marconi, *La Pittura dei Romani*, p. 11.
[2] Volume of Plates iv, 82, *a*.
[3] B.M. Cat. Sculp. i, 11, No. D. 69, fig. 89.

From the time of the Samnite wars whole legions of painters settled in Rome, and Livy and other literary sources bear witness to the numbers of pictures in the temples and buildings of the city, but of all this few visible records remain. We are fortunate, however, in the recovery of the wall-paintings of the podium-façade of the Tomb of the Scipios (p. 834), which have only quite recently been brought to light. The subjects, nearly obliterated by time and damp, are no longer clear, though from the best preserved parts[1] it is evident that soldiers and parleys were represented, as in the Esquiline fragment. The costumes—a tunic of pinkish-red and white stripes, a yellow sash and high black boots—are mystifying and we can point to no parallel. What colour remains is still singularly vivid and shows that the façades of tombs, and presumably also of houses, were as brilliantly adorned with paintings in Republican Rome as in Pompeii.

From a columbarium tomb on the Esquiline, which may be set in the second half of the first century, we have a long frieze representing episodes from the legendary history of Rome (battle between Latins and Rutuli, building of Lavinium and of Alba Longa, story of Rhea Silvia and Exposure of the Twins), which ran above the niches for the urns[2]. The figures, with their somewhat elongated limbs resemble those on the Tomb of the Baker (p. 830). The method of composition is that of the older Esquiline fresco; but picturesque detail has now expanded into landscape: foreground and distant scenery having become an integral part of the composition so that the figures would lose their significance if dissociated from their setting. Landscape painting, however, only found its true scope in the prospect and vista pictures of the architectural style of wall-decoration.

Wall-painting has long been reckoned among the great achievements of Roman art. In its earliest phase, an example of which occurs in Italy as early as in the François Tomb at Vulci[3], the marble revetments fashionable in the Hellenistic East were simply imitated in paint. Therefore, in a sense, the origin of this style of decoration may be claimed for Greece; but it was left to Roman artists to exploit the discovery throughout a succession of phases that lead up from the early, severe imitation of marble panellings to the architectural triumphs of the second style. In this phase, which alone concerns us here, the wall-surface was broken up by painted architectural frame-work intended to pro-

---

[1] Volume of Plates iv, 82, *b*.   [2] *Ib.* 82, *c*.

[3] See A. V. Gerkan in F. Messerschmidt, *Nekropole von Vulci*, p. 80 *sq.* and fig. 69; cf. p. 113.

duce the illusion of extra space: a dark line painted along the bottom of the wall was made to appear as a continuation of the floor; above this line was painted a podium supporting a wall, above which again ran a frieze; pedestals, sustaining columns that carried an architrave, projected boldly from the podium. The aim was to enlarge the room by letting the actual wall appear indefinitely recessed by means of the architectural members painted in front of it. This earlier phase of the second style appears in Rome in a room of approximately Sullan date under the *lararium* of the Flavian palace on the Palatine[1]. The hall in the Villa of the Mysteries at Pompeii is another more famous example, also of Sullan date or very little later. The principle here is identical with that of the Palatine room, *i.e.* the enlargement of the actual space is from within—but a new, purely human motive is introduced in the long scene of the Mysteries, which, taken from some Greek model and originally doubtless historical and descriptive in intention, is here introduced in such a manner as to appear to be a living ceremony within the hall.

In the later architectural style, openings were imitated, first in the frieze, then in the panels, to disclose whole landscapes, enlivened as a rule by figures, and conceived not as isolated pictures but as representing the open country outside and beyond the wall. In one room from the house of Republican date discovered in 1848 on the Esquiline, the frieze—now in the Vatican—was treated as a clerestory disclosing between the pillars a 'continuous' landscape, within which are depicted the adventures of Odysseus (Laestrygones, isle of Circe, mouth of the underworld, punishment of the damned, etc.). To arrange different episodes—whether from the same story or not is immaterial—against a landscape background made to appear continuous is a novel and thoroughly Roman idea, though the actual scenes may very well be borrowed from Hellenistic art (vol. viii, p. 700[2]).

This more advanced manner may be further illustrated from wall-paintings in the Terme Museum, from the house by the Farnesina. Among the best—and nearly all are of the first order—may be cited the frieze with landscapes and seascapes in the beautiful 'Room of the Caryatids,' or the vista pictures on the wall of the principal bedroom, disclosing a Dionysiac precinct, outside which sits a Maenad nursing the babe Dionysus, while other priestesses look on. The so-called House of Livia on the Palatine, which may be the house of the orator Hortensius that Augustus

---

[1] Volume of Plates iv, 84, *a*.   [2] *Ib.* iii, 180.

later occupied, is decorated in the same style. Whatever the
history of the house, the mid-first century B.C. character of its
paintings can scarcely be doubted[1]. The so-called *triclinium* on the
right of the garden court, with its two simulated openings from
which we look into sacred woods and glades, is peculiarly characteristic; so, too, is the central room of the three on the principal
side of the court, with its vista pictures in which Greek subjects
(Galatea and Polyphemus and Hermes and Io) are used, as in
the Odyssey frieze, to animate the landscape by defining planes
and distances. The simulated three-fold division of the right wall
is effected by a portico of Corinthian columns supported on bases
projecting from a high podium. The same divisions reappear in
the beautiful 'white room' where great swags of fruit and foliage
are suspended between the imitation columns to enhance the
suggestion of real space between these and the wall. Above runs
a delightful landscape frieze composed in the continuous style
and carried out in yellow monochrome[2].

In spite of the close connection between the two arts, Roman
sculpture in relief was slower to develop than painting. Its
triumphs were not till the Imperial arches and columns of the
second century A.D. The Italic passion for space and depth revealed
in the reliefs of Etruscan urns had passed north and found expression in the monuments of Southern Gaul (p. 818), before it
asserted itself in the City. Towards the close of the second century
B.C., when relief makes its first appearance in the monuments of
Rome, strong Hellenistic influences were in the air. This is at once
obvious in the friezes from an altar said to belong to the temple
of Neptune *in circo Flaminio*. On the principal slab, now in the
Louvre, a sacrifice to Mars is represented[3], while the remaining
three slabs, now in Munich, are decorated in honour of the temple
divinity with the *thiasos* of Poseidon and Amphitrite[4]. It has
recently been pointed out that the main scene is of a *lustrum* after
a *census*, and should probably be connected with Cn. Domitius
Ahenobarbus, who had been censor in 115 B.C., and whose family

---

[1] If the house really is that of Hortensius, who died in 50 B.C., this would
afford a further proof for the date of its pictures. Recently, however, the
whole question of the House of Livia has been reopened by Professor Bartoli's
discovery under the small Flavian palace of an earlier palace which he holds
may be that of Augustus, with its temple of Vesta and other appurtenances
(see *Not. Scav.* 1929, pp. 1 *sqq.*).

[2] Volume of Plates iv, 84, *b*.

[3] *Ib.* 86, *a, b, c*.   [4] *Ib.* 86, *d*.

had been patrons or devotees of the temple[1]. This dating is confirmed by the Hellenistic character of the technique and by the
fact that the civilians wear the same short, early toga noted in
the *Aules Metilis* and the *Aurelius Hermia*. It also explains the
hybrid art of the monument—the curious juxtaposition it offers
of a Roman official scene with a Greek mythical subject, and its
odd mixture of Italic and late Hellenistic elements. In the *thiasos*,
the artist, in imitation of Greek models, allows no detail of the
composition either to project beyond the front plane or to cut
into the background. Yet this Roman attempt to treat a Greek
subject in a Greek manner remains cold and unimpressive, owing
to the deadness of the ground and the harsh silhouetting of the
figures against it. In the lustral sacrifice in honour of Mars, on
the other hand, we have a less monotonous sequence and the
background is transformed into space around the figures, which
are drawn with an Italic feeling for both mass and depth, though
many of the motives are of Hellenistic derivation. Technically the
relief is poor; the outline is lacking in sharpness, the forms heavy
and dull—characteristics which have recently been shown to per-
tain to this period of Hellenistic art in Greece as well as in Italy,
and to have affected architecture as well as sculpture[2]. It is difficult
to decide whether the work as a whole is that of a Roman,
endeavouring, not altogether successfully, to work in the Greek
manner, or of a Greek who has fallen under Roman influence. The
same method of composition and disagreeable technique, the same
conflict between Greek and Roman principles, reappear on a frieze
from a capital or statue base in the Villa Borghese, showing a scene
recently re-interpreted as a Sacrifice to Hercules Victor[3], while as
further proof of the mingling of Greek and Roman features
about the time of Sulla, we may recall the stele of Aurelius Hermia
and his wife, facing one another like figures on a Greek sepulchral
relief[4].

   Little by little the Italic element tends to suppress the Hellenistic—or else a compromise is effected between the two. A modest
little frieze belonging to a circular altar or more probably to a base
supporting a trophy, now to be seen in the vestibule of the Cathedral of Civita Castellana, brings us near to the period of Caesar[5]
and shows a return to the sharp crisp outlines of Etruscan relief.
It represents a bearded general (Aeneas or Romulus) offering liba-
tion in presence of a triad of divinities—Venus Genetrix between

---

[1] See Goethert, *op. cit.* pp. 7 *sqq.*   [2] *Ib.* p. 31.
[3] Volume of Plates iv, 88   [4] *Ib.* 52, *a.*   [5] *Ib.* 90, *b, c.*

Mars (?) and Vulcan. The spacing of the figures is Hellenistic, but the Italic tradition is evident in the attempts at fore-shortenings and in the manner in which various details are so drawn as to appear to penetrate the background and to bring it into the composition.

A fragment at Munich[1] which though found in the north of Italy is Roman in spirit brings us to the Caesarian period. It represents a gladiatorial scene—possibly part of a frieze: on the left are two trumpeters (note the bold action of the arms, and the trumpets which, held vigorously aloft, cut into the cornice in Italic fashion); on the right two armed gladiators, one of whom, drawn and modelled with the vigour of Mantegna, is seen in three-quarters view from the back, recalling the foreshortened figures of the Trojan prisoners in the Italic versions of the Sacrifice at the Tomb of Achilles (p. 818). As in the Domitius relief, the effort is made to suggest space behind and beyond. It is needless to multiply examples, we will only quote in conclusion the little friezes that adorn the Tomb of the Baker, likewise probably of Caesarian date (p. 826). The slender limbs of the men and their long strides have already been noticed as connecting these friezes with the contemporary paintings from a tomb on the Esquiline (p. 826). In the friezes, as in the Gladiator slab, relief was gradually reverting to the Italic tradition; it only needed the stimulus of the Imperial *res gestae* to bring out the full force of its native elements.

VII. ARCHITECTURE AND TOWN PLANNING

The origins of Roman architecture, like those of Roman art, must be looked for in the earliest Italic culture, among the peoples of the Neolithic and Chalcolithic settlements and those of the *terremare* (vol. VII, pp. 333 *sqq.*). From the round and other huts of the Neolithic peoples were evolved in time the circular structures so characteristic of Rome; in the Chalcolithic period we find the first settlements arranged on regular plan (*cf.* Remedello near Brescia), which were developed by the people of the *terremare* into the axial and rectangular schemes (with trapezoidal variations) afterwards adopted for cities and camps[2]. To this period also may be traced back the *templum* marked off by augural lines, the high podium, and the saddle roof with high pediments. It would take too long to follow out in detail the process by which these rudiments were gradually elaborated into the architecture of

[1] Volume of Plates iv, 90, *a*.   [2] See Plan 1, facing p. 829.

ancient Italy and Rome. For our purpose it is sufficient to concentrate attention upon Rome, where various strata of the old Republican city are being daily laid bare in the course of modern building operations. Phenomena outside the city need only be touched upon here in so far as they throw light upon Roman problems.

The temples first claim attention. These were of the well-ascertained Italic type, as modified by the Etruscans. They differed from the Hellenic in having a high podium in place of a stepped stylobate, in the greater depth of the vestibule, often equal in size to the broad cella, in the absence of a second vestibule at the back, and in the steep pitch of the saddle roof which, resting on *columen* or tie-beam, and on *mutuli* or side-beams, projected beyond the columns like a balcony and was left open[1]. These differences were fundamental. The podium, though lowered in time, remained a constant feature of Italico-Roman architecture; together with the steep roof, it contributed to heighten the structure in accordance with the Roman principle of verticalism, which is in marked contrast to the Greek predilection for horizontal lines. Moreover, since the podium only admitted of steps in the front, and the back had neither vestibule nor pedimental projection, it followed that both architectural and decorative emphasis was laid on the façade, which thus became a dominant feature and imposed a symmetrical arrangement of buildings in relation to itself. A good example of third-century date is afforded by Gabii, where the temple stands in the centre of a cloistered precinct, axially to this and to the theatre immediately below[2]. A further stage was reached when the temple was pushed against the rear wall of the court as in most of the Imperial *fora*; by this device space was gained and the temple front made still more dominant. In time the temple was yet further recessed so that only the façade remained flush with the rear wall of the court, an arrangement typical of Roman-Syrian temples (Baalbek) and of Christian basilicas, and which attained its perfected form in the seventeenth century in the piazza of St Peter's.

In the earliest stages only the foundations of temples appear to have been of stone, the walls being of sun-dried brick, the columns and the whole superstructure of wood. All this woodwork was cased in terracotta slabs, picked out in contrasting colours of black and white, or red and blue. Friezes and tile-ends

[1] Volume of Plates iv, 94, *a*.   [2] See Plan 2, facing p. 829.

were decorated with conventional patterns or with figures; the *columen* and *mutuli* were faced with slabs representing groups of divinities or of warriors; while tall floral acroteria, whose place might be taken by figures or groups, rose above the apex and the angles of the pediment.

The temple of Juppiter on the Capitol, part of the podium and substructures of which are now visible in the Museo Mussolini, was strictly Italic in character[1]. It was almost square and rose on a high platform which, according to recent investigations, measured 60 × 55 m., corresponding roughly to the 200 ft. square (Greek) given by Dionysius of Halicarnassus. These imposing dimensions suggest that the Rome of the Tarquins shared to some extent the culture and splendour attributed to the age of the Tyrants[2]. Nor was the Roman temple of Juppiter unique in this respect; and the recently excavated temple (of Juno?) at Ardea has been found to be approximately of the same size[3]. The great breadth of the cella of the Capitoline and of other Etrusco-Italic temples is due to their being tripartite in order to lodge a divine Triad. Others are the temple of Ceres, Liber and Libera at the north foot of the Aventine, not far from the Circus Maximus, a temple at Marzabotto near Bologna, the Capitolium of Veii[4], where the three cellae are clear on the ground plan, and the Capitolium of Signia in Latium, on its high podium.

The older type of wooden column was soon replaced by columns of peperino or later of travertine, no longer cased in terracotta but stuccoed, the decoration of the superstructure remaining of terracotta, as appears from various fragments of tile-ends in the shape of satyr-masks and other fantastic heads found here and there in Rome. The temple of Ceres, Liber and Libera, though Italic in shape and tripartite, as suited a Triad, was, it is said, decorated in a new style by two Greek artists, Damophilus and Gorgasus, who probably came from Southern Italy. This decoration was still of terracotta, and the innovation may have consisted in the introduction of a less heavy manner of modelling, offering the same hellenizing variations from the older Etrusco-Italic style as may be noted in the terracottas of Campania or in those of Latin Satricum. This change would explain Varro's dictum that before this 'everything in temples had been Etruscan[5].'

[1] Volume of Plates iv, 92, *a*.
[2] For the latest plan see Paribeni in *Not. Scav.* 1921, pp. 38 *sqq.*; Platner and Ashby, *Top. Dict.* s.v.   [3] *Ib.* 92, *b, c.*
[4] *I.e.* the so-called temple of Apollo; but see T. Ashby in *The Year's Work in Classical Studies*, 1930, p. 117.   [5] *ap.* Pliny, *N.H.* xxxv, 154.

Round buildings, derived from the round huts of the Neolithic peoples, were largely adopted for the habitations of the dead (cf. Etruscan *tumuli*) and for cults of great antiquity, such as those of Vesta and of the Latin Hercules. The tugurium Vestae in the Forum kept its circular plan throughout all later transformations and embellishments[1]; Hercules had round temples in the Forum Boarium, another near the Circus Flaminius, and a third in the Porticus Philippi. The high antiquity and venerable traditions attaching to round tombs are emphasized in the magnificent revival of the type in late Republican Rome; the shape, sanctified by religion, outlived every fashion and was given by Augustus to his family Mausoleum and by Hadrian to his own tomb and to the Pantheon.

Very little is known of the appearance of the city between the fifth century and the time of the Punic Wars and our knowledge of Republican architecture may be said to begin with the third century. The recent clearance of a group of four temples in what was once an enclosed area or sacred precinct east of the theatre of Pompey (modern Largo Argentina)[2] has given us a starting point of importance. The second temple from the south, which is the most ancient of the four, is not yet satisfactorily identified. It was of tufa originally coated with stucco, and has a high archaic podium and a cella of pure Italic type without vestibule or columns at the back. North of this archaic temple is a well-preserved circular podium of concrete which supports sixteen columns of tufa: from its shape and its locality possibly the temple of Hercules Custos, so called from its being near the entrance to the Circus Flaminius[3]. It was celebrated by Ovid:

> Si titulum quaeris:...Sulla probavit opus,
>
> *(Fasti,* vi, 209, 212.)

Sulla having presumably restored it. Its rectangular porch and steps, with traces of an altar, has an exact resemblance to that of the round temple of Hercules Musarum in the Porticus Philippi as we now know it from a newly identified fragment of the *Forma Urbis*[4]. The likeness to the porch of the Pantheon is evident. The northernmost temple, later incorporated into the medieval church of S. Nicola de Calcarario, is datable to the third century, but is still unidentified. The first on the south which was the last to

---

[1] Volume of Plates iv, 94, *b.*   [2] *Ib.* 96, *a, b,* and Plan 3, facing p. 829.

[3] See B. Wijkström in *Eranos,* xxviii, 1930, pp. 148 *sqq.*

[4] The identification is V. Lundström's in *Undersökningar i Roms Topografi,* Svenskt Arkiv for Humanistiska Avhandlingar, ii, 1929, p. 96; cf. C. A. Boethius in *Athenaeum,* N.S. ix, 1931, p. 122.

be completely excavated, is also the latest; being of travertine, it can scarcely be earlier than the last century of the Republic. That these temples were of great sanctity is evident from the careful manner in which they were preserved throughout Imperial times. Though complete evidence is still lacking, it would seem that all four were surrounded by a *porticus* like that of Metellus.

The architectural ornament of the Argentina temples has disappeared except for two mutilated capitals; better preserved and more interesting architecturally are the three temples—two Ionic and one Doric[1]—dedicated respectively to Spes, Juno and Janus, that stood on the west of the old vegetable market. They are partly built into the church of S. Nicola in Carcere, which accounts for their unusually good preservation. Though erected at different times, the temples are axially parallel and so close together that they must have given the impression of a single structure with three cellas. All three have Italic podia, the northern one having no columns at the back and the others being, it would seem, peripteral. The architectural forms both of Doric and Ionic are somewhat heavy and clumsy, but the effect may have been helped out by the addition of details in stucco. With these Roman Republican temples may be compared the lovely temple at Gabii, the Italic podium of which is still archaic in character, though the ornamental mouldings are Hellenic in style. Characteristic of the Republican period is the small size of temples: nothing approaching in grandeur to the old Capitoline Temple was attempted until the Empire.

The Tomb of the Scipios (*Sepulchrum Scipionum*) to the left of the Via Appia is a structure of the third century B.C., only recently cleared. The sepulchral chambers, which were excavated in the rock like an Etruscan tomb, were entered from a door in the long podium already mentioned for its paintings (p. 826). Above the podium rose a façade of four columns, with statues in the inter-spaces, which masked the cliff. In spite of its Ionic volutes and Hellenistic ornament the sarcophagus of Scipio Barbatus[2], from the central niche of his family mausoleum, was as severe in structure as the tomb itself. Its Graeco-Etruscan frieze of triglyphs and rosettes derives from Etruscan models (p. 810) and recurs in the time of Sulla on the podium of the Praenestine temple[3] and on the little monument of the flute-players in the Museo Mussolini.

[1] The names have been variously assigned, the more usually adopted view being that the northern temple is that of Janus (260 B.C.), the central one that of Juno Sospita (194 B.C.), and the southernmost that of Spes (258 B.C.).
[2] Volume of Plates iv, 98, *a*. [3] *Ib.* 98, *b.*

Among the many Republican tombs in Rome, that of the Baker Vergilius Eurysaces, which is datable to about 50 B.C., deserves another mention here for its quaintly conceived podium consisting of round coupled pilasters alternating with rectangular supports[1]. The round pilasters themselves are said to be built up of corn measures, or, according to a recent theory, of mixing bowls for the dough[2]; and similar measures or bowls, neatly rimmed and turned on their sides, adorn the superstructure, which carries the charming frieze with baking operations already described (p. 822). Aeolic capitals impart a classic touch to the curious little monument.

Whoever the people were who first invented the arch, no one would deny that the Romans were the first to develop its possibilities to the utmost. Its earliest appearance in Italy is actually in Rome, where certain arches over drains in the Forum are to be attributed to the sixth century B.C.[3], thus antedating the beautiful gate of Etruscan Volterra, which belongs to the fifth century. At first arches developed along utilitarian lines, being used for drains, city gates, and later for aqueducts and bridges. A fine stretch survives of the arches of the Aqua Marcia, the aqueduct constructed in 144 B.C. by Q. Marcius Rex to bring water thirty-six miles to Rome from the Sabine mountains. Traces of the Pons Aemilius of 142 B.C., built into an arch and pier of Augustan date, are still visible in mid-stream; of the Pons Mulvius, which carried the Flaminian Way across the Tiber, and which was rebuilt in stone at the end of the second century, two ancient arches are partially extant; even earlier is the one-arched bridge on the Via Praenestina which was retained below the seven arches of the later Ponte di Nona, itself 'by far the finest road bridge in the neighbourhood of Rome[4].'

In the second century likewise the arches, honorary or triumphal, whose origin may be traced back to the ancient rites prescribed for the purification of the victorious army[5], began to exhibit those forms and systems of decoration which were brought to perfection under the Empire. Triumphal arches, to com-

[1] Volume of Plates iv, 100.
[2] The theory (not yet published) is Mr I. A. Richmond's, who has an account of the tomb in his *Walls of Rome*, pp. 12, 205, etc.
[3] T. Ashby and Spiers, *Architecture of Ancient Rome*, p. 3; cf. Platner-Ashby, *op. cit.* p. 464.
[4] T. Ashby, *The Roman Campagna in Classical Times*, p. 132.
[5] F. Noack, *Römische Triumphbogen*. (Vorträge der Bibliothek Warburg 1925–26 (1928).)

memorate victories and serving as a rule as pedestals for statues of the *triumphatores*, were put up by L. Stertinius in 196 B.C., in the Cattle Market; in 190 B.C. by Scipio on the Clivus Capitolinus; in 121 B.C. in the Forum by Q. Fabius Allobrogicus. It is an open problem when and where the system of two columns flanking an arch, known from triumphal arches and monumental gates and from the Sullan *tabularium*, was invented, though the arch itself is an old Italic form as we know from Volterra and from the later gates of *Falerii Novae*.

It is often asserted that anything like regular town-planning was impossible in Rome because of the hills[1]. This is true so far as the city as a whole is concerned; but repeated and successful efforts were made to improve one or other of the quarters of Rome and to dispose new buildings on a symmetrical plan. Already a road such as the first stretch of the Via Flaminia, the Via Lata, corresponding to the modern Corso, provided Rome as early as 220 B.C. with the backbone for a piece of town-planning still respected in every *piano regolatore*. On the west the Circus Flaminius, one of the earliest stone buildings in Rome, was the centre of a building district known as *ad circum Flaminium* and together with the precinct of the four temples (p. 833) formed the nucleus of a well-planned group on the west of the Via Lata. Another group, immediately south of the Circus, but with a different orientation, comprised the Porticus Octavia, of 163 B.C., and the Porticus Metelli, of 147 B.C. and provided Rome with still further emplacements for recreation and for the transaction of business. This western region of theatres, amphitheatres and colonnades was later matched by the chain of Imperial Fora on the east, the first of which, the Forum Caesaris, was laid out for the great Dictator in 54 B.C.

Early in the second century, however, long before the idea of fora to supplement the crowded Roman Forum had dawned, the congestion on this eastern side was relieved by the erection in 179 B.C. of a large market-place on the north-east of the Basilica Aemilia, which absorbed among others the old Fish Market, and a market dedicated to the sale of sweetmeats; the very markets,

---

[1] Good examples of Italico-Roman axial planning ranging from the fourth to the second centuries B.C. are provided by the small *castrum* (only 193 × 120 m.) of Ostia of *c.* 330 B.C., by Cosa of 273 B.C., Falerii 241 B.C., Bononia 189 B.C., Aquileia 181 B.C. That Italic axial planning developed independently and earlier than Greek seems now accepted; see D. S. Robertson, *Greek and Roman Architecture*, p. 193.

probably, whose loungers, vendors, catering parasites, and even less reputable characters are so gaily described by Plautus; like the street markets recently abolished in modern Rome, they were assuredly more picturesque than hygienic. The new Macellum itself disappeared to make way for a line of Imperial Fora; but it was doubtless the model for the Imperial market-places on the Coelian and Esquiline: a central round hall in the midst of a square enclosure lined by shops. In the years that followed the successful close of the Hannibalic War (201 B.C.), when building activity was at its height, the basilica, a new type of roofed structure, was introduced from Magna Graecia or the East. The earliest was the Basilica Porcia, erected in 184 by Cato the Elder, and followed in 179–174 B.C. by the famous Basilica Aemilia; the oldest surviving is the basilica of Pompeii which differs, however, from the accepted type in being open to the sky. Basilicas were mostly of considerable size; they were used as law courts, as halls for the transaction of business, as meeting places, as shelters from rain or sun, and eventually became a popular feature of almost every Roman city. To them also European architecture owes the principle of clerestory lighting. Another innovation of the second century was a stone theatre, the first of the kind erected in Rome, but soon pulled down again owing to the outcry raised against the introduction of Greek customs (p. 805).

Domestic architecture also flourished at this time. Besides the more patrician atrium-houses of the richer quarters of the city there is now full evidence that tenement houses, heralding the Imperial *insulae*, were erected in Rome from the end of the third century B.C.[1] They were of the type first known from Ostia and which is now being ascertained for Pompeii and elsewhere.

That the high standard of Roman architecture was acknowledged outside Italy itself as early as the beginning of the second century B.C. is evident from the fact that in 174 Antiochus IV summoned a Roman architect of the name of Cossutius to complete the Olympieum at Athens left untouched since the days of Peisistratus (see vol. VIII, p. 701).

Any discussion of building material falls outside the scope of this chapter, yet it is impossible to speak of Republican Rome of the second century without mentioning the introduction of concrete. It makes a first modest appearance in Rome between 120 and 117 B.C. for the podia of the temples of Castor and of

---

[1] C. A. Boethius, *De nya utgravningarne i Rom*; cf. A. Maiuri in *Atti del I Congresso Nazionale di Studi Romani*, I, 1929, pp. 163 *sqq.*; K. Lehmann-Hartleben in *P. W. s.v. Städtebau*, cols. 2040, 2058.

Concord—but the innovation must fairly have revolutionized building, opening out new constructional possibilities which eventually led to the audacious vaults and domes of the great edifices of the Empire.

The remarkable progress made under Sulla, great town-planner and master-builder, was due to the closer welding together of forces and principles already present in Italic architecture, rather than, as is generally stated, to new Hellenic influence. There can be no doubt that Sulla, fresh from the conquest of Greece, dreamt of creating a Rome that should vie with the great capitals of the Hellenic East, but he did not necessarily conceive of a Rome copied from these, or even of one modelled upon the same plan. Similarly, although Hellenistic forms had for a long period been slowly filtering into Rome, affecting and modifying architectural detail, there is no sign, either in Sullan or in pre-Sullan Italy, of a reversal of accepted architectural principles. The Italic element remained dominant throughout the peninsula, but a new inspiration is evident in details such as the enrichment of the Corinthian capital notable at that time. Typical of the new tendencies is the Capitoline temple of Juppiter (burnt down in 83 B.C.) as restored by Sulla; this retained its full Italic plan, but received new and high columns of Greek style—an architectural luxury hitherto unheard of. In the same way the arcaded façade of the *tabularium* towards the Forum on its high Italic podium offers us the apotheosis of the combination Roman arch and Greek pilaster.

The two temples of Sullan epoch at Cori[1] are Italic in plan, without columns at the rear; the better preserved of the two has the characteristic high pediment and broad spacing of the columns. The less well-preserved—dedicated to the Castores according to the inscription—shows Hellenic detail in its Corinthian capitals, the fashion for Corinthian having been enthusiastically adopted under Sulla, but remains strictly Italic in plan. Purely Italic, likewise, are the temples of Tivoli on their imposing podia, although much of the trimming may be Hellenistic[2]. The so-called 'Temple of Peace' at Paestum, set up by the Lucanians after the expulsion of the Greek rulers, shows a return to the Italic type with deep vestibule and no columns at the back[3]. At Pompeii the principal temples of the Sullan Colonia Pompeiana have Italic plan: the temple of Juppiter[4], though not tripartite, has the characteristic broad cella, deep vestibule, high podium and no peristyle; the

---

[1] Volume of Plates iv, 102, *a, b*.   [2] *Ib.* 102, *c*.
[3] See Plan 4, facing p. 829.   [4] Volume of Plates iv, 104, *a*.

temple of Apollo, it is true, has a peristyle, but otherwise follows the 'Etruscan' plan[1].

Nowhere does Sullan architecture show itself more magnificent than in the great pilgrimage shrines which Sulla built or restored. Of these the temple of Juppiter Anxur at Terracina, the platform of which still dominates the town from a slope of Monte S. Angelo, was perhaps the most imposing. The platform is supported by arched galleries in the characteristic Sullan *opus incertum*[2]; the temple itself, with its precinct and rest-houses for the priests, was one of the most splendid edifices of Latium, comparable with the shrine of Fortuna at Praeneste or that of Hercules at Tivoli.

The Praenestine sanctuary, in reality a kind of 'Holy city' containing a temple with all its appurtenances, was rebuilt by Sulla after the Social War. It rose in terraced slopes, covering the whole hillside as with a great baroque façade[3]. The lower principal terrace formed a long covered court whose rear wall was broken up by windows in Hellenistic style: at the one end was the oracular cave with the beautiful mosaic of the inland bay; at the other was a long hall, with domed apse identified as the temple and paved with the great mosaic of the Nile[4]. This hall is specially noteworthy for its internal architecture, consisting of a high podium which supported columns in a manner imitated in the 'second style' of Roman wall-painting. The podium[5], moreover, was adorned with a delicately carved pattern of triglyphs and rosettes already familiar from the sarcophagus of Scipio Barbatus and from Etruscan sarcophagi (p. 834).

Together with the two smaller temples above the Anio, the once celebrated Sanctuary of Hercules at Tivoli also belongs to the Sullan period: like that of Fortune at Praeneste, it consisted of a series of terraces which supported the actual temple—now embedded in the cathedral—minor shrines, offices for the 'college' in charge of the temple ritual, and the like.

Outside Rome the Sullan age left its mark not only in these famous sanctuaries and temples, but also in a multitude of villas which, though restored and altered, often lasted late into the Empire. Fine remains are to be seen at Terracina, at the neighbouring Monte Circeo, while under the Villa of Hadrian near Tivoli an original villa of the Sullan period has lately been discovered.

In Rome, Sulla, hardly more fortunate in this than Caesar,

---

[1] See A. Mau, *Pompeii*, new English ed. 1907, p. 82.
[2] See Plan 5, facing p. 829 and Volume of Plates iv, 106, *a, b*.
[3] *Ib.* 108.
[4] On its Hellenistic character see Marion E. Blake, *Mem. Amer. Ac.* viii, 1930, pp. 139 *sqq.*   [5] Volume of Plates iv, 98, *b*.

planned more than he achieved. His Capitol was completed in the consulship of Q. Catulus, who is also responsible for the *tabularium*[1] with its vault and chambers of Roman concrete and its Hellenistic arcading, which Sulla had planned to unite Capitol and Arx and also to provide the north end of the Forum with a façade. The Curia and Rostra which he remodelled and enlarged were burnt down in 52 B.C., and his further schemes for improving the Forum came to an end with his abdication.

The great work of planning the city was next taken up by Pompey, whose theatre, erected in 55 B.C., gave another splendid civic building to the Flaminian region (p. 615). Though inspired, it is said, by the Theatre of Mitylene, the ground-plan of Pompey's theatre reveals the usual Roman arrangement by which *auditorium* and stage-house are united into one building instead of being separated by wide passages as in Greece. The huge *cavea* conceived, it was said, as steps leading to a shrine of Venus, in order that another protest against a permanent theatre of stone might be averted, had a façade in three tiers of arcades, the flanking columns of which imparted to the whole edifice the coveted Hellenistic appearance. South of the stage-house opened a colonnaded portico to which spectators resorted for fresh air and which was much frequented as a promenade. Behind the colonnades were halls for the transaction of business, in one of which, large enough to accommodate a meeting of the Senate, Caesar was murdered. It is probable that Pompey, flushed with the success of his Eastern expeditions, dreamed like Sulla of a greater Rome of which his theatre was to be a leading feature; but at heart he remained Italian and Roman, and the temple which he consecrated to Hercules was built, as Vitruvius is careful to point out, in the same archaic and barycephalic or 'top-heavy' style as the temple of Ceres, Liber and Libera.

To the transition period between Pompey and Caesar may be attributed the charming Ionic temple by the Tiber—an Italic structure on high podium[2] with engaged Ionic columns simulating a Greek peristyle and with delicate mouldings carried out in stucco. Here again the decorative motives are borrowed from Greece while the structural principles are those traditional to ancient Italy. As to the celebrated round temple near by, which in its present condition can scarcely be earlier than Augustus, all that can be said is that it possibly conceals beneath its later marble casing an earlier structure, the tufa podium of which, afterwards used as core of the marble stylobate, is still visible.

[1] Volume of Plates iv, 104, *b*.   [2] *Ib.* 110.

Among the many building enterprises connected with Caesar one of the most significant was the forum called after him, by which he planned to relieve the overcrowding of the Roman Forum. It was thus the first in the series of *fora* which are among the Empire's most lasting contributions to the embellishment of the city. Recent excavation shows that the new forum was planned in Italico-Roman fashion as the court of a temple, but it marks an advance on Gabii in that the temple, according to well-considered calculation, was placed against the back wall of the precinct, though Appian[1] seems to imply that it stood out free within the enclosure. The forum itself, planned as early as 54 B.C. and begun when Caesar was still in Gaul, covered an area of some 6–7000 sq. m., about a third of which (longitudinally) was uncovered early in 1932. The enclosing wall rises to a height of 17 m.; behind it are three superimposed galleries (the upper one arched) divided into small chambers of unequal depth serving apparently as *tabernae* or offices looking on the forum. The construction, so far as at present revealed, was throughout of tufa with travertine details. In front of the shops ran a street, separated by a colonnaded portico from the inner temple precinct. The temple, vowed at Pharsalus and therefore later than the forum, still lies buried under the modern street. The capitals of two columns found fallen on the west side of the temple reveal late Flavian character. They presumably belong to a restoration necessitated by a fire or other catastrophe of which there is no record in history. The podium, however, seems to have been high, of Italic type and Caesarian date. Forum and temple were completed by Augustus but by what precise date is uncertain.

Other buildings of Caesar, such as his curia and rostra, have disappeared under later constructions, but it is interesting to note that behind the *Saepta Julia* (a building planned by Caesar but built after his death) on a site south of the later Pantheon, stood, according to recent investigations[2], that mysterious *tumulus* (or *aedes*) *Juliorum* in which the great Dictator was laid to rest by the side of his daughter Julia. Systematic excavation is making it daily more evident that the Republican City to which Caesar intended to put the finishing touch was the worthy predecessor of the 'city of marble.' Fundamental architectural principles based on the experience of centuries had been laid, and Augustus found ready to his hand and already fully developed every architectural form with which the name of Rome is indissolubly connected.

[1] *Bell. Civ.* ii, 102, 424.
[2] V. Lundström, *Undersökningar i Roms Topografi*, pp. 130 *sqq.*

CHAPTER XXI

THE DEVELOPMENT OF LAW UNDER THE REPUBLIC

I. PERIODS IN THE HISTORY OF REPUBLICAN LAW: STATE OF THE EVIDENCE

UP to the beginning of the second century B.C. the national Latin law ran a course of normal native development, but during the last century or so of the Republic it was obliged to adapt itself to the radically changed conditions of the Roman State, and to enter on a process of shedding its national archaism and of reception of ideas from subject nations which was continued under the Empire. Thus the periods in the history of law do not coincide with those of constitutional history; the fall of the Republic found private law in an early stage of its second period, during which it had ceased to be purely national and was becoming Romano-Hellenic like the civilization in which it was rooted. Though the climax of this second period, the classical age of Roman law, came under the Empire, nevertheless the middle of the last century B.C. is a convenient point from which to take stock of the essential contrast between the earlier and later periods. The decisive turn in the new direction had by then been taken, and already the main categories of juristic thought had been fixed, the fundamental institutions established, the full juristic method acquired. In comparison, the classical period of the Empire was not creative; what was left for the jurists was to elaborate and refine, to work out consequences in detail. The central point of a short sketch of Republican legal history must therefore be the most important and interesting phase of the whole of Roman legal history, namely that of the acquisition of ideas and institutions which were the germ of the subsequent development.

The state of the evidence is briefly that, while we can form fairly correct general ideas of the primitive and late Republican law, so that there can be no doubt of the wide gulf that separates them, we have to rely largely on conjecture for the intervening history. The contrast is great, but no greater than that between the conditions of the Roman State and Roman society at the same two epochs. Of the law at the end of the Republic we can obtain a general picture from Cicero, the contemporary jurists and their immediate successors; and again, the Twelve Tables were so freely quoted by grammarians and antiquarians, and so fondly appealed to by jurists, whenever appeal was possible, that however little value can be attached to the modern conventional grouping of fragments as a reconstruction of the work of the Decemvirs, it must be admitted that a fair idea of the primitive law is attainable. In this matter the technical form assumed by classical law is of much assistance, because its statement involves a constant contrast between the old civil law rules and their practical nullification by praetorian and later rules.

On the other hand, the evidence of how and when the primitive law was modified and the later law came into being is poor. That from contemporary documents, whether juristic literature or statutory texts, is insignificant, as can be seen from a glance at Bremer's *Iurisprudentia Antehadriana* or Bruns' *Fontes*. The only professed legal history that has come down to us is the long extract from Pomponius' (*aet.* Hadrian) *liber singularis enchiridii* in the Digest (*Dig.* 1, 2, 2), of which the third part (*Dig.* 1, 2, 2, 35–53), dealing with the succession of *prudentes* up to his own time, is a practically unique source. But the mistakes made in the first two parts, which we have some means of checking, together with the rhetorical colour and bad Latin of the whole extract, greatly impair its authority. The best opinion, however, accepts it as an authentic work of Pomponius, that is of one who, whatever his qualifications for writing legal history, was a jurist having access to all sorts of information denied to us, but a work which has been subjected to extremely careless 'interpolation,' taking the form chiefly of copious excision by Justinian's compilers of what must have seemed to busy practical men wholly unnecessary historical details, accompanied by gross neglect in joining the loose ends.

II. THE SOURCES OF LAW

The organs of development were custom, statute, Edict and jurisprudence. Custom requires no separate consideration, not that it is unimportant, but because, except so far as taken up by one of the other sources, it is imperceptible. Historical Roman law begins with a code, which, so far as we can judge, was a model of draftsmanship, bearing witness to a remarkable prehistoric jurisprudence: they were no novices who in the short time allowed by tradition for its preparation achieved this expression of hard practical thinking in terse, plain and painfully accurate language.

But statute stands still and life moves on. Sooner or later arises
a discord for which the two possible remedies are fresh legislation
and adjustment by doctrine and practice. In private law the
Romans chose on the whole the latter method, with the result
that the Twelve Tables stood for centuries as the basic statute, the
lex per eminentiam. But though the hard-won equality and certainty of law which it established caused the code to be cherished
as a sort of *Magna Carta* in the nature of a treaty between the
Orders, it would be an exaggeration to say that it was regarded as
the unalterable and final word of the legislature, even if the statement be confined to private law. The legislation of the assemblies,
though not abundant in this department, proves the contrary. The
real explanation of the formal endurance of the Twelve Tables is
that the necessary changes were satisfactorily carried out by other
means.

The reform of private law has never been a favourite occupation
of legislative assemblies, and therefore the fact that many of the
leges (including *plebiscita*) touching private law are attributable
to social or economic motives is perfectly natural and normal.
Though statutes so inspired do in fact modify private law, and
though technical defects of private law may in themselves constitute a grave social evil, it remains true that public opinion is
slow to demand legislative action against the *vis inertiae* of an
inherited private law, while lawyers themselves, who could best
formulate the defects and their remedies, have an instinctive dislike
of appeals to the legislature, preferring to deal with what they
regard as their own troubles in their own ways. Now when the
need to reform the primitive law had outstripped the powers of
even the liberal Roman conception of *interpretatio*, the lawyers had
in the praetor's Edict an instrument of reform which was practically as potent as statute, and far more congenial. For example,
the primitive law of damage to property was reformed by a statute
(Lex Aquilia, ? 287 B.C.), whereas that of injury to the person was
reformed by the Edict; and the explanation is that at the date of
the Lex Aquilia the praetor did not possess or did not realize his
power, whereby he later modernized the law of *iniuria*.

We have not space in which even to name the Republican
statutes on private law. Whatever may have been their motive,
their total effect was not small. The most far-reaching importance
belongs to those which concern procedure, because of the opportunities for the development of law by practice which they
created, and among these the Lex Aebutia is outstanding. Our
information as to its exact contents is very scanty, but, whatever

view is taken of them, it is common ground that its introduction of the formulary procedure between citizens marks the beginning if not of all praetorian law, at least of the grand period of the Edict. Its enactment, which may be put about 150 B.C., seems to have terminated a sudden outbreak of legislative activity; at any rate, few relevant statutes can be placed certainly later. But there is one observation which should be made before leaving the subject of statute law: what Cicero (*de legibus* III, 20, 46, 48) tells us of the carelessness with which *leges* were preserved warns us that, in considering how this or that development may have taken place, we must sometimes reckon with the possibility of forgotten legislation, so that what appears to be common law may be 'statute worn out.' Still, in view of the tenacity of the tradition of private law, a forgotten statute is likely to have been an ineffectual statute.

The two organs of development with which an outline such as this must deal are the Edict and jurisprudence. In a broad sense jurisprudence covers the whole field, because the Edict, though formally the magistrate's contribution to practice, was substantially the work of the jurists. The grand epoch of the Edict was, as has been said, under the formulary system introduced by the Lex Aebutia, and at the end of the Republic *ius praetorium* had already profoundly modified the whole law. But the scope of the pre-Aebutian Edict, or, to use a wider expression, of the powers of the magistrate under the pure system of *legis actiones*, is the most controversial question in the history of Republican law. It will be convenient, before discussing this question in connection with the development of the law in the pre-Aebutian period, to give a preliminary account of the legal profession, which can be short, since the subject is well known. The work of that profession, jurisprudence, as being always with us and as containing within itself the precipitate of all the other factors, will occupy the greater part of the chapter.

III. THE REPUBLICAN JURISTS[1]

The consent of tradition traces the origin of jurisprudence to the college of *pontifices*, which, it may be conjectured, acted as the *consilium* of the king on questions of *fas* and *ius*. But whereas

[1] The fundamental authority, freely followed here as far as it goes, is P. Jörs, *Röm. Rechtswiss. zur Zeit der Republik*, I: *Bis auf die Catonen*. Constant use has also been made of F. P. Bremer, *Iurisprudentia Antehadriana*, I.

consultation of the college in matter of *fas* is historical, the function of giving *responsa* on private law belonged in historical times to the individual *pontifex*, from whom it passed unchanged in essentials to the individual practising jurist. Pomponius (*Dig.* 1, 2, 2, 6) indeed makes a statement pointing to a more regulated institution: from the college of *pontifices* one was appointed annually *qui praeesset privatis*. Since there is no evidence that the *pontifices*, whether as individuals or as a college, ever exercised a proper jurisdiction, this must be understood to refer simply to a division of the work of consultation, an interesting symptom of the separation of *fas* and *ius*, and of the abandonment of collegiate counsel in matter of *ius*, if such counsel ever existed.

The Romans put the function of the consulting lawyer very high: no list of sources omits the *auctoritas prudentium* in one form or another. Gaius (1, 7; 4, 30) actually speaks of their authority *iura condere*, but this is a recognition[1], in an age of reflection, of practical effects, not of formal competence. The authority of the *pontifices* rested on superior knowledge, derived from oral and written collegiate tradition, and that of the later *prudentes* was an inheritance of theirs. In an age of formalism, when in order to obtain a desired sacral or legal result one had to make a literally exact use of the appropriate traditional formulary, it was but prudent to be guided by those who, possessing archives, were supposed to possess the tradition, and whose pronouncements were accepted by all as final. Formalism, in fact, was only tolerable on condition of *copia iurisconsulti*. A magistrate or a citizen having important business to transact with heaven or man would, as a matter of course, betake himself to the *indigitamenta* or *actiones*, which could only be arrived at through a *pontifex*. The *actiones*, according to earlier technical usage, covered not only the formularies of court-procedure, but also those of business transactions generally. The selection of the proper *actio* and its adaptation to the matter in hand required, besides access to the pontifical archives, knowledge of and practice in the law. Moreover, a magistrate might not exercise jurisdiction on a *dies nefastus*, and the *dies fasti* and *nefasti* could only be ascertained from the pontifical calendar.

Thus the famous pontifical monopoly was merely a *de facto* monopoly of knowledge, not unlike the familiar professional monopoly of the present day, except that the authority of a modern legal opinion rests on argument brought before the bar of an

[1] To be found also in Cicero, and in Pomponius, who probably derived it from Varro.

instructed public opinion, whereas the *responsa* of the *pontifices*, who no doubt were careful to present an unbroken front, were the oracular utterances of members of a close college of five.

A monopoly of knowledge is broken down by its divulgation. The decisive steps in the divulgation of jurisprudence were the public declaration of the law by the Twelve Tables, the publication of the *ius Flavianum* and of the calendar, and the opening of the college to plebeians by the Lex Ogulnia (300 B.C.). The Twelve Tables did not, as we shall see, supersede the traditional lore of the *pontifices*, but they introduced a new and controlling factor. Though knowledge of the old forms remained essential, and though their application became increasingly beyond the powers of a layman, yet the concrete formulations uttered by the *pontifices* had to accord with a statute which was public property, and not merely with a mass of custom the definition of which lay in their own hands. The *responsa* and the formularies prescribed by them were indeed no secret. A man who chose to collect them as given, and to take note of the decisions of the courts and of the course of the calendar, would in time provide himself with the materials which the *pontifices* still monopolized in their archives. And, since there is no reason to endow Appius Claudius with the pontificate, this is roughly the course that he and his secretary Cn. Flavius must have pursued before they published in 304 B.C. the *actiones* or precedents and the calendar (vol. VII, p. 533).

What could not be divulged so easily was the traditional technique of application and adaptation. The science that lay behind the precedents must have been unformulated, a simple craftsmanship incommunicable save by practical demonstration. It is unlikely that the early *responsa* were argued so as to permit of their method being inferred. But almost contemporaneous with Appius Claudius's publications is the Lex Ogulnia admitting plebeians and with them fresh air to the college. It is no accident that the first plebeian *pontifex maximus*, Ti. Coruncanius (*cos.* 280 B.C.), was also the first *publice profiteri* (Pomponius, *Dig.* 1, 2, 2, 35, 38), by which phrase we must understand at least that he argued and expounded the questions arising in his practice before those desirous of learning the law. Thereby he was disclosing the last secret, and completing the change from oracular to professional jurisprudence which the Twelve Tables had rendered inevitable in the long run. It does not seem that the pontifical monopoly had constituted a political grievance, but with the removal of the last class-barrier the last motive for preserving it disappeared.

To the public the opening of the profession of jurisconsult can have made little difference. Certain members of the governing classes continued to control with unquestioned authority the interpretation of the law by their *responsa*, but who they should be was settled by educated public opinion instead of election to the college. Besides their jurisprudence, the *pontifices* bequeathed to posterity two valuable traditions: to the governing classes the tradition that the practice of law was a branch of statesmanship worthy of them, a public service to be given freely without reward, to the people that of unquestioning acceptance of learned opinion. Thus the primeval authority of the *pontifices* continued as the *auctoritas prudentium*, and for a time no change of juristic method is discernible. The science of Coruncanius and his successors was for nearly a century a simple continuation of that of the *pontifices*, but with Sextus Aelius Paetus (*cos.* 198 B.C.) we reach the end of the national period of law.

Sextus Aelius is a figure of the first importance. Pomponius tells us (*Dig.* 1, 2, 2, 7) that owing to the *ius Flavianum* having become inadequate (*deerant quaedam genera agendi*) Aelius *alias actiones composuit et librum populo dedit, qui appellatur ius Aelianum.* In a second notice (*ib.* 38) he relates that there was still extant in his own day a work by Aelius containing as it were the cradle of the law, called *Tripertita* because *lege duodecim tabularum praeposita iungitur interpretatio, deinde subtexitur legis actio.* The questions of the relation of the *ius Aelianum* to the *Tripertita*, and of the way in which the threefold division of the *Tripertita* was applied, are of no great moment. What matters is that the *Tripertita* were still extant in Pomponius' day, that he regarded them as the earliest known monument of the law (*veluti cunabula iuris*), and that what he says of the early law is almost certainly derived, immediately or ultimately, from them. In describing that law (*ib.* 5–6, cf. 12) Pomponius uses the Aelian triad, *lex, interpretatio* and *legis actiones*, and perhaps the most important point in our meagre information about the *Tripertita* is that by about 200 B.C. the juristic law or *interpretatio*, which was the product of practice (*disputatio fori*), was recognized as a distinct mass and known as *ius civile quod sine scripto in sola prudentium interpretatione consistit* (Pomponius, *ib.* 12, cf. 5). It should be added that, though the aim of the *Tripertita* was doubtless practical, it seems to be the starting point of Roman legal literature and the first step towards a systematic treatment of the whole law. Till then there can have been little beyond collections of formularies and of *responsa*, and possibly commentaries on portions of the Twelve Tables. Moreover, standing at a momentous parting of ways, it belongs to that small class of books which, whatever their intrinsic merits, are remembered as representative of a whole period.

Aelius lived long enough to see the beginning of the succeeding age. The consul of 198 was a friend of Laelius, and was even remembered by Q. Mucius Scaevola the Augur, who seems to have been born about 160. He must have witnessed, perhaps with eyes less totally unsympathetic than those of the elder Cato, the spring of the intellectual awakening which followed the Second Punic War, but to judge by his favourite quotation from Ennius[1] he was averse from speculation. One may guess that he was the typical successful lawyer, too keen a mind not to be in touch with the intellectual movement, but absorbed by his practice, *cordatus*, but eminently *catus*.

His contemporary, M. Porcius Cato (234–149 B.C.), is interesting rather as a statesman and man of business than as a jurist. The corrupt notice of Pomponius (*Dig.* 1, 2, 2, 38) seems to ascribe him, as one would expect, to the old school of jurisprudence, though no doubt the forms of contract recommended in the treatise on agriculture by a man certainly not easily *captus* were the last word in the *ars cavendi*. Our tradition generally fails to distinguish him as a lawyer from his son (*c.* 192–152 B.C.), but what Pomponius says entitles us to attribute anything of importance to the latter, who is to be reckoned the founder of the new school[2].

The son's name lives in the *regula Catoniana* (*Dig.* 34, 7, 1), and a valiant and not wholly unsuccessful attempt has been made by Jörs to represent him as the introducer of a new method, that of *regulae*, the novelty of which would consist in not arguing from the concrete solutions of previous *responsa* to that of the case in hand, but in deriving the principle to be applied by generalization from them. But, as Jörs himself recognizes, it is hazardous to make the mere disengagement of general propositions implied in all argument a novelty of the Catonian age. That much of the older law was remembered by the classical jurists in the form of *regulae* or *definitiones* of the *veteres* must be admitted, but those who drafted the Twelve Tables were already capable of some

---

[1] Cicero, *De Rep.* 1, 18, 30: philosophari velle, sed paucis; nam omnino haud placere.

[2] Pomponius, *Dig.* 1, 2, 2, 38: hos (*i.e.* the school of Aelius) sectatus ad aliquid est [Cato. deinde] Marcus Cato princeps Porciae familiae, cuius et libri extant: sed plurimi filii eius, ex quibus ceteri oriuntur [ordiuntur. Mommsen]. Cf. Jörs, *op. cit.* 1, p. 279 n. 1.

generalization and, on the other hand, not every *regula* in the Digest is old. If we could feel sure that the Catonian fragment in *Dig.* 45, 1, 4, 1 has not been recast, we should say that before 150 B.C. the lawyers were arguing in modern style. That about this time they were busily arguing is shown by the emergence of *ius controversum*[1]. On some disputed points we have the views of the men who according to Pomponius (*Dig.* 1, 2, 2, 39) *fundaverunt ius civile:* M. Junius Brutus (*praetor* about 150 B.C.), M'. Manilius (*cos.* 149) and P. Mucius Scaevola (*cos.* 133, *pont. max.* 131). The formularies of stipulations in sale, the *Manilii actiones*, some of which are preserved by Varro, come probably from this Manilius, perhaps from his *Monumenta*. Brutus is to be noted as having adopted in his *de iure civili libri tres* the Greek form of dialogue, and P. Mucius as having upheld the tradition of legal science in the pontifical college; he also left books. A few *responsa* of these men survive in one form or another.

The signs are now plentiful that we have reached a new age with which the classical lawyers felt at home. Its characterization had best be deferred, though it is convenient to complete here our notice of the leading jurists. The names multiply, and they are names which we meet occasionally in the Digest. We must be content with the bare mention of P. Rutilius Rufus (*cos.* 105) who, like his older contemporary Q. Aelius Tubero (*cos. suff.* 118), was a Stoic pupil of Panaetius. He is thrice cited by Ulpian (through Sabinus), and was the author of more than one reform.

In the last years of the Republic three great names stand out: Q. Mucius Scaevola (*cos.* 95 B.C.), C. Aquilius Gallus, a pupil of Mucius, praetor of the *quaestio de ambitu* 66 B.C., who died between 55 and 44, and his pupil Servius Sulpicius Rufus (105–43), the close friend of Cicero. Born of a family of lawyers and *pontifices* and an ardent member of the senatorial party, Q. Mucius was the natural champion of tradition. To the classical jurists he represented their law in its earliest stage; he was much used by Labeo and Masurius Sabinus, and he is quoted as late as Ulpian and Paul. Tribonian professes to extract from his *liber ὅρων*, but may have drawn his knowledge from Pomponius' *libri ex Q. Mucio*. Safer sources for us are Cicero, Varro and Gellius. The son and pupil of P. Mucius was undoubtedly a conservative lawyer, but he was also the friend of Rutilius and a Stoic, and in the freer field of provincial administration he signalized his governorship of Asia in 100 B.C. by an Edict which Cicero

---

[1] Jörs, *op. cit.* 1, p. 84; P. Krüger, *Geschichte der Quellen und Literatur des röm. Rechts*[2], pp. 53, 62 n. 37; Bremer, *op. cit.* 1, 22, 25, 32.

fifty years later took as his model in Cilicia. It was doubtless pure joy to repress the *publicani*, but he also allowed *autonomia* to the Greeks, and he propounded an *exceptio doli* which anticipated by a good few years, at least, that of the urban Edict. In him we see the conflict of the old civil law tradition with the new philosophical and rhetorical doctrines. If he came out on the wrong side in the *causa Curiana*[1], it was a mistake with which any lawyer will sympathize. His utterance on the *bonae fidei arbitria*[2] shows that his heart was in the right place, but it is balanced by his adherence to the old rule that land sold was not warranted free of servitudes unless expressed to be *optimus maximus*, and he seems to have been incapable of appreciating the natural reasonableness of partnership between a capitalist and a skilled man. Yet he was perhaps the first to hold that a borrower was responsible for negligent as well as intentional damage and that a right to sue in theft descended to the heir. What is most noteworthy is that he was the first to attempt a systematic treatment of the law: *ius civile primus constituit generatim in libros decem et octo redigendo* (Pomponius, *Dig.* 1, 2, 2, 41), a great advance on the *ordo legalis* of Aelius' work. Such treatment involved the use and definition of general concepts; we see Greek influence at work in his attention to ὅροι or *definitiones*, and to distinction by *genera* and *species*.

C. Aquilius Gallus appears to have been a lawyer of much the same stamp, but of a more purely practical bent; no literary work is attributed to him, and his remains are a product of practice. His greatest achievement was the introduction of a remedy for fraud. It is uncertain whether he was responsible for the defence (*exceptio doli*) as well as for the action for damages (*iudicium*); but the *exceptio* was an inevitable deduction from the *iudicium*, and this proved one of the most potent instruments in the modernization of the old law. Since he was never *praetor urbanus*, he must have proposed his *formulae de dolo malo* as jurisconsult, and since he was not an author, probably in a *responsum* or *responsa*. To the same origin must be ascribed the *stipulatio Aquiliana* (*Inst.* 3, 29, 2; *Dig.* 46, 4, 18, 1) and his precedent for institution as *heredes* or the disinheriting of certain *postumi* (*Dig.* 28, 2, 29 pr.; 28, 6, 33, 1). He was *iudex* in the *pro Quinctio*, where his decision is not certainly known, and in a scandalous case in which he seems to have pronounced void a promise based on immoral consideration. His equity is celebrated by Cicero (*pro Caecina*, 27, 78) in an eloquent passage.

[1] See below, p. 870 *sq.*; Bremer, *op. cit.* 1, 49; J. Stroux, *Summum ius summa iniuria*, p. 29.   [2] Cicero, *de off.* iii, 17, 70.

Servius Sulpicius Rufus is rated by Cicero above Mucius and Gallus as a jurist and below only himself as an orator, a suspicious antithesis. He was a prolific writer, but the little that we know of his works suggests that he wrote no great systematic treatise, confining himself to criticism of Mucius and to monographs. He is credited, however, with the first commentary on the Edict, two books *ad Brutum, perquam brevissimi*—a significant occurrence. He was very active as consultant and teacher, a large number of his *responsa* being preserved by his highly distinguished school. It is impossible to enter here upon the various points which suggest comment as one reads these texts. Though modern opinion inclines to think Cicero's estimate (*Brutus*, 41, 152 *sq.*) unduly laudatory, he seems to have judged correctly enough that Servius introduced and exploited the dialectical method, and that he frankly adopted equity as his aim. In short he brought to the service of jurisprudence the full Graeco-Roman culture, and in him the adoption of the new jurisprudential method was complete[1].

IV. THE DEVELOPMENT OF THE LAW IN THE NATIONAL PERIOD

The Twelve Tables did not supersede the national jurisprudence to whose pre-existence they bear witness, but played straight into the hands of its exponents. The short gnomic sentences of the code state sometimes a wide principle, sometimes a detail, but throughout an existing body of custom is presupposed. Procedure receives the most detailed treatment (Twelve Tables 1–3), but though the Decemvirs regulated the old rituals for the enforcement of rights in such points as they thought fit, they did not describe their forms as a whole, but left their application to practice. Still more is this true of mancipation and the making of wills (Twelve Tables, 5, 3. 6, 1). In short the *lex* required *interpretatio*, which was the province of the *pontifices* and their successors, and for a time the magistrate having *iurisdictio* (the consuls and later their *collega* the praetor) was silenced. We enter upon a period of some 250 years during which the development of law was preponderantly juristic. There does not seem to have been much legislation, and the Edict, so far as it existed at all, must have been a small matter. It was also a period of development upon national lines, when the Romanism of Roman law struck deep roots.

---

[1] Bruns-Lenel, *Holtzendorffs Enzykl*[7]. 1, 345.

Pomponius following Aelius classifies the law of the period as *lex*, *legis actiones* and *interpretatio*, but the *legis actiones* are properly a branch of *interpretatio* which acquired special fixity. The first preoccupation of the *pontifices* seems to have been their determination. The four general forms of enforcing rights (to which before the end of the period legislation added the *condictio*) were already fixed by custom, with such regulation as the Twelve Tables had superimposed, but the assertion through them of rights sanctioned by the code involved a new piece of work, namely the filling in of the blanks in the appropriate general form in accordance with the definitions of rights provided by the *lex*. Thus the *pontifices* settled the specific form by which each particular right was to be enforced, and the catalogue of these forms (*legis actiones*) became the core of the pontifical secret. Ihering's view must be accepted, that jurisprudence in framing the *legis actiones* was tied to *lex*, and this accounts for the fixity assumed by the list. The *legis actiones* were *legum verbis accommodatae*; a cause of action was given by *lex*, and the pleading showed its dependence on *lex* by following its very words (Gaius 4, 11; 4, 24). We read, it is true, that Sextus Aelius made additions to the forms of the *ius Flavianum*, but it is hardly likely that these were further inferences from the Twelve Tables made in the course of the third century; more probably new *leges* had created new causes of action. In any case, Aelius is at the very end of our period, when the principle *nulla actio sine lege* was about to break down completely.

This fixing of the *legis actiones* was necessary to the object of the Twelve Tables. Like other ancient laws, Roman law was a system of rights of action, and only if the *actiones* were fixed was the law itself fixed. The expansive power of the material law only existed within the framework of the *legis actiones*. Hence when, owing to fundamental changes in social and economic conditions, a great expansion of the law became necessary, reform took the shape of the adoption of a new procedure, the essence of which was, or came to be, that the *actiones* were determined no longer by immobile *lex*, but by the annually renewed and amendable Edict.

The question what scope there was within the limits of *lex* and *legis actio* for development by jurisprudence (including custom) involves consideration of the judicial system. The division of functions in private suits between the magistrate and a lay authority is a well-known feature of the whole Republican period. Modern study has led to the well-ascertained conclusion that this peculiar arrangement represents the combination of State authorization and regulation with a system of voluntary arbitration. It may be taken as proven that the *iudicium privatum* was based on an act of the parties, *litis contestatio*, which was a formal agreement to submit to a fellow-citizen, the *iudex*, an issue which the *litis contestatio* formulated and which was reached before the praetor (*in iure*), in early days by *legis actio*, in later times by informal proceedings culminating in a written *formula*. *Legis actio* or *formula* there could not be without the concurrence of the praetor, and the *iudex* only became seised of the case by the praetor's order (*iussum iudicandi*), but till the end of the classical period there was sufficient survival of the original idea of agreement to make it impossible to go to trial without the adhesion of both parties to the *litis contestatio*. However, the practical results to a defendant of refusing his adhesion were as bad as any that could follow from an unfavourable judgment. The characteristic feature is that they did not take the form of judgment by default.

The part of the praetor was thus to organize the issue and to empower the trial-authority, but there his functions ceased, unless and until the question of execution arose. He was incompetent to decide a suit between citizens. But it is plain that if he had power to deny to plaintiffs any forms of issue but those which seemed right to him, and to impose such issues, by indirect pressure, upon defendants, he could in effect alter the law. Such indeed was his power at the end of the Republic under the formulary system, but it is very doubtful if he exercised anything like it under the *legis actiones*. Here we are reduced to guess-work, based chiefly on our imperfect knowledge of the *legis actio sacramenti*.

The *legis actiones* seem to have been rites in which stereotyped acts and utterances were assigned to praetor and parties by custom and jurisprudence. There were typical forms, the blanks in which had been filled up to suit the various causes of action. If the typical form were not observed, one may suppose that the praetor could stop the case; if he did not, the question of nullity of *litis contestatio* would be for the *iudex*. But if within a typical form an unprecedented cause of action was stated, *i.e.* if plaintiff departed from the recognized list of *legis actiones*, then the question of law —was there a *meum esse ex iure Quiritium* or an *oportere*?—would seem to have been for the *iudex*, guided by the *prudentes*, not for the praetor. Thus Gaius (4, 11) tells us of a suitor who lost his case because he claimed for *vites succisae* instead of keeping to the statutory *arbores succisae*. The *responsum* laying this down must have been made when the case had reached the *iudex*, because if the case had been stopped *in iure* before *litis contestatio*, the plaintiff might have amended his claim, whereas we read that he had lost it (*rem perdidisse*).

According to this account, admittedly highly conjectural, the most that the praetor could do was to connive at changes in the *ius civile* accepted by *iudices* on the authority of the juristic *interpretatio*. There seems to be no room for *ius praetorium*, a conclusion which harmonizes with the fact that Aelius' *Tripertita*, which summed up the law as it stood at the very end of this period, contained besides the *lex* and the *legis actiones* only the *interpretatio*, which was pure civil law, pre-eminently *ius civile*. Further, if the praetor had been free to make *ius praetorium*, what would have been the certainty of law and wherein would have been the abolition of magistratual caprice which were the prime objects of the Twelve Tables? Why should the *actiones* have been qualified as *legis*, and why in order to overcome the literal adherence of jurisprudence to *lex* was it necessary to pass the Lex Aebutia, which sent suitors to find their causes of action formulated in the Edict?

The objections to the view put forward are nevertheless weighty. Apart from special arguments, with which we cannot deal here, consisting in signs of pre-Aebutian praetorian activity, there are important general considerations. The humble position assigned to the consuls and later to the praetor is difficult to accept, while the supposed contrast between the magistrate's position before and after the Lex Aebutia makes that law contradict the whole course of constitutional development. The Lex Aebutia, in fact, figures much more prominently in modern books than in the ancient texts. And further, if any development of law by way of *ius praetorium* is necessarily after the Lex Aebutia, which it is common ground cannot be earlier than the *Tripertita* and was possibly not before 150 B.C., certain institutions, notably the *bonae fidei iudicia*, which are plausibly accounted for as receptions from praetorian into civil law, are made impossibly late. The *bonae fidei iudicia* were civil by the time of Q. Mucius Scaevola, the *pontifex maximus*[1], so that we have to suppose that they did not exist in any shape till at the earliest 200 B.C., and had in the course of at most a hundred and perhaps less than fifty years passed from being praetorian to civil, without a trace being left of their originally praetorian character. These and other arguments have led writers of the highest authority to maintain pre-Aebutian *ius praetorium*, and even praetorian use of the formulary procedure between *cives*.

Upon so fundamental a question it is necessary to take up some

---

[1] Cicero, *de off.* III, 17, 70.

position. The present writer believes that during the prime of the *legis actiones* the praetor was powerless to give effect to new causes of action, but that the Lex Aebutia must have been preceded by a period in which the old system was strained to breaking-point by the advent of radically altered conditions, and the demand for some mitigation of the excessive adherence to *lex* became irresistible. The possibilities of expansion by tendencious interpretation on the lines shortly to be mentioned must by this time have been pretty well exhausted, and the old *ius civile* was ready to crystallize in the definitive work of Sextus Aelius. Legislation was not out of the question, as the Lex Aquilia shows, and probably some at least of the procedural statutes cited by Gaius belong to the period of dissatisfaction with the old system. Ultimately it was a procedural statute, the Lex Aebutia, which saved the situation. But before this reform it is probable that expedients of all sorts were attempted—partial reforms, botching and patchwork. It was undoubtedly time for the dormant powers of the *imperium* to wake up, and there may well have been some sprouting of what would afterwards have been called *ius praetorium*. It is worth considering for a moment how much the praetor may have done without actually infringing the civil law.

The case for his power to put pressure on a plaintiff by simply refusing to concur in the *legis actio* does not rest on the slight and equivocal evidence of pre-Aebutian *denegatio actionis*, but on incontrovertible *a priori* grounds. The limit on his power so to act can at any time only have been political, and with public opinion behind him he may have used it freely. The same is true of *missio in possessionem* or other administrative methods of coercing a defendant. By *denegatio* of the traditional remedy the praetor might oblige a plaintiff to adopt a new one or forgo his right, and by *missio* a defendant to accept it. In this way he may, without creating a praetorian action, have compelled parties to go to arbitration instead of to *legis actio*. For such compulsion he may often have had moral justification in the terms of their agreement: the forms of contract recommended by Cato for sales of produce or placing of work contain clauses referring questions of damage to *boni viri arbitratus*. A constant practice of reference to arbitration under the compulsion of the praetor or of heavy penalties provided by contract may have developed standards of contractual obligation which were ripe for recognition as new civil law when the Lex Aebutia was passed. Another possibility is suggested by the appearance, probably in this period, of *sponsio praeiudicialis*. It is that if the praetor could thus compel parties to alter their civil law position, though only to a nominal extent, as a procedural convenience, he may have been able also, in the interests of equity, to insist on substantial stipulations of the same nature as the compulsory praetorian stipulations of later practice. It is useless to pile hypothesis on hypothesis. Our point is that before the Lex Aebutia made possible the frank creation of praetorian law, the praetor, once he had public opinion behind him, was far from helpless. Nevertheless we believe that the Twelve Tables were followed by a long period during which the development of law necessarily took the form of *interpretatio* of *lex*. The civil law that was thus gradually formed when the *legis actiones* were in their prime ultimately, like all law, lost its power of expansion, but up to a certain point it proved capable of sufficient adjustment to the changing needs of a society which, although conservative, was by no means stationary.

Within the limits of *lex* and *legis actio* there was for a time room for development by custom and jurisprudence[1]. Thus, the formulation of a claim of inheritance (*hereditatis petitio*) was fixed, but this would not prevent the jurists from varying their answer to the questions who was *heres* and what was included in a *hereditas*. Or again, if one sued *de glande legenda* or *de tigno iuncto*, the *iudex* might be guided by a *responsum* to broaden the interpretation of *glans* or *tignum*[2]. The one change that could not be made was to alter the statutory *wording* of the *legis actio*. It is unnecessary to labour this point, because Ihering has shown once for all that the old *interpretatio*, under a parade of literalness, was extremely tendencious. When we find literalness carried *ad absurdum*, we ought to seek for a motive which might render the result arrived at desirable, as when it is deduced from Twelve Tables, 5, 4 that only the nearest agnate could succeed as *legitimus heres*, so that if he failed to succeed the next nearest had no title. But the recognition of the fictitious character of interpretation came later; and so long as the fiction obtained, the letter of the *lex* was a real limitation. The *lex xii tabularum* was, however, in certain respects a liberal *lex*, which did not condescend to undue particularity. Two clauses especially, *uti legassit* (5, 3) and *ubi nexum faciet* (6, 1), left the *paterfamilias* to make his own *ius*. His word was to be law, but again what he had once said became matter for strict interpretation. Hence, if he were wise, he would follow the formulary recommended as suiting his need by a jurist. The development of business formu-

---

[1] R. von Ihering, *Geist des röm. Rechts*[4], II, pp. 441 *sqq.*
[2] Gaius, *Dig.* 50, 16, 236, 1; 50, 16, 62.

laries thus became a most important side of the jurist's craft. On this matter also it is only necessary to refer to Ihering[1].

The achievements of the early school of interpretation are best known to us in those branches of the law which were still archaic in the time of Gaius, the law of the family and of inheritance, and to a smaller extent the law of property. A marked feature is the abuse of institutions, well-known examples of which are the exploitation of the rule of three sales (Twelve Tables 4, 2) for the purposes of adoption and emancipation, the conversion of *coemptio* to non-matrimonial uses, the employment of *mancipatio* as form of conveyance outside sale. The extreme case is the *testamentum per aes et libram*. These topics have long been exhausted. It is more to our purpose to examine shortly certain institutions which formed within the civil law itself the starting-point of the law of the future.

V. THE BEGINNINGS OF FREER LAW IN THE NATIONAL PERIOD

The free marriage, which did not subject the wife to the husband, but left her in her existing *patria potestas* or *tutela*, is found as early as Ennius and Cato as an accepted institution. But a patriarchal family system of the extreme Roman type presupposes the subjection of the wife, in other words *manus*-marriage, and it is a paradox that the free marriage should, as it did, have placed the children *in patria potestate*. The predominant and typical primitive Roman marriage was therefore *manus*-marriage, and the diffusion of free marriage must be in some sense an innovation. But a pure innovation of such gravity in the most conservative branch of the law is unthinkable in these early times, and there is reason to believe that free marriage had roots stretching as far back as *manus*-marriage. Precise statement of its legal position at the time of the Twelve Tables is impossible: we only know of the decemviral provision enabling a woman married without *manus* to avoid falling into it by *usus* if she absented herself for three nights in each year (Twelve Tables 6, 4). One can hardly avoid the conclusion that *usus* was intended to operate between persons who were considered already man and wife, but who for their part had not cared to use *confarreatio* or *coemptio*, and might prefer to avoid *manus* altogether. Evidence has been given elsewhere of a considerable mingling of races in early Rome (vol. VII, chaps. XI, XII); if there were people who disposed

---

[1] *Op. cit.* II, pp. 300, 470, 577 *sqq.*

of their dead otherwise than the majority, there may equally well have been some who had a different conception of marriage. The ease with which the free marriage became fully recognized is in sharp contrast to the slow and laborious progress of the emancipation of women from *tutela*, to the roundabout and very gradual substitution of *cognatio* for *agnatio* in intestate succession, and to the tenacity of the *patria potestas* itself. The contrast would be explained if in this one case of marriage the Twelve Tables left open a chink, however small, in the armour of patriarchalism. No words need be wasted in expatiating on the momentous character of this development.

In classical times land in Italy and certain easements, slaves and beasts of draught and burden (*res mancipi*), could be fully conveyed only by either *mancipatio* or surrender in court (*in iure cessio*). To other property (*res nec mancipi*) *mancipatio* was inapplicable, and though *res nec mancipi* might be ceded *in iure*, their normal conveyance was by simple delivery (*traditio*). But how were *res nec mancipi* alienated in primitive law? Great objection has been felt to allowing that *dominium ex iure Quiritium* in them could be passed by informal *traditio* in the days of primitive formalism. Conveyance by *in iure cessio* is a theoretical solution, but not practical. Hence it has been held that ownership of *res nec mancipi* was not originally *dominium ex iure Quiritium*, but a possessory relation transferable by mere delivery. But if so, the early real action, including *in iure cessio*, must have been confined to *res mancipi*, a limitation of which there is not the faintest trace. The simple way out is to put the postulate of formalism in proper perspective[1]. So long as uncoined copper remained the medium of exchange, sales of any kind of property must have been *per aes et libram*, though only those of the future *res mancipi* may have required a *libripens*, five witnesses and a customary ritual, and to such alienations alone certain subsidiary effects (*actio auctoritatis, de modo agri*) attached. Once counting coin took the place of weighing metal, the weighing was dropped where it was only a natural necessity, *i.e.* in the conveyance of *res nec mancipi*. But for *res mancipi* some legal requirement, probably statutory, saved the old ritual, which had the advantage of the subsidiary effects above mentioned. And sale fixed the general type of conveyance suitable for *res nec mancipi* as for *res mancipi*.

Nexum, the application of the ceremony *per aes et libram* to contract, disappeared early owing to the Lex Poetelia (? 326 B.C.).

[1] K. Polenske, *Einführung in die Geschichte des röm. Privatrechts*, I, pp. 34 *sqq.*

It is often assumed that its place was taken by *mutuum*, but if, as seems probable, provision for interest was an integral part of a loan by *nexum*, this cannot have been so. The only obligation to which *mutuum* could give rise was to return an equal quantity of things similar in kind to those lent (for consumption) by informal delivery. It could not incorporate agreement for interest, which had to be secured by a distinct contract. *Mutuum*, in fact, though analysable as an informal contract, has another aspect: a man who will not repay a sum lent is keeping the lender out of his money, and in the view of Roman law is in the same position as a man who will not repay money paid to him by mistake or otherwise without just cause. The postulate of formalism can apply to such cases no more than to the commission of a delict. In short, *mutuum* is but an example, though perhaps the earliest, of a general principle formulated by later law, that one who has acquired another's property *non ex iusta causa* must make it good.

The contracts which came to the front after the departure of *nexum* and passed into the next period were *stipulatio* and *expensilatio*. Of the latter we must say nothing. The stipulation of classical law was a unique combination of the new and the old, being a formal *stricti iuris* contract, but except in one form (*sponsio*) *iuris gentium*: in other words, it had become applicable to *peregrini*, but its character had evidently been fixed in the early period. That it was in general use in its presumably oldest form, *sponsio*, at the time of the Twelve Tables is very unlikely, since it is not mentioned by them. The form was in all probability originally an oath, and Mitteis[1] may be said to have established that its original function was guarantee and that it developed by way of self-guarantee into an abstract form of contract. He suggests that its original sphere of application was procedural. But, accepting this latter hypothesis or not, one cannot say how and when the evolution took place; there is no trace of confinement to the procedural sphere in the early Lex Publilia (Gaius 3, 127; 4, 22). Other unanswerable questions are whether the clearly ancient *fidepromissio* was an alternative form from the beginning, whether the fact that later this form was open to *peregrini* indicates early recognition of a common Italian form of engagement, how soon and in what sense such recognition occurred, and how soon other forms became valid, so that the two older forms became merely special cases of *stipulatio*. The second chapter of the Lex Aquilia (? 287 B.C.) does not appear to

---

[1] *Z. d. Sav.-Stift., Rom. Abt.*, XXII, 1901, p. 97; *Festschr. f. Bekker*, p. 110; *Röm. Privatrecht*, I, p. 266; P. F. Girard, *Manuel élém. de droit romain*[8], pp. 515 *sqq.*

be confined to *sponsio* and *fidepromissio*. These two forms had in the time of Gaius, in what we have accepted as their earliest function, guarantee, the peculiarity of not binding the heirs of the promissor, from which it may be inferred, but against other evidence, that contractual liabilities originally resembled delictual in not being hereditary.

The early history of Roman contract is thus very obscure, but at any rate it is clear that the Romans possessed from a comparatively remote date a general form for binding any sort of promise. Even if *stipulatio* was confined by the nature of early remedies to promises of *certa pecunia* and *certa res*, one could stipulate for a pecuniary *poena* conditionally upon a non-performance of any kind, for unlike other civil law *negotia* stipulation could be conditional. Thus if the economic development at a given date requires the existence of a contract of sale, it does not follow that this must have been the classical consensual contract, because essential needs may have been met, though less conveniently, by two stipulations. Undoubtedly stipulation offered a fair field for the development of a general theory of contract, and the precedents of stipulation (*e.g. Manilii actiones*) settled by jurisprudence for different economic purposes fixed the main categories of contracts and the natural obligations of the parties. Thus the *stipulatio duplae* and the *stipulatio dotis*, doubtless elaborated in our period, eventually engendered implied common law obligations of a seller and of a receiver of *dos*, just as the practice of English conveyancers has in various cases been adopted by the general law.

The essential doctrines of contractual obligation may well have been settled in outline before the beginning of the last century of the Republic, but it is otherwise with the law of delict. The very fact that the Twelve Tables, silent on contracts, were rich in the regulation of delicts, provoked an early *interpretatio* which, in spite of statutory (Lex Aquilia) and praetorian (*iniuria*) reforms, stereotyped ideas and rules only to be explained as survivals of a primitive system of vengeance. The law built up later on these foundations is a triumph of juristic construction, but we cannot be blind to the imperfection of even the final result. The most satisfactory achievement is the developed law of personal injury (*iniuria*), precisely the delict which was reformed most completely and at a comparatively late date, the delict also in which the principle of retribution was most justifiable. The two wrongs (*furtum manifestum* and *membrum ruptum*) for which the Decemvirs did not ordain pecuniary composition of the right of vengeance were also ultimately dealt with by praetorian actions, but it is likely that long before the days of *ius praetorium* practice made the acceptance of composition compulsory. Composition was the primitive conception of the pecuniary penalties given in other cases by the *lex*, and the persistence of this conception is the best explanation of the survival of rules based on vengeance (non-descent of liability, noxal actions, etc.). Indeed the classification of rights of action *ex delicto* as obligations, that is as pecuniary elements in the *patrimonium*, is probably late, perhaps not earlier than the second century A.D.[1] The theory of obligations was based on contract, and its application to delict was never satisfactory.

VI. THE LEX AEBUTIA. *IUS PRAETORIUM*

The general conditions of the legal movement during the last century and a half of the Republic are the intellectual and moral, social, economic and political changes resulting from the victory over Carthage and intimate contact with the Hellenistic East (see above, vol. VIII, chaps. XII–XIV). What must be emphasized here at the outset is that the legal movement, in spite of its radical nature, was controlled by the national jurisprudence. There was no break in the juristic tradition, and Q. Mucius is the true heir of Sextus Aelius. As we have tried to show, the old *ius civile* had been by no means stationary; under the guise of literal interpretation the function of jurisprudence had always been to adapt the law to changing needs. But the change in conditions with which it was confronted in the second century amounted almost to a revolution, and demanded a rapidity of legal evolution, a reception and digestion of new customs, which might well have proved beyond the capacity of jurisprudence, even if armed with a new method. The solution was found in the Lex Aebutia. This was a half-hearted reform, for it seems to have made the formulary procedure, already known outside the *ius civile*[2], merely an alternative to the *legis actiones*, which were not abolished till the Lex Julia de iudiciis privatis of Augustus. The *ius civile* was not assaulted frontally, but, almost unintentionally perhaps, its position was turned. In itself the substitution of issues based on *formula* for issues based on *legis actio* was merely a change from one form to another. The principle of formalism still lived in the *formula*; it was strict pleading, which the *iudex* was bound to observe most literally. If all that the Lex Aebutia had meant was the conversion

---

[1] F. de Visscher, *Rev. hist. de droit français et étranger*, VII, 1928, p. 355.

[2] J. Partsch, *Die Schriftformel im röm. Provinzialprozesse*.

of, say, the spoken *aio te mihi dare oportere* into the written *si paret
Numerium Negidium Aulo Agerio dare oportere*, the change would
have been merely from a difficult and perilous form to a simple
one: the *iudex* must still decide on the *oportere* by strict civil law.
More must have been intended than this; one would think that
it was intended to give scope to more liberal ideas of causes of
action and their content, and not merely to sanction an improved
formulation of existing causes. The most obvious step in this
direction was the granting of *formulae* for *arbitria bonae fidei*, an
advance, as the writer thinks, already half-made by pre-Aebutian
custom. These *formulae* appear never to have been praetorian;
they left the question of *oportere* to the *iudex*, but with the qualification *ex fide bona*, which seems to have removed all scruples.
The result of this act of faith in the progressiveness of *iudices* and
responding jurists proved that they were only waiting for their
opportunity to recognize the new custom as part of the civil law.

But on the assumption—a grave one—that the *iudex* was bound
by the terms of whatever formula was incorporated in the *iussum
iudicandi*, it was possible for the praetor to operate outside the *ius
civile*, in a word, to create *ius praetorium*. On the positive side a
formula might be granted leaving the *iudex* still a question of civil
law, but with the modification that he must assume for fact what
possibly was not fact (*formula ficticia*), or one withdrawing the law
from him by ordering condemnation or absolution according as
he found certain facts (*formula in factum concepta*). On the negative
side the *formula*, while representing a good civil cause of action,
might make condemnation conditional on the defendant failing
to prove certain, from the civil point of view irrelevant, facts, the
existence of which thus constituted a special defence (*exceptio*).
By such action the praetor, though incapable of altering the
civil law, except so far as *iudices* and jurists were willing to
recognize new custom, could proceed to the development of new
law, *ius praetorium*. We must not hesitate to regard his power in
this respect as, from the point of view of substance, one of legislation, legally unlimited save by the general conditions of his
office (*intercessio*, impeachment, Lex Cornelia 67 B.C., see p. 343).

The Edict was the praetor's annual announcement of his intentions in respect of his *officium iurisdictionis*. He therefore said
not: *familiam habeto*, but: *bonorum possessionem dabo*, not *dupli
poena esto*, but: *in duplum iudicium dabo*. But when praetor after
praetor said the same thing, when a clause had become traditional,
it was legislation. The final state of the Edict as codified by
Salvius Julianus under Hadrian is well known, but the earlier

history of incorporation of new clauses is largely unknown. All we can say in general is that by the end of the Republic the Edict had attained considerable size and fixity, and the body of new law resulting from it stood out as distinct from the *ius civile*. Cicero's remarks on it[1] are interesting as being the reflections of a cultivated layman, but technically the contrast between *ius civile* and *ius praetorium* was absolute. Receptions from one to the other were not unknown, but, though important, were exceptional. On a larger view the distinction was a needless technicality, like our own between law and equity, but its tentacles became so well set in the legal system that complete unification proved beyond the powers of even Justinian. As legal historians we have no reason to regret its survival, because otherwise we should have known much less of the successive strata of Roman law.

The power of virtual legislation which thus reinforced a jurisprudence which had grown antiquated was intimately in touch with practice. This is an important observation, because it means that the formulary system was almost as much in the hands of the jurists as the *legis actiones*. One may think that a prudent layman confronted with the task of *praetor urbanus* for a year only would be tempted simply to take over his predecessor's Edict, but the fact remains that praetors did innovate, and that early post-Aebutian praetors must have innovated a great deal. But no one who has studied the Edict can doubt that its real authors were professional jurists of the highest quality. The lawyers on the praetor's *consilium* certainly took a hand; they must at least have approved. But recent researches[2] into the formulary system have made us realize more fully the place occupied by the drawing of pleadings in the practice of the *prudentes*. The Edict showed the pleadings that would be allowed of course, and usually the jurist's business would be to select the appropriate *formula*, not necessarily an easy matter. But the praetor's powers were not exhausted by the Edict, so that if a suitable *formula* could not be found in it, it was for the jurist to consider whether he could not draft an original *formula* which he could support in his *responsum*. It was not the praetor's duty to draw up the pleadings. The plaintiff had to choose and give notice of his *formula*, and, though the praetor was more ready to help defendants, it was for the defendant to be ready with grounds for refusing the proposed *formula* or with any *exceptio* he wished to have inserted. Hence

---

[1] II *in Verr.* 1, 42, 109; *de inv.* II, 22, 67. More significant: *de legibus*, 1, 5, 17.

[2] M. Wlassak, *Die klassische Prozessformel*, I.

the jurists who assisted an incoming praetor to draw up his Edict must have found many suggestions in recent practice. The draft of some bold pleader would thus make its way into the Edict, provided the profession agreed *dandam actionem* or *exceptionem*. It is therefore now no longer a stumbling-block that Aquilius Gallus, the author of the *formulae de dolo*, was never *praetor urbanus*, and the temptation has vanished to endow Cascellius with that office against the evidence of Pomponius (*Dig.* 1, 2, 2, 45). The manipulation of the formulary system was work for which the tradition of the *ius civile* had eminently fitted the Roman lawyer.

The *ius praetorium*, *i.e.* those parts of the Edict which did not simply carry out, but amended, the civil law, whether by correction or addition, is an accumulation of reforms of detail, large and small, gradually made and touching every branch of the law, which could only be described in the course of a systematic treatment of the whole law; it cannot be summarized under large leading ideas. Reforms were provoked, one by one, by the experience of litigation, by the new demands created by new conditions. Amongst the latter was the freer conception of law prevailing in the last years of the Republic, making itself felt in proposals from authoritative practising jurists. A reform once made would itself become the object of *interpretatio*, as will be illustrated below from the history of the *exceptiones doli* and *pacti*. But the dominant considerations in the Edict were practical, not dogmatic, however much its reforms as a whole were, as might be expected, in harmony with the general trend of juristic thought. For example, it is reasonable to regard the *actio Publiciana* (Gaius 4, 36) as a manifestation of the general movement away from formalism, and thus to connect it with the *ius gentium*, but the *actio* is no part of the *ius gentium* and might well have been invented if the *ius gentium* had never been heard of.

Again, many an idea in the Edict is a loan from Greek law, but this is a point to be established in the individual case. A clear example, the only one we can mention here, is the replacement of the civil law of personal wrongs (*iniuria*) based on the Twelve Tables (8, 2–4) by the Edict *de iniuriis*. The law of the Decemvirs was so primitive that it must have been reformed sooner or later in the ordinary course of national development, but actually the definitive reform was by a praetorian reception of Greek law[1]. The defects of the early system were that the wrong of personal

---

[1] H. F. Hitzig, *Injuria*; J. Partsch, *Arch. Pap.* vi, p. 54; F. de Visscher, *Études de droit romain*, p. 327.

injury was conceived as purely physical and that, except in the case of *talio ni cum eo pacit* for *membrum ruptum*, it gave damages according to a tariff. The total result of the Edict was to give an action for assessable damages for any act falling under the concept *ὕβρις*. The widening and refining of the concept came gradually, as is shown by the historical succession of the edictal clauses, but the first and earliest introduces an *actio aestimatoria* which we know from the Alexandrian *Dikaiomata* to have existed in Hellenistic law. Its original applicability must have been to the recognized cases of corporeal *iniuria*; then it was extended by special clauses to offences against honour. From them Labeo (*Coll.* 2, 5, 1) was able to generalize: *iniuria* equals *ὕβρις*.

VII. THE *IUS GENTIUM*

Maiores aliud ius gentium, aliud ius civile esse voluerunt, writes Cicero[1]. *Maiores* must include the second-century jurists, and the distinction is not likely to be older than them. Probably they took the phrase *ius gentium* from popular speech; almost certainly it is national, and was not introduced by the Greek teachers of philosophy and rhetoric who from about the middle of the second century dominated Roman intellectual circles[2]. From Cicero onwards, however, it became so closely identified with the Greek doctrine of natural law that its original national meaning is hard to recover. In the popular use of the phrase, *gentium* probably meant the same as in the phrases *ubi, nusquam, minime gentium*[3], which occur as early as Plautus. 'The law of the world' is the sort of phrase the ordinary man of that age might coin to designate a felt antithesis to national law. The reason of the jurists for appropriating the distinction must, one would think, have been practical; there is no ground for attributing to the second century the ornamental use of it which we find in the classical age. Thus no light is thrown on the original meaning of *ius gentium* by compiling a list of the institutions which under the influence of the doctrine of natural law one or other classical writer declares to be *iuris gentium*; this in its speculative sense might be predicated of any piece of Roman law not greatly encumbered with national technicality. But there are a few classical passages in which the

---

[1] *de off.* III, 17, 69. H. Nettleship, J. P. XIII, 1885, p. 169 (= *Contributions to Latin Lexicography*, p. 500).

[2] What can be said in favour of Greek influence is to be found in Weiss, *PW.*, *s.v. Ius gentium*, col. 1218. But Nettleship's view seems preferable.

[3] The observation is due to E. C. Clark, *Practical Jurisprudence*, p. 354. See now E. Schönbauer, *Z. d. Sav.-Stift., Rom. Abt.*, XLIX, 1929, p. 388.

statement bears a practical meaning, namely that the institution in question will be applied in a Roman court to *peregrini*. Here, if anywhere in later literature, must be the clue to the original meaning.

Ius gentium in this practical sense covers the law of contract and the informal methods of acquiring property (thus *traditio* as opposed to *mancipatio* and *in iure cessio*), in fact commercial law[1]. We have seen that some of these constituents were native civil law and older than the second century: thus *traditio, stipulatio* (with its release, *acceptilatio*) and *mutuum* (possibly with further applications of the *condictio non ex iusta causa*). The remaining constituents are the *bonae fidei* contracts, among which the real were not developed till after our period and are in any case unimportant, but the four consensual certainly formed part of the civil law at the end of the second century B.C. This is proved by the inclusion of the actions on sale, hire, mandate and *societas* in the list of *arbitria bonae fidei* to which Q. Mucius attributed *summa vis*[2]. How and at what date they got into the civil law are obscure questions which have already been discussed (p. 855 *sq.*). A custom seems somehow to have been formed in pre-Aebutian times which was strong enough to enable the earliest post-Aebutian Edicts to offer *formulae in ius conceptae*, which means that the praetors could presume that *iudices* would recognize an *oportere* in these cases, provided it were qualified as *ex fide bona*.

In spite of objections that have been made it is surely obvious that the practice of the *praetor peregrinus* must have been a powerful factor in the evolution both of this new custom of *bonae fidei* contracts and of the general conception *ius gentium*. A magistrate of the Roman Republic (for short the *praetor peregrinus*) when exercising jurisdiction over *peregrini* was, in default of provision by treaty, free to take such measures as seemed best to him. The principle of personality of law being absolute, the *ius civile* did not apply to *peregrini*, and the order of ideas which has produced our modern private international law did not exist to make it a duty to apply their own law[3]. It was inevitable that the *praetor peregrinus* should evolve a practice indistinguishable from law, and that it should reflect his national stock of legal ideas. Hence the fact that the *ius gentium* was not based on Greek law, but was a modernized Roman law, is not inconsistent with its having corresponded to the practice of the *praetor peregrinus*. Strong

---

[1] The delicts have some claim to be included: Gaius, 4, 37.
[2] Cicero, *de off.* III, 17, 70.
[3] Schönbauer, Z. d. Sav.-Stift., Rom. Abt., XLIX, 1929, p. 395.

practical considerations would keep the commercial custom applied at Rome *inter peregrinos* and *inter cives et peregrinos* as close as possible to that applied *inter cives*, but it is not to be denied that if among the commercial classes of Rome there was from the beginning of the second century need of a modernized law, the *praetor peregrinus* was in a far better position than the pre-Aebutian *praetor urbanus* to satisfy it. *A priori* considerations are confirmed by the probability that the formulary procedure was known at Rome before the Lex Aebutia authorized it as between *cives*, and by the practical sense of *ius gentium*, which may well have been the early sense, though its known usage is much later.

At any rate there is no doubt that by the beginning of the first century the civil law in both senses, that is of law *inter cives* and of law not resting merely on the Edict, had incorporated the essential constituents of the *ius gentium*. The main part of it was a law of contract, which might be improved by additions (the *bonae fidei* real and innominate contracts), but which only required further modernization in one of its members, the stipulation. This was a contract of the old *ius civile*, therefore, in spite of the simplicity and elasticity of its form, a formal contract; also a unilateral contract, which abstracted from the give and take of real business. The modernization of this contract, partly by a deeper juristic analysis and partly by means of praetorian *exceptiones* as interpreted, is the best illustration that can be given of the legal movement in the last years of the Republic. But for the moment the point to be insisted on is that substantially the whole of the institutions of the *ius gentium* and their union under that general concept were the product of native Roman jurisprudence, stimulated no doubt by the circumstances of the newly acquired empire. Their common characteristics, namely the rule of good faith, the determination of the effects of acts and facts in the law by the intention of the parties and not merely by the words used, formed an obvious antithesis to the formalism of the old civil law.

VIII. THE EFFECT OF GREEK THOUGHT ON JURISPRUDENCE

Forms being national and intention universal, the practical needs of an empire must in any case have given over the future to the *ius gentium*, but the same period which saw the consolidation of the *ius gentium* saw also the beginning of the reign of Greek thought at Rome. An inevitable result was the identification of the national antithesis of *ius civile* and *ius gentium* with that of νομικὸν δίκαιον and φυσικόν (τὸ πανταχοῦ τὴν αὐτὴν ἔχον δύναμιν)[1]. Thus the Greek doctrine of natural law found its entry into Roman legal thought well prepared, but it was too speculative ever directly to produce much practical law. Naturally the philosophic basis which it furnished for the universality of the principles of the *ius gentium* served in all departments of the law as a strong support of rationalism against traditionalism, of ethical as opposed to strictly legal views. But the fact that no special school of philosophy is indicated by the ordinary expressions of the classical jurists on the subject of *ius naturale* shows that their philosophy was not very deep. The Stoic philosophy has figured largely in books about Roman law, and doubtless the ethical theory by which the republican jurists were most affected was that of the Stoa, made fashionable by the Scipionic circle. But there was nothing specially Stoic in the method of definition by *genera* and *species* introduced into legal literature by Q. Mucius, nor in the dialectic for using which Cicero praised Servius Sulpicius. The truth is that the jurists were not philosophers, but just educated men[2].

The direct source of Greek influence on Roman law was not philosophy but rhetoric, and he who would trace this influence to its ultimate sources must be competent to pronounce on the philosophical derivations of the rhetorical theory. The radical nature of the influence of rhetorical method of interpretation on the jurisprudence of the end of the Republic has been demonstrated, for the first time in convincing detail, by a recent monograph[3]. To put it shortly, the logical or equitable method of interpretation was largely substituted for the literal. But from an English lawyer's point of view the epithet 'equitable' is misleading. To adopt *voluntas* as the test of legal meaning instead of *verba* may be equitable in the general sense, but it is not equity in the English technical sense; it is a change of civil law. An English lawyer would find applications of Aristotle's definition of equity: ἐπανόρθωμα νόμου ᾗ ἐλλείπει διὰ τὸ καθόλου[4], in the *ius praetorium* rather than in the transformation of the legal method of interpretation. This last is the matter to be examined.

---

[1] *Nic. Eth.* 1134 *b*, 18.

[2] W. W. Buckland, *Text-book of Roman Law*, pp. 53–4.

[3] Stroux, *Summum ius summa iniuria.* Cp. E. Cuq, *Manuel des institutions juridiques des romains*[1], pp. 40 *sqq.*; P. Jörs, *Geschichte und System des röm. Privatrechts*, pp. 58 *sqq.*

[4] *Nic. Eth.* 1137 *b*, 26: 'an amendment of the law, in those points where it fails through the generality of its language' (F. H. Peters' translation, ed. 7, p. 176).

Rhetoric professed to classify cases under general types (στάσεις, *status*), and to provide the advocate with the appropriate arguments on either side under each type. Among the questions arising under these *status* are questions of interpretation, whether of statute or of the expressions of parties, and here the oratorical programmes of ready-made arguments constitute a complete theory of interpretation, which Stroux has analysed from its presentment in Cicero's *De inventione* (II, 40, 116 *sq.*), a work based on Greek models. The most important debate is that between *scriptum* or *verba* and *voluntas* or *sententia*. We find that every possible argument *pro* and *contra* on the question of grammatical or literal versus logical or equitable interpretation had been exhausted by the rhetorical method in which the youth of Rome was being trained. It is impossible that their education in this fundamental problem of jurisprudence should have had any but a very considerable effect on advocates, jurists and judges. The impression to be derived from Cicero is that of a sweeping victory for the equitable method, a final defeat for the *callida interpretatio* attacked by him in the *pro Murena* and the *pro Caecina*; but after all it was the jurists, Mucius, Aquilius and Servius, who had the last word. The arguments in favour of equitable interpretation (*voluntas*) were undoubtedly timely, in that they touched the weak spot of the traditional method of the civil law, its literalness (*verba*). But those in favour of *verba* have also a universal validity which was not likely to have been lost on lawyers. To speak of a complete victory would be, to say the least, an exaggeration, because that would mean that the jurists lost their heads and threw over their national jurisprudence for the *doctrina transmarina atque adventicia*[1]. A closer reading of Cicero shows that he was fully conscious that there were two sides to the question[2].

Still, an almost revolutionary reinforcement of the tendencies which had in a previous age produced a national development of the institutions of the *ius gentium*, and secured the enactment of the Lex Aebutia, must be admitted, and it must be attributed very largely to the rhetorical method. The exact nature of the victory was that the principle of equitable interpretation secured a firm foothold in the civil law itself: there is a notable example in the *causa Curiana*, a *cause célèbre* of the Sullan period, in which L. Licinius Crassus argued successfully against Q. Mucius

---

[1] Cicero, *de orat.* III, 33, 135.
[2] *De orat.* I, 44, 197; 3, 33, 133–5; *pro Caecina*, 24, 67–9; 25, 70. Cf. [Quintilian] *Decl.* 264.

Scaevola that, where a testator had appointed an expected post-humous son his *heres*, and had provided a successor to him in the event of his dying before puberty, effect must be given to his obvious intention in the event which happened, but had not been expressly provided for, of no posthumous son being born; and the arguments on both sides were derived from rhetoric[1]. That was an important precedent, but, though *in medio iure civili*, a centumviral precedent. The Digest can be cited in favour of equitable interpretation, but also, though not equally, in favour of literal. A wholesale and immediate abandonment of formalism and of the accepted interpretations of traditional formularies could only have been effected by legislation, and such may have been the intention of Caesar's project of codification. But what actually happened was that, the unconscious equity obtainable by literal interpretation having been exhausted, its place was taken by a conscious equity based on *voluntas*, which produced a gradual reform, proceeding from case to case and from institution to institution, the final results of which were not obtained till long after our period. There is weight in the fact that Cicero's judgments of the three greatest jurists of his time lay special stress on their justice and equity, but they remained lawyers.

There are limits, however, to the reforms that can be effected by change of doctrine even in so vital a point as the theory of interpretation. The modernization of Roman law could not have been accomplished, as accomplished it was, by practice, if practice had not disposed of the Edict as an engine of reform. The Edict enabled practice to respect tradition, to leave the civil law formally untouched, and yet to set it aside. In this respect, though they are quite different in technique, praetorian law and English Equity present a striking resemblance.

The modernization of the stipulation by the combined operation of the new doctrines and the *ius praetorium* is the best illustration of the movement begun in our period, although the developments about to be mentioned fall largely within the imperial period. The ambiguous position of this contract must be recalled: a formal contract which was nevertheless *iuris gentium*. That last character it doubtless owed to the simplicity and rationality of its form, which is really the ultimate analysis of a promise. But in spite of its simplicity, the form remained a form. It was necessary that the question and answer should be exchanged orally *inter praesentes*. It is most significant that as late as Gaius we have no hint that the oral solemnity, attenuated as it then was, could be replaced by

---

[1] Stroux, *op. cit.* pp. 29 *sqq.*; cf. Girard, *op. cit.*, p. 883, 1.

writing. The use of sealed evidentiary documents was, indeed, a republican practice not only in stipulations, but in wills and mancipations; no doubt in business transactions generally *cavere* spelt *scribere*. But, in contrast to Hellenistic practice, such documents remained mere evidence, creating a strong presumption that the oral solemnity had in fact taken place, but displaceable by sufficient evidence to the contrary. This is proof positive that, in contrast to the all-pervading influence of Greek speculation, the adoption of practical Greek law, where it took place, was an act of choice, not one of obedience to an irresistible tendency.

The formalism of the stipulation meant more than that a certain solemnity must be observed. It meant also that the promissor was bound strictly to what was said and to that only. He might have promised more than he intended, or less than what the parties manifestly meant: he was bound *verbis*, not *sententia* or *voluntate*. It was not until the jurists had analysed stipulation as a form embodying *consensus*, and to which *consensus* was essential, that any attention could be given to intention as such. We have no evidence of such an analysis before the beginning of the Empire, but in course of time it was held that essential mistake nullified a stipulation *ab initio*. That, however, was far short of substituting the presumable intention for the expression. In the interpretation of stipulations the Romans held fast to *strictum ius*, that is to the exact meanings attributed to words by tradition. One can only applaud their wisdom. But the case was different where some hoary technicality prevented effect being given to words actually used. Thus if a man promised by stipulation to advance another a certain sum up to a certain date (*i.e.* if requested on or before that date), the resulting obligation at civil law was perpetual, but *iure praetorio* effect was given to the void words. If the stipulator sued disregarding them, he would be met by the *exceptio pacti*. A simpler application of the same *exceptio* was where the stipulator had made an informal pact, devoid of civil effect, not to sue (Gaius 4, 116 *b*). This may well have been the original case under the *exceptio*; the pact in our previous case exists only by construction of law.

The formalism of stipulation also meant that the promise and the resulting obligation were isolated from the surrounding circumstances. Thus, if a promise had been obtained by fraud, the promissor was none the less bound at civil law. Crude cases of this kind were probably the occasion of the introduction of the *formulae de dolo* on the proposal of Aquilius Gallus, but the *exceptio doli* was interpreted to cover cases where the sharp practice of the plaintiff arose out of events subsequent to the stipulation. Thus, if a promise had been made in view of some counter-performance not mentioned in it, and that counter-performance was withheld, the promise was absolutely binding at civil law, but its enforcement could be resisted by the *exceptio doli* (Gaius 4, 116 *a*). The result was that stipulation became a causal instead of an abstract contract. A very real defect was thus at least partially cured.

It is not likely that the more refined applications of the *exceptiones*, first devised to meet gross bad faith, can be attributed to our period, but it can claim the credit of having founded the principle that inequitable claims, however well grounded at civil law, must be defeated: *saepe enim accidit ut quis iure civili teneatur, sed iniquum sit eum iudicio condemnari* (Gaius 4, 116).

IX. CRIMINAL LAW

Criminal law falls under the general concept of *ius*, but in paying comparatively little attention to it modern civilians do but follow the tradition, at any rate up to a comparatively late period, of Roman jurisprudence. The jurists elaborated their system of private law as a thing apart from public; the scientific treatment of criminal law hardly dates from before Hadrian, and was never carried to the same perfection as that of private law. This in spite of the fact that the Twelve Tables made no distinction between the two. We find there, along with the private law, a number of cases in which the death penalty is ordained as a public punishment in the sense that there is no sign that it represents a legalization of private revenge, or anything but the direct repression by the community of acts done to its prejudice. But private law was segregated at least as early as 366 B.C., when *iudicia privata* were assigned to a special magistrate, the *praetor*, who had nothing to do with criminal cases; indeed the seeds of separation had been sown even earlier, if we may trust the tradition which attributes to the first days of the Republic the declaration of the citizen's right *provocare ad populum* from the death-sentence of a magistrate (see vol. VII, pp. 445 *sqq.*).

The problem of fettering the *imperium* of the magistrates, which in the sphere of private law did not arise owing to the peculiar form taken by the *iudicium privatum* (above p. 853 *sq.*), appears in the criminal sphere as the fundamental point in the establishment of the rule of law. It was dealt with by the clumsy method, just referred to, of *provocatio* from death-sentences. For death was the one criminal punishment of primitive Rome; mutilation was unknown, scourging of citizens occurs only as part of the capital penalty, confiscation appears only incidentally, exile and lesser political penalties are a later phenomenon, and imprisonment is met with only as an occasional administrative expedient[1]. Fines, it is true, soon made their appearance, but at an early date they too, if above a certain maximum, were subjected to *provocatio*.

The result of *provocatio* was thus to make one or other of the assemblies the criminal court in all graver cases. The proceedings there (*iudicium populi*) were formally a petition for remission of the sentence pronounced by the magistrate after public *anquisitio*. But in substance the magistrate, after having convicted and sentenced upon such grounds as seemed good to him, was obliged, in order to give effect to his sentence, to assume the position of prosecutor before the people. Probably for this reason among others criminal jurisdiction under the Republic was not exercised by the consuls, but by minor magistrates, quaestors, aediles, duumvirs and tribunes. Now under such a system it is evident that only a rudimentary jurisprudence would be possible, though the native Roman legal sense established the elementary principles of publicity of proceedings, notice to the accused, and facilities for defence. The only traces of literary treatment of criminal law under the Republic are manuals for the conduct of magistracies; the subject fell outside the admirable institution of *responsa*.

Nevertheless, save in exceptional cases (above, pp. 304 *sqq.*), the *iudicia populi* seem to have worked tolerably till the last century of the Republic. Apart from their defects in cases bearing or capable of being given a political colour, their vice seems to have lain in the slackness engendered by the magistrates being obliged to weigh the chances of a tribunician *intercessio* or of a rebuff from the assembly, instead of considering simply the maintenance of law and order. There is no reason to suppose that in the best period of the Republic common criminals were frequently rescued by a tribune, or that the assemblies did not ordinarily confirm sentences pronounced by the magistrates in accordance with law and custom.

But by the beginning of the last century of the Republic another undesirable feature had appeared. Polybius (vi, 14, 7) tells us that in a capital trial the accused was free, until the last vote had been cast, 'to depart openly, sentencing himself to voluntary exile; and the banished man will be safe if he retires to Tibur, Praeneste, or Neapolis,' or any other state with which Rome has a sworn treaty.'

---

[1] Mommsen, *Röm. Strafrecht*, p. 42 n. 1; E. Levy, *Die röm. Kapitalstrafe*, Heid. S.B. 1930–1, Abh. 5, p. 17, n. 4.

The custom (ἔθος) was indeed already even more lax: self-exile seems to have been allowed in practice even after condemnation, and before the end of the second century the custom was confirmed by statutes[1]. What this means is that the preliminary arrest of accused persons, which was well within the natural competence of the magistrates, had been abandoned, and that even the condemned were given a period of grace in which to exempt themselves from Roman jurisdiction by withdrawing from Roman soil and adopting another *civitas*. The magistrate's answer to such conduct was to procure from one or other of the popular assemblies a decree of interdiction from fire and water, which made the exile's return to Italy punishable by summary execution. We have thus to face the fact that a decadent public opinion had become opposed to the execution of citizens even for crimes so serious as treason and murder. Some authorities[2] hold that the mitigation did not extend to the common criminal, but the generality of Polybius' statement is confirmed by the later history of criminal penalties.

It must be borne in mind that the scope of the true criminal law, of the *iudicia populi*, was narrow: *provocatio* was confined to citizens, perhaps to male citizens; *peregrini*, slaves and perhaps women were subject to the unlimited *coercitio* of the magistrates. Of citizens themselves the majority were subject to the unlimited domestic discipline of the *paterfamilias*, as were of course slaves. Thus the less responsible elements of the population were sufficiently under control without recourse to the *iudicia populi*. And lastly the commonest offences of even independent male citizens were dealt with by civil, not criminal, penal law. Our English system of private rights of action for wrongs or torts is mainly compensatory, though it by no means lacks a penal element, but the Roman private delicts, as they came to be called, were essentially rights to sue for a money penalty in lieu of vengeance; compensation of the injury was only incidental, indeed in some cases might be recovered by independent action. Wrongs to another's physical person or honour, and unlawful appropriation of or damage to his property, these, which are the staple crimes, were not yet treated as such, but were visited with a pecuniary penalty recoverable by the injured party in a civil action, a penalty often much greater than the injury.

It should further be noted that, although theft of and damage to public property were punishable by *multa* exacted under the *coercitio* or by comitial proceedings, it might also be open to the

---

[1] Sallust, *Cat.* 51, 22 and 40. Levy, *op. cit.* p. 19.
[2] Levy, *op. cit.* p. 19 n. 1.

magistrate to sue for the penalty provided for the protection of private property under the forms of private law, *i.e.* before the *praetor urbanus*. The private action was extended to the recovery of fines, in the strict sense, imposed by statute or edict, and frequent use was made in the later period of the device of allowing such actions to be brought by any citizen (*actio popularis*), his zeal as informer being stimulated by the prospect of pocketing the penalty recovered[1].

But in the long run private law cannot be made to do the work of public. The common thief would not be likely to be able to pay double or quadruple the value of what he had stolen, though it must be admitted that if he failed to do so, he would be reduced to the unpleasant position of an *adiudicatus*, and again, that if he was *alieni iuris*, there might well be some substantial person behind him to answer in the noxal action. But the proof that the remedy became unsatisfactory lies in the fact that in the ordinary practice of the Empire the civil *actio furti* was displaced by criminal prosecution *extra ordinem*. Again, the reform of the private suit for *iniuria* mentioned above as having taken place in the last century of the Republic did not re-establish its adequacy as a remedy for all forms of that wrong, notably the more violent. Accordingly we shall find that certain cases of *iniuria* were brought by Sulla within the jurisdiction of one of his new courts, and under the Empire this delict also became subjected to criminal process *extra ordinem*.

A comprehensive reform was carried out by Sulla, following lines suggested by previous legislation from the Lex Calpurnia of 149 onwards. The Leges Corneliae[2], without constituting a criminal code, form a closely connected group. They defined each some offence or offences, and laid them open to prosecution, in general by any qualified citizen, before a court consisting of a large jury drawn from the upper classes and presided over (normally) by a praetor. From the sentence of these courts there was no appeal to the *comitia*, and the old procedure of the *iudicia populi*, though not formally abolished, was superseded in practice. The utilitarian

---

[1] Mommsen, *Die Popularklagen, Juristische Schriften*, III, p. 375. But see L. Wenger, *Institutionen des röm. Zivilprozessrechts*, p. 159 n. 27.

[2] On the Lex Calpurnia see vol. VIII, p. 375, and on the Leges Corneliae see above, pp. 304 *sqq.* The chief later Republican criminal statutes are: Lex Plautia de vi (?77), Lex Tullia ambitus (63), Lex Julia repetundarum (59), Lex Pompeia de parricidis (?55), Lex Licinia de sodaliciis (55), and various Leges Juliae more or less certainly attributed to Caesar's dictatorship, as to which see P. F. Girard, *Z. d. Sav.-Stift., Rom. Abt.*, XXXIV, 1913, p. 295.

and opportunist character of Roman legislation precludes the idea that the Leges Corneliae, or even the Lex Julia de iudiciis publicis of Augustus, amounted to a systematic code. There are common ideas running through them, but the constituting statute of each of the *quaestiones perpetuae*, as the new courts are called, fixed its own procedure, penalties and sphere of jurisdiction. As a whole Sulla's legislation amounted to a great reform. From the point of view of procedural theory it meant the substitution of the accusatory for the inquisitorial form, from that of substantive law a better definition of crimes and penalties, from the political a recognition of the breakdown of the popular assemblies on their judicial side.

Mommsen regards the novelty of the new system as consisting essentially in the adoption by criminal law of the forms of civil procedure[1]. The office of accuser was taken away from the examining magistrate and thrown open to the volunteer private citizen; the commission of the decision to *iudices* resembles the fundamental institution of private procedure, except for the presidence of a magistrate; the definition of the charge by the constituting statute conferred on the *nominis receptio* by the magistrate a function analogous to that of *litis contestatio*. By a system of challenges the parties, as we may call them, were given a part in the selection of the *iudices*, though not so great as in an ordinary private suit. The accuser, it is true, was accorded, as representing the public interest, an exceptional right to compel the appearance of witnesses, which by an injustice more apparent than real was not extended to the accused. From the decision of the court, which was declared by its president, there was, as in private law, no appeal, the penalty was an automatic statutory deduction from it, the terms of the statute thus constituting a sort of *formula*.

Criticisms are obvious. The volunteer prosecutor was not necessarily actuated by public spirit; his motive might well be private revenge, or, since there might be substantial rewards for success, cupidity. Hence provision for a countercharge of *calumnia* or malicious prosecution is a feature of the Cornelian legislation; and there were corresponding precautions against collusive prosecution. Again, exactly by whom and how questions of law were decided does not appear. One thinks of the presiding magistrate, but his position in the course of the trial does not seem to have approached that of an English judge in a jury case.

---

[1] H. F. Hitzig, *Die Herkunft des Schwurgerichts*, suggests imitation of Greek law. Cf. P. Koschaker, *Z. d. Sav.-Stift., Rom. Abt.*, L, 1930, pp. 679, 724.

Certainly the jury, whose size must have diminished the sense of individual responsibility, were neither protected by a law of evidence nor assisted by a judicial summing up, and had not the advantage even of mutual consultation before giving their verdict: the speeches and proofs of the parties having been concluded, they simply voted.

It has been the prevailing view[1] that *aquae et ignis interdictio*, in effect exile with loss of citizenship, was adopted by Sulla as a legal penalty, being the highest that could be placed within the competence of an inappellable *quaestio*. But recently it has been demonstrated[2] that his laws, as one would expect, preserved the old death-penalty, and that the appearance to the contrary is due simply to the continuance of the lax practice, now inveterate, described above. Not till the very end of the Republic does exile figure as a statutory penalty[3].

With all these reservations the new system marks a great advance on the old, and might well have formed the starting point of a jurisprudential and statutory development which would have put criminal law on a nearer level to private. But it came too late. Though, as reformed by Augustus and stiffened by the superior administration of the Empire, it survived for two centuries, and though evidence is not lacking in the Digest of developments by juristic interpretation and Senatusconsult, the *ordo iudiciorum publicorum*, as we may call it, was the most certain victim of the return to the principle of an absolute magistracy. Even if we leave out of account the abuses of State trials, the required extensions of the criminal law took more and more the form of *crimina extraordinaria*, which meant that offences were defined and punished at the discretion of a magistracy regulated in the last resort not by law, but by the administrative instructions of the supreme magistrate, under a procedure which, though it did not altogether shed the accusatory form, was in substance once more inquisitorial.

The mere list of the crimes for which *quaestiones* existed in Cicero's[4] day reveals the preponderating interest of the legislator

---

[1] Mommsen, *Röm. Strafrecht*, pp. 73, 201, 907, 941.

[2] Levy, *op. cit.* Substantially the view of J. L. Strachan-Davidson, *Problems of the Roman Criminal Law*, II, chaps. XV and XVI; but he does not altogether shake off Mommsen's influence.

[3] Levy, *op. cit.* pp. 30 *sqq.*: Lex Tullia de ambitu (63), Fufia de religione (61), Clodia (58), Leges Caesaris de maiestate (46), Pedia (43).

[4] *Plagium* and the Lex Fabia are here omitted, because of the highly uncertain date of that law, and because Mommsen, *Strafrecht*, p. 780 hardly bears out what is implied on p. 203.

in offences directly affecting the State: they are *maiestas*, which practically absorbed the oldest crime, *perduellio*, under a more elastic conception, *vis publica* or seditious violence, *ambitus*, covering besides bribery the organization of electoral clubs, the *crimen repetundarum*, which needs no comment here, *peculatus* and *sacrilegium*, and *corruptio iudicis*. The offences directly against individuals, to which we shall confine our attention, are murder (with connected offences), *iniuria* in the forms of assault and housebreaking, and *falsum*. Even here we have evidence that the prevalent evils were violence and brigandage.

The submission of certain forms of *iniuria* to a *quaestio* is deceptive; they were not thereby constituted public crimes in the full sense, for the charge could only be brought by the injured party, and condemnation, as in the civil action, was in a sum of money payable to him. The purpose of this Lex Cornelia may be conjectured to have been an acceleration and aggravation of the remedy. Though the procedure resembled that of a criminal prosecution, it was under the direction of the *praetor urbanus* or his substitute. As already stated, true criminal process was applied to this offence under the Empire.

For murder there appears to have been a standing *quaestio* established before Sulla. The crimes dealt with by the Lex Cornelia de sicariis et veneficis[1] were various: not merely murder, but also going about within the first milestone of Rome armed for the purpose of murder or robbery; not merely the murderous administration of poison, but also its manufacture, sale, purchase or keeping; corruption against the accused in a capital charge; giving false witness against the accused in such a case; arson[2]. These diverse categories can be resumed under the general idea of the protection of life, but Mommsen holds the real cause of their conjunction to have been the ancient practice of referring all capital charges other than *perduellio* to the *quaestores parricidii*. The frequency of the crimes coming under this statute led naturally to the constitution of additional courts presided over by quasi-magistrates, and the work may have been divided according to the categories of crime.

There seems to be no ground for holding[3] that murder of near relatives, *parricidium*, was, at least till the Lex Cornelia, reserved to the old comitial procedure, nor that the Lex Cornelia expressly

---

[1] The original title seems to have been *inter sicarios et de veneficiis*.

[2] Later extensions to magic, procuring abortion, castration and the like.

[3] Mommsen, *Röm. Strafrecht*, pp. 643 *sqq.*; E. Costa, *Cicerone Giureconsulto*, II, pp. 123–4.

saved the *poena cullei*, which was reduced to the normal banishment by a Lex Pompeia de parricidis (? 55 B.C.). The evidence rather is that *parricidium* came under the *quaestio*-procedure along with other murders, and that the death-penalty, had it been exacted, would have been carried out *more maiorum*[1].

It is certain that the statute dealt only with homicide committed *dolo*, not with that resulting from negligence, *i.e.* with murder, not manslaughter. This is in accord with a general principle running through the criminal law, as is the punishment of accomplices equally with principals. But it is doubtful whether the punishment of attempts and preparatory acts was not a peculiarity of this statute: *in lege Cornelia dolus pro facto accipitur* (*Dig.* 48, 8, 7). The more usually held view is that this was a general principle of criminal law already established in Cicero's time, in admitted opposition to the rule in private delicts. Another view is that the criminal principle is a generalization made only under Hadrian from the Lex Cornelia de sicariis[2].

The remaining statute to be mentioned is that later known as the Lex Cornelia de falsis, originally as the Lex Cornelia testamentaria nummaria. It was a characteristically casuistic enactment, dealing with specific forms of dishonesty: forging of a false or tampering with a genuine testament, putting false metal in circulation, and various offences against the public coinage, not however the several heads of corruption in litigation later included under *falsum*. The statute indeed received some notable extensions under the Empire, but no comprehensive conception of *falsum* was evolved. *Falsum* simply meant any charge that could be brought under this Lex Cornelia and its extensions, but the list of such charges, as befitted criminal law, was definite; prosecution for *falsum* had not the elasticity of the civil *actio doli*, and hence later law gave birth to the complementary semi-public *actio stellionatus*. This Lex Cornelia, at any rate, punished only the consummated crime.

It may have been noticed that we have said nothing of sexual offences, not even of incest, which last may have fallen within the scope of *iudicium populi* in early times. It seems that the criminal law of the later Republic took no account of these matters, apart from measures repressing *lenones* and a Lex Scantinia of uncertain date punishing paederasty. The point of view in sexual matters was that a Roman woman was bound to respect her unmarried or married state, but that the Roman man was only bound to

---

[1] Levy, *op. cit.* p. 28.
[2] Costa, *op. cit.* II, p. 69 n. 4.

respect these her duties, so that he could only offend as her partner in wrong. Over women the domestic tribunal was capable of exercising a severe control; moreover, a guilty wife might be made to suffer in respect of her *dos*. This seems to have been found sufficient, though it is obvious that, apart from the *actio iniuriarum* and the possibility of justifiable or excusable self-redress, the man might easily escape any punishment. The great reform in this sphere came from the Lex Julia de adulteriis of Augustus.

APPENDIX

THE LITERARY AUTHORITIES FOR ROMAN HISTORY, 133–44 B.C.[1]

The object of this note is to provide a clue to the extant literary authorities on which our knowledge of Roman history during this period depends, and also to give some rough indication of the nature and value of the matter which these various works enshrine. It does not set out to do more than this, and it is to be understood that there are many questions on the relation of these writers to each other which are still topics of controversy. Reference is made in the several Bibliographies to the epigraphic and numismatic material, which is of the first importance.

As a necessary preliminary to an account, however brief, of the authorities whose writings survive, something must be said of the records left by writers contemporary with the events they describe which we may reasonably assume to have been available for consultation during the whole or part of later antiquity. Raw material for the historian was to be found in the speeches and memoirs of leading men, several of whom, like Sulla, are known to have left behind them something in the nature of an autobiography. Direct use, however, of such documents as these seems rarely, if ever, to have been made in post-Republican times, and their influence on the majority of the surviving authorities has been exercised through the mediation of writers whose works have now mostly disappeared.

Among authors of what may be described as complete Histories of Rome the earliest who were able to deal with any considerable part of the period here in question were the group known collectively as the 'Sullan Annalists,' though their publications are to be dated after Sulla's death and in the neighbourhood of 70 B.C. The outstanding figures were Q. CLAUDIUS QUADRIGARIUS, VALERIUS ANTIAS and C. LICINIUS MACER, of whom the last was tribune in 73 B.C. (see pp. 766 *sqq.*). The reputation of these annalists is bad, but this is due above all to their imaginative handling of early Roman history. For later events, and especially for the events of their own age, their authority is by no means to be despised, though even here the length at which they wrote—Valerius Antias, the most verbose of all, seems to have devoted almost a whole book to every year from the time of the Gracchi onwards—suggests that, like Livy, they aimed at producing a readable story rather than a sober account of such features of the past as deserved the notice of later generations.

To be distinguished from the school which took as its theme the whole history of Rome is that which was content to deal with a briefer period. Two members of the latter, both roughly coeval with the Gracchi, were C. FANNIUS, a man of liberal outlook whose work covered the greater part of the

[1] For the modern literature on these writers see in general the survey of A. Rosenberg, *Einleitung und Quellenkunde zur römischen Geschichte*, Berlin, 1921, and the works cited below in the Bibliographies on the ancient sources. On those authors who belong to the period of this volume see also above, chap. XVIII.

last fifty years of the second century B.C., and a certain SEMPRONIUS ASELLIO, whose narrative is known to have been carried down as far as 91 B.C. These were succeeded in the same tradition by L. CORNELIUS SISENNA, praetor in 78 B.C., whose *Historiae* gave an account, conservative in its political sympathies, of events from the outbreak of the Social War to the death of Sulla; and this was continued by the *Historiae* of SALLUST, a work of which the extant fragments are numerous enough to have made possible a reconstruction of its general scheme. Sallust took as his subject the period in which the constitutional work of Sulla collapsed—a subject congenial to one who was a lifelong supporter of the *populares*. He began with 78 B.C. and continued with a detailed narrative of events, abroad as well as at home, until in the fifth book he had reached the year 67. The *Historiae* were written in the early thirties of the last century B.C., and it is possible that at his death in 35 B.C. Sallust left them incomplete. For Sallust's other works see below, p. 889 *sq*.

The chief successor of Sallust among Roman historians is ASINIUS POLLIO. Born in 76 B.C., he began a career under Caesar's protection with the opening of the Civil War and continued to play a part in public affairs which reached its highest distinction in the consulship in 40 B.C. and a triumph in the next year. After Actium had decided the struggle for power between Antony and Octavian, Pollio wrote *Historiae* which began with the formation of the First Triumvirate in the consulship of Metellus (60 B.C.) and extended to a point later than the Battle of Philippi. He died at the age of eighty in A.D. 4 or 5. Such evidence as there is for the character of his work suggests that he did not underrate his own part in the events which he described, and that he was at pains to correct the tradition set by Caesar's *Commentaries*. He was apparently no partisan and praised Cicero, Brutus and Cassius. He followed Antony at first but found it possible to be well seen by Octavian. Pollio appears to have had more influence on the historical tradition of Caesar's later career than any writer except Caesar himself (see further below, pp. 885 *sqq*.).

By the side of Pollio may be set a more shadowy figure, TANUSIUS GEMINUS, whose *Historiae* began not later than Sertorius and ended not earlier than 55 B.C. The few references to his work that survive suggest that it was anti-Caesarian, and Tanusius may have been the opposite, and possibly the opponent of Sallust, as a partisan writer (see below, p. 889 *sq*.).

Next must be noticed a figure of the first importance, standing somewhat outside the main Roman succession. Among the many undertakings to which POSIDONIUS OF APAMEA devoted his encyclopaedic mind was a large work on history. Posidonius, who was born in the thirties of the second century B.C., lived for the greater part of his life at Rhodes, and he came into contact with Rome both as an official representative of the Rhodians and as a friend of the many prominent Romans who were attracted by the fame of his erudition. His *Universal History*, which is said to have counted fifty-two books, opened in 146 B.C., where the narrative had been left by Polybius, and ended at some time in the Sullan age. Like Polybius, Posidonius was a philosophic historian, with an outlook on affairs at Rome which may be described as one of critical conservatism. And, like Polybius again, Posidonius had travelled in the West, where he seems to have collected information of value about people who lived outside the Roman Empire.

The work of Polybius was also continued in the time of Augustus by STRABO OF AMASIA, in Pontus, who wrote a 'general history,' the greater part of which covered the years from 146 B.C. to towards the end of this period. This work is lost, though it may be traced in Josephus and has been suspected as underlying much of Plutarch and Appian. The geographical work of Strabo which survives contains some historical material, more particularly for the Greek East. A slightly earlier contemporary of Strabo, NICOLAUS OF DAMASCUS, also wrote a general history which has suffered the same fate as that of Strabo. What remains of his work belongs to the biographical tradition, being the beginning of a *Life of Augustus* which affords some good evidence for events during the year 44 B.C.

Roman achievements were naturally the theme of Greek panegyric: a prominent writer in this kind was THEOPHANES OF MITYLENE, who devoted himself to the glorification of his patron Pompey. A more distinguished figure is JUBA II, king of Mauretania under Augustus. He was a scholar—'studiorum claritate memorabilior etiam quam regno'—even if his method of writing was compilation rather than creation. Among his works was a *History of Rome*, apparently in two books, which reached the period of the civil wars. This *History*, and still more a substantial work on comparative customs and institutions ('Ομοιότητες), were used by Plutarch, and the citations suggest that Juba enjoyed a considerable reputation in antiquity.

The writing of Republican history was continued under the Principate by historians whose works have perished, but who were largely the immediate sources of most of the extant authorities for the period which they described. It is, however, uncertain whether any of the known writers of the early Principate after Augustus were concerned with general Roman history before the beginning of the Civil War. The resemblances between Appian (see p. 886) and Plutarch (p. 887) may perhaps be explained best by the hypothesis that both draw largely upon a general history of Rome, based on a succession of writers mostly contemporary with the events which they described. But it is not possible either to isolate with certainty all the material due to this source or to assign a name to the compiler of it.

It remains to mention the school of biographers which grew up in the last years of the Republic. Of the *Imagines* of VARRO we can say little but that they appear to have introduced this particular form of literature to Rome, but the *Vitae* of his contemporary, CORNELIUS NEPOS, seem, so far at least as some of the Roman *Lives* are concerned, to have been based on an amount of independent research which made the result one of serious value. Unfortunately, none of the Roman *Lives* has survived except those of Cato the Elder and of Atticus from his *de Latinis historicis* (p. 769). There is one other figure which here deserves notice—that of C. JULIUS HYGINUS, the freedman of Augustus who became Prefect of the Palatine Library. Hyginus wrote a work in several books *de vita rebusque inlustrium virorum*, possibly for purposes connected with the *elogia* set up by Augustus in his new Forum, and this has left undoubted traces on the surviving records.

Of the extant authorities the first to be considered are those of the LIVIAN SCHOOL. Livy's narrative of this period was contained in the books numbered from 58 to 116 inclusive, of which our knowledge is wholly indirect. But, although the original text is lost, we have the *Periochae* of all these books—short summaries derived from an abbreviated form (*Epitome*) of the author's text. The extant *Periochae*[1] are thus separated from the work of Livy by an intermediate version, and it is clear that in course of transmission the views of Livy have at times suffered some misrepresentation. But on the whole it may be assumed that the *Periochae* give us access to the opinions of Livy on such subjects as they mention, and they are not in conflict with the conclusion, to which other evidence points, that for the greater part of this period Livy was dependent on the Sullan annalists—particularly on Claudius Quadrigarius and Valerius Antias—and at times apparently also on the *Histories* of Posidonius. For the period covered by Caesar's *Commentaries* and the Caesarian corpus (p. 767 and p. 889) Livy no doubt used these authorities, together with an independent source which it is not too hazardous to describe as Asinius Pollio. The trend of the Livian tradition can be reconstructed for part of the Civil War from Lucan and in general from Dio, who made a great use of this tradition. Indeed it is from writers in later centuries who relied on his authority that much of our knowledge of the Livian tradition is derived.

Two such, who lived in the second century A.D., were a certain FLORUS whose brief account of the wars of Rome is concerned with this period from bk I, 35 (II, 20) to Bk II, 13 (IV, 2), and one GRANIUS LICINIANUS whose treatment of the years down to 78 B.C., partly preserved in a palimpsest at the British Museum, is of interest rather for its antiquarian digressions than for the framework, which is ultimately derived from Livy. From the fourth century comes the *Breviarium historiae Romanae* of EUTROPIUS, published in the year A.D. 363 and here relevant in the section from Bk IV, 18 to Bk VI, 25 (20), and from the fifth the apologetic *Historia adversum paganos* of PAULUS OROSIUS, a friend and pupil of Augustine. The *History* of Orosius was published in A.D. 417, and in the parts dealing with the Roman Republic it provides our fullest information about Livy's version of the facts. The treatment of this period is to be found in the section from Bk V, 8 to Bk VI, 17. There is also a small amount of material derived from Livy preserved in the *Chronicon* of CASSIODORUS, which appeared in A.D. 519. Finally, under this head must be mentioned the names of JULIUS OBSEQUENS, who at an unknown date used some version of Livy as a source from which to compile a list of the prodigies recorded in Roman history, and of Cassius Dio. CASSIUS DIO COCCEIANUS[2], a native of Nicaea, was consul for the second time as colleague of the emperor Severus Alexander in A.D. 229, and his *Roman History* was written with a knowledge of the Imperial constitution, rare among the Greeks, which makes it, in its later parts at least, a work of the greatest value. Unhappily of the books from XXIV to XXXV, which contained his account of the period 133 B.C. to 69 B.C., nothing has been preserved but a few fragments so scanty as to make conjecture about the source of the narrative and its value virtually impossible. The beginning of Book XXXVI is lost, but what remains of that book and its successors to XLIV presents a continuous narrative of events from 68 to 44 B.C. It is generally agreed, and with reason, that

[1] Cited, according to common practice, as *Epit*.
[2] His *praenomen* is unknown.

in these books his main source was Livy, who in his day still ranked as the standard authority for the history of the Republic. In general his annalistic arrangement derives from Livy, but in places he groups his material otherwise in such a way as to obscure the chronological and, indeed, logical order of events. He was a convinced admirer of the revived Imperial authority of Septimius Severus and it may be suspected that this admiration has coloured his picture of Caesar, and rendered him uncritical of traditions which lent themselves to an interpretation upon these lines. Of the ideas and working of the Republican institutions he has not the knowledge or understanding which he displays in writing of the Imperial régime. But it cannot be denied that he practised independent criticism, and had a high ideal of history, although his desire to be a second Thucydides, coupled with his incapacity to achieve his desire, have deprived that part of his work which deals with the Republic of colour and life, and often of detail.

A work which requires special treatment is that of APPIAN—an Alexandrine Greek, born towards the end of the first century A.D., who secured a place in the imperial civil service during the principate of Antoninus Pius through the influence of Fronto, the tutor of M. Aurelius and L. Verus. The virtues of Appian as an historian are not high. He was chiefly interested in wars, on which he supplies information of value, but he had no eye for the themes of more significance and his ignorance of the Republican constitution betrayed him into frequent misunderstandings of his authorities. Nevertheless, the thirteenth book of his Ῥωμαϊκά, more commonly known as the first book of the *Civil Wars*, contains evidence of outstanding value for some part of the period with which it deals—the years from 133 to 70 B.C. In the later chapters, besides the usual annalistic material, the influence of Posidonius and subsequently of Sallust is plain, though it is unlikely that Appian drew on either of these sources direct. But in the earlier sections, and particularly from ch. 7 to ch. 17, where Appian gives his account of the tribunate of Tiberius Gracchus and of the economic situation which his legislation was designed to meet, he is using an authority contemporary with the events. The identity of this writer has been much discussed. Conceivably he was the historian C. Fannius (see above, p. 882), but it is of less importance to ascertain his name than to appreciate the penetrating insight with which he states the problem which Tiberius Gracchus essayed to solve—an insight not to be concealed by the jejuneness of Appian's reproduction. The second book of the *Civil Wars* continues the narrative to the death of Caesar. There are traces of the use of Asinius Pollio, which may explain the increasing fullness of treatment as the history approaches Pollio's own time. In general it may be said that nothing in the second book of the *Civil Wars* possesses for political history the value of the Gracchan sections of the first book. In his account of the wars in Illyria Appian gives some information of value, and this is truer still of the *Mithridatica*, which supplies the only continuous account of these wars as a whole, and of events geographically connected with them, such as the campaign against the pirates. For the First War, Appian appears to have drawn on Livy rather than Posidonius, who may have been his source for the preceding relations of Rome and Pontus. In the Second and Third Wars the narrative appears to come from a Greek source, probably Nicolaus of Damascus, with additions, for the Third War, from the poems of Archias, who accompanied Lucullus on his campaigns.

At this point there may be mentioned the surviving fragments from Books XXXIV to XXXIX of the *Bibliotheke* of DIODORUS SICULUS—a dull and inaccurate compilation made in the last years of the Republic, which is nevertheless a valuable source of information for various episodes, particularly the Sicilian Slave Wars, and which is of interest because the *History* of Posidonius was among the works whereon its author regularly drew. The information on geographical and ethnical matters collected by Posidonius is to some extent preserved by Strabo, whose remarks in Books IV and VII of his *Geography* on the Germanic invasions are evidence of value for that episode.

The second group among the extant authorities is composed of those who may in some sense be called biographers (see above, p. 884). Of these the earliest is C. VELLEIUS PATERCULUS, an army officer of no great intellectual distinction, who in A.D. 30 published a brief general history up to his own time. For the affairs of Rome, Velleius depends in the first place on the later annalists, but into the framework thus supplied he inserts a certain amount of matter derived from other sources, among which the earlier biographical compilations hold a prominent place. The chapters in which he treats the period here in question are those from 2 to 57 in the Second Book. In his account of the closing decade of the Republic signs of the age in which he lived can be detected: for example, Antony is made to appear as largely responsible for such acts of Caesar as did not suit the policy of the Principate.

Of far greater significance than Velleius is PLUTARCH, a native of Chaeronea born in the principate of Claudius, whose *Parallel Lives* of famous Greeks and Romans, though varying through every degree of value, often supply evidence of high importance. In the *Lives of the Gracchi*, besides material from an annalistic source, Plutarch had access, indirect indeed, to an early biography of which the author may plausibly be identified with Cornelius Nepos. Similar authorities are to be detected in the *Life of Marius*, another of Plutarch's more valuable compilations, and in the *Life of Sulla*—a disappointing record largely dependent, though not directly, on the *Memoirs* of the dictator—and in the *Lives of L. Lucullus, Sertorius, Pompey* and *Crassus*. In the last four the influence of the *Histories* of Sallust is clear in the treatment of those years with which Sallust had been concerned. The biographies of Crassus, Pompey and Caesar show marked resemblances in their general historical setting which point to the use of a source of considerable range, which may be the same as that followed by Appian in the corresponding parts of his *Civil Wars* (see above, p. 886). Within this setting there is a varied biographical tradition in which no doubt Asinius Pollio played a part. For the *Life of Cato the Younger* Plutarch appears to have made direct use of a work by the Stoic Thrasea, which in turn went back to an older biography by Munatius Rufus. In the biography of Cicero there is much excellent material derived ultimately from his freedman Tiro. The *Brutus* is drawn from some existing combination of memoirs in the same historical setting as the other lives of this period.

A later contemporary of Plutarch, C. SUETONIUS TRANQUILLUS, born *c.* A.D. 75, wrote eight books *de vita Caesarum*, of which the first is the life of Julius Caesar. His interests and his reading were wide, and he has the merit of using sources at first hand; but part of his sources were full of scandals which are not the truer for having been concocted by contemporaries. In others of his *Lives* he occasionally cited official sources by name, but it cannot be said with certainty that he did this in the *Divus Iulius*. Though well acquainted with the speeches and letters both of Caesar and Cicero, he shows little sign of having used them extensively. Resemblances to Plutarch suggest that he referred to the work of Pollio, which he cites twice. On the other hand he does not mention either Sallust or Livy. Although not impeccable in point of accuracy, he provides a valuable collection of facts, though his practice of grouping the material for his lives according to topics blurs his chronology.

In the same tradition stands the anonymous tract *de viris illustribus urbis Romae*, a work not earlier than the second century A.D. which in the chapters from 58 to 81 briefly sketches the careers of numerous outstanding figures from Scipio Aemilianus to Julius Caesar. The work is so short that its value is small, but such information as it does preserve is largely the common currency of the biographies, even if it be right to recognize scattered signs that the author was acquainted with the work of Florus.

Connected with biography, though to be distinguished therefrom, is the literature which culled from history *Exempla* of various virtues and vices. Of this form there is one specimen which yields a considerable amount of casual information about the later Republic—the *Libri novem factorum et dictorum memorabilium* published in instalments by a certain VALERIUS MAXIMUS during the principate of Tiberius. The sources of this work are to be seen in the biographical literature, behind which stood the later annalists and the contemporary memoirs to which the early biographers had recourse. Among the sources used by Valerius Maximus it is fairly certain that a similar selection of *Exempla* by C. Julius Hyginus (see above, p. 884) is to be included. Finally, though most important for the historian, remain contemporary works of various kinds.

For his own age the writings of CICERO provide evidence on a scale which makes the last years of the Republic a period more intimately known to posterity than any other of the same length before the invention of printing, but they also contain abundant references to earlier periods of Roman history. About the value of these, which is very far from uniform, nothing can here be said. There is, however, a work normally included in the Ciceronian corpus, though it is not by Cicero, which calls for special mention—the four books *de ratione dicendi ad C. Herennium*. This work was probably composed about the time of Sulla's dictatorship, and it has value as an historical authority, not only on account of the information contained in the passages cited by way of illustration, but because the author was an opponent of the Senate and so belonged to a school of thought whose opinions are very ill represented in our other authorities. The correspondence of Cicero (see above, pp. 773 *sqq.*) that has survived contains more than the orator's own letters. In particular, it includes letters written both by Caesar and Pompey in the first year of the Civil War, and the especially valuable commentary on the political situation at Rome sent by Caelius to Cicero during his absence in Cilicia. The great majority of the letters in the whole correspondence can be dated precisely or fairly closely, and their historical value in themselves and as a test of other sources is obviously very great. It has to be remembered that while some of them are calculated political documents, the majority, especially those written to Atticus, present the mood of a moment and are to be interpreted accordingly. In the same way the speeches, despite re-touches before publication, are governed by the political events which evoked them or the case which the orator had to plead.

Fragments of speeches which have perished and extremely well-informed notes are to be found in what remains of the commentary to Cicero's speeches which was composed not later than A.D. 57 and possibly after 54 by Q. ASCONIUS PEDIANUS. Unfortunately notes to only five speeches have survived. Some good information is also to be obtained from the *Scholia Bobiensia* to a number of speeches. The Gronovian scholiasts contribute little, and the same is true of the pseudo-Asconius' commentary to part of the Verrines. References to post-Gracchan and contemporary history are to be found also in the philosophical and rhetorical works of Cicero, and what remains of the *de Re publica* is evidence for Cicero's own political thought in the period during which the work was composed (see above, p. 623 *sq*.).

CAESAR'S *Commentarii* (and those of the so-called Caesarian corpus) are in form the raw material of history (see pp. 763 *sqq*.). Those on the Gallic Wars are based in part on the reports of Caesar's *legati* to him; and although the work was put into final form at one time, it embodies in part despatches of Caesar himself to the Senate at the end of each year (see above, p. 537 *Note*). Criticism has failed to prove extensive lapses from the truth, although no doubt Caesar placed a favourable colour on his actions, particularly in the first year of his governorship. The *Commentarii* on the Civil War were incomplete at the time of the dictator's death and contain gaps in the narrative. Caesar naturally takes his own part in the political narrative, but on the military side the details are almost wholly to be trusted, and in general his opponents are treated fairly and with respect. The *Gallic War* was completed by Hirtius, a member of Caesar's staff. Though not as devoid of military knowledge as has sometimes been supposed, Hirtius was more employed on the political side and was no doubt in Caesar's personal confidence. It is not improbable that he is the author of the *Bellum Alexandrinum* which continues the story of the Civil War where Caesar's own work ended. If this is so, he was not present at most of the varied events which he describes in that book, but the writer, whoever he was, had excellent sources of information. Of the remaining works in the Caesarian corpus the *Bellum Africum*, which treats of the campaign that ended with Thapsus, is from the pen of a soldier on the spot who views the operations from the angle of an officer of rank but not in Caesar's immediate confidence. The book is an excellent piece of military history. The writer of the *Bellum Hispaniense* was also a soldier who had first-hand information of what he attempted to describe. The attempt is only partly successful because of a pitiful illiteracy shot with strands of misapplied rhetoric. The text is badly transmitted and incapable of satisfactory emendation. The account of Munda can be supplemented from Dio, who retains a Livian tradition which is not without value.

To these may be added two extant works by SALLUST, which, though in form historical monographs, partake largely of the character of pamphlets.

These are the *Bellum Catilinae* and the *Bellum Jugurthinum*. The first was probably inspired by the publication in 42 B.C., from among Cicero's papers, of a pamphlet *de consiliis*, in which Caesar was declared to have been the true originator of the Catilinarian conspiracy. Sallust seeks to refute an allegation which was probably false, partly by an appeal to the attitude of Cicero at the time, partly by an alternative and far more elaborate falsification in which Catiline was made a great revolutionary, the result of the moral breakdown induced by the bad government of the *nobiles*. This attack on the *nobiles* was carried further in the *Bellum Jugurthinum*, in which the alleged faults of Senatorial foreign policy and the earlier career of Marius are placed in a setting of war on which Sallust, although he had been a governor in Africa, plainly did not lavish overmuch attention (see also pp. 113 *sqq.* and p. 767 *sq.*). More clearly pamphlets are the *Invectiva in M. Tullium* (see p. 619), apparently regarded as Sallustian in antiquity, and the two brochures '*ad Caesarem senem de re publica*,' which many scholars regard as from his hand. The question of these two pamphlets cannot be discussed here. It may be said that the results of stylistic study incline to the conclusion that both pamphlets are authentic rather than imitations of the Imperial period, whereas the difficulties presented by the contents, more particularly of the second, have not been solved. In chapter XVI above, the second is not adduced as contemporary evidence.

There remain a group of writers who were not primarily concerned with Rome or Roman history, but who incidentally supply information at points at which Rome entered their field. In the Augustan period POMPEIUS TROGUS wrote *Historiae Philippicae*, apparently in continuation and imitation of the work of Theopompus (vol. VII, p. 257). Trogus concerned himself with the States of the ancient world apart from Rome, and though his work has perished, the abridgement of it made by M. JUNIANUS[1] JUSTINUS in the third century A.D. provides some information not found in any other surviving sources. The reputation of the work has suffered from the inability of Justin to make an accurate and intelligent abstract.

For Roman contacts with the Jews and with Syria evidence is afforded by FLAVIUS JOSEPHUS, who was born in A.D. 37 or 38 of a Jewish priestly family. After taking a leading part in the great Jewish revolt he settled in Rome, enjoying the favour of the Flavian emperors. He wrote on the history of the Jewish people and of their wars since the time of the Maccabees, in which he supplies evidence for Roman foreign policy and warfare in the East, based, apparently, on the general histories of Nicolaus and Strabo (p. 884).

Josephus is concerned with his own people and his works provide a distinguished example of national or local history-writing. Another example of this last *genre* is the local history of Heraclea in Pontus written by Memnon about A.D. 100. More fortunately for us than for Heraclea the city came within the range of the Mithridatic Wars, and its local tradition preserved a record of these operations. The parts of the work which survive are of considerable value, though it may be said that their value varies in inverse proportion to the distance of the events from Heraclea.

---

[1] Or Junianius. See Kroll in *P. W. s.v.* Iunianus (4).

NOTES

1. THE DATE OF THE LEX RUBRIA DE COLONIA IN AFRICAM DEDUCENDA

On the authority of Velleius Paterculus (1, 15, 4), who places the foundation of Junonia in the year after that of Fabrateria—a colony planted in 124
(Vell.Pat. *ib.*)—and of Eutropius (IV, 21) and Orosius (V, 12, 1), who connect
the settlement at Carthage with the consular year 123, it is often held that
Rubrius was tribune for 124/3. On the other hand the Epitomator of Livy
(60) puts the colonial schemes of Gracchus in his second tribunate (123/2) and
Plutarch (*Gracchi*, 31) definitely assigns the Lex Rubria to a date after the
counter-stroke of Drusus, who was undoubtedly a tribune of 123/2 (Cicero,
Brutus, 28, 109). Confidence is impossible; but the present writer is inclined
to follow Livy and Plutarch at least in their suggestion that Rubrius held office
in 123/2. Various arguments in favour of this course are adduced by Kornemann (*Zur Geschichte der Gracchenzeit*, pp. 44 *sqq.*), and to these may be added
another consideration. The desertion of those former friends of Gracchus
who finally went over to the Senate can scarcely be placed later than the passing
of the final *lex iudiciaria*: if their loyalty survived that measure, it would have
survived to the end. Now the *volte-face* of Fannius is described as if it happened during his consulship—*i.e.* in 122, so that the final *lex iudiciaria* should
belong to that year and not to 123. If then, as is highly probable, this *lex
iudiciaria* was passed by M'. Acilius Glabrio, Glabrio was tribune for 122;
and, since it is virtually certain that Rubrius and Glabrio were tribunes in
the same year (see below, p. 892), 122 is indicated again as Rubrius' year of
office.

The argument used by Gsell (*Histoire ancienne de l'Afrique du Nord*, VII,
p. 59, n. 3 and p. 61) to show that Rubrius was tribune for the year 124/3 is
not wholly convincing. It depends on the belief that Gracchus, who
admittedly went to Carthage in order to make the site ready for his colonists
by marking out the plots and so on, took at least the bulk of the settlers with
him. Such a belief, as Gsell allows (*ib.* p. 61), is in direct conflict with
evidence of Appian (*Bell. Civ.* 1, 24, 104). That Gracchus was accompanied
by a certain number, who would supply such labour as was required for the
preliminary survey, is not only probable but is implied by Plutarch (*Gracchi*,
32, 1): but it is less easy to believe that the whole body landed in Africa
before any preparations for their reception had been made.

The present writer does not accept the theory of Carcopino (*Autour des
Gracques*, pp. 266 *sqq.*) that Rubrius proposed the colonization of Carthage
in order to secure the removal of Gracchus from Italy and so to gain a respite
from the Italian activities of the Gracchan land-commission. The theory
rests on an assumption which is improbable—that the Gracchan land-commission was still dangerously active: it is more likely that almost all the
available land in Italy had been assigned even before 123 (see above, p. 67).
Moreover, such a view, for which there is no direct evidence, conflicts with
the frequent statements that much was done to destroy the influence of
Gracchus by reports of difficulties at Carthage. It is not altogether easy to

believe that the prestige of Gracchus in Rome would have been affected by the misfortunes of Junonia if the colony was not a scheme of his own conception, but a device forced on him by rival politicians in order to tie his hands. This, however, is not to deny the truth of Appian's statement (*Bell. Civ.* I, 24, 102) that the Senate was relieved to see his back when he went off to Africa.   H. M. L

2. THE LEX ACILIA

On the sheet of bronze of which the fragments are now at Naples and Vienna the texts of two laws are in part preserved, and of these the earlier[1] is a *lex de rebus repetundis* (Bruns, *Fontes*[7], 10). The general character of this measure shows beyond all doubt that it belongs to the tribunician career of Gaius Gracchus, and there are some who still believe that the reference to a Lex Rubria in line 22 is conclusive evidence that it falls after the passing of the Lex Rubria de colonia in Africam deducenda and before the repeal of that law in 121 B.C[2]. Moreover, since the text in question reproduces all the recorded provisions of a Lex Acilia which is more than once mentioned by Cicero and his commentators, it must be admitted that this document contains either the Lex Acilia itself or something which was indistinguishable from that enactment in all respects on which evidence is available. In the complete absence of reasons for regarding this as an unrecorded measure different from the Lex Acilia though identical with it in all ascertainable details, the multiplication of hypotheses may be avoided and the first of the extant texts may be accepted as part of the Lex Acilia to which Cicero refers. In that case there is a further clue to its date. From an inscription found at Astypalaea[3], wherein a Lex Rubria Acilia[4] is cited in the course of a *senatus consultum*, it appears that a Rubrius and an Acilius were colleagues in some office and that together they passed a law which was the latest legislation on its particular subject, whatever precisely that may have been, in 105 B.C. Here again, in spite of the difficulty caused by the unusual double designation of the enactment[5], the most obvious identification is the least objectionable: Rubrius is the colleague of Gaius Gracchus, and [M'.] Acilius Glabrio was another member of the same tribunician board, which the present writer believes to be that of 123/2 B.C. Thus the earlier of the two epigraphic texts is connected by internal evidence with the activities of Gracchus: with this law a certain Acilius is associated by the casual remarks of Cicero about the provisions of a Lex Acilia: and by the inscription from Astypalaea an Acilius is revealed in an office, which may now be regarded as the tribunate, at the same time as one Rubrius, in whom it is natural to see the author of the Lex

---

[1] J. Carcopino (*Autour des Gracques*, pp. 228 *sqq.*) argues that this is the later of the two texts; but the facts adduced by Mommsen (*Gesammelte Schriften*, I, pp. 11 *sqq.*) in favour of the other view, which is here adopted, appear to the present writer to be conclusive.

[2] For a different view see Carcopino, *op. cit.*, pp. 220 *sqq.*

[3] *I.G.R.R.* IV, 1028.

[4] The vital words are in lines 12–13—[κατὰ] τὸν νόμον [τόν τε] Ῥόβριον καὶ τὸν Ἀκίλιον.

[5] On this see Mommsen, *Staatsrecht*, III, p. 315, n. 2.

de colonia in Africam deducenda. There are thus independent indications that Acilius and the earlier of the laws on our inscription are to be connected with one another and with the tribunate of Gaius Gracchus. For these reasons the extant document may be regarded as part of the Lex Acilia, and in what follows it will so be called.

The Lex Acilia concerns itself wholly with the court for the trial of charges of extortion; and, though later authorities often speak as if the judiciary reforms of Gracchus had a wider scope than this, there is a lack of evidence to show that other permanent *quaestiones* had been set up so early as 122 B.C. Even if it could be proved that other *iudicia publica* were already in existence, the peculiar purpose of the *repetundae*-court (see above, p. 75) would make it easy to believe that in his judicial reforms Gaius Gracchus confined his attention to the needs of this particular tribunal. In fact, however, the *quaestio de rebus repetundis* is the only court of the new type known for certain to have been instituted before 123 B.C. The authorities for the Gracchan Lex ne quis iudicio circumveniatur no more prove that Gracchus established a standing court for the trial of this offence than the evidence for the Lex Cornelia Baebia de ambitu of 181 B.C. (vol. VIII, p. 374) or for the consequential law of 159 B.C. (Livy, *Epit.* 47) shows that a *iudicium publicum* was created on either of these occasions. Indeed, the passage of Cicero's speech *pro Cluentio* (55, 151) which is often quoted as proof that Gaius Gracchus set up a permanent court for the trial of this charge rather suggests that the first standing *quaestio* on this subject, as on many others, was due to Sulla. Nor is it necessary to infer from other remarks of Cicero[1] that a *iudicium publicum* for cases of murder had been established by 142 B.C.

Writers who lived after the Sullan age may well have assumed that Gracchus was dealing with a system which, if it was not as elaborate as that which it was the work of Sulla to create, included more *quaestiones* than one; and the assumption was perhaps made easier by the fact that the issue raised by Gracchus about the solitary standing court of his own day affected all later courts of the same kind as they were successively established. But by itself the general phraseology used by Velleius, Plutarch, Tacitus and Appian is not enough to prove the existence of other courts for which no explicit evidence is to be had, and it may therefore be said that, so far as is known to us, the famous measure whereby Gracchus set strife between the Senate and the next order in the State was confined to the *quaestio de rebus repetundis*[2].

The surviving sections of the law are enough to show that it made comprehensive arrangements for the conduct of the court, but its political significance is due almost wholly to its change in the recruitment of the *iudices*. Hitherto they had been drawn exclusively from the Senate; henceforward no senator was to be empanelled[3]. But at this point uncertainty begins. It is

[1] *de finibus*, II, 16, 54: cf. *de nat. deor.* III, 30, 74. On these passages see A. W. Zumpt, *Das Criminalrecht der röm. Republik*, I, 2, p. 106.

[2] Criticisms of the view here adopted, that the Lex Acilia is the famous Gracchan judiciary law, may be found in *Hist. Zeitschr.* 3te Folge, XV, 1913, pp. 491 *sqq.* (W. Judeich) and in *Hermes*, LVI, 1921, pp. 281 *sqq.* (E. von Stern).

[3] For a different view see M. A. Levi in *Riv. Fil.* N.S. VII, 1929, pp. 383 *sqq.*

true that the general effect of the reform allows of little doubt: in the place of senators there were put jurors drawn from the most substantial stratum of society outside the Senate itself. But beyond this everything is conjecture. By one of those tantalizing accidents which are too frequent in the fortunes of epigraphic monuments, both passages of the Lex Acilia in which the positive qualifications of the new *iudices* were set out have been destroyed, and over their restoration by conjecture much fruitless effort has been expended. In its main lines the issue is plain: it lies between a qualification expressed in an amount of property and one which demands that the jurors should have been enrolled in certain specified centuries of the Servian organization.

At this point the *equites* must for the first time be introduced, and in order that speculation, however hazardous, may rest on at least a foundation of certainty the uses of the term first to be examined must be those which prevailed in the Ciceronian age. Though the evidence is copious, an adequate summary of the facts is to be found in a single passage. In the pamphlet entitled *De petitione consulatus*, which may very well be an authentic work written by Quintus Cicero at the end of the year 65 B.C., Quintus advises his brother Marcus to secure the support of the 'equitum centuriae,' the famous eighteen centuries of knights: the task, he says, will be easy because the members of these centuries are few, and also because they are young men who readily respond to the seductions of a skilful canvass. But, what is more, since Marcus has the *equester ordo* in his pocket, the youthful *equites* of the eighteen centuries will be induced to give him their votes by the 'ordinis auctoritas' (8, 33). Thus there are two bodies to be distinguished—the *equites equo publico*, who are a small body of rich cadets, and the *equester ordo* itself. Of this *ordo* it is enough to say that, so far from being an organized corporation, it can scarcely be described more precisely than as a stratum of Roman society—a stratum consisting of those citizens with the wealth required for membership of the equestrian centuries and who were not members of the Senate. Such men, though not included in the *centuriae equitum*, had some claim to describe themselves as *equites* because, possibly since the time of Camillus, they were theoretically liable to be called upon for service as *equites equo privato*: but, though it was customary for the *equites equo publico* to surrender their horse at the age of forty-six at latest and so to join the *equester ordo* in its wider sense, it is beyond doubt that the *ordo* contained many men who had never held the *equus publicus* at all. Their connection with the *equitatus* was simply this—that, while they were not senators, they had property of an amount which made them liable for equestrian service if such service was required. The ownership of this property was the only positive differentia by which they could be legally described, and if it was they who were made eligible for choice as *iudices* it must have been a qualification expressed in value of property which stood in the two famous lacunae of the Lex Acilia. Words meaning 'holders of the public horse' would cover none but men actually enrolled in the *centuriae equitum*: words like 'holders of the public horse, past or present' would include a larger number by admitting men who had been members of the eighteen centuries in the earlier days and had since retired: but, if the whole *equester ordo* in the sense of the Ciceronian usage was to be described, the description, after senators had been ruled out, could only be made by setting out a minimum assessment—in all probability one of 400,000 sesterces.

Though it is perhaps less than enough for demonstrative proof, there is a certain amount of evidence to suggest that, when the Lex Aurelia of Lucius Cotta in 70 B.C. constituted juries of three elements—senators, *equites* and *tribuni aerarii* in equal numbers, the two latter categories were not specified by a merely pecuniary definition: it is at least possible to argue that, by Cotta's law, service on the equestrian panels was confined to those who either were or had been members of the *equitum centuriae* (see above, pp. 338 *sqq.*). If that were so, and if it were legitimate to assume, as is regularly done, that the *equites* of Cotta are the same as those mentioned by our authorities for the judicial reforms of Gaius Gracchus, the question about the missing definitions of the Lex Acilia would be answered: the lacunae must have been filled by words which would restrict service on the juries for the trial of extortion to some or all of those 'who hold, have held, shall hold or shall have held the *equus publicus.*'

Such in outline is the view which on the whole has found most favour in the past, and it is a view which may well be true. But it would be misleading to state it thus without adding a word on the other side. Surviving documents of the Gracchan age are scarce, and it is no matter for surprise that in the few fragments which remain there is nothing to show by what name Gaius Gracchus and his contemporaries normally called the class on whom his favour was bestowed. The earliest extant passage in which the term 'equites' is used to describe the *iudices Gracchani* seems to be one belonging to the year 70 B.C.[1], though it should perhaps be said as well that Cicero, in references to the period between 110 and 70 B.C., frequently uses the word to indicate what corresponded to the whole *equester ordo* of his own day. Such evidence is little enough, and by itself it would do nothing to justify the suspicion that this application of the name 'equites' to the Gracchan jurors is an illicit transference to the second century B.C. of a usage proper only in the first. There remains, however, the testimony of Pliny. In his brief account of what Cicero knew as the *ordo equester*[2] he traces its origin as a separate section in the State to the tribunates of the Gracchi; and then come some words most relevant to the present issue. Its members, he says, were first of all called 'iudices,' until in course of time, when the repute of the courts was low, this title was dropped and 'publicani' for a while held its place. Finally, the name 'equites' was fixed in the consulship of Cicero, and the familiar use of the phrase 'ordo equester' only dates from the year 63 B.C. This account is open to some criticism in detail: it has been noticed above that Cicero speaks of 'equites' in the political sense seven years before his consulship. But, unless Pliny's story is mere invention, it is evidence of value for the intentions of Gaius Gracchus.

Nothing can be proved to demonstration, and the issue is between mere possibilities: all that the present writer would do is to express his own opinion that, if the Gracchan *iudices*—the nucleus of Cicero's *ordo equester*—had been defined as 'equites' in the judiciary law of 122 B.C., it would be a matter for some surprise that fifty or sixty years should have been spent in looking for the name which, on this theory, Gracchus himself had already supplied. So far as it goes, this evidence tells in favour of the belief that the lacunae of the Lex Acilia contained a property-qualification and nothing more; and such a

[1] Cicero, I *in Verr.* 15, 38.　　　　　　　　[2] *N.H.* XXXIII, 34.

conclusion is supported by the general consideration that what Gracchus sought was a certain kind of ability and outlook—qualities which might normally go with a high degree of wealth and education, but which it is difficult to connect in any essential way with service in the equestrian centuries. For these and other reasons[1], though certainty cannot be attained, it may be thought probable that the vital passages in lines 12 and 16 of the Lex Acilia should be so restored as to say that every juror should be one 'quei in hac civitate sestertium quadringentorum milium nummum plurisve census siet,' or something to a similar effect.   H. M. L.

3. THE DATES OF THE LEX ANTONIA DE TERMESSIBUS MAIORIBUS AND THE LEX PLAUTIA DE REDITU LEPIDANORUM

The view that Sulla deprived the tribunes of their power to initiate legislation has often been challenged on the ground that in the so-called Lex Antonia de Termessibus Maioribus (Bruns, *Fontes*[7], 14) we have a tribunician measure passed while the arrangements of Sulla were still in force. This, however, is by no means certain. The law apparently belongs to a year not earlier than 72 B.C., and is usually assigned to 71: but to 71 it can scarcely belong. The names of the ten tribunes of the year in which the Lex Antonia was passed are almost certainly known from an inscription (Dessau 5800), and among them there is no place for M. Lollius Palicanus, whose tribunate should probably be placed in the year which began on 10 December 72 B.C. (see Drumann-Groebe, *Geschichte Roms*, III, p. 57, n. 14 and IV, p. 400, n. 1). If—as is perhaps slightly more likely than not, unless the reading in col. 1, line 22 is corruptly preserved, though it is by no means certain—the measure is later than 72 B.C., then it cannot be earlier than the tribunate which began on 10 December 71 and coincided, for the greater part, with the first consulships of Pompeius and Crassus. But in that case who shall say whether this law was prepared before or after the consuls had restored the tribunate to its pristine power (see J. M. Sundén, *De tribunicia potestate a L. Sulla imminuta quaestiones*, pp. 10 *sqq.*)?

The only other measure almost certainly of tribunician origin which may fall between 74 and 70 B.C. is the Lex Plautia de reditu Lepidanorum. Mommsen's reasons (*Strafrecht*, p. 654, n. 2) for putting in it 77 B.C. will scarcely bear examination. All that can be said with certainty is that it falls before Caesar's quaestorship in (?) 68 B.C. (Suet. *Div. Iul.* 5); but it may be added that no date earlier than the death of Sertorius in 73 is easy to accept. Within these limits, however, precision is impossible: 73 B.C. itself—the year favoured by Lange (*Römische Alterthümer*, III[2], p. 185) and Maurenbrecher (*Sallusti Historiarum Reliquiae*, Prol. p. 78, n. 8)—is commended by the probability that the claims of the Lepidans called for consideration during the settlement which followed the end of the war in Spain, but it is scarcely less likely that this particular problem, which required a law for its solution, was reserved until Pompeius had returned to Rome, and that Drumann (*Geschichte Roms* (ed. 1) III, p. 139) was right in referring it, as he seems to do though he is not altogether explicit, to 70 B.C. or the following year.   H. M. L.

[1] Some of which may be found set out by A. Stein in *Der römische Ritterstand*, p. 20 *sq.*

4. LUCULLUS' OPERATIONS IN THE LYCUS VALLEY[1]

The date adopted in the text (spring of 72 B.C.) for Lucullus' advance into the valley of the Lycus rests on the authority of Sallust, who states (*ap.* Plutarch, *Lucullus*, 33 = *Hist.* V, 10 M.) that the sieges of Cyzicus and Amisus took place in two succeeding winters. Phlegon, *Frag.* 12, states that in 72–1 B.C. Lucullus, leaving Murena in charge of the siege of Amisus, proceeded towards Cabeira, where he wintered. From Plutarch, *Lucullus*, 15, it is clear that Lucullus left Amisus in the spring following the first winter of the siege; accordingly Phlegon's reference to Lucullus wintering at Cabeira, which implies that he was in possession of the town, must be dated to the winter of 72/1 after the flight of Mithridates. The operations in the Lycus valley took place therefore in 72 B.C.

Considerable uncertainty attaches to the date at which certain of the Pontic fortresses fell. For the reasons given on page 363 it seems better to reject the statement of Memnon, 45, that Eupatoria was not assaulted and captured until after the operations at Cabeira were finished. There is equal uncertainty with regard to Themiscyra. Appian (*Mithr.* 78) describes an assault on the town at the same time as Amisus and Eupatoria were being attacked: Λεύκολλος δ᾽ Ἀμισόν τε καὶ Εὐπατορίαν...περικαθήμενος ἐπολιόρκει, καὶ ἑτέρῳ στράτῳ Θεμίσκυραν. It would appear therefore that Lucullus' first measures, before entering the Lycus valley, were aimed at the reduction of these three important fortresses. Amasia he could afford for the present to neglect. The only alternative to the rejection of Memnon's date for the fall of Eupatoria is to stress Appian's statement (*Mithr.* 79) Λεύκολλος διὰ τῶν ὀρῶν ἐπὶ τὸν Μιθριδάτην ἐχώρει, and to assume that Lucullus reached the Lycus valley by a circuitous route through the hills. Such a route might be found in that described by Munro (*J.H.S.* XXI, 1901, p. 54) from Themiscyra along the coast to Oenoe and thence over the Paryadres range to Cabeira. But even if this were a possible route for a large army, it can be ruled out on the ground that it would have brought Lucullus directly on to Cabeira, which he clearly did not reach till a later stage.

The existence, however, of this route northwards from Cabeira to the coast does explain the later position which Lucullus took up immediately above Cabeira, when he had been driven from the low ground by Mithridates' cavalry. Plutarch's language is quite definite (*Lucullus*, 15): ἐπὶ τόπῳ ἀσφαλεῖ τῷ στρατοπέδῳ καὶ φρούριον ἔχοντι τοῖς Καβείροις ἐπικρεμάμενον. Munro, rejecting the statement of Plutarch, would place Lucullus' φρούριον on the ridge which (15 miles from Eupatoria and 12 from Cabeira) divides the Lycus valley into two sections. His supplies from Cappadocia, according to the same writer, reached him by the road from Comana to Herek (in the lower section of the valley). But if Plutarch, as appears from the unusual precision of topographical detail in his narrative, is correct, Lucullus' position above Cabeira secured him from attack, constituted a permanent threat to Cabeira itself and provided a line of retreat northwards by the hill-road Cabeira–Oenoe in the event of a

[1] See p. 364 *sq.* and Map 7, facing p. 211.

serious reverse. His convoys would in any case have to fight their way across the Lycus valley, whether they used the road Comana–Herek or Comana–Niksar (Cabeira). H.A.O.

5. LEGIONS IN THE CIVIL WAR[1]

In the winter of 50–49 B.C. Caesar had legion XIII in North Italy and eight legions in Gaul (Hirtius *B.G.* VIII, 54, 3–4). In the view of the present writer, these eight are *legiones civium Romanorum*, VI–XII and XIV, and to them should be added the Gallic formation the Alaudae, which afterwards received the number V. Caesar has thus ten legions. Of these VIII and XII and 22 cohorts not yet organized into legions joined Caesar and XIII at Corfinium. The six legions which remained in Gaul then fought in Spain[2]. These conclusions appear to make the best of the evidence, but are open to the objection that the Alaudae are not recorded as active during 49. In 48 legions VI–XIV and the Alaudae served with Caesar in the Balkans together with a non-veteran legion XXVII. After Pharsalus three legions were formed of Pompeian troops[3]. Two of these were XXXVI and XXXVII, the third presumably either XXXV or XXXVIII. Thus before the battle Caesar had under arms legions VI–XXXIV or XXXV, less, possibly, two legions lost with Curio in Africa, if new legions did not take their numbers. A legion II was in Spain at this time (*Bell. Alex.* 53, 4) and a legion III is found with Caesar in Spain in 45 B.C. (*Bell. Hisp.* 30, 7), and may have been in existence in 48. Nothing is heard of a legion I or III. We may estimate the sum of Caesarian legions on the day of Pharsalus at within one or two of thirty. The new legions were made up partly of 70 Pompeian cohorts who surrendered in Italy and some 20 cohorts out of the Pompeian legions in Spain. Caesar says that Pompey lost 130 cohorts of Roman citizens in Italy and Spain. The number of cohorts lost in Italy is reached by subtracting either 60 or 70 cohorts for Spain. It seems slightly more probable that Caesar, when speaking of cohorts *civium Romanorum*, is not including the *legio vernacula*, which was the seventh Pompeian legion in Spain (*B.C.* I, 85, 6; II, 20, 4). The remainder of the new legions would be composed of the 22 cohorts already raised by Caesar at the outbreak of the war together with new enrolments in Cisalpine Gaul, now enfranchised, and Italy.

At the time of Pharsalus there were three legions in Sardinia and Sicily, five in Further Spain, at least two in Illyricum and the remainder in Nearer Spain, Gaul and Italy itself. During the year which followed Pharsalus VI was with Caesar, the remaining veteran legions were in Italy. Of the three legions formed from Pompeians after the battle Domitius kept XXXVI in Syria, sent XXXVII to Alexandria and another legion to Syria where it stayed. Caesar left in Egypt XXVII, which had accompanied him from Greece, and

---

[1] For a detailed discussion see A. von Domaszewski in *Neue Heid. Jahrb.* IV, 1894, Drumann-Groebe, III, pp. 704 *sqq.*, Veith in *Geschichte der Feldzüge C. Julius Caesars* and works on separate campaigns; Rice Holmes, *The Roman Republic*, Vol. III, and H. M. D. Parker, *The Roman Legions*. To the last-named works this brief statement of conclusions is especially indebted.

[2] Parker, *op. cit.* p. 59.

[3] Rice Holmes, *op. cit.* III, p. 476.

xxxvii. A third legion is found in Egypt; this was probably formed from soldiers of the old army of occupation[1].

In the African campaign Caesar used in all v (Alaudae), ix, x, xiii and xiv, together with five non-veteran legions, of which the numbers xxvi, xxviii and xxix are certain[2]. In the campaign of Munda Caesar had eight legions of which iii, v (Alaudae), vi, x are certain; the other four are probably xxviii and xxx (found in Spain after Caesar's death), ii and xxi[3]. In March 44 the total number of Caesarian legions was about thirty-five. It is to be remembered that it was Caesar's practice to allow legions to dwindle rather than to replenish them with recruits. It is very doubtful if in this period there was any regular conventional strength for a legion; a maximum complement for a Caesarian legion would be about 4000 men, the normal strength of a legion after several campaigns about 2000 to 2500. At Zela the sixth legion was less than 1000 strong (*Bell. Alex.* 69), at Munda the soldiers of the tenth are described as 'pauci' (*Bell. Hisp.* 31, 4).

Pompey took from Italy five legions. At Pharsalus he had in the line 110 cohorts[4]. He had added to his army four new legions from Cilicia, Crete and Macedonia, and Asia, the 15 cohorts captured from C. Antonius who were drafted into his legions, the legions from Syria and the *Afranianae cohortes*. As seven cohorts were stationed in his camp, we may assume that their place was taken by the Afranians. The fact that Pompey's Cilician legion was formed from two weak legions, which had been in that province during Cicero's governorship, suggests that it was his policy to keep legions at full strength rather than to multiply them. This is consistent with the distribution of Antonius' men throughout his legions. The reason for this policy would be the lack of experienced centurions. Caesar states that Pompey's 110 cohorts contained 45,000 men. This is probably an exaggeration. He gives 7000 for Pompey's cavalry both at Pharsalus and at the beginning of the campaign (*B.C.* iii, 4, 3 and 84, 4)[5]. Scipio brought some cavalry from Syria but it is very unlikely that it made up for the losses in the Dyrrhachium campaign. Caesar may equally reckon the strength of the infantry without making due account for wastage. On the number of cohorts he would be accurately informed but not on their strength. Pompey's cohorts at Pharsalus may then be rated at an average of rather under 400 men. There is no evidence, and small probability, that he included in his army any considerable proportion of orientals, for his number can fairly be reached without that assumption. In Spain Afranius and Petreius had six legions *civium Romanorum* and had raised a *legio vernacula*; otherwise, they used Spaniards in cohorts without legionary formation. In Asia Minor Deiotarus

[1] v. Domaszewski, *op. cit.* p. 173.
[2] Rice Holmes, *op. cit.* p. 523.
[3] Parker, *op. cit.* p. 68.
[4] Caesar, *B.C.* iii, 88, 4. Orosius, vi, 15, 23, says 88 cohorts. This figure is apparently reached by assigning to Pompey eleven legions and subtracting 15 cohorts for the garrison of Dyrrhachium and seven for the guard of the camp. But the cohorts that garrisoned Dyrrhachium were probably auxiliaries, and the subtraction of the camp-guard was, as has been said, probably balanced by the addition of the *Afraniani*.
[5] Rice Holmes, *op. cit.* p. 476 n. 1.

and in Africa Juba trained natives in the Roman fashion and formed legions. These experiments were not a success. The Pompeians in Africa had ten legions apart from Juba's four. It is difficult to see how they can have had so many legions at reasonably full strength without admitting non-Italians. Cn. Pompeius in Spain was in worse case, for he gave legionary formation to a considerable number of cohorts of Spanish birth. The attitude of the Roman professional soldier towards any but regular legions *civium Romanorum* is shown by *Bell. Hisp.* 7, 4. 'Aquilas et signa habuit XIII legionum; sed ex quibus aliquid firmamenti se existimabat habere duae fuerant vernaculae....'

F. E. A.

6. THE *TRIBUNICIA POTESTAS* OF CAESAR

Dio (XLII, 20, 3) states that after Pharsalus Caesar received the right to be consul for five years without intermission, to be appointed dictator not for six months but for a whole year, 'and he added to these offices the power of the tribunes for life, so to speak—τήν τε ἐξουσίαν τῶν δημάρχων διὰ βίου ὡς εἰπεῖν προσέθετο.' Dio then explains what he means by 'the power of the tribunes,' namely, 'to sit with the tribunes on the same benches and in other respects to be reckoned one of them, a thing that was allowed to no one else.' L. Wiegandt[1] argues that the words ὡς εἰπεῖν must qualify the words διὰ βίου. This, he points out, is required by Dio's usage (cf. XLI, 7, 1; XLII, 19, 1; XLIII, 22, 1), and by the balance of the sentence, and the qualification is in place because he is only deducing that the grant was made for life by the absence of any fixed term. Dio (XLIV, 4, 2; 5, 3) further states that in 44 B.C. there were conferred on Caesar sacrosanctity and the right to sit upon the tribunician benches at the games. Either the first statement says the same as the second or it says more, and in either case it is difficult to see why there should be conferred on Caesar in 44 what he already possessed since 48. Wiegandt further shows that before 44 B.C. there is no other evidence of Caesar's possession of the rank or functions of a tribune or of tribunician sacrosanctity. His view of ὡς εἰπεῖν appears to be correct and it goes against the suggestion[2] that in 48 Caesar received what may be called quasi-tribunician power only, so that the conferment in 44 B.C. was necessary. It seems therefore preferable to reject the first statement as an anticipation of the second. Eight years later[3] Wiegandt was inclined to argue, with less probability, that some form of *tribunicia potestas* was offered to Caesar in 48 B.C. but not accepted by him. M. A. Levi[4] advances the theory that in 48 B.C. Caesar was granted the tribunician veto and that alone to complement his powers as dictator, which he believes to have been *rei gerendae* not *rei publicae constituendae*. To this view the text of Dio gives little support, especially if ὡς εἰπεῖν is rightly applied, and it appears improbable that this particular power of the tribune would be conferred alone, or that the dictatorship conferred on Caesar in 48 was not *rei publicae constituendae*.

[1] *C. Julius Caesar und die tribunizische Gewalt*, p. 7.
[2] Rice Holmes, *The Roman Republic*, III, p. 515.
[3] In *Jahresbericht des Kgl. Gymnasiums zu Dresden-Neustadt*, 1898.
[4] *Atti del I Congresso Nazionale di Studi Romani*, I, 1929, pp. 353–7.

If what Dio says in connection with 48 B.C. is rejected as an exaggerated anticipation of what in fact happened in 44 B.C., then Caesar received neither powers nor functions but only sacrosanctity. This is apparently what Dio means in the second passage. In the speech which he puts into Antony's mouth after the murder he describes Caesar as ὃν ἐξ ἴσου τοῖς δημάρχοις ἄσυλον ἐπεποιήκεσαν[1]. Sacrosanctity was associated in the minds of the Romans with the tribunate, and the most obvious way of marking this tribune-like sacrosanctity was to permit its possessor to appear with the tribunes on great public occasions. In the view of the present writer it was this sacrosanctity which was conferred on Octavian in 36 B.C. (Dio XLIX, 15, 5–6) and which he in turn caused to be conferred on Octavia and Livia in the next year (Dio, XLIX, 38, 1) rather than *tribunicia potestas* in any active sense. What is important for Caesar is that it was not he but Augustus who later devised the active *tribunicia potestas* which reached its full development in 23 B.C.

F. E. A.

[1] XLIV, 50, 1.

LIST OF ABBREVIATIONS

Abh. Arch.-epig.	Abhandlungen d. archäol.-epigraph. Seminars d. Univ. Wien.
A.J.A.	American Journal of Archaeology.
A.J.Num.	American Journal of Numismatics.
A.J.Ph.	American Journal of Philology.
Am. Hist. Rev.	American Historical Review.
Arch. Anz.	Archäologischer Anzeiger (in J.D.A.I.).
Ἀρχ.	Ἀρχαιολογικὴ Ἐφημερίς.
Arch. Pap.	Archiv für Papyrusforschung.
Arch. Relig.	Archiv für Religionswissenschaft.
Ath. Mitt.	Mitteilungen des deutschen arch. Inst. (Athenische Abteilung).
Atti Acc. Torino	Atti della r. Accademia di scienze di Torino.
Bay. Abh.	Abhandlungen d. bayerischen Akad. d. Wissenschaften.
Bay. S.B.	Sitzungsberichte d. bayerischen Akad. d. Wissenschaften.
B.C.H.	Bulletin de Correspondance hellénique.
Berl. Abh.	Abhandlungen d. preuss. Akad. d. Wissenschaften zu Berlin.
Berl. S.B.	Sitzungsberichte d. preuss. Akad. d. Wissenschaften zu Berlin.
Boll. Fil. Class.	Bollettino della Filologia Classica.
B.P.W.	Berliner Philologische Wochenschrift.
B.S.A.	Annual of the British School at Athens.
B.S.R.	Papers of the British School at Rome.
Bursian	Bursian's Jahresbericht.
C.I.G.	Corpus Inscriptionum Graecarum.
C.I.L.	Corpus Inscriptionum Latinarum.
C.J.	Classical Journal.
C.P.	Classical Philology.
C.Q.	Classical Quarterly.
C.R.	Classical Review.
C.R. Ac. Inscr.	Comptes rendus de l'Académie des Inscriptions et Belles-Lettres.
Dessau	Dessau, Inscriptiones Latinae Selectae.
Ditt.³	Dittenberger, Sylloge Inscriptionum Graecarum. Ed. 3.
D.S.	Daremberg and Saglio, Dictionnaire des antiquités grecques et romaines.
E. Brit.	Encyclopaedia Britannica. Ed. 11.
F. Gr. Hist.	F. Jacoby's Fragmente der griechischen Historiker.
F.H.G.	C. Müller's Fragmenta Historicorum Graecorum.
G.G.A.	Göttingische Gelehrte Anzeigen.
Gött. Abh.	Abhandlungen d. Gesellschaft d. Wissenschaften zu Göttingen.
Gött. Nach.	Nachrichten der Gesellschaft der Wissenschaften zu Göttingen. Phil.-hist. Klasse.
Harv. St.	Harvard Studies in Classical Philology.
Head H.N.²	Head's Historia Numorum. Ed. 2.
Heid. S.B.	Sitzungsberichte der Heidelberger Akademie der Wissenschaft.
H.Z.	Historische Zeitschrift.
I.G.	Inscriptiones Graecae.
I.G.R.R.	Inscriptiones Graecae ad res Romanas pertinentes.
Jahreshefte	Jahreshefte d. österr. archäol. Instituts in Wien.
J.D.A.I.	Jahrbuch des deutschen archäologischen Instituts.
J.E.A.	Journal of Egyptian Archaeology.

J.H.S.	Journal of Hellenic Studies.
J.I. d'A.N.	Journal International d'Archéologie Numismatique.
J.P.	Journal of Philology.
J.R.A.S.	Journal of the Royal Asiatic Society.
J.R.S.	Journal of Roman Studies.
Klio	Klio (Beiträge zur alten Geschichte).
Mém. Ac. Inscr.	Mémoires de l'Académie des Inscriptions et des Belles-Lettres.
Mem. Acc. Lincei	Memorie della r. Accademia nazionale dei Lincei.
Mem. Acc. Torino	Memorie della r. Accademia di scienze di Torino.
Mnem.	Mnemosyne.
Mus. B.	Musée belge.
N. J. f. Wiss.	Neue Jahrbücher für Wissenschaft und Jugendbildung.
N.J. Kl. Alt.	Neue Jahrbücher für das klassische Altertum.
N.J.P.	Neue Jahrbücher für Philologie.
N.S.A.	Notizie degli Scavi di Antichità.
Num. Chr.	Numismatic Chronicle.
Num. Z.	Numismatische Zeitschrift.
O.G.I.S.	Orientis Graeci Inscriptiones Selectae.
O.L.Z.	Orientalistische Literaturzeitung.
Phil.	Philologus.
Phil. Woch.	Philologische Wochenschrift.
P.W.	Pauly-Wissowa-Kroll's Real-Encyclopädie der classischen Altertumswissenschaft.
Rend. Linc.	Rendiconti della r. Accademia dei Lincei.
Rev. Arch.	Revue archéologique.
Rev. Belge	Revue Belge de philologie et d'histoire.
Rev. Bib.	Revue biblique internationale.
Rev. Celt.	Revue des études celtiques.
Rev. E. A.	Revue des études anciennes.
Rev. E.G.	Revue des études grecques.
Rev. E.J.	Revue des études juives.
Rev. E.L.	Revue des études latines.
Rev. H.	Revue historique.
Rev. N.	Revue numismatique.
Rev. Phil.	Revue de philologie, de littérature et d'histoire anciennes.
Rh. Mus.	Rheinisches Museum für Philologie.
Riv. Fil.	Rivista di filologia.
Riv. stor. ant.	Rivista di storia antica.
Röm. Mitt.	Mitteilungen des deutschen arch. Inst. Römische Abteilung.
S.B.	Sitzungsberichte.
S.E.G.	Supplementum epigraphicum Graecum.
S.G.D.I.	Sammlung der griechischen Dialektinschriften.
St. Fil.	Studi italiani di filologia classica.
Trans. A.P.A.	Transactions of the American Philological Association.
Wien Anz.	Anzeiger d. Akad. d. Wissenschaften in Wien.
Wien S.B.	Sitzungsberichte d. Akad. d. Wissenschaften in Wien.
Wien. St.	Wiener Studien.
Z. d. Sav.-Stift.	Zeitschrift d. Savigny-Stiftung f. Rechtsgeschichte.
Z.N.	Zeitschrift für Numismatik.

BIBLIOGRAPHIES

These bibliographies do not aim at completeness. They include modern and standard works and, in particular, books utilized in the writings of the chapters. Some technical monographs, especially in journals, are omitted, but the works that are registered below will put the reader on their track.

The works given in the General Bibliography are, as a rule, not repeated in the bibliographies to the separate chapters. The first page only of articles in journals is given if the whole article is cited.

GENERAL BIBLIOGRAPHY

I. General Histories and Treatises

A. *Hellenistic*

Beloch, K. J. *Griechische Geschichte seit Alexander.* (In Gercke-Norden, *Einleitung in die Altertumswissenschaft,* III, Ed. 2.) Leipzig-Berlin, 1914.

Bevan, E. R. *The House of Seleucus.* London, 1902.

—— *A History of Egypt under the Ptolemaic Dynasty.* London, 1927.

Bouché-Leclercq, A. *Histoire des Lagides.* Paris, 1903.

—— *Histoire des Séleucides.* Paris, 1913.

Ferguson, W. S. *Hellenistic Athens.* London, 1911.

Neumann, K. J. *Die hellenistischen Staaten und die römische Republik.* (In J. von Pflugk-Harttung's *Weltgeschichte: Altertum.*) Berlin, n.d. [1909].

Tarn, W. W. *Hellenistic Civilisation.* Ed. 2. London, 1930.

B. *Roman*

Barbagallo, C. *Roma antica.* I. *Dalle origini alla fine della Repubblica.* Turin, 1931.

Beloch, K. J. *Römische Geschichte bis zum Ende der Republik,* in *Einleitung in die Altertumswissenschaft,* herausgegeben von A. Gercke und E. Norden, vol. III (zweite Auflage; Leipzig-Berlin, 1914), pp. 160 *sqq.*

Bloch, G. *La République romaine : les conflits politiques et sociaux.* Ed. 2. Paris, 1922.

De Sanctis, G. *Der Hellenismus und Rom,* in *Propyläen-Weltgeschichte,* herausgegeben von W. Goetz. Vol. II (Berlin, n.d.), pp. 241 *sqq.*

Drumann, W. *Geschichte Roms in seinem Übergange von der republikanischen zur monarchischen Verfassung.* Zweite Auflage, herausgegeben von P. Groebe. Vol. I, 1899. Berlin. Vol. II, 1902; vol. III, 1906; vol. IV, 1908; vol. V, 1919; vol. VI, 1929. Leipzig.

Ferrero, G. *The Greatness and Decline of Rome,* vols. I–II, translated by A. Zimmern, London, 1907; vol. III, translated by H. J. Chaytor, 1908.

Frank, T. *A History of Rome.* London, n.d. [1923].

—— *An Economic History of Rome.* Ed. 2. Baltimore, 1927.

—— *Roman Imperialism.* New York, 1914.

Heitland, W. E. *The Roman Republic.* 3 vols. Cambridge, 1909, new impression, 1923.

Ihne, W. *The History of Rome.* London. Vol. III, 1877; vol. IV, 1882; vol. V, 1882.

Lange, L. *Römische Alterthümer.* Berlin. Vol. I (ed. 3), 1876; vol. II (ed. 3), 1879; vol. III (ed. 2), 1876.

Meyer, Ed. *Caesars Monarchie und das Principat des Pompejus.* Ed. 2. Stuttgart-Berlin, 1919.

Mommsen, Th. *The History of Rome,* translated by W. P. Dickson. London. Vols. I–III, 1894; vols. IV and V, 1895.

Neumann, C. *Geschichte Roms während des Verfalles der Republik.* Breslau, 1881.

Neumann, K. J. *Op. cit.* above.

Niese, B. *Grundriss der römischen Geschichte nebst Quellenkunde.* 5te Auflage neubearbeitet von E. Hohl. (Müller's *Handbuch der klassischen Altertumswissenschaft,* Band III, Abt. 5.) Munich, 1923.

Nitsch, K. W. *Geschichte der römischen Republik.* Zweiter Band: bis zur Schlacht bei Actium. Leipzig, 1885.

Pais, E. *Dalle guerre puniche a Cesare Augusto.* 2 vols. Rome, 1918.

Piganiol, A. *La conquête romaine.* Ed. 2. Paris, 1931.

Rice Holmes, T. *The Roman Republic and the Founder of the Empire.* 3 vols. Oxford, 1923.

Rostovtzeff, M. *A History of the Ancient World.* Vol. II. *Rome.* Oxford, 1927.

Vogt, J. *Die römische Republik.* Freiburg i/B. 1932.

II. WORKS OF REFERENCE, DICTIONARIES, ETC.

Daremberg, Ch. et E. Saglio. *Dictionnaire des antiquités grecques et romaines d'après les textes et les monuments.* Paris, 1877–1919. (D.S.)

De Ruggiero, G. *Dizionario epigrafico di Antichità romane.* Rome. 1895– .

Gercke, A. und E. Norden. *Einleitung in die Altertumswissenschaft.* Ed. 2, Leipzig-Berlin, 1914. Ed. 3 in course of publication.

Lübker, Friedrich. *Reallexikon des klassischen Altertums.* Ed. 8 (by J. Geffcken and E. Ziebarth). Leipzig-Berlin, 1914. (Lübker.)

von Müller, Iwan. *Handbuch der Altertumswissenschaft.* (In course of revision under the editorship of W. Otto.) München, 1886– . (Müllers Handbuch.)

Platner, S. B. *A Topographical Dictionary of Ancient Rome.* (Completed and revised by T. Ashby.) Oxford, 1929.

Sandys, Sir J. E. *A Companion to Latin Studies.* Ed. 3. Cambridge, 1929.

Stuart Jones, H. *A Companion to Roman History.* Oxford, 1912.

Wissowa, G. *Pauly's Real-Encyclopädie der classischen Altertumswissenschaft.* Neue Bearbeitung. (Under the editorship of W. Kroll and K. Mittelhaus.) Stuttgart, 1894– . (P.W.)

Roscher, W. H. *Ausführliches Lexikon der griechischen und römischen Mythologie.* (Under the editorship of K. Ziegler.) Leipzig, 1884– . (Roscher.)

CHAPTERS I–IV, VI–VII

TIBERIUS GRACCHUS; GAIUS GRACCHUS; THE WARS OF THE AGE OF MARIUS; THE ENFRANCHISEMENT OF ITALY; SULLA; THE BREAKDOWN OF THE SULLAN SYSTEM AND THE RISE OF POMPEY

(Separate bibliographies will be found below for Chap. IV, sections VI and VII, Chap. VI, section IV, and Chap. VII, section IV.)

I. ANCIENT AUTHORITIES

1. *Inscriptions*

Corpus Inscriptionum Latinarum. Berlin. Vol. I. Inscriptiones Latinae antiquissimae ad C. Caesaris mortem. Editio altera. 1893–1918.
Dessau, H. *Inscriptiones Latinae Selectae.* Berlin. Vol. I, 1892; vol. II, 1, 1902; vol. II, 2, 1906; vol. III, 1, 1914; vol. III, 2, 1916.
Inscriptiones Graecae ad res Romanas pertinentes auctoritate et impensis Academiae Inscriptionum et Litterarum Humaniorum collectae et editae. Paris. Vol. I, 1911; vol. III, 1906; vol. IV, 1927.
Dittenberger, W. *Orientis Graeci Inscriptiones Selectae.* Lipsiae. Vol. I, 1903; vol. II, 1905.
—— *Sylloge Inscriptionum Graecarum.* Ed. 3. Lipsiae. Vol. I, 1915; vol. II, 1917; vol. III, 1920; vol. IV (indices), 1924.
Pais, E. *Fasti triumphales populi Romani.* Rome, 1920.
L'Année Épigraphique, 1922, No. 88. (Fasti Antiates); †1931, No. 135.

2. *Coins*

Grueber, H. A. *Coins of the Roman Republic in the British Museum.* 3 vols. London, 1910.

3. *Legal Documents*

Digesta, rec. Th. Mommsen, retractavit P. Krueger, in *Corpus Iuris Civilis*, vol. I. Editio stereotypa quarta decima. Berolini, 1922.
Bruns, C. G. *Fontes Iuris Romani Antiqui*, septimum edidit O. Gradenwitz. Tubingae, 1909.
Girard, P. F. *Textes de droit romain.* Ed. 5. Paris, 1923.
Hardy, E. G. *Roman Laws and Charters.* Oxford, 1912.
Rotondi, G. *Leges publicae populi Romani.* (Estratto dalla *Enciclopedia Giuridica Italiana*.) Milan, 1912.

4. *Literary Sources*

Historicorum Romanorum reliquiae. Rec. H. Peter. Lipsiae. Vol. I, ed. 2, 1914; vol. II, 1906.
Oratorum Romanorum fragmenta. Rec. H. Malcovati. 3 vols. Augustae Taurinorum, 1930.
Corpus Agrimensorum Romanorum. Rec. C. Thulin. Vol. I, fasc. I, Opuscula Agrimensorum Veterum. Lipsiae, 1913.
Appiani Historia Romana. Lipsiae. Vol. I. Ed. L. Mendelssohn, 1879. Vol. II. Ed. L. Mendelssohn: editio altera correctior curante P. Viereck, 1905.
Appian, Civil Wars: Book I. Edited by J. L. Strachan-Davidson. Oxford, 1902.

Q. Asconii Pediani orationum Ciceronis quinque enarratio. Recognovit A. C. Clark. Oxonii, 1907.

Sexti Aurelii Victoris Liber de Caesaribus, praecedunt Origo gentis Romanae et Liber de viris illustribus urbis Romae. Rec. F. Pichlmayr. Lipsiae, 1911.

C. Iuli Caesaris Commentarii. Recensuit R. Du Pontet. 2 vols. Oxonii, 1900.

Cassii Dionis Cocceiani Historiarum Romanarum quae supersunt. Ed. U. P. Boissevain. Vol. 1. Berolini, 1895.

M. Tulli Ciceronis scripta quae manserunt omnia. Rec. C. F. W. Mueller. Lipsiae.

Partis 1 vol. 11 continens de oratore libros, Brutum, Oratorem, de optimo genere oratorum, Partitiones oratorias, Topica. Rec. G. Friedrich. 1893.

Partis iv vol. 11 continens libros de natura deorum, de divinatione, de fato, de re publica, de legibus, etc. 1898.

M. Tulli Ciceronis scripta quae manserunt omnia. Lipsiae. Incerti auctoris de ratione dicendi ad C. Herennium libri iv. Iterum rec. F. Marx. 1923.

Rhetorici libri duo qui vocantur de inventione. Rec. E. Stroebel. 1915.

De Re publica librorum sex quae manserunt. Iterum rec. K. Ziegler. 1929.

Academicorum reliquiae, cum Lucullo. Rec. O. Plasberg. 1922.

De Finibus bonorum et malorum libri quinque. Rec. Th. Schiche. 1915.

Tusculanae disputationes. Rec. M. Pohlenz. 1918.

De natura deorum. Rec. O. Plasberg. 1917.

Cato Maior, Laelius. Rec. K. Simbeck. De gloria. Rec. O. Plasberg. 1917.

De officiis. Rec. C. Atzert. De virtutibus. Rec. O. Plasberg. 1923.

M. Tulli Ciceronis Orationes. Oxonii. Divinatio in Q. Caecilium. In C. Verrem. Recognovit G. Peterson. Editio altera. 1917.

Pro Sex. Roscio. De imperio Cn. Pompei. Pro Cluentio. In Catilinam. Pro Murena. Pro Caelio. Rec. A. C. Clark. 1908.

Pro Milone. Pro Marcello. Pro Ligario. Pro Rege Deiotaro, Philippicae. Rec. A. C. Clark. Editio altera. 1918.

Pro Quinctio. Pro Q. Roscio. Pro Caecina. De lege agraria. Pro C. Rabirio perduellionis reo. Pro Flacco. In Pisonem. Pro C. Rabirio Postumo. Rec. A. C. Clark. 1909.

Cum Senatui gratias egit. Cum populo gratias egit. De domo sua. De haruspicum responso. Pro Sestio. In Vatinium. De provinciis consularibus. Pro Balbo. Rec. G. Peterson. 1911.

Pro Tullio. Pro Fonteio. Pro Sulla. Pro Archia. Pro Plancio. Pro Scauro. Rec. A. C. Clark. 1911.

The Correspondence of M. Tullius Cicero, arranged according to its chronological order; with a revision of the text, a commentary, and introductory essays by R. Y. Tyrrell and L. C. Purser. Dublin and London. Vol. 1 (ed. 3), 1904; vol. 11 (ed. 2), 1906; vol. 111 (ed. 2), 1914; vol. iv (ed. 2), 1918; vol. v (ed. 2), 1915; vol. vi, 1899; vol. vii (indices), 1901.

Ciceronis Orationum Scholiastae. Rec. T. Stangl. Volumen 11, commentarios continens. Vindobonae-Lipsiae, 1912.

Diodori Bibliotheca Historica, ex recensione et cum annotationibus L. Dindorfii. Vol. v. Lipsiae, 1868.

Eutropi Breviarium ab urbe condita. Rec. F. Ruehl. Lipsiae, 1887.

Sexti Pompeii Festi de uerborum significatu quae supersunt cum Pauli epitome. Ed. W. M. Lindsay. Lipsiae, 1913.

L. Annaei Flori Epitomae libri 11 et P. Annii Flori fragmentum de Vergilio oratore an poeta. Ed. O. Rossbach. Lipsiae, 1896.

Iuli Frontini Strategematon libri quattuor. Ed. G. Gundermann. Lipsiae, 1888.

A. Gellii Noctium Atticarum libri xx. Ed. C. Hosius. 2 vols. Lipsiae, 1903.

M. Iuniani Iustini Epitoma historiarum Philippicarum Pompei Trogi ex recensione Francisci Ruehl. Lipsiae, 1886.

Grani Liciniani quae supersunt rec. M. Flemisch. Lipsiae, 1904.

Titi Livi ab urbe condita. Recc. R. S. Conway et C. F. Walters. Oxonii. Tom. I: libri I–v, 1914. Tom. II: libri VI–x, 1919.

Titi Livi ab urbe condita libri. Editionem primam curavit Gulielmus Weissenborn; editio altera, quam curavit Mauritius Müller. Lipsiae. Pars III, Fasc. II, 1909; Pars IV, Fasc. I, 1912; Pars IV, Fasc. II, 1912.

Titi Livi ab urbe condita libri. Rec. Wilh. Weissenborn. Lipsiae. Pars v. 1897.

Titi Livi ab urbe condita libri. Editionem primam curavit Gulielmus Weissenborn; editio altera, quam curavit Gulielmus Heraeus. Pars v, Fasc. II. Lipsiae, 1912.

T. Livi periochae omnium librorum, fragmenta Oxyrhynchi reperta, Iulii Obsequentis prodigiorum liber. Ed. O. Rossbach. Lipsiae, 1910.

Macrobius. Franciscus Eyssenhardt iterum recognovit. Lipsiae, 1893.

Pauli Orosii Historiarum adversus paganos libri VII, ex recogn. C. Zangemeister. Lipsiae, 1889.

C. Plini Secundi Naturalis Historiae libri XXXVII. Ed. C. Mayhoff. Lipsiae. Vol. I, 1906; vol. II, ed. 2, 1909; vol. III, 1892; vol. IV, 1897; vol. v, 1897.

Plutarchi Vitae Parallelae. Recc. Cl. Lindskog et K. Ziegler. Lipsiae. Vol. I, fasc. I, 1914; fasc. II, 1914; vol. III, fasc. I, 1915; fasc. II, 1926.

Plutarchi Vitae Parallelae. Iterum rec. C. Sintenis. Vol. III. Lipsiae, 1881.

Plutarch's Lives of the Gracchi, edited by G. E. Underhill. Oxford, 1892.

Plutarchos: Tiberius und Gaius Gracchus. Mit Einleitung, kritischem Apparat und Sachkommentar von K. Ziegler. Heidelberg, 1911.

Polybii Historiae. Editionem a L. Dindorfio curatam retractavit T. Büttner-Wobst. Lipsiae. Vol. I, 1882; vol. II, 1889; vol. III, 1893; vol. IV, 1904; vol. v (indices), 1904.

C. Sallusti Crispi Catilina, Iugurtha, orationes et epistulae excerptae de historiis. Rec. A. W. Ahlberg. Lipsiae, 1919.

C. Sallusti Crispi Historiarum reliquiae. Ed. B. Maurenbrecher. Lipsiae. Fasc. I: Prolegomena. 1891. Fasc. II: Fragmenta. 1893.

C. Sallusti Crispi Epistulae ad Caesarem senem de re publica. Iterum ed. A. Kurfess. Lipsiae, 1930.

Strabonis Geographica. Rec. A. Meineke. Lipsiae. Vol. I, 1895; vol. II, 1877; vol. III, 1898.

C. Suetoni Tranquilli De vita Caesarum libri VIII. Rec. M. Ihm. Lipsiae, 1907.

C. Suetoni Tranquilli quae supersunt omnia. Rec. Carolus Ludovicus Roth. Lipsiae, 1902.

Cornelii Taciti Annalium ab excessu divi Augusti libri. Rec. C. D. Fisher. Oxonii, 1906.

Tacitus Germania, mit Beiträgen von A. Dopsch, H. Reis, K. Schumacher, unter Mitarbeit von H. Klenk herausgegeben und erläutert von W. Reeb. Leipzig, 1930.

Cornelii Taciti Historiarum libri. Rec. C. D. Fisher. Oxonii, 1911.

M. Terenti Varronis De lingua Latina quae supersunt. Recc. G. Goetz et F. Schoell. Lipsiae, 1910.

M. Terentii Varronis Rerum rusticarum libri tres. Post H. Keil iterum ed. G. Goetz Lipsiae, 1912.

Valerii Maximi Factorum et Dictorum Memorabilium libri novem. Iterum rec. C. Kempf. Lipsiae, 1888.

Vellei Paterculi ad M. Vinicium libri duo. Ed. A. Bolaffi. Augustae Taurinorum, 1930.

Ioannis Zonarae Epitome Historiarum. Cum Caroli Ducangii suisque adnotationibus ed. Ludovicus Dindorfius. Lipsiae. Vol. I, 1868; vol. II, 1869; vol. III, 1870; vol. IV, 1871; vol. V, 1874; vol. VI, 1875.
Greenidge, A. H. J. and A. M. Clay. *Sources for Roman History*, B.C. 133–70. Oxford, 1903.

The more important literary authorities for the general course of Roman History in the period covered by these chapters (133–66 B.C.) are the Epitomes of Livy's Books LVIII to C, Appian's *Bella Civilia* I, the *Bellum Jugurthinum* and the fragments of the *Historiae* of Sallust, and Plutarch's Lives of the *Gracchi*, *Marius*, *Sulla* and *Pompey*. These provide the framework of our knowledge into which the information derived from less continuous sources has to be inserted. In chapters I–IV and VI–VII an attempt has been made to give detailed references for all but the most trivial statements based on the minor authorities, about which further information will be found in the Appendix (pp. 882 *sqq.*).

II. Criticism of Authorities

Rosenberg, A. *Einleitung und Quellenkunde zur römischen Geschichte*. Berlin, 1921.
Wachsmuth, C. *Einleitung in das Studium der alten Geschichte*. Leipzig, 1895.
Busolt, G. *Quellenkritische Beiträge zur Geschichte der römischen Revolutionszeit*. N.J.P. CXLI, 1890, pp. 321 and 405.
Cichorius, C. *Untersuchungen zu Lucilius*. Berlin, 1908.
Hendrickson, G. L. *Literary Sources in Cicero's Brutus and the Technique of Citation in Dialogue*. A.J.Ph. XXVII, 1906, p. 184.

Works on the authorities for short periods of the history will be found in the bibliographies of the periods with which they deal.

III. Modern Works

The lists which follow are intended, not to survey the whole modern literature, but to indicate works to which the writer desires to acknowledge his indebtedness and those wherein references to other publications may conveniently be found. A few books and articles are included which, owing to their inaccessibility, it has been impossible to consult direct, and there are also added certain works of which the writer would gladly have availed himself had they not reached him after the relevant chapters of this volume had been finally paged; all these are marked with a †.

1. *General*

The works here cited are additional to the historical works given above in the General Bibliography I.

Bloch, G. et J. Carcopino, *Histoire romaine*, II. *La République romaine de 133 avant J.-C. à la mort de César*. Paris. Fasc. I, 1929; Fasc. II, n.d.
Bouché-Leclercq, A. *Leçons d'histoire romaine*. Paris, 1909.
Cavaignac, E. *Histoire de l'antiquité*. Vol. III: *La Macédoine, Carthage et Rome* (330–107). Paris, 1914.
Greenidge, A. H. J. *A History of Rome from the Tribunate of Tiberius Gracchus to the End of the Jugurthine War*, B.C. 133–104. London, n.d. [1904].
Cichorius, C. *Römische Studien*. Leipzig, 1922.
†De Sanctis, G. *Problemi di storia antica*. Bari, 1932.
Meyer, Ed. *Kleine Schriften*. Vol. I (ed. 2); vol. II. Halle (Saale), 1924.

Mommsen, Th. *Gesammelte Schriften.* Berlin. Juristische Schriften: vol. I, 1905; vol. II, 1905; vol. III, 1907. Historische Schriften: vol. IV, 1906; vol. V, 1908; vol. VI, 1910. Philologische Schriften: vol. VII, 1909. Epigraphische und numismatische Schriften: vol. VIII, 1913.

In the following sections of this bibliography, works are grouped, so far as possible, in the order in which they become relevant to the texts of the chapters concerned.

---

2. *The Constitution*

Rotondi, G. *Leges publicae Populi Romani.* Milan, 1912.
de Francisci, P. *Storia del diritto romano.* Rome. Vol. I, 1926; vol. II, parte I, 1929.
Greenidge, A. H. J. *Roman Public Life.* London, 1911.
Herzog, E. *Geschichte und System der römischen Staatsverfassung.* Vol. I. *Königszeit und Republik.* Leipzig, 1884.
Homo, L. *Les institutions politiques romaines: de la cité à l'état.* Paris, 1927.
Levi, M. A. *La costituzione romana dai Gracchi a Giulio Cesare.* Florence, n.d.[1928].
Madvig, J. N. *Die Verfassung und Verwaltung des römischen Staates.* Leipzig. Vol. I. 1881; vol. II, 1882.
Marquardt, J. *Römische Staatsverwaltung.* Leipzig. Ed. 2. Vol. I, 1881; vol. II, 1884; vol. III, 1885.
Mommsen, Th. *Römisches Staatsrecht.* Leipzig. Vol. I (ed. 3), 1887; vol. II, I (ed. 3), 1887; vol. II, 2 (ed. 3), 1887; vol. III, I, 1887; vol. III, 2, 1888.
Neumann, K. J. *Römische Staatsaltertümer,* in *Einleitung in die Altertumswissenschaft,* herausgegeben von A. Gercke und E. Norden, vol. III (zweite Auflage; Leipzig-Berlin, 1914), pp. 435 *sqq.*
Schönbauer, E. *Untersuchungen zum römischen Staats- und Wirtschaftsrecht.* I. *Wesen und Ursprung des römischen Principats.* Z. d. Sav.-Stift. XLVII, 1927, romanistische Abteilung, p. 264.
Willems, P. *Le droit public romain.* Ed. 7. Louvain-Paris, 1910.
Botsford, G. W. *The Roman Assemblies from their Origin to the End of the Republic.* New York, 1909.
Abbott, F. F. *The Referendum and the Recall among the Ancient Romans.* The Sewanee Review, XXIII, 1915, p. 84.
Cavaignac, E. *La répartition tribuaire des citoyens romains et ses conséquences démographiques.* Rev. Belge, IX, 1930, p. 815.
Willems, P. *Le Sénat de la République romaine: sa composition et ses attributions.* Louvain. Vol. I, 1878; vol. II, 1883; Appendices du Tome I et registres, 1885.
de Boor, C. *Fasti censorii.* Berlin, n.d. [1873].
Frank, T. *Roman Census Statistics from 225 to 28 B.C.* C.P. XIX, 1924, p. 329.
†Niccolini, G. *Il tribunato della plebe.* Milan, 1932.
—— *Fasti tribunorum plebis ab an. 260/494 usque ad an. 731/23.* Pisa, 1898.
Ziegler, M. *Fasti tribunorum plebis,* 133–70. Beilage zum Programm des kgl. Gymnasiums in Ulm. Ulm, 1903.
Carcopino, J. On Festus, p. 246 Müller = p. 290 Lindsay. *Bulletin de la Société nationale des Antiquaires de France,* 1929, p. 75.
Costa, E. *Cicerone giureconsulto.* Ed. 2. Two vols. Bologna, n.d. [1927].

3. *Criminal Law and Procedure*

Greenidge, A. H. J. *The Legal Procedure of Cicero's Time.* Oxford, 1901.

Mommsen, Th. *Römisches Strafrecht.* Leipzig, 1899.

Strachan-Davidson, J. L. *Problems of the Roman Criminal Law.* 2 vols. Oxford, 1912.

Zumpt, A. W. *Das Criminalrecht der römischen Republik.* Berlin. Vol. I, 1865; vol. II, 1, 1868; 2, 1869.

Plaumann, G. *Das sogennante Senatus consultum ultimum, die Quasidiktatur der späteren römischen Republik.* Klio, XIII, 1913, p. 321.

Hardy, E. G. *Some Notable* Iudicia Populi *on Capital Charges,* in *Some Problems in Roman History* (Oxford, 1924), p. 1.

Hitzig, H. F. *Die Herkunft des Schwurgerichts im römischen Strafprozess.* Zürich, 1909.

Fraccaro, P. *Sulle "leges iudiciariae" romane. I. Osservazioni preliminari. Giurati e corti sino a Gaio Gracco.* Rendiconti del R. Istituto Lombardo di Scienze e Lettere, Serie II, vol. LII, 1919, p. 382.

Lohse, G. C. *De quaestionum perpetuarum origine, praesidibus, consiliis.* Leipzig Diss. Plaviae, 1876.

Zumpt, C. T. *De legibus iudiciisque repetundarum in Republica Romana.* Berolini, 1845.

Ferguson, W. S. *The Lex Calpurnia of* 149 B.C. J.R.S. XI, 1921, p. 86.

Hardy, E. G. *Notes on the Lex Judiciaria of C. Gracchus, the Lex Servilia of Caepio and the Lex Thoria.* J.P. XXXII, 1913, p. 96.

Levi, M. A. *A proposito della "Lex repetundarum" delle tavole del Bembo.* Riv. Fil. LVII, 1929, p. 383.

Mommsen, Th. *Lex repetundarum a.u.c.* DCXXXI *vel* DCXXXII, CXXIII *vel* CXXII *ante Chr.* Gesammelte Schriften, I, p. 1.

—— *Über die leges iudiciariae des* VII. *Jahrhunderts bis zur lex Aurelia.* Gesammelte Schriften, III, p. 339.

†Scialoja, V. *Frammenti inediti di legge romana del* I° *sec. av. Cr.* in *Studi in onore di Pietro Bonfante,* vol. I (Milan, 1930), pp. 3–10.

Madvig, J. N. *De tribunis aerariis disputatio,* in *Opuscula academica altera* (Hauniae, 1842), pp. 242 *sqq.*

4. *Rome and Italy*

Pais, E. *Storia della colonizzazione di Roma antica.* Vol. I. Rome, 1923.

—— *Serie cronologica delle colonie romane e latine dalla età regia fino all' impero.* Mem. Acc. Lincei, Serie quinta, XVII, 1924, p. 311; Serie sesta, I, 1925, p. 345.

Mommsen, Th. *Die italischen Bürgercolonien von Sulla bis Vespasian.* Gesammelte Schriften, V, p. 203.

Beloch, J. *Die Bevölkerung der griechisch-römischen Welt.* Leipzig, 1886.

—— *Die Bevölkerung Italiens im Altertum.* Klio, III, 1903, p. 471.

—— *Der italische Bund unter Roms Hegemonie.* Leipzig, 1880.

Drzerga, E. *Die römische Bundesgenossenpolitik von den Gracchen bis zum Ausbruch des Bundesgenossenkrieges.* Diss. Breslau, 1907.

Kubitschek, W. *De romanarum tribuum origine ac propagatione.* (Abhandlungen des archäologisch-epigraphischen Seminars der Universität Wien, Heft III.) Wien, 1882.

Mommsen, Th. *Die römische Tribuseintheilung nach dem marsischen Krieg.* Gesammelte Schriften, V, p. 262.

Gelzer, M. *Gemeindestaat und Reichsstaat in der römischen Geschichte.* Frankfurt a/M. n.d. [1924.]

5. Social and Economic History

Tarn, W. W. *Hellenistic Civilisation.* Ed. 2. London, 1930.

von Pöhlmann, R. *Geschichte der sozialen Frage und des Sozialismus in der antiken Welt.* Dritte Auflage durchgesehen und um einen Anhang vermehrt von F. Oertel. 2 vols. Munich, 1925.

Oertel, F. *Die soziale Frage im Altertum.* N.J. f. Wiss. III, 1927, p. 1.

Kromayer, J. *Staat und Gesellschaft der Römer,* in *Staat und Gesellschaft der Griechen und Römer bis zum Ausgang des Mittelalters.* (Die Kultur der Gegenwart, Teil II, Abt. IV, I.) Ed. 2. Berlin, 1923.

Gelzer, M. *Die Nobilität der römischen Republik.* Leipzig, 1912.

Münzer, F. *Römische Adelsparteien und Adelsfamilien.* Stuttgart, 1920.

Belot, E. *Histoire des chevaliers romains.* Paris. Vol. I, 1866; vol. II, 1873.

Marquardt, J. *Historiae equitum Romanorum libri* IV. Berolini, 1840.

Stein, A. *Der römische Ritterstand.* Munich, 1927.

Deloume, A. *Les manieurs d'argent à Rome jusqu'à l'Empire.* Ed. 2. Paris, 1892.

Hatzfeld, J. *Les trafiquants italiens dans l'Orient hellénique.* Paris, 1919.

Salvioli, G. *Le capitalisme dans le monde antique.* Paris, 1906.

Kahrstedt, U. *Die Grundlagen und Voraussetzungen der römischen Revolution,* in *Neue Wege zur Antike,* IV (Leipzig, n.d.), p. 97.

Frank, T. *An Economic History of Rome.* Ed. 2. Baltimore, 1927.

Oliver, E. H. *Roman Economic Conditions to the Close of the Republic.* Toronto, 1917.

Toutain, J. *L'économie antique.* Paris, 1927.

Kromayer, J. *Die wirtschaftliche Entwicklung Italiens im* II. *und* I. *Jahrhundert vor Chr.* N.J. Kl. Alt. XXXIII/IV, 1914, p. 145.

Dickson, A. *The Husbandry of the Ancients.* 2 vols. Edinburgh, 1788.

Heitland, W. E. *Agricola: a study of agriculture and rustic life in the Greco-Roman world from the point of view of labour.* Cambridge, 1921.

Vančura, J. Art. *Leges agrariae.* P.W. XII, col. 1150.

Gummerus, H. *Der römische Gutsbetrieb als wirtschaftlichen Organismus nach den Werken des Cato, Varro und Columella.* Klio, Beiheft V: Leipzig, 1906.

†Scalais, R. *La politique agraire de Rome depuis les guerres puniques jusqu'aux Gracques.* Mus.B. XXXIV, 1930–1932, p. 195.

Stuart Jones, H. *Land Problems in Ancient Rome.* Edinburgh Rev., vol. 224, 1916, p. 60.

Kaïla, E. *L'unité foncière en droit romain.* Paris, 1927.

Maschke, R. *Zur Theorie und Geschichte der römischen Agrargesetze.* Tübingen, 1906.

Weber, M. *Die römische Agrargeschichte in ihrer Bedeutung für das Staats- und Privatrecht.* Stuttgart, 1891.

von Schilling, C. *Studien aus der römischen Agrargeschichte.* Abhandlungen des Herder-Instituts zu Riga. Vol. II, no. 1, p. 15. Riga, 1926.

Beaudouin, E. *La limitation des fonds de terre dans ses rapports avec le droit de propriété: étude sur l'histoire du droit romain de la propriété.* Nouvelle revue historique de droit français et étranger, Année XVII, 1893, p. 397 and p. 567; Année XVIII, 1894, p. 157 and p. 309.

Kontchalovsky, D. *Recherches sur l'histoire du mouvement agraire des Gracques.* Rev. H. 153, 1926, p. 161.

Levi, M. A. *Una pagina di storia agraria romana.* Atene e Roma, N.S. III, 1922, p. 239.

Rostowzew, M. Art. *Frumentum.* P.W. VII, col. 126.

Corsetti, R. *Sul prezzo dei grani nell' antichità classica.* Studi di storia antica, II, 1893, p. 63.

Francotte, H. *Le pain à bon marché et le pain gratuit dans les cités grecques*, in *Mélanges (Jules) Nicole* (Geneva, 1905), pp. 135 *sqq.*

Wiegand, Th. und U. von Wilamowitz-Moellendorff, *Ein Gesetz von Samos über die Beschaffung von Brotkorn aus öffentlichen Mitteln.* Berl. S.B., 1904, p. 917.

6. The Gracchi

Carcopino, J. *Autour des Gracques: études critiques.* Paris, 1928.

—— *Les lois agraires des Gracques et la guerre sociale.* Bulletin de l'Association Guillaume Budé, No. 22, Janvier 1929, p. 3.

Cardinali, G. *Studi Graccani.* Genoa, 1912.

De Sanctis, G. *Dopoguerra antico.* Atene e Roma, N.S. i, 1920, p. 3 and p. 73.

—— *Rivoluzione e reazione nell' età dei Gracchi.* Atene e Roma, N.S. ii, 1921, p. 209.

Felsberg, A. *The Brothers Gracchi.* Jurjev (Dorpat: Tartu), 1910. In Russian.

Fraccaro, P. *Studi sull' età dei Gracchi.* Studi storici per l'antichità classica, v, 1912, p. 317; vi, 1913, p. 42.

—— *Sui Fanni dell' età Graccana.* Rend. Linc., Serie quinta, vol. xix, 1910, p. 656.

Gerlach, F. O. *Tiberius und Cajus Gracchus.* Basel, 1843.

Klimke, Dr. *Die ältesten Quellen zur Geschichte der Gracchen.* Kgl. Gymnasium zu Königshütte O.-S. Beilage zum 9. Jahres-Berichte. Beuthen O.-S., 1886.

—— *Beiträge zur Geschichte der Gracchen.* Jahresbericht der Kgl. Katholischen Gymnasiums zu Sagan, 1891/2. Sagan, 1892.

Kornemann, E. *Zur Geschichte der Gracchenzeit.* Klio, Beiheft i: Leipzig, 1903.

—— *Velleius' Darstellung der Gracchenzeit* (ii, 1–8). Klio, ix, 1909, p. 378.

Loew, H. *Untersuchungen zur Vorgeschichte der gracchischen Bewegung.* Giessen Diss. Darmstadt, 1920.

Meyer, Ed. *Untersuchungen zur Geschichte der Gracchen,* in *Kleine Schriften,* i (ed. 2), p. 363. Halle (Saale), 1924.

Münzer, F. *Die Fanniusfrage.* Hermes, lv, 1920, p. 427.

Nitzsch, K. W. *Die Gracchen und ihre nächsten Vorgänger.* Berlin, 1847.

Piganiol, A. *L'œuvre des Gracques.* Annales d'histoire économique et sociale, i, 1929, p. 382.

von Pöhlmann, R. *Zur Geschichte der Gracchenzeit.* Bay. S.B. philos.-philol. u. hist. Klasse, 1907, p. 443.

Schwartz, E. Review of E. Meyer, *Untersuchungen zur Geschichte der Gracchen.* G.G.A. 158, 1896, p. 792.

Soergel, J. *De Tiberio et Gaio Gracchis commentationis Particula* i. Jahresbericht von der königlichen Studienanstalt zu Erlangen bekannt gemacht den 8 August, 1860. Erlangen. *Particula* ii. 7 August, 1863. *Particula* iii. Sollemnia anniversaria in Gymnasio Regio Erlangensi rite celebranda. Erlangae, 1856 (by error for 1866). *Particula* iv. Jahres-Bericht von der königlichen Studien-Anstalt zu Hof im Studien Jahre 1868/69. Hof.

von Stern, E. *Zur Beurteilung der politischen Wirksamkeit des Tiberius und Gaius Gracchus.* Hermes, lvi, 1921, p. 229.

7. The Slave Wars in Sicily

Bücher, K. *Die Aufstände der unfreien Arbeiter* 143–129 *v. Chr.* Frankfurt a/M., 1874.

Carcopino, J. *La loi de Hiéron et les Romains.* Paris, 1914.

—— *La Sicile agricole au dernier siècle de la République romaine.* Vierteljahrsschrift für Social- und Wirthschaftsgeschichte, iv, 1906, p. 128.

Ciaceri, E. *Roma e le guerre servili in Sicilia,* in *Processi politici e relazioni internazionali* (Rome, 1918), pp. 55 *sqq.*

Giacobbe, A. *Sulla duplicazione delle guerre servili in Sicilia.* Rend. Linc., Serie sesta, I, 1925, p. 655.

Mahaffy, J. P. *The Slave Wars against Rome.* Hermathena, XVI, 1890, p. 167.

Pareti, L. *I supposti 'sdoppiamenti' delle guerre servili in Sicilia.* Riv. Fil. LV, 1927, p. 44.

Rathke, G. *De Romanorum bellis servilibus capita selecta.* Diss. Berlin, 1904.

Scalais, R. *La prospérité agricole et pastorale de la Sicile depuis la conquête romaine jusqu'aux guerres serviles.* Mus. B. XXVIII, 1924, p. 77.

—— *La restauration de l'agriculture sicilienne par les Romains.* Mus. B. XXVII, 1923, p. 243.

8. *Tiberius Gracchus*

Bijvanck, W. G. C. *Studia in Ti. Gracchi historiam.* Lugduni Batavorum, 1879.

Fraccaro, P. *Studi sull' età dei Gracchi. La tradizione storica sulla rivoluzione graccana,* Fasc. I. Città di Castello, 1914.

Geffcken, P. *Ein Wort des Tiberius Gracchus.* Klio, XXIII, 1930, p. 453.

Münzer, F. Art. *Ti. Sempronius Gracchus, der Volkstribun von* 621＝133. P.W. II A, col. 1409.

Pfeifer, G. *Agrargeschichtlicher Beitrag zur Reform des Tiberius Gracchus.* Munich Diss. Altenburg, S. A., 1914.

Riecken, G. *Die Quellen zur Geschichte des Tiberius Gracchus.* Erlangen Diss. Leipzig, 1911.

Taeger, F. *Untersuchungen zur römischen Geschichte und Quellenkunde: Tiberius Gracchus.* Stuttgart, 1928.

Terruzzi, P. *La legislazione agraria in Italia all' epoca dei Gracchi.* Rivista d' Italia, 15 May, 1926.

—— *Studi sulla legislazione agraria di Roma. Enigmi graccani e post-graccani.* Archivio giuridico. Vol. XCVII (Quarta Serie, Vol. XIII), 1927, p. 3.

—— *Intorno all' applicazione della legge Sempronia agraria.* Athenaeum, VI, 1928, p. 85.

Lincke, E. *P. Cornelius Scipio Æmilianus.* Jahresbericht des Wettiner Gymnasiums zu Dresden. Dresden, 1898.

Münzer, F. Art. *P. Cornelius Scipio Aemilianus Africanus.* P.W. IV, col. 1439.

9. *Gaius Gracchus*

Häpke, N. *C. Semproni Gracchi oratoris Romani fragmenta collecta et illustrata.* Diss. Munich, 1915.

†Callegari, E. *La legislazione sociale di Cajo Gracco.* Padua, 1896.

Corradi, G. *Gaio Gracco e le sue leggi.* St. Fil., N.S. V, 1927, p. 235; VI, 1928, pp. 55 and 139.

Warde Fowler, W. *Gaius Gracchus and the Senate: Note on the Epitome of the Sixtieth Book of Livy.* C.R. X, 1896, p. 278.

—— *Notes on Gaius Gracchus.* Eng. Hist. Rev. XX, 1905, pp. 209 and 417.

Fraccaro, P. *Ricerche su Gaio Graccho.* Athenaeum, N.S. III, 1925, pp. 76 and 156.

Judeich, W. *Die Gesetze des Gaius Gracchus.* H.Z. 111, 3 F. 15, 1913, p. 473.

Mommsen, Th. *Über zwei römische Colonien bei Velleius Paterculus.* Gesammelte Schriften, V, p. 254.

Münzer, F. Art. *C. Sempronius Gracchus, der Volkstribun von* 631＝123 *und* 632＝122. P.W. II A, col. 1375.

Pelham, H. F. *On the Lex Sempronia C. Gracchi de provincia Asia.* Transactions of the Oxford Philological Society, 1881–1882, p. 1.

Prodinger, K. *Das Tribunat des C. Gracchus.* Dritter Jahresbericht des k. k. Staatsgymnasiums zu Gottschee. Gottschee, 1908, p. 1.

(10) *Junonia*

Barthel, W. *Römische Limitation in der Provinz Africa.* Bonner Jahrbücher, cxx, 1911, p. 39.

Carcopino, J. *L'Afrique au dernier siècle de la République romaine.* Rev. H. 162, 1929, p. 88.

Gsell, S. *Histoire ancienne de l'Afrique du Nord.* Vol. vii (Paris, 1928), pp. 58 *sqq.*

Saumagne, Ch. *Colonia Iulia Karthago.* Bulletin archéologique du Comité des Travaux historiques et scientifiques, 1924, p. 131.

Schulten, A. *L'arpentage romain en Tunisie.* Bulletin archéologique du Comité des Travaux historiques et scientifiques, 1902, p. 129.

11. *Agrarian Legislation after the Gracchi*

Ensslin, W. *Die Ackergesetzgebung seit Ti. Gracchus im Kampfe der politischen Parteien.* N.J. Kl. Alt. liii/liv, 1924, p. 15.

Caspari, M. O. B. *On Some Problems of Roman Agrarian History.* Klio, xiii, 1913, p. 184.

Hardy, E. G. *Were the Lex Thoria of 118 b.c. and the Lex Agraria of 111 b.c. Reactionary Laws?* J.P. xxxi, 1910, p. 268.

Levi, M. A. *Intorno alla legge agraria del 111 a.c.* Riv. Fil. lvii, 1929, p. 231.

Mommsen, Th. *Lex agraria a.u.c. dcxliii, ante Chr. 111.* Gesammelte Schriften, i, p. 65.

Niccolini, G. *Spurius Thorius, tribunus plebis, e la lex agraria del 111.* Rend. Linc., Serie quinta, xxviii, 1920, p. 189.

Rudorff, A. A. F. *Das Ackergesetz des Spurius Thorius.* Zeitschrift für geschichtliche Rechtswissenschaft, x, 1842, p. 1.

Saumagne, Ch. *Sur la loi agraire de 643/111; essai de restitution des lignes 19 et 20.* Rev. Phil., 3me série, i, 1927, p. 50.

Thompson, F. C. *The Agrarian Legislation of Spurius Thorius.* C.R. xxvii, 1913, p. 23.

Cary, M. *The Land Legislation of Julius Caesar's First Consulship.* J.P. xxxv, 1920, p. 174.

—— *Notes on the Legislation of Julius Caesar.* J.R.S. xix, 1929, p. 113.

Fabricius, E. *Ueber die lex Mamilia Roscia Peducaea Alliena Fabia.* Heid. S.B., philos.-hist. Klasse, 1924/5, 1 Abh.

Hardy, E. G. *The Lex Mamilia Roscia Peducaea Alliena Fabia.* C.Q. xix, 1925, p. 185.

12. *The Romans in Asia*

Cardinali, G. *Il regno di Pergamo.* (Studi di storia antica, pubblicati da Giulio Beloch, Fasc. v.) Rome, 1906.

—— *La morte di Attalo III e la rivolta di Aristonico,* in *Saggi di storia antica e di archeologia* (Rome, 1910), p. 269.

Chapot, V. *La province romaine proconsulaire d'Asie depuis ses origines jusqu'à la fin du Haut-Empire.* Paris, 1904.

Foucart, P. *La formation de la province romaine d'Asie.* Mémoires de l'Institut national de France: Académie des Inscriptions et Belles Lettres, vol. xxxvii, 1904, p. 297.

Meyer, Ernst. *Die Grenzen der hellenistischen Staaten in Kleinasien.* Zürich-Leipzig, 1925.

Reinach, Th. *Mithridate Eupator, roi de Pont.* Paris, 1890.

13. The Romans in South-Eastern Europe

Perdrizet, P. *Inscriptions de Delphes,* v. *Le proconsul M. Minucius Rufus vainqueur des Gaulois Scordistes et des Thraces.* B.C.H. xx, 1896, p. 481.

Pomtow, H. *Die Datierung der* xii. *delph. Priesterzeit.* Phil. liv, 1895, p. 356, especially p. 367 f.

—— *Die drei Brände des Tempels zu Delphi.* Rh. Mus., N.F. li, 1896, p. 329.

Tod, M. N. *The Macedonian Era.* B.S.A. xxiii, 1918–1919, p. 206, and xxiv, 1919–1920, 1920–1921, p. 54.

Zippel, G. *Die römische Herrschaft in Illyrien bis auf Augustus.* Leipzig, 1877.

14. The Jugurthine War and its Significance

Gsell, S. *Histoire ancienne de l'Afrique du Nord.* Vol. vii, *La République romaine et les rois indigènes.* Paris, 1928.

Bosselaar, D. E. *Quomodo Sallustius historiam belli Iugurthini conscripserit.* Utrecht Diss. Amsterdam, 1915.

van der Hock, M. *Quaestiones Sullanae et Sallustianae.* Amsterdam Diss. Leovardiae, 1901.

Bloch, G. *M. Aemilius Scaurus: étude sur l'histoire des partis au* vii*e siècle de Rome,* in *Mélanges d'histoire ancienne* (Université de Paris: Bibliothèque de la Faculté des Lettres, Tome xxv). Paris, 1909, pp. 1 *sqq.*

Pais, E. *M. Emilio Scauro: i suoi processi e la sua autobiografia,* in *Dalle guerre puniche a Cesare Augusto* (Rome, 1918), i, pp. 91 *sqq.*

—— *L'autobiografia ed il processo "repetundarum" di P. Rutilio Rufo,* in *Dalle guerre puniche a Cesare Augusto* (Rome, 1918), i, pp. 35 *sqq.*

De Sanctis, G. *Quinto Cecilio Metello Numidico.* Atti del 2° Congresso Nazionale di Studi Romani (Rome, 1931), vol. i, p. 343. Reprinted in part in *Problemi di storia antica,* pp. 215 *sqq.*

Holroyd, M. *The Jugurthine War: was Marius or Metellus the real victor?* J.R.S. xviii, 1928, p. 1.

† Levi, M.A. *Chi ha vinta la guerra giugurtina?* Atti del 2° Congresso Nazionale di Studi Romani (Rome, 1931), vol. i, p. 508.

Meinel, G. *Zur Chronologie des jugurthinischen Krieges.* Programm. Augsburg, 1883.

Mommsen, Th. *Zu Sallustius.* Gesammelte Schriften, vii, p. 77.

Wirz, H. *Die stoffliche und zeitliche Gliederung des Bellum Jugurthinum des Sallust,* in *Festschrift der Kantonsschule in Zürich zur Begrüssung der vom* 28. *September bis* 1. *Oktober* 1887 *in Zürich tagenden* xxxix. *Versammlung deutscher Philologen und Schulmänner,* p. 1. Zürich, 1887.

Carcopino, J. *Salluste, le culte des* Cereres *et les Numides.* Rev. H. 158, 1928, p. 1.

Saumagne, Ch. *Sur la bataille de Zama.* Rend. Linc., Serie sesta, vol. i, 1925, p. 678.

—— *Le champ de bataille du Muthul.* Revue tunisienne, N.S. i, 1930, p. 3.

Cagnat, R. Art. *Exercitus: II. Rome.* D.S. ii, p. 912.

Couissin, P. *Les armes romaines.* Paris, 1926.

Kromayer, J. und G. Veith. *Heerwesen und Kriegführung der Griechen und Römer* (Müller's *Handbuch der Altertumswissenschaft,* Abt. iv, Teil iii, Band ii). Munich, 1928.

Parker, H. M. D. *The Roman Legions.* Oxford, 1928.

Schulten, A. *Zur Heeresreform des Marius.* Hermes, lxiii, 1928, p. 240.

Gelzer, M. *Die römische Gesellschaft zur Zeit Ciceros.* N.J. Kl. Alt. xlv/vi, 1/2, 1920, p. 1.

Vogt, J. *Homo novus: ein Typus der römischen Republik.* Stuttgart, 1926.

Schur, W. *Homo novus.* Bonner Jahrbücher, cxxxiv, 1929, p. 54.

15. *The Romans in the West: the Germanic Invasions*

Jullian, C. *Histoire de la Gaule.* Vol. III: La conquête romaine et les premières invasions germaniques. Ed. 2. Paris, 1920.

Constans, L. A. *Esquisse d'une histoire de la Basse-Provence dans l'antiquité.* Marseilles, 1923. (Extrait du Tome II des *Bouches-du-Rhône*, Encyclopédie départementale.)

——— *Arles antique.* Paris, 1921.

Clerc, M. *Massalia: histoire de Marseille dans l'antiquité.* Vol. II. Marseilles, 1929.

Bieder, Th. *Geschichte der Germanenforschung.* Leipzig. Teil I, 1921; Teil II, 1922; Teil III, 1925.

Capelle, W. *Die Germanen im Frühlicht der Geschichte.* Leipzig, 1928.

Meyer, Ed. *Tougener und Teutonen,* in *Kleine Schriften,* vol. II [Halle (Saale), 1924], pp. 497 *sqq.*

Norden, E. *Die germanische Urgeschichte in Tacitus Germania.* Leipzig, 1922.

Schmidt, L. *Zur Kimbern- und Teutonenfrage.* Klio, XXII, 1929, p. 95.

Stähelin, F. *Die Schweiz in römischer Zeit.* Ed. 2. Basel, 1931.

Clerc, M. *Aquae Sextiae. Histoire d'Aix-en-Provence dans l'antiquité.* Aix-en-Provence, 1916.

——— *La bataille d'Aix: études critiques sur la campagne de Marius en Provence.* Paris, 1906.

16. *Internal History of Rome from 121 to 91 B.C.*

Wende, M. *De Caeciliis Metellis commentationis pars* I. Diss. Bonn, [1875].

Paape, C. *De C. Mario quaestiones selectae.* Diss. Regimonti, 1888.

thor Straten, W. *Rettungen des Kajus Marius.* Meldorf, 1869.

Weiland, F. *C. Marii* VII *cos. vita.* Programme d'invitation à l'examen public du Collège Royal Français fixé au 30 Septembre 1845. Berlin.

Bardey, E. *Das sechste Consulat des Marius oder das Jahr* 100 *in der römischen Verfassungsgeschichte.* Rostock Diss. Brandenburg, 1884.

Niccolini, G. *Note cronologiche su alcuni tribuni della plebe.* Historia, IV, 1930, p. 38.

Lengle, J. *Die Verurteilung der römischen Feldherrn von Arausio.* Hermes, LXVI, 1931, p. 302.

Münzer, F. Art. *C. Servilius Glaucia.* P.W. II A, col. 1796.

Klebs, E. Art. *L. Apuleius Saturninus.* P.W. II, col. 261.

Niccolini, G. *L. Appuleio Saturnino e le sue leggi.* St. Fil. V, 1897, p. 441.

Robinson, F. W. *Marius, Saturninus und Glaucia. Beiträge zur Geschichte der Jahre* 106–100 *v. Chr.* Jenaer historische Arbeiten, Heft 3. Bonn, 1912.

Vonder Mühll, F. *De L. Appuleio Saturnino tribuno plebis.* Diss. Basel, 1906.

Gwynn, A. *Roman Education from Cicero to Quintilian.* Oxford, 1926.

Asbach, J. *Das Volkstribunat des jüngeren M. Livius Drusus.* Programm des kgl. Gymnasiums zu Bonn, Schuljahr 1887–88. Bonn, 1888.

Hardy, E. G. *Three Questions as to Livius Drusus.* C.R. XXVII, 1913, p. 261.

Lanzani, C. *Ricerche sul tribunato di M. Livio Druso il giovane.* Riv. Fil. XL, 1912, p. 272.

Seymour, P. A. *The Policy of Livius Drusus the Younger.* Eng. Hist. Rev. XXIX, 1914, p. 417.

Strehl, W. *M. Livius Drusus, Volkstribun im Jahre* 91 *a. Chr.* Diss. Marburg, 1887.

17. *Sulla, and the Collapse of the Sullan Constitution*

†Bennett, H. *Cinna and his Times.* Diss. Menasha, 1923.

†Berve, H. *Sulla.* N.J. f. Wiss. VII, 1931, p. 673.

†Carcopino, J. *Sylla, ou la monarchie manquée.* Paris, 1931.

Fröhlich, F. Art. *L. Cornelius L. f. P. n. Sulla Felix.* P.W. IV, col. 1522.

Zachariä, K. S. *Lucius Cornelius Sulla, genannt der Glückliche, als Ordner des römischen Freistaates.* Neue Auflage. Mannheim, 1850.

Linden, E. *De bello civili Sullano.* Diss. Friburgi Brisigavorum, 1896.

Meyer, Ed. *Die angebliche Centurienreform Sullas.* Hermes, XXXIII, 1898, p. 652.

Münzer, F. *De gente Valeria.* Berlin Diss. Oppoliae, 1891.

Lanzani, C. *La legge "Valeria de aere alieno" dell' anno 86 av. Cr.* Studi storici per l'antichità classica, II, 1909, p. 426.

†—— *La rivoluzione Sillana.* Historia, V, 1931, p. 353.

Warde Fowler, W. *On the Date of the* Rhetorica ad Herennium, in *Roman Essays and Interpretations* (Oxford, 1920), pp. 91 *sqq.*

Boak, A. E. R. *The Extraordinary Commands from* 80 *to* 48 B.C.: *a study in the origins of the Principate.* Am. Hist. Rev. XXIV, 1918/9, p. 1.

Wiehn, E. *Die illegalen Heereskommanden in Rom bis auf Caesar.* Marburg Diss. Leipzig, 1926.

Fritzsche, H. *Die sullanische Gesetzgebung.* Königliches Gymnasium zu Essen: Jahres-Bericht über das Schuljahr 1881–1882. Essen, 1882.

Lengle, J. *Untersuchungen über die sullanische Verfassung.* Diss. Freiburg i/B., 1899.

Levi, M. A. *Silla: saggio sulla storia politica di Roma dell'* 88 *all'* 80 *a.C.* Milan, 1924.

McFayden, D. *The* Lex data *as a Source of Imperial Authority,* in *Papers on Classical Subjects in Memory of John Max Wulfing* (Washington University Studies— New Series; Language and Literature, No. 3. St Louis, 1930), pp. 64 *sqq.*

Hardy, E. G. *The Number of the Sullan Senate.* J.R.S. VI, 1916, p. 59.

Hill, H. *Sulla's Military Oligarchy.* Proceedings of the Classical Association, XXVIII, 1931, p. 63.

Sundén, J. M. *De tribunicia potestate a L. Sulla imminuta quaestiones.* Skrifter utgifna af K. Humanistiska Vetenskapssamfundet i Upsala, V, 5. Upsala, 1897.

Nipperdey, K. *Die "leges annales" der römischen Republik.* Abhandlungen der philol.-hist. Classe der königl. sächsischen Gesellschaft der Wissenschaften, V, 1865. p. 1.

Neunheuser, J. *M. Aemilius Lepidus: die Reformen des Sulla und die ersten Versuche, sie im römischen Staate rückgängig zu machen.* Münster Diss. Essen, 1902.

Deutsch, M. E. *The Death of Lepidus, Leader of the Revolution of* 78 B.C. University of California Publications in Classical Philology, Vol. V, No. 3, p. 59.

Münzer, F. *Der erste Gegner des Spartacus.* Phil. LV, 1896, p. 387.

Lévy-Bruhl, H. *La* denegatio actionis *sous la Procédure Formulaire.* Lille, 1924.

CHAPTER IV. SECTIONS VI AND VII

A. Ancient Sources

(a) Epigraphical

C.I.L. I (ed. 2), Part i (1893). *Acta triumphorum*, p. 177, Part ii, i (1918). 588, 708 (= Dessau, 29), 709 (= Dessau, 8888), 848–884 (*Glandes Asculanae*). For *Glandes Asculanae* see also *C.I.L.* IX (1883), 6086 and C. Zangemeister, *Glandes Asculanae et reliquae Picenae* in *Ephemeris Epigrafica*, VI (1885), pp. 5–47 and 142.

(b) Coins

Grueber, H. A. *Coins of the Roman Republic in the British Museum.* Vol. II, London (1910), pp. 317–339.

(c) Literary

Appian, *Bell. Civ.* I, 38–53.
Asconius, pp. 3, 14, 22, 73, 74, 79 C.
Auctor *ad Herennium*, II, 28, 45; III, 2, 2.
Auctor *de viris illustribus*, 63, 66, 75.
Cicero, *pro Archia*, 4, 7; *pro Balbo*, 8, 21; 22, 50; *Brutus*, 89, 304; *pro Cluentio*, 7, 21; *de div.* I, 33, 72; II, 30, 65; *pro Fonteio*, 18, 41; 19, 43: *de lege agraria*, II, 29, 80; II, 33, 90; *Phil.* III, 3, 6; VIII, 10, 31; XII, 11, 27; *in Pisonem*, 36, 87; *in Verrem*, II, 2, 5.
Claudius Quadrigarius, frag. 80, P. (= Seneca, *de Ben.* III, 23, 2).
Dio Cassius (ed. Boissevain), XXIX, frag. 98; XXX–XXXV, frag. 100.
Diodorus Siculus (ed. Dindorf), frags. of bk. XXXVII.
Frontinus, *Strat.* I, 5, 17; II, 4, 15–16 (= IV, 7, 40–41); III, 17, 8.
Gellius, *N.A.* II, 27, 2; IV, 4, 3; XV, 4, 4.
Justin, XXXVIII, 4, 13.
Licinianus, p. 32 F.
Macrobius, *Sat.* I, 11, 23 (= Seneca, *de Ben.* III, 23, 5); I, 11, 24; I, 11, 32.
Memnon, 29 (*F.H.G.* III, p. 540).
Obsequens, 54 (114), 55 (115), 56 (116).
Orosius, V, 18, 1–29.
Ovid, *Fasti*, VI, 563–568.
Pliny, *N.H.* II, 83, 199; III, 5, 70; III, 20, 138; VII, 3, 34; VII, 43, 135; VIII, 57, 221; XV, 29, 121; XXII, 6, 12; XXV, 5, 52; XXXIII, 1, 20; XXXIII, 3, 55.
Plutarch, *Cato*, 2; *Cicero*, 3; *Lucullus*, 1, 2; *Marius*, 32–33; *Pompey*, 4; *Sertorius*, 4; *Sulla*, 6.
Polyaenus, VIII, 9.
Schol. Bob. ed Stangl, II, p. 175.
Servius, *ad Aen.* IX, 587.
Sisenna, frags. 1–124 P.
Strabo, V, 541.
Sulla, frags. 8–10, 10 A P.
Valerius Maximus, I, 6, 4; V, 4, 7; VI, 3, 3; VI, 9, 9; VIII, 6, 4; IX, 7, 4; IX, 8, 3.
Velleius Paterculus, II, 15–16; 21, 1.

B. Modern Works

Besides the relevant portions of the histories cited in the General Bibliography see also:

Beloch, K. J. *Römische Geschichte.* Berlin-Leipzig, 1926. pp. 621–627. (*Die* Lex Pompeia de Gallia Citeriore.)

Cichorius, C. *Das Offiziercorps eines römischen Heeres aus dem Bundesgenossenkriege.* Römische Studien, Leipzig-Berlin, 1922. pp. 130–185.

von Domaszewski, A. *Bellum Marsicum.* Abh. Arch.-epig., Wien und Leipzig, 1924.

Frank, T. *Representative Government in Ancient Politics.* C.J. xiv, 1919, p. 547.

—— *Representative Government in the Macedonian Republics.* C.P. ix, 1914, p. 50, note 2.

Hardy, E. G. *The Transpadane Question and the Alien Act of* 65 *or* 64 B.C. J.R.S. vi, 1916, p. 65. (= *Some Problems in Roman History.* Oxford, 1924. pp. 46–9.)

Hill, G. F. *Historical Roman Coins.* London, 1909. pp. 85–92.

Hirschfeld, O. *Der Treuschwur der Italiker für Marcus Livius Drusus.* Kleine Schriften. Berlin, 1913. p. 288.

Kiene, A. *Der römische Bundesgenossenkrieg.* Leipzig, 1845.

Marcks, E. *Die Überlieferung des Bundesgenossenkrieges.* Marburg, 1884.

Mattingly, H. *Roman Coins.* London, 1928. p. 79.

Nissen, H. *Italische Landeskunde.* Berlin, 1883. See the paragraphs on various Italian towns, especially vol. i, p. 340 (Corfinium); vol. ii, p. 426 (Asculum).

Reid, J. S. *Municipalities of the Roman Empire.* Cambridge, 1913. pp. 111–120.

Rice Holmes, T. *The Roman Republic and the Founder of the Empire.* Oxford, 1923. Vol. i, p. 356.

Stevenson, G. H. *Cn. Pompeius Strabo and the Franchise Question.* J.R.S. ix, 1919, p. 95.

Articles in P.W., *Aesernia* (Hülsen); *Asculum* (Hülsen); *Bovianum Vetus* (Hülsen); *Q. Caecilius* (98) *Metellus Pius* (Münzer); *Corfinium* (Hülsen); *L. Cornelius* (392) *Sulla* (Frölich); *C. Cosconius* (3) (Münzer); *T. Didius* (5) (Münzer); *Grumentum* (Weiss); *L. Julius* (142) *Caesar* (Münzer); *T. Lafrenius* (Münzer); *Lex Calpurnia* (1) (Weiss); *Lex Plautia* (2) *Iudiciaria* (Weiss); *Lex Plautia* (3) *Papiria* (Weiss); *Lex Pompeia* (1) (Weiss); *Lex Varia* (s.v. *Maiestas*) (Kübler); *P. Licinius* (61) *Crassus* (Münzer); *Marius Egnatius* (10) (Münzer); *Marsi* (Philipp); *Minatius Magius* (8) (Münzer); *P. Rutilius* (26) *Lupus* (Münzer); *Samnites* (Philipp); *Q. Sertorius* (3) (Schulten); *Q. Servilius* (50) *Caepio* (Münzer).

Outlines of the parts played by various Italian towns in the Social War are to be found in the historical introductions in the appropriate volumes of *C.I.L.,* namely: ix (Mommsen), x (Mommsen), xi (Bormann), xiv (Dessau).

CHAPTER VI. SECTION IV

A. Ancient Sources

(*a*) *Epigraphical*

C.I.L. i (ed. 2), Part ii, i (1918). 719 (= Dessau, 26), 722.

(*b*) *Literary*

Appian, Bell. Civ. i, 75–96; 100; 104.

Asconius, pp. 75, 84 c.

Auctor *de viris illustribus,* 68, 75.

Cicero, *ad Att.* IX, 10, 3; *de domo*, 17, 43; *in Cat.* III, 4, 9; *de legibus*, II, 22, 56–57; *de leg. agr.* I, 7, 21; II, 21, 56; II, 29, 81; II, 33, 89; II, 34, 92–93; *de nat. deorum*, III, 32, 80; *de officiis*, II, 8, 27; II, 14, 51; *paradoxa*, VI, 2, 46; *de pet. cons.* 2, 9; 3, 10; *Phil.* XII, 11, 27; XIII, 1, 2; *pro Quinctio*, 24, 76; *pro Roscio Amerino*, 2, 6; 43, 125–126; 45, 130; *pro Sulla*, 26, 72; *in Verr.* I, 16, 43; IV, 31, 69.

Claudius Quadrigarius, frag. 84 P. (= Orosius, V, 20, 6).

Dio Cassius (ed. Boissevain), XXX–XXXV, frags. 106–109.

Diodorus (ed. Dindorf), frags. of bks. XXXVIII, XXXIX.

Dionysius of Halicarnassus, IV, 62.

Eutropius, V, 7, 4; 8.

Florus, 11, 9, [III, 21] 18–22.

Frontinus, *Strat.* II, 9, 3.

Licinianus, p. 32 F.

Livy, *Epit.* 85–89.

Obsequens, 57 (118).

Orosius, V, 20–21.

Pliny, *N.H.* VII, 43, 137; XXXIII, 1 16.

Plutarch, *Caesar*, 1; *Cato*, 3; *Crassus*, 6; *Pompey*, 6–8; *Sertorius*, 6; *Sulla*, 27–32.

Sallust, *Hist.* I, 34–53; V, 20 M.

Strabo, V, 249.

Sulla, frags. 18–19 P.

Tacitus, *Ann.* VI, 12; *Hist.* III, 72.

Valerius Maximus, V, 2, 9; VI, 8, 2; VII, 6, 4; IX, 2, 1.

Velleius Paterculus, II, 24, 3–29, 2.

Zonaras, X, 1.

B. Modern Works

Besides the relevant portions of the histories cited in the General Bibliography see also:

Cantalupi, P. *La guerra civile Sillana in Italia.* Rome, 1892.

Ensslin, W. *Appian und die Liviustradition zum ersten Bürgerkrieg.* Klio, **xx**, 1926, p. 446.

Gardner, R. *The Siege of Praeneste.* J.P. XXXV, 1919, p. 1.

Lanzani, C. *Le battaglie di Fidentia e di Placentia nella guerra civile Sillana.* Rend. Linc., Ser. VI, vol. II, 1926, p. 7.

Linden, E. *De bello civili Sullano.* Diss. Freiburg, 1896.

Articles in P.W., Q. *Caecilius* (98) *Metellus Pius* (Münzer); C. *Carrinas* (1) (Münzer); *Cornelii* (4) (Münzer); L. *Cornelius* (338) *Scipio Asiagenus* (Münzer); L. *Cornelius* (392) *Sulla* (Frölich); *Gutta* (Münzer); L. *Junius* (58) *Brutus Damasippus* (Münzer); M. *Licinius* (68) *Crassus* (Gelzer); M. *Licinius* (109) *Lucullus* (Münzer); Q. *Lucretius* (25) *Ofella* (Münzer); L. *Marcius* (75) *Philippus* (Münzer); C. *Marius* (15) (Münzer); M. *Marius* (42) *Gratidianus* (Münzer); *Sacriportus* (Philipp); Q. *Sertorius* (3) (Schulten).

Outlines of the parts played in the Civil War by various towns in Italy and Cisalpine Gaul are to be found in the historical introductions in the appropriate volumes of *C.I.L.*, namely: V (Mommsen), IX (Mommsen), X (Mommsen), XI (Bormann), XIV (Dessau).

CHAPTER VII. SECTION IV

A. Ancient Sources

(a) Epigraphical

C.I.L. i (ed. 2), Part i (1893). *Acta triumphorum*, p. 177.

(b) Literary

Ammianus Marcellinus, xxiv, 6, 7; xxvi, 9, 9; xxx, 1, 23.
Appian, *Bell. Civ.* 1, 67, 85–86, 108–15; *Iber.* 99–101; *Mithr* 68.
Auctor *de viris illustribus*, 63, 77.
Caesar, *B.G.* iii, 23, 5.
Cicero, *Brutus*, 48, 180; *de fin.* ii, 20, 63; *pro Balbo*, 2, 5; 6, 14; *pro Fonteio*, 6,
    14; 7, 16; 20, 46; *de imp. Cn. Pompeii*, 4, 10; 11, 30; 16, 46; 21, 62;
    Phil. xi, 8, 18; *Verr.* i, 34, 87; v, 28, 72; v, 56, 146; v, 58, 153; v, 59, 154.
Claudius Quadrigarius, frag. 85 P. (= Gellius, *N.A.* ix, 1, 1).
Diodorus (ed. Dindorf), xxxvii, 22a.
Frontinus, *Strat.* 1, 1, 12; 1, 5, 1; 1, 5, 8; 1, 8, 5; 1, 10, 1–2 (= iv, 7, 6); 1, 11,
    13; 1, 12, 4; ii, 1, 2–3; ii, 3, 5; ii, 3, 10–11; ii, 5, 31–32; ii, 7, 5; ii, 10,
    1; ii, 11, 2; ii, 12, 2; ii, 13, 3; iv, 5, 19.
Gellius, *N.A.* ii, 27, 2; ix, 1, 1; xv, 22, 1–9.
Obsequens, 58 (119), 59 (120), 60 (121).
Orosius, v, 19, 9; 20, 1; 23, 1–15.
Pliny, *Epist.* iii, 9, 10.
Pliny, *N.H.* iii, 3, 18; vii, 26, 96; viii, 32, 117; xxii, 6, 12; xxxvii, 6, 15.
Plutarch, *Lucullus*, 5; *Marius*, 6, 44; *Pompey*, 17–20; *Sertorius*.
Polyaenus, viii, 22.
Sallust, *Hist.* i, 84–126; ii, 28–35, 53–70, 88–98; iii, 45–6, 81–9 M.
Strabo, iii, 156–162; iv, 178.
Tacitus, *Ann.* iii, 73.
Valerius Maximus, i, 2, 4; viii, 15, 8; ix, 1, 5; ix, 15, 3.
Velleius Paterculus, ii, 24, 4; 29, 5–30, 1; 90, 3.
Zonaras, x, 2.

B. Modern Works

Besides the relevant portions of general histories cited in the General Bibliography,
see also:

Berve, H. *Sertorius*. Hermes, lxiv, 1929, p. 199.
von Bienkowski, P. R. *Kritische Studien über Chronologie und Geschichte des
    sertorianischen Krieges*. Wien. St. xiii, 1891, pp. 129–58; pp. 210–30.
Cavaignac, E. *Métellus contre Hirtuléius*. Rev. E.A. xxx, 1928, p. 98.
Cichorius, C. *Römische Studien*. Leipzig-Berlin, 1922, esp. pp. 167, 196, 230, 256.
Dronke, G. *Kritische Studien zur Geschichte des sertorianischen Kämpfe*. Zeitschrift
    für d. Altertumswissenschaft, xi, 1853, Nr. 63 and 64.
Hauler, E. *Zu den Orleaner Bruchstücken des* iii. *Buches von Sallusts Historien*.
    Wien. St. xliv, 1924–5, p. 188.
Mattingly, H. *Some Historical Coins of the late Republic*. J.R.S. xii, 1922, p. 234.
Maurenbrecher, B. *C. Sallusti Crispi Historiarum Reliquiae*. Leipzig, 1891. Vol. i,
    pp. 20–40.
Rice Holmes, T. *The Roman Republic and the Founder of the Empire*. Oxford, 1923.
    Vol. i, pp. 138–53; pp. 369–84.
Schulten, A. *Sertorius*. Leipzig, 1926.

Schulten, A. *Ein römisches Lager aus dem sertorianischen Kriege.* J.D.A.I. xxxiii, 1918, p. 75.

—— *Eine unbekannte Topographie von Emporion.* Hermes, lx, 1925, p. 66.

—— *Fontes Hispaniae Antiquae.* Vol. ii. Barcelona, 1925.

—— *Numantia.* Vol. i, München, 1914, pp. 379–82; pp. 293–317. Vol. iv, München, 1929 (Die Lager bei Renieblas), esp. pp. 180–4; pp. 246–8.

Schulten, A. und R. Paulsen. *Castra Caecilia.* Arch. Anz., Beiblatt zum J.D.A.I. xliii, 1928, cols. 1–29.

Stahl, W. *De bello Sertoriano.* Diss. Erlangen, 1907.

Wilsdorf, D. *Fasti Hispaniarum provinciarum.* Diss. Leipzig, 1878.

Articles in P.W., *C. Annius* (9) *Luscus* (Klebs); *Q. Caecilius* (98) *Metellus Pius* (Münzer); *P. Calpurnius* (49) *Lanarius* (Münzer); *Caracca* (Hübner); *Celtiberi* (Hübner); *Consabura* (Hübner); *Contrebia* (Hübner); *L. Cornelius* (392) *Sulla* (Frölich); *T. Didius* (5) (Münzer); *M. Domitius* (44) *Calvinus* (Münzer); *L. Fufidius* (4) (Münzer); *C. Herennius* (7) (Münzer); *L. Hirtuleius* (3) (Münzer); *Hispania* (Schulten); *Italica* (Hübner-Schulten); *Lauro* (2) (Schulten); *P. Licinius* (61) *Crassus* (Münzer); *Lusitani* (Schulten); *L. Marcius* (75) *Philippus* (Münzer); *Segovia* (1) (Keune); *Q. Sertorius* (3) (Schulten).

Outlines of the parts played by Spanish towns in the Sertorian War are given in the historical introductions in *C.I.L.* ii (Spain) by Hübner.

CHAPTER V

PONTUS AND ITS NEIGHBOURS: THE FIRST MITHRIDATIC WAR

A. ANCIENT SOURCES

1. *Literary Texts*

The main literary sources are Appian's *Mithridatica*, Florus, Justin, Plutarch's *Lives of Lucullus, Pompey*, and *Sulla*, Strabo, and Velleius Paterculus. A complete survey and analysis of all the texts and of questions relating to the source-material is given in the monograph of Th. Reinach, *Mithridate Eupator*, quoted below.

For the campaigns narrated in sections v–vIII of the chapter the following passages are specifically relevant:

Ammianus Marcellinus, xvi, 12, 41.
Appian, *Mithr.* 1–63.
Auctor *De vir. illustr.* 70, 75.
Cicero, II *in Verr.* II, 21, 51; 65, 159: *de imp. Cn. Pompei*, 3, 7; 5, 11: *pro Flacco* 14, 32; 25, 60: *pro Rab. Post.* 10, 27.
Dio Cassius, fr. 99, 101, 104.
Diodorus, xxxvii, 26–28; xxxviii, 6, 7, 8.
Eutropius, v, 5–7.
Florus, I, 40 (III, 5).
Frontinus, *Strat.* II, 3, 17; II, 8, 12; III, 17, 5.
Josephus, *Ant. Jud.* xiv, 112 (7, 2).
Justin, xxxviii, 1–7.
Licinianus (ed. Flemisch), fragments of book xxxv.
Livy, *Epit.* 76, 77, 78, 81, 82, 83.
Memnon, fragments of *History of Heraclea*, 30–35. (F. H. G. III, pp. 541 *sqq.*)
Orosius, vi, 2.
Pausanias, I, 20, 4–7: IX, 7, 4–6; 33, 6; 40, 7: X, 34, 4.
Plutarch, *Lucullus*, 2–3: *Sulla*, 11–26: *Moralia*, 259 A–D; 809 C.
Posidonius, frag. 39 (= Nicolaus Dam., fr. 79): frag. 41 (*ap.* Athenaeus, v, 211 *sqq.*).
Strabo, IX, 396, 398; XII, 579, 654; XIII, 594, 614, 621; XIV, 641, 649.
Tacitus, *Ann.* III, 62; IV, 14; 56.
Velleius Paterculus, II, 18, 23, 24.

2. *Inscriptions*

All the inscriptions bearing upon the history of Pontus which were known down to 1890 will be found in Reinach, *op. cit.* pp. 456 *sqq.* For these and for more recent discoveries consult also the *Recueil des Inscriptions grecques et latines du Pont et de l'Arménie* in *Studia Pontica*, III, 1910 (see below).

See also H. Grégoire, *Rapport sur un voyage d'exploration dans le Pont et en Cappadoce*, B.C.H. xxxvi, 1909, p. 1: G. de Jerphanion, *Inscriptions de Cappadoce et du Pont*, Mélanges de la Faculté Orientale de Beyrouth, vii, 1917–21, p. 1 and p. 395: *S.E.G.* IV, 1930, 727–33: A. Souter, *Two new Cappadocian Greek Inscriptions* (Anatolian Studies presented to Sir William Ramsay), 1923, p. 399. Inscriptions of Sinope will be found in D. M. Robinson, *Ancient Sinope*, quoted below. For inscriptions from South Russia bearing on the history of Pontus see B. Latyschev, *Inscriptiones Orae Septentrionalis Ponti Euxini*, I, ed. 2, 1916.

See also *C.I.L.* III, 238–40, 6979–80, 12220, 14402; Th. Reinach in *Rev. Arch.* (5ᵐᵉ sér.) III, 1916, p. 329, and XII, 1920, p. 185; A. Salač, in *B.C.H.* XLIV, 1920, p. 354; D. M. Robinson, in *A.J.Ph.* XLIII, 1922, p. 71; Ἀρχ. Δελτ. XI, 1927–28, παραρτ. p. 27, No. 12 (Chios), and M. Segre in *Il Mondo Classico*, II, 1932, p. 129.

3. *Coins*

See E. Babelon et Th. Reinach, *Recueil Général des Monnaies grecques d'Asie Mineure*, I, i, ed. 2, 1925; and cf. E. S. G. Robinson, in *Num. Chr.* XX (4ᵗʰ ser.), 1920, p. 1, and X (5ᵗʰ ser.), 1930, p. 1. Also K. Regling in *Klio*, XXII, 1928, p. 292.

B. MODERN WORKS

(Titles marked with an asterisk are in Russian)

Anderson, J. G. C., Cumont, E., Cumont, F. and Grégoire, H. *Studia Pontica*, I, 1903; II, 1906; III, 1 (Inscriptions), 1910; 2 (in preparation).

Beloch, K. J. *Griechische Geschichte.* Vol. IV. Ed. 2. Berlin-Leipzig, 1925–27, pp. 214 *sqq.*

Delagarde, A. Berthier. *On Chersonesus.* Bull. de la Comm. Imp. Arch. XXI, 1907, p. 177. (See also *Memoirs of the Odessa Society for History and Antiquities*, XIV, p. 266.)

Chantre, E. *Recherches Archéologiques dans l'Asie Occidentale.* (Mission en Cappadoce.) Paris, 1898.

Grinevitch, K. *Exhibition of the Results of the Excavations in the Heracleotic Peninsula.* Sevastopol, 1929.

—— *Chersonesky Sbornik.* (Materials for the Archaeology of the Tauric Chersonese.) Sevastopol, I, 1926; II, 1927.

de Jerphanion, G. *Mélanges d'archéologie anatolienne.* (Monuments préhelléniques, gréco-romains, byzantins et musulmans de Pont, de Cappadoce, de Galatie.) Mélanges de l'Univ. Saint-Joseph. Beyrouth (Liban), XIII, 1928.

Leonhard, R. *Paphlagonia.* Berlin, 1915.

Loeper, R. Chr. *A Greek Inscription from Ineboli.* Bull. de l'Inst. Arch. Russe à Constantinople, VIII, 1903, p. 153.

—— *Inscriptions of Chersonese.* Bull. de la Comm. Imp. Arch. XLV, 1912, p. 23.

Meyer, Ed. *Geschichte des Königreichs Pontos.* Leipzig, 1879.

—— *Kappadokien.* Ersch und Gruber Encycl. 2, Sect. 32, p. 383.

Meyer, Ernst. *Die Grenzen der hellenistischen Staaten in Kleinasien.* Zürich-Leipzig, 1925.

Minns, E. H. *Scythians and Greeks.* Cambridge, 1913.

Munro, J. A. R. *Roads in Pontus, Royal and Roman.* J.H.S. XXI, 1901, p. 52.

Niese, B. *Straboniana.* VI. *Die Erwerbung der Küsten des Pontus durch Mithridates VI.* Rh. Mus. XLII, 1887, p. 559.

von der Osten, H. H. *Explorations in Hittite Asia Minor.* (Oriental Institute of the University of Chicago Communications, No. 2.) 1927.

Patsch, C. *Beiträge zur Völkerkunst von Südosteuropa*, v. *Aus 500 Jahren vorröm. und röm. Gesch. Südosteuropas*, I. Vienna, 1932.

Pechonkin, N. M. *Archaeological Excavations on the site of Strabo's Old Chersonese.* Bull. de la Comm. Imp. Arch. XLII, 1911, p. 108.

Reinach, Th. *Trois Royaumes de l'Asie Mineure.* Paris, 1888.

—— *Mithridate Eupator.* Paris, 1890.

—— *Monnaie inédite des rois Philadelphes du Pont.* Rev. N. 1902, p. 52.

—— *L'Histoire par les monnaies.* Paris, 1903, pp. 127 *sqq.*

—— *A Stele from Abonuteichos.* Num. Chr. V (4ᵗʰ ser.), 1905, p. 113.

Robinson, David M. *Ancient Sinope.* New York, 1906. (Cf. *A.J.Ph.* xxvii and *A.J.A.* ix.)

Rostovtzeff, M. **Syriscus, the Historian of the Tauric Chersonese.* Journ. of the Min. of Publ. Educ. 1915, April, p. 151.

—— *Pontus, Bithynia and the Bosporus.* B.S.A. xxii, 1918, p. 1.

—— Ἐπιφάνειαι. Klio, xvi, 1920, p. 203.

—— *Caesar and the South of Russia.* J.R.S. vii, 1917, p. 39.

—— **Strabo as a source for the history of the Bosporus.* (Volume in honour of V. Buzeskul. Kharkov, 1914, pp. 366 *sqq.*)

—— *Skythien und der Bosporus.* Berlin, 1930.

Stähelin, F. *Geschichte der Kleinasiatischen Galater.* Ed. 2. Leipzig, 1907.

von Stern, E. *Bemerkungen zu Strabons Geographie der Taurischen Chersonesos.* Hermes, lii, 1917, p. 1. (See also his contributions* in *Memoirs of the Odessa Society for History and Antiquities,* xix, 1896, Minutes, no. 296, p. 92; *ib.* xxviii, 1907, Minutes, no. 383, p. 89; also *Hittler's Zeitschrift für Alte Geschichte,* i, 2, p. 63.)

Articles in P.W., *Amaseia, Amisos* (Hirschfeld); *Ariamnes* (Judeich); *Ariarathes* (Niese); *Bithynia* (Ed. Meyer), cols. 510–24; *Galatia* (Bürchner and Brandis); *Galli* (Niese); and *Kappadokien* (Ruge).

In addition to these books and articles, the following should also be consulted for the First Mithridatic War:

Chapot, V. *La Province romaine proconsulaire d'Asie.* Paris. 1904.

Ferguson, W. S. *Hellenistic Athens.* London, 1911. pp. 437–459.

Kromayer, J. *Antike Schlachtfelder,* ii, Berlin, 1907. pp. 351–397.

—— *Die Entwickelung der römischen Flotte vom Seeräuberkrieg des Pompeius bis zur Schlacht von Actium.* Phil. lvi, 1897. p. 470.

Articles in P.W., *Apellicon* (Dziatzko); *Aristion, Athenion* (Wilcken).

CHAPTER VIII

ROME AND THE EAST

A. ANCIENT SOURCES

1. *Inscriptions*

The principal inscriptions dealing with the kingdom of Pontus and the Mithridatic Wars are collected in Th. Reinach, *Mithridate Eupator*, quoted below, pp. 456–472, the most important of which are cited in the text of sections I–VI from Ditt.[3] and *O.G.I.S.* Inscriptions relating to the Pirate Wars are collected in E. Ziebarth, *Beiträge zur Geschichte des Seeraubs und Seehandels*, quoted below, Anhang I, nos. 92, 93, 94, 96, 111. See also *S.E.G.* I, 335, III, 378, on the date of which see H. Stuart Jones, *J.R.S.* XVI, 1926, pp. 155 *sqq.* and the literature there cited.

2. *Literary Sources*

Appian, *Mithr.* 64–119; *Sic.* 6; *Syr.* 48, 69–70.
Cicero, *Brutus*, v, 168; *de imp. Cn. Pompei*; *de lege agraria*, I, ii, 5; II, xix, 50; *pro Murena*, xv, 33.
Dio Cassius, XXXVI–XXXVII, 23.
Diodorus, XL, 1; 4.
Eutropius, VI, 2–14; 16 (13).
Florus, I, 39–42 (III, 4–7).
Frontinus, *Strat.* I, 1, 7; II, 1, 12; 3, 14; 5, 33; III, 7, 1; 13, 6.
Josephus, *Antiq. Jud.* XIV, 2–5, 1; *Bell. Jud.* I, 6–7.
Justin, XXXVIII–XL.
Livy, *Epit.* 90–102.
Memnon, fragments of *History of Heraclea*, 36–60, F.H.G. III, pp. 544 *sqq.*
Obsequens, p. 104.
Orosius, v, 23; VI, 2–6, 4.
Phlegon, in *F. Gr. Hist.* no. 257, fr. 12.
Pliny, *Hist. Nat.* VI, 17, 52; 26, 97–99; XXXVII, 5, 16.
Plutarch, *Lucullus*, 5–37; *Pompey*, 24–45; *Sertorius*, 7; 23–24.
Sallust, *Historiae* (M.), I, 1, 127–132; II, 47, 71, 80–81, 87; III, 2, 5–6, 19, 54; IV, 12, 18, 56, 58–59, 61, 63, 64–65, 67, 69, 79–80; v, 13–14.
Strabo, XI, 499–502; 522; 527–533; XII, 540–562; 567–569; XIV, 668–671; XVI, 747.
Velleius Paterculus, II, 31–34, 40, 42.

B. MODERN WORKS

i. *General*

Besides general Roman histories (for which see the General Bibliography) the following works should be consulted:

Bevan, E. R. *A History of Egypt under the Ptolemaic Dynasty.* London, 1927. pp. 342–52.
—— *The House of Seleucus.* London, 1902. Vol. II, pp. 263–8.
Bouché-Leclerq, A. *Histoire des Lagides.* Paris, 1904. Vol. II, pp. 125–35.
—— *Histoire des Séleucides.* Paris, 1913–14. Vol. II, pp. 438–43.
Dobiáš, J. *Les premiers rapports des Romains avec les Parthes et l'occupation de la Syrie.* Archiv Orientalni, III, 1931, p. 215.

Reinach, Th. *Mithridate Eupator, Roi de Pont.* Paris, 1890.
Stähelin, F. *Geschichte der kleinasiatischen Galater.* Ed. 2. Leipzig, 1907. pp. 88–90.

ii. *Special Topics*

(a) *The Pirates of Cilicia*

Ormerod, H. A. *Piracy in the Ancient World.* Liverpool, 1924. pp. 190–247.
Ziebarth, Erich. *Beiträge zur Geschichte des Seeraubs und Seehandels im alten Griechenland.* Hamburg, 1929. pp. 31–43.

(b) *Individual episodes of the Pirate War*

Ormerod, H. A. *The Campaigns of Servilius Isauricus against the Pirates.* J.R.S. XII, 1922, p. 35. (Criticized by Sir W. M. Ramsay, *J.H.S.* XLVIII, 1928, p. 46, and *Klio*, XXII, 1929, p. 381.)
Foucart, P. *Les campagnes de M. Antonius Creticus contre les Pirates,* 74–71. Journal des Savants, N.S. IV, 1906, p. 569.
Groebe, P. *Zum Seeräuberkriege des Pompeius Magnus.* Klio, X, 1910, p. 374.
Kromayer, J. *Die Entwicklung der röm. Flotte vom Seeräuberkrieg des Pompeius bis zur Schlacht von Actium.* Phil. LVI, 1897, p. 426.
Ormerod, H. A. *The Distribution of Pompeius' Forces in the Campaign of 67 B.C.* Liverpool Annals of Archaeology and Anthropology, X, 1923, p. 46.

(c) *Campaigns in Pontus and its topography*

(See also the Bibliography to Chapter V, B)

Anderson, J. G. C. *Pompey's Campaigns against Mithridates.* J.R.S. XII, 1922, p. 99.
Guse, F. *Die Feldzüge des dritten Mithradatischen Krieges in Pontus und Armenien.* Klio, XX, 1926, p. 332.
Hogarth, D. G. and J. A. R. Munro. *Modern and ancient roads in Eastern Asia Minor.* Royal Geog. Soc., Suppl. Papers, vol. III, 1893, part 5.
Munro, J. A. R. *Roads in Pontus, Royal and Roman.* J.H.S. XXI, 1901, p. 52.

(d) *The invasion of Armenia and its topography*

Sachau, E. *Über die Lage von Tigranokerta.* Abhandl. der kgl. Akad. d. Wissensch. z. Berlin, Phil.-Hist.-Kl. II, 1880, pp. 1–92.
Belck, W. *Majafarkin und Tigranokerta.* Z. für Ethnologie, XXXI, 1899, p. 263.
Lynch, H. F. B. *Armenia.* London, 1901.
Lehmann-Haupt, C. F. *Maiafar(i)kin und Tigranokerta.* Verhandl. Berliner anthrop. Gesellsch. 1899, pp. 600–608.
—— *Eine griechische Inschrift aus der Spätzeit Tigranokerta's.* Klio, VIII, 1908, p. 497.
—— *Armenien Einst und Jetzt,* I. Berlin, 1910.
Henderson, B. W. *Controversies in Armenian Topography.* J.P. XXVIII, 1903, p. 98.
Eckhardt, K. *Die Armenischen Feldzüge des Lukullus.* Klio, IX, 1909, p. 400; X, 1910, p. 192.
Rice Holmes, T. *The Roman Republic.* Oxford, 1923. I, pp. 409–426.
Guse, F. *Die Feldzüge des dritten Mithradatischen Krieges in Pontus und Armenien.* Klio, XX, 1926, p. 332.

CHAPTER IX

THE JEWS

A. ANCIENT AUTHORITIES

1. *Texts.*

Nicolaus of Damascus, *De Vita sua*, and a History of the World in 144 Books (precise title unknown), of which Books cxxiii and cxxiv dealt with the history of Herod. Named quotations in *F.H.G.* iii, pp. 343 *sqq.* (*F. Gr. Hist.* no. 90, pp. 324 *sqq.*).

Material from Nicolaus in Josephus.

Josephus, *Ant.* xiii, 284–end of xiv; *Wars*, i, 70–357.

Strabo, xvi, 2 and fragments of lost books, quoted by Josephus; see T. Reinach, *Textes d'Auteurs Grecs et Romains, relatifs au Judaïsme.* Paris, 1895, pp. 89 *sqq.*

Cornelius Alexander Polyhistor, named quotations in *F.H.G.* iii, pp. 206 *sqq.*

The Septuagint (*The Old Testament in Greek*), H. B. Swete, Cambridge, 1891–95; N. McLean, A. E. Brooke and H. St J. Thackeray. Cambridge, 1917, 1927 (in progress).

The Wisdom of Jesus the son of Sirach, called also *Ecclesiasticus*. R. Smend, *Die Weisheit des Jesus Sirach*, Hebrew and German, with commentary, Berlin, 1906; J. H. A. Hart, *Ecclesiasticus: the Greek text of Codex* 248, *with textual commentary and prolegomena.* Cambridge, 1909.

The Psalms of Solomon (Greek text with Introduction, Translation and Notes), H. E. Ryle and M. R. James, Cambridge, 1891. *Les Psaumes de Salomon* (introduction, text and translation into French). J. Viteau, Paris, 1911.

The Book of Enoch (Ethiopic text, together with fragmentary Greek and Latin versions), R. H. Charles, Oxford, 1906.

The Assumption of Moses (Latin text, with translation). R. H. Charles, London, 1897.

The Testaments of the Twelve Patriarchs. For editions of fragments of Hebrew original, and of Greek and Armenian versions see Bibliography in Charles, *Apocrypha and Pseudepigrapha*, ii, p. 295.

The Book of Jubilees (R. H. Charles, *The Ethiopic Version of the Book of Jubilees with the Hebrew, Syriac, Greek, and Latin fragments*, Oxford, 1895).

Pirkē Abōth (Hebrew and English, C. Taylor, *Sayings of the Jewish Fathers.* Ed. 2. Cambridge, 1897; also R. T. Herford, New York, 1925).

Demetrius, Περὶ τῶν ἐν τῇ Ἰουδαίᾳ βασιλέων. Eupolemus, Περὶ τῶν ἐν τῇ Ἰουδαίᾳ βασιλέων. Artapanus, Περὶ Ἰουδαίων. Cleodemus, Περὶ Ἰουδαίων (?). Philo "the Elder," Epic Poet. *F.H.G.* iii, pp. 211–30.

Theodotus, Samaritan Epic Poet (Fragment in Eusebius, *Praep. Evang.* ix, 22).

Ezekiel, Tragic Poet (fragments of his *Exodus* in Clement of Alexandria and in Eusebius, *Praep. Evang.*).

Aristobulus, philosopher (fragments in Clement of Alexandria and in Eusebius, *Praep. Evang.*; cf. also *Hist. eccl.* vii, 32, 16–19).

The Sibylline Oracles (J. Geffcken, Leipzig, 1902).

Pseudo-Hecataeus, named quotations in *F. H. G.* ii, pp. 393–396.

Pseudo-Aristeas, *Ad Philocratem Epistula* (P. Wendland, Leipzig, 1900).

Pseudo-Phocylides. Diehl, *Anth. Lyr.* 1922, lv, pp. 194–208.

Philo of Alexandria. All the works preserved in Greek, with Index, L. Cohn,
    P. Wendland, S. Reiter, and J. Leisegang, 7 vols. Berlin, 1896–1930. (This
    unfortunately does not include either the fragments of lost works, preserved in
    the original Greek, or a translation of the works preserved in the Armenian
    version.) The works preserved in Armenian, J. B. Aucher. (Armenian and
    Latin version.) *Philonis Judaei sermones tres hactenus inediti ex Armena
    versione nunc primum in Latium* [sic] *fideliter translati.* Venice, 1822. *Philonis
    Judaei paralipomena Armena...ex Armena versione etc. nunc primum in
    Latium fideliter translata.* Venice, 1826. See also Hans Lewy, *Neue Philon-
    texte in der Ueberarbeitung des Ambrosius.* Berlin, 1932. Lewy announces
    that he is preparing a new critical edition of the Armenian with a translation.

2. *Translations and Commentaries (without text)*

Apocrypha and Pseudepigrapha as a whole

Charles, R. H. *The Apocrypha and Pseudepigrapha of the Old Testament in English
    with Introductions and Critical and Explanatory Notes.* 2 vols. Oxford, 1913.
Kautzsch, E. *Apokryphen und Pseudepigraphen des Alten Testaments.* 2 vols. Tübin-
    gen, 1900.

Enoch

Martin, F. *Le Livre d' Hénoch.* Paris, 1906.

Ecclesiasticus

Oesterley, W. O. E. *The Wisdom of Jesus the Son of Sirach with Introduction and
    Notes.* Cambridge, 1912.
Peters, N. *Das Buch Jesus Sirach übersetzt und erklärt.* Münster, 1913.

Wisdom

Feldmann, F. *Das Buch der Weisheit.* Bonn, 1926.
Goodrick, A. T. S. *The Book of Wisdom with Introduction and Notes.* London, 1913.
Gregg, J. A. F. *The Book of Wisdom with Introduction and Notes.* Cambridge, 1909.
Oesterley, W. O. E. *The Wisdom of Solomon with Introduction and Notes.* London,
    1917.

Pseudo-Aristeas

Thackeray, H. St J. *The Letter of Aristeas translated into English with Introduction
    and Notes.* London, 1904.

Philo

Heinemann, I. *Philos von Alexandria Werke in deutscher Uebersetzung* (with
    commentary). Breslau, 1919.

B. Modern Literature

Works earlier than 1900 are not given, since for these reference may be made to
the bibliography in Schürer, vol. 1 (4th ed.), pp. 4–31 (see below). In Volumes xi
and xii of the *C.A.H.* there will be bibliographies dealing with the rise of Christianity.

1. *General Histories*

Felten, J. *Neutestamentliche Zeitgeschichte.* Regensburg, 1910.
Klausner, J. *Israelite History* (in Hebrew), vol. ii. Jerusalem, 1923.
Lagrange, M.-J. *Le Judaïsme avant Jésus-Christ.* Paris, 1931.
Margolis, M. L. and A. Marx. *A History of the Jewish People.* Philadelphia,
    1927.
Meyer, E. *Ursprung und Anfänge des Christentums,* vol. ii. Stuttgart-Berlin, 1921
Oesterley, W. O. E. *A History of Israel,* vol. ii. Oxford, 1932.

Schlatter, A. *Geschichte Israels von Alexander dem Grossen bis Hadrian*. Ed. 3. Stuttgart, 1925.

Schürer, E. *Geschichte des jüdischen Volkes im Zeitalter Jesu Christi*. Leipzig. Vol. I, Ed. 4, 1901; vols. II and III, Ed. 3, 1898. Eng. trans. (from Ed. 2), *A History of the Jewish People in the Time of Jesus Christ*. London, 1880, etc.

Staerk, W. *Neutestamentliche Zeitgeschichte*. Leipzig, 1907.

Wellhausen, J. *Israelitische und jüdische Geschichte*. Ed. 8. Berlin, 1921.

2. *History of Herod.* (See further, bibliographies in Volume x.)

Otto, W. Art. *Herodes* in *P.W.* Suppl. zum VIII. Bande, Heft 2, 1913.

Willrich, H. *Das Haus des Herodes*. Heidelberg, 1929.

3. *Social and Economic Conditions*

Grant, F. C. *The Economic Background of the Gospels*. Oxford, 1926.

Jeremias, J. *Jerusalem zur Zeit Jesu*. Leipzig, 1923–4.

Klausner, J. *Jesus of Nazareth*. Eng. translation from Hebrew by H. Danby. London, 1925.

4. *Topography*

Dalman, G. *Jerusalem und seine Gelände*. Gütersloh, 1930.

Haefeli, L. *Geschichte der Landschaft Samaria*. Münster, 1923.

Klein, S. *Neue Beiträge zur Geschichte und Geographie Galiläas*. Vienna, 1923.

—— *Galiläa von der Makkabäerzeit bis 67* (in *Jüdische Studien J. Wohlgemuth zu seinem 60ten Geburtstag gewidmet*). Frankfurt, 1928.

Kirmis, F. *Die Lage der alten Davidsstadt und die Mauern des alten Jerusalem*. Breslau, 1919.

Krauss, S. *Contributions à la topographie de Jérusalem*. Rev. E. J. Vol. LXXI, 1920, p. 148; Vol. LXXII, 1921, p. 48; Vol. LXXIII, 1921, p. 59.

Smith, G. A. *Jerusalem*. 2 vols. London, 1908.

Vincent, L. H. *Jérusalem: recherches de topographie, d'archéologie et d'histoire*. Paris, 1912.

Weill, R. *La Cité de David*. Paris, 1920.

5. *Literature*

General

Stählin, O. *Die hellenistisch-jüdische Literatur*, in W. von Christ's *Geschichte der griechischen Literatur*, Ed. 6 (1920), 2, 1, pp. 535 *sqq*. (Contains ample references to previous literature.)

The Septuagint

Deissmann, A. *Die Hellenisierung des semitischen Monotheismus*, N. J. Kl. Alt. XI, 1903, p. 161.

Herrmann, J. und F. Baumgärtel. *Beiträge zur Entstehungsgeschichte der Septuaginta*. Stuttgart, 1923.

Kaminka, A. *Studien zur Septuaginta*. Frankfurt, 1928.

Procksch, O. *Studien zur Geschichte der Septuaginta*. Leipzig, 1910.

Sperber, A. *Septuaginta-probleme*. Stuttgart, 1920.

Swete, H. B. *An Introduction to the Old Testament in Greek*. Cambridge, 1914.

Thackeray, H. St J. *The Septuagint and Jewish Worship*. London, 1921.

—— *Some Aspects of the Greek Old Testament*. London, 1927.

Book of Jubilees

Büchler, A. *Traces des idées et des coutumes hellénistiques dans le Livre des Jubilés.*
Rev. E. J. LXXXIX, 1930, p. 320.

Ecclesiastes[1]

Levy, L. *Das Buch Koheleth.* Leipzig, 1912.
Ranston, H. *Ecclesiastes and the Early Greek Wisdom Literature.* London, 1925.
Thilo, M. *Der Prediger Salomo.* Bonn, 1923.

[1] Ecclesiastes is included in all the series of Old Testament commentaries, on
which see vol. III, p. 732.

Book of Enoch

Kuhn, G. *Beiträge zur Erklärung des Buchs Henoch.* Zeitsch. f. Alttest. Wiss.
XXXIX, 1921, p. 240.

Wisdom of Solomon

Focke, F. *Die Entstehung der Weisheit Salomos* (Forschungen zur Religion und
Literatur des Alten und Neuen Testaments, Neue Folge, 5). Göttingen, 1913.
Gärtner, E. *Komposition und Wortlaut des Buches der Weisheit* (Schriften der
Lehranstalt für die Wiss. d. Judentums, II, 2–4). Berlin, 1912.
Heinemann, J. *Poseidonios Metaphysische Schriften.* Vol. I. Breslau, 1921. (*Die
griechische Quelle des Buchs der Weisheit*, pp. 136 *sqq.*).

Ecclesiasticus

Hart, J. H. A. *Ecclesiasticus.* Jewish Quart. Rev. XIX, 1906–7, p. 284.

Pseudo-Aristeas

Bickermann, A. *Zur Datierung des Pseudo-Aristeas.* Zeitschr. f. d. Neutest. Wiss.
XXIX, 1930, p. 280.
Février, J. G. *La Date, la Composition et les Sources de la Lettre d'Aristée à Philo-
crate* (Bibliothèque de l'École des Hautes Études, Sciences Historiques, 1924).
Lumbroso, G. *Lettera al Sig. Prof. Wilcken* (on the Jewish feast at Alexandria
commemorative of the composition of the Septuagint). Arch. Pap. V, 1913,
pp. 402 *sqq.*

Philo of Alexandria

Adler, M. *Studien zu Philon von Alexandreia.* Breslau, 1929.
Bentwich, N. *Philo Judaeus of Alexandria.* Philadelphia, 1910.
Bevan, E. *Hellenistic Judaism*, in *The Legacy of Israel*, pp. 29 *sqq.* Oxford, 1927.
Billings, T. H. *The Platonism of Philo Judaeus.* Chicago, 1919.
Bréhier, E. *Les Idées de Philon d'Alexandrie.* Paris, 1925.
Guthrie, K. S. *The Message of Philo Judaeus.* London, 1910.
Hart, J. H. A. *Philo of Alexandria.* Jewish Quart. Rev. XVII, 1904–5, p. 78;
p. 726; XVIII, 1905–6, p. 330; XX, 1907–8, p. 294.
Heinemann, I. *Philons Lehre vom Heiliger Geist und der intuitiven Erkenntniss.*
Monatsschrift f. Gesch. u. Wiss. d. Judentums, Neue Folge, XXVIII, 1920,
p. 101.
—— *Philons griechische und jüdische Bildung.* Breslau, 1932.
Kennedy, H. A. A. *Philo's Contribution to Religion.* London, 1919.
Massebieau, L. et E. Bréhier. *Essai sur la chronologie de la vie et des œuvres de
Philon.* Rev. de l'Histoire des Religions, 1906, p. 25; p. 164; p. 267.

Stein, E. *Die allegorische Exegese des Philo aus Alexandreia.* Giessen, 1929.

Treitel, L. *Philonische Studien.* Breslau, 1915.

—— *Gesammt-Theologie und Philosophie Philos von Alexandreia.* Berlin, 1923.

Windisch, H. *Die Frömmigkeit Philos und ihre Bedeutung für das Christentum.* Leipzig, 1909.

6. *Jewish Religion*

(*a*) *General*

Bertholet, A. *Die jüdische Religion von der Zeit Esras zum Zeitalter Christi* (Grundriss der theol. Wissensch., Abt. 18). Tübingen, 1911.

Bousset, W. *Die Religion des Judentums im späthellenistischen Zeitalter.* Ed. 3, edited and enlarged by H. Gressmann. Tübingen, 1926. (Review by I. Heinemann in *Monatsschrift f. Gesch. u. Wiss. d. Jud.* LXXXI, 1927, p. 71. See also Perles cited below.)

Browne, L. E. *Early Judaism.* Cambridge, 1920.

Charles, R. H. *Religious Development between the Old and New Testaments.* London, 1914.

von Dobschütz, E. *Das Judentum der Zeit Jesu in neuer Beleuchtung.* Theol. Stud. u. Krit. CI, 1929, p. 122.

Fiebig, P. *Die Umwelt des Neuen Testaments.* Göttingen, 1926. (A collection of extracts from ancient documents, with notes).

Graham, W. C. *The Jewish World in which Jesus lived.* Journ. of Religion, VIII, 1928, p. 566.

Gressmann, H. *Die Aufgaben der Wissenschaft des nachbiblischen Judentums.* Zeit. f. d. Alttest. Wissens. XLIII, 1915, p. 1. Giessen, 1925.

Herford, R. T. *Judaism in the New Testament Period.* London, 1928.

Hölscher, G. *Geschichte der israelitischen und jüdischen Religion.* Giessen, 1922.

—— *Urgemeinde und Spätjudentum.* Oslo, 1928.

Jackson, F. J. Foakes, and Kirsopp Lake. *The Beginnings of Christianity.* Vol. I, London, 1920. (pp. 1–168, *The Jewish World,* by the Editors and C. G. Montefiore.)

Kittel, G. *Die Probleme des palästinischen Spätjudentums und das Urchristentum.* Stuttgart, 1926.

—— *Urchristentum, Spätjudentum, Hellenismus.* Stuttgart, 1926.

Montefiore, C. G. *The Old Testament and After.* London, 1923.

Moore, G. F. *Judaism in the first centuries of the Christian Era.* 2 vols. Cambridge, U.S.A., 1927.

Oesterley, W. O. E. and T. H. Robinson. *Hebrew Religion, its Origin and Development.* London, 1930.

Perles, F. *Boussets Religion des Judentums im neutestamentlichen Zeitalter kritisch untersucht.* Berlin, 1903.

Strack, H. L. und P. Billerbeck. *Kommentar zum Neuen Testament aus Talmud und Midrasch.* 4 (really 5) vols. Munich, 1922–1928.

(*b*) *Jewish Sects and Piety*

Abrahams, I. *Studies in Pharisaism and the Gospels,* 2 Series. Cambridge, 1917, 1924.

Aptowitzer, V. *Parteipolitik der Hasmonäerzeit im rabbinischen und pseudepigraphischen Schrifttum.* Vienna, 1927. (Review of this book by A. Marmorstein in *Monatsschrift f. Gesch. u. Wiss. d. Jud.* XXXVII, 1929, p. 244; reply by Aptowitzer, *ib.* pp. 403; reply to this by Marmorstein, *ib.* p. 478).

Bauer, W. Art. *Essenes* in P.W. Suppl. IV (in which a survey of previous literature dealing with the Essenes will be found). (Review of this article by A. Bertholet in *O.L.Z.* XXVII, 1924, col. 478 *sqq.*)

Büchler, A. *Der galiläische Am ha-Aretz.* Vienna, 1906.
—— *Types of Jewish-Palestinian Piety from* 70 B.C.E. *to* 70 C.E. London, 1922.
(Review by A. Kaminka in *Monatsschrift f. Gesch. u. Wiss. d. Jud.* XXXIII, 1925,
p. 393).
—— *Studies in Sin and Atonement in the Rabbinic Literature of the First Century.*
Oxford, 1928.
Causse, A. *Les Pauvres d'Israël.* Strasbourg, 1922.
Eppel, R. *Le Piétisme Juif dans les Testaments des Douze Patriarches.* Paris, 1930.
Finkelstein, L. *The Pharisees, their Origin and their Philosophy.* Cambridge, Mass.,
1929.
Friedländer, I. *The Rupture between Alexander Jannai and the Pharisees.* Jewish
Quart. Rev., N.S. IV, 1913–14, p. 443.
Friedländer, M. *Die religiösen Bewegungen innerhalb des Judentums im Zeitalter
Jesu.* Berlin, 1905.
Herford, R. T. *Pharisaism, its aim and methods.* London, 1903.
—— *The Pharisees.* London, 1924.
Hölscher, G. *Der Sadduzäismus.* Leipzig, 1906.
Leszynsky, R. *Die Sadduzäer.* Berlin, 1912. (Review, by B. Revel, Jewish Quart.
Rev. VII, 1916–7, p. 429.)
Lévy, I. *La Légende de Pythagore de Grèce en Palestine.* Paris, 1927. (Deals
with the Pharisees and Essenes, both of whom Lévy regards as offshoots of
Pythagoreanism.)
Marmorstein, A. *The Doctrine of Merits in old Rabbinical Literature.* London,
1920. (Review by J. Weill, Rev. E. J. LXXII, 1920, p. 212.)
Montefiore, C. G. *Rabbinic Literature and Gospel Teaching.* London, 1930.
Wellhausen, J. *Die Pharisäer und die Sadducäer.* Ed. 2. Greifswald, 1924.
Ziegler, J. *Die sittliche Welt des Judentums.* 2te Teil. Leipzig, 1928.

(c) *The Samaritans*

Creten, J. *La Pâque des Samaritains.* Rev. Bib. XXXI, 1922, p. 434.
Gaster, M. *The Samaritans: their History, Doctrines and Literature.* London, 1925.
Montgomery, J. A. *The Samaritans.* Philadelphia, 1907.

(d) *The Damascus Community of the New Covenant*

Büchler, A. *Jewish Sectaries.* Jewish Quart. Rev., N.S. III, 1912–13, p. 428.
(Reply of Schechter to Büchler, Jewish Quart. Rev., N.S. IV, 1913–14, p. 449).
Ginzberg, L. *Eine unbekannte jüdische Sekte.* (Series of articles in *Monatsschrift f.
Gesch. u. Wiss. d. Judentums,* XIX [1911]—XXII [1914].)
Gutmann, J. Art. *Damaskusschrift* in *Encyclopædia Judaica,* Vol. V, Berlin, 1930.
Hölscher, G. *Zur Frage nach Alter und Herkunft der sogenannten Damaskusschrift.*
Zeitsch. f. Neutest. Wiss. XXVIII, 1929, pp. 21–46.
Meyer, E. *Ursprung u. Anfänge d. Christentums,* II, pp. 47 *sqq.* (with references).
Segal, M. H. *Notes on "Fragments of a Zadokite Work."* Jewish Quart. Rev., N.S.
II, 1911–12, p. 133.
Staerk, W. *Die jüdische Gemeinde des Neuen Bundes in Damaskus.* Gütersloh, 1922.

(e) *The Synagogue*

Box, G. H. and W. O. E. Oesterley. *The Religion and Worship of the Synagogue.*
Ed. 2. London, 1911.
Elbogen, J. *Der jüdische Gottesdienst in seiner geschichtlichen Entwickelung.* Ed. 2.
Frankfurt, 1924.

Finkelstein, L. *The Origin of the Synagogue.* Proc. of the Amer. Acad. for Jewish Research, 1928–30, p. 49.

Kohler, K. *The Origins of the Synagogue and the Church.* New York, 1929.

Krauss, S. *Synagogale Altertümer.* Berlin, 1922.

Rankin, O. S. *The Origin of the Festival of Hanukkah.* Edinburgh, 1930.

7. *Mysticism*

Abelson, J. *The Immanence of God in Rabbinical Literature.* London, 1912.

—— *Jewish Mysticism.* London, 1913.

Box, G. H. *The Idea of Intermediation in Jewish Theology. A note on Memra and Shekinah.* Jewish Quart. Rev., N.S. [1932].

Hertz, J. H. *Mystical Currents.* London, 1929.

Kittel, R. *Die hellenistische Mysterienreligion und das Alte Testament.* Stuttgart, 1924.

Kohler, K. Art. *Memra* in the *Jewish Encyclopaedia.* Vol. VIII. New York, 1925.

Lewy, H. *Sobria Ebrietas: Untersuchungen zur Geschichte d. antiken Mystik.* Giessen, 1929.

Moore, G. F. *Intermediaries in Jewish Theology (Memra, Shekinah, Metatron).* Harvard Theological Review, Jan. 1922. (See also Burkitt, F. C. *Memra, Shekinah, Metatron,* Journ. of Theol. Studies, XXIV, 1922–3, p. 158.)

Odeberg, H. *3 Enoch.* Cambridge, 1928.

8. *Eschatology and the Messianic Idea*

Burkitt, F. C. *Jewish and Christian Apocalypses.* London, 1913.

Causse, A. *Judaïsme et syncrétisme oriental à l'époque perse.* Rev. de l'Histoire et d. Philosophie Relig. VIII, 1928, pp. 301–328.

Dürr, L. *Ursprung und Ausbau der israelitischen-jüdischen Heilandserwartung.* Berlin, 1925.

von Gall, A. Freiherr. Βασιλεία τοῦ θεοῦ. Heidelberg, 1926.

Gressmann, H. *Der Ursprung der israelitisch-jüdischen Eschatologie.* Göttingen, 1905.

—— *Der Messias.* Göttingen, 1929.

Heinemann, I. *Messianismus und Mysterienreligion.* Monatsschrift f. Gesch. u. Wiss. d. Judentums, LXIX, 1925, pp. 337 *sqq.*

Hölscher, G. *Die Ursprünge der jüdischer Eschatologie.* Giessen, 1925.

Klausner, J. *Die messianischen Vorstellungen des jüdischen Volkes im Zeitalter der Tanaïten kritisch untersucht.* Berlin, 1904.

—— *Messianic Doctrines in Israel from their first appearance to the closing of the Mishna* (in Hebrew). Jerusalem, 1927.

Lagrange, M.-J. *Le Messianisme chez les Juifs 150 av. J.-C. à 200 ap. J. C.* Paris, 1909.

Lemann, A. *Histoire complète de l'idée messianique chez le peuple d'Israël.* Lyons, 1909.

Messel, N. *Die Einheitlichkeit der jüdischen Eschatologie.* Upsala, 1915.

—— *Der Menschensohn in den Bilderreden Henochs.* Upsala, 1922. (Review by M.-J. Lagrange in *Rev. Bib.* 1922, p. 624.)

Montefiore, C. G. IV *Ezra: A Study in the Development of Universalism.* London, 1929.

Nötscher, F. *Altorientalischer und alttestamentlicher Auferstehungsglauben.* Würzburg, 1926.

Perles, F. *Traces des Apocryphes et des Pseudépigraphes dans la liturgie juive.* Rev. E. J. LXXIII, 1921, p. 173.

Scheftelowitz, J. *Die altpersische Religion und das Judentum.* Berlin, 1920.

Volz, P. *Jüdische Eschatologie.* Tübingen, 1903.

9. *The Diaspora*

Axenfeld, K. *Die jüdische Propaganda als Verläuferin und Wegbereiterin der urchristlichen Mission.* (Festschrift zu G. Warnecks 70 Geburtstag.) Berlin, 1904.

Bell, H. I. *Jews and Christians in Egypt.* London, 1924.

Bentwich, N. *Hellenism.* Philadelphia, 1919.

Bickermann, E. *Ritualmord und Eselskult.* Monatsschrift f. Gesch. u. Wiss. d. Jud. LXXI, 1927, pp. 171–187, 255–264.

Bousset, W. *Jüdisch-christlicher Schulbetrieb in Alexandreia und Rom.* Forsch. z. Rel. u. Lit., N.F. 6, 1915.

Causse, A. *Les Origines de la Diaspora.* Rev. de l'Hist. des Religions, May–June, 1924.

—— *Les Dispersés d'Israël.* Paris, 1929.

von Dobschütz, E. Art. *Proselyten* in Herzog, *Real-Enzyklopädie f. Protest. Theol. u. Kirche.* Leipzig, 1905.

Frey, J. B. *Les communautés juives de Rome aux premiers temps de l'Église.* Recherches de science relig. XX, 1930, p. 269.

Friedländer, M. *Geschichte der jüdischen Apologetik als Vorgeschichte des Christentums.* Zürich, 1903.

Fuchs, L. *Die Jüden Aegyptens in ptolemäischer und römischer Zeit.* Vienna, 1924.

Geffcken, J. *Komposition und Entstehungszeit der Oracula Sibyllina.* Leipzig, 1902.

Goodenough, E. R. *The Jurisprudence of the Jewish Courts in Egypt.* Yale Univ. Press, 1929. (Puts forward a very questionable thesis in regard to Philo.)

Guttmann, M. *Das Judentum und seine Umwelt.* Vol. I, Teil 1. Berlin, 1927.

Heinemann, I. *Posidonios über die Entwickelung der jüdischen Religion.* Monatsschrift f. Gesch. u. Wiss. d. Jud., N.F. XXVII, 1919, p. 113.

—— *Hellenistica.* Ib., N.F. XXXVII, 1929, pp. 425 *sqq.*

—— Art. *Antisemitismus* in *P.W.* Suppl. Band V (which gives references to previous literature on the subject).

Juster, J. *Les Juifs dans l'empire romain.* Paris, 1914.

Modona, A. N. *La Vita pubblica e privata degli Ebrei in Egitto nell' età ellenistica e romana.* Milan, 1922. (Reprinted from *Aegyptus*, II, 1921 and III, 1922)

Montefiore, C. G. *Liberal Judaism and Hellenism.* London, 1918.

Motzo, B. R. *Saggi di storia e letteratura giudeo-ellenistica.* Florence, 1926.

Petrie, Sir W. Flinders. *The Status of the Jews in Egypt.* London, 1922.

Radin, M. *The Jews among the Greeks and Romans.* Philadelphia, 1915.

Rzach, A. Articles *Sibyllen, Sibyllinische Orakel* in *P.W.*

Windisch, H. *Die Orakel des Hystaspes.* Amsterdam, 1929.

CHAPTER X

THE PROVINCES AND THEIR GOVERNMENT

The authorities, ancient and modern, for the historical events referred to in this chapter will be found in the bibliographies to the relevant chapters, where they are treated in fuller detail. The works mentioned below are concerned rather with provincial administration than with the growth of the Roman Empire.

I. ANCIENT SOURCES

The writings of Cicero are our chief source of information upon the provincial government of the later Republic. Among his speeches the most important are: *in Verrem, in Pisonem, pro Flacco, pro Fonteio, de provinciis consularibus, de imperio Cn. Pompeii*. To these must be added his letters from Cilicia (Tyrrell and Purser, vol. III) and to his brother Quintus (book I). Incidental details of importance are found in the later books of Livy and in the works of Appian, Dio Cassius, Plutarch and Sallust.

Original documents bearing on the subject are to be found in:

Abbott, F. F. and A. C. Johnson. *Municipal Administration in the Roman Empire*. Cited below.
Bruns, C. G. *Fontes Iuris Romani Antiqui*. Ed. 7. Tübingen, 1909.
Hardy, E. G. *Roman Laws and Charters*. Oxford, 1912.

II. MODERN WORKS

Abbott, F. F. and A. C. Johnson. *Municipal Administration in the Roman Empire*. Princeton, 1926.
Arnold, W. T. *Roman Provincial Administration*. Ed. 2. Oxford, 1906.
Broughton, T. R. S. *The Romanization of Africa Proconsularis*. Baltimore, 1929.
Chapot, V. *La province romaine proconsulaire d'Asie*. Paris, 1904.
—— *Le monde romain*. Paris, 1927. (English translation, *The Roman World*, London, 1928.)
De Sanctis, G. *Storia dei Romani*. Vol. IV. Chap. v. Turin, 1923.
Dessau, H. *Geschichte der römischen Kaiserzeit*. Vol. II, ii. Berlin, 1930. (Mainly concerned with the Principate.)
Frank, Tenney. *Roman Imperialism*. New York, 1914.
—— *Economic History of Rome*. Ed. 2. London, 1927.
Greenidge, A. H. J. *Roman Public Life*. London, 1901. (pp. 316 *sqq*.)
—— *The Legal Procedure of Cicero's Time*. Oxford, 1901.
Gsell, S. *Histoire ancienne de l'Afrique du Nord*. Vols. VII and VIII. Paris, 1928.
Jullian, C. *Histoire de la Gaule*. Vol. III. Paris, 1920.
Marquardt, J. *Römische Staatsverwaltung*. Vol. I. Ed. 2. Leipzig, 1881. (Still the most useful book of reference.)
Mommsen, Th. *Römisches Staatsrecht*. Leipzig. Vol. III, 1, 1887, vol. III, 2, 1909.
—— *The Provinces of the Roman Empire*. London, 1909.
Reid, J. S. *The Municipalities of the Roman Empire*. Cambridge, 1913.
Stevenson, G. H. *The Roman Empire*. London, 1930. Chapters VIII–X.

Articles in P.W. upon the different provinces, *s.vv. Asia* (Brandis); *Bithynia* (Brandis); *Gallia* (Weiss); *Hispania* (Schulten); *Macedonia* (Geyer); *Sardinia* (Philipp); *Sicilia* (Ziegler).

For the study of Taxation and Finance the following will be found useful:

Carcopino, J. *La Loi de Hiéron et les Romains.* Paris, 1919.

Ciccotti, E. *Lineamenti dell' Evoluzione Tributaria nel Mondo Antico.* Milan, 1921.

Deloume, A. *Les Manieurs d'Argent à Rome.* Ed. 2 Paris, 1892.

Kniep, F. *Societas Publicanorum.* Jena, 1896.

Marquardt, J. *Römische Staatsverwaltung.* Vol. II. Ed. 2. Leipzig, 1881.

Rostowzew, M. *Geschichte der Staatspacht in der römischen Kaiserzeit.* (Phil. Suppb. IX, Heft 3.)

—— *Studien zur Geschichte des römischen Kolonats.* Berlin, 1910.

Articles in P.W., *Ager*(Kubitschek); *Decuma*(Liebenam); *Frumentum* (Rostowzew); *Manceps* (Steinwenter).

CHAPTERS XI AND XII

ROME IN THE ABSENCE OF POMPEY: THE FIRST TRIUMVIRATE

A. ANCIENT SOURCES

1. *Texts*

Appian, *Bell. Civ.* II, 1–25.
Asconius Pedianus, *Orationum Ciceronis Quinque Enarratio* (ed. Clark).
M. Cicero: *ad Att.* I–IV; *ad Fam.* I, V, 2, 3, 7; *ad Q. F.* I–III; *de Lege Agraria*, I–III; *pro C. Rabirio perduellionis reo; in Catilinam*, I–IV; *pro Murena; pro Sulla; pro Flacco; cum Senatui gratias egit; cum Populo gratias egit; de Domo Sua; de Haruspicum Responso; pro Sestio; in Vatinium; pro Caelio; de Provinciis Consularibus; in Pisonem*; frags. in vol. II of the editions by Kayser and Baiter; *de Officiis*, II, 84.
Q. Cicero (?), *de Petitione Consulatus*.
Dio Cassius, XXXVI, 21–7; XXXVII, 8–58; XXXVIII, 1–30; XXXIX, 6–37.
Diodorus Siculus, XL, frags. 5, 5a.
Livy, *Epit.* 102–5.
Orosius, VI, 6.
Plutarch, *Cato Minor*, 17–43; *Caesar*, 5–15, 19, 21; *Cicero*, 9–34; *Crassus*, 13–16; *Lucullus*, 37–43; *Pompey*, 43–52.
Sallust, *Bellum Catilinae*.
Suetonius, *Divus Iulius*, 9–24, 28.
Valerius Maximus, IV, 8, 3.
Velleius Paterculus, II, 40–6.

2. *Commentaries and Discussions*

Abbott, F. F. *Cicero's Letters in 59 B.C.* A.J.Ph. XIX, 1898, p. 389.
Beltrami, A. *De Commentariolo Petitionis Q. Tullio Ciceroni Vindicando.* Annali della Regia Scuola Normale Superiore di Pisa, Filosofia e Filologia, vol. IX, 1892.
Besser, J. *De Coniuratione Catilinaria.* Neustadt, 1880.
Bücheler, F. *Q. Ciceronis Reliquiae.* Leipzig, 1869.
Butler, H. E. and M. Cary. *Cicero, De Provinciis Consularibus.* Oxford, 1924.
——— ——— *Suetonius, Divus Iulius.* Oxford, 1927.
Cook, A. M. *Gaii Sallusti Crispi Bellum Catilinae.* London, 1884.
Dübi, H. *De Catilinae Sallustiani Fontibus ac Fide.* Bern, 1872.
——— *Die jüngeren Quellen der catilinarischen Verschwörung.* Jahrbücher für classische Philologie, XXII, 1876, p. 851.
Eussner, A. *Commentariolum Petitionis examinatum atque emendatum.* Würzburg, 1872.
Halm, K. *Cicero's Ausgewählte Reden*, vols. 3, 4, 7. New edd. by G. Laubmann, Berlin, 1886–93.
Heitland, W. E. *Ciceronis pro C. Rabirio Oratio ad Quirites.* Cambridge, 1882.
Hendrickson, G. L. *On the Authenticity of the Commentariolum Petitionis of Quintus Cicero.* A.J.Ph. XIII, 1892, p. 200.
——— *On the Commentariolum Petitionis of Q. Cicero.* Decennial Publications of the University of Chicago, Series I, vol. 6, 1904, pp. 69–94.

Humbert, J. *Les Plaidoyers écrits de Cicéron*. Paris, 1925.
—— *Contributions à l'étude des sources d'Asconius*. Paris, 1925.
Pocock, L. G. *A Commentary on Cicero In Vatinium*. London, 1926.
Reid, J. S. *M. Tulli Ciceronis Pro P. Cornelio Sulla Oratio ad Iudices*. Cambridge, 1882.
Reuter, F. *Disputatio de veteribus rei Catilinariae auctoribus*. Kiel, 1869.
Schwarz, E. *Berichte über die catilinarische Verschwörung*. Hermes, XXXII, 1897, p. 554.
Seel, O. *Sallust von den Briefen* ad Caesarem zur Coniuratio Catilinae. Leipzig-Berlin, 1930.
Sternkopf, W. Reviews of Hendrickson in *B.P.W.* 1904, cols. 265–272, 296–301.
Thouret, G. *De Cicerone, Asinio Pollione, G. Oppio rerum Caesarianarum Scriptoribus*. Leipziger Studien, vol. I, 1878, pp. 305–324.
Tyrrell, R. Y. and L. C. Purser. *The Correspondence of Cicero*. Vol. I (3rd ed.); vol. II (2nd ed.); vol. III, app. 1 and 2 (2nd ed.). Dublin and London, 1904–14.
Ullmann, R. *Essai sur le Catiline de Salluste*. Rev. Phil. XLII, 1918, p. 5.
Watson, A. *Cicero, Select Letters*, parts 1 and 2. (Ed. How.) Oxford, 1925.
Wellrich, H. *De Coniurationis Catilinae Fontibus*. Göttingen, 1893.

B. Modern Works

1. *General*

Besides the relevant portions of the histories by Bloch (*République romaine*), Drumann-Groebe, Ferrero, Heitland, Meyer, Mommsen, Neumann, Rice Holmes, mentioned in the General Bibliography, see also:

Boak, A. E. R. *The Extraordinary Commands from 81 to 48 B.C.* Am. Hist. Rev. XXIV, 1918–19, p. 14.
Botsford, G. W. *The Roman Assemblies*. New York, 1909. (Chapter 17.)
Deloume, A. *Les Manieurs d'argent à Rome jusqu'à l'Empire*. Ed. 2. Paris, 1892.
Warde Fowler, W. *Social Life in Rome in the days of Cicero*. London, 1908.
Gelzer, M. *Die römische Gesellschaft zur Zeit Ciceros*. N.J. Kl. Alt. XXIII, 1920, p. 1.
Greenidge, A. H. J. *The Legal Procedure of Cicero's Time*. Oxford, 1901.
Groebe, P. *Die Obstruktion im römischen Senat*. Klio, V, 1905, p. 229.
Kroll, W. *Die römische Gesellschaft in der Zeit Ciceros*. N.J.f. Wiss. IV, 1928, p. 308.
—— *Die Privatwirtschaft in der Zeit Ciceros*. N.J.f. Wiss. V, 1929, p. 419.
Marsh, F. B. *The Founding of the Roman Empire*. Ed. 2. Oxford, 1927. (Chapters 3 and 4: Appendix 1.)
Mispoulet, J. B. *La Vie parlementaire à Rome sous la République*. Paris, 1899. (Bk. III, chapters 1–12.)
Plaumann, G. *Das sogenannte* Senatus Consultum Ultimum. Klio, XIII, 1913, p. 321.
Strachan-Davidson, J. L. *Problems of the Roman Criminal Law*. Oxford, 1912. (Vol. I, chapters, 10, 11, 13; vol. II, chapters 17, 18.)

2. *The Catilinarian Conspiracy*

Backmund, J. *Catilina und die Parteikämpfe im Jahre 63 v. Chr.* Würzburg, 1870.
Baur, E. *Zur Chronologie der catilinarischen Verschwörung*. Strassburg, 1875.
Beesly, E. S. *Catiline, Clodius and Tiberius*. London, 1878. (Chapters 1 and 2.)
Bertrin, G. *Num legitime prudenterque se gesserit M. Tullius Cicero consul in puniendis coniurationis Catilinariae sociis*. Paris, 1900.

Bloch, G. *Note sur un passage de Diodore de Sicile à propos de la première Catilinaire.* Mélanges Boissier. Paris, 1903. pp. 65–70.

Boissier, G. *La Conjuration de Catilina.* Paris, 1905.

Ciaceri, E. *Processi Politici e Relazioni Internazionali.* Rome, 1918. (Chapter 3.)

Hagen, E. *Untersuchungen über römische Geschichte.* I. Catilina. Königsberg, 1854.

Hardy, E. G. *The Catilinarian Conspiracy.* Oxford, 1924.

John, C. *Die Entstehungsgeschichte der catilinarischen Verschwörung.* Jahrb. f. Klass. Phil. Supplementband VIII, 1876, p. 703. (Indispensable.)

—— *Sallustius über Catilina's Candidatur im Jahre 688.* Rh. Mus. XXXI, 1876, p. 401.

Lang, E. *Das Strafverfahren gegen die Catilinarier.* Heilbronn, 1884.

Martha, J. *Comment Cicéron est arrivé aux honneurs.* Mélanges Boissier. Paris, 1903. pp. 365–9.

Mérimée, P. *Études sur l'histoire romaine.* II. Conjuration de Catilina. Paris, 1844.

Nutting, H. C. *The Attempt to murder Cicero at his House.* Trans. A.P.A. XXXV, 1904, pp. lxxxiii.

—— *The Conspiracy at Rome in 66–5 B.C.* (Univ. of California Publ. in Class. Phil. Vol. II, 1910, no. 3, p. 43).

von Pöhlmann, R. *Geschichte des antiken Kommunismus und des Sozialismus in der antiken Welt.* Munich, 1901. (Vol. II, bk 2, chapter 3.)

Rabe, A. *Die Senatssitzung am 8 November des Jahres 63 v. Chr. und die Entstehung der ersten catilinarischen Rede Ciceros.* Klio, XXIII, 1930, p. 74.

Reinach, Th. *Catulus ou Catilina?* Rev. E.G. XVII, 1904, p. 5.

Seel, O. *Sallust von den Briefen* ad Caesarem zur Coniuratio Catilinae. Leipzig-Berlin, 1930.

Speck, H. *Katilina im Drama der Weltliteratur.* Leipzig, 1906.

von Stern, E. *Catilina und die Parteikämpfe in Rom der Jahre 66–3.* Dorpat, 1883.

Thiaucourt, C. *Étude sur la Conjuration de Catilina.* Paris, 1887.

Ullmann, R. *Senatsmotet 5te december 63.* Nordisk Tidskrift for Filologi: 4th series, vol. 6, 1917, part 1, p. 1.

Wirtz, R. *Beiträge zur catilinarischen Verschwörung.* Aachen, 1910.

Wirz, H. *Catilina's und Cicero's Bewerbung um den Consulat für das Jahr 63.* Zürich, 1863.

3. *The Transpadanes and the* Lex Papia

Hardy, E. G. *Op. cit.* Chapter II.

Husband, R. W. *The expulsion of foreigners from Rome.* C.P. XI, 1916, p. 323.

4. *The Agrarian Law of* 63 B.C.

Hardy, E. G. *Op. cit.* Chapter III.

Sage, E. T. *Cicero and the Agrarian Proposals of* 63 B.C. C.J. XVI, 1920–1, p. 230.

5. *The Trial of Rabirius*

Ciaceri, E. *Op. cit.* Chapter IV.

Hardy, E. G. *Op. cit.* Chapter IV.

Huschke, P. E. *Die Multa und das Sacramentum.* Leipzig, 1874. Appendix II.

Lallier, R. *Le Procès de C. Rabirius.* Rev. H. 12, 1878, p. 257.

Renkema, E. H. *De iudicio perduellionis sublato.* Mnem. LV, 1927, p. 395.

Schneider, A. *Der Prozess des C. Rabirius betreffend verfassungswidrige Gewaltthat.* Zürich, 1889.

Schulthess, O. *Der Prozess des C. Rabirius vom Jahre 63 v. Chr.* Frauenfeld, 1891.

Strachan-Davidson, J. L. *Op. cit.* Vol. I, Chapter II.

6. Caesar's First Consulship

Bersanetti, G. M. *Quando fu conchiusa l'alleanza tra Cesare Pompeo e Crasso?* Palermo, 1924.

Cary, M. *The Land Legislation of Julius Caesar's First Consulship.* J.P. xxxv, 1920, p. 174.

Frank, T. *The Date of the Vatinian Law.* A.J.Ph. xli, 1920, p. 276.

Gelzer, M. *Die Lex Vatinia de imperio Caesaris.* Hermes, lxiii, 1928, p. 113.

Hardy, E. G. *Op. cit.* Chapter v.

Laqueur, R. *Cäsars gallische Statthalterschaft und der Ausbruch des Bürgerkriegs.* N.J. Kl. Alt. xxiii, 1920, p. 241.

Marsh, F. B. *The Chronology of Caesar's Consulship.* C.J. xxii, 1926–7, p. 504.

—— *Op. cit.* App. i.

Pocock, L. G. *A Commentary on Cicero in Vatinium.* London, 1926. (App. ii, iv, v.)

Riepl, W. *Das Nachrichtenwesen bei den Griechen und Römern.* Leipzig, 1913. pp. 380–94.

Sage, E. T. *The Date of the Vatinian Law.* A.J. Ph. xxxix, 1918, p. 367.

Schmidt, O. E. *Flugschriften aus der Zeit des ersten Triumvirats.* N.J. Kl. Alt. vii, 1901, p. 620.

7. 58–56 B.C.

Bouché-Leclercq, A. *La question d'Orient au temps de Cicéron.* Rev. H. lxxix, 1902, p. 241; lxxx, 1902, p. 1.

Cary, M. *Asinus Germanus.* C.Q. xviii, 1923, p. 103.

De Benedetti, Gina. *L'Esilio di Cicerone e la sua importanza storico-politica.* Historia, iii, 1929, p. 331.

Greenidge, A. H. J. *The Leges Aelia and Fufia.* C.R. vii, 1893, p. 158.

Gurlitt, L. *Lex Clodia de Exilio Ciceronis.* Phil. lix, 1900, p. 578.

Hoff, L. *Die beiden Gesetze des P. Clodius gegen M. Tullius Cicero.* Coesfeld, 1894.

Marsh, F. B. *The Policy of Clodius.* C.Q. xxii, 1927, p. 30.

McDonald, W. F. *Clodius and the Lex Aelia Fufia.* J.R.S. xix, 1929, p. 164.

Pocock, L. G. *P. Clodius and the Acts of Caesar.* C.Q. xix, 1924, p. 59.

—— *A Note on the Policy of Clodius.* C.Q. xx, 1925, p. 182.

—— *Pompeiusve Parem.* C.P. xxii, 1927, p. 301.

Saunders, Catherine. *The παλινῳδία of Cicero.* C.P. xiv, 1919, p. 201.

Smith, C. L. *Cicero's Journey into Exile.* Harv. St. vii, 1896, p. 65.

Sternkopf, W. *Über die Verbesserung des clodianischen Gesetzentwurfes de exilio Ciceronis.* Phil. lix, 1900, p. 272.

—— *Noch einmal die correctio der lex Clodia de exilio Ciceronis.* Phil. lxi, 1902, p. 42.

—— *Die Senatssitzung vom 14ten Januar 56.* Hermes, xxxviii, 1903, p. 28.

8. Biographies

(a) General

Oman, Sir Charles. *Seven Roman Statesmen.* London, 1902.

(b) Caesar

Birt, T. *Römische Charakterköpfe.* Leipzig, 1913. pp. 141–64.

Brandes, G. *G. Julius Caesar.* Copenhagen, 1918 (German trans., Berlin, 1925).

Deutsch, M. E. *The Year of Caesar's Birth.* Trans. A.P.A. xlv, 1914, p. 17.

—— *Concerning Caesar's Appearance.* C.J. xii, 1916–17, p. 247.

Warde Fowler, W. *Julius Caesar and the Foundation of the Roman Imperial System.* New York and London, 1904.

—— *An unnoticed trait in the character of Julius Caesar.* C.R. xxx, 1916, p. 68.

Froude, J. A. *Caesar, a Sketch.* London, 1879.

Gelzer, M. *Cäsar, der Politiker und Staatsmann.* Stuttgart and Berlin, 1921.

von Mess, A. *Caesar.* Leipzig, 1913.

Napoléon III. *Vie de César.* Paris, 1865.

Russell, A. *Julius Caesar.* London, 1915.

Sihler, E. G. *Annals of Caesar.* New York, 1911.

(c) Cicero

Boissier, G. *Cicéron et ses Amis.* Paris, 1865. (Eng. Trans., London, 1897.)

Ciaceri, E. *Cicerone e i suoi tempi.* Milan-Rome-Naples, I, 1926; II, 1930.

Cauer, F. *Cicero's Politisches Denken.* Berlin, 1903.

Forsyth, W. *Life of M. Tullius Cicero.* London, 1864.

Masè-Dari, E. *Cicerone e le sue idee sociali ed economiche.* Turin, 1901.

Petersson, T. *Cicero.* Berkeley, 1920.

Schwartz, E. *Charakterköpfe aus der antiken Literatur.* Leipzig, 1903. pp. 96–160.

Sihler, E. G. *Cicero of Arpinum.* New Haven, 1914.

—— *Cicero, an appreciation.* A.J.Ph. xxxv, 1914, p. 1.

—— *Caesar, Cicero and Ferrero.* A.J.Ph. xxxv, 1914, p. 379.

Strachan-Davidson, J. L. *Cicero and the Fall of the Roman Republic.* New York and London, 1898.

Taylor, H. *Cicero, a sketch of his Life and Works.* London, 1916.

Zielinski, T. *Cicero im Wandel der Jahrhunderte.* Leipzig, 1912.

(d) Crassus

Deknatel, C. *De Vita M. Crassi.* Leyden, 1901.

(e) Pompey

Birt, T. *Op. cit.* pp. 113–40.

(f) Miscellaneous

See the various biographies in P.W., especially *T. Annius* (67) *Milo* (Klebs), *C. Antonius* (19) *Hybrida* (Klebs), *P. Clodius* (48) (Fröhlich), *C. Julius* (131) *Caesar* (Groebe), and *M. Licinius* (68) *Crassus* (Gelzer).

CHAPTER XIII

THE CONQUEST OF GAUL

I. ANCIENT LITERARY SOURCES

1. *Contemporary*

Caesar, *De Bello Gallico commentarii* I–VII.
Cicero, *Epistulae ad Atticum*, I, 19, 2, 1, 20, 5, IV, 14–19; *Epistulae ad Familiares*, VII, 5–18; *Epistulae ad Q. fratrem*, II, 11–14, III, 1, 3, 8–9; *Oratio pro M. Fonteio*.
Hirtius, *De Bello Gallico commentarius octavus*.

2. *Secondary*

Dio Cassius, XXXVII, 47–8 (on the revolt of the Allobroges), XXXVIII, 31–50, XXXIX, 1–5, 40–54, XL, 1–11, 31–43.
Diodorus Siculus, V, 21–32.
Frontinus, *Strat.* II, 6, 3; 13, 11.
Pliny, *N.H.* II, 67, 170.
Plutarch, *Caesar*, 15–27.
Strabo, IV.
Suetonius, *Divus Iulius*, 22; 24–25; 47; 56; 58, 1; 67, 2.
Valerius Maximus, III. 2. 23.

For other references see Appian, ἐκ τῆς Κελτικῆς, I, 3–5, II, 15–21; Eutropius, VI, 17; Florus, I, 45 (III, 10), Livy, *Epit.* 103–9; Lucan, I, 392–465, III, 399–425; Orosius, VI, 7–12, and for references in ancient writers to the Druids see the collection of passages in T. D. Kendrick, *The Druids* (cited below).

3. *Modern works on the sources*

Bojkowitsch, A. *Hirtius als Offizier und als Stilist.* Wien. St. XLIV, 1924–5, p. 178; XLV, 1926–7, p. 71 and p. 221.
Ebert, C. *Über die Entstehung von Caesars Bellum Gallicum.* Nürnberg, 1909.
Klotz, A. *Cäsarstudien.* Leipzig and Berlin, 1910.
—— *Zu Caesars Bellum Gallicum.* Rh. Mus. LXVI, 1911, p. 629.
Koller, R. *Geographica in Cäsars Bellum Gallicum.* Wien. St. XXXVI, 1914, p. 140.
Radin, M. *The date of composition of Caesar's Gallic War.* C. P. XIII, 1918, p. 283.
Sternkopf, W. *Cäsars gallischer Feldzug in Ciceros Briefen.* N. J. Kl. Alt. XXIII, 1909, p. 638.
Strack, M. L. *Aulus Hirtius.* Bonner Jahrbücher, CXVIII, 1909, p. 139.

II. MODERN WORKS

A. GENERAL

Beckmann, F. *Geographie und Ethnographie in Caesars Bellum Gallicum.* Dortmund, 1930.
Beloch, J. *Die Bevölkerung Galliens zur Zeit Caesars.* Rh. Mus. LIV, 1899, p. 414.
Constans, L.-A. *Guide illustré des campagnes de César en Gaule.* Paris, 1930.
Delbrück, H. *Geschichte der Kriegskunst.* Ed. 3. Berlin, 1920. pp. 489–554.
Ebert, M. *Reallexicon der Vorgeschichte.* Berlin, 1924–9 (now completed).
Ferrero, G. *The Greatness and Decline of Rome* (English translation by A. E. Zimmern of *Grandezza e decadenza di Roma*), vols. I and II. London, 1907.
Frahm, F. *Cäsar und Tacitus als Quellen für die altgermanische Verfassung.* Hist. Vierteljahrschrift, XXIV, 1927–9, p. 145.
Fröhlich, F. *Das Kriegswesen Cäsars.* Zürich, 1889.

Gelzer, M. *Cäsar der Politiker und Staatsmann.* Stuttgart and Berlin, 1921.

Howorth, H. H. *The Germans of Caesar.* Eng. Hist. Review, XXIII, 1908, p. 417 and p. 625.

Jullian, C. *Histoire de la Gaule.* Vol. II. Ed. 4. Paris, 1921. Vol. III. Ed. 2. Paris, 1920.

—— *Notes Gallo-Romaines* in Rev. E. A. (started in vol. I and still continue).

Kromayer, J. (with G. Veith). *Schlachten-Atlas zur antiken Kriegsgeschichte.* Part 5. Leipzig, 1929.

von Mess, A. *Caesar.* Leipzig, 1913.

Napoléon III. *Histoire de Jules César,* vol. II. Paris, 1865 (authorized English translation: London, 1865).

Norden, E. *Die germanische Urgeschichte in Tacitus Germania.* Ed. 2. Leipzig and Berlin, 1922.

Radin, M. *The international law of the Gallic campaigns.* C.J. XII, 1916–17, p. 8.

Rice Holmes, T. *Caesar's Conquest of Gaul.* Ed. 2. Oxford, 1911.

—— *Ancient Britain and the invasions of Julius Caesar.* Oxford, 1907.

Veith, G. *Geschichte der Feldzüge C. Julius Caesars.* Vienna, 1906.

—— Section on Caesar's army in *Heerwesen und Kriegführung der Griechen und Römer. Müllers Handbuch,* IV. 3, part 2 (Munich, 1928), pp. 376–454.

B. SPECIAL

1. On Section I[1]

Blanchet, A. *Traité des monnaies gauloises.* Paris, 1905.

Bulliot, J. G. *Fouilles de Mont Beuvray de 1867 à 1895.* Autun, 1899.

Bushe-Fox, J. P. *Excavation of the Late-Celtic Urn-Field at Swarling, Kent* (Reports of the Research Committee of the Society of Antiquaries of London, No. 5). Oxford, 1925.

Déchelette, J. *Les fouilles du Mont Beuvray de 1897 à 1901.* Paris, 1904 (contains a comparative study of the finds at Bibracte and Stradonitz).

—— *Manuel d'archéologie,* II, 3. Paris, 1914.

Dottin, G. *Manuel pour servir à l'étude de l'Antiquité celtique.* Ed. 2. Paris, 1915.

Hastings, J. *Encyclopaedia of Religion and Ethics.* Edinburgh and New York, 1908–1926.

Holder, A. *Altceltischer Sprachsatz.* Leipzig, 1896.

Jullian, C. *De l'origine de l'assemblée druidique.* Rev. E. A. XXI, 1919, p. 27.

—— *Nouvelles questions sur les Druides.* Rev. E.A. XXI, 1919, p. 102.

Kendrick, T. D. *The Druids.* London, 1927.

Krappe, A. H. *Sur le passage de César de bell. Gall.* VI. 19. Rev. Celt. XLIV, 1927, p. 374.

MacBain, A. *Celtic Mythology and Religion.* Stirling, 1917 (a collection of three papers written 1883–1893).

MacCulloch, J. A. *The Religion of the Ancient Celts.* Edinburgh, 1911.

Meyer, Kuno, and E. Nutt. *The Voyage of Bran.* London, 1895–7.

Reinach, S. *Catalogue illustré du Musée…de Saint-Germain-en-Laye,* II. Paris, 1921.

—— *Le mot* orbis *dans le latin de l'Empire.* Rev. Celt. XXII, 1901, p. 447.

—— *Teutates, Esus, Taranis.* Rev. Celt. XVIII, 1897, p. 137.

Smith, R. A. *British Museum Guide to Early Iron Age Antiquities.* Ed. 2. London, 1925.

2. On Sections II–III

Bircher, H. *Bibracte Eine kriegsgeschichtliche Studie.* Aarau, 1904.

Colomb, G. *Campagne de César contre Arioviste.* Rev. Arch. XXXIII, 1898, p. 21.

---

[1] See further the works cited in the bibliography to chapter II of volume VII.

Ferrero, G. *Le premier livre des commentaires et les critiques de Mr. T. Rice Holmes.* C.Q. IV, 1910, p. 28.

Fröhlich, F. *Die Glaubwürdigkeit Cäsars in seinem Bericht über den Feldzug gegen die Helvetier 58 v. Chr.* Aarau, 1903.

Klotz, A. *Der Helvetierzug.* N.J. Kl. Alt. XXXV, 1915, p. 609.

Müller, B. A. *Die Zahl der Teilnehmer am Helvetierzug im Jahre 58.* Klio, IX, 1909, p. 69.

Rau, R. *Die Örtlichkeit der Helvetierschlacht.* Klio, XXI, 1927, p. 374.

Rice Holmes, T. *Signor Ferrero's reconstruction of Caesar's first commentary.* C.Q. III, 1909, p. 203.

—— *Signor Ferrero or Caesar?* C.Q. IV, 1910, p. 239.

Stoffel, E. G. *Guerre de César et d'Arioviste.* Paris, 1890.

Täubler, E. *Bellum Helveticum.* Stuttgart, 1924.

—— *Tyche. Historische Studien.* Leipzig and Berlin, 1926. pp. 137–166.

Wachsmuth, C. *Die Zahl der Teilnehmer an dem Helvetierzuge 58 v. Chr.* Klio, III, 1903, p. 281.

Walker, A. T. *The movements of Ariovistus before his interview with Caesar.* C.J. I, 1905–6, p. 213.

3. On Sections IV–VII

Colomb, G. *L'Énigme d'Alésia.* Paris, 1922.

Constans, L.-A. *Les débuts de la lutte entre César et Vercingétorix.* Rev. Belge, XXVII, 1923, p. 201.

—— *Notes critiques et historiques sur quelques passages de César de bello Gallico.* Rev. Phil. XLVIII, 1924, p. 131.

Haverfield, F. *Portus Itius.* C.R. XXVII, 1913, p. 258 and XXVIII, 1914, p. 82.

Jullian, C. *Vercingétorix.* Ed. 5. Paris, 1911.

Klotz, A. *Zu Caesar bell. Gall.* VII. 75. Phil. LXXXIII, 1928, p. 390.

Koehne, C. *Die Gründe von Cäsars schnellem Rückzug aus Deutschland im Jahre 53 v. Chr.* Hist. Vierteljahrschrift, XXIV, 1927–9, p. 529.

Lehmann, C. *Die Örtlichkeit des Kampfes Cäsars an der Axona.* Klio, VI, 1906, p. 237.

Münzer, F. *Caesars Legaten in Gaul.* Klio, XVIII, 1923, p. 200.

Pro Alesia. Began in 1906 as a monthly review of the excavations at Alise-Sainte-Reine and of questions relating to Alesia, and continued till 1910. Resumed as a quarterly in 1914 (vol. I issued Paris, 1914–15) and still continues.

Pro Nervia. Vol. I. Avesnes, 1923 (in progress).

Rice Holmes, T. *Portus Itius.* C.R. XXVIII, 1914, p. 45 and p. 193.

Sadée, E. *Caesars Feldzug am Rhein im Jahre 55 v. Chr.* Bonner Jahrbücher, CXXIII, 1916, p. 99.

Schulz, O. T. *Über die wirtschaftlichen und politischen Verhältnisse bei den Germanen zur Zeit des C. Julius Caesar.* Klio, XI, 1911, p. 48.

Walker, A. T. *Where did Caesar defeat the Usipetes and Tencteri?* C.J. XVII, 1921–2, p. 77.

Warburg, H. D. *Caesar's first expedition to Britain.* Eng. Hist. Review, XXXVIII, 1923, p. 226.

The above bibliography is merely an introduction to the vast literature on Caesar's campaigns in Gaul and Britain. The general works of T. Rice Holmes contain references to most of the literature prior to their publication, and in his later work, *The Roman Republic* (Oxford, 1923), vol. II, pp. 271–92, he deals with the more important books and articles on Caesar which appeared between 1911 and 1922.

A detailed bibliography by E. Kalinka of the Caesar literature for 1898–1928 will be found in Bursian, vol. 224 (Leipzig, 1929), pp. 1–256.

CHAPTER XIV

PARTHIA

I. SOURCES

1. PRIMARY

Coins of Parthia, Elymaïs, Characene and Persis (see I, 3).

Greek. (*a*) Literary texts: Polybius, x, 28–31; fragments of Apollodorus of Artemita, *F.H.G.* IV, p. 308, and of Posidonius, *F.Gr.Hist.* II, no. 87, frags. 5, 11–13, 71 (pp. 226, 228, 267); Herodicus' epigram, Athen. v, 222 A; Herodorus' ode, Fr. Cumont, *Mémoires de la délégation en Perse*, XX, 1928, p. 89 n. 6.

(*b*) Inscriptions: *O.G.I.S.* 430; Fr. Sarre and E. Herzfeld, *Iranische Felsreliefs*, 1910, p. 226; A. Dumont, *Mélanges d'archéologie et d'épigraphie*, 1892, p. 134; B. Haussoullier, *Klio*, IX, 1909, pp. 352 *sqq.* (one also in *Brit. Mus. Inscr.* IV, 2, no. 1052), with M. I. Rostovtzeff's readings, *Yale Classical Studies*, II, 1930, p. 40. The following, though later, are also material: Fr. Cumont, *Fouilles de Doura-Europos*, 1926, nos. 91, 118, 124; *C.R. Ac. Inscr.* 1930, p. 212 (the first poem from Susa in praise of Zamaspes). The second poem, *C. R. Ac. Inscr.* 1931, p. 241, could not be used for this chapter.

(*c*) Parchments: no. 1 from Avroman, E.H. Minns, *J.H.S.* XXXV, 1915, p. 22 and see above, p. 586, n. 2. Also material, though later, are Fr. Cumont, *Fouilles de Doura-Europos*, no. 2, p. 296; M. I. Rostovtzeff and C. B. Welles, *Yale Classical Studies*, II, 1930.

Latin. Cicero: *de fin.* III, 75; *de div.* I, 29 *sq.*, II, 84; *ad Att.* v, 18, 1; 20, 2–4; 21, 2; VI, 5, 3; *ad fam.* XV, 1; 4, 3–7. Sallust, *Hist.* IV, fr. 69 M.

Babylonian. Two astronomical tables (chronicles), S.H. 108 and S.P. 1, 176: F. X. Kugler, *Von Moses bis Paulus*, pp. 339, 342. Tablet of Hyspaosines' reign (see II, C). Contracts and astronomical documents (see II, C).

Chinese. Ssu-ma-ch'ien, *Shi-ki*, ch. 123 (see II, B).

Jewish. 1 Macc. xiv, 1–3; 2 Macc. i, 13.

Aramaic. The inscriptions from Ashur and Hatra (see II, D) are material, though many are later.

2. SECONDARY

(*a*) Classical

Isidore of Charax, *Parthian Stations* (material largely contemporary).

Strabo, XI, 508–17, 522, 524–5, 532; XVI, 743–5, 748–9.

Diodorus, XXXIII, 18; XXXIV, 15–19, 21.

Justin, XXXVI, 1, XXXVIII, 9, 10, XLI, XLII, with Trogus' *Prologues*.

Plutarch, *Crassus*; *Sulla*, 5, *Pompey*, 36, 38–9, *Lucullus*, 21, 28, 30, 36; *Moralia*, 184 D, 204 A, 605 B.

Dio Cassius, XXXVI, 1, 3, 45, 51; XXXVII, 5–7; XL, 12–30.

[Livy] represented by: *Epit.* 59, 106; Florus, I, 46; Eutropius, VI, 18; Obsequens, 28, 124; Valerius Maximus, I, 6, 11.

Appian, *Syr.* 51, 67–8; *Mithr.* 104–6; *Bell. Civ.* II, 65–6, 201.

Josephus, *Ant.* XIII, 184–6, 250–3, 344, 371, 384–6; XIV, 98, 103, 105, 119; *Bell. Jud.* I, 175–9.

Pliny, *N.H.* VI, 44–52, 111–16, 121–2, 134–41, 145–6, and scattered notices.

Orosius, v, 4, 16–17; 10, 8; VI, 13.

Herodian, III, 1, 2; 4, 8–9; IV, 10, 4; VI, 5, 4–5.

Lucan, *Pharsalia*, VIII, 368–410.

Fragments of Arrian, *Parthica*, *F. Gr. Hist.* II, no. 156, 30–51, and in Roos' *Arrian*; Memnon, *F.H.G.* III, 541, 549; John of Antioch, *ib.* IV, 661; Phlegon, *F. Gr. Hist.* II, no. 257, frag. 12, p. 1164; Nicolaus of Damascus, *ib.* no. 90, frags. 79, 92, pp. 378, 381; Porphyry, *ib.* no. 260, pp. 1217 *sq.*

Notices in Polyaenus, VII, 39–41; Frontinus, II, 5, 35; Ammianus Marcellinus, XXIII, 6, 4–6; Athenaeus, 513 F; Aelian, *H.N.* 10, 34; Velleius Paterculus, II, 46; Suidas, Arsaces, ἀγαθός, θώραξ; Stephanus, Ἀπασιακαί, Ἀρσακία, Παρθυαῖοι; Hesychius, βίσταξ; Ovid, *Fasti*, VI, 465. Many allusions to Carrhae in Latin literature.

The description of Parthia in Philostratus, *Life of Apollonius*, does not belong to history.

(b) Chinese

Ts'ien Han Shoo (*Annals of the Former Han*), chs. 96, part 1 and part of 61 (see II, B).

Hoo Han Shoo (*Annals of the Later Han*), ch. CXVIII (*ib.*).

3. Coins

(a) Parthia

Dayet, M. *Divinité nabatéenne sur une monnaie Parthe*, Aréthuse, fasc. 26, 1930, p. 39.

—— *Un tétradrachme arsacide inédit*. Ib., fasc. 7, 1925, p. 63.

—— *Une trouvaille de monnaies séleucides et arsacides*. Ib., fasc. 9, 1925, p. 131.

De la Fuye, A. *Nouveau classement des monnaies arsacides*. Rev. N. 1904, p. 317.

—— *Inventaire des monnaies trouvées à Suse*. Mém. Délégation en Perse, XX, 1928, pp. 27, 55.

Dressel, H. *Ein tetradrachmon des Arsakiden Mithradates III*. Z.N. XXXIII, 1922, p. 156.

Gardner, P. *The Parthian Coinage*. London, 1877.

Head, *H.N.*² pp. 817–823.

Hill, G. F. *Andragora*. Atti e memorie dell' Inst. Italiano di num. III, 2, 1919, p. 23.

—— in *Num. Chr.* 1927, p. 206 (Himerus).

de Morgan, J. *Observations sur le monnayage des premiers Arsacides de Perse*. Rev. N. XVI, 1912, p. 169.

—— *Étude sur la décadence de l'écriture grecque dans l'empire Perse sous la dynastie des Arsacides*. Rev. Arch. 1912, II, p. 1.

—— *Numismatique de la Perse antique: Introduction—Arsacides*. In Babelon's *Traité des monnaies grecques et romaines*, III, 1, fasc. 1. Paris, 1927.

Newell, E. T. *A Parthian Hoard*. Num. Chr. 1924, p. 141.

—— *Mithridates of Parthia and Hyspaosines of Charax*. Num. Notes and Monographs, XXVI. New York, 1925.

von Petrowicz, A. *Arsaciden-Münzen*. Vienna, 1904.

Wroth, W. *Parthia*. British Museum Catalogue, 1903.

(b) Persis, Elymaïs, Characene

Babelon, E. *Sur la numismatique et la chronologie des dynastes de Characene*. J.I. d'A.N. I, 1898, p. 381.

De la Fuye, A. *La dynastie de Kamnaskirès*. Rev. N. 1902, p. 92.

—— *Monnaies de l'Élymaïde*. Mém. Délégation en Perse, VIII, 1905, p. 177.

—— *La numismatique de la Perside*. Corolla Numismatica, p. 63. London, 1906.

De la Fuye, A. *Les monnaies de l'Élymaïde.* Rev. N. 1919, p. 45.
—— *Élymaïde.* Mém. Délégation en Perse, xx, 1928, p. 33.
Hill, G. F. *Arabia, Mesopotamia, and Persia.* British Museum Catalogue, 1922.
de Morgan, J. *Notes sur la succession des princes mazdéens de la Perside.* C.R. Ac. Inscr. 1920, p. 132.

II. MODERN LITERATURE

A. HISTORICAL

1. *General histories*

von Gutschmid, A. *Geschichte Irans.* Tübingen, 1888.
Huart, C. *La Perse antique et la civilisation iranienne,* Paris, 1925; translated as *Ancient Persia and Iranian civilisation,* London and New York, 1927.
Justi, F. *Geschichte Irans,* in Geiger and Kuhn, *Grundriss der iranischen Philologie,* vol. II. Strassburg, 1896–1904.
Meyer, Ed. Art. *Parthia* and *Persia* in *E. Brit.* 1911.
Rawlinson, G. *The sixth great oriental monarchy.* London, 1873.
Sykes, Sir P. *A history of Persia,* vol. I. Ed. 2. London, 1921.

2. *Special*

Bevan, Edwyn. *The House of Seleucus,* vol. II. London, 1902.
Bouché-Leclercq, A. *Histoire des Séleucides.* Paris, 1913–14.
Breccia, E. *Mitridate I. il Grande di Partia.* Klio, v, 1905, p. 39.
Chapot, V. *Les destinées de l'Hellénisme au delà de l'Euphrate.* Mém. soc. nat. des antiquaires de France, LXIII, 1904, p. 207.
—— *La frontière de l'Euphrate de Pompée à la conquête Arabe.* Paris, 1907.
Cumont, Fr. *Nouvelles Inscriptions grecques de Suse.* C. R. Ac. Inscr. 1930, pp. 208, 212.
Dobiáš, J. *Le proconsulat syrien de M. Calpurnius Bibulus, de 51 à 50 av. J.-C.* Rozpravy České akademie Cl. 1 no. 65, Prague, 1923. (See Rev. d. travaux scientifiques tchékoslovaques, IV–VI, 1922–4, p. 259.)
—— *Les premiers rapports des Romains avec les Parthes et l'occupation de la Syrie.* Archiv Orientalni, III, 2, 1931.
Duval, R. *Histoire politique, religieuse, et littéraire d'Édesse.* Paris, 1892.
von Gutschmid, A. *Untersuchungen über die Geschichte des königreichs Osroene.* Mém. Ac. des sciences de St Pétersbourg, sér. 7, xxxv, 1887, no. 1.
Herzfeld, E. *Hatra.* Zeit. d. deutsch. morg. Gesellschaft, LXVIII, 1914, p. 655.
Kennedy, J. *The secret of Kanishka,* part II. J.R.A.S. 1912, p. 981 (Characene).
Kiessling, A. Art. *Hekatompylos, Hydaspes* (2), *Hyrkania,* in *P.W.*
Kugler, F. X. *Von Moses bis Paulus* (pp. 337–44). Münster-i.-W., 1922.
Lehmann-Haupt, C. F. Art. *Satrap* in *P.W.*
Marquart, J. *Untersuchungen zur Geschichte von Eran.* Göttingen, 1896–1905.
Meyer, Ed. *Blüte und Niedergang des Hellenismus in Asien.* Berlin, 1925.
Minns, E. H. *Parchments of the Parthian period from Avroman in Kurdistan.* J.H.S. xxxv, 1915, p. 22.
Mommsen, Th. *Provinces of the Roman Empire* (Eng. Tr. 1886), vol. II, ch. IX.
Niese, B. *Geschichte der griechischen und makedonischen Staaten,* vols. II, III. Gotha, 1899, 1903.
Otto, W. Art. *Himeros, Hyrodes,* in *P.W.*
Rostovtzeff, M. I. and C. B. Welles. *A parchment contract of loan from Dura-Europus on the Euphrates.* Yale Classical Studies, II, 1930, p. 1. (Preliminary publication by M. I. Rostovtzeff in *C.R. Ac. Inscr.* 1930, p. 148.)

Schoff, W. H. *Parthian Stations, by Isidore of Charax.* Philadelphia, 1914.
Streck, M. *Seleukeia und Ktesiphon.* Der alte Orient, xvi, 3–4. Leipzig, 1917.
—— Art. *Hatra, Seleukeia am Tigris,* in *P.W.*
Weissbach, F. H. Art. *Characene, Elymais, Isidoros* (20), Κάρραι, Σίννακα, in *P.W.*

B. The nomad invasion

Cambridge History of India, vol. i: chs. xvii by Sir G. Macdonald and xxiii by
   E. J. Rapson. Cambridge, 1922.
Chavannes, E. *Les mémoires historiques de Se-ma Ts'ien,* vol. i: Introduction, pp.
   lxx *sqq.* 1895.
—— *Les Pays d'Occident d'après le Heou Han Chou.* T'oung Pao, viii, 1907, p. 149.
   (Translation of ch. cxviii.)
Franke, O. *Beiträge aus chinesischen Quellen zur Kenntnis der Turkvölker und
   Skythen Zentralasiens.* Berl. Abh. 1904, No. 1.
Herrmann, A. Art. *Sacaraucae, Sakai, Sakastene,* in *P.W.*
Hirth, Fr. *China and the Roman Orient.* Shanghai and Hongkong, 1885.
—— *The story of Chang K'ien.* J. Amer. Oriental Soc. xxxvii, 1917, p. 89. (Trans-
   lation of ch. 123 of Ssu-ma-ch'ien's *Shi-ki.*)
Kennedy, J. *The Indians in Armenia.* J.R.A.S. 1904, p. 309.
Kiessling, A. Art. *Hunni* in P.W.
von Le Coq, A. *Auf Hellas' Spuren in Ostturkistan.* Leipzig, 1926.
—— *Von Land und Leuten in Ostturkistan.* Leipzig, 1928.
Lüders, H. *Die Sakas und die 'nordarische' Sprache.* Berl. S.B. 1913, p. 406.
—— *Ueber die literarischen Funde von Ostturkistan.* Ib., 1914, p. 85.
Marquart, J. *Ērānšahr,* Exkurs iii: Τοχαριστᾶn. Gött. Abh. iii, 1901.
Minns, E. H. *Scythians and Greeks.* Cambridge, 1913.
Müller, F. W. K. Τοχρῑ *und Kuišan (Kūšän).* Berl. S.B. 1918, p. 566.
Sieg, E. *Ein einheimischer Name für* Τοχρῑ. Ib., 1914, p. 643.
Smith, V. A. *The Sakas in Northern India.* Zeit. d. deutsch. morg. Gesellschaft,
   lxi, 1907, p. 403.
von Staël-Holstein, Baron A. *Was there a Kuṣana race?* J.R.A.S. 1914, p. 79.
Tarn, W. W. *Seleucid-Parthian Studies.* Proc. Brit. Acad. 1930.
Thomas, F. W. *Sakastana.* J.R.A.S. 1906, p. 181.
Wylie, A. *Notes on the Western Regions.* J. Anthrop. Inst. x, 1881, p. 20. (Transla-
   tion of *Ts'ien Han Shoo,* chs. 96, pt. 1 and 61, fol. 1–6.)

C. Babylonian documents and chronology

Clay, A. T. *Babylonian records in the Library of J. Pierpont Morgan,* part ii, nos.
   52, 53. New York, 1913.
Epping, J. and Strassmaier, J. N. *Neue babylonische Planeten-Tafeln.* Zeitschrift
   für Assyriologie, v, 1890, p. 341; vi, 1891, p. 217.
Kohler, J. and Ungnad, A. *Hundert ausgewählte Rechtsurkunden aus der Spätzeit
   des babylonischen Schrifttums,* nos. 94–100. Leipzig, 1911.
Kolbe, W. *Beiträge zur syrischen und jüdischen Geschichte,* Kap. 1. Stuttgart, 1926.
Kugler, F. X. *Sternkunde und Sterndienst in Babel,* ii, pp. 438 *sqq.* Münster-i.-W.
   1909–1924.
Lehmann-Haupt, C. F. *Zur Arsakiden-Aera.* Klio, v, 1905, p. 128.
Minns, E. H. *Parchments of the Parthian period from Avroman.* J.H.S. xxxv,
   1915, p. 22.
Pinches, T. G. *A Babylonian Tablet dated in the reign of Aspasine.* Babylonian and
   Oriental Record, iv, 1890, p. 131 (see T. de Lacouperie, *ib.* p. 141).
Rostovtzeff, M. I. and C. B. Welles in *Yale Classical Studies,* ii (see A 2 above).

Schrader, E. *Die Datierung der babylonischen so-genannten Arsakideninschriften.* Berl. S.B. 1890, p. 1319; 1891, p. 3. (Only material now for certain criticisms.)

Schroeder, O. *Kontrakte der Seleukidenzeit aus Warka,* no. 37. Vorderasiatische Schriftdenkmäler d. k. Mus. zu Berlin, xv. Leipzig, 1916.

Strassmaier, J. N. *Arsakiden-Inschriften.* Zeit. f. Assyr. iii, 1888, p. 129.

——— *Zur Chronologie der Seleukiden.* Ib., viii, 1893, p. 106 (largely Arsacid).

D. Miscellaneous (Parthia)

Andrae, W. *Die zwei Kalksteinstelen aus Assur.* Mitt. d. deutsch. Orient-Gesellschaft, xxii, 1904, p. 48.

Andrae, W. und P. Jensen. *Aramäische Inschriften aus Assur und Hatra aus der Partherzeit.* Ib., lx, 1920, p. 1.

Baur, P. V. C. and M. I. Rostovtzeff. *The excavations at Dura-Europos,* 1928–9. New Haven and London, 1931.

Cowley, A. *The Pahlavi document from Avroman.* J.R.A.S. 1919, p. 147.

Cumont, Fr. *Les religions orientales dans le paganisme romain,* ch. vi. Ed. 4. Paris, 1929.

——— *Les fouilles de Doura-Europos* (1922–3). Paris, 1926.

Drouin, E. *Onomastique arsacide.* Rev. N. 1895, p. 360.

Ebeling, E. *Die babylonische Fabel.* Leipzig, 1927.

Gauthiot, R. *Iranica.* Mém. de la Soc. de Linguistique, xix, 1916, p. 125.

Herzfeld, E. *Paikuli*: ch. iv, *Essay on Pahlavi.* Berlin, 1924.

——— *The hoard of the Kâren Pahlavs.* Burlington Magazine, lii, 1928, p. 21.

Hilprecht, H. V. *Explorations in Bible Lands during the nineteenth century,* pp. 556 *sqq.* Edinburgh, 1903.

Hopkins, Clark. *The Palmyrene gods at Dura-Europos.* J. Amer. Or. Soc. li, p. 119.

Jensen, P. *Erschliessung der aramäischen Inschriften von Assur und Hatra.* Berl. S.B. 1919, p. 1042.

Jordan, J. *Uruk-Warka.* Leipzig, 1928.

Laufer, B. *Sino-Iranica.* Chicago, 1919.

Meillet, A. *De l'influence parthe sur la langue arménienne.* Rev. des Études arméniennes, i, 1920, p. 9.

Moulton, J. H. *Early Zoroastrianism.* London, 1913.

Perrot, G. et C. Chipiez. *Histoire de l'art dans l'antiquité,* vol. v, 1890, pp. 561–88. (Persis.)

Pettazoni, R. *La religione di Zarathustra.* Bologna, 1921.

Pinches, T. G. *Greek transcriptions of Babylonian tablets.* Proc. Soc. Bibl. Arch. xxiv, 1902, p. 108. (See A. H. Sayce, *ib.* p. 120, F. C. Burkitt, *ib.* p. 143.)

Reuther, O. *The German excavations at Ctesiphon.* Antiquity, 1929, p. 434.

Robinson, D. M. *A Graeco-Parthian portrait head of Mithridates I.* A.J.A. xxxi, 1927, p. 338.

Sarre, Fr. *Die altorientalischen Feldzeichen.* Klio, iii, 1903, p. 333.

——— *Die Kunst des alten Persien.* Berlin, 1922.

Sarre, Fr. und E. Herzfeld. *Iranische Felsreliefs.* Berlin, 1910.

Schilieco, W. G. *Ein babylonischer Weihtext in griechischer Schrift.* Archiv für Orientforschung, v, 1928, p. 11.

Smith, Sidney. *Notes on "The Assyrian Tree."* Bull. School Oriental Studies, iv, 1926, p. 29.

Strzygowski, J. *Die Baukunst der Armenier und Europa,* vol. ii, pp. 634 *sqq.* Vienna, 1918.

Tarn, W. W. *Hellenistic military and naval developments.* Cambridge, 1930.

Unvala, J. M. *Observations on the religion of the Parthians.* Bombay, 1925.

Unvala, J. M. *Ancient sites in Susiana.* Rev. d'Assyriologie, xxv, 1928, p. 83.
—— *On the three parchments from Avroman in Kurdistan.* Bull. School Oriental Studies, i, 1917–20, p. 125.
Waterman, L. *Preliminary Report upon the excavations at Tel Umar, Irak.* Univ. of Michigan Press, 1931.

E. THE INVASION OF CRASSUS

[For histories of Rome see the general bibliography.]

Gelzer, M. Art. *Licinius (Crassus)* (68) in *P.W.*
Groebe, P. *Der Schlachttag von Karrhae.* Hermes, XLII, 1907, p. 315.
Günther, A. *Beiträge zur Geschichte der Kriege zwischen Römer und Parthern.* Berlin, 1922.
Hartmann, K. *Ueber das Verhältnis des Cassius Dio zur Parthergeschichte des Flavius Arrianus.* Phil. LXXIV, 1917, p. 73.
Holzapfel, L. reviewing Regling, *B.P.W.* XXI, 1901, col. 850.
Lammert, F. *Die römische Taktik zu Beginn der Kaiserzeit und die Geschicht-schreibung*, pp. 12 *sqq.* Leipzig, 1931. (Phil. Supp. XXIII, 2.)
Regling, K. *De belli Parthici Crassiani fontibus.* Berlin, 1899.
—— *Zur historischen Geographie des mesopotamischen Parallelogramms.* Klio, I, 1901, p. 443.
—— *Crassus' Partherkrieg.* Klio, VII, 1907, p. 357.
Schwartz, E. Art. *Cassius* (40) in *P.W.*
Smith, Fr. *Die Schlacht bei Carrhä.* H. Z. cxv, 1916, p. 237.

[The present writer has been unable to see Manfrin, *La cavalleria dei Parti.*]

CHAPTERS XV–XVII

FROM THE CONFERENCE OF LUCA TO THE RUBICON; THE CIVIL WAR; CAESAR'S DICTATORSHIP

A. ANCIENT SOURCES

1. *Inscriptions*

Bruns[7], *Fontes*, 15, 16, 17, 18, 28.
Dessau, 72, 73, 73*a*, 6343, 5406.
Ditt.[3], 757, 759, 760, 762.
Fasti Ostienses, *C.I.L.* XIV, *supp.* 4531. Capitoline Fasti.
I.G.R.R. IV, 57, 303, 304, 305, 307, 929.
I.G. XII, 2, 165*b*; XII, 5, 557.

2. *Coins*

Grueber, H. A. *Coins of the Roman Republic in the British Museum*, London, 1910. Vol. I, pp. 471, 487–553; Vol. II, 361–9, 390 *sq.*, 469 *sq.*, 477–80, 570–76.

3. *Literary Sources*

(*a*) *Primary*

Caesar, *De Bello Gallico commentarii* I–VIII; *De Bello Civili commentarii* I–III; *Bellum Alexandrinum, Bellum Africum, Bellum Hispaniense.*
Cicero, Correspondence of the years 55–54 in R. Y. Tyrrell and L. C. Purser, *The Correspondence of Cicero*, Vols. III–V; *de provinciis consularibus*; *in Pisonem, pro Milone, pro Marcello, pro* Q. *Ligario, pro rege Deiotaro, Philippics* I and II; *de Re publica, de legibus.* References in other works of Cicero.
(?) Sallust, *in Caesarem senem de republica*; *in Ciceronem et invicem invectivae* (ed. Kurfess).

(*b*) *Secondary*

Appian, *Bell. Civ.* II, 18–117; *Illyr.* 12–15; *Mithr.* 120–1.
Asconius, Comm. on *in Pisonem, pro Scauro, pro Milone.*
Dio Cassius, XXXIX, 32–XLIV, 19.
Eutropius, VI, 18–25.
Florus, II, 13 [III, 2].
Josephus, *Ant.* XIV, 98; [VI, I–XI, I]–27.
Livy, *Epit.* 105–116.
Lucan, *Belli Civilis libri decem.*
Malalas, *Corp. Scr. Hist. Byz.* VIII, p. 216.
Nicolaus Damascenus, *F.H.G.* III, pp. 427 *sqq.*; *F.Gr. Hist.* II, no. 90, pp. 391 *sqq.*
Plutarch, *Antony, Brutus, Caesar, Cato minor, Cicero, Crassus, Pompey.*
Strabo, III, 160; IV, 181; V, 236; VII, 298, 303 *sqq.*; VIII, 381; XII, 546 *sq.*; XIII, 594 *sq.*, 625; XIV, 649; XVII, 792, 796, 833.
Suetonius, *Divus Iulius* (edition with historical notes by H. E. Butler and M. Cary. Oxford, 1927).
Velleius Paterculus, II, 46–59.
Scattered references of no great value, in Frontinus, *Strategemata* and Valerius Maximus.

B. Modern Works

The lists which follow are intended, not to survey the whole modern literature, but to indicate works to which the author wishes to acknowledge his indebtedness and those wherein references to other publications may conveniently be found. Works are grouped, so far as possible, in the order of their relevance to the text or of their relevance to each other. A few works are cited which the writer was unable to consult direct or which appeared too late to be used in writing these chapters. They are marked with a †.

1. Political history of Rome, 55–50 B.C.

Fabricius, E. *Ueber die* Lex Mamilia Roscia Peducaea Alliena Fabia. Heid. S.B., philos.-hist. Klasse, xv, 1924/5, 1 Abh.

Hardy, E. G. *The Lex Mamilia Roscia Peducaea Alliena Fabia.* C.Q. xix, 1925, p. 185.

Cary, M. *The Land legislation of Julius Caesar's First Consulship.* J.P. xxxv, 1920, p. 174.

—— *Notes on the legislation of Julius Caesar.* J.R.S. xix, 1929, p. 1.

Reitzenstein, R. und E. Schwarz. *Pseudo-Sallusts Invective gegen Cicero.* Hermes, xxxiii, 1898, p. 87.

Bardt, C. *Zur Provenienz von Ciceros Briefen ad familiares,* 2. Hermes, xxxii, 1897, p. 267.

Ciaceri, E. *Processi politici e Relazioni internazionali.* Rome, 1918, pp. 197–247.

—— *Cicerone e i suoi tempi,* Vol. ii. Milan-Rome-Naples, 1930, p. 10.

Dessau, H. *Gaius Rabirius Postumus.* Hermes, xlvi, 1911, p. 613.

Reitzenstein, R. *Die Idea des Principats bei Cicero und Augustus.* Gött. Nach. 1917, p. 399; p. 436.

—— *Zu Cicero* de republica. Hermes, lix, 1924, p. 356.

Ciaceri, E. *Il Trattato de Cicerone* 'De Republica' *e le teorie di Polibio sulla costituzione romana,* iii. Rend. Linc. xxvii, 1918, p. 303.

Meyer, Ed. *Caesars Monarchie und das Principat des Pompejus.* Ed. 2, pp. 177 *sqq.*

Heinze, R. *Ciceros 'Staat' als politische Tendenzschrift.* Hermes, lix, 1924, p. 73.

Sprey, K. *De M. Tulli Ciceronis politica doctrina.* Amsterdam Diss. Zutphen, 1928.

Sabine, G. H. and S. B. Smith. *Cicero on the Commonwealth.* Transl. with notes and introduction, Columbus, Ohio, State Univ. Press, 1929.

How, W. W. *Cicero's Ideal in his* de Republica. J.R.S. xx, 1930, p. 24

Clark, A. C. *Cicero, pro Milone.* Oxford, 1895. Historical introduction.

Bardt, C. *Die Übergabe des Schwertes an Pompejus im Dezember,* 50 *v. Chr.* Hermes, xlv, 1910, p. 337.

Sanford, F. W. *The narrative in the eighth book of the 'Gallic War,' chapters* 50–55; *a study in chronology.* Nebraska Univ. Studies, xi, 1911, no. 4.

2. The term of Caesar's command

Mommsen, Th. *Die Rechtsfrage zwischen Caesar und dem Senat.* Abh. d. phil-hist. Gesellschaft in Breslau, i, 1857, p. 1 = Gesammelte Schriften, iv, pp. 92 *sqq.*

Zumpt, A. W. *Studia Romana.* Berlin, 1859.

Guiraud, P. *Le Différend entre César et le Sénat.* Paris, 1878.

Nissen, H. *Der Ausbruch des Bürgerkriegs* 49 *v. Chr.* i, H.Z. xliv, 1880, p. 409; ii, 1881, p. 48.

Hirschfeld, O. *Der Endtermin der Gallischen Statthalterschaft Caesars.* Klio, iv, 1904, p. 76; v, 1905, p. 236.

Holzapfel, L. *Die Anfänge des Bürgerkrieges zwischen Caesar und Pompejus,* ii, iii. Klio, iv, 1904, p. 327.

Merrill, E. T. *On Caes.* B.C. 1, 2, 6 *Ante Certam Diem.* C.P. VII, 1912, p. 248.

Judeich, W. *Das Ende von Caesars gallischer Statthalterschaft und der Ausbruch des Bürgerkrieges.* Rh. Mus. LXVIII, 1913, p. 1.

Hardy, E. G. *The evidence as to Caesar's legal position in Gaul.* J.P. XXXIV, 1918, p. 163.

Rice Holmes, T. *Hirschfeld and Judeich on the Lex Pompeia Licinia.* C.Q. X, 1916, p. 49. (See further, *The Roman Republic,* II, pp. 299 *sqq.*)

Frank, Tenney. *Pompey's Compromise; Cicero,* ad fam. VIII, 11, 3. C.R. XXXIII, 1919, p. 68.

Cary, M. *Pompey's Compromise.* C.R. XXXIII, 1919, p. 109.

Laqueur, R. *Cäsars gallische Statthalterschaft und der Ausbruch des Bürgerkrieges.* N.J. Kl. Alt. XLV, 1920, p. 241; XLVII, 1921, p. 233.

Marsh, F. B. *The Founding of the Roman Empire.* Ed. 2. Oxford, 1926. Appendix II.

Perpillon, A. *La question de droit entre César et le Sénat.* Rev. H. 158, 1928, p. 272.

Gelzer, M. *Die Lex Vatinia de imperio Caesaris.* Hermes, LXIII, 1928, p. 113.

Stone, C. G. *March* 1, 50 B.C. C.Q. XXII, 1928, p. 193; XXIII, 1929, p. 60.

Adcock, F. E. *The Legal Term of Caesar's Governorship in Gaul.* C.Q. XXVI, 1932, p. 14.

3. *Military, topographical and chronological questions connected with the Civil War (including the ampaign of Munda)*

(Full and most valuable discussions of these matters will be found in the notes and essays at the end of Rice Holmes' *Roman Republic,* vol. III.)

Heuzey, L. *Les opérations militaires de Jules César.* Paris, 1886.

Stoffel, E. G. H. C. *Histoire de Jules César.* Paris, 1887.

von Göler, A. *Caesars gallischer Krieg und Theile seines Bürgerkriegs.* Ed. 2 Tübingen, 1880.

Veith, G. *Geschichte der Feldzüge C. Julius Caesars.* Vienna, 1906. (Largely superseded by subsequent writings by the same author cited below.)

Delbrück, H. *Geschichte der Kriegskunst.* Ed. 3, vol. 1. Berlin, 1920.

Kromayer, J. und G. Veith. *Heerwesen und Kriegführung der Griechen und Römer.* (*Müllers Handbuch,* IV, 3, part 2.) Munich, 1928.

Lammert, F. *Die römische Taktik zu Beginn der Kaiserzeit und die Geschichtschreibung.* Leipzig, 1931. Phil. Supp. XXIII, 2.

Stolle, Fr. *Das Lager und Heer der Römer.* Strassburg, 1912.

Parker, H. M. D. *The Roman Legions.* Oxford, 1928. pp. 47 *sqq.*

Mommsen, Th. *Das Militärsystem Caesars.* Gesammelte Schriften, IV, pp. 156 *sqq*

von Domaszewski, A. *Die Heere der Bürgerkriege in den Jahren* 49 *bis* 42 *vor Christus.* Neue Heid. Jahrb. IV, 1894, p. 157.

Kromayer, J. *Die Entwicklung der röm. Flotte vom Seeräuberkrieg des Pompeius bis zur Schlacht von Actium.* Phil. LVI, 1897, p. 426.

—— *Antike Schlachtfelder.* Berlin, 1903–1931.

—— and Veith, G. *Schlachten-Atlas.* Röm. Abt. IV. Leipzig, 1924.

Schmidt, O. E. *Der Briefwechsel des M. Tullius Cicero.* Leipzig, 1893.

Peaks, M. P. *Caesar's Movements Jan.* 21 *to Feb.* 14, 49 B.C. C.R. XVIII, 1904, p. 346.

Veith, G. *Corfinium, eine kriegsgeschichtliche Studie.* Klio, XIII, 1913, p. 1.

How, W. W. *Domitianae Cohortes.* C.Q. XVIII, 1924, p. 65.

Clerc, M. *Massalia: Histoire de Marseille dans l'antiquité.* Vol. II. Marseilles, 1929. pp. 65 *sqq.*

Gsell, S. *Histoire ancienne de l'Afrique du Nord.* Vol. VIII. *Jules César et l'Afrique. Fin des Royaumes indigènes.* Paris, 1928.

Ferrabino, A. *Curione in Africa:* 49 *a.C.* Atti Acc. Torino, 1912, p. 499.

Veith, G. *Zu den Kämpfen der Caesarianer in Illyrien.* Strena Buliciana, Zagreb, 1924, pp. 267–274.
—— *Der Feldzug von Dyrrhachium zwischen Caesar und Pompejus.* Vienna, 1920.
Menegetti, N. *Quel che Cesare non dice nel suo capolavoro,* Milan, n.d. [1931].
Art. Labienus (6), in *P.W.* (Münzer).
Lucas, F. L. *The Battlefield of Pharsalos.* B.S.A. xxiv, 1919–21, p. 34.
Stählin, F. *Das hellenische Thessalien.* Stuttgart, 1924. p. 142*sq.*
—— *Pharsalica* iii. Phil. lxxxii, 1926–7, p. 115.
†—— *Das Schlachtfeld von Pharsalos.* Bay. Blätter für Gymn.-Schulwesen, 1931.
Veith, G. *Bericht über eine Reise zur Untersuchung der caesarianischen Schlachtfelder in Griechenland.* Wien Anz. 1923, no. xxiv, p. 86.
Judeich, W. *Caesar im Orient.* Leipzig, 1885.
†Jung, H. *Caesar in Aegypten, 48/47 v. Chr.* Progr. Mainz, 1900.
Teggart, F. J. *Caesar and the Alexandrian Library.* Centralbl. f. Bibliothekswesen, xvi, 1899, p. 470.
†Graindor, P. *La Guerre d'Alexandrie.* (Rec. de trav. publ. par la Faculté des Lettres, fasc. 7.) Cairo, 1931.
Fourer, E. *Ephemerides Caesarianae rerum inde ab ineunte Bello Africano usque ad extremum Bellum Hispaniense gestarum.* Diss. Bonn, 1889.
Steinwender, Th. *Ruspina.* Klio, xvii, 1921, p. 204.
Krueger, E. *De rebus inde a Bello Hispaniensi usque ad Caesaris necem gestis.* Diss. Bonn, 1895.
Klotz, A. *Kommentar zum Bellum Hispaniense.* Leipzig, 1927. (With essay on the military history by L. C. Lammerer.)
—— *Die literarische Überlieferung über Caesars letztem Feldzug.* ἐπιτύμβιον H. Swoboda dargetracht. Reichenberg, 1927. pp. 123–132.

4. *Caesarian Legislation, etc.*

Rostovtzeff, M. *The Social and Economic History of the Roman Empire.* Oxford, 1926, chap. i. (Revised German edition, Leipzig, n.d. [1931].)
Girard, P. F. *Les leges Iuliae iudiciorum publicorum et privatorum.* Z. d. Sav.-Stift., Roman. Abt. xxxiv, 1913, p. 295.
Mommsen, Th. *Über den Inhalt des rubrischen Gesetzes.* Gesammelte Schriften, i, pp. 162 *sqq.*
—— *Ein zweites Bruchstück des rubrischen Gesetzes vom Jahre 705 Roms.* Ib., i, pp. 175 *sqq.*
—— *Zu C.I.L.* xi, 1146. Ib., i, p. 192*sq.*
Hardy, E. G. *The Table of Veleia or the Lex Rubria.* Eng. Hist. Rev. xxxi, 1916, p. 353.
Heitland, W. E. *A Great Agricultural emigration from Italy?* J.R.S. viii, 1918, p. 34.
Fabricius, E. *Zum Stadtrecht von Urso.* Hermes, xxxv, 1900, p. 205.
Mancini, G. *Fasti Antiates.* N.S.A. xviii, 1921, p. 73. (See Bursian, 227, 1930, p. 111.)
Hardy, E. G. *Roman Laws and Charters.* Translated with introduction and notes. Oxford, 1912.
—— *Three Spanish Charters and other Documents.* Translated with introduction and notes. Oxford, 1912.
—— *The Table of Heraclea and the Lex Julia Municipalis.* J.R.S. iv, 1914, p. 65.
Elmore, J. *The Professiones of the Heraclean Tablet (Lex Julia Municipalis).* J.R.S. v, 1915, p. 125.
Reid, J. S. *The so-called 'Lex Iulia Municipalis.'* J.R.S. v, 1915, p. 207.

von Premerstein, A. *Die Tafel von Heraclea und die Acta Caesaris.* Z. d. Sav.-Stift., Roman. Abt. XLIII, 1922, p. 45. (This article supersedes earlier discussions on the date and scope of the laws contained in these tables.)

Cary, M. *Notes on the legislation of Julius Caesar.* J.R.S. XIX, 1929, p. 113.

5. *Foreign policy and colonies*

Frank, Tenney. *Roman Imperialism*, New York, 1914, pp. 329 *sqq.*

Niese, B. *Straboniana* IV; *Strabo* XII, 567. *Galatien und seine Tetrachen.* Rh. Mus. XXXVIII, 1883, p. 583.

Zippel, G. *Die römische Herrschaft in Illyrien bis auf Augustus.* Leipzig, 1877.

Täubler, E. *Imperium Romanum.* Leipzig-Berlin, 1913. pp. 159–79.

Kromayer, J. *Die Militärcolonien Octavians und Caesars in Gallia Narbonensis.* Hermes, XXXI, 1896, p. 1.

Jullian, C. *Histoire de la Gaule*, IV. Ed. 2, 1921, pp. 28–38.

Kornemann, E. *Die cäsarische Kolonie Karthago und die Einführung röm. Gemeindeordnung in Afrika.* Phil. LXX, 1901, p. 402.

Barthel, W. *Zur Geschichte der römischen Städte in Afrika.* Greifswald, 1904. (Cf. his later additions and remarks in Bonn. Jahrb. CXX, 1911, pp. 81 *sqq.*)

Gsell, S. *Les premiers temps de la Carthage romaine.* Rev. H. 156, 1927, p. 228.

Carcopino, J. *L'Afrique au dernier siècle de la république romaine.* Rev. H. 162, 1929, p. 86.

Broughton, T. R. S. *The Romanization of Africa Proconsularis.* Baltimore-Oxford, 1929.

Rostovtzeff, M. *Caesar and the South of Russia.* J.R.S. VII, 1917, p. 27.

Mommsen, Th. *Zur Geschichte der Caesarischen Zeit*, I. *Die Provinzen Caesars.* Gesammelte Schriften, IV, pp. 169 *sqq.*

Schwarz, E. *Die Vertheilung der roem. Provinzen nach Caesars Tod.* Hermes, XXXIII, 1898, p. 185.

Sternkopf, W. *Die Verteilung der röm. Provinzen vor dem Mutinensischen Kriege.* Hermes, XLVII, 1912, p. 231.

6. *Caesar's position in the State*

Heinen, H. *Zur Begründung des röm. Kaiserkultes.* Klio, XI, 1911, p. 129.

Ferguson, W. *Legalized Absolutism en route from Greece to Rome.* Am. Hist. Rev. XVIII, 1912–3, p. 29.

Warde Fowler, W. *Roman Ideas of Deity in the last century before the Christian era.* London, 1914, pp. 107 *sqq.*

Reid, J. S. *Roman Ideas of Deity.* J.R.S. VI, 1916, p. 170.

Taylor, L. R. *The Divinity of the Roman Emperor.* Middletown, Conn., U.S.A., 1931, chap. III.

Pohlenz, M. *Eine politische Tendenzschrift aus Caesars Zeit.* Hermes, LIX, 1924, p. 157.

Gelzer, M. *Die römische Gesellschaft zur Zeit Ciceros.* N.J. Kl. Alt. XLV, 1920, p. 1.

Shipley, F. W. *Cicero's Attitude towards Caesar in the years 45 B.C. and 44 B.C.* Washington Univ. Stud., Hum. Ser. V, 1, 1917, pp. 33–50.

Wiegandt, L. *C. Julius Caesar und die tribunizische Gewalt.* Dresden, 1890.

—— *Studien zur staatsrechtlichen Stellung des Diktators Caesar: Das Recht über Krieg und Frieden.* Jahresbericht d. Kgl. Gymnasiums zu Dresden-Neustadt. Dresden, 1898.

Levi, M. A. *La 'tribunicia potestas' di C. Giulio Cesare.* Atti del I Congresso naz. di Studi Romani, 1928, p. 353.

—— *La costituzione romana dai Gracchi a Giulio Cesare* Florence, n.d. [1928]. pp. 106–10, 207–10.

†Niccolini, G. *Il tribunato della plebe.* Milan, 1932. pp. 157 *sqq.*

Pais, E. *L' Aspirazione di Cesare al regno e l' opposizione tribunicia durante gli anni 45–44 b.c.* Atti d. reale accad. di archeol. lett. e belle arti (Soc. Reale di Napoli), 1913, N.S. II (Part I), p. 149.

Deutsch, M. E. *Caesar's Son and Heir.* Univ. of California Public. in Class. Phil. IX, 1928, no. 6, p. 149.

McFayden, D. *The History of the title Imperator under the Roman Empire.* Chicago Diss. 1920.

Cichorius, C. *Ein Bündnisvertrag zwischen Rom und Knidos.* Rh. Mus. LXXVI, 1927, p. 327.

Täubler, E. *Imperium Romanum.* Leipzig-Berlin, 1913, pp. 157 *sqq.*

Ganter, F. L. *Die Diktaturen Caesars und die Münzen der funf ersten* IIII viri a.a.a.f.f. Z.N. XIX, 1895, p. 183.

Schnabel, P. *Die zweite Diktatur Caesars.* Klio, XIX, 1924, p. 354.

McFayden, D. *The* Lex Data *of the Roman Republic as a precedent for the legislation of the Princeps.* Washington Univ. Stud. Lang. and Lit. No. 3. St Louis, 1930, pp. 64–72.

Kromayer, J. *Die rechtliche Begründung des Principats.* Marburg, 1888.

Marsh, F. B. *The Roman Aristocracy and the Death of Caesar.* C.J. XX, 1924–5, p. 451.

7. *The Suasoriae attributed to Sallust*

Last, Hugh. *On the Sallustian* Suasoriae. C.Q. XVII, 1923, p. 87, p. 151 and XVIII, 1924, p. 83. (Contains a full list of earlier literature.)

Holborn-Bettmann, A. *De Sallustii epistulis ad Caesarem senem de re publica.* Heidelberg Diss. 1926.

Kroll, W. *Sallust's Staatsschriften.* Hermes, LXII, 1927, p. 373.

—— *Die Sprache des Sallust.* Glotta, XV, 1927, p. 280.

Post, L. A. *The Second Sallustian Suasoria.* Class. Weekly, XXI, 1928.

Arnaldi, F. *L'autenticità delle due epistole sallustiane "ad Caesarem."* St. Fil., N.S. VI, 1928, no. 6.

Seel, O. *Sallust von den Briefen* ad Caesarem *zur* Coniuratio Catilinae. Leipzig-Berlin, 1930.

Gelzer, M. Review of Seel above in *Deutsche Literaturzeitung,* 1931, col. 1985 *sqq.*

Sprey, K. *De C. Sallustio Crispo nomine populari.* Mnem. LIX, 1931, p. 103.

Edmar, B. *Studien zu den Epistulae ad Caesarem senem de re publica.* Lund, 1931.

Skard, E. *Studien zur Sprache der Epistulae ad Caesarem.* Symbolae Osloenses, x, 1932, p. 61.

8. *Studies of Caesar and of his historical importance*

Apart from the works on Caesar cited above p. 942 *sq.* and appreciations of him in general histories there are very many studies of his personality and of his importance in history. Among the most recent may be mentioned, G. Veith, *Cäsar.* Ed. 2. Leipzig, 1922; W. Schur, *Caesars Aufsteig und Fall.* Schlesische Jahrb. für Geistes- und Naturwissenschaft, XI, 1923, no. 1; E. Hohl, *Caesar.* Rostock, 1930; R. S. Conway, in *Makers of Europe.* Harv. Univ. Press, 1931; J. Buchan, *Julius Caesar.* London, 1932.

See further:

Levi, M.A. *La caduta della Repubblica Romana (rassegna degli studi recenti),* Riv. stor. ital. XLI (N.S. II), 1924, p. 253.

Groag, E. *Neue Literatur über Caesar und Augustus.* N.J. f. Wiss. II, 1926, p. 129.

Gundolf, F. *Caesar, Geschichte seines Ruhms.* Berlin, 1924. Eng. trans. The Mantle of Caesar. London, n.d. [1929].

CHAPTER XVIII
LITERATURE IN THE AGE OF CICERO

1. *Fragments*

The fragments of the Historians in this period are to be found in H. Peter, *Historicorum Romanorum Fragmenta*, Leipzig, 1883. The fragments of the Republican Orators will be found in H. Malcovati, *Oratorum Romanorum Fragmenta* (with full notes), 3 vols., Turin, 1930. For fragments of the Poets see Aemilius Baehrens, *Fragmenta Poetarum Romanorum*, Leipzig, 1886, and also W. Morel, *Fragmenta Poetarum Latinorum*, Leipzig, 1927.

2. *Rhetoric in Latin Literature* (see also under *Cicero*)

Broadhead, H. D. *Latin Prose Rhythm.* Cambridge, 1928.
Clark, A. C. *Fontes Prosae Numerosae.* Oxford, 1909.
de Groot, A. W. *Handbook of Antique Prose Rhythm.* Groningen, 1918.
—— *De numero oratorio Latino.* Groningen, 1919.
Norden, E. *Die antike Kunstprosa.* Ed. 2. Leipzig, 1909.
Novotný, Fr. *État actuel des études sur la rhythme de la prose latine.* Paris, 1929.

3. *Caesar*

(*a*) *Text.*
B. Kübler, 3 vols. Leipzig, 1893–96; A. Klotz, 3 vols. Leipzig (i, ed. 2, 1927, ii, 1926, iii, 1927); R. L. A. du Pontet, 2 vols., Oxford, 1900; T. Rice Holmes, Oxford, 1914 (Gallic War); R. Schneider, Berlin, 1888 (Alexandrine War) and 1905 (African War); F. Kraner and F. Hofmann, ed. 11, by H. Meusel (Civil War), Berlin, 1906; A. Klotz (Spanish War), Leipzig, 1927; L. A. Constans, 2 vols. (text and French transl.), Paris, 1926.

(*b*) *English Translations.*
H. J. Edwards (*Gallic War*). Loeb series, 1917.
F. P. Long (*Civil War*). Oxford, 1906.

(*c*) *Works on Caesar.*
Beckmann, F. *Geographie und Ethnographie in Caesars Bellum Gallicum.* Dortmund, 1930.
Klotz, A. *Cäsarstudien.* Leipzig and Berlin, 1910.
Rice Holmes, T. *Caesar's Conquest of Gaul.* Ed. 2, Oxford, 1911.
Sihler, E. G. *Annals of Caesar.* New York, 1911.

4. *Catullus*

(*a*) *Text.*
E. Baehrens, 2 vols. (vol. i, ed. 2, by K. P. Schulze), Leipzig, 1893; R. Ellis (with comm.), ed. 2, Oxford, 1899; J. P. Postgate, London, 1899; S. G. Owen, London, 1893; E. T. Merrill (with comm.), Boston, 1893; W. Kroll, Leipzig, 1923, ed. 2, 1929; G. Lafaye, Paris, 1922; C. Pascal, Turin, 1916.
There are numerous editions of select poems: in English, F. P. Simpson, ed. 2, London, 1880; H. V. Macnaghten and A. B. Ramsay, London, 1899.

(*b*) *English Translations.*
Prose: F. W. Cornish (Loeb series), 1912. Verse: F. A. Wright (Broadway Translations), 1926 (the whole); H. V. Macnaghten, Cambridge, 1925.

(*c*) *Works on Catullus.*
Frank, T. *Catullus and Horace: Two Poets in their Environment.* New York and Oxford, 1928.

Harrington, K. P. *Catullus and his Influence*. Boston and London, 1924.
Lafaye, G. *Catulle et ses modèles*. Paris, 1894.
Munro, H. A. J. *Criticisms and Elucidations of Catullus*. Cambridge, 1878; ed. 2 (J. D. Duff), London, 1905.

5. *Cicero*

(*a*) *Text*.
A. C. Clark, Oxford, 1900–; H. de la Ville de Mirmont, Paris, 1921–; Teubner text (various editors), Leipzig, 1914–.
The very numerous editions of separate works cannot here be mentioned.

(*b*) Text and translation of the speeches, by W. C. A. Ker, L. H. G. Greenwood and others, in progress, Loeb series; of the letters, by E. S. Shuckburgh (4 vols.), London, 1899–1900; letters to Atticus, by E. O. Winstedt (3 vols.), Loeb series, to his Friends, (3 vols.), W. Glynn Williams, Loeb series.

(*c*) *Works on Cicero*.
The following are among the more recent works bearing on the general study of Cicero; see also under 'Rhetoric.'

Arnaldi, F. *Cicerone*. Bari, 1929.
Ciaceri, E. *Cicerone ed i suoi tempi*. 2 vols. Milan-Rome-Naples, 1926–1930.
Greenidge, A. H. J. *The legal procedure of Cicero's time*. Oxford, 1901.
Humbert, J. *Les plaidoyers écrits et les plaidoiries réelles de Cicéron*. Paris, 1925.
Kubik, J. *De M. Tullii Ciceronis poetarum Latinorum studiis* (diss. phil. Vind. i). Leipzig, 1887.
Laurand, L. *De M. Tullii Ciceronis studiis rhetoricis*. Paris, 1907.
—— *Études sur le style des discours de Cicéron*. Paris, 1907. Vol. I, ed. 3, 1928, vol. II, ed. 2, 1926, vol. III, ed. 2, 1927.
Petersson, T. *Cicero, a Biography*. Berkeley, 1920.
Rolfe, J. C. *Cicero and his Influence*. Boston and London, 1923.
Sihler, E. G. *Cicero of Arpinum*. Yale Univ. Press, 1914.
Sprey, K. *De M. Tullii Ciceronis politica doctrina*. Amsterdam Diss. Zutphen, 1928.
Strachan-Davidson, J. L. *Cicero and the Fall of the Roman Republic*. New York, 1894.
Zander, C. *Eurythmia Ciceronis*. Leipzig, 1914.
Zielinski, Th. *Cicero im Wandel der Jahrhunderte*. Ed. 4. Leipzig, 1929.
—— *Der constructive Rhythmus in Ciceros Reden*. Leipzig, 1920.
Zillinger, W. *Cicero und die altrömischen Dichter*. Würtzburg, 1911.

6. *Cornelius Nepos*

(*a*) *Text*.
C. Halm and A. Fleckeisen, Leipzig, 1884; E. O. Winstedt, Oxford, 1904; A. M. Guillemin (with French translation), Paris, 1923.

(*b*) *English Translation*.
J. C. Rolfe (with text), Loeb series, 1929.

7. *Lucretius*

An account of recent work on Lucretius, by F. Merbach, is given in Bursian, 1923, part 2, pp. 39–108. A few of these references are included in the following list.

(*a*) *Text*. H. A. J. Munro, ed. 4, vol. I (text), Cambridge, 1886; vol. II (notes and introductory essay on the science of Lucretius by E. N. da C. Andrade), London, 1928; A. Brieger, Leipzig, 1894 (appendix, 1898); C. Giussani (text with Italian comm. and essays), Turin, 1896–8; new ed. by E. Stampini in progress; C. Bailey (text only), Oxford, 1900, ed. 2, 1922; W. A. Merrill (with comm.), Berkeley, 1917; H. Diels, 2 vols. (text and German transl.), Berlin, 1923–4; A. Ernout and L. Robin (with French transl.), Paris (Budé), 1925–8.

Editions of separate books are numerous; of these may be specially noted J. D. Duff, books i, iii, v, published separately, Cambridge, 1923–30.

(c) English Translations.

Besides the translation in Munro's ed. there are prose translations by C. Bailey, Oxford, 1910, ed. 2, 1921, by W. H. D. Rouse (with text), Loeb series, 1924. Verse translations by W. E. Leonard, London, 1916, Sir R. Allison, London, ed. 2, 1925, T. Jackson, Oxford, 1929 (in rhythmical prose).

(c) Works on Lucretius (selected list).

Alfieri, V. E. *Lucrezio.* Florence, 1929.

Herford, C. H. *The Poetry of Lucretius.* Manchester, 1918.

Martha, J. *Le poème de Lucrèce.* Paris, ed. 1, 1869, ed. 6, 1905.

Masson, J. *Lucretius, Epicurean and poet.* 2 vols. London, 1907–9.

Santayana, G. *Three philosophical poets* (Lucretius, Dante, Goethe). (Harvard Studies in Class. Phil. i.) Cambridge, Mass. 1910.

8. *Sallust*

(a) Text.

Catiline and Jugurtha. A. W. Ahlberg, Leipzig, 1919; editio minor, Leipzig, 1926.

Fragments of Histories. B. Maurenbrecher. 2 vols. Leipzig, 1891–3.

Letters, etc. A. Kurfess. Leipzig (*in Ciceronem*), 1914 (*ad Caesarem*), 1923.

(b) English Translation.

J. C. Rolfe (with text), Loeb series, 1921.

9. *Varro*

(a) Text.

De re rustica. H. Keil, Leipzig, 1889, ed. 2 (revised by G. Goetz), 1929.

De lingua Latina. G. Goetz and F. Schoell, Leipzig, 1910.

Menippean satires. A. Riese, Leipzig, 1865.

F. Bücheler, ed. of Petronius, with Varro's *Satires*, ed. 4, 1922.

(b) English Translation.

Ll. Storr-Best, *Varro on Farming.* London, 1912.

CHAPTER XIX

CICERONIAN SOCIETY

A. Ancient Sources.

Apart from contemporary sources such as Caesar, Catullus, Cicero, Lucretius, Nepos, Sallust and Varro (for which see the Bibliography to chapter xviii), important material will also be found in later works such as Appian's *Civil Wars*, Aulus Gellius, Dio Cassius, Plutarch's *Lives* (especially the eleven which treat figures of the Ciceronian age, *Marius, Sulla, Sertorius, Lucullus, Crassus, Pompey, Cicero, Caesar, M. Junius Brutus, Cato the Younger, Antony*), Suetonius' *Life of Julius Caesar*, Valerius Maximus, and Velleius Paterculus. It is impossible to give detailed reference here to all the passages; some of the more important will be found in the footnotes to the text of this chapter.

B. Modern Works

The older lives of Cicero by Conyers Middleton (ed. 2, London, 1741, reissued with translation of Letters by Melmoth and Heberden, Edinburgh, 1892), by W. Forsyth (ed. 3, London, 1869), by B. R. Abeken (transl. C. Merivale, London, 1854), and by Anthony Trollope (London, 1880) retain in different degrees matter of social interest.

Baker, G. P. *Sulla the Fortunate*. London, 1927.

Bardt, C. *Römische Charakterköpfe in Briefen vornehmlich aus Caesarischer und Traianischer Zeit.* pp. 3–313. Leipzig, 1925.

Barrow, R. H. *Slavery in the Roman Empire*. London, 1928. [Partly concerns Republican period: bibliography.]

Boissier, G. *Cicéron et ses amis* (étude sur la société romaine du temps de César). Ed. 10. Paris, 1895. (Eng. trans. in several edns., London, Melbourne and Toronto.)

Cagnat, R. *Étude historique sur les impôts indirects chez les Romains* [bears on relationship of *publicani* to tariffs and trade]. Paris, 1882.

—— *s.v.v. Negotiator* and *Publicani* in D.S.

Cavaignac, E. *Peut-on reconstituer l'échelle des fortunes dans la Rome républicaine?* in *Annales d'hist. écon. et sociale*, I, 4, pp. 481 *sqq.* Paris, 1929.

Chapot, V. *Le monde romain*. Paris, 1927. Eng. trans. [Hist. of Civilization series.] London and New York, 1928.

Ciaceri, E. *Cicerone e i suoi tempi*. 2 vols. Milan-Rome-Naples, 1926–30.

Drumann, W. *Geschichte Roms in seinem Übergange von d. republikan. zur monarch. Verfassung, oder Pompeius Caesar Cicero u. ihre Zeitgenossen.* Ed. 2. P. Groebe. v–vi. 'M.T. Cicero.' Berlin, 1919, 1929.

Duff, Arnold M. *Freedmen in the Early Roman Empire*. Oxford, 1928 [partly concerns Republican period: bibliography].

Duff, J. Wight. "Education, Roman" in *Enc. of Rel. and Ethics*, v, pp. 208–16. Edinburgh, 1912 [bibliography].

Warde Fowler, W. *Roman Essays and Interpretations*. Oxford, 1920 (on history of word 'religio,' pp. 7–15: on 'Laudatio Turiae,' pp. 126–138).

—— *Social Life at Rome in the Age of Cicero*. London, 1909.

—— *The Religious Experience of the Roman People* (to the age of Augustus). London, 1911; ed. 2, 1922.

Frank, Tenney. *An Economic History of Rome to the end of the Republic*. Ed. 2. Baltimore, 1927.

Frank, Tenney. *Life and Literature in the Roman Republic.* Cambridge, 1930.

Froude, J. A. *Society in Italy in the last days of the Roman Republic* (based on Cicero *pro Cluentio*) in 'Short Studies on Great Subjects,' vol. III, pp. 260 *sqq.* London, 1879.

Gelzer, M. *Die Nobilität der römischen Republik.* Leipzig, 1912. Cf. N.J. f. Wiss. (from political standpoint), XLV, pp. 1–27. Leipzig, 1920.

Heitland, W. *Agricola, A Study of Agriculture and Rustic Life in the Greco-Roman world from the point of view of labour.* Cambridge, 1921.

Kroll, W. *Die Römische Gesellschaft in der Zeit Ciceros* in N.J. f. Wiss. Heft 3. Leipzig, 1928.

—— *Die Religiosität in der Zeit Ciceros.* Ib., Heft 5, pp. 519–31. 1928.

—— *Die Privatwirtschaft der ciceronischen Zeit* in *Forschungen und Fortschritte, Nachrichtenblatt der deutschen Wissenschaft u. Technik*, I, p. 3. Berlin, 1930.

Lichtenberger, A. *De Ciceronis re privata.* Paris, 1895.

Litchfield, H. W. *Cicero's Judgement on Lucretius.* Harv. St. XXIV, 1913.

Marquardt, J. *Das Privatleben der Römer*, vol. VII of *Handb. d. römisch. Altert.* by T. Mommsen and J. Marquardt. Ed. 2. A. Mau, Leipzig, 1886. (*La vie privée des Romains*, French trans.)

Masè-Dari, E. *M.T. Cicerone e le sue idee sociali ed economiche.* Torino, 1901.

McDaniel, W. B. *Roman Private life and its Survivals.* [Bibliography.] London-Calcutta-Sydney, n.d.

Merrill, W. *Cicero's knowledge of Lucretius' poem.* Univ. of California Publ. in Class. Phil., vol. II. Berkeley, 1909.

Münzer, F. *Römische Adelsparteien und Adelsfamilien.* Stuttgart, 1920.

Paribeni, R. *La Famiglia Romana.* Rome, 1929.

Park, M. E. *The Plebs in Cicero's Day.* Pennsylvania, 1918. [A study of their provenance and of their employment.]

Petersson, T. *Cicero: A Biography.* Berkeley, 1921.

Plasberg, O. *Cicero in seinen Werken und Briefen.* Leipzig, 1926.

Pütz, P. T. *M.T. Ciceronis Bibliotheca.* Münster Diss. 1925.

Ramsay, A. M. *The Speed of the Roman Imperial Post.* J.R.S. XV, 1925, p. 60.

Ramsay, W. *A Manual of Roman Antiquities*, revised by R. Lanciani. Ed. 17. London, 1901.

Reure, L'abbé. *Les gens de lettres et leurs protecteurs à Rome.* Paris, 1891 (esp. 'Memmius et ses amis,' pp. 30–46).

Rice Holmes, T. *The Roman Republic.* Vol. I, ch. II. Oxford, 1923.

Rolfe, J. C. *Cicero and his Influence.* London, 1923.

Rostovtzeff, M. *The Social anad Economic History of the Roman Empire.* (Ch. I, 'Italy and the Civil War,' for wealth among aristocrats of Cicero's days.) Oxford, 1926.

Salvioli, G. *Il capitalismo nel mondo antico* (for equestrian wealth and Atticus). Bari, 1929.

Schmidt, O. E. *Arpinum: eine topographisch-historische Skizze* (map). Meissen, 1900.

—— *Ciceros Villen* (plans and illustrations). Leipzig, 1899.

Sihler, E. G. *Cicero of Arpinum: A political and literary biography.* Oxford, 1914.

Stein, A. *Der römische Ritterstand* (ein Beitrag zur Sozial- und Personengeschichte des röm. Reiches). München, 1927.

Strachan-Davidson, J. L. *Cicero and the Fall of the Roman Republic.* New York and London, 1894 (esp. chs. I, II, III, VI).

Stuart Jones, H. *Companion to Roman History* (esp. chapters on Architecture, Religion, Public Amusements, Art). Oxford, 1912.

Suringar, W. H. D. *Ciceronis commentarii rerum suarum sive de vita sua: accesserunt annales Ciceroniani.* Leiden, 1854. [A useful collection of Ciceronian and other ancient sources.]

Toutain, J. *L'Économie Antique.* Paris, 1927. Eng. trans. (Hist. of Civilization series), Part III, ch. IV, pp. 227–50 on 'The Economic Life of Rome, 264 B.C.–A.D. 14' (with Bibliography). London, 1930.

Wissowa, G. *Religion und Kultus der Römer* (Handb. der Altertumswissenschaft). Ed. 2. München, 1912.

Zillinger, W. *Cicero u. die altrömischen Dichter.* Würzburg Diss. 1911

Articles in P.W.: *Auspicium* (Wissowa); *Industrie und Handel* (Gummerus), esp. cols. 1454 *sqq.*; *Religio* (Kobbert).

CHAPTER XX

THE ART OF THE ROMAN REPUBLIC

A. General

For older works on Etruscan Art see the Bibliography in vol. iv, p. 643.
See also the Bibliography to Hellenistic Art in vol. viii, p. 794

Ashby, T. *Rome*. London, 1929.
Della Seta, A. *Italia Antica*. Bergamo, 1928.
Homo, L. *La Civilisation romaine*. Paris, 1930.
—— *L'Italie primitive et les débuts de l'impérialisme romain*. Paris, 1925.
Koch, H. *Römische Kunst*. Breslau, 1925.
Kluge, K. und K. Lehmann-Hartleben. *Die antiken Grossbronzen*. 3 vols. Berlin and Leipzig, 1927.
Sieveking, J. *Das römische Relief*. Festschrift Arndt. Munich, 1925, pp. 14 *sqq*.

B. Etrusco-Italic and Campanian Art

See in general *Studi Etruschi*, i–, 1927–.

Anti, C. *Il Problema dell'Arte Italica*. Studi Etruschi, iv, 1930, p. 51.
Bianchi-Bandinelli, R. *I Caratteri della Scultura Etrusca a Chiusi*. Dedalo, vi, 1925, p. 5.
—— *Clusium*. Mon. ant. dei Lincei, xxx, 1925, p. 210.
—— *Sovana*. Florence, 1929.
—— *La Posizione dell' Etruria nell' arte dell' Italia antica*. (Nuova Antologia, Sept. 1928.)
Cultrera, G. *Arte Italica e limiti della questione etrusca*, Studi Etruschi, i, 1927, p. 71.
Devoto, G. *Gli Antichi Italici*. Florence, 1931.
Ducati, P. *Etruria Antica*. Turin, 1925.
—— *Storia dell'Arte Etrusca*. Florence, 1927.
van Essen, C. C. *Chronologie der Latere Etruskische Kunst*. Mededeelingen van het Nederlandsch Historisch Institut te Rome, vi, 1926, p. 29.
Giglioli, G. Q. *Etruskische Terrakottafiguren aus Veii*. Antike Denkmäler, iii, 5. Berlin, 1926.
Hill, I. Thallon. *Rome of the Kings*. New York, 1925.
Karo, G. *Etruskisch-Römische Bildkunst*, Antike Plastik, 1928 (Festschrift Amelung), pp. 100 *sqq*.
McCartney, E. S. *The military indebtedness of early Rome to Etruria*, Memoirs of the American Academy in Rome, i, 1915–16, p. 121.
Merlin, A. et L. Poinssot. *Cratères et Candélabres de Marbre, trouvés en mer près de Mahdia*. Tunis and Paris, 1930.
Messerschmidt, F. und A. von Gerkan. *Nekropoli von Vulci*. Berlin, 1930.
Pareti, L. *Le Origini Etrusche*. Florence, 1926.
Pryce, F. N. *Catalogue of Sculpture in the Department of Greek and Roman Antiquities in the British Museum*. Vol. 1, 2. Etruscan, 1931.
Randall-MacIver, D. *The Etruscans*. Oxford, 1927.
—— *Greek Cities in Italy and Sicily*. Oxford, 1931.
Schachermeyer, F. *Etruskische Frühgeschichte*. Berlin-Leipzig, 1929.
Solari, A. *Vita Pubblica e Privata degli Etruschi*. Florence, 1931.

C. Republican Sculpture and Portraiture (with Coins and Gems)

Bernoulli, J. J. *Römische Ikonographie.* 4 vols. Stuttgart, 1882.
Bianchi-Bandinelli, R. *Il Bruto Capitolino: Scultura Etrusca.* Dedalo, VIII, 1927–8, p. 5.
Curtius, L. *Physiognomik des römischen Porträts.* Die Antike, VII, 1931, p. 226.
Delbrueck, R. *Antike Porträts.* Bonn, 1912.
van Essen, C. C. *Chronologie van de Romeinische Sculptuur Tijdens de Republiek.* Mededeelingen van het Nederlandsch Historisch Instituut te Rome, VIII, 1928, p. 29.
Goethert, F. W. *Zur Kunst der römischen Republik.* Berlin, 1931.
Grueber, H. A. *Coins of the Roman Republic.* 3 vols. London, 1910.
Hekler, A. *Greek and Roman Portraits.* London, 1912.
Kaschnitz-Weinberg, G. *Ritratti Fittili Etruschi e Romani dal Secolo III al I av. Cr.* Rendiconti della Pont. Acc. rom. di Archeologia, 1925, p. 325.
—— *Studien zur Etruskischen und Frührömischen Porträtkunst.* Röm. Mitt. XLI, 1926, pp. 133–211.
Mattingly, H. *Roman Coins. From the Earliest Times to the Fall of the Western Empire.* London, 1928.
Regling, K. *Die Antike Münze als Kunstwerk.* Berlin, 1924.
Sieveking, J. *Ein Altitalischer Porträtkopf.* Münchner Jahrbuch der bildenden Kunst, V, 1928, p. 21.
Weickert, C. *Gladiatoren-Relief der Münchner Glyptothek.* Münchner Jahrbuch der bildenden Kunst, N.F. II, 1/2.
—— *Ein römisches Relief aus der Zeit Caesars.* Festschrift Arndt. Munich, 1925.
Zadoks-Josephus Jitta, A. *Ancestral portraiture in Rome, and the art of the last century of the Republic.* Allard Pierson Stichting, Amsterdam, 1932. (This monograph appeared too late to be used in the chapter.)

D. Painting

Curtius, L. *Die Wandmalerei Pompejs.* Leipzig, 1929.
Marconi, P. *La Pittura dei Romani.* Rome, 1929.
Reinach, S. *Répertoire des Peintures Grecques et Romaines.* Paris, 1922.
Rizzo, G. E. *La Pittura Ellenistico-Romana.* Milan, 1929.
Spinazzola, V. *Le Arti Decorative in Pompei.* Milan, 1928.
Swindler, M. H. *Ancient Painting.* New Haven-London, 1929.

E. Architecture and Town-planning

Anderson, W. J. and R. P. Spiers. *The Architecture of Ancient Rome.* Edition revised by T. Ashby, London, 1927.
Ashby, T. and S. B. Platner. *Topographical Dictionary.* Oxford, 1929.
Cultrera, G. *Architettura Ippodamea.* Mem. Acc. Lincei. Rome, 1924.
von Gerkan, A. *Griechische Städteanlagen.* Berlin and Leipzig, 1924.
Lehmann-Hartleben, K. *s.v. Städtebau Italiens und des Römischen Reiches* in *P.W.* (cols. 2017–2124).
Loewy, E. *Die Anfänge des Triumphbogens.* Jahrbuch der Kunsthistorischen Sammlungen in Wien, N.F. XI, 1928, p. 1.
Noack, F. *Triumph und Triumphbogen* (Bibliothek Warburg Vorträge, 1925–6). Leipzig, 1928.
Owen, A. S. and T. B. L. Webster. *Excerpta ex Antiquis Scriptoribus quae ad Forum Romanum spectant.* Oxford, 1930.
Robertson, D. S. *Handbook of Greek and Roman Architecture.* Cambridge, 1929.

CHAPTER XXI

THE DEVELOPMENT OF LAW UNDER THE REPUBLIC

Few works on Roman law deal even mainly with the Republic, most touch on it. Thus completeness would only be obtained by giving a full bibliography of Roman law. The attempt is made here to indicate from comparatively recent literature what is most helpful to an English reader in the study of the Republican period. Fuller bibliographies will be found in Girard's *Manuel* and in Jörs' *Geschichte und System* (both mentioned below).

I. TEXTS

Bremer, F. P. *Iurisprudentiae antehadrianae quae supersunt, Pars prior, Liberae rei publicae iuris consulti.* Leipzig, 1896.

Bruns, C. G. *Fontes iuris romani antiqui*, ed. 7, O. Gradenwitz, I, *Leges et negotia*, II, *Scriptores*. Tübingen, 1909. *Index*, Tübingen, 1912.

Girard, P. F. *Textes de droit romain.* Ed. 5. Paris, 1923.

Huschke, Ph. E. *Iurisprudentiae anteiustinianae reliquias ed.* (6), E. Seckel *et* B. Kübler, I, II (1, 2). Leipzig, 1908, 1911, 1927.

Iustiniani Institutiones rec. P. Krüger, *Digesta rec.* Th. Mommsen, *retract.* P. Krüger (=Vol. I of the stereotyped Berlin *Corpus Iuris Civilis*).

Kniep, F. *Gai institutionum commentarii*, I–III. Jena, 1911–17.

Krüger, P., Mommsen, Th., Studemund, G. *Collectio librorum iuris anteiustiniani*, I, II, III. Berlin, 1923, 1878, 1890.

Kübler, B. *Gaii institutionum commentarii quattuor.* Ed. 6. Leipzig, 1928 (*cum supplemento*).

—— *Lesebuch des römischen Rechts.* Ed. 3. Leipzig-Erlangen, 1925.

Lenel, O. *Palingenesia iuris civilis*, I, II. Leipzig, 1889.

Moyle, J. B. *Imperatoris Iustiniani institutionum libri quattuor.* Ed. 5. Oxford, 1912.

Poste, E. *Gai institutiones.* Ed. 4, E. A. Whittuck, Oxford, 1904.

Riccobono, S., Baviera, J., Ferrini, C. *Fontes iuris romani anteiustiniani*, I, II. Florence, 1909.

II. SOURCES AND HISTORY OF JURISPRUDENCE

Clark, E. C. *Roman Private Law*, I, II (1, 2), III. Cambridge, 1906, 1914, 1921.

Costa, E. *Cicerone Giureconsulto*, I, II. Ed. 2. Bologna, 1927–8.

Jörs, P. *Römische Rechtswissenschaft zur Zeit der Republik*, I: *bis auf die Catonen* (not continued). Berlin, 1888.

Kipp, Th. *Geschichte der Quellen des römischen Rechts.* Ed. 4. Leipzig-Erlangen, 1919.

Krüger, P. *Geschichte der Quellen und Literatur des römischen Rechts.* Ed. 2. Munich-Leipzig, 1912.

Lenel, O. *Das Edictum perpetuum. Ein Versuch zu seiner Wiederherstellung.* Ed. 3. Leipzig, 1927.

Pernice, A. *Marcus Antistius Labeo. Das römische Privatrecht im ersten Jahrhunderte der Kaiserzeit.* Halle, 1873–1900.

Riccobono, S. *Fasi e fattori dell' evoluzione del diritto romano*, in *Mélanges de droit romain dédiés à Georges Cornil*, II, pp. 235 *sqq.* Ghent-Paris, 1926.

—— *Storia del diritto antico e studio del diritto romano di Lodovico Mitteis* (translation of Mitteis's lecture, with commentary) in *Annali del Seminario giuridico di Palermo*, XII, pp. 477 *sqq.* Cortona, 1928.

Rotondi, G. *Leges publicae populi romani.* Milan, 1912.

Stroux, J. *Summum ius summa iniuria,* extr. *Festschrift P. Speiser-Sarasin.* Leipzig-Berlin, 1926. Italian translation with commentary by S. Riccobono, *Annali del Seminario giuridico di Palermo,* xii, pp. 639 *sqq.* Cortona, 1929. Cp. E. Levy, *Z. d. Sav.-Stift. (Rom. Abt.),* xlviii, 1928, pp. 668 *sqq.,* and S. Riccobono, *Gnomon,* v, 1929, pp. 65 *sqq.*

III. General and Miscellaneous Works

Arangio-Ruiz, V. *Istituzioni di diritto romano.* Naples, 1927.

Bonfante, P. *Storia del diritto romano,* i, ii. Ed. 3. Milan, 1923. Revised French translation (J. Carrère *et* F. Fournier). Paris, 1928.

—— *Corso di diritto romano,* i, ii, vi–. Rome, 1925, 1928, 1930.

Bruns, C. G., Pernice, A., Lenel, O. *Geschichte und Quellen des römischen Rechts* in *Holtzendorffs Enzyklopädie der Rechtswissenschaft,* i, pp. 303 *sqq.* Ed. 7. Berlin, 1915.

Buckland, W. W. *The main institutions of Roman private law.* Cambridge, 1931.

—— *A textbook of Roman law from Augustus to Justinian.* Ed. 2. Cambridge, 1932.

—— *A manual of Roman private law.* Cambridge, 1925.

Corbett, P. E. *The Roman law of marriage.* Oxford, 1930.

Cornil, G. *Droit romain. Aperçu historique sommaire.* Brussels, 1921.

—— *Ancien droit romain.* Brussels-Paris, 1930.

Cuq, E. *Manuel des institutions juridiques des romains.* Ed. 2. Paris, 1928.

de Francisci, P. *Storia del diritto romano,* i, ii, i. Rome, 1926, 1929.

Girard, P. F. *Manuel élémentaire de droit romain.* Ed. 8. F. Senn. Paris, 1929.

von Ihering, R. *Geist des römischen Rechts auf den verschiedenen Stufen,* i, ii, iii 1. Ed. 4. Leipzig, 1878–88. i, ii. Ed. 5, 1891–99.

Jolowicz, H. F. *Historical introduction to the study of Roman law.* Cambridge, 1932.

Jörs, P. *Geschichte und System des römischen Privatrechts.* Berlin, 1927.

Kübler, B. *Geschichte des römischen Rechts.* Leipzig-Erlangen, 1925.

Mitteis, L. *Römisches Privatrecht bis auf die Zeit Diokletians,* i (not continued). Leipzig, 1908.

Muirhead, J. *Historical introduction to the private law of Rome.* Ed. 3. A. Grant. London, 1916.

Perozzi, S. *Istituzioni di diritto romano.* Ed. 2. i, ii. Rome, 1928.

Rabel, E. *Grundzüge des römischen Privatrechts* in *Holtzendorffs Enzyklopädie der Rechtswissenschaft,* i, pp. 399 *sqq.* Ed. 7. Berlin, 1915.

Siber, H. *Römisches Privatrecht,* i, ii. Berlin, 1925, 1928.

Sohm, R. *Institutionen: Geschichte und System des römischen Privatrechts.* Ed. 17. L. Mitteis und L. Wenger. Munich-Leipzig, 1923. English translation of Ed. 12 (J. C. Ledlie). Oxford, 1907 (Ed. 3).

IV. Special Works on Civil Procedure

Costa, E. *Profilo storico del processo civile romano.* Rome, 1918.

Girard, P. F. *Histoire de l'organisation judiciaire des romains,* i. Paris, 1901 (not continued).

Greenidge, A. H. J. *The legal procedure of Cicero's times.* Oxford, 1901.

Jobbé-Duval, E. *La legis actio avec formule à l'époque de Cicéron,* in *Mélanges de droit romain dédiés à Georges Cornil,* i, pp. 515 *sqq.* Ghent-Paris, 1926.

Lévy-Bruhl, H. *La denegatio actionis sous la procédure formulaire.* Lille, 1924. Cp. *Tijdschrift voor Rechtsgeschiedenis,* v, p. 383. Haarlem, 1924. *Rev. hist. de droit français et étranger,* v, p. 5. Paris, 1926.

Partsch, J. *Die Schriftformel im römischen Provinzialprozesse.* Breslau, 1905.
—— *Formules de procédure civile romaine.* Geneva, 1909.
Wenger, L. *Institutionen des römischen Zivilprozessrechts.* Munich, 1925.
—— *Prätor und Formel.* Bay. S.B. 1926, 3.
—— *Abriss des römischen Zivilprozessrechts,* in P. Jörs' *Geschichte und System des römischen Privatrechts,* pp. 259 *sqq.* Berlin, 1927.
Numerous important works noted by L. Wenger, *Institutionen des römischen Zivilprozessrechts,* pp. 3 *sqq.,* to which add M. Wlassak, *Die klassische Prozessformel,* I. Wien S.B. 202, 3, 1924.

V. Special Works on Criminal Law

Ferrini, C. *Diritto penale romano.* Milan, 1899.
Hitzig, H. F. *Die Herkunft des Schwurgerichts im römischen Strafprozess.* Zürich, 1909.
Levy, E. *Die römische Kapitalstrafe.* Heid. S.B. 1930–1. Abh. 5.
Mommsen, Th. *Römisches Strafrecht.* Leipzig, 1899. French translation (J. Duquesne), I–III. Paris, 1907, in *Manuel des antiquités romaines.*
Strachan-Davidson, J. L. *Problems of the Roman criminal law,* I, II. Oxford, 1912.

VI. Collected Works

Bonfante, P. *Scritti giuridici varii,* I, II, III. Turin, 1916, 1918, 1921.
Girard, P. F. *Mélanges de droit romain,* I, II. Paris, 1912, 1923. Add especially *Les leges Iuliae iudiciorum publicorum et privatorum,* Z. d. Sav.-Stift. (Roman. Abt.), XXXIV, 1913, pp. 295 *sqq.*
Mommsen, Th. *Gesammelte Schriften,* I–III, *Juristische Schriften.* Berlin, 1905–7.
Ferrini, C. *Opere di,* I–V. Milan, 1929–31.
de Visscher, F. *Études de droit romain.* Paris, 1931.

VII. Periodicals

The following are the principal, but there are many others, especially German and Italian, in which articles on Roman law appear. See P. Jörs, *Geschichte und System des römischen Privatrechts,* pp. xiv–xv.

Archivio giuridico. Modena (now), 1868–.
Bullettino del Istituto di diritto romano. Rome, 1888–.
The Law Quarterly Review. London, 1885–.
Nouvelle revue historique de droit français et étranger. Paris, 1877–1921. Continued as *Revue hist. de dr. fr. et étr.* Paris, 1922–.
Tijdschrift voor Rechtsgeschiedenis = Revue d'histoire du droit. Haarlem, 1918–.
Zeitschrift der Savigny-Stiftung für Rechtsgeschichte, Romanistische Abteilung. Weimar, 1880–.

Much valuable matter is to be found in testimonial volumes, but these are too numerous to catalogue.

GENERAL INDEX

Romans are entered under their gentile names, and, for purposes of identification, the year of their first or most significant tenure of office, usually the consulship (cos.), is inserted. Laws are entered under the general heading of Lex, leges.

INDEX OF MAPS

Maps have each their own index, and reference is made here only to the number of the map. The alphabetical arrangement ignores the usual prefixes (lake, etc.).

INDEX OF PASSAGES REFERRED TO

(References to pages include the notes at the foot of the page. For the texts used see the Bibliography, pp. 906–9)

---

[1] See above, p. 1. Note.

HELLENISTIC DYNASTIES

I. Egypt: The Ptolemies

	B.C.
Ptol. I Soter	–283
Ptol. II Philadelphus	285–246
Ptol. III Euergetes I	246–221
Ptol. IV Philopator	221–203
Ptol. V Epiphanes	203–181/0
Ptol. VI Philometor	181/0–145
Ptol. VII Euergetes II (Physcon)	145–116
Ptol. VIII Soter II (Lathyrus)	116–108/7
	88–80
Ptol. IX Alexander I	108/7–88
Ptol. X Alexander II	80
Ptol. XI Auletes	80–51
⎱Ptol. XII	51–48
⎰Cleopatra VII	
⎱Ptol. XIII	
⎰Cleopatra VII	47–44
⎱Cleopatra VII	
⎰Ptol. XIV Caesar (Caesarion)	?44–30

II. Syria: The Seleucids

	B.C.
Seleucus I Nicator	–280
Antiochus I Soter	280–262/1
Antiochus II Theos	261–247
Seleucus II Callinicus	247–226
Seleucus III Soter	226–223
Antiochus III (the Great)	223–187
Seleucus IV Philopator	187–175
Antiochus IV Epiphanes	175–163
Antiochus V Eupator	163–162
Demetrius I Soter	162–150
Alexander I Balas	150–145
Demetrius II Nicator	145–139/8
	129–125
Antiochus VI Epiphanes	145–142/1
Antiochus VII Sidetes	139/8–129
[Alexander II Zabinas	128–123]
Antiochus VIII Grypus	125–121
	121–96
Seleucus V	125
Antiochus IX Cyzicenus	115–95
Seleucus VI Epiphanes Nicator	96–95
Antiochus X Eusebes Philopator	95–83
Antiochus XI Philadelphus	92
Philippus I Philadelphus	92–83
Demetrius III Eukairos Philopator Soter	95–88
Antiochus XII Dionysus	87–84
[Tigranes of Armenia	83–69[1]]
Antiochus XIII Asiaticus	69–64
Philippus II	65–64

III. Pontus: The Mithridatids

The dynasty begins with Mithridates I, dynast of Cius from B.C. 337/6 to 302/1, and then runs:

	B.C.
Mithridates II[2] (*vulgo* Ktistes)	302/1–266/5
Ariobarzanes[3]	266/5–c. 250
Mithridates III	c. 250–c. 185
Pharnaces I[4] [adelphus	c. 185–c. 170
Mithridates IV Philopator Phil-	c. 170–c. 150
Mithridates V Euergetes	c. 150–121/0
Mithridates VI Eupator Dionysus[5]	121/0–63
Pharnaces II	63–47
Darius	39–?37

V. Cappadocia

The first ruler to assert independence was Ariarathes III, 262/1–220, who began as *epistates* and later assumed the diadem and kingly title. The list then runs:

Ariarathes IV Eusebes	220–163
Ariarathes V Eusebes Philopator[7]	163–c. 130

The kingdom was in disorder for some years under the regency of the queen-mother Nysa.

Ariarathes VI Epiphanes Philopator	c. 126–111
Ariarathes VII Philometor	111–c. 100
Ariarathes Eusebes Philopator[8]	c. 100–96
Ariarathes VIII	96–95

With the death of Ariarathes VIII the dynasty came to an end and the Cappadocians elected a noble, Ariobarzanes, as their king.

Ariobarzanes I Philoromaios[9]	c. 95–62
Ariobarzanes II Philopator	62–51
Ariobarzanes III Eusebes Philoromaios	51–42

IV. Bithynia

	B.C.
Ziboetes	327–c. 279
Nicomedes I	c. 279–c. 250
Ziaelas	c. 250–c. 230
Prusias I	c. 230–c. 180
Prusias II	c. 180–149
Nicomedes II Epiphanes	149–c. 94
Nicomedes III Epiphanes Philopator[6]	c. 94–75/4

VI. Commagene

Ptolemaeus, who began to rule about 170 B.C. as dependent *epistates* of Commagene, asserted his independence of Syria *circa* 163/2. The list then runs:

Ptolemaeus	c. 163/2–c. 130
Samus II Theosebes Dikaios	c. 130–c. 100
Mithridates I Callinicus	c. 100–c. 70
Antiochos I Theos Dikaios Epiphanes Philoromaios Philhellen	c. 70–c. 35

---

[1] See p. 357.

[2] See pp. 216 *sqq.*

[3] Ariobarzanes died during the rule of Antiochos II Theos of Syria (261–247).

[4] Pharnaces is mentioned for the first time in 183; see p. 219.

[5] For the first few years the queen-mother (?Laodice) ruled, but Mithridates had certainly seized power by 115 B.C.; see p. 226, n. 2.

[6] A younger brother of Nicomedes III, Socrates, was put forward as a pretender in 91/90 by Mithridates Eupator of Pontus and reigned for a time as Nicomedes IV but was ejected later. (p. 238.)

[7] During the early years of Ariarathes V there was another claimant to the throne, Orophernes, supported by Demetrius I of Syria, but put down by c. 155. (vol. VIII, p. 281, p. 522.)

[8] Really a son of Mithridates Eupator but it was claimed that he was a son of Ariarathes V. After the death of Ariarathes VIII Mithridates again set him upon the throne. (pp. 236–9.)

[9] During the first eight years of this reign Ariobarzanes I and Ariarathes IX alternated upon the throne according to the fortunes of the war; in 85 Ariobarzanes was finally restored by Sulla. (p. 259.)